www.rxprep.com

RxPrep® | THE REVIEW
BY TOP STUDENT

The RxPrep® Difference

NAPLEX,® MPJE® & CPJE Reviews

Not sure how to learn it all? The RxPrep Videos and the Test Bank Assessments match to each chapter in this Course Book. The questions in the Test Banks cover the must-know basic competency drug information. Find out what you know and what you need to know before you take the exam. Watch videos and take assessments on your phone or tablet; download the RxPrep app to access on the go.

READ: ***Includes the simplest and most complete calculations and biostatistics reviews. It's all here, in easy steps, for complete exam know-how.***
The RxPrep Course Book is the student-preferred resource for NAPLEX. Includes all topics tested with must-know key drugs and study tips.

WATCH: ***Pair the Course Book with video lectures that emphasize the required drug information.***
Focus on topics that need a fresh review, or use a video to bring up a topic score.

ATTEND: Live or streaming video review sessions.

PRACTICE: ***No need to guess— exam-style tests let you know when you are ready to test – and do well.***
The RxPrep Test Banks contain case-rich, exam-style questions that cover all the required material. Includes cumulative practice exam.

UPDATED: Annually. Current, complete and ready for exam preparation.

ORDER THE VIDEO AND TEST BANKS ONLINE AT WWW.RXPREP.COM

CONTACT RXPREP FOR LIVE REVIEWS AND GROUP RATES AT SUPPORT@RXPREP.COM

Download the RxPrep app to study on the go

GET IT ON Google Play | Download on the App Store

RxPrep's
MPJE *AND*
CPJE REVIEWS
Course Manual, Practice Tests, Videos and Live review

The authors in good faith have made every attempt to ensure that the information included in this book is accurate and up to date. However, the content is intended for instructional purposes only, therefore the authors make no guarantees, offer no warranties or representations, nor accept any liabilities with respect to the accuracy of the content contained within.

The RxPrep Test Bank assessments and Video Lectures for NAPLEX, and the MPJE and CPJE law review courses can be found on the RxPrep website at www.rxprep.com. Click on "Store."

2020 NAPLEX
COURSE BOOK

Study Guide for the **NAPLEX**® and **Clinical Content** for the **CPJE** for those **testing** in **2020**

KAREN SHAPIRO, PHARMD, BCPS

CHELSEA BOMBATCH, PHARMD, BCPS

AMY DREW, PHARMD, BCPS

STEPHANIE D. GARRETT, PHARMD, BCPS

ANGIE VEVERKA, PHARMD, BCPS

2020 Contributors

CAITLIN DAVIS
PHARMD, BCPS

KAREN GOUD
PHARMD, BCPS

MINDY HOLCOMBE
PHARMD, BCPS, BCPPS

DACY LIM
EDITORIAL ASSISTANT

TESSA OVERMAN
PHARMD, BCPS

REZA TAHERI
PHARMD, MBA

MICHAEL J. FREUDIGER
PHARMD, APH, BCPS, BCGP

D. RAYMOND WEBER
PHARMD, BSPHARM, BCOP, BCPS, RPH

AND

MS. SHANNON ZINDA
BOOK DESIGN AND PRODUCTION

NEW AND IMPROVED COURSE BOOK FOR 2020 GRADUATES

PREPARING FOR NAPLEX 1

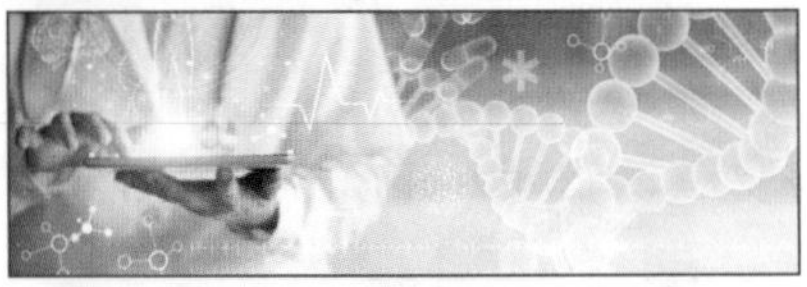

1. Preparing for NAPLEX with the RxPrep Course 3
Quick Guides....13
How to Use the RxPrep Course Book....14
Top Outpatient Drugs....15
Top Inpatient Drugs....19
Top OTC Drugs....23
Required Formulas....25
Diagnostic Tests....27
Medical Terms....30
Common Medical Abbreviations....39

PHARMACY FOUNDATIONS PART 1 44

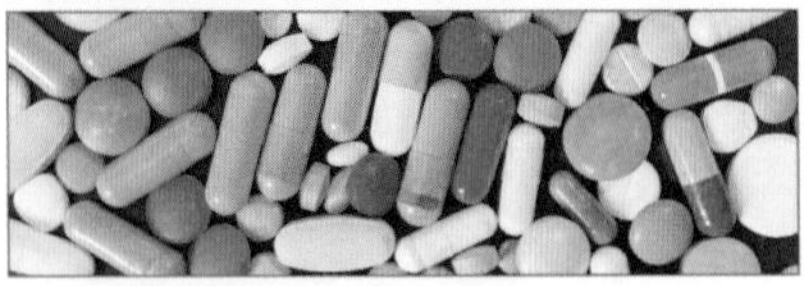

2. Learning Basic Science Concepts 46
3. Learning Drug Interactions....55
4. Learning Lab Values & Drug Monitoring 71
5. Learning Drug References 81
6. Learning Drug Formulations 91
7. Learning IV Medications.... 99
8. Answering Case-Based Exam Question 106
Temperature Conversions (Fahrenheit ↔ Celsius)....108

CALCULATIONS.......... 114

9. Calculations I: Math Basics 116
Liquid (Volume) Conversions....117
Solid (Weight) Conversions....117
Height Conversions....117
10. Calculations II: Compounding 128
Percentage Strength....128
Ratio Strength....132
Parts Per Million (PPM)....134
Specific Gravity (SG)....135
Dilution & Concentration (Changing Strength or Volume)....136
Alligation....137
Osmolarity....139
Isotonicity (E Value)....142
Moles and Millimoles....144
Milliequivalents....146
KCl Solution (Oral) to Tablets....see #61
11. Calculations III: Parenteral and Enteral Nutrition 148
Determining Fluid Needs....149
Total Energy Expenditure....150
Parenteral Nutrition....151
Enteral Nutrition....151
Grams of Nitrogen From Grams of Protein....152
Corrected Calcium for Albumin < 3.5....159
12. Calculations IV: Clinical....166
Body Mass Index (BMI)....166
Ideal Body Weight (IBW)....167
Adjusted Body Weight ($AdjBW_{0.4}$)....167
Selecting and Calculating Patient Weights....168
Flow Rates....169
Drop Factor....172
Dehydration....174
Cockcroft-Gault Equation....175
Arterial Blood Gases (ABG)....177
Anion Gap....178
pH Calculations....179
Percent Ionization....182
Drug Conversions....183
Absolute Neutrophil Count (ANC)....184
13. Calculations V: Exam-Style Math Practice....185

BIOSTATISTICS.......... 198

14. Biostatistics 200
Mean, Medium and Mode....202
Risk, Relative Risk (RR)....207
Relative Risk Reduction (RRR)....208
Absolute Risk Reduction (ARR)....208
Number Needed to Treat (NNT)....209
Number Needed to Harm (NNH)....210
Odds Ratio (OR)....210
Hazard Ratio (HR)....211
Sensitivity and Specificity....214

COMPOUNDING & HAZARDOUS DRUGS.......... 223

15. Compounding I: Basics 225
16. Compounding II: Equipment, Stability & Excipients 249
Min Weighable Qty (MWQ)....252
17. Compounding III: Documentation & Preparation....267

RENAL & LIVER DISEASE...... 288

18. Renal Disease 290
19. Hepatitis & Liver Disease 302

IMMUNIZATIONS & TRAVELERS.......... 314

20. Immunizations 316
21. Travelers 333

INFECTIOUS DISEASES......... 340

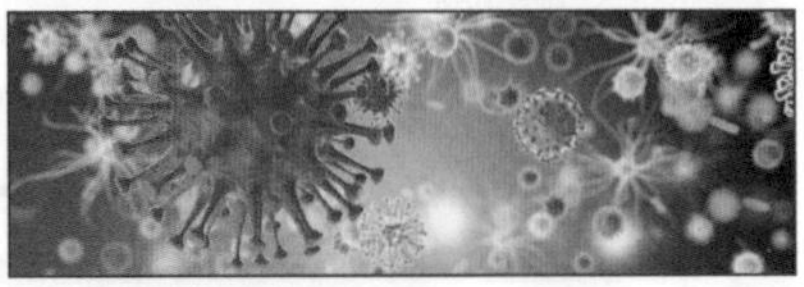

22. ID I: Background & Antibacterials by Drug Class....342
23. ID II: Bacterial Infections....375
24. ID III: Antifungals & Antivirals.... 398
25. ID IV: Opportunistic Infections 412
26. Human Immunodeficiency Virus 415

CARDIOVASCULAR CONDITIONS.......... 440

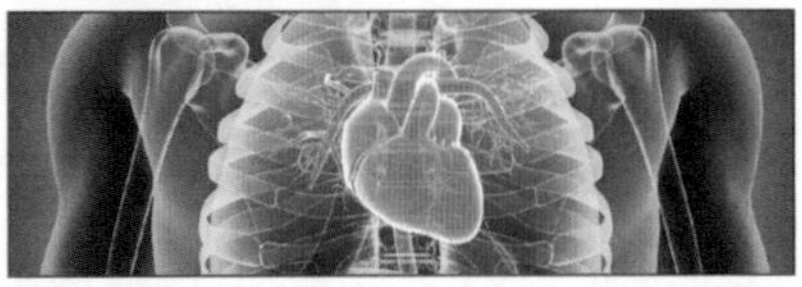

27. Dyslipidemia.... 442
Friedewald Equation.... 443
28. Hypertension.... 458
29. Ischemic Heart Disease....474
30. Acute Coronary Syndromes....481
31. Chronic Heart Failure....489
32. Arrhythmias.... 505
33. Stroke....517

ANTICOAGULATION & BLOOD DISORDERS.......... 524

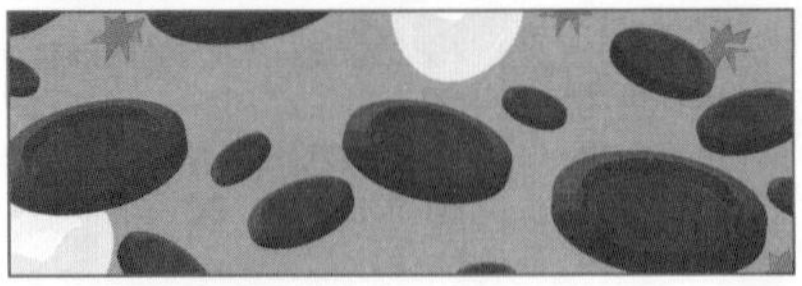

34. Anticoagulation....526
35. Anemia....542
36. Sickle Cell Disease.... 550

EYES, EARS, NOSE & SKIN CONDITIONS.......... 554

37. Allergic Rhinitis, Cough & Cold 556
38. Common Conditions of the Eyes and Ears. 566
39. Common Skin Conditions....573
Time to Burn (TTB)....587

PULMONARY CONDITIONS & TOBACCO CESSATION.......... 590

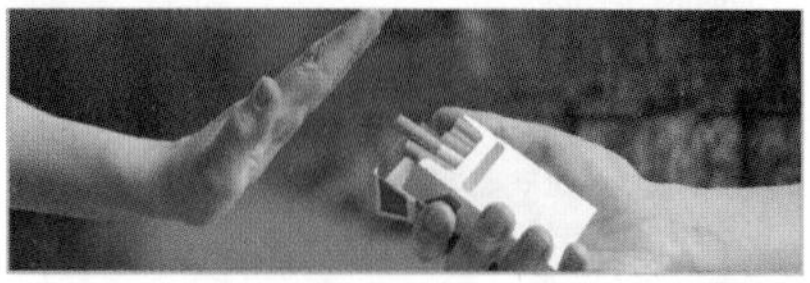

40. Pulmonary Arterial Hypertension 592
41. Asthma.. 599
42. Chronic Obstructive Pulmonary Disease... 617
43. Tobacco Cessation.................................. 629

ENDOCRINE CONDITIONS.. 634

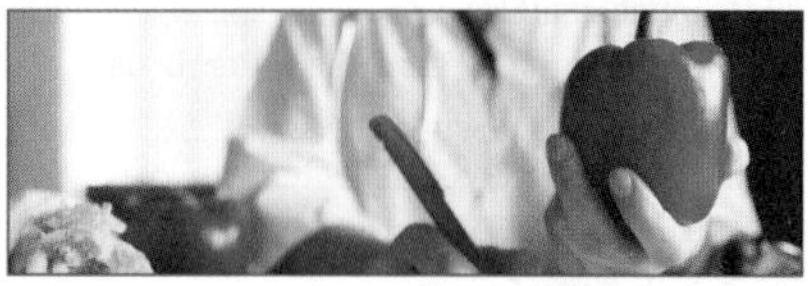

44. Diabetes 636
    - Insulin Conversions: .... *begins at* 656
        - Initiating Basal-Bolus Insulin in Type 1 Diabetes
        - Insulin-to-Carbohydrate Ratio: Rule of 500 for Rapid-Acting Insulin
        - Insulin-to-Carbohydrate Ratio: Rule of 450 for Regular Insulin
        - Correction Factor: 1,800 Rule for Rapid-Acting Insulin
        - Correction Factor: 1,500 Rule for Regular Insulin
        - Correction Dose
45. Thyroid Disorders.................................. 664
46. Systemic Steroids & Autoimmune Conditions 671

MALE & FEMALE HEALTH.... 692

47. Contraception & Infertility........................ 694
48. Drug Use in Pregnancy & Lactation............707
49. Osteoporosis, Menopause & Testosterone Use..713
50. Sexual Dysfunction 729
51. Benign Prostatic Hyperplasia (BPH) 734
52. Overactive Bladder 740

SPECIAL POPULATIONS....... 746

53. Acute & Critical Care Medicine 748
54. Pediatric Conditions......................................763
55. Cystic Fibrosis 773
56. Transplant..779
57. Weight Loss.. 789

PAIN/RELATED CONDITIONS.......................... 794

58. Pain 796
59. Migraine..818
60. Gout..825

ONCOLOGY............................. 831

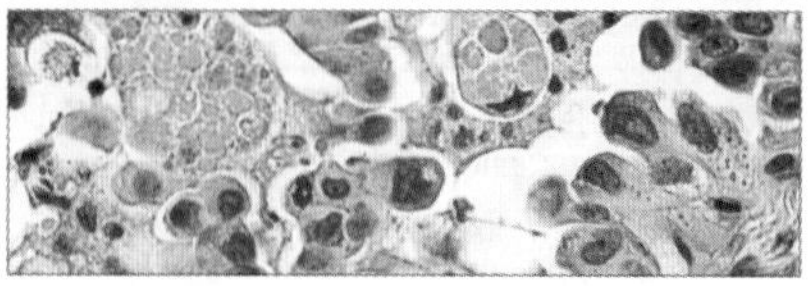

61. Oncology I: Overview & Side Effect Management..832
62. Oncology II: Common Cancer Types & Treatment 851
    - BSA Calculations, using Mosteller 861

PSYCHIATRIC CONDITIONS..878

63. Depression 880
64. Schizophrenia/Psychosis.......................... 892
65. Bipolar Disorder 901
66. Attention Deficit Hyperactivity Disorder (ADHD) 905
67. Anxiety Disorders 913
68. Sleep Disorders: Insomnia, Restless Legs Syndrome (RLS) & Narcolepsy.................... 918

NEUROLOGIC CONDITIONS .924

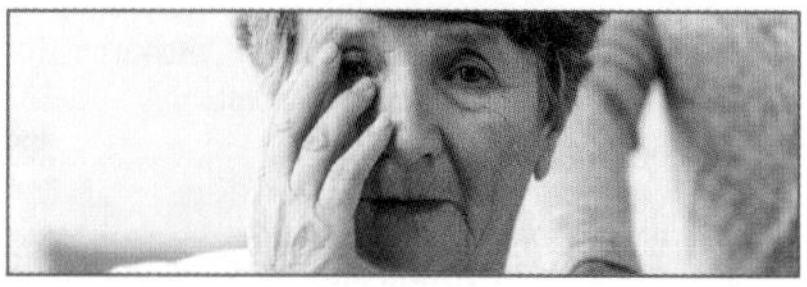

69. Parkinson Disease...................................... 926
70. Alzheimer's Disease....................................932
71. Seizures/Epilepsy..937
    - Phenytoin Correction for Albumin < 3.5 946

GASTROINTESTINAL CONDITIONS.......................... 954

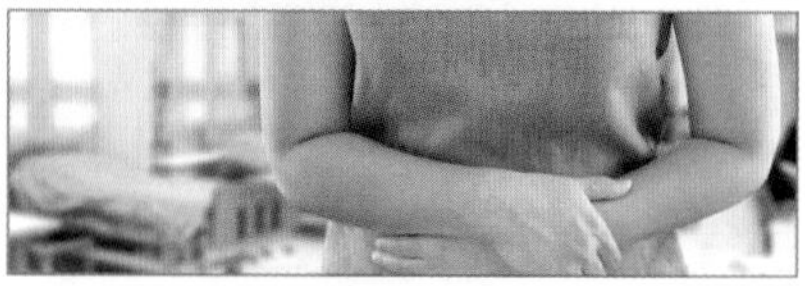

72. Gastroesophageal Reflux Disease & Peptic Ulcer Disease................................. 956
73. Constipation & Diarrhea 966
74. Inflammatory Bowel Disease......................975
75. Motion Sickness.. 983

PHARMACY FOUNDATIONS PART 2 986

76. Medication Safety & Quality Improvement... 988
77. Drug Allergies & Adverse Drug Reactions 1000
78. Pharmacokinetics 1009
    - Bioavailability (F).. 1011
    - Volume of Distribution (Vd) 1012
    - Clearance 1013
    - Elimination Rate Constant (Ke)...................... 1016
    - Predicting Drug Concentrations 1016
    - Half-Life (T1/2) 1017
    - Loading Dose (LD).. 1019
79. Pharmacogenomics....................................1020
80. Dietary Supplements, Natural & Complementary Medicine 1024
81. Emergency Preparedness, Toxicology & Antidotes.. 1033

PATIENT CASES 1041

82. Cases, Exam-Style Practice 1042

INDEX....................................... 1050

By Classification + Drug Name 1050

CONTENT LEGEND

(symbol) = Required Formula

KEY DRUG GUY AND STUDY TIP GAL TABLE OF CONTENTS

PHARMACY FOUNDATIONS PART 1 44

2. Learning Basic Science Concepts 46
- Receptor Pharmacology 49

3. Learning Drug Interactions 55
- Pharmacodynamics: Pharmaco + Dynamics 55
- Risk with Concurrent Use of Benzodiazepines and Opioids 56
- Pharmacokinetics: Pharmaco + Kinetics 57
- CYP Inducers 59
- CYP Inhibitors 60

4. Learning Lab Values & Drug Monitoring 71
- Therapeutic Drug Levels 80

5. Learning Drug References 81
- "Color" Drug References 89

6. Learning Drug Formulations 91
- Patch Frequency 97

7. Learning IV Medications 99
- Drugs with Leaching/Adsorption/Absorption Issues with PVC Containers 101
- Common Drugs with Diluent Solution Requirements 101
- Common Drugs with Filter Requirements 103
- Do Not Refrigerate 103
- Protect From Light During Administration 104

8. Answering Case-Based Exam Question 106
- Select Drugs and Conditions that Alter Vital Signs 109
- Identifying Medication Therapy Problems 110

CALCULATIONS 114

9. Calculations I: Math Basics 116
- Common Conversions 117
- How to Round on the Exam 117
- Setting Up Proportions 118
- Drug Conversions 125
- Ratio Relationships 125
- Follow the Rules of Math 127
- Ready to Submit Your Answer? 127

10. Calculations II: Compounding 128
- Common IV Fluids 129
- Dissociation Particles vs. Valence 146

11. Calculations III: Parenteral and Enteral Nutrition 148
- Calories Provided from Macronutrients 151

12. Calculations IV: Clinical 166
- Height in Inches 168
- Final Volume of Compounded IV Solutions 171
- Interpreting ABGs 177

13. Calculations V: Exam-Style Math Practice 185
- Math is Ready for NAPLEX When 197

BIOSTATISTICS 198

14. Biostatistics 200
- Central Tendency Calculations 202
- Interpreting Confidence Intervals 205
- Rounding Rules for NNT and NNH 210

COMPOUNDING & HAZARDOUS DRUGS 223

15. Compounding I: Basics 225
- Pharmacopeias 226
- Hazardous Drugs on the NIOSH List 228
- ISO Air Quality in the PEC 233

16. Compounding II: Equipment, Stability & Excipients 249
- The HLB Number 257

17. Compounding III: Documentation & Preparation 267
- Reducing Particle Size & Cake Baking 271
- Suppositories 277
- Determining the BUD For CSPs 284

RENAL & LIVER DISEASE 288

18. Renal Disease 290
- Select Drugs that Cause Kidney Disease 292
- CrCl vs. GFR 292
- ACE Inhibitors and ARBs for Albuminuria 293
- Select Drugs that Require ↓ Dose or ↑ Interval in CKD 294
- Select Drugs that are Contraindicated in CKD 294
- Select Drugs that Raise Potassium Levels 298
- Steps for Treating Severe Hyperkalemia 299

19. Hepatitis & Liver Disease 302
- Comparison of Hepatitis Viruses 303
- DAA Mechanisms and Regimens 303
- Interferons 307
- Lab Tests for Liver Disease 309
- Select Drugs with Boxed Warning for Liver Damage 310

IMMUNIZATIONS & TRAVELERS 314

20. Immunizations 316
- Vaccine Timing & Spacing 319
- Invalid Contraindications to Vaccination 320
- Influenza Vaccine Tips 325
- Pneumococcal Vaccine Indications, Sequence and Intervals 328

21. Travelers 333
- Drugs for Travelers' Diarrhea 335
- Travel Vaccines 336

INFECTIOUS DISEASES 340

22. ID I: Background & Antibacterials by Drug Class 342
- Common Resistant Pathogens 346
- Key Features of Penicillins 350
- Key Features of Cephalosporins 352
- Key Features of Carbapenems 353
- Aminoglycosides: Good News, Bad News 355
- Key Features of Quinolones 358
- Key Features of Macrolides 359
- Key Features of Tetracyclines 360
- Key Features of Sulfamethoxazole/Trimethoprim 361
- Key Features of Nitrofurantoin 368
- Drugs of Choice/Active Drugs for Specific Pathogens 369
- No Renal Dose Adjustment Required 370

23. ID II: Bacterial Infections 375
- Timing of Perioperative Antibiotics 377
- AOM Treatment in Kids: When to Consider Observation 379
- CAP Patient Assessment (Stepwise Approach) 382
- RIPE Therapy for TB 386
- *C. difficile* Guideline Recommendations 394
- Symptoms of Common STIs 395
- Gonorrhea & Chlamydia: They Often Go Together 396
- Penicillin Pregnancy Puzzler 396
- Lyme Disease or Ringworm? 397

24. ID III: Antifungals & Antivirals 398
- Key Issues with Azole Antifungals 400

25. ID IV: Opportunistic Infections 412

26. Human Immunodeficiency Virus 415
- INSTI-Based Regimen (INSTI + 2 NRTIs) 418
- Single Tablet Regimens 419
- Key Features of NRTIs 420
- Key Features of NNRTIs 423
- Key Features of PIs 425
- PI and PK Booster Drug Interactions 429
- Key Features of INSTIs 430
- Administration (Food) Requirements 434
- ART Adverse Effects by Class and Agent 435
- Dispense in Original Container 436

CARDIOVASCULAR CONDITIONS 440

27. Dyslipidemia 442
- Select Drugs/Conditions that Can Raise LDL and/or Triglycerides 443
- Determining Statin Treatment Intensity Based on Patient Risk 445
- Statin Equivalent Doses 446
- Managing Myalgias 446
- Determining Add-On Treatment Based on Patient Risk 448

28. Hypertension 458
- Blood Pressure Monitoring 460
- Drugs that Can Increase Blood Pressure 460
- Hypertension Guideline Recommendations 461
- Key IV Hypertension Medications 472

29. Ischemic Heart Disease 474
- Treatment Approach for Stable Ischemic Heart Disease 475

30. Acute Coronary Syndromes 481
- Drug Treatment of ACS 482
- Drugs for Secondary Prevention After ACS 488

31. Chronic Heart Failure 489
- Signs and Symptoms of Systolic Heart Failure 490
- Select Drugs that Cause or Worsen Heart Failure 491
- Treatment of Chronic Systolic Heart Failure 492

32. Arrhythmias 505
- The Heart's Natural Pacemaker and Arrhythmias 505
- Select Drugs that Can Increase or Prolong the QT Interval 508
- Classifying Drugs with Vaughan Williams 508
- AFib: Rate vs. Rhythm Control 509

33. Stroke 517
- Signs and Symptoms of Stroke 518

ANTICOAGULATION & BLOOD DISORDERS 524

34. Anticoagulation 526
- Anticoagulants are for Blood Clots 526
- Coagulation Cascade 527
- Conversion between Anticoagulants 532
- Warfarin Tablet Colors 535

35. Anemia 542
- Assessing and Treating Iron Deficiency Anemia 544
- Select Drugs that Can Cause Hemolytic Anemia 549

36. Sickle Cell Disease 550
- Key Vaccines in Sickle Cell Disease 551

EYES, EARS, NOSE & SKIN CONDITIONS 554

37. Allergic Rhinitis, Cough & Cold 556
- Diphenhydramine In Pharmacy; It's Everywhere 559
- Pediatric Cough and Cold Treatment - Caution Needed 564
- Cough and Cold Combo Products: What's in a Name? 565

38. Common Conditions of the Eyes and Ears 566
- Drugs that Can Increase IOP 567
- Glaucoma Treatment Goal: Decrease IOP 567
- Common Drugs Known to Cause Vision Changes or Damage 571

39. Common Skin Conditions 573
- Acne Treatment Summary 574

PULMONARY CONDITIONS & TOBACCO CESSATION 590

40. Pulmonary Arterial Hypertension 592
- Select Drugs that Can Cause Pulmonary Fibrosis 598

41. Asthma 599
- Spirometry: Tests Lung Function (How Well the Lungs Work) 600
- MDIs and DPIs 607
- With a Spacer, More Drug Gets Into The Lungs 611

42. Chronic Obstructive Pulmonary Disease 617
- COPD vs Asthma 618

43. Tobacco Cessation 629
- Treatment Considerations for Tobacco Cessation 631
- Nicotine Patch Administration 632
- How to Chew Nicotine Gum 632

ENDOCRINE CONDITIONS 634

44. Diabetes 636
- Diagnostic Criteria 638
- Complications of Diabetes 639
- Adult Treatment Goals (ADA) 641
- Drugs that Can Raise Blood Glucose 641
- Treatment Algorithm 642
- Concentrated Insulin Products 656
- Initiating Basal-Bolus Insulin 656
- Insulin Conversions 657
- Multidose Pens (No Needle Included) 659
- Select Drugs that Can Lower Blood Glucose 660
- Hyperglycemic Crises Treatment 661
- Factors to Consider When Selecting Drug Treatment 662

45. Thyroid Disorders 664
- S/Sx of Hypothyroidism 665
- Select Drugs and Conditions that can Cause Hypothyroidism 665
- Levothyroxine Tablet Colors 667
- S/Sx of Hyperthyroidism 668
- S/Sx of Thyroid Storm 669

46. Systemic Steroids & Autoimmune Conditions 671
- Steroids: Least Potent to Most Potent 673
- Immunosuppression from Steroids 674
- Treating Acute Inflammation with Steroids 674
- Select Drugs That Can Cause Drug-Induced Lupus Erythematosus (DILE) 682
- Drug-Induced Raynaud's 686

MALE & FEMALE HEALTH 692

47. Contraception & Infertility 694
- Select Contraceptive Types 699
- Severe & Rare Adverse Effects of Estrogen 700
- Infertility Drugs Act Like Endogenous Hormones to Trigger Ovulation 706

48. Drug Use in Pregnancy & Lactation 707
- Teratogens: Danger in Pregnancy 709

49. Osteoporosis, Menopause & Testosterone Use 713
- Select Factors and Conditions with Osteoporosis Risk 714
- Diagnosis of Osteoporosis 714
- Calcium and Vitamin D 715
- Drug Summary for Osteoporosis Treatment and Prevention 716
- Hormone Therapy: Health Risks and Appropriate Use 722

50. Sexual Dysfunction 729
- Drugs that Can Cause Erectile/Sexual Dysfunction 730
- PDE-5 Inhibitor Dosing Guide 731

51. Benign Prostatic Hyperplasia (BPH) 734
- Drugs that Can Worsen BPH 734

52. Overactive Bladder 740
- Anticholinergic Side Effects 742
- Decreasing Risk of Dry Mouth 742

SPECIAL POPULATIONS 746

53. Acute & Critical Care Medicine 748
- Dopamine Dosing 753
- General Principles for Treating Shock 755
- Two Common Causes of ICU Infections 756
- Treating ADHF 756

54. Pediatric Conditions 763
- Avoid in Pediatrics 770

55. Cystic Fibrosis 773
- Inhaled Medications for CF 774
- Common Issues with Pancreatic Enzyme Products 776

56. Transplant 779
- Transplant Drugs: What's Used, When 785
- Vaccine-Preventable Illness in Transplant Recipients 786

57. Weight Loss 789
- Select Drugs/Conditions that Can Cause Weight Gain 790
- Select Drugs/Conditions that Can Cause Weight Loss 790
- Prescription Weight Loss Drugs: Avoid or Use Caution 791

PAIN/RELATED CONDITIONS 794

58. Pain 796
- Acetaminophen Overdose 798
- NSAIDs and the Ductus Arteriosus 799
- Opioid Boxed Warnings 802
- Opioid Allergy 808
- Opioid-Induced Constipation 808
- Opioid Induced Respiratory Depression (OIRD) Risks 811
- Opioid Overdose Management 811

59. Migraine 818
- Common Migraine Triggers 819
- Triptan Formulations 821

60. Gout 825
- Drugs that Increase Uric Acid 826
- Gout Treatment Basics 827

ONCOLOGY 831

61. Oncology I: Overview & Side Effect Management 832
- Dosing Considerations for Select Highly Toxic Drugs 835
- ChemoMan and Major Toxicities of Common Chemotherapy Drugs 837
- Chemotherapy Adjunctive Medications 838
- Hydration, To Reduce Toxicity 838
- Irinotecan (I-Run-To-The-Can) 846

62. Oncology II: Common Cancer Types & Treatment 851
- To Reduce Doxorubicin Cardiotoxicity 864
- Hints for Understanding Monoclonal Antibodies 872

PSYCHIATRIC CONDITIONS 878

63. Depression 880
- Select Drugs that Cause or Worsen Depression 881
- Depression Diagnosis 881
- Antidepressants: Select Adverse Effects 885
- MAO Inhibitors – Keep Them Separated 887
- Selecting the Best Antidepressant 888

64. Schizophrenia/Psychosis 892
- Medications/Illicit Drugs that Can Cause Psychotic Symptoms 893
- Picking the Best Antipsychotic 895

65. Bipolar Disorder 901
- Lithium-Not Easy to Initiate 904

66. Attention Deficit Hyperactivity Disorder (ADHD) 905
- Patient-Friendly Formulations for Stimulants 906

67. Anxiety Disorders 913
- Select Drugs that Cause Anxiety 913
- Safe Use of Benzodiazepines 916

68. Sleep Disorders: Insomnia, Restless Legs Syndrome (RLS) & Narcolepsy 918
- Select Drugs That Can Worsen Insomnia 919
- Ez Tip for Excellent Zzzzzz (Sleep) 919

NEUROLOGIC CONDITIONS 924

69. Parkinson Disease 926
- Dopamine Blocking Drugs that Can Worsen PD 926
- Parkinson Disease: The Cause, Symptoms and Primary Drug Treatment 927

70. Alzheimer's Disease 932
- Key Drugs that Can Worsen Dementia 933

71. Seizures/Epilepsy 937
- Drugs that Can Lower the Seizure Threshold 938
- Diastat Acudial Dispensing 939
- AED Cousins 940
- Take Your Vitamins on AEDs! 940
- Lamictal Starter Kits: Colors Help Safety 941
- Phenytoin/Fosphenytoin Administration 946
- Adjusting Phenytoin Doses 949
- AEDs Have a Lot of Drug Interactions 949
- AEDs are CNS Depressants 949

GASTROINTESTINAL CONDITIONS 954

72. Gastroesophageal Reflux Disease & Peptic Ulcer Disease 956
- Key Drugs that Can Worsen GERD Symptoms 957
- H2RA and PPI Formulations to Know 959
- Key Drugs with Decreased Absorption 960

73. Constipation & Diarrhea 966
- Drugs that are Constipating 967
- Which OTC to Recommend for Constipation 967
- Select Drugs that Can Cause Diarrhea 972

74. Inflammatory Bowel Disease 975
- Maintenance of Remission: Comparison of Common CD and UC Treatments 977

75. Motion Sickness 983
- Scopolamine *(Transderm Scop)* Patch 985

PHARMACY FOUNDATIONS PART 2 986

76. Medication Safety & Quality Improvement 988
- Select National Patient Safety Goals 990
- Do Not Use Abbreviations 991

77. Drug Allergies & Adverse Drug Reactions 1000
- Intolerance or Allergy? 1003
- Drugs Most Commonly Associated w/Photosensitivity 1004
- Drugs Commonly Associated w/TTP 1004
- Drugs Commonly Associated w/Severe Skin Reactions 1005
- Epinephrine Auto-Injector Administration 1006
- A Penicillin Allergy, or Not? 1007

78. Pharmacokinetics 1009
- Drug Absorption 1010
- Dose Adjustments for Michaelis-Menten Kinetics 1015

79. Pharmacogenomics 1020
- Does a Positive or Negative Test Require Action? 1023
- Select Drugs with Pharmacogenomic Implications 1023

80. Dietary Supplements, Natural & Complementary Medicine 1024
- Differences Between Dietary Supplements and Drugs 1025

81. Emergency Preparedness, Toxicology & Antidotes 1033
- Common Symptomatic Treatment 1035
- N-Acetylcysteine Treatment 1036
- Initial Management of Suspected Opioid Overdose 1036

CONTENT LEGEND

= Study Tip Gal   = Key Drug Guy

PREPARING FOR NAPLEX

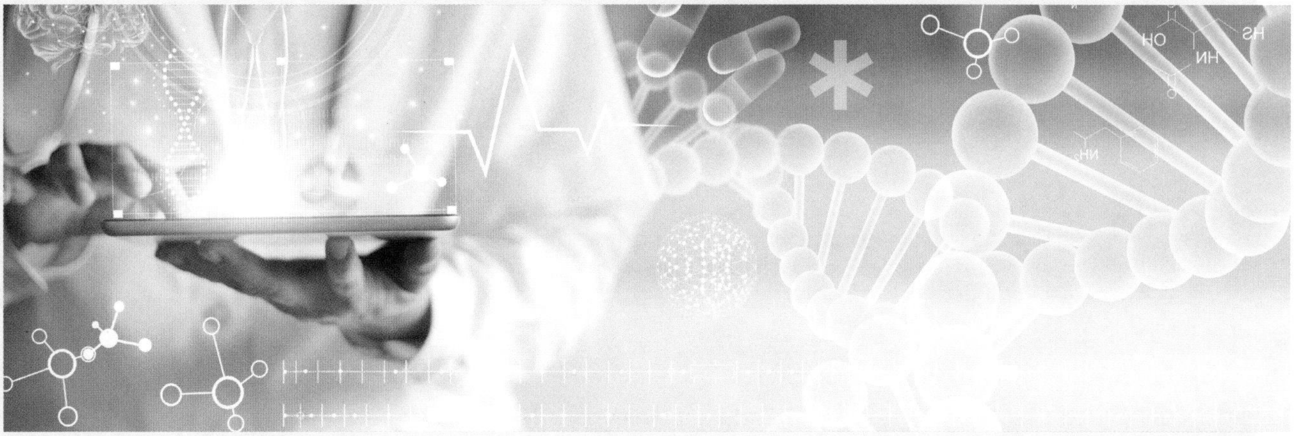

CONTENTS

CHAPTER 1

PREPARING FOR NAPLEX WITH THE RxPREP COURSE | **3**

QUICK GUIDES | 13

HOW TO USE THE RxPREP COURSE BOOK | **14**

TOP OUTPATIENT DRUGS | **15**

TOP INPATIENT DRUGS | **19**

TOP OTC DRUGS | **23**

REQUIRED FORMULAS | **25**

DIAGNOSTIC TESTS | **27**

MEDICAL TERMS | **30**

COMMON MEDICAL ABBREVIATIONS | **39**

CHAPTER CONTENT

How to Study When Passing is the Only Option 3
RxPrep's Roadmap to Passing 4
Step 1 Take the Two Free Assessment Tests 4
Step 2 Create a Study Plan 5
Step 3 Studying Clinical & Math Chapters 6
Step 4 Take the RxPrep Practice NAPLEX Exam 9
Required Formulas Checklist 10
The NAPLEX Competency Statements 11
Format of the Exam 11
Arrival Details, Tutorial 12
Case Practice 12
Pharmacy Law Exams 12
Quick Guides 13
How to Use the RxPrep Course Book 14
Top Outpatient Drugs 15
Top Inpatient Drugs 19
Top OTC Drugs 23
Required Formulas 25
Diagnostic Tests 27
Medical Terms 30
Common Medical Abbreviations 39

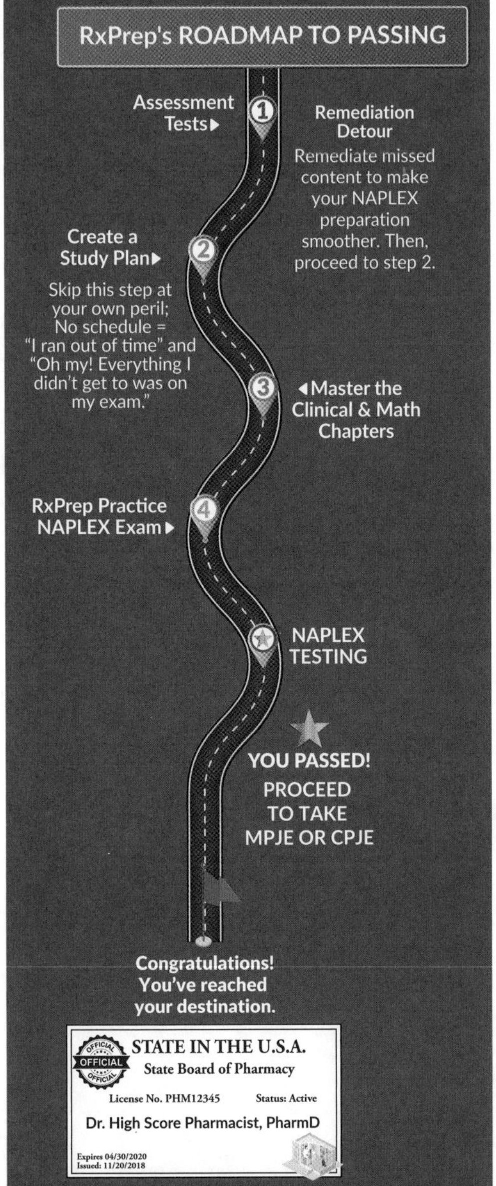

CHAPTER 1
PREPARING FOR NAPLEX WITH RxPREP

HOW TO STUDY WHEN PASSING IS THE ONLY OPTION

RxPREP STUDY MATERIALS

The RxPrep Course Book is a companion to the RxPrep Online Video Course, available at www.rxprep.com. The Course Book is updated annually to be current for the pharmacist licensure exam. The date on the cover (such as the 2020 RxPrep CourseBook) should be the year in which you are testing.

Additional resources for NAPLEX preparation are unnecessary.

NO SUCH THING AS LUCK; IT'S DRUG KNOWLEDGE AND SKILL

There is no such thing as luck in taking licensure exams; there is only drug knowledge and the skill required to apply the knowledge to case-based questions. All topics must be mastered, and all calculations must be completed with adequate speed and accuracy.

If passing is the only option, follow the steps outlined in this chapter. Do not skimp on the preparation; the steps outlined in this chapter work well when used as-directed.

*COURSE BOOK UPDATES AVAILABLE, WHEN NEEDED

The RxPrep pharmacists summarize new guidelines that are released after the current Course Book went to press. When the new information could be relevant for testing, a summary of the changes will be posted under the Student Resources tab at www.rxprep.com. Any corrections are posted in the same location.

*For the CPJE (California) law exam, refer to the last page of this chapter.

RxPREP'S ROADMAP TO PASSING

1 TAKE THE TWO FREE ASSESSMENT TESTS

Begin preparation by taking the free assessment tests at www.rxprep.com. Click on the 'Store' tab and scroll down to find them. The assessments are important to determine if you are ready to jump into NAPLEX preparation or will require remediation in basic math skills and/or basic drug information, such as brand and generic drug names.

1 FREE DRUG BASICS & TERMINOLOGY ASSESSMENT

- **≥ 80%** → **Proceed to Step 2** 'Creating a Study Plan'
- **< 80%** → **REMEDIATE** Study the Quick Guides in the back of this chapter or use the individual chapters to study.

> *Learn what you missed!*

2 FREE MATH BASICS ASSESSMENT

- **≥ 80%** → **Proceed to Step 2** 'Creating a Study Plan'
- **< 80%** → **REMEDIATE** Watch the video for Calculations I: Math Basics. Follow and repeat the steps to solve each problem with the instructor. Complete all problems in each section, then retake the Math Basics assessment and proceed to Step 2 when each missed item is mastered.

2 CREATE A STUDY PLAN

To make it simpler to plan your study schedule, the RxPrep pharmacists have put together a list of the time it usually takes to complete each Test Bank, with a blank Excel template. The spreadsheet includes drop-down topic lists to easily populate (fill-in) your study schedule. The Excel template can also be opened in Google Sheets. Look under the 'Student Resources' tab at www.rxprep.com. Click on 'How to ACE Your Exams.'

Helpful Pointers for Creating your Study Schedule

- **Fill in the schedule by allocating adequate time for each of the chapters (topics).**
  - ❑ Use the time estimates from the following chart, with your best-guess if you will need more or less time for a topic.
- **Practice math daily.**
  - ❑ Schedule math for 1 – 2 hours (at night), or 3 – 4 hours during the day, until you are on "auto pilot" when calculating any of the math problems. If you are trying to remember a formula or how to set up a calculation when you are taking the actual exam, you should not be taking the exam. Repetition is required for mastery.
- **Alternate between math and clinical topics.**
  - ❑ The time you devote to math on a daily basis should be roughly equal to the time given to other topics, until the math is completed.
- **Always leave weekly catch-up time. It is normal to fall behind; the catch-up time will help you stay on schedule.**
  - ❑ If you are unable to stick to your schedule it is best to postpone the exam. The topics you did not prepare for can be on the exam.
- **Leave the two weeks before your estimated test date open.**
  - ❑ The last two weeks are used to take the RxPrep NAPLEX Practice Exam, remediate (learn) any missed areas, and review the math and other topics that may have been forgotten. This is covered in Step 4.

Estimated Topic Completion Time for an APPE Student

~ 1 weekday night	~1-2 weekday nights	~2-5 weekday nights or 1-2 weekend days
Allergic Rhinitis, Cough & Cold	Acute Coronary Syndromes	Anticoagulation
Alzheimer's Disease	ADHD	Biostatistics
Anemia	Arrhythmias	Calculations II
Answering Case-Based Exam Questions	Asthma	Calculations III
Anxiety Disorders	Calculations I	Calculations IV
Benign Prostatic Hyperplasia (BPH)	Calculations V	Common Skin Conditions
Bipolar Disorder	Chronic Heart Failure	Diabetes
Common Conditions of the Eyes and Ears	Contraception & Infertility	Dyslipidemia
Constipation & Diarrhea	Compounding I	HIV
COPD	Compounding II	Infectious Diseases I
Cystic Fibrosis	Compounding III	Infectious Diseases II
Drug Allergies & Adverse Drug Reactions	Acute & Critical Care Medicine	Oncology I
Drug Use in Pregnancy & Lactation	Depression	Oncology II
Emergency Preparedness	Dietary Supplements, Natural & Complementary Medicine	Osteoporosis, Menopause & Testosterone Use
Gout	GERD & PUD	Pain
Infectious Diseases IV	Hepatitis & Liver Disease	Seizures/Epilepsy
Ischemic Heart Disease	Hypertension	Systemic Steroids & Autoimmune Conditions
Learning Basic Science Concepts	Immunizations	
Learning Drug Formulations	Infectious Diseases III	
Learning Drug References	Inflammatory Bowel Disease	
Migraine	Learning Drug Interactions	
Motion Sickness	Learning Lab Values & Drug Monitoring	
Overactive Bladder	Medication Safety & Quality Improvement	
Parkinson Disease	Pharmacokinetics	
Pediatric Conditions	Renal Disease	
Pharmacogenomics	Schizophrenia/Psychosis	
Learning IV Medications	Transplant	
Pulmonary Arterial Hypertension		
Sexual Dysfunction		
Sickle Cell Disease		
Sleep Disorders		
Stroke		
Thyroid Disorders		
Tobacco Cessation		
Travelers		
Weight Loss		

3 STUDYING CLINICAL & MATH CHAPTERS

HOW TO STUDY CLINICAL CHAPTERS

DECIDE IF YOU KNOW A TOPIC WELL BY REVIEWING THE CHAPTER IN THE COURSE BOOK

> ***Alternate your study time between the math test banks, and the clinical topics.***

Yes, I know this chapter well. It is a piece of cake.

- Complete a quick review of the chapter, then proceed to the Test Bank/s for that chapter. Several chapters have multiple test banks. Do not skip any.
- If the score is less than 70% in a Test Bank, proceed to the next step; you need to relearn the content in the chapter. If the score is 70% or higher, you need only to learn the missed items by following the steps in the diagram on the next page.

No, I do not know this chapter well. I forgot what I learned in school!

- Begin by reading the chapter or (preferably) begin by watching the video for the chapter with the Course Book open to the right page. Follow along with the instructor. The RxPrep instructors know the content well and can help you focus on the important information. Highlight in the Course Book the information you will need to review, and review it before taking the matching Test Bank/s.

Learning the Missed Test Bank Questions

- If a question was answered incorrectly, or the correct answer was chosen with a guess, you need to learn the information in the question. The same content can appear on the NAPLEX in a patient scenario or question that is different from the RxPrep Test Bank.

There are two options to learn the missed content described here, and shown in the diagram on the next page.

- **BEST METHOD:** make your own flashcard by writing the question on the front of an index card, and the answer on the back. Any information in the question feedback that you need to learn can be added to the card.
- **ALTERNATIVE METHOD:** let the computer make a "flashcard" for you: select the heart in the upper right hand corner of the question. The heart will turn red. The questions with red hearts will be kept together as online "flashcards" that are stored with the chapter topic on the Student Dashboard page.

WITH BOTH methods: DO NOT SKIP THIS STEP! Explain aloud, in your own words, why the answer is correct. Pretend you are explaining the question to someone you care about, such as your mother (for a patient) or another pharmacist (for content a patient would not need to know, such as a drug's mechanism of action). If you change the information into your own words and hear yourself explain it, your brain can more easily store the information. If using index cards, put the new card in the very back of the box. Every day, pull a small stack of cards from the front of the box and review them using the method in the last step of the diagram on the next page. If using hearts, review with the older flashcard sets first.

Mastering Cases

- NAPLEX questions are based on cases. You will need to pull information from a case to answer questions, such as:
  - How many grams of protein per day are being provided by the parenteral nutrition?
  - Which drug is the best option to treat the infection?
- Evaluating cases and making patient-specific recommendations about drug therapy requires practice. This is what the last year of most pharmacy school curriculum is focused on; do not take it for granted. Help with case-based questions can be found in several chapters: in Answering Case-Based Exam Questions, in Calculations V, and at the end of the Course Book in the chapter called Cases, Exam-Style Practice. There are more cases in the Test Banks, and in the cumulative NAPLEX-style Practice Exam, which is included with the RxPrep Test Banks. Do not skip any of the case-based practice.

3 ▶ *Continued*

HOW TO STUDY CLINICAL CHAPTERS *CONTINUED*

Must know topic well → TAKE TEST BANK

Know topic so-so or not well

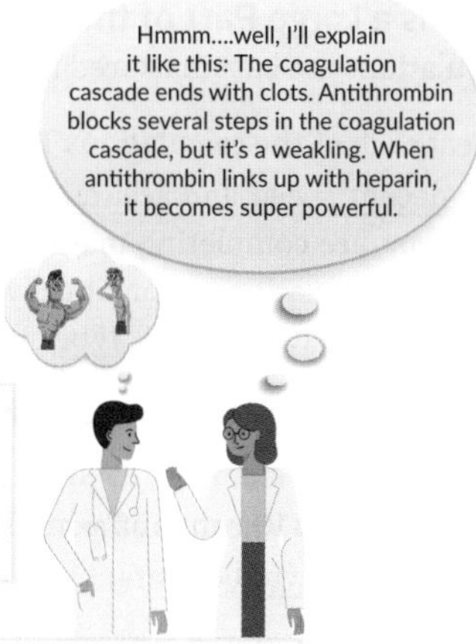

REMEDIATE

✓ Watch Video with Course Book, or read Course Book

✓ Highlight information to learn

✓ Review your highlights

↓

TAKE TEST BANK

Mark missed/near miss questions by selecting heart ♡→♥ or (higher retention rate!) prepare index card; see next.

↓

MAKE INDEX CARDS FOR MISSED QUESTIONS

With both index cards or flash cards made from ♥'s, master the concept by pretending to explain (teach) the concept to someone you care about. (see above)

What is the mechanism of action of heparin?

Heparin potentiates antithrombin. That means it makes antithrombin much more effective for anticoagulation.

↓

Review ♥ or index cards

When the question is known well, deselect the heart ♥→♡ or put the index card in a 'done' pile.
Do not test until all questions with a ♥ or on index cards from all test banks have been mastered.

This Course Book Has Built-in Goodies

- Important drugs for NAPLEX are **bolded** in the drug tables. Bolded drugs should be mastered.
- There are some drugs that are not bolded but have a small number of items **underlined**; again, focus on learning the information that is underlined.
- The **Study Tip Gals** are explaining how to learn something, or summarizing key points. Do not skip them.
- The **Key Drugs Guys** are there to help you learn the drugs that cause a condition (such as low blood glucose) or have preparation requirements (such as drugs that are put into saline only). Do not skip them.
- **Exam Scenarios** and **Clinical Scenarios** are located throughout the Course Book. Use these to test your knowledge; they represent the type of cases that can be seen on NAPLEX. Practice cases are also found in the Cases, Exam-Style Practice chapter and the RxPrep Test Banks.
- **Quick Guides** are located at the end of this chapter; these will help you to master formulas, terminology/abbreviations, medical tests and top selling medications.

BOLDED DRUG = TOP SELLER "MUST KNOW"

UNDERLINED INFORMATION = ESSENTIAL "MUST KNOW"

DRUG	DOSING	SAFETY/SIDE EFFECTS/MONITORING
Metformin *(Glucophage, Glucophage XR, Fortamet, Glumetza,* *Riomet)* IR: 500, 850, 1,000 mg	IR: 500 mg BID or 850 mg daily initially ER: 500-1,000 mg daily with dinner Titrate by 500 mg weekly or 850 mg every 2 weeks	**BOXED WARNING** Lactic acidosis – risk ↑ with hypoxic states (e.g., acute HF, sepsis), dehydration, hepatic or renal impairment, age ≥ 65 years, intravascular iodinated contrast media **CONTRAINDICATIONS** eGFR < 30 mL/min/1.73 m^2, acute or chronic metabolic acidosis (includes DKA), with or without coma

STUDY TIP GAL

- The gal with the light bulb points out a study tip.
- The study tips include an approach to complex concepts, a way to organize the information or a way to remember the information.

KEY DRUGS GUY

These are the MUST KNOW drugs for testing (e.g., drugs that cause hypoglycemia)

KEY DRUG LIST

The guy with the key points out key drugs.

These drugs have the same concern, but are less well-known.

3 ▶ *Continued*

HOW TO STUDY MATH

Math is a Large Part of the Exam

Calculations are best mastered through repetition.

Repeat each of the calculations Test Banks until you can do all of the problems with decent speed and accuracy. You will be ready for math on the NAPLEX when you are completing math problems on "auto pilot"; you see a problem, and the calculation automatically flows out from your pen. This happens because you have seen this type of problem many times.

Most of the calculations are in these chapters:

- Calculations chapters I, II, III and IV. The last Calculations chapter (Calculations V) contains exam-style math practice.
- Biostatistics chapter.
- Pharmacokinetics chapter.

> ***Repeat the math Test Banks until all the formulas on the Required Formulas Sheet are easily known and easy to calculate.***
> ***Math starts out difficult. With practice, math becomes automatic. Like learning to drive!***

The rest of the calculation problems are dispersed throughout the Course Book:

- Use the Required Formulas Checklist in this chapter to make sure none have been missed before taking the Practice NAPLEX Exam. Make sure you can check them off; a check mark means: I've got this one down.
- The formulas on the Required Formulas Sheet must be memorized.

When you can say: I have mastered everything on the Required Formulas Checklist, you have mastered NAPLEX math.

Keep Track of your Math Scores

- Use an index card to keep track of your math scores (see following index card example). Continue until you are easily scoring 100% on each Test Bank and can complete a 50-item test in 75 minutes.
- Follow the same instructions for the math in the Pharmacokinetics and Biostatistics chapters. You will need to learn all of the formulas, and how to use them, that are listed on the Required Formulas Sheet (and which you will check-off on the Required Formulas Checklist).

When scores are 100% in each section, cut back to 1 hour of practice per week. Increase the time 2 weeks prior to the NAPLEX. Formulas can be quickly forgotten.

Repeat for all of the chapters, until 100%. Practice at least 1 hr/day and ↑ on days off. When scores are > 80%, turn off feedback mode and focus on timing. Goal: 50 questions in 75 minutes.

Record your scores for the Test Banks for Calculations Chapters I, II, III and IV on the front of an index card. Record the scores for Biostatistics and Pharmacokinetics on the back. Re-do the Test Banks until you can easily score 100%, on all of them.

Test yourself on the matching Test Bank
Stuck? Click on the video link in the question's feedback section to watch the problem type be solved.

Complete Calculations chapters—solve each problem
Stuck? Read through the explanation +/- watch the instructor on the video solve each type of problem simply, step-by-step. Pause the videos and complete the rest of the problems in that section.

	Calc I	Calc II	Calc III	Calc IV
1st Attempt	46	54	33	44
2nd Attempt	72	88	50	67
3rd Attempt	94	92	78	88
4th Attempt	98	100	88	91

My Scores

Biostatistics	Pharmacokinetics
44	67
64	88
80	94

My Scores

These steps apply to Calculation chapters, I, II, III and IV, Biostatistics and Pharmacokinetics.

4 TAKE THE RxPREP PRACTICE NAPLEX EXAM

> *Calm your mind; you've done the work required to do well. Go and knock the exam out of the universe!*

YOU ARE READY TO TAKE THE PRACTICE EXAM WHEN:

1. The Math is a Piece of Cake

Each calculation is marked off on the Required Formulas Checklist, which indicates that the formula is known by heart, and the math can be completed flawlessly.*

2. The Index Card Box is Empty, or the Hearts Have Been De-Selected

This indicates that you have mastered the clinical questions.**

THEN, TAKE THE RxPREP PRACTICE NAPLEX EXAM. FIND IT WITH THE OTHER TEST BANKS IN THE NAPLEX COURSE.

- The practice exam has 150 questions. To have the same time per question as the NAPLEX exam, it should be taken as a timed, 3.5 hour exam.
- Any unanswered questions will receive zero points (the same as on the actual NAPLEX exam).
- Use a calculator only – no books or formula sheets.

Scored 80% or Higher on the Practice Exam? Almost Ready to Go.

- Take a couple of weeks before the exam to review a few items that are easily forgotten:
  - ❑ Review all of the math. Use the Required Formulas Checklist in this chapter to make sure none have been missed. This includes Calculations, Biostatistics, Pharmacokinetics and the individual formulas in other chapters (e.g., phenytoin adjustment and others).
  - ❑ Review the Compounding topics.
  - ❑ Review any topics in which you missed questions on the practice exam.

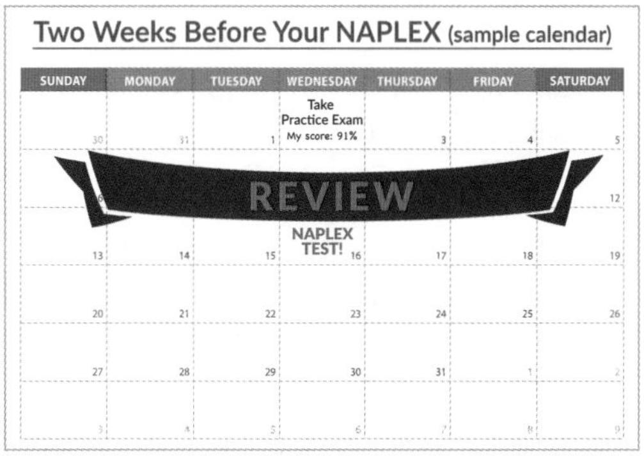

READY TO GO ON TO THE NAPLEX!

See the Required Formulas Checklist in this chapter.
***See the instructions for using index cards or hearts earlier in this chapter.*

REQUIRED FORMULAS CHECKLIST

Calculations
- ❑ Liquid (Volume) Conversions p. 117
- ❑ Solid (Weight) Conversions p. 117
- ❑ mEq to mmol, Height Conversions p. 117
- ❑ Percentage Strength p. 128
- ❑ Ratio Strength p. 132
- ❑ Parts Per Million (PPM) p. 134
- ❑ Specific Gravity (SG) p. 135
- ❑ Changing Strength or Volume (Q1C1, Dilution or Concentration p. 136
- ❑ Alligation p. 137
- ❑ Osmolarity p. 139
- ❑ Isotonicity (E-value) p. 142
- ❑ Moles and Millimoles p. 144
- ❑ Milliequivalents p. 146
- ❑ KCl Solution (Oral) to Tablets p. 147 (see #61)
- ❑ Corrected Calcium for ↓ Albumin p. 159
- ❑ Selecting and Calculating Patient Weights p. 168
- ❑ Body Mass Index (BMI) p. 166
- ❑ Ideal Body Weight (IBW) p. 167
- ❑ Adjusted Body Weight ($AdjBW_{0.4}$) p. 167
- ❑ Dehydration p. 174
- ❑ Parenteral Nutrition Calories p. 151
- ❑ Enteral Nutrition Calories p. 151
- ❑ Determining Fluid Needs p. 149
- ❑ Total Energy Expenditure p. 150
- ❑ Grams of Nitrogen From Protein p. 152
- ❑ Flow Rates (drops/min) p. 169
- ❑ Cockcroft-Gault Equation p. 175
- ❑ Arterial Blood Gases (ABG) p. 177
- ❑ Anion Gap p. 178
- ❑ pH Calculation p. 179
- ❑ Percent Ionization p. 182
- ❑ Absolute Neutrophil Count (ANC) p. 184

Answering Case-Based Exam Questions
- ❑ Fahrenheit ↔ Celsius, p. 108

Biostatistics
- ❑ Mean, Median and Mode p. 202
- ❑ Risk, Relative Risk (RR) p. 207
- ❑ Relative Risk Reduction (RRR) p. 208
- ❑ Absolute Risk Reduction (ARR) p. 208
- ❑ Number Needed to Treat (NNT) p. 209
- ❑ Number Needed to Harm (NNH) p. 210
- ❑ Odds Ratio (OR) p. 210
- ❑ Hazard Ratio (HR) p. 211
- ❑ Sensitivity and Specificity p. 214

Common Skin Conditions
- ❑ Time to Burn (TTB) p. 587

Diabetes
- ❑ Initiating Basal-Bolus Insulin p. 656
- ❑ Insulin-to-Carbohydrate Ratio: Rule of 500 for Rapid-Acting Insulin p. 656
- ❑ Insulin-to-Carbohydrate Ratio: Rule of 450 for Regular Insulin p. 656
- ❑ Correction Factor: 1,800 Rule for Rapid-Acting Insulin p. 657
- ❑ Correction Factor: 1,500 Rule for Regular Insulin p. 657
- ❑ Correction Dose p. 657

Dyslipidemia
- ❑ Friedewald Equation p. 443

Epilepsy/Seizures
- ❑ Phenytoin Correction for ↓ Albumin p. 949

Compounding
- ❑ Min Weighable Qty (MWQ) p. 252

Oncology II
- ❑ BSA Calculations, using Mosteller p. 861

Pharmacokinetics
- ❑ Bioavailability (F) p. 1011
- ❑ Volume of Distribution (Vd) p. 1012
- ❑ Clearance p. 1013
- ❑ Elimination Rate Constant (ke) p. 1016
- ❑ Predicting Drug Concentrations p. 1016
- ❑ Half-Life ($t_{1/2}$) p. 1017
- ❑ Loading Dose (LD) p. 1019

Dose Conversions (Oral, unless noted)
- ❑ Calcium Salts p. 148
- ❑ Aminophylline ↔ Theophylline p. 148
- ❑ Statins p. 446
- ❑ Loop Diuretics p. 493
- ❑ Metoprolol IV: PO Conversion p. 496
- ❑ Iron, Elemental p. 544
- ❑ Insulin Conversions p. 657
- ❑ Steroids p. 673
- ❑ Opioids (methodology) p. 806

NOTE: The Required Formulas can be found in the Quick Guides section at the end of this chapter, plus in an easy "tear out" page at the end of the Course Book.

THE NAPLEX COMPETENCY STATEMENTS

EXAM QUESTIONS MATCH TO THE COMPETENCY STATEMENTS

The NAPLEX Competency Statements are available on the National Association of Boards of Pharmacy (NABP) website at www.nabp.net. The competency statements provide a blueprint (outline) of tested items, split into two sections: Area #1 and Area #2.

Interpreting the meat and potatoes of the exam from some of the competency statements can be challenging. No worry; the RxPrep pharmacists have done that for you. Follow the recommendations in this chapter to do well on the exam.

AREA #1: ENSURE SAFE AND EFFECTIVE PHARMACOTHERAPY AND HEALTH OUTCOMES (67% OF THE EXAM)

- This section includes mechanism of action, indications, side effects, contraindications and drug interactions.
- Brand/generics are tested, along with common dosage forms.
- Questions are largely asked in a case-based format. It will be important to quickly identify pertinent information from a case (e.g., abnormal labs, past medical history, medication use history, etc.) and recognize appropriate or inappropriate treatments. It is critical to master the chapter called Learning Lab Values & Drug Monitoring; lab ranges will be provided.
- Learning Drug Interactions is an overview chapter; it is not necessary to know every drug interaction, nor is it possible. Most pharmacists will know the big inhibitors, big inducers and the drugs that interact commonly (e.g., warfarin and theophylline). Review this chapter prior to tackling the disease state chapters to cover the interactions that appear repeatedly.
- Patient counseling is critical, especially for formulations that come in delivery vehicles other than tablets and capsules, including inhalers, self-injectables, patches and topicals.
- It will be important to be able to read study summaries and interpret the data. Biostatistics must be mastered. Many pharmacists are not particularly endeared to biostatistics; yet, the math is simpler than with many other calculations. Follow the steps, one at a time, and you will find biostatistics math is simpler than expected.
- Be able to apply Pharmacokinetic and Pharmacogenomic parameters to individualize drug treatment.
- Pulling data from drug references is required to respond to questions from other healthcare professionals and patients. Complete the questions at the end of the Learning Drug References chapter. There is an answer sheet under the Student Resources tab at www.rxprep.com. Additional drug reference questions are in the Test Bank.
- Vaccination rates have increased because of pharmacists, and providing vaccinations is a required skill. Vaccines are covered in the Immunizations and Travelers chapters.
- The other chapters are essential. Cases which are centered on the material in any chapter (Diabetes, Chronic Heart Failure, Oncology, Cystic Fibrosis... all the rest) can be on your exam, and will test Area #1 competencies.

AREA #2: SAFE AND ACCURATE PREPARATION, COMPOUNDING, DISPENSING, AND ADMINISTRATION OF MEDICATIONS AND PROVISION OF HEALTH CARE PRODUCTS (33% OF THE EXAM)

- This section includes calculations. It covers nutritional requirements and basic nutritional calculations. Flow rates for drugs administered by IV infusion are essential, along with drug concentrations, and the other general calculations.
- Techniques, procedures and equipment used for sterile and non-sterile compounding, including hazardous drugs, are a requirement.
- Be familiar with storage, packaging, handling and medication disposal. These are all important to discuss with a patient when counseling on a new prescription.
- Instructions and techniques for medication administration are tested in this section.

FORMAT OF THE EXAM

NAPLEX is a 6-hour exam with 250 questions. Most questions are based on a patient case. Of these, 200 questions are used to calculate the score. The other 50 questions are pre-test questions that are being evaluated for inclusion on future exams. Pre-test questions are interspersed throughout the exam; it is not possible to identify the pre-test questions. The total test time is 6 hours. The computer screen will display a prompt for two optional 10-minute breaks. Any other non-scheduled breaks you request will be subtracted from the total time.

- There are 5 question types on the NAPLEX. Each of the 5 types are in the RxPrep Test Banks:
  - Multiple-Choice: select the one correct answer.
  - Multiple-Response: select all of the correct responses and no incorrect response/s for credit.
  - Constructed-Response: enter the answer using the computer keyboard (usually for math problems).
  - Ordered-Response: put the items in a specified order.
  - Hot Spot: select the correct area on a diagram or picture by clicking on it.
- The majority of the questions (including calculations) are asked in a case-based format (such as patient profiles with accompanying questions). There are also stand alone questions.
- All questions must be answered in the order in which they are presented. It is not possible to skip questions, or go back to a question at a later time.
- Personal calculators may not be used during the exam. The Pearson VUE testing center console uses an on-screen calculator which looks similar to the Texas Instruments TI-30XS Multiview, and other similar hand-held, non-graphing calculators. The on-screen calculator can be opened in a pop-up window during the exam at any time (a similar on-screen calculator is available in the RxPrep Test Bank for practice, when taking the tests on a computer browser). A candidate requesting a handheld calculator will be given a five function calculator. The hand-held calculator is useful for simple calculations, such as 65.5 mg x 5. Some of the calculations may require advanced functions only available on the on-screen calculator (e.g., order of operands, exponents, and most problems with multiple steps). Refer to the Calculations chapters for detailed information.

ARRIVAL DETAILS, TUTORIAL

On the day of the exam, arrive at least 30 minutes prior to your appointment for check-in procedures (ID verification, palm vein scan, digital signature and photograph). Review the Candidate Registration Bulletin for details on acceptable forms of ID, prohibited items and exam misconduct.

- If you arrive 30 minutes or later than your scheduled appointment, and are refused admission to sit for the exam, you will be required to forfeit your appointment.
- Take the online exam tutorial before starting the exam. The tutorial will explain how to open up lab screens, navigate the cases, enter answers, etc. The tutorial is important, and does not take away from your time.

CASE PRACTICE

Interpreting cases requires knowledge of medical terms, diagnostic tests and commonly-used abbreviations. The terms, tests and abbreviations that appear throughout this Course Book and in the Test Banks are pulled together on the following pages.

- Diagnostic Tests
- Medical Terms
- Medical Abbreviations

Case-Based Math

The majority of the math questions will appear in cases (e.g., calculating the amount of glucose received from IV fluids and piggybacks over the past 24 hours, or locating the renal function in a lab report to calculate an antibiotic dose or a flow rate). You must memorize and understand how to use the Required Formulas. You can find the Required Formulas with the Quick Guides after this chapter. There is a Required Formulas Checklist earlier in this chapter. Check off a formula only when you have the formula memorized, and you know how to use it. Each formula must be checked off prior to taking the exam.

PHARMACY LAW EXAMS

MPJE POINTERS

It is best to study for the MPJE when the NAPLEX has been completed. The scores from the NAPLEX arrive quickly, and at that point law preparation can begin. Unlike the law exam in California (the CPJE), there is little overlap between the NAPLEX and MPJE.

Depending on the person's prior knowledge (i.e., experience working in a pharmacy setting), students will take from 2 - 5 weeks for MPJE preparation. The RxPrep MPJE course will provide the content needed to do well.

CPJE POINTERS

This text includes the topics that overlap with the CPJE (Medication Safety, Infectious Diseases, Immunizations, HIV, others). The clinical topics not covered on the NAPLEX that are tested on the CPJE are included in the separate CPJE course (e.g., therapeutic interchange). California law is covered completely. The CPJE course is available at www.rxprep.com.

Best wishes for your exam preparation.

The RxPrep Pharmacy Team.

QUICK GUIDES

CONTENTS

TOP OUTPATIENT DRUGS | 15

Brand names are provided as a study aid; with some drugs, the generic is more commonly used, and the brand name is not as important. This applies to inpatient and OTC drugs; i.e., the drug can be referred to with the generic name.

Medications used in the outpatient (community) pharmacy setting are commonly oral formulations. The Quick Guide lists when the formulation is not oral.

TOP INPATIENT DRUGS | 19

The common medication formulations used in the inpatient setting are noted.

TOP OTC DRUGS | 23

For drugs that are available in both OTC and Rx (prescription) versions: the Rx doses are generally higher than the OTC doses. The brand names can be different, e.g., orlistat OTC *(Alli)* is 60 mg/dose, orlistat Rx *(Xenical)* is 120 mg/dose.

REQUIRED FORMULAS FOR THE NAPLEX | 25

The formulas on this list are the must-know formulas for the exam. Do not expect them to be provided.

DIAGNOSTIC TESTS | 27

Common diagnostic tests are pulled together for use as a study guide. The diagnostic tests can be found again in the individual chapters.

MEDICAL TERMS | 30

Common medical terminology is pulled together for use as a study guide. The terms can appear in a case question. Do not expect the case to explain the meaning of the terminology. Additional terminology can be found in Lab Values & Drug Monitoring (this chapter is very helpful as a study guide), Anemia, Compounding and Oncology.

COMMON MEDICAL ABBREVIATIONS | 39

The abbreviations on this list are used commonly, in many practice settings. They can appear in cases on the exam, and the meaning may not be provided.

HOW TO USE THE RXPREP COURSE BOOK

Drugs that are top-sellers in the outpatient setting are bolded. Drugs with key safety considerations and important hospital drugs are also bolded; they could be tested, even though they are not top sellers. If information is underlined, it is essential to know for the exam.

BOLDED DRUG = TOP SELLER "MUST KNOW"

DRUG	DOSING	SAFETY/SIDE EFFECTS/MONITORING
MetFORMIN ***(Glucophage, Glucophage XR,*** *Fortamet, Glumetza, Riomet)* IR: 500, 850, 1,000 mg	IR: 500 mg BID or 850 mg daily initially ER: 500-1,000 mg daily with dinner initially Titrate by 500 mg weekly or 850 mg every 2 weeks	**BOXED WARNING** Lactic acidosis – risk ↑ with hypoxic states (e.g., acute HF, sepsis), dehydration, hepatic or renal impairment, age ≥ 65 years, intravascular iodinated contrast media, alcohol or certain drugs (see Drug Interactions) **CONTRAINDICATIONS** eGFR < 30 mL/min/1.73 m^2, acute or chronic metabolic acidosis (includes DKA), with or without coma

UNDERLINED INFORMATION = ESSENTIAL "MUST KNOW"

Study Tip Gal Box

STUDY TIP

- The gal with the light bulb points out a study tip.
- The study tips include an approach to complex concepts, a way to organize the information or a way to remember the information.

Guidelines/References
The main source of information about the medications in this book is the FDA-approved package labeling (package inserts).

Key Drug Guy Box

OTHER DRUGS

KEY DRUGS

These are the MUST KNOW drugs for testing purposes

The guy with the key points out key drugs.

This part of the box includes a list of drugs that cause something (like hypoglycemia or hypertension).

Practice Cases, Questions and Exam Scenarios
Practice cases and sample questions can be found at the end of the Coursebook and in several chapters. These are designed to be somewhat similar to cases you might see on the exam. They allow you to test your knowledge. Exam scenarios can be found throughout the Course Book in grey shaded boxes. The RxPrep Test Bank contains > 3,500 additional practice questions (including case-based practice) and a practice exam.

Updates
Refer to ***www.rxprep.com*** (Student Resources page) for updates throughout the year and other helpful information.

TOP OUTPATIENT DRUGS

DRUG	BRAND NAME
Acetaminophen/ Codeine	*Tylenol with Codeine #2, #3, #4*
Acyclovir	*Zovirax*
Albuterol	*ProAir HFA, ProAir RespiClick, Proventil HFA, Ventolin HFA*
Albuterol/Ipratropium	*Combivent Respimat*
Alendronate	*Fosamax*
Allopurinol	*Zyloprim, Aloprim*
Alprazolam	*Xanax*
Amiodarone	*Pacerone*
Amitriptyline	
Amlodipine	*Norvasc*
Amlodipine/ Benazepril	*Lotrel*
Amoxicillin	*Moxatag*
Amoxicillin/ Clavulanate	*Augmentin*
Amphetamine/ Dextroamphetamine	*Adderall*
Anastrozole	*Arimidex*
Apixaban	*Eliquis*
Aripiprazole	*Abilify*
Atenolol	*Tenormin*
Atenolol/ Chlorthalidone	*Tenoretic*
Atomoxetine	*Strattera*
Atorvastatin	*Lipitor*
Azelastine	
Azithromycin	*Zithromax, Zithromax Z-Pak, Zmax*
Bacitracin/Neomycin/ Polymyxin B/ Hydrocortisone	*Cortisporin*
Baclofen	*Lioresal*
Beclomethasone	*QVAR RediHaler*

DRUG	BRAND NAME
Benazepril	*Lotensin*
Benzonatate	*Tessalon Perles*
Benztropine	*Cogentin*
Bimatoprost	*Lumigan, Latisse*
Bisoprolol/HCTZ	*Ziac*
Brompheniramine/ Pseudoephedrine/ Dextromethorphan	*Bromfed DM*
Budesonide	*Pulmicort, Pulmicort Flexhaler*
Buprenorphine	*Belbuca (Buccal Film), Butrans (Patch)*
Buprenorphine/ Naloxone	*Suboxone (SL Film), Bunavail (Buccal Film), Zubsolv (SL Tablet)*
Bupropion	*Wellbutrin SR, Wellbutrin XL, Zyban*
Buspirone	
Butalbital/ Acetaminophen/ Caffeine	*Fioricet*
Canagliflozin	*Invokana*
Carbidopa/Levodopa	*Sinemet*
Carisoprodol	*Soma*
Carvedilol	*Coreg*
Cefdinir	
Cefuroxime	*Ceftin*
Celecoxib	*Celebrex*
Cephalexin	*Keflex*
Cetirizine	*Zyrtec*
Chlorhexidine, Topical Antiseptic	*Hibiclens*
Chlorthalidone	
Cholecalciferol, Vitamin D3	

DRUG	BRAND NAME
Ciprofloxacin	*Cipro*
Ciprofloxacin/ Dexamethasone	*Ciprodex*
Citalopram	*Celexa*
Clarithromycin	*Biaxin*
Clindamycin, Topical	*Cleocin, Clindagel*
Clobetasol, Topical	*Clobex, Temovate, Olux*
Clonazepam	*Klonopin*
Clonidine	*Catapres, Catapres-TTS, Kapvay*
Clopidogrel	*Plavix*
Clotrimazole/ Betamethasone, Topical	*Lotrisone*
Codeine/ Promethazine	
Colchicine	*Colcrys*
Cyanocobalamin, Vitamin B-12	
Cyclobenzaprine	*Amrix, Fexmid*
Cyclosporine	*Restasis*
Desvenlafaxine	*Pristiq*
Dexamethasone	*DexPak*
Dexlansoprazole	*Dexilant*
Dextromethorphan/ Promethazine	
Diazepam	*Valium*
Diclofenac, Topical	*Voltaren Gel*
Dicyclomine	*Bentyl*
Digoxin	*Digitek, Lanoxin*
Diltiazem	*Cardizem, Tiazac*
Diphenhydramine, OTC	*Benadryl*
Diphenoxylate/ Atropine	*Lomotil*
Divalproex/Valproate	*Depakene, Depakote*

Top Outpatient Drugs Continued

DRUG	BRAND NAME
Docusate Sodium	*Colace*
Donepezil	*Aricept*
Doxazosin	*Cardura*
Doxepin	
Doxycycline	*Vibramycin*
Dulaglutide	*Trulicity*
Duloxetine	*Cymbalta*
Empagliflozin	*Jardiance*
Enalapril	*Vasotec*
Epinephrine	*EpiPen, EpiPen Jr, Adrenaclick*
Ergocalciferol, Vitamin D2	*Calciferol*
Erythromycin	*E.E.S. 400, Ery-Tab*
Escitalopram	*Lexapro*
Esomeprazole	*Nexium, Nexium 24HR, Nexium IV*
Estradiol, Patch	*Vivelle-Dot, Alora, Climara*
Estradiol, Topical/ Ring	*Estrace, Estring, Vagifem*
Estrogens, Conjugated	*Premarin*
Eszopiclone	*Lunesta*
Ethinyl Estradiol and Norgestimate	*Ortho Tri-Cyclen, Sprintec, TriNessa*
Ethinyl Estradiol/ Etonogestrel	*NuvaRing*
Ethinyl Estradiol/ Norethindrone Fe	*Junel, Loestrin*
Ezetimibe	*Zetia*
Famotidine	*Pepcid*
Fenofibrate	*Antara, Tricor, Trilipix*
Fentanyl, Patch	*Duragesic*
Finasteride	*Proscar*
Fluconazole	*Diflucan*
Fluocinonide, Topical	*Vanos*
Fluoxetine	*Prozac, Prozac Weekly, Sarafem*

DRUG	BRAND NAME
Fluticasone	*Flovent Diskus, Flovent HFA, Arnuity Ellipta*
Fluticasone Furoate/ Vilanterol	*Breo Ellipta*
Fluticasone Propionate	*Flonase Allergy Relief, Veramyst*
Fluticasone/ Salmeterol	*Advair Diskus, Advair HFA*
Folic acid, Vitamin B9	
Formoterol/ Budesonide	*Symbicort*
Furosemide	*Lasix*
Gabapentin	*Neurontin*
Gemfibrozil	*Lopid*
Glimepiride	*Amaryl*
Glipizide	*Glucotrol, Glucotrol XL*
Glyburide	*Glynase*
Guanfacine	*Intuniv, Tenex*
Hydralazine	
Hydrochlorothiazide	*Microzide*
Hydrocodone/ Acetaminophen	*Lortab, Lorcet, Norco, Vicodin*
Hydrocortisone, Topical	*Cortaid, others*
Hydromorphone	*Dilaudid*
Hydroxychloroquine	*Plaquenil*
Hydroxyzine	*Vistaril*
Ibuprofen (high dose)	
Inactivated Influenza Vaccine	*Fluarix, Fluzone High Dose,* others with *Flu* in name
Inactivated Quadrivalent Influenza Vaccines (IIV4)	*Fluarix Quadrivalent, Flucelvax Quadrivalent,* others
Indomethacin	*Indocin*
Insulin Aspart	*NovoLOG, NovoLOG FlexPen*

DRUG	BRAND NAME
Insulin Detemir	*Levemir, Levemir FlexTouch*
Insulin Glargine	*Lantus, Lantus SoloStar, Toujeo SoloStar*
Insulin Lispro	*HumaLOG, HumaLOG KwikPen*
Irbesartan	*Avapro*
Isosorbide Mononitrate	
Ketoconazole, Topical	*Nizoral, Nizoral A-D (OTC)*
Ketorolac	*Acular*
Labetalol	
Lamotrigine	*Lamictal, Lamictal ODT, Lamictal Starter Kit*
Lansoprazole	*Prevacid, Prevacid 24HR, Prevacid SoluTab*
Latanoprost	*Xalatan*
Levetiracetam	*Keppra*
Levocetirizine	*Xyzal*
Levofloxacin	*Levaquin*
Levothyroxine	*Levoxyl, Synthroid, Unithroid*
Lidocaine Viscous Solution	
Linaclotide	*Linzess*
Linagliptin	*Tradjenta*
Liothyronine	*Cytomel*
Liraglutide	*Victoza, Saxenda*
Lisdexamfetamine	*Vyvanse*
Lisinopril	*Prinivil, Zestril*
Lisinopril/HCTZ	*Zestoretic*
Lithium	*Lithobid*
Loratadine	*Claritin*
Lorazepam	*Ativan*

Top Outpatient Drugs Continued

DRUG	BRAND NAME
Losartan	*Cozaar*
Losartan/HCTZ	*Hyzaar*
Lovastatin	*Altoprev*
Medroxyprogesterone	*Provera*
Meloxicam	*Mobic*
Memantine	*Namenda*
Metformin	*Glucophage, Glucophage XR, Fortamet, Glumetza*
Methadone	*Dolophine*
Methocarbamol	*Robaxin*
Methotrexate	*Trexall*
Methylphenidate	*Concerta, Daytrana, Ritalin*
Methylprednisolone	*Medrol*
Metoclopramide	*Reglan*
Metoprolol Succinate ER	*Toprol XL*
Metoprolol Tartrate IR	*Lopressor*
Metronidazole	*Flagyl*
Minocycline	*Minocin, Solodyn*
Mirtazapine	*Remeron, Remeron SolTab*
Mometasone, Topical	*Elocon*
Mometasone/ Formoterol	*Dulera*
Montelukast	*Singulair*
Morphine	*MS Contin, Kadian, Duramorph*
Mupirocin, Topical	*Bactroban*
Nabumetone	
Naproxen (high dose)	
Nebivolol	*Bystolic*

DRUG	BRAND NAME
Neomycin/Polymyxin B/ Dexamethasone	*Maxitrol*
Nifedipine ER	*Adalat CC, Procardia XL*
Nitrofurantoin	*Macrobid, Macrodantin*
Nitroglycerin	*Nitrostat, Nitrolingual, NitroMist*
Nortriptyline	*Pamelor*
Nystatin	*Bio-Statin*
Ofloxacin	*Ocuflox*
Olanzapine	*Zyprexa*
Olmesartan	*Benicar*
Olmesartan/HCTZ	*Benicar HCT*
Olopatadine	*Pataday, Patanol*
Omega-3 Fatty Acids	*Lovaza, Vascepa*
Omeprazole	*Prilosec*
Ondansetron	*Zofran, Zofran ODT*
Oseltamivir	*Tamiflu*
Oxcarbazepine	*Trileptal*
Oxybutynin	*Ditropan XL, Oxytrol*
Oxycodone ER	*Oxycontin*
Oxycodone/ Acetaminophen	*Percocet, Endocet*
Pantoprazole	*Protonix*
Paroxetine	*Paxil*
Penicillin VK	
Phenazopyridine	*Pyridium*
Phenobarbital	
Phentermine	*Adipex-P*
Phenytoin	*Dilantin*
Pioglitazone	*Actos*

DRUG	BRAND NAME
Pneumococcal Conjugate Vaccine (13-Valent)	*Prevnar 13*
Polymyxin/ Trimethoprim	*Polytrim*
Potassium Chloride	*Klor-Con, Klor-Con 10, Micro-K*
Pramipexole	*Mirapex, Mirapex ER*
Pravastatin	*Pravachol*
Prednisolone	*Omnipred, Pred Forte, Pred Mild*
Prednisolone	*Millipred, Orapred ODT*
Prednisone	*Deltasone*
Pregabalin	*Lyrica*
Progesterone	*Prometrium*
Promethazine	*Phenergan*
Propranolol	*Inderal*
Quetiapine	*Seroquel*
Quinapril	*Accupril*
Ramipril	*Altace*
Ranitidine	*Zantac*
Risperidone	*Risperdal*
Rivaroxaban	*Xarelto*
Ropinirole	*Requip*
Rosuvastatin	*Crestor*
Sertraline	*Zoloft*
Sildenafil	*Viagra, Revatio*
Simvastatin	*Zocor*
Sitagliptan	*Januvia*
Sitagliptan/Metformin	*Janumet*
Sodium/Potassium/ Magnesium Sulfate	*Suprep Bowel Prep Kit*

Top Outpatient Drugs Continued

DRUG	BRAND NAME
Solifenacin	*Vesicare*
Spironolactone	*Aldactone*
Sucralfate	*Carafate*
Sulfamethoxazole/ Trimethoprim	*Bactrim*
Sumatriptan	*Imitrex, Imitrex STATdose*
Tadalafil	*Cialis, Adcirca*
Tamsulosin	*Flomax*
Temazepam	*Restoril*
Terazosin	
Testosterone Cypionate, Injection	
Testosterone, Topical	*AndroGel*
Thyroid, Desiccated	*Armour Thyroid*
Timolol	*Timoptic, Istalol, Timoptic-XE*
Timolol/Dorzolamide	*Cosopt, Cosopt PF*
Tiotropium	*Spiriva HandiHaler, Spiriva Respimat*
Tizanidine	*Zanaflex*
Topiramate	*Topamax*

DRUG	BRAND NAME
Tramadol	*Ultram, Ultram ER*
Travoprost	*Travatan Z*
Trazodone	
Tretinoin, Topical	*Atralin, Renova, Retin-A*
Triamcinolone, Topical	*Kenalog*
Triamterene/HCTZ	*Dyazide, Maxzide*
Valacyclovir	*Valtrex*
Valsartan	*Diovan*
Valsartan/HCTZ	*Diovan HCT*
Varenicline	*Chantix*
Venlafaxine	*Effexor*
Verapamil	*Calan*
Warfarin	*Coumadin, Jantoven*
Zolpidem	*Ambien, Ambien CR, Edluar, Intermezzo*

RxPrep thanks Iqvia and Mr. Robert Hunkler for providing this list to assist the students preparing for licensure.

TOP INPATIENT DRUGS

DRUG	BRAND NAME
Abacavir/Lamivudine, Oral	*Epzicom*
Abciximab, Injection	*Reopro*
Acetaminophen, Oral, Rectal, Injection	*Tylenol (Oral/ Suppository), Ofirmev (Injection)*
Acyclovir, Oral Capsule/Tablet, Injection	*Zovirax*
Adalimumab, Injection	*Humira*
Albumin	
Albuterol, Oral Inhaler	*ProAir HFA, ProAir RespiClick, Proventil HFA, Ventolin HFA*
Alteplase, Injection	*Activase*
Amikacin, Injection	
Amiodarone, Oral, Injection	*Pacerone (Oral), Nexterone (comes in non-PVC IV bag)*
Amphotericin B Liposomal, Injection	*Ambisome*
Ampicillin, Oral Capsule/Suspension, Injection	
Ampicillin/Sulbactam, Injection	*Unasyn*
Antithymocyte Globulin (Equine), Injection	*Atgam*
Antithymocyte Globulin (Rabbit), Injection	*Thymoglobulin*
Apixaban, Oral	*Eliquis*
Aprepitant, Oral	*Emend*
Argatroban, Injection	
Aripiprazole, Oral, Injection	*Abilify, Abilify Maintenna (4-weeks)*
Atazanavir, Oral	*Reyataz*
Azithromycin, Oral Tablet/Suspension, Injection	*Zithromax*

DRUG	BRAND NAME
Aztreonam, Injection	*Azactam*
Baclofen, Oral	*Lioresal*
Basiliximab, Injection	*Simulect*
Belimumab, Injection	*Benlysta*
Bevacizumab, Injection	*Avastin*
Bivalirudin, Injection	*Angiomax*
Bleomycin, Injection	
Budesonide, Oral	*Entocort EC, Uceris*
Budesonide/ Formoterol, Oral Inhaler	*Symbicort*
Busulfan, Injection	*Busulfex, Myleran*
Calcitonin, Intranasal, Injection	*Miacalcin*
Carboplatin, Injection	
Carmustine, Injection	*BiCNU*
Caspofungin, Injection	*Cancidas*
Cefazolin, Injection	
Cefepime, Injection	*Maxipime*
Cefotaxime, Injection	*Claforan*
Cefotetan, Injection	*Cefotan*
Ceftaroline, Injection	*Teflaro*
Ceftazidime, Injection	*Fortaz*
Ceftriaxone, Injection	*Rocephin*
Certolizumab Pegol, Injection	*Cimzia (2-weeks or 4-weeks)*
Cetuximab, Injection	*Erbitux*
Cinacalcet, Oral	*Sensipar*
Ciprofloxacin, Oral, Injection	*Cipro*
Ciprofloxacin/ Dexamethasone, Otic Suspension	*Ciprodex*
Cisatracurium, Injection	*Nimbex*
Cisplatin, Injection	

DRUG	BRAND NAME
Clindamycin Oral, Topical, Injection	*Cleocin*
Cyclophosphamide, Oral, Injection	*Cytoxan*
Cyclosporine, Oral, Injection	*Cyclosporine, modified (Neoral, Gengraf)-Oral Cyclosporine, non-modified (Sandimmune)- Oral, IV*
D5W	
Daptomycin, Injection	*Cubicin*
Darbepoetin, Injection	*Aranesp*
Darunavir, Oral	*Prezista*
Denosumab, Injection	*Prolia, Xgeva*
Desflurane, Inhalation	*Suprane*
Dexamethasone Oral, Injection	*DexPak, Decadron*
Dexmedetomidine, Injection	*Precedex*
Diazepam, Oral, Injection	*Valium*
Digoxin Immune Fab, Injection	*Digifab*
Diphenhydramine, Oral, Injection	*Benadryl*
Diphtheria and Tetanus Toxoids, Acellular Pertussis (Tdap) Vaccine	*Adacel, Boostrix*
Docetaxel, Injection	*Taxotere*
Dolutegravir, Oral	*Tivicay*
Dolutegravir/ Abacavir/ Lamivudine, Oral	*Triumeq*
Donepezil, Oral	*Aricept*
Dopamine, Injection	
Dornase Alfa, Inhalation	*Pulmozyme*
Doxorubicin Liposomal, Injection	*Doxil*
Doxycycline, Oral Capsule, Injection	*Vibramycin, Doxy 100*

Top Inpatient Drugs Continued

DRUG	BRAND NAME
DTaP-HepB-IPV Vaccine, IM Injection	*Pediarix*
Elvitegravir/ Cobicistat/ Emtricitabine/ Tenofovir Alafenamide, Oral	*Genvoya*
Elvitegravir/ Cobicistat/ Emtricitabine/ Tenofovir Disoproxil Fumarate, Oral	*Stribild*
Emtricitabine/ Tenofovir Alafenamide, Oral	*Descovy*
Emtricitabine/ Tenofovir Alafenamide/ Rilpivirine, Oral	*Odefsey*
Emtricitabine/ Tenofovir Disoproxil Fumarate, Oral	*Truvada*
Emtricitabine/ Tenofovir Disoproxil Fumarate/ Efavirenz, Oral	*Atripla*
Emtricitabine/ Tenofovir Disoproxil Fumarate/ Rilpivirine, Oral	*Complera*
Enalaprilat, Injection	*Vasotec IV*
Enoxaparin, Injection	*Lovenox*
Epinephrine, Injection	*Adrenalin*
Epoetin Alfa, Injection	*Epogen, Procrit*
Epoprostenol, Injection	*Flolan*
Ertapenem, Injection	*Invanz*
Erythromycin, Oral Capsule/Tablet/ Suspension, Injection	*Erythrocin*
Esmolol, Injection	*Brevibloc*
Esomeprazole, Oral, Injection	*Nexium*
Etanercept, Injection	*Enbrel (twice-weekly or weekly)*
Etonogestrel, Implant	*Nexplanon*
Everolimus, Oral	*Afinitor*

DRUG	BRAND NAME
Famotidine, Oral, Injection	*Pepcid*
Fentanyl, Patch, Injection	*Sublimaze (Injection), Duragesic (Patch)*
Ferumoxytol, Injection	*Feraheme*
Fidaxomicin, Oral	*Dificid*
Filgrastim, Injection	*Neupogen*
Fluconazole Oral Tablet/Suspension, Injection	*Diflucan*
Flucytosine, Oral Capsule	*Ancobon*
Flumazenil, Injection	
Fluorouracil, 5-FU, Injection	*Adrucil*
Fluticasone, Oral Inhaler	*Flovent Diskus, Flovent HFA, Arnuity Ellipta*
Fluticasone/ Salmeterol, Oral Inhaler	*Advair Diskus, Advair HFA*
Fosphenytoin, Injection	*Cerebyx*
Four Factor Prothrombin Complex Concentrate, Injection	*Kcentra*
Fulvestrant, Injection	*Faslodex*
Furosemide, Oral, Injection	*Lasix*
Ganciclovir, injection	*Cytovene*
Gentamicin, Injection	
Glatiramer Acetate, Injection	*Copaxone*
Glucagon, Injection	*GlucaGen*
Golimumab, Injection	*Simponi (monthly or 2-months)*
Goserelin, Injection	*Zoladex*
Granisetron, Oral, Injection	*Sancuso*
Haloperidol, Oral, Injection (stat relief), Decanoate Injection (long-lasting)	*Haldol, Haldol Decanoate (4-weeks)*
Heparin, Injection	

DRUG	BRAND NAME
Hepatitis A Vaccine, Injection	*Havrix, VAQTA*
Hepatitis B Vaccine, Injection	*Engerix-B, Recombivax HB*
Human Papillomavirus (HPV) Vaccine (9-valent), Injection	*Gardasil 9*
Hydralazine, Injection	
Hydrocortisone, Injection	*Solu-Cortef*
Hydromorphone HCl, Oral, Injection	*Dilaudid*
Ibandronate, Oral (monthly), Injection (3-months)	*Boniva*
Ibuprofen Oral, Injection	*Motrin (Oral), Caldolor (Injection)*
Idarucizumab, Injection	*Praxbind*
Ifosfamide, Injection	*Ifex*
Imatinib, Oral Tablet	*Gleevec*
Inactivated Influenza Vaccine, Injection	*Fluarix, Fluzone High Dose,* others with *Flu* in name
Inactivated Quadrivalent Influenza Vaccines (IIV4)	*Fluarix Quadrivalent, Flucelvax Quadrivalent,* others
Infliximab, Injection	*Remicade (4-8 weeks)*
Insulin Aspart, SC Injection	*Novolog, Novolog Flexpen*
Insulin Detemir, SC Injection	*Levemir*
Insulin Glargine, SC Injection	*Lantus Solostar, Lantus, Toujeo Max Solostar, Toujeo Solostar*
Insulin Lispro, SC Injection	*Humalog*
Ipratropium bromide, Oral Inhaler	*Atrovent HFA*
Irinotecan, Injection	*Camptosar*
Iron Sucrose, Injection	*Venofer*
Ketorolac Oral, Nasal, Injection	*Toradol*

Top Inpatient Drugs Continued

DRUG	BRAND NAME
Labetalol, Injection	
Lactated Ringer's	
Lactulose, Oral	*Enulose*
Leuprolide: Injection	*Lupron Depot*
Levofloxacin, Oral Tablet/Solution, Injection	*Levaquin*
Levonorgestrel, IUD	*Mirena*
Levothyroxine, Oral, Injection	*Synthroid*
Lidocaine, Injection	
Linezolid, Oral Tablet/ Suspension, Injection	*Zyvox*
Lorazepam, Oral, Injection	*Ativan*
Lurasidone, Oral	*Latuda*
Mannitol, Injection	
Measles-Mumps-Rubella Vaccine (MMR), Injection	*M-M-R-II*
Measles-Mumps-Rubella-Varicella Vaccine (MMRV); Injection	*ProQuad*
Medroxyprogesterone Acetate, Oral	*Provera*
Memantine, Oral	*Namenda*
Meningococcal Vaccine (MCV4), Injection	*Menactra, Menveo*
Meperidine Oral, Injection	*Demerol*
Meropenem, Injection	*Merrem*
Methotrexate, Oral, Injection	*Trexall (Oral)*
Methylprednisolone, Injection	*Solu-Medrol*
Metoprolol Tartrate, Oral, Injection	*Lopressor*
Metronidazole, Oral, Injection	*Flagyl*
Micafungin, Injection	*Mycamine*
Mitoxantrone, Injection	

DRUG	BRAND NAME
Morphine, Oral, Injection	*Kadian, MS Contin (Oral), Infumorph, Duramorph (Injection)*
Moxifloxacin, Oral Tablet, Injection	*Avelox*
Mycophenolate Mofetil, Oral, Injection	*Cellcept*
Naloxone, Injection	*Narcan*
Natalizumab, Injection	*Tysabri*
Nicardipine, Injection	*Cardene IV*
Nimodipine, Oral	
Nitroglycerin Oral, Injection, Dermal	*Nitrostat (SL) Nitro-BID (ointment)*
Nitroprusside, Injection	*Nitropress, Nipride*
Norepinephrine, Injection	*Levophed*
NS (1/2 NS, 1/4 NS)	
Octreotide, Injection	*Sandostatin*
Olanzapine, Oral, Injection	*Zyprexa*
Omalizumab, Injection	*Xolair*
Ondansetron, Oral Tablet/Solution/Film, Injection	*Zofran*
Oseltamivir Oral Capsule/Suspension	*Tamiflu*
Oxycodone, Oral	*Roxicodone, OxyContin*
Paclitaxel, Injection	*Taxol*
Paliperidone, Oral, Injection	*Invega, Invega Sustenna (4-weeks), Invega Trinza (3-months)*
Palivizumab, Injection	*Synagis*
Palonosetron, Oral Capsule, Injection	*Aloxi*
Pantoprazole, Injection	*Protonix IV*
Paritaprevir/ Ritonavir/Ombitasvir/ Dasabuvir, Oral	*Viekira Pak*

DRUG	BRAND NAME
Pegfilgrastim, Injection	*Neulasta*
Penicillin G Benzathine, Injection	*Bicillin LA*
Phenytoin, Oral, Injection	*Dilantin*
Piperacillin/ Tazobactam, Injection	*Zosyn*
Plasma-Lyte A	
Pneumococcal Conjugate Vaccine (PCV13), Injection	*Prevnar 13*
Pneumococcal Polysaccharide Vaccine (PPSV23), Injection	*Pneumovax 23*
Polyethylene Glycol, Oral	*Colyte, GoLYTELY, MoviPrep, NuLYTELY*
Posaconazole, Oral Tablet/Suspension, Injection	*Noxafil*
Pregabalin, Oral	*Lyrica*
Propofol, Injection	*Diprivan*
Propylthiouracil, Oral	
Protamine, Injection	
Quetiapine, Oral	*Seroquel*
Raltegravir, Oral	*Isentress*
Ranitidine, Oral, Injection	*Zantac*
Rasburicase, Injection	*Elitek*
Regular insulin, Injection	*Humulin R, Novolin R*
Ribavirin, Oral, Inhalation	*Ribasphere (Oral)-Hepatitis C Virazole (Inhalation)- RSV*
Rifaximin	*Xifaxan*
Risperidone, Oral, Injection	*Risperdal, Risperdal Consta (2-weeks)*
Ritonavir, Oral	*Norvir*
Rituximab, Injection	*Rituxan*

Top Inpatient Drugs Continued

DRUG	BRAND NAME
Rivaroxaban, Oral	*Xarelto*
Rosuvastatin, Oral	*Crestor*
Rotavirus Vaccine, Oral	*Rotarix; RotaTeq*
Scopolamine Patch	*Transderm-Scop*
Sevelamer, Oral	*Renvela, Renagel*
Sildenafil, Oral, Injection	*Revatio*
Sitagliptin, Oral	*Januvia*
Sodium Phosphates, Oral, Injection	*Osmoprep (Oral)*
Sofosbuvir/Ledipasvir, Oral	*Harvoni*
Sofosbuvir/ Velpatasvir, Oral	*Epclusa*
Sulfamethoxazole/ Trimethoprim, Oral Tablet/Suspension, Injection	*Bactrim*
Tacrolimus, Oral, Injection	*Prograf*
Tbo-filgrastim, Injection	*Granix*
Tenecteplase, Injection	*TNKase*
Tigecycline, Injection	*Tygacil*
Tiotropium, Oral Inhaler	*Spiriva Handihaler, Spiriva Respimat*
Tobramycin, Inhalation, Injection	
Tolvaptan, Oral	*Samsca*
Tranexamic Acid, Injection	*Cyklokapron*
Trastuzumab, Injection	*Herceptin*
Triamcinolone, Injection	*Kenalog*
Valganciclovir Oral Tablet/Solution	*Valcyte*
Vancomycin, Oral Capsule, Injection	*Vancocin*
Varicella (Chickenpox) Vaccine, Injection	*Varivax*

DRUG	BRAND NAME
Vedolizumab, Injection	*Entyvio*
Vinblastine, Injection	
Vincristine, Injection	
Vitamin K1, Phytonadione, Oral, Injection	*Mephyton*
Voriconazole, Oral Tablet/Injection	*Vfend, Vfend IV*
Warfarin, Oral	*Coumadin, Jantoven*
Zidovudine, Oral, Injection	*Retrovir*
Ziprasidone, Oral, Injection	*Geodon*
Zoledronic Acid, Injection	*Reclast, Zometa*
Zoster (Shingles) Vaccine, Injection	*Zostavax*

RxPrep thanks IQVIA and Mr. Robert Hunkler for providing this list to aid the student's study.

TOP OTC DRUGS

For drugs that are available in both OTC and Rx (prescription) versions: the Rx doses are generally higher than the OTC doses. The brand names can be different, e.g., orlistat OTC *(Alli)* is 60 mg/dose, orlistat Rx *(Xenical)* is 120 mg/dose. *Brand names are provided as a study aid (generic may be top-seller).*

DRUG
ALLERGIC RHINITIS, COUGH AND COLD
Antihistamines, Non-Sedating
Fexofenadine *(Allegra)*
Loratadine *(Claritin)*
Cetirizine *(Zyrtec)* **(more sedating)**
Levocetirizine *(Xyzal Allergy 24 HR)* **(more sedating)**
Antihistamines, Sedating
Diphenhydramine *(Benadryl)*
Cough Suppressant
Dextromethorphan *(Delsym, Robitussin DM)* – some states impose sales restrictions such as minimum age
Mucolytic-Expectorant
Guaifenesin *(Mucinex)*
Decongestants
Oxymetazoline *(Afrin)* – nasal
Phenylephrine *(Sudafed PE)* – systemic
Pseudoephedrine *(Sudafed, Nexafed, Zephrex-D)* – systemic – behind the counter, federal and/or state restrictions on sales, in all formulations)
Decongestants/Antihistamines, Non-Sedating
Cetirizine/Pseudoephedrine *(Zyrtec D)*
Loratadine/Pseudoephedrine ER *(Claritin D)*
Fexofenadine/Pseudoephedrine *(Allegra D)*
Loratadine/Pseudoephedrine ER *(Claritin D)*
Nasal Steroid Inhalers, OTC and Rx
Budesonide *(Rhinocort Allergy Spray)*
Fluticasone *(Flonase Allergy Relief, Flonase Sensimist, Children's Flonase)*
Triamcinolone *(Nasacort Allergy 24HR)*
COMMON SKIN CONDITIONS
Acne
Adapalene *(Differin)*
Azelaic acid

DRUG
Benzoyl peroxide
Salicylic acid
Alopecia
Minoxidil *(Rogaine)* - topical
Cold Sores, for Herpes Simplex
Docosanol *(Abreva)*
Dandruff
Ketoconazole *(Nizoral A-D)*
Pyrithione zinc *(Head & Shoulders)*
Selenium sulfide *(Selsun)*
Coal tar *(T/Gel)*
Topical Antifungals, for Tinea Infections
Butenafine *(Lotrimin Ultra cream)*
Clotrimazole *(Lotrimin AF cream)*
Miconazole *(Lotrimin AF powder and spray)*
Terbinafine *(Lamisil AT)*
Tolnaftate *(Tinactin powder, cream, spray)*
Undecylenic acid *(Fungi-Nail)*
Vaginal Antifungals, for Candida Infections
Butoconazole *(Gynazole-1, others)*
Clotrimazole *(Gyne-Lotrimin, others)*
Miconazole *(Monistat, others)*
Terconazole *(Terazol 7, others)*
Hemorrhoids
Phenylephrine *(Preparation H)*
Lice
Permethrin 1% *(Nix)*
Piperonyl butoxide/Pyrethrin *(RID)*
Minor wounds
Polymyxin/Bacitracin/Neomycin *(Neosporin)* – topical antibiotic
Pinworm
Pyrantel pamoate

DRUG
Inflammation and Rash
Hydrocortisone cream 0.5% and 1% – topical, **OTC and Rx**
CONSTIPATION AND DIARRHEA
Antidiarrheals
Bismuth subsalicylate *(Pepto-Bismol)*
Loperamide *(Imodium A-D)*
Constipation
Bisacodyl *(Dulcolax)*
Calcium polycarbophil *(FiberCon)*
Docusate sodium *(Colace)*
Glycerin suppository
Magnesium hydroxide *(Milk of Magnesia)*
Methylcellulose *(Citrucel)*
Mineral oil
Polyethylene glycol 3350 *(MiraLax)*, **OTC and Rx**
Psyllium *(Metamucil)*
Saline enema *(Fleet)*
Senna *(Ex-Lax, Senokot)*
Wheat dextrin (Benefiber)
CONTRACEPTION
Condoms
Diaphragm
Nonoxynol-9 spermicide
Levonorgestrel *(Plan B One-Step, Others)* - emergency contraception, **OTC and Rx**
DIABETES: INSULIN, OTC and Rx
NPH Insulin
Humulin N, Humulin N KwikPen, Novolin N
Pre-Mixed Insulins
Humulin 70/30, Humulin 70/30 KwikPen, Novolin 70/30
Regular Insulin
Humulin R, Novolin R

Top OTC Drugs Continued

DRUG
DIETARY SUPPLEMENTS, NATURAL & COMPLEMENTARY MEDICINE
Acetyl-l-carnitine
Calcium carbonate *(Tums, Oscal)*
Calcium citrate *(Citracal, Cal-Citrate)*
CoQ10
Ferrous sulfate *(SlowFe, Fer-In-Sol)*
Fish oil supplements
Magnesium citrate
Magnesium oxide
Melatonin
Probiotics
Lactobacillus (Culturelle)
Bifidobacterium infantis, L. acidophilus, B. bifidum/B. lactis (Align)
Saccharomyces boulardii (Florastor)
Vitamins
Niacin Controlled Release *(Slo-Niacin)*
Multivitamin *(One-A-Day)*
Prenatal multivitamin, **OTC and Rx**
Vitamin B complex
Vitamin B12, cyanocobalamin, **OTC and Rx**
Vitamin B9, folic acid, **OTC and Rx**
Vitamin C, ascorbic acid
Vitamin D2, **OTC and Rx**
Vitamin D3, **OTC and Rx**
GASTROESOPHAGEAL REFLUX DISEASE & PEPTIC ULCER DISEASE
Proton Pump Inhibitors, OTC and Rx
Esomeprazole 20 mg *(Nexium 24HR)*
Omeprazole 20 mg *(Prilosec)*
Lansoprazole 15 mg *(Prevacid 24HR)*, Lansoprazole 15 mg ODT
H2-Receptor Antagonists, OTC and Rx
Cimetidine 200 mg
Famotidine 10/20 mg *(Pepcid)*
Ranitidine 75/150 mg *(Zantac)*

DRUG
Antacids & Antigas
Aluminum/Magnesium/Simethicone *(Maalox, Mylanta)*
Calcium carbonate *(Tums)*
Anhydrous citric acid, Aspirin & Sodium bicarbonate *(Alka-Seltzer)*
Simethicone 125 mg *(Gas-X)*
Alpha-Galactosidase enzyme *(Beano)*
Lactase enzyme *(Lactaid)*
MOTION SICKNESS
Dimenhydrinate *(Dramamine)*
Meclizine *(Dramamine Less Drowsy)*
OPHTHALMICS AND OTICS
Artificial tears *(Systane, Refresh, Clear Eyes)* – dry eye
Carbamide peroxide *(Debrox)* – ear wax removal
Naphazoline eye drops *(Clear Eyes Maximum Redness Relief)* – red eye
Tetrahydrozoline eye drops *(Visine)* – red eye
OVERACTIVE BLADDER (OAB)
Oxybutynin *(Oxytrol for Women)*, **OTC and Rx**
PAIN
Acetaminophen 325 mg, 500 mg, 650mg *(Tylenol, Feverall rectal suppository)*
Acetaminophen/Caffeine *(Excedrin Tension Headache)*
Acetaminophen/Aspirin/Caffeine *(Excedrin Extra Strength, Excedrin Migraine)*
Acetaminophen/Caffeine/Pyrilamine *(Midol)*
Aspirin *(Ecotrin, Bufferin, Ascriptin)*
Capsaicin 0.025% and 0.075% cream *(Zostrix, Zostrix HP)*
Ibuprofen 200 mg *(Motrin, Advil)*, **OTC and Rx**
Lidocaine patches *(LidoPatch 4%)*, **OTC and Rx** *(Lidoderm 5%)*
Magnesium salicylate *(Doans, Doans ES)*
Methyl salicylate and menthol topical *(BenGay, Salonpas, Icy Hot)*
Naproxen sodium 220 mg *(Aleve)*, **OTC and Rx**
Trolamine salicylate *(Aspercreme)*

DRUG
SLEEP DISORDERS
Diphenhydramine *(Benadryl)*
Doxylamine *(Unisom)*
TOBACCO CESSATION
Nicotine Gum *(Nicorette)*
Nicotine Lozenge*(Nicorette)*
Nicotine Transdermal Patch *(Nicoderm)*
WEIGHT LOSS
Orlistat *(Alli)*, **OTC and Rx**

REQUIRED FORMULAS

Calculations

Liquid (Volume) Conversions p. 117
tsp (t) = 5 mL, tbsp (T) = 15 mL
1 fl oz = 30 mL (approx.); 29.57 mL (actual)
1 cup = 8 oz, 240 mL (approx.); 236.56 mL (actual)
1 pint = 16 oz, 480 mL (approx.); 473 mL (actual)
1 quart = 2 pints, 960 mL (approx.); 946 mL (actual)
1 gallon = 4 quarts, 3,840 mL (approx.); 3,785 mL (actual)

Solid (Weight) Conversions p. 117
1 kg = 2.2 pounds (lbs)
1 oz = 28.4 grams (g)
1 lb = 454 g
1 grain = 65 mg (approx.); 64.8 mg (actual)
mEq to mmol is 1:1 for monovalent ions, 1:0.5 for divalent ions

Height Conversions p. 117
1 inch (in) = 2.54 centimeters (cm)
1 meter (m) = 100 cm

Percentage Strength p. 128

$$\% \text{ w/v} = \frac{\text{X g}}{\text{100 mL}} \qquad \% \text{ w/w} = \frac{\text{X g}}{\text{100 g}} \qquad \% \text{ v/v} = \frac{\text{X mL}}{\text{100 mL}}$$

Ratio Strength p. 132
Percentage strength = 100 / Ratio strength
Ratio strength = 100 / Percentage strength

Parts Per Million (PPM) p. 134
PPM → Percentage strength — Move the decimal left 4 places
Percentage strength → PPM — Move the decimal right 4 places

Specific Gravity (SG) p. 135

$$\text{SG} = \frac{\text{weight of substance (g)}}{\text{weight of equal volume of water (g)}} \quad \text{or} \quad \text{SG} = \frac{\text{g}}{\text{mL}}$$

Dilution & Concentration (Changing Strength or Volume) p. 136
Q1 x C1 = Q2 x C2 — Q1 = old quantity, Q2 = new quantity, C1 = old concentration, C2 = new concentration

Alligation p. 137

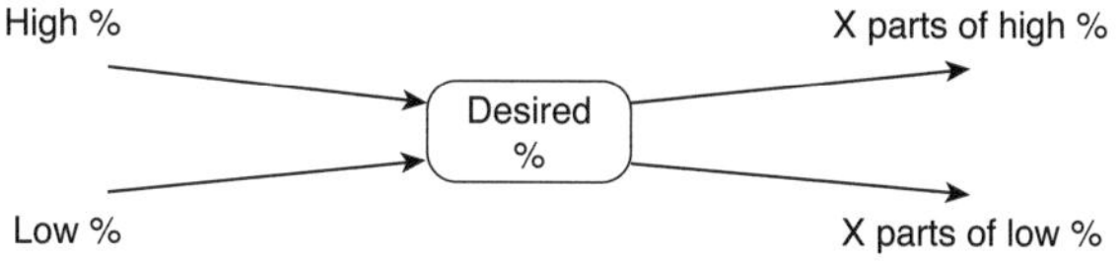

Use proportions to calculate amount of high % and/or low % required

Osmolarity p. 139

$$\text{mOsmol/L} = \frac{\text{Wt of substance (g/L)}}{\text{MW (g/mole)}} \times \text{(\# of particles)} \times 1{,}000$$

Isotonicity (E Value) p. 142

$$E = \frac{(58.5)(i)}{\text{(MW of drug)(1.8)}}$$

Moles and Millimoles p. 144

$$\text{mols} = \frac{\text{g}}{\text{MW}} \quad \text{or} \quad \text{mmols} = \frac{\text{mg}}{\text{MW}}$$

Milliequivalents p. 146

$$\text{mEq} = \frac{\text{mg x valence}}{\text{MW}} \quad \text{or} \quad \text{mEq} = \text{mmols x valence}$$

Corrected Calcium for Albumin < 3.5 (not needed with ionized Ca) p. 159
$Ca_{corrected}$ (mg/dL) = $calcium_{reported(serum)}$ + [(4.0 – albumin) x (0.8)]

Parenteral Nutrition Calories p. 151
Dextrose Monohydrate = 3.4 kcal/gram
Amino Acid Solutions = 4 kcal/gram
ILE 10% = 1.1 kcal/mL
ILE 20% = 2 kcal/mL
ILE 30% = 3 kcal/mL

Determining Fluid Needs p. 149
When weight > 20 kg: 1,500 mL + (20 mL)(weight in kg – 20)
**can estimate using 30-40 mL/kg/day*

Enteral Nutrition Calories p. 151
Carbs, Protein = 4 kcal/gram — Fat 9 kcal/gram

Total Energy Expenditure p. 150
TEE = BEE x activity factor x stress factor

Grams of Nitrogen From Protein p. 152

$$\text{Nitrogen (g)} = \frac{\text{protein intake (g)}}{6.25}$$

Cockcroft-Gault Equation p. 175

$$\text{CrCl (mL/min)} = \frac{140 - \text{(age of patient)}}{72 \times \text{SCr}} \times \text{weight (kg) (x 0.85 if female)}$$

Body Mass Index (BMI) p. 166

$$\text{BMI (kg/m}^2) = \frac{\text{weight (kg)}}{[\text{height (m)}]^2} \quad \text{or} \quad \frac{\text{weight (lb)}}{[\text{height (inches)}]^2} \times 703$$

Ideal Body Weight (IBW) p. 167
IBW (males) = 50 kg + (2.3 kg) (number of inches over 5 feet)
IBW (females) = 45.5 kg + (2.3 kg) (number of inches over 5 feet)

Adjusted Body Weight ($AdjBW_{0.4}$) p. 167
$AdjBW_{0.4}$ = IBW + 0.4(TBW – IBW)

Selecting Patient Weights p. 168

All drugs (if underweight)	Total Body Weight (TBW)
Most drugs (if normal weight or obese)	TBW
Exceptions	
Acyclovir, Aminophylline, Levothyroxine, Theophylline (normal weight, obese)	IBW
Aminoglycosides (obese)	$AdjBW_{0.4}$

Flow Rates Drop Factor (drops/min) p. 169

$$\frac{\text{\# drops}}{\text{mL}} \times \frac{\text{mL}}{\text{hr}} \times \frac{\text{hr}}{\text{60 min}} = \frac{\text{\# drops}}{\text{min}}$$

Dehydration p. 174
BUN:SCr > 20:1

Arterial Blood Gas (ABG) p. 177
ABG: pH/pCO_2/pO_2/HCO_3/O_2 Sat

1. pH < 7.35 → acidosis and pH > 7.45 → alkalosis
2. Respiratory: pCO_2 < 35 → alkalosis and pCO_2 > 45 → acidosis
   Metabolic: HCO_3 > 26 → alkalosis and HCO_3 < 22 → acidosis
3. Which abnormal value (pCO_2 or HCO_3) matches the pH from Step #1?
   Ex: ↓ pH + ↑ pCO_2 → respiratory acidosis
   Ex: ↓ pH + ↓ HCO_3 → metabolic acidosis

Anion Gap p. 178
Anion gap (AG) = Na – Cl – HCO_3

pH Calculations p. 179
Weak acid

$$\text{pH} = pK_a + \log\left[\frac{\text{salt}}{\text{acid}}\right]$$

Weak base

$$\text{pH} = pK_a + \log\left[\frac{\text{base}}{\text{salt}}\right]$$

Percent Ionization p. 182
Weak acid

$$\% \text{ ionization} = \frac{100}{1+10^{(pKa-pH)}}$$

Weak base

$$\% \text{ ionization} = \frac{100}{1+10^{(pH-pKa)}}$$

Absolute Neutrophil Count (ANC) p. 184
ANC (cells/mm^3) = WBC x [(% segs + % bands)/100]

Answering Case-Based Exam Questions

Temperature Conversions (Fahrenheit ↔ Celsius) p. 108
°C = (°F – 32)/1.8 — °F = (°C x 1.8) + 32

Biostatistics

Mean, Median and Mode p. 202

Mean - average value

Median - value in the middle of an ordered list

Mode - value that occurs most frequently

Risk, Relative Risk (RR) p. 207, Relative Risk Reduction (RRR) & Absolute Risk Reduction (ARR) p. 208

$$\text{Risk} = \frac{\text{Number of subjects with unfavorable event in group}}{\text{Total number of subjects in group}}$$

$$\text{RR} = \frac{\text{Risk in treatment group}}{\text{Risk in control group}}$$

$$\text{RRR} = \frac{(\text{\% risk in control group} - \text{\% risk in treatment group})}{\text{\% risk in the control group}}$$

ARR = (% risk in control group) – (% risk in treatment group)

Number Needed to Treat or Harm (NNT, NNH) pp. 209-210

$$\text{NNT or NNH} = \frac{1}{\text{ARR*}}$$

*expressed as decimal

Odds Ratio (OR) p. 210

Exposure	Outcome Present	Outcome Absent
Present-Cases	A	B
Absent-Controls	C	D

$$\text{OR} = \frac{AD}{BC}$$

Hazard Ratio (HR) p. 211

$$\text{HR} = \frac{\text{Hazard rate in the treatment group}}{\text{Hazard rate in the control group}}$$

Sensitivity and Specificity p. 214

Test Result	HAVE Condition	No Condition
Positive	A	B
Negative	C	D
Total	A + C	B + D

Sensitivity = [A/(A + C) x 100]

Specificity = [D/(B + D) x 100]

Common Skin Conditions

Time to Burn (TTB) p. 514

TTB (with sunscreen in min) = SPF X TTB (without sunscreen)

Diabetes

Initiating Basal-Bolus Insulin in Type 1 Diabetes p. 656

1. Calc TDD 0.6 units/kg/day using TBW
2. Divide into 1/2 basal & 1/2 rapid-acting. If using NPH/R, use 2/3 & 1/3.
3. Split rapid-acting among meals

Insulin-to-Carbohydrate Ratio: Rule of 500 for Rapid-Acting Insulin p. 656

$$\frac{500}{\text{total daily dose of insulin (TDD)}} = \text{grams of carbohydrate covered by 1 unit of rapid-acting insulin}$$

Insulin-to-Carbohydrate Ratio: Rule of 450 for Regular Insulin p. 656

$$\frac{450}{\text{total daily dose of insulin (TDD)}} = \text{grams of carbohydrate covered by 1 unit of regular insulin}$$

Correction Factor: 1,800 Rule for Rapid-Acting Insulin p. 657

$$\frac{1{,}800}{\text{total daily dose of insulin (TDD)}} = \text{correction factor for 1 unit of rapid-acting insulin}$$

Correction Factor: 1,500 Rule for Regular Insulin p. 657

$$\frac{1{,}500}{\text{total daily dose of insulin (TDD)}} = \text{correction factor for 1 unit of regular insulin}$$

Correction Dose p. 657

$$\frac{\text{(blood glucose now) - (target blood glucose)}}{\text{correction factor}} = \text{correction dose}$$

Dyslipidemia

Friedewald Equation p. 443

$$\text{LDL} = \text{TC} - \text{HDL} - \frac{\text{TG*}}{5}$$

*do not use if TG > 400

Non-Sterile Compounding

Minimum Weighable Quantity (MWQ) p. 252

$$\text{MWQ} = \frac{\text{Sensitivity Requirement}}{0.05}$$

Oncology II

BSA Calculations, using Mosteller p. 861

(review how to use Dubois-Dubois)

$$\text{BSA (m}^2) = \sqrt{\frac{\text{Ht (cm) x Wt (kg)}}{3{,}600}}$$

Pharmacokinetics

Bioavailability (F) p. 1011

$$\text{F (\%)} = 100 \times \frac{\text{AUC}_{\text{extravascular}}}{\text{AUC}_{\text{intravenous}}} \times \frac{\text{Dose}_{\text{intravenous}}}{\text{Dose}_{\text{extravascular}}}$$

Volume of Distribution (Vd) p. 1012

$$\text{Vd} = \frac{\text{Amount of drug in body}}{\text{Concentration of drug in plasma}}$$

Clearance p. 1013

$$\text{Cl} = \frac{\text{F x Dose}}{\text{AUC}} \quad \text{or} \quad \text{Cl} = \text{ke x Vd}$$

Elimination Rate Constant (ke) p. 1016

$$\text{ke} = \frac{\text{Cl}}{\text{Vd}}$$

Predicting Drug Concentrations p. 1016

$$C_2 = C_1 \times e^{-kt}$$

$$\text{ke} = \frac{\ln (C_1/C_2)}{t}$$

Half-Life ($t_{1/2}$) p. 1017

$$t_{½} = \frac{0.693}{\text{ke}}$$

Loading Dose (LD) p. 1019

$$\text{LD} = \frac{\text{Desired Concentration x Vd}}{\text{F}}$$

Seizures/Epilepsy

Phenytoin Correction for Albumin < 3.5 (not needed with free phenytoin) p. 949

$$\text{Phenytoin}_{\text{corrected}}\ \text{(mcg/mL)} = \frac{\text{Total phenytoin measured}}{(0.2 \times \text{albumin}) + 0.1}$$

(can also be used for valproic acid)

DOSE CONVERSIONS *(ORAL, UNLESS NOTED)*

KCl Solution (Oral) to Tablets p. 147 (see problem #61)

KCl 10% = 20 mEq/15 mL, KCl 20% = 40 mEq/15 mL

Calcium Salts p. 148

Calcium Carbonate = 40% elemental calcium

Calcium Citrate = 21% elemental calcium

Aminophylline ↔ Theophylline p. 148

Aminophylline to Theophylline: Multiply by 0.8 (remember: **ATM**)

Theophylline to Aminophylline: Divide by 0.8

Loop Diuretics p. 493

Ethacrynic acid	50 mg	Bumetanide	1 mg
Furosemide	40 mg	Furosemide IV:PO = 1:2	
Torsemide	20 mg	Other Loops IV:PO = 1:1	

Metoprolol Conversions p. 496 (IV:PO = 1:2.5)

Iron, Elemental Conversions p. 544

Ferrous Sulfate = 20% elemental iron (e.g., 325 mg x 0.2 = 65 mg)

Insulin Conversions p. 657

Usually, 1:1 conversion

Exceptions:

NPH dosed BID → glargine dosed daily, use 80% of NPH dose

Toujeo → *Lantus* or *Basaglar*, use 80% of *Toujeo* dose

Steroids p. 673

Cortisone	25 mg	Methylprednisolone	4 mg
Hydrocortisone	20 mg	Triamcinolone	4 mg
Prednisone	5 mg	Dexamethasone	0.75 mg
Prednisolone	5 mg	Betamethasone	0.6 mg

(remember: **C**ute **H**ot **P**harmacists and **P**hysicians **M**arry **T**ogether & **D**eliver **B**abies)

Opioids (methodology) p. 806

Statins p. 446

Pitavastatin	2 mg	Lovastatin	40 mg
Rosuvastatin	5 mg	Pravastatin	40 mg
Atorvastatin	10 mg	Fluvastatin	80 mg
Simvastatin	20 mg		

(remember: **P**harmacists **R**ock **A**t **S**aving **L**ives and **P**reventing **F**atty-deposits.)

DIAGNOSTIC TESTS

DISORDER/CONDITION	DIAGNOSTIC TEST/S; REFER TO SPECIFIC CHAPTER FOR MORE INFORMATION
AUTOIMMUNE	
Autoimmune, Various	↑ Erythrocyte Sedimentation Rate **(ESR)**, ↑ C-Reactive Protein **(CRP)**, Rheumatoid Factor **(RF)**, Anti-Nuclear Antibody **(ANA)**
Rheumatoid Arthritis	Above autoimmune tests; specific for RA: Anti-Citrullinated Peptide Antibody (ACPA)
Systemic Lupus Erythematosus (SLE)	Above autoimmune tests; specific for SLE: anti-ssDNA, anti-dsDNA
Multiple Sclerosis	Magnetic Resonance Imaging **(MRI)**
CARDIOVASCULAR	
Acute Coronary Syndromes (ACS), Coronary Artery Disease (CAD)	Electrocardiogram **(**ECG, or EKG**)**, Cardiac Enzymes [Creatine Kinase Muscle/Brain (CK-MB), Troponin I, T]
Arrhythmia	**ECG** (or EKG), records heart electrical activity, provides heart rhythm, heart rate (HR), **Holter Monitor** is a portable ECG device
Atrial Fibrillation/Atrial Flutter, Stroke Prevention Treatment	**CHADS2** or **CHA2DS2-VASc** Scoring System (score directs need for anticoagulation treatment)
Cerebrovascular Accident (CVA, Stroke)	Computed Tomography **(CT)**, **MRI**
Chronic Heart Failure	Echocardiogram **(ECHO)**, ↑ B-Type Natriuretic Peptide (BNP), ↑ N-Terminal ProBNP (NT-proBNP)
Coronary Artery Calcium (CAC)	A non-invasive CT scan of the heart that measures calcium-containing plaque
Ischemic Heart Disease (IHD)/ Chronic Stable Angina	**Cardiac Stress Test**, CK-MB, Troponins (I or T), ECG
Deep Vein Thrombosis (DVT)	D-Dimer Test (marker of fibrinolysis), **Ultrasound (US)**; if US is negative with DVT symptoms: Venography, MRI
Pulmonary Embolism (PE)	D-Dimer Test; if positive, pulmonary Computed Tomographic Angiography (CTA)
Dyslipidemia	↑ **TC, Non-HDL**, **LDL**, Triglycerides **(TG)**
Hypertension	↑ Systolic Blood Pressure (SBP)/Diastolic Blood Pressure (DBP)
Hypertensive Emergency	**↑ BP (≥ 180/120 mmHg) with acute target organ damage**
Hypertensive Urgency	**↑ BP (≥ 180/120 mmHg) without acute target organ damage**
10-Year Cardiovascular Risk of Myocardial Infarction (MI, heart attack) or Stroke	10-year **ASCVD Risk Tool** (use if no history of MI or stroke)
ENDOCRINE	
Diabetes	Prediabetes: Fasting Plasma Glucose **(FPG)**, Oral Glucose Tolerance Test **(OGTT)**, Hemoglogin A1C **(A1C)** Diabetes: same tests as prediabetes, but with higher values, and **classic symptoms of diabetes (e.g., polyuria, polydipsia and polyphagia)**
Hyperthyroidism	↓ Thyroid Stimulating Hormone **(TSH)**, ↑ Free T4 **(FT4)** (mostly Graves' Diesase, autoimmune)
Hypothyroidism	↑ **TSH**, ↓ **FT4** (mostly Hashimoto's Disease, autoimmune)
FEMALE HEALTH	
Ovulation	**Luteinizing Hormone (LH)**, peak value provides optimal timing for intercourse for pregnancy
Pregnancy	**Human Chorionic Gonadotropin (hCG)**, positive value, in urine (outpatient test kit) or in blood
Bacterial Vaginitis	**Fishy odor, pH > 4.5**, clear, white or gray vaginal discharge, little or no pain
Candida Vaginitis	**White, thicker** vaginal discharge, **pruritus**
Trichomoniasis	**Yellow, green frothy** vaginal discharge, soreness, pain with intercourse

Diagnostic Tests Continued

DISORDER/CONDITION	DIAGNOSTIC TEST/S; REFER TO SPECIFIC CHAPTER FOR MORE INFORMATION
GASTROINTESTINAL	
Peptic Ulcer Disease	Epigastric (upper, central part of abdomen) pain, Upper Gastrointestinal Endoscopy (mouth to small intestine) **Duodenal Ulcer:** pain 2-3 hrs after eating **(without food in stomach); pain relief** with food/antacids **Gastric Ulcer:** pain right after eating **(with food in stomach)**; little/**no pain relief** with food/antacids
GERD	Symptoms and patient presentation, **Esophageal pH Monitoring,** Endoscopy
H. pylori	**Urea Breath Test (UBT)**, Fecal Antigen Test
Inflammatory Bowel Disease	**Ulcerative Colitis** (rectum and colon affected): Sigmoidoscopy (end part of intestine closest to rectum), Colonoscopy (large intestine), Biopsy, Imaging Tests (CT, MRI) **Crohn's Disease** (extensive; more of GI tract affected): Endoscopy, Colonoscopy, Biopsy, Imaging Tests (CT, MRI)
PULMONARY DISORDERS	
Bronchospastic Diseases	Spirometry measures how much and how quickly a person can exhale air. There are three main results: **FEV1**: how much air can be forcefully exhaled in one second **FVC**: the maximum amount of air that can be forcefully exhaled **FEV1/FVC**: the percentage of total air capacity ("vital capacity") that can be forcefully exhaled in one second
Asthma	Spirometry **(FVC and FEV1)** and peak expiratory flow (PEF) Allergic Asthma (in response to an allergen/s): **Skin Test** (to detect an allergen)
Chronic Obstructive Pulmonary Disease (COPD)	**Post-Bronchodilator FEV1/FVC < 0.7** Eosinophils $\geq$ 300 cells/μL indicates inflammation and better response to inhaled steroids
ACID/BASE DISORDERS	
Metabolic Acidosis	Low pH, Low HCO3; Compensation: Respiratory Alkalosis
Respiratory Acidosis	Low pH, High CO2; Compensation: Metabolic Alkalosis
Metabolic Alkalosis	High pH, High HCO3; Compensation: Respiratory Acidosis
Respiratory Alkalosis	High pH, Low CO2; Compensation: Metabolic Acidosis
High Anion Gap Metabolic Acidosis	Anion Gap > 12 mEq/L
INFECTIONS	
C. difficile	***C. difficile* Stool Culture, Toxin A and B**, cytotoxin, Glutamate Dehydrogenase (GDH) Test
ELISA	Enzyme-Linked Immunosorbent Assay (ELISA) a test that measures antibodies in the blood
HIV	**HIV Ab and Antigen Immunoassay** (ELISA test performed 1st), confirm with **HIV-1/HIV-2 Antibody** Differentiation Immunoassay, **HIV RNA viral load** and the **Western Blot** are alternative tests for confirmation
Infective Endocarditis	ECHO, Blood Culture (for organism)
Lyme Disease	Round, red bullseye rash; Enzyme-Linked Immunosorbent Assay **(ELISA)** Test
Meningitis	**Lumbar Puncture (LP)**, plus symptoms of severe headache, stiff neck and altered mental status
Onychomycosis (toenail, fingernail fungal infection)	**20% KOH smear**
Lice (*Pediculosis*)	**Pruritus,** visible lice on the scalp and **nits (eggs)** on hair shafts
Pinworm (*Vermicularis*)	**Tape Test** (on skin adjacent to anus, for presence of eggs); otherwise, test for **helminths** (worms) in blood, feces or urine
Pneumonia	**Chest X-Ray** showing infiltrates, consolidations or opacity, with symptoms
Syphilis	**Rapid Plasma Reagin (RPR) Test**, also called the Venereal Diseases Research Laboratory (VDRL) blood test
***Toxoplasma gondii* Encephalitis**	Toxoplasma IgG Test
Tuberculosis (TB)	Tuberculin Skin Test **(TST)**, also called purified protein derivative (PPD) test

Diagnostic Tests Continued

DISORDER/CONDITION	DIAGNOSTIC TEST/S; REFER TO SPECIFIC CHAPTER FOR MORE INFORMATION
CANCER	Initial screenings; all followed by biopsy (tissue sample sent to pathology)
Breast	**Mammogram, Ultrasound, MRI**
Carcinoembryonic Antigen (CEA)	A test, or marker, used in identifying cancer
Cervical	**Pap Smear, HPV Test**
Colon	**Colonoscopy, Sigmoidoscopy,** Double-Contrast Barium Enema, CT Colonography, Stool DNA, Fecal Occult Blood Test (FOBT), Fecal Immunochemical Test
Lung	**CT Chest**
Skin	Skin Biopsy
Prostate	**Digital Rectal Exam (DRE), Prostate Specific Antigen (PSA)**
ADDITIONAL COMMON CONDITIONS	
Abnormal Involuntary Movement Scale (AIMS)	Rating scale used to measure involuntary movements, or tardive dyskinesias, as monitoring for patient improvement
Anemia, Macrocytic (or B12 or Folate Deficiency)	**↓ Hgb/Hct/RBC,** ↑ Mean Corpuscular Volume **(MCV)** (cell size is larger, MCV > 100 fL), Schilling Test
Anemia, Microcytic (or Fe-Deficiency)	**↓ Hgb/Hct/RBC, ↓ MCV** (cell size is smaller, MCV < 80 fL)
Allergic Reactions	**Skin Prick** (Scratch) Test (immediate), Immunoglobulin E **(IgE) Antibodies** (blood)
Cholestasis (Bile Duct Blockage)	↑ Alkaline Phosphatase (Alk Phos), ↑ Total Bilirubin (Tbili), ↑ Gamma-Glutamyltransferase (GGT)
Cognitive Impairment (e.g., Alzheimer's)	Mini-Mental State Exam **(MMSE),** score < 24 indicates impairment; a simple exam, others are more complex
Cystic Fibrosis	**Sweat Test**
Glaucoma	↑ Intraocular Pressure **(IOP)**, Visual Field Test (to identify optic nerve damage)
Gout	↑ Uric Acid **(UA)** level
Liver Disease	↑ AST/ALT, ↑ PT/INR, ↓ Albumin, ↑ Alk Phos, ↑ Tbili, ↑ Lactate Dehydrogenase (LDH) **Alcoholic Liver Disease:** ↑ AST > ↑ ALT; ↑ GGT **Hepatic Encephalopathy:** ↑ Ammonia Level (blood)
Myopathy	↑ Creatinine Kinase or **Creatinine Phosphokinase (CPK)**
Neuropathy, Peripheral	↓ sensation, with **10-g Monofilament Test**, Pinprick Tests, Temperature, Vibration
Osteoarthritis	X-Ray, MRI
Osteoporosis	Bone Mineral Density (BMD) using Dual Energy X-ray Absorptiometry **(DEXA** or DXA), **T-Score ≤ -2.5** **Osteopenia: T-score -1 to -2.4**
Pain	**Pain scales**, non-verbal signs (e.g., moaning, grimacing, agitation)
Pancreatitis	**↑ Amylase/Lipase**
Psychiatric Disease (e.g., Depression, Schizophrenia)	**DSM-5** Diagnostic Criteria Depression-specific: **Ham-D or HDRS Assessment Scale**
Renal Disease	**↑ BUN/SCr** **Dehydration: BUN/SCr Ratio** > **20:1**, plus symptoms (e.g., ↓ urine output, dry mucus membranes, tachycardia)
Seizures/Epilepsy	Electroencephalogram **(EEG)**, records brain electrical activity
Sickle Cell Disease	Hemoglobin S (Hgb S) test
Weight: Underweight, Normal Weight, Overweight, Obesity	**BMI** (plus **waist circumference** for risks associated with overweight/obesity)

MEDICAL TERMS

Lab values and drugs that affect them are in the Learning Lab Values & Drug Monitoring chapter. Blood cell terminology is in the Learning Lab Values & Drug Monitoring chapter and the Anemia chapter.

Compounding terminology is in the Compounding chapters. Oncology terminology is in the Oncology I chapter.

PREFIXES, SUFFIXES, THAT ARE COMMON	
A, as in atypical	An A in front of a word becomes it's opposite. Atypical means not typical. Agranulocytosis means no granulocytes.
Algia, as in arthralgia	Algia = pain/soreness; arth = joint; arthralgia is joint pain/soreness.
Au, as in audiologist	Au = ears/hearing; an audiology consult (to assess hearing) is ordered with ototoxic drugs (e.g., vancomycin or aminoglycosides).
Brady, as in bradykinesia	Brady = slow, kinesia = movement; bradykinesia is slow movement. Card = heart, bradycardia is a slow heart rate, [< 60 beats per minute (BPM)].
Dys, as in dysmenorrhea	Dys = painful, dysmenorrhea is painful menorrhea (menstruation).
Hem, as in hematuria	Hem = blood, ur = urine, hematuria is blood in the urine.
Hep, as in hepatotoxicity	Hep = liver; hepatotoxicity means liver toxicity.
Hyper, as in hyperkalemia	Hyper = high; hyperkalemia means high potassium.
Hypo, as in hypokalemia	Hypo = low; hypokalemia means low potassium.
Itis, as in arthritis	itis = inflammation/pain; arthritis is a disease with joint inflammation/pain (e.g., osteoarthritis).
My, as in myocarditis	My = muscle, card = heart, itis = inflammation; myocarditis is inflammation of the heart muscle.
Path, as in pathology	Path = disease; arth = joint, arthropathy is joint disease.
Pnea, as in tachypnea	Pnea = breathing; tachypnea is rapid breathing, sleep apnea is a temporary cessation (stop) in breathing, usually during sleep (sleep apnea).
Tachy, as in tachycardia	Tachy = fast; tachycardia is a rapid heart rate (> 100 BPM), tachypnea is a rapid respiratory rate (breathing quickly).

MEDICAL TERMS	
Abscess	A painful collection of pus on the skin, often caused by a bacterial infection. Can be due to a pressure ulcer (bed sore) from lying in the same position (over a bone) for long periods.
Akathisia	Inability to stay still with constant movement (restlessness), can be due to antipsychotics (e.g., aripiprazole).
Akinesia	Kinesia means movement; akinesia is the lack of voluntary movement; can be a symptom of Parkinson disease (i.e., freezing or off-moments). Bradykinesia is slow movement. Dyskinesias are abnormal, involuntary movements; can be due to levodopa and (to a lesser degree) dopamine agonists. Dyskinesias are an extrapyramidal symptom (with dystonic reactions and tardive dyskineas; see below). Tardive dyskinesia (TD) is involuntary movements in the tongue, face, trunk, and extremities (caused by dopamine blockade); can be due to antipsychotics (not quetiapine or clozapine) and metoclopramide. When TD is present, the drug should be discontinued; TD can be irreversible.
Alogia	Lack of speech; a negative symptom of schizophrenia.
Alopecia	Hair loss, can be due to valproate, methotrexate, chemotherapy drugs (e.g., taxanes).
Amenorrhea	Absence of menstruation, can be due to spironolactone, and drugs that ↑ prolactin (risperidone, paliperidone).
Amnesia, anterograde	Loss of memory when the drug is taken (i.e., going forward in time); past memory is not affected; can be due to benzodiazepines (and varenicline, if the patient has a blackout).
Amnesia, retrograde	Loss of memory to past events.
Anaphylaxis	Severe, life-threatening allergic reaction, occurs soon after a drug is taken; many drugs can cause anaphylaxis; drugs with high-risk include penicillins, carbapenems, omalizumab and other monoclonal antibodies (MABs), injectable iron (especially iron dextran, which requires a small test dose prior to use), pegloticase, rasburicase, IV phytonadione. When a drug causes anaphylaxis, the drug is contraindicated for that patient (except penicillin, to treat syphilis in pregnancy, will require desensitization).

Medical Terms Continued

Angioedema	The swelling of tissue layers under the skin; includes swelling of the dermis and lower layers [subcutaneous (SC) tissue, mucosa, submucosal layers—swelling in these layers causes breathing difficulty]; can be due to ACE inhibitors, angiotensin receptor blockers (ARBs), monoclonal antibodies (MABs).
Anorexia	Loss of appetite, can be psychological (anorexia nervosa – bupropion is contraindicated), due to AIDS (AIDS wasting syndrome) or due to drugs (generally, drugs ↓ appetite, versus causing a loss of appetite, see Weight Loss chapter). Digoxin toxicity causes anorexia (acutely), which is a loss of appetite due to nausea/not able to stomach food.
Anorgasmia	Inability to have an orgasm, despite stimulation, can be due to SSRIs, SNRIs [both cause other sexual side effects, including ↓ libido (sexual desire)].
Anuria	Lack of urine output, can be due to acute renal failure (oliguria is low urine output); with urinary retention (e.g., from anticholinergics, including antihistamines), the urine comes out but takes longer to begin to flow.
Apoptosis	Cell death, can be due to medical conditions (e.g., alcoholic cirrhosis) or from several chemotherapy drugs.
Arrhythmia	Irregular heart rhythm, with low HR (bradycardia) or fast HR (tachycardia); can be due to antiarrhythmics, and (if the arrhythmia is torsades de pointes) from drugs that prolong the QT interval (see Arrhythmias chapter).
Arthralgia	Joint pain, can be due to erythropoiesis-stimulating agents (ESAs, e.g., erythropoietin), colony stimulating factors (CSFs, e.g., filgrastim), aromatase inhibitors (AIs), quinupristin/dalfopristin *(Synercid)*, parathyroid hormone (e.g., teriparatide), statins.
Arthritis	Joint disease/inflammation; 3 common types include osteoarthritis (OA), rheumatoid arthritis (RA) and gout.
Ascites	Fluid accumulation within the peritoneal space that can lead to spontaneous bacterial peritonitis (SBP) and hepatorenal syndrome (HRS); can be caused by liver disease, volume overload with acute decompensated heart failure (ADHF), infection or (uncommonly) as an adverse reaction to a drug (e.g., rifaximin).
Asplenia	Decreased or absent spleen function (e.g., spleen was removed after an injury, such as a gunshot wound), asplenia causes altered immunocompetency, with ↑ infection risk; infection precautions will be needed, including meningococcal and both pneumococcal (conjugate and polysaccharide) vaccines, and avoiding live vaccines.
Asthenia	Abnormal lack of energy and strength, can be due to levetiracetam, some chemotherapy drugs.
Ataxia	Loss of full control and uncoordinated body movement (e.g., an intoxicated individual has ataxia, and cannot walk in a straight line); can be due to alcohol, benzodiazepines, barbiturates, drug toxicity from antiepileptic drugs (AEDs, e.g., phenytoin) and lithium. Ataxia can be due to ototoxicity that causes vestibular (inner ear) damage.
Atherosclerosis	The buildup of fats, cholesterol and other substances in and on the artery walls (atherosclerotic plaques), which restrict blood flow. If the plaque ruptures, the artery can become occluded (closed up/blocked).
Attenuated	Weakened; used to refer to weakened live vaccines that are able to replicate, but will not be able to cause disease (except in immunocompromised patients).
Atypical	Not the usual symptoms or presentation; e.g., a woman having a heart attack may have back pain or abdominal pain and not the classic (typical) symptom of chest pain.
Auscultation	Listening to internal organs (e.g., heart and lungs) with a stethoscope.
Axillary temperature	Temperature taken under the arm (in the armpit)
Avolition	Lack of motivation; a negative symptom of schizophrenia.
Bilateral	On both (bi) sides of the body, versus unilateral, which is on one side of the body.
Bioavailability	The extent to which an oral drug is absorbed into the systemic circulation; an IV drug has 100% bioavailability (none is lost to oral absorption); a drug that has 1:1 oral (PO) to IV dosing has 100% bioavailability. A 100 mg IV dose would be equivalent to a 100 mg PO dose.
Blepharitis	Eyelid inflammation.
Bolus	A relatively large dose of an IV drug given at once to quickly achieve an effect or serum level; in contrast, an IV infusion delivers a steady rate of drug over a longer period.
Bradycardia	↓ Heart Rate (HR); < 60 BPM; see Vital Signs table in Answering Case-Based Exam Questions chapter.
Bradykinesia	Slow movement; see akinesia.
Bronchitis	Inflammation of the bronchial tubes with difficulty breathing and clearing mucus, often due to an infection, from long-term smoking, second-hand smoke, or airborne irritants.
BUD (Beyond Use Date)/Expiration Date	Expiration dates are used for manufactured drugs and relate to the drug's chemical/physical stability after opening or dilution. Expiration dates are provided by the manufacturer. Beyond use dates (BUDs) are applied to products by the pharmacist, and relate to the preparation's microbial sterility. A BUD is the last date the drug may be used. The BUD is usually shorter than the chemical/physical stability. When labeling drugs in use, always choose the shortest date.
Bulimia	An eating disorder characterized by binging (over-eating) and compensatory self-induced vomiting.

Medical Terms Continued

Cachexia	Extreme weight loss and muscle wasting due to a chronic illness, commonly seen in frail, thin elderly patients who have been sick for some time.
Carbuncle – cluster of furuncles (boils)	A furuncle is a hair follicle infection, most are *S. aureus* infections. A carbuncle is a red, inflamed cluster of furuncles that contains pus, and can form an abscess.
Cardiomegaly	An abnormally enlarged heart. Most cardiomegaly is due to thin, stretched out ventricles (i.e., dilated cardiomyopathy).
Cataplexy	A sudden loss of muscle control that causes temporary paralysis on both sides, often triggered by laughing, crying or fear. The person remains conscious (is aware) but is temporarily unable to move. Cataplexy occurs most often with narcolepsy, a disorder of excessive sleepiness (i.e., narcolepsy with cataplexy).
Cataract	A cataract is a cloudiness covering the lens in the eye/s. As the cataract grows, the vision becomes progressively worse; can be due to sunlight exposure, chronic use of systemic steroids or steroid eye drops (e.g., *Pred Forte*).
Cellulitis	A bacterial infection (usually due to *Staphylococcus* or *Streptococcus*) in the skin or subcutaneous tissue, most commonly on the lower legs. Skin is red, swollen and painful.
Central line	A central line (catheter) empties into a large vein (e.g., the superior vena cava). In contrast, a peripheral line empties into a smaller vein (e.g., the cephalic vein). Some drugs can only be infused with a central line (e.g., vasopressors).
Cerebrovascular Accident (CVA) - stroke	Blood flow to a part of the brain is blocked by a thrombus (ischemic CVA) or a blood vessel rupture (hemorrhagic CVA).
Cerumen	Ear wax, build-up ↓ hearing; can be removed in a medical office, or with OTC products.
Chancre	A painless ulcer (e.g., a chancre on the genitals due to syphilis).
Chelation	A chemical complex in which ions and molecules bind to metal ions; e.g., the antidote EDTA chelates to heavy metals to reduce toxicity, quinolones and tetracyclines can chelate with polyvalent metallic cations, including Fe, Al, Mg and Ca, making them less effective. With both EDTA and quinolones/tetracyclines, the complexes are not absorbed and will be excreted in the feces.
Cholelithiasis	The formation of gallstones (calculi), often preceded by biliary sludge (a mixture of bilirubin, cholesterol and other substances). Neonates can develop biliary sludge from ceftriaxone. Cholelithiasis can also be due to parenteral nutrition, ezetimibe, fibrates, orlistat and octreotide.
Cholestasis	Reduction or blockage of bile flow; can be due to parenteral (versus enteral) nutrition. Pregnancy, liver disease, cancer and bile duct tumors can cause cholestasis.
Cinchonism	Quinine or quinidine (Cinchona alkaloids) overdose, with symptoms of tinnitus, hearing loss, blurred vision, headache, delirium.
Cirrhosis	Advanced, frequently irreversible fibrosis (scarring) of the liver.
Conjunctivitis - pinkeye	Inflammation of the thin clear tissue that lies over the white part of the eye, can be due to an infection (viral, bacterial) or an inflammatory response to an allergen (e.g., pollen) or a substance (e.g., dust).
Crystalluria	The excretion of crystals in the urine; can be due to sulfamethoxazole/trimethoprim, sulfasalazine, quinolones. Keep hydrated to reduce risk (i.e., drink water).
Cystitis	Bladder inflammation, usually due to a bacterial infection. Hemorrhagic cystitis (with hematuria, pain, difficulty with voiding) can be due to ifosfamide and high-doses of cyclophosphamide. Ifosfamide is always given with mesna to reduce risk.
Delirium	An acutely disturbed mind with incoherent thought and speech and agitation; can be due to infection, illicit drug use, anticholinergic toxicity in elderly.
Delusion/Hallucination	Delusions are incorrect (misinterpreted) perceptions; persecutory delusions are most common (e.g., the nurse hates me and is trying to kill me; the nurse is there, but the perceptions are delusional). Hallucinations are hearing/seeing/feeling something that is not there, and not based in any reality; auditory hallucinations are most common (e.g., hearing voices that are tormenting the patient).
Dementia	Memory loss, difficulty with judgement, attention, planning and personal care. The most common type of dementia is Alzheimer's.
Desiccant	An agent that keeps something dry; drugs that come in a bottle with a desiccant packet usually require that the drug is dispensed in the original container. Common (not inclusive): *Pradaxa, Effient, Nitrostat, Cresemba* Sofosbuvir (*Sovaldi*) and sofosbuvir-combo products (*Epclusa, Harvoni, Vosevi*), tenofovir alafenamide (*Vemlidy*), tenofovir disoproxil fumarate (*Viread*) and tenofovir-combo products (*Atripla, Biktarvy, Cimduo, Complera, Descovy, Genvoya, Odefsey, Stribild, Symtuza, Truvada, Symfi*), raltegravir (*Isentress*), elvitegravir and elvitegravir-combo products (*Genvoya, Stribild*)
Diabetic Ketoacidosis (DKA)	A life-threatening complication of type 1 diabetes (and occasionally type 2 diabetes—type 2 diabetes patients are much more likely to get HHS), with signs/symptoms of fatigue, weakness, hyperglycemia, anion gap metabolic acidosis and ketonuria. Mainly due to not taking insulin, an insulin pump failure, or can be the initial presentation in type 1 diabetes.

Medical Terms Continued

Dialysis (different types: hemodialysis, peritoneal dialysis)	Dialysis replaces the function of the kidneys to remove waste products, electrolytes and excess fluid from the patient's blood. A dialysis machine filters the blood, which circulates back (cleaner) blood into the patient.
Diaphoresis	Sweating; in addition to normal sweating due to heat, diaphoresis can be due to an acute coronary syndrome (ACS, e.g., an MI), anxiety, vasomotor (menopausal) symptoms, hypoglycemia, tuberculosis (TB), SNRIs/SSRIs and opioids. Night sweats are common with vasomotor symptoms (i.e., hot flashes in the day, night sweats at night), active TB and can be present with HIV infection.
Diplopia	Double vision, can be due to alcohol or drug toxicity (e.g., CNS-depressant drugs, AEDs, including phenytoin, alcohol).
Dyscrasia	A blood disorder in one or more of the cell lines (e.g., agranulocytosis, pancytopenia).
Dysentery	Severe diarrhea, with abdominal pain and bloody stool, usually due to a *Shigella* infection and treated with azithromycin.
Dysgeusia	Bad, bitter or metallic taste in the mouth; metallic taste can be due to metronidazole, metallic ions (in antacids, potassium iodide, zinc lozenges), nasal antihistamines (e.g., olopatadine), telavancin, phenytoin, macrolides, loxapine in the *Adasuve* powder formulation. Fish oils *(Lovaza)* can cause a fishy taste. Tenofovir powder has a bitter taste. The hyperthyroid drugs methimazole and propylthiouracil can cause loss of taste.
Dyskinesia	Abnormal, involuntary movement; see akinesia.
Dysmenorrhea	Discomfort and pain during the menstrual period.
Dyspepsia	Indigestion.
Dysphagia	Difficulty swallowing. Can be due to stroke and neuromuscular disorders.
Dysphonia	Physical difficulty speaking; can be due to use of oral steroid inhalers.
Dyspnea	Difficult or labored breathing; can be due to pulmonary toxicity, including fibrosis, cardiac damage (e.g., with heart failure). In many cases, the patient is fine until ↑ oxygen is required that the patient is unable to provide [dyspnea on exertion (DOE)].
Dystonia/Dystonic reaction	Prolonged contraction of muscles, including painful muscle spasms; can be due to antipsychotics (dopamine-blockade) and levodopa. Centrally-acting anticholinergics are ued for prophylaxis and treatment of dystonias.
Ectopic	In an abnormal place or position (e.g., ectopic pregnancy is a pregnancy outside of the uterus).
Emboli/Embolism	Embolism is obstruction of a blood vessel by an emboli that has traveled through the blood. Most emboli are blood clots (a thrombus), and most come from DVTs. A thrombus that has traveled through the blood is called a thromboembolus. Eventually, the thrombus comes to a vessel that it cannot fit through and gets stuck. The tissue on the other side of the emboli starts to die from lack of oxygen-rich blood. An emboli that stops in the lungs is called a pulmonary embolism (PE); it will block oxygen transfer, and can cause suffocation/death. An emboli that stops in a cerebral (brain) artery will cause a CVA (stroke) or transient ischemic attack (TIA). An emboli that stops in a coronary artery will cause an MI (heart attack). See Anticoagulation, Stroke and Acute Coronary Syndrome chapters.
Encephalitis	Inflammation of the brain; can be due to infections (e.g., herpes, toxoplasmosis).
Encephalopathy	A disease in the brain that alters brain function or structure; the key presentation is progressive loss of consciousness, with declines in memory and cognition. Can be due to liver disease (hepatic encephalopathy) or brain infection/cancer/trauma/toxin exposure.
Endocarditis	An infection in the lining of the heart chambers or heart valves; infection (growth) on the valves changes the shape of the valve, which can cause the blood to leak out or flow backwards (regurgitation, heard as a murmur). Can require open-heart surgery to repair/replace heart valves. Major risk factor is IV drug abuse (IVDA).
Endometriosis	A painful condition in which tissue that normally lines the uterus (endometrium) has grown outside the uterus; combination oral contraceptives (COCs, which contain estrogen and a progestin) are the drugs-of-choice to reduce pain and bleeding.
Enteral	Refers to the gut; enteral administration [through the gastrointestinal (GI) tract] is the preferred route (versus IV) for drug delivery. Other forms of drug delivery may be preferable (e.g., topical delivery for a skin rash).
Enuresis	Bed wetting, treated behaviorally (1st), then possibly with desmopressin (oral).
Epistaxis	Nosebleed; can be due to anticoagulants, some risk with antiplatelets.
Eructation	Burping: can be due to fish oils, mesalamine (oral).

Medical Terms Continued

Erythema	Skin redness, caused by ↑ blood (capillary dilation) in an area, commonly caused by receiving an injection, and from patch irritation. Erythema migrans is the bulls-eye rash from Lyme disease (tick bite). Erythema multiforme is a type of severe rash.
Etiology	The cause (e.g., of a disease).
Euphoria	A feeling of happiness, elation; can be due to opioids, or mild euphoria due to pregabalin.
Exacerbation	An acute ↑ in the severity of a disease.
Exophthalmos	Bulging (protruding) eyeballs. If bilateral, it is often due to Graves' Disease (hyperthyroidism).
Extravasation (with vesicant)	Extravasation occurs when a vesicant (a drug that will cause severe tissue damage) is being given by intravenous (IV) injection through a catheter (a line), and the catheter tip falls out of the vein, which allows the drug to seep into the surrounding tissues. Vesicants are in the Learning IV Medications chapter.
Fibromyalgia	A painful condition with both physical pain (diffuse musculoskeletal pain) and psychological pain, with fatigue.
Fibrosis	Scarring (with stiffness) in connective tissue [e.g., liver cell fibrosis is present in cirrhosis, pulmonary fibrosis (PF) lungs]. Drugs that cause PF are in the Pulmonary Arterial Hypertension chapter.
Flatulence	Excess gas in the GI tract, which is expelled by belching or through the anus (i.e., farting).
Folliculitis	Hair follicle infection that looks like a red pimple; primarily caused by *Staphylococcus* or *Streptococcus*.
Galactorrhea	The production of breast milk in men or women who are not breastfeeding, can be due to ↑ prolactin (risperidone, paliperidone).
Gastritis	Inflammation, irritation, or erosion of the lining of the stomach; can be due to NSAIDs, dabigatran.
Gastroparesis	Peristalsis is the movement of food/liquids through the GI tract by muscle contractions; gastroparesis causes ↓ peristalsis.
Genotype, Phenotype	Specific sequence of nucleotides that code (provide instructions) for a protein. A specific type of gene is called an allele; e.g., "she must have gotten the brown hair allele (the genotype) from her father." The brown hair is the phenotype, what is expressed.
Gingival Bleeding	Gingiva is gums; gingival bleeding is gum bleeding; the most common cause is poor dental care. Can be due to anticoagulants (e.g., warfarin) and (less commonly) from other drugs with bleeding risk.
Gingival Hyperplasia	Gingival hyperplasia is gum overgrowth; can be due to chronic use of phenytoin, verapamil and other calcium channel blockers (CCBs).
Glossitis	Tongue inflammation; can be due to anemia (e.g., iron deficiency anemia), an infection (e.g., herpes sore) or an allergic reaction or injury (e.g., a burn).
Gynecomastia	Breast enlargement in men; can be due to spironolactone, estrogen, testosterone, GnRH agonists, antiandrogens, drugs that ↑ prolactin (risperidone, paliperidone).
Hematemesis	Vomiting blood.
Hematoma	A collection of blood can be due to hemorrhagic stroke, injury, clopidogrel, heparin and vitamin K if given IM (do not give IM). Low molecular weight heparins (LMWHs), fondaparinux, oral direct factor Xa inhibitors and oral and some injectable direct thrombin inhibitors have a risk for hematoma (and subsequent paralysis) if given with epidural or spinal neuraxial anesthesia or spinal puncture. Caution: anesthesia is used for surgical procedures.
Hematuria	Blood in the urine; can be due to urinary tract infection (UTI), or over-anticoagulation.
Hemolysis	Destruction of red blood cells (RBCs).
Hemoptysis	Coughing or spitting up blood from the respiratory tract.
Hemorrhoid	An enlarged or swollen blood vessel, usually located near the anus or the rectum.
Hemostasis	Causing bleeding to stop.
Hepatotoxicity	Liver toxicity, from various causes (e.g., viral infections, cancer, alcohol, hepatotoxic drugs).
Hirsutism	Male-pattern hair growth in women.
Hot Flashes – vasomotor symptoms	Temporary but recurring episodes of flushing with a sensation of warmth or heat on the upper body and face. They are one of the hallmarks of perimenopause, and are due to the decline in estrogen, which has feedback regulation of luteinizing hormone (LH), resulting in ↑ LH; this causes temperature dysregulation.
Hyperbilirubinemia	↑ bilirubin in the blood, resulting in clay-colored stools and dark urine; can be due to ceftriaxone in neonates (i.e., < 30 days old), quinupristin/dalfopristin *(Synercid)*, rasburicase *(Elitek)*, several older HIV drugs.

Medical Terms Continued

Hyperhidrosis	Excessive sweating, commonly due to vasomotor (menopausal) symptoms.
Hyperosmolar Hyperglycemic State (HHS)	Hyperosmolar hyperglycemic state (HHS) is a hyperglycemic crisis that most often occurs in type 2 diabetes due to some type of severe stress (e.g., very high BG levels, severe infection). Serum ketones are not present, or negligible (present in DKA).
Hyperthermia	Body temperature well above normal; can be caused by heat stroke, drugs (e.g., from antipsychotics in neuroleptic malignant syndrome).
Hypertrichosis	Excessive hair growth, can be all over the body or in patches.
Hypertrophy	The enlargement of an organ or tissue from the ↑ in size of its cells (e.g., benign prostatic hypertrophy, BPH), versus hyperplasia, which is an ↑ in the number of cells.
Intracranial Hemorrhage (ICH)	A hemorrhage in the brain; fibrinolytics (e.g., alteplase, tenecteplase) are contraindicated with a history of ICH.
Intraarticular	Into the joint (e.g., intraarticular steroid injections are an option to treat acute gout).
Intrathecal	Introduced into or occurring in the space under the arachnoid membrane of the brain or spinal cord; intrathecal injection is used for drug delivery, including for some chemotherapy regimens; vincristine, a chemotherapy drug, can cause fatality if given by intrathecal injection.
Ischemia	An inadequate blood supply to an organ or part of the body.
Libido	Sexual desire; see Sexual Dysfunction chapter for drugs that can ↓ libido.
Lyophilized	Freeze-dried; IV drugs that come as lyophilized powders are reconstituted (brought back to a liquid form) by the addition of sterile water for injection (SWFI) or bacteriostatic water for injection.
Malaise	A general feeling of discomfort or illness.
Malignant	Virulent, uncontrolled, potentially fatal, used to refer to cancer (versus benign, or harmless).
Medication Guide (MedGuide)	A handout that alerts the patient to toxicities associated with a drug; additionally, the MedGuide will include useful information, such as what to expect, and administration.
Menorrhagia	Heavy menstrual bleeding; drugs that treat menorrhagia include *Natazia* (estrogen-progestin oral contraceptive), *Mirena* (levonorgestrel-releasing IUD) and *Lysteda* (oral form of tranexamic acid).
Metatarsophalangeal Joint	The big toe joint; often the location for a gout attack.
Morbidity, Mortality	Simply, morbidity refers to disease and mortality refers to death. These are population terms, and are used for the disease burden in a population (morbidity), or the number of people who died within a population (mortality). The population could be the subjects in a clinical trial.
Mucositis	Mucositis (inflammation/ulceration of the mucous membranes in the mouth and throat).
Myalgias	Muscle pain can be due to statins, quinupristin/dalfopristin *(Synercid)*.
Mydriasis	Pupil dilation
Myelosuppression (Bone Marrow Suppression)	Low WBC, RBC and platelets; usually due to chemotherapy drugs.
Myocardial Infarction	A heart attack, there are 3 types (see Acute Coronary Syndromes chapter): STEMI: most severe; due to complete coronary artery blockage. No blood can flow to heart tissue, which begins to die. Cardiac enzymes will be elevated in the blood and the ECG will have ST-segment elevations. NSTEMI: the coronary artery is partially blocked, severely restricting blood flow to the heart. Cardiac enzymes will be elevated in the blood; the ECG may be normal or may have abnormalities. Unstable angina: the coronary artery is partially blocked, restricting blood flow to the heart. Cardiac enzymes will not be elevated in the blood; the ECG may be normal or may have abnormalities.
Myocarditis	Inflammation of the myocardium (heart muscle).
Myoclonus	Muscle twitching.
Myopathy	Muscle damage.
Necrosis	The death of all or most of the cells in a part of the body, or in an organ.
Nephrolithiasis	Kidney stones; urolithiasis can refer to kidney, or bladder stones; painful to pass.

Medical Terms Continued

Nephrotoxicity	Renal toxicity/damage.
Neuropathy, peripheral	Peripheral nerve damage, can be due to diabetes, and from some types of chemotherapy.
Nosocomial	Hospital-acquired, such as a nosocomial infection (e.g., nosocomial (hospital-acquired) pneumonia).
NPO	Nothing by mouth; unable to take oral medication, food or drinks.
Nystagmus	Repetitive, uncontrolled movements of the eyes; can be due to phenytoin toxicity.
Oligohidrosis	Deficient sweat, can cause heat stroke, occurs primarily in children due to use of the AEDs (e.g., topiramate, zonisamide).
Orthopnea	Shortness of breath when lying flat; patients can assess if heart failure is worsening by the number of pillows they prop themselves up with to get to sleep; they are making their body more vertical (with more pillows) to keep congestion out of the lungs; this is referred to as pillow orthopnea.
Orthostasis	A ↓ in blood pressure that happens soon after standing; postural hypotension.
Osteomalacia, versus Osteoporosis	In osteomalacia, the bones are too soft. In osteoporosis (low bone density), the bones are porous (full of holes) and brittle.
Osteomyelitis	Infection inside the bone; osteomyelitis is difficult to treat, and requires long-term antibiotics, and in some cases amputation (i.e., when the infection cannot be treated).
Otalgia	Ear pain.
Otorrhea	Middle ear effusion/fluid, indicates infection.
Ototoxicity	Ear damage, which can cause hearing loss, tinnitus.
Palliative care	Medical care directed towards providing relief from the symptoms of a serious illness, including adequate relief from pain.
Pallor	Pale skin color.
Parasomnias	Unusual actions while sleeping, such as sleepwalking.
Paresthesia	A burning or prickling sensation.
Peak Level	The highest concentration of a drug in the patient's bloodstream; taken after the dose has been given, and has distributed through the blood.
Pediculosis	Lice infestation (head and/or body).
Pegylated	Addition of polyethylene glycol (PEG) to a compound to ↓ toxicity, ↑ half-life (to extend dosing interval).
Pharmacodynamics	What a drug does to the human body (e.g., loop diuretics cause a person to lose fluids).
Pharmacokinetics	What the human body does to a drug (e.g., enzyme metabolism, which can destroy the drug).
Pharyngitis	Sore throat can be due to viral or bacterial (streptococcal) infection.
Phlebitis	Vein inflammation, with pain, swelling, redness; can be due to injection of long-term antibiotics, hypertonic or cytotoxic solutions or a clot (thrombophlebitis).
Photosensitivity	Sun allergy; an immune system reaction to sunlight, most often causes an itchy red rash.
PICC (Peripherally Inserted Central Line)	A central line inserted peripherally (in a vein in the arm), and advanced through the vein until the tip reaches a large vessel (often the superior vena cava). See Learning IV Medications chapter.
Pleural Effusion	Fluid between the layers of the pleura, the thin membranes that line the outside of the lungs.
Pneumonia	Lung infection.
Polydipsia	Extreme thirst.
Polyp	An abnormal growth of tissue projecting from a mucous membrane.
Polyphagia	Excessive hunger or increased appetite.
Polyuria	↑ urination.
Porphyria	A group of disorders that result from a buildup of natural chemicals that produce porphyrin in your body. Porphyrin is important for hemoglobin (which carries oxygen) to function normally.

Medical Terms Continued

Postprandial	After a meal, often used in referencing after-meal blood glucose control.
Preprandial	Before a meal, often used in referencing pre-meal medication administration with diabetes (e.g., regular or rapid-acting insulin, meglitinides and alpha-glucosidase inhibitors).
Priapism	Prolonged erection > 4 hours, will become painful, and requires emergency medical care; can be a complication of sickle cell disease, or due to phosphodiesterase-5 inhibitors (e.g., sildenafil), alprostadil, trazodone, alpha-1 blockers, levodopa, atomoxetine.
Prophylaxis	Preventing a condition or drug side effect, e.g., medications are used for malaria prophylaxis (to protect a person from contracting malaria).
Pruritus	Itching.
Purulent	Consisting of, containing, or discharging pus.
Pyelonephritis	A type of urinary tract infection where one or both kidneys become infected.
Pyrexia	Fever.
Rales, Rhonchi, Stridor (lung sounds)	Abnormal lung sounds heard with auscultation (via a stethoscope) during inspiration (when breathing in): Rales/crackles: rattling, crackling sounds, can be due to infection (pneumonia), pulmonary fibrosis, pulmonary edema due to congestion with heart failure. Wheezes/rhonchi: deeper rattling sounds that resemble snoring sounds, due to fluid build-up [infection, COPD and cystic fibrosis (CF) cause rhonchi, which may go away with mucus secretion or coughing]. Stridor: high-pitched whistling sounds; specific causes, including croup (see Pediatrics chapter).
Risk Evaluation and Mitigation Strategy (REMS)	A strategy to manage the risks from an especially toxic drug (e.g., requiring prescribers to warn patients about the risks from opioids, in addition to pharmacist's counseling). The specifics for each REMS depends on the toxicity from the drug.
Retrograde ejaculation	Semen enters the bladder instead of exiting through the penis during orgasm; can occur with the BPH drug solodosin.
Rhabdomyolysis	Skeletal muscle breaks down rapidly, releasing myoglobin and other muscle components into the blood. This causes complications, including acute renal failure from muscle pieces flooding into the kidney and causing severe damage.
Rhinitis	Inflammation and swelling in the nose, usually caused by a cold or allergic rhinitis.
Rhinorrhea	Runny nose, due to excessive mucus.
Rigidity	Stiffness; nuchal rigidity (unable to bend neck) can indicate meningitis; "lead-pipe" rigidity can indicate neuroleptic malignant syndrome, which can be due to antipsychotics.
Rigors	Shivering, in which the patient feels cold but the body temperature is hot; can be due to amphotericin B deoxycholate injection, and occurs post-operatively; meperidine ↓ rigor severity.
Scabies	Itchy, contagious mite *(Sarcoptes scabiei)* infestation (not infection); mites burrow into the skin and cause severe itching. Treated topically with permethrin (OTC) or systemically with ivermectin (Rx).
Sepsis	Life-threatening organ dysfunction caused by dysregulated host response to infection. Organ dysfunction can be identified by an acute change in the total Sequential Organ Failure Assessment (SOFA) score ≥ 2 points due to infection. The quick SOFA (qSOFA) is a simplified version that uses only three criteria: altered mental status, systolic blood pressure ≤100 mmHg and respiratory rate ≥ 22 breaths per min.
Septicemia	A severe bloodstream infection. Also known as bacteremia, or commonly referred to as blood poisoning.
Shock	A medical emergency (with high mortality), characterized by hypoperfusion usually in the setting of hypotension.
Sialorrhea	Hypersalivation; can be due to Parkinsons disease.
Sinusitis	Inflammation of the sinuses (the hollow areas of the skull around the nose) can be due to infection or allergies; can cause a severe headache (sinus headache).
Somnambulism	Sleep walking; can be caused by varenicline, or part of parasomnias (unusual actions during sleep) due to non-benzodiazepines (e.g., zolpidem).
Somnolence	Sedation, caused by CNS depressants, dopamine agonists (e.g., ropinirole), many AEDs, benzodiazepines, barbiturates, opioids, muscle relaxants (e.g., carisoprodol), flibanserin *(Addyi)*, THC-derived or synthetic drugs (e.g., dronabinol), sedating antihistamines (e.g., diphenhydramine), centrally-acting anticholinergics (e.g., benztropine), clonidine, guanfacine, many antipsychotics (all first-generation, most second-generation), benzonatate *(Tessalon Perles)* and intentionally from hypnotics (e.g., zolpidem).
Spirometry	The pulmonary (lung) test that is used to diagnose and assess asthma and COPD; measures how much air someone can inhale, exhale, and how fast they can exhale; see Asthma chapter.
Steatorrhea	Fat globules in the feces due to ↓ intestinal fat absorption; present in CF.

Medical Terms Continued

Steatosis	Abnormal collection of fat somewhere in the body; liver steatosis, in which fat collects in the liver, is referred to as fatty liver.
Stenosis	Narrowing of space/s in the body; bilateral renal artery stenosis is narrowing of both renal arteries, which provide the major source of blood to the kidneys. Renal artery stenosis is caused by atherosclerosis.
Stevens Johnsons Syndrome/Toxic Epidermal Necrolysis (SJS/TEN)	A severe skin reaction can be due to use of many drugs. SJS is the less-severe end of the spectrum, which may/may not proceed to TEN, which is more severe. Begins with fever and flu-like symptoms, followed by skin blisters (initially on face and chest) that are bright red, and spread rapidly. Mucus membranes, nerves, eyes and genitalia can be affected. Can cause sepsis/shock/organ failure and death. A drug that caused SJS or SJS/TEN will be contraindicated in that patient.
Stomatitis	Mouth inflammation can be due to pancreatic enzyme products (PEPs, if held in the mouth) and from methotrexate, which can cause stomatitis with mucositis (inflammation/ulceration of the mucous membranes in the mouth and throat).
Striae	Stretch marks on the skin can be due to losing weight quickly, pregnancy, and the use of chronic steroids, including heavy use of topical steroids.
Stricture	An abnormal narrowing of a body passage, often seen in esophageal strictures, which are caused when acid refluxes into the esophagus, causing esophagitis with ulceration and leaving scar tissue that narrows the tube. Chronic acid exposure causes the cells to become abnormal, which is called Barrett's esophagitis, and is a pre-cancerous condition.
Syncope	Temporary loss of consciousness caused by a quick drop in blood pressure.
Synergy	An effect greater than the sum of the parts; drugs used for synergistic benefit include opioids with non-opioids (e.g., acetaminophen + hydrocodone) and aminoglycosides + beta-lactams.
Tachycardia	↑ Heart Rate (HR) > 100 BPM; see Vital Signs table in Answering Case-Based Exam Questions chapter.
Tachyphylaxis	↓ response to the effect of a drug; occurs with nitrates (not with *Bidil*), which require a 10-12 hour nitrate-free period, H2-blockers and neuromuscular blockers.
Teratogenic	A drug that will cause birth defects if taken during pregnancy; see Drug Use in Pregnancy chapter.
Thrombocytopenia	↓ platelets; if due to heparin (heparin-induced thrombocytopenia, HIT), there is a > 50% drop in platelets from baseline (that is not due to an acute blood loss).
Thrombotic Thrombocytopenic Purpura (TTP)	Blood clots form throughout the body. The clots consume platelets, which leads to bleeding under the skin and the formation of purpura (bruises) and petechiae (dots), that are seen on the skin surface; can be due to clopidogrel.
Thrush	Oral candidiasis infection inside of the mouth (called thrush), can be due to severe immunocompromised state (e.g., AIDS), and localized immunocompromise from oral steroid inhaler use. Thrush can be avoided by rinsing the steroid off the oral cavity (rinse and spit out).
Tinnitus	Ringing in the ears; can be due to salicylate toxicity, or ototoxicity from aminoglycosides, vancomycin, IV loop diuretics, cisplatin, mefloquine (with other neurotoxicity) and phosphodiesterase-5 inhibitors (with hearing loss).
Torsades de Pointes (TdP)	A deadly type of ventricular tachycardia can be due to drugs. See Arrhythmias chapter.
Trough Level	The lowest concentration of a drug in the blood; troughs are usually measured at steady-state, right before a dose. In contrast, a peak is measured after the drug has been given and has had time to distribute.
Uremia	A build up of urea (a nitrogen waste product) in the blood (e.g., elevated BUN, blood urea nitrogen); can be due to kidney failure.
Urethra	The tube that carries urine from the bladder, and out of the body, runs through the penis (in males) and through the vaginal opening (in females).
Ureter	The tubes that run from each kidney into the bladder, delivering the "renal filtrate" that will be excreted as urine.
Urolithiasis	Kidney/bladder stones, that are very painful to pass.
Urticaria	Hives. Raised, itchy areas of skin; affects top skin layer only (dermis) can be due to a drug reaction.
Xerophthalmia	Dry eyes; can be due to Sjögren's syndrome, long daily use of contact lenses, dehydration or anticholinergics.
Xerostomia	Dry mouth; can be due to Sjögren's syndrome, dehydration or anticholinergics.

COMMON MEDICAL ABBREVIATIONS

ABBREVIATION	MEANING
AAA	Abdominal Aortic Aneurysm
A&O	Alert & Oriented
ABG	Arterial Blood Gas
ac	Before Meals
ACE	Angiotensin Converting Enzyme
ACIP	Advisory Committee on Immunization Practices
ACOG	American Congress of Obstetricians and Gynecologists
ACS	Acute Coronary Syndrome
ACTH	Adrenocorticotropic Hormone
ad	Right Ear
ADH	Anti-Diuretic Hormone
ADR	Adverse Drug Reaction
ADT	Alternate Day Therapy
AF	Atrial Fibrillation, or A.Fib.
AGEP	Acute Generalized Exanthematous Pustulosis
AIN	Acute Interstitial Nephritis
ALT	Alanine Aminotransferase
ANA	Antinuclear Antibody
ANC	Absolute Neutrophil Count
ANS	Autonomic Nervous System
APTT	Activated Partial Thromboplastin Time
ARA	Aldosterone Receptor Antagonist
ARB	Angiotensin Receptor Blocker
ARDS	Acute Respiratory Distress Syndrome
ARF	Acute Renal Failure
ARNI	Angiotensin Receptor and Neprilysin Inhibitor
as	Left Ear
ASCVD	Atherosclerotic Cardiovascular Disease
AST	Aspartate Aminotransferase
ATC	Around the Clock
ATN	Acute Tubular Necrosis
au	Each Ear
AVP	Arginine Vasopressin
BEE	Basal Energy Expenditure
BID	Twice a Day
BIW	Two Times Per Week

ABBREVIATION	MEANING
BM	Bowel Movement
BMI	Body Mass Index
BMP	Basic Metabolic Panel
BP	Blood Pressure
BPH	Benign Prostatic Hypertrophy
BPM	Beats Per Minute, Breaths Per Minute
BUN	Blood Urea Nitrogen
C or w/	With
C-I, C-II, C-III, C-IV, C-V	Refers to Controlled Drug Categories
C&S	Culture and Sensitivity
C/O	Complaining of
CA	Cancer
CABG	Coronary Artery Bypass Graft
CAD	Coronary Artery Disease
cAMP	Cyclic Adenosine Monophosphate
CA-MRSA	Community-Acquired MRSA
CAPES	*Citrobacter, Acinetobacter, Providencia, Enterobacter, Serratia*
CBC	Complete Blood Count
CC	Chief Complaint
CCB	Calcium Channel Blocker
CD	Crohn's Disease
CDI	C. *difficile* infection
CF	Cystic Fibrosis
CH	Cholesterol
CHF	Congestive Heart Failure
CI	Cardiac Index, Contraindicated
CMV	*Cytomegalovirus*
CNS	Central Nervous System
CO	Cardiac Output
COPD	Chronic Obstructive Pulmonary Disease
CP	Chest Pain or Cerebral Palsy
CPAP	Continuous Positive Airway Pressure
CPK	Creatine Phosphokinase
CPR	Cardiopulmonary Resuscitation
CrCl	Creatinine Clearance
CRE	Carbapenem-Resistant *Enterobacteriaceae*

Common Medical Abbreviations Continued

ABBREVIATION	MEANING
CRF	Chronic Renal Failure
CRP	C-reactive Protein
CSF	Cerebrospinal Fluid
CT	Computerized Tomography
CV	Cardiovascular
CVA	Cerebrovascular Accident
CVP	Central Venous Pressure
CXR	Chest X-Ray
D1	Dopamine 1 Receptor
D2	Dopamine 2 Receptor
D/C	Discontinue or Discharge
D5W	5% Dextrose in Water
DDIs	Drug-Drug Interactions
DHP CCB	Dihydropyridine Calcium Channel Blockers
DJD	Degenerative Joint Disease (Osteoarthritis)
DKA	Diabetic Ketoacidosis
DM	Diabetes Mellitus
DOC	Drug of Choice
DOE	Dyspnea on Exertion
DPI	Dry Powder Inhaler
DRESS	Drug Reaction with Eosinophilia and Systemic Symptoms
dtd	Of Such Doses
DVT	Deep Venous Thrombosis
Dx	Diagnosis
EC	Enteric Coated
ECG	Electrocardiogram
EIAD	Extended-Interval Aminoglycoside Dosing (PK chapter)
ERA	Endothelin Receptor Antagonist
ESBL	Extended Spectrum Beta Lactamases
ESR	Erythrocyte Sedimentation Rate
ESRD	End Stage Renal Disease
ETOH	Ethanol
F/U	Follow-Up
FBS	Fasting Blood Sugar
FDA	Food and Drug Administration
FEV1	Forced Expiratory Volume in 1 second

ABBREVIATION	MEANING
FT4	Free Thyroxine (T4)
GFR	Glomerular Filtration Rate
GI	Gastrointestinal
GNR	Gram Negative Rod
gtt, gtts	Drop, Drops
GTT	Glucose Tolerance Test
H/O	History of
HA	Headache
HACEK	*Haemophilus, Actinobacillus, Cardiobacterium, Eikenella, Kingella*
HBV	Hepatitis B Virus
HCG	Human Chorionic Gonadotropin
HCT	Hematocrit
HCTZ, HCT	Hydrochlorothiazide
HCV	Hepatitis C Virus
HDL, HDL-C	High Density Lipoprotein
HF	Heart Failure
HFrEF	Heart Failure with Reduced Ejection Fraction
HFpEF	Heart Failure with Preserved Ejection Fraction
Hgb	Hemoglobin
HIT	Heparin-Induced Thrombocytopenia
HIV	Human Immunodeficiency Virus
HJR	Hepatojugular Reflex
HNPEK	*Haemophilus influenzae, Neisseria spp, Proteus mirabilis, E. coli, Klebsiella pneumonia*
HPA	Hypothalamic-Pituitary-Adrenal
HPI	History of Present Illness
HR	Heart Rate
HS	At Bedtime
HSV	Herpes Simplex Virus
HTN	Hypertension
HUS/TTP	Hemolytic-Uremic Syndrome and Thrombotic Thrombocytopenic Purpura
Hx	History
I&O	Intake and Output, Input and Output
IBD	Inflammatory Bowel Disease
IBS	Irritable Bowel Syndrome
IBW	Ideal Body Weight
ICU	Intensive Care Unit

Common Medical Abbreviations Continued

ABBREVIATION	MEANING
ID	Intradermal
IE	Infective Endocarditis
IHD	Ischemic Heart Disease
IM	Intramuscular
Inj	Injection
INR	International Normalized Ratio
IV	Intravenous
IVP	Intravenous Push
IVPB	Intravenous Piggyback
LD	Loading Dose
LDH	Lactate Dehydrogenase
LDL, LDL-C	Low-Density Lipoprotein
LFTs	Liver Function Tests
LLSB	Left Lower Sternal Border
LR	Lactated Ringers
LVH	Left Ventricular Hypertrophy
M. ft.	Mix and Make
MAO	Monoamine Oxidase
MAO Inhibitor	Monoamine Oxidase Inhibitor
MAP	Mean Arterial Pressure
MCH	Mean Cell Hemoglobin
MCHC	Mean Cell Hemoglobin Concentration
MCV	Mean Corpuscular Volume
MD	Maintenance Dose
MDI	Metered-Dose Inhaler
MDR	Multidrug-Resistant
MI	Myocardial Infarction
MIC	Minimum Inhibitory Concentration
mL	Milliliter
mPAP	Mean Pulmonary Artery Pressure
MRI	Magnetic Resonance Imaging
MRSA	Methicillin-Resistant *Staphylococcus Aureus*
MS	Multiple Sclerosis (Do not use this abbreviation for Morphine Sulfate – potential med error)
MSSA	Methicillin-Sensitive *Staphylococcus Aureus*
MVA	Motor Vehicle Accident
MVI	Multivitamin Injection
N/V, N&V	Nausea and Vomiting

ABBREVIATION	MEANING
N/V/D	Nausea, Vomiting, Diarrhea
NG	Nasogastric
NKA	No Known Allergies
NKDA	No Known Drug Allergies
NOAC	New Oral Anticoagulant
Non-DHP	Non-Dihydropyridine Calcium Channel Blockers
nPEP	Nonoccupational Post-Exposure Prophylaxis
NPO	Nothing By Mouth
NR	No Refills
NRT	Nicotine Replacement Therapy
NS	Normal Saline
NSAIDs	Nonsteroidal Anti-Inflammatory Drugs
NSR	Normal Sinus Rhythm
NTE	Not To Exceed
NTG	Nitroglycerin
OB-GYN	Obstetrics and Gynecology
OD	Right Eye
ODT	Orally Disintegrating Tablet
OROS	Osmotic Release Delivery System
OS	Left Eye
OTC	Over-The-Counter
OU	Each Eye
P-gp	P-glycoprotein
PAP	Pulmonary Artery Pressure
pc	After Meals
PCC	Prothrombin Complex Concentrate
PCI	Percutaneous Coronary Intervention
PCN	Penicillin
PCOS	Polycystic Ovary Syndrome
PCP	Primary Care Physician
PCV13	Pneumococcal conjugate vaccine (13-valent)
PCWP	Pulmonary Capillary Wedge Pressure
PE	Pulmonary Embolus or Physical Exam
PEK	*Proteus mirabilis, E. coli, Klebsiella pneumonia*
PEP	Occupational Post-Exposure Prophylaxis
PET	Positron Emission Tomography (PET)
PKU	Phenylketonuria

Common Medical Abbreviations Continued

ABBREVIATION	MEANING
PMH	Past Medical History
PO	By mouth, Oral
PPD	Purified Protein Derivative
PPI	Proton Pump Inhibitor
PPSV23	Pneumococcal Polysaccharide Valent (23-valent)
PRBC	Packed Red Blood Cells
PR	Per Rectum
PrEP	Pre-Exposure Prophylaxis
PRN	As Needed
PT	Prothrombin Time or Physical Therapy
Pt	Patient
PTCA	Percutaneous Transluminal Coronary Angioplasty
PTH	Parathyroid Hormone
PUD	Peptic Ulcer Disease
PVC	Polyvinyl Chloride
Q	Every
QD	Every Day
QID	Four Times a Day
QOD	Every Other Day
QS	Sufficient Quantity
QS AD	A Sufficient Quantity to Make
R/O	Rule Out
RA	Rheumatoid Arthritis
RASS	Richmond Agitation and Sedation Scale
RBC	Red Blood Cell
RML	Right Middle Lobe
ROS	Review of Systems
RSI	Rapid Sequence Intubation
RSV	Respiratory Syncytial Virus
Rx	Prescription
rxn	Reaction
S or w/o	Without
S/P	Status Post
SCr	Serum Creatinine
SIADH	Syndrome of Inappropriate Antidiuretic Hormone
SIG	Write on Label

ABBREVIATION	MEANING
SJS	Stevens Johnson Syndrome
SL	Sublingual
SLE	Systemic Lupus Erythematous
SOAP	Subjective, Objective, Assessment, Plan
SOB	Shortness of Breath
SC, SQ, subc, subq	Subcutaneous
Spp.	Species
ss	One-half
S/Sx	Signs and Symptoms
SSTI	Skin and Soft-Tissue Infection or Skin and Skin-Structure Infection
STAT	Immediately
STD	Sexually Transmitted Disease
STI	Sexually Transmitted Infection
Supp, sup	Suppository
SVR	Systemic Vascular Resistance
Sx	Symptoms
TB	Tuberculosis
TC	Total Cholesterol
TdP	Torsade de Pointes
TEG	Thromboelastography
TEN	Toxic Epidermal Necrolysis
TG	Triglycerides
TIA	Transient Ischemic Attack
TIBC	Total Iron Binding Capacity
TID	Three Times a Day
TIW	Three Times Per Week
TOP	Topically
TPN	Total Parenteral Nutrition
TSH	Thyroid Stimulating Hormone
TTP	Thrombotic Thrombocytopenic Purpura
TBW	Total Body Weight
Tx	Treatment
UA	Urinalysis
UC	Ulcerative Colitis
UFH	Unfractionated Heparin
ULN	Upper Limit of Normal
UNG	Ointment

Common Medical Abbreviations Continued

ABBREVIATION	MEANING
URTI	Upper Respiratory Tract Infection
UTI	Urinary Tract Infection
V1	Vasopressin 1 Receptor
V2	Vasopressin 2 Receptor
VF	Ventricular Fibrillation
VRE	Vancomycin-Resistant Enterococcus
VT	Ventricular Tachycardia
VTE	Venous Thromboembolism
WA	While Awake
WBC	White Blood Cells
WNL	Within Normal Limits
WPW	Wolff-Parkinson-White Syndrome
x	Times
y/o	Years Old
yr	Year

Meanings of abbreviations may vary. Not all of these abbreviations are considered safe, but all are used outpatient. In hospital settings, avoid unapproved abbreviations (See Medication Safety & Quality Improvement chapter).

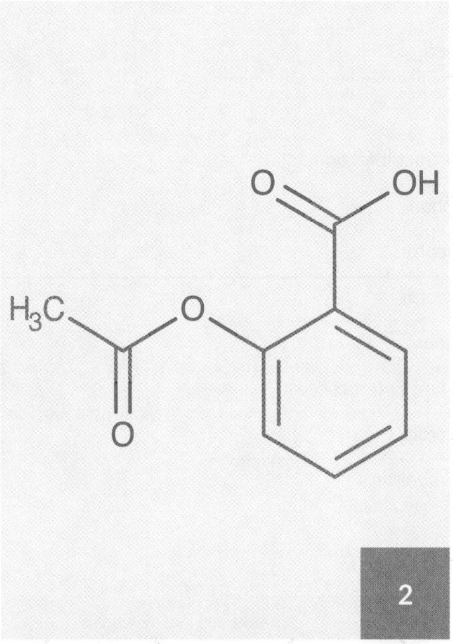

2

?
Is that a protein, carbohydrate, fat, vitamin, mineral or other type of nutrient?
No. It could be a toxin. I will eliminate it. Hmm...renal or hepatic clearance?

3

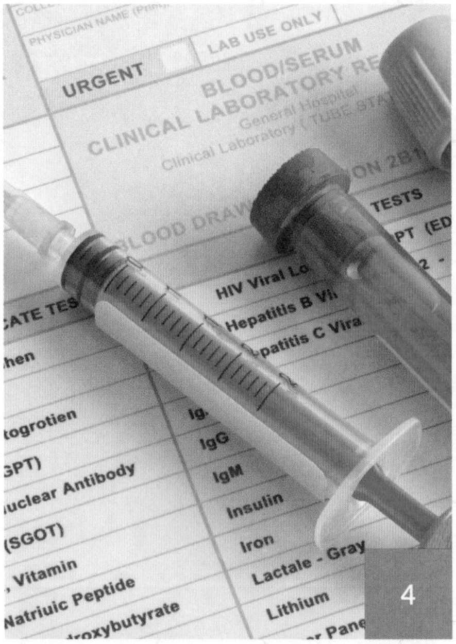
URGENT
LAB USE ONLY
BLOOD/SERUM
HIV Viral Lo
IgG
IgM
Insulin
Iron
Lithium

4

5

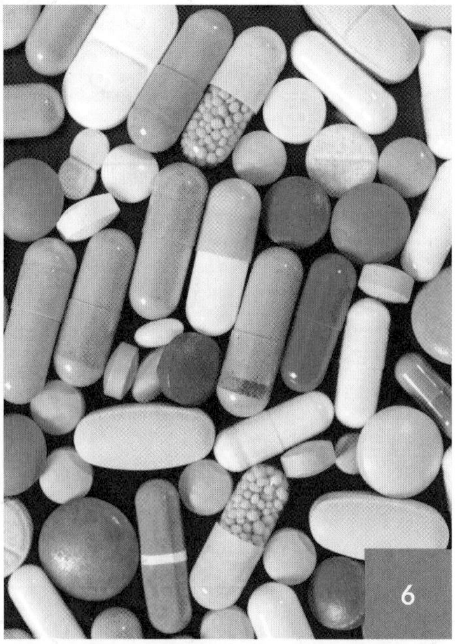

6

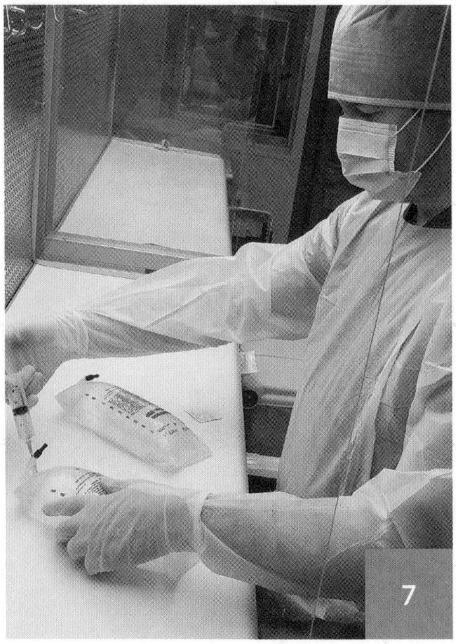

7

8

PHARMACY FOUNDATIONS PART 1

CONTENTS

CHAPTER 2
LEARNING BASIC SCIENCE CONCEPTS | **46**

CHAPTER 3
LEARNING DRUG INTERACTIONS | **55**

CHAPTER 4
LEARNING LAB VALUES & DRUG MONITORING | **71**

CHAPTER 5
LEARNING DRUG REFERENCES | **81**

CHAPTER 6
LEARNING DRUG FORMULATIONS | **91**

CHAPTER 7
LEARNING IV MEDICATIONS | **99**

CHAPTER 8
ANSWERING CASE-BASED EXAM QUESTIONS | **106**

CHAPTER CONTENT

Background 46
Drugs Interactions with Receptors or Enzymes 46
Overview of the Nervous System 47
Parts of the Nervous System 47
Autonomic Nervous System 48
Receptor Pharmacology 49
Monoamine Oxidase Inhibitors 49
Functional Groups 50
Common Functional Groups 51
Commonly Used Structures 52

CONTENT LEGEND

= Study Tip Gal

Acetylsalicylic Acid

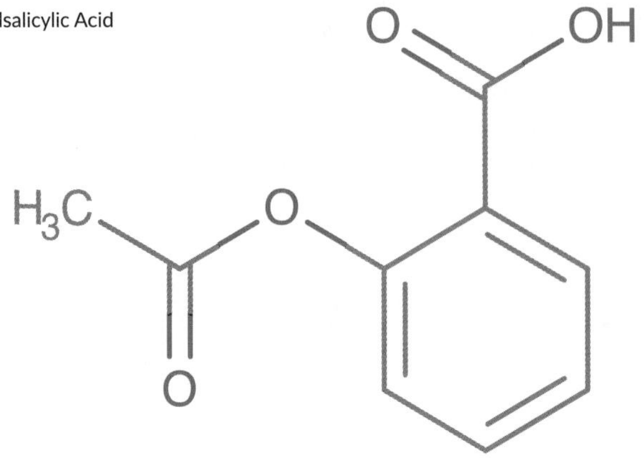

CHAPTER 2
LEARNING BASIC SCIENCE CONCEPTS

BACKGROUND

Medications can be referred to by their mechanism of action [e.g., beta-adrenergic blockers or phosphodiesterase-5 (PDE-5) inhibitors] or by their main purpose (e.g., antihypertensives or decongestants). The expected effect of a drug can be predicted from its mechanism of action and chemical structure. The relationship between the structure of a compound and its activity is referred to as structure activity relationship.

This chapter describes some of the common neurotransmitter pathways, structure-activity relationships and mechanisms of action of drugs. Important drug mechanisms are also reviewed in the specific disease state chapters.

DRUGS INTERACTIONS WITH RECEPTORS OR ENZYMES

A substrate (or ligand) is a compound that binds to a receptor and starts a chain reaction that produces an effect, such as altering a second messenger system. An agonist is a drug that behaves in a similar manner to an endogenous (produced by the body) substrate. For example, albuterol is a beta-2 agonist that behaves similarly to epinephrine. It binds to beta-2 receptors in the lungs, which activates several steps [e.g., increased cyclic adenine monophosphate (cAMP) production and decreased intracellular calcium] that result in bronchial smooth muscle relaxation.

A drug that blocks an endogenous substrate from binding to its receptor is an antagonist (also called a blocker). For example, beta-1 blockers prevent adrenergic neurotransmitters (e.g., epinephrine) from binding to beta-1 receptors in the heart. Epinephrine normally increases heart rate and contractility when it binds to beta-1 receptors.

By blocking the receptor, beta-1 blockers decrease heart rate and contractility, which decreases blood pressure.

Some drugs exert their effects through activating or inhibiting enzymes. Enzymes are compounds that speed up (catalyze) a reaction (e.g., creating a new compound or breaking down a compound into smaller parts). For example, theophylline blocks the phosphodiesterase (PDE) enzyme, which increases the second messenger cAMP, which in turn causes the smooth muscles of the bronchioles to relax.

The interaction of a drug with a receptor or an enzyme can be competitive or non-competitive. Competitive inhibition occurs when a drug binds to the same active site of a receptor or enzyme as the endogenous substrate, preventing the activity. For example, cyclic guanosine monophosphate (cGMP), which is involved in smooth muscle relaxation, is degraded by the PDE-5 enzyme. Sildenafil is a PDE-5 inhibitor, which binds at the same active site as cGMP and prevents the breakdown of cGMP. In non-competitive inhibition the drug binds to the enzyme or receptor at a site other than the active site, and reduces the activity of the substrate.

Some drugs bind with receptors inside the cell, leading to alterations in DNA replication. Antibodies and hormones can amplify, or provide a normal, cellular process. An example is erythropoiesis-stimulating agents, which stimulate RBC production in patients who cannot produce the hormone erythropoietin, or administering testosterone gel to provide a substitute for low endogenous testosterone. Monoclonal antibodies are clones of a parent compound. They can be used to block a cell receptor [such as infliximab, which inhibits tumor necrosis factor (TNF)-alpha] or they can act as an agonist (such as immune globulin).

OVERVIEW OF THE NERVOUS SYSTEM

The central nervous system (CNS) includes the brain and the spinal cord. It controls the functions of the rest of the body by sending signals to the peripheral nervous system (PNS). Neurotransmitters (NT) are the body's chemical messengers, used to transmit signals in the nervous system. They are released from the presynaptic neuron into the synaptic cleft, then travel to the postsynaptic neuron (or other parts of the body) to exert their effect (see image).

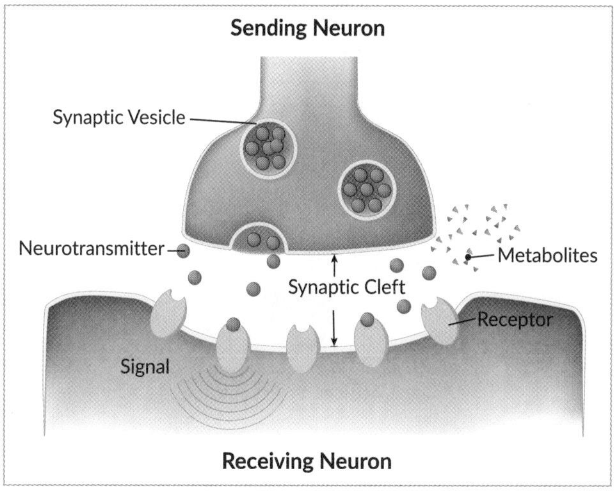

The PNS has two main systems (somatic and autonomic). The somatic nervous system (voluntary) controls muscle movement by sending signals through neurons to release acetylcholine (ACh). ACh then acts on nicotinic receptors (Nn) in skeletal muscles. The autonomic nervous system (involuntary) controls other bodily functions, such as digestion, cardiac output (CO) and blood pressure (BP). It is made up of two types of neurons, those that carry the signal from the brain through the spinal cord, and those that carry the signal to the rest of the body. The electrical signal is transmitted from one neuron to the next by the release of ACh from pre-synaptic neurons, which acts on nicotinic receptors located on the post-synaptic neuron.

PARTS OF THE NERVOUS SYSTEM

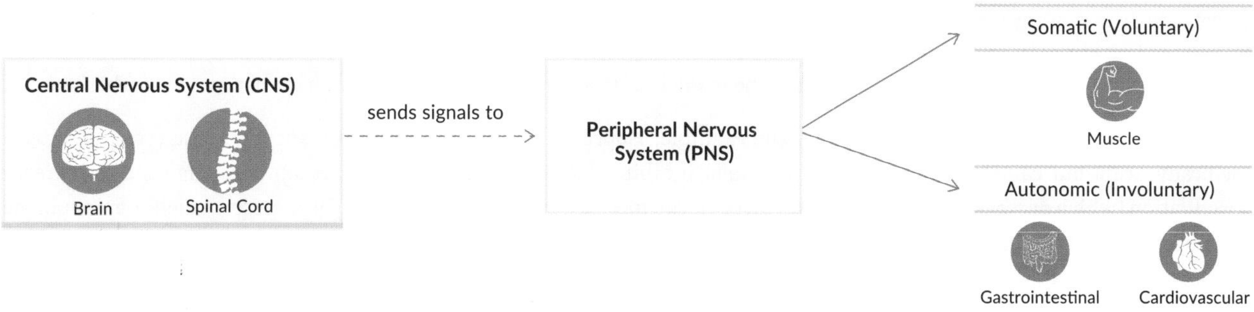

AUTONOMIC NERVOUS SYSTEM

There are two main divisions of the autonomic nervous system (parasympathetic and sympathetic). The parasympathetic nervous system (PSNS) is known as the "rest and digest" system. The PSNS works by releasing ACh on to muscarinic receptors located throughout the body, including the GI tract, the bladder and the eyes. This results in a physiologic response, such as salivation, defecation and urination. The sympathetic nervous system (SNS) is known as the "fight or flight" system. The SNS works by releasing epinephrine (Epi) and norepinephrine (NE), which act on adrenergic receptors (alpha-1, beta-1 and beta-2) in the cardiovascular and respiratory systems. Activation of this system results in increased BP, heart rate (HR) and bronchodilation. Stimulation of beta-2 receptors in the GI tract increases glucose production to provide muscles with oxygen and energy. When the SNS is activated, functions like digestion and urination are minimized to focus on the more important bodily functions for "fight or flight."

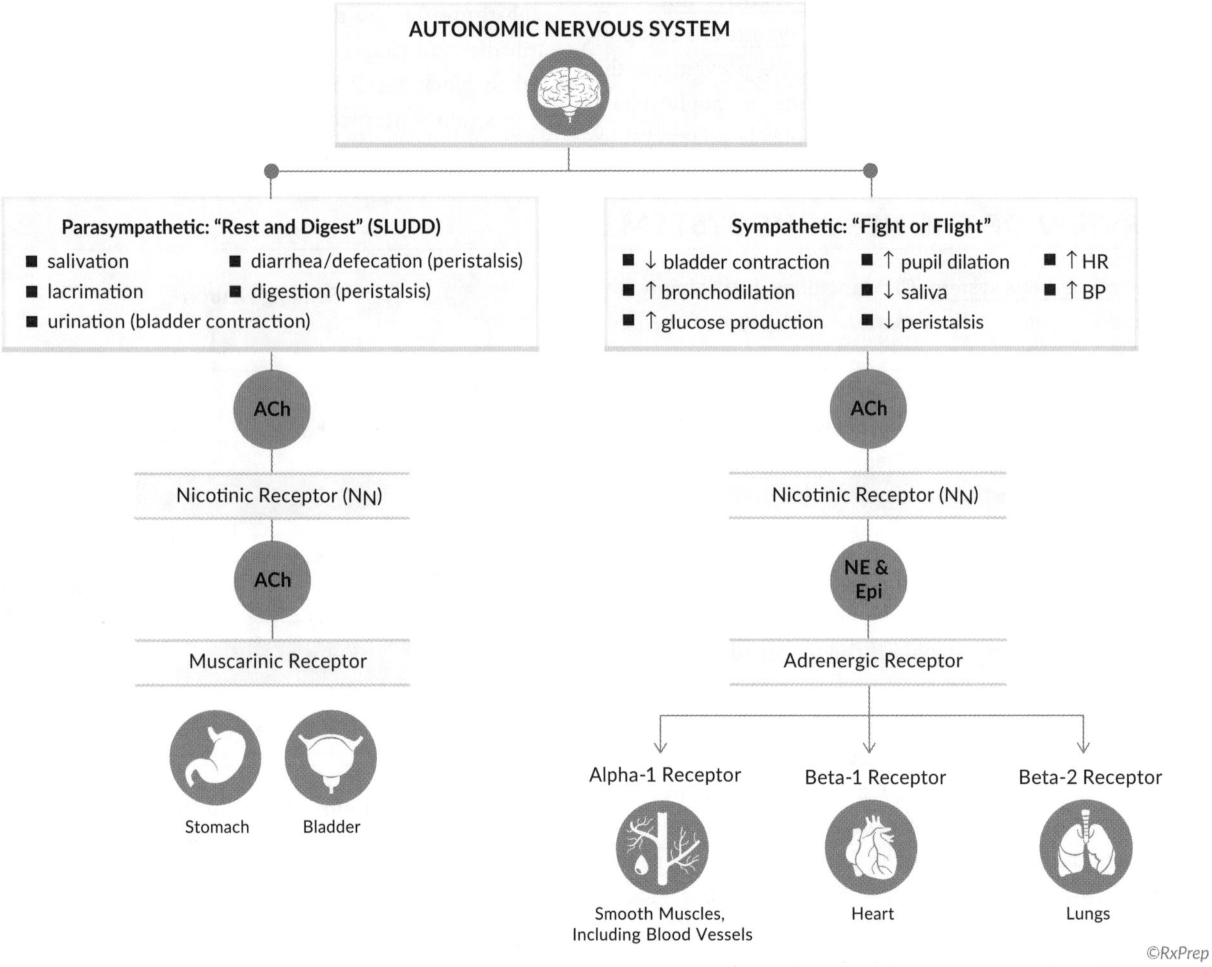

An understanding of receptor pharmacology is essential for pharmacists. Adrenergic and muscarinic receptors can be used as targets for drug therapy (see Study Tip Gal on the following page). For example, muscarinic and alpha-1 receptors are targets for medications used to reduce bladder contractions and relax the bladder, respectively (see the Overactive Bladder and the Benign Prostatic Hyperplasia chapters). Terbutaline is solely a beta-2 agonist used in acute, severe asthma exacerbations.

Some medications affect multiple receptors. For example, isoproterenol is a mixed beta-1 and beta-2 agonist; it is used for bradycardia but causes bronchodilation. Labetalol inhibits alpha-1, beta-1 and beta-2 receptors. It is used to increase vasodilation (which decreases BP) and decrease HR, but it can increase bronchoconstriction. Vasopressors, such as epinephrine and norepinephrine, stimulate multiple receptors, including alpha-1 and beta-1, leading to increased vasoconstriction, HR and BP. Non-selective beta-blockers (e.g., propranolol, nadolol) block beta-1 and beta-2 receptors.

Other medications work in the CNS to affect neurotransmitter release and availability to act on PNS receptors. Clonidine is a centrally acting alpha-2 adrenergic agonist. When alpha-2 receptors located in the brain are stimulated, there is a decrease in overall sympathetic output. This means less ACh is available to nicotinic receptors, leading to decreased release of NE and Epi. Less NE and Epi binding to adrenergic receptors results in vasodilation (decreased BP) and a decrease in HR.

RECEPTOR PHARMACOLOGY

RECEPTOR	AGONIST ACTION	AGONIST EXAMPLES	ANTAGONIST ACTION	ANTAGONIST EXAMPLES
Muscarinic	↑ SLUDD	Pilocarpine, bethanechol	↓ SLUDD	Atropine, oxybutynin
Alpha-1	↑ vasoconstriction, BP	Phenylephrine, dopamine (dose-dependent)	↑ vasodilation via smooth muscle relaxation, ↓ BP	Alpha-1 blockers (e.g., doxazosin, carvedilol, phentolamine)
Beta-1	↑ contractility, CO, HR	Dobutamine, isoproterenol, dopamine (dose-dependent)	↓ CO, HR	Selective beta-1 blockers (e.g., metoprolol) and non-selective beta-blockers (e.g., propranolol)
Beta-2	↑ bronchodilation	Albuterol, terbutaline	↑ bronchoconstriction	Non-selective beta-blockers

MONOAMINE OXIDASE INHIBITORS

Monoamine oxidase (MAO) is an enzyme responsible for breaking down monoamines. Monoamines, a specific sub-type of neurotransmitters called (or sometimes referred to as) catecholamines, include:

- Catecholamine neurotransmitters
  - Dopamine
  - Norepinephrine (NE)
  - Serotonin (5-HT)
- Tyramine (an amino acid that releases catecholamines)

If the MAO enzyme is blocked, monoamine levels increase, which can cause beneficial effects in treating depression and other diseases. If these monoamines build up too much (due to additive effects with other drugs or foods), toxic effects such as hypertensive crisis or serotonin syndrome can occur (see diagram below and on the following page).

MAO INHIBITORS

Phenelzine *(Nardil)*
Tranylcypromine *(Parnate)*
Isocarboxazid *(Marplan)*
Rasagiline, selegiline
Methylene Blue
Linezolid

The older MAO inhibitor antidepressants are non-selective (they inhibit MAO A and B). They bind irreversibly to the MAO enzyme and prevent it from working. The newer drugs are specific for MAO A or MAO B, but the specificity is dose-related.

Catecholamines (Epinephrine, Norepinephrine and Dopamine) and Hypertensive Crisis

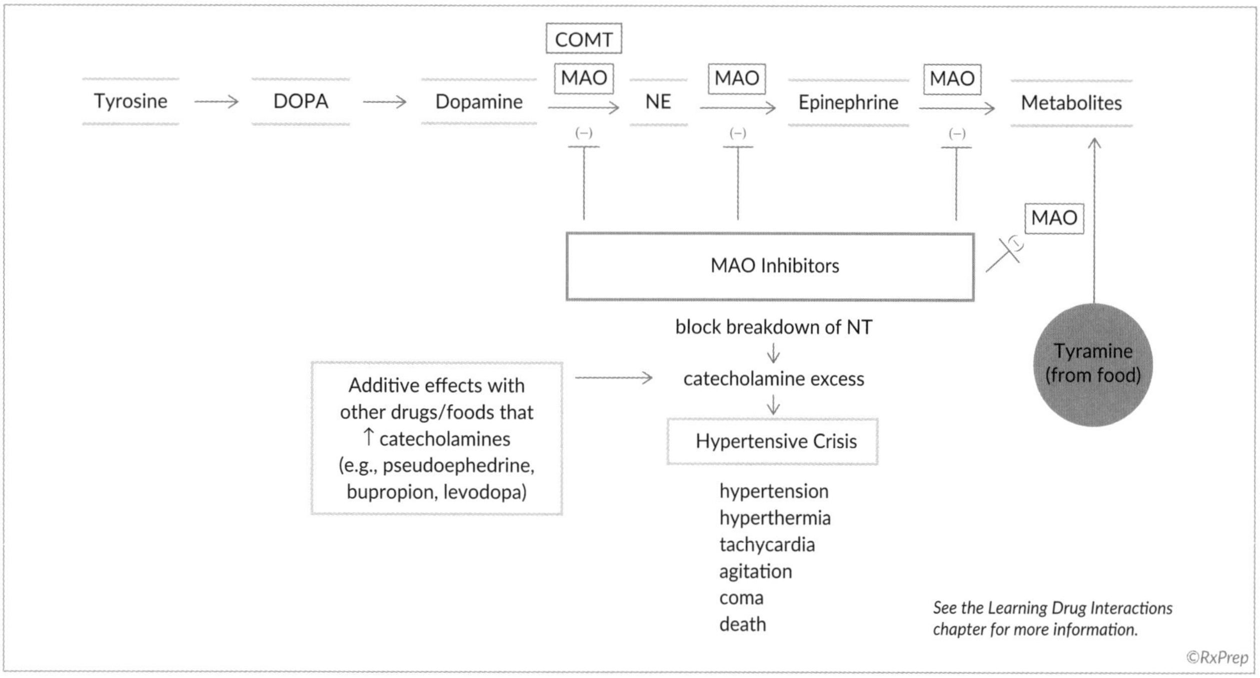

Serotonin and Serotonin Syndrome

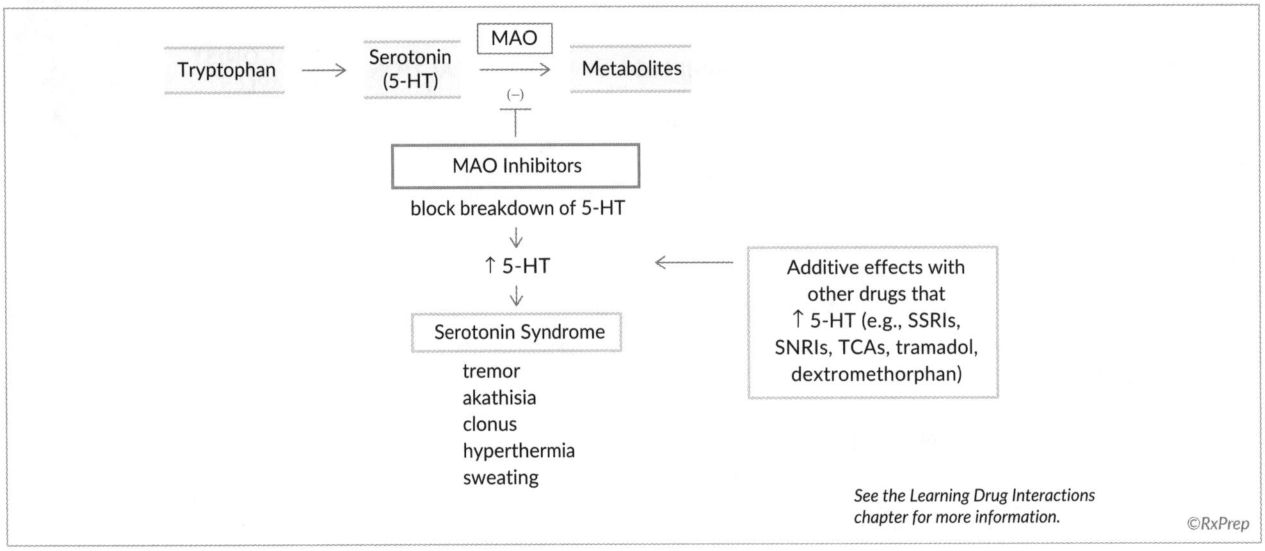

To avoid potentially fatal interactions, separate medications and foods that increase these monoamine neurotransmitters (dopamine, NE and 5-HT) from MAO inhibitors. Allow a wash-out period (usually 14 days) between a drug that increases a neurotransmitter and an MAO inhibitor. Once taking an MAO inhibitor, avoid foods that contain tyramine. See the Learning Drug Interactions chapter for more information.

FUNCTIONAL GROUPS

Some of the common functional groups are depicted in the table on the following page. Knowledge of these functional groups allows a pharmacist to predict certain effects or adverse effects of drugs. For example, identification of the sulfonamide functional group on the celecoxib compound explains why the product labeling for celecoxib states that it is contraindicated in patients with allergic-type reactions to sulfonamides.

Differences in functional groups within a drug class can be important. If a patient has a hypersensitivity reaction to one type of drug in the class, another type of drug can sometimes be used instead. For example, procaine is an ester-type anesthetic and lidocaine is an amide-type anesthetic (see the ester functional group of procaine and the amide functional group of lidocaine enclosed in the dotted lines of each structures below). If a patient has a reaction to procaine, other ester-type drugs (e.g., benzocaine) should be avoided due to the potential for cross-reactivity, but it is reasonable to try an amide-type anesthetic. Amide-type anesthetics can be recognized by the "i" in their name before the "-caine" ending (e.g., lidocaine, bupivacaine, ropivacaine). The rest of this chapter shows common functional groups and drug structures that should be recognized for the exam.

Celecoxib *(Celebrex)*

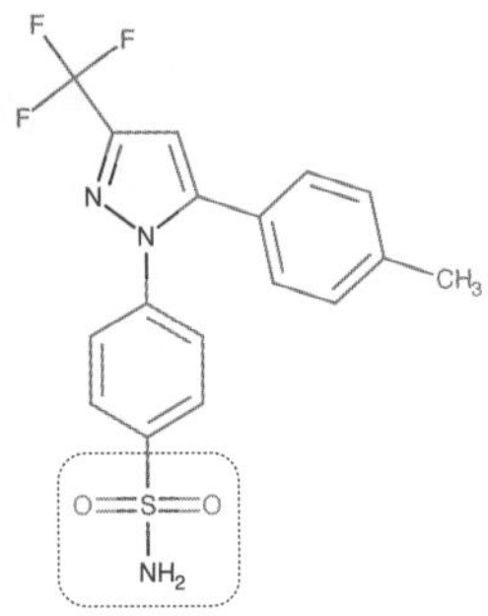

Procaine

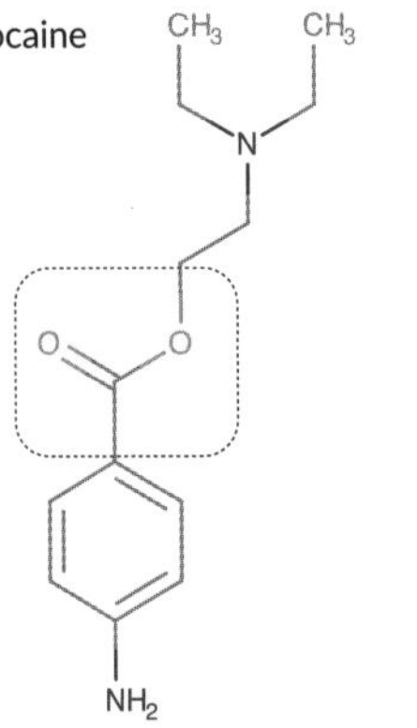

Lidocaine

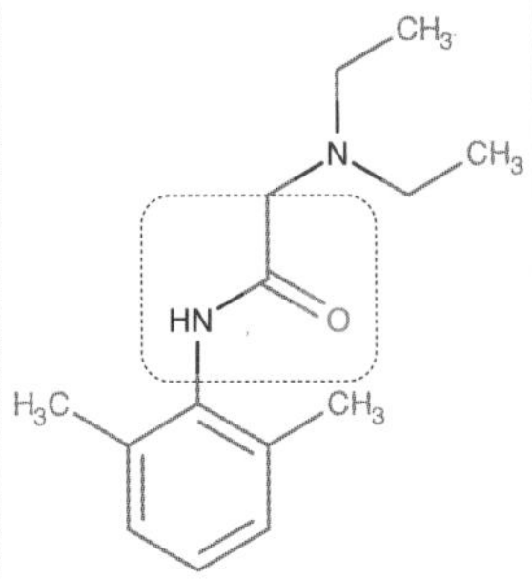

COMMON FUNCTIONAL GROUPS

Neutral Functional Groups

HYDROXYL OR ALCOHOL (PRIMARY)	KETONE	ALDEHYDE	AMIDE
	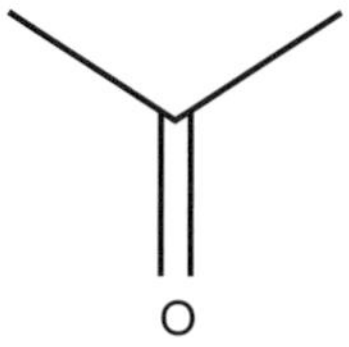	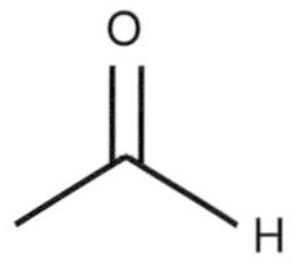	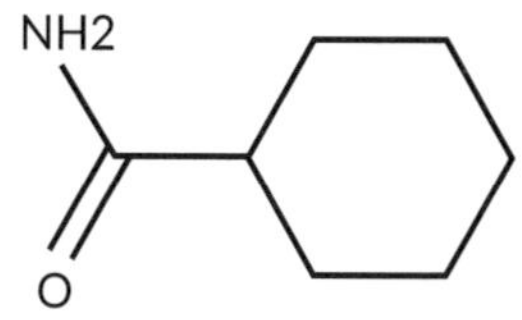

NITRATE	NITRO	AROMATIC (BENZENE) RING	UREA
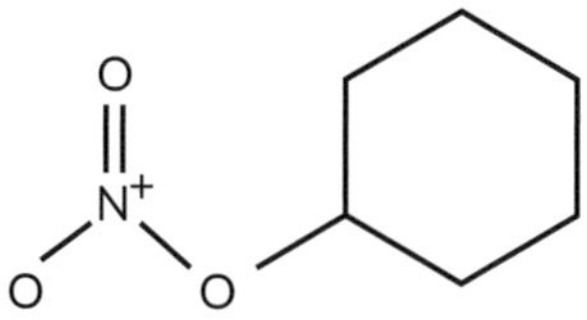	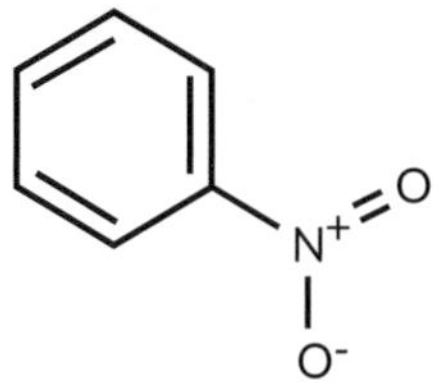	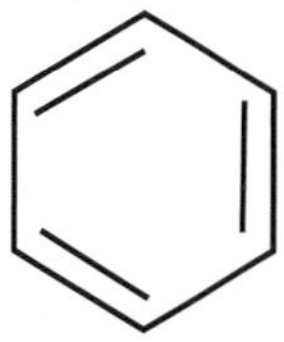	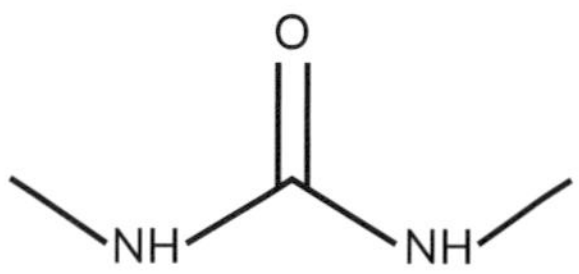

CARBONATE	CARBAMATE	ETHER	THIOETHER
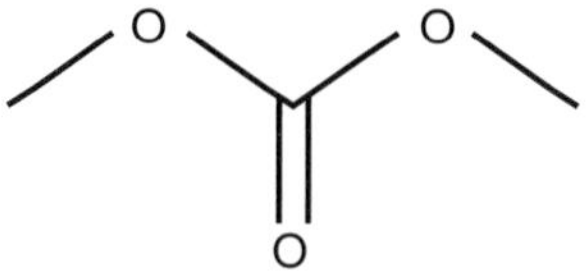	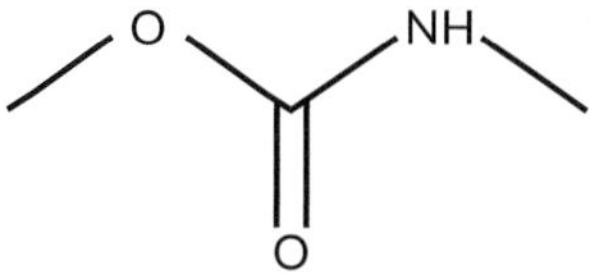		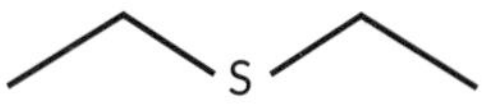

Acidic Functional Groups

CARBOXYL	PHENOL	IMIDE	SULFONAMIDE
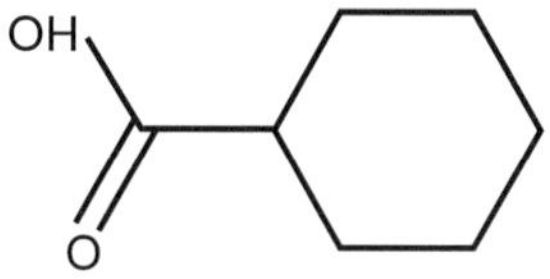	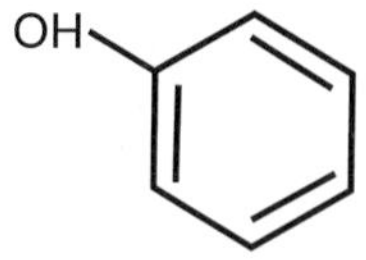	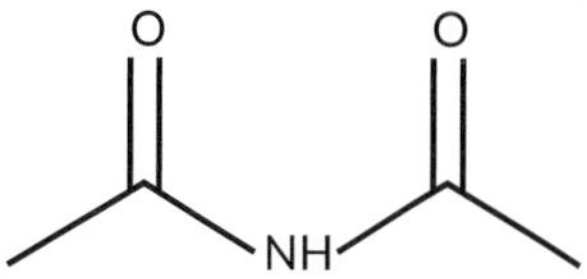	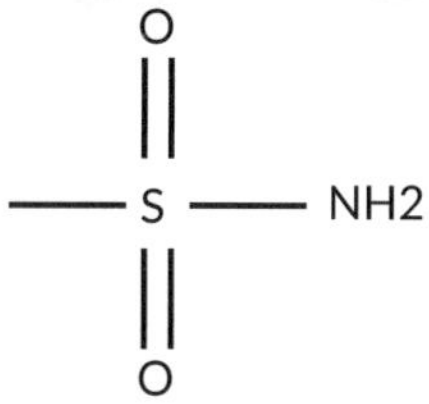

Basic Functional Groups

AMINE (PRIMARY)	AMINE (TERTIARY)	IMINE	AMIDINE
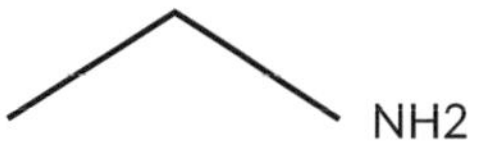	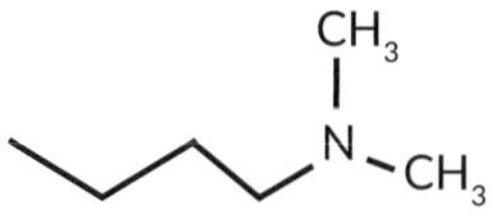	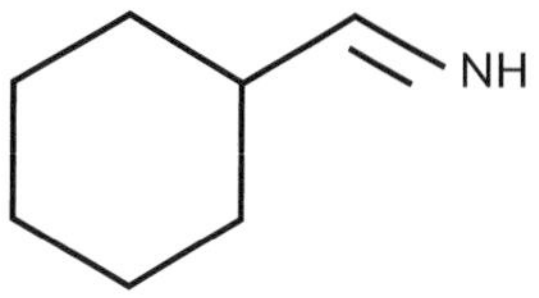	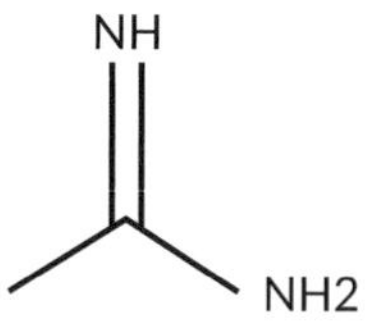

COMMONLY USED STRUCTURES

AMITRIPTYLINE

Tricyclic antidepressant

Contains 3 rings in the structure (note the "tri" in the name)

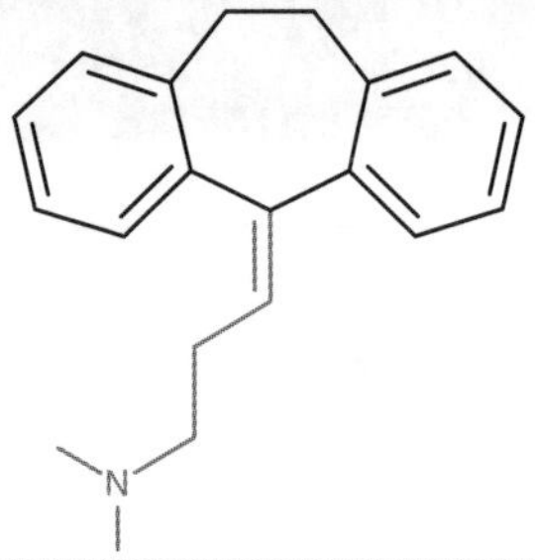

AMIODARONE

Class III antiarrhythmic

Contains two iodine molecules in the structure (note "iod" in the name)

Explains the hyper- and hypothyroid effects and contraindication in patients with an iodine allergy

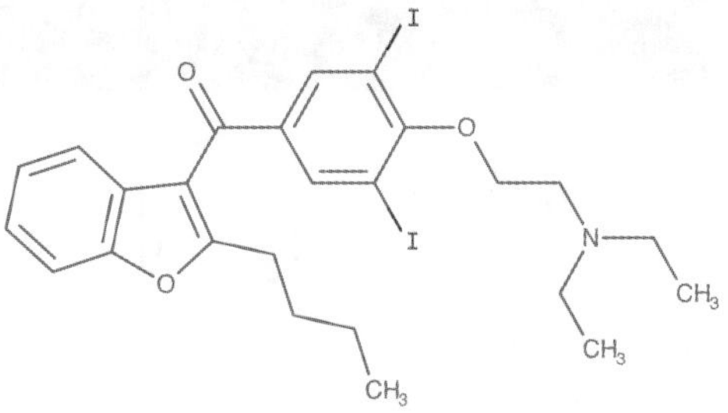

AMOXICILLIN

Beta-lactam, penicillin antibiotic

Contains a beta-lactam ring fused to a 5-sided ring

Hypersensitivity: cross-reactive to other drugs with a beta-lactam ring (see ceftriaxone, ertapenem)

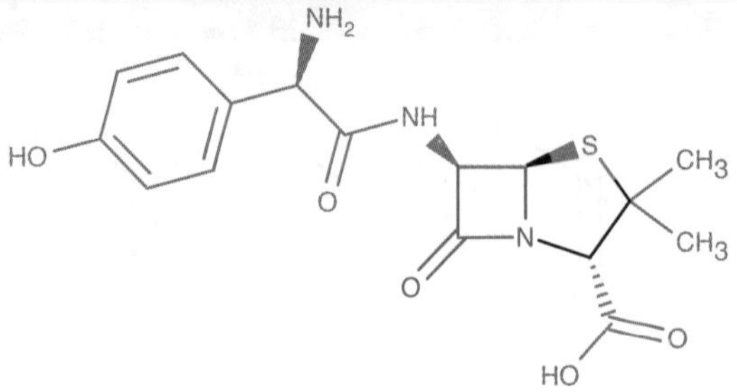

AMPHETAMINE

Stimulant, for ADHD

Contains a primary amine functional group (note "amine" in the name)

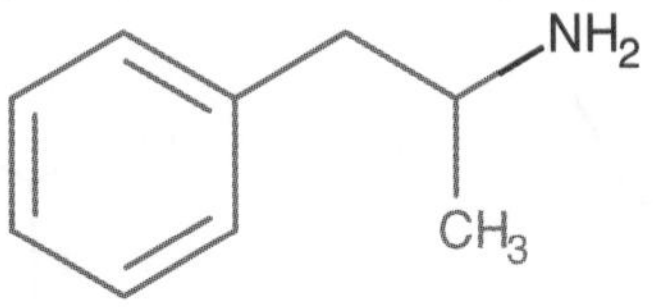

ASPIRIN

Salicylate non-steroidal anti-inflammatory analgesic

Contains an acidic, carboxyl functional group

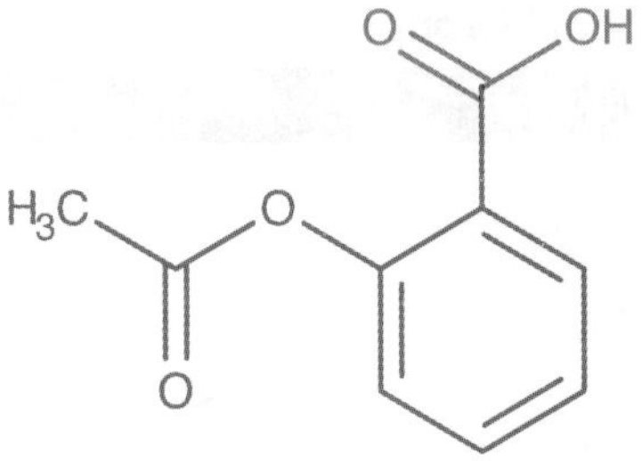

AZTREONAM

Monobactam antibiotic

Contains a lactam ring not fused to another ring (note "mono" in monobactam means one)

Hypersensitivity: not cross-reactive with beta-lactam antibiotics

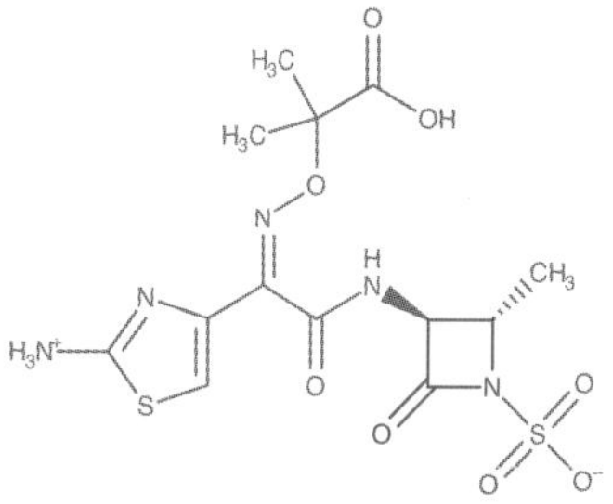

CEFTRIAXONE

Beta-lactam, cephalosporin antibiotic

Contains a beta-lactam ring fused to a 6-sided ring

Hypersensitivity: cross-reactive to other drugs with a beta-lactam ring (see amoxicillin, ertapenem)

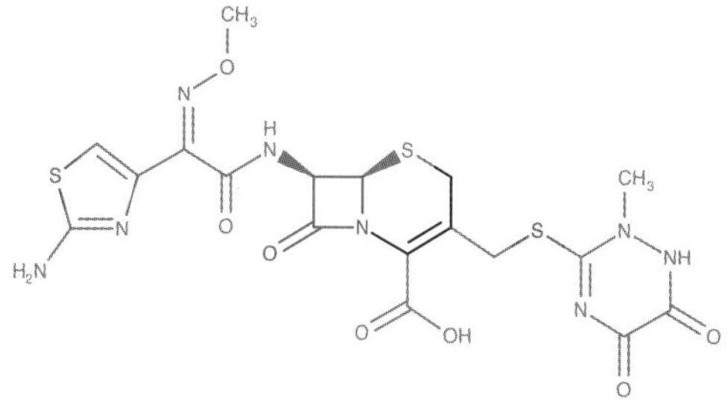

CHLORPROMAZINE

Phenothiazine antipsychotic

Contains a thioether group

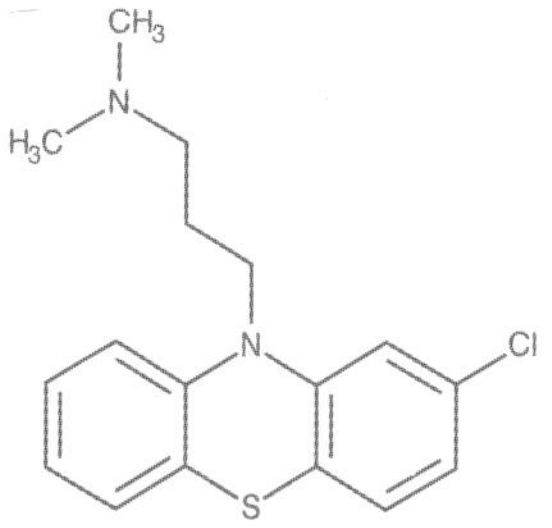

ERTAPENEM

Beta-lactam, carbapenem antibiotic

Contains a beta-lactam ring fused to a 5-sided ring

Hypersensitivity: cross-reactive to other drugs with a beta-lactam ring (see amoxicillin, ceftriaxone)

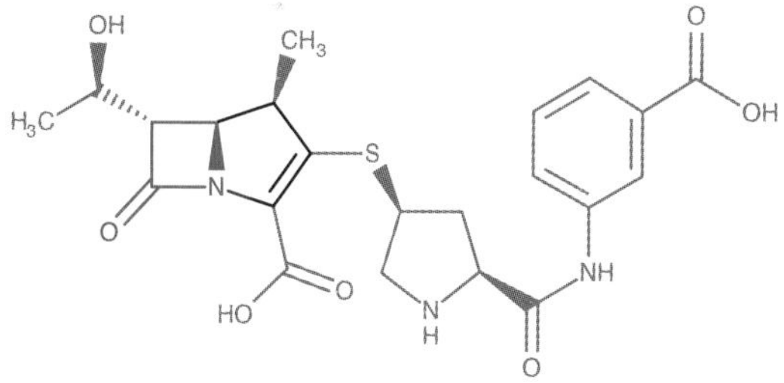

FENOFIBRATE

Fibrate, for high cholesterol

Contains ketone groups

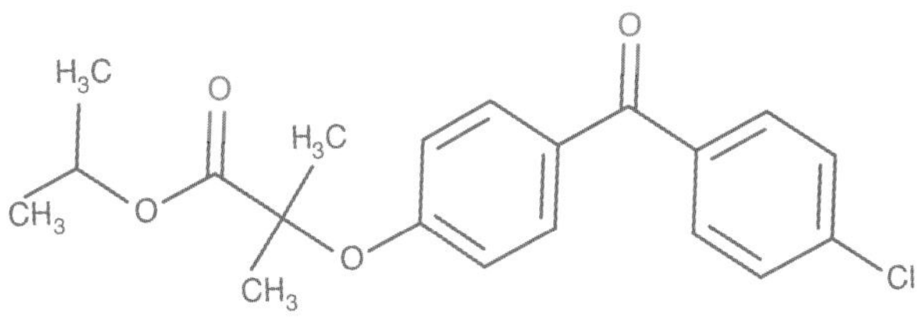

GENTAMICIN

Aminoglycoside antibiotic

Contains an amine (amino) group* and a sugar (glycoside) group**

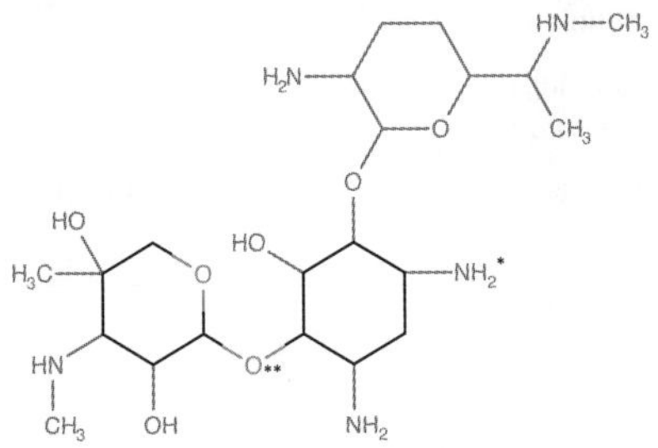

IBUPROFEN

Non-steroidal anti-inflammatory analgesic

Contains a carboxyl group

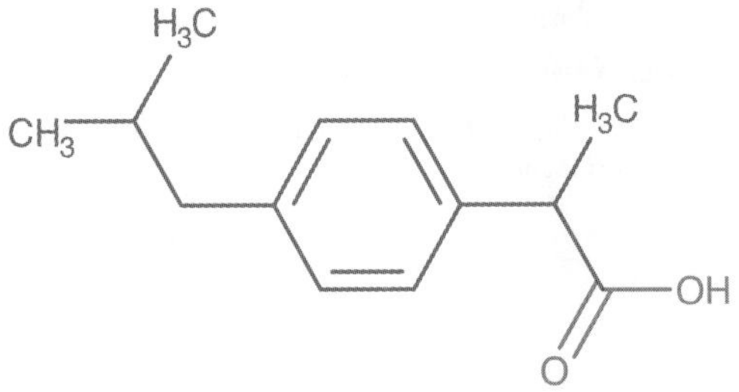

LEVOTHYROXINE

Thyroid hormone (T4)

Contains 4 iodine molecules in the structure (note the "4" in T4); converted to T3 (triiodothyronine) in the body (note "tri" meaning 3 and "iod" for iodine)

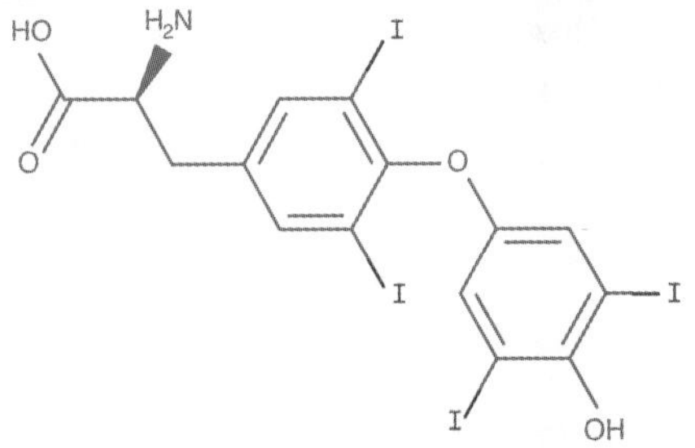

SULFAMETHOXAZOLE

Sulfonamide antibiotic

Contains a sulfonamide group

Hypersensitivity: cross-reactive to other drugs containing this group (e.g., celecoxib)

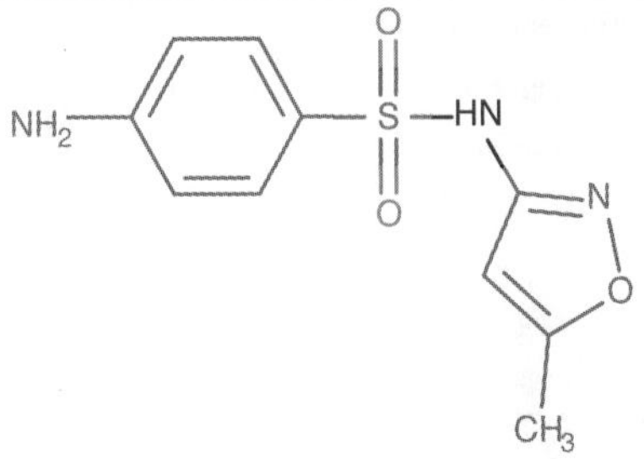

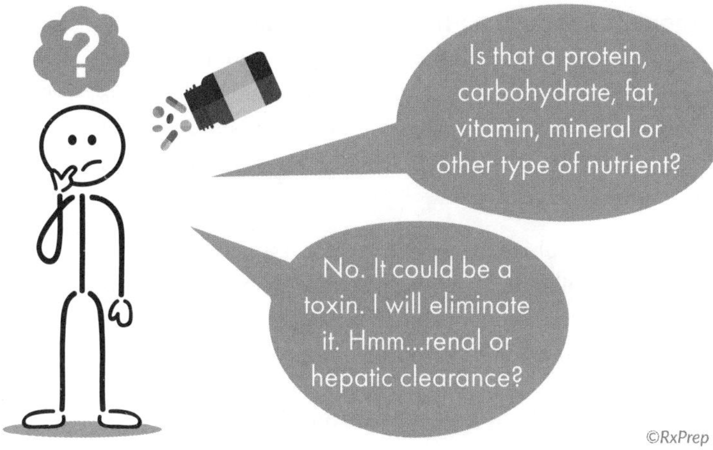

©RxPrep

CHAPTER CONTENT

Types of Drug Interactions ... 55
Pharmacodynamic Drug Interactions ... 55
Pharmacodynamics: Pharmaco + Dynamics ... 55
Risk with Concurrent Use of Benzodiazepines and Opioids ... 56
Pharmacokinetic Drug Interactions ... 57
Pharmacokinetics: Pharmaco + Kinetics ... 57
Drug Breakdown and Removal ... 58
Renal Excretion: In The Urine ... 58
Drug Metabolism ... 58
Cytochrome P450 Enzymes ... 58
Enzyme Inducers Decrease The Concentration of the Substrate Drugs ... 59
CYP Inducers ... 59
Enzyme Inhibitors Increase The Concentration of the Substrate Drugs ... 60
CYP Inhibitors ... 60
"Lag" Time for Enzyme Induction ... 60
Prodrugs: Inactive Drugs Converted by CYP Enzymes to Active Drugs ... 60
Non-CYP450 Enzymes ... 61
Gut Excretion: In The Feces ... 62
P-Glycoprotein Efflux Pumps ... 62
Enterohepatic Recycling ... 62
Common Drug Interactions ... 62
CYP 450 Enzymes Substrates, Inducers & Inhibitors ... 69
Common Prodrugs ... 70

CONTENT LEGEND

= Study Tip Gal

CHAPTER 3
LEARNING DRUG INTERACTIONS

TYPES OF DRUG INTERACTIONS

PHARMACODYNAMIC DRUG INTERACTIONS

"Pharmaco" refers to a drug, and "dynamic" refers to an activity, such as a type of process, or a change. Pharmacodynamics refers to the effect or change that a drug has on some type of organism, such as a human body (see Study Tip Gal).

PHARMACODYNAMICS: PHARMACO + DYNAMICS

"Pharmaco" refers to a drug. "Dynamic" refers to an activity, such as a type of process or change.

Pharmacodynamics refers to the effect or change that a drug has on the body. The effect can be therapeutic (e.g., morphine provides pain relief when it binds to the mu receptor) or toxic (excessive morphine can be fatal).

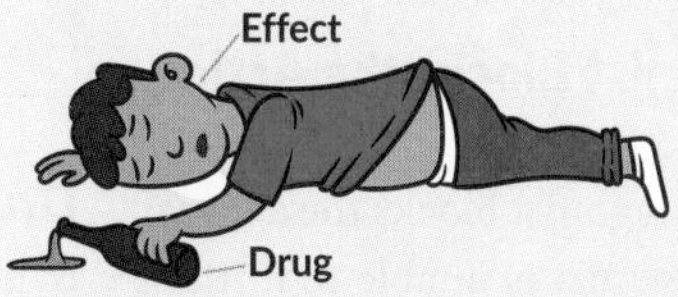

PD drug interactions can occur when two or more drugs are given together. The effects can be additive (such as more sedation), antagonistic (one drug blocks the effect of another drug) or synergistic, with an amplified (versus additive) effect.

Drugs are designed to be given at a therapeutic dose. When a dose is less than intended, the effect can be subtherapeutic, with poor treatment efficacy. When the dose is higher than intended, the effect can be supratherapeutic, with risk of toxicity (e.g., respiratory depression risk due to an excessive opioid dose). A pharmacodynamic (PD) drug interaction occurs when two or more drugs are given together, with some type of beneficial or harmful effect.

Agonists Produce a Pharmacodynamic Event

An agonist is a chemical compound that binds to and activates a receptor, producing some type of response. Endogenous compounds, such as endorphins, are agonists at opioid receptors. Endorphins bind to the receptor, which results in pain relief (analgesia).

Example: morphine is a mu-receptor agonist. It causes an effect similar to (but much greater than) endogenous compounds that mute pain. Excessive morphine causes toxicity, including fatality from respiratory depression.

Antagonists Block a Pharmacodynamic Event

An antagonist binds to the same receptor as an agonist but does not produce a subsequent reaction; the antagonist simply blocks the agonist from binding to the same receptor. The reaction that would have been produced by the agonist is blocked.

Example: epinephrine (EPI) is an endogenous agonist at the beta receptor. When EPI is bound to the receptor in a fight or flight response, the heart rate (HR) increases to provide adequate blood flow to enable the response (i.e., to fight, or run away). Metoprolol is a beta-blocker (antagonist) that blocks EPI from docking to the receptor, which lowers HR.

Drug Interaction: Multiple Agonists Cause Additive Effects

Multiple drugs that are agonists at the same receptor can cause additive effects.

Example: morphine is a mu-receptor agonist, providing analgesia, but with risk of fatal toxicity when overdosed. Oxycodone binds to the same receptor, with similar effects. If both opioids are taken concurrently, the drug interaction would be additive, with increased side effects (e.g., excessive sedation) and a higher degree of respiratory depression, and death.

Drug Interaction: An Antagonist Blocks the Action of an Agonist

In a competitive interaction, an antagonist blocks the agonist from docking to a receptor. The agonist is unable to initiate a change that would have resulted in some effect (e.g., analgesia, with respiratory depression when the dose is excessive).

Example: naloxone is a mu-receptor antagonist, and floods the mu-receptor, which blocks the opioid from the receptor. Naloxone reverses respiratory depression. Naloxone will also reverse the analgesic effect.

Drug Interaction: Additive Effects from Agonists Binding to Different Receptors

Drugs that have similar end effects through different mechanisms/receptors can cause additive effects.

Example: benzodiazepines, like opioids, are sedating and suppress respiration. The effects are similar but caused by a different mechanism. Benzodiazepines enhance the effect of the endogenous neurotransmitter gamma-aminobutyric acid (GABA), which binds to the GABA receptor, causing anxiolytic, hypnotic, anticonvulsant, and muscle relaxant effects (including relaxing the diaphragm, which suppresses respiration). Benzodiazepines taken concurrently with opioids increases the risk of fatal overdose from the additive effects; one-third of the opioid overdose fatalities in 2017 involved opioids with benzodiazepines (see Study Tip Gal).

Another example: warfarin causes anticoagulation through inhibition of vitamin K dependent clotting factors. Aspirin blocks the effects of platelets. Although they work through different mechanisms, both can cause increased bleeding, and when used together the risk is greater.

RISK WITH CONCURRENT USE OF BENZODIAZEPINES AND OPIOIDS

Due to the heightened fatality risk when opioids and benzodiazepines are taken together, the FDA added a boxed warning to all drugs, in both classes:

WARNING: RISKS FROM CONCOMITANT USE WITH OPIOIDS

Concomitant use of benzodiazepines and opioids may result in profound sedation, respiratory depression, coma, and death.

- Reserve concomitant prescribing of these drugs for use in patients for whom alternative treatment options are inadequate.
- Limit dosages and durations to the minimum required.
- Follow patients for signs and symptoms of respiratory depression and sedation.

Drug Interaction: Synergism

Synergism is present when the effect from two drugs taken in combination is greater than the effect from simply adding the two individual effects together.

Example: oxycodone provides analgesia as a mu-receptor agonist. Acetaminophen provides analgesia by different mechanisms, which are not fully understood. Acetaminophen is thought to provide some of the analgesic effect by inhibiting prostaglandin synthesis in the central nervous system. The mechanisms that produce analgesia with opioids and with acetaminophen do not overlap. Acetaminophen taken with oxycodone produces more analgesia than the effect that would be expected from adding together the analgesic effects provided by each drug.

PHARMACOKINETIC DRUG INTERACTIONS

"Pharmaco" refers to a drug, and "kinetic" refers to motion. Pharmacokinetics (PK) refers to the effect or change that the body has on a drug (see Study Tip Gal).

PHARMACOKINETICS: PHARMACO + KINETICS

"Pharmaco" refers to a drug. "Kinetics" refers to motion.

Pharmacokinetics refers to the effect the body has on the drug as it travels (moves) through the Absorption, Distribution, Metabolism and Excretion (ADME) processes.

- Absorption (with oral drugs, typically occurring in the small intestine)
- Distribution (through the blood and dispersed throughout the tissues)
- Metabolism (including enzymatic reactions), and
- Excretion (to remove the drug or end products (metabolites) from the body

PK drug interactions occur when one drug alters the absorption, distribution, metabolism or excretion of another drug. PK drug interactions can beneficial or harmful.

PK Drug Interaction: A Drug Reduces the Absorption of Another Drug

Chelation occurs when a drug binds to charged ions in another compound. The chelated complex cannot dissolve in the gut fluid and will pass out in the stool.

Tetracyclines or quinolones, when taken with positively-charged metallic compounds (e.g., Mg++, Ca++), form a compound that cannot dissolve, will not be absorbed, and the infection may not be adequately treated. Magnesium is present in many antacids and multivitamin-mineral tablets. Calcium is present in many supplements and in dairy products.

Other interactions occur by different binding mechanisms. For example, bisphosphonates are "sticky". Most drugs and foods will decrease bisphosphonate absorption from the (already low) level of 0.8 - 1.8%. Bisphosphonates can be taken only with plain water.

Many drugs have poor absorption when the gut fluid is not acidic. The Gastroesophageal Reflux Disease and Peptic Ulcer Disease chapter contains a chart of the many drugs that require an acidic gut for adequate absorption.

Example: antacids decrease the absorption of some antivirals and antifungals. The interaction can result in untreated/ resistant infections.

PK Drug Interaction: Inducers and Inhibitors Alter the Metabolism of Other (Substrate) Drugs

The majority of PK drug interactions occur during metabolism. Drug-drug interactions can be harmful or beneficial.

Example of a beneficial interaction: ritonavir and darunavir are used concurrently; ritonavir inhibits the metabolism of darunavir, which provides a higher level of darunavir, and increased efficacy in treating HIV.

Example of a harmful interaction: quinolones and macrolides inhibit warfarin metabolism (which increases the INR) and rifampin induces warfarin metabolism (which decreases the INR). Both reactions are potentially harmful, but may be necessary. The dose of warfarin will be decreased (with either antibiotic) or increased (with rifampin).

PK Drug Interaction: A Drug Decreases or Increases the Excretion of Another Drug

Renal excretion is the primary route of drug excretion and is described further in this chapter. Drug interactions can block or enhance renal excretion.

Example: probenecid blocks the renal excretion of penicillin. High penicillin levels are needed to cross the blood-brain barrier (BBB) and provide effective treatment of neurosyphilis. Probenecid is given with penicillin to increase the penicillin serum level, which creates a higher concentration gradient, resulting in more penicillin moving across the BBB.

Another example: salicylate (e.g., aspirin) overdose results in toxicity. Sodium bicarbonate given IV alkalinizes the urine, which causes the salicylates to become ionized. Compounds that are ionized are more hydrophilic (less lipophilic) and will stay in the watery urine. Less will be reabsorbed through the renal tubules (i.e., across a lipid membrane) and move back into the blood. Compounds that stay in the urine will be renally excreted.

There are many other examples of PK drug-drug interactions in the remainder of this chapter. Enzymes are not present to cause drug-drug interaction problems in order to keep pharmacists gainfully employed. The purpose of the enzymes that metabolize drugs is to get rid of the drugs (i.e., to remove the drugs from the body). The human body, as smart as it may seem, does not recognize that warfarin is being given to prevent a stroke and darunavir is being given to fight an infection. To the human body, the drugs are toxins that need to be removed.

DRUG BREAKDOWN AND REMOVAL

The breakdown of drugs in the body into forms that can be removed is called metabolism. Primary sites for drug metabolism include the liver and the gut, due to high levels of metabolic enzymes in these areas.

Removal of drugs from the body is called excretion. The majority of drugs are excreted in the urine. Most of the remainder are excreted in the feces. Minor routes of excretion include the skin, tears, breast milk and lungs (via exhalation).

RENAL EXCRETION: IN THE URINE

The urine is mostly water, and drugs and drug metabolites need to be water-soluble to have a high degree of renal excretion. Many drugs are lipid-soluble (non-polar, uncharged) and will need to be converted to a more water-soluble (polar, charged) compound in order to concentrate in the renal filtrate (urine).

DRUG METABOLISM

Metabolism is the process of converting a drug into a form that can be excreted. The drug that is subject to the reactions is called the substrate. Phase I and Phase II metabolism refers to the enzyme-catalyzed transformation reactions that take place in the intestine and liver.

These two phases involve:

- Phase I: chemical reactions that change the parent molecule into a metabolite. Most are oxidation reactions, but can be hydrolysis or reduction reactions. Phase I reactions usually inactivate the compound.
- Phase II: mainly conjugation reactions. Conjugation means "joined together." In these reactions, an enzyme binds the compound to another substance (e.g., glucuronide, glutathione or sulfate) to increase water solubility and facilitate elimination.

A small number of drugs are renally excreted without any transformation reactions, including the water-soluble drug penicillin G, and lithium. Some compounds require only one phase of metabolism, and some require both Phase I and Phase II reactions for adequate renal excretion.

First-pass metabolism refers to the changes made to a drug in Phase I and Phase II reactions prior to the drug reaching the systemic (blood) circulation. This reduces bioavailability of the drug, and results in the inactivation of some fraction of ~75% of oral drugs. These concepts are discussed further in the Pharmacokinetics chapter.

CYTOCHROME P450 ENZYMES

The purpose of the cytochrome (CYP) enzymes is to catalyze reactions for production of essential compounds (e.g., cholesterol and cortisol), and to catalyze reactions that uncover or insert a polar group into a compound to facilitate renal excretion.

How CYP 450 Enzymes Metabolize Drugs

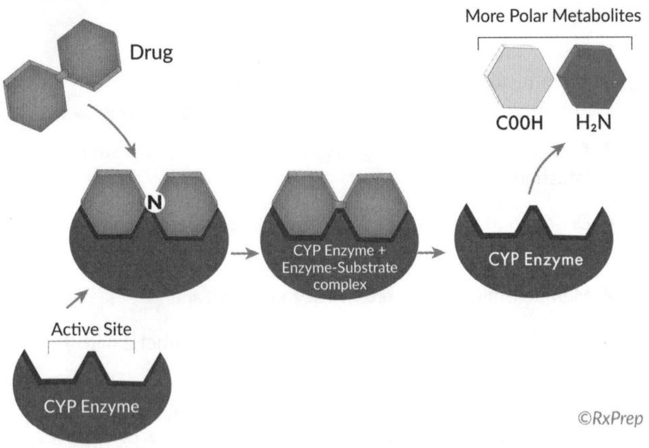

More than 50 CYP enzymes have been identified, with 6 of them metabolizing most drugs. The big work horse is CYP 3A4, which metabolizes ~34% of all CYP 450-metabolized drugs. The reactions catalyzed by CYP enzymes occur in Phase I metabolism. The function of CYP enzymes can be effected by genetics (discussed on the right) and other drugs that act as inhibitors or inducers (discussed on the following page).

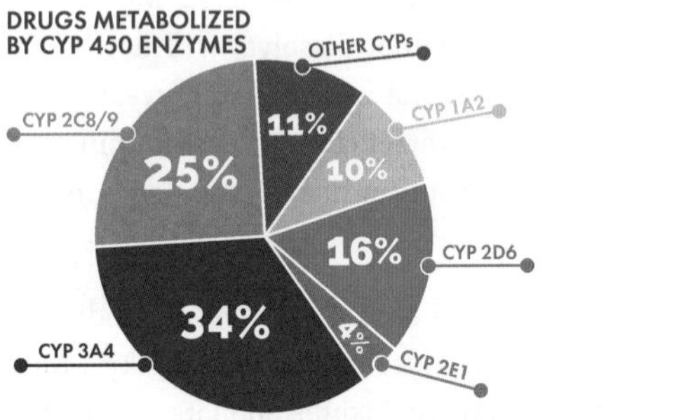

Reproduced with permission from Joseph McGraw, Concordia Univ Wisc

CYP Enzymes are Polymorphic

The CYP 450 enzymes are polymorphic, which means there are different forms of the same enzyme. The changes are due to a single nucleotide polymorphism (SNP) in the DNA that codes for the enzyme. A SNP can cause the enzyme production in an individual to increase or decrease, which will increase or decrease the rate of drug metabolism and, consequently, the serum level of the substrate drug.

The major types of variations are classified into 4 groups, based on the effect on the rate of metabolism: ultra-rapid metabolizer (UM), extensive metabolizer (EM), intermediate metabolizer (IM) and poor metabolizer (PM).

Enzyme inhibitors and PMs cause drug levels to increase because there are less functional enzymes to metabolize the enzyme's substrate drugs. Enzyme inducers and UMs cause drug levels to decrease because there are more enzymes to metabolize the enzyme's substrate drugs. This is discussed further on the following page.

CYP Enzymes Vary by Ethnicity and Among Individuals

Gene variants are most often inherited, and the variant enzyme expression can be measured among ethnic groups. Using CYP 2D6 as an example, 6-10% of Caucasians are PMs and produce little or no CYP 2D6, while 30% of Ethiopians are UMs and produce about double the usual amount (see table).

GENETIC TYPE	CYP2D6 ACTIVITY	ETHNIC DIFFERENCES (APPROX.)
Poor Metabolizers	None	Caucasians 6%-10% Mexican Americans 3%-6% African Americans 2%-5% Asians ~1%
Intermediate Metabolizers	Low	Not established
Extensive Metabolizers	Normal	Most people are extensive metabolizers
Ultrarapid Metabolizers	High	Finns and Danes 1% North Americans (white) 4% Greeks 10% Portuguese 10% Saudis 20% Ethiopians 30%

Reprinted with Permission from Dr. John Horn

ENZYME INDUCERS DECREASE THE CONCENTRATION OF THE SUBSTRATE DRUGS

Inducers cause more enzyme production or increase enzyme activity, which increases the rate of drug metabolism. Substrates for the enzyme will then have a decrease in serum drug level. In some cases, more drug will be lost to first pass metabolism. Inducers can cause therapeutic failure. The FDA labels inducers (and inhibitors) as strong, moderate and weak, based on the effect on metabolism of the enzyme's substrate drugs.

CYP INDUCERS

PS PORCS (BIG INDUCERS)

Phenytoin

Smoking

Phenobarbital

Oxcarbazepine (and eslicarbazepine)

Rifampin (and rifabutin, rifapentine)

Carbamazepine (and is an auto-inducer)

St. John's wort

Effects

- Increased metabolism of substrates
- Decreased serum concentrations and decreased clinical effect of substrates
- In**D**ucers = **D**ecreased levels/effects of substrates
- Effect on prodrugs: inducers ↑ levels of active drug form

Recognizing the Problem

- Review labs for therapeutic drug monitoring
- Monitor for therapeutic effect

Possible Actions: increase dose of substrate (unless a prodrug), use alternate agent to avoid combination

CLINICAL CASE: SUBTHERAPEUTIC LEVEL WITH AN INDUCER

A 34-year-old female has been taking warfarin chronically for VTE prophylaxis secondary to mechanical mitral valve replacement.

Warfarin dose: 5 mg PO daily

INR range for the past 6 months: 2.6 – 3.1 (INR goal 2.5 – 3.5)

She was admitted for infective endocarditis and started on gentamicin, ceftriaxone, rifampin and vancomycin.

Recognizing the Problem

Rifampin is a broad-spectrum inducer of P-gp, CYP 2C9, 3A4, 1A2 and 2C19.

Warfarin is metabolized by CYP2C9 (major) and CYP 1A2, 2C19 and 3A4.

Pharmacist Actions

Monitor INR more frequently; increase warfarin dose PRN.

ENZYME INHIBITORS INCREASE THE CONCENTRATION OF THE SUBSTRATE DRUGS

Inhibitors result in less functional enzymes, which decreases the rate of drug metabolism. Substrates for the enzyme will then have an increase in serum drug level. In some cases, less drug will be lost to first pass metabolism. Inhibitors can result in drug toxicity. Inhibitors increase drug levels soon after they are taken. Drugs that are enzyme inhibitors are sometimes used deliberately to block drug metabolism. The two common inhibitors used for this purpose are ritonavir and cobicistat, which are used to increase the levels of other HIV drugs taken concurrently. The FDA labels inhibitors (and inducers) as strong, moderate and weak, based on the effect on metabolism of the enzyme's substrate drugs.

CYP INHIBITORS

G ♥ PACMAN (BIG INHIBITORS)

Grapefruit

♥

PIs Protease Inhibitors (don't miss ritonavir) but check all PIs since many are potent inhibitors

Azole antifungals (fluconazole, itraconazole, ketoconazole, posaconazole, voriconazole and isavuconazonium)

C - cyclosporine, cimetidine, cobicistat

Macrolides (clarithromycin and erythromycin, but not azithromycin)

Amiodarone (and dronedarone)

Non-DHP CCBs (diltiazem and verapamil)

Effects

- Decreased metabolism of substrates
- Increased serum concentrations and increased clinical effect of substrates
- **IN**hibitors = **IN**creased effects/levels/ADR/toxicities of substrates
- Effect on prodrugs: inhibitors ↓ levels of active drug form

Recognizing the Problem

- Review labs for therapeutic drug monitoring
- Monitor for therapeutic effect, ADRs, toxicity

Possible Actions: Decrease dose of substrate (unless a prodrug), use alternate agent to avoid combination

CLINICAL CASE: TOXICITY RISK WITH AN INHIBITOR

A 76-year-old male presents to the pharmacy with a voriconazole prescription for aspergillosis from an ID specialist.

The medication profile includes betaxolol 1 drop OU BID, simvastatin 40 mg PO QHS and hydrochlorothiazide 25 mg PO QAM.

Recognizing the Problem

Voriconazole is a strong CYP 3A4 inhibitor and will increase the simvastatin level, increasing the risk of muscle toxicity and risk of rhabdomyolysis.

Pharmacist Actions

The combination of voriconazole and simvastatin is contraindicated.

Ensure that the drugs are not used concurrently. Recommend an alternative statin, such as rosuvastatin.

"LAG" TIME FOR ENZYME INDUCTION

Inhibition of an enzyme is fast; effects are seen within a few days and will end quickly when the inhibitor is discontinued.

Induction most often requires additional enzyme production, which takes time. The full effect on drug levels due to enzyme induction may not be seen for up to 4 weeks. When the inducer is stopped it could take 2-4 weeks for the induction to disappear completely; the excess enzymes will degrade based on their half-lives.

PRODRUGS: INACTIVE DRUGS CONVERTED BY CYP ENZYMES TO ACTIVE DRUGS

With prodrugs, inhibitors and inducers have an opposite effect on drug levels. Prodrugs are taken by the patient in an inactive form and are converted by CYP 450 enzymes into the active form. With a prodrug, the active drug concentration decreases with an inhibitor because there are less functional enzymes to convert the prodrug to the active form. With an inducer, the prodrug's active drug concentration increases because there are more enzymes to catalyze the conversion to the active drug.

For example, clopidogrel is a commonly used prodrug, which is converted to an active form via CYP2C19. Common inhibitors of CYP2C19 include omeprazole and esomeprazole. If taken together, omeprazole and esomeprazole may block the conversion of clopidogrel to the active form and prevent its antiplatelet effects.

How CYP 450 Enzymes Metabolize Prodrugs

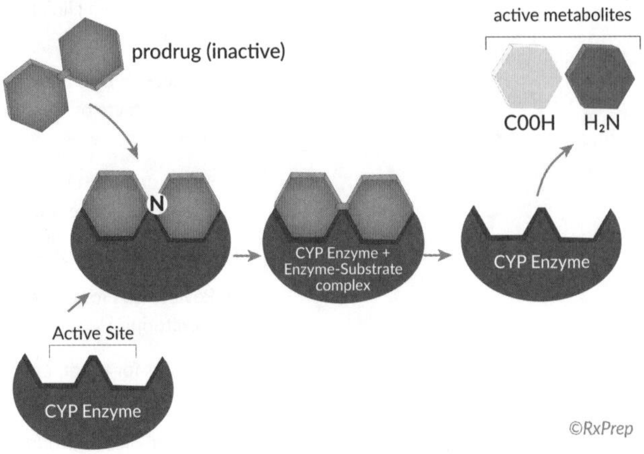

Prodrugs are designed by drug manufacturers to take advantage of the CYP enzymes for some type of beneficial effect, such as longer dosing intervals and reduced abuse potential.

Prodrugs to Extend Dosing Intervals

A drug that has 50% bioavailability (written as F = 0.5) loses half of the dose to first-pass metabolism. A prodrug version could be designed to use the CYP enzymes to catalyze a reaction that converts an inactive drug to an active form—instead of converting an active drug to an inactive metabolite. This would increase the drug's oral bioavailability, which could make a longer dosing interval feasible.

An example of this concept is the prodrug valacyclovir, which is metabolized to the active drug acyclovir. Valacyclovir has higher bioavailability than acyclovir, and is dosed less frequently.

Prodrugs to Prevent Drug Abuse

Lisdexamfetamine *(Vyvanse)*, comes in a prodrug formulation with an amino acid (lysine) attached to the amphetamine. The attachment renders the amphetamine inactive until the lysine is detached by enzymatic cleavage during first-pass. Opioid abusers commonly extract opioids and stimulants for injection or to snort as a powder. There is no fast stimulant "rush" to a user who injects or snorts lisdexamfetamine drug powder because the first-pass conversion has been bypassed. Several of the extended-release opioids utilize prodrug technology with different mechanisms for abuse-deterrence.

Prodrugs and Toxicity Risk

Codeine, an inactive prodrug, lacks analgesic effects. About 10% of a dose is metabolized by CYP2D6 to the active drug morphine, which provides the analgesia. Opioids, including morphine, can cause respiratory depression when overdosed. PMs or patients taking CYP2D6 inhibitors would have little or no conversion to morphine, the active drug, and would receive little or no analgesia. A more dangerous situation arises when an UM is given codeine, with sometimes fatal consequences. See the Clinical Case example.

CLINICAL CASE: TOXICITY RISK WITH CODEINE, A PRODRUG

A breast feeding mother had taken codeine. The codeine was rapidly converted to morphine, which passes readily into breast milk. Her infant suffered fatal respiratory depression. She was found to be an UM of CYP2D6.

Several children who were UMs of CYP2D6 have suffered fatality from the use of codeine for post-tonsillectomy/adenoidectomy pain. This is the most common operation in children; codeine would have risk with other procedures in CYP2D6 UMs. The pharmacogenomic profile is most often unknown.

NON-CYP450 ENZYMES

CYP450 enzymes are common Phase I enzymes. Other enzymes, including those active in Phase II metabolism, can alter drug levels. The impact is typically not as substantial as from CYP450 enzymes but with individual drugs, it can be. As one example, bictegravir, an antiviral for HIV, is a substrate of CYP3A4 and a substrate of the Phase II enzyme uridine diphosphate glucuronosyltransferase (UGT) 1A1. Inducers or inhibitors of CYP3A4 or UGT 1A1 will change the metabolism of bictegravir.

Another type of Phase II enzyme, N-acetyltrasferase (NAT), is well known due to its role in the early history with the study of pharmacogenomics. Differences in isoniazid toxicities were found to be due to differences in the rate of acetylation by NAT enzymes. NATs are highly polymorphic. The differences in the NAT enzymes caused the differences in the degree of toxicity.

GUT EXCRETION: IN THE FECES

P-GLYCOPROTEIN EFFLUX PUMPS

Permeability glycoprotein (P-gp) efflux pumps (or transporters) are located in many tissues where they provide protection against foreign substances by moving them out of critical areas. The term efflux means to flow out, and P-gp transports drugs and their metabolites out of the body by pumping them into the gut, where they can be excreted in the stool. When p-gp is blocked (or inhibited), less substrate will be removed and the drug level will increase. There are other transporters in other parts of the body that are not described here, including efflux pumps that cause resistance by pumping chemotherapeutics out of cancer cells, and the organic ion transporter OATP1B1/3, which pumps drugs and other compounds from the blood into the liver.

There is overlap among the enzymes and transporters that protect the body from perceived toxins, including drugs. Many drugs which are substrates, inhibitors or inducers of P-gp serve the same role as CYP 450 enzymes, including many of the drugs in the table below. A chart of common CYP 450 substrates, inducers and inhibitors can be found at the end of this chapter.

P-gp Common Substrates, Inducers & Inhibitors

SUBSTRATES	INDUCERS	INHIBITORS
Anticoagulants (apixaban, edoxaban, rivaroxaban, dabigatran) **Cardiovascular drugs** (carvedilol, digoxin, ranolazine) **Immunosuppressants** (cyclosporine, tacrolimus, sirolimus) **HCV drugs** (dasabuvir, ombitasvir, paritaprevir, sofosbuvir) **Others** (atazanavir, colchicine, dolutegravir, posaconazole, raltegravir, saxagliptin)	Carbamazepine, dexamethasone, phenobarbital, phenytoin, rifampin, St. John's wort, tipranavir	**Anti-infectives** (clarithromycin, itraconazole, posaconazole) **Cardiovascular drugs** (amiodarone, carvedilol, conivaptan, dronedarone, diltiazem, quinidine, verapamil) **HIV drugs** (cobicistat, ritonavir) **HCV drugs** (daclatasvir, ledipasvir, paritaprevir) **Others** (cyclosporine, flibanserin, ticagrelor)

ENTEROHEPATIC RECYCLING

After a drug has been metabolized, it can be transported through the bile back to the gut. From the gut, the drug can be reabsorbed again (primarily in the small intestine, where most drugs are absorbed), enter into the portal vein and travel back to the liver. The recycling of an already-metabolized drug is called enterohepatic recycling, which increases the duration of action of many drugs, including some antibiotics, some NSAIDs, and the cholesterol-lowering drug ezetimibe.

COMMON DRUG INTERACTIONS

Drug interactions can be important for drugs not covered in this chapter; such as warfarin, lithium and theophylline. These are reviewed in the individual drug chapters. Several of the commonly used drugs for cardiovascular disease, including arrhythmias and heart failure (HF), interact with each other; these are reviewed first, followed by the sections listed below. The last page of the chapter is a chart of CYP 450 substrates, inducers and inhibitors.

1. Common Cardiovascular Drugs with Drug Interactions
2. Inhibitors Increase Substrate Drugs
3. Inducers Decrease Substrate Drugs
4. Additional Common, Well-Known Drug Interactions
5. Drugs with Similar Side Effects, When Used in Combination, Have More Side Effects

1. Common Cardiovascular Drug Interactions

INTERACTION	RISK	ACTIONS BY PHARMACIST
CARDIOVASCULAR (CV) DRUGS THAT INTERACT WITH EACH OTHER		
AMIODARONE **+ Warfarin** Can be used together for atrial fibrillation treatment: amiodarone (for rhythm), warfarin (to reduce clot risk). Dronedarone has similar drug interaction issues.	Amiodarone inhibits multiple enzymes, including CYP2C9, which metabolizes the major warfarin isomer. ↓ warfarin metabolism, ↑ INR, bleeding risk increased.	**If using amiodarone 1st** ■ Start warfarin at a low dose of ≤ 5 mg. **If using warfarin 1st** ■ When starting amiodarone, ↓ warfarin dose 30-50%, depending on the INR. **Both** ■ Monitor INR; adjust as needed.
AMIODARONE **+ Digoxin** Can be given together for arrhythmia treatment: amiodarone (for rhythm), digoxin (for rate control, ↓ HR, or for symptom improvement in a patient with HF).	Amiodarone inhibits P-gp; digoxin is P-gp substrate. ↓ digoxin excretion, ↑ ADRs/toxicity. Amiodarone and digoxin both ↓ HR, ↑ risk of bradycardia, arrhythmia, fatality.	**If using amiodarone 1st** ■ Start digoxin at low dose, such as 0.125 mg daily instead of 0.25 mg daily. **If using digoxin 1st** ■ ↓ digoxin dose 50%; if oral, change 0.25 mg daily to 0.125 mg daily, or change 0.125 mg daily to 0.125 mg other day. **Both** ■ Check for other enzyme inhibitors that can increase digoxin level. ■ Instruct patient to monitor for initial sx of digoxin toxicity: nausea, anorexia; if present, check HR, contact prescriber. ■ Monitor HR; normal rate is 60-100 BPM, (can be lower, based on patient's history and physical state); check for other drugs that ↓ HR: beta-blockers, clonidine, diltiazem, verapamil, dexmedetomidine *(Precedex)*. ■ If digoxin is being used for rate control, inform prescribers to consider beta-blockers or non-DHP CCBs (preferred). ■ Monitor electrolytes and correct if abnormal. ■ Renal impairment: ↓ digoxin dose or frequency, or discontinue.
DIGOXIN **+ Loop Diuretic** Caution: HF and renal impairment often concurrent. Digoxin is cleared by P-gp and directly excreted by kidneys; renal impairment ↑ digoxin level and toxicity risk.	Loops ↓ K, Mg, Ca and Na. (Even without the use of a loop, electrolyte deficiencies are common with CVD.) Low K, Mg or Ca will worsen arrhythmias. Low K and Mg ↑ risk of digoxin toxicity. High Ca also ↑ risk.	
DILTIAZEM/VERAPAMIL **+ Other drugs that ↓ HR** Preferred for rate control (over digoxin); beta-blockers also preferred.	Additive effect with other drugs that ↓ HR, including amiodarone, digoxin, beta-blockers, dexmedetomidine (*Precedex*) and clonidine.	Monitor HR; normal rate is 60-100 BPM, (can be lower, based on patient's history and physical state; fit persons can have ↓ HR).
STATINS **+** **CYP3A4 Inhibitors** Diltiazem, verapamil, ritonavir & other PIs, cobicistat, clarithromycin, erythromycin, azole antifungals, *Viekira Pak*, cyclosporine, grapefruit juice/fruit, amiodarone, dronedarone, nefazodone	↑ levels with CYP3A4 substrates, risk toxicity; lovastatin, simvastatin, atorvastatin are CYP3A4 substrates. ↑ risk myopathy, if severe (with high CPK) can cause rhabdomyolysis, with acute renal failure (ARF).	With statins, recommend statin not metabolized by CYP450 enzymes (pitavastatin, pravastatin, rosuvastatin), or use lower doses of other statins, such as simvastatin 10-20 mg (see Dyslipidemia chapter). There are significant interactions between grapefruit and cardiovascular drugs, including some of the statins and amiodarone. See the next section for details.
WARFARIN **+** **CYP2C9 Inhibitors and Inducers** Inhibitors: azole antifungals, sulfamethoxazole/trimethoprim, amiodarone, gemfibrozil Inducers: rifampin, St. John's wort	↑ levels of warfarin (and ↑ INR) with CYP2C9 inhibitors, bleeding risk ↓ levels of warfarin (and ↓ INR) with CYP2C9 inducers, clotting risk	Monitor INR; therapeutic range is 2-3 for most conditions (2.5-3.5 for some high-risk indications, such as mechanical mitral valve). Some drugs (e.g., amiodarone) require prophylactic warfarin dose adjustment when started (see above).

2. Inhibitors Increase Substrate Drugs

INTERACTION	RISK	ACTION BY PHARMACIST/NOTES
CYP3A4 INHIBITORS + **CYP3A4 substrates (many)** Includes the opioids fentanyl, hydrocodone, oxycodone, methadone	↓ substrate metabolism, ↑ ADRs/ toxicity. If an opioid is the substrate, sedation will increase, followed by respiratory depression, which can quickly cause fatality.	Monitor drug levels/side effects; the majority of drugs will increase when used with drugs that inhibit CYP enzymes. Do not use a CYP3A4 inhibitor with an opioid metabolized by 3A4; the combination will certainly cause increased ADRs, including sedation, and can be fatal. Grapefruit/Juice: do not take with CYP3A4 substrates. Drugs that specifically include instructions not to take with grapefruit include amiodarone, simvastatin, lovastatin, nifedipine and tacrolimus; many other drugs have similar risk.
VALPROATE **+ Lamotrigine** Valproate is an inhibitor of lamotrigine metabolism	Valproate ↓ lamotrigine metabolism, ↑ lamotrigine level which ↑ risk of serious skin reactions, including SJS/TEN (can be fatal). Risk is highest in pediatrics.	Initiate lamotrigine using the starter kit dosing that begins with lower lamotrigine doses. Titrate carefully Q 2 weeks. Counsel patients to get emergency help if rash develops.
MONOAMINE OXIDASE (MAO) INHIBITORS **Isocarboxazid, phenelzine, tranylcypromine, linezolid, methylene blue** + **Drugs that ↑ epinephrine (Epi), norepinephrine (NE), dopamine (DA)** Pseudoephedrine, phenylephrine, epinephrine, norepinephrine, dobutamine, SNRIs, bupropion and stimulants, including amphetamines used for ADHD (e.g., methylphenidate, lisdexamfetamine, dextroamphetamine) + **Drugs that ↑ serotonin (5HT)** Antidepressants: SSRIs, SNRIs, TCAs, MAO inhibitors, mirtazapine, trazodone Opioids: fentanyl, methadone, tramadol Others: buspirone, dextromethorphan (high doses taken as drug of abuse), lithium, St. John's wort	The monoamine oxidase (MAO) enzyme metabolizes epinephrine (Epi), norepinephrine (NE), dopamine (DA) and serotonin (5HT); blocking MAO with an MAO-inhibitor will ↑ Epi, NE, DA and 5HT. High Epi, NE, DA can cause hypertensive crisis. High 5HT can cause serotonin syndrome; see serotonergic drugs in the Additive Drug Interactions section.	Do not use together. Use a 2-week washout period between serotonergic drugs and another antidepressant (AD); if changing fluoxetine to an MAO inhibitor, wait 5 weeks.
MAO INHIBITORS **Non-selective (listed above) and selective MAO-B inhibitors (rasagiline, selegiline)** + **Tyramine-rich foods/drinks**	MAO metabolizes tyramine; if blocked, tyramine causes ↑ NE, with risk of hypertensive crisis.	Tyramine-rich foods have been aged, pickled, fermented or smoked, including aged cheeses, air-dried meats, sauerkraut, some wines and beers. Do not eat foods rich in tyramine.
CYP2D6 INHIBITORS **Amiodarone, fluoxetine, paroxetine, fluvoxamine** + **CYP2D6 substrates (many)**	↓ drug metabolism, ↑ ADRs/ toxicity.	Avoid using together or ↓ dose of the substrate.
CYP3A4, P-GP INHIBITORS + **Calcineurin Inhibitors (CNIs)** Tacrolimus, cyclosporine + **mTOR Kinase Inhibitors** Sirolimus, everolimus	↓ drug metabolism, ↑ ADRs/ toxicity, including ↑ blood pressure, nephrotoxicity, metabolic syndrome and other adverse effects (see Transplant chapter).	Avoid using together or ↓ dose of CNI or mTOR kinase inhibitor cautiously and based on drug levels. Monitor transplant drug level (trough).

3. Inducers Decrease Substrate Drugs

INTERACTION	RISK	ACTION BY PHARMACISTS
PHENYTOIN, PHENOBARBITAL, PRIMIDONE, CARBAMAZEPINE, OXCARBAZEPINE **+** **Other drugs metabolized by CYP enzymes, including oral contraceptives, other AEDs and carbamazepine** (auto-inducer, which induces it's own metabolism)	↑ metabolism, ↓ substrate drug or carbamazepine level; with AEDs, loss of seizure control.	Monitor for change in drug levels; induction takes up to 4 weeks for the full effect. Consider increasing the dose of the substrate drug. If substrate is lamotrigine, use the starter kit dosing that begins with higher lamotrigine doses.
RIFAMPIN **+** **CYP and P-gp substrates (most drugs)**	The concentration of substrate drugs will greatly decrease.	Monitor drug levels, or monitoring parameter, such as INR with warfarin. Increase the dose of the substrate drug as necessary, or replace with rifabutin to reduce interactions.
CYP3A4 INDUCERS **+** **Opioids that are substrates of CYP3A4** fentanyl, hydrocodone, oxycodone, methadone	↑ metabolism, ↓ opioid concentration; analgesia (pain relief) will decrease.	Assess the patient's use of breakthrough pain medication to determine if an increased dose is necessary. Use caution; opioids cause respiratory depression when overdosed, and induction has a lag time.
CYP2D6 UMs **+** **Prodrugs codeine, tramadol**	There are no CYP2D6 inducers, however, with 2D6 UMs (who produce about twice as many enzymes), the effect is similar to the effect from an inducer. With UMs: the active drug concentration will increase, which can cause toxicity/risk fatality.	Do not use codeine or tramadol in patients ≤ 12 years and in children < 18 years following tonsillectomy +/or adenoidectomy (contraindication). Do not use an opioid prodrug that is metabolized by CYP2D6 (codeine, tramadol) in a breast-feeding mother unless it is known that she is not a 2D6 UM. Never crush or chew any extended-release opioid, including prodrugs.
CYP3A4, P-GP INDUCERS **+** **Calcineurin inhibitors (CNIs)** Tacrolimus, cyclosporine **+** **mTOR Kinase Inhibitors** Sirolimus, everolimus	↑ metabolism, ↓ transplant drug level, with ↑ risk of transplant (organ) rejection.	Risk of transplant rejection; avoid using together or ↑ dose of CNI or mTOR kinase inhibitor carefully. Monitor transplant drug level (trough) for efficacy.
SMOKING **+** **Some antipsychotics, antidepressants, hypnotics, anxiolytics, caffeine, theophylline, insulin, warfarin (R-isomer)** Smoking primarily induces CYP1A2; this includes smoking tobacco and marijuana	**Smokers who quit** When the inducer (cigarettes) is stopped, drug concentration (primarily CYP1A2 substrates) will ↑, and could cause toxicity.	Counsel/advocate for smoking cessation. When a smoker quits, monitor INR; the R-isomer of warfarin (less potent isomer) is metabolized by CYP1A2, but the therapeutic range is narrow and could be affected.
	Current smoker The substrate drugs (primarily CYP1A2 substrates) will have ↓ levels.	When a current smoker starts a drug (primarily CYP1A2 substrates), a higher dose can be required. When a smoker quits, a lower dose of drug may be needed; if not reduced, toxicity can result. Nicotine replacement products (NRT, such as the patch and gum) do not induce CYP enzymes.

4. Additional Common, Well-Known Drug Interactions

INTERACTION	RISK	ACTION BY PHARMACISTS
PDE-5 inhibitors: avanafil, sildenafil, tadalafil, vardenafil **+** **CYP3A4 Inhibitors**	↓ PDE-5 inhibitor metabolism, ↑ side effects, including headache, dizziness, flushing (causing ↑ risk of falls/injury).	Start with half usual starting dose of PDE-5 inhibitor; change 50 mg sildenafil to 25 mg, change 10 mg vardenafil/tadalafil to 5 mg, avanafil 100 mg to 50 mg.
PDE-5 inhibitors **+** **Nitrates**	Magnified adverse effects, which are similar in both classes: risk of severe hypotension and death-concurrent use contraindicated.	Do not use together; check fill history for sublingual nitroglycerin for PRN use with chest pain; for acute use (UA/NSTEMI) can consider use if 24-hours after sildenafil; monitor blood pressure.
PDE-5 inhibitors **+** **Alpha-Blockers**	Additive (increased) adverse effects, which are similar in both classes: hypotension/orthostasis, dizziness and falls. Non-selective alpha-blockers ↑ risk of hypotension/orthostasis.	Start with low dose when adding a drug from either classes; e.g., do not use > 1 mg doxazosin (non-selective alpha-blocker) or if on alpha-blocker initially, use lower doses of PDE-5 inhibitor (listed above).
DRUGS THAT PROLONG THE QT-INTERVAL **+** **Antiarrhythmics** Including amiodarone, dofetilide, dronedarone, ibutilide, sotalol **Antibiotics/Antifungals** Quinolones and macrolides Azole antifungals, except isavuconazonium *(Cresemba)* **Antidepressants** Tricyclics SSRIs, highest risk: citalopram, escitalopram **Antipsychotics (most)** Including phenothiazines (end in -azine, such as thioridazine), haloperidol, ziprasidone **Antiemetics** 5-HT3 receptor antagonists (e.g., ondansetron), droperidol and phenothiazines (e.g., prochlorperazine) **Others** Donepezil, fingolimod, methadone	QT prolongation ↑ the risk of torsades de pointes (TdP), an often fatal arrhythmia. The risk increases with: ■ Higher doses. ■ Higher drug levels due to concurrent enzyme inhibitors. ■ Higher drug levels due to reduced drug clearance, such as with renal or liver disease. ■ Multiple QT-prolonging drugs. ■ Elderly (60+ years) and patients with CVD, including with other arrhythmias, HF, MI.	With all QT-prolonging drugs, avoid/reduce risk of TdP: ■ Carefully dose QT-prolonging drugs; do not use excessive doses. Use lower doses/caution with use in elderly patients. ■ If possible, do not use QT-prolonging drugs at all or select drugs with lower QT risk, especially with arrhythmias and any type of CVD or with CVD risk (exception: amiodarone is the common drug of choice to treat arrhythmia in patients with HF). ■ Avoid use of inhibitors that block a QT-prolonging drug's metabolism. ■ Avoid concurrent QT-prolonging drugs, if possible. ■ Do not exceed 40 mg/day citalopram or 20 mg/day in elderly (60+ years), liver disease or with enzyme inhibitors that decrease clearance. ■ Do not exceed 20 mg/day escitalopram or 10 mg/day with higher risk (see above). Among SSRIs, sertraline is considered safer with CVD. ■ Do not use droperidol for inpatient N/V (droperidol is injection-only); 5HT-3 receptor antagonists have less QT-risk.
Quinolones, tetracyclines, levothyroxine or oral bisphosphonates **+ antacids, sucralfate, bile acid resins, magnesium, aluminum, calcium, iron, zinc, multivitamins, phosphate binders** *Drugs that require an acidic gut for absorption are in the GERD chapter.	↓ drug absorption, ↓ efficacy. Drugs need to dissolve to be absorbed; drugs chelated together will not be absorbed and will be excreted in stool. Oral bisphosphonates cannot be taken with any other medications or supplements, including these; must take with plain water.	Separate these medications from compounds with cations. **Quinolones** ■ Give ciprofloxacin 2 hours before or 6 hours after these drugs. ■ Give levofloxacin 2 hours before or 2 hours after these drugs. ■ Give moxifloxacin 4 hours before or 8 hours after these drugs. **Tetracyclines** ■ Give doxycycline 1 – 2 hours before, or 4 – 6 hours after these drugs ■ Tetracycline is separated, but rarely used. Minocycline does not require separation.

5. Drugs with Similar Side Effects, When Used in Combination, Have More Side Effects

ADDITIVE SIDE EFFECTS	RISK	ACTIONS BY PHARMACIST
SEROTONERGIC TOXICITY		
Antidepressants SSRIs, SNRIs, TCAs, mirtazapine, trazodone **MAO inhibitors** Antidepressants: isocarboxazid, phenelzine, tranylcypromine Selective MAO-B inhibitors: selegiline, rasagiline Others: linezolid, metaxalone, methylene blue **Buspirone** **Dextromethorphan** taken in excess (as a drug of abuse) **Dihydroergotamine** **Lithium** **Lorcaserin** **Opioids** Fentanyl, meperidine, methadone, tramadol, tapentadol and risk with any other opioids when used in combination **Metoclopramide** **Triptans** one serotonergic drug with occasional (PRN) triptan use may be safe; more serotonergic drugs increase risk. **Natural products** St. John's wort, l-tryptophan	Serotonin syndrome risk increases when 2 or more drugs that affect serotonin are used together. Higher doses ↑ risk. Symptoms range from mild to severe and fatal: ■ Agitation, confusion, delirium, fever. ■ Diarrhea, mydriasis, hyperhidrosis. ■ Hyperreflexia, tremor, muscle rigidity, tachycardia.	Avoid using serotonergic drugs together; if used, doses should be reasonable. Check for inhibitors of serotonergic drugs. Counsel to report symptoms, even if mild. If severe symptoms, counsel to go to the emergency department. Recommend eliminating an initial serotonergic drug prior to starting a new serotonergic drug by using a washout period: use 2-weeks between the drugs, or use 6-weeks for drugs with longer duration of action, such as fluoxetine.
BLEEDING RISK		
Anticoagulants Warfarin, dabigatran, apixaban, betrixaban, edoxaban, rivaroxaban, heparin, enoxaparin, dalteparin, fondaparinux, argatroban, bivalirudin **Antiplatelets** Salicylates, including aspirin, dipyridamole, clopidogrel, prasugrel, ticagrelor **NSAIDs, SSRIs, SNRIs** **Natural products** 5G's: garlic, ginger, ginkgo biloba (inhibits PAF), ginseng and glucosamine, and vitamin E, willow bark, fish oils (high doses)	↑ bleeding risk, which can increase without changing an anticoagulation monitoring parameter, such as the INR (with warfarin).	Avoid using in combination, with a few exceptions: ■ Aspirin (for cardio-protection) and occasional NSAID for pain, fever or inflammation (acetaminophen preferred; NSAIDs should not be used with cardiac conditions). ■ SSRIs, SNRI use/occasional NSAID for pain, fever or inflammation. ■ Dual antiplatelets, when recommended. ■ Bridging/overlap treatment, such as enoxaparin + warfarin, until INR therapeutic ≥ 24 hrs.
HYPERKALEMIA RISK		
Spironolactone, eplerenone—highest risk **Renin-Angiotensin-Aldosterone Drugs** ACE inhibitors, ARBs, aliskiren, sacubitril/valsartan **Amiloride, triamterene, salt substitutes (KCl), calcineurin inhibitors (tacrolimus and cyclosporine), canagliflozin, pentamidine, SMX/TMP and drospirenone-containing oral contraceptives**	Risk of hyperkalemia; symptoms include weakness, heart palpitations, arrhythmia. Higher risk with renal impairment.	Do not use ACE inhibitor with ARB. Do not use sacubitril/valsartan with ACE inhibitor or ARB. With risk of hyperkalemia, suggest alternative diabetes medication for canagliflozin, alternative antibiotic for SMX/TMP, alternative birth control using a progestin that is not drospirenone. Counsel patient to avoid salt substitutes that contain KCl. Monitor potassium.

5. DRUGS WITH SIMILAR SIDE EFFECTS, WHEN USED IN COMBINATION, HAVE MORE SIDE EFFECTS CONTINUED

ADDITIVE SIDE EFFECTS	RISK	ACTIONS BY PHARMACIST
CNS DEPRESSION		
CNS Depressants: opioids, skeletal muscle relaxants, antiepileptic drugs, benzodiazepines, barbiturates, hypnotics, mirtazapine, trazodone, dronabinol, nabilone, propranolol, clonidine, sedating antihistamines, cough syrups with antihistamine or opioid, some NSAIDs **Highest risk for fatality when used in combination:** **Opioids** **+** **Benzodiazepines or other CNS depressants**	CNS depressant-effects; including somnolence, dizziness, confusion/ cognitive impairment, altered consciousness/delirium, gait instability/imbalance/risk of falls/ accidents, including motor vehicle accidents. Benzodiazepines are a drug of abuse, and are often prescribed inappropriately (for anxiety, less frequently for insomnia), adding unnecessary CNS-depressant risk. See alternatives in right column. Benzodiazepines are appropriate for status epilepticus, alcohol withdrawal, as an antidote for stimulant overdose, prior to medical procedures, in acute high-anxiety situations, and for anticipatory emesis with chemotherapy. Opioids: due to the risks of abuse, dependence and addiction, reserve for severe pain that is not responsive to other measures. See alternatives in right column.	Counsel not to use alcohol with these drugs. Counsel not to operate car or other potentially dangerous vehicles/machines when starting/using CNS depressants. Counsel on increased risk of falls, confusion. Avoid combining CNS-depressants, when possible. Suggest alternatives for anxiety: SSRI (not paroxetine due to more withdrawal symptoms, weight gain and sedation, and not any SSRI in patients with fall/ fracture risk), SNRI, buspirone Suggest alternatives for insomnia: non-drug treatments (lifestyle) preferred. Suggest alternatives for pain: acetaminophen, NSAIDs, antiepileptic drugs (AEDs), antidepressant drugs (ADs), physical therapy, acupuncture, other complementary treatments. **For opioids specifically:** ■ Do not use opioids when not medically necessary. ■ Do not use opioids in combination with benzodiazepines; other CNS-depressants, including alcohol, have high risk of fatality with opioids. ■ Extended-release formulations (many opioids) have additional risk: several become shorter-acting when taken with alcohol, with high risk of fatality; do not use in anyone who uses alcohol. ■ Recommend naloxone self-injector (to patient, or for caregiver) with at-risk patients, including anyone using high doses, receiving rapid dose increases or with reduced clearance (e.g., renal impairment with morphine). ■ Avoid codeine if pharmacogenomic profile is unknown (highest risk with CYP2D6 UMs). ■ See other CYP3A4 and 2D6 substrate cautions in previous section. ■ Monitor for sedation, slow and shallow breathing, shortness of breath.
OTOTOXICITY RISK		
Aminoglycosides, cisplatin, loop diuretics (especially IV), salicylates (including aspirin, salsalate, magnesium salicylate), vancomycin	Hearing loss, tinnitus, vertigo.	■ Order audiology consult at start of treatment for baseline hearing assessment, continue to monitor. ■ Among loop diuretics, ethacrynic acid is highest risk for ototoxicity; in at-risk patients, recommend a different loop. ■ Avoid concurrent use of ototoxic drugs, when possible.

5. DRUGS WITH SIMILAR SIDE EFFECTS, WHEN USED IN COMBINATION, HAVE MORE SIDE EFFECTS CONTINUED

ADDITIVE SIDE EFFECTS	RISK	ACTIONS BY PHARMACIST
NEPHROTOXICITY RISK		
Aminoglycosides, amphotericin B, vancomycin **Cisplatin, methotrexate with high chemo doses** **CNIs: cyclosporine, tacrolimus** **Loop diuretics (especially IV)** **NSAIDs**	Worsening renal function/ acute renal failure (ARF), can be evidenced by ↓ in urine output, ↑ in SCr/BUN in < 20:1 ratio.	■ Cisplatin: use amifostine to protect kidneys. ■ Cisplatin, methotrexate, other nephrotoxic/ bladder toxic drugs: hydration with fluids, including hypertonic solutions to increase urine output (mannitol, hypertonic saline). ■ Cyclosporine, tacrolimus: recommend an adjunctive agent to enable lower CNI dose, such as mycophenolate. ■ Discontinue NSAIDs with renal impairment. ■ Monitor urine output, SCr/BUN.
ANTICHOLINERGIC TOXICITY		
Paroxetine, tricyclic antidepressants, first-generation antipsychotics **Sedating antihistamines, including: diphenhydramine, brompheniramine, chlorpheniramine, doxylamine, hydroxyzine, cyproheptadine** **Atropine, belladonna, dicyclomine, meclizine** **Benztropine, trihexyphenidyl** **Muscle relaxants, including baclofen, carisoprodol, cyclobenzaprine** **Overactive bladder antimuscarinics, such as oxybutynin, darifenacin, tolterodine**	Anticholinergic symptoms of CNS depression, including sedation, and peripheral anticholinergic side effects of dry mouth, dry/ blurry vision, constipation, urinary retention. Highest risk in elderly	■ Recommend alternatives to sedating antihistamines, such as loratadine, fexofenadine, cetirizine or use of saline nasal spray/drops that clear allergens out of the nasal passages. ■ If using diphenhydramine or other sedating antihistamine for sleep, suggest lifestyle changes (sleep hygiene). ■ Recommend treatments for dry mouth, dry eyes (see Sjogren's Syndrome in Systemic Steroids & AutoImmune Conditions chapter); recommend laxative for constipation (see Constipation & Diarrhea chapter).

CYP 450 ENZYMES: COMMON SUBSTRATES, INDUCERS & INHIBITORS

CYP	SUBSTRATES	INDUCERS	INHIBITORS
3A4	**Analgesics** (buprenorphine, diclofenac, fentanyl, hydrocodone, meloxicam, methadone, oxycodone, tramadol) **Anticoagulants** (apixaban, rivaroxaban, R-warfarin) **Antidiabetic drugs** (nateglinide, pioglitazone, repaglinide, saxagliptin, sitagliptin) **Antiplatelet drugs** (cilostazol, prasugrel, ticagrelor) **Cardiovascular drugs** (amiodarone, amlodipine, bosentan, diltiazem, eplerenone, ivabradine, nifedipine, quinidine, ranolazine, tolvaptan, verapamil); **Immunosuppressants** (cyclosporine, tacrolimus, sirolimus) **Statins** (atorvastatin, lovastatin, simvastatin) **Key HIV drugs** (atazanavir, efavirenz, ritonavir, tipranavir) **PDE-5 inhibitors** (avanafil, sildenafil, tadalafil, vardenafil) **Others** (alfuzosin, aprepitant, aripiprazole, benzodiazepines, brexpiprazole, buspirone, carbamazepine, citalopram, clarithromycin, colchicine, dapsone, dutasteride, erythromycin, escitalopram, ethinyl estradiol, felbamate, haloperidol, ketoconazole, levonorgestrel, mirtazapine, modafinil, ondansetron, paritaprevir, progesterone, quetiapine, tamoxifen, trazodone, venlafaxine, zolpidem)	Carbamazepine, efavirenz, nevirapine, oxcarbazepine, phenobarbital, phenytoin, primidone, rifabutin, rifampin, rifapentine, smoking, St. John's wort	**Anti-infectives** (clarithromycin, erythromycin, fluconazole, isoniazid, itraconazole, ketoconazole, posaconazole, voriconazole) **Cardiovascular drugs** (amiodarone, diltiazem, dronedarone, quinidine, ranolazine, verapamil) **Key HIV drugs** (atazanavir, cobicistat, efavirenz, darunavir, ritonavir) **Other HIV drugs** (fosamprenavir, indinavir, nelfinavir, saquinavir) **Others** (aprepitant, cimetidine, cyclosporine, fluvoxamine, grapefruit juice, haloperidol, nefazodone, sertraline)
1A2	Alosetron, aprepitant, clozapine, cyclobenzaprine, duloxetine, ethinyl estradiol, fluvoxamine, methadone, mirtazapine, olanzapine, ondansetron, pimozide, propranolol, rasagiline, ropinirole, theophylline, R-warfarin	Carbamazepine, phenobarbital, phenytoin, primidone, rifampin, ritonavir, smoking, St. John's wort	Atazanavir, cimetidine, ciprofloxacin, fluvoxamine, zileuton

CYP	SUBSTRATES	INDUCERS	INHIBITORS
2C8	Amiodarone, dasabuvir, pioglitazone, repaglinide, rosiglitazone	Phenytoin, rifampin	Amiodarone, atazanavir, clopidogrel, gemfibrozil, ketoconazole, trimethoprim/sulfamethoxazole, ritonavir
2C9	Alosetron, carvedilol, celecoxib, diazepam, diclofenac, fluvastatin, glyburide, glipizide, glimepiride, meloxicam, netaglinide, phenytoin, ramelteon, S-warfarin, tamoxifen, zolpidem	Aprepitant, carbamazepine, phenobarbital, phenytoin, primidone, rifampin, rifapentine, ritonavir, St. John's wort	Amiodarone, atazanavir, capecitabine, cimetidine, efavirenz, etravirine, gemfibrozil, fluconazole, fluvoxamine, fluorouracil, isoniazid, ketoconazole, metronidazole, oritavancin, tamoxifen, trimethoprim/sulfamethoxazole, valproic acid, voriconazole, zafirlukast
2C19	Clopidogrel, phenytoin, thioridazine, voriconazole	Carbamazepine, phenobarbital, phenytoin, rifampin	Cimetidine, esomeprazole, efavirenz, etravirine, fluoxetine, fluvoxamine, isoniazid, ketoconazole, modafinil, omeprazole, topiramate, voriconazole
2D6	**Analgesics** (codeine, hydrocodone, meperidine, methadone, oxycodone, tramadol) **Antipsychotics/Antidepressants** (aripiprazole, brexpiprazole, doxepin, fluoxetine, haloperidol, mirtazapine, risperidone, thioridazine, trazodone, tricyclic antidepressants, venlafaxine) **Others** (atomoxetine, carvedilol, dextromethorphan, flecainide, methamphetamine, metoprolol, propafenone, propranolol, tamoxifen)		Amiodarone, bupropion, cimetidine, cobicistat, darifenacin, dronedarone, duloxetine, fluoxetine, mirabegron, paroxetine, propafenone, quinidine, ritonavir, sertraline

COMMON PRODRUGS

COMMON PRODRUGS AND THEIR ACTIVE METABOLITES	SELECT SAFETY CONSIDERATIONS
Codeine → Morphine Clopidogrel → Active metabolite Lisdexamfetamine → Dextroamphetamine Primidone → Phenobarbital Capecitabine → Fluorouracil Fosaprepitant → Aprepitant Fosphenytoin → Phenytoin Enalapril → Enalaprilat Tramadol → Active metabolite Valacyclovir → Acyclovir Valganciclovir → Ganciclovir Other prodrugs include: Calcifediol → Calcitriol, Colistimethate → Colistin, Isavuconazonium sulfate → Isavuconazole, Famciclovir → Penciclovir, Fosamprenavir → Amprenavir, Cortisone → Cortisol, Prednisone → Prednisolone, Leflunomide → Teriflunomide, Levodopa → Dopamine and some of the abuse-deterrent opioids.	Codeine, by itself, and in combo products, such as *Tylenol #3* ■ Risk of toxicity with UMs of CYP2D6; higher conversion to morphine. See discussion on prodrugs earlier in chapter. ❑ Do not use codeine in UMs of 2D6. ■ Risk of poor analgesia with PMs of CYP2D6. ❑ Use an alternative analgesic in patients identified as PMs of 2D6. Clopidogrel *(Plavix)* ■ Risk with CYP2C19 inhibitors, which may block conversion to active form: ❑ Do not use with 2C19 inhibitors, including omeprazole and esomeprazole. ■ Risk with PMs of CYP2C19; low conversion to active form, with reduced effect of drug on platelet activity. ❑ Use an alternative P2Y12 inhibitor in patients identified as PMs of 2C19.

CHAPTER CONTENT

Background 71
Definitions 71
Complete Blood Cell Count 71
Basic Metabolic Panel/Comprehensive Metabolic Panel 72
Blood Cell Lines 72
Lab Results 72
Common Laboratory Reference Ranges - Adult 73
Assessing Patient Cases Quickly 79
Therapeutic Drug Monitoring 80
Therapeutic Drug Levels 80

CONTENT LEGEND

= Key Drug Guy

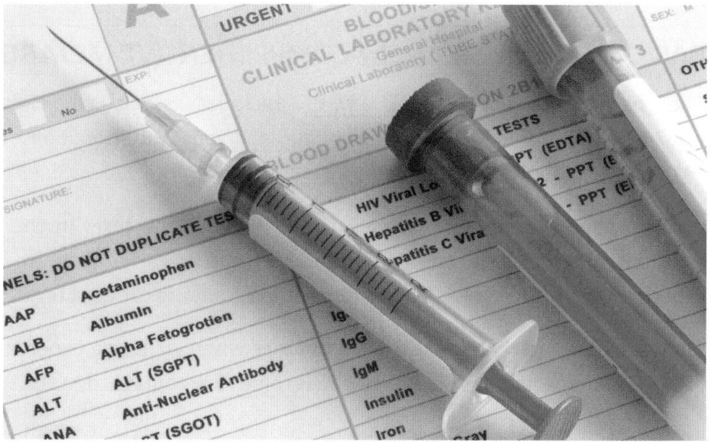

CHAPTER 4
LEARNING LAB VALUES & DRUG MONITORING

BACKGROUND

Laboratory values assist healthcare providers in diagnosing and monitoring diseases and drug therapies. Blood or other samples can be sent to a hospital or outside laboratory, but there are newer methods. Point-of-care (POC) testing provides quick results at the site of patient care. There are many POC tests including tests for cardiac enzymes, A1C, INR, various infections and others. Home testing kits provide convenience and privacy and are available to test for pregnancy, ovulation, HIV infection, herpes, fecal occult blood and presence of illicit substances or opioids. Many are available OTC.

Therapeutic drug monitoring (TDM) involves obtaining a drug level or related labs to monitor for efficacy and safety. TDM is reviewed in detail at the end of this chapter.

Pharmacists in many states can order and interpret lab tests for a variety of purposes, including tests to screen for and diagnose disease, to monitor drug levels and lab values, to check for medication adherence or to screen for drugs of abuse. Prescribing privilege is advancing in many states.

DEFINITIONS

COMPLETE BLOOD CELL COUNT

The complete blood count (CBC) is a commonly ordered lab panel that analyzes the white blood cells (WBCs), or neutrophils, the red blood cells (RBCs) and the platelets (PLTs). The CBC includes the hemoglobin (oxygen-carrying protein in RBCs) and the hematocrit (the level of RBCs in the fluid component of the blood, or plasma). When a CBC with differential is ordered, the types of neutrophils are analyzed. RBCs have an average life span of 120 days. Platelets have an average life span of 7 – 10 days.

BASIC METABOLIC PANEL / COMPREHENSIVE METABOLIC PANEL

The basic metabolic panel (BMP) includes seven to eight tests that analyze electrolytes and glucose, acid/base (with the HCO3, or bicarbonate) and renal function. Some labs calculate and report the anion gap along with the BMP (see Calculations IV chapter).

A comprehensive metabolic panel (CMP) includes the tests in the BMP plus albumin, alanine aminotransferase (ALT), aspartate aminotransferase (AST), total bilirubin and total protein. The additional tests are used primarily to assess liver function. The BMP and CMP are groups of labs that are ordered together for convenience.

The stick diagrams below are used in practice when writing a paper chart note to denote the primary components of the CBC or BMP. Pharmacists should know which values are contained in the stick diagrams below.

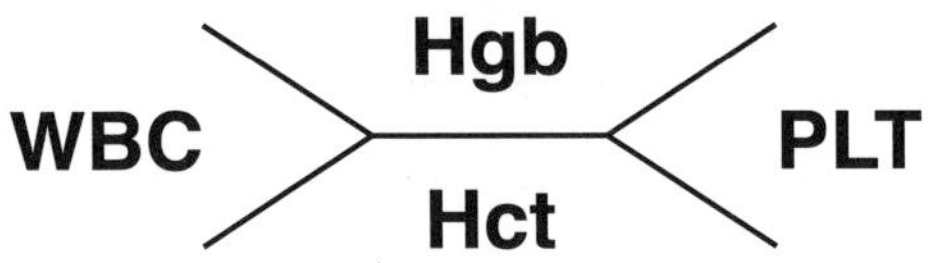

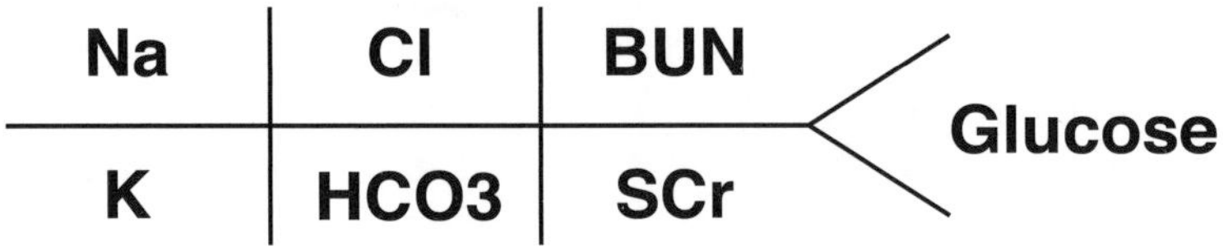

BLOOD CELL LINES

Stem cells in the bone marrow produce red blood cells, white blood cells and platelets (see figure). White blood cells can be called leukocytes and red blood cells can be called erythrocytes. An immature red blood cell is called a reticulocyte (discussed in the Common Laboratory Reference Ranges table).

Changes in Blood Cell Lines

Increase in Individual Cell Lines	
↑ WBC	Leukocytosis
↑ RBC	Polycythemia
↑ Platelets	Thrombocytosis
Decrease in Individual Cell Lines	
↓ WBC	Leukopenia
↓ RBC (or ↓ Hgb)	Anemia
↓ Platelets	Thrombocytopenia
Decrease in Multiple Cell Lines	
Agranulocytosis Can be due to: propylthiouracil, methimazole, procainamide, clozapine, carbamazepine, sulfamethoxazole/trimethoprim and isoniazid	↓ granulocytes (WBCs that have secretory granules in the cytoplasm); includes ↓ neutrophils, basophils and eosinophils

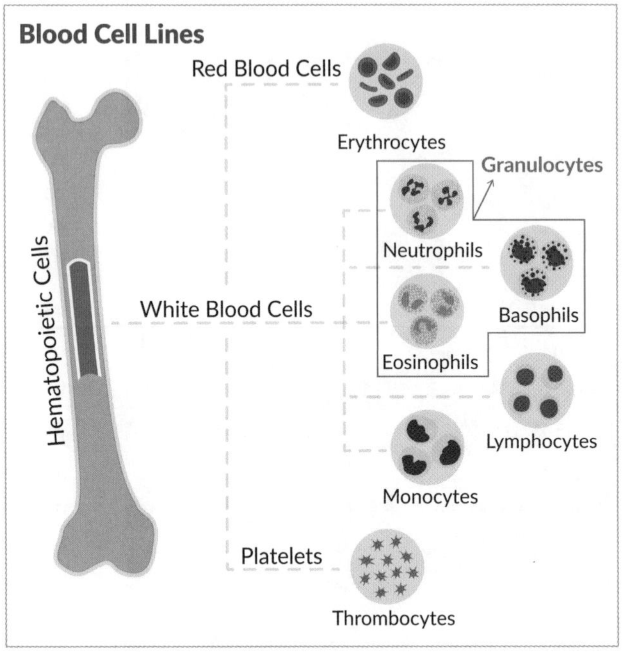

LAB RESULTS

Lab results are usually reported as a numerical value (e.g., sodium = 139 mEq/L). Some are reported as "positive" or "negative" or indicate a specific item, such as "Gram-positive cocci." Reference ranges can vary slightly from one facility to another (due to slight variances in products and techniques) and between pediatric and adult populations. A patient's lab results may be within the reference ranges (normal) or outside of the reference ranges (can indicate a serious condition that needs to be addressed rapidly). A value that is termed critical can be life-threatening unless a corrective action is taken quickly. The Joint Commission requires that all accredited facilities create and follow a protocol to identify and report critical values to the responsible healthcare provider, who has an established time frame to manage the result. This applies to critical lab values and diagnostic procedure results.

COMMON LABORATORY REFERENCE RANGES – ADULT

Reference ranges for labs are generally provided on NAPLEX, but may not be provided on the California law exam (CPJE). Familiarity with lab tests and their interpretation will greatly reduce the time required to evaluate cases on the exam. "Must know" labs for pharmacists are bolded in the table, though others are likely to be included in patient cases. The reference range for a healthy adult is provided, unless otherwise noted. Drugs specifically indicated to treat a lab abnormality (e.g., urate lowering therapies) are included in the respective chapter (e.g., the Gout chapter). Studying this table will be much easier after mastering all of the associated disease state chapters in this book.

ITEM	COMMON REFERENCE RANGE	NOTES
BMP and Electrolytes		
Calcium, total Calcium, ionized **(Ca)**	8.5–10.5 mg/dL 4.5–5.1 mg/dL	Calculate corrected calcium if albumin is low (see Calculations III chapter for formula). Correction is not needed for ionized calcium. ↑ due to calcium supplementation, vitamin D, thiazide diuretics. ↓ due to systemic steroids, long-term heparin, loop diuretics, bisphosphonates, cinacalcet, calcitonin, foscarnet, topiramate. Supplement calcium in pregnancy, other conditions and with certain drugs (see Dietary Supplements & Natural and Complementary Medicine chapter).
Chloride (Cl)	95–106 mEq/L	Used with other labs to assess acid-base status and fluid balance.
Magnesium (Mg)	1.3–2.1 mEq/L	↑ due to magnesium-containing antacids and laxatives with renal impairment. ↓ due to PPIs, diuretics, amphotericin, foscarnet, echinocandins, diarrhea, chronic alcohol intake.
Phosphate (PO4)	2.3–4.7 mg/dL	↑ in renal failure. ↓ due to phosphate binders, foscarnet, oral calcium intake.
Potassium (K)	3.5–5 mEq/L	↑ due to ACE inhibitors, ARBs, aldosterone receptor antagonists (ARAs), aliskiren, canagliflozin, cyclosporine, tacrolimus, mycophenolate, potassium supplements, sulfamethoxazole/trimethoprim, drospirenone-containing oral contraceptives, chronic heparin use, NSAIDs, pentamidine. ↓ due to steroids, beta-2 agonists, conivaptan, diuretics, insulin, mycophenolate (both ↑ and ↓ reported).
Sodium (Na)	135–145 mEq/L	↑ due to hypertonic saline. ↓ due to carbamazepine, oxcarbazepine, SSRIs, diuretics, desmopressin.
Bicarbonate **(HCO3 or "bicarb")**	Venous: 24–30 mEq/L Arterial: 22–26 mEq/L (varies by method)	Used to assess acid-base status. ↑ due to loop diuretics, systemic steroids. ↓ due to topiramate, zonisamide, salicylate overdose.
Blood Urea Nitrogen **(BUN)**	7–20 mg/dL	↑ in renal impairment and dehydration. Used with SCr (e.g., BUN:SCr ratio) to assess fluid status and renal function.
Serum Creatinine **(SCr)**	0.6–1.3 mg/dL	↑ due to many drugs that impair renal function (e.g., aminoglycosides, amphotericin B, cisplatin, colistimethate, cyclosporine, loop diuretics, polymyxin, NSAIDs, radiocontrast dye, tacrolimus, vancomycin). False ↑ due to sulfamethoxazole/trimethoprim, H2RAs, cobicistat. ↓ with low muscle mass, amputation, hemodilution.
Anion Gap (AG)	5–12 mEq/L	A calculated value, but often reported on the BMP (see Calculations IV chapter). Presence of ↑ anion gap suggests metabolic acidosis.

ITEM	COMMON REFERENCE RANGE	NOTES
WBC and Differential Many drugs (including chemotherapy, immunosuppressants and antivirals) have the potential to affect WBC, Hgb and PLTs.		
White Blood Cells (WBC)	4,000–11,000 cells/mm^3	Used to diagnose and monitor infection/inflammation. Can ↑ as an acute phase reactant, indicating a systemic reaction to inflammation or stress (e.g., surgery). ↑ due to systemic steroids, colony stimulating factors, epinephrine. ↓ due to clozapine, chemotherapy that targets the bone marrow, carbamazepine, cephalosporins, immunosuppressants (e.g., DMARDs, biologics), procainamide, vancomycin.
Neutrophils	45–73%	Neutrophils and bands are used with clinical s/sx to assess likelihood of acute infection and with WBC in absolute neutrophil count (ANC) calculation (see Calculations IV chapter). Neutrophils are also called polymorphonuclear cells (PMNs or polys) and segmented neutrophils (segs). Bands are immature neutrophils released from bone marrow to fight infection (called a "left shift").
Bands	3–5%	
Eosinophils	0–5%	↑ in drug allergy, asthma, inflammation, parasitic infection.
Basophils	0–1%	↑ in inflammation, hypersensitivity reaction, leukemia.
Lymphocytes	20–40%	↑ in viral infections, lymphoma. ↓ in bone marrow suppression, HIV or due to systemic steroids.
Monocytes	2–8%	↑ in chronic infections, inflammation, stress.
Anemia		
Red Blood Cells (RBC)	Males: 4.5–5.5 x 10^6 cells/μL Females: 4.1–4.9 x 10^6 cells/μL	↑ due to erythropoiesis-stimulating agents (ESAs), smoking, and in polycythemia (a condition that causes high RBCs). ↓ due to chemotherapy that targets the bone marrow, low production, blood loss, deficiency anemias (e.g., B12, folate), hemolytic anemia, sickle cell anemia.
Hemoglobin (Hgb, Hb)	Males: 13.5–18 g/dL Females: 12–16 g/dL	Hgb is the iron-containing protein that carries oxygen in the RBCs. The Hct mirrors the Hgb result (providing the same clinical information). ↑ due to ESAs (see Anemia chapter). ↓ in anemias and bleeding (risk with anticoagulants, antiplatelets, P2Y12 inhibitors, fibrinolytics). See Coombs Test and G6PD for drug-induced anemias.
Hematocrit (Hct)	Males: 38–50% Females: 36–46%	
Mean Corpuscular Volume (MCV)	80–100 fL	↑ due to B12 or folate deficiency. ↓ due to iron deficiency.
Mean Corpuscular Hemoglobin (MCH)	26–34 pg/cell	Additional tests used in an anemia workup. Together MCV, MCHC and RDW are called "RBC indices."
Mean Corpuscular Hgb Concentration (MCHC)	31–37 g/dL	
RBC Distribution Width (RDW)	11.5–14.5%	RDW measures the variability in the RBC size.
Iron	65–150 mcg/dL	↑ due to iron supplementation. ↓ due to blood loss or poor nutritional intake.
Total Iron Binding Capacity (TIBC)	250–400 mcg/dL	Monitored as part of the workup and treatment for iron deficiency anemia, anemia of chronic disease or anemia of chronic kidney disease (CKD). Often parenteral iron is required in conjunction with an ESA for patients on dialysis (see Anemia chapter).
Transferrin	> 200 mg/dL	
Transferrin Saturation (TSAT)	Males: 15–50% Females: 12–45%	
Ferritin	11–300 ng/mL	
Erythropoietin	2–25 mIU/mL	

ITEM	COMMON REFERENCE RANGE	NOTES
Folic acid (folate)	5–25 mcg/L	B12 and folate are ordered for further workup of macrocytic anemia. ↓ due to phenytoin/fosphenytoin, phenobarbital, primidone, methotrexate, sulfamethoxazole/trimethoprim, sulfasalazine. Supplement folate in women of childbearing age and alcoholism (see Dietary Supplements & Natural and Complementary Medicine chapter).
Vitamin B12	> 200 pg/mL	↓ due to PPIs, metformin, colchicine, chloramphenicol.
Methylmalonate (MMA)	Varies	Used for further workup of macrocytic anemia when B12 deficiency is suspected. Schilling test has also been used.
Reticulocyte count	0.5–2.5%	Measures the amount of reticulocytes (immature red blood cells) being made by the bone marrow; reticulocyte count is ↑ in blood loss and ↓ in bone marrow suppression.
Coombs Test, Direct Also known as: Direct Antiglobulin Test (DAT)	Negative	Used to determine cause of hemolytic anemia (autoimmune vs. drug-induced) and in assessment of transfusion compatibility (see Anemia chapter). Positive in drug-induced hemolysis caused by penicillins and cephalosporins (prolonged use/high concentrations), levodopa, methyldopa, quinidine, rifampin, sulfonamides (see Anemia chapter). If positive, discontinue offending drug.
Glucose-6-phosphate dehydrogenase **(G6PD)**	5–14 units/gram	Used to determine if hemolytic anemia is due to G6PD deficiency (the result will be low). The RBC destruction with G6PD deficiency is triggered by stress, foods (fava beans) or these drugs: dapsone, methylene blue, nitrofurantoin, pegloticase, primaquine, rasburicase, sulfonamides (see Anemia chapter).
Anticoagulation **These tests monitor different aspects of clotting and are used to monitor specific drugs.**		
Antifactor Xa Activity **(Anti-Xa)**	1.0-2.0 IU/mL (therapeutic LMWH) Obtain a peak anti-Xa 4 hours after SC LMWH dose for proper interpretation	Used to monitor low molecular weight heparins (LMWHs). Monitoring is recommended in pregnancy and possibly in obesity, low body weight, pediatrics, elderly, renal insufficiency (see Anticoagulation chapter). ↑ due to heparin, LMWHs, fondaparinux.
Prothrombin Time/ International Normalized Ratio **(PT / INR)**	PT: 10–13 seconds (varies) INR: < 1.2 (for those not on warfarin)	Used to monitor warfarin. INR ↑ (without warfarin) due to liver disease. False ↑ from daptomycin, oritavancin, telavancin. Many drugs ↑ or ↓ INR (see Anticoagulation chapter).
Activated Partial Thromboplastin Time **(aPTT or PTT)**	22–38 seconds (varies, this is called the "control") Treatment goal (on UFH): 1.5–2.5x control	Used to monitor unfractionated heparin (UFH) and direct thrombin inhibitors (e.g., argatroban). False ↑ from oritavancin, telavancin.
Activated Clotting Time (ACT)	70–180 seconds (varies)	Used to monitor anticoagulation in the cardiac catheterization lab during percutaneous coronary intervention (PCI) and in surgery.
Platelets **(PLTs)**	150,000–450,000/mm^3	Platelets are required for clot formation. Spontaneous bleeding can occur when platelets are < 20,000/mm^3. ↓ due to heparin, LMWHs, fondaparinux, glycoprotein IIb/IIIa receptor antagonists, linezolid, valproic acid, chemotherapy that targets the bone marrow, rarely other drugs.
Heparin-induced platelet antibodies: 1st ELISA test, then 2nd Serotonin release assay (SRA)	Negative	To confirm diagnosis of heparin-induced thrombocytopenia (HIT). If the ELISA test is positive, a positive SRA is confirmatory.

ITEM	COMMON REFERENCE RANGE	NOTES
Liver and Gastroenterology		
Albumin	3.5–5 g/dL	↓ due to cirrhosis and malnutrition. Highly protein bound drugs (e.g., warfarin) are impacted by changes in albumin; phenytoin, valproic acid and calcium serum concentrations require correction for low albumin (see Seizures/Epilepsy, Pharmacokinetics and Calculations III chapters).
Alkaline Phosphatase (Alk Phos or ALP)	33–131 IU/L	Used with other labs to assess liver, biliary tract (cholestatic) and bone disease.
Aspartate Aminotransferase **(AST)**	10–40 units/L	AST and ALT are enzymes released from injured hepatocytes (liver cells). Numerous medications and herbals can ↑ AST and ALT (see Hepatitis & Liver Disease chapter).
Alanine Aminotransferase **(ALT)**	10–40 units/L	
Gamma-Glutamyl Transpeptidase (GGT)	9–58 units/L	Used with other labs to assess liver, biliary tract (cholestasis) and pancreas.
Bilirubin, total (T Bili)	0.1–1.2 mg/dL	Used along with other liver tests to monitor drug toxicity, determine other cause of liver damage and detect bile duct blockage.
Ammonia	19–60 mcg/dL	Though not diagnostic, often measured in suspected hepatic encephalopathy (HE). ↑ due to valproic acid, topiramate. ↓ due to lactulose.
Pancreatitis		
Amylase	60–180 units/L	↑ in pancreatitis which can be caused by didanosine, stavudine, GLP-1 agonists, DPP-4 inhibitors, valproic acid, hypertriglyceridemia.
Lipase	5–160 units/L	
Cardiovascular		
Creatine Kinase or **Creatine Phosphokinase** **(CK** or **CPK)**	Males: 55–170 IU/L Females: 30–135 IU/L	To assess muscle inflammation (myositis) or more serious muscle damage and to diagnose cardiac conditions. ↑ due to daptomycin, quinupristin/dalfopristin, statins, fibrates (especially if given with a statin), emtricitabine, tenofovir, tipranavir, raltegravir, dolutegravir.
CK-MB isoenzymes, total	≤ 6.0 ng/mL	As a group, these are called "cardiac enzymes" and are used in the diagnosis of MI. The troponins can be elevated with a few other conditions (e.g., sepsis, PE, CKD). BNP and NT-proBNP are both markers of cardiac stress. They are not HF nor heart disease-specific, but higher values indicate higher likelihood of HF when consistent with HF symptoms. Renal failure is the second most common cause of ↑ in BNP and NT-proBNP. Myoglobin and CK-MB are not interchangeable; they are 2 separate markers. Myoglobin is a sensitive marker for muscle injury but has relatively low specificity for acute MI and therefore is not routinely used for diagnosis (see Acute Coronary Syndrome chapter).
Troponin T **(TnT)**	0–0.1 ng/mL (assay dependent)	
Troponin I **(TnI)**	0–0.5 ng/mL (assay dependent)	
B-Type Natriuretic Peptide **(BNP)**	< 100 pg/mL or ng/L	
N-Terminal-ProBNP **(NT-proBNP)**	Males: < 61 pg/mL Females: 12–151 pg/mL	
Respiratory		
Eosinophil count	< 100 cells/mcL	Used to determine if inhaled corticosteroids (ICS) will be beneficial in COPD treatment, along with history of COPD exacerbations (See Chronic Obstructive Pulmonary Disease chapter).

ITEM	COMMON REFERENCE RANGE	NOTES
Lipids and Cardiovascular Risk		
Total Cholesterol (TC)	< 200 mg/dL	For complete discussion, see Dyslipidemia chapter. Fasting begins 9-12 hours prior to lipid blood draw. Non-HDL = TC - HDL. Guidelines do not support specific TC, HDL or TG goals; they support a statin intensity level for LDL-C reductions based on those most likely to benefit. This means that the target values are not being used as goals for treatment, but elevations should be recognized. In some individuals, additional treatment is considered if LDL ≥ 70 mg/dL.
Low Density Lipoprotein **(LDL)**	< 100 mg/dL, desirable	
High Density Lipoprotein **(HDL)**	< 40 mg/dL, low (male) ≥ 60 mg/dL, desirable	
Non-HDL	< 130 mg/dL, desirable	
Triglycerides **(TG)**	< 150 mg/dL	
Lipoprotein-a, Lp(a) Apolipoprotein-B, Apo B	< 10 mg/dL < 130 mg/dL	↑ Lp(a) and ↑ ApoB are being used more commonly; these are associated with ↑ coagulation and ↑ risk of CVD.
C-reactive Protein **(CRP)**	0–0.5 mg/dL	↑ CRP indicates inflammation, which could be due to many conditions (infection, trauma, malignancy). Higher levels indicate ↑ risk. High-sensitivity CRP (hs-CRP) is more sensitive for CVD.
Coronary Artery Calcium score	< 300 Agatston units or < 75 percentile for age, sex and ethnicity; higher is at risk	The coronary artery calcium score measures calcium build-up in the coronary arteries.
Ankle Brachial Index (ABI)	1–1.4	The ankle brachial index measures the ratio of the BP in the lower legs to the BP in the arms. It is used to assess severity of peripheral artery disease (PAD). An ABI < 1 indicates some degree of PAD.
Diabetes		
Fasting Plasma Glucose **(FPG)**	≥ 126 mg/dL is positive for diabetes 100–125 mg/dL is positive for pre-diabetes	Fasting is 8+ hours. See Diabetes chapter for complete information and medications that can cause hyper and hypoglycemia.
Hemoglobin A1C **(A1C)**	< 7% (ADA), ≤ 6.5% (AACE)	Average blood glucose over the past 3 months; based on attachment of glucose to hemoglobin; ↑ glucose = ↑ BG attached to Hgb = ↑ A1C.
Estimated Average Glucose (eAG)	< 154 mg/dL (ADA)	Used to correlate a finger stick glucose with an A1C; an eAG of 126 mg/dL corresponds to an A1C of 6%.
Preprandial blood glucose	80–130 mg/dL (ADA), < 110 mg/dL (AACE)	Blood glucose measurement taken before a meal.
Postprandial blood glucose	< 180 mg/dL (ADA), < 140 mg/dL (AACE)	Blood glucose measurement taken after a meal (1-2 hours after the start of eating).
C-peptide (fasting)	0.78–1.89 ng/mL	Insulin breakdown product used to evaluate beta-cell function (distinguish type 1 from type 2 diabetes).
Urine Albumin to Creatinine Ratio or Albumin to Creatinine Ratio (UACR or ACR) or **Urinary Albumin Excretion** **(UAE)**	Males: < 17 mg/gram Females: < 25 mg/gram < 30 mg/24 hours	See Diabetes and Renal Disease chapters.

ITEM	COMMON REFERENCE RANGE	NOTES
Thyroid Function		
Thyroid Stimulating Hormone (TSH)	0.3–3 mIU/L	TSH is used with FT4 to diagnose hypothyroidism and is used alone (sometimes with FT4) to monitor patients being treated. ↑ or ↓ due to amiodarone, interferons. ↑ (hypothyroidism) due to interferons, tyrosine kinase inhibitors, lithium, carbamazepine.
Total thyroxine (T4)	4.5–10.9 mcg/dL	T4 and FT4 are two of several tests used for a detailed assessment of thyroid function (see Thyroid chapter for additional interacting drugs).
Free thyroxine (FT4)	0.9–2.3 ng/dL	
Uric Acid/Gout		
Uric acid	Males: 3.5–7.2 mg/dL Females: 2–6.5 mg/dL	Used in diagnosis/treatment of gout. ↑ due to diuretics, niacin, low doses of aspirin, pyrazinamide, cyclosporine, tacrolimus, select pancreatic enzyme products, select chemotherapy (tumor lysis syndrome).
Inflammation/Autoimmune Disease		
C-Reactive Protein (CRP)	Normal: 0–0.5 mg/dL High risk: > 3 mg/dL	Nonspecific tests used in autoimmune disorders, inflammation, infections. Drug-induced lupus erythematosus (DILE) can be caused by many drugs. More likely with anti-TNF agents, hydralazine, isoniazid, methimazole, methyldopa, minocycline, procainamide, propylthiouracil, quinidine, terbinafine. If ANA is positive, histone antibody and anti-dsDNA tests will help establish diagnosis. The causative drug must be discontinued (see Systemic Steroids & Autoimmune Conditions chapter).
Rheumatoid Factor, serum (RF)	Negative, or ≤ upper limit of normal (ULN) for the lab (usually < 20 IU/mL)	
Erythrocyte Sedimentation Rate (ESR)	Males: ≤ 20 mm/hr Females: ≤ 30 mm/hr	
Antinuclear Antibodies (ANA)	Negative (titers may be provided)	
Antihistone Antibodies (Detected by ELISA)	Negative	
HIV		
CD4+ T Lymphocyte Count	800–1,100 cells/mm³	Used to assess HIV and monitor treatment (see HIV chapter).
HIV RNA Concentration (Viral Load)	Undetectable Measured in copies/mL	
HIV Antibody (Ab)	Negative (non-reactive)	Detects infection with the virus; may not become positive until several weeks after exposure.
HIV DNA PCR	Negative	Useful for early detection.
HIV p24 Antigen	Undetectable	
Acid-Base (arterial sample)		
pH	7.35–7.45	Together these values are called an arterial blood gas (ABG) sample. Often written in chart notes with a stick diagram: pH/pCO2/pO2/HCO3/O2 Sat (see Calculations IV chapter for ABG interpretation). Bicarbonate on the ABG is a calculated value and reference range may differ from venous samples.
pCO2	35–45 mmHg	
pO2	80–100 mmHg	
HCO3	22–26 mEq/L	
O2 Sat	> 95%	

ITEM	COMMON REFERENCE RANGE	NOTES
Hormonal		
Testosterone total, free	Males: 300–950 ng/dL	↑ with testosterone supplementation.
Prostate-Specific Antigen (PSA)	< 4 ng/mL	Can ↑ with testosterone supplementation. Used in detecting prostate cancer and BPH.
Human Chorionic Gonadotropin **(hCG)**	Varies by test	Tested in blood or urine to determine pregnancy. A positive value in a female indicates she is pregnant.
Luteinizing Hormone **(LH)**	Varies during cycle	Rises mid-cycle, causing egg release from the ovaries (ovulation). Tested in urine with ovulation predictor kits for women attempting pregnancy.
Parathyroid Hormone (PTH)	Varies	Used in evaluation of parathyroid disorders, hypercalcemia and chronic kidney disease (CKD) (see Renal Disease chapter).
Other		
Cosyntropin Stimulation Test	Baseline and timed increase are measured	Used to test for adrenal suppression; medications that affect baseline cortisol or suppress adrenal response will impact test and may need to be held prior (e.g., steroids).
Lactic acid (lactate)	0.5–2.2 mEq/L	Lactic acidosis indicates anaerobic metabolism, which occurs in long distance running and in certain medical conditions (e.g., sepsis). ↑ due to NRTIs (see HIV chapter), metformin (low risk/mostly with renal disease and heart failure), alcohol, cyanide.
Procalcitonin	≤ 0.15 ng/mL	↑ due to systemic bacterial infections or severe localized infections.
Prolactin	1–25 ng/mL	Secretion is regulated by dopamine; can ↑ with haloperidol, risperidone, paliperidone, methyldopa. Can ↓ with bromocriptine.
Purified Protein Derivative or Mantoux test **(PPD)**	No induration (raised area); induration is measured for diagnosis of TB exposure	TB skin test (TST) administered by intradermal injection. Not used alone for diagnosis of active TB. Response is measured by diameter (mm) of induration at 48-72 hours (see ID II: Bacterial Infections chapter for interpretation of the PPD).
Rapid Plasma Reagin **(RPR)**	Negative	Antibody test used to screen for syphilis. If the RPR is positive, confirmatory testing is performed. Titers may be reported and are used to monitor response to therapy.
Serum osmolality	275–290 mOsm/kg H2O	Used with Na, BUN/SCr, and clinical volume status to evaluate hypo/hypernatremia. ↑ due to mannitol, toxicities (e.g., ethylene glycol, methanol, propylene glycol).
Thiopurine Methyltransferase **(TPMT)**	≥ 15 units/mL	Those with genetic deficiency of TPMT are at ↑ risk for myelosuppression (bone marrow suppression) and may require lower doses with azathioprine and mercaptopurine.
Vitamin D, serum 25(OH)	> 30 ng/mL	↓ levels increase risk of osteoporosis, osteomalacia (rickets), CVD, diabetes, hypertension, infectious diseases and other conditions. Supplement vitamin D with various conditions and drugs (see Dietary Supplements & Natural and Complementary Medicine chapter).

ASSESSING PATIENT CASES QUICKLY

Cases can be evaluated more quickly by recognizing lab patterns and signs and symptoms that provide a clue to the patient's diagnosis. Watch for drug-induced signs/symptoms and lab changes. Look for lab contraindications to drugs (e.g., +hCG, hyperkalemia). Additional information can be found in the chapters on these disease states.

Lab patterns and likely diagnoses can be located in the first chapter of this Course Book. Lab patterns due to an infectious disease can be found in the Infectious Diseases chapters.

THERAPEUTIC DRUG MONITORING

Drug levels or other values (such as anti-Xa levels for LMWHs) are used to reach dosing goals and to avoid toxicity. Therapeutic drug monitoring (TDM) is increasingly common due to the need to target highly resistant organisms and dose medications properly in overweight and obese patients. The peak level is the highest concentration in the blood the drug will reach and requires time for the drug to distribute in the body's tissues. The trough level is the lowest concentration the drug will reach in the blood and is drawn right before the next dose or some short period of time before the next dose (30 minutes is common). This allows time for assessment of the level before another dose is given and time to hold the next dose if the level is high. The time that drug levels are drawn is critical for accurate interpretation. For example, a tobramycin level of 6 mcg/mL would be interpreted differently if the level was a trough versus a peak. Obtaining drug levels at steady state is often (but not always) preferred. See Pharmacokinetics chapter for further discussion.

Narrow therapeutic index (NTI) drugs have a narrow separation between the subtherapeutic (low), therapeutic (desired) and supratherapeutic (high) drug levels. Supratherapeutic drug levels can be toxic.

TDM is commonly performed by pharmacists. The following table lists drugs that are routinely monitored. These drugs and usual therapeutic ranges are felt to be essential for NAPLEX.

THERAPEUTIC DRUG LEVELS

DRUG	USUAL THERAPEUTIC RANGE
Carbamazepine	4-12 mcg/mL
Digoxin	0.8-2 ng/mL (AFib) 0.5-0.9 ng/mL (HF)
Gentamicin (traditional dosing)	Peak: 5-10 mcg/mL Trough: < 2 mcg/mL
Lithium	0.6-1.2 mEq/L (up to 1.5 mEq/L for acute symptoms)
Phenytoin/Fosphenytoin Free Phenytoin	10-20 mcg/mL; if albumin is low, correct serum level; see Seizures/Epilepsy chapter 1-2.5 mcg/mL
Procainamide NAPA (procainamide active metabolite) Combined	4-10 mcg/mL 15-25 mcg/mL 10-30 mcg/mL
Theophylline	5-15 mcg/mL
Tobramycin (traditional dosing)	Peak: 5-10 mcg/mL Trough: < 2 mcg/mL
Valproic acid	50-100 mcg/mL (up to 150 mcg/mL in some patients); if albumin is low, correct serum level; see Seizures/Epilepsy chapter
Vancomycin	Trough: 15-20 mcg/mL for most serious infections (pneumonia, endocarditis, osteomyelitis, meningitis, and bacteremia) Trough: 10-15 mcg/mL for others
Warfarin	Goal INR is 2-3 for most indications, use higher range (2.5-3.5) with mechanical mitral valves

Refer to the Pharmacokinetics chapter for detailed information.

Select Guidelines/References

Lab Tests Online. https://labtestsonline.org (accessed 2018 November 27).
Lee M. Basic Skills in Interpreting Laboratory Data. 6th ed. Betheseda, MD: ASHP; 2017.
Schmidt J, Wieczorkiewicz J. Interpreting Laboratory Data: A Point-of-Care Guide. Betheseda, MD: ASHP; 2012.

CHAPTER CONTENT

Background 81
Package Inserts 82
The PI Includes The Drug's Safety Information 83
General Drug Information Resources 83
Paid Subscriptions Versus Free Access 84
Unique Features of Common Drug Information Resources 85
The Pharmacist's Letter 85
OTC Drug Information 86
Labeling Requirements for OTC Drugs 86
Locating Specific-Types of Information 87
Selecting the Correct "Color" Drug Reference 88
"Color" Drug References 89
Locating Clinical Study Data And Research Summaries 89
Consumer Resources 89
Practice Scenarios 90

> ***Pharmacists respond to drug questions ATC (around the clock). Knowing where to locate drug information is a must in all practice settings.***

CONTENT LEGEND

= Study Tip Gal

© Michael J. Freudiger

CHAPTER 5
LEARNING DRUG REFERENCES

BACKGROUND

Providing drug information to patients and other healthcare professionals is a critical function of pharmacists, the drug therapy experts. To provide adequate responses, pharmacists need to select the most appropriate resource/s, using current drug information.

The first part of this chapter covers the package insert (PI). The next section covers the general drug information resources that include drug monographs based largely (but not completely) on the PI. A review of resources to locate specific information follows, such as where to find information about a drug shortage or vaccines to administer prior to travel, followed by sources for clinical studies and consumer information.

CLINICAL SCENARIO

MJ presents with a prescription for *Keppra* 500 mg tablets by mouth BID for her 5-year-old, 80 kg daughter. She asks the pharmacist a few questions:

- Is the medication dosed properly for her daughter's age and weight?
- Is it possible to crush the tablets or switch to a liquid?
- Is it safe to take melatonin for sleep with *Keppra*?

Resources

- Drug dosing in a child may (or may not) be in the drug's package insert (PI), which includes only FDA-approved indications. It may be included in the off-label section of a general drug information resource, such as *Lexicomp*. A pediatric resource such as The *Harriet Lane Handbook* includes pediatric dosing that might otherwise be unavailable. The clinical guidelines for the condition might have recommended dosing for children, especially for conditions that are common in children, such as epilepsy, and various infectious diseases.
- Administration recommendations (e.g., if the tablets can be crushed) and the product availability (e.g., if a solution is available) will be included in the PI, which will be reflected in the general drug information resources. If a formulation is not available, a compounding pharmacist might be able to prepare an oral formulation, under the preparation recommendations in USP 795, and according to a master formula (recipe) for oral *Keppra* liquid.
- A drug-natural product interaction reference should be used to evaluate the safety of taking melatonin and *Keppra*, which can be found in most of the general drug information resources. A specific natural medicine resource might provide more detail.

PACKAGE INSERTS

COMMON CONTENT CATEGORIES IN THE DRUG'S PACKAGE INSERT

Package Insert Contents (and consequently, in the general drug information monographs).

PRESCRIBING INFORMATION

EVISTA (raloxifene hydrochloride) Tablet for Oral Use

BOXED WARNING

Increased Risk of Venous Thromboembolism and Death from Stroke.

-----------------------Recent Major Changes-----------------------

None.

-----------------------Indications and Usage-----------------------

EVISTA is an estrogen agonist/antagonist indicated for:

- Treatment and prevention of osteoporosis in postmenopausal women.
- Reduction of risk of invasive breast cancer in postmenopausal women.

--------------------Dosage and Administration--------------------

60 mg tablet orally once daily.
Calcium and vitamin D should be added if insufficient.

-------------------Dosage Forms and Strengths-------------------

Tablets (not scored) 60 mg.

-------------------------Contraindications-------------------------

- Active or past venous thromboembolism.
- Pregnancy, nursing mothers, women who might become pregnant.

--------------------Warnings and Precautions--------------------

- Venous thromboembolism.
- Death due to stroke, cardiovascular disease.
- Hypertriglyceridemia.

-------------------------Adverse Reactions-------------------------

Adverse reactions (> 2% and more common than with placebo) include: hot flashes, leg cramps, peripheral edema, arthralgia...

--------------------------Drug Interactions--------------------------

- Cholestyramine: use with EVISTA is not recommended. Reduces raloxifene absorption.
- Warfarin: monitor prothrombin time.

--------------------Use in Specific Populations--------------------

Renal impairment: EVISTA should be used with caution in patients with moderate or severe renal impairment.

------------------Drug Abuse and Dependence------------------

Not Applicable.

---------------------Overdosage/Toxicology---------------------

In an 8-week study of 63 postmenopausal women, a dose of raloxifene HCl 600 mg/day was safely tolerated.
In clinical trials, no raloxifene overdose has been reported.

-------------Pharmacology/Mechanism of Action----------------

Raloxifene is an estrogen agonist/antagonist, commonly referred to as a selective estrogen receptor modulator (SERM). The biological actions of raloxifene are largely mediated through binding to estrogen receptors.

-----------------------Additional Categories-----------------------

Pharmacokinetics and Pharmacodynamics

Clinical Studies

Storage and Handling

Patient Counseling Information

Revised; not actual Evista Package Insert.

The package insert (PI) is the FDA-approved drug information that is part of the drug's official labeling. The FDA provides the PIs to the National Library of Medicine (NLM), which puts the current PIs on the *DailyMed* website, and a manufacturer's website will have PIs for the manufacturer's drugs. The current PIs can also be located on the FDA website directly. Pharmacists who are in the vicinity of the actual drug (i.e., in a community or hospital pharmacy) can take the PI directly from the product (e.g., removing the PI off the top of a bottle of *Eliquis* and check the product's contraindications).

> ***The FDA approves drugs and their labeling. The PI is part of the labeling. PIs do not contain information not approved by the FDA, such as off-label use, or the drug's cost.***

THE PI INCLUDES THE DRUG'S SAFETY INFORMATION

Important safety information is split into the categories described below. There may be separate handouts that alert the patient to the drug's toxicity (Medication Guides) and/or a strategy to manage the risk (REMS). These are discussed in the Drug Allergies and Adverse Drug Reactions chapter. A decision whether or not to prescribe a drug (and the decision by the patient to take a drug) should involve a risk-benefit assessment. When a drug is used, the benefit must outweigh the risk. All drugs, OTC and prescription, have some degree of risk.

- Boxed Warnings: the strictest warning. The black box around the warning (see example on previous page) alerts prescribers to the risk of death or permanent disability (e.g., increased risk of venous thromboembolism and death from stroke with raloxifene).
- Contraindications: when a patient has a contraindication to a drug, the drug cannot be used in that patient. The risk will outweigh any possible benefit (e.g., a history of venous thromboembolism is a contraindication to the use of raloxifene). If there are no known contraindications for a drug, the section will state "None."
- Warnings and Precautions: include serious reactions that can result in death, hospitalization, medical intervention, disability or teratogenicity (e.g., raloxifene has a warning for venous thromboembolism). Warnings and precautions may or may not change a prescribing decision.
- Adverse Reactions: refer to undesirable, uncomfortable or dangerous effects from a drug (e.g., arthralgia from raloxifene). The risk-benefit assessment is patient-specific (e.g., arthralgia from raloxifene will be more of a concern in a patient with chronically sore joints, versus a patient with no sore joints).

PRESCRIBING INFORMATION	FORMATS	DESCRIPTION
FDA-approved Package Inserts can be found at:		FDA label information for Rx and OTC drugs.
■ DailyMed (NLM) https://dailymed.nlm.nih.gov	Online	
■ Drugs@FDA www.accessdata.fda.gov/scripts/cder/daf/index.cfm	Online and Mobile App	In addition to the FDA and DailyMed websites, the PI can be located at the manufacturer's website (e.g., www.pfizer.com) or (especially with newer drugs) the manufacturer will have a website for the specific drug; the website URL will be the drug's brand name (e.g., www.eliquis.com).
■ The Drug Manufacturer's Website	Individual URL Addresses	

GENERAL DRUG INFORMATION RESOURCES

General drug information resources rely on the PI for much of their content. These resources are developed by different companies, and the additional information they contain varies. The next page summarizes the general drug information resources. The following page highlights some of the specific content that different general drug information resources provide.

> **"**
>
> ***General drug information resources contain monographs on each drug. The monographs include the FDA-approved information from the drug's PI, plus some other items, depending on the resource.***

The *American Hospital Formulary Service* (*AHFS*) provides comprehensive monographs that link to supporting evidence and references, which makes it a very useful resource for researching a topic in detail. The off-label drug use section is well-researched, with linked references.

Clinical Pharmacology, Facts and Comparisons, Lexicomp and *Micromedex* are commonly used by pharmacists, and each contains information that pharmacists find useful, including *Trissel's* IV drug compatibility and stability data, drug class comparisons, natural products, drug (tablet/capsule) identification and international drug names. Most of the sites provide drug pricing, with either the drug's average wholesale price (AWP), which is usually reported by the manufacturer, or the average price charged at pharmacies, which tends to be lower (~17% less than the AWP). The pricing provides a rough ball-park estimate.

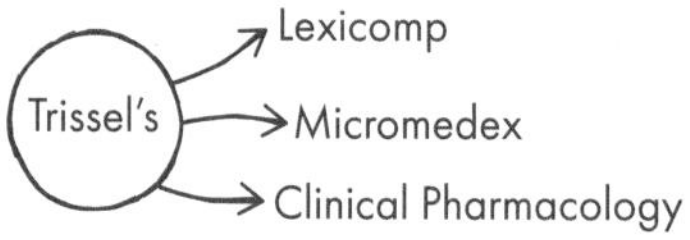

Caution: pharmacists rely on the data in the drug information resource at their practice site, but when a PI is updated, there can be a lag time until the drug's monograph includes the update. Pharmacists may need to check the PI directly.

Drug Monograph sites pull in information from the PI and other sources (e.g., *Trissel's* IV info is contained in many sites).

PAID SUBSCRIPTIONS VERSUS FREE ACCESS

The general drug information resources used by most healthcare professionals requires a paid subscription. The last two listings in the following table, *Drugs.com* and *RxList*, can be accessed by anyone, at no-cost to the user. The National Library of Medicine (NLM) is a government organization, and the drug monographs are provided at no-charge.

GENERAL DRUG INFORMATION RESOURCES	FORMATS	DESCRIPTION
American Hospital Formulary Service (AHFS)* www.ahfsdruginformation.com An ASHP product	AHFS Drug Information: Book	Collection of drug monographs for medications available in the U.S.
	AHFS DI Essentials: Book	Select drug monographs from AHFS Drug Information re-formatted for point-of-care decision making; expands on therapeutic evidence and includes additional information (e.g., patient counseling).
	AHFS Clinical Drug Information (AHFS CDI): Online and Mobile App Included with Lexicomp Online	AHFS Drug Information and AHFS DI Essentials databases, plus real-time updates (e.g., drug shortages, FDA safety alerts).
Clinical Pharmacology www.clinicalpharmacology.com	Online and Mobile App	Monographs for Rx and OTC drugs, natural products and investigational drugs.
Drug Information Portal (NLM) https://druginfo.nlm.nih.gov/drugportal/	Online	Drug searches link directly to other NLM databases for related information (e.g., DailyMed for the PI, LactMed for effect on breastfeeding, Pillbox for drug identification and images).
Epocrates/Epocrates Plus www.epocrates.com	Online and Mobile App	Free with registration; drug information plus guideline summaries. Epocrates Plus (fee required) expands into evidence-based disease management and includes sections on natural products, lab and diagnostic information and ICD-10 coding (for billing purposes).
Facts & Comparisons www.wolterskluwercdi.com/facts-comparisons-online/	Drug Facts and Comparisons: Book	Monographs of Rx and OTC drugs organized by therapeutic class.
	Facts & Comparisons eAnswers: Online	Collection of databases; includes drug monographs, comparative drug charts and other unique resources (e.g., search drugs based on a specific adverse reaction).
Lexicomp www.wolterskluwercdi.com/lexicomp-online/	Drug Information Handbook: Book	Drug monographs organized alphabetically; includes useful appendices (e.g., drug class comparisons, equivalent dosing charts).
	Lexi-Drugs: Online and Mobile App Included with UpToDate	Multiple clinical databases (beyond Lexi-Drugs) depending on subscription level purchased (see the Locating Specific Types of Information table).
Micromedex truvenhealth.com/Products/Micromedex	DRUGDEX: Online and Mobile App	Multiple clinical databases beyond DRUGDEX (see the Locating Specific Types of Information table).
Prescriber's Digital Reference (*mobile*PDR) www.pdr.net/resources/mobilePDR/	Mobile App	Free with registration; previously the Physician's Desk Reference (no longer in print); includes information for drugs, vaccines and biologics. Detail is more than the drug's PI, and includes practical information, such as where injections can be given, and time to reach clinical effect.
Drugs.com www.drugs.com	Online and Mobile App	Free for professionals and consumers; drug information is primarily sourced from other products, including AHFS Drug Information, Micromedex, Facts & Comparisons and the FDA.
RxList www.rxlist.com	Online and Mobile App	Free for professionals and consumers; drug information is primarily sourced from other products, including the FDA, Cerner Multum and First Databank, Inc.

Only resource designated by the U.S. Congress as acceptable for determining reimbursement for off-label uses under Medicare Part D and Medicaid.

UNIQUE FEATURES OF COMMON DRUG INFORMATION RESOURCES

The electronic versions of these references offer additional tools (beyond the routine content provided in general drug monographs) that are useful in daily practice. The table below describes some of the popular features that are commonly accessed by pharmacists. Many of the online databases link to external sites that have public access (e.g., *Lexicomp* includes monographs and immunization schedules for vaccines and provides links to immunization resources on the CDC website).

REFERENCE	Off-Label Uses	IV Drug Compatibility	Drug/Pill Identification	Natural Products	Drug Class Comparisons	Pricing	International Drug Names
AHFS/AHFS CDI	√	√ (AHFS CDI*)					√ (via USP Dictionary of USAN and International Drug Names)
Clinical Pharmacology	√	√ (via Trissel's**)	√	√	√	√	√ (via Index Nominum)
Drugs.com	√		√	√		√	√
Epocrates/ Epocrates Plus	√		√	√ (Epocrates Plus)	√	√	
Facts & Comparisons eAnswers	√	√ (via Trissel's**)	√	√	√		√ (via Martindale)
Lexicomp	√	√ (via Trissel's**)	√ (Lexi-Drugs ID)	√ (Lexi-Natural Products)	√ (via Facts & Comparisons)	√	√ (via Martindale)
Micromedex	√	√ (via Trissel's**)	√ (IDENTIDEX)	√ (AltMedDex)	√	√ (Red Book)	√ (via Martindale, Index Nominum and others)
***mobile*PDR**			√		√		

**Data from ASHP's Handbook on Injectable Drugs*
***Data from Trissel's 2 Clinical Pharmaceutics Database*

PHARMACIST'S LETTER

Pharmacist's Letter does not contain traditional drug monographs, but is a valuable resource that provides evidence-based drug information. The same company provides similar products called *Prescriber's Letter, Nurse's Letter* and *Pharmacy Technician's Letter*. Subscribers receive a monthly newsletter in the mail, and have online access to helpful practice tools:

- New drug approvals, drug withdrawals, new dosage forms and first time generics
- Charts (e.g., drug class comparisons, disease-state treatment summaries)
- Lists of medications with MedGuides, with links to the MedGuide on the FDA website
- Patient education summaries and patient flyers
- Continuing education (CE)
- Training materials for technicians and intern pharmacists
- Forum for peer discussions and comments

OTC DRUG INFORMATION

OTC, or nonprescription drugs, are considered safe and effective for self-diagnosed conditions by the general public, have adequate written directions for self-use, and do not require physician supervision. No prescription is therefore required for the purchase of OTC products.

LABELING REQUIREMENTS FOR OTC DRUGS

The labeling on prescription drugs is written for healthcare providers. The labeling on OTC drugs is written for patients who may not have medical training. The language needs to be written in a manner that a layperson can understand, in order to be able to use the drug safely, and for the purpose/s for which it is intended. The labeling information is written on the package of OTC drugs in the Drug Facts Panel (see figure), which must include:

- The active ingredients, including the amount in each dosage unit, with dosage instructions.
- The uses (simpler word than indications) for the product.
- Specific warnings, including circumstances when the drug should not be used (e.g., in kidney disease), and when it is appropriate to consult with a doctor or pharmacist.
- Side effects, and substances or activities to avoid.
- The inactive ingredients.

OTC Drug Approval

There are two methods that a manufacturer can use to market an OTC product:

1. The New Drug Application (NDA) Process
2. The OTC Monograph Process

The NDA approval process for prescription drugs is managed through the FDA's Center for Drug Evaluation and Research (CDER). OTC drugs can go through the same drug approval process, or the manufacturer can opt to stick to the standards in the OTC monograph for that therapeutic drug class. The monograph for the class will cover the acceptable ingredients, doses, formulations, and labeling, plus study data on the drug's safety and effectiveness.

Locating OTC Drug Status and Labeling

OTC drugs that have gone through the NDA approval process become FDA-approved drugs, and will be listed in common general drug information resources (e.g., *Lexicomp, Micromedex*). The OTC drug labeling can also be found in the same location on the FDA website that contains the labeling (package inserts) for prescription drugs: *Drugs@FDA*. The labeling for OTC drugs does not need to be a separate document, but can be the container itself, as long as the items specified above are included.

LOCATING SPECIFIC TYPES OF INFORMATION

The table below highlights select specialty references that may be encountered on the licensure exam. General drug information resources described previously (e.g., *Lexicomp* and *Micromedex*) provide some of the same information.

> ***This chart provides the sites for specific information, such as where to locate drug shortage information. Do not forget that the general drug information sources will have some of the same information, such as Drug Interactions.***

LOCATING SPECIFIC TYPES OF INFORMATION

ADVERSE REACTIONS

ASHP's Drug-Induced Diseases: Prevention, Detection, and Management

Meyler's Side Effects of Drugs

FDAble: FDA searchable database of adverse reactions caused by medicines, vaccines, devices, tobacco products, dietary supplements

- MedWatch: The FDA Safety Information and Adverse Event Reporting System (FAERS)
- Vaccine Adverse Event Reporting System (VAERS)
- Manufacturer and User Facility Device Experience (MAUDE)
- Safety Reporting Portal

COMPOUNDING AND PHARMACEUTICS

Allen's The Art, Science, and Technology of Pharmaceutical Compounding

ASHP Guidelines on Compounding Sterile Preparations

Handbook of Pharmaceutical Excipients

Merck Index: An Encyclopedia of Chemicals, Drugs, and Biologicals

Remington: The Science and Practice of Pharmacy

Trissel's Stability of Compounded Formulations

USP Compounding Compendium:

- USP 795: Non-Sterile Preparations
- USP 797: Sterile Preparations
- USP 800: Hazardous Drugs - Handling in Healthcare Settings
- USP-NF: monographs for drug substances, dosage forms, compounded preparations and excipients

ASHP's Extemporaneous Formulations for Pediatric, Geriatric, and Special Needs Patients

Pediatric Drug Formulations

DRUG IDENTIFICATION

Pillbox (NLM)

Ident-A-Drug (Therapeutic Research Center)

DRUG INTERACTIONS

Hansten and Horn's Drug Interactions Analysis and Management

Drug Interaction Facts (Facts & Comparisons)

DRUG PRICING

Red Book (Micromedex)

Medi-Span Price Rx

DRUG SHORTAGES

ASHP Current Drug Shortages

FDA Drug Shortages

CDC Current Vaccine Shortages & Delays

American Hospital Formulary Service Clinical Drug Information (AHFS CDI)

DRUG SUBSTITUTION

FDA's Orange Book: Approved Drug Products with Therapeutic Equivalence Evaluations

FDA's Purple Book: Lists of Licensed Biological Products with Reference Product Exclusivity and Biosimilarity or Interchangeability Evaluations

GERIATRICS

American Geriatrics Society (AGS) Beers Criteria for Potentially Inappropriate Medication Use in Older Adults

ASHP's Fundamentals of Geriatric Pharmacotherapy

Geriatric Dosage Handbook (Lexicomp)

IMMUNIZATIONS (ADULT AND PEDIATRIC)

CDC Advisory Committee on Immunization Practices (ACIP)

- Updates published in the Morbidity and Mortality Weekly Report (MMWR)

CDC Pink Book: Epidemiology and Prevention of Vaccine Preventable Disease

Immunization Action Coalition

American Pharmacists Association (APhA) Immunization Center

Vaccines, Blood & Biologics (FDA)

INFECTIOUS DISEASES

Infectious Diseases Society of America (IDSA) Practice Guidelines

Sanford Guide to Antimicrobial Therapy

Sanford Guide to HIV/AIDS Therapy

Johns Hopkins ABX and HIV Guides

AIDSinfo.nih.gov (U.S. Dept. of Health and Human Services)

INTERNATIONAL DRUG INFORMATION

Index Nominum: International Drug Directory

Martindale: The Complete Drug Reference

USP Dictionary of United States Adopted Names (USAN) and International Drug Names

Drug Information Handbook with International Trade Names Index (Lexicomp)

Monograph-type resources sometimes include one or more of the above (e.g., AHFS includes USP Dictionary of USAN and International Drug Names, and Lexicomp includes Martindale)

INVESTIGATIONAL DRUGS

Clinicaltrials.gov (NIH)

IV DRUG COMPATIBILITY AND STABILITY

ASHP's Handbook on Injectable Drugs (formerly Trissel's)

King Guide to Parenteral Admixtures

Trissel's 2 Clinical Pharmaceutics Database

LOCATING SPECIFIC TYPES OF INFORMATION (CONTINUED)

MEDICATION SAFETY

FDA MedWatch (report adverse events and medication errors)

NIOSH List of Antineoplastic (Chemotherapy) and Other Hazardous Drugs in Healthcare Settings

Institute for Safe Medication Practices (ISMP)

- Report medication errors to the ISMP Medication Errors Reporting Program (ISMP MERP)

Crediblemeds.org (QT Drugs Lists)

FDA:

- Drug and Biologic Recalls
- Drug Safety Label Changes database
- Medication Guides
- Safety Alerts

NATURAL PRODUCTS/ALTERNATIVE MEDICINE

Natural Medicines Database (Therapeutic Research Center)

Dietary Supplements Label Database (NIH)

USP Dietary Supplements Compendium

OTHER CLINICAL GUIDELINES

Professional organizations and guidelines (listed at the end of the relevant chapter, examples included below)

- Infectious Diseases Society of America (IDSA) Practice Guidelines
- American Diabetes Association (ADA) Standards of Medical Care

OVERDOSES, POISONING AND TOXICOLOGY

Lexi-Tox (Lexicomp)

Micromedex Toxicology Management (previously POISONDEX)

TOXNET (NLM)

Goldfrank's Toxicologic Emergencies

State Poison Control Center

The American Association of Poison Control Centers

PEDIATRICS

NeoFax and Pediatrics (Micromedex)

Pediatric & Neonatal Dosage Handbook (Lexicomp)

Red Book: Report of the Committee on Infectious Diseases (AAP)

The Harriet Lane Handbook

American Academy of Pediatrics (AAP)

ASHP's Pediatric Injectable Drugs (The Teddy Bear Book)

Nelson Textbook of Pediatrics

PHARMACOLOGY

Goodman and Gilman's The Pharmacological Basis of Therapeutics

Katzung's Basic and Clinical Pharmacology

PREGNANCY AND LACTATION

Briggs' Drugs in Pregnancy and Lactation

CDC: Medications and Pregnancy

Hale's Medications and Mothers' Milk

LactMed (NLM TOXNET)

Reprotox and Reprorisk (Micromedex)

MotherToBaby

PSYCHIATRY

Diagnostic and Statistical Manual of Mental Disorders: Fifth edition (DSM-5)

REGULATORY AND BUSINESS DEVELOPMENT

FDA Center for Drug Evaluation and Research (CDER)

Pink Sheet

THERAPEUTICS AND DISEASE MANAGEMENT

DiPiro's Pharmacotherapy: A Pathophysiologic Approach

Handbook of Nonprescription Drugs: An Interactive Approach to Self-Care (OTC)

Koda-Kimble's Applied Therapeutics: The Clinical Use of Drugs

The Merck Manual

UpToDate

CDC: Diseases & Conditions

Harrison's Principles of Internal Medicine

Medscape

TRAVEL MEDICINE

CDC

- Health Information for International Travel (Yellow Book): for healthcare professionals who care for international travelers
- Travelers' Health: resources for travelers and healthcare professionals

International Society of Travel Medicine (ISTM)

International Association For Medical Assistance To Travelers (IAMAT)

SELECTING THE CORRECT "COLOR" DRUG REFERENCE

A number of important references are referred to by a color (see Study Tip Gal on next page). One of the more frequently accessed resources is the FDA's *Orange Book*, available online at www.accessdata.fda.gov/scripts/cder/ob/. This resource is used to determine if a generic substitution of a branded product is acceptable based on an AB rating, which indicates therapeutic equivalence to the brand.

"COLOR" DRUG REFERENCES

Orange Book (FDA)
List of approved drugs that can be interchanged with generics based on therapeutic equivalence.

Pink Book (CDC)
Information on epidemiology and vaccine-preventable diseases.

Pink Sheet (Pharma Intelligence)
News reports on regulatory, legislative, legal and business developments.

Purple Book (FDA)
List of biological drug products, including biosimilars.

Red Book, Pharmacy
Drug pricing information.

Red Book, Pediatrics (AAP)
Summaries of pediatric infectious diseases, antimicrobial treatment and vaccinations.

Yellow Book (CDC)
Information on the health risks of international travel, required vaccines and prophylaxis medications.

Green Book (FDA)
Information on approved animal drug products.

Below is an example of the methylphenidate extended-release tablet entry from the online *Orange Book* indicating therapeutic equivalence to *Concerta*.

Mkt. Status	Active Ingredient	Proprietary Name	Appl No	Dosage Form	Route	Strength	TE Code	RLD	RS	Applicant Holder
RX	METHYLPHENIDATE HYDROCHLORIDE	CONCERTA	N021121	TABLET, EXTENDED RELEASE	ORAL	18MG	AB	RLD		JANSSEN PHARMACEUTICALS INC
RX	METHYLPHENIDATE HYDROCHLORIDE	CONCERTA	N021121	TABLET, EXTENDED RELEASE	ORAL	27MG	AB	RLD		JANSSEN PHARMACEUTICALS INC
RX	METHYLPHENIDATE HYDROCHLORIDE	CONCERTA	N021121	TABLET, EXTENDED RELEASE	ORAL	36MG	AB	RLD		JANSSEN PHARMACEUTICALS INC
RX	METHYLPHENIDATE HYDROCHLORIDE	CONCERTA	N021121	TABLET, EXTENDED RELEASE	ORAL	54MG	AB	RLD	RS	JANSSEN PHARMACEUTICALS INC

LOCATING CLINICAL STUDY DATA AND RESEARCH SUMMARIES

There are a number of databases that pharmacists use to search for published studies, systematic reviews, including meta-analyses and review articles. Two of the more common databases are:

- *PubMed*: accesses MEDLINE (journal articles in medicine, nursing, dentistry, veterinary medicine, life sciences and more) and is a free service available from the NLM (www.ncbi.nlm.nih.gov/pubmed/).
- *Cochrane Library*: provides evidence-based information to guide clinical decision making. The database of Cochrane Systematic Reviews contains > 7,500 reviews (e.g., *Diagnostic Tests for Autism Spectrum Disorder (ASD) in Preschool Children)*. This important work is supported by government funds and donations, with no-cost access for users. Available at www.cochranelibrary.com.

CONSUMER RESOURCES

Pharmacists should be able to recommend reputable websites for patient-friendly information on medical conditions, and drug treatment.

- *Drugs.com* (www.drugs.com) and *RxList* (www.rxlist.com) provide drug monographs and other information (see earlier description in the General Drug Information Resources table). *Drugs.com* provides patient-level material on natural products, international drugs, drug use in pregnancy and breastfeeding, pill identifiers, information on disease states and drug interaction tools. *RxList.com* contains some of the same information.
- The CDC (www.CDC.gov) provides information on infectious diseases, immunizations, travelers health and has a symptom-checker.
- FDA For Consumers (www.fda.gov/ForConsumers/default.htm) provides comprehensive information on drugs (including recalls), food products, medical devices, vaccines, tobacco products and other topics that fall under the FDA's jurisdiction. Content can be selected by audience type (e.g., women, children or minority health).
- The U.S. Department of Health and Human Services website *Healthfinder.gov* (https://healthfinder.gov/) has a mission to encourage healthy living, through various topics (e.g., how to eat in a healthy manner, types of physical activity).
- *Mayo Clinic* (www.mayoclinic.org) provides comprehensive patient information for diseases, symptoms, tests and procedures, and drugs and supplements.
- *MedlinePlus* (medlineplus.gov/, from the NLM) has sections on health topics, drugs and supplements, health-related videos, lab tests and a medical encyclopedia, with images.
- *SafeMedication* (www.safemedication.com, from ASHP) includes medication tips and tools and a searchable database for patient-focused drug monographs, pulled from AHFS.
- *WebMD* (www.webmd.com) covers diseases, healthy living, pregnancy, prescription and OTC drug information, plus a pill identifier and interaction checker.

PRACTICE SCENARIOS

Fill in your answers below. Answers are located under the Student Resources tab at www.rxprep.com. Practice questions in the NAPLEX-style exam formats can be found in RxPrep's Drug References Test Bank.

WHERE CAN THE PHARMACIST LOCATE INFORMATION TO....

Recommend antibiotics for CAP treatment in a 34-year-old

Identify a blue oval tablet, F 8 on one side, 3 on the other side

Identify several medications brought from Mexico.

Find the common adverse effects from *Requip*

Locate the generic equivalent for *Plavix* 75 mg

Confirm that topiramate is indicated for migraine prophylaxis

Review the boxed warnings for oral isotretinoin

See if there are any biosimilars for filgrastim 300 mcg/0.5 mL

Check to see if DVT is a contraindication to *NuvaRing*

Review the required vaccines for a nurse

Locate the needle length & gauge for *Shingrix*

Find the AWP for a *Clomid* cash sale

Counsel a patient on the *Bevespi* inhaler

Recommend appropriate treatment for impetigo in a 6-year-old

Review recommended vaccinations for a traveler going to Ghana

Find a list of drugs that can harm a pregnant pharmacist's offspring

Dispose of an unused 500 mL chemo infusion safely

Identify what to include in a compounding log record

Locate air flow requirements for a sterile compounding room

Read about clinical pearls on *Keppra* for a seminar presentation

Locate off-label information for gabapentin use in restless legs syndrome

Check if it is safe to dispense *Sporanox* with *Altoprev*

Select an antibiotic for Strep throat for a mom who is breast-feeding

Find if ivermectin is available OTC

Find if oxybutynin comes in an extended-release formulation

CHAPTER CONTENT

Drug Formulation Considerations 91
Example: Olanzapine 91
Example: Ondansetron 92
Warning: Sweeteners Are Not Sweet for All 92
Select Medications in Unique Formulations 92
Self-Administered Injections 95
Patches 97
Patch Sites 97
Patch Frequency 97
Common Concerns with Patches 98

CONTENT LEGEND

= Study Tip Gal

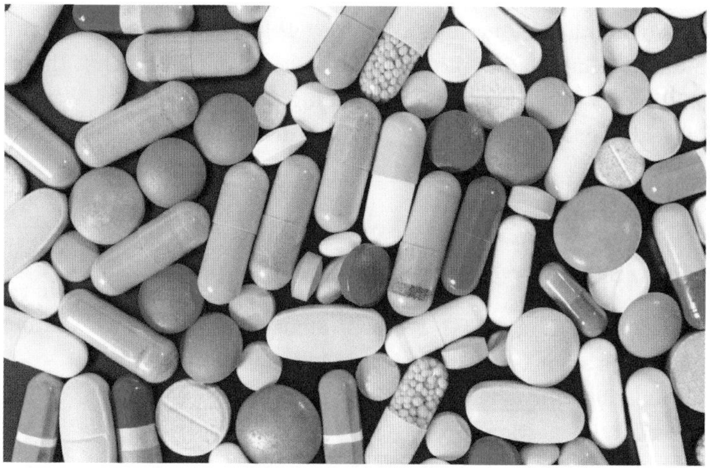

CHAPTER 6
LEARNING DRUG FORMULATIONS

DRUG FORMULATION CONSIDERATIONS

Compressed tablets are the most common formulation type and the least expensive to manufacture. Capsules are also relatively inexpensive to make. If a pharmaceutical company develops a drug in any other formulation, the cost will be higher and there must be a patient group that would benefit from the new formulation. For example, prednisolone 10 mg tablets cost < 25¢ per tablet. The branded oral disintegrating tablet (ODT), *Orapred ODT,* is ~$16 per tablet. The higher-priced formulation might be beneficial in a child with facial swelling who might choke on a hard tablet or who cannot swallow tablets.

It is helpful to recall drug formulation types by asking two questions:

1. Who typically uses this drug?
2. Would there be a reason to have this type of formulation for this patient population?

This can be useful on the exam when unsure if a particular formulation exists.

EXAMPLE: OLANZAPINE

Olanzapine is an antipsychotic with various formulations available: immediate-release (IR) tablet, ODT, short-acting injection and long-acting injection.

Who uses this drug?

People with schizophrenia, bipolar disorder or some type of psychosis.

Why are different formulations beneficial?

The majority of patients with schizophrenia discontinue antipsychotics. A long-acting injection can improve adherence. ODTs dissolve quickly in the mouth; they are useful to prevent the patient from hiding the medication in the mouth ("cheeking") and then spitting it out when no one is watching. The likelihood of "cheeking" is further reduced by giving a drink of water after the ODT. The short-acting injection works quickly and is useful for acute agitation.

EXAMPLE: ONDANSETRON

Ondansetron is a 5HT-3 receptor antagonist (5HT3-RA) used to prevent or treat nausea. It is available in various formulations: IR tablet, oral solution, ODT, oral film and short-acting injection.

Who uses this drug?

Patients receiving emetogenic drugs (e.g., chemotherapy), post-surgical patients or patients with any condition that causes nausea/vomiting.

Why are different formulations beneficial?

Oral medications will not be very effective when the patient is vomiting; an injection would be useful if the patient is in a medical setting. An ODT, oral film or injection can be given for nausea without vomiting. Dysphagia (difficulty swallowing) is common in patients receiving chemotherapy and other patients (e.g., post-stroke, elderly). It would be difficult to swallow tablets with painful esophageal ulcers, strictures or tumors. An oral solution would be preferred in many of these cases. Though tablets can sometimes be crushed and put down a nasogastric (NG) tube, oral solutions are ideal for giving medications via NG tube.

Another 5HT3-RA, granisetron, comes in a long-acting patch *(Sancuso)* that prevents chemotherapy-induced nausea for up to seven days. The patch is applied before the chemotherapy, since patches usually require time for the drug to be absorbed through the skin.

WARNING: SWEETENERS ARE NOT SWEET FOR ALL

Formulations that are exposed to taste buds often contain sweeteners (e.g., aspartame, saccharin), which are generally well-tolerated, with exceptions. Sorbitol metabolism produces gas, cramping and bloating in sensitive patients, including those with IBS. Phenylalanine is used in many ODT, chewable and granule medication formulations. It is a dangerous sweetener for those with phenylketonuria (PKU), a genetic defect in which the enzyme that degrades phenylalanine is absent. Lactose is the most commonly used excipient in drug formulations. It is tolerated by some, but not all, patients with lactose-intolerance. Sensitivity to lactose is variable and changes with age. Additional sweeteners and excipients are reviewed in the Compounding chapters.

SELECT MEDICATIONS IN UNIQUE FORMULATIONS

Medications are increasingly offered in new, unique formulations (e.g., *Onzetra Xsail*, a nasal powder for migraine or *Cotempla XR-ODT*, a long-acting ODT for ADHD). These formulations are reviewed in the disease state chapters of this book. The following tables summarize commonly encountered unique formulations with select examples.

FORMULATION	EXAMPLES	REASONS FOR USE
Oral		
ODTs Placed on the tongue and disintegrates rapidly in saliva Films that dissolve in the mouth are similar to ODTs (e.g., *Zuplenz* – ondansetron film)	*Lamictal ODT* – lamotrigine, for children *Remeron SolTab* – mirtazapine, for nausea, dysphagia *Zyprexa Zydis* – olanzapine, for non-adherence ondansetron ODT – for nausea, dysphagia	Dysphagia (difficulty swallowing) due to a variety of reasons. Paralysis of the throat muscles from stroke is the most common cause. Other causes of dysphagia include: esophagitis, esophageal tumors, ↓ LES pressure/reflux, facial swelling from an allergic reaction and conditions that worsen motor function, including Parkinson disease. Children are often too young to swallow tablets or capsules. Nausea can make it difficult to tolerate anything orally; some patients can take an ODT when they cannot swallow whole tablets/capsules due to nausea. If vomiting is present or is likely, a non-oral route should be used. Non-adherence: ODTs dissolve quickly. This can help with compliance since it is harder for uncooperative patients to spit the drug out.

FORMULATION	EXAMPLES	REASONS FOR USE
Sublingual (SL) or buccal delivery with a tablet, film, powder or spray	*Edluar* and *Intermezzo* – zolpidem SL tablets, fast onset *Nitrostat* – nitroglycerin SL tablet, fast onset *Subsys, Actiq, Fentora, Abstral* – fentanyl (various formulations), fast onset	Has same benefits of ODTs, and with SL/buccal absorption: Onset of action is faster than with a tablet or capsule that is swallowed; the drug is readily absorbed into the venous circulation right under the absorption site (e.g., under the tongue). Less drug is lost to gut degradation and first-pass metabolism.
Lozenges for oral mucosa drug administration	*Mycelex* – clotrimazole troche, for oral thrush	Used to treat a condition in the oral mucosa; the drug is held in the mouth while the troche slowly dissolves.
Chewable tablets	*Suprax* – cefixime, for children *Singulair* – montelukast, for children *Lamictal CD* – lamotrigine, for children	Primarily used for children who are unable to swallow tablets. A few chewable products are used by adults. Chewable calcium products are popular because calcium tablets are large and hard for many people to swallow. *Fosrenol* (a phosphate binder) must be chewed for the drug to bind phosphate in the gut.
Granules, powders or capsules that can be opened and sprinkled into soft food or water	**On Applesauce*** *Adderall XR* – dextroamphetamine/amphetamine ER *Coreg CR* – carvedilol *Dexilant* – dexlansoprazole *Focalin XR* – dexmethylphenidate *Namenda XR* – memantine *Nexium* – esomeprazole *Ritalin LA* – methylphenidate **Other Specific Instructions** *Cambia*- diclofenac potassium powder, in water *Creon* and other pancreatic enzyme products – pancrelipase, on soft food with low pH (applesauce, pureed pears or banana) *Depakote Sprinkles* – valproic acid, on soft food *Kadian* – morphine, on applesauce or soft food *Micro-K* – potassium, on applesauce or pudding *Questran, Questran Light* – cholestyramine, in 2-6 oz water or non-carbonated liquid *Singulair* – montelukast granules, in 5 mL baby formula or breast milk or in a spoonful of applesauce, carrots, rice or ice cream *Vyvanse* – lisdexamfetamine, in water, yogurt or orange juice	These formulations are primarily for geriatric and pediatric patients who have difficulty swallowing. Hospital implications: it is usually cheaper to give an oral medication via NG tube rather than converting to IV administration. Some medications are not available in IV formulations. Instruct the patient on the following: ■ Do not chew any long-acting pellets or beads that are emptied out from a capsule. ■ If capsule contents are mixed in food or liquid, do not let the mixture sit too long (take within the time directed). ■ Do not add to anything warm or hot (the contents will dissolve too quickly). *Always refer to the product labeling for instructions; not all capsule medications should be opened and administered (refer to long-acting capsules in this chapter). The medication should only be mixed in the specific foods/liquids that were studied, because the pH of the food/liquid could be critical. Many medications have specific instructions for oral vs NG tube administration.

FORMULATION	EXAMPLES	REASONS FOR USE
Long-acting oral tablets/ capsules	*Concerta* – methylphenidate *Detrol LA* – tolterodine Do not crush or chew any drug that has the following suffix that indicates it is a long-acting formulation: XL, XR, ER, LA, SR, CR, CRT, SA, TR, TD, or has 24 in the name, or the ending "cont" (for controlled release), or timecaps or sprinkles. **Osmotic Release Oral System (OROS)** *Concerta, Cardura XL, Procardia XL* and about a dozen other long-acting medications use an OROS to provide fast drug delivery, followed by an extended-release in one drug. Water from the gut is absorbed into the delivery system by osmosis, which increases the pressure inside and forces the drug out through a small opening. The tablet/capsule shell may be visible in the patient's stool (called a ghost tablet/capsule), but the drug has been released (important counseling).	Drugs may be designed to release slowly to avoid nausea or to provide a long-duration of action. Providing a smooth level of drug release over time reduces high "peaks" which reduces side effects (e.g., less drug hitting the "wrong" receptor) and provides a safe level of drug over the dosing interval. Note the danger if long-acting formulations are crushed: a fatal dose could be released. This includes ER opioids. Be sure to look for the suffix and counsel the patient. Some long-acting opioid capsules (e.g., *Kadian, Xtampza ER*, others) can be opened and the contents sprinkled on certain foods (discussed previously). The capsule contents should not be crushed or chewed. Always consult package labeling, as not all formulations have been studied in this way. ISMP's "Do Not Crush List" contains a list of drugs that should not be crushed. There are a few long-acting formulations that can be cut at the score line – but still not crushed (e.g., *Toprol XL, Sinemet CR*).
Nasal		
Nasal sprays	*Imitrex* – sumatriptan, fast onset, alternative to injection *Afrin* – oxymetazoline, local effect *Flonase Allergy Relief* – fluticasone, local effect	The nasal route has a faster onset than the GI route, and is useful for acute conditions that should be treated quickly, including pain. Nasal sprays bypass gut absorption; proteins that would get destroyed in the gut (e.g., calcitonin) can be given nasally. Some patients may absorb a drug better nasally vs. orally (e.g., patients lacking intrinsic factor needed for oral absorption of vitamin B12). *Afrin* and *Flonase* are used primarily to treat localized nasal symptoms.
Topical (can be used for localized or systemic effect) *Patches are discussed later in this chapter*		
Creams, ointments, gels, solutions for localized effect	*Voltaren* – diclofenac gel, treats pain near skin surface *Bactroban* – mupirocin ointment, for skin infections	Topical treatments used for topical conditions have a decreased incidence of systemic side effects and generally provide faster relief. Common conditions treated topically include muscle/joint pain, cold sores, acne, eczema, inflammation, mild infections, hair loss, rash, fungal infections.
Topicals for systemic effect	*AndroGel*, others – testosterone, alternative route (oral route destroys the hormone)	
Rectal		
Suppositories/enemas	*Rowasa* – mesalamine enema, treats local disease (distal ulcerative colitis) *Babylax* – glycerin suppository, treats constipation (stool is in rectum) *FeverAll* – acetaminophen suppository, avoids need for injection	Used either for localized treatment (e.g., constipation, hemorrhoids) or for systemic treatment (e.g., mesalamine rectal formulations for distal ulcerative colitis). Suppositories can be used when the patient is NPO and systemic treatment is needed (e.g., acetaminophen for treating pain or fever in an infant).

FORMULATION	EXAMPLES	REASONS FOR USE
Inhaled		
Oral inhalations that patients self-administer	See Asthma and COPD chapters	Inhaled medications provide immediate (rescue) and long-lasting (maintenance) benefits in lung disorders (e.g., asthma or COPD). The drug is delivered directly to the lungs and this minimizes systemic toxicities.
Injectable		
Injections that patients can self-administer (mostly SC)	*Forteo* – teriparatide *Imitrex* – sumatriptan, avoids worsening nausea (from migraine), fast onset Insulins, GLP-1 agonists – see Diabetes chapter *Lovenox* – enoxaparin *Tymlos* – abaloparatide	SC administration is used for rapid effect [for pain, opioid overdose reversal (with naloxone, *Evzio*)] or for drugs that would get destroyed or not absorbed if given by oral administration (e.g., enoxaparin, etanercept).
Long-acting intramuscular (IM) injections	*Abilify Maintena* – aripiprazole *Haldol* – haloperidol decanoate *Invega Sustenna* – paliperidone *Lupron Depot* – leuprolide *Risperdal Consta* – risperidone *Vivitrol* – naltrexone *Zyprexa Relprevv* – olanzapine	Various drugs come as long-acting injections to improve adherence (such as antipsychotics) or to ↓ the need for more frequent (painful) injections.
Intravenous (IV) injections	Many, acute care drugs	Bypasses the oral route for patients who are intubated or sedated; fast response, can achieve high concentrations, avoids loss of drug due to N/V.

SELF-ADMINISTERED INJECTIONS

Injections that patients give themselves are almost always given by subcutaneous (SC) injection. Intramuscular (IM) injection generally hurts more due to the longer needle length and subsequent muscle soreness. *EpiPen* is an IM injection, which is given in the thigh, for acute need (i.e., bronchoconstriction, wheezing).

Injection Sites

	ROOM TEMP	INJECTION LOCATION	FREQUENCY
Refrigerated*			
Glatiramer (*Copaxone*)	Up to 30 d	Abdomen, arms, hips, thighs	Daily, or 3x/week
Etanercept (*Enbrel*)	Up to 14 d	Thigh (preferred), abdomen, upper arm	Weekly
Adalimumab (*Humira*)	Up to 14 d	Abdomen, thigh	Every other week
Certolizumab pegol (*Cymzia*)	Requires reconstitution Prefilled syringes: up to 7 d	Abdomen, thigh	Every 2-4 weeks
Golimumab (*Simponi*)	Up to 30 d	Thigh, lower abdomen (below navel), upper arm	Monthly
Teriparatide (*Forteo*)	Minimize, should be stored refrigerated at all times	Thigh, abdomen	Daily
Abaloparatide (*Tymlos*)	Up to 30 d	Abdomen	Daily
Insulin**	Variable	Abdomen, thigh, buttocks, upper arms	Variable

Not Refrigerated			
Enoxaparin *(Lovenox)*		Abdomen > 1 inch from navel	Once or twice daily
Fondaparinux *(Arixtra)*		Abdomen > 1 inch from navel	Once or twice daily
Methotrexate (*Otrexup*, others)		Abdomen, thigh	Weekly
Sumatriptan *(Imitrex)*		Upper arm, thigh	PRN, at first sign of migraine
Sumatriptan *(Sumavel DosePro)*		Abdomen > 2 inch from navel, thigh	PRN, at first sign of migraine

**Let sit at room temp for 15-30 min prior to injecting. **See Diabetes chapter.*

EpiPen is stored at room temp, IM injection into outer thigh, and held to skin for 3 secs; see Drug Allergies & Adverse Reactions chapter.

Injection Basics

- Inject at least 1-inch away from previous injection site.
- Some injections "click" when the needle enters the skin and/or "click" when the injection is complete.
- If single-use, discard needle or entire assembly (with attached needle) in sharps container.
- Do not rub skin near anticoagulant injections; will bruise badly (enoxaparin, fondaparinux).
- Do not use any device to heat up cold injections; let sit at room temp for ~20 minutes.
- Liquids can degrade; if solution is discolored or contains particles, do not use. Do not use beyond expiration date.

STEP 1	STEP 2	STEP 3	STEP 4	STEP 5
Wash hands. 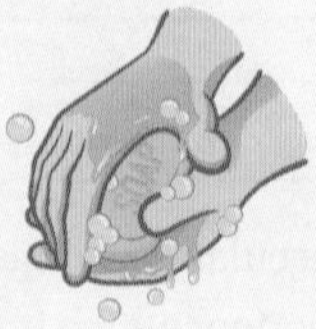	Prepare injection 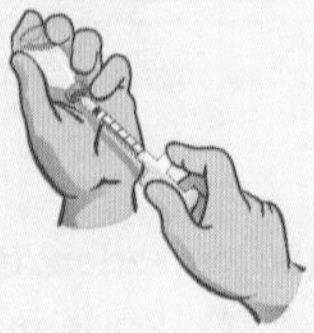	Select and clean injection site 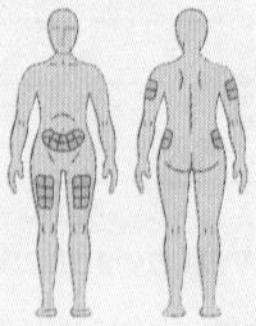	Inject 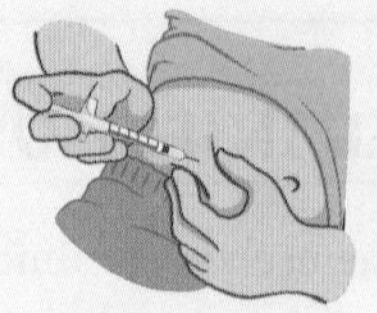	Discard syringes, pen needles or entire assembly in sharps container 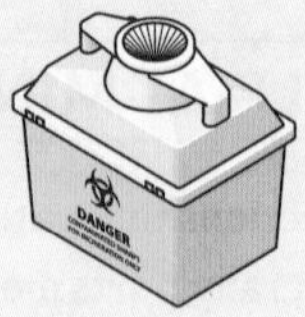

PATCHES

PATCH SITES

Common sites for patch application, including *Duragesic* and *Catapres-TTS* include these sites, on either side of the body:

- The chest (upper)
- The back (upper and lower)
- The upper arm (on the part facing out)
- The flanks (sides of the body, abdomen level)

Exelon is the same sites, but no flanks. *Butrans* is the same sites, except rather than the sides of the body near the abdomen, it is applied to the sides, level to the chest. Some pain patches (such as *Flector, Lidoderm* and *Salonpas)* treat local pain, and are applied over the painful area/s. Never apply patches to skin that is oily, or irritated in any manner. Patches have to be smoothed out on the skin, and then pressed down for a number of seconds, usually 10 – 30 seconds (*Duragesic* is 30 seconds). The patches in the figures have unusual application sites. *Daytrana* is applied on the hip, alternating right and left hips daily. *Transderm Scop* is applied behind the ear, at least four hours before needed, alternating ears Q72H. Sites where the patch is placed, with the exception of the topical pain patches, should be alternated. Patches can irritate the skin.

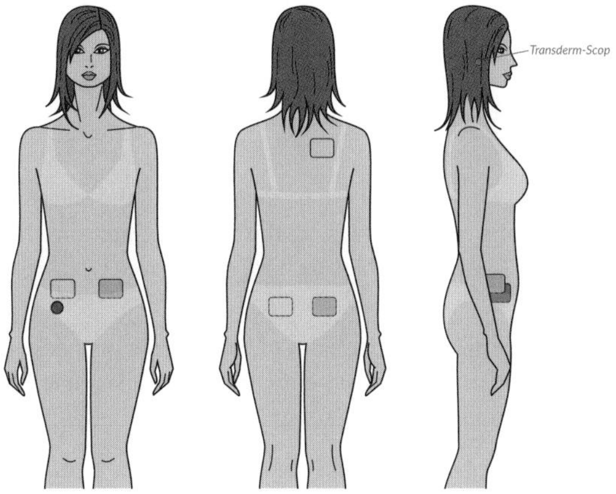

Xulane (back, abdomen, or buttock)
Daytrana (hip)
Oxybutynin (abdomen, hip, or buttock)
Vivelle-Dot (lower abdomen)
Transderm-Scop (behind the ear)

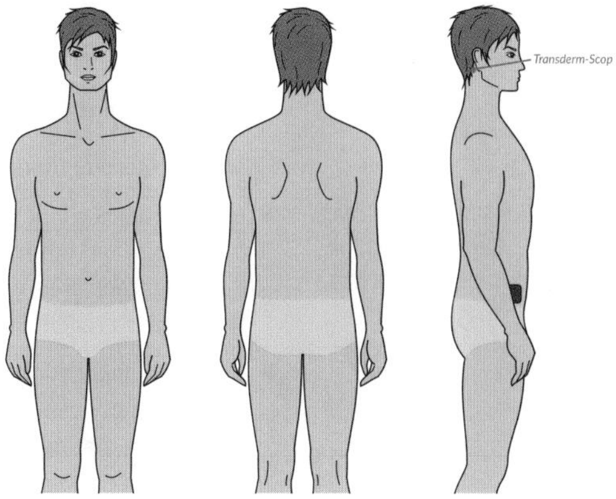

Daytrana (hip)
Transderm-Scop (behind the ear)

PATCH FREQUENCY

Daily
Methylphenidate *(Daytrana)*: QAM, 2 hours prior to school

Nicotine *(NicoDerm CQ)*

Rivastigmine *(Exelon)*

Rotigotine *(Neupro)*

Selegiline *(Emsam)*

Testosterone *(Androderm)*: nightly, not on scrotum

Daily (With Special Instructions)
Lidocaine *(Lidoderm)*: 1-3 patches on for 12 hours, then off for 12 hours (as needed)

Nitroglycerin *(Minitran, Nitro-Dur)*: on for 12-14 hours, then off for 10-12 hours/day

Twice Daily
Diclofenac *(Flector)*

Twice Weekly
Estradiol* *(Alora, Vivelle-Dot)*

Oxybutynin *(Oxytrol)*

Weekly
Buprenorphine *(Butrans)*

Clonidine *(Catapres-TTS)*

Estradiol* *(Climara, Menostar)*

Estradiol/levonorgestrel *(ClimaraPro)*

Ethinyl estradiol/norelgestromin *(Xulane)*: weekly for 3 weeks, off for the 4th week

Other
Fentanyl *(Duragesic)*: Q72H, if it wears off after 48 hours, change to Q48H

Scopolamine *(Transderm Scop)*: Q72H, if needed

**Estradiol patches may be used on continuous or cyclic (3 weeks on, 1 week off) schedules at the frequency listed above.*

COMMON CONCERNS WITH PATCHES

QUESTION	RESPONSE
Can I cut the patch into pieces?	■ Usually no, except *Lidoderm*, which is designed to be cut and applied over the painful regions.
Can the patch be exposed to heat from an electric blanket, heating pad, or body temperature > 38 °C (> 100.4 °F)?	■ Avoid heat exposure with most patches. Heat causes rapid absorption of the medication from the patch, resulting in toxicity. With fentanyl and buprenorphine, this can be quickly toxic (fatal).
The patch is bothering my skin. What can I do?	■ Alternate the application site. An alternative site (if permitted) may be beneficial. ■ The skin should not be shaved shortly before applying; shaving is irritating to the skin. If needed, cut the hair short with a scissors. A topical steroid, such as hydrocortisone, can be applied after the patch is removed.
Which patches need to be removed prior to an MRI?	■ Patches containing metal (e.g., aluminum) need to be removed prior to an MRI or the metal will burn the skin. ❑ Clonidine *(Catapres-TTS)* ❑ Diclofenac *(Flector)* ❑ Estrogen (some, including *Alora)* ❑ Rotigotine *(Neupro)* ❑ Scopolamine *(Transderm Scop)* ❑ Testosterone *(Androderm)*
The patch does not stick (it falls or peels off). Can the patch be covered with tape if it will not stick?	■ Most patches cannot be covered with tape. A few patches can be taped around the edges. Fentanyl *(Duragesic)* and buprenorphine *(Butrans)* can be covered only with the permitted adhesive film dressings *Bioclusive* or *Tegaderm*. *Catapres-TTS* comes with its own adhesive cover, which goes over the patch to hold it in place.
Where is the patch applied?	■ Common application sites include the upper chest or upper/sides of back (below the neck), upper thigh or upper outer arm (see picture in this chapter). Always verify with product labeling. Most require alternating sites to reduce skin irritation. ❑ *Daytrana* is applied on the hip, alternating right and left hips daily. ❑ *Transderm Scop* is applied behind the ear, alternating ears Q72H. ❑ Estrogen patches are mostly applied on the lower abdomen; some can be applied to upper buttock. Never to breasts. ❑ Testosterone patch is never applied to the scrotum (testicles and surrounding sac). ❑ Some pain patches (such as *Flector, Lidoderm* and *Salonpas)* are applied over the painful area/s. ❑ Systemic pain patches, such as *Duragesic*, are applied to the chest, back, flank or upper arm.
How do I dispose of used patches?	■ In most cases, remove and fold the patch to press adhesive surfaces together for disposal. Used drugs should be disposed of according to the manufacturer's instructions, which can include throwing it away in a lidded container or flushing it down the toilet. ■ Some highly potent narcotic patches *(Duragesic, Butrans, Daytrana)* can be fatal, especially if ingested by a child or pet. For these drugs, the FDA and/or manufacturer may recommend flushing the used patch down the toilet to remove it from the home immediately.
Where is the drug located?	■ The drug can be in a raised pouch, a reservoir (containing a gel or a semi-solid form) or it is directly incorporated into the adhesive of the patch (the side that adheres to the patient's skin).

CHAPTER CONTENT

Background 99
IV Drug Delivery 99
Venous Catheters 100
Peripheral Lines 100
Central Lines 100
Incompatibilities 100
Chemical and Physical Incompatibility 101
Container Incompatibility 101
Drugs with Leaching/Adsorption/ Absorption Issues with PVC Containers 101
Common Drugs with Diluent Solution Requirements 101
Diluent Incompatibility 101
Drug-Drug Incompatibility 101
High-Risk Incompatibilities 102
Reference Table Interpretation 102
Filters 103
Common Drugs with Filter Requirements 103
Temperature & Stability 103
Do Not Refrigerate 103
Protect From Light During Administration 104

We gratefully acknowledge the assistance of Michael J. Freudiger, PharmD, APh, BCPS, BCGP, in preparing this chapter.

CONTENT LEGEND

= Key Drug Guy

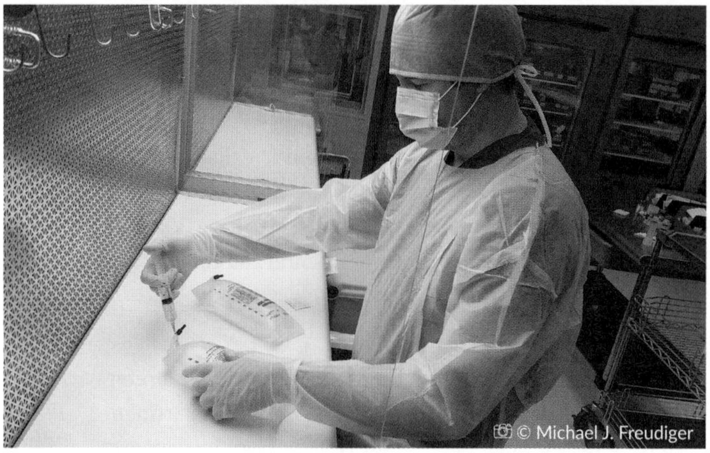

© Michael J. Freudiger

CHAPTER 7
LEARNING IV MEDICATIONS

BACKGROUND

Enteral administration [through the gastrointestinal (GI) tract] is the preferred route for drug delivery. When the enteral route is not feasible, a parenteral route (outside of the GI tract) is used. Common routes for parenteral drug administration include intravenous (IV), intramuscular, subcutaneous or transdermal administration. There are other parenteral routes that are used for specific purposes; a couple that are well-known to pharmacists include intra-articular (into the joint) and intrathecal (into the space under the arachnoid membrane of the brain/spinal cord). The intrathecal route is often used by anesthesiologists and for some chemotherapy, but when contraindicated (e.g., with vincristine), intrathecal administration can be fatal.

IV DRUG DELIVERY

The IV route is required in hospitalized patients who are NPO (not able to take anything by mouth) and with gastrointestinal conditions when the gut needs to be bypassed (e.g., surgery, malabsorption). Drugs with poor oral availability are often given IV (e.g., vancomycin for conditions other than *C. difficile* treatment). In a critical situation where fast (stat) onset is required (e.g., use of a vasopressor to quickly raise cardiac output), IV administration is a must. Oral medications require gut dissolution and absorption, which takes time.

This chapter focuses on the aspects of intravenous administration that are important to the pharmacist, including venous access (IV lines), compatibility and stability issues and administration requirements.

VENOUS CATHETERS

A catheter is a piece of plastic tubing that goes into a part of the body to put in fluids, or take them out (e.g., with a urinary catheter). A catheter inserted into a vein is called a venous catheter, and is used for fluid and drug delivery. A venous catheter is called a line, and the patient is said to have IV-access. Lines come in two primary types: peripheral and central.

PERIPHERAL LINES

Percutaneous means through the skin, and peripheral refers to locations away from the body's central compartment, including the arms and legs. Most IV drugs can be delivered through percutaneous, peripheral venous catheters that are inserted into smaller veins. Common veins used for peripheral venous catheters are the cephalic vein in the arm and the saphenous vein near the ankle.

Peripheral lines are simpler and less expensive to insert than central lines, but they have limitations. Administering drugs into smaller veins can cause phlebitis (vein irritation), venous thrombosis (clots) and interstitial fluid extravasation; this is when the catheter becomes dislodged from the vein and the infusion contents enter surrounding tissue.

CENTRAL LINES

A central line empties into a larger vein, and the contents are quickly diluted. Central lines provide secure, long-term vascular (i.e., blood vessel) access and are required for administration of highly concentrated drugs (e.g., potassium chloride > 20 mEq/ 100 mL), long-term antibiotics (e.g., to treat osteomyelitis), for delivery of toxic drugs that would cause severe phlebitis [e.g., chemotherapy, especially with vesicants (see next column)] and for drugs with a pH or osmolality that is not close to blood pH or osmolality (e.g., parenteral nutrition). Central lines are sometimes used for patients with poor peripheral venous access (e.g., patients with IV drug addiction with collapsed veins). Additional benefits with a central line are the ability to administer higher volumes and use faster infusion rates.

Central Line Placement

There are options with central line placement. A catheter can be placed directly through the skin and into a large vessel [e.g., into the superior vena cava (near the top of the chest) or into the jugular or femoral vein]. Dialysis catheters are placed in this manner. The other option is placing the line into a smaller vein and advancing (pushing) the catheter through the vein until the tip ends in the superior vena cava (where the infusion contents will be released). This is called a peripherally inserted central catheter (PICC). It is simpler to insert a PICC line than a direct central line; a PICC line can be inserted at the bedside, and a quick x-ray will confirm that the tip has reached the right location.

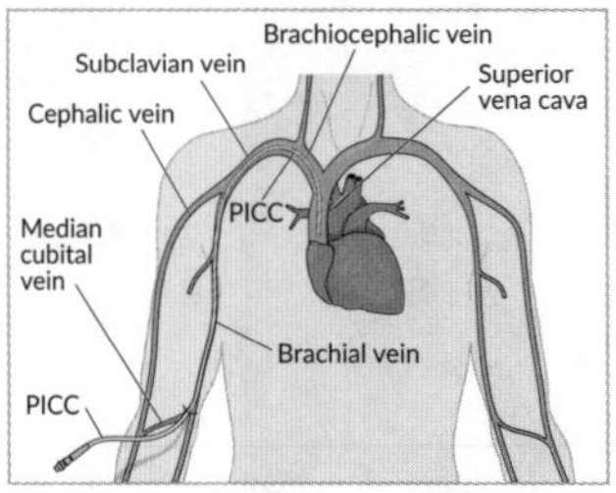

A peripherally inserted central catheter (PICC) empties into the superior vena cava from a line placed into a peripheral vein (see figure on left).

Vesicants are Safer with a Central Line

A vesicant is a drug that will cause severe tissue damage if the catheter tip falls out of the vein, allowing the drug to seep into the surrounding tissues. Vesicants are preferentially administered through a central line because the line is less likely to become dislodged from the vein. Vesicants include vasopressors (e.g., dopamine, norepinephrine), anthracyclines (e.g., doxorubicin), vinca alkaloids (e.g., vincristine, vinblastine), digoxin, foscarnet, nafcillin, mannitol, mitomycin and promethazine.

PROMETHAZINE CAN CAUSE SEVERE TISSUE INJURY

Some hospitals have removed it from formulary due to this risk.

Not to be given intra-arterial or SC; IM is preferred but this has tissue injury risk, too.

Minimally: do not give to children < 2 years, dilute the drug, limit the dose and concentration and be careful.

INCOMPATIBILITIES

The pharmacist is the primary resource for questions concerning parenteral medication administration. There are many drugs, and drug information changes; reputable resources are required. The *Handbook on Injectable Drugs* (commonly called *Trissel's*) or the *King Guide to Parenteral Admixtures* (commonly called *King's*) are the primary compatibility and stability resources, along with the drug's package insert. Some drug information databases, including *Micromedex, Clinical Pharmacology and Lexicomp*, use the IV compatibility information from *Trissel's* (see Learning Drug References chapter). A reputable group of pharmacists prepare lists of compatibility issues on a periodic basis that are published in *Pharmacy Practice News* and in *Hospital Pharmacy*. These lists are used for handy reference purposes; the pharmacist may need to verify that the information has not changed.

CHEMICAL AND PHYSICAL INCOMPATIBILITY

Chemical incompatibility causes drug degradation or toxicity due to a hydrolysis, oxidation or decomposition reaction.

Physical incompatibilities occur between a drug and one of the following:

- The container (e.g., polyvinyl chloride containers)
- The diluent (solution) (e.g., dextrose or saline)
- Another drug

CONTAINER INCOMPATIBILITY

DEHP from the Container

The majority of polyvinyl chloride (PVC) containers use diethylhexyl phthalate (DEHP) as a "plasticizer" to make the plastic bag more flexible. DEHP can leach from the container and into the solution. DEHP is toxic, and can harm the liver and testes.

Container Absorption/Adsorption

Absorption occurs when drug moves into the PVC container and adsorption occurs when drug adheres (or "sticks") to the container; either will reduce the drug's concentration.

Alternative (Non-PVC) Containers

Drugs that have leaching or absorption/adsorption issues with PVC containers can be placed in polyolefin, polypropylene or glass containers (although glass is heavy and can break).

Insulin and PVC Containers

Insulin adsorbs to PVC. Clinicians adjust the rate of insulin infusions to obtain blood glucose control, regardless of the type of IV container and tubing that is used. It might be useful to know that insulin does adsorb to PVC for testing purposes.

DRUGS WITH LEACHING/ ADSORPTION/ABSORPTION ISSUES WITH PVC CONTAINERS

KEY DRUGS

These drugs have sorption or leaching issues with PVC:

Lorazepam
Amiodarone
Tacrolimus
Taxanes*
Insulin
Nitroglycerin

Remember: **L**each **A**bsorbs **T**o **T**ake **I**n **N**utrients

*Paclitaxel and most taxanes require non-PVC. Exception: Paclitaxel-albumin bound *(Abraxane)* can be placed into PVC.

Others:
Carmustine
Cyclosporine
Ixabepilone
Sufentanil
Temsirolimus
Teniposide
Thiopental

Sufentanil is an IV opioid used in acute care settings. Besides sufentanil, the other drugs that cannot be put into PVC containers are chemo drugs.

COMMON DRUGS WITH DILUENT SOLUTION REQUIREMENTS

KEY DRUGS

SALINE (No Dextrose)

Remember:
A DIAbetic **C**an't **E**at **P**ie

Ampicillin
Daptomycin *(Cubicin)*
Infliximab *(Remicade)*
Ampicillin/Sulbactam *(Unasyn)*
Caspofungin *(Cancidas)*
Ertapenem *(Invanz)*
Phenytoin *(Dilantin)*

DEXTROSE (No Saline)

Remember: **O**bese **B**aker **A**voids **S**alt

Oxaliplatin
Bactrim – SMX/TMP
Amphotericin B (all)
S*ynercid* – Quinupristin/Dalfopristin

Others:

Saline (No Dextrose)
Abatacept *(Orencia)*
Azacitidine *(Vidaza)*
NS
Belimumab *(Benlysta)*
Bevacizumab *(Avastin)*
Idarucizumab *(Praxbind)*
Iron Sucrose *(Venofer)*
Sodium Ferric Gluconate Complex *(Ferrlecit)*
Natalizumab *(Tysabri)*
Trastuzumab *(Herceptin)*

Dextrose (No Saline)
Carfilzomib *(Kyprolis)*
Mycophenolate *(CellCept IV)*
Pentamidine

DILUENT INCOMPATIBILITY

When drugs are put into solution for IV administration in the pharmacy, they are commonly placed into 50 mL or larger IV piggybacks that contain 5% dextrose (D5W) or 0.9% sodium chloride (normal saline, NS). For most drugs, either solution is acceptable, but some drugs cannot be put into dextrose, and others cannot be put into saline (see Key Drugs Guy above).

DRUG-DRUG INCOMPATIBILITY

Hospitalized patients most often are receiving IV fluids with multiple IV medications. In order to avoid turning the patient into a pin cushion, the lines of infusion bags are often joined together in a Y-site and run together in the same line during administration.

Y-Site Administration: Mixing Drugs in the Line

INTERMITTENT WITH CONTINUOUS THERAPY SET-UP

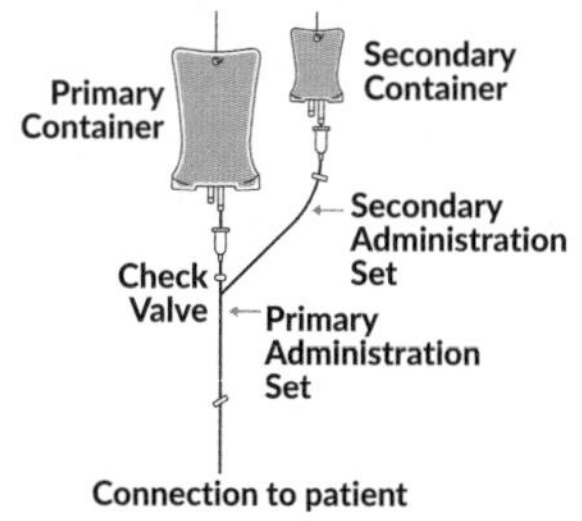

A Y-site describes the shape that forms when the lines (from different IV containers) are joined prior to entering the patient. Often, the large (1 liter) container is the patient's fluids and the smaller IV piggybacks contain the drugs. Since the drugs mix together briefly in the common portion of the IV tubing, it is important that the drugs and solutions are compatible with Y-site administration.

Additive Compatibility: Mixing Drugs in the Same Container

Additive compatibility needs to be confirmed when putting multiple drugs together in the same container or syringe. Additive compatibility and Y-site compatibility are listed separately in *Trissel's* and other drug reference sources.

There are more compatibility issues with mixing drugs in the same container (compared to Y-site administration) because the drugs are together for a longer period of time. Y-site incompatibilities are important because this type of administration is common, and many drugs that cannot be mixed in the same container are compatible when the drugs are mixed together for a short period in the line.

HIGH-RISK INCOMPATIBILITIES

A dangerous example of incompatibility involves ceftriaxone and calcium. Ceftriaxone cannot be mixed with any calcium-containing solutions due to the risk of precipitates. Lactated Ringer's contains calcium and cannot be mixed with ceftriaxone, including Y-site administration. This combination must be avoided in all age groups; neonates have the highest risk for lethal effects.

Calcium and phosphate are the Romeo and Juliet of the IV pharmacy world. They will meet, fall in love, bind together, and the resulting precipitate kills the patient. Methods to prevent calcium-phosphate precipitate when preparing parenteral nutrition are discussed in Calculations III chapter.

Amphotericin B and sodium bicarbonate are incompatible with the majority of IV drugs with any type of IV administration. The common hospital drug piperacillin/tazobactam forms a precipitate when it mixes with acyclovir, amphotericin B and many other IV drugs.

Heparin is incompatible when administered with many drugs, including those which are often given concurrently in a patient requiring heparin (e.g., nitroglycerin, alteplase and hydromorphone). Caspofungin, another common hospital drug for treating *Candida* infections, has many Y-site incompatibilities. All of the IV quinolones are incompatible with Y-site infusion of many drugs. Information is extensive for incompatibilities; there are many others.

BEWARE!

Mixing Together Can Be Fatal

Risk of precipitates→ emboli→ fatality

Calcium & Ceftriaxone*

Calcium & Phosphate**

*Lactated Ringer's contains calcium.

**When calcium and phosphate are both put into PN, methods must be used to reduced the risk of a precipitate; see the PN section in Calculations.

REFERENCE TABLE INTERPRETATION

The tables shown in this section are similar to tables that a pharmacist would need to interpret to check drug compatibility. The reference drug is listed in the table (cefepime, in the example below). The drug tested with it for compatibility issues is listed in the row below (gentamicin). A pharmacist can check to see if cefepime can be mixed with gentamicin in the same container. The table below reports that cefepime and gentamicin are incompatible (I in the last column) when mixed together in either D5W or NS, at the concentrations listed. In addition to the C/I rating, the remarks include that a precipitate had formed.

Cefepime

DRUG	MFR	CONC/L	MFR	CONC/L	TEST SOLN	REMARKS	REF	C/I
Gentamicin	ES	1.2 g	BR	40 g	D5W, NS	Cloudiness forms in 18 hr at room temp	588	I

C = compatible; I = incompatible

Y-Site Injection Compatibility (1:1 Mixture)

In this next example, a pharmacist can check if cefepime can be given in the same line when gentamicin is infusing (Y-site administration). The pharmacist will find that cefepime and gentamicin are compatible for Y-site administration at the concentrations listed, indicated by the "C" in the far right column, and by the remarks.

Cefepime

DRUG	MFR	CONC	MFR	CONC	REMARKS	REF	C/I
Gentamicin	ES	6 mg/mL	BMS	120 mg/mL	Physically compatible with less than 10% cefepime loss. Gentamicin was not tested.	2212	C

C = compatible; I = incompatible

FILTERS

In-line filters (attached to the IV tubing) are used with drugs that have a risk of particulates, precipitates, crystals, contaminants or entrapped air in the final solution. The size of the filter required is determined by the size of the particles to be removed. The majority of drugs in which filters are necessary use a 0.22 micron filter (1 micron = 1/1,000 mm); another common filter size is 1.2 microns which is used for lipids. Some drugs come packaged with the required filter. If compounding IV medications packaged in glass ampules, filter needles or filter straws are used to prevent particulates from entering the IV bag and a filter may be required in the line. Parenteral nutrition is filtered with a 0.22 micron filter, which will catch a calcium-phospate particulate. If lipids are included, the filter size will need to be larger.

Some drugs must not be filtered due to the size of the drug particle, including many liposomal formulations of chemotherapy drugs.

TEMPERATURE & STABILITY

A drug that is "stable" will be stable only at a given concentration, for a certain time, at a certain temperature and with a certain degree of light exposure.

Time in Solution

Solutions decompose faster than solid (e.g., powder) formulations. The likelihood of a chemical reaction that would degrade the drug increases with time. Compatibility concerns due to longer infusion times have become an important issue in recent years with piperacillin/tazobactam (*Zosyn*) extended infusions. The same drug is commonly used with shorter infusions, without stability issues. The longer infusion period is used to increase time above the minimum inhibitory concentration (T > MIC) in order to counter drug resistance with nosocomial pathogens, including *Pseudomonas*, *Enterobacter* and *Acinetobacter*. The higher T > MIC is beneficial, but the longer infusion times result in more compatibility issues. Interactions with various antibiotics (e.g., piperacillin/tazobactam, azithromycin, ciprofloxacin, tobramycin, vancomycin), insulin and some of the vasopressors occur more commonly when given as a longer infusion.

Temperature

Higher temperatures speed up chemical reactions. The majority of IV drugs are kept cold in order to permit longer stability (i.e., a longer period until the beyond-use-date). There are exceptions; for example, furosemide and phenytoin crystallize if kept cold, and are stored at room temperature. See the Key Drugs Guy to the right of IV drugs that do not require refrigeration.

Light Exposure

Light exposure causes photo-degradation, which destroys some drugs, and in some cases, increases a drug's toxicity (e.g., nitroprusside). Many medications should be protected from light during storage to avoid degradation. Some medications are supplied in amber (light-protected) vials, and others are stored in the original packaging (foil overwrap or box) until needed. A small number of drugs are so light-sensitive that they require protection from light during administration. Pharmacy staff dispense these medications with a light-protective cover. In some cases, light-protective tubing (generally amber-colored) is needed. See the Key Drugs Guy on the following page for a list of photosensitive drugs that require light-protection during administration.

COMMON DRUGS WITH FILTER REQUIREMENTS

KEY DRUGS

That's my **GAL, PLAT**
(who's head is flat)

Golimumab *(Simponi)*
Amiodarone
Lorazepam*

Phenytoin*
Lipids—1.2 micron**
Amphotericin B (lipid formulations)**
Taxanes, except docetaxel

*Phenytoin & lorazepam require filters when administered by continuous infusion; a filter is not required for IV push.

**Larger pore size filter required; ampho: prepare using a 5 micron filter

Others:

Abatacept *(Orencia)*

Abciximab *(ReoPro)*

Infliximab *(Remicade)*

Isavuconazonium *(Cresemba)*

Mannitol *(Osmitrol)*

Thiotepa

(& some albumin products require a filter)

DO NOT REFRIGERATE

KEY DRUGS

Remember: **D**ear **S**weet **P**harmacist, **F**reezing **M**akes **M**e **E**dgy!

Dexmedetomidine *(Precedex)**

Sulfamethoxazole/Trimethoprim *(Bactrim)*

Phenytoin – crystallizes

Furosemide – crystallizes*

Metronidazole

Moxifloxacin *(Avelox)*

Enoxaparin *(Lovenox)*

*Optional: diluted *Precedex* and furosemide can be kept cold.

Others:

Acetaminophen *(Ofirmev)*

Acyclovir – crystallizes

Deferoxamine *(Desferal)* – precipitates

Levetiracetam *(Keppra)*

Pentamidine – crystallizes

Valproate

Do Not Shake/Agitate

Agitation destroys some drugs, including hormones and other proteins. Drugs that are easily destroyed include albumin, alteplase, immune globulins, insulins, rasburicase and some vaccines, including zoster. Quinupristin/Dalfopristin *(Synercid)* and etanercept *(Enbrel)* form a foam and should only be swirled when reconstituting. Do not shake; wait for the foam to dissolve.

Check Solutions for Color Changes

Most intravenous medications are clear and colorless. In some cases discoloration can be of little or no consequence. However, in most cases, discoloration indicates oxidation or another type of decomposition.

PROTECT FROM LIGHT DURING ADMINISTRATION

KEY DRUGS

Remember: **P**rotect **E**very **N**ecessary **M**ed from **D**aylight

Phytonadione (vitamin K; *Mephyton)*
Epoprostenol *(Flolan)*
Nitroprusside *(Nitropress)*
Micafungin *(Mycamine)*
Doxycycline

Others:

Ampho B Deoxycholate

Anthracyclines

Dacarbazine (if extravasates, protect exposed tissues from light)

Thiotepa

Pentamidine

DRUG	DO NOT USE WITH COLOR CHANGE	NOTES
Chlorpromazine	Darker than slight yellow	Slight yellow: potency retained, okay to use
Dacarbazine	Pink	
Dobutamine		Oxidation turns the solution slightly pink, but potency is not lost.
Dopamine	Darker than slight yellow	Slight yellow: potency retained, okay to use Extravasation antidote: phentolamine
Epinephrine	Pink, then brown	
Isoproterenol	Pink or darker	Damaged by air, light, heat
Morphine	Dark	
Nitroprusside	Orange → brown → blue	Blue indicates nearly complete dissociation to cyanide. Antidote: *Cyanokit*
Norepinephrine	Brown or any discoloration	Normal color: yellow/orange
Tigecycline	Green/black	

IV Drugs that Come as Colored Solutions (i.e., not clear)

DRUG	COLOR OF IV FLUID	SKIN AND SECRETIONS DISCOLORATION
Anthracyclines (e.g., doxorubicin)	Red 	Sweat and urine
Rifampin	Red 	Body fluids and teeth
Methotrexate	Yellow 	None
Multivitamins for Infusion (MVI)	Yellow 	None
Tigecycline	Yellow/Orange 	Teeth (if used during teeth development)
Mitoxantrone	Blue 	Skin, eyes, urine
IV Iron, various	Brown 	Urine

Check Solutions for Particulates

The clinician (or the patient if using a self-injectable) should always check parenteral solutions for particulate matter. If particulates are present, the drug should be discarded.

Select Guidelines/References

Handbook on Injectable Drugs, 19th Ed. American Society of Health-System Pharmacists. 2016.

King Guide to Parenteral Admixtures. https://www.kingguide.com/online.html (accessed 2019 April 16).

CHAPTER CONTENT

Background 106
The Patient Medical Record 106
Electronic Health Records 106
Sections of the Patient Medical Record 107
Requirements for Reimbursement: Documentation and Quality of Care 107
The SOAP Note Format 108
Subjective 108
Objective 108
Temperature Conversion 108
Select Drugs and Conditions that Alter Vital Signs 109
Assessment 110
Plan 110
Military Time 110
Answering Case-Based Questions on the Exam 110
Identifying Medication Therapy Problems 110
How to Look for Medication Problems in a Patient Case 110
Matching Drugs to Medical Problems 111
Questions About the Medication Profile 111
Recommending Drug Therapy 112
Patient Communication 112
Health Literacy 112
Effective Communication and Education Strategies 112
Example Electronic Health Record SOAP Note 113

CONTENT LEGEND

= Study Tip Gal   = Required Formula

CHAPTER 8
ANSWERING CASE-BASED EXAM QUESTIONS

BACKGROUND

Increased use of electronic health records (EHRs) provides pharmacists with greater access to patient-specific information, including labs, test results and progress notes from other healthcare providers. Pharmacists must be prepared to effectively use all of this information to make decisions about drug therapy.

Questions on NAPLEX are presented mainly in a case-based format. Some of the information provided in the case will be needed to correctly answer the questions. The goal is to assess whether the pharmacist can make the best choices for a specific patient vs. simply recalling facts. This better reflects the role of pharmacists in healthcare today.

This chapter reviews the patient medical record and discusses how to use the information to correctly answer case-based questions on the exam.

THE PATIENT MEDICAL RECORD

ELECTRONIC HEALTH RECORDS

The patient medical record (PMR) provides complete documentation of a patient's medical history at a particular institution. The PMR can be referred to using older terminology such as the medical record or the patient chart. These terms are from the era of paper records, when all records of the patient's medical care were gathered into ring binders. Paper charts remain in some healthcare settings, but are being phased out and replaced by EHRs. Once implemented, EHRs improve accuracy and efficiency.

The EHR is quicker and easier to review. For example, if a patient is admitted to the hospital with an elevated SCr, the EHR provides current and previous lab results (by selecting a date range that can go back years in time) which are used to determine if this is a new or an old finding, and what recent work-up has been completed. With paper charts, time is required to look back and compile this history or to gather history with calls and faxes, papers can be missing (sometimes the entire chart can be lost) and time is required to transport the chart to wherever the patient is going next. Labs and tests are often duplicated because it may be easier to reorder them rather than locating them in the paper records. Procedures with results recorded on paper can be quickly scanned into the EHR. EHRs allow providers to have immediate access to information when they are off-site. Some community pharmacies have access to EHRs of affiliated clinics.

When the EHR is linked to Computerized Prescriber Order Entry (CPOE) and electronic prescribing (e-prescribing), the problem of illegible handwriting is eliminated. The CPOE system can be designed to present only formulary drugs with proper dosing as options. As a result, pharmacists spend less time clarifying orders or changing to a formulary drug. Clinical decision support (CDS) tools can be built into the order entry process. Examples include order sets, pathways, limited drop-down menus that reflect the preferred drug/s, drug interaction and dose checking alerts and others. Refer to the Medication Safety & Quality Improvement chapter for additional information.

The Health Insurance Portability and Accountability Act of 1996 (HIPAA) requires security protections for all individually identifiable health information, which is called protected health information (PHI). These protections apply to both paper records and electronic records. For electronic records, access is limited with PINs and passwords, information is encrypted so unauthorized users cannot read it and an "audit trail" is used to track access. Security can still be violated. Individuals can access medical records for patients they are not involved with, an employee can forget to log out or the system can be hacked from the outside. All personnel using the EHR are responsible for security; education on security must be continual, and the software must be continuously evaluated for breaches. As part of the HIPAA requirements, patients have a right to access their own medical records that are kept in either paper or electronic formats.

The list of "Do Not Use" abbreviations should be easily available. It is important to avoid abbreviations that could be interpreted to mean something else (refer to the Medication Safety & Quality Improvement chapter).

SECTIONS OF THE PATIENT MEDICAL RECORD

The first additions to the PMR (paper or EHR) are the patient's demographic data (including insurance information), admission sheet, a service agreement form ("this is what I am having done at this facility"), a page describing the patient's rights (a Joint Commission requirement), and an advance directive to document the patient's wishes concerning medical treatment if he or she is unable to make decisions on their own behalf. Allergies may be here or listed later in the chart.

Certain religious groups will request a refusal form for blood transfusions and blood products which will need to be included in the PMR. Blood products primarily involve albumin and immune globulins, but some patients will refuse drugs buffered in blood (*Epogen/Procrit, Kogenate* – used for hemophilia), natural clotting factors/tissue adhesives/interferons and a few other uncommon agents. A few vaccines contain porcine-derived gelatin as a stabilizer. The major religious groups consider this use acceptable, but a specific patient may not.

Other forms or sections in the PMR include progress notes, the vital signs record, labs, medication records used for some medications (such as warfarin to track the INR history), medication administration records and procedure records, including the diagnostic and operating room (OR) records. At the end of the hospital stay the planning and discharge forms are added to the EHR.

REQUIREMENTS FOR REIMBURSEMENT: DOCUMENTATION AND QUALITY OF CARE

Pharmacists are involved with many patient care activities and frequently make verbal recommendations concerning patient care. While verbal recommendations may be effective, they are not part of the PMR and do not allow the information to be shared with other healthcare providers involved in the patient's care who are not present at that time. Interventions require documentation for reimbursement since the quality of the care is (increasingly) tied to the payment. Departments of pharmacy should have policies in place that describe the authority of pharmacists to document in the PMR, what activities will be documented and the proper format for documentation. Some activities that pharmacists document in the PMR include patient counseling, medication histories, consultations (e.g., pharmacokinetics, anticoagulation) and dosage adjustments. Documenting in the PMR is critical to establishing pharmacists as central members of the healthcare team.

The Centers for Medicare and Medicaid Services (CMS) provides health insurance to many Americans; CMS is directly involved with quality measurements and cost control. CMS has penalties for poor care and incentives for quality care. Two areas in which the penalties are steep are the rate of hospital-acquired infections and the hospital's readmission rate. These measures are chosen because they are expensive and are often, but not always, avoidable.

The Joint Commission, the Pharmacy Quality Alliance (PQA) and the Agency for Healthcare Research and Quality (AHRQ) are also involved in setting the criteria to measure the quality of care. The PQA quality measurements focus on medications.

Specific goals that involve medications include increasing adherence, avoiding unnecessary or unsafe medications (such as high-risk medications in the elderly) and increasing the use of medications indicated for certain conditions.

MEDICARE & MEDICAID

Medicare is the federal health insurance program for people ≥ 65 years old, < 65 with disability and all ages with end stage renal disease (ESRD).

The prescription drug benefit under Medicare is called Part D.

Part A covers the hospital visit and Part B covers medical costs, such as doctor visits, and some vaccines.

Medicaid provides health insurance for all ages with very low income (< 133% of the federal poverty level). Medicaid is a federal and state program. A senior who qualifies for both Medicare and Medicaid has "dual coverage".

THE SOAP NOTE FORMAT

A progress note records a patient encounter. One common method of organizing a note is in the SOAP format. The SOAP note is organized into four parts: Subjective, Objective, Assessment and Plan (SOAP). Prior to the use of SOAP notes it was difficult to understand patient chart entries, because the format was not standardized. Pharmacists may write SOAP notes to document their activities and read the SOAP notes of others while providing patient care. An example SOAP note from an EHR is included at the end of this chapter.

SUBJECTIVE

The 1st section in a SOAP note is the subjective information recorded from the patient. It is the patient's own narrative of their symptoms. Only the relevant information is recorded. The person conducting the interview should use only open-ended and direct questions while avoiding closed-ended and leading questions. For example, the leading question: "You always take your blood pressure pills, right?" is not likely to get a useful response. Phrasing the question in a direct manner that is worded to avoid a "yes or no" response will be more useful: "In a typical week, about how many mornings do you forget to take the blood pressure pills?"

The subjective section begins with a one-line Chief Complaint (CC). This is the specific reason the patient is being seen today, such as "I've had a stabbing pain in my right hip for three days" or "I feel like I need to go all the time but nothing much comes out." The subjective section includes the history of the present illness (HPI): the onset and duration of the specific complaint, the quality and severity (for example, with a pain complaint, descriptive words should be used to identify the type of pain, with a numerical pain rating), any modifying factors (what reduces or aggravates the condition), and treatment that has been tried to resolve the condition and the effect of the treatment, if any.

This section includes the past medical history (PMH), social history (alcohol, tobacco and illicit drug use), family history (first-degree relatives only - parents and siblings), allergies and medication use. Medication use includes prescriptions, samples, and OTCs, including vitamins and natural products. Information on start date and last refill is important when recording medication information.

OBJECTIVE

The 2nd section in a SOAP note is the objective information obtained by the clinician, either through observation or analysis. This includes the vital signs (respiration rate, heart rate, blood pressure and temperature). Note that on the top of the sample EHR at the end of this chapter the vitals are recorded at the top of the page, but vital signs are objective data. Any other measurements (e.g., height and weight, spirometry), physical findings, tests performed (e.g., ECG, chest x-ray, urinalysis) and laboratory results go into this section. If the medication list is obtained from a source other than the patient (e.g., recording information from prescription bottles or calling another pharmacy) it is occasionally recorded in the objective section of the SOAP because it was objectively verified.

Critical results are lab values significantly outside the reference range. Since these can indicate a life-threatening situation, they must be reported to a healthcare provider and addressed quickly. This is a Joint Commission National Patient Safety Goal.

Units of Measure

It is important to document measurements according to the policies of the institution. Documentation is generally done in metric system units (e.g., kg, cm). Recording weights and heights with incorrect units (150 pounds vs 150 kg) can have fatal consequences in terms of dosing medications. Refer to the Calculations chapters to practice common height and weight conversions.

In the U.S., temperatures are still frequently recorded in degrees Fahrenheit and may need to be converted to degrees Celsius. Temperatures taken rectally or orally are more accurate than if taken by axillary (under the arm) or tympanic (in the ear) methods.

Temperature Conversions

°C = (°F - 32)/1.8	°F = (°C x 1.8) + 32

EXAM SCENARIO

A patient presented with a temperature of 101.6°F. What is this temperature in degrees Celsius? Round to the nearest tenth.

$$°C = \frac{(101.6°F - 32)}{1.8} = 38.7°C$$

Select Drugs and Conditions that Alter Vital Signs

Make note of drugs that cause "↓ HR" or "↑ BP" while studying. On the exam, you might be asked about the possible cause of an abnormal vital sign. The table below is not all-inclusive; some conditions have variable effects on vital signs depending on severity (infection, withdrawal, poisoning). This information will be covered in more detail in the individual disease state chapters.

VITAL SIGN	INCREASED	DECREASED
Blood Pressure (BP)	"Hypertension" **Drugs** See Key Drugs Guy in Hypertension chapter **Conditions** ■ Renal insufficiency/failure ■ Pregnancy ■ Excess salt intake ■ Obesity ■ Adrenal tumors	"Hypotension" **Drugs** ■ Antihypertensives ■ Vasodilators ■ Opioids ■ Benzodiazepines ■ Anesthetics ■ Phosphodiesterase inhibitors **Conditions** ■ Anaphylaxis ■ Blood loss ■ Infection (esp. sepsis) ■ Dehydration (orthostatic hypotension)
Heart Rate (HR)	"Tachycardia" **Drugs** ■ Stimulants (ADHD, weight loss drugs) ■ Decongestants ■ Beta agonist use (esp. overuse) ■ Theophylline (esp. in toxicity) ■ Anticholinergics (tricyclics, antihistamines) ■ Bupropion ■ Antipsychotics ■ Excess caffeine/nicotine, illicit drug use ■ Vasodilators (e.g., nitrates, hydralazine, dihydropyridine CCBs) cause reflex tachycardia **Conditions** ■ Some arrhythmias (e.g., atrial fibrillation, ventricular tachycardia) ■ Hyperthyroidism ■ Anemia ■ Dehydration ■ Anxiety, stress, pain ■ Hypoglycemia ■ Infection ■ Drug withdrawal ■ Serotonin syndrome	"Bradycardia" **Drugs** ■ Beta-blockers ■ Non-dihydropyridine CCBs ■ Digoxin ■ Clonidine, guanfacine ■ Antiarrhythmics (esp. Class III) ■ Opioids ■ Sedatives ■ Anesthetics ■ Neuromuscular blockers ■ Acetylcholinesterase inhibitors **Conditions** ■ Some arrhythmias (sinus bradycardia) ■ Hypothyroidism
Respiratory Rate (RR)	"Tachypnea" **Drugs** ■ Stimulant drug use **Conditions** ■ Asthma and COPD (esp. when poorly controlled) ■ Anxiety, stress ■ Ketoacidosis ■ Pneumonia	"Respiratory depression" **Drugs** ■ Opioids ■ Sedatives **Conditions** ■ Hypothyroidism
Temperature (Temp)	"Hyperthermia" **Drugs** ■ Inhaled anesthetics (malignant hyperthermia) ■ Antipsychotics (neuroleptic malignant syndrome) ■ Topiramate **Conditions** ■ Fever ■ Hyperthyroidism ■ Trauma ■ Cancer ■ Serotonin syndrome	"Hypothermia" **Conditions** ■ Exposure to cold ■ Hypothyroidism (esp. myxedema coma) ■ Hypoglycemia

ASSESSMENT

The 3rd section is the assessment. This is the provider's thought process of possible causes of the current situation. Many conditions present with similar signs and symptoms; the assessment will often include multiple possible diagnoses. The differential diagnosis is a list of possible diagnoses that could explain the patient's current signs and symptoms. Each diagnosis on the list will be investigated.

PLAN

The 4th section is the plan. This is how the problem/s will be addressed. The plan should be as specific as possible. Labs might be ordered, the patient might require diagnostic exams, referrals may be requested or the patient may require education (e.g., suspected nonadherence, poor device technique, nutritional education or smoking cessation support). If there is a differential diagnosis there will be multiple steps in the plan to eliminate ("rule out") some of the possible conditions. Patients often have many medical problems that must be addressed, and they may be vastly different from the complaint that prompted the patient to seek medical attention.

MILITARY TIME

In all medical records, including the SOAP note, time is recorded with a 24-hour clock, rather than splitting the day into two 12-hour segments (AM/PM). The 24-hour clock is called "military time." The day begins at midnight, which is called 24:00 (pronounced "twenty-four hundred"). This is actually the start of the day and is sometimes referred to as 00:00. After 12:00 noon the time continues on the same number scale for the rest of the day: 1:00 PM is 13:00, 2:00 PM is 14:00, and so on. The last minute of the day is 23:59, then 24:00 (midnight), and then the next day begins. Some clocks are labeled for military time (see image).

To convert military time back to 12-hour segments (AM/PM), simply subtract 12 from any number ≥ 13 (e.g., 16:00 = 4 pm, because 16 - 12 = 4).

ANSWERING CASE-BASED QUESTIONS ON THE EXAM

Pharmacists caring for patients (or taking NAPLEX) are often faced with complex medication regimens. In order to provide the best care possible, a systematic approach to assessment of the treatment plan and medication regimen is warranted.

IDENTIFYING MEDICATION THERAPY PROBLEMS

Pharmacists should assess for medication therapy problems, intervene when appropriate and document the intervention/s in the PMR as policy permits. Cases on the exam will require the same type of systematic assessment to identify risks to the patient and potential solutions to problems.

Pharmacists develop a process for thoroughly identifying medication problems. One method is shown below (see Study Tip Gal). Ask yourself each question listed: Are there any therapeutic duplications? Are there any drug interactions? You may not be able to answer every question with the information provided. Strong mastery of the material (e.g., brand/generic name identification, drug interactions, guidelines) is essential. The Exam Scenario below illustrates how you could be asked several different types of questions about a case.

HOW TO LOOK FOR MEDICATION PROBLEMS IN A PATIENT CASE

Review the case for the following medication problems:

- Untreated medical condition
- Medications used without an indication
- Improper drug selection
- Dose that is too low or high
- Therapeutic duplication
- Lack of patient understanding about medication
- Drug allergy
- Drug interaction
- Improper use of medication
- Failure to receive medication
- Adverse drug reaction
- Nonadherence

Practice reviewing cases until it becomes routine to check for each of these problems, every time. This is essential for a pharmacist.

EXAM SCENARIO

A new patient transfers the following prescriptions to a community pharmacy on December 15th: *Benicar* 20 mg daily, *Zocor* 20 mg daily, *Stribild* 1 daily (last refilled November 1st) and *Avapro* 150 mg TID. All are written for a 30-day supply.

Identify the potential problems (see Study Tip Gal above):

- Therapeutic duplication: two ARBs
- Drug interaction: cobicistat is contraindicated with simvastatin
- Dose too high: *Avapro* should be dosed once daily
- Potential nonadherence: *Stribild* should be refilled every 30 days

MATCHING DRUGS TO MEDICAL PROBLEMS

How will you determine whether there are untreated medical conditions, drugs without an indication or duplications of therapy? Pharmacists are skilled at matching up medical problems and drugs as a quick way to assess this.

EXAM SCENARIO

Match the medications to the condition being treated. Some conditions may require more than one medication.

Past Medical History	**Medications**
Hypertension	*Keflex*
Arthritis	*Synthroid*
Depression	Hydrochlorothiazide
Cellulitis	*Renova* cream
Diabetes	*Ambien*
	Meloxicam
	Cymbalta

Past Medical History		**Medications**
Hypertension	⟶	Hydrochlorothiazide
Arthritis	⟶	Meloxicam
Depression		*Cymbalta*
Cellulitis	⟶	*Keflex*
Diabetes	⟶	?
? Insomnia		*Ambien*
? Hypothyroidism		*Synthroid*
? Acne		*Renova* cream

- There are several medications without a documented indication in the patient's past medical history. The pharmacist should interview the patient and/or review labs/vitals (PRN) to determine if these medications are still required or were possibly prescribed in error. It is very common for the medical record to be incomplete or incorrect, but pharmacists must ensure that medications are used properly.
- There is one condition (diabetes) that is not being treated with a medication. Many patients are able to control type 2 diabetes with diet alone, which might be the case. A review of the labs (blood glucose, A1C) would help answer this question. Again, notice that mastery of brand/generic names is critical.

QUESTIONS ABOUT THE MEDICATION PROFILE

Use the Exam Scenario below to answer questions about the medication profile.

EXAM SCENARIO

The pharmacist is filling new prescriptions for a patient with the following home medication list:

Advair
Clozapine
Daliresp
Depakote ER
Dutasteride
Fenofibrate
Hyzaar
ProAir
Spiriva
Tamsulosin

Based on the medication profile, which group of medical problems does this patient have?

A. Asthma, glaucoma and gout
B. Atrial fibrillation, depression and schizophrenia
C. Hypertriglyceridemia, migraine and Parkinson Disease
D. BPH, COPD and hypertension
E. Seizures, diabetes and anemia

One of the new prescriptions is for *Flomax*. This is a duplication of therapy with which of the patient's current medications?

A. *Advair*
B. *Daliresp*
C. Dutasteride
D. *Hyzaar*
E. Tamsulosin

The patient's labs reveal an increased ammonia level. Which of the home medications is most likely responsible?

A. *Advair*
B. Clozapine
C. *Depakote ER*
D. *Spiriva*
E. Tamsulosin

Answers:
D, E, C

RECOMMENDING DRUG THERAPY

Some exam questions will ask you to make a drug therapy recommendation. This requires strong knowledge of guidelines and indications/contraindications for drugs. Read the question and answer choices first, before extensively evaluating the case. After you read the question, you should be able to quickly determine what information you need from the case.

EXAM SCENARIO

A case is provided regarding a patient with a past medical history of type 2 diabetes who is currently taking no medications. The first question is:

Which of the following medications should be recommended to treat the patient's diabetes?

A. *Glucophage XR*
B. *Actos*
C. *Invokana*
D. *Victoza*
E. Regular insulin given by IV infusion

How will you decide which answer to pick? Here is the correct approach to the question:

- Metformin is recommended as the first-line medication along with lifestyle modifications for type 2 diabetes. It is very likely the right answer, but the question may be testing something more advanced than simple recall of the recommended first-line medication. Before selecting metformin, make sure it is a safe choice in this specific patient and that nothing was missed in the case that would make another choice better:
  - ❑ Insulin is one of the answer choices. Could this patient have hyperglycemia hyperosmolar state (HHS) or diabetic ketoacidosis (DKA), which would require an insulin infusion? Read the HPI. Look for signs, symptoms and labs that help (e.g., very high blood glucose, altered mental status, extreme dehydration; refer to the Diabetes chapter).
  - ❑ Metformin should not be started if eGFR is < 45 mL/min/1.73 m^2. If eGFR is not provided, calculate the patient's CrCl and use this as an eGFR estimate. Metformin may not be safe for this patient.
  - ❑ Check the progress notes and other information provided. Metformin should not be used within 48 hours of receiving IV iodinated contrast media.

If the patient does not require an insulin infusion to treat DKA or HHS, and there are no contraindications or safety concerns with starting metformin, select it as the correct answer choice. If metformin is not a safe choice, use a similar process to determine which of the other choices is best for this patient.

PATIENT COMMUNICATION

HEALTH LITERACY

Good communication skills are essential for pharmacists and are linked to patient satisfaction and trust. Pharmacists provide valuable information to patients, but the effort is wasted if the information is not understood. Only about 12% of adults have proficient health literacy. Health literacy is the degree to which individuals are able to obtain, process and understand basic health and medication information to make appropriate health decisions. An example of this is being able to correctly interpret a prescription label. Health literacy is different than simply being able to read or being well educated; many educated people have difficulty understanding medical information. Low health literacy is common in the elderly, minority populations, those with lower income, poor health, and limited English proficiency but can be an issue for any patient. A person's health literacy is dependent on age, communication skills, knowledge, experience and culture. Low health literacy is linked to poor health outcomes.

EFFECTIVE COMMUNICATION AND EDUCATION STRATEGIES

- Approach all patients as if they may not understand the health information presented. Do not assume that it is easy to tell who has low health literacy.
- Use everyday, non-medical language that patients can understand.
  Example: Say "high blood pressure" instead of "hypertension" or "tired" instead of "fatigued".
- Ask open-ended questions that require more than a "yes" or "no" answer.
  Example: Ask "what questions can I answer about your new medication today?" instead of "do you have any questions?"
- Avoid leading questions.
  Example: Ask "what about your high blood pressure concerns you?" instead of "are you most concerned about the side effects from the high blood pressure medication?"
- Confirm understanding. Ask the patient to repeat the information or ask what they would tell their spouse or friend about the new medication.
- Use different communication strategies (verbal, written, visual aids) to enhance understanding. Ask the patient how he/she prefers to receive the information.
- Use active listening. Clarifying or summarizing what the patient has said is helpful and gives the patient an opportunity to offer correction.
- Speak clearly, make eye contact, introduce yourself and refer to patients by their name. Avoid "sweetie", "dear" and other similar terms.

EXAMPLE ELECTRONIC HEALTH RECORD SOAP NOTE

Juanita Burrows (PRN: JB747114): SOAP Note for 09/25
Age on DOS: 40 yrs, DOB 03/13/1974
Allergies: NKDA

San Diego Medical Group
35 La Jolla Drive Suite 100 San Diego, CA 92130
(444) 444-4444

seen by: Alison James
seen on: Thursday 25 September

VS

Height:	Weight:	BMI:	Blood Pressure:	Temp:	Pulse:	Resp Rate:
67.0 in	195.0 lb	30.5	154/92 mmHg	97.9 F	80 bpm	12 rpm

CC "I feel limp."

S

JB is a 40y/o female who presents with a 3 month history of increasing fatigue. She first noticed that she felt tired when she was working long hours to get a job done at work, but has been working her usual 8 hours a day for the past 2 months and has not regained her energy. She described her fatigue as "feeling limp". It is present throughought the day, but worse with significant exertion (e.g., walking > 3-4 blocks or going up stairs). She has tried to go to bed earlier, but even sleeping up to 10 hours/night (increased from 8 hours/night) has not helped. She is concerned that there is something seriously wrong, as she is usually full of energy and her family and friends are starting to ask if she is sick. She has also not been able to exercise, which she usually enjoys. She denies chest pain, SOB, abdominal pain, N/V/D, or changes in her stool. She has no alopecia or skin changes. She has had no fever, chills or night sweats. She has gained about 6-7 lbs in the last few months, which she attributes to inactivity due to fatigue. She denies depressed mood, sadness, or anhedonia. She states that she goes to bed at 10pm and wakes feeling tired at 6am on weekdays and 8am on weekends. Her husband states that she has "always" snored quite loudly. Her menses are regular on timing, heavy flow for 1-2 days, then lighter for another 2-3 days. The pattern is unchanged from prior to the onset of her fatigue. Her last menstrual period was one week ago. When asked about compliance with her medications, she states that she takes everything regularly "except for the one for her blood pressure because she doesn't feel like her pressure is high".

She reports a history of GERD, HTN, and depression.
Her medications include: Zantac 150 mg PO QHS, Chlorthalidone 25 mg PO Daily, Zoloft 100 mg Daily, and Caltrate + D 600 mg BID.

O

Well-appearing black female in no acute distress.
SKIN: not pale, no rashes
NECK: no thyromegaly or thyroid nodules
NODES: no cervical, axillary or inguinal lymphadenopathy
CHEST: clear to auscultation and percussion bilaterally
CV: RRR, 2/6 systolic ejection murmur heard best at the LLSB that radiates to the apex, no S3 or S4
ABD: normal active bowel sounds, no hepatosplenomegaly by palpation or percussion, no abdominal tenderness
EXT: no edema, pulses normal

A

Recent onset of fatigue with no obvious inciting event. Hypothyroidism is possible especially given her weight gain, though this also may have occurred from her inactivity. It is possible that she is anemic though her menstrual periods have not lengthened or increased and there is no other obvious sources of blood loss. A recent menses makes pregnancy unlikely. Given her history of snoring, sleep apnea is possible, but her history of snoring over many years is not entirely consistent with her more recent onset of fatigue. She does not seem to have a recurrence of her depression since she has no new symptoms. She does not have symptoms of infection, nor has her murmur changed, so subacute bacterial endocarditis is possible but unlikely. BP is elevated and she has been noncompliant with prescribed therapy for HTN.

P

#1. Check TSH to rule out hypothyroidism
#2. Check CBC to rule out anemia
#3. If the above are unremarkable, consider a sleep study to rule out sleep apnea
#4. Consider blood cultures to rule out subacute bacterial endocarditis
#5. Pharmacy consult for medication adherence
#6. Follow-up visit in 1 week to discuss test results and further work-up

26 September 5:23 PM
page 1 of 1

Select Guidelines/References

American Society of Health-System Pharmacists. ASHP Guidelines on Pharmacist-Conducted Patient Education and Counseling. *Am J Health-Syst Pharm.* 1997;54:431-4.

Office of Disease Prevention and Health Promotion. Health Literacy and Communication at http://health.gov/communication/ (accessed 2019 Jan 15).

9

10

Serving Size 1 cup (228g)
Servings Per Container
Amount Per Serving
11

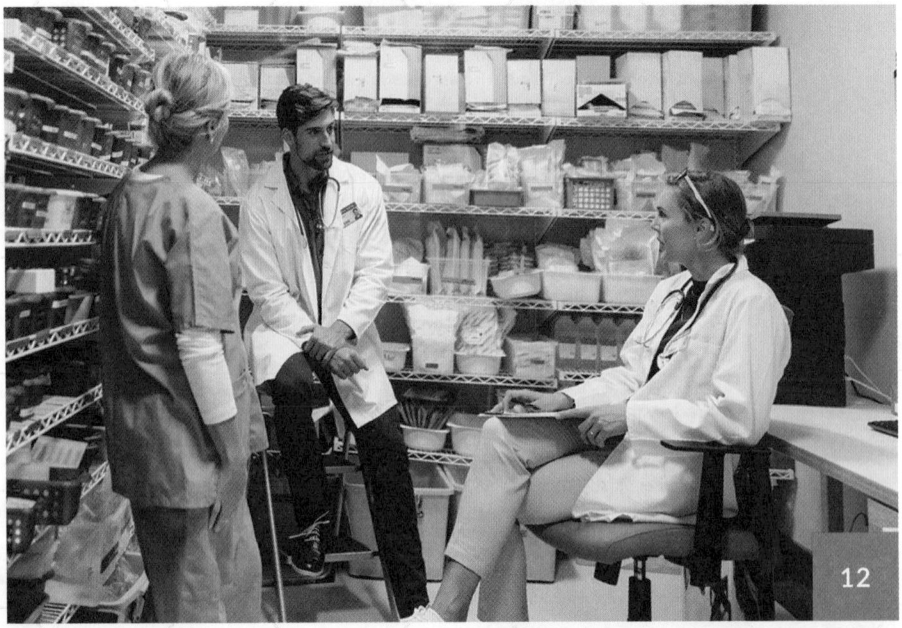
12

13

CALCULATIONS

CONTENTS

CHAPTER 9
I: MATH BASICS | **116**

CHAPTER 10
II: COMPOUNDING | **128**

CHAPTER 11
III: PARENTERAL AND ENTERAL NUTRITION | **148**

CHAPTER 12
IV: CLINICAL | **166**

CHAPTER 13
V: EXAM-STYLE MATH PRACTICE | **185**

CHAPTER CONTENT

Equivalent Measurements....116
Common Conversions....117
Rounding....117
How to Round on the Exam....117
Proportions and Dimensional Analysis....118
Proportions....118
Setting Up Proportions....118
Dimensional Analysis....117
Converting Common Units....119
Larger → Smaller Volume....119
Smaller → Larger Volume....119
Larger → Smaller Weight....119
Smaller → Larger Weight....119
Calculations Involving Prescriptions....120
Converting From One Drug to Another....125
Drug Conversions....125
Ratios....125
Ratio Relationships....125
Decimals and Percentage Conversion....126
Squaring a Number....126
Exponents....126
Order of Operations....127
Follow the Rules of Math....127
Ready to Submit Your Answer?....127

> ***This chapter covers basic math concepts that must be mastered for NAPLEX. These topics may be a review for some, but they are the foundation for solving more complex problems.***

CONTENT LEGEND

(Study Tip icon) = Study Tip Gal (Key Drug icon) = Key Drug Guy

CHAPTER 9

CALCULATIONS I: MATH BASICS

EQUIVALENT MEASUREMENTS

Drugs can be measured in different ways:

- As weights [grams (g), milligrams (mg), micrograms (mcg), nanograms (ng)].
- As liquid volumes [liters (L), milliliters (mL)].
- As percentage strengths (g in 100 mL, g in 100 g, or mL in 100 mL).
- As concentrations of a given amount of a drug in a given volume of liquid (mcg/mL or mg/L). Very small amounts are measured in ng/mL. BUN and serum creatinine concentrations are measured in mg/dL (one liter is 10 dL).
- As concentrations using milliequivalents (mEq) per liter (mEq/L) (e.g., lithium and common electrolytes).

Common conversions must be known for the exam (see Study Tip Gal on the next page); they may or may not be provided. Actual or approximate conversions can be used. The rounding instructions provided on the exam questions will account for any differences in using actual vs. approximate conversions. If a specific conversion is provided on an exam question, always use it.

1. A prescription reads: "take 2 tsp PO Q6H x 7 days." How many milliliters must be dispensed to complete 7 days of therapy?

$$2 \text{ tsp} \times \frac{5 \text{ mL}}{1 \text{ tsp}} = 10 \text{ mL per dose}$$

$$\frac{10 \text{ mL}}{\text{dose}} \times \frac{4 \text{ doses}}{\text{day}} \times 7 \text{ days} = 280 \text{ mL}$$

COMMON CONVERSIONS

LIQUID (VOLUME) CONVERSION

tsp (t)	5 mL
tbsp (T)	15 mL
1 fl oz	30 mL (approx.); 29.57 mL (actual)
1 cup	8 oz 240 mL (approx.); 236.56 mL (actual)
1 pint	16 oz 480 mL (approx.); 473 mL (actual)
1 quart	2 pints 960 mL (approx.); 946 mL (actual)
1 gallon	4 quarts 3,840 mL (approx.); 3,785 mL (actual)

SOLID (WEIGHT) CONVERSION

1 kg	2.2 pounds
1 oz	28.4 g
1 pound (lb)	454 g
1 grain (gr)	65 mg approx.); 64.8 mg (actual)

MILLIEQUIVALENTS (mEq) & MILLIMOLES (mmol)	
K^+, Na^+ & other monovalent ions	1 mEq = 1 mmol*
Ca^{++} & other divalent ions	1 mEq = 0.5 mmol*

**If mEq are provided for potassium, and the answer requires mmol, use the same numbers. When mEq are provided for calcium, and the answer requires mmol, use half of the number.*

HEIGHT CONVERSION	
Inch (in)	2.54 centimeters (cm)
Meter (m)	100 cm

ROUNDING

The majority of problems that require rounding will specify to round to the nearest whole number. It may be necessary to round differently, such as rounding to the nearest tenth, the nearest ten milligrams or the nearest whole tablet.

2. A pediatric patient is receiving 5.25 mL of drug every 4 hours. How many milliliters will be required for the entire day? Round to the nearest whole number.

5.25 mL (per dose) x 6 times/day = 31.5 mL
Round to the nearest whole number = 32 mL

3. A patient requires 410.9 mg of a drug daily. The daily dose will be divided for BID administration. How many milligrams will the patient receive BID? Round to the nearest whole number.

410.9 mg daily/2 times per day = 205.45 mg BID
Round to the nearest whole number = 205 mg BID

HOW TO ROUND ON THE EXAM

- Underline the number to the right of what is being rounded. If rounding to the nearest whole number, underline the 4 in this example: 347.<u>4</u>8
- Look at the number that is underlined and apply one of these rules:
  - ❑ If the underlined number is 5, 6, 7, 8, or 9, round up.
  - ❑ If the underlined number is 0, 1, 2, 3, or 4, round down.
- 347.48 rounded to the nearest whole number is 347.

***Never round until the last step in the calculation.**

**Round only once on the last step; use the calculator's memory or parentheses function on the exam for the intermediate steps. In the RxPrep Course Book, some intermediate steps (that do not affect the final answer) have been rounded for simplicity and space.*

What if the problem said "round to the nearest tenth"? The correct answer would then be 205.5 mg. <u>Rounding to the nearest tenth is the same</u> as rounding to <u>one decimal place</u>.

4. Enoxaparin 56.5 mg was ordered for a patient. The hospital rounds enoxaparin doses to the nearest 10 mg. What dose should be dispensed?

Correct answer: 60 mg. Rounding to the nearest 10 mg is different than rounding to the nearest tenth.

5. A patient is 5'2" tall. What is her height in centimeters? Round to the nearest whole number.

$$5 \text{ feet} \times \frac{12 \text{ inches}}{1 \text{ foot}} = 60 \text{ inches} + 2 \text{ inches} = 62 \text{ inches}$$

$$62 \text{ inches} \times \frac{2.54 \text{ cm}}{1 \text{ inch}} = 157.48 \text{ cm}$$

Round to the nearest whole number = 157 cm

PROPORTIONS AND DIMENSIONAL ANALYSIS

These methods are very important for most of the math that pharmacists do routinely. Pharmacists tend to either love dimensional analysis, or they prefer to do individual proportion calculations (or a combination of the two). When performed correctly, both methods provide the same answer. Pick the method that works best for you.

PROPORTIONS

Proportions are two fractions (ratios) that are set equal to each other. One variable is unknown and labeled "X." When setting up proportions, make sure that the units for the numerators match to each other and the units for the denominators match to each other or make sure the items in the left fraction match and the items in the right fraction match (see Study Tip Gal and problem #6 for an example).

DIMENSIONAL ANALYSIS

Dimensional analysis allows multiple proportion calculations to be completed quickly. Diagonal units that are the same can be crossed out ("canceled out"), leaving the desired units. The numbers can be plugged into the calculator exactly as written. Converting from one common unit of measure to another (e.g., pounds to kilograms) is a simple way to illustrate both methods.

SETTING UP PROPORTIONS

Two methods of matching:

Match both numerators and both denominators: Every item in the left numerator (drug, route, units) must match to every item in the right numerator (except the values of the numbers).

Every item in the left denominator must match to every item in the right denominator (except the values of the numbers).

Match numerator and denominator of each fraction: Items in the left fraction (numerator and denominator) must match and items in the right fraction (numerator and denominator) must match (except the value of the numbers).

Carefully review Problem #6 to see how both methods provide the same answer.

6. A patient weighs 176 pounds. What is the patient's weight in kilograms?

Method 1: Proportion. Solve for X by multiplying diagonally and then dividing. Set up in either of the two ways shown.

$$\frac{176 \text{ lbs}}{X \text{ kg}} = \frac{2.2 \text{ lbs}}{1 \text{ kg}} \quad X = 80 \text{ kg}$$

or

$$\frac{176 \text{ lbs}}{2.2 \text{ lbs}} = \frac{X \text{ kg}}{1 \text{ kg}} \quad X = 80 \text{ kg}$$

Method 2: Dimensional analysis. Cancel out the same units diagonally, leaving the desired units.

$$176 \cancel{\text{lbs}} \times \frac{1 \text{ kg}}{2.2 \cancel{\text{lbs}}} = 80 \text{ kg}$$

Notice that there is an equal sign (=) between the fractions in a proportion and a multiplication symbol (x) between the fractions in dimensional analysis.

CONVERTING COMMON UNITS

LARGER → SMALLER VOLUME

Liters (L) → milliliters (mL)

7. How many milliliters are in 5 liters?

Method 1: Proportion

$$\frac{5\ \text{L}}{\text{X mL}} = \frac{1\ \text{L}}{1{,}000\ \text{mL}} \qquad \text{X} = 5{,}000\ \text{mL}$$

or

Method 2: Dimensional analysis

$$5\ \cancel{\text{L}} \times \frac{1{,}000\ \text{mL}}{1\ \cancel{\text{L}}} = 5{,}000\ \text{mL}$$

SMALLER → LARGER VOLUME

Milliliters (mL) → liters (L)

8. Convert 5,000 mL to liters.

$$5{,}000\ \cancel{\text{mL}} \times \frac{1\ \text{L}}{1{,}000\ \cancel{\text{mL}}} = 5\ \text{L}$$

LARGER → SMALLER WEIGHT

Kilogram (kg) → grams (g) → milligrams (mg) → micrograms (mcg) → nanograms (ng)

9. How many nanograms are equal to 5 kg?

This example requires 4 separate proportions or dimensional analysis (shown).

$$5\ \cancel{\text{kg}} \times \frac{1{,}000\ \cancel{\text{g}}}{1\ \cancel{\text{kg}}} \times \frac{1{,}000\ \cancel{\text{mg}}}{1\ \cancel{\text{g}}} \times \frac{1{,}000\ \cancel{\text{mcg}}}{1\ \cancel{\text{mg}}} \times \frac{1{,}000\ \text{ng}}{1\ \cancel{\text{mcg}}} = 5\ \text{trillion ng (or } 5 \times 10^{12}\ \text{ng)}$$

SMALLER → LARGER WEIGHT

Nanograms (ng) → micrograms (mcg) → milligrams (mg) → grams (g) → kilograms (kg)

10. How many grams are equal to 50,000,000 nanograms?

$$50{,}000{,}000\ \cancel{\text{ng}} \times \frac{1\ \cancel{\text{mcg}}}{1{,}000\ \cancel{\text{ng}}} \times \frac{1\ \cancel{\text{mg}}}{1{,}000\ \cancel{\text{mcg}}} \times \frac{1\ \text{g}}{1{,}000\ \cancel{\text{mg}}} = 0.05\ \text{g}$$

When dimensional analysis is presented from this point forward, the strike through lines will be omitted for readability.

CALCULATIONS INVOLVING PRESCRIPTIONS

Interpretation of prescriptions, orders and compounding instructions will be necessary on the exam. Refer to Chapter 1 for common abbreviations used in prescriptions and medical charts.

11. A pharmacist receives this prescription for *Vicodin*. How many tablets should be dispensed?

A. 6 tablets
B. 8 tablets
C. 12 tablets
D. 16 tablets
E. 24 tablets

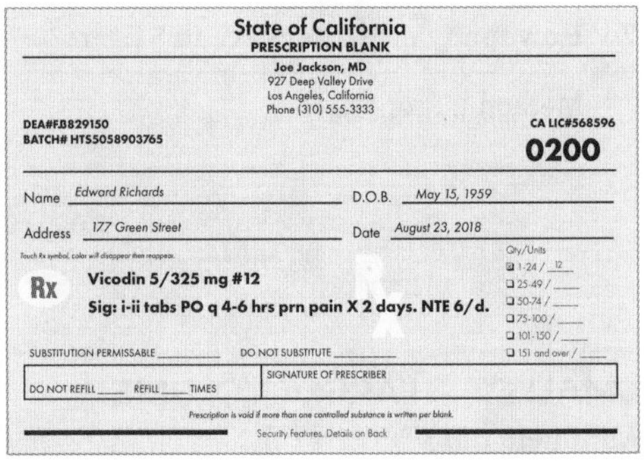
State of California
PRESCRIPTION BLANK
Joe Jackson, MD
927 Deep Valley Drive
Los Angeles, California
Phone (310) 555-3333
DEA#FJ3829150
BATCH# HTS5058903765
CA LIC#568596
0200
Name Edward Richards D.O.B. May 15, 1959
Address 177 Green Street Date August 23, 2018
Touch Rx symbol, color will disappear then reappear.
Rx Vicodin 5/325 mg #12
Sig: i-ii tabs PO q 4-6 hrs prn pain X 2 days. NTE 6/d.
Qty/Units
☒ 1-24 / 12
☐ 25-49 / ____
☐ 50-74 / ____
☐ 75-100 / ____
☐ 101-150 / ____
☐ 151 and over / ____
SUBSTITUTION PERMISSABLE ________ DO NOT SUBSTITUTE ________
DO NOT REFILL ____ REFILL ____ TIMES
SIGNATURE OF PRESCRIBER
Prescription is void if more than one controlled substance is written per blank.
Security Features. Details on Back

The correct answer is (C). The dispense quantity is indicated and consistent with the "not to exceed" instructions.

12. A pharmacist receives a prescription for "*Vigamox* 0.5%. Dispense 3 mL. 1 gtt tid ou x 7d." How many drops will the patient use per day?

A. 1 drop
B. 2 drops
C. 3 drops
D. 6 drops
E. 21 drops

The correct answer is (D).

13. A 7-year-old male child (48 pounds) presents to the urgent care clinic with a fever of 102°F, and nausea/vomiting that started the previous day. He will receive an acetaminophen 5 grain suppository for the fever. A pharmacist receives a prescription for the suppository with the instructions: Use 1 PR Q4-6H PRN temperature > 102°F. How many milligrams per kilogram (mg/kg) will the child receive per dose? Round to the nearest whole number.

$$5 \text{ grains} \times \frac{65 \text{ mg}}{1 \text{ grain}} = 325 \text{ mg per suppository}$$

$$48 \text{ lbs} \times \frac{1 \text{ kg}}{2.2 \text{ lbs}} = \sim 21.8182 \text{ kg}$$

Note: if a proportion is used to solve the step above, the repeating decimals must be addressed. It is best to use the calculator's memory or parentheses function on the exam so that all decimals can be carried forward to the next step. Round only once on the last step.

$$325 \text{ mg}/21.8182 \text{ kg} = \sim 14.896 \text{ mg/kg, round to } 15 \text{ mg/kg}$$

Try the problem again with the actual conversion (64.8 mg/grain). Notice that the answer will be the same.

14. How many milliliters of *Mylanta* suspension are contained in each dose of the prescription below? Round to the nearest whole number.

PRESCRIPTION	QUANTITY
Belladonna Tincture	10 mL
Phenobarbital	60 mL
Mylanta susp. qs. ad	120 mL
Sig. 5 mL BID	

The total prescription is 120 mL; 10 mL belladonna, 60 mL of phenobarbital, and that leaves 50 mL for the *Mylanta*.

$$\frac{50 \text{ mL } Mylanta}{120 \text{ mL total Rx}} = \frac{X \text{ mL } Mylanta}{5 \text{ mL total Rx dose}} \quad X = 2.08, \text{ or } 2 \text{ mL } Mylanta \text{ per dose}$$

---

15. A pharmacist received this sulfamethoxazole/trimethoprim prescription and dispensed 3 oz to Ms. Brooks. How many days of therapy will Ms. Brooks be short? Use 30 mL for 1 fluid ounce.

A. 1
B. 3
C. 9
D. 10
E. 90

Gene Tran, MD
5445 Grand Ave.
Fallbrook, California
Phone (760) 555-2112

005-1015

CA LIC. #A19666
D.E.A. #SK456789

Name *Angelina Brooks* Date *January 22, 2019*

Address *33 Walden Rd. N Falls* D.O.B. *May 5, 1951*

℞

TMP/SMX 40-200 mg/5 mL
Sig: 1 tsp PO BID x 10 days, until all taken.

❑ Do Not Substitute Refill _____ Times

Quantity Units
❑ 1-24 _____
❑ 25-49 _____
❑ 50-74 _____
❑ 75-100 _____
❑ 101-150 _____
❑ 151 and over _____

Physician Signature

Prescription is void if more than one controlled substance is written per blank.

The correct answer is (A).

5 mL (per dose) x 2 times/day x 10 days = 100 mL

Quantity dispensed: 3 oz x 30 mL/oz = 90 mL dispensed

Difference: 100 mL - 90 mL = 10 mL, which is 1 day of therapy

A common mistake is selecting answer (D). Yes, the patient will be 10 mL short, but the question asked for "days of therapy." Each tsp (t) is 5 mL. The patient must take 2 tsp (t) daily (or 10 mL), so she is one day short for her prescribed course of therapy.

16. A pharmacist has tablets that contain 0.25 mg of levothyroxine per tablet. The tablets will be crushed and mixed with glycerol and water to prepare a prescription for a 36 pound child. How many levothyroxine tablets will be needed to compound the following prescription?

PRESCRIPTION	QUANTITY
Levothyroxine Liq.	0.1 mg/mL
Disp.	60 mL
Sig. 0.01 mg per kg PO BID	

$$60 \text{ mL total Rx} \times \frac{0.1 \text{ mg levo}}{\text{mL}} = 6 \text{ mg of levothyroxine needed}$$

$$6 \text{ mg levo} \times \frac{1 \text{ tab}}{0.25 \text{ mg levo}} = 24 \text{ tabs of levothyroxine needed}$$

The first step can also be performed as a proportion. If the proportion is set up correctly, the answers will be the same.

$$\frac{0.1 \text{ mg levo}}{1 \text{ mL}} = \frac{X \text{ mg levo}}{60 \text{ mL}} \qquad X = 6 \text{ mg of levothyroxine needed}$$

$$6 \text{ mg levo} \times \frac{1 \text{ tab}}{0.25 \text{ mg levo}} = 24 \text{ tabs of levothyroxine needed}$$

Or, it can be solved by dimensional analysis:

$$\frac{1 \text{ tab levo}}{0.25 \text{ mg levo}} \times \frac{0.1 \text{ mg levo}}{\text{mL}} \times 60 \text{ mL total Rx} = 24 \text{ tabs of levothyroxine needed}$$

---

17. How many milligrams of codeine will be contained in each capsule?

PRESCRIPTION	QUANTITY
Codeine Sulfate	0.6 g
Guaifenesin	1.2 g
Caffeine	0.15 g
M. ft. caps. no. 24	
Sig. One capsule TID PRN cough	

Begin by converting to the units requested in the answer (mg).

$$0.6 \text{ g codeine} \times \frac{1{,}000 \text{ mg}}{1 \text{ g}} = 600 \text{ mg of codeine for the total prescription}$$

The prescription order is for 24 capsules.

$$\frac{600 \text{ mg codeine total}}{24 \text{ caps}} = 25 \text{ mg of codeine/capsule}$$

After solving the problem, read the question again to be certain the question was answered with the correct units (mg of codeine per capsule).

18. How many grains of aspirin will be contained in each capsule? Round to the nearest tenth.

PRESCRIPTION	QUANTITY
Aspirin	6 g
Phenacetin	3.2 g
Caffeine	0.48 g
M. ft. no. 20 caps	
Sig. One capsule Q6H PRN pain	

$$6\text{ g aspirin} \times \frac{1{,}000\text{ mg}}{1\text{ g}} \times \frac{1\text{ grain}}{65\text{ mg}} = 92.3\text{ grains}$$

We have 92.3 grains of aspirin that will be divided into 20 capsules.

$$\frac{92.3\text{ grains}}{20\text{ capsules}} = 4.6\text{ grains/capsule}$$

After solving the problem, read the question again to be certain the question was answered with the correct units (grains per capsule).

---

19. A 45 milliliter nasal spray delivers 20 sprays per milliliter of solution. Each spray contains 1.5 mg of active drug. How many milligrams of drug are contained in the 45 mL package?

First calculate the amount of drug per mL.

$$\frac{1.5\text{ mg drug}}{\text{spray}} \times \frac{20\text{ sprays}}{\text{mL}} = 30\text{ mg/mL}$$

Then solve for milligrams of drug in 45 mL.

$$\frac{30\text{ mg}}{\text{mL}} = \frac{X\text{ mg}}{45\text{ mL}} \quad X = 1{,}350\text{ mg}$$

---

20. A metered dose inhaler provides 90 micrograms of albuterol sulfate with each inhalation. The canister provides 200 inhalations. If the patient uses the entire canister, how many total milligrams will the patient have received?

$$200\text{ inhalations} \times \frac{90\text{ mcg}}{\text{inhalation}} \times \frac{1\text{ mg}}{1{,}000\text{ mcg}} = 18\text{ mg}$$

21. Digoxin injection is supplied in ampules of 500 mcg per 2 mL. How many milliliters must a nurse administer to provide a dose of 0.2 mg?

Method 1: Two steps using a proportion.

First, convert micrograms to milligrams.

$$500 \text{ mcg} \times \frac{1 \text{ mg}}{1{,}000 \text{ mcg}} = 0.5 \text{ mg}$$

Then use a proportion to calculate the number of milliliters for a 0.2 mg dose.

$$\frac{0.5 \text{ mg digoxin}}{2 \text{ mL}} = \frac{0.2 \text{ mg digoxin}}{X \text{ mL}} \qquad X = 0.8 \text{ mL}$$

Method 2: Dimensional analysis.

$$0.2 \text{ mg} \times \frac{1{,}000 \text{ mcg}}{1 \text{ mg}} \times \frac{2 \text{ mL}}{500 \text{ mcg}} = 0.8 \text{ mL}$$

---

22. If one 10 mL vial contains 0.05 g of diltiazem, how many milliliters should be administered to provide a 25 mg dose of diltiazem?

Method 1: Two steps using a proportion.

First, convert grams to milligrams. It is usually best practice to convert to the units required for the answer when beginning the problem.

$$0.05 \text{ g diltiazem} \times \frac{1{,}000 \text{ mg}}{1 \text{ g}} = 50 \text{ mg}$$

Next, calculate the number of milliliters for a 25 mg dose.

$$\frac{50 \text{ mg}}{10 \text{ mL}} = \frac{25 \text{ mg}}{X \text{ mL}} \qquad X = 5 \text{ mL}$$

Method 2: Dimensional analysis.

$$25 \text{ mg dose} \times \frac{1 \text{ g}}{1{,}000 \text{ mg}} \times \frac{10 \text{ mL}}{0.05 \text{ g}} = 5 \text{ mL}$$

CONVERTING FROM ONE DRUG TO ANOTHER

Another common application for proportions is converting from one drug and dose to another drug and dose. Common conversions that pharmacists perform are shown (see Key Drugs Guy).

23. The pharmacist is consulted to convert a patient from prednisone 10 mg PO BID to an equivalent dose of oral dexamethasone given once daily. What is the equivalent daily dose? Prednisone 5 mg = dexamethasone 0.75 mg.

$$\frac{\text{20 mg prednisone}}{\text{X mg dexamethasone}} = \frac{\text{5 mg prednisone}}{\text{0.75 mg dexamethasone}} \quad \text{X = 3 mg of dexamethasone daily}$$

Notice that the numerators match each other (drug name and units) and the denominators match each other. For the exam, the equivalencies (e.g., prednisone 5 mg = dexamethasone 0.75 mg) must be memorized (see Systemic Steroids & Autoimmune Conditions chapter for steroid equivalencies).

DRUG CONVERSIONS

These drug conversions must be known for the exam. The conversions are discussed in the disease state chapters noted.

- Aminophylline/theophylline (Asthma)
- Calcium salts (Osteoporosis, Menopause & Testosterone Use, Calculations IV)
- Insulin (Diabetes)
- Iron salts (Anemia)
- Loop diuretics (Chronic Heart Failure)
- Opioids (Pain)
- Potassium chloride (Chronic Heart Failure)
- Statins (Dyslipidemia)
- Steroids (Systemic Steroids & Autoimmune Conditions)
- IV:PO conversions
  - Furosemide (Chronic Heart Failure)
  - Levothyroxine (Thyroid Disorders)
  - Metoprolol (Chronic Heart Failure)

RATIOS

A ratio is a comparison between two numbers. Ratios can be used to describe how ingredients should be mixed. If compounding instructions state "mix petrolatum and lanolin in a 3:1 ratio," it means 3 parts of petrolatum should be mixed with 1 part of lanolin. The pharmacist needs to know the weight of one part in order to calculate the weight of the other or the weight of the final mixture. The ratio is usually converted to a fraction (e.g., 3:1 = 3/1) for use in math.

24. How many grams of bacitracin and nystatin are required to prepare 150 g of a 2:3 topical bacitracin:nystatin ointment?

Since the total weight is provided (150 g) and the total number of parts can be calculated (2 parts + 3 parts = 5 total parts), the value of 1 part can be determined using a proportion.

$$\frac{\text{5 total parts}}{\text{150 g}} = \frac{\text{1 part}}{\text{X g}} \quad \text{X = 30 g per 1 part}$$

$$\text{2 parts bacitracin} \times \frac{\text{30 grams}}{\text{1 part}} = \text{60 g bacitracin}$$

$$\text{3 parts nystatin} \times \frac{\text{30 grams}}{\text{1 part}} = \text{90 g nystatin}$$

Add the weights to confirm that they match the total weight:

$$\text{60 g bacitracin + 90 g nystatin} = \text{150 g of 2:3 bacitracin:nystatin ointment}$$

RATIO RELATIONSHIPS

$$4{:}8 = \frac{4}{8} = \frac{1}{2}$$ Or, 1 part to 2 parts

DECIMALS AND PERCENTAGE CONVERSION

To convert a decimal to a percentage, multiply the decimal by 100.

To convert a percentage to a decimal, divide the percentage by 100.

25. HT is a 16-year-old female who complains of weakness, fatigue and heavy menstrual periods. She is diagnosed with anemia. HT takes ferrous sulfate 220 mg once daily. How many milligrams of elemental iron does HT receive from the supplement? Ferrous sulfate is 20% elemental iron.

Divide the percentage by 100: 20%/100 = 0.2

Multiply the total amount of ferrous sulfate by 0.2 to determine the amount of elemental iron in mg:

220 mg x 0.2 = 44 mg elemental iron

SQUARING A NUMBER

26. Calculate 3.5^2.

Either method will provide the answer:

Method 1: Multiply the number by itself:

3.5 x 3.5 = 12.25

Method 2: Use the x^2 key on the calculator:

1. Enter the number to square on the calculator: 3.5
2. Hit the x^2 key
3. This will provide the same answer: 12.25

EXPONENTS

27. Calculate 2^4.

1. Enter the first number (in this example, enter 2)
2. Hit the x^y key
3. Enter the exponent (in this example, enter 4)
4. This will provide the answer; in this example, the answer is 16

ORDER OF OPERATIONS

Math calculations that involve more than one function need to be completed in a specified order (see Study Tip Gal). The order is brackets (first), then parenthesis, then exponents, then multiplication and division (left to right), then addition and subtraction (left to right). In fractions, the fraction bar is a grouping symbol; the entire numerator and the entire denominator are calculated before dividing the denominator into the numerator.

FOLLOW THE RULES OF MATH

Brackets → Parentheses (and other grouping symbols)→ Exponents → Multiplication and Division → Addition and Subtraction

Remember: **B-PEMDAS**

Billy, **P**lease **E**at **M**om's **D**elicious **A**pple **S**trudel

Phenytoin and valproate require a specific formula to calculate the corrected drug level when the albumin is low (< 3.5 g/dL). Refer to the Seizures/Epilepsy chapter for additional discussion. The order of operations must be followed in order to get the correct result.

28. SJ is a female patient in the internal medicine unit receiving treatment following a motor vehicle accident. Her medications include lorazepam, morphine and phenytoin. Her serum albumin is 1.8 g/dL and her phenytoin level is 9.6 mcg/mL. Calculate SJ's corrected phenytoin level using the formula provided. Round to the nearest one decimal place.

$$\text{Phenytoin corrected* (mcg/mL)} = \frac{\text{Total phenytoin measured}}{(0.2 \times \text{albumin}) + 0.1} \quad \dagger$$

**Same formula is used for valproic acid correction*

† Use serum phenytoin in mcg/mL and albumin in g/dL (standard units in the U.S.) in the corrected phenytoin formula. The units are not intended to cancel out.

$$\text{Phenytoin corrected} = \frac{9.6}{(0.2 \times 1.8) + 0.1} = \ \sim 20.8696 \text{ mg/L}$$

Round to the nearest one decimal place = 20.9 mg/L

1. Do the math inside parentheses first: 0.2 x 1.8 = 0.36
2. Add 0.1 to the answer: 0.36 + 0.1 = 0.46
3. Divide 9.6 by the answer: 9.6 divided by 0.46 = 20.9 (per rounding instructions provided)

READY TO SUBMIT YOUR ANSWER?

Not so fast. Do a double check first!

Ask yourself these questions to avoid common mistakes:

- Does the answer match the question?
  - ❑ Re-read the question. Did you solve for the right thing? Remember many problems on the exam require more than one step.
- Is the answer in the correct units? This is a common mistake. The problem may have been done correctly, but one more step is required to convert the answer to the specified units.
- Is the answer rounded correctly? The rounding instructions must be followed to get the problems right on the exam.
- Does the answer make sense?
  - ❑ If the problem asks how many liters of fluid a patient will receive in one day, 20,000 liters is unlikely to be the right answer. It does not make sense.

CHAPTER CONTENT

Percentage Strength......128
Common IV Fluids......129
Ratio Strength......132
Parts Per Million......134
Specific Gravity......135
Dilution and Concentration (Q1C1)......136
Alligation......137
Osmolarity......139
Isotonicity......142
Moles and Millimoles......144
Milliequivalents......146
Dissociation Particles vs. Valence......146

CONTENT LEGEND

= Study Tip Gal

CHAPTER 10
CALCULATIONS II: COMPOUNDING

PERCENTAGE STRENGTH

Drug concentrations can be expressed in many ways, but they are a ratio of the amount of an ingredient to the total amount of the product. A percent is the number of parts in 100. Percents are often written as decimals or fractions (e.g., 25% = 0.25 = 25/100). The types of percentage concentrations are defined as follows:

- Percent weight-in-volume (% w/v) is expressed as g/100 mL (a solid mixed into a liquid). This applies to common IV fluids (see Study Tip Gal on the next page).
- Percent volume-in-volume (% v/v) is expressed as mL/100 mL (a liquid mixed into a liquid).
- Percent weight-in-weight (% w/w) is expressed as g/100 g (a solid mixed into a solid).

1. How many grams of NaCl are in 1 liter of normal saline (NS)?

Normal saline contains 0.9 g NaCl per 100 mL of solution (see Study Tip Gal on the next page). Percentage strength problems are solved with simple proportions (reviewed in detail in Calculations I).

$$\frac{0.9\text{ g}}{100\text{ mL}} = \frac{X\text{ g}}{1{,}000\text{ mL}} \quad X = 9\text{ g}$$

2. How many grams of NaCl are in 500 mL of 1/2NS? Round to the nearest hundredth.

Since NS is 0.9% NaCl, 1/2NS is 0.45%.

$$\frac{0.45\text{ g}}{100\text{ mL}} = \frac{X\text{ g}}{500\text{ mL}} \quad X = 2.25\text{ g}$$

---

3. How many grams of dextrose are in 250 mL of D5W? Round to the nearest tenth.

$$\frac{5\text{ g}}{100\text{ mL}} = \frac{X\text{ g}}{250\text{ mL}} \quad X = 12.5\text{ g}$$

---

4. How many milligrams of triamcinolone should be used in preparing the following prescription? Round to the nearest whole number.

PRESCRIPTION	QUANTITY
Triamcinolone (w/v)	5%
Glycerin qs	60 mL
Sig. Two drops in right ear once daily	

$$\frac{5\text{ g}}{100\text{ mL}} = \frac{X\text{ g}}{60\text{ mL}} \quad X = 3\text{ g, or 3,000 mg}$$

COMMON IV FLUIDS

- Normal saline (NS) = 0.9% (w/v) NaCl
  - 1/2NS (called "half normal saline") = 0.45% (w/v) NaCl
  - 1/4NS (called "quarter normal saline") = 0.225% (w/v) NaCl
- D5W (called "D-5-W") = 5% (w/v) dextrose in water
- D20W = 20% (w/v) dextrose in water
- Combination fluid examples
  - D5NS (called "D-5-N-S") = 5% dextrose and 0.9% NaCl in water
  - D51/2NS (called "D-5-Half-N-S") = 5% dextrose and 0.45% NaCl in water

---

5. A prescription reads as follows: "Prepare a 3% w/w coal tar preparation; qs with petrolatum to 150 grams." How many grams of petrolatum are required to compound the prescription? Round to the nearest tenth.

$$\frac{3\text{ g coal tar}}{100\text{ g preparation}} = \frac{X\text{ g coal tar}}{150\text{ g preparation}} \quad X = 4.5\text{ g coal tar}$$

150 g (total weight of preparation) − 4.5 g (coal tar) = 145.5 g petrolatum

---

6. A pharmacist is compounding a vancomycin oral suspension. The master formulation record says to reconstitute a 5 g vial of vancomycin powder with 50 mL of sterile water, then dilute with sterile water to 200 mL. What is the final percentage strength of the compounded product (% w/v)?

$$\frac{5\text{ g}}{200\text{ mL}} = \frac{X\text{ g}}{100\text{ mL}} \quad X = 2.5\text{ g, which is 2.5\%}$$

---

7. If 1,250 grams of a mixture contains 80 grams of drug, what is the percentage strength (w/w) of the mixture? Round to the nearest tenth.

$$\frac{80\text{ g}}{1{,}250\text{ g}} = \frac{X\text{ g}}{100\text{ g}} \quad X = 6.4\text{ g, which is 6.4\%}$$

8. A mouth rinse contains 1/12% (w/v) of chlorhexidine gluconate. How many grams of chlorhexidine gluconate should be used to prepare 18 liters of mouth rinse? Round to the nearest whole number.

First, convert 1/12% to a decimal. 1/12% = 0.083 g per 100 mL (w/v).

Next, convert L to mL. 18 L x 1,000 mL/L = 18,000 mL.

Then, solve for grams of chlorhexidine gluconate needed.

$$\frac{0.083\ g}{100\ mL} = \frac{X\ g}{18{,}000\ mL} \quad X = 14.94\ g\text{, rounded to } 15\ g$$

9. SS is a 79-year-old female with dry mouth and dry eyes from Sjögren's syndrome. She is picking up the prescription below. What is the maximum milligrams of pilocarpine she will receive per day?

PRESCRIPTION	QUANTITY
Pilocarpine	1% (w/v)
Sodium Chloride qs ad	15 mL
Sig: 2 gtts (0.05 mL/gtt) po TID prn up to 5 days for dry mouth	

First, calculate the amount of pilocarpine in the prescription.

$$\frac{1\ g}{100\ mL} = \frac{X\ g}{15\ mL} \quad X = 0.15\ g$$

Then, convert to mg since the problem asks for mg of pilocarpine.

$$0.15\ g \times \frac{1{,}000\ mg}{1\ g} = 150\ mg\text{ of pilocarpine}$$

The patient will receive up to 3 doses per day (0.1 mL x 3 = 0.3 mL). Calculate the amount of pilocarpine in 0.3 mL.

$$\frac{150\ mg\text{ pilocarpine}}{15\ mL} = \frac{X\ mg}{0.3\ mL} \quad X = 3\ mg\text{ pilocarpine}$$

10. A pharmacist dissolves 6 tablets. Each tablet contains 250 mg of metronidazole. The pharmacist will put the drug into a liquid base to prepare 60 mL of a topical solution. What is the percentage strength (w/v) of metronidazole in the prescription? Round to the nearest tenth.

$$6\text{ tablets} \times \frac{250\ mg}{1\text{ tab}} = 1{,}500\ mg\text{, or } 1.5\ g$$

$$\frac{1.5\ g}{60\ mL} = \frac{X\ g}{100\ mL} \quad X = 2.5\ g\text{, which is } 2.5\%\ w/v$$

11. If 12 grams of lanolin are combined with 2 grams of white wax and 36 grams of petrolatum to make an ointment, what is the percentage strength (w/w) of lanolin in the ointment?

$$\frac{12\ g\text{ lanolin}}{50\ g\text{ ointment}} = \frac{X\ g}{100\ g} \quad X = 24\%\ w/w$$

12. A pharmacist adds 5.3 grams of hydrocortisone to 150 grams of a 2.5% hydrocortisone ointment. What is the percentage (w/w) of hydrocortisone in the finished product? Round to the nearest whole number.

First, determine the amount of hydrocortisone (HC) in the current product.

$$\frac{2.5 \text{ g HC}}{100 \text{ g ointment}} = \frac{X \text{ g HC}}{150 \text{ g ointment}} \quad X = 3.75 \text{ g HC}$$

5.3 grams of HC is being added to the existing product which contains 3.75 g of HC: 5.3 g + 3.75 g = 9.05 g.

Next, find the percent concentration of the final product (5.3 g + 150 g = 155.3 g).

$$\frac{9.05 \text{ g HC}}{155.3 \text{ g ointment}} = \frac{X \text{ g HC}}{100 \text{ g ointment}} \quad X = 5.8274 \text{ g, rounded to } 6\%$$

---

13. How many milliliters of hydrocortisone liquid (40 mg/mL) will be needed to prepare 30 grams of a 0.25% cream (w/w)? Round to the nearest hundredth.

First, calculate the amount of hydrocortisone needed in the final product.

$$\frac{0.25 \text{ g}}{100 \text{ g}} = \frac{X \text{ g}}{30 \text{ g}} \quad X = 0.075 \text{ g or } 75 \text{ mg}$$

Then, solve for mL of hydrocortisone liquid needed.

$$\frac{40 \text{ mg}}{\text{mL}} = \frac{75 \text{ mg}}{X \text{ mL}} \quad X = 1.875 \text{ mL, rounded to } 1.88 \text{ mL}$$

After solving the problem, read the question again to be certain the question was answered with the correct units (mL).

---

14. What is the percentage strength of imiquimod in the following prescription? Round to the nearest hundredth.

PRESCRIPTION	QUANTITY
Imiquimod 5% cream	15 g
Xylocaine	20 g
Hydrophilic ointment	25 g

First, calculate the amount of imiquimod (5%) in the prescription.

$$\frac{5 \text{ g}}{100 \text{ g}} \times 15 \text{ g} = 0.75 \text{ grams of imiquimod}$$

The total weight of the prescription is 60 g (15 g + 20 g + 25 g).

$$\frac{0.75 \text{ g}}{60 \text{ g}} = \frac{X \text{ g}}{100 \text{ g}} \quad X = 1.25 \text{ g, which is } 1.25\%$$

RATIO STRENGTH

The concentration of a weak solution can be expressed as a ratio strength. It is denoted as one unit of solute contained in the total amount of the solution or mixture (e.g., 1:500). Ratio strength is another way of presenting a percentage strength. This makes sense because percentages are ratios of parts per hundred.

In clinical practice, ratio strengths have been associated with medication errors. The FDA now requires removal of ratio strengths from the labeling of injectable drug products with only one active ingredient (e.g., epinephrine, isoproterenol). Ratio strength is still commonly used in compounding.

SHORTCUT FOR RATIO STRENGTH

Most multi-step calculations will require converting ratio strength to percentage strength. If a ratio strength is presented in a problem, convert it to a percentage strength and convert it back if needed.

- Ratio strength → Percentage strength
  - % strength = 100 / ratio strength
- Percentage strength → Ratio strength
  - Ratio strength = 100 / % strength

15. Express 0.04% as a ratio strength.

$$\frac{0.04}{100} = \frac{1 \text{ part}}{X \text{ parts}} \quad X = 2{,}500. \text{ Ratio strength is } 1{:}2{,}500$$

Convert back to 0.04% by taking 1/2,500 x 100 or simply 100/2,500. Try it.

On the exam, you will be provided with instructions on how to enter your answer. Usually you will enter just the numbers after the colon in the ratio strength (e.g., for this problem, you would enter 2500). The instructions could read "Calculate the ratio strength. Enter only the numbers after the colon, as shown here with Xs: 1:XXX."

16. Express 1:4,000 as a percentage strength.

$$\frac{1 \text{ part}}{4{,}000 \text{ parts}} = \frac{X}{100} \quad X = 0.025, \text{ which is } 0.025\%$$

Problem #16 can be done using the shortcut in the box above for converting between ratio and percentage strength:

Percentage strength = 100 / 4,000 = 0.025%

17. There are 50 mg of drug in 50 mL of solution. Express the concentration as a ratio strength.

First, convert 50 mg to grams. 50 mg x 1 g/1,000 mg = 0.05 g

Then, calculate grams per 100 mL.

$$\frac{0.05 \text{ g}}{50 \text{ mL}} = \frac{X \text{ g}}{100 \text{ mL}} \quad X = 0.1 \text{ g}$$

Now solve for ratio strength.

$$\frac{0.1 \text{ g}}{100 \text{ mL}} = \frac{1 \text{ part}}{X \text{ parts}} \quad X = 1{,}000, \text{ or } 1{:}1{,}000$$

18. How many milligrams of iodine should be used in compounding the following prescription?

ITEM	QUANTITY
Iodine	1:400
Hydrophilic ointment qs ad	10 g
Sig. Apply as directed.	

First, convert the ratio strength to a percentage strength.

$$\frac{1 \text{ part}}{400 \text{ parts}} = \frac{X \text{ g}}{100 \text{ g}} \quad X = 0.25\%$$

Then, determine how much iodine will be needed for the prescription.

$$\frac{0.25 \text{ g}}{100 \text{ g}} = \frac{X \text{ g}}{10 \text{ g}} \quad X = 0.025 \text{ g, or } 25 \text{ mg}$$

Or, solve another way:

1:400 means 1 g in 400 g of ointment.

$$\frac{1 \text{ g}}{400 \text{ g}} = \frac{X \text{ g}}{10 \text{ g}} \quad X = 0.025 \text{ g, or } 25 \text{ mg}$$

---

19. A 10 mL mixture contains 0.25 mL of active drug. Express the concentration as a percentage strength (% v/v) and a ratio strength.

First, find out how much drug is in 100 mL.

$$\frac{0.25 \text{ mL drug}}{10 \text{ mL}} = \frac{X \text{ mL drug}}{100 \text{ mL}} \quad X = 2.5 \text{ mL, or } 2.5\% \text{ (v/v)}$$

Now solve for ratio strength.

$$\frac{2.5 \text{ mL drug}}{100 \text{ mL}} = \frac{1 \text{ part}}{X \text{ parts}} \quad X = 40; \text{ or } 1:40$$

---

20. What is the concentration, in ratio strength, of a trituration made by combining 150 mg of albuterol sulfate and 4.05 grams of lactose?

First, add up the total weight of the prescription.

$$0.150 \text{ g} + 4.05 \text{ g} = 4.2 \text{ g}$$

Now solve for ratio strength.

$$\frac{0.150 \text{ g}}{4.2 \text{ g}} = \frac{1 \text{ part}}{X \text{ parts}} \quad X = 28, \text{ or } 1:28$$

Refer to the Compounding chapters for discussion of trituration and other compounding terminology.

PARTS PER MILLION

Parts per million (PPM) and parts per billion (PPB) are used to express the strength of very dilute solutions. They are defined as the number of parts of the drug per 1 million (or 1 billion) parts of the whole. The same designations are used as for percentage strength (% w/w, % w/v and % v/v).

SHORTCUT FOR PARTS PER MILLION

- PPM → Percentage strength
  - Move the decimal left 4 places
- Percentage strength → PPM
  - Move the decimal right 4 places

21. Express 0.00022% w/v as PPM. Round to the nearest tenth.

$$\frac{0.00022\ g}{100\ mL} = \frac{X\ parts}{1{,}000{,}000} \quad X = 2.2\ PPM$$

22. Express 30 PPM of copper in solution as a percentage.

$$\frac{30\ parts}{1{,}000{,}000} = \frac{X\ g}{100\ mL} \quad X = 0.003\%$$

23. Express 5 PPM of iron in water as a percentage.

$$\frac{5\ parts}{1{,}000{,}000} = \frac{X\ g}{100\ mL} \quad X = 0.0005\%$$

24. A patient's blood contains 0.085 PPM of selenium. How many micrograms of selenium does the patient's blood contain if the blood volume is 6 liters?

$$\frac{0.085\ parts}{1{,}000{,}000} = \frac{X\ g}{6{,}000\ mL} \quad X = 0.00051\ g,\ or\ 510\ mcg$$

25. A sample of an intravenous solution is found to contain 0.4 PPM of DEHP. How much of the solution, in milliliters, will contain 50 micrograms of DEHP?

$$\frac{0.4\ parts}{1{,}000{,}000} = \frac{0.00005\ g}{X\ mL} \quad X = 125\ mL$$

If asked to express something in PPB (parts per billion), divide by 1,000,000,000 (9 zeros).

SPECIFIC GRAVITY

Specific gravity (SG) is the ratio of the density of a substance to the density of water. SG can be important for calculating doses of IV medications, in compounding and in interpreting a urinalysis. Water has a specific gravity of 1; 1 g water = 1 mL water. Substances with a SG < 1 are lighter than water and those with SG > 1 are heavier than water.

$$SG = \frac{\text{weight of substance (g)}}{\text{weight of equal volume of water (g)}} \quad \text{or more simply:} \quad SG = \frac{g}{mL}$$

26. What is the specific gravity of 150 mL of glycerin weighing 165 grams? Round to the nearest tenth.

$$SG = \frac{165\ g}{150\ mL} \qquad SG = 1.1$$

Check the answer: 150 mL x 1.1 = 165 g

27. What is the weight of 750 mL of concentrated acetic acid (SG = 1.2)?

$$1.2 = \frac{X\ g}{750\ mL} \qquad X = 900\ g$$

Check the answer: 900 g/750 mL = 1.2

28. How many milliliters of polysorbate 80 (SG = 1.08) are needed to prepare a prescription that includes 48 grams of the surfactant/emulsifier (polysorbate)? Round to the nearest hundredth.

$$1.08 = \frac{48\ g}{X\ mL} \qquad X = 44.44\ mL$$

29. What is the specific gravity of 30 mL of a liquid weighing 23,400 milligrams? Round to the nearest hundredth.

$$SG = \frac{23.4\ g}{30\ mL} \qquad SG = 0.78$$

30. What is the weight of 0.5 L of polyethylene glycol 400 (SG = 1.13).

$$1.13 = \frac{X\ g}{500\ mL} \qquad X = 565\ grams$$

31. Nitroglycerin has a specific gravity of 1.59. How much would 1 quart weigh in grams? Use 1 quart = 946 mL. Round to the nearest whole number.

$$1.59 = \frac{X\ g}{946\ mL} \qquad X = 1{,}504\ g$$

Check the answer: 1,504 g/946 mL = 1.59

Note that the SG is equivalent to the density in g/mL (with units). If asked for the density in the above problem, the answer would be 1.59 g/mL.

DILUTION AND CONCENTRATION (Q1C1)

Often the strength of a product must be increased or decreased, or a new quantity is required. This formula can be used to change the strength or quantity. Be careful: the units on each side must match and one or more may need to be changed, such as mg to gram, or vice-versa. Q1C1 is used when the problem deals with two concentrations.

Q1 x C1 = Q2 x C2	
Q1 = old quantity	Q2 = new quantity
C1 = old concentration	C2 = new concentration

32. A pharmacist has an order for parenteral nutrition that includes 550 mL of D70%. The pharmacist checks the supplies and finds the closest strength he has available is D50%. How many milliliters of D50% will provide an equivalent energy requirement?

550 mL x 70% = Q2 mL x 50%

Q2 = 770 mL of D50%

33. How many grams of petrolatum (diluent) should be added to 250 grams of a 20% ichthammol ointment to make a 7% ichthammol ointment? Round to the nearest tenth.

Note the difference from the previous problem. In this example, the problem asks how much diluent should be added to make the final weight.

250 g x 20% = Q2 x 7%

Q2 = 714.3 g of 7% ichthammol ointment

If the prescription calls for an ingredient that is pure, the concentration is 100%.

If a diluent is mentioned (e.g., petrolatum, lanolin, alcohol, ointment base, inert base, lactose, *Aquaphor*), the concentration of the diluent is 0%.

Read the question again to be certain about what is being asked. Since the question did not ask how much of the 7% ointment can be prepared, but rather how much diluent is required, an additional step is needed:

714.3 g total weight - 250 g (already present) = 464.3 g petrolatum required

34. Using 20 grams of a 9% boric acid ointment base, the pharmacist will manufacture a 5% ointment. How much diluent is required?

20 g x 9% = Q2 x 5%

Q2 = 36 g of the 5% ointment can be prepared

36 g total weight - 20 g (already present) = 16 g diluent required

35. If 1 gallon of a 20% (w/v) solution is evaporated to a solution with a 50% (w/v) strength, what will be the new volume (in milliliters)? Round to the nearest 100 mL.

3,785 mL x 20% = Q2 x 50%

Q2 = 1,514 mL, rounded to the nearest 100 mL = 1500 mL

This answer will be the same regardless of which conversion is used for gallon to mL.

36. A patient has been receiving 200 mL of an enteral mixture that contains 432 mOsm/L. The pharmacist will reduce the contents to 278 mOsm/L. How many milliliters of bacteriostatic water should be added to the bag? Round to the nearest mL.

200 mL x 432 mOsm/L = Q2 x 278 mOsm/L X = 311 mL

Q2 = 311 mL of the 278 mOsm/L enteral mixture can be prepared

There are 200 mL in the original bag. The final volume will be 311 mL.

311 mL - 200 mL = 111 mL of bacteriostatic water

ALLIGATION

Alligation is used to obtain a new strength (percentage) that is between two strengths the pharmacist has in stock. It is used when the problem deals with three concentrations. Sometimes no math is required to solve this type of problem if the new strength needed is exactly in the middle of the two strengths that are available.

37. A pharmacist must prepare 100 grams of a 50% hydrocortisone powder using the 25% and 75% powders that she has in stock. How much of each is required?

Since the desired strength is exactly in the middle of the strengths available, divide the desired quantity in half (100 g / 2 = 50 grams). Use 50 g of the 75% and 50 g of the 25% to prepare 100 g of a 50% powder.

---

38. A pharmacist is asked to prepare 80 grams of a 12.5% ichthammol ointment with 16% and 12% ichthammol ointments that she has in stock. How many grams of the 16% and 12% ointment are required?

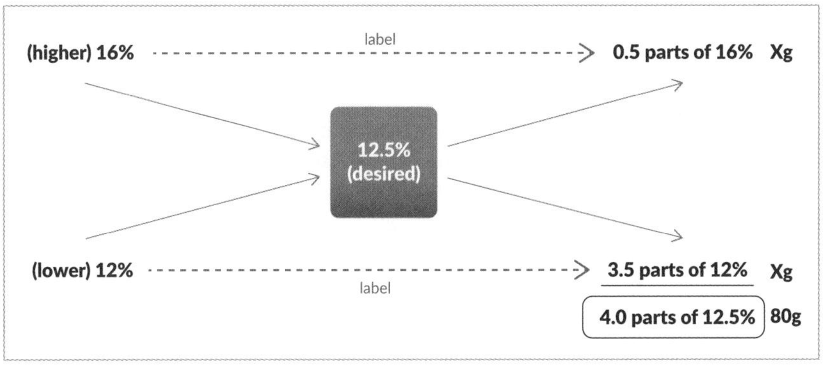

Setting Up An Alligation

- High goes high: write the higher concentration at the top left.
- Low goes low: write the lower concentration on the lower left.
- Write the desired concentration in the middle.
- Subtract diagonally along the X lines to obtain the number of parts. Write the absolute number (no negative sign) on the right side of the X.
  - ❑ 16% - 12.5% = 3.5 parts
  - ❑ 12% - 12.5% = 0.5 parts
- Label horizontally along the dashed lines; the starting concentrations are carried across.
- For some problems, it will be necessary to add up the total number of parts (as shown).

Divide the total weight (80 g) by the number of parts to get the weight per part.

$$\frac{80\ g}{4\ parts} = 20\ grams\ per\ part$$

Take the amount per part (20 g) and multiply it by the parts from each of the concentrations (from the high, and from the low).

$$0.5\ parts\ of\ 16\% \times \frac{20\ g}{part} = 10\ g\ of\ the\ 16\%\ ichthammol\ ointment$$

$$3.5\ parts\ of\ 12\% \times \frac{20\ g}{part} = 70\ g\ of\ the\ 12\%\ ichthammol\ ointment$$

When the two quantities are mixed together, the pharmacist will have 80 g of a 12.5% ichthammol ointment.

39. A pharmacist is asked to prepare 1 gallon of tincture containing 5.5% iodine. The pharmacy has 3% iodine tincture and 8.5% iodine tincture in stock. How many milliliters of the 3% and 8.5% iodine tincture should be used? (Use 1 gallon = 3,785 mL)

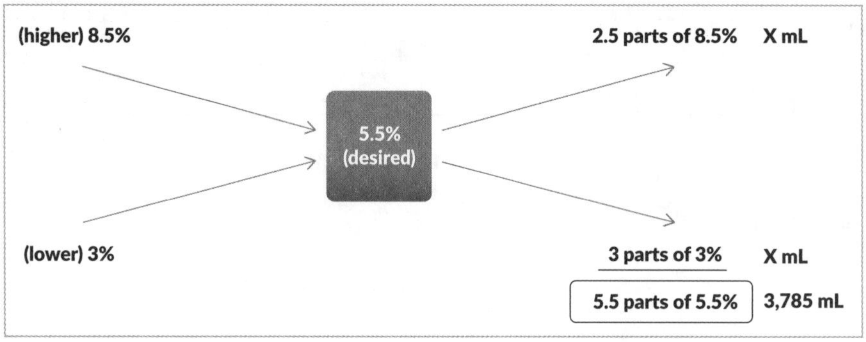

Divide the total volume (3,785 mL) by the number of parts to obtain the volume per part.

$$\frac{3{,}785 \text{ mL}}{5.5 \text{ parts}} = 688.2 \text{ mL per part}$$

$$2.5 \text{ parts} \times \frac{688.2 \text{ mL}}{\text{part}} = 1{,}720 \text{ mL of the 8.5\% iodine tincture}$$

$$3 \text{ parts} \times \frac{688.2 \text{ mL}}{\text{part}} = 2{,}065 \text{ mL of the 3\% iodine tincture}$$

The end product provides 3,785 mL of a 5.5% iodine tincture. Alligation can also be used when the final volume is not known, as shown in the next problem.

---

40. A hospice pharmacist receives a prescription for 1% morphine sulfate oral solution. She has a 120 mL bottle of morphine sulfate labeled 20 mg/5 mL and a 240 mL bottle of morphine sulfate labeled 100 mg/5 mL. How much of the 100 mg/5 mL product must be mixed with the contents of the 20 mg/5 mL morphine sulfate bottle to prepare the desired percentage strength for the patient?

First determine the percentage strengths of the two available products.

20 mg/5 mL $\quad \frac{0.02 \text{ g}}{5 \text{ mL}} = \frac{X \text{ g}}{100 \text{ mL}} \quad X = 0.4\%$

100 mg/5 mL $\quad \frac{0.1 \text{ g}}{5 \text{ mL}} = \frac{X \text{ g}}{100 \text{ mL}} \quad X = 2\%$

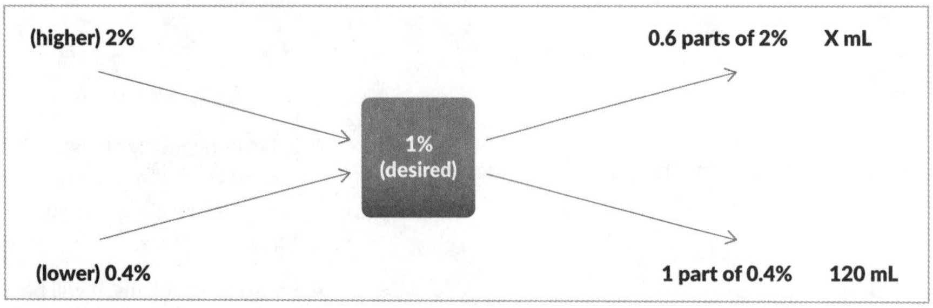

In this case, we do not know the final volume of the product, but we know the proper ratio of the parts (0.6:1).

$$\frac{\text{1 part of 0.4\% morphine}}{\text{0.6 parts of 2\% morphine}} = \frac{\text{120 mL of 0.4\% morphine}}{\text{X mL of 2\% morphine}} \quad X = 72 \text{ mL of 2\% morphine sulfate}$$

72 mL of 2% (100 mg/5 mL) morphine sulfate must be added to the 120 mL of 0.4% (20 mg/5 mL) morphine sulfate to get a 1% solution. Ultimately, 192 mL of 1% product can be prepared, but the alligation must be solved to determine that.

OSMOLARITY

The total number of particles in a given solution is directly proportional to its osmotic pressure. The particles are usually measured in milliosmoles. Osmolarity is the measure of total number of particles (or solutes) per liter of solution, defined as osmoles/liter (Osmol/L) or, more commonly as milliosmoles/liter (mOsmol/L). Solutes can be either ionic (such as NaCl, which dissociates into two solutes in solution, Na^+ and Cl^-) or non-ionic, which do not dissociate (such as glucose and urea).

COMPOUND	# OF DISSOCIATION PARTICLES
Dextrose	1
Mannitol	1
Potassium chloride (KCl)	2
Sodium chloride (NaCl)	2
Sodium acetate ($NaC_2H_3O_2$)	2
Magnesium sulfate ($MgSO_4$)	2
Calcium chloride ($CaCl_2$)	3
Sodium citrate ($Na_3C_6H_5O_7$)	4

Since the volume of water changes according to temperature, the term osmolality (mOsmol/kg) is used in clinical practice; it is independent of temperature. When solute concentrations are very low, osmolarity and osmolality are similar.

Milliosmole calculation problems differ from osmolarity calculation problems in that osmolarity will always need to be normalized to a volume of 1 liter. Math problems usually use osmolarity. The compounds and dissociation particles shown in the table should be known for the exam.

$$\text{mOsmol/L} = \frac{\text{Wt of substance (g/L)}}{\text{MW (g/mole)}} \times (\text{\# of particles}) \times 1{,}000$$

Step 1. Add up the number of particles into which the compound dissociates.

Step 2. Calculate the number of grams of the compound present in 1 L.

Step 3. Use the molecular weight (M.W.) to solve the problem.

Milliosmole calculations do not normalize to 1 liter.

---

41. What is the osmolarity, in mOsmol/L, of normal saline (0.9% NaCl)? M.W. = 58.5. Round to the nearest whole number.

NaCl dissociates into 2 particles; Na^+ and Cl^-.

Calculate the number of grams of the compound (NaCl) present in 1 L.

$$\frac{0.9\ \text{g}}{100\ \text{mL}} = \frac{X\ \text{g}}{1{,}000\ \text{mL}} \quad X = 9\ \text{g}$$

Use the molecular weight to solve for mOsmol/L.

$$\text{mOsmol/L} = \frac{9\ \text{g/L}}{58.5\ \text{g/mole}} \times 2 \times 1{,}000 = 308\ \text{mOsmol/L}$$

---

42. What is the osmolarity, in mOsmol/L, of D5W? M.W. = 198. Round to the nearest tenth.

Dextrose does not dissociate and is counted as 1 particle.

$$\frac{5\ \text{g}}{100\ \text{mL}} = \frac{X\ \text{g}}{1{,}000\ \text{mL}} \quad X = 50\ \text{g}$$

Use the molecular weight to solve for mOsmol/L.

$$\text{mOsmol/L} = \frac{50\ \text{g/L}}{198\ \text{g/mole}} \times 1 \times 1{,}000 = 252.5\ \text{mOsmol/L}$$

43. How many milliosmoles of $CaCl_2$ (M.W.= 111) are represented in 150 mL of a 10% (w/v) calcium chloride solution? Round to the nearest whole number.

$$\frac{10\ g}{100\ mL} = \frac{X\ g}{150\ mL} \quad X = 15\ g$$

$$mOsmol = \frac{15\ g}{111\ g/mol} \times 3 \times 1{,}000 = 405\ mOsmol$$

Note that the problem is asking for milliosmoles and not osmolarity. The answer is in milliosmoles and not mOsmol/L. It is not normalized to 1 liter.

---

44. A solution contains 373 mg Na ions per liter. How many milliosmoles are represented in the solution? M.W. = 23. Round to the nearest tenth.

First, convert the units to match the formula.

$$\frac{373\ mg\ Na}{L} \times \frac{1\ g}{1{,}000\ mg} = 0.373\ g/L$$

$$mOsmol = \frac{0.373\ g/L}{23\ g/mole} \times 1 \times 1{,}000 = 16.2\ mOsmol$$

The problem asks for milliosmoles and not osmolarity. Since the problem provides the amount of Na ions in 1 liter, the numerical answer is the same (mOsmol or mOsmol/L).

---

45. How many grams of potassium chloride are needed to make 200 mL of a solution containing 250 mOsmol/L? Round to the nearest hundredth. (M.W. K = 39, M.W. Cl = 35.5)

First calculate the M.W. of KCl.

M.W. of KCl = M.W. of K + M.W. of Cl = 39 + 35.5 = 74.5

$$250\ mOsmol/L = \frac{X}{74.5} \times 2 \times 1{,}000 \quad X = 9.31\ g/L$$

$$\frac{9.31\ g}{1{,}000\ mL} = \frac{X\ g}{200\ mL} \quad X = 1.86\ g$$

You may be provided with the molecular weight on the exam or asked to calculate it.

---

46. A solution contains 200 mg Ca ions per liter. How many milliosmoles are represented in the solution? M.W = 40.

$$mOsmol = \frac{0.2\ g/L}{40\ g/mole} \times 1 \times 1{,}000 = 5\ mOsmol$$

The problem is asking for milliosmoles and not osmolarity. The answer is in milliosmoles and not mOsmol/L. It is not normalized to 1 liter.

47. Calculate the osmolar concentration, in milliosmoles, represented by 1 liter of a 10% (w/v) solution of anhydrous dextrose (M.W. = 180) in water. Round to the nearest one decimal place.

$$\frac{10\ g}{100\ mL} = \frac{X\ g}{1{,}000\ mL} \quad X = 100\ g$$

$$mOsmol = \frac{100\ g/L}{180\ g/mole} \times 1 \times 1{,}000 = 555.6\ mOsmol$$

The problem asks for milliosmoles and not osmolarity. Since the problem asks for mOsmol of dextrose in 1 liter, the numerical answer is the same (mOsmol or mOsmol/L).

---

48. A patient was ordered 1 liter of D5NS with 20 mEq KCl for dehydration. How many milliosmoles are in 1 liter of this fluid (MW dextrose = 198, Na = 23, K = 39, Cl = 35.5)? Round to the nearest whole number.

First, solve for the osmolarity of the dextrose component.

$$\frac{5\ g\ Dextrose}{100\ mL} \times \frac{X\ g}{1{,}000\ mL} = 50\ g/L$$

$$mOsmol = \frac{50\ g/L}{198\ g/mole} \times 1 \times 1{,}000 = 252.5252\ mOsmol/L$$

Next, solve for the osmolarity of the NS component.

$$\frac{0.9\ g\ NaCl}{100\ mL} \times \frac{X\ g}{1{,}000\ mL} = 9\ g/L$$

$$mOsmol = \frac{9\ g/L}{58.5\ g/mole} \times 2 \times 1{,}000 = 307.6922\ mOsmol/L$$

Then, solve for the osmolarity of the KCl component, using the milliequivalent formula (reviewed later in this chapter).

$$20\ mEq = \frac{X\ mg \times 1}{74.5} = 1490\ mg = 1.49\ g$$

$$mOsmol = \frac{1.49\ g/L}{74.5\ g/mole} \times 2 \times 1{,}000 = 40\ mOsmol/L$$

The final step is to add the three components together to find the total osmolarity.

252.5252 + 307.6922 mL + 40 = 600.217 mOsmol/L, or 600 mOsmol/L

ISOTONICITY

When discussing osmotic pressure gradients between fluids, the term tonicity is used; solutions can be isotonic (osmolality is the same as blood, which is ~300 mOsmol/kg), hypotonic or hypertonic. When solutions are prepared, they need to match the tonicity of the body fluid as closely as possible. If the osmolality is higher in one cellular compartment, it will cause water to move from the lower to the higher concentration of solutes. If a PN solution is injected with a higher osmolality than blood, fluid will flow into the vein, resulting in edema, inflammation, phlebitis and possible thrombosis. Isotonicity is commonly used when preparing eye drops and nasal solutions.

Since isotonicity is related to the number of particles in solution, the dissociation factor (or ionization), symbolized by the letter *i*, is determined for the compound (drug). Non-ionic compounds do not dissociate and will have a dissociation factor, *i*, of one. The table shows the dissociation factors (*i*) based on the percentage that dissociates into ions; for example, a dissociation factor of 1.8 means that 80% of the compound will dissociate in a weak solution.

NUMBER OF DISSOCIATED IONS	DISSOCIATION FACTOR (OR IONIZATION) *i*
1	1
2	1.8
3	2.6
4	3.4
5	4.2

As mentioned above, body fluids are isotonic, having an osmotic pressure equivalent to 0.9% sodium chloride. When making a medication to place into a body fluid, the drug provides solutes to the solvent and needs to be accounted for in the prescription in order to avoid making the prescription hypertonic. The relationship between the amount of drug that produces a particular osmolarity and the amount of sodium chloride that produces the same osmolarity is called the sodium chloride equivalent, or "E value" for short. This is the formula for calculating the E value of a compound:

$$E = \frac{(58.5)(i)}{(\text{MW of drug})(1.8)}$$

The "E value" formula takes into account the molecular weight of NaCl (58.5) and the dissociation factor of 1.8 since normal saline is around 80% ionized; adding 0.8 for each additional ion beyond 1 into which the drug dissociates. The reason the compound is compared to NaCl is because NaCl is the major determinant of the isotonicity of body fluid.

Once the "E value" is determined, the following steps outline the process of doing isotonicity problems:

Step 1. Calculate the total amount of NaCl needed to make the final product/prescription isotonic by multiplying 0.9% NS by the desired volume of the prescription.

Step 2. Calculate the amount of NaCl represented by the drug. To do this, multiply the total drug amount (in milligrams or grams) by the "E value."

Step 3. Subtract step 2 from step 1 to determine the total amount of NaCl needed to prepare an isotonic prescription.

49. Calculate the E value for mannitol (M.W. = 182). Round to the nearest hundredth.

$$\frac{(58.5)(i)}{(\text{MW of drug})(1.8)} = \frac{58.5\ (1)}{182\ (1.8)} = 0.18$$

50. Calculate the E value for potassium iodide, which dissociates into 2 particles (M.W. = 166). Round to two decimal places.

$$\frac{(58.5)(i)}{(\text{MW of drug})(1.8)} = \frac{58.5\ (1.8)}{166\ (1.8)} = 0.35$$

51. Physostigmine salicylate (M.W. = 413) is a 2- ion electrolyte, dissociating 80% in a given concentration (i.e., use a dissociation factor of 1.8). Calculate its sodium chloride equivalent. Round to two decimal places.

$$\frac{(58.5)(i)}{(\text{MW of drug})(1.8)} = \frac{58.5\ (1.8)}{413\ (1.8)} = 0.14$$

---

52. The E value for ephedrine sulfate is 0.23. How many grams of sodium chloride are needed to compound the following prescription? Round to 3 decimal places.

PRESCRIPTION	QUANTITY
Ephedrine sulfate	0.4 g
Sodium chloride	q.s.
Purified water qs	30 mL
Make isotonic soln.	
Sig. For the nose.	

Step 1. Determine how much NaCl would make the product isotonic.

$$\frac{0.9\text{ g}}{100\text{ mL}} = \frac{X}{30\text{ mL}} \quad X = 0.27\text{ g}$$

Step 2. Determine amount of sodium chloride represented from ephedrine sulfate.

0.4 g x 0.23 ("E value") = 0.092 g of sodium chloride

Step 3. Subtract step 2 from step 1.

0.27 g – 0.092 g = 0.178 g of NaCl are needed to make an isotonic solution

---

53. The pharmacist receives an order for 10 mL of tobramycin 1% ophthalmic solution. He has tobramycin 40 mg/mL solution. Tobramycin does not dissociate and has a M.W. of 468. Find the E value for tobramycin and determine how many milligrams of NaCl are needed to make the solution isotonic. Round to two decimal places.

$$\frac{(58.5)(i)}{(\text{MW of drug})(1.8)} = \frac{58.5\ (1)}{468\ (1.8)} = 0.07\text{, which is the "E value" for tobramycin}$$

The "E value" for tobramycin is 0.07. The prescription asks for 10 mL of 1% solution.

Step 1. Determine how much NaCl would make the product isotonic (if that is all you were using).

$$\frac{0.9\text{ g}}{100\text{ mL}} = \frac{X}{10\text{ mL}} \quad X = 0.09\text{ g, or 90 mg}$$

Step 2. Determine amount of sodium chloride represented from tobramycin.

$$\frac{1\text{ g}}{100\text{ mL}} = \frac{X}{10\text{ mL}} \quad X = 0.1\text{ g, or 100 mg}$$

100 mg x 0.07 ("E value") = 7 mg of sodium chloride

Step 3. Subtract step 2 from step 1. You are using tobramycin, so you do not need all the NaCl. Subtract out the equivalent amount of tonicity provided by the tobramycin, which is 7 mg.

90 mg - 7 mg = 83 mg (83 mg additional sodium chloride is needed to make an isotonic solution)

MOLES AND MILLIMOLES

A mole (mol) is the molecular weight of a substance in grams, or g/mole. A millimole (mmol) is 1/1,000 of the molecular weight in grams, or 1/1,000 of a mole. For monovalent species, the numeric value of the milliequivalent and millimole are identical.

$$\text{mols} = \frac{\text{g}}{\text{MW}} \quad \text{or} \quad \text{mmols} = \frac{\text{mg}}{\text{MW}}$$

54. How many moles of anhydrous magnesium sulfate (M.W. = 120.4) are present in 250 grams of the substance? Round to the nearest hundredth.

$$\text{mols} = \frac{250\text{ g}}{120.4} = 2.076\text{, or }2.08\text{ mols}$$

55. How many moles are equivalent to 875 milligrams of aluminum acetate (M.W. = 204)? Round to 3 decimal places.

First, convert 875 mg to grams.

$$875\text{ mg} \times \frac{1\text{ g}}{1{,}000\text{ mg}} = 0.875\text{ g}$$

Next, solve for mols.

$$\text{mols} = \frac{0.875\text{ g}}{204} = 0.004\text{ mols}$$

56. How many millimoles of sodium phosphate (M.W. = 138) are present in 90 g of the substance? Round to the nearest whole number.

$$\text{mmols} = \frac{90{,}000\text{ mg}}{138} = 652\text{ mmols}$$

Or, solve another way:

$$\frac{90\text{ g}}{138} = 0.652\text{ mols, which is }652\text{ mmols}$$

57. How many moles are equivalent to 45 grams of potassium carbonate (M.W. = 138)? Round to the nearest thousandth.

$$\text{mols} = \frac{45\text{ g}}{138} = 0.326\text{ mols}$$

58. How many millimoles of calcium chloride (M.W. = 147) are represented in 147 mL of a 10% (w/v) calcium chloride solution?

Step 1: Calculate the amount (g) of $CaCl_2$ in 147 mL of 10% $CaCl_2$ solution.

$$\frac{10\ g}{100\ mL} = \frac{X\ g}{147\ mL} \quad X = 14.7\ g$$

Step 2: Calculate the mols of $CaCl_2$ in 147 mL of 10% $CaCl_2$ solution.

$$mols = \frac{14.7\ g}{147} = 0.1\ mol$$

Step 3: Solve the problem by converting moles to millimoles:

$$0.1\ mol \times 1{,}000 = 100\ mmols$$

---

59. How many milligrams of sodium chloride (MW = 58.5) represent 0.25 mmol? Do not round the answer.

$$0.25\ mmols = \frac{X\ mg}{58.5} \quad X = 14.625\ mg$$

---

60. How many grams of sodium chloride (M.W. = 58.5) should be used to prepare this solution? Do not round the answer.

PRESCRIPTION	QUANTITY
Methylprednisolone	0.5 g
NaCl solution	60 mL
Each 5 mL should contain 0.6 mmols of NaCl	

First determine how many mmols of NaCl will be in 60 mL of the compounded preparation.

$$\frac{0.6\ mmols}{5\ mL} = \frac{X\ mmols}{60\ mL} \quad X = 7.2\ mmols\ NaCl$$

Next, use the total mmols of NaCl to calculate grams of NaCl.

$$7.2\ mmols = \frac{X\ mg}{58.5} \quad X = 421.2\ mg\ or\ 0.4212\ g\ NaCl$$

MILLIEQUIVALENTS

Drugs can be expressed in solution in different ways:

- Milliosmoles refers to the number of particles in solution.
- Millimoles refers to the molecular weight (MW).
- Milliequivalents (mEq) represent the amount, in milligrams (mg), of a solute equal to 1/1,000 of its gram equivalent weight, taking into account the valence of the ions. Like osmolarity, the quantity of particles is important - but so is the electrical charge. Milliequivalents refers to the chemical activity of an electrolyte and is related to the total number of ionic charges in solution and considers the valence (charge) of each ion.

To count the valence, divide the compound into its positive and negative components, and then count the number of either the positive or the negative charges. For a given compound, the milliequivalents of cations equals that of anions. Some common compounds and their valences are listed in the table. A comparison of valence and dissociation particles is presented in the figure below (see Study Tip Gal). Remember, there are a lot of chelation drug interactions with "polyvalent" cations (calcium, magnesium and iron). Use that interaction to remember which compounds have a valence of 2!

COMPOUND	VALENCE
ammonium chloride (NH_4Cl)	1
potassium chloride (KCl)	1
potassium gluconate ($KC_6H_{11}O_7$)	1
sodium acetate ($NaC_2H_3O_2$)	1
sodium bicarbonate ($NaHCO_3$)	1
sodium chloride (NaCl)	1
calcium carbonate ($CaCO_3$)	2
calcium chloride ($CaCl_2$)	2
ferrous sulfate ($FeSO_4$)	2
magnesium sulfate ($MgSO_4$)	2

$$\text{mEq} = \frac{\text{mg x valence}}{\text{MW}} \quad \text{or} \quad \text{mEq} = \text{mmols x valence}$$

DISSOCIATION PARTICLES VS. VALENCE

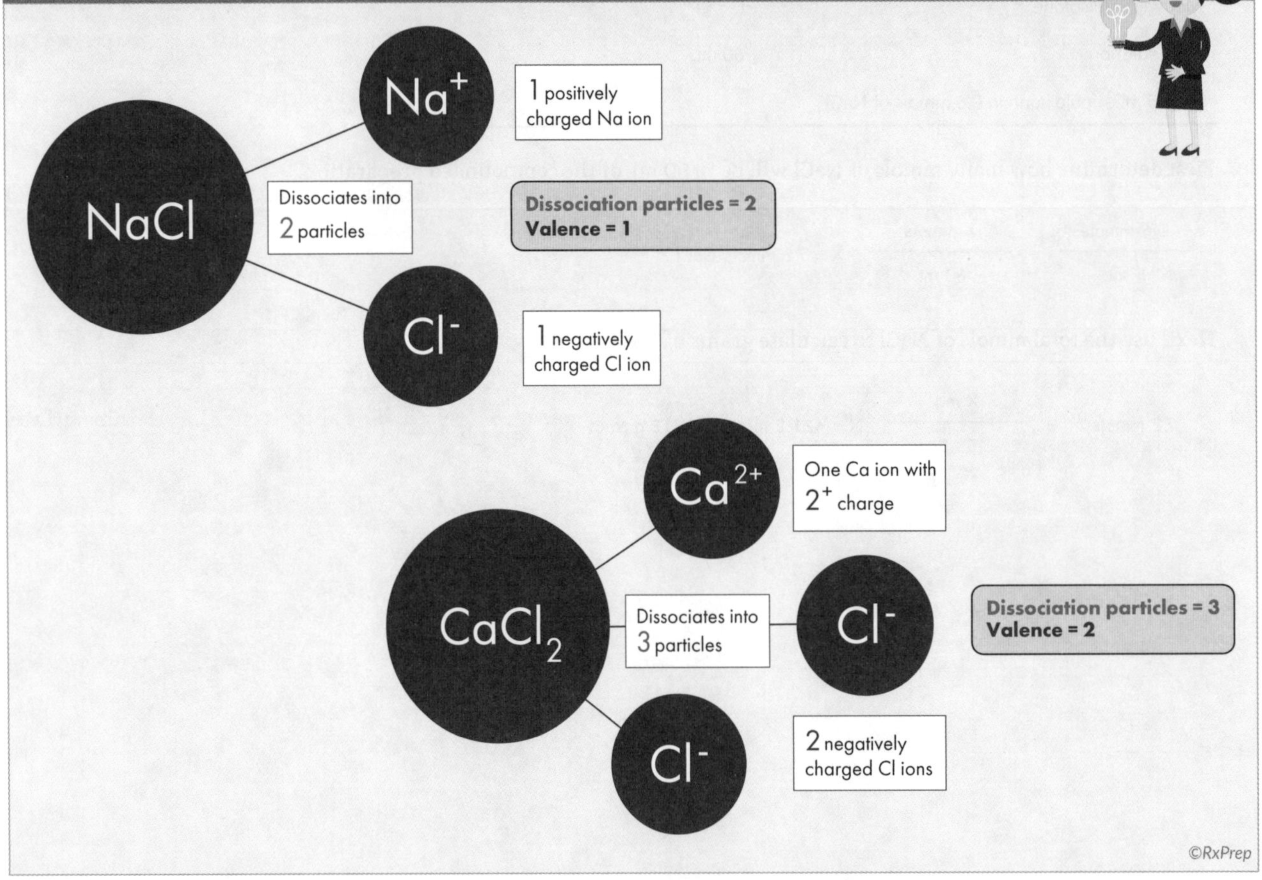

61. A 20 mL vial is labeled potassium chloride (2 mEq/mL). How many grams of potassium chloride (M.W. = 74.5) are present? Round to the nearest hundredth.

$$20 \text{ mL} \times \frac{2 \text{ mEq}}{\text{mL}} = 40 \text{ mEq KCl total}$$

$$40 \text{ mEq} = \frac{\text{mg} \times 1}{74.5} = 2{,}980 \text{ mg, which is } 2.98 \text{ g}$$

If asked to convert KCl liquid to tablets or vice versa, use a simple proportion since <u>KCl 10% = 20 mEq/15 mL</u>. For example, if someone is using Klor-Con 20 mEq BID, the total daily dose is 40 mEq. Convert to KCl 10%, as follows:

$$\frac{40 \text{ mEq}}{X \text{ mL}} = \frac{20 \text{ mEq}}{15 \text{ mL}} \quad X = 30 \text{ mL of KCl 10\% liquid is equal to Klor-Con 20 mEq PO BID}$$

---

62. How many milliequivalents of potassium chloride are present in a 12 mL dose of a 10% (w/v) potassium chloride (M.W. = 74.5) elixir? Round to 1 decimal place.

$$\frac{10 \text{ g}}{100 \text{ mL}} = \frac{X \text{ g}}{12 \text{ mL}} \quad X = 1.2 \text{ g, or } 1{,}200 \text{ mg}$$

$$\text{mEq} = \frac{1{,}200 \text{ mg} \times 1}{74.5} = 16.1 \text{ mEq}$$

---

63. Calculate the milliequivalents of a standard ammonium chloride (M.W. = 53.5) 21.4 mg/mL sterile solution in a 500 mL container.

$$\frac{21.4 \text{ mg}}{\text{mL}} \times 500 \text{ mL} = 10{,}700 \text{ mg}$$

$$\text{mEq} = \frac{10{,}700 \text{ mg} \times 1}{53.5} = 200 \text{ mEq}$$

---

64. How many milliequivalents of $MgSO_4$ (M.W. = 120.4) are represented in 1 gram of anhydrous magnesium sulfate? Round to the nearest tenth.

$$\text{mEq} = \frac{1{,}000 \text{ mg} \times 2}{120.4} = 16.6 \text{ mEq}$$

---

65. How many milliequivalents of sodium are in a 50 mL vial of sodium bicarbonate (M.W. = 84) 8.4%?

$$\frac{8.4 \text{ g}}{100 \text{ mL}} = \frac{X \text{ g}}{50 \text{ mL}} \quad X = 4.2 \text{ g, or } 4{,}200 \text{ mg}$$

$$\text{mEq} = \frac{4{,}200 \text{ mg} \times 1}{84} = 50 \text{ mEq}$$

CHAPTER CONTENT

Background 148
Calorie Sources 148
Parenteral Nutrition 149
Determining Fluid Needs 149
Determining Caloric Needs 150
Calories Provided from Macronutrients 151
Protein 151
Nitrogen Balance 152
Amino Acid Calculations 153
Carbohydrates 154
Fat 156
Electrolytes 157
Sodium 157
Potassium 158
Phosphate 158
Calcium 159
Other Additives 160
Multivitamins 160
Trace Elements 160
Insulin 160
Enteral Nutrition 160
Drug-Nutrient Interactions 161
Tube Names 161
Additional PN Practice 163

CONTENT LEGEND

= Study Tip Gal

CHAPTER 11
CALCULATIONS III: PARENTERAL AND ENTERAL NUTRITION

BACKGROUND

When a patient cannot eat enough to stay healthy, nutrition support may be required. Examples include patients with coma, stroke, cancer and GI disorders (e.g., bowel obstruction, Crohn's disease, ulcerative colitis). Enteral nutrition (EN) uses the GI tract to deliver all or part of a patient's caloric needs (e.g., eating food orally or delivering a formula via a "feeding tube" into the stomach or intestine), while parenteral nutrition (PN) delivers those calories into a vein through a peripheral or central line. When the GI tract is working, enteral nutrition is preferred; it is most physiologic, has fewer complications and is generally less expensive. Parenteral nutrition can be used for patients whose GI tract is not functioning, who cannot/will not eat or who cannot maintain nutritional status enterally.

CALORIE SOURCES

A calorie is a measurement of the energy, or heat, it takes to raise the temperature of 1 gram of water by 1° C. Calories are associated with nutrition because humans obtain energy from the food they consume or from EN/PN. Calories are provided by these 3 components: carbohydrates, fat and protein (called macronutrients).

A calorie is a very small unit, and these are therefore measured in kilocalories, or kcals, where 1,000 calories = 1 kcal. It is common to find the term "calories" used interchangeably for kcals. For example, the "Nutrition Facts" box on the side of a container of Honey Nut Cheerios® states that a ¾ cup serving of the cereal provides 110 Calories. Precisely, this is 110 kcals. Looking at the box, the word "Calories" is written with a capital "C" which is sometimes used to indicate kcals, versus a lower case "c". For pharmacy calculations, "calories" or "Calories" are meant to refer to kilocalories, or kcals.

PARENTERAL NUTRITION

It is preferable to use the least invasive and most physiologic method of feeding. Parenteral nutrition (PN) is neither and has a higher risk of complications, including infection and thrombosis. It may be indicated when the patient is not able to absorb adequate nutrition via the GI tract for ≥ 5 days. Usual conditions that require PN include bowel obstruction, ileus, severe diarrhea, radiation enteritis and untreatable malabsorption.

There are 2 types of PN admixtures. Mixtures that contain dextrose, amino acids, sterile water for injection, electrolytes, vitamins and minerals are referred to as 2-in-1 formulations, while the lipids are infused separately. When the lipids are mixed in the same bag, it is referred to as a total nutrient admixture (TNA), or 3-in-1, or all-in-one formulation.

If the PN is expected to be short-term (< 1 week), peripheral administration may be possible, but has a high risk of phlebitis (inflammation of the vein) and vein damage. Central line placement allows for a higher osmolarity and a wider variation in pH. Common types of central lines include peripherally-inserted central catheters ("PICC" lines), Hickman, Broviac, Groshong and others.

Each patient's fluid, kcal, protein and lipid requirements, plus the initial electrolyte, vitamin and trace element requirements will be determined. PN requires careful monitoring, including assessing the degree of glucose intolerance and the risk of refeeding syndrome, which is an intracellular loss of electrolytes, particularly phosphate, which causes serious complications. The calculations that follow are basic and should be known by pharmacists who work in the hospital setting. Nutrition pharmacy itself is more complex and is a specialty area.

DETERMINING FLUID NEEDS

Fluid requirements are determined first when designing a PN regimen. Enough (but not too much) fluid needs to be given to maintain adequate hydration. Daily fluid needs can be calculated using this formula:

When weight > 20 kg: 1,500 mL + (20 mL)(weight in kg* - 20)

**Total body weight (the patient's weight on the scale) is used for most PN calculations, unless the question specifies otherwise.*

Some institutions estimate adult fluid requirements using a general guideline of 30 – 40 mL/kg/day. The PN and fluid volume should be tailored to the patient. If the patient has problems with fluid accumulation (e.g., heart failure or renal dysfunction), the amount of fluid provided should be reduced. Fluid volume from medications (including IVPBs) should be included in the calculation of the overall volume the patient is receiving.

1. **GG is a 57-year-old female admitted to the hospital with bowel obstruction. She will be NPO for the next 5 - 7 days. The decision was made to start PN therapy. She weighs 65 kg. Her SCr is 1.3 mg/dL. Calculate GG's daily fluid requirements.**

   1,500 mL + (20 mL) (65 - 20) = 2,400 mL/day

2. **A 76-year-old, 154 pound patient is NPO and needs hydration. She is afebrile and does not have HF, renal disease, or ascites. What volume of fluid should the patient receive per day?**

   1,500 mL + (20 mL) (70 - 20) = 2,500 mL/day

DETERMINING CALORIC NEEDS

Basal Energy Expenditure

The basal energy expenditure (BEE), otherwise referred to as the basal metabolic rate (BMR), is the energy expenditure in the resting state, exclusive of eating and activity. It is estimated differently in male and female adults using the Harris-Benedict equations below. Most pharmacists do not memorize these equations; they are likely to be provided on the exam.

BEE (males): 66.47 + 13.75 (weight in kg*) + 5 (height in cm) - 6.76 (age in years)
BEE (females): 655.1 + 9.6 (weight in kg*) + 1.85 (height in cm) - 4.68 (age in years)

**Total body weight (the patient's weight on the scale) is used for most PN calculations, unless the question specifies otherwise.*

Total Energy Expenditure

Total energy expenditure (TEE; or total daily expenditure, TDE) is a measure of basal energy expenditure plus excess metabolic demands as a result of stress, the thermal effects of feeding, and energy expenditure for activity. Once the BEE is calculated, calculate the TEE by taking the BEE calories and multiplying by the appropriate activity factor and stress factor. This will increase the calories required. Energy requirements are increased 12% with each degree of fever over 37° C.

TEE = BEE x activity factor x stress factor

The activity factor is either 1.2 if confined to bed (non-ambulatory), or 1.3 if out of bed (ambulatory). Commonly used stress factors are listed in the table. The formula for BEE and patient-specific stress factors are likely to be provided if needed on the exam.

STATE OF STRESS	STRESS FACTOR
Minor surgery	1.2
Infection	1.4
Major trauma, sepsis, burns up to 30% BSA	1.5
Burns over 30% BSA	1.5–2

3. Using the Harris-Benedict equation, calculate the basal energy expenditure for a 66-year-old male with major trauma (stress factor 1.5). He weighs 174 pounds and is 5'10". Activity factor is 1.2. Round to the nearest whole number.

Height = 70 inches x 2.54 cm/inch = 177.8 cm. Weight = 174 pounds x 1 kg/2.2 pounds = 79.0909 kg.

BEE (males): 66.47 + 13.75 (weight in kg) + 5 (height in cm) - 6.76 (age in years)

BEE = 66.47 + (13.75 x 79.0909) + (5 x 177.8) - (6.76 x 66)

BEE = 66.47 + 1,087.5 + 889 - 446.16 = 1,596.81, or 1,597 kcal/day

The stress factor is not needed in this calculation, because you were asked to calculate BEE only. The BEE can be estimated using 15 – 25 kcal/kg (adults). It may be helpful to check the calculation with this estimate and see if the numbers are close. In this case, an estimation using 20 kcal/kg/day would provide 1,582 kcal/day (very close to 1,597 kcal/day as above).

4. Calculate the total energy expenditure for a major trauma patient (stress factor is 1.5, activity factor is 1.2) who is a 66-year-old male, weighing 174 pounds and measuring 5'10" in height. (Use the BEE calculated from the patient in the previous problem.) Round to the nearest whole number.

TEE = BEE x activity factor x stress factor. BEE was calculated above.

TEE = 1,597 kcal/day x 1.2 x 1.5 = 2,875 kcal/day

5. A 25-year-old female major trauma patient survives surgery and is recovering in the surgical intensive care unit. The medical team wants to start PN therapy. She is 122 pounds, 5'7" with some mild renal impairment. Calculate her BEE using the Harris-Benedict equation and her TEE (stress factor = 1.7 and activity factor = 1.2). Round each to the nearest whole number.

Height = 67 inches x 2.54 cm/inch = 170.18 cm. Weight = 122 pounds x 1 kg/2.2 pounds = 55.4545 kg.

BEE (females): 655.1 + 9.6 (weight in kg) + 1.85 (height in cm) - 4.68 (age in years)

```
BEE = 655.1 + (9.6 x 55.4545) + (1.85 x 170.18) - (4.68 x 25)
```

```
BEE = 655.1 + 532.3636 + 314.833 - 117 = 1,385.2966, or 1,385 kcal/day
```

TEE = BEE x activity factor x stress factor

```
TEE = 1,385 kcal/day x 1.2 x 1.7 = 2,825 kcal/day
```

Once the total caloric needs are determined, the calories provided from each macronutrient can be calculated using the conversions shown in the Study Tip Gal below.

Calories Provided from Macronutrients

USUAL DIET*			EN FORMULAS*		PN FORMULAS	
Carbs	Bread, Rice....	4 kcal/g	Corn syrup solids, cornstarch, sucrose....	The components contribute the same as from the diet, but are measured (together) as kcal/mL Examples of EN formulas: *Ensure, Osmolite, Jevity, Glucerna* and others	Dextrose Monohydrate	3.4 kcal/gram
					Glycerol/ Glycerin**	4.3 kcal/gram
Fat	Butter, Oil....	9 kcal/g	Borage oil, canola oil, corn oil....		Injectable Lipid Emulsion (ILE)10%	1.1 kcal/mL
					Injectable Lipid Emulsion (ILE) 20% (*Intralipid, Smoflipid*)	2 kcal/mL
					Injectable Lipid Emulsion (ILE) 30%	3 kcal/mL
Protein	Fish, Meat....	4 kcal/g	Casein, soy, whey....		Amino Acid Solutions (*Aminosyn, FreAmine*, others)	4 kcal/gram

**The diet and enteral formula components shown are common examples; there are others.*
***Glycerol may be used to decrease hyperglycemia; more commonly, the dextrose load is decreased or the insulin dose is increased.*

PROTEIN

Protein is used either to repair or build muscle cells, or as a source of energy. Protein in enteral intake is present in various forms, and in PN as the constituent amino acids. Because critically ill patients are catabolic (protein breakdown occurs faster than synthesis), many clinicians prefer to use "protein sparing" techniques in this population. This means that most or all of the TEE calories are provided by dextrose and fat. If adequate energy is provided by carbohydrates and fat, the protein may be "spared" and can be used by muscle (although the protein calories may not end up in the intended location). If "protein sparing" is used, the energy required by the patient will come from only the dextrose and lipids, which are the "non-protein calories" (NPC). Overall, whether to include the calories from protein in the total calories provided by a PN regimen is controversial.

Protein calories from food, enteral nutrition formulas or as parenteral amino acid solutions each provide 4 kcal/gram. The typical protein requirement for a non-stressed, ambulatory patient is 0.8 – 1 g/kg/day. Protein requirements increase if the patient is placed under stress, which is defined as illness severity. The more severely ill, the greater the protein requirements will be. In patients with a high degree of metabolic stress the protein requirements can be as high as 2 g/kg/day. The desired weight is likely to be specified (if needed) in an exam scenario. Some prescribers order protein based on the patient's ideal body weight (IBW).

CONDITION	PROTEIN REQUIREMENTS
Ambulatory, non-hospitalized (non-stressed)	0.8–1 g/kg/day
Hospitalized, or malnourished	1.2–2 g/kg/day

6. MK is a 62-year-old female who has been admitted with enteritis and pneumonia. She has a history of Crohn's disease and COPD. Her IBW is 54.7 kg. The staff gastroenterologist has ordered PN therapy with 1.5 g/kg IBW/day of protein. How many grams of protein will MK receive per day? Round to the nearest whole number.

54.7 kg x 1.5 g/kg IBW/day = 82 g protein/day

---

7. PP is a 46-year-old male who weighs 207 pounds. He is admitted for bowel resection surgery. Post surgery, he is to be started on PN therapy. The physician wants the patient to receive 1.3 g/kg/day of protein. Calculate his protein requirement. Round to the nearest whole number.

First, convert pounds to kg: 207 pounds x 1 kg/2.2 pounds = 94.1 kg.

Then, calculate the protein requirement.

94.1 kg x 1.3 g/kg/day = 122 g protein/day

NITROGEN BALANCE

Grams Of Nitrogen From Protein

Nitrogen is released during protein catabolism and is mainly excreted as urea in the urine. Nitrogen balance is the difference between the body's nitrogen gains and losses. While grams of protein are calculated in a nutritional plan, grams of nitrogen are used as an expression of the amount of protein received by the patient. There is 1 g of nitrogen (N) for each 6.25 g of protein. To calculate the grams of nitrogen in a certain weight of protein, divide the protein grams by 6.25.

$$\text{Nitrogen intake} = \frac{\text{grams of protein intake}}{6.25}$$

---

8. A patient is receiving PN containing 540 mL of 12.5% amino acids per day. How many grams of nitrogen is the patient receiving? Round to the nearest tenth.

$$\frac{12.5 \text{ g}}{100 \text{ mL}} = \frac{X \text{ g}}{540 \text{ mL}} \quad X = 67.5 \text{ g of protein}$$

$$\frac{67.5 \text{ g of protein}}{6.25} = 10.8 \text{ g of nitrogen}$$

Non-Protein Calories to Nitrogen Ratio

The non-protein calorie to nitrogen ratio (NPC:N) is calculated as follows:

- First, calculate the grams of nitrogen supplied per day (1 g N = 6.25 g of protein).
- Then, divide the total non-protein calories (dextrose + lipids) by the grams of nitrogen.

Desirable NPC:N ratios are:

- 80:1 the most severely stressed patients
- 100:1 severely stressed patients
- 150:1 unstressed patient

9. A patient is receiving PN containing 480 mL of dextrose 50% and 50 grams of amino acids plus electrolytes. Calculate the non-protein calories to nitrogen ratio for this patient.

First, calculate the nitrogen intake.

$$\text{Nitrogen} = \frac{\text{50 g of protein}}{6.25} = \text{8 g}$$

Next, calculate the non-protein calories.

$$\frac{\text{50 g dextrose}}{\text{100 mL}} = \frac{\text{X g}}{\text{480 mL}} \quad \text{X = 240 g dextrose}$$

$$\text{240 g dextrose} \times \frac{\text{3.4 kcal dextrose}}{\text{1 g}} = \text{816 kcal of dextrose}$$

Then, set up the NPC:N ratio.

NPC:N ratio is 816:8, or 102:1

AMINO ACID CALCULATIONS

Amino acids are the protein source in PN. Amino acids come in stock preparations of 5%, 8.5%, 10%, 15% and others. They all provide 4 kcal/gram. Branded amino acid solutions commonly used for PN include *Aminosyn, FreAmine, Travasol, TrophAmine, Clinisol* and others.

10. If the pharmacy stocks *Aminosyn* 8.5%, how many milliliters will be needed to provide 108 grams of protein? Round to the nearest whole number.

$$\frac{\text{8.5 g}}{\text{100 mL}} = \frac{\text{108 g}}{\text{X mL}} \quad \text{X = 1,270.58, or 1,271 mL}$$

11. How many calories are provided by 108 grams of protein?

$$\frac{\text{4 kcal}}{\text{g}} \times \text{108 g} = \text{432 kcal of protein}$$

12. The pharmacy stocks *FreAmine* 10%. A patient requires 122 grams of protein per day. How many milliliters of *FreAmine* will the patient need?

$$\frac{\text{10 g}}{\text{100 mL}} = \frac{\text{122 g}}{\text{X mL}} \quad \text{X = 1,220 mL}$$

13. JR is a 55-year-old male (weight 189 pounds) who is confined to bed (activity factor 1.2) due to his current infection (stress factor 1.5). JR requires 1.4 g/kg/day of protein and the pharmacy stocks *Aminosyn* 8.5%. Calculate the amount of *Aminosyn*, in milliliters, JR should receive. Round to the nearest whole number.

First, convert weight to kg: 189 pounds x 1 kg/2.2 pounds = 85.90 kg

Next, calculate protein requirement: 1.4 g/kg/day x 85.9090 kg = 120.27 g/day

Then, calculate the amount of *Aminosyn* (mL) needed. Note that the activity factor and stress factor are not required to calculate the protein requirement.

$$\frac{8.5\text{ g}}{100\text{ mL}} = \frac{120.27\text{ g}}{X\text{ mL}} \quad X = 1{,}414.97\text{, or } 1{,}415\text{ mL}$$

---

14. JR is receiving 97 grams of protein in an *Aminosyn* 8.5% solution on day 8 of his hospitalization. How many calories are provided by this amount of protein?

$$\frac{4\text{ kcal}}{\text{g}} \times 97\text{ g} = 388\text{ kcal of protein}$$

---

15. A PN order is written to add 800 mL of 10% amino acid solution. The pharmacy only has 15% amino acid solution in stock. Using the 15% amino acid solution instead, how many milliliters should be added to the PN bag? Round to the nearest whole number.

First, calculate the grams of protein that would be provided with the 10% solution.

$$\frac{10\text{ g}}{100\text{ mL}} = \frac{X\text{ g}}{800\text{ mL}} \quad X = 80\text{ g}$$

Next, calculate how much of the 15% amino acid solution will supply 80 grams of protein.

$$\frac{15\text{ g}}{100\text{ mL}} = \frac{80\text{ g}}{X\text{ mL}} \quad X = 533\text{ mL}$$

CARBOHYDRATES

Glucose is the primary energy source. Unless a patient purchases glucose tablets or gel, carbohydrates are consumed as simple sugars, such as fruit juice, or complex "starchy" sugars, such as legumes and grains. These are hydrolyzed by the gut into the monosaccharides fructose, galactose and glucose, which are absorbed. The liver converts the first two into glucose, and excess glucose is stored as glycogen.

Carbohydrates from food or in enteral nutrition formulas provide 4 kcal/gram. In PN, dextrose monohydrate provides the carbohydrate source. This is the isomer of glucose (D-glucose) which can be metabolized for energy. The dextrose in PN provides 3.4 kcal/gram. Occasionally, glycerol is used as an alternative to dextrose in patients with impaired insulin secretion. Glycerol provides 4.3 kcal/gram and comes pre-mixed with amino acids.

The usual distribution of non-protein calories is 70 – 85% as carbohydrate (dextrose) and 15 – 30% as fat (lipids). Dextrose comes in concentrations of 5%, 10%, 20%, 30%, 50%, 70% and others. The higher concentrations are used for PN. When calculating the dextrose, do not exceed 4 mg/kg/min (some use 7 g/kg/day). These are conservative estimates of the maximum amount of dextrose that the liver can handle.

---

16. Using 50% dextrose in water, how many milliliters are required to fulfill a PN order for 405 grams of dextrose?

$$\frac{50\text{ g}}{100\text{ mL}} = \frac{405\text{ g}}{X\text{ mL}} = 810\text{ mL}$$

17. DF, a 44-year-old male, is receiving 1,235 mL of D30W, 1,010 mL of *FreAmine* 8.5%, 200 mL of *Intralipid* 20% and 50 mL of electrolytes/minerals in his PN. How many calories from dextrose is DF receiving from the PN? Round to the nearest whole number.

$$\frac{30\text{ g}}{100\text{ mL}} \times \frac{1{,}235\text{ mL}}{\text{day}} \times \frac{3.4\text{ kcal}}{\text{g}} = 1{,}260\text{ kcal/day}$$

---

18. A pharmacist has mixed 200 mL of D20% with 100 mL of D5%. What is the final concentration in the bag?

The 200 mL bag has 40 g of dextrose (20 g/100 mL x 2).

The 100 mL bag has 5 g of dextrose. There are a total of 45 g of dextrose in the bag.

$$\frac{45\text{ g}}{300\text{ mL}} = \frac{X\text{ g}}{100\text{ mL}} \quad X = 15\text{ g; the percentage is }15\%$$

---

19. If a 50% dextrose injection provides 170 kcal in each 100 mL, how many milliliters of a 70% dextrose injection would provide the same caloric value? Round to the nearest tenth.

There are several ways to solve this problem. Option 1:

$$\frac{70\text{ g}}{100\text{ mL}} = \frac{50\text{ g}}{X\text{ mL}} = 71.4\text{ mL}$$

Option 2:

$$\frac{100\text{ mL}}{70\text{ g}} \times \frac{1\text{ g}}{3.4\text{ kcal}} \times 170\text{ kcal} = 71.4\text{ mL}$$

Option 3: since the calories are from 50% dextrose and the pharmacist is using 70% dextrose, Q1C1 can be used (this method is reviewed in the Calculations II chapter)

$$100\text{ mL} \times 50\% = Q2 \times 70\%$$

$$Q2 = 71.4\text{ mL}$$

---

20. AH is receiving 640 mL of D50W in her PN. How many calories does this provide?

$$\frac{50\text{ g}}{100\text{ mL}} \times \frac{640\text{ mL}}{\text{day}} \times \frac{3.4\text{ kcal}}{\text{g}} = 1{,}088\text{ kcal}$$

---

21. A PN order is written for 500 mL of 50% dextrose. The pharmacy only has D70W in stock. How many milliliters of D70W should be added to the PN bag? Round to the nearest whole number.

First, calculate the grams of dextrose needed for the PN as written.

$$\frac{50\text{ g}}{100\text{ mL}} = \frac{X\text{ g}}{500\text{ mL}} \quad X = 250\text{ g}$$

Next, calculate how much of the 70% dextrose solution provides 250 grams of dextrose.

$$\frac{70\text{ g}}{100\text{ mL}} = \frac{250\text{ g}}{X\text{ mL}} \quad X = 357\text{ mL of D70W}$$

FAT

Fats, or lipids, are used by the body for energy or for various critical functions, including being an essential component of cell membranes, a solvent for fat soluble vitamins, in hormone production and activity, in cell signaling and other functions. In food or from EN formulas, fat is provided as four types: saturated, *trans*, monounsaturated and polyunsaturated. Each of these provides 9 kcal/gram. In PN, injectable lipid emulsion (ILE) is the fat source. Lipids in PN are not measured in grams but in kcal/mL due to the caloric contribution provided by the egg phospholipid and glycerol components in the ILE. 10% ILE provides 1.1 kcal/mL, 20% provides 2 kcal/mL and 30% provides 3 kcal/mL.

The standard distribution of non-protein calories is 70 – 85% as carbohydrate (dextrose) and 15 – 30% as fat (lipids). Lipids are available as 10%, 20% or 30% emulsions, with brand names *Intralipid* (all concentrations) and *Smoflipid* (20% only); *Smoflipid* contains 4 oils, while traditional ILE contains only soybean oil, so they are not interchangeable. ISMP has received numerous reports of mix-ups between them.

Lipids do not need to be given daily; if triglycerides are high lipids may be given 3 times per week or once weekly. If lipids are given once weekly, divide the total calories by 7 to determine the daily amount of fat the patient receives. Due to the risk of infection, the recommended hang time limit for ILE is 12 hours when infused alone. However, an admixture containing fat emulsion, such as a TNA, may be administered over 24 hours. Lipid emulsions cannot be filtered through 0.22 micron filters; 1.2 micron filters are commonly used for lipids. PN requires a filter itself due to the risk of a precipitate.

Some medications are formulated in a lipid emulsion (propofol and clevidipine) that provides fat calories. If a patient is receiving PN along with one or both of these medications, the calorie contribution from the medication must be considered. Refer to the Acute & Critical Care Medicine and Hypertension chapters for further discussion.

22. A patient is receiving 500 mL of 10% lipids. How many calories is the patient receiving from the lipids? Round to the nearest whole number.

$$\frac{1.1\text{ kcal}}{\text{mL}} = \frac{X\text{ kcal}}{500\text{ mL}} \qquad X = 550\text{ kcal}$$

23. The total energy expenditure (TEE) for a critically ill patient is 2,435 kcal/day. The patient is receiving 1,446 kcal from dextrose and 810 kcal from protein. In this critical care unit, clinicians do not include protein calories in the TEE estimation. How many kcal should be provided by the lipids?

As stated in the problem, at this institution TEE refers to the non-protein calories.

2,435 kcal (total non-protein) – 1,446 kcal (dextrose) = 989 kcal remaining from lipids

24. Using 20% *Smoflipid*, how many milliliters are required to meet 989 calories? Round to the nearest whole number.

$$\frac{2\text{ kcal}}{\text{mL}} = \frac{989\text{ kcal}}{X\text{ mL}} \qquad X = 495\text{ mL}$$

25. A patient is receiving 660 mL of 10% *Intralipid* on Saturdays along with his normal daily PN therapy of 1,420 mL of D20W, 450 mL *Aminosyn* 15%, and 30 mL of electrolytes. What is the daily amount of calories provided by the lipids? Round to the nearest whole number.

$$\frac{1.1\text{ kcal}}{\text{mL}} = \frac{X\text{ kcal}}{660\text{ mL}} \qquad X = 726\text{ kcal/week. Divide by 7 to get kcal/day} = 104\text{ kcal/day}$$

26. A patient is receiving 180 mL of 30% lipids. How many calories is the patient receiving from the lipids?

$$\frac{3\text{ kcal}}{\text{mL}} = \frac{X\text{ kcal}}{180\text{ mL}} \qquad X = 540\text{ kcal}$$

27. A PN order calls for 475 calories to be provided by lipids. The pharmacy has 10% lipid emulsion in stock. How many milliliters should be administered to the patient? Round to the nearest whole number.

$$\frac{1.1\text{ kcal}}{\text{mL}} = \frac{475\text{ kcal}}{X\text{ mL}} \qquad X = 432\text{ mL}$$

ELECTROLYTES

Electrolytes are another component of the PN that must be individualized to the patient's needs. This includes sodium, potassium, phosphate, chloride and calcium. More or less of an electrolyte may be needed based on the patient's conditions (e.g., renal disease).

SODIUM

Sodium is the principal extracellular cation. Sodium may need to be reduced in renal dysfunction or cardiovascular disease, including hypertension. Sodium chloride comes in many concentrations, such as 0.9% (NS), 0.45% (1/2 NS) and others. Sodium chloride 23.4% is used for PN preparation and contains 4 mEq/mL of sodium. Hypertonic saline (greater than 0.9%) is dangerous if used incorrectly and is discussed in the Medication Safety & Quality Improvement chapter.

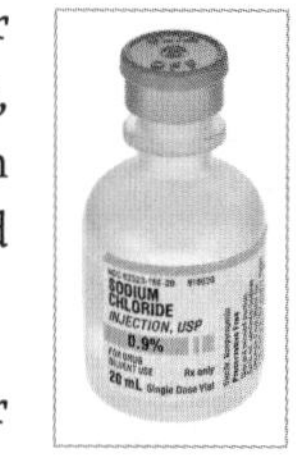

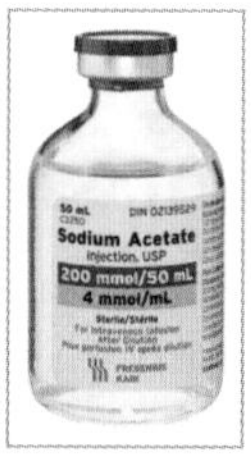

Sodium can be added to PN as either sodium chloride, sodium acetate, sodium phosphate or combinations of these. If a patient is acidotic, sodium acetate should be added. Sodium acetate is converted to sodium bicarbonate and may help correct the acidosis.

28. The pharmacist is going to add 80 mEq of sodium to the PN; half will be given as sodium acetate (2 mEq/mL) and half as sodium chloride (4 mEq/mL). How many milliliters of sodium chloride will be needed?

40 mEq will be provided by the NaCl.

$$\frac{4\text{ mEq}}{\text{mL}} = \frac{40\text{ mEq}}{X\text{ mL}} \qquad X = 10\text{ mL}$$

29. The pharmacist is making PN that needs to contain 80 mEq of sodium and 45 mEq of acetate. The available pharmacy stock solutions contain 4 mEq/mL sodium as sodium chloride and 2 mEq/mL sodium as sodium acetate. The final volume of the PN will be 2.5 liters to be infused at 100 mL/hr. What quantity, in milliliters, of each stock solution should be added to the PN to meet the requirements? Round to the nearest hundredth.

First, calculate the acetate component as this contributes sodium as well.

$$\frac{2\text{ mEq}}{\text{mL}} = \frac{45\text{ mEq}}{X\text{ mL}} \qquad X = 22.5\text{ mL of sodium acetate}$$

Next, determine how many mEq of sodium are supplied by 22.5 mL sodium acetate.

$$\frac{2\text{ mEq}}{\text{mL}} \times 22.5\text{ mL sodium acetate} = 45\text{ mEq of sodium}$$

So, 45 mEq of sodium acetate also supplies 45 mEq of sodium. How many mEq of sodium are left to be provided from sodium chloride?

80 mEq Na total − 45 mEq Na from Na Acetate = 35 mEq of sodium still needed from NaCl

Calculate how much sodium chloride will supply the remaining sodium (35 mEq).

$$\frac{4\text{ mEq}}{\text{mL}} = \frac{35\text{ mEq}}{X\text{ mL}} \qquad X = 8.75\text{ mL of sodium chloride}$$

30. A 2 liter PN solution is to contain 60 mEq of sodium and 30 mEq of acetate. The pharmacy has in stock sodium chloride (4 mEq/mL) and sodium acetate (2 mEq/mL). What quantity, in milliliters, of each solution should be added to the PN? Round to the nearest tenth.

First, calculate the amount of sodium acetate needed.

$$\frac{2 \text{ mEq}}{\text{mL}} = \frac{30 \text{ mEq}}{X \text{ mL}} \quad X = 15 \text{ mL of sodium acetate}$$

This amount (15 mL of sodium acetate) supplies 30 mEq of sodium (15 mL x 2 mEq/mL = 30 mEq). The additional amount of sodium required is 30 mEq from NaCl (60 mEq - 30 mEq).

Now, calculate the amount of sodium chloride needed.

$$\frac{4 \text{ mEq}}{\text{mL}} = \frac{30 \text{ mEq}}{X \text{ mL}} \quad X = 7.5 \text{ mL of NaCl}$$

POTASSIUM

Potassium is the principal intracellular cation. Potassium may need to be reduced in renal or cardiovascular disease. Potassium can be provided by potassium chloride (KCl), potassium phosphate (K Phos, KPO4) or potassium acetate or combinations of these. The normal range for serum potassium is 3.5 – 5 mEq/L.

PHOSPHATE

Phosphorus (or phosphate, PO4) is present in DNA, cell membranes and ATP. It acts as an acid-base buffer and is vital in bone metabolism. Phosphate can be provided by sodium phosphate (NaPO4) or potassium phosphate (K Phos, KPO4). The two forms do not provide equivalent amounts of phosphate. The order should be written in mmol of phosphate, followed by the type of salt form (potassium or sodium). Phosphate will often need to be reduced in renal disease.

31. The pharmacist has calculated that a patient requires 30 mmol of phosphate and 80 mEq of potassium. The pharmacy has stock solutions of potassium phosphate (3 mmol of phosphate with 4.4 mEq of potassium/mL) and potassium chloride (2 mEq K/mL). How much potassium phosphate and how much potassium chloride will be required to meet the patient's needs?

First, calculate the phosphate required (since phosphate can only be provided by KPO4 and potassium will also be provided by this solution).

$$\frac{3 \text{ mmol phosphate}}{\text{mL}} = \frac{30 \text{ mmol phosphate}}{X \text{ mL}} \quad X = 10 \text{ mL KPO4}$$

Each mL of the potassium phosphate (KPO4) supplies 4.4 mEq of potassium. Calculate the amount of potassium the patient will receive from the 10 mL of KPO4.

10 mL x 4.4 mEq/mL = 44 mEq potassium from KPO4

The remaining potassium will be provided by KCl.

80 mEq K required - 44 mEq potassium (from KPO4) = 36 mEq to be obtained from KCl

$$\frac{2 \text{ mEq K}}{\text{mL}} = \frac{36 \text{ mEq K}}{X \text{ mL}} \quad X = 18 \text{ mL KCl}$$

The patient requires 10 mL of potassium phosphate and 18 mL of potassium chloride.

CALCIUM

Calcium is important for many functions including cardiac conduction, muscle contraction, and bone homeostasis. The normal serum calcium level is 8.5 - 10.5 mg/dL. Almost half of serum calcium is bound to albumin. Low albumin will lead to a falsely low serum calcium concentration. If albumin is low (< 3.5 g/dL), the calcium level must be corrected with this equation prior to the addition of calcium into the PN or providing calcium replacement in any manner:

$$Ca_{corrected}\ (mg/dL) = calcium_{reported(serum)} + [(4.0 - albumin) \times (0.8)]\ †$$

† Use serum calcium in mg/dL and albumin in g/dL (standard units in the U.S.) in the corrected calcium formula

32. Calculate the corrected calcium value for a patient with the following lab values:

LAB	REFERENCE RANGE	RESULT
Calcium (mg/dL)	8.5–10.5	7.6
Albumin (g/dL)	3.5–5	1.5

$$Ca_{corrected} = 7.6 + [(4.0 - 1.5) \times (0.8)] = 9.6\ mg/dL$$

The corrected calcium provides an estimate of what the patient's serum calcium would be if the albumin was normal. In this example, the patient's corrected calcium is within the reference range for the lab.

33. A patient is to receive 8 mEq of calcium. The pharmacy has calcium gluconate 10% in stock which provides 0.465 mEq/mL. How many milliliters of calcium gluconate should be added to the PN? Round to the nearest whole number.

$$8\ mEq\ Ca \times \frac{1\ mL}{0.465\ mEq\ Ca} = 17.2,\ or\ 17\ mL\ calcium\ gluconate$$

Calcium and Phosphate Solubility

Phosphate and calcium need to be added to the PN carefully, or they can bind together and precipitate, which can cause a pulmonary embolus. This can be fatal. The following steps can help reduce the risk of a calcium-phosphate precipitate:

- Choose calcium gluconate over calcium chloride ($CaCl_2$) because it is less reactive and has a lower risk of precipitation with phosphates. Calcium gluconate has a lower dissociation constant compared to calcium chloride, leaving less free calcium available in solution to bind phosphates.
- Add phosphate first (after the dextrose and amino acids), followed by other PN components, agitate the solution, then calcium should be added near the end to take advantage of the maximum volume of the PN formulation.
- The calcium and phosphate added together (units must be the same to do this) should not exceed 45 mEq/L.
- Maintain a proper pH (lower pH; less risk of precipitation) to eliminate binding and refrigerate the bag once prepared (PNs are kept in the refrigerator until they are needed). When temperature increases, more calcium and phosphate dissociate in solution and precipitation risk increases.

34. A patient is receiving 30 mmol of phosphate and 8 mEq of calcium. The volume of the PN is 2,000 mL. There are 2 mEq PO4/mmol. Confirm that the sum of the calcium and phosphorus does not exceed 45 mEq/L.

First, calculate mEq from the phosphate.

$$\frac{2\ mEq\ PO4}{mmol} \times 30\ mmol\ PO4 = 60\ mEq\ phosphate$$

Then, add the phosphate and calcium. 60 mEq phosphate + 8 mEq calcium = 68 mEq.

Read the question again. Has it been answered? The volume of the PN is 2,000 mL, or 2 L. Calculate the mEq per liter.

68 mEq/2 L = 34 mEq/L, which is less than 45 mEq/L.

OTHER ADDITIVES

Multivitamins and trace elements are usually added to the PN formula. Insulin and histamine-2 receptor antagonists (H2RAs) are occasionally added. Adding any other IV medications to the PN is generally discouraged, because the entire PN would be wasted if a medication was discontinued or changed during the day.

MULTIVITAMINS

There are 4 fat-soluble vitamins (A, D, E and K) and 9 water-soluble vitamins (thiamine, riboflavin, niacin, pantothenic acid, pyridoxine, ascorbic acid, folic acid, cyanocobalamin, biotin) in the standard MVI-13 mixture. The MVI-12 mixture does not contain vitamin K since certain patients may need less or more of this vitamin. If patients on PN therapy are taking warfarin, the INR must be monitored.

TRACE ELEMENTS

The standard mix includes zinc, copper, chromium and manganese (and may include selenium). Manganese and copper should be withheld in severe liver disease. Chromium, molybdenum and selenium should be withheld in severe renal disease. Iron is not routinely given in a PN.

INSULIN

Because of the large carbohydrate component of PNs, insulin may be required (even in patients without diabetes). Half the previous day's sliding scale requirement or less can be added to the PN as regular insulin to safely control blood glucose. This can be supplemented by SC insulin as needed. PN formulas are often titrated on and off (e.g., started at less than the goal rate and not abruptly stopped) to facilitate physiologic glucose regulation.

ENTERAL NUTRITION

Enteral nutrition (EN) is the provision of nutrients via the gastrointestinal (GI) tract. Sometimes this is achieved through a feeding tube (often called tube feeding). Nasogastric (NG) tubes are often used, primarily for short-term administration. For longer-term, or if the stomach cannot be used, tubes are placed further down the GI tract. EN is the preferred route for patients who cannot meet their nutritional needs through voluntary oral intake. Tube feedings can range from providing adjunctive support to providing complete nutrition support. Examples of EN formulas include *Ensure, Osmolite, Jevity, Glucerna, Novasource* and many others. Each formula contains different amounts of macro/micronutrients and calories (see previous Study Tip Gal). Some are specialized for certain types of patients (e.g., *Nepro* is a renal formula, *Glucerna* is for patients with diabetes), and some can be purchased OTC for meal replacement or those needing additional calories.

Several advantages of EN over PN include lower cost, using the gut (which prevents atrophy and other problems), and a lower risk of complications (less infections, less hyperglycemia, reduced risk of cholelithiasis and cholestasis). The most common risk associated with enteral feeding is aspiration which can lead to pneumonia. Enteral feedings can cause drug interactions. The general rule for preventing drug/enteral feeding interactions is to hold the feedings one hour before or two hours after the drug is administered. Some drugs may require further separation.

Tube feeds do not, by themselves, provide enough water. Water is given in addition to the tube feeds. If fluid intake is inadequate, it will be uncomfortable for the patient and put them at risk for complications, including hypernatremia.

DRUG-NUTRIENT INTERACTIONS

- Warfarin: many enteral products bind warfarin, resulting in low INRs and the need for dose adjustments. Hold tube feeds one hour before and one hour after warfarin administration. EN formulas contain varying amounts of vitamin K, which can complicate warfarin dosing in some patients.
- Tetracyclines, quinolones and levothyroxine: will chelate with metals, including calcium, magnesium, and iron, which reduces drug availability; separate from tube feeds.
- Ciprofloxacin: the oral suspension is not used with tube feeds because the oil-based suspension adheres to the tube. The immediate-release tablets are used instead; crush and mix with water, flush line with water before and after administration.
- Phenytoin (*Dilantin* suspension): levels are reduced when the drug binds to the feeding solution, leading to less free drug availability and sub-therapeutic levels. Separate tube feeds by 2 hours.

TUBE NAMES

- A tube in the nose to the stomach is called a nasogastric (NG), or nasoenteral, tube.
- A tube that goes through the skin into the stomach is called a gastrostomy, or percutaneous endoscopic gastrostomy (PEG, or G) tube.
- A tube into the small intestine is called a jejunostomy, or percutaneous endoscopic jejunostomy (PEJ, or J) tube.

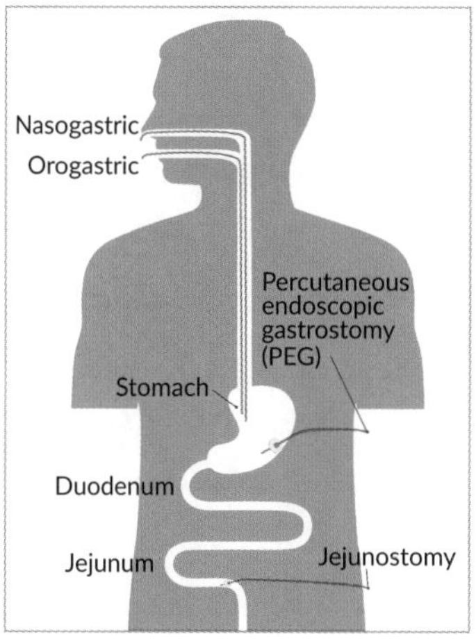

Patient Case (For Questions 35 – 37)

WT is a patient starting enteral nutrition therapy. She has a past medical history significant for type 2 diabetes. She will be started on *Glucerna* Ready-to-Drink Vanilla shakes. See the nutrient label provided.

35. According to the case, what percent of calories will WT receive from the protein component? Round to the nearest whole number.

First, calculate the amount of calories provided by the protein component.

$$19.6 \text{ g protein} \times \frac{4 \text{ kcal}}{\text{g}} = 78.4 \text{ kcal}$$

Next, find the percentage of protein calories.

$$\frac{78.4 \text{ kcal}}{356 \text{ kcal}} \times 100 = 22\%$$

Nutrition Facts	
Serving Size: 8 fl oz (237 mL)	
Amount Per Serving	
Calories	356 kcal
Total Fat	17.8 g
Protein	19.6 g
Total Carbohydrate	31.5 g
Dietary Fiber	3.8 g
L-Carnitine	51 mg
Taurine	40 mg
m-Inositol	205 mg
Vitamin A	
Viamin C	
Iron	

36. How many calories will WT receive from the fat component of 1 (8 fl oz.) shake? Round to the nearest whole number.

$$17.8 \text{ g} \times \frac{9 \text{ kcal}}{\text{g}} = 160.2, \text{ or } 160 \text{ kcal}$$

37. What percent of calories are derived from the fat component? Round to the nearest whole number.

$$\frac{160.2 \text{ kcal}}{356 \text{ kcal}} \times 100 = 45\%$$

Patient Case (For Questions 38 - 40)

JB is a patient receiving *Osmolite* (a high-protein, low-residue formula) enteral nutrition through a PEG tube. See the nutrient label provided.

Nutrition Facts

Serving Size: 8 fl oz (237 mL)

Amount Per Serving	
Calories	285 kcal
Total Fat	9.2g
Protein	13.2 g
Total Carbohydrate	37.4 g
L-Carnitine	36 mg
Taurine	36 mg
Vitamin A	
Viamin C	
Iron	

38. According to the case above, how many calories will JB receive from the carbohydrate component in 4 fl oz? Round to the nearest whole number.

First, calculate the total calories from carbohydrates per 1 can (8 fl oz).

$$37.4 \text{ g carbohydrate} \times \frac{4 \text{ kcal}}{\text{g}} = 149.6 \text{ kcal from 8 fl oz}$$

The question asks about calories in 4 fl oz (1/2 can).

$$\frac{149.6 \text{ kcal}}{2} = 74.8, \text{ or } 75 \text{ kcal from 4 fl oz}$$

39. What percent of calories will JB receive from the carbohydrate component? Round to the nearest whole number.

First, calculate the amount of calories from the carbohydrate component.

$$37.4 \text{ g carbohydrate} \times \frac{4 \text{ kcal}}{\text{g}} = 149.6 \text{ kcal}$$

Next, find the percentage of carbohydrate calories.

$$\frac{149.6 \text{ kcal}}{285 \text{ kcal}} \times 100 = 52.49, \text{ or } 52\%$$

40. The nurse was administering 1 can (8 fl oz.) of *Osmolite* to JB when she accidentally spilled 2 fl oz. onto the floor. The remaining amount in the can was accurately delivered to the patient. How many calories did he actually receive? Do not round the answer.

$$\frac{8 \text{ fl oz}}{285 \text{ kcal}} = \frac{6 \text{ fl oz}}{X \text{ kcal}} \quad X = 213.75 \text{ kcal}$$

ADDITIONAL PN PRACTICE

41. TE is a 35-year-old female who is receiving 325 grams of dextrose, 85 grams of amino acids, and 300 mL of 10% lipids via her PN therapy. What percentage of total calories is provided by the protein content? Round to the nearest whole number.

First, calculate the calories from all sources; dextrose, amino acids, and lipids.

Dextrose

$$\frac{3.4 \text{ kcal}}{\text{g}} \times 325 \text{ g} = 1{,}105 \text{ kcal of dextrose}$$

Protein

$$\frac{4 \text{ kcal}}{\text{g}} \times 85 \text{ g} = 340 \text{ kcal of protein}$$

Lipids

$$\frac{1.1 \text{ kcal}}{\text{mL}} \times 300 \text{ mL} = 330 \text{ kcal of fat}$$

Then, add up the total calories from all the sources. 1,105 + 340 + 330 = 1,775 kcal

Finally, calculate the percent of calories from protein.

$$\frac{340 \text{ kcal}}{1{,}775 \text{ kcal}} \times 100 = 19\%$$

Use the following PN order to answer questions 42 – 51:

ITEM	QUANTITY
Dextrose 70%	250 g
Amino acids	50 g
Sodium chloride (M.W. 58.5)	44 mEq
Sodium acetate (M.W. 82)	20 mEq
Potassium	40 mEq
Magnesium sulfate	12 mEq
Phosphate	18 mmol

ITEM	QUANTITY
Calcium	4.65 mEq
MVI-12	5 mL
Trace elements-5	1 mL
Vitamin K-1	0.5 mg
Famotidine	10 mg
Regular insulin	20 units
Sterile water qs ad	960 mL

42. Calculate the amount, in milliliters, of dextrose 70% that should be added to the PN. Round to the nearest whole number.

$$\frac{70 \text{ g}}{100 \text{ mL}} = \frac{250 \text{ g}}{X \text{ mL}} \quad X = 357 \text{ mL of dextrose 70\%}$$

43. Using amino acids 10%, calculate the amount of amino acids that should be added to the PN.

$$\frac{10 \text{ g}}{100 \text{ mL}} = \frac{50 \text{ g}}{X \text{ mL}} \quad X = 500 \text{ mL of 10\% amino acids}$$

44. Using the potassium phosphate (3 mmol of phosphate and 4.4 mEq of potassium/mL) vials in stock, calculate the amount of potassium phosphate that should be added to the PN to meet the phosphate requirement.

$$\frac{3 \text{ mmol phosphate}}{\text{mL}} = \frac{18 \text{ mmol phosphate}}{X \text{ mL}} \quad X = 6 \text{ mL potassium phosphate}$$

---

45. The PN contains 6 mL of potassium phosphate (3 mmol of phosphate and 4.4 mEq of potassium/mL). The daily potassium requirement from the PN order is 40 mEq. How much potassium chloride (2 mEq/mL), in milliliters, should be added to the PN? Round to the nearest tenth.

First, calculate the amount of K already added to the PN in the form of potassium phosphate.

$$\frac{4.4 \text{ mEq K}}{\text{mL}} \times 6 \text{ mL} = 26.4 \text{ mEq K}$$

Total K needed is 40 mEq. 40 mEq - 26.4 mEq = 13.6 mEq still needed from KCl

$$\frac{2 \text{ mEq K}}{\text{mL}} = \frac{13.6 \text{ mEq K}}{X \text{ mL}} \quad X = 6.8 \text{ mL KCl}$$

---

46. The PN order calls for 4.65 mEq of calcium. The pharmacy has calcium gluconate 10% (0.465 mEq/mL) in stock. How many milliliters of calcium gluconate 10% should be added to the PN?

$$\frac{0.465 \text{ mEq Ca}}{\text{mL}} = \frac{4.65 \text{ mEq Ca}}{X \text{ mL}} \quad X = 10 \text{ mL calcium gluconate } 10\%$$

---

47. The PN calls for 18 mmol of phosphate and 4.65 mEq of calcium (provided by 10 mL of calcium gluconate 10%, as calculated in the previous problem) in a volume of 960 mL. There are 2 mEq PO4/mmol. Confirm that the sum of the calcium and phosphorus do not exceed 45 mEq/L.

First, calculate mEq from the phosphate.

$$\frac{2 \text{ mEq PO4}}{\text{mmol}} \times 18 \text{ mmol PO4} = 36 \text{ mEq phosphate}$$

Then, add the phosphate to the calcium. 36 mEq phosphate + 4.65 mEq calcium = 40.65 mEq.

The volume of the PN is 960 mL, or 0.96 L. Calculate the mEq per liter

40.65 mEq/0.96 L = 42.3 mEq/L, which is less than 45 mEq/L

---

48. Calculate the amount of magnesium sulfate (4 mEq/mL) that should be added to the PN.

$$\frac{4 \text{ mEq}}{\text{mL}} = \frac{12 \text{ mEq}}{X \text{ mL}} \quad X = 3 \text{ mL magnesium sulfate}$$

49. What percentage of the total calories from the PN are represented by the protein component? Round to the nearest whole number.

First, calculate the total calories.

Dextrose

$$\frac{3.4 \text{ kcal dextrose}}{\text{g}} \times 250 \text{ g dextrose} = 850 \text{ kcal of dextrose}$$

Protein

$$\frac{4 \text{ kcal protein}}{\text{g}} \times 50 \text{ g protein} = 200 \text{ kcal of protein}$$

Total calories = 850 + 200 = 1,050 kcal. Now, calculate the percent of calories from protein.

$$\frac{200 \text{ kcal}}{1{,}050 \text{ kcal}} \times 100 = 19\%$$

Questions 50 & 51 require knowledge of milliequivalents from the Calculations II chapter.

50. How many milliliters of 23.4% sodium chloride should be added to the PN.

$$44 \text{ mEq} = \frac{X \text{ mg} \times 1}{58.5} \qquad X = 2{,}574 \text{ mg, or } 2.574 \text{ g}$$

$$\frac{23.4 \text{ g}}{100 \text{ mL}} = \frac{2.574 \text{ g}}{X \text{ mL}} \qquad X = 11 \text{ mL of } 23.4\% \text{ NaCl}$$

This concentration of NaCl is hypertonic and is a high-alert drug due to heightened risk of patient harm when dosed incorrectly. Refer to the Medication Safety & Quality Improvement chapter.

51. Calculate the amount of 16.4% sodium acetate that should be added to the PN.

$$20 \text{ mEq} = \frac{X \text{ mg} \times 1}{82} \qquad X = 1{,}640 \text{ mg, or } 1.64 \text{ g}$$

$$\frac{16.4 \text{ g}}{100 \text{ mL}} = \frac{1.64 \text{ g}}{X \text{ mL}} \qquad X = 10 \text{ mL of } 16.4\% \text{ sodium acetate}$$

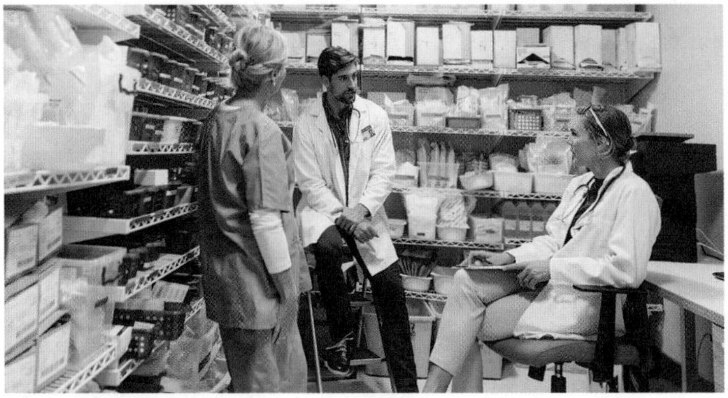

CHAPTER 12
CALCULATIONS IV: CLINICAL

CHAPTER CONTENT

Body Mass Index 166
BMI Classifications 166
Body Weight 167
Actual Body Weight or Total Body Weight 167
Ideal Body Weight 167
Adjusted Body Weight 167
Height in Inches 168
Flow Rates 169
Final Volume of Compounded IV Solutions 171
Drop Factor 172
Renal Function and Creatinine Clearance Estimation 174
The Cockcroft-Gault Equation 175
Acid-Base and Arterial Blood Gases 177
pH 177
Arterial Blood Gases 177
Interpreting ABGs 177
Anion Gap 178
Buffer Systems and Ionization 179
The pH of a Solution 179
Calculating the Log of a Number 180
Percentage of Drug Ionization in a Solution 182
Drug Conversions 183
Calcium Salt Conversions 183
Aminophylline to Theophylline 183
Absolute Neutrophil Count 184

CONTENT LEGEND

= Study Tip Gal

BODY MASS INDEX

Overweight and obesity are health problems associated with increased morbidity from hypertension, dyslipidemia, diabetes, coronary heart disease, stroke, gallbladder disease, osteoarthritis and some other conditions. Higher body weights are also associated with increases in all-cause mortality. Body mass index (BMI) is a measure of body fat based on height and weight that applies to adult men and women. BMI is a useful measure of body fat, but the BMI can over-estimate body fat in persons who are muscular, and can under-estimate body fat in frail elderly persons and others who have lost muscle mass. Waist circumference is used concurrently with BMI. If most of the fat is around the waist, there is higher disease risk. High risk is defined as a waist size > 35 inches for women or > 40 inches for men. Underweight can be a problem if a person is fighting a disease such as a frail, hospitalized patient with an infection.

BMI should be calculated as follows:

$$\text{BMI (kg/m}^2) = \frac{\text{weight (kg)}}{[\text{height (m)}]^2}$$

Alternatively, BMI can be calculated with weight in pounds and height in inches using a conversion factor to convert to units of kg/m^2:

$$\text{BMI (kg/m}^2) = \frac{\text{weight (pounds)}}{[\text{height (in)}]^2} \times 703 \text{ (to convert to kg/m}^2)$$

BMI CLASSIFICATIONS

BMI (kg/m^2)	CLASSIFICATION
< 18.5	Underweight
18.5 – 24.9	Normal weight
25 – 29.9	Overweight
≥ 30	Obese

1. A male patient comes to the pharmacy and tells the pharmacist he is 6'7" tall and 250 pounds. His waist circumference is 43 inches. Calculate his BMI. Round to the nearest whole number. Is the patient underweight, normal weight, overweight or obese?

- Convert weight to kg: 250 pounds x 1 kg/2.2 lbs = 113.6363 kg
- Convert height to cm: 6'7" = 79 inches x 2.54 cm/inch = 200.66 cm

$$200.66 \text{ cm} \times \frac{\text{m}}{100 \text{ cm}} = 2.0066 \text{ m}$$

$$\text{BMI (kg/m}^2) = \frac{113.6363 \text{ kg}}{(2.0066 \text{ m})^2} = 28.2 \text{ kg/m}^2\text{, rounded to 28, overweight}$$

Because of the rounding specifications in the question, the answer is the same regardless of the formula used. Expect the same on the exam.

---

2. Calculate the BMI for a male who is 6' tall and weighs 198 lbs. Round to the nearest tenth. Is the patient underweight, normal weight, overweight or obese?

$$\text{BMI (kg/m}^2) = \frac{198 \text{ pounds}}{(72 \text{ in})^2} \times 703 = 26.9 \text{ kg/m}^2\text{, overweight}$$

Because of the rounding specifications in the question, the answer is the same regardless of the formula used. Expect the same on the exam.

BODY WEIGHT

There are three potential measures of body weight for a patient: actual (or total) body weight, ideal body weight and adjusted body weight. In pharmacy, weights are used to calculate drug doses, flow rates, creatinine clearance and more. The weight that should be used for each type of calculation (in an individual patient) is not always the same. This chapter discusses rules that should be followed for the exam with example problems.

ACTUAL BODY WEIGHT OR TOTAL BODY WEIGHT

Actual body weight or total body weight (TBW) is the weight of the patient when weighed on a scale.

IDEAL BODY WEIGHT

Ideal body weight (IBW) is the healthy (ideal) weight for a person. The IBW formula must be memorized:

IBW (males) = 50 kg + (2.3 kg)(number of inches over 5 feet)

IBW (females) = 45.5 kg + (2.3 kg)(number of inches over 5 feet)

There are alternate methods of calculating IBW in children and adults < 5 feet.

ADJUSTED BODY WEIGHT

Adjusted body weight is calculated when patients are obese or overweight. The adjusted body weight formula must be memorized:

$$AdjBW_{0.4} = IBW + 0.4(TBW - IBW)$$

Adult doses are generally the same for all patients (e.g., lisinopril 10 mg daily, memantine 5 mg BID). Weight-based (mg/kg) dosing is common in pediatrics and is recommended for some medications in adult patients. Total body weight is used for weight-based dosing of most drugs in adults, but there are some exceptions. Some drugs with a narrow therapeutic index (e.g., aminophylline, theophylline) are dosed based on IBW to avoid toxicity. Some drugs (e.g., enoxaparin, vancomycin) are dosed based on actual body weight (even if a patient is obese) because that has been determined to be the best weight to use in clinical trials. Dosing drugs in obesity is challenging because there is a risk of underdosing (when standard doses are used) and overdosing (when dosing with total body weight). In clinical practice, it will be necessary to consult primary literature for the best dosing strategy in obese patients. For the exam, the figure on the following page can be used.

Which Weight to Use for Drug Dosing (mg/kg)?

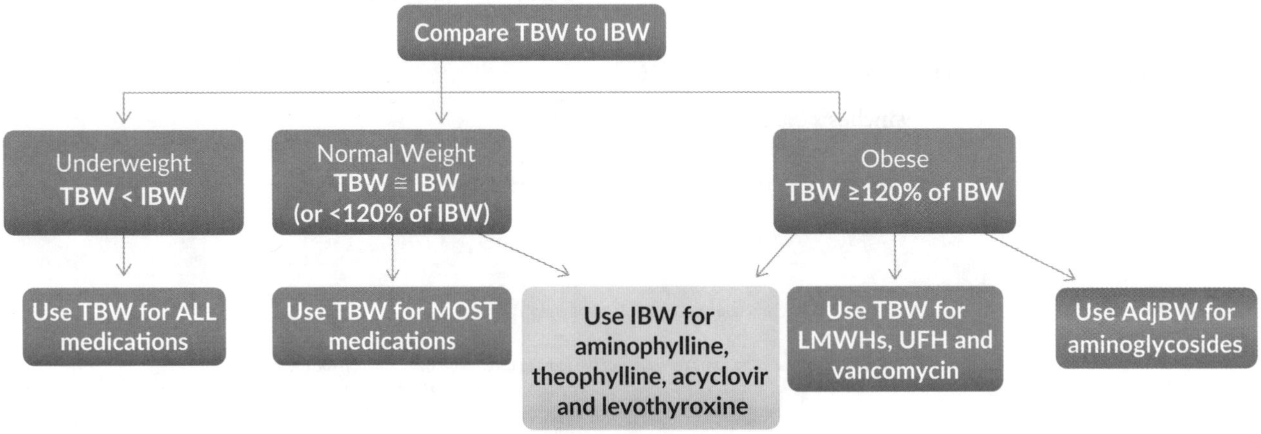

If a question specifies what weight to use (even if different from above), use it. Follow all instructions on the exam.
**Aminoglycosides are dosed based on TBW or IBW, unless the patient is obese, then AdjBW is used.*

---

3. A female patient is to receive 5 mg/kg/day of theophylline. The patient is 5'7" and weighs 243 pounds. Calculate the daily theophylline dose the patient should receive.

$$\text{Total Body Weight} = 243 \text{ lb} \times \frac{1 \text{ kg}}{2.2 \text{ lbs}} = 110.4545 \text{ kg}$$

$$\text{IBW (female)} = 45.5 \text{ kg} + (2.3 \times 7 \text{ in}) = 61.6 \text{ kg}$$

$$\% \text{ above IBW} = \frac{110.4545 \text{ kg}}{61.6 \text{ kg}} = \text{~}1.8\text{, she is 180\% of her IBW or 80\% above her IBW}$$

Use the flowchart to determine which weight to use to dose the theophylline. This patient is obese. Theophylline, aminophylline, acyclovir and levothyroxine are narrow therapeutic index drugs. They are dosed on IBW in normal weight and obese patients for safety.

$$\text{Theophylline } 5 \text{ mg/kg} \times 61.6 \text{ kg} = 308 \text{ mg}$$

---

4. A 34-year-old male (height 6'7", weight 287 pounds) is hospitalized after a motor vehicle accident. He develops a *Pseudomonas aeruginosa* infection. The physician orders tobramycin 2 mg/kg IV Q8H. Calculate the tobramycin dose. Round to the nearest 10 milligrams.

$$\text{Total Body Weight} = 287 \text{ lb} \times \frac{1 \text{ kg}}{2.2 \text{ lbs}} = 130.4545 \text{ kg}$$

$$\text{IBW (male)} = 50 \text{ kg} + (2.3 \times 19 \text{ in}) = 93.7 \text{ kg}$$

$$\% \text{ above IBW} = \frac{130.4545 \text{ kg}}{93.7 \text{ kg}} = \text{1.39, he is 139\% of his IBW or 39\% above his IBW}$$

Use the flowchart to determine which weight to use to dose the aminoglycoside. This patient is obese. Aminoglycosides are dosed on adjusted body weight in obese patients.

$$AdjBW_{0.4} = 93.7 + 0.4\,(130.4545 - 93.7) = 108.4 \text{ kg}$$

$$\text{Tobramycin } 2 \text{ mg/kg} \times 108.4 \text{ kg} = \text{216.8 mg, round to 220 mg IV Q8H}$$

HEIGHT IN INCHES

In the U.S., heights are generally presented in feet and inches vs using the metric system.

- Example 1: A patient is 5 feet 6 inches tall (often written 5'6"). How many inches tall is the patient?
  - 1 ft = 12 inches, so 5 ft = 60 inches
  - Next, add the additional 6 inches
  - 5'6" = 66 inches
  - For IBW calculation: patient is 6 inches over 5 feet
- Example 2: A patient is 6'3". How many inches tall is this patient?
  - 6 ft x 12 inches/ft = 72 inches
  - Next, add the additional 3 inches
  - 6'3" = 75 inches
  - For IBW calculation: patient is 15 inches over 5 feet

FLOW RATES

Intravenous (IV) infusions or continuous infusions are commonly used to deliver medications in different settings, including hospitals. Flow rates are used to specify the volume or amount of drug a patient will receive over a given period of time. An order can specify the flow rate in many ways. Some examples include: milliliters per hour, milligrams per hour, mcg /kg/ min or as the total time to administer the entire volume of the infusion (e.g., give over 8 hours). Sometimes flow rates are expressed in drops/min, which is discussed later in this chapter.

Flow rate problems can be performed with proportions or dimensional analysis. Principles of each are reviewed in Calculations I. Some of the following problems will be illustrated using both methods, but not all. Feel free to use whichever method is most comfortable.

5. A patient will receive 400 mg of a drug that has been put in a 250 mL IV bag. The rate of drug administration is 375 mcg per minute. Calculate the flow rate in milliliters per hour. Round to the nearest whole number.

The order specifies the rate of administration as 375 mcg/min. Many infusion pumps are set to deliver a certain volume of fluid per unit of time (e.g., mL/hr). This requires a conversion.

Dimensional analysis works well for flow rate problems. Here is a breakdown of the steps:

1. The 1st fraction is the drug concentration. Since you are solving for mL/hr, milliliters needs to be in the numerator.
2. The 2nd fraction converts the drug weight from mg to micrograms.
3. The 3rd fraction is the rate of drug administration.
4. The 4th fraction converts minutes to hours.
5. This combines the individual steps into one calculation. If using dimensional analysis, make sure that all units cancel out to leave the correct units:

$$\frac{250\ \text{mL}}{400\ \cancel{\text{mg}}} \times \frac{1\ \cancel{\text{mg}}}{1000\ \cancel{\text{mcg}}} \times \frac{375\ \cancel{\text{mcg}}}{\cancel{\text{min}}} \times \frac{60\ \cancel{\text{min}}}{1\ \text{hr}} = 14\ \text{mL/hr}$$

Flow rates depend on the dose of the medication and the concentration available. If the concentration of the medication is 400 mg/250 mL (in the example above), then the IV needs to run at 14 mL/hr to deliver 375 mcg/min.

If the pharmacy prepared a more concentrated product (e.g., 800 mg/250 mL or twice as concentrated), then the IV will only need to run at 7 mL/hr to deliver the same dose. See math below:

$$\frac{250\ \text{mL}}{800\ \text{mg}} \times \frac{1\ \text{mg}}{1000\ \text{mcg}} \times \frac{375\ \text{mcg}}{\text{min}} \times \frac{60\ \text{min}}{1\ \text{hr}} = 7\ \text{mL/hr}$$

6. The pharmacist has an order for heparin 25,000 units in 250 mL D5W to infuse at 1,000 units/hour. The pharmacy has the following premixed heparin bags in stock: 25,000 units in 500 mL ½ NS, 10,000 units in 250 mL D5W, and 25,000 units in 250 mL D5W. What should the infusion rate be set at in mL/hour?

The pharmacy has the heparin product that was ordered. First, calculate the concentration (units per mL).

$$\frac{25{,}000\ \text{units}}{250\ \text{mL}} = 100\ \text{units/mL}$$

Next calculate the infusion rate.

$$\frac{1{,}000\ \text{units}}{1\ \text{hr}} \times \frac{1\ \text{mL}}{100\ \text{units}} = 10\ \text{mL/hr}$$

Since 1,000 units/hour must be delivered to the patient and there are 100 units in each mL, the pump should be programmed for an infusion rate of 10 mL/hr.

Question 6 continued on next page

A second way to solve flow rate problems is using dimensional analysis:

$$\frac{250 \text{ mL}}{25{,}000 \text{ units}} \times \frac{1{,}000 \text{ units}}{1 \text{ hr}} = 10 \text{ mL/hr}$$

Another way to solve these problems is to use a proportion:

$$\frac{25{,}000 \text{ units}}{250 \text{ mL}} = \frac{1{,}000 \text{ units}}{X \text{ mL}} \quad X = 10 \text{ mL (10 mL/hr since we need to administer 1,000 units in 1 hour)}$$

Try solving the problems in this section both ways and decide which you prefer.

---

7. If 200 mg of drug are added to a 500 mL bag, what rate of flow, in milliliters per hour, will deliver 500 mcg of drug per hour? Round to the nearest hundredth.

$$200 \text{ mg} \times \frac{1{,}000 \text{ mcg}}{1 \text{ mg}} = 200{,}000 \text{ mcg}$$

$$\frac{200{,}000 \text{ mcg}}{500 \text{ mL}} = \frac{500 \text{ mcg}}{X} \quad X = 1.25 \text{ mL/hour}$$

---

8. A nurse is hanging a 4% lidocaine drip for a patient. If the dose ordered is 6 mg/min, how many hours will a 250 mL bag last? Round to the nearest tenth.

$$\frac{4 \text{ g}}{100 \text{ mL}} = \frac{X \text{ g}}{250 \text{ mL}} \quad X = 10 \text{ g or } 10{,}000 \text{ mg}$$

$$\frac{6 \text{ mg}}{\text{min}} = \frac{10{,}000 \text{ mg}}{X \text{ min}} \quad X = 1{,}666.67 \text{ minutes}$$

Convert to hours = 27.777 hrs, or 27.8 hrs

Or, solve another way:

$$\frac{1 \text{ hr}}{60 \text{ min}} \times \frac{1 \text{ min}}{6 \text{ mg}} \times \frac{1{,}000 \text{ mg}}{1 \text{ g}} \times \frac{4 \text{ g}}{100 \text{ mL}} \times 250 \text{ mL} = 27.8 \text{ hours}$$

---

9. A 68 kg patient is receiving a drug in a standard concentration of 400 mg/250 mL of ½ NS running at 15 mL/hr. Calculate the dose in mcg/kg/min. Round to the nearest hundredth.

$$\frac{15 \text{ mL}}{\text{hr}} \times \frac{400 \text{ mg drug}}{250 \text{ mL}} = 24 \text{ mg drug/hr}$$

$$\frac{24 \text{ mg drug}}{\text{hr}} \times \frac{1{,}000 \text{ mcg}}{1 \text{ mg}} = 24{,}000 \text{ mcg/hr}$$

$$\frac{24{,}000 \text{ mcg}}{\text{hr}} \times \frac{1 \text{ hr}}{60 \text{ min}} = 400 \text{ mcg/min}$$

$$\frac{400 \text{ mcg/min}}{68 \text{ kg}} = 5.88 \text{ mcg/kg/min}$$

10. The pharmacist has an order for heparin 25,000 units in 250 mL D5W to infuse at 1,000 units/hour. How many hours will it take to infuse the entire bag?

$$25{,}000 \text{ units} \times \frac{1 \text{ hr}}{1{,}000 \text{ units}} = 25 \text{ hrs}$$

---

11. If 50 mg of drug are added to a 500 mL bag, what rate of flow, in milliliters per hour, will deliver 5 mg of drug per hour?

$$\frac{500 \text{ mL}}{50 \text{ mg}} \times \frac{5 \text{ mg}}{\text{hr}} = 50 \text{ mL/hour}$$

---

12. A patient is to receive *Keppra* at a rate of 5 mg/min. The pharmacy has a 5 mL *Keppra* vial (100 mg/mL) which will be diluted in 100 mL of NS. What is the *Keppra* infusion rate, in mL/min? Do not include the volume of the 5 mL additive.

First, calculate the amount of *Keppra* in the vial.

$$\frac{100 \text{ mg}}{\text{mL}} = \frac{X \text{ mg}}{5 \text{ mL}} \quad X = 500 \text{ mg}$$

Then, solve for the answer in mL/min.

$$\frac{100 \text{ mL}}{500 \text{ mg}} \times \frac{5 \text{ mg}}{\text{min}} = 1 \text{ mL/min}$$

FINAL VOLUME OF COMPOUNDED IV SOLUTIONS

Why does problem #12 say "do not include the volume of the 5 mL additive"? Because the answer might be different (depending on the rounding instructions) if you used 100 mL vs 105 mL for the final volume.

- Exam scenarios:
  - ❑ Explicit instructions (e.g., #12).
  - ❑ Language stating that a specific volume is "added to" some volume of a fluid (e.g., #22).
  - ❑ Rounding instructions are such that either method will yield the correct answer or volumes of additives are not provided.
  - ❑ Language stating that a specific volume is added "to make 1 liter" or "for a final volume of 1 L."

This can be handled in many ways in clinical practice, but institutions should have clear policies to avoid medication errors.

---

13. A patient is to receive 600,000 units of penicillin G potassium in 100 mL D5W. A vial of penicillin G potassium 1,000,000 units is available. The manufacturer states that when 4.6 mL of diluent is added, a 200,000 units/mL solution will result. How many milliliters of reconstituted solution should be withdrawn and added to the bag of D5W?

$$\frac{200{,}000 \text{ units}}{\text{mL}} = \frac{600{,}000 \text{ units}}{X \text{ mL}} \quad X = 3 \text{ mL}$$

---

14. A patient is to receive *Flagyl* at a rate of 12.5 mg/min. The pharmacy has a 5 mL (100 mg/mL) *Flagyl* injection vial to be diluted in 100 mL of NS. How much drug in milligrams will the patient receive over 20 minutes?

$$\frac{12.5 \text{ mg}}{\text{min}} \times 20 \text{ minutes} = 250 \text{ mg}$$

---

15. A physician has ordered 2 grams of cefotetan to be added to 100 mL NS for a 56-year-old female with an anaerobic infection. Using a reconstituted injection containing 154 mg/mL, how many milliliters should be added to prepare the order? Round to the nearest whole number.

$$2{,}000 \text{ mg} \times \frac{1 \text{ mL}}{154 \text{ mg}} = 13 \text{ mL}$$

16. JY is a 58-year-old male hospitalized for a total knee replacement. He was given unfractionated heparin and developed heparin-induced thrombocytopenia (HIT). Argatroban was ordered at a dose of 2 mcg/kg/min. The pharmacy mixes a concentration of 100 mg argatroban in 250 mL of D5W. JY weighs 187 lbs. At what rate (mL/hour) should the nurse infuse argatroban to provide the desired dose? Round to the nearest whole number.

First, determine the amount of drug needed based on the body weight provided.

$$2 \text{ mcg/kg/min} \times 85 \text{ kg} = 170 \text{ mcg/min}$$

Then, calculate mL/hr.

$$\frac{250 \text{ mL}}{100 \text{ mg}} \times \frac{1 \text{ mg}}{1{,}000 \text{ mcg}} \times \frac{170 \text{ mcg}}{\text{min}} \times \frac{60 \text{ min}}{\text{hr}} = 25.5 \text{ mL/hr, rounded to } 26 \text{ mL/hr}$$

17. A 165 pound patient is to receive 250 mL of a dopamine drip at a rate of 17 mcg/kg/min. The pharmacy has dopamine premixed in a concentration of 3.2 mg/mL in D5W. Calculate the infusion rate in mL/minute. Round to the nearest tenth.

Step 1: Calculate amount of drug in the 250 mL bag.

$$\frac{3.2 \text{ mg}}{\text{mL}} \times 250 \text{ mL} = 800 \text{ mg}$$

Step 2: Calculate amount of drug the patient needs per minute.

$$\frac{17 \text{ mcg}}{\text{kg/min}} \times \frac{1 \text{ kg}}{2.2 \text{ lbs}} \times 165 \text{ lbs} = 1{,}275 \text{ mcg/min or } 1.275 \text{ mg/min}$$

Step 3: Solve for milliliters per minute.

$$\frac{250 \text{ mL}}{800 \text{ mg}} \times \frac{1.275 \text{ mg}}{\text{min}} = 0.4 \text{ mL/min}$$

18. An order is written for phenytoin IV. A loading dose of 15 mg/kg is to be infused at 0.5 mg/kg/min for a 33 pound child. The pharmacy has phenytoin injection solution 50 mg/mL in a 5 mL vial in stock. The pharmacist will put the dose into 50 mL NS. Over how many minutes should the dose be administered? Round to the nearest whole number.

First, calculate the child's body weight in kg.

$$33 \text{ lbs} \times \frac{1 \text{ kg}}{2.2 \text{ lbs}} = 15 \text{ kg}$$

Next, find the dose the child will receive.

$$\frac{15 \text{ mg}}{\text{kg}} \times 15 \text{ kg} = 225 \text{ mg}$$

Then, calculate the time it will take to infuse this amount of drug at the given rate.

$$0.5 \text{mg/kg/min} \times 15 \text{ kg} = 7.5 \text{ mg/min}$$

$$\frac{1 \text{ min}}{7.5 \text{ mg}} \times 225 \text{ mg} = 30 \text{ minutes}$$

DROP FACTOR

IV tubing is set to deliver a certain number of drops per minute (gtts/min). There are various types of IV tubing and each has a hollow plastic chamber called a drip chamber. The number of drops per minute can be counted by looking at the drip chamber. It is important to know how big the drops are to calibrate the tubing in terms of drops/mL. This is called the drop factor. Calculating flow rates from a drop factor is not as common with the prevalence of programmable "smart" pumps. It is a good skill to know for situations when a programmable pump is not available (or fails) and as a "double check."

19. A physician orders an IV infusion of D5W 1 liter to be delivered over 8 hours. The IV infusion set delivers 15 drops/mL. How many drops/min will the patient receive? Round to the nearest whole number.

$$\frac{15 \text{ drops}}{1 \text{ mL}} \times \frac{1{,}000 \text{ mL}}{8 \text{ hr}} \times \frac{1 \text{ hr}}{60 \text{ min}} = 31.25 \text{ drops/min, rounded to 31 drops/min}$$

---

20. A physician orders 15 units of regular insulin to be added to a liter of D5W to be given over 10 hours. What is the infusion rate, in drops/minute, if the IV set delivers 15 drops/mL? Do not include the insulin volume in the calculation.

$$\frac{15 \text{ drops}}{\text{mL}} \times \frac{1{,}000 \text{ mL}}{10 \text{ hrs}} \times \frac{1 \text{ hr}}{60 \text{ min}} = 25 \text{ drops/min}$$

---

21. The pharmacy has insulin vials containing 100 units of insulin/mL. A physician orders 15 units of regular insulin to be added to a liter of D5W to be given over 10 hours. How many units of insulin will the patient receive each hour if the IV set delivers 15 drops/mL? Do not round the answer.

$$\frac{15 \text{ units}}{10 \text{ hrs}} = \frac{X \text{ units}}{1 \text{ hr}} \quad X = 1.5 \text{ units/hr}$$

---

22. An order is written for 10 mL of a 10% calcium chloride injection and 10 mL of multivitamin injection (MVI) to be <u>added to</u> 500 mL of D5W. The infusion is to be administered over 6 hours. The IV set delivers 15 drops/mL. What should be the rate of flow in drops/minute to deliver this infusion? Round to the nearest whole number.

Total volume of the infusion = 500 mL (D5W) + 10 mL ($CaCl_2$) + 10 mL (MVI) = 520 mL

$$\frac{15 \text{ drops}}{\text{mL}} \times \frac{520 \text{ mL}}{6 \text{ hr}} \times \frac{1 \text{ hr}}{60 \text{ min}} = 21.6666\text{, rounded to 22 drops/min}$$

---

23. RS is a 45-year-old male, 5'5", 168 pounds, hospitalized with a diabetic foot infection. The pharmacist prepared a 500 mL bag of D5W containing 1 gram of vancomycin to be infused over 4 hours using a 20 gtts/mL IV tubing set. How many mg of vancomycin will the patient receive each minute? Round to the nearest tenth.

$$\frac{1{,}000 \text{ mg vanco}}{4 \text{ hrs}} \times \frac{1 \text{ hr}}{60 \text{ min}} = 4.16 \text{ mg/min, rounded to 4.2 mg/min}$$

Notice that the patient's height and weight are not needed to solve this problem.

---

24. A patient is to receive 1.5 liters of NS running at 45 gtts/min using a 15 gtts/mL IV tubing set. Calculate the total infusion time in hours. Round to the nearest tenth.

$$\frac{15 \text{ gtts}}{1 \text{ mL}} = \frac{45 \text{ gtts}}{X \text{ mL}} \quad X = 3 \text{ mL}$$

$$\frac{3 \text{ mL}}{\text{min}} = \frac{1{,}500 \text{ mL}}{X \text{ min}} \quad X = 500 \text{ min}$$

$$500 \text{ min} \times \frac{1 \text{ hr}}{60 \text{ min}} = 8.3 \text{ hrs}$$

25. The 8 a.m. medications scheduled for a patient include *Tygacil* dosed at 6 mg/kg. The patient weighs 142 pounds. The nurse has *Tygacil* labeled 500 mg/50 mL NS. The dose will be administered over thirty minutes. The IV tubing in the unit delivers 15 drops per milliliter. What is the correct rate of flow in drops per minute? Round to the nearest drop.

$$\frac{142 \text{ pounds}}{2.2 \text{ pounds/kg}} \times \frac{6 \text{ mg}}{\text{kg}} = 387.27 \text{ mg required dose}$$

$$387.27 \text{ mg} \times \frac{50 \text{ mL}}{500 \text{ mg}} = 38.727 \text{ mL}$$

$$\frac{38.727 \text{ mL}}{30 \text{ min}} \times \frac{15 \text{ drops}}{\text{mL}} = 19.36 \text{ drops/min, rounded to 19 drops/min for 30 minutes}$$

RENAL FUNCTION AND CREATININE CLEARANCE ESTIMATION

Creatinine is a break-down product produced when muscle tissue makes energy. The normal range for serum creatinine is approximately 0.6 – 1.3 mg/dL. If kidney function declines and creatinine cannot be cleared (excreted), the creatinine level will increase in the blood and the creatinine clearance (CrCl) will decrease. This tells us that the concentration of drugs that are renally cleared will also increase and a dose reduction may be required. Sometimes the serum creatinine can appear normal even when renal function is compromised (e.g., in the elderly). Refer to the Learning Lab Values & Drug Monitoring and Renal Disease Chapters.

Patients should be assessed for dehydration when the serum creatinine is elevated. Dehydration can cause both the serum creatinine (SCr) and the blood urea nitrogen (BUN) to increase. A BUN:SCr ratio > 20:1 indicates dehydration. Correcting the dehydration will reduce both BUN and SCr, and can prevent or treat acute renal failure. Signs of dehydration should also be assessed and these can include decreased urine output, tachycardia, tachypnea, dry skin/mouth/mucous membranes, skin tenting (skin does not bounce back when pinched into a fold) and possibly fever. Dehydration is usually caused by diarrhea, vomiting and/or a lack of adequate fluid intake.

26. Looking at the laboratory values below, make an assessment of the patient's hydration status.

	PATIENT'S VALUE	REFERENCE RANGE
BUN	54 mg/dL	7-20 mg/dL
Creatinine	1.8 mg/dL	0.6-1.3 mg/dL

A. The patient appears to be well hydrated.
B. The patient appears to be too hydrated.
C. The patient is not experiencing dehydration.
D. The patient is experiencing dehydration and may need to be started on fluids.
E. The patient has subjective information indicating dehydration but the patient needs to be assessed objectively as well.

The correct answer is (D). The patient's BUN:SCr ratio is 54/1.8 = 30:1. Since 30:1 > 20:1, the BUN is disproportionately elevated relative to the creatinine, indicating that the patient is dehydrated.

27. NK is receiving a furosemide infusion at 5 mg/hr. The nurse notices her urine output has decreased in the last hour. Laboratory values are drawn and the patient has a SCr of 1.5 mg/dL and a BUN of 26 mg/dL. The nurse wants to know if she should stop the furosemide infusion due to the patient becoming dehydrated. What is the correct assessment of the patient's hydration status?

A. The patient appears to be too hydrated given the laboratory results.
B. The patient is not experiencing dehydration given the laboratory results.
C. The patient is experiencing dehydration and may need to be started on fluids.
D. The patient has objective information indicating dehydration but the patient needs to be assessed subjectively as well.
E. None of the above are correct.

The correct answer is (B). The BUN:SCr ratio is 26/1.5 = 17.3:1, which is < 20:1. Continue to monitor the patient.

THE COCKCROFT-GAULT EQUATION

This formula is used by pharmacists to estimate renal function. It is not commonly used in very young children, ESRD patients or when renal function is fluctuating rapidly. There are different methods used to estimate renal function in these circumstances. The Cockcroft-Gault equation should be known, as it is commonly used in practice.

$$\text{CrCl (mL/min)} = \frac{140 - \text{(age of patient)}}{72 \times \text{SCr}} \times \text{weight in kg (x 0.85 if female)}$$

Use age in years, weight in kg and SCr in mg/dL (same as mmol/L) in the Cockcroft-Gault equation

Which Weight to Use for Calculating CrCl?

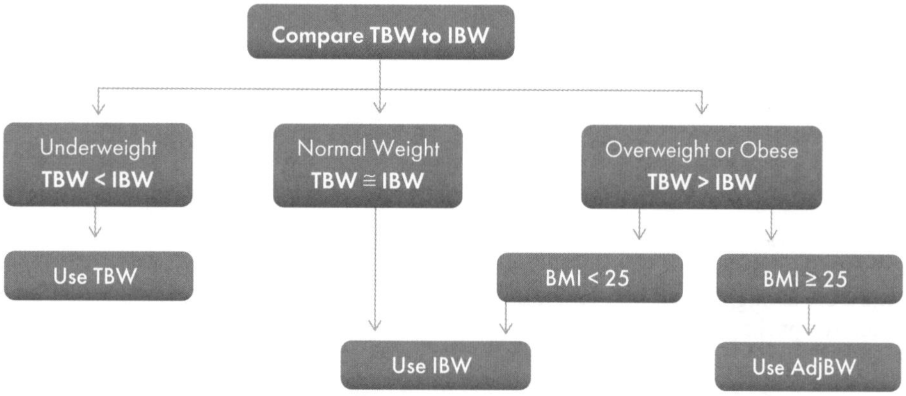

Once the CrCl has been calculated, it is used to renally adjust all necessary medications (unless serum creatinine changes). The proper weight to use in the Cockcroft-Gault equation will not always be the same weight used to calculate a weight-based (mg/kg) dose (see previous algorithm). The following examples illustrate this point.

28. A 64-year-old female patient (height 5'5", weight 205 pounds) is hospitalized with a nosocomial pneumonia which is responding to treatment. Her current antibiotic medications include ciprofloxacin, *Primaxin* and vancomycin. Her morning laboratory values include: K 4 mEq/L, BUN 60 mg/dL, SCr 2.7 mg/dL and glucose 222 mg/dL. Based on the renal dosage recommendations from the package labeling below, what is the correct dose of *Primaxin* for this patient?

CrCl	≥ 71 mL/min	41-70 mL/min	21-40 mL/min	6-20 mL/min
Primaxin Dose	500 mg IV Q6H	500 mg IV Q8H	250 mg IV Q6H	250 mg IV Q12H

Use the flowchart to determine which weight to use to calculate CrCl.

Total Body Weight = 93.1818 kg

IBW = 45.5 kg + (2.3 x 5 in) = 57 kg

$$\text{BMI} = \frac{205 \text{ lbs}}{(65 \text{ inches})^2} \times 703 = 34.1 \text{ kg/m}^2\text{, obese}$$

Now calculate her adjusted body weight:

$$\text{AdjBW}_{0.4} = 57 + 0.4\,(93.1818 - 57) = 71.47 \text{ kg}$$

Then, solve using the Cockcroft-Gault equation:

$$\text{CrCl} = \frac{140 - 64}{72 \times 2.7} \times 71.47\,(0.85) = 23.75 \text{ mL/min}$$

The correct dose of *Primaxin* is 250 mg IV Q6H.

---

29. Levofloxacin, dosing per pharmacy, is ordered for an 87-year-old female patient (height 5'4", weight 103 pounds). Her labs include BUN 22 mg/dL and SCr 1 mg/dL. Choose the correct dosing regimen based on the renal dosage adjustments from the package labeling below.

CrCl	≥ 50 mL/min	20-49 mL/min	< 20 mL/min
Levofloxacin Dose	500 mg Q24 hours	250 mg Q24 hours	250 mg Q48 hours

First, determine which weight to use in calculating the CrCl.

Total Body Weight = 46.8181 kg

IBW = 45.5 kg + (2.3 x 4 in) = 54.7 kg

Use total body weight for calculating CrCl since the patient's total body weight is less than her IBW.

$$\text{CrCl} = \frac{140 - 87}{72 \times 1} \times 46.8181 \text{ kg } (\times\, 0.85) = 29 \text{ mL/min}$$

The correct dose of levofloxacin is 250 mg Q24H.

30. A 50-year-old male (height 6'1", weight 177 pounds) has HIV and is being started on tenofovir, emtricitabine and efavirenz therapy. His laboratory values include K 4.4 mEq/L, BUN 40 mg/dL, SCr 1.8 mg/dL, and CD4 count of 455 cells/mm³. Using the renal dosage recommendations from the package labeling below, what is the correct dose of tenofovir for this patient?

CrCl	≥ 50 mL/min	30–49 mL/min	10–29 mL/min	< 10 mL/min
Tenofovir Dose	300 mg daily	300 mg Q48 hours	300 mg Q72-96 hours	300 mg weekly

First, determine which weight to use in calculating the CrCl.

Total Body Weight = 80.4545 kg

IBW = 50 kg + (2.3 x 13 in) = 79.9, or 80 kg

The IBW is almost the same as the actual weight. Either weight will yield a similar CrCl.

Next, calculate the CrCl.

$$CrCl = \frac{140 - 50}{72 \times 1.8} \times 80\ kg = 55\ mL/min$$

The dose of tenofovir should be 300 mg daily.

ACID-BASE AND ARTERIAL BLOOD GASES

pH

The pH refers to the acidity or basicity of the solution. As a solution becomes more acidic (the concentration of protons increases), the pH decreases. Conversely, when the pH increases, protons decrease, and the solution is more basic, or alkaline. Pure water is neutral at a pH of 7, and blood, with a pH of 7.4, is slightly alkaline. Stomach acid has a pH of ~2, and is therefore acidic, with many protons in solution.

ARTERIAL BLOOD GASES

The acid-base status of a patient can be determined with an arterial blood gas (ABG). The primary buffering system of the body is the bicarbonate/carbonic acid system. The kidneys help to maintain a neutral pH by controlling bicarbonate (HCO3) reabsorption and elimination. Bicarbonate acts as a buffer and a base. The lungs help maintain a neutral pH by controlling carbonic acid (which is directly proportional to the partial pressure of carbon dioxide or pCO2) retained or released from the body. Carbon dioxide acts as a buffer and an acid. Alterations from the normal values lead to acid-base disorders. Diet and cellular metabolism lead to a large production of H^+ ions that need to be excreted to maintain acid-base balance. ABGs are presented as follows in a written chart note:

ABG: pH/pCO2/pO2/HCO3/O2 Sat

INTERPRETING ABGs

- Step #1: Is it an acidosis or alkalosis?
  - ↓ pH = acidosis
  - ↑ pH = alkalosis
- Step #2: What other value(s) are abnormal?
  - Respiratory: ↓ CO2 = alkalosis ↑ CO2 = acidosis
  - Metabolic: ↑ HCO3 = alkalosis ↓ HCO3 = acidosis
- Step #3: Which of the abnormal values in Step #2 matches with the pH in Step #1?
  - Example: ↓ pH, ↑ CO2 and normal HCO3
  - pH = acidosis and ↑ CO2 = acidosis; this is a respiratory acidosis
- Step #4: What if both CO2 and HCO3 are abnormal?
  - Usually only one of the values will match the pH, the other will go in the opposite direction from the pH. This is called compensation.
  - Example: ↓ pH, ↓ CO2 and ↓ HCO3
  - pH = acidosis, ↓ HCO3 = acidosis and ↓ CO2 = alkalosis; this is a metabolic acidosis with some degree of respiratory compensation

An acid-base disorder that leads to a pH < 7.35 is called an acidosis. If the disorder leads to a pH > 7.45, it is called an alkalosis. These disorders are further classified as either metabolic or respiratory in origin. The primary disturbance in a metabolic acid-base disorder is the plasma HCO3 (bicarbonate) concentration. A metabolic acidosis is characterized primarily by a decrease in plasma HCO3 concentration. In a metabolic alkalosis, the plasma HCO3 concentration is increased. Metabolic acidosis may be associated with an increase in the anion gap (see next page). In respiratory acidosis, the pCO2 is primarily elevated and in respiratory alkalosis, the pCO2 is decreased. Each disturbance has a compensatory (secondary) response that attempts to correct the imbalance toward normal and keep the pH neutral (see Study Tip Gal on previous page for the steps to interpret ABGs).

REFERENCE RANGE	
pH	7.35 – 7.45
pCO2	35 – 45 mmHg
pO2	80 – 100 mmHg
HCO3	22 – 26 mEq/L
O2 Sat	> 95%

Reference range for arterial sample. Bicarbonate reported on ABG is a calculated value and reference range will differ from venous sample

31. A babysitter brings a 7-year-old boy to the Emergency Department. He is unarousable. Labs are ordered and an ABG is drawn. The ABG results are as follows: 6.72/40/89/12/94%. What acid base disorder does the child have?

Based on the pH, this is an acidosis. The pCO2 is normal and the HCO3 is decreased (low bicarbonate indicates acidosis). This is a metabolic acidosis.

32. An elderly female is admitted to the hospital after a motor vehicle accident. She suffered a head injury and is in the ICU. An ABG is obtained and the results are as follows: 8.25/29/97/26/98%. What acid base disorder does the patient have?

Based on the pH, this is an alkalosis. The pCO2 is decreased (low pCO2 indicates alkalosis) and the HCO3 is normal. This is a respiratory alkalosis.

ANION GAP

When a patient is experiencing metabolic acidosis, it is common to calculate an anion gap. The anion gap is the difference in the measured cations and the measured anions in the blood. An anion gap assists in determining the cause of the acidosis. A mnemonic to remember the causes of a gap acidosis is CUTE DIMPLES [cyanide, uremia, toluene, ethanol (alcoholic ketoacidosis), diabetic ketoacidosis, isoniazid, methanol, propylene glycol, lactic acidosis, ethylene glycol, salicylates]. The anion gap is considered high if it is > 12 mEq/L (meaning the patient has a gap acidosis). The anion gap can also be low, which is less common. A non-gap acidosis is caused by other factors, mainly hyperchloremic acidosis. Anion gap is calculated with this formula, using the values from the basic metabolic panel (venous sample).

Anion gap (AG) = Na - Cl - HCO3

33. A patient in the ICU has recently developed an acidosis. Using the laboratory parameters below, calculate the patient's anion gap.

Na	139
Cl	101
K	4.6
HCO3	19
SCr	1.6
BUN	38

Anion Gap = 139 - 101 - 19 = 19; therefore, the patient has a positive anion gap acidosis

34. SJ was recently admitted to the ICU with a pH of 7.27. Below is her laboratory data. Calculate SJ's anion gap.

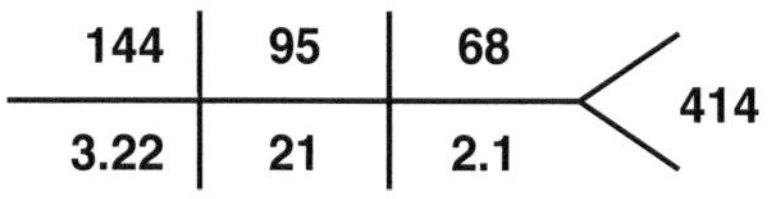

Anion Gap = 144 - 95 - 21 = 28; therefore, SJ has a positive anion gap acidosis

BUFFER SYSTEMS AND IONIZATION

Buffer systems help to reduce the impact of too few or too many hydrogen ions in body fluids. These hydrogen ions could cause harm including degrading some drugs, destabilizing proteins, inhibiting cellular functions, and with too much of a change outside of the narrow range, cells die and death can occur. Therefore, buffers minimize fluctuations in pH so that harm is avoided. Buffer systems are common in the body and are composed of either a weak acid and salt of the acid (e.g., acetic acid and sodium acetate), or weak base and salt of the base (e.g., ammonium hydroxide and ammonium chloride). An acid is a compound that dissociates, releasing (donating) protons into solution. Once the proton is released, the compound is now a conjugate base, or its salt form. For example, HCl in solution is an acid and dissociates (giving up the proton) into H^+ and Cl^-. A base picks up, or binds, the proton. For example, NH_3 is a base that can pick up a proton and become NH_4^+.

Acid-base reactions are equilibrium reactions; there is drug moving back and forth between the acid and base state. The pH and the pKa are used to determine if the drug is acting as an acid or a base. When the pH = pKa, the molar concentration of the salt form and the molar concentration of the acid form of the buffer acid-base pair will be equal: 50% of the buffer will be in salt form and 50% in acid form. Notice that the percentage of buffer in the acid form when added to the percentage of buffer in the salt form will equal 100%. When the pH = pKa, this is the point at which half the compound is not protonated (ionized), and half is protonated (un-ionized).

A 'strong' acid or base means 100% dissociation and a 'weak' acid or base means very limited dissociation. Any time a pKa is provided, it refers to the acid form losing protons to give to the base, or salt, form.

If the 'pKb' is provided, think 'base' simply because of the definitions of the two terms.

If the pH > pKa, more of the acid is ionized, and more of the conjugate base is un-ionized.

If the pH = pKa, the ionized and un-ionized forms are equal.

If the pH < pKa, more of the acid is un-ionized, and more of the conjugate base is ionized.

The percentage of drug in the ionized versus un-ionized state is important because an ionized drug is soluble but cannot easily cross lipid membranes. An un-ionized drug is not soluble but can cross the membranes and reach the proper receptor site. Most drugs are weak acids. They are soluble, and can pick up a proton to cross the lipid layer.

Most drug molecules are weak acids (or weak bases). These molecules can exist in either the un-ionized or the ionized state, and the degree of ionization depends on the dissociation constant (Ka) of the drug and the pH of the environment. This leads to the Henderson-Hasselbalch equation, also known as the buffer equation, which is used to solve for the pH.

THE pH OF A SOLUTION

Weak acid formula

$$pH = pK_a + \log\left[\frac{\text{salt}}{\text{acid}}\right]$$

Weak base formulas

$$pH = (pK_w^* - pK_b) + \log\left[\frac{\text{base}}{\text{salt}}\right] \quad \text{or} \quad pH = pK_a + \log\left[\frac{\text{base}}{\text{salt}}\right]$$

where pKw = 14

CALCULATING THE LOG OF A NUMBER

35. Calculate log (1/0.5). Round to the nearest tenth.

$$\log\left[\frac{1}{0.5}\right]$$

1. **If there is a division, solve the division first.** 1/0.5 = 2
2. **The number 2 will be on the calculator screen. Solve for log[2] by hitting the $\log_{10}$ or log key.**

   Some hand-held and on-screen calculators may require you to press the log key first, followed by "2" to solve this problem.
3. **This will provide the answer, in this example, the answer is 0.3 (rounded to the nearest tenth).**

   Some calculators have parenthesis that allow you to enter the calculation as written in the problem, rather than performing each step separately. Practice these steps until you are familiar with them.

36. What is the pH of a solution prepared to be 0.5 M sodium citrate and 0.05 M citric acid (pKa for citric acid = 3.13)? Round to the nearest hundredth.

$$pH = pK_a + \log\left[\frac{salt}{acid}\right]$$

$$pH = 3.13 + \log\left[\frac{0.5M}{0.05M}\right]$$

$$pH = 3.13 + \log[10]$$

$$pH = 3.13 + 1$$

$$pH = 4.13$$

37. What is the pH of a solution prepared to be 0.4 M ammonia and 0.04 M ammonium chloride (pKb for ammonia = 4.76)? Round to the nearest hundredth.

$$pH = (pK_w - pK_b) + \log\left[\frac{base}{salt}\right]$$

$$pH = (14 - 4.76) + \log\left[\frac{0.4}{0.04}\right]$$

$$pH = 9.24 + \log(10)$$

$$pH = 9.24 + 1$$

$$pH = 10.24$$

38. What is the pH of a buffer solution containing 0.5 M acetic acid and 1 M sodium acetate in 1 liter of solution (pKa for acetic acid = 4.76)? Round to the nearest hundredth.

$$pH = pK_a + \log\left[\frac{\text{salt}}{\text{acid}}\right]$$

$$pH = 4.76 + \log\left[\frac{1}{0.5}\right]$$

$$pH = 4.76 + \log(2)$$

$$pH = 4.76 + 0.301$$

$$pH = 5.06$$

---

39. A buffer solution is prepared using 0.3 mole of a weakly basic drug and an unknown quantity of its salt (pKa of the drug = 10.1). The final solution has a pH of 8.99. How much of the salt was used? Round to the nearest hundredth.

$$pH = pK_a + \log\left[\frac{\text{base}}{\text{salt}}\right]$$

$$8.99 = 10.1 + \log\left[\frac{0.3}{X}\right]$$

$$8.99 - 10.1 = \log\left[\frac{0.3}{X}\right]$$

$$10^{-1.11} = \frac{0.3}{X}$$

$$X = 3.86 \text{ mole of the salt}$$

PERCENTAGE OF DRUG IONIZATION IN A SOLUTION

The Henderson-Hasselbalch equation can be modified to calculate the percent of ionization of a drug. Since the pH is a measurement of the hydrogen ions (protons) in the solution, the percent ionization is the percentage of the drug in the solution that has unprotonated.

To calculate the % ionization of a weak acid:

$$\% \text{ ionization} = \frac{100}{1+10^{(pKa-pH)}}$$

To calculate % ionization of a weak base:

$$\% \text{ ionization} = \frac{100}{1+10^{(pH-pKa)}}$$

40. What is the percent ionization of amitriptyline, a weak base with a pKa = 9.4, at a physiologic pH of 7.4?

Use the weak base formula:

$$\% \text{ ionization} = \frac{100}{1+10^{(pH-pKa)}}$$

$$\% \text{ ionization} = \frac{100}{1+10^{(7.4-9.4)}}$$

$$\% \text{ ionization} = \frac{100}{1+10^{(-2)}}$$

$$\% \text{ ionization} = \frac{100}{1.01}$$

$$\% \text{ ionization} = 99\%$$

41. What is the percent ionization of naproxen, a weak acid with a pKa of 4.2, in the stomach at a pH of 3? Round to the nearest whole number.

Use the weak acid formula:

$$\% \text{ ionization} = \frac{100}{1+10^{(pKa-pH)}}$$

$$\% \text{ ionization} = \frac{100}{16.85}$$

$$\% \text{ ionization} = 6\%$$

DRUG CONVERSIONS

CALCIUM SALT CONVERSIONS

Calcium carbonate (*Oscal, Tums*) has acid-dependent absorption and should be taken with meals. Calcium carbonate is a dense form of calcium and contains 40% elemental calcium. A tablet that advertises 500 mg of elemental calcium weighs 1,250 mg. If 1,250 mg is multiplied by 0.40 (which is 40%), it will yield 500 mg elemental calcium.

Calcium citrate (*Citracal*) has acid-independent absorption and can be taken with or without food. Calcium citrate is less dense and contains 21% elemental calcium. A tablet that advertises 315 mg calcium weighs 1,500 mg. If 1,500 mg is multiplied by 0.21 (or 21%), it will yield 315 mg elemental calcium. This is why the larger calcium citrate tablets provide less elemental calcium per tablet. They may be preferred if the gut fluid is basic, rather than acidic.

Calcium acetate (*PhosLo*) is used as a phosphate binder and not for calcium replacement. Though the capsules contain 25% elemental calcium, absorption from this formulation is poor. Calcium carbonate and citrate are most commonly used for calcium replacement.

42. A patient is taking 3 calcium citrate tablets daily (one tablet, TID). Each weighs 1,500 mg total (non-elemental) weight. She wishes to trade her calcium tablets for the carbonate form. If she is going to use 1,250 mg carbonate tablets (by weight), how many tablets will she need to take to provide the same total daily dose?

1,500 mg/tablet x 3 tablets/day x 0.21= 945 mg elemental calcium daily

Each of the carbonate tablets (1,250 mg x 0.4) has 500 mg elemental calcium per tablet.

$$\frac{945 \text{ mg elemental calcium}}{X \text{ tablets}} = \frac{500 \text{ mg elemental calcium}}{1 \text{ tablet}} \qquad X = 1.89 \text{ tablets}$$

She would need to take 2 tablets daily to provide a similar dose. Calcium absorption increases with lower doses, so this patient should be instructed to take one tablet with the morning meal and one with the evening meal.

AMINOPHYLLINE TO THEOPHYLLINE

Aminophylline and theophylline are narrow therapeutic index drugs. They are dosed on IBW in normal weight and obese patients for safety (see Body Weight section at the beginning of this chapter). Conversions between aminophylline and theophylline must be known for the exam. To convert aminophylline to theophylline, remember "ATM":

- **A**minophylline to **T**heophylline: **M**ultiply by 0.8
- Theophylline to Aminophylline: Divide by 0.8

43. A physician writes an order for aminophylline 500 mg IV, dosed at 0.5 mg per kg per hour for a female patient (185 pounds, 5'1"). There is only theophylline in stock. How many milligrams (mg) of theophylline will the patient receive per hour? Round to the nearest whole number.

IBW (female) = 45.5 kg + (2.3 x 1 in) = 47.8 kg

$$\frac{0.5 \text{ mg aminophylline}}{\text{kg/hr}} \times 47.8 \text{ kg} = 23.9 \text{ mg/hr aminophylline}$$

The aminophylline dose must now be converted to theophylline.

23.9 mg/hr aminophylline x 0.8 = 19.12 mg/hr, rounded to the nearest whole number = 19 mg/hr of theophylline

After solving the problem, read the question again to be certain the question was answered with the correct units (mg per hour of theophylline).

ABSOLUTE NEUTROPHIL COUNT

Neutrophils are our body's main defense against infection. The lower a patient's neutrophil count, the more susceptible that patient is to infection (see table below). The Clozapine REMS Program is designed to reduce the risk of severe clozapine-induced neutropenia; clozapine cannot be refilled if the ANC is < 1,000 cells/mm^3. A neutropenic patient should be monitored for signs of infection, including fever, shaking, general weakness or flu-like symptoms. Precautions to reduce infection risk, such as proper hand-washing and avoiding others with infection, should be followed. Further information is in the Learning Lab Values & Drug Monitoring chapter.

ANC (CELLS/MM^3)	DEFINITION
2,200 – 8,000	Normal
< 1,000	Neutropenia (at risk for infection)
< 500	Severe neutropenia
< 100	Profound neutropenia

Calculating the ANC

Multiply the WBC (in total cells/mm^3) by the percentage of neutrophils (the segs plus the bands) and divide by 100. Neutrophils can be labeled polymorphonuclear cells (PMNs or polys) or segmented neutrophils (segs) on a lab report.

ANC (cells/mm^3) = WBC x [(% segs + % bands)/100]

44. A patient is being seen at the oncology clinic today after her first round of chemotherapy one week ago. A CBC with differential is ordered and reported back as WBC = 14.8 x 10^3 cells/mm^3, segs 10% and bands 11%. Calculate this patient's ANC.

WBC = 14,800 cells/mm^3, Segs = 10% Bands = 11%

ANC = 14,800 x [(10% + 11%)/100] = 14,800 x 0.21 = 3,108 cells/mm^3

45. A patient is taking clozapine and is at the clinic for a routine visit. Today's labs include WBC = 4,300 cells/mm^3 with 48% segs and 2% bands. Calculate this patient's ANC.

WBC = 4,300 cells/mm^3, Segs = 48% Bands = 2%

ANC = 4,300 x [(48% + 2%)/100] = 4,300 x 0.5 = 2,150 cells/mm^3

CHAPTER CONTENT

Practice What You've Learned 185
Exam-Style Math Practice 186
Answer Key and Explanations 191
Are You Ready for the Math on NAPLEX? 197
Math is Ready for NAPLEX When 197

CHAPTER 13
CALCULATIONS V: EXAM-STYLE MATH PRACTICE

PRACTICE WHAT YOU'VE LEARNED

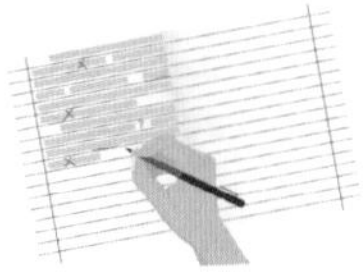

After all of the math concepts in Calculations I-IV have been mastered, test yourself with this exam-style math practice. Put all of your notes and formula sheets away. Grab a calculator and some scrap paper. Time yourself to finish the following 30 questions in ≤ 45 minutes. An answer key with detailed explanations follows.

TOOLS YOU WILL NEED

- Pen or Pencil

- Scrap paper

- Calculator
  (use yours or an online scientific calculator)

CONTENT LEGEND

= Study Tip Gal

EXAM-STYLE MATH PRACTICE

1. **A pharmacist receives a prescription for a 1.5% (w/w) hydrocortisone cream using cold cream as the base. She will use hydrocortisone injection (100 mg/mL, SG 1.5) to prepare the prescription because she has no hydrocortisone powder in stock. How many grams of cold cream are required to compound 60 grams of the preparation?**

2. **How many milliliters of a 1:2,500 (w/v) solution of aluminum acetate can be made from 100 mL of a 0.2% solution?**

3. **A pharmacist will prepare an *Amoxil* suspension to provide a 1600 mg daily dose for a child with an otitis media infection. The dose will be divided BID. To prepare an *Amoxil* suspension containing 200 mg/5 mL the pharmacist should add 76 mL of water to the powder for a final volume of 100 mL. The pharmacist should add approximately $^1/_3$ of the water first, shake vigorously, add the remaining water, and shake again to form the suspension. The pharmacist mistakenly adds too much water and finds that the final volume is 110 mL. The pharmacy has no other bottles of *Amoxil*, so the pharmacist will dispense the bottle with the extra water added. How many milliliters should the patient take twice daily to receive the correct dose? Round to the nearest whole number.**

4. **What is the ratio strength (w/v) of 50 mL containing a 1:20 (w/v) ammonia solution diluted to 1 liter?**

5. **A pharmacist receives an order for sodium chloride 4 mEq/kg/day for a patient who weighs 165 pounds. Using ½NS, how many liters will the patient require per day? Round to the nearest tenth. (M.W. of Na = 23, M.W. of Cl = 35.5)**

6. **How many milligrams of aminophylline will Mike receive per day based on the order in the profile? Round to the nearest whole number.**

PATIENT PROFILE

Patient Name	Mike Kelly
Address	65 Laney Road
Age:	22 **Sex:** M **Race:** Caucasian
Allergies	NKDA

DIAGNOSES

Asthma
Allergies

MEDICATIONS

Date	Prescriber	Drug/Strength/Sig
8/23	Sanchez	*Singulair* 10 mg 1 tablet in the evening daily
8/23	Sanchez	*Qvar* 1 puff (40 mcg) BID
9/29	Williams	Methylprednisolone 40 mg IV Q12H
9/29	Williams	Aminophylline 0.5 mg/kg/hr
9/29	Williams	D5$^1/_2$NS at 80 ml/hr
9/29	Williams	Albuterol nebulization 2.5 mg Q6H

LAB/DIAGNOSTIC TESTS

Test	Normal Value	Results Date: 9/1	Date: 1/7	Date: 9/29
Weight		125 pounds	141 pounds	160 pounds
Height		5'9"		5'9"
WBC	4,000-11,000 cells/mm^3	12,000		11,225
K	3.5-5 mEq/L	3.7	4.1	3.6
Glu	65-99 mg/dL	101		142

7. A patient is receiving D5½NS with potassium chloride at 20 drops/min. After 10 hours, the patient has received a total of 40 mEq of potassium chloride using tubing that delivers 15 drops/mL. What is the percentage concentration of potassium chloride in the patient's IV fluid? Round to 2 decimal places. (M.W. of K = 39, M.W. of Cl = 36)

---

8. An order is written for a dopamine drip in the ICU. The order reads: "Start dopamine drip at 3 mcg/kg/min, titrate by 5 mcg/kg/min Q5 minutes to achieve SBP > 100 mmHg. Page the critical care resident for additional orders if maximum dose of 20 mcg/kg/min is reached." The patient weighs 165 pounds and the ICU stocks premixed dopamine drips (400 mg/250 mL) in the automated dispensing cabinet (ADC). What rate (mL/hr) should the dopamine drip be started at? Round to the nearest whole number.

---

9. A 46-year-old female with radiation enteritis is receiving 1,800 kcal from her parenteral nutrition. The solution contains amino acids, dextrose and electrolytes. There are 84.5 grams of protein in the PN and it is running at 85 mL/hour over 24 hours. What is the final concentration of dextrose in the PN solution? Express the answer as a percentage. Round to the nearest whole number.

---

10. ML is a 165 pound male receiving a premixed dopamine drip (400 mg/250 mL) in the ICU. The order states that the drip can be titrated to a maximum dose of 20 mcg/kg/min. What is the maximum rate (mL/hr) at which the drip can be run? Round to the nearest whole number.

---

11. A pharmacist in an oncology clinic receives the following prescription for a patient with Hodgkin lymphoma: "Prednisone 40 mg/m^2/day PO on days 1-14." The patient is 5'1" and weighs 116 pounds. The hospital uses the following formula for BSA (m^2) = 0.007184 x height(cm)$^{0.725}$ x weight(kg)$^{0.425}$. How many 20 mg prednisone tablets should be dispensed to the patient?

---

12. A nephrologist is treating a patient with hyponatremia. She estimates the patient's sodium deficit to be 210 mEq. How many milliliters of normal saline (M.W. Na = 23, M.W. Cl = 35.5) will be required to replace the deficit?

---

13. A pharmacy technician is asked to compound three 500 mL doses of 5% albumin. How many 50 mL vials of 25% albumin will be required?

---

14. A patient is to receive a potassium acetate infusion prepared by adding 9 mL of 39.2% potassium acetate ($KC_2H_3O_2$) to 0.45% NS to make 1 liter. The patient is to receive the potassium acetate at 5 mEq/hr. What rate (mL/hr) will provide this dose? Round to the nearest whole number. (M.W. of K = 39, M.W of $C_2H_3O_2$ = 59)

---

15. An intravenous infusion contains 2 mL of a 1:1,000 (w/v) solution of epinephrine and 250 mL of D5W. At what flow rate (mL/min) should the infusion be administered to provide 0.3 mcg/kg/min of epinephrine to an 80 kg patient? Round to the nearest whole number.

Use the following case to answer questions 16-18:

PATIENT PROFILE

Patient Name	Helene Gudot
Address	1365 Stephens Avenue
Age:	64 **Sex:** F **Race:** African American **Height:** 5'5" **Weight:** 135 pounds
Allergies	Bactrim

DIAGNOSES

Type 2 Diabetes	Dyslipidemia
Hypertension	Heart Failure

MEDICATIONS

Date	Prescriber	Drug/Strength/Sig
12/10	Marks	Metformin 1 gram BID
12/10	Marks	Regular insulin sliding scale per protocol
12/11	Marks	*Lantus* 10 units at HS
12/12	Ventrakhan	D51/4NS + 20 mEq KCL at 75 mL/hr
12/12	King	*Coreg* 6.25 mg BID
12/13	Marks	D51/2NS + 10 mEq KCL at 60 mL/hr
12/13	Marks	Lasix 40 mg IV Q12H
12/13	Ventrakhan	*Altace* 5 mg BID

LAB/DIAGNOSTIC TESTS

Test	Normal Value	Results Date: 12/13	Date: 12/12	Date: 12/11
WBC	4,000-11,000 cells/mm^3	10.7	10.1	12.2
Na	135-146 mEq/L	139	142	145
K	3.5-5.3 mEq/L	4.3	4.1	3.3
Cl	98-110 mEq/L	104	105	101
HCO3	22-28 mEq/L	26	26	25
BUN	7-25 mg/dL	23	26	28
Creatinine	0.6-1.2 mg/dL	1.1	1.3	1.4
Glu	65-99 mg/dL	180 @ 0700	140 @ 0700	260 @ 0700
Glu	65-99 mg/dL	280 @ 1100	280 @ 1100	320 @ 1100
Glu	65-99 mg/dL	220 @ 1700	300 @ 1700	280 @ 1700
Glu	65-99 mg/dL	100 @ 2100	220 @ 2100	220 @ 2100

16. Mrs. Gudot uses the following regular insulin sliding scale: "take 1 unit of insulin SC for every 20 mg/dL of blood sugar > 160 mg/dL." How many units of sliding scale insulin should have been administered on December 12th?

17. The pharmacist is asked to convert several of Mrs. Gudot's labs to different units so her case can be compared to a published case report. Convert her serum potassium level on December 13th to mg/dL. (M.W. of potassium = 39)

18. Convert Mrs. Gudot's serum sodium level on December 11th to mmol/L. (M.W. of Na = 23)

19. A patient received 4 mg of IV morphine. What is an equivalent dose of oral hydromorphone? (10 mg of IV morphine is equivalent to 7.5 mg of oral hydromorphone)

20. If 200 capsules contain 500 mg of an active ingredient, how many milligrams of the active ingredient will 76 capsules contain?

21. If phenobarbital elixir contains 18.2 mg of phenobarbital per 5 mL, how many grams of phenobarbital would be used in preparing a pint of the elixir? Round to the nearest tenth.

22. WC, a 57-year-old male, is receiving 1,145 mL of D30W, 850 mL of *FreAmine* 8.5%, and 350 mL of *Intralipid* 10% in his PN. What percentage of the non-protein calories is represented by dextrose? Round to the nearest whole number.

---

23. A penicillin V 250 mg tablet equals 400,000 units of penicillin activity. A patient is taking penicillin V 500 mg tablets QID for 7 days. How much penicillin activity, in units, will this patient receive in the total prescription?

---

24. A cough syrup contains 4 grams of brompheniramine maleate per liter. How many milligrams are contained in one teaspoonful of the elixir?

---

25. A patient is to receive acyclovir 5 mg/kg every 8 hours for an acute outbreak of herpes zoster. What daily dose, in milligrams, should a 110 pound female receive?

---

26. MH is a 72-year-old male patient hospitalized with decompensated heart failure and fever. Cultures are positive for aspergillosis. MH weighs 110 kg and will receive 0.25 mg/kg per day of amphotericin B (reconstituted and diluted to 0.1 mg/mL) by IV infusion. How many milliliters of amphotericin solution are required to deliver the daily dose?

---

27. Oral potassium chloride 20% solution contains 40 mEq of potassium per 15 milliliters of solution. A patient needs 25 mEq of potassium daily. What amount, in milliliters, of 20% potassium chloride should the patient take? Round to the nearest tenth.

---

28. The pharmacist reviews Ms. Hoydt's *Lovenox* order and labs in the profile. At this hospital, pharmacists have the authority to make renal dosage adjustments per package labeling when necessary. What is the correct *Lovenox* dose for Ms. Hoydt?

PATIENT PROFILE

Patient Name	Carolyn Hoydt								
Address	13 Windgate Road								
Age:	37	**Sex:**	F	**Race:**	Caucasian	**Height:**	5'6"	**Weight:**	175 pounds
Allergies	NKDA								

DIAGNOSES

DVT confirmed by ultrasound

MEDICATIONS

Date	Rx #	Prescriber	Drug/Strength/Sig
7/5	98732	Langston	*Ortho Tri-Cyclen* 1 PO Daily
7/5	98733	Langston	Centrum 1 PO Daily
11/15	102345	Mason	*Lovenox* 1 mg/kg SC Q12H
11/15	102347	Mason	D51/2NS @ 70 ml/hr

LAB/DIAGNOSTIC TESTS

Test	Normal Value	Results Date: 7/5	Results Date: 11/15	Date:
Na	135-146 mEq/L	136	142	
K	3.5-5.3 mEq/L	3.5	5.2	
Cl	98-110 mEq/L	109	105	
HCO3	22-28 mEq/L	25	26	
BUN	7-25 mg/dL	10	22	
Creatinine	0.6-1.2 mg/dL	0.7	1.4	
Glu	65-99 mg/dL	100	120	
Hgb	12-16 g/dL	12	13.6	
Hct	36-46%	37	41	

A. 175 mg SC Q12H
B. 175 mg SC once daily
C. 80 mg SC once daily
D. 80 mg SC Q12H
E. 60 mg SC Q12H

29. The pharmacist reviews the order for IV *Bactrim* and the labs for Mr. Ross in the profile. What dose should Mr. Ross receive given the renal dosage recommendations below?

CrCl	> 30 mL/min	15–30 mL/min	< 15 mL/min
Sulfamethoxazole/ trimethoprim (SMX/TMP)	No dosage adjustment required	Administer 50% of the recommended dose	Use is not recommended

PATIENT PROFILE

Patient Name	Jeremy Ross
Address	22 Harris Lane
Age:	41 **Sex:** M **Race:** Hispanic **Height:** 6'1" **Weight:** 70 kg
Allergies	NKDA

DIAGNOSES

Depression	Dyslipidemia
HIV	

MEDICATIONS

Date	Prescriber	Drug/Strength/Sig
5/5	Sangler	Nicotine patch 21 mg/day – apply 1 patch daily
5/5	Sangler	*Stribild* 1 tablet daily
6/15	Sangler	*Celexa* 20 mg 1 tablet daily
11/15	Mason	*Lipitor* 10 mg 1 tablet daily
12/1	Hern	*Bactrim* 20 mg TMP/kg/day IV divided Q6H

LAB/DIAGNOSTIC TESTS

Test	Normal Value	Results Date: 12/1	Date: 5/5	Date:
WBC	4,000-11,000 cells/mm^3	10.7	9.5	
CD4	800-1,100 cells/mm^3	187	226	
Na	135-146 mEq/L	139	142	
K	3.5-5.3 mEq/L	3.7	4.1	
Cl	98-110 mEq/L	109	105	
HCO3	22-28 mEq/L	24	26	
BUN	7-25 mg/dL	7	9	
Creatinine	0.6-1.2 mg/dL	0.6	0.8	
Glu	65-99 mg/dL	120	136	

A. 1400 mg TMP IV Q6H
B. 700 mg TMP IV Q6H
C. 400 mg TMP IV Q12H
D. 350 mg TMP IV Q6H
E. Mr. Ross should not receive *Bactrim*

---

30. What is the pH of a solution containing 0.2 mole of a weakly basic drug and 0.02 mole of its salt per liter of solution (pKa of the drug = 9.36)? Round to the nearest hundredth.

ANSWER KEY AND EXPLANATIONS

1. First, calculate the grams of hydrocortisone required for the prescription.

$$\frac{1.5\text{ g}}{100\text{ g}} = \frac{X\text{ g}}{60\text{ g}} \quad X = 0.9 \text{ grams of hydrocortisone required}$$

Calculate the volume of hydrocortisone injection required.

$$\frac{100\text{ mg}}{1\text{ mL}} = \frac{900\text{ mg}}{X\text{ mL}} \quad X = 9\text{ mL}$$

Calculate the weight of 9 mL of hydrocortisone injection using the SG provided.

$$1.5 = \frac{X\text{ g}}{9\text{ mL}} \quad X = 13.5 \text{ grams (weight of hydrocortisone injection)}$$

Calculate the grams of cold cream required.

60 g final product − 13.5 g (weight of hydrocortisone) = 46.5 g of cold cream

2. Both concentrations must be in the same units to use the Q1C1 = Q2C2 formula. So, 1:2,500 must be converted to a percentage strength first.

$$\frac{1\text{ part}}{2{,}500\text{ parts}} = \frac{X\text{ g}}{100\text{ mL}} \quad X = 0.04\text{ g, or } 0.04\%$$

Now use the formula.

100 mL x 0.2% = Q2 x 0.04%

Q2 = 500 mL

3. Two methods to solve this calculation are shown:

$$\frac{200\text{ mg}}{5\text{ mL}} = \frac{X\text{ mg}}{100\text{ mL}} \quad X = 4{,}000\text{ mg}$$

$$\frac{4{,}000\text{ mg}}{110\text{ mL}} = \frac{800\text{ mg}}{X\text{ mL}} \quad X = 22\text{ mL}$$

$$\frac{4{,}000\text{ mg}}{110\text{ mL}} = \frac{X\text{ mg}}{\text{mL}} \quad X = 36.36\text{ mg/mL}$$

$$\frac{36.36\text{ mg}}{1\text{ mL}} = \frac{800\text{ mg}}{X\text{ mL}} \quad X = 22\text{ mL}$$

4. First, convert 1:20 to a percentage strength.

$$\frac{1\text{ part}}{20\text{ parts}} = \frac{X\text{ g}}{100\text{ mL}} \quad X = 5\text{ g, or } 5\%$$

50 mL x 5% = 1,000 mL x C2

C2 = 0.25%

Convert 0.25% to ratio strength = 1:400

5.

$$\frac{4 \text{ mEq}}{\text{kg}} \times 75 \text{ kg} = 300 \text{ mEq/day}$$

$$300 \text{ mEq} = \frac{X \text{ mg} \times 1}{58.5} = 17{,}550 \text{ mg, or } 17.55 \text{ g}$$

$$\frac{0.45 \text{ g}}{100 \text{ mL}} = \frac{17.55 \text{ g}}{X \text{ mL}} \quad X = 3{,}900 \text{ mL or } 3.9 \text{ L}$$

---

6. Aminophylline is dosed based on IBW.

IBW (male) = 50 kg + (2.3 x 9 in) = 70.7 kg

Aminophylline 0.5 mg/kg/hr x 70.7 kg x 24 hrs = 848.4 mg/day, round to 848 mg/day

---

7.

$$40 \text{ mEq} = \frac{X \text{ mg} \times 1}{75} = 3{,}000 \text{ mg, or 3 g of KCl have been given in 10 hours}$$

$$\frac{20 \text{ drops}}{\text{min}} \times \frac{60 \text{ min}}{1 \text{ hr}} \times 10 \text{ hrs} = 12{,}000 \text{ drops infused in 10 hours}$$

$$\frac{15 \text{ drops}}{\text{mL}} = \frac{12{,}000 \text{ drops}}{X \text{ mL}} \quad X = 800 \text{ mL have infused in 10 hours}$$

$$\frac{3 \text{ g KCl}}{800 \text{ mL}} = \frac{X \text{ g}}{100 \text{ mL}} \quad X = 0.375 \text{ g, or } 0.38\%$$

8.

3 mcg/kg/min x 75 kg = 225 mcg/min

$$\frac{250 \text{ mL}}{400 \text{ mg}} \times \frac{1 \text{ mg}}{1000 \text{ mcg}} \times \frac{225 \text{ mcg}}{\text{min}} \times \frac{60 \text{ min}}{1 \text{ hr}} = 8.4 \text{ mL/hr, or 8 mL/hr}$$

---

9. First, calculate the amount of dextrose the patient is receiving by subtracting out the protein component.

$$84.5 \text{ g} \times \frac{4 \text{ kcal}}{\text{g}} = 338 \text{ kcal}$$

1,800 kcal − 338 kcal of protein = 1,462 kcal from dextrose

Next, calculate the grams of dextrose in this PN.

$$1{,}462 \text{ kcal} \times \frac{1 \text{ g}}{3.4 \text{ kcal}} = 430 \text{ grams of dextrose}$$

Then, calculate the final concentration. This requires calculating the total volume the patient is receiving.

$$\frac{85 \text{ mL}}{\text{hr}} \times 24 \text{ hours} = 2{,}040 \text{ mL}$$

$$\frac{430 \text{ g dextrose}}{2{,}040 \text{ mL}} = \frac{X \text{ g}}{100 \text{ mL}} \quad X = 21\%$$

10.

$$20\ mcg/kg/min \times 75\ kg = 1500\ mcg/min$$

$$\frac{250\ mL}{400\ mg} \times \frac{1\ mg}{1000\ mcg} \times \frac{1500\ mcg}{min} \times \frac{60\ min}{1\ hr} =$$ 56.25 mL/hr – max rate per order
Round to nearest number = 56 mL/hr

11.

$$BSA\ (m^2) = 0.007184 \times (154.94)^{0.725} \times (52.7272)^{0.425} = 1.5\ m^2$$

$$40\ mg/m^2/day \times 1.5\ m^2 = 60\ mg/day$$

Refer to Oncology II chapter for discussion of BSA.

The patient will take 60 mg of prednisone (three 20 mg tablets) per day for 14 days. The pharmacist should dispense 42 of the 20 mg prednisone tablets.

12.

$$210\ mEq = \frac{mg \times 1}{58.5}$$ 12,285 mg or 12.285 g

$$\frac{0.9\ g}{100\ mL} = \frac{12.285\ g}{X\ mL}$$ X = 1,365 mL of NS are required

13.

$$\frac{5\ g}{100\ mL} = \frac{X\ g}{500\ mL}$$ X = 25 g, or 75 g for the three required doses

$$\frac{25\ g}{100\ mL} = \frac{X\ g}{50\ mL}$$ X = 12.5 g per 50 mL vial

$$75\ g\ required \times \frac{1\ vial}{12.5\ g}$$ X = 6 vials of 25% albumin required

14.

$$\frac{39.2\ g}{100\ mL} = \frac{X\ g}{9\ mL}$$ X = 3.528 g or 3,528 mg

$$X\ mEq = \frac{3{,}528\ mg \times 1}{98} = 36\ mEq$$

$$\frac{1{,}000\ mL}{36\ mEq} \times \frac{5\ mEq}{hr} =$$ 138.88 mL/hr, or 139 mL/hr

15.

1:1,000 ratio strength = 0.1% (w/v)

$$\frac{0.1\text{ g}}{100\text{ mL}} = \frac{X\text{ g}}{2\text{ mL}} \quad X = 0.002\text{ g, or }2\text{ mg}$$

The patient is 80 kg x 0.3 mcg/kg/min = 24 mcg/min

$$\frac{252\text{ mL}}{2\text{ mg}} \times \frac{1\text{ mg}}{1{,}000\text{ mcg}} \times \frac{24\text{ mcg}}{\text{min}} = 3\text{ mL/min}$$

16.

140 mg/dL = no insulin

280 mg/dL - 160 mg/dL = 120 mg/dL; 120 mg/dL / 20 mg/dL = 6 units

300 mg/dL - 160 mg/dL = 140 mg/dL / 20 mg/dL = 7 units

220 mg/dL - 160 mg/dL = 60 mg/dL / 20 mg/dL = 3 units

Total sliding scale units for December 12th = 6 + 7 + 3 = 16 units

---

17.

$$4.3\text{ mEq} = \frac{X\text{ mg} \times 1}{39} \quad X = 167.7\text{ mg}$$

4.3 mEq = 167.7 mg. The patient's serum potassium is reported as 4.3 mEq/L, which equals 167.7 mg/L.

$$\frac{167.7\text{ mg}}{1\text{ L}} \times \frac{1\text{ L}}{10\text{ dL}} = 16.77\text{ mg/dL}$$

18.

$$145\text{ mEq} = \frac{X\text{ mg} \times 1}{23} \quad X = 3{,}335\text{ mg}$$

$$X\text{ mmols} = \frac{3{,}335\text{ mg}}{23} \quad X = 145\text{ mmols, therefore }145\text{ mEq/L} = 145\text{ mmol/L for sodium}$$

Note that mmols = mEq in this problem. For Na and K, the mmol and mEq are the same; 1 mmol = 1 mEq.

19.

$$\frac{4\text{ mg IV morphine}}{X\text{ mg oral hydromorphone}} = \frac{10\text{ mg IV morphine}}{7.5\text{ mg oral hydromorphone}} \quad X = 3\text{ mg oral hydromorphone}$$

20.

$$\frac{200\text{ caps}}{500\text{ mg}} = \frac{76\text{ caps}}{X\text{ mg}} \quad X = 190\text{ mg}$$

21. First, convert milligrams to grams.

$$18.2 \text{ mg} \times \frac{1 \text{ g}}{1{,}000 \text{ mg}} = 0.0182 \text{ g}$$

Use a proportion to calculate the grams needed for 1 pint.

$$\frac{0.0182 \text{ g}}{5 \text{ mL}} = \frac{X \text{ g}}{473 \text{ mL}} \quad X = 1.7 \text{ g}$$

Because of the rounding specifications in the question, the answer is the same regardless of the pint conversion used. Expect the same on the exam.

---

22. First, calculate the non-protein calories (dextrose and lipids).

Dextrose

$$\frac{3.4 \text{ kcal}}{\text{g}} \times \frac{30 \text{ g}}{100 \text{ mL}} \times 1{,}145 \text{ mL} = 1{,}168 \text{ kcal}$$

Lipids

$$\frac{1.1 \text{ kcal}}{\text{mL}} \times 350 \text{ mL} = 385 \text{ kcal}$$

Then, add up the calories from the non-protein sources. 1,168 + 385 = 1,553 kcal

Finally, calculate the percent of non-protein calories from dextrose.

$$\frac{1{,}168 \text{ kcal from dextrose}}{1{,}553 \text{ kcal non-protein}} \times 100 = 75\%$$

---

23. If 250 mg contains 400,000 units, then 500 mg contains 800,000 units. The patient is taking 4 tablets daily, for 7 days (or 28 total tablets), at 800,000 units each.

$$\frac{800{,}000 \text{ units}}{1 \text{ tab}} = \frac{X \text{ units}}{28 \text{ tabs}} \quad X = 22{,}400{,}000 \text{ units}$$

---

24. First, convert grams to milligrams.

$$4 \text{ g} \times \frac{1000 \text{ mg}}{1 \text{ g}} = 4{,}000 \text{ mg per 1 liter}$$

1 L = 1,000 mL

1 teaspoonful = 5 mL

Next, solve using a proportion.

$$\frac{4{,}000 \text{ mg}}{1{,}000 \text{ mL}} = \frac{X \text{ mg}}{5 \text{ mL}} \quad X = 20 \text{ mg}$$

25. Begin by converting the patient's weight in pounds (lbs) to kilograms (kg).

$$110 \text{ pounds} \times \frac{1 \text{ kg}}{2.2 \text{ pounds}} = 50 \text{ kg}$$

$$\frac{5 \text{ mg}}{1 \text{ kg}} = \frac{X \text{ mg}}{50 \text{ kg}} \quad X = 250 \text{ mg/dose} \times 3 \text{ doses/day} = 750 \text{ mg/day}$$

---

26. Begin by calculating the total daily dose (mg) for this patient.

$$\frac{0.25 \text{ mg}}{1 \text{ kg}} = \frac{X \text{ mg}}{110 \text{ kg}} \quad X = 27.5 \text{ mg daily}$$

Calculate the volume of reconstituted amphotericin B solution needed per day.

$$\frac{27.5 \text{ mg}}{X \text{ mL}} = \frac{0.1 \text{ mg}}{1 \text{ mL}} \quad X = 275 \text{ mL}$$

27.

$$\frac{40 \text{ mEq K}}{15 \text{ mL}} = \frac{25 \text{ mEq K}}{X \text{ mL}} \quad X = 9.375\text{, or } 9.4 \text{ mL}$$

---

28. The correct answer is (D). Total body weight is used to determine the weight-based dose of LMWHs. Since the patient's BMI is 28.3 kg/m2 (overweight), her adjusted body weight is used in the Cockcroft-Gault equation to calculate CrCl. Her CrCl is 58.5 mL/min (well above the threshold of 30 mL/min, for changing the dosing interval of *Lovenox* to once daily).

---

29. The correct answer is (D). Mr. Ross is of normal weight per BMI (BMI = 20.4 kg/m2). His *Bactrim* dose will be calculated with his total body weight (20 mg TMP/kg/day x 70 kg = 1400 mg TMP/day or 350 mg TMP Q6H for normal renal function). His TBW is less than his IBW, so his CrCl should be calculated with his TBW and is ~160 ml/min. Renal dose adjustments will not be needed for any medications at this level of CrCl.

30.

$$pH = pK_a + \log\left[\frac{\text{base}}{\text{salt}}\right]$$

$$pH = 9.36 + \log\left[\frac{0.2}{0.02}\right]$$

$$pH = 9.36 + 1$$

$$pH = 10.36$$

ARE YOU READY FOR THE MATH ON NAPLEX?

How will you know that you have sufficiently studied the math for NAPLEX? This small sample of questions is not enough to make that determination. Remember: math is very important on NAPLEX. See the Study Tip Gal below and Preparing for NAPLEX with RxPrep chapter.

Want more practice? Check out the RxPrep Online Course, which includes Test Bank access and Video Course.

The RxPrep Test Bank contains case-rich, exam-style questions that cover all the required material, including > 200 additional calculation problems.

FIND THE TEST BANK AND VIDEO COURSE ONLINE AT WWW.RXPREP.COM

MATH IS READY FOR NAPLEX WHEN:

- The formula/s can be quickly recalled in response to a problem ("automatic recall") [exclude the Basal Energy Expenditure (BEE) formula, which is likely to be provided].
- Math mistakes have become a thing of the past.

Track Your Scores	
Calculations #1	48, 78, 96, 100 Yeah!
Calculations #2	55, 82, 92, 100 Yeah!
Calculations #3	60, 77 keep going...
Calculations #4	66, 74 keep going...
Calculations #5	48, 65 keep going...
Biostats math	48, 59 don't give up...

Make a score sheet like this. Keep going until the math is flawless. Math mistakes cause a cliff-dive in the exam score. A math mistake in pharmacy means the patient got the wrong dose.

BIOSTATISTICS

CONTENTS

CHAPTER 14
BIOSTATISTICS | **200**

CHAPTER CONTENT

Purpose of Biostatistics.......200
Types of Study Data.......201
Continuous Data.......201
Discrete (Categorical) Data.......201
Summarizing the Data.......202
Measures of Central Tendency.......202
Mean, Median and Mode.......202
Spread (Variability) of Data.......202
Central Tendency Calculations.......202
Gaussian (Normal) Distributions.......202
Skewed Distributions.......203
Dependent and Independent Variables.......203
Testing the Hypothesis for Significance.......204
The Null Hypothesis and Alternative Hypothesis.......204
Alpha Level: The Standard for Significance.......204
Confidence Intervals.......205
Interpreting Confidence Intervals.......205
Type I and Type II Errors.......206
Risk.......207
Relative Risk (or Risk Ratio).......207
RR Formula.......207
Relative Risk Reduction.......208
RRR Formula.......208
Absolute Risk Reduction.......208
ARR Formula.......208
Number Needed to Treat or Harm.......209
Number Needed to Treat.......209
NNT Formula.......209
Number Needed to Harm.......210
Rounding Rules for NNT and NNH.......210
Odds Ratio and Hazard Ratio.......210
Odds Ratio.......210
Odds Ratio Formula (OR).......210
Hazard Ratio.......211
Hazard Ratio Formula (HR).......211
OR and HR Interpretation.......211
Primary and Composite Endpoints.......212
Types of Statistical Tests.......212
Discrete (Categorical) Data.......212
Examples of Test Type Selection.......213
Correlation and Regression.......213
Sensitivity and Specificity.......214
Sensitivity and Specificity.......214
Intention to Treat and Per Protocol Analysis.......215
Noninferiority and Equivalence Trial Design.......215
Forest Plots and Confidence Intervals.......216
Types of Medical Studies.......217
Pharmacoeconomics.......220
Average and Incremental Cost Effectiveness Ratios.......221
Pharmacoeconomic Methodologies.......221
Health Related Quality of Life.......222

CONTENT LEGEND

= Study Tip Gal   = Required Formula

CHAPTER 14
BIOSTATISTICS

PURPOSE OF BIOSTATISTICS

Statistics involves the collection and analysis of all types of data, from the average number of cars on a freeway to the blood pressure reduction expected from a calcium channel blocker. When statistics are used to understand the effects of a drug or medical procedure on people and animals, the statistical analysis is called biostatistical analysis, or simply, biostatistics.

A basic understanding of biostatistics is required to interpret studies in medical and pharmacy journals, such as the *New England Journal of Medicine* and *Pharmacotherapy*. Simple formulas and definitions, described here, prepare the reader to interpret most journal articles and feel confident tackling common practice-based situations, such as:

A physician asks if a patient should be switched from standard of care treatment to a new drug based on the relative risk reduction reported in the clinical trial.

A warfarin patient wants to know if he should switch to Xarelto because he saw a commercial claiming that "it prevents DVT or PE in 98% of patients."

STEPS TO JOURNAL PUBLICATION

The path to publication for the classic type of research study is shown in the figure on the next page. A study manuscript (description of the research, with results) can be submitted for publication in a professional, peer-reviewed journal. The editor of the journal selects potential publications and sends them to experts in the topic area for peer-review. Peer review is intended to assess the design and methods of the research, the value of the results and conclusions to the field of study, how well the manuscript is written, and whether it is appropriate for the readership of the journal. The reviewers make a recommendation to the editor to either accept the article (usually with revisions) or reject it (e.g., if it is too flawed). Data that contradicts a previous recommendation, or presents new information, can change treatment guidelines.

BEGIN with a RESEARCH QUESTION	DESIGN the STUDY	ENROLL the SUBJECTS	COLLECT the DATA	ANALYZE the DATA	PUBLISH
Write a null hypothesis to answer the research question, such as: New drug is not as effective as current drug.	Is it randomized, placebo-controlled, a case-control or other type of study?	Assign to a treatment group or control group, or identify subjects belonging to a cohort or other group.	Prospectively (going into the future for a set period of time) or retrospectively (looking back in time using medical records).	Enter the data into statistical software; assess the results (e.g., risk reductions, confidence intervals).	

©RxPrep

ORGANIZATION OF A PUBLISHED CLINICAL TRIAL

A published clinical trial begins with an abstract that provides a brief summary of the article. The introduction to the study comes next, which includes background information, such as disease history and prevalence, and the research hypothesis. This is followed by the study methods, which describe the variables and outcomes, and the statistical methods used to analyze the data.

The results section includes figures, tables and graphs. A reader needs to interpret basic statistics and common graphs in order to understand the study results. The researchers conclude the article with an interpretation of the results and the implications for current practice.

TYPES OF STUDY DATA

When data points, or values, are collected during a study, they can be analyzed to determine the degree of difference between groups, or some other type of association. The type of statistical tests used to perform the analysis depends on the type of data.

CONTINUOUS DATA

Continuous data has a logical order with values that continuously increase (or decrease) by the same amount (e.g., a HR of 120 BPM is twice as fast as a HR of 60 BPM). The two types of continuous data are interval data and ratio data. The difference between them is that interval data has no meaningful zero (zero does not equal none) and ratio data has a meaningful zero (zero equals none). The Celsius temperature scale is an example of interval data, because it has no meaningful zero (0°C does not mean no temperature; it is the freezing point of water). Heart rate is an example of ratio data; a HR of 0 BPM is cardiac arrest (zero equals none; the heart is not beating).

DISCRETE (CATEGORICAL) DATA

The two types of discrete data, nominal and ordinal, have categories, and are sometimes called categorical data. Nominal and name are derived from the same word; with nominal data, subjects are sorted into arbitrary categories (names), such as male or female (0 = male, 1 = female or 0 = female, 1 = male). It is sometimes described as "yes/no" data. Ordinal comes from the word order; ordinal data is ranked and has a logical order, such as a pain scale. In contrast to continuous data, ordinal scale categories do not increase by the same amount; a pain scale rating of 4 is worse than a pain scale rating of 2, but it does not mean that there is twice as much pain.

CONTINUOUS DATA Data is provided by some type of measurement which has unlimited options (theoretically) of continuous values		DISCRETE (CATEGORICAL) DATA Data fits into a limited number of categories	
RATIO DATA Equal difference between values, with a true, meaningful zero (0 = NONE) **Examples:** age, height, weight, time, blood pressure **Ordered, Equal**	**INTERVAL DATA** Equal difference between values, but without a meaningful zero (0 ≠ NONE) **Example:** Celsius and Fahrenheit temperature scales **Ordered, Equal**	**NOMINAL DATA** Categories are in an arbitrary order *Order of categories does not matter* **Examples:** gender, ethnicity, marital status, mortality **No Set Order**	**ORDINAL DATA** Categories are ranked in a logical order, but the difference between categories is not equal *Order of categories matters* **Examples:** NYHA Functional Class I-IV; 0-10 pain scale **Ordered, Ranked**

©RxPrep

SUMMARIZING THE DATA

MEASURES OF CENTRAL TENDENCY

Descriptive statistics provide simple summaries of the data. The typical descriptive values are called the measures of central tendency, and include the mean, the median and the mode (see Study Tip Gal below for mean, median and mode calculation examples).

- Mean: the average value; it is calculated by adding up the values and dividing the sum by the number of values. The mean is preferred for continuous data that is normally distributed (described below).
- Median: the value in the middle when the values are arranged from lowest to highest. When there are two center values (as with an even number of values), take the average of the two center values. The median is preferred for ordinal data or continuous data that is skewed (not normally distributed).
- Mode: the value that occurs most frequently. The mode is preferred for nominal data.

SPREAD (VARIABILITY) OF DATA

Two common methods of describing the variability, or spread, in data are the range and the standard deviation (SD).

- Range: the difference between the highest and lowest values.
- Standard deviation (SD): indicates how spread out the data is, and to what degree the data is dispersed away from the mean (i.e., spread out over a smaller or larger range). A large number of data values close to the mean has a smaller SD. Data that is highly dispersed has a larger SD.

CENTRAL TENDENCY CALCULATIONS

Example

The diastolic blood pressure (DBP mmHg) reduction for 9 patients in a trial

3, 2, 3, 8, 6, 3, 4, 4, 3

Put the numbers in order:

2 + 3 + 3 + 3 + 3 + 4 + 4 + 6 + 8

The MEAN is 4 (36 ÷ 9 = 4).

The MODE is 3, the value that occurs most frequently.

The MEDIAN is 3, the value in the middle of the ranked (ordered) list.

The RANGE is the highest value (8) minus the smallest value (2). The range in DBP reduction is 6.

GAUSSIAN (NORMAL) DISTRIBUTIONS

Large sample sets of continuous data tend to form a Gaussian, or "normal" (bell-shaped), distribution (see the figure at the top of the next page). For example, if a researcher collects 5,000 blood pressure measurements (continuous data) from Idaho residents and plots the values, the graph would form a normal distribution.

Characteristics of a Gaussian Distribution

When the distribution of data is normal, the curve is symmetrical (even on both sides), with most of the values closer to the middle. Half of the values are on the left side of the curve, and half of the values are on the right side. A small number of values are in the tails. When data is normally distributed:

- The mean, median and mode are the same value, and are at the center point of the curve.
- 68% of the values fall within 1 SD of the mean and 95% of the values fall within 2 SDs of the mean.

Normal Distribution Shapes

The examples to the right show how the curve of normally distributed data changes based on the spread (or range) of the data. The curve gets taller and skinnier as the range of data narrows. The curve gets shorter and wider as the range of data widens (or is more spread out).

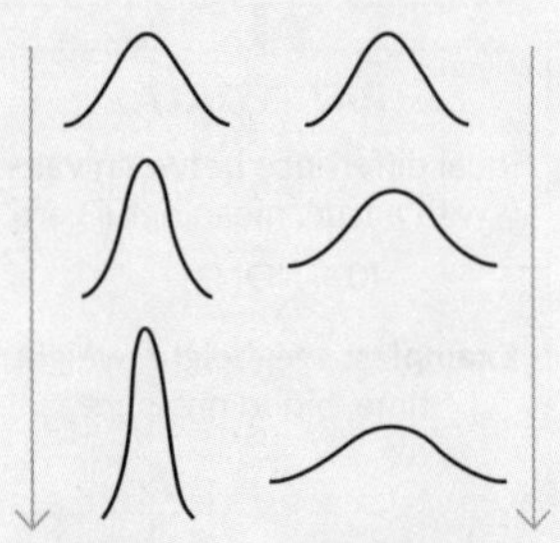

GAUSSIAN (NORMAL) DISTRIBUTION

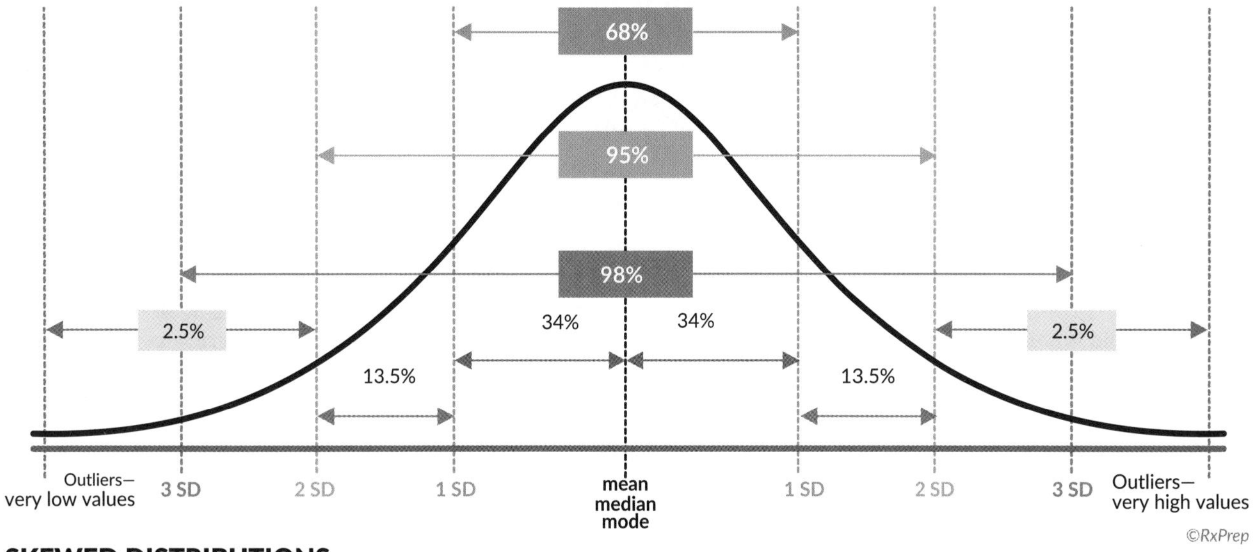

SKEWED DISTRIBUTIONS

Data that are skewed do not have the characteristics of a normal distribution; the curve is not symmetrical, 68% of the values do not fall within 1 SD from the mean and the mean, median and mode are not the same value. This usually occurs when the number of values (sample size) is small and/or there are outliers in the data.

Outliers (Extreme Values)

An outlier is an extreme value, either very low or very high, compared to the norm. For example, if a study reports the mean weight of included adult patients as 90 kg, then a patient in the same study with a weight of 40 kg or 186 kg is an outlier. When there are a small number of values, an outlier has a large impact on the mean and the data becomes skewed. In this case, the median is a better measure of central tendency. In the examples to the right, the median is right in the middle of the data, and is not affected by outliers.

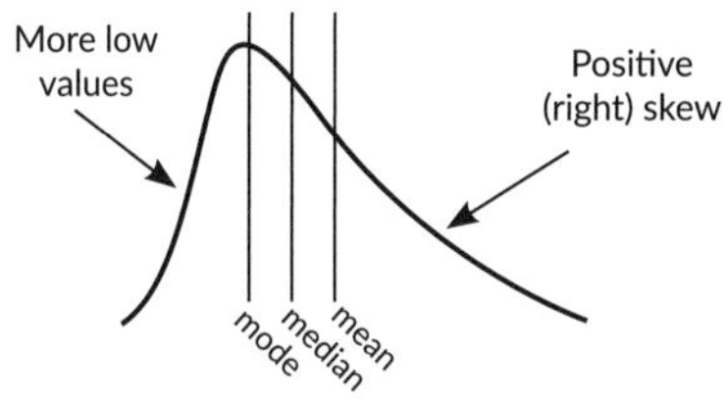

The distortion of the central tendency caused by outliers is decreased by collecting more values; as the number of values increases, the effect of outliers on the mean decreases.

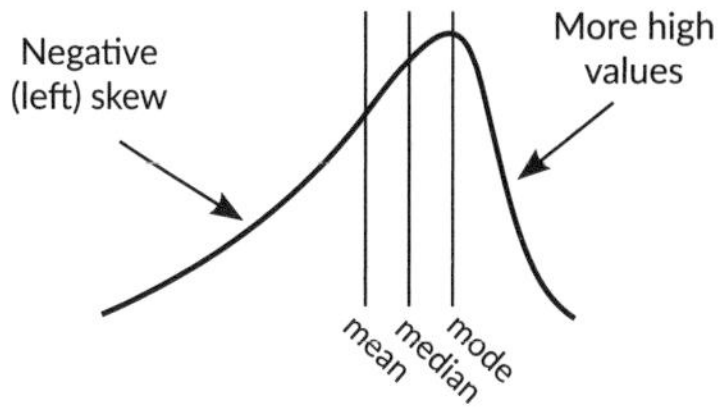

Skew Refers to the Direction of the Tail

Data is skewed towards outliers. When there are more low values in a data set and the outliers are the high values, data is skewed to the right (positive skew). When there are more high values in the data set and the outliers are the low values, the data is skewed to the left (negative skew).

DEPENDENT AND INDEPENDENT VARIABLES

A variable in a study is any data point or characteristic that can be measured or counted. Examples include age, gender, blood pressure and pain. Variables can be clinical endpoints such as death, stroke, hospitalization or an adverse event, or they can be intermediate (or surrogate) endpoints used to assess an outcome, such as measuring serum creatinine to assess the degree of renal impairment.

Independent variables are changed by the researcher	→	**The dependent variables can be effected by the independent variables**
Examples: drug, drug dose/s, placebos, patients included (e.g., age, gender, comorbid conditions)		Examples: HF progression, hemoglobin A1C, blood pressure, cholesterol values, mortality

An independent variable is changed (manipulated) by the researcher in order to determine whether it has an effect on the dependent variable (the outcome). Independent variables are the characteristics of the subject groups (treatment and control) selected for inclusion (e.g., age, gender, presence or absence of hypertension, diabetes or other comorbid conditions), or any other characteristic that could have an effect on the dependent variable.

TESTING THE HYPOTHESIS FOR SIGNIFICANCE

If a drug or device manufacturer wants to sell their product and make money, they will want research data which demonstrates that their product is significantly better (or superior) than the current treatment or a placebo (no treatment). To show significance, the trial needs to demonstrate that the null hypothesis is not true and should be rejected, and the alternative hypothesis can be accepted. The null hypothesis and alternative hypothesis are always complementary; one is accepted and the other is rejected, or vice-versa.

THE NULL HYPOTHESIS (H_0) AND ALTERNATIVE HYPOTHESIS (H_A)

Null means none or no; a null hypothesis states that there is no statistically significant difference between groups. A researcher who is studying a drug versus a placebo would write a null hypothesis that states that there is no difference in efficacy between the drug and the placebo (drug efficacy = placebo efficacy). The null hypothesis is what the researcher tries to disprove or reject.

The alternative hypothesis states that there is a statistically significant difference between the groups (drug efficacy ≠ placebo efficacy). The alternative hypothesis is what the researcher hopes to prove or accept.

ALPHA LEVEL: THE STANDARD FOR SIGNIFICANCE

When investigators design a study, they select a maximum permissible error margin, called alpha (α). Alpha is the threshold for rejecting the null hypothesis. In medical research, alpha is commonly set at 5% (or 0.05). A smaller alpha value can be chosen (e.g., 1%, or 0.01), but this requires more data, more subjects (which means more expense) and/or a larger treatment effect.

ALPHA CORRELATES WITH THE VALUES IN THE TAILS WHEN DATA HAS A NORMAL DISTRIBUTION

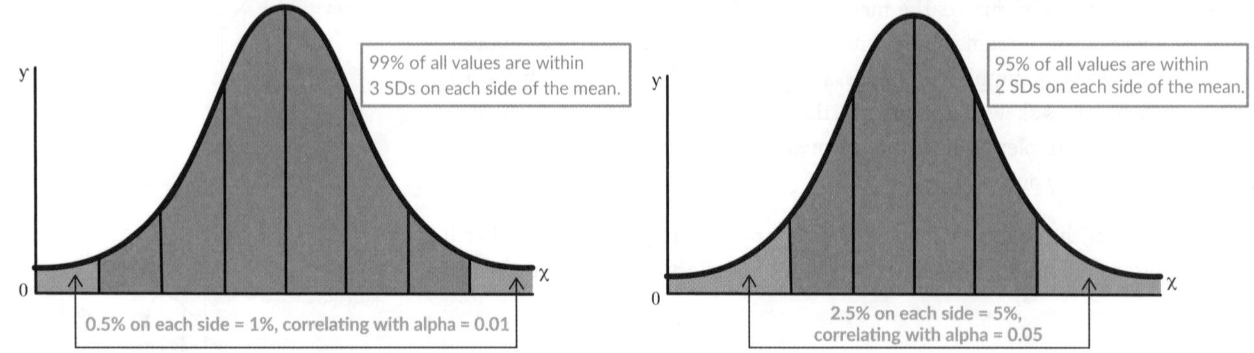

©RxPrep

Comparing the P-Value to Alpha

Once the alpha value is determined, statistical tests are performed to compare the data, and a p-value is calculated. The p-value is compared to alpha. If the alpha is set at 0.05 and the p-value is less than alpha ($p < 0.05$), the null hypothesis is rejected, and the result is termed statistically significant. If the p-value is greater than or equal to alpha ($p \geq 0.05$), the study has failed to reject the null hypothesis, and the result is not statistically significant.

THE NULL HYPOTHESIS: REJECT OR ACCEPT?

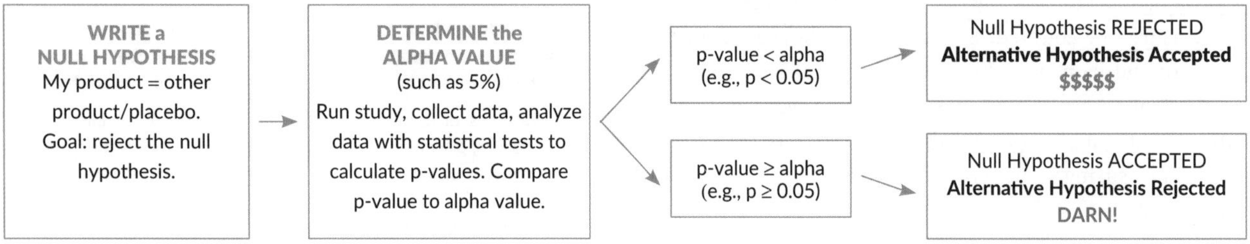

©RxPrep

CONFIDENCE INTERVALS

A confidence interval (CI) provides the same information about significance as the p-value, plus the precision of the result. Alpha and the CI in a study will correlate with each other.

$$CI = 1 - \alpha$$

If alpha is 0.05, the study reports 95% CIs; an alpha of 0.01 corresponds to a CI of 99%. The relationship between alpha, the p-value and the CI is described in the table here and in the figure on the previous page.

ALPHA	P-VALUE	MEANING	
0.05	≥ 0.05	Not statistically significant	
0.05	< 0.05	95% probability (confidence) that the conclusion is correct; less than 5% chance it's not.	*Statistically Significant*
0.01	< 0.01	99% probability (confidence) that the conclusion is correct; less than 1% chance it's not.	*Statistically Significant*
0.001	< 0.001	99.9% probability (confidence) that the conclusion is correct; less than 0.1% chance it's not.	*Statistically Significant*

INTERPRETING CONFIDENCE INTERVALS

The values in the CI range are used to determine whether significance has been reached

Determining statistical significance using the CI alone (without a p-value) is required for the exam

COMPARING DIFFERENCE DATA (MEANS)

- Difference data is based on subtraction [e.g., the difference in Δ FEV1 between roflumilast and placebo (below) was 38 (46 – 8 = 38)]
- The result is statistically significant if the CI range does not include zero (e.g., zero is not present in the range of values)
- In the example below:
  - The 95% CI for the difference in Δ FEV1 between roflumilast and placebo (18-58 mL) does not include zero → the result is statistically significant
  - The 95% CI for the difference in Δ FEV1/FVC (-0.26-0.89) includes zero → the result is not statistically significant

LUNG FUNCTION	DRUG* (N = 745)	PLACEBO (N = 745)	DIFFERENCE (95% CI)
Δ FEV1 (mL)	46	8	38 (18-58)
Δ FEV1/FVC (%)	0.314	0.001	0.313 (-0.26-0.89)

*Roflumilast

COMPARING RATIO DATA (RELATIVE RISK, ODDS RATIO, HAZARD RATIO)

- Ratio data is based on division [e.g., the ratio of severe exacerbations between roflumilast and placebo (below) was 0.92 (0.11/0.12 = 0.92)]
- The result is statistically significant if the CI range does not include one (e.g., one is not present in the range of values)
- In the example below:
  - The 95% CI for the relative risk of moderate exacerbations between roflumilast and placebo (0.72-0.99) does not include one → the result is statistically significant
  - The 95% CI for the relative risk of severe exacerbations (0.61-1.29) includes one → the result is not statistically significant

EXACERBATIONS*	DRUG** (N = 745)	PLACEBO (N = 745)	RELATIVE RISK (95% CI)
Severe	0.11	0.12	0.92 (0.61-1.29)
Moderate	0.94	1.11	0.85 (0.72-0.99)

*Mean rate, per patient per year

**Roflumilast

Confidence Intervals and Estimation (Extent and Variability in the Data)

The goal of the majority of medical research is to use the study results to promote the procedure or drug for use in the general population of patients with the same medical condition. Clinicians need to understand how their patients would benefit. The CI includes the treatment effect, and the range; both are helpful in estimating the effect on others.

A narrow CI range implies high precision, and a wide CI range implies poor precision. A CI can be written in slightly different formats. For example, a study comparing metoprolol to placebo finds a 12% absolute risk reduction (ARR) in heart failure progression, with a 95% CI range of 6 – 35%. This can be written as ARR 12% (95% CI 6% – 35%) or as decimals, with commas in the range, such as ARR 0.12 (0.95 CI 0.06, 0.35). The CI indicates that you are 95% confident that the true value of the ARR for the general (or true) population lies somewhere within the range of 6% – 35%, with some values as low as 6%, and others as high as 35%. If the reported range was 4% – 68%, the true value would still be within the range, but where? The range is wider, and therefore less precise. Cardiologists who interpret the results for their patients would not know whether to expect a result closer to 4% or 68%. A large range correlates to a large dispersion in the data. A narrower range is preferable.

In some studies, specific patient types will cause a wider distribution in data. For example, fibrates are used to lower triglyceride levels; they cause a greater reduction in patients with higher triglycerides. The consideration of where the patient is likely to fall within the range will become part of the assessment of the individual's baseline risk.

TYPE I AND TYPE II ERRORS

Consider what would happen if a pharmaceutical manufacturer developed a new drug and marketed the drug as better for heart failure than the standard of care, when in fact the new, expensive drug has similar benefit to the old drug (it is not better at all). The null hypothesis stated that the new drug and the old drug are equal. The statistical tests found a significant benefit with the new drug, and the null hypothesis was rejected, when it should have been accepted.

Type I Errors: False-Positives

In the scenario described above, the conclusion was wrong and a type I error was made. The alternative hypothesis was accepted and the null hypothesis was rejected in error. The probability, or risk, of making a type I error is determined by alpha and it relates to the confidence interval.

CI	=	1 - α (type I error)

When alpha is 0.05 and a study result is reported with $p < 0.05$, it is statistically significant and the probability of a type I error (making the wrong conclusion) is < 5%. You are 95% confident (0.95 = 1 – 0.05) that your result is correct and not due to chance.

Type II Errors: False-Negatives

The probability of a type II error, denoted as beta (β), occurs when the null hypothesis is accepted when it should have been rejected. Beta is set by the investigators during the design of a study. It is typically set at 0.1 or 0.2, meaning the risk of a type II error is 10% or 20%. The risk of a type II error increases if the sample size is too small. To decrease this risk, a power analysis is performed to determine the sample size needed to detect a true difference between groups.

Study Power

Power is the probability that a test will reject the null hypothesis correctly (i.e., the power to avoid a type II error). Power = $1 - \beta$. As the power increases, the chance of a type II error decreases. Power is determined by the number of outcome values collected, the difference in outcome rates between the groups, and the significance (alpha) level. If beta is set at 0.2, the study has 80% power (there is a 20% chance of missing a true difference and making a type II error). If beta is set at 0.1, the study has 90% power. A larger sample size is needed to increase study power and decrease the risk of a type II error.

DISTINGUISHING BETWEEN A TYPE I AND TYPE II ERROR

The sample of patients in a trial may not reflect the population. A type I error occurs when an investigator rejects a null hypothesis that is actually true in the population. A type II error occurs when an investigator accepts a null hypothesis that is not actually true in the population.

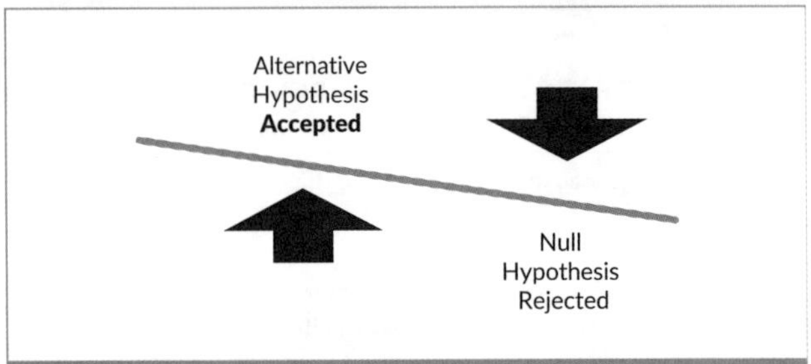

If wrong conclusion, a Type I error has been made.

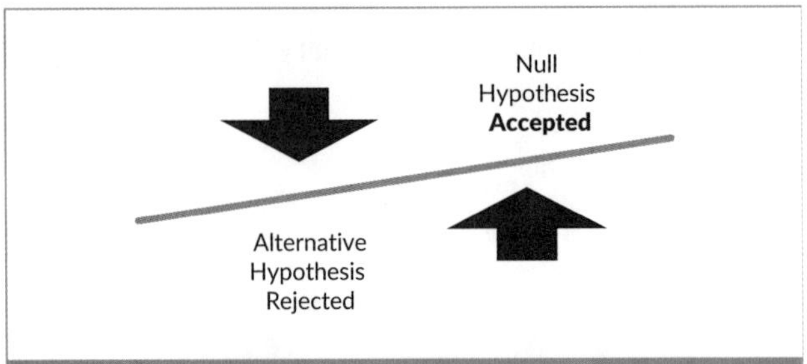

If wrong conclusion, a Type II error has been made.

RISK

In healthcare, risk refers to the probability of an event (how likely it is to occur) when an intervention, such as a drug, is given. The lack of intervention is measured as the effect in the placebo (or control) group.

RELATIVE RISK (OR RISK RATIO)

The relative risk (RR) is the ratio of risk in the exposed group (treatment) divided by risk in the control group.

RR Formula

$$\text{Risk} = \frac{\text{Number of subjects in group with an unfavorable event}}{\text{Total number of subjects in group}}$$

$$\text{RR} = \frac{\text{Risk in treatment group}}{\text{Risk in control group}}$$

RR Calculation

A placebo-controlled study was performed to evaluate whether metoprolol reduces disease progression in patients with heart failure (HF). A total of 10,111 patients were enrolled and followed for 12 months. What is the relative risk of HF progression in the metoprolol-treated group versus the placebo group?

Calculate the risk of HF progression in each group. Then calculate RR.

	METOPROLOL N = 5,123	CONTROL N = 4,988
HF progression	823	1,397

Metoprolol Risk	Control Risk
$\frac{823}{5,123} = 0.16$	$\frac{1,397}{4,988} = 0.28$

$$\text{RR} = \frac{0.16}{0.28} = 0.57 \times 100 = 57\%$$

Answer can be expressed as a decimal or a percentage; the exam question will specify with instructions

RR Interpretation

RR = 1 (or 100%) implies no difference in risk of the outcome between the groups.
RR > 1 (or 100%) implies greater risk of the outcome in the treatment group.
RR < 1 (or 100%) implies lower risk (reduced risk) of the outcome in the treatment group.

In the metoprolol study, the RR of HF progression was 57%. Patients treated with metoprolol were 57% as likely to have progression of disease as placebo-treated patients.

INTERPRETING THE RELATIVE RISK (RR)

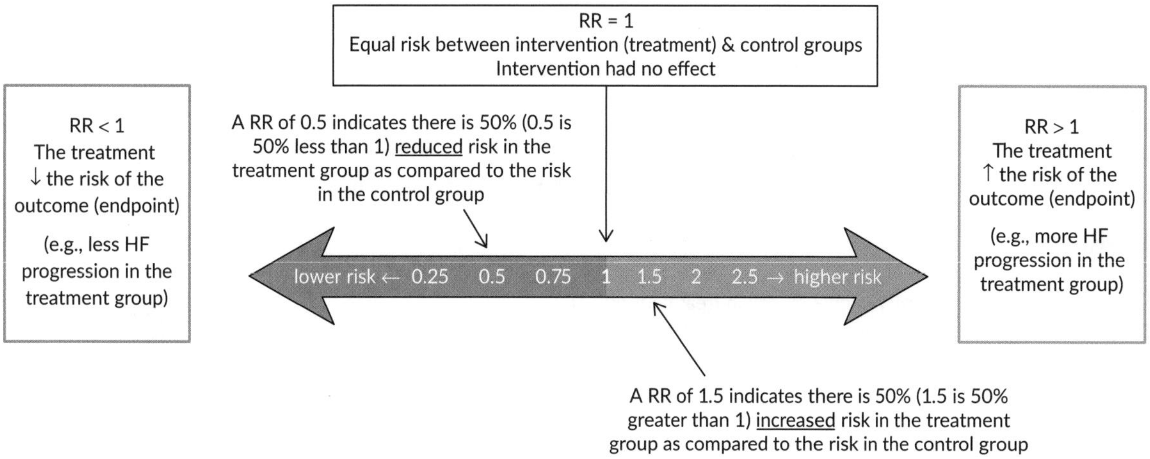

©RxPrep

RELATIVE RISK REDUCTION

The RR calculation determines whether there is less risk (RR < 1) or more risk (RR > 1). The <u>relative risk reduction</u> (RRR) is calculated after the RR and indicates <u>how much the risk is reduced</u> in the treatment group, compared to the control group.

RRR Formula

$$RRR = \frac{(\text{\% risk in control group} - \text{\% risk in treatment group})}{\text{\% risk in the control group}} \quad \text{or} \quad 1 - RR^*$$

Decimals or percentages may be used for risks

**Must use decimal form of RR*

RRR Calculation

Using the risks previously calculated for HF progression in the treatment and control groups (metoprolol: 16% and placebo: 28%), calculate the RRR of HF progression.

$$RRR = \frac{(28\% - 16\%)}{28\%} = 0.43 \quad \text{or} \quad RRR = 1 - 0.57 = 0.43$$

Answer can be expressed as a decimal or percentage; the exam question will specify with instructions

RRR Interpretation

The RRR is 43%. Metoprolol-treated patients were 43% <u>less likely</u> to have HF progression than placebo-treated patients.

INTERPRETING THE RELATIVE RISK REDUCTION (RRR)

RR: metoprolol patients were 57% <u>as likely</u> (as the control group) to suffer from HF progression.

RRR: metoprolol patients were 43% <u>less likely</u> (than the control group) to suffer from HF progression.

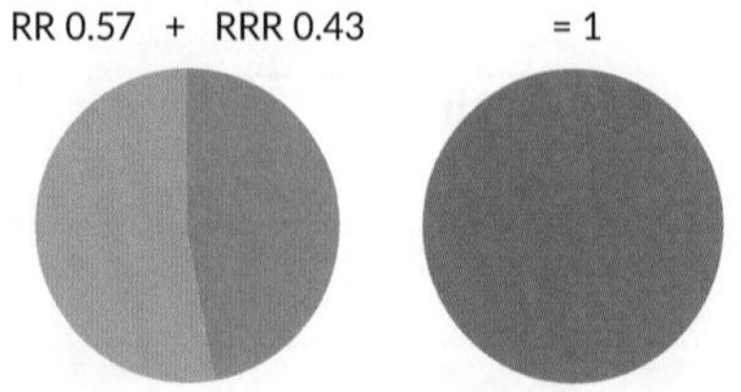

RR	**AS likely (vs. the control)**
RRR	**LESS likely (vs. the control)**
Therefore	**RR + RRR = 100%**

©RxPrep

ABSOLUTE RISK REDUCTION

A clinician is listening to a presentation on a drug. The drug manufacturer representative reports that the drug causes 48% less nausea than the standard treatment. The result sounds great; the clinician asks the pharmaceutical representative: what is the absolute risk reduction (ARR)?

The RR and RRR provide relative (proportional) differences in risk between the treatment group and the control group; they have no meaning in terms of absolute risk.

<u>Absolute risk reduction</u> is more useful because it includes the <u>reduction</u> in risk <u>and</u> the <u>incidence rate</u> of the outcome. If the risk of nausea is reduced, but the risk was small to begin with (perhaps the drug caused very little nausea), the large risk reduction has little practical benefit.

It is best if a study reports both ARR and RRR, and for clinicians to understand how to interpret the risk for their patients. If the ARR is not reported, it is possible that the risk reduction, in terms of a decrease in absolute risk, is minimal.

ARR Formula

$$ARR = (\text{\% risk in control group}) - (\text{\% risk in treatment group})$$

ARR Calculation

Using the risks previously calculated for HF progression in the metoprolol study, calculate the ARR of HF progression.

Metoprolol Risk	Control Risk
$\frac{823}{5,123} = 0.16$	$\frac{1,397}{4,988} = 0.28$

ARR = 0.28 − 0.16 = 0.12 x 100 = 12%

Answer can be expressed as a decimal or a percentage; the exam question will specify with instructions

ARR Interpretation

The ARR is 12%, meaning 12 out of every 100 patients benefit from the treatment. Said another way, for every 100 patients treated with metoprolol, 12 fewer patients will have HF progression.

An additional benefit of calculating the ARR is to be able to use the inverse of the ARR to determine the number needed to treat (NNT) and number needed to harm (NNH). These concepts are discussed next.

INTERPRETING THE ABSOLUTE RISK REDUCTION (ARR)

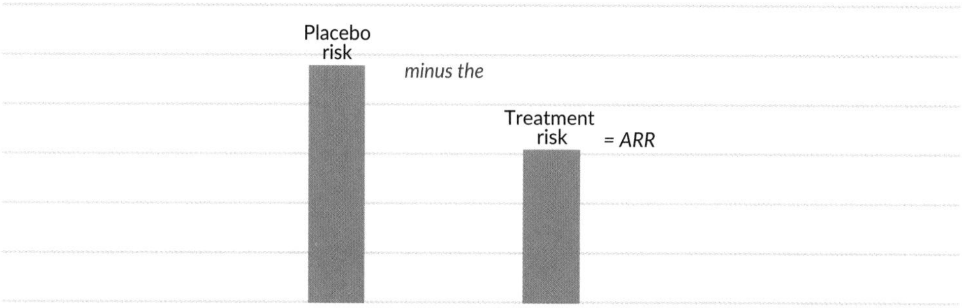

The absolute risk reduction is the true difference in risk between the treatment and the placebo groups.
Said another way, the ARR is the net effect (benefit) beyond the effect obtained from a placebo.

©RxPrep

NUMBER NEEDED TO TREAT OR HARM

NNT and NNH help clinicians answer the question: how many patients need to receive the drug for one patient to get benefit (NNT) or harm (NNH)? This information, taken into consideration with the patient's individual risk, helps guide decisions.

NUMBER NEEDED TO TREAT

<u>NNT</u> is the <u>number of patients</u> who <u>need to be treated</u> for a <u>certain period of time</u> (e.g., one year) in order for <u>one patient</u> to <u>benefit</u> (e.g., avoid HF progression).

NNT Formula

$$\text{NNT} = \frac{1}{\text{(risk in control group)} - \text{(risk in treatment group)*}} \quad \text{or} \quad \frac{1}{\text{ARR*}}$$

**Risk and ARR are expressed as decimals*

NNT Calculation

The ARR in the metoprolol study was 12%. The duration of the study period was one year. Calculate the number of patients that need to be treated with metoprolol for one year in order to prevent one case of HF progression.

$$\text{NNT} = \frac{1}{0.12} = \text{8.3, rounded up to 9*}$$

**Numbers greater than a whole number are rounded up*

NNT Interpretation

For every 9 patients who receive metoprolol for one year, HF progression is prevented in one patient.

NUMBER NEEDED TO HARM

NNH is the number of patients who need to be treated for a certain period of time in order for one patient to experience harm.

NNT and NNH are calculated with the same formula (see the NNT formula above). There are two differences: 1. NNT is rounded up, and NNH is rounded down (see Study Tip Gal) and 2. The absolute value of the ARR is used with NNH, as shown in the following example.

NNH Calculation

A study evaluated the efficacy of clopidogrel versus placebo, both given in addition to aspirin, in reducing the risk of cardiovascular death, MI and stroke. The study reported a 3.9% risk of major bleeding in the treatment group and a 2.8% risk of major bleeding in the control group.

ROUNDING RULES FOR NNT AND NNH

Normal rounding rules do not apply:

- For NNT, anything greater than a whole number, round up to the next whole number. This avoids overstating the potential benefit of an intervention.
  - Example: NNT of 52.1 → round up to 53
- For NNH, anything greater than a whole number, round down to the nearest whole number. This avoids understating the potential harm of an intervention.
  - Example: NNH of 41.9 → round down to 41

ARR = 2.8% – 3.9% = –1.1%; the absolute value is the difference between the two groups. There is a 1.1% higher risk of major bleeding in the treatment group.

$$NNH = \frac{1}{0.011} = 90.9, \text{ rounded down to } 90^*$$

**Numbers greater than a whole number are rounded down*

NNH Interpretation

One additional case of major bleeding is expected to occur for every 90 patients taking clopidogrel instead of placebo.

ODDS RATIO AND HAZARD RATIO

ODDS RATIO

Odds is the probability that an event will occur, versus the probability that it will not occur. Case-control studies, described in the Types of Medical Studies section, are not suitable for relative risk calculations. In order to estimate the risks associated with a treatment or some type of intervention in a case-control study, the odds of unfavorable events are calculated instead.

Case-control studies enroll patients who have a clinical outcome or disease that has already occurred (e.g., lung cancer). The patient medical charts are reviewed retrospectively (in the past) to search for possible exposure/s (e.g., smoking) that increased the risk of the clinical outcome or disease. In this case, the odds ratio (OR) is used to calculate the odds of an outcome occurring with an exposure, compared to the odds of the outcome occurring without the exposure. ORs are used most commonly with case-control studies, but can be used in cohort and cross-sectional studies.

OR Formula

EXPOSURE/TREATMENT	OUTCOME PRESENT	OUTCOME ABSENT
Present	A	B
Absent	C	D

A = # that have the outcome, with exposure
B = # without the outcome, with exposure
C = # that have the outcome, without exposure
D = # without the outcome, without exposure

$$OR = \frac{AD}{BC}$$

OR Calculation

A case-control study was conducted to assess the risk of falls with fracture (outcome) associated with serotonergic antidepressant (AD) use (exposure) among a cohort of Chinese females ≥ 65-years-old. Cases were matched with 33,000 controls (1:4, by age, sex, and cohort entry date).

EXPOSURE/ TREATMENT	FALLS W/ FRACTURE (CASES)	FALLS W/O FRACTURE (CONTROLS)
Serotonergic AD-YES	4,991	18,270
Serotonergic AD-NO	3,259	14,730

AD = 4,991 x 14,730 = 73,517,430

BC = 3,259 x 18,270 = 59,541,930

$$OR = \frac{73{,}517{,}430}{59{,}541{,}930} = 1.23$$

Conclusion: serotonergic ADs are associated with a 23% increased risk of falls with fracture (see OR and HR Interpretation below).

HAZARD RATIO

In a survival analysis (e.g. analysis of death or disease progression), instead of using "risk," a hazard rate is used. A hazard rate is the rate at which an unfavorable event occurs within a short period of time. Similar to RR, the hazard ratio (HR) is the ratio between the hazard rate in the treatment group and the hazard rate in the control group.

HR Formula

$$HR = \frac{\text{Hazard rate in the treatment group}}{\text{Hazard rate in the control group}}$$

HR Calculation

A placebo-controlled study was performed to evaluate whether niacin, when added to intensive statin therapy, reduces cardiovascular risk in patients with established cardiovascular disease. The primary endpoint was the first event of the composite endpoint (death from coronary heart disease, nonfatal myocardial infarction, ischemic stroke, hospitalization for an acute coronary syndrome or coronary or cerebral revascularization). A total of 3,414 patients were enrolled and followed for three years.

Calculate the hazard ratio.

	NIACIN N = 1,718	PLACEBO N = 1,696
Primary endpoint	282	274

Niacin Hazard	Control Hazard
$\frac{282}{1{,}718} = 0.16$	$\frac{274}{1{,}696} = 0.16$

$$HR = \frac{0.16}{0.16} = 1 \times 100 = 100\%$$

Answer can be expressed as a decimal or a percentage; the exam question will specify with instructions

Conclusion: there is no benefit to cardiovascular risk when adding niacin to intensive statin therapy (see OR and HR Interpretation below).

OR AND HR INTERPRETATION

OR and HR are interpreted in a similar way to RR:

OR or HR = 1: the event rate is the same in the treatment and control arms. There is no advantage to the treatment.

OR or HR > 1: the event rate in the treatment group is higher than the event rate in the control group; for example, a HR of 2 for an outcome of death indicates that there are twice as many deaths in the treatment group.

OR or HR < 1: the event rate in the treatment group is lower than the event rate in the control group; for example, a HR of 0.5 for an outcome of death indicates that there are half as many deaths in the treatment group.

PRIMARY AND COMPOSITE ENDPOINTS

The primary endpoint is the main (primary) result that is measured to see if the treatment had a significant benefit. In the metoprolol trial, the primary endpoint was HF progression.

A composite endpoint combines multiple individual endpoints into one measurement. This is attractive to researchers, as combining several endpoints increases the likelihood of reaching a statistically significant benefit with a smaller, less costly trial.

When a composite endpoint is used, each individual endpoint gets counted toward the same (composite) outcome.

Primary Endpoints (distinct and separate)	Composite Endpoint (combined into one)
Death from cardiovascular causes	Death from cardiovascular causes
or	and
Nonfatal stroke	Nonfatal stroke
or	and
Nonfatal MI	Nonfatal MI

COMPOSITE ENDPOINTS: CAUTION

All endpoints in a composite must be similar in magnitude and have similar, meaningful importance to the patient. For example, the composite endpoint of blood pressure reduction should not be included with heart attack and stroke reduction. The FDA requires each individual endpoint to be measured and reported when a composite endpoint is used. When assessing a composite measurement, it is important to use the composite endpoint value, rather than adding together the values for the individual endpoints. The value of the sum of the individual endpoints will not equal precisely with the value of the composite endpoint, since a patient can have more than one non-fatal endpoint during a trial.

TYPES OF STATISTICAL TESTS

The next step following data collection (and calculation of risks, RR, ARR, HR, etc.) is to analyze the data to check if differences between the treatment and control groups are statistically significant, or to determine an association or relationship in the data. Selecting the correct test to analyze the data depends on the type of data, and the outcomes measured.

CONTINUOUS DATA

With continuous data, the type of test used to determine statistical significance depends on the distribution of data (discussed previously). If it is normally distributed, parametric methods are appropriate. If the data is not normally distributed, nonparametric methods are appropriate.

T-Tests

This is a parametric method used when the endpoint has continuous data and the data is normally distributed. When data from a single sample group is compared with known data from the general population, a one-sample t-test is performed. If a single sample group is used for a pre-/post-measurement (i.e., the patient serves as their own control), a paired t-test is appropriate.

A student t-test is used when the study has two independent samples: the treatment and the control group. For example, a study comparing the reduction in hemoglobin A1C values between metformin and placebo would use an independent or unpaired student t-test.

Analysis of Variance

Analysis of variance (ANOVA), or the F-test, is used to test for statistical significance when using continuous data with 3 or more samples, or groups.

DISCRETE (CATEGORICAL) DATA

Chi-Square Test

For nominal or ordinal data, a chi-square test is used to determine statistical significance between treatment groups. For example, if a study assesses the difference between two groups in mortality (nominal data), or pain scores based on a pain scale (ordinal data), a chi-square test could be used.

SELECTING A TEST TO ANALYZE THE DATA

Numerical/Continuous Data: PARAMETRIC TESTS (Data has a normal distribution)	Numerical/Continuous Data: NON-PARAMETRIC TESTS (Data does not have a normal distribution)	Discrete/Categorical Data
One group One-sample t-test	**One group** Sign test	**One group** Chi-square test
Dependent/paired t-test (if one group has before and after measures)	Wilcoxon Signed-Rank test (if one group has before and after measures)	Wilcoxon Signed-Rank test (if one group has before and after measures)
Two groups (e.g. treatment and control groups) Independent/unpaired student t-test	**Two groups (e.g. treatment and control groups)** Mann-Whitney (Wilcoxon Rank-Sum) test	**Two groups (e.g. treatment and control groups)** Chi-square test or Fisher's exact test Mann-Whitney (Wilcoxon Rank-Sum) test (may be preferred for ordinal data)
Three or more groups ANOVA (or F-test)	**Three or more groups** Kruskal-Wallis test	**Three or more groups** Kruskal-Wallis test

EXAMPLES OF TEST TYPE SELECTION

Example 1

A study is performed to assess the safety and efficacy of ketamine-dexmedetomidine (KD) versus ketamine-propofol (KP) for sedation in patients after coronary artery bypass graft surgery.

ENDPOINT (MEAN VALUES)	KD	KP
Fentanyl dose, mcg	41.94 ± 20.43	152.8 ± 51.2
Weaning/extubation time, min	374.05 ± 20.25	445.23 ± 21.7

Measurements of dose and time are both continuous data. The trial has two independent samples, or groups (KD and KP). An appropriate test is an independent/unpaired student t-test. If the trial included a third group, ANOVA would be used.

Example 2

An emergency medical team wants to see if there is a statistically significant difference in death due to multiple drug overdose (OD) with at least one opioid taken, versus no opioid taken. Which test can determine a statistically significant difference in death?

ENDPOINT	YES OPIOID N = 250	NO OPIOID N = 150
Death (n, %)	52 (20.8%)	35 (23.3%)

The variable (dead or alive) is nominal. The chi-square test is used to test for significance when there are two groups.

CORRELATION AND REGRESSION

CORRELATION

Correlation is a statistical technique that is used to determine if one variable (such as number of days hospitalized) changes, or is related to, another variable (such as incidence of hospital-acquired infection). When the independent variable (number of hospital days) causes the dependent variable (infections) to increase, the direction of the correlation is positive (increases to the right). When the independent variable causes the dependent variable to decrease, the direction of the correlation is negative (decreases to the right).

Different types of data require different tests for correlation. Spearman's rank-order correlation, referred to as Rho, is used to test correlation with ordinal, ranked data. The primary test used for continuous data is the Pearson's correlation coefficient, denoted as *r*, which is a calculated score that indicates the strength and direction of the relationship between two variables. The values range from –1 to +1, and are described in the figure on the next page.

It is not possible to conclude from a correlation analysis that the change in a variable causes the change in another variable. A correlation, whether positive or negative, does not prove a causal relationship.

REGRESSION

Regression is used to describe the relationship between a dependent variable and one or more independent (or explanatory) variables, or how much the value of the dependent variable changes when the independent variables changes. Regression is common in observational studies where researchers need to assess multiple independent variables or need to control for many confounding factors. There are three typical types of regressions: 1) linear, for continuous data, 2) logistic, for categorical data, and 3) Cox regression, for categorical data in a survival analysis.

TESTING FOR CORRELATION WITH THE PEARSON CORRELATION COEFFICIENT

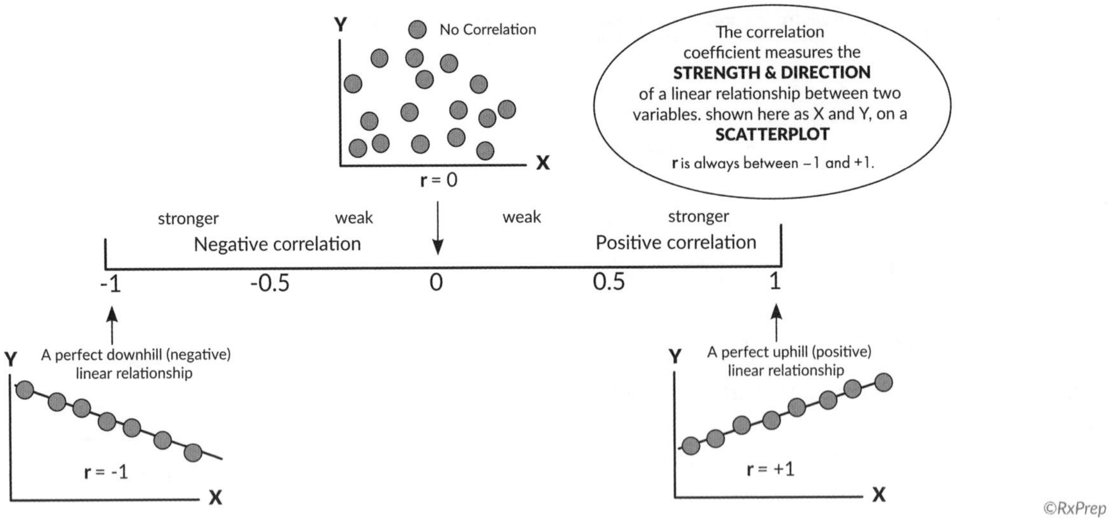

SENSITIVITY AND SPECIFICITY

Lab and diagnostic tests are used to screen for and diagnose medical conditions. Interpreting sensitivity and specificity correctly is required to answer these two questions concerning the validity of lab or diagnostic test results:

- If the result is positive, what is the likelihood of having the disease?
- If the result is negative, what is the likelihood of not having the disease?

SENSITIVITY, THE TRUE POSITIVE

Sensitivity describes how effectively a test identifies patients with the condition. The higher the sensitivity, the better; a test with 100% sensitivity will be positive in all patients with the condition. Sensitivity is calculated from the number who test positive, out of those who actually have the condition (sensitivity is the percentage of "true-positive" results).

SPECIFICITY, THE TRUE NEGATIVE

Specificity describes how effectively a test identifies patients without the condition. The higher the specificity the better; a test with 100% specificity will be negative in all patients without the condition. Specificity is calculated from the number who test negative, out of those who actually do not have the condition (specificity is the percentage of "true-negative" results).

Sensitivity and Specificity Formula

TEST RESULT	HAVE CONDITION	NO CONDITION
Positive	A	B
Negative	C	D
Total	A + C	B + D

$$\text{Sensitivity} = \frac{A}{A + C} \times 100$$

$$\text{Specificity} = \frac{D}{B + D} \times 100$$

A = # that have the condition, with a positive test result
B = # without the condition, with a positive test result
C = # that have the condition, with a negative test result

D = # without the condition, with a negative test result

Sensitivity and Specificity Calculation and Interpretation

The tables below show how sensitivity and specificity is calculated for two lab tests used in the diagnosis of rheumatoid arthritis (RA), cyclic citrulline peptide (CCP) and rheumatoid factor (RF). Based on study data, CCP has a sensitivity of 98% and a specificity of 98% for RA, while RF has a sensitivity of 28% and a specificity of 87%.

Using the RF lab test as an example, a sensitivity of 28% means that only 28% of patients with the condition will have a positive RF result; the test is negative in 72% of patients with the disease (and the diagnosis can be missed). A specificity of 87% means that the test is negative in 87% of patients without the disease; but 13% of patients without the disease can test positive (potentially causing an incorrect diagnosis).

CCP RESULTS	HAVE CONDITION	NO CONDITION
Positive	A = 147	B = 9
Negative	C = 3	D = 441
Total	A + C = 150	B + D = 450
Sensitivity	147/150 x 100 = 98%	
Specificity		441/450 x 100 = 98%

RF RESULTS	HAVE CONDITION	NO CONDITION
Positive	A = 21	B = 26
Negative	C = 54	D = 174
Total	A + C = 75	B + D = 200
Sensitivity	21/75 x 100 = 28%	
Specificity		174/200 x 100 = 87%

Sensitivity and Specificity Application

If an elderly female patient with swollen finger joints is referred to a rheumatologist and lab tests reveal a positive CCP and a positive RF, the positive CCP indicates a very strong likelihood that the patient has RA, because it has a high sensitivity and specificity (98%). If the RF is positive and the CCP is negative, the rheumatologist would consider the possibility of other autoimmune/inflammatory conditions that could be contributing to swollen joints, because of the low sensitivity of RF (28%).

INTENTION TO TREAT AND PER PROTOCOL ANALYSIS

Data from clinical trials can be analyzed in two different ways; intention-to-treat or per protocol. Intention-to-treat analysis includes data for all patients originally allocated to each treatment group (active and control) even if the patient did not complete the trial according to the study protocol (e.g., due to non-compliance, protocol violations or study withdrawal). This method provides a conservative (real world) estimate of the treatment effect. A per protocol analysis is conducted for the subset of the trial population who completed the study according to the protocol (or at least without any major protocol violations). This method can provide an optimistic estimate of treatment effect since it is limited to the subset of patients who were adherent to the protocol.

NONINFERIORITY AND EQUIVALENCE TRIAL DESIGNS

The standard design of most trials is to establish that a treatment is superior to another treatment; the researcher wishes to show that the new drug is better than the old drug, or a placebo. Perhaps a new treatment is developed that is less expensive, or less toxic than the standard of care. Researchers would hope to demonstrate that the new drug is roughly equivalent, or at least not inferior, to the standard of care. Two types of trials are used for this purpose: equivalence and non-inferiority trials.

Equivalence trials attempt to demonstrate that the new treatment has roughly the same effect as the old (or reference) treatment. Non-inferiority trials attempt to demonstrate that the new treatment is not much worse than the old treatment. Equivalence trials tests in two directions, for higher or lower effectiveness. This is called a two-way margin. Non-inferiority trials test for effect in one direction (a one-way margin).

FOREST PLOTS AND CONFIDENCE INTERVALS

Forest plots are graphs that have a "forest" of lines. Forest plots are used either for a single study, in which individual endpoints are pooled (gathered together) into a composite endpoint (see figure labeled Pogue et al. below) or, more commonly, when the results from multiple studies are pooled into a single study, such as with a meta-analysis (see figure labeled Miller et al. below).

Forest plots provide CIs for difference data or ratio data. Interpreting the forest plots correctly can help identify whether a statistically significant benefit has been reached. When interpreting statistical significance using a forest plot:

- The boxes show the effect estimate. In a meta-analysis, the size of the box correlates with the size of the effect from the single study shown. Diamonds (at the bottom of the forest plot) represent pooled results from multiple studies.
- The horizontal lines through the boxes illustrate the length of the confidence interval for that particular endpoint (in a single study) or for the particular study (in a meta-analysis). The longer the line, the wider the interval, and the less reliable the study results. The width of the diamond in a meta-analysis serves the same purpose.
- The vertical solid line is the line of no effect; a significant benefit has been reached when data falls to the left of the line; data to the right of the line indicates significant harm. The vertical line is set at zero for difference data and at one for ratio data.

COMPARING DIFFERENCE DATA

The study shown to the right (a meta-analysis by Miller et al.) uses a forest plot to test for significance with difference data. Recall for difference data, a result is not statistically significant if the confidence interval crosses zero, so the vertical line (line of no difference), is set at zero. Examples (high-dosage vitamin E):

- 3rd study (PPS): shows a statistically significant benefit; the data point, plus the entire confidence interval, is to the left of the vertical line and does not cross zero.
- 5th study (CHAOS): the result is not statistically significant; the confidence interval crosses zero.
- 9th study (WAVE): shows a statistically significant harmful outcome; the data point, plus the entire confidence interval, is all to the right of the vertical line and does not cross zero.

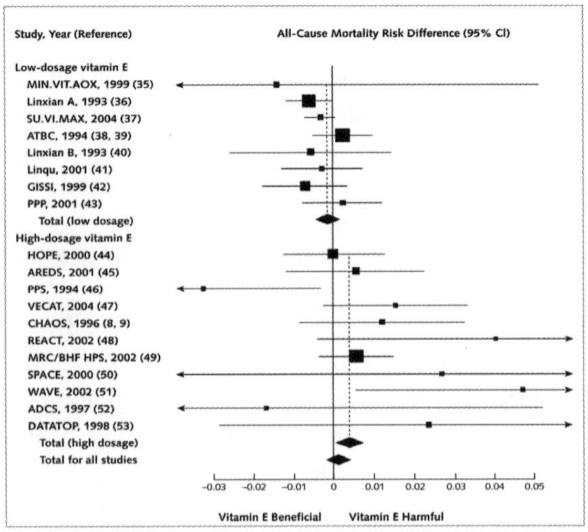

Miller, et al. Ann Intern Med. 2005 Jan 4;142(1):37-46.

COMPARING RATIO DATA

The study shown to the right (by Pogue et al.) uses a forest plot to test for significance of a composite endpoint reported as ratio data, in this case hazard ratio. Recall for ratio data, the result is not statistically significant if the confidence interval crosses one, so the vertical line (line of no difference), is set at one. Examples:

- Primary composite endpoint: shows a statistically significant benefit with treatment; the CI (0.7 – 0.99) does not cross one (and the horizontal line representing the CI does not touch or cross the vertical line at one).
- CV death: shows no statistically significant benefit (or harm); the CI (0.92 – 1.83) crosses one (and the horizontal line representing the CI crosses the vertical line at one).

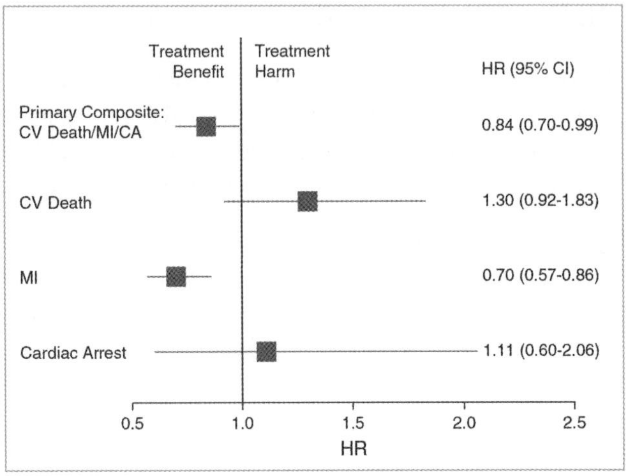

Pogue, et al. PLoS One 2012; 7(4): e34785.

TYPES OF MEDICAL STUDIES

Evidence-based medicine (EBM), which is largely guideline and protocol-driven, is the foundation of practice and most patient care recommendations are based on valid study data. The type of study that a researcher chooses is a major factor in determining the quality of the study data and the clinical value or impact. The pyramid figure to the right depicts the reliability of each of the major study types.

Common types of studies include:

- Case-control studies: retrospective; compare cases (patients with a disease) to controls (without a disease).
- Cohort studies: retrospective or prospective; compare patients with an exposure to those without an exposure.
- Randomized controlled trials: prospective; compare patients who were randomly assigned to groups.
- Meta-analyses: analyzes the results of multiple studies.

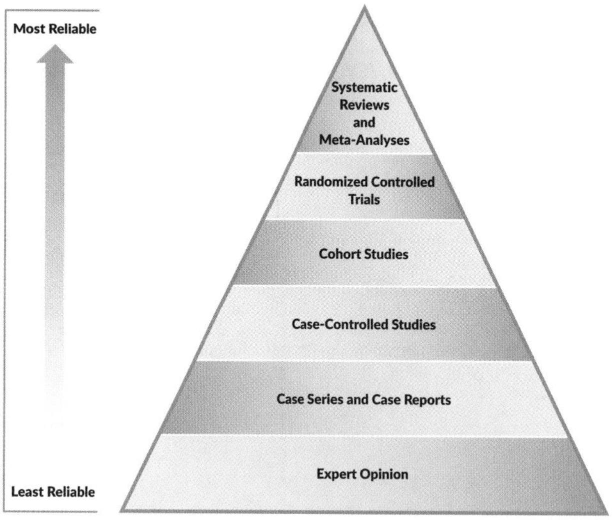

Each type of study has benefits and limitations. The table below describes the various study types and provides an example of each study.

STUDY TYPE, BENEFITS AND LIMITATIONS	STUDY TYPE EXAMPLE
CASE-CONTROL STUDY Compares patients with a disease (cases) to those without the disease (controls); the researcher looks back in time (retrospectively) to see if a relationship exists between the disease and various risk factors. **Benefits** Data is easy to get from medical records. Good for looking at outcomes when the intervention is unethical (e.g., exposing patients to a pesticide to test an association with cancer; cases that occurred are used instead). Less expensive than RCT. **Limitations** Cause and effect cannot reliably be determined (associations may be proven to be non-existent).	***Predictors of surgical site infection after open lower extremity bypass (LEB) revascularization.*** **Methods** Data was pulled from 35 hospitals for all patients who had LEB during a 3-year period. Cases of surgical site infection (SSI) were identified and compared to those who did not develop a SSI (controls). An odds ratio (OR) was calculated for various risk factors that might increase SSI risk. **Statistical Data** Renal failure OR: 4.35 (95% CI 3.45-5.47; $p < 0.001$). Hypertension OR: 4.29 (95% CI 2.74-6.72; $p < 0.001$). BMI ≥ 25 kg/m^2 OR: 1.78 (95% CI 1.23-2.57; $p = 0.002$). **Conclusion** Renal failure, hypertension and BMI ≥ 25 kg/m^2 were all associated with an increased risk of SSI.
COHORT STUDY Compares outcomes of a group of patients exposed and not exposed to a treatment; the researcher follows both groups prospectively (in the future) or retrospectively (less common) to see if they develop the outcome. **Benefits** Good for looking at outcomes when the intervention would be unethical. **Limitations** More time consuming and expensive than a retrospective study. Can be influenced by confounders, which are other factors that affect the outcome (e.g., smoking, lipid levels).	***Statin use and cognitive function in adults with type 1 diabetes.*** **Methods** Patients with type 1 diabetes who were taking statins (exposed) were compared to those not taking statins (not exposed) and followed for 7-12 years to see if statin use was associated with cognitive impairment (outcome). **Statistical Data** Statin use and odds of cognitive impairment OR: 4.84 (95% CI 1.63-14.44; $p = 0.005$). **Conclusion** In type 1 diabetes, patients taking statins were more likely to develop cognitive impairment compared to those who did not take statins.

STUDY TYPE, BENEFITS AND LIMITATIONS	STUDY TYPE EXAMPLE
CROSS-SECTIONAL SURVEY Estimates the relationship between variables and outcomes (prevalence) at one particular time (cross-section) in a defined population. **Benefits** Can identify associations that need further study (hypothesis-generating). **Limitations** Does not determine causality (further studies needed if association found).	***Association of selective serotonin reuptake inhibitors and bone mineral density (BMD) in elderly women.*** **Methods** A cross-sectional analysis of 250 elderly women (defined population) from August 2010 to April 2015 (time period) was performed. Data was collected retrospectively for two groups: SSRI users (variable) and SSRI nonusers (variable) to compare the prevalence of low BMD. **Statistical Data** No difference in the prevalence of low BMD at the femoral neck ($p=0.887$) or the spine ($p = 0.275$). **Conclusion** There was no difference in the prevalence of BMD between elderly women on SSRIs and not on SSRIs.
CASE REPORT AND CASE SERIES Describes an adverse reaction or a unique condition that appears in a single patient (case report) or a few patients (case series). **Benefits** Can identify new diseases, drug side effects or potential uses. Generates hypotheses that can be tested with other study designs. **Limitations** Conclusions cannot be drawn from a single or few cases.	***Tardive oculogyric crisis during treatment with clozapine: report of three cases.*** **Methods** A psychiatrist identified three cases of patients at his center who experienced the adverse effect, wrote it up, and it was printed in a medical journal. **Statistical Data** No statistical validity; risk cannot be compared to the general population as there is no control. **Conclusion** The findings of oculogyric crisis in patients treated with clozapine are interesting, but do not provide important information on prevalence.
RANDOMIZED CONTROLLED TRIAL (RCT) Compares an experimental treatment to a control (placebo or existing treatment) to determine which is better. Subjects with the desired characteristics (inclusion criteria) are carefully selected and patients with characteristics that may influence the outcome are excluded (exclusion criteria). Patients are randomized and sometimes blinded (unaware if they are receiving treatment or control). **Benefits** Preferred study type to determine cause and effect, or superiority. Less potential for bias. **Limitations** Time consuming and expensive. May not reflect real-life scenarios (when rigorous exclusion criteria are used).	***Angiotensin-neprilysin inhibition versus enalapril in heart failure (PARADIGM-HF study).*** **Methods** Patients with heart failure were randomized in a double-blind manner to receive a new drug (angiotensin-neprilysin inhibitor) or the current standard of care (enalapril). The effectiveness of the treatments was measured as a primary composite outcome of death from cardiovascular causes or hospitalization for heart failure. **Statistical Data** Primary outcome HR: 0.8 (95% CI 0.73-0.87, $p < 0.001$). **Conclusion** The new drug demonstrated a statistically significant benefit in reducing death from cardiovascular causes or hospitalizations due to heart failure. The null hypothesis (that there was no difference between the two arms) was rejected.
PARALLEL RCT Subjects are randomized to the treatment or control arm for the entire study.	The PARADIGM-HF study (discussed above) is an example of a parallel study design and is the most common type of RCT.

STUDY TYPE, BENEFITS AND LIMITATIONS	STUDY TYPE EXAMPLE
CROSSOVER RCT Patients are randomized to one of two sequential treatments: Group 1 – receive treatment A first, then crossover (change) to treatment B. Group 2 – receive treatment B first, then crossover (change) to treatment A. **Benefits** Patients serve as their own control; this minimizes the effects from confounders. **Limitations** A washout period is needed to minimize the influence of the first drug during the second treatment.	***Crossover comparison of timolol and latanoprost in chronic primary angle-closure glaucoma.*** **Methods** Patients with chronic primary angle-closure glaucoma were randomized after surgery to latanoprost or timolol. Three months after treatment with the first drug, the second drug was substituted. Intraocular pressure (IOP) was recorded before starting and at 3 and 7 months in both groups. **Statistical Data** Decrease in IOP from baseline was 8.2 ± 2 mmHg with latanoprost ($p < 0.001$) and 6.1 ± 1.7 mmHg with timolol ($p = 0.01$). **Conclusion** Latanoprost was associated with a greater decrease in IOP from baseline than timolol.
FACTORIAL DESIGN Randomizes to more than the usual two groups to test a number of experimental conditions. **Benefits** Evaluates multiple interventions (multiple drugs or dosing regimens) in a single experiment. **Limitations** With each arm added, more subjects are needed to have adequate power.	***Prednisolone or pentoxifylline for alcoholic hepatitis.*** **Methods** A 2-by-2 factorial design was used to evaluate the effect of prednisolone or pentoxifylline on 28-day mortality in patients with alcoholic hepatitis. Patients were randomized to 1 of 4 groups: prednisolone (PR)-pentoxifylline (PE), PR-placebo, PE-placebo, or placebo-placebo. **Statistical Data** Pentoxifylline (PE-PR and PE-placebo groups) OR: 1.04 (95% CI 0.77-1.49; $p = 0.69$). Prednisolone (PR-placebo) OR: 0.72 (95% CI 0.52-1.01; $p = 0.06$). **Conclusion** Pentoxifylline (alone or in combination with prednisolone), and prednisolone alone did not reduce mortality in patients with alcoholic hepatitis.
META-ANALYSIS Combines results from multiple studies in order to develop a conclusion that has greater statistical power than is possible from the individual smaller studies. **Benefits** Smaller studies can be pooled instead of performing a large, expensive study. See previous forest plot explanation for how data can be presented. **Limitations** Studies may not be uniform (size, inclusion and exclusion criteria, etc). Validity can be compromised if lower quality studies are weighted equally to higher quality studies.	***Antioxidants for chronic kidney disease (CKD).*** **Methods** The authors searched the PubMed database to locate studies investigating the use of antioxidants in people with CKD. Ten studies were identified, and the results were pooled to try and identify whether antioxidants had an effect on cardiovascular disease and mortality in patients with CKD. **Statistical Data** Antioxidant use and cardiovascular disease RR: 0.78 (95% CI 0.52-1.18; $p = 0.24$). All-cause mortality RR: 0.93 (95% CI 0.76-1.14; $p = 0.48$). **Conclusion** Antioxidant use did not reduce cardiovascular disease or mortality in CKD patients.
SYSTEMATIC REVIEW ARTICLE Summary of the clinical literature that focuses on a specific topic or question (e.g., treatment options for a condition). Begins with a question followed by a literature search, then the information is summarized, and sometimes includes a meta-analysis to synthesize results. **Benefits** Inexpensive (studies already exist).	***The evolving treatment landscape of advanced renal cell carcinoma (RCC) in patients progressing after VEGF inhibition.*** **Methods** It is still unclear which patients benefit most from VEGF and mTOR inhibitors and the ideal sequence, timing and duration of therapy. The review wanted to define the appropriate treatment sequence after first-line treatment failure. **Statistical Data** No statistical tests reported. **Conclusion** There are no predictive biomarkers that determine best therapy for the right patient or the best sequence of treatment. More studies are needed.

PHARMACOECONOMICS

BACKGROUND

Healthcare costs in the United States rank among the highest of all industrialized countries. In 2017, total healthcare expenditures reached $3.5 trillion, which translates to an average of $10,739 per person, or about 17.9% of the national gross domestic product. The increasing costs have highlighted the need to understand how our limited resources can be used most effectively and efficiently in the care of our patients and society as a whole. It is necessary to scientifically evaluate the value (i.e., costs vs. outcomes) of interventions such as medical procedures or drugs.

DEFINITIONS

Pharmacoeconomics is a collection of descriptive and analytic techniques for evaluating pharmaceutical interventions (drugs, devices, procedures, etc.) in the healthcare system. Pharmacoeconomic research identifies, measures and compares the costs (direct, indirect and intangible) and the consequences (clinical, economic and humanistic) of pharmaceutical products and services.

Various research methods can be used to determine the impact of the pharmaceutical product or service. These methods include: cost-effectiveness analysis, cost-minimization analysis, cost-utility analysis and cost-benefit analysis. The term "pharmacoeconomics" is sometimes referred to as "outcomes research," but they are not the same thing. Pharmacoeconomic methods are specific to assessing the costs and consequences of pharmaceutical products and services. Outcomes research represents a broader research discipline that attempts to identify, measure and evaluate the end result of healthcare services.

Healthcare providers, payers and other decision makers use these methods to evaluate and compare the total costs and consequences of pharmaceutical products and services. The results of pharmacoeconomic analyses can vary significantly based on the point of view of the analyst; the study perspective is critical for interpretation. What may be viewed as good value for society or for the patient may not be deemed as such from an institutional or provider perspective (e.g., the costs of lost productivity due to illness are critically important to a patient or employer, but perhaps less so to a health plan).

Pharmacoeconomic analyses provide useful supplemental evidence to traditional efficacy and safety endpoints. They help translate important clinical benefits into economic and patient-centered terms, and can assist providers and payers in determining where, or if, a drug fits into the treatment paradigm for a specific condition. Pharmacoeconomic studies serve to guide optimal healthcare resource allocation, in a standardized and evidence-based manner.

The ECHO model (Economic, Clinical and Humanistic Outcomes) provides a broad evaluative framework to assess the outcomes associated with diseases and treatments.

- Economic outcomes: include direct, indirect and intangible costs of the drug compared to a medical intervention.
- Clinical outcomes: include medical events that occur as a result of the treatment or intervention.
- Humanistic Outcomes: include consequences of the disease or treatment as reported by the patient or caregiver (e.g., patient satisfaction, quality of life).

MEDICAL COST CATEGORIES: DIRECT, INDIRECT AND INTANGIBLE

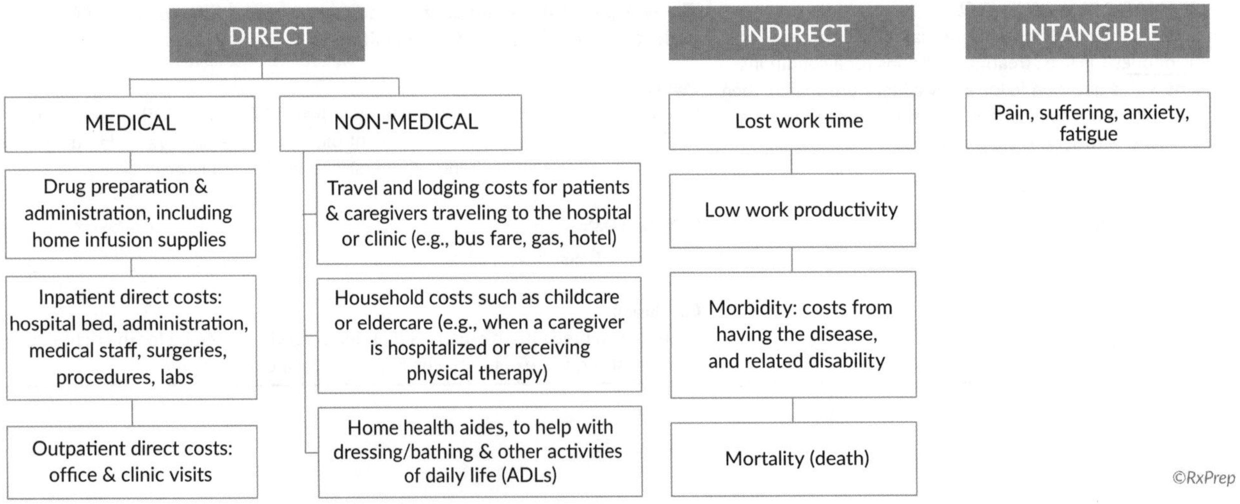

AVERAGE AND INCREMENTAL COST-EFFECTIVENESS RATIOS

The results of a pharmacoeconomic analysis are commonly expressed in terms of a cost ratio, representing the costs incurred to achieve a particular outcome [e.g., cost per case cured, cost per treatment success, cost per quality-adjusted life year (QALY) gained]. Two fundamental cost ratios are commonly used to communicate results of a pharmacoeconomic analysis.

Average Cost-Effectiveness Ratios

Average cost-effectiveness ratios reflect the cost per outcome of one treatment independent of other treatment alternatives. For example, if a treatment costs $50 to generate successful outcomes in two patients, the average cost-effectiveness ratio is $25/treatment success ($50/2 successfully treated patients).

Incremental Cost-Effectiveness Ratios

Incremental cost-effectiveness ratios represent the change in costs and outcomes when two treatment alternatives are compared. An incremental cost-effectiveness ratio is calculated when evaluating costs and outcomes between competing alternatives, and represents the additional costs required to produce an additional unit of effect. It is calculated as shown to the right, where C is for costs and E is for effects.

$$\text{Incremental Cost Ratio} = \frac{(C_2 - C_1)}{(E_2 - E_1)}$$

- Example: if spending $200 on Drug A results in 5 treatment successes while spending $300 on Drug B results in 7 treatment successes, what is the incremental cost ratio?

$$\text{Incremental Cost Ratio} = \frac{(\$300 - \$200)}{(7 - 5)} = \frac{\$100}{2} = \$50$$

Conclusion: Drug B costs $50 more relative to Drug A for each additional treatment success.

PHARMACOECONOMIC METHODOLOGIES

Cost-Minimization Analysis

Cost-minimization analysis (CMA) is used when two or more interventions have demonstrated equivalence in outcomes and the costs of each intervention are being compared. CMA measures and compares the input costs of treatment alternatives that have equivalent outcomes. This determination of equivalence is a key consideration in adopting this methodology. Ideally, evidence exists to support the clinical equivalence of the alternatives. In some instances, assumptions are made in the absence of relevant evidence.

For example, two ACE inhibitors, captopril and lisinopril, are considered therapeutically equivalent in the literature, but the acquisition cost (the price paid for the drug) and administrative costs may be different (captopril is administered TID and lisinopril is administered once daily). A CMA looks at "minimizing costs" when multiple drugs have equal efficacy and tolerability. Another example of CMA is looking at the same drug regimen given in two different settings (e.g., hospital versus home health care). CMA is considered the easiest analysis to perform, but use of this method is limited given its ability to compare only alternatives with demonstrated equivalent outcomes.

Cost-Benefit Analysis

Cost-benefit analysis (CBA) is a systematic process for calculating and comparing benefits and costs of an intervention in terms of monetary units (dollars). CBA consists of identifying all the benefits from an intervention and converting them into dollars in the year that they will occur. The costs associated with the intervention are identified, allocated to the year when they occur, and then discounted back to their present day value. Given that all other factors remain constant, the program with the largest present day value of benefits minus costs is the best economic value. In CBA, it can be difficult to assign a dollar amount to a benefit (e.g., measuring the benefit of patient quality of life, which is difficult to quantify, and assigning a dollar value to it). One advantage to using CBA is the ability to determine if the benefits of the intervention exceed the costs of implementation. CBA can also be used to compare multiple programs for similar or unrelated outcomes, as long as the outcome measures can be converted to dollars.

Cost-Effectiveness Analysis

Cost-effectiveness analysis (CEA) is defined as a series of analytical and mathematical procedures that aid in the selection of a course of action from various alternative approaches. Inputs are usually measured in dollars and outputs are usually measured in natural units (e.g., LDL values in mg/dL, % clinical cures, length of stay). The main advantage of this method is that the outcomes are easier to quantify when compared to other analyses, and clinicians are familiar with these types of outcomes since they are similar to outcomes seen in clinical trials and practice. CEA is the most common pharmacoeconomic methodology seen in biomedical literature.

A disadvantage of CEA is the inability to directly compare different types of outcomes. For example, one cannot compare the cost effectiveness of implementing a diabetes program with implementing an asthma program where the outcome units are different (i.e., blood glucose values versus asthma exacerbations). It is also difficult to combine two or more outcomes into one value of measurement (e.g., comparing one chemotherapeutic agent that prolongs survival, but has significant side effects, to another chemotherapeutic agent that has less effect on prolonging survival but fewer side effects).

Cost-Utility Analysis

Cost-utility analysis (CUA) is a specialized form of CEA that includes a quality-of-life component of morbidity assessments, using common health indices such as quality-adjusted life years (QALYs) and disability-adjusted life years (DALYs). CEA can measure the quantity of life (years gained) but not the "quality" or "utility" of those years. In CUA, the intervention outcome is measured in terms QALYs gained. QALY takes into account both the quality (morbidity) and the quantity (mortality) of life gained.

CUA measures outcomes based on years of life that are adjusted by utility weights, which range from 1 for "perfect health" to 0 for "dead." These weights can take into account patient and society preferences for specific health states. There is no consensus on the measurement, since both patient and society preferences can vary based on culture. An advantage of CUA is that different types of outcomes, and diseases with multiple outcomes of interest, can be compared (unlike CEA which can only compare one common unit).

Four Basic Pharmacoeconomic Methodologies

METHODOLOGY	COST MEASUREMENT UNIT	OUTCOME UNIT
Cost-minimization analysis	Dollars	Demonstrated or assumed to be equivalent in comparative groups
Cost-benefit analysis	Dollars	Dollars
Cost-effectiveness analysis	Dollars	Natural units (e.g., life-years gained, mmHg blood pressure, % at treatment goal)
Cost-utility analysis	Dollars	Quality-adjusted-life-year (QALY) or other utilities

HEALTH-RELATED QUALITY OF LIFE

Health-related quality of life (HRQOL) refers to the effects of a disease and its treatment on an individual's function and well being, as perceived by that individual. It is commonly included under a broad umbrella of assessments known as patient-reported outcomes (PROs). HRQOL is comprised of several important domains, including physical and mental functioning, role functioning, vitality, social functioning and general health perceptions.

HRQOL assessments can provide important patient-centered information related to the effects of a disease or treatment on patient functioning and well-being. These assessments are typically developed as either general (or generic) health status instruments that can be used across a number of disease areas (e.g., the SF-36 Health Survey can be used for asthma, diabetes and other conditions) or disease-specific measures applicable to a limited disease population (e.g., the Asthma Quality of Life Questionnaire). Prior to their use in practice, it is critical that the reliability and validity of HRQOL assessments in specific patient populations has been documented.

15
16
17

COMPOUNDING & HAZARDOUS DRUGS

CONTENTS

CHAPTER 15
COMPOUNDING 1: BASICS | **225**

CHAPTER 16
COMPOUNDING II:
EQUIPMENT, STABILITY & EXCIPIENTS | **249**

CHAPTER 17
COMPOUNDING III:
DOCUMENTATION & PREPARATION | **267**

CHAPTER CONTENT

What Are Compounded Drugs? 225
The Different Types Of Compounding 225
Hazardous Drugs are Toxic to Healthcare Workers 225
Compounding Standards and Resources 226
Pharmacopeias 226
Compounding "101" (The Basics) 227
Non-Sterile Preparations 227
Sterile Preparations 227
Hazardous Drugs 227
Hazardous Drugs on the NIOSH List 228
PECs, SECs, CSTDs and Other Such Terms 228
Physical Space Basics 229
Interpreting USP Terminology 231
USP Space Requirements for Sterile Compounding 231
Air Quality and HEPA Filters 231
Primary Engineering Control 232
Secondary Engineering Control 232
ISO Air Quality in the PEC 233
Air Pressure 233
Two Types of Locations that Can House a PEC 234
Compounding Personnel (Staff) Training 237
Required Training and Testing for CSPs 237
Gloved Fingertip Test 237
Media-Fill Test 237
Temperature Monitoring 238
Air and Surface Testing 239
Keeping the Sterile Compounding Area Clean 240
Keep the PECs Running 240
Clean the PEC Continuously 240
Hazardous Drug Compounding Cleaning Specifics 241
Sanitization 241
"Risk" and Compounded Formulations 242
Risk with Hazardous Drugs 242
Risk with Sterile Drugs 242
Risk with Non-Sterile Drugs 242
Drug Exposure 243
Hazardous Drug Exposure & Spill Management 243
Respiratory Protection 243
Hazardous Drug Spills 244
Administration of Hazardous Drugs 244
Disposal 245
Transporting Hazardous Drugs 245
Garbing 245
Garb for Hazardous Drugs 245
Garbing for Sterile Compounding 246
When to Re-Garb 247
Garbing for Hazardous Drugs 248

CONTENT LEGEND

= Study Tip Gal   = Key Drug Guy

CHAPTER 15
COMPOUNDING I: BASICS

WHAT ARE COMPOUNDED DRUGS?

Compounded drugs are prepared by pharmacists for individual patients. They are not mass-produced in a manufacturing plant like the drugs used for most conditions. The pharmacist prepares a unique dose or formulation for a patient, based on a prescription written for that patient. The dose or formulation cannot be already available as a manufactured product. If it was, compounding would not be needed.

THE DIFFERENT TYPES OF COMPOUNDING

Compounded drugs are either Non-Sterile or Sterile. Both Non-Sterile and Sterile compounded drugs can be further subdivided into two categories: Non-Hazardous and Hazardous.

HAZARDOUS DRUGS ARE TOXIC TO HEALTHCARE WORKERS

Hazardous drugs (HDs) can cause toxicity to the healthcare workers who handle the drugs in any manner, including unloading the drugs in the receiving dock, stocking the shelves, preparing the drugs in the pharmacy, administering the drugs to a patient, and obtaining and cleaning up body fluids that contain hazardous drug residues.

HDs require work spaces, equipment and devices that are designed to reduce exposure of the drug to the staff.

The figure on the following page splits HDs into non-sterile (such as methotrexate oral tablets crushed to make a topical preparation) or sterile (such as preparing an IV chemotherapy infusion).

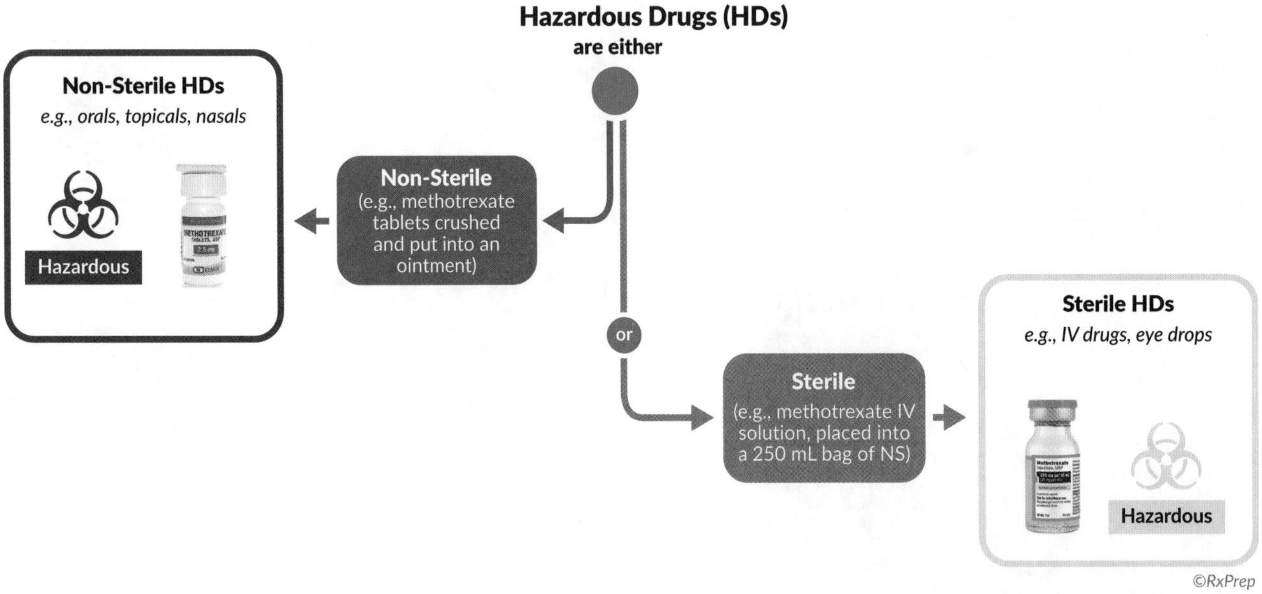

©RxPrep

COMPOUNDING STANDARDS AND RESOURCES

U.S. Pharmacopeia

The U.S. Pharmacopeia (USP) sets the standards for compounding preparations.

The USP Chapters related to Compounding include USP 795 (Non-Sterile Compounding), USP 797 (Sterile Compounding) and USP 800 (Handling Hazardous Drugs).

USP does not determine which drugs are hazardous; USP simply sets the requirements for safe handling of HDs.

PHARMACOPEIAS

Pharmacopeia refers to a list of medicinal drugs, with preparation instructions.

Pharmacopeias have been around for a very long time.

The U.S. Pharmacopeia (USP) sets the standards for preparation, strength, quality and purity of human and animal drugs, including both manufactured and compounded drugs.

Old Pharmacopeia

U.S. Pharmacopeia (USP) Compounding Chapter

USP 795, 797 and 800 are considered to be minimum acceptable standards for pharmacy compounding by the Food and Drug Administration (FDA), the state boards of pharmacy, and the Joint Commission.

National Institute for Occupational Safety and Health

The National Institute for Occupational Safety and Health (NIOSH) determines which drugs are hazardous. NIOSH keeps a list of all HDs called the *NIOSH List of Antineoplastic and Other Hazardous Drugs in Healthcare Settings.*

When a drug is on the NIOSH list, the pharmacist knows that the drug is hazardous, and handles it according to the USP 800 requirements in order to reduce the risk of exposure.

American Society of Health-System Pharmacists

ASHP Guidelines on Compounding Sterile Preparations

Purpose

Legal and Regulatory Considerations

Accreditation Considerations

In addition to the USP Chapters, hospital pharmacists rely on the American Society of Health-System Pharmacists (ASHP) for detailed guidance on implementing USP standards.

COMPOUNDING "101" (THE BASICS)

Non-Sterile Preparations
—Standards in USP Chapter 795

The Compounding Requirements for Non-Sterile Preparations

Non-sterile compounding is made by a pharmacist, based on a prescription for a preparation that meets a patient's individual requirements. The dose and formulation type cannot be commercially available (e.g., a pharmacist cannot compound atorvastatin 10 mg tablets).

Non-Sterile Compounding is Primarily Used To:

- Change the formulation of a medication, such as changing a solid tablet into a liquid to help a patient who cannot swallow the tablet
- Avoid an excipient that a patient cannot tolerate
- Formulate a dose or formulation that is not commercially available
- Add a flavor to a medication to make it more palatable

Non-Sterile Preparation Examples

- Estradiol cream for a post-menopausal woman
- Chicken-flavored chewable levothyroxine tablets for a dog
- Calamine and hydrocortisone topical ointment
- Antifungal lollipops for thrush
- Cherry-flavored antiviral suspension for a child
- Acetaminophen + lidocaine suppositories

Sterile Preparations
—Standards in USP Chapter 797

The Compounding Requirements for Sterile Preparations

Sterile-compounding requires the pharmacist to follow strict procedures to keep the products free from contamination.

The most common preparations made by pharmacists are sterile intravenous (IV) drugs that are injected into a patient's vein. The blood is sterile, which means it is free of microorganisms (e.g., bacteria, viruses, fungi) and other contaminants (e.g., glass shards, precipitates, particles of any type). The IV drugs injected into the blood must also be sterile.

Sterile Compounding Is Primarily Used To:

- Prepare non-hazardous sterile IV drugs
- Prepare hazardous sterile IV drugs
- Prepare radiopharmaceuticals (i.e., radioactive drugs that are used in nuclear medicine)
- Prepare eyedrops
- Prepare eardrops
- Prepare irrigations (liquid 'washes' that go into a body cavity, such as into the bladder)

Sterile Preparation Examples

- 1 gram of vancomycin taken from a vial and injected into a 250 mL D5W IV bag
- Piperacillin-tazobactam 3.375 grams in 50 mL NS IV bag
- 3-in-1 parenteral nutrition 1000 mL
- 1000 mL of NS with 40 mEq KCl
- Moxifloxacin and prednisolone 10 mL eye drops
- Boric acid 2% in isopropyl alcohol ear drops
- Gentamicin bladder irrigation solution for cystitis

Hazardous Drugs
—Standards in USP Chapter 800

The Requirements for Handling Hazardous Drugs

Hazardous Drugs Pose a Danger to Staff, including:

- Pharmacists
- Technicians
- Nurses, lab staff, janitors, any other worker in the facility that can come into contact with the drug

Characteristics that Make a Drug Hazardous (≥ 1)

- Carcinogenic (cancer-causing)
- Teratogenic (causes birth defects)/reproductive toxicity (such as infertility)
- Causes organ toxicity at low doses
- Genotoxic (damages the DNA, which can cause cancer)

HD Preparation Examples

- Antineoplastics (chemotherapy drugs, the majority of HDs), e.g., 100 mg epirubicin in 50 mL sterile water
- Non-Antineoplastics (e.g., hormones and transplant drugs), e.g., progesterone 5 g in *Lipoderm* cream 100 g

The list of NIOSH drugs is on the following page

> Prior to handling any HDs, both men and women with reproductive capability (the ability to have children) must confirm in writing that they understand the risks associated with handling HDs.

HAZARDOUS DRUGS ON THE NIOSH LIST

Others:

- Botulinum toxin-urinary incontinence, migraine, cosmetic use
- Cabergoline-hyperprolactinemia
- Cetrorelix, Urofollitropin-infertility
- Deferiprone-iron overload (chelator)
- Dexrazoxane-chemo (cardiac) protectant
- Dinoprostone-cervical ripening
- Icatibant-hereditary angioedema
- Mifepristone-abortifacient
- Miltefosine-antiparasite
- Mipomersin-familial hypercholesterolemia
- Misoprostol-abortifacient, prevention of NSAID-induced gastric ulcers
- Nafarelin-endometriosis
- Oxytocin-labor induction
- Pasireotide-acromegaly, Cushings
- Pentetate calcium trisodium-antidote for plutonium, americium and curium toxicity
- Phenoxybenzamine-pheochromocytoma

HAZARDOUS KEY DRUGS

Antineoplastic Drugs (Chemotherapeutics)

Non-Antineoplastic Hazardous Drugs on the NIOSH List

Antibiotics
Chloramphenicol
Telavancin

Anticoagulants
Warfarin

Antifungals
Fluconazole, Voriconazole

Antiretrovirals, HIV
Abacavir, Entecavir, Nevirapine, Zidovudine

Antivirals, Cytomegalovirus
Cidofovir, Ganciclovir, Valganciclovir

Acne
Isotretinoin

Arrhythmias
Dronedarone

Autoimmune Conditions
Acitretin (psoriasis), Leflunomide, Teriflunomide

Benign Prostatic Hypertrophy (BPH)
Dutasteride, Finasteride

Contraception
Estrogens, Progestins (in birth control), Ulipristal

Depression
Paroxetine

Diabetes
Exenatide

Dyslipidemia
Lomitapide

Seizures/Epilepsy
Clobazam, Clonazepam
Carbamazepine, Oxcarbazepine, Eslicarbazepine
Divalproex, Fosphenytoin, Phenytoin, Topiramate, Vigabatrin, Zonisamide

Gout
Colchicine

Heart Failure
Ivabradine, Spironolactone

Hepatitis
Ribavirin

Hormones
Androgens (e.g., testosterone)
Estrogens (e.g., estradiol)
Progesterones (e.g., medroxyprogesterone)
SERMS (e.g., raloxifene)

Hypercalcemia of Malignancy
Pamidronate
Zoledronic Acid (& Osteoporosis)

Hyperthyroidism
Methimazole, Propylthiouracil

Insomnia
Temazepam
Triazolam

Migraine
Dihydroergotamine

Multiple Sclerosis
Fingolimod
Interferon Beta-1b

Parkinson Disease
Apomorphine, Rasagiline

Pulmonary Arterial Hypertension (PAH)
Ambrisentan, Bosentan, Macitentan, Riociguat

Renal Disease
Darbepoetin alfa

Schizophrenia
Ziprasidone

Transplant
Azathioprine, Cyclosporine, Mycophenolate, Tacrolimus, Sirolimus

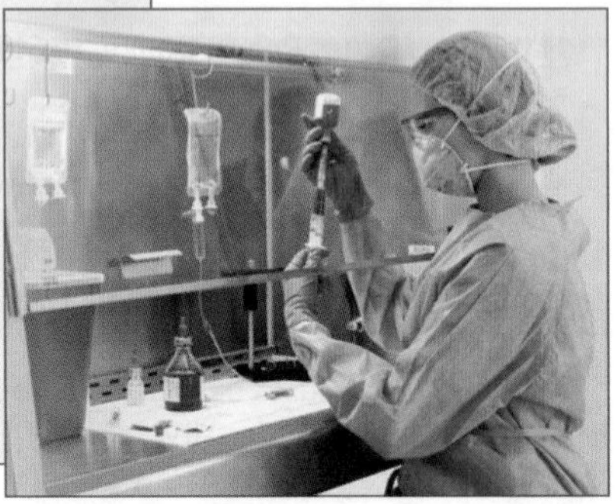

The pharmacist is using a closed-system transfer device (CSTD) to reduce her exposure to a HD (doxorubicin)

PECs, SECs, CSTDs and Other Such Terms

The Primary Engineering Control (PEC) refers to the sterile hood. The pharmacist in the above image is reaching her hands into the PEC to compound a doxorubicin infusion. The Secondary Engineering Control (SEC) refers to the buffer room that houses most PECs. In this image, the pharmacist is standing inside the SEC. These terms are described in more detail after the next two pages on the basic requirements for physical space.

CSTDs (see image above) are used to keep hazardous drugs contained inside the device to prevent spills and fumes from leaking out. The CSTD also protects the drug, by blocking entry of contaminants. CSTDs are described later in this chapter.

PHYSICAL SPACE BASICS

Non-Sterile Compounding

Non-Sterile Compounding Requires Dedicated Space

USP 795 requires non-sterile preparation to be "separate and distinct" from sterile preparation.

Non-sterile compounding can be done in ambient (room air), but must be separated from the dispensing part of the pharmacy. Non-sterile compounding should not take place in the sterile, ISO space (i.e., controlled amount of air particulates). The exception is non-sterile HDs, discussed under HDs, in the bottom right section of this page.

Powder Containment Hoods

Powders can cause air contamination, and are best when compounded within a powder containment hood. The hood does not contain ISO-rated air; rather, it is a box designed to contain powder, which tends to fly-away. Powder hoods can have ventilation, including HEPA filtered air, pressurized air (negative pressure, to keep the powder inside the hood) and exhaust systems. This type of hood is called a Ventilated Compounding Enclosure (VCE).

Adequate Space for Orderly Work

Space to organize equipment and materials is needed to avoid mix-ups of ingredients, containers, and other components. The space should include shelving and storage.

No Storage on the Floor

All components, equipment, and containers must be stored off the floor. This requirement can be met by having a raised section in the bottom of cabinets and shelves.

Water and Sinks

There needs to be adequate plumbing and two types of water:

1. Potable (from the tap), for hand and equipment washing, and
2. Purified (e.g., distilled), for use in compounded formulations that include water, and for rinsing equipment and utensils.

The sink needs to be easily accessible to the compounding areas. Soap, detergent and an air hand dryer or single-use towels should be included.

Other Space Requirements

Waste must be held and disposed of in a sanitary, timely manner. The space should be well-lit. Heating, Ventilation and Air Conditioning (HVAC) should be controlled, with temperature and humidity monitoring.

Sterile Compounding

Sterile Compounding has Detailed Space Requirements

The sterile compounding space must include an anteroom, a buffer area and a primary engineering control (PEC) or a segregated compounding area (SCA). There are ISO air requirements. These requirements are important and are described later. The basic requirements, described next, are straight-forward.

Basic Requirements

Surfaces of ceilings, walls, floors, fixtures, shelving, counters and cabinets must be smooth, impervious, free from cracks and crevices, and non-shedding,* to make them easy to clean and to minimize the risk of microorganisms or other contaminants accumulating. Work surfaces must be easy to clean and disinfect. Stainless steel or molded plastic are smooth, impervious and easy to clean and disinfect.

Walls must be constructed of durable material with locked, sealed panels. Floors must be overlaid with wide, sheet vinyl flooring with heat-welded seams.

The buffer area or area inside the perimeter of an SCA cannot contain water sources or floor drains.

There are temperature and humidity requirements, and required air and surface sampling to test for microbial contamination (described later).

**Shedding means that particles are coming off, such as dust, powder, dirt and dead skin.*

Hazardous Drugs

C is for Containment

Hoods and buffer rooms used for compounding HDs begin with the word Containment:

- Containment-PEC (C-PEC) and
- Containment-SEC (C-SEC)

Containment is required to keep hazardous drugs/particles/vapors contained within the space—due to toxicity risk.

Non-Sterile and Sterile HD Compounding in the Same Space

While it is preferable to keep non-sterile and sterile compounding space separate, an exception can be made to prepare non-sterile hazardous drugs in a C-PEC inside a C-SEC, if these requirements are met:

- The C-SEC must maintain ISO 7 (discussed later) air even when it is being used for non-sterile HD compounding.
- There must be separate sterile and non-sterile C-PECs, kept at least 1 meter apart.
- Particle-generating activity, such as working with powders, cannot be performed when any sterile compounding is being performed in the same C-SEC.

Hazardous Drugs continued on following page

Physical Space Basics continued...

Hazardous Drugs continued

Negative Air Pressure
C-PECs and C-SECs must have negative air pressure.

- Negative air flow in the C-PEC causes the air to flow into the C-PEC (away from the staff who is standing at the front of the hood), and then to flow out of the C-PEC, through the external exhaust at the top of the hood.
- Negative air flow in the C-SEC keeps the air from exiting the room. The air is removed through the room exhaust.

Air Changes
Air in spaces used for HD compounding can get contaminated and needs to be regularly replaced. The air changes per hour (ACPH) is the number of times (per hour) that the air is replaced in the room.

- In space where non-sterile HDs are compounded there must be at least 12 ACPH.
- In the sterile HD space there must be at least 30 ACPH.

External Exhaust
Air that has been contaminated with HDs should be externally exhausted. This means that the air is moved out of the space (from the C-PEC, from the C-SEC or from the non-sterile HD compounding space) and cannot be recirculated and returned to the room. It is sent outside (goodbye possibly toxic air) and takes any contamination out with it.

- In a non-sterile HD room, the air should be externally vented (preferably) or redundant-HEPA filters can be used.

Redundant HEPA Filters Instead of External Exhaust
Community pharmacies can be located in areas that would not welcome contaminated air exhaust, such as a compounding pharmacy that prepares hormone creams for postmenopausal women that is located adjacent to a park where owners walk their dogs.

- An alternative option to an external exhaust (for non-sterile HD compounding only) is to use redundant-HEPA filters (see the illustration below).

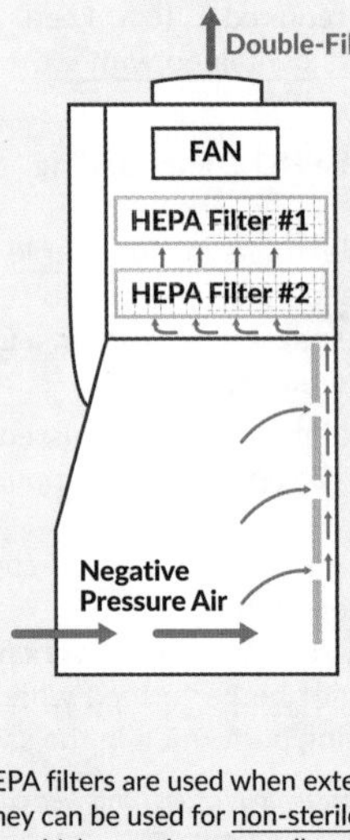

Redundant HEPA filters are used when external venting is not reasonable. They can be used for non-sterile HD only (i.e., not for sterile HDs, which must be externally vented).

Hazardous, Non-Sterile Powder Compounding

INTERPRETING USP TERMINOLOGY

Before getting into the details, review the terminology used by USP, and consequently, by pharmacists who compound according to the USP requirements. The comic below includes some common USP terminology.

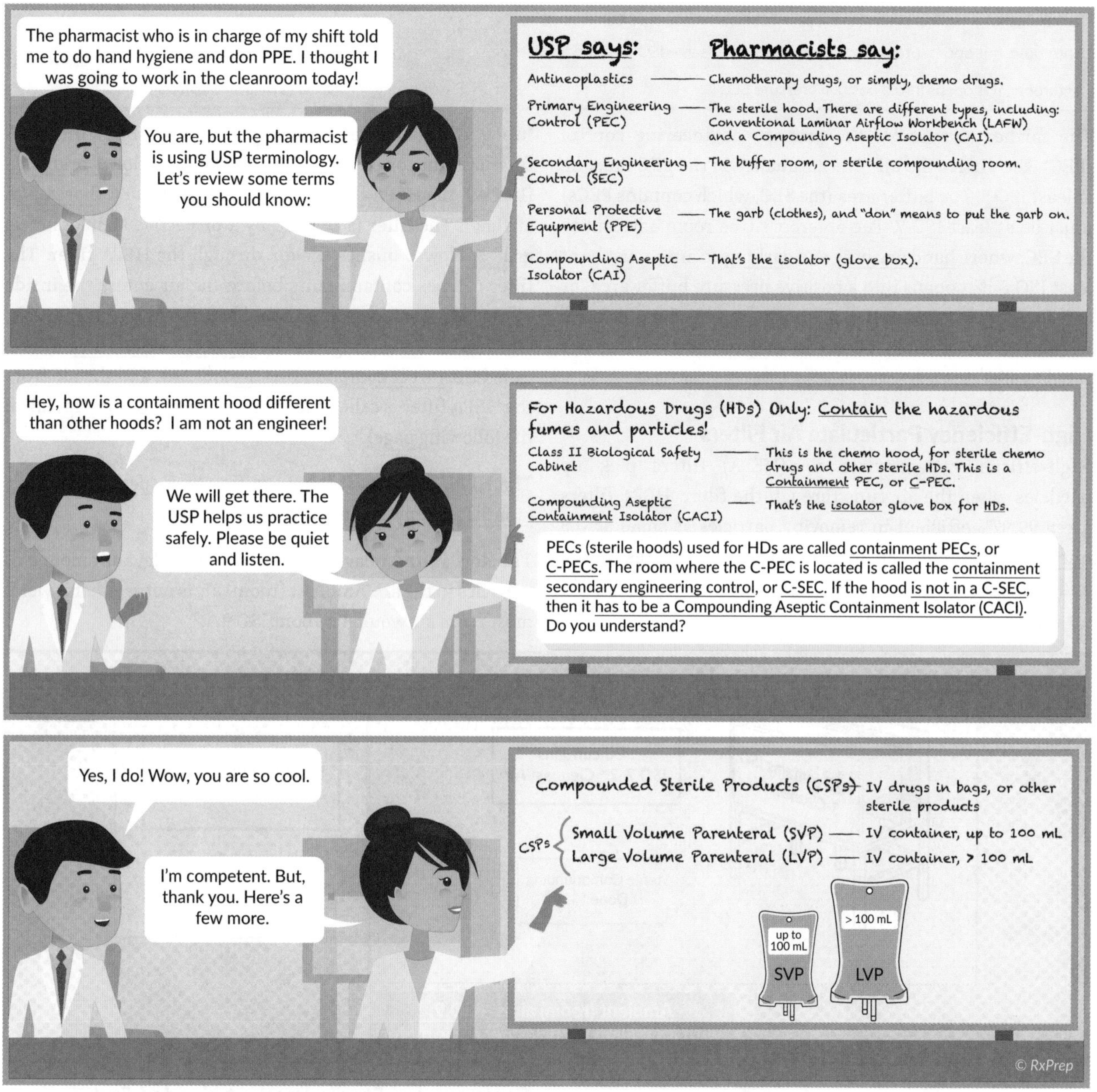

USP SPACE REQUIREMENTS FOR STERILE COMPOUNDING

Sterile compounding space has many more requirements than non-sterile compounding space. Sterile compounding for HDs has even more.

AIR QUALITY AND HEPA FILTERS

Clean air is important in the compounding area in order to reduce the risk of contamination. The International Standards Organization (ISO) sets the standards for air quality, which is determined by the number of particles per volume of air of a specified particle size. The lower the particle count, the cleaner the air.

In critical areas that are closest to exposed sterile drugs and containers (i.e., inside the sterile hood) the air must be at least ISO 5. This means that there are no more than 3,520 particles per cubic meter. Particles are included in this count if they are 0.5 microns (micrometers) in size or larger.

COMPOUNDING AREA	ISO RATING	PARTICLES/m³
Primary engineering control (PEC, called the hood, or isolator, if using a glove box)	5	3,520
Not applicable (ISO 6 is not used for pharmacy spaces)	6	35,200
Secondary engineering control (SEC, called the buffer room or buffer area) Anteroom, if it opens into a negative pressure SEC (same ISO # as the SEC)	7	352,000
Anteroom, if it opens into a positive pressure SEC	8	3,520,000

The farther away from the primary engineering control (PEC), the dirtier the air. The air quality in the PEC must be at least ISO 5. The buffer area (the SEC, which contains PECs) must be at least ISO 7. The anteroom (the room adjacent to the SEC, where hand washing and garbing occurs) must be at least ISO 8 if it opens into a positive pressure buffer area, or at least ISO 7 if it opens into a negative pressure buffer area. Regular room or "ambient" air is unclassified (i.e., it is not rated by ISO).

High-Efficiency Particulate Air Filters

High-efficiency particulate air (HEPA) filters pick up particles when the air runs through the filter. HEPA filters are > 99.97% efficient in removing particles as small as 0.5 microns wide or larger, including bacteria, viruses, fungi, and dust.

In a vertical airflow biological safety cabinet (BSC), the HEPA filter is at the top of the PEC. In a laminar airflow workbench (LAFW), the HEPA filter is at the back of the PEC (horizontal airflow). The filter is covered by a protective stainless-steel grill. A blower pushes the air through the HEPA filter. The filter catches contaminants before the air enters the inside of the PEC. Compounding should be done in the cleanest air, which is the air coming directly out of the HEPA filter. This is called the direct compounding area (DCA), and the air from the HEPA filter is called the first air (see the Study Tip Gal on the following page).

The HEPA filter must be recertified by a specialist every 6 months and anytime a PEC has been moved.

The dots in the image below show the relevant amount of particles in the air. Ambient (room) air is not rated; if it were, most room air would be about ISO 9.

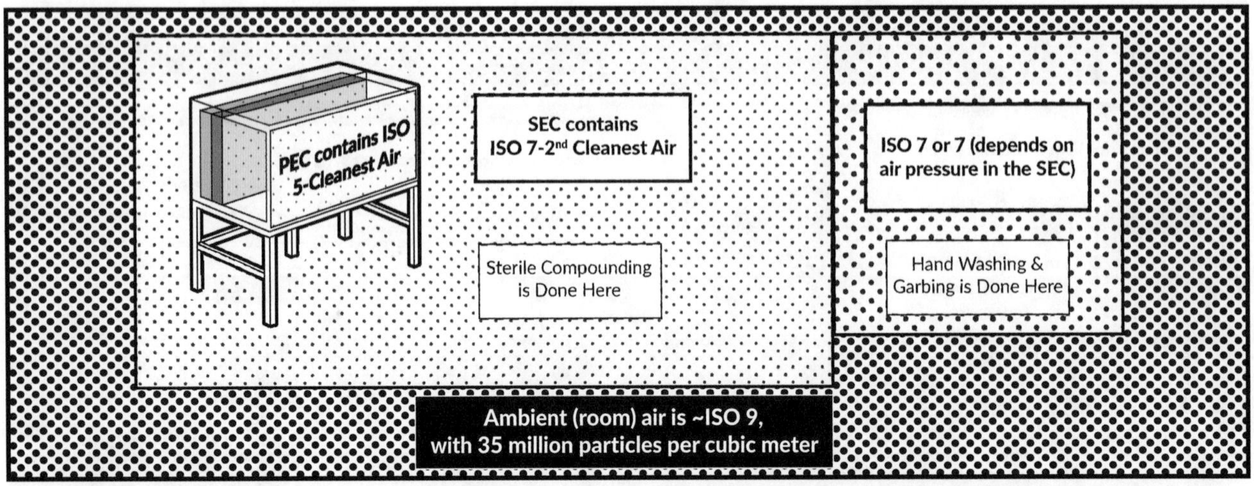

PRIMARY ENGINEERING CONTROL

The sterile hood is the primary engineering control (PEC).

SECONDARY ENGINEERING CONTROL

The secondary engineering control (SEC) is the room that contains the PEC or multiple PECs. The SEC is commonly called the buffer area or buffer room because it provides a "buffer" of relatively clean air (ISO 7) around the PEC (ISO 5).

There are PECs that are not located in a SEC. These are isolator PECs, described later in this chapter.

Compounded Sterile Product Needed *Stat*

The requirements described in this chapter for aseptic compounded sterile product (CSP) preparation, including putting on protective garb and cleaning the PEC (described later), takes time.

In certain circumstances, IV drugs are needed stat (i.e., immediately), with no time for aseptic preparation, such as in an ambulance or during a code blue when quick action is needed to save a life. This is emergency use, and because the drug has been prepared for that patient under suboptimal conditions for sterility, the CSP will have a very short beyond use date (BUD) of 1 hour, after which the drug can no longer be used and must be discarded. BUDs are described in the Compounding III chapter.

ISO AIR QUALITY INSIDE THE PEC

The air quality in the PEC is ISO 5, which is very clean air. Some of the air in the PEC is cleaner than the rest. It is called the first air.

The cleanest air is coming directly out of the HEPA filter into the direct compounding area (DCA). The air comes out in a unidirectional flow, and is called the first air.

The DCA is where the critical sites to keep clean, such as the injection port on the CSP, and the syringe needle that will inject into the port, can receive the cleanest air, that is the first air (see image).

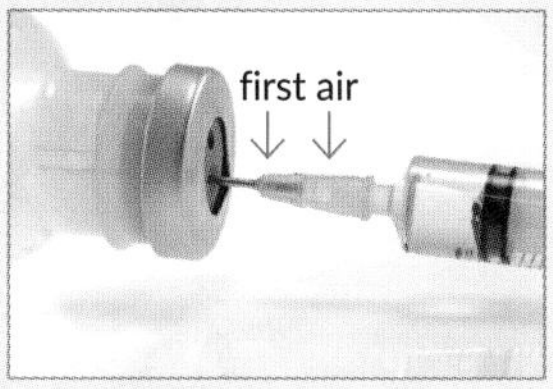

Do not obstruct the first air, especially around the area where the needle enters the vial or ampule.

- Do not block airflow from the HEPA filter with anything, including hands or supplies.
- It is imperative to line up items correctly inside the PEC (see the Compounding III chapter) to avoid creating turbulence.
- If the airflow is obstructed, it will become turbulent, rather than laminar flow with parallel lines of air. In turbulent air, particles can hit each other and land on the CSPs, similar to two small jets in turbulent air hitting each other and landing in a cornfield.

Keep the air inside the PEC as clean as possible.

- Wipe off the outside of vials, syringes, etc. with 70% isopropyl alcohol (IPA) prior to bringing them into the PEC. Open packages along the designated tear line, if present; do not rip open, which produces particles.
- All work must be performed at least 6 inches from the front edge of the PEC (i.e., compounding work should be done at least 6 inches into the hood). This helps keep the ISO 7 air in the SEC from co-mingling with the cleaner air in the PEC.
- Move waste out shortly after it is created; do not let waste accumulate inside the PEC.
- Most contamination to CSPs comes from the compounding staff, largely from inadequate hand hygiene and garbing; correct technique is essential, and is described later in this chapter.

AIR PRESSURE

In addition to the ISO air quality in a space, the air pressure in the space relative to the adjacent space is important.

There must be a differential (i.e., a difference) in air pressure between spaces to keep the air inside a space enclosed, or conversely, to permit the air to enter adjacent areas.

The air pressure inside the PEC and inside a non-hazardous SEC can both be positive since the air will not cause toxicity if it moves into adjacent spaces. With hazardous compounding, the containment PEC (C-PEC) and the containment SEC (C-SEC) must have negative pressure to keep the toxic air contained in the space. Non-sterile hazardous compounding that is not prepared in an ISO-rated space must be done in a room with negative air pressure.

POSITIVE PRESSURE (NON-HD) CLEANROOM

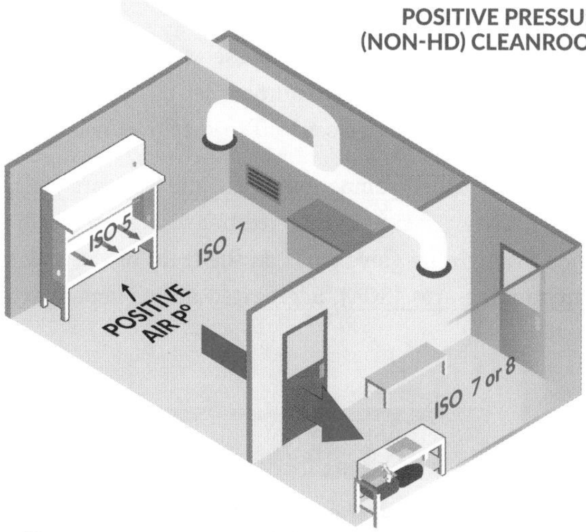

Let me show you our non-HD cleanroom. The primary engineering controls (PECs) in a non-HD cleanroom can be either:

- A compounding aseptic isolator (CAIs, these are glove boxes, and are usually outside of a cleanroom) or
- A laminar airflow workbench (LAFW)

The air pressure in the SEC and PEC can be positive as it is not used for HDs.

The anteroom should be ISO 7 (if opening into a SEC with negative air pressure). It can be ISO 8 (if opening into a SEC with positive air pressure).

NEGATIVE PRESSURE (HD) CLEANROOM

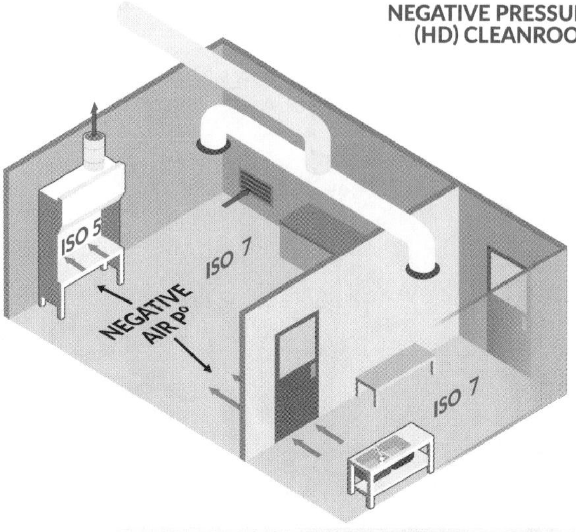

Let me show you our cleanroom where the pharmacists and technicians compound hazardous sterile drugs.

The air in here is changed most frequently: At least 30 times per hour (≥ 30 ACPH).

This is because the air can get contaminated from the HDs. Toxic air? Not in our cleanroom.

The air pressure in the room is negative, which pulls the contaminated air out of the room, through the external vents in the room and from the PEC; see the red arrows in the picture.

The PEC in an HD cleanroom has the word containment in the name because the hazardous fumes and particles are contained in the hood. The PEC is called a C-PEC, and can be either;

- A compounding aseptic containment isolator (CACI), or
- A biological safety cabinet (BSC)

The anteroom must have ISO 7 air (as it opens into a negative pressure SEC and pulls air in with it).

TWO TYPES OF LOCATIONS THAT CAN HOUSE A PEC

A cleanroom refers to the complete set-up of one or more PECs within an SEC, with an adjacent anteroom. Keep in mind that not every pharmacy has a cleanroom set-up available to the pharmacists. An isolator PEC can be used instead. The isolator is designed with the front closed-off to keep the unclassified room air around it from mixing with the clean air inside the PEC.

Isolators are called compounding aseptic isolators (CAIs), or if used for HDs, compounding aseptic containment isolators (CACIs). They are simply referred to as isolators or glove boxes because the pharmacist or technician inserts their gloved hands through the glove ports on the front of the isolator (see lower left image). The isolators are located in a segregated compounding area (SCA). Segregated means kept apart from other areas of the pharmacy to minimize interruptions and noise.

Segregated Compounding Area (SCA)
—with an Isolator as PEC

- An option when a cleanroom is not viable.
- An SCA does not have a buffer area or anteroom. It can only be used for low-risk CSPs compounded in an isolator (glove box) PEC (see image below).
- The PEC (the isolator) is located in a space with unclassified air, such as in a corner of the regular pharmacy space.
- SCAs are useful for satellite pharmacies a distance away from the main pharmacy in a large hospital, for infusion centers and clinics, and in small hospitals.
- SCAs cannot be located adjacent to food preparation, warehouse or construction sites, or unsealed windows/doors near busy areas (e.g., not near the pharmacy pick-up area).
- The maximum beyond use dates (BUDs) for CSPs made in an isolator in an SCA is 12 hours.

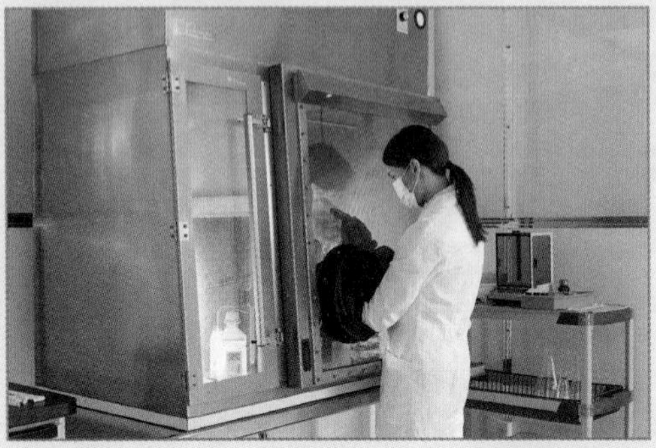

© Terra Universal. Inc

Cleanroom
—Complete Sterile Set-up

- This is the typical sterile compounding space that has an ISO 5 primary engineering control (PEC), which (if compounding non-hazardous drugs) can include laminar airflow workbenches (LAFW) and compounding aseptic isolators (CAIs).
- The PEC sits inside an ISO 7 secondary engineering control (SEC, the buffer area).
- An ISO 7 or 8 anteroom is adjacent to the SEC.

  If the anteroom is ISO 8, the air will be dirtier than inside the SEC. To keep the air from the anteroom out, the SEC will need to have positive air pressure to push the air out of the SEC and into the anteroom. Positive air pressure is used in a PEC and SEC for compounding non-HDs.

  If the SEC has negative air pressure, the air in the anteroom would mingle with the air in the SEC. In this case, the anteroom air must be ISO 7, which is the same cleanliness as the air in the SEC. Negative air pressure is required in all HD compounding spaces, including C-SECs and C-PECs.

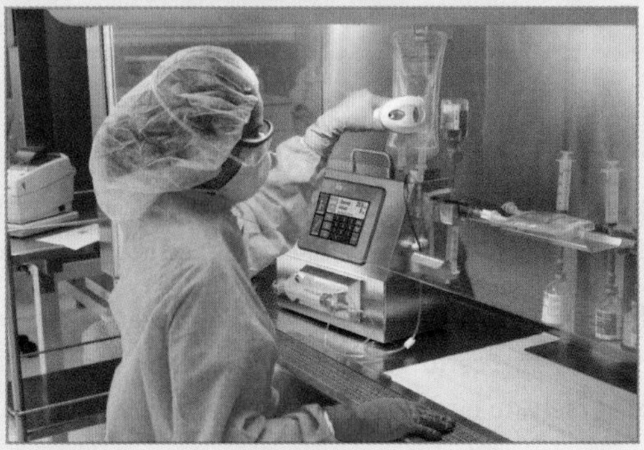

© Production Automation Corporation

Open-Front Primary Engineering Controls (PECs) are Located in the Secondary Engineering Control (SEC)

For Sterile Preparation, Non-Hazardous
—Protects the CSPs

NO EXTERNAL VENT
Positive air pressure protects the CSPs from coughs, sneezes, or any particles from the compounding staff or from the air in the SEC.

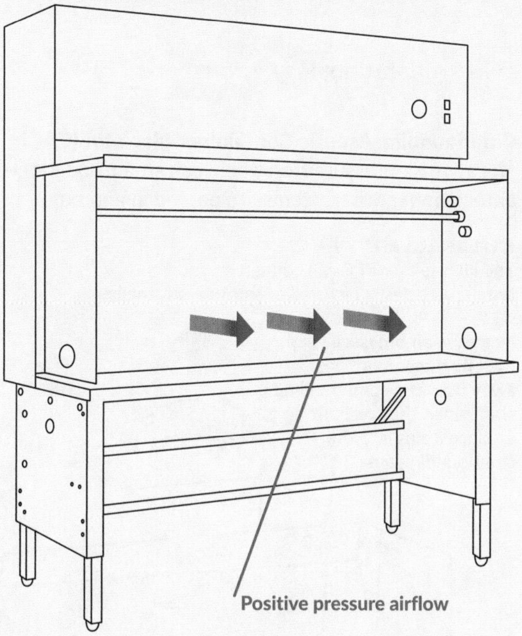

Conventional Laminar Airflow Workbench (LAFW)
"sterile hood, cabinet, or workbench"

- HEPA-filtered air and positive air pressure protects the CSPs
- Horizontal laminar airflow

Horizontal laminar airflow is when the air flows in parallel lines from the HEPA filter at the back of the hood. This keeps particles from colliding with each other, and landing on the DCA surface or CSPs.

For Sterile Preparation, Hazardous
—Protects the CSPs and the Pharmacy Staff

EXTERNAL VENT
The HD C-PEC (chemo hood), or the HD isolator PEC (the CACI), contains hazardous fumes/particles, which will be externally vented.

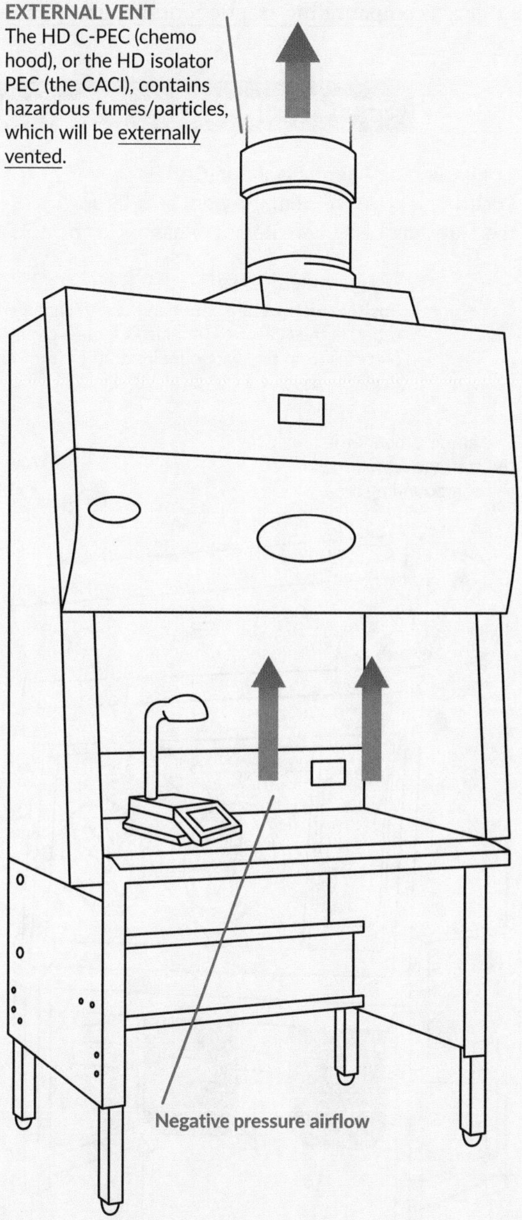

Class II Biological Safety Cabinet "chemo hood"

- HEPA-filtered air and negative air pressure protects the CSPs and the compounding staff
- Vertical laminar airflow

Closed-Front PECs Do Not Need to be Placed Inside an SEC

These are isolators. They can be placed in an SEC, but are most often located in a corner of the pharmacy or other space, in a segregated (i.e., separate) compounding area (SCA). The pharmacist or technician performs hand hygiene, dons sterile, powder-free gloves (minimally; the garb required when compounding in an isolator depends on the manufacturer's instructions), and inserts their gloved hands into the interior of the hood through the glove ports, which are the two circular openings on the front. The two types of isolators are (on the left) a compounding aseptic isolator (CAI, for non-HDs) and (on the right) a compounding aseptic containment isolator (CACI, for HDs).

Sterile Preparation, Non-Hazardous

Compounding Aseptic Isolator (CAI)
Positive air pressure from the work area through the antechamber, where items are passed in and out.

NO EXTERNAL VENT
Positive air pressure between the antechamber protects the CSPs from coughs, sneezes, or any particles from the compounding staff or from the air in the SEC.

The antechamber—the area where the staff move items in and out of the compounding area.

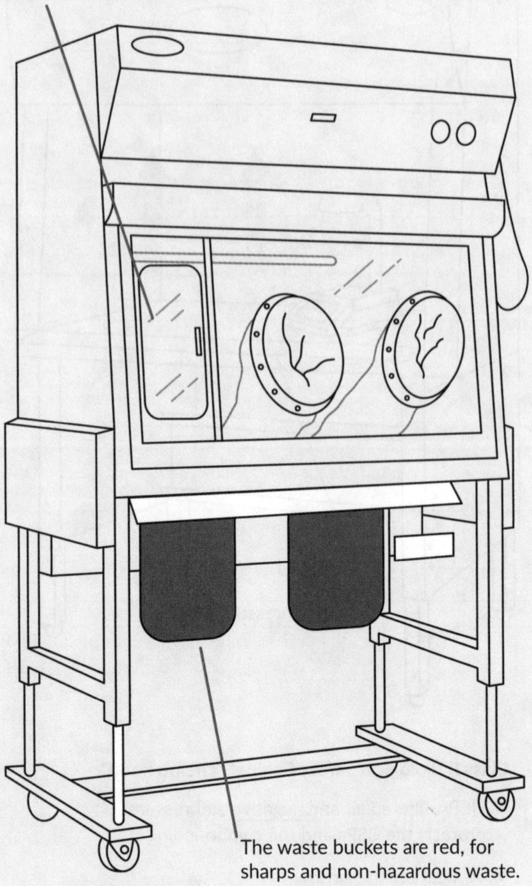

The waste buckets are red, for sharps and non-hazardous waste.

Sterile Preparation, Hazardous

Compounding Aseptic Containment Isolator (CACI)
Negative air pressure from the work area through the antechamber, where items are passed in and out.

EXTERNAL VENT
The HD isolator PEC will contain hazardous fumes/particles, which will be **vented externally.**

Negative air pressure keeps the HD fumes/particles away from the compounding staff, when they pull out or place items into the compounding area.

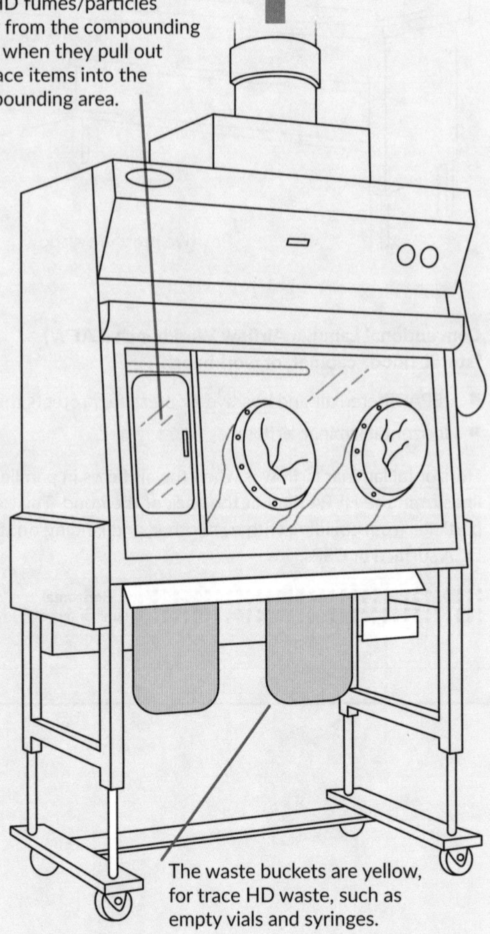

The waste buckets are yellow, for trace HD waste, such as empty vials and syringes.

COMPOUNDING PERSONNEL (STAFF) TRAINING

Staff Training

Personnel (i.e., staff) must have proper training for each type of compounding they perform. All training must be documented.

Initial Training

Initial training has two parts:

- Didactic training (teaching, with lectures or videos).
- Hands-on training (compounding), which must be observed by the compounding supervisor, or by a staff expert.

Continuous Training

When work is new or different for any reason, the compounding staff must receive additional training. This can include new drugs, revised drug information, changes in equipment and new or revised procedures.

REQUIRED TRAINING AND TESTING

Staff must demonstrate that they can follow adequate aseptic procedures for each of these items prior to independently compounding sterile products:

- Hand hygiene
- Garbing and gloving technique
- Cleaning and disinfecting procedures for the sterile space and equipment
- Sterile drug preparation

Adequate aseptic technique in hand hygiene, garbing and gloving is demonstrated by passing the gloved fingertip test.

Adequate aseptic technique in sterile drug preparation is demonstrated by passing the media-fill test.

GLOVED FINGERTIP TEST

A passing score on the gloved fingertip test is required initially, then annually (if compounding only low- and medium-risk CSPs) and semi-annually (if compounding high-risk CSPs). Immediately after completing hand hygiene and garbing/gloving, the evaluator collects a gloved fingertip sample from both hands of the compounder by lightly pressing each fingertip onto a separate petri dish (a "plate") that contains tryptic soy agar (TSA).

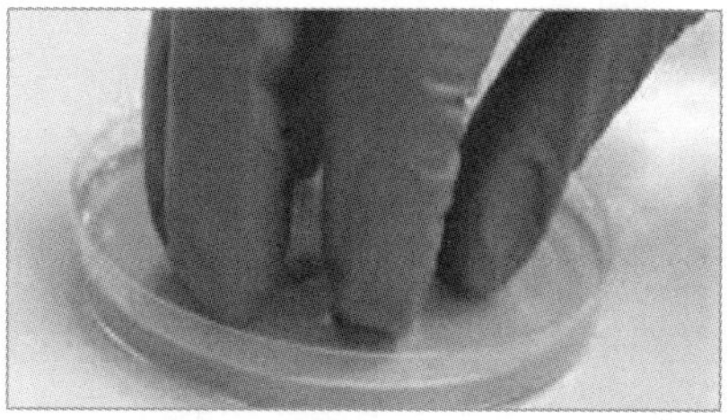

USP 797 requirements for gloved fingertip and media fill testing apply to staff who perform sterile compounding (for both non-hazardous and hazardous drugs).

If microorganisms are present, they will use the TSA as a food source and replicate. The plates are incubated (heated, to facilitate growth) for 2 – 3 days and then inspected for microbial growth, which will be visible as spots on the plates. Spots that form are called colony-forming units (CFUs) and indicate contamination was present on the gloves.

Passing a Gloved Fingertip Test

Passing requires three consecutive gloved fingertip samples with zero CFUs for both hands.

MEDIA-FILL TEST

The media-fill test is used to determine if a compounder is preparing CSPs in an aseptic manner (i.e., free from contamination). The test container holds soybean-casein digest medium, which is also called tryptic soy broth (TSB). TSB is taking the place of the drug in the preparation. TSB is a growth medium used by the organisms to replicate. The amount of growth medium required is small, and the test can be done in a small IV bag or a syringe. Turbidity (cloudiness) indicates contamination is present.

Passing a Media-Fill Test

If the liquid stays clear after 14 days of incubation, the compounder passed the test.

TEMPERATURE MONITORING

Temperatures must be kept in the appropriate range (see clipboard). They must be monitored at least once daily in the SEC. The temperature should be documented on the temperature log sheet. The SEC (compounding room) should be kept at 20 °C (68 °F), or cooler. It can get hot for the staff wearing garb, with their clothes underneath, and the room should be kept comfortable. The refrigerator and freezer should be monitored twice daily; this is the same requirement for refrigerators and freezers containing vaccines. The refrigerator temperature should be between 2 – 8 °C and the freezer temperature should be between -50 and -15 °C.

Pharmacy TEMPERATURE Log

Form PH-246

	ONCE Daily	TWICE Daily			
Date	SEC Room ≤ 20 °C ≤ 68 °F	Vaccine Refrigerator 2-8 °C 36-46 °F		Vaccine Freezer -50-15 °C -58-5 °F	
2/1					
2/2					
2/3					
2/4					
2/5					
2/6					
2/7					
2/8....end of month					

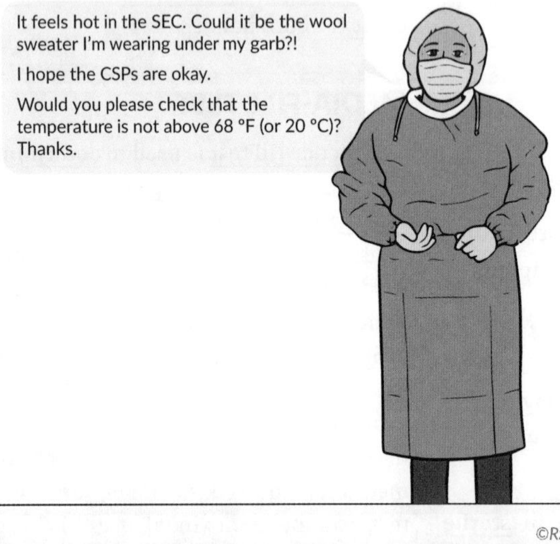

©RxPrep

AIR AND SURFACE TESTING

In addition to personnel testing with the gloved fingertip test and the media-fill test, there are two other tests that are used to ensure that the environment for compounding sterile products is acceptably free of contaminants. The two tests are sampling the air and sampling the surfaces in the sterile compounding space.

©RxPrep

Air Sampling

Air sampling identifies contaminants in the air. It should be performed at least every 6 months by a person certified in air sampling, or by a qualified compounding staff member.

Surface Sampling

USP requires that surfaces be tested periodically. Tryptic soy agar (TSA) provides a good growth medium. Polysorbate 80 and lecithin are added to the TSA to neutralize the effect of any disinfecting agents on the surfaces.

The testing should occur at the end of the day when the surfaces are in the poorest state. All surfaces that are regularly exposed to staff (e.g., inside the PECs and other work surfaces, door handles, equipment) should be tested. At least one surface sample must be taken from each ISO 5, 7 and 8 area. After the plates have been incubated for 2 – 3 days, the results should indicate zero CFUs (preferred); action must be taken if > 3 CFUs are identified in the ISO 5 area and > 5 CFUs in the ISO 7 area. If action is needed, Gram stains can be used to identify the microorganisms present, which can help identify the source (e.g., *Staphylococcus* are likely from the compounding staff; Gram-negative organisms can be from water condensation, which could be due to poor air conditioning).

Air Pressure Testing

The air pressure testing confirms there is the correct differential (difference in pressures) between two spaces and ensures that the airflow is unidirectional (i.e., in one direction out from or into a space). Pressure gauges are installed in the cleanroom space, and checked (minimally) once daily or with every work shift. The results are documented, by the staff, or the pharmacy can install a device that continually records the air pressure readings.

ENVIRONMENTAL PARAMETER	MONITORING INTERVAL	
Air sampling	**At least every 6 months**	Performed by a compounding personnel or qualified certifier.
Surface sampling	**Periodically**	Use plates containing tryptic soy agar with polysorbate 80 and lecithin. Sample surfaces at the end of the day to simulate the dirtiest condition. After the plates have been incubated, the results should indicate zero CFUs (preferred); action must be taken if > 3 CFUs in the ISO 5 area or > 5 CFUs in the ISO 7 area.
Air pressure	**Each shift (preferably) or daily (minimally)**	

©RxPrep

KEEPING THE STERILE COMPOUNDING AREA CLEAN

KEEP THE PEC RUNNING

All PECs, including C-PECs, are preferably kept running at all times to help keep the surfaces clean. If there is a power outage, all compounding must stop, and the PECs will need to be cleaned with a germicidal detergent and then disinfected with sterile 70% isopropyl alcohol (IPA) prior to re-initiation of compounding activity.

If the PEC is a C-PEC, sanitization will need to be done if the power has been turned off. The sanitization process is more complex, and is described later in this chapter.

If the power has been off, in addition to cleaning and disinfecting (or sanitization for C-PECs) the PEC or C-PEC must be on for at least 30 minutes before compounding can begin.

CLEAN THE PEC CONTINUOUSLY

The PEC is cleaned throughout the day (see below), and at the end of the day it is cleaned again (first), followed by the SEC, then the anteroom. Lint-free sterile wipes are used to clean the PEC. First, the PEC is cleaned with a germicidal detergent, then disinfected with 70% IPA. There are wipes that come pre-soaked with the appropriate agent. Alternatively, a spray bottle can be used to wet a dry wipe. Never spray inside the PEC. Use slightly overlapping, unidirectional strokes rather than circular motions. Use a new side of the wipe for the next area cleaned, and replace used wipes often.

PECs are cleaned from top to bottom, back to front.

This means that the cleanest areas will be cleaned first, and the dirtiest areas will be cleaned last.

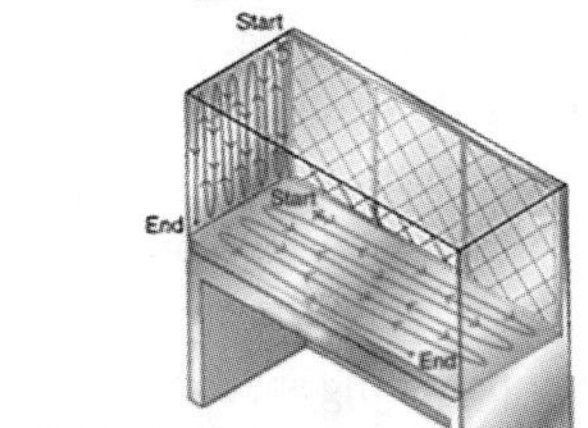

Start cleaning at the back, and move side to side. Do not wipe down a little distance at a time; starting and stopping creates turbulence. Use long sweeps.

Example of how to clean the side walls and work surface

Cleaning a Horizontal Laminar Airflow PEC

This is an example of the order of cleaning for a common type of PEC.

1. Clean the ceiling of the hood, from back to front.
2. Clean the grill over the HEPA filter, from top to bottom.
3. Clean the side walls starting from back to front, wiping up and down in a long sweeping motion. Clean the IV bar and hooks. Either the side walls or the bar can be cleaned first.
4. Clean anything kept in the hood [e.g., automated compounding device (used for parenteral nutrition), or other equipment].
5. Clean the bottom surface (the work area) starting from back to front, with a side to side motion.

Do not start compounding until the surfaces have dried.

DAILY		WEEKLY	MONTHLY
All Sterile Work	**For Hazardous Drugs**	**Walls**	**Ceiling**
Before entering the cleanroom, wipe the outside containers of all supplies Clean with germicidal cleaner and disinfect with sterile 70% IPA, every day: Counters, Floors & Carts	Always sanitize the work area at the end of a shift: Deactivate, Decontaminate, Clean, Disinfect Leaving HD residue for the next shift is NOT acceptable and is likely a justification for termination.	**Windows** **Shelving** **Bins** **Chairs**	

ISO 5 PECs, all types, are cleaned *often*:

√ Before each shift

√ Every 30 minutes while working

√ Before and after each batch of CSPs

√ Whenever needed, including after spills

HAZARDOUS DRUG COMPOUNDING CLEANING SPECIFICS

SANITIZATION

All areas and equipment used for handling HDs must be sanitized, which includes deactivating, decontaminating, and cleaning at least once daily. Sterile compounding areas and equipment must be disinfected as a final step. It is important to perform the sanitizing steps in the correct order; if the disinfecting step is done before deactivating, it will spread the HD residue.

DEACTIVATION and **DECONTAMINATION**
2% Bleach (Sodium Hypochlorite) or Peroxide
Reduce HD toxicity, then remove HD residues

CLEANING
Germicidal Detergent, such as Quat, Ammonium, Phenolics
Removes dirt and microbial contamination

DISINFECTION
Sterile 70% Isopropyl Alcohol (IPA)
Inhibits or destroys microorganisms; Required step in sterile compounding

When using the sanitizing agents, wetted wipes should be used instead of using a spray bottle to directly spray onto the surfaces and equipment. This is because the spray can cause any HD residue to aerosolize and spread to other areas. All workers performing these activities must wear appropriate PPE. A NIOSH approved fit-tested respirator should be used if the sash of the BSC or the front cover of the CACI is opened.

There are several commercially available kits which simplify the sanitization process, and multi-purpose agents that combine deactivation and decontamination, such as *Peridox RTU*. Bleach or peroxide can be used for both steps. Bleach can cause corrosion on stainless steel surfaces, which includes the surfaces of C-PECs. To prevent corrosion, neutralize the bleach by wiping surfaces afterwards with sodium thiosulfate, sterile alcohol, sterile water, or a germicidal detergent.

All areas where HDs are handled (receiving, transporting, compounding, administering, disposal) must be routinely deactivated/decontaminated and cleaned. All reusable equipment and devices must be routinely deactivated/decontaminated and cleaned. The cleaning and disinfecting schedule from USP 800 applies to both sterile and non-sterile HD compounding areas. Decontamination must be done anytime a spill occurs.

"RISK" AND COMPOUNDED FORMULATIONS

USP defines risk differently in USP 795, 797 and 800.

- For sterile (USP 797) and non-sterile (USP 795) drug compounding, higher risk means a higher chance of an unsafe preparation getting to the patient.
- With hazardous drug compounding (USP 800), higher risk means a higher chance of causing harm to the workers exposed to the drug.

RISK WITH HAZARDOUS DRUGS

The USP 800 requirements for safe handling of HDs are extensive, including working in a C-PEC in a C-SEC, specialized garb and so forth; but, some HDs are not as risky as others. A couple of examples of lower risk HDs include finasteride tablets and methotrexate tablets. A pharmacy can opt to conduct a risk assessment for drugs with lower risk. The pharmacy will need to develop a plan to handle the lower-risk HDs, which will include actions to limit staff exposure, such as:

- Packaging drugs inside a powder hood to keep particles and fumes out of the pharmacy. A hood with an external exhaust is recommended.
- Putting drugs in distinctive bins on the shelf to alert staff to the content.
- Wearing ASTM-rated gloves when counting or packaging drugs.
- Dedicating a counting tray and spatula for counting HDs and decontaminate both after use.
- Placing prepared HD containers into a sealable plastic bag.

If the pharmacy does not conduct a risk assessment for the lower risk HDs, the full USP 800 requirements must be followed.

RISK WITH STERILE DRUGS

USP 797 risk categories apply to the risk of contamination of the sterile product, which can cause severe patient harm. Risk categories include:

- Low risk
- Medium risk
- High risk
- Immediate use has higher risk, but is acceptable when the preparation is needed urgently to save a life.

The risk level of a sterile drug preparation determines the beyond use date (BUD), and is described further in the Compounding III chapter.

RISK WITH NON-STERILE DRUGS

USP 795 categorizes the risk based on the complexity of the preparation. There are three categories:

- Simple
- Moderate
- Complex

Simple requires (simply) following instructions.

Examples:
- Adding 59 mL of purified water, according to the package labeling instructions, to amoxicillin oral suspension, USP, to make a final concentration of 250 mg/5 mL.
- Preparing a medication from a compounding kit that comes with clear, step-by-step instructions.
- Following the instructions on most of the USP monographs to prepare a formulation.

Moderate requires compounding a preparation that has no established stability data, or a preparation with specialized calculations or procedures.

Example:
- Mixing two topical ingredients without stability data for either of them.

Complex requires specialized training, facilities, equipment or procedures.

Example:
- Compounding transdermal patches or extended-release tablets or capsules.

DRUG EXPOSURE

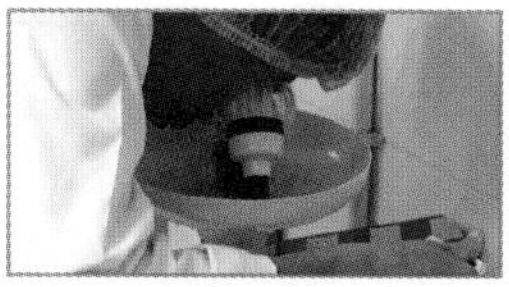

The most urgent action to take when a staff member has an exposure to non-hazardous drugs, any chemical used in the work place, and certainly for hazardous drugs where the hazard is well-established, is to get the drug or chemical off the person as soon as possible. The first 10 to 15 seconds after exposure are critical. Delaying treatment, even for a few seconds, may cause serious injury.

Protocols for emergency procedures should be kept at the pharmacy. Minimal actions to take:

1. For an exposure to gloves or gown, immediately remove the garb that has the drug on it.
2. Immediately cleanse any affected skin with soap and water.
3. For an eye exposure, flood the affected eye at an eyewash fountain (see image), or with water or an isotonic eyewash for at least 15 minutes. Depending on the chemical, the time required for flushing can be longer.
4. Obtain medical attention, when warranted.
5. Document the exposure in the employee's record.

HAZARDOUS DRUG EXPOSURE & SPILL MANAGEMENT

Remove any HD exposed to the skin as soon as possible. See details above. Additionally, emergency medical treatment must be sought with significant skin exposure (see following section on managing a spill) and with mucus membrane and inhalation exposure. Chemotherapeutics and some other HDs can irritate the eyes and mucus membranes in the nose and mouth and cause lung damage.

Eye and face protection must be worn when there is a risk for spills or splashes, including when working in a PEC and when working outside of a PEC (e.g., when administering the drug to the patient or cleaning up a spill).

Goggles are used for eye protection. Eye glasses alone or safety glasses with side shields do not protect the eyes adequately from splashes; face shields in combination with goggles is preferable and provides complete protection against splashes to the face and eyes.

Face shields alone do not provide full eye and face protection, which is why they are used with goggles.

RESPIRATORY PROTECTION

When HDs are unpacked and they are not contained in plastic, the staff member should wear an elastomeric half-mask, with a multi-gas cartridge and P100-filter, until assessment of the packaging integrity ensures that no breakage or spillage occurred during transport.

Respiratory protection is needed in circumstances with direct HD exposure:

- Cleaning up spills that need more supplies to clean up than provided by a spill kit.
- Deactivating, decontaminating, and cleaning underneath the work surface of a C-PEC
- There is a known or suspected airborne exposure to HD powders or vapors.
- Disposal of PPE used when handling HDs, which will be contaminated with (minimally) trace amounts.

There are three types of acceptable respirators. The type often used for HD compounding is the N95-respirator, which is sufficient, but does not provide the most preferable protection. Surgical masks are insufficient, and are not used for this purpose. There are two other preferable options, (in addition to the N95 respirator mask), which include:

- A fit-tested respirator mask with attached gas canisters (a "gas mask"), see below.

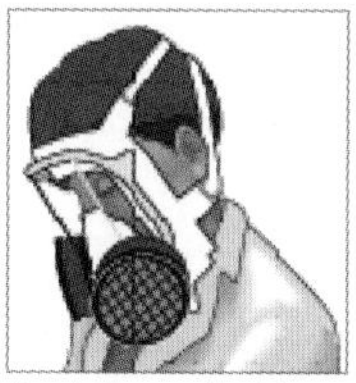

Respirator mask with gas canisters

Powered Air-Purifying Respirator (PAPR)

- A powered air-purifying respirator (PAPR) that blows air through the filter to the user (see upper right). PAPRs are easier to breathe through than the gas mask type but require a fully charged battery to work properly. They use the same filters as gas masks.

A sufficient option is an N95 respirator mask with side shields. This type of mask prevents particle inhalation, and is commonly used. It does not prevent gas/vapor inhalation, and for cleaning up a spill would be acceptable, but not optimal.

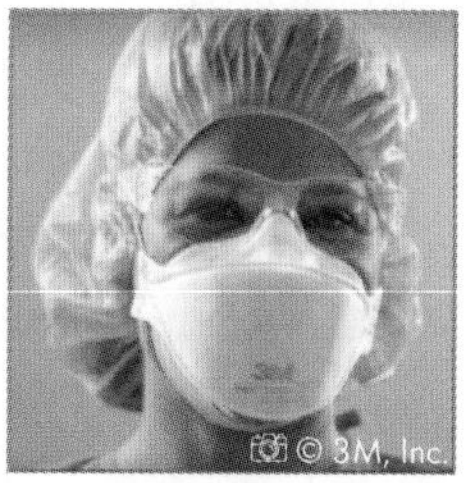

N95 Respirator Mask plus Goggles with Side Shields

HAZARDOUS DRUG SPILLS

Spills must be cleaned up immediately. Depending on the facility, all of the compounding staff can be trained to handle HD spills, or the facility can have a trained spill response team.

Establish the Who, What and When

- Who refers to the staff who will respond to assist with people exposed to the spill and who will respond to clean up the spill. If HD exposure has occurred, emergency medical help will be needed.
- What refers to the rapid assessment of the situation to determine if additional help will be needed.
- When refers to the urgent need to clean up hazardous spills immediately.

Managing the Spill

- Spill kits for HDs must be kept in areas where HDs are prepared, stored and administered. The spill kits must be available immediately wherever hazardous drugs travel, which is where they can spill.
- Quickly limit access to the area, and post warning signs around the perimeter of the spill. Multiple signs can be needed if more than one entry opens into the area with the spill. Pregnant women should not be involved with any clean-up activities and should immediately leave the area.
- The warning sign should state ***Caution: Hazardous Spill, Proceed with Care!*** or something similar.

Spill Kit Contents

- Protective gown, latex gloves, (minimally) N95 respirator mask plus goggles with side shields
- HD waste bag, scoop and scraper to get spill waste into the waste bag, chemo pads to absorb hazardous liquid
- HD spill report exposure form to document HD exposure

Procedure for Cleaning up a Spill

Open the spill kit. The PPE should be donned immediately to protect the staff cleaning up the spill.

- Put the heavy-duty gloves over the ASTM-rated gloves, which are the type used for HD compounding. The heavy-duty gloves protect the hands from broken glass.
- Clean up macro amount (big amounts) of spilled drug and broken glass.
  - Never use a brush to clean up broken glass and powder that is contaminated with HDs. Brushes can cause particles to become airborne.
- If liquid is present, cover the liquid with an absorbent spill pad.
- Next, decontaminate the surfaces on which the HD has spilled from the area of lesser contamination to areas of greater contamination to avoid spreading the hazard.
- If moistened pads are not available, pour the solution on the pads. Do not spray.
- Put trash into a hazardous waste bag, and seal. This is bulk hazardous waste, which is discarded in the black bulk hazardous waste bin.

After the Spill is Cleaned

- Doff (remove) garb and perform hand hygiene.
- Decontaminate the respirator and replace the cartridges.
- Replace the spill kit.

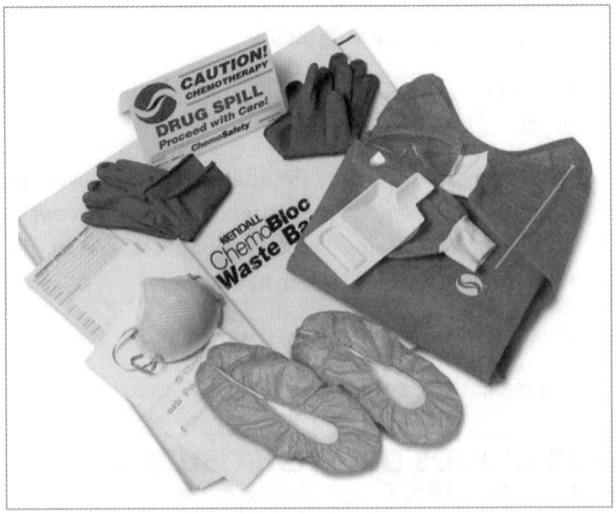

ADMINISTRATION OF HAZARDOUS DRUGS

Appropriate PPE must be worn when administering HDs. Two pairs of chemotherapy gloves and a chemotherapy gown are required when administering IV drugs and are recommended when administering other HDs that are not in tablet or capsule form. Single chemotherapy gloves are acceptable when administering intact tablets or capsules.

Closed system drug transfer devices (CSTDs) must be used by nurses for drug administration, if available for the formulation being used. CSTDs are described on the next page. Chemotherapy pins are used to prevent HDs from aerosolizing by reducing air pressure with venting. They can be used during reconstitution and during administration. The pins attach with a luer lock connection, described in the Compounding II chapter.

Pharmacy and nursing should try to avoid manipulating oral HDs, such as crushing tablets and opening capsules. If a liquid formulation of the drug is available, it should be used. If manipulation is required (e.g., crushing tablets) it should be done in a plastic bag to contain any dust or particles.

DISPOSAL

All PPE worn when handling HDs are considered contaminated with trace amounts. The outer chemotherapy gloves worn during compounding are discarded in a yellow trace chemotherapy waste bin located inside the C-PEC or put in a sealable bag if discarding outside the C-PEC. Remove the outer glove before handling and labeling the compounded preparation. The chemotherapy gown and outer shoe cover must be taken off before exiting the negative pressure area and thrown away in the yellow trace chemotherapy waste bin. The rest of the garb is removed when leaving the ante-room or C-SCA when the compounding session is complete.

Trace antineoplastic waste (i.e., empty vials, empty syringes, empty IV bags, IV tubes, used gloves, used gowns, used pads) are thrown away in a yellow container, which will be destroyed by incineration (burning) at a waste facility.

Bulk antineoplastic waste, which includes unused or partially empty IV bags, syringe and vials are thrown away in a black container, which will be incinerated at a waste facility.

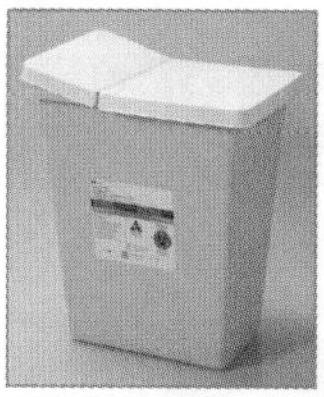

Trace Chemo Waste Bin: Yellow

Bulk Chemo Waste Bin: Black

TRANSPORTING HAZARDOUS DRUGS

When HDs need to be transported, they must be properly labeled and packaged to minimize the risk of spillage or breakage. Pneumatic tube systems cannot be used to transport any liquid HDs or any antineoplastics because of the potential for breakage and contamination.

GARBING FOR ALL TYPES OF COMPOUNDING

Garb attire includes hair covers (bonnets), beard covers, special shoes or shoe covers, gowns, gloves, face masks, eye shields and aprons. The garb attire required depends on the type of compounding performed. The staff have to be protected from chemical exposure (some drugs are more toxic than others), and the drug needs to be protected from contamination. Hand hygiene and garbing is more detailed for sterile compounding.

GARB FOR HAZARDOUS DRUGS

Appropriate PPE must be worn with each step involving HDs: receiving, storage, transporting, compounding (sterile and non-sterile), administration, sanitation, and during spill control. Double ASTM (chemotherapy)-rated gloves are required when compounding or cleaning up spills. Single gloves can be used for HD receiving and storage.

Non-Sterile Hazardous Drugs

Placing intact tablets or capsules into unit-dose or multidose containers on an occasional basis poses relatively low risk to the healthcare worker. A single pair of gloves may be adequate. When USP 800 is not being followed completely (which requires 2 pairs of gloves), it must be based on a risk-assessment that has identified the drugs which will have less stringent requirements, and the procedures put in place to reduce risk.

Repeatedly counting, cutting, or crushing tablets poses a higher risk for worker exposure and contamination to the workplace if exposure controls are not in place. If a BSC or CACI is not available, then PPE should be used that includes:

- Double gloves, a gown, a mask, and
- A disposable pad to protect the work surface

Sterile Hazardous Drugs

PPE for sterile hazardous drug compounding includes:

- Head covers and (if applicable) beard covers
- Two pairs of shoe covers
- An impermeable gown
- Two pairs of ASTM (chemotherapy)-rated gloves.
- A full-facepiece respirator or a face shield with goggles when there is a risk for spills or splashes.

Non-PPE Protection for the Environment and CSPs

CSTDs should be used to transfer drugs whenever possible to keep the HDs contained within (inside) the device. CSTDs reduce leaks and spills when withdrawing solution from vials, injecting solution into IV bags, reconstituting dried powders into solutions, and for syringe to syringe transfers. CSTDs are recommended when compounding HDs and required when administering antineoplastics, if available. CSTDs have built-in pressure equalization. When CSTDs are used to reconstitute or withdraw the HD, the manual negative pressure technique (see Compounding III chapter) is not needed.

The following pages illustrate how to don garb for sterile compounding, followed by requirements for sterile hazardous garb. Note that removing coats, sweaters, makeup and visible jewelry should be done before entering the ante area. Some pharmacies have compounders change into scrubs at work; these may be cleaner than street clothes, and are light and comfortable.

Garbing for Sterile Compounding

—Garbing is donned in the ante area. The order in which the garb should be donned is from dirtiest to cleanest.

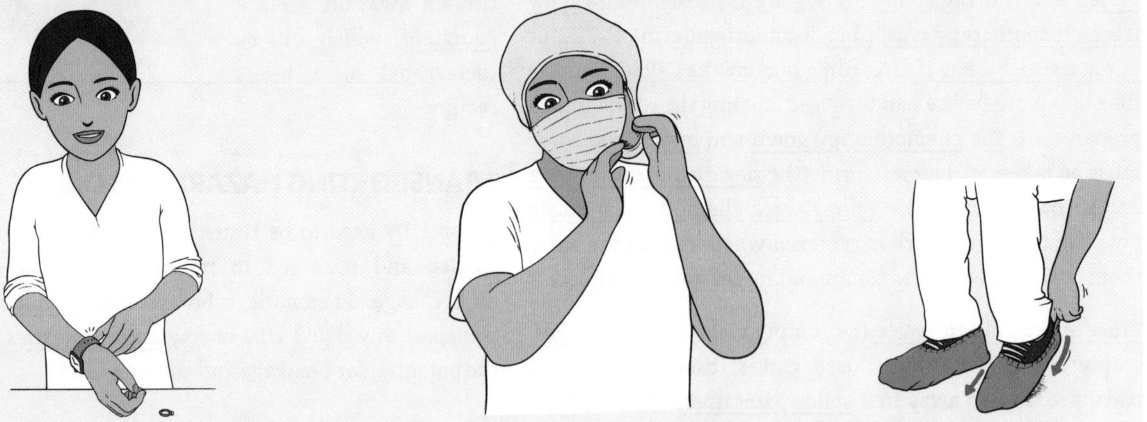

- Remove coats, rings, watches, bracelets and makeup. Artificial or long nails are not permitted.
- No make-up is permitted because it sheds.

- Don dedicated shoes or shoe covers, head and facial hair covers, and face masks. A second pair of shoe covers are needed for compounding hazardous drugs (HDs). The ante area should have a mirror that is used to check that the hair is completely covered. An eye shield is optional, except if preparing a hazardous drug.

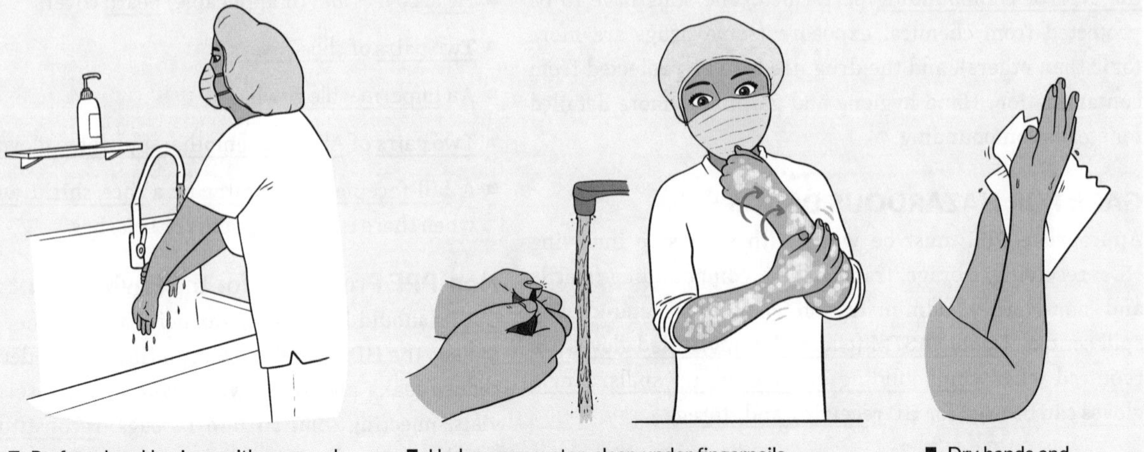

- Perform hand hygiene with soap and warm water. Most contamination of CSPs comes from the hands.

- Under warm water, clean under fingernails to remove debris.
- Working from the fingertips to the elbows, wash vigorously in circular motions for 30 seconds.

- Dry hands and forearms with lint-free disposable towels (preferred) or an electronic hand dryer.

Garbing for Sterile Compounding *continued*

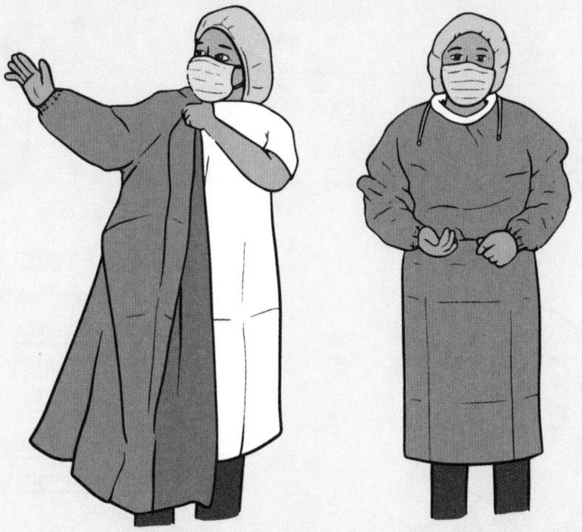

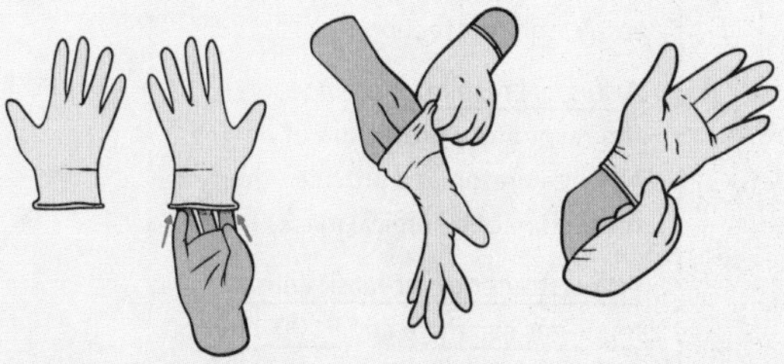

- Don a non-shedding gown that fits snugly around the wrists and has an enclosure at the neck. Disposable gowns are required for HD compounding and preferred for non-HD compounding. If gowns are reusable, they must be laundered prior to reuse.
- Enter the buffer area (IV room).
- Apply an alcohol-based surgical hand scrub with persistent antimicrobial activity for the recommended amount of time (per manufacturer) and allow to dry. The FDA has issued a warning for serious allergic reactions to chlorhexidine, which many compounders use. Another option is povidone-iodine *(Betadine)*, which can be used if there has been an allergic reaction to chlorhexidine.
- Don sterile, powder-free gloves. Two pairs of ASTM (chemotherapy)-rated gloves are required for compounding HDs. Tuck one pair under the cuffs of the gown. The second pair goes over the cuffs.
- Sanitize the gloves with 70% IPA routinely during compounding and whenever the gloves touch non-sterile surfaces. Do not resume compounding until the alcohol has dried. Continually inspect gloves for tears.

- All garb must be used when compounding with an isolator (glove box) unless the isolator's manufacturer provides written documentation that garb is not required.
- When the compounding is completed and the compounding personnel leaves the cleanroom/compounding area, all garb except for the gown goes into the disposal container. If the gown is not visibly soiled, it can be taken off and kept in the compounding area in order to be re-worn for the current work shift. The gown cannot leave the ante area if it is going to be re-worn. Hand hygiene is repeated, and all other garb is replaced when re-entering the compounding area.

When to Re-Garb

- Garb should not be worn outside of the anteroom; if the anteroom has been exited, complete regarbing is required, including hand hygiene.
- If working in a segregated compounding area (SCA) and the SCA is left for any reason, regarbing is required.

Garbing for Hazardous Drugs

—Garbing is donned in the ante area. The order in which the garb should be donned is from dirtiest to cleanest.

RESPIRATOR

A fit tested NIOSH-certified N95 respirator is appropriate for most activities that need respiratory protection.

A surgical respirator provides the respiratory protection of an N95 respirator, and provides the protection of a surgical mask.

An elastomeric half-mask with a multi-gas cartridge and P100-filter should be used for unpacking HDs which are not wrapped in plastic.

A full-face piece, chemical cartridge-type respirator or powered air-purifying respirator (PAPR) should be worn for cleaning up large HD spills, sanitizing the undertray of a C-PEC, or when there is a known or suspected airborne exposure to powders or vapors.

FACE MASK

Required for sterile compounding

HEAD AND HAIR COVERS

EYE/FACE PROTECTION

Must be worn when there is a risk for HD spills or HD splashes when working outside of a C-PEC.

A full-facepiece respirator or a face shield with goggles is acceptable.

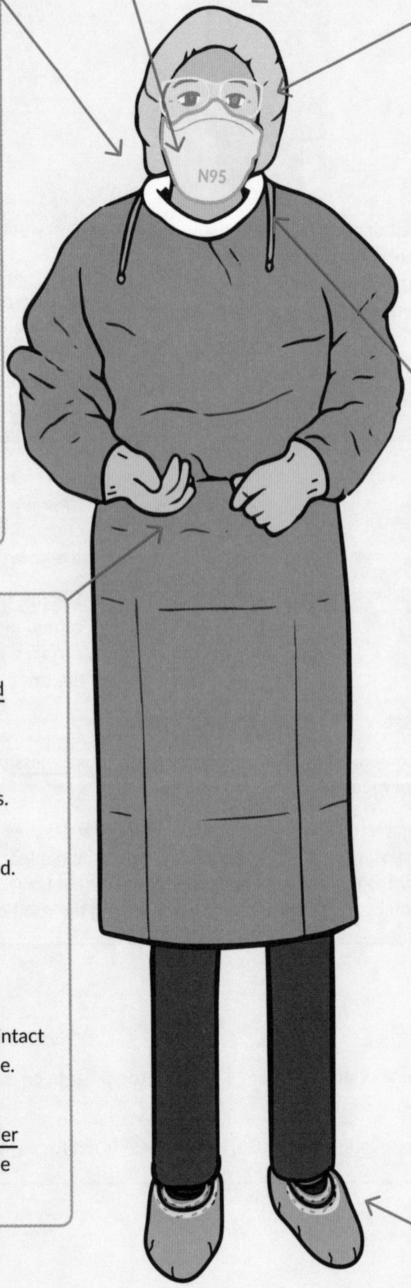

CHEMOTHERAPY GOWN

Must be disposable.

Must be impermeable; best is polyethylene-coated polypropylene or other laminate material.

Must close in the back, be long sleeved, and have closed cuffs (elastic or knit).

No seams or closures that can trap HD particles.

Must be changed per manufacturer's schedule, or if unknown, change Q 2–3 hours or immediately after a spill or splash.

Disposable sleeve covers made of coated materials can be used with the gown.

CHEMOTHERAPY GLOVES

Must meet the American Society for Testing and Materials (ASTM) standard D6978 (or its successor).

Powder-free.

Must not have pin holes or weak spots.

Must be changed every 30 minutes or when torn, punctured, or contaminated.

Two pairs must be worn while administering chemotherapy drugs and while compounding sterile and higher-risk non-sterile HDs.

For low-risk non-sterile HDs, such as intact tablets, one pair of gloves is acceptable.

When two pairs of gloves are worn with a gown, one glove should go under the cuff of the gown and the other one should go over the cuff of the gown.

SHOE COVERS

Two pairs are required when compounding sterile HDs.

CHAPTER CONTENT

Equipment 249
Measuring Equipment 250
Syringes 250
Luer Locks Improve Patient Safety 252
Weighing Equipment 252
Grinding, Mixing and Transferring Equipment 253
Mixing Equipment 253
Heating Devices 254
Molds, Tablet Presses and Capsule Machines 254
Compounding Ingredients 254
Surfactants 255
Salad Dressing Chemistry 255
Surfactant Mechanism of Action 255
Surfactants Have Many Uses 256
Types of Surfactants 256
The Hydrophilic-Lipophilic Balance 257
The HLB Number 257
Stability and Degradation 258
Stability of Compounded Preparations 258
Oxidation 259
Hydrolysis 260
Photolysis 261
Additional Processes that Degrade Drugs 261
Excipients 261
Excipients to be Avoided in Some Patients 266

CONTENT LEGEND

= Study Tip Gal

CHAPTER 16

COMPOUNDING II: EQUIPMENT, STABILITY & EXCIPIENTS

EQUIPMENT

Equipment for Different Types of Compounding

The first section of this chapter covers equipment used for compounding. Most equipment is used for non-sterile compounding (e.g., ointment mills and tablet molds), some is used for both non-sterile and sterile compounding (e.g., syringes and graduated cylinders) and a small number is used for sterile compounding only (e.g., the automated compounding equipment used to prepare parenteral nutrition).

Dedicated Equipment for Hazardous Drugs

The Compounding I chapter includes a cautionary statement that equipment (and spaces) used for hazardous drug (HD) preparation should not be used for non-hazardous drug preparation. HDs cause contamination. Equipment used for HDs, including routine equipment such as counting trays and spatulas, should be dedicated for HD preparation and sanitized after use.

Cautionary Note on Calibration and Materials

Equipment must be calibrated regularly to confirm accuracy. The calibration can be frequent; e.g., electronic balances are calibrated routinely before use. Complex equipment can require calibration by an outside expert. Equipment maintenance should be done with care to keep the equipment clean, working properly, and free from contamination.

Equipment should be made of material that does not react with the compounding ingredients (e.g., metal spatulas should not be used with compounds containing metal ions).

MEASURING EQUIPMENT

Pharmacists use various equipment to measure ingredients, and nurses and patients use some of the same equipment (such as oral syringes and pipettes) to administer medication.

Selecting the Size of the Measuring Equipment

When measuring, select a device that has a measuring capacity equal to or slightly larger than the amount being measured to get the most accurate measurement (e.g., if an 8 mL dose is needed, and the syringe sizes available are 1 mL, 3 mL, 5 mL, 7.5 mL and 10 mL, the 10 mL syringe should be used). Measurements should be made in the metric system.

Cylindrical and Conical Graduates

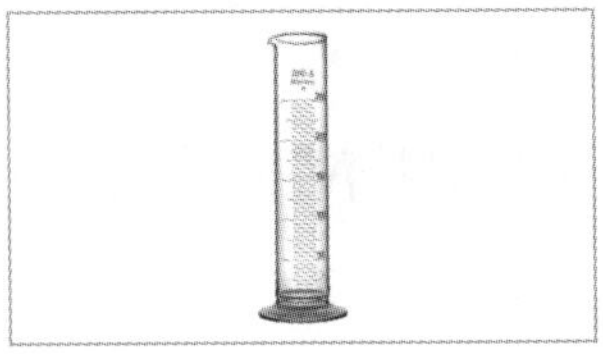

Graduated cylinder

Conical graduate

Graduates are measuring equipment with lines on the glass that are used to measure the volume, and include graduated cylinders (above left), conical graduates (above right), graduated beakers and graduated medication containers.

A graduated cylinder has the same diameter from the top to the bottom of the container and provides more accurate measurements than conical graduates, which have a wide mouth.

A graduate should not be used to measure volumes less than 20% of the graduate's capacity.

- The smaller the percentage of the graduate's measuring capacity that is used, the higher the measuring error (e.g., measuring 5 mL in a 100 mL graduate will have a higher measuring error than measuring 87 mL in a 100 mL graduate. A 5 mL measurement needs a smaller graduate.)

To read the volume in a graduate, place on a flat surface and view the height of the liquid in the cylinder at eye-level.

- The liquid can curve downward from both sides, especially with viscous liquids. This curve is called the meniscus.
- The bottom of the meniscus, at the center, is where the liquid measurement is read (see image; the measurement is 20 mL).

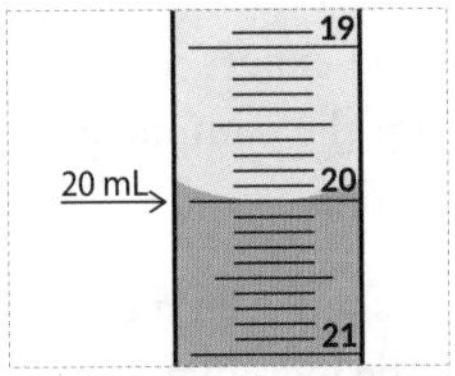

Liquids measured in a graduated cylinder can form a curve called a meniscus. Measure the level at the bottom (center) of the meniscus, at eye level.

A conical (cone-shaped) graduate has a wide mouth (see image, above) to make it easier to stir the mixture using a glass stirring rod.

- The wider the mouth, the lower the measuring accuracy.

SYRINGES

Syringes used for Non-Sterile Compounding

Oral syringes and hypodermic (injection) syringes (also called parenteral syringes), with or without the cannula (needle), can be used for measuring. See images, next page.

- Syringes are most accurate for measuring small volumes.
- They are especially useful for measuring viscous (thick) liquids, such as glycerin and mineral oil.
- Patients receiving a liquid who require a very accurate dose should use an oral syringe for measurement rather than a small dosing cup, which have lower accuracy.
- Oral syringes are useful for squirting the medication into the side of the mouth (as are small pipettes or droppers), which can be useful for children and animals. Oral syringes can be used to deliver small amounts of topical preparations.

Caution with Oral Syringes in an Acute Care Setting

There have been multiple deaths due to patient's receiving oral medications as an injection. This can cause quick fatality.

- A useful method to prevent this mishap is to cover the tip of the syringe with a sticker that says: **For Oral Use Only.**
- Pharmacy should communicate the correct route of administration with nursing.
- Oral syringes do not fit onto a luer lock connection (see next page), which helps prevent some of these mishaps.

Caution with Hypodermic Syringe Needle-Sticks

Recapping needles leads to needle-stick injuries. In sterile compounding, a needle-stick can injure the staff and cause contamination to the compounded sterile products (CSPs). In patient care settings, needle-stick injuries carry infection risk.

- In general, do not recap syringes.
- It is preferable to use syringes with safety features, e.g., safety shields, that cover the needle immediately after use.
- If the needle must be recapped, it is safer to place the cap on the work surface (rather than holding it) and slip the tip of the needle into the cap, without letting the needle tip touch the work surface.

Syringes used for Sterile Compounding

Hypodermic syringes are also called parenteral syringes. In addition to use in patients, they are commonly used for sterile compounding to transfer drugs and additives into IV bags.

- All syringe and other packages, prior to being brought into the secondary engineering control (SEC) or into an isolator primary engineering control (PEC) should be wiped off with IPA 70% to remove contaminants, including dust.
- Sterile syringes will be individually wrapped, and must be opened along the seal (not torn open) in order to avoid shedding (i.e., release of particles into the sterile compounding space).

Syringe Parts

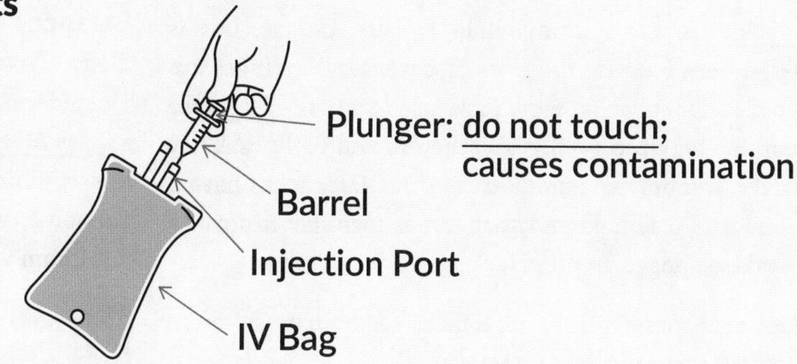

Syringes can be injected into the IV bag (as shown) or can be used to inject directly into a vein or into a catheter if the patient has IV access [i.e., a port (vein entry) placed under the skin, with IV tubing extended out for the entry of injections or infusions].

Providing a quick bolus dose into a vein (directly) or into a vein through a catheter is called an IV push.

Syringe Types

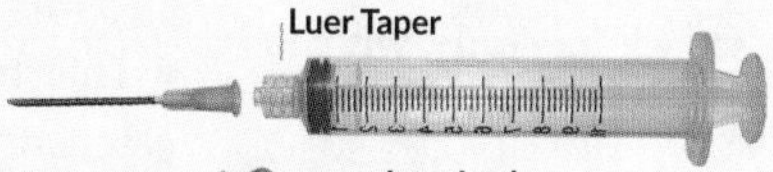

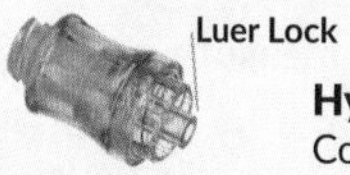

Luer Locks

The syringe above has an end called a luer taper. It is designed to screw into a luer lock (such as the purple luer lock, shown above) to give a medication by IV push. Oral syringes do not have a luer taper. Syringes such as this one are used to give a drug directly (with the needle attached) or via a port, as shown below. They should never be used for oral medications. This can cause a fatal error if the syringe is used to administer the oral drug intravenously.

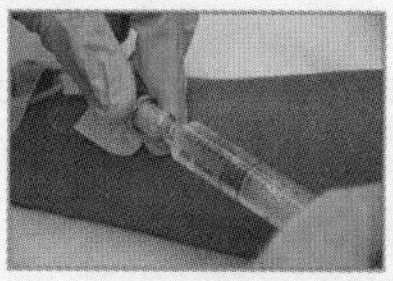

The patient is receiving an IV push through a luer lock connection. The syringe is screwed onto the female part of the luer lock at the opening where the patient has a catheter (a port) that provides IV access (i.e., access to the patient's vein).

An IV line will be attached the same way, using a luer lock connection. Multiple IV lines can be attached together using luer locks.

Hypodermic (Injection) Syringes

Come with cannulas (needles) attached, or the cannula will separate and is screwed onto the tip of the syringe. Syringes are available in many sizes, e.g., 1 mL, 5 mL, 7.5 mL, 10 mL and others.

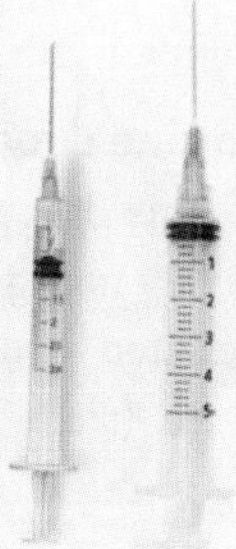

Choose the Correct Size Syringe

For drawing up medication, use the exact size syringe needed or (if exact size is not available) the closest syringe size above the size needed. Do not add two different syringe sizes for a dose. Use the next size up.

Oral Syringes

For Oral Use Only sticker can be placed over the tip to prevent accidental injection, which can cause fatality. These are used to administer drugs orally by mouth or through a nasogastric (NG) tube. They are sometimes used to deliver small amounts of topical preparations.

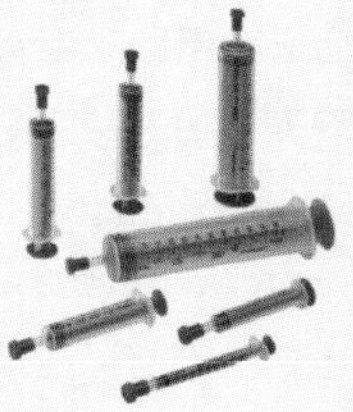

LUER LOCKS IMPROVE PATIENT SAFETY

Luer locks are not a compounding issue, per se, but is discussed here because the ends of parenteral syringes are designed for luer locks, which are used to make leak-free connections between syringes, catheters and IV lines. They are used commonly in patient care units. Luer locks have a male-end and a female-end that screw together to form a tight seal (see image on previous page).

The luer lock connection forms a more secure connection to prevent leaks and accidental removal.

Pipettes and Droppers

Pipettes are thin plastic or glass tubes used to measure small volumes. Pipettes can be used by patients to take medication because they are easy to draw up a dose (insert tip into liquid medication, squeeze, remove). If the pipette is being inserted into an opening such as a mouth or nose, it is important to keep the bulb squeezed when withdrawing it, to avoid contaminating the inside of the pipette.

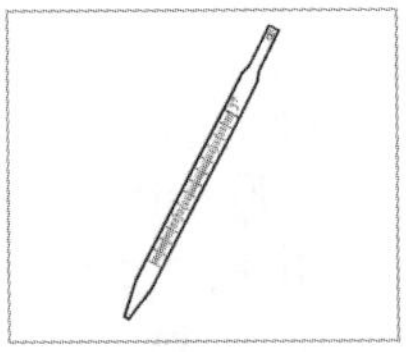

Mohr Pipette (graduated)

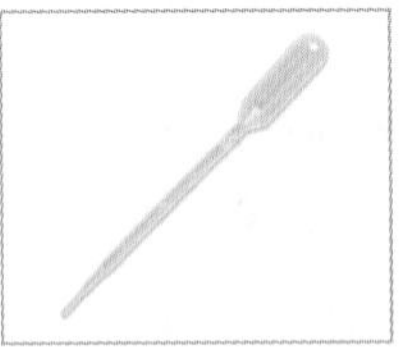

Disposable Pipette

Pipettes can be referred to as droppers, because they release drops. Medicine droppers are also called droppers.

- A volumetric pipette draws up a set volume only, which is the volume the pipette can hold.
- A Mohr pipette is graduated and is used to measure small (different) volumes. Mohr pipettes are commonly used in compounding.

Medicine Droppers

Medicine droppers come in graduated and non-graduated versions. Graduated droppers that meet USP criteria (such as the dropper in the image) release drops of water that weigh 45-55 mg, when held vertically.

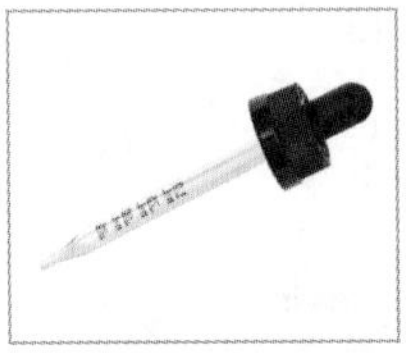

Graduated Dropper

- The weight is given for water drops; other compounds will have different weights for the same size drops, depending on the liquid's specific gravity.
- Non-graduated medicine droppers that meet the USP criteria release a similarly-sized drop.

WEIGHING EQUIPMENT

Balances

There are two types of balances used to weigh ingredients. The older balance is the Class III torsion balance (also called a Class A balance). This type of balance is still used, though less commonly than the electronic balance [see "Ye Old Torsion Balance" for a description and the calculation for the minimum weighable quantity (MWQ)].

YE OLD TORSION BALANCE

Class III (Class A) torsion balances have internal weights, which are used to weigh quantities ≤ 1 gram. When weighing > 1 gram, external weights (see picture) are placed on one pan and the substance to be weighed is placed on the other. The external weights must be handled with a forceps (pincers) to avoid getting oil from the skin on the weights.

Torsion balances have a sensitivity requirement (SR) that is most often 6 mg, which means 6 mg can be added or removed before the dial moves 1 division. The minimum weighable quantity (the minimum amount that can be weighed) is calculated as shown:

MWQ = SR / acceptable error rate (0.05 or 5%)

MWQ = 6 mg / 0.05 = 120 mg

The top-loading electronic balance (also called an analytical balance or a scale) is used most commonly.

- This type of balance is simple to use and has higher sensitivity (i.e., can weigh with more precision, including very small amounts). It is not necessary to calculate the MWQ with a modern electronic balance.
- When using an electronic balance, the compounder must "tare" or "zero out" the balance after placing the weigh boat or glassine paper on the scale (see next section). This ensures that only the ingredients are weighed and the container or paper used to hold the ingredients are not included in the weight.

With either balance, never place material to be weighed (e.g., powder) directly on the balance. The material will be placed on a weigh boat (a shallow dish) or on glassine weighing paper, which is coated to reduce moisture penetration. The weigh boats are made of plastic or other material.

Electronic balance

Torsion balance

Weigh boats

GRINDING, MIXING AND TRANSFERRING EQUIPMENT

Mortars and Pestles

Mortars and pestles are used to grind substances into a finer consistency, and can be used to stir and mix small amounts of ingredients. The mortar is the bowl, and the pestle is the blunt, heavy stick. A compounding pharmacy needs at least one glass and one Wedgwood or porcelain mortar and pestle.

- Glass mortars are used for liquids, such as suspensions and solutions, and for mixing compounds that are oily or can stain.
- Wedgwood mortars have a rougher surface than porcelain, and are preferred for grinding dry crystals and hard powders.
- Porcelain mortars have a smoother surface, and are preferred for blending powders and pulverizing gummy consistencies.

Glass mortar and pestle

Wedgwood mortar & pestle

Porcelain mortar and pestle

Spatulas

Spatulas are used to mix and transfer (move) ingredients from one place (such as an ointment slab) to another place (such as a container). The flat part of the blade can be used to flatten and grind down ingredients, and to pack preparations such as ointments into containers. Spatulas are made of stainless steel, plastic or hard rubber. Stainless steel and disposable plastic spatulas are used commonly. The type of spatula to use depends on what ingredients are being transferred or mixed.

- A steel (metal) spatula would not be used if making a mixture that contains metallic ions.
- A rubber spatula is used to handle corrosive material.

Ointment Slabs

Ingredients are mixed into ointments on a compounding (or ointment) slab, which is a flat board made of porcelain or glass.

Slab and spatula

- Ointment slabs are used as a work surface for other purposes besides making ointments since the material is hard and non-reactive. An ointment slab can be used to form pills (in which case it can be referred to as a pill tile), for rolling out suppositories, and for other uses.
- Alternatively, disposable parchment ointment pads can be used as a work surface for working with ingredients if the water content of the mixture will not cause the paper to tear.
- Mixtures that have a higher water content than an ointment, such as a cream, can be mixed on an ointment slab if the mixture will hold its shape (and not flow off the slab). Otherwise, different equipment can be used to hold the preparation, such as a mortar bowl or a beaker.

Powder Sieves

Sieves are sifters similar to those used in baking.

Sieve

- After a powder has been ground fine, it is sifted in order to ensure a uniform particle size.

MIXING EQUIPMENT

Electric Mixing Equipment Saves Time

Mixing can be performed manually or with electric mixing equipment. Electric mixing speeds up the process.

- Ointment mills, homogenizers and grinders are used to mix ingredients.
- Ointment mills and grinders reduce the particle size (and in so doing, increase the surface area, which increases the rate of drug absorption.
- Hot plates with stirrer bars are used to heat and mix.

Ointment Mills

An ointment mill draws the ointment (or another semi-solid preparation) between rollers that grind and homogenize (i.e., make uniform) the ingredients in the preparation (see image).

Ointment mill

- In addition to making the ointment homogeneous, the ointment mill will make the ointment feel smoother by grinding down large particles and removing any grittiness, which is undesirable.

Homogenizers

A homogenizer (also called an electric mortar and pestle) can be used to mix ointments, creams, or other semi-solid preparations.

Homogenizer (also called an electric mortar & pestle)

- The homogenizer is similar to a smoothie blender, although with more power, and at a higher cost (see image). Homogenizers can be small and hand-held.
- A popular brand of homogenizer is called the *Unguator*.
- There are other homogenizer manufacturers that make various models (e.g., *PharmaRAM* or *Mazerustar Mixer*).

Grinders

Electric grinders are similar to coffee bean grinders. In fact, coffee bean grinders are used in some pharmacies. When used for compounding, they must be dedicated for compounding use only (i.e., not for coffee bean grinding or other food-use).

- A strong coffee bean grinder is useful for grinding hard tablets down. The powder will need further preparation to produce a fine powder.

Hot Plate with Magnetic Stirrer

A hot plate (see next section) with a magnetic stirrer can save time by continuously stirring the mixture, in order to dissolve and mix the ingredients.

- The stirrer has a rotating magnet under the ceramic plate, which causes the stir bar (placed inside the glass) to spin, which stirs the components (see image below).
- Hot plates are used without the stirrer bar to heat only; see next section.
- Glass stirring rods are used to manually stir the contents.

HEATING DEVICES

Heating with Hot Plates

Hot plates provide direct heat to soften and melt ingredients, and to hasten chemical reactions. Heat must be carefully controlled to avoid burning.

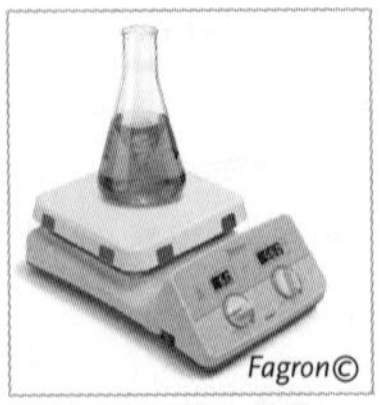

Hot plate with a stir bar in the glass. A magnet inside the hot plate moves the stir bar.

- A water bath is helpful when the temperature needs to be carefully controlled. The water bath protects the ingredients from overheating and burning.
- The ingredients to be melted will be in a container (e.g., a beaker) that is placed into a larger container filled with water.
- The water in the outer container separates the inner container from the direct heat source, to prevent burning.

Heating with Microwave Ovens

Microwave ovens heat quickly; be careful that the heat is applied uniformly as some microwaves provide uneven heat.

MOLDS, TABLET PRESSES AND CAPSULE MACHINES

Reusable or disposable molds are used to prepare tablets, lozenges/troches (orally-dissolving tablets), and suppositories.

- With soft delivery vehicles, such as suppositories and lozenges, the medication is often dispensed in a disposable plastic mold. This helps keep the product in the correct shape. Refrigeration helps soft products retain shape.

Tablets

A tablet press (or tablet mold) is two plastic or metal plates used to compress damp powder into tablets.

- Similar to forcing *Play-Doh* into a mold to form a shape, the compounder takes the pasty mass and uses the tablet press to form tablet shapes.
- After the mold shapes the tablets, the tablets are removed, and given time to dry.

Capsules

Capsules can be soft gels or hard shells, which are more commonly used for compounding. The shells are made of gelatin, which is pork-derived and will not be suitable for some patients, or from hypromellose or a similar plant-derived product. Hypromellose is a cellulose product, as the name implies.

- Capsule sizes for human use range from 000 (the largest size) to 5 (the smallest size). Veterinary pharmacists can order larger capsule sizes for use in large animals.
- Capsule bodies are filled with the drugs and excipients, and the capsule caps are placed over the bodies by hand or with a capsule machine.

Tube Sealers

Tube-sealers heat and squeeze the ends of tubes shut; the end will look similar to the crimped end of a toothpaste tube.

- In the image below right, a filled tube is being sealed shut.

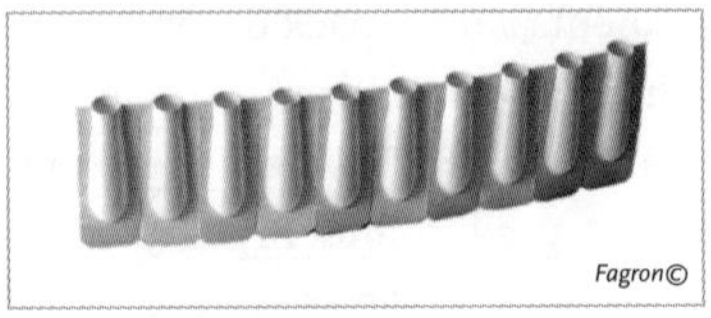

Suppository mold

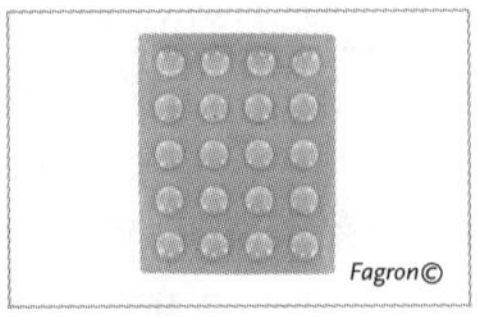

Lozenge mold

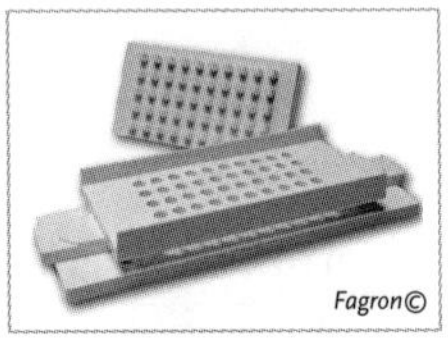

Tablet press

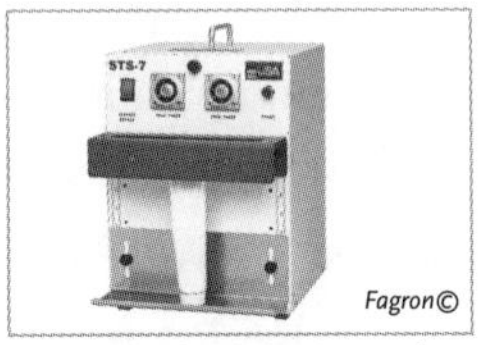

Tube sealer (sealed at bottom)

COMPOUNDING INGREDIENTS

All medications, whether compounded or not, include the drug/s (called the active pharmaceutical ingredients, or APIs) and the excipients. Excipients do not produce therapeutic effect, but are needed to make the dosage form stable, functional, palatable and pleasing to the patient.

High Quality Ingredients Required

High-quality ingredients ensure the purity and safety of the formulation. Recommended compounding ingredients are listed in a reputable source:

- The USP National Formulary (USP-NF)

- The Food Chemicals Codex (FCC) substances list.

Preferably, the approved substances should be manufactured at an FDA-registered facility.

- If any substance comes from a non-FDA registered facility, a Certificate of Analysis (CoA) should be obtained that confirms the specifications and quality.

If any component is moved to a different container, the new container should be labeled with the component name, original supplier, lot or control number, transfer date and expiration date.

Missing Expiration Date

Ingredients degrade, and expiration dates are important to ensure that the product retains potency and is non-toxic. If there is an ingredient without an expiration date, the pharmacist will assign a conservative (cautious) date that is no more than 3 years from the date of receipt (the day the pharmacy received the item). The label on the container should include:

- The date of receipt, and
- The assigned expiration date.

SURFACTANTS

SALAD DRESSING CHEMISTRY

Preparations can have multiple phases, similar to an oil and vinegar salad dressing, which has an oil phase that will become dispersed in the watery phase (the vinegar) when shaken. The dressing will quickly settle back into the two distinct phases because the "tension" between the two surfaces is high; the oil and water will repel each other. A surfactant added to the salad dressing will lower the tension between the two surfaces, and keep the phases from quickly separating.

Lowering the Surface Tension

Surfactant is a contraction of the words surface active agent. Surfactants lower the surface tension (i.e., the interfacial tension) between two ingredients (or phases) in a preparation to make them more miscible (i.e., easier to mix together). The side of the phase that is close to the other phase is the "face" of the phase, and the interfacial tension is the tension at the interface. The surfactant lowers the interfacial tension, to help the phases move closer together.

SURFACTANT MECHANISM OF ACTION

The common mechanism of action of a surfactant involves forming a micelle structure (see micelle figure, in first box below), which can reverse (turn inside-out). If oil and water are mixed, the oil will interact with the lipophilic (lipid-loving) end of the surfactant, and the water will interact with the hydrophilic (water-loving) end of the surfactant. Surfactants are amphiphilic; they are both hydrophilic (on one side) and hydrophobic (on the other side).

Non-Micelle Mechanisms

Surfactants do not always form micelles when used as surfactants; some form a film between the surfaces, or form an electrically-charged layer to keep the phases separate. With all mechanisms, the surface tension is lowered, which helps with drug preparation and stabilization.

SURFACTANTS HAVE MANY USES

Surfactants have practical uses in addition to aiding in the formation of homogenous preparations. By keeping the drug dispersed, a consistent dose is delivered. In manufacturing, the micelles formed by surfactants are used to facilitate gut absorption of lipophilic drugs, similar to the way bile acids facilitate absorption of cholesterol, and are used to control the rate of drug release.

When the surface tension is lowered, it is easier to grind particles down, and to mix ingredients. Surfactants are called by a variety of names, depending on the use or the type of preparation. For example, when a surfactant is used to reduce the surface tension between an insoluble drug and a liquid (such as in a suspension) it can be referred to as a suspending agent.

TYPES OF SURFACTANTS

Wetting agents

Wetting agents are substances that reduce the surface tension of water or another substance to permit the substance to more easily spread. A fine powder that will be incorporated into a suspension is wetted with a wetting agent and stirred into a thick paste prior to being put into the delivery vehicle. Levigating agents (see next column) can be referred to as wetting agents.

Emulsifiers

An emulsion is a liquid dispersed in a different liquid, such as water droplets dispersed in oil, or oil droplets dispersed in water. Emulsifiers are added to an emulsion to help keep the liquid droplets dispersed throughout the liquid vehicle. This helps prevent the two liquids from separating into distinct (separate) phases. Emulsifiers can be called emulgents.

Suspending Agents

A suspension is a solid dispersed in a liquid (e.g., sulfamethoxazole powder does not dissolve in water, and is delivered as a suspension). Suspending agents are added to suspensions to help keep the solid particles from settling.

Suspending agents do not keep suspensions separated for long, and suspensions must be shaken to redisperse the solid prior to use. Suspending agents can be called dispersants (or a dispersing agent or a plasticizer, where plasticizer means that it will make the preparation easier to shape or mold.

Levigating Agents

Levigation and trituration are both used to grind down (i.e., make particles smaller); the difference is that levigation uses a levigating agent (also called a levigant) such as glycerin or mineral oil to aid in the grinding. Mineral oil is commonly used for lipophilic (oil-soluble) compounds, and glycerin or propylene glycol are used for aqueous (water-soluble) compounds.

Foaming Agent

Foaming agents help foam to form (e.g., in soap) by lowering the surface tension of water. An enormous use of surfactants in manufacturing is in detergents, where they foam and remove dirt. In non-sterile compounding, anti-foaming agents are more commonly used (e.g., simethicone).

Glycols & Gels are used as Surfactants and Delivery Vehicles

The commonly used products polyethylene glycol (PEG) and poloxamer by itself, or as the P in PLO gel, described later) are both delivery vehicles and surfactants.

PEG and poloxamer have both hydrophilic and hydrophobic parts, which makes them useful for a variety of preparations. For example, poloxamer gel can be used to distribute ingredients in a preparation into the "like" phase (i.e., the hydrophobic compound distributes into the organic (lipophilic) phase, and the hydrophilic compound distributes into the water-based phase). Poloxamer is useful for topical drug delivery, and is used commonly.

THE HYDROPHILIC-LIPOPHILIC BALANCE

When a pharmacist wishes to disperse a liquid into a liquid to form an emulsion, selecting the right surfactant is important to keep the liquid droplets adequately dispersed.

A primary consideration in selecting the surfactant to use in an emulsion will be whether the emulsion is a water-in-oil (w/o) emulsion or an oil-in-water (o/w) emulsion.

The type of emulsion will determine which values on the hydrophilic-lipophilic balance (HLB) scale will be useful.

The HLB scale has a range of 0 - 20, with a midpoint value of 10.

- Surfactants with a low HLB number (< 10) are more lipid-soluble and are used for water-in-oil (w/o) emulsions.
- Surfactants with a high HLB number (> 10) are more water-soluble and are used for oil-in-water (o/w) emulsions.

The following table has examples of surfactants and their HLB values. There are many available surfactants; these are just a handful.

In the table, PEG 400 and *Tween 85* have HLB values greater than 10, and would be possible options for forming an o/w emulsion. The HLB values that are less than 10 would be possible options for forming a w/o emulsion.

THE HLB NUMBER

The HLB scale range is 0 – 20. The midpoint is 10.

Surfactants with a low HLB number (< 10) are more lipid-soluble and are used for water-in-oil (w/o) emulsions.

Surfactants with a high HLB number (> 10) are more water-soluble and are used for oil-in-water (o/w) emulsions.

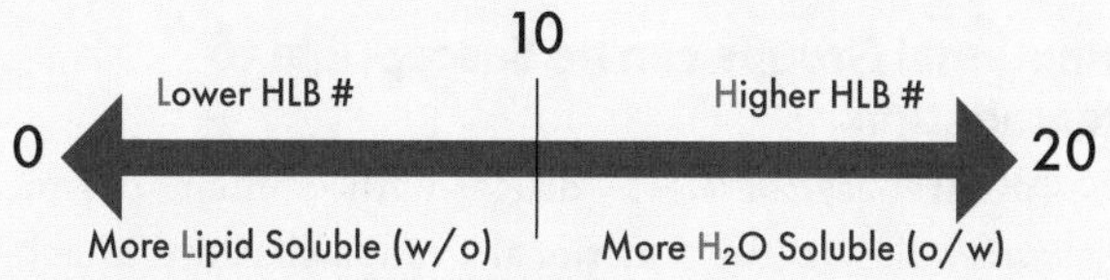

Examples of Surfactants and their HLB Values

COMMERCIAL NAME	CHEMICAL NAME	HLB VALUE
Glyceryl monostearate	Glyceryl monostearate	3.8
PEG 400 monooleate	Polyoxyethylene monooleate	11.4
Span 65	Sorbitan tristearate	2.1
Tween 81	Polyoxyethylene sorbitan monooleate	10
Tween 85	Polyoxyethylene sorbitan trioleate	11

STABILITY AND DEGRADATION

STABILITY OF COMPOUNDED PREPARATIONS

USP defines stability as the extent to which a product retains, within specified limits, and throughout its period of storage and use (i.e., the shelf-life), the same properties and characteristics it possessed at the time of it was made. It is not difficult to compromise the stability of compounded products if they are not prepared or stored properly.

Functional Groups can be Susceptible to Degradation

The differences between drugs with similar chemical structures lies in the functional groups that are attached to the compound's core structure, and the bonds that hold the compound together. Reactions to the functional groups can make the drug ineffective, become unpalatable, and occasionally, become toxic. Reactions to the functional groups are common causes of drug degradation.

Reactions that Cause Drug Degradation

USP identifies these three types of chemical reactions that cause most drug products to become unstable and degrade:

- Oxidation-Reduction
- Hydrolysis, and
- Photolysis

The next section describes each of these reactions, with examples.

Methods that reduce the likelihood of the reaction (e.g., light and moisture protection) are important to extend the stability of the preparation.

Instability can cause changes in texture, color or smell

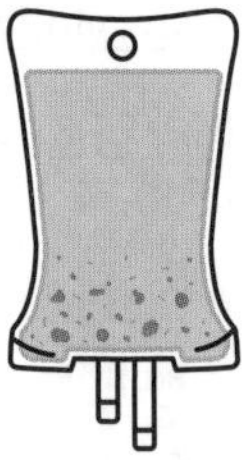

IV preparations must be examined for turbidity or any visual color changes or precipitates

The compounder uses methods that limit drug degradation and help the product remain stable, including:

Excipients, such as buffers to retain the pH in an adequate range and antimicrobials to prevent the growth of microorganisms.

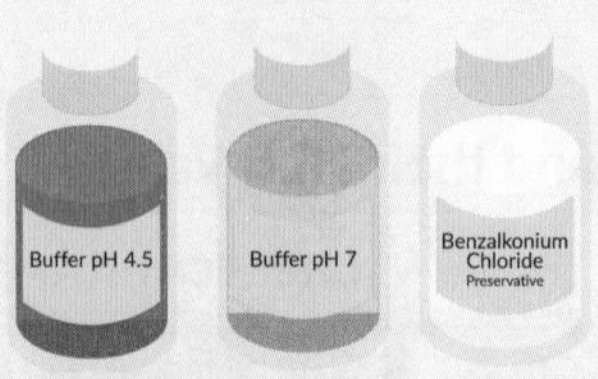

Light Protection, to block degradation from UV light exposure, causing photolysis.

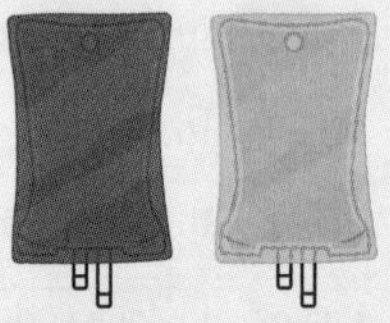

Packages that seal tightly to keep out light and moisture.

Proper storage, including refrigeration when a product is subject to damage from heat; heat causes molecules to vibrate (move), which speeds up chemical reactions.

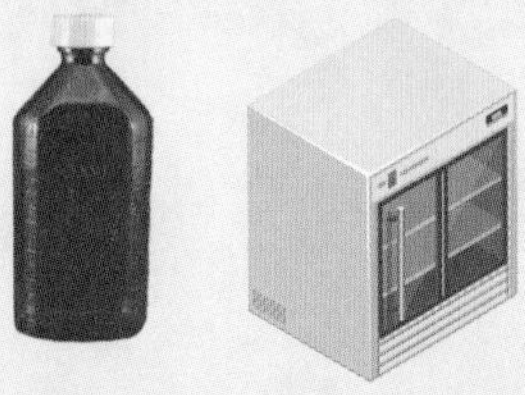

OXIDATION

What is Oxidation?

A compound is oxidized when it loses electrons and is reduced when it gains electrons. Oxidation and reduction reactions occur together; when one compound is oxidized, another must be reduced at the same time. This is called the re-dox reaction (re from reduction and ox from oxidation). An example of oxidation that can be seen (and enjoyed) is cooking onions to cause caramelization. The sugar is carmelized in a series of reactions, which begins when the alcohol functional group in the sugar is oxidized. An alcohol is a hydroxyl functional group (-OH) bound to a carbon. The water is removed when the steam evaporates. The end product has a visible color change and a change in taste (i.e., brown, caramel-flavored onions).

With some drugs, oxidation is visible with a color change, such as epinephrine becoming amber-colored (yellow/orange-ish). Other compounds turn pink/red-ish when oxidized. Oxidation will not always be apparent with a color change.

Which Compounds are Likely to Become Oxidized?

The molecular structures most likely to oxidize are those with a hydroxyl group directly bonded to an aromatic ring, such as catecholamines (e.g., epinephrine), phenolics (e.g., phenylephrine), phenothiazines (e.g., chlorpromazine), aldehydes (e.g., various structures used as flavorings), and some others.

Oxidation can increase in the presence of oxygen, light, increased temperature, changes in pH and some metal anions.

Example: Oxidation of Epinephrine. The presence of the hydroxyl groups on the ring make oxidation more likely.

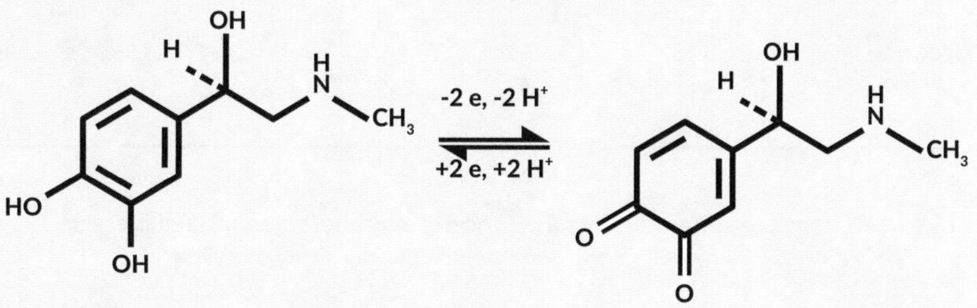

Epinephrine

How can Oxidation be Prevented?

Oxidation is catalyzed by heat, light and metal ions. Changes in temperature and pH must be carefully controlled; either can exponentially increase oxidation (and will do the same for hydrolysis reactions, described next).

Light-protection	With amber glass and plastic containers that seal out light, and light-protective sleeves (bags) for IV bags, IV lines and syringes.
Adequate storage	Temperature control with refrigeration, control of room temperatures and (occasionally) freezer storage.
Chelating agent	Use chelators to chelate metal ions that have an unshared electron in the outer shell. These are free radicals, which can catalyze oxidation chain reactions. The chelating agent ties up the catalyst, which prevents the reaction. Remember common chelators by Mr. **ED** Chelator: EDetate disodium (EDTA), EDetate calcium disodium and EDetic Acid.
Antioxidants Also called: free radical scavengers	Oxidation produces free radicals, which have an unshared electron in the outer shell. Free radicals are highly reactive with other compounds, and cause a chain reaction that damages the compound (see chelating agents, above). Autoxidation are oxidation reactions that occur routinely during preparation and storage. Antioxidants inhibit free radicals. Common antioxidants include ascorbic acid (vitamin C), tocopherols (vitamin E), ascorbyl palmitate, sodium (Na) ascorbate, Na bisulfate, Na sulfoxylate and Na thiosulfate.
Control pH	Maintain pH with a buffer; see pH discussion that follows.

HYDROLYSIS

What is Hydrolysis?

Hydrolysis occurs when water causes the cleavage of a bond in a molecule. Important protection will require that moisture is blocked from damaging the preparation. Counseling should include to avoid storing products susceptible to hydrolysis in the bathroom and to close containers tightly. Desiccants are sometimes used to soak up any moisture that enters the container.

Which Compounds are Likely to Become Hydrolyzed?

The most common functional groups susceptible to hydrolysis are esters, amides and lactams. The carbonyl group is subject to hydrolysis. Lactams are called cyclic amides.

Ester Carbonyl group bonded to an OR group	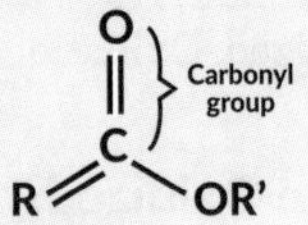
Amide Carbonyl group bonded to a Nitrogen	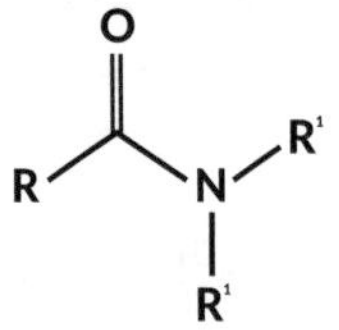
Lactam, a cyclic amide This is a beta-lactam ring, present in penicillins, carbapenems, cephalosporins and monobactams.	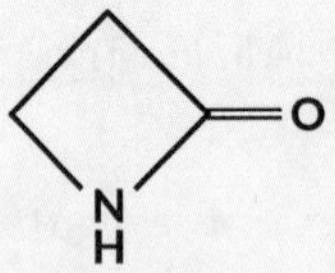

Example: Hydrolysis of the ester group on acetylsalicylic acid (aspirin) to acetic acid and salicylic acid (if moisture is present). In this example, hydrolysis is beneficial. The analgesic is salicylic acid, which is formed by a hydrolysis reaction from the prodrug acetylsalicylic acid.

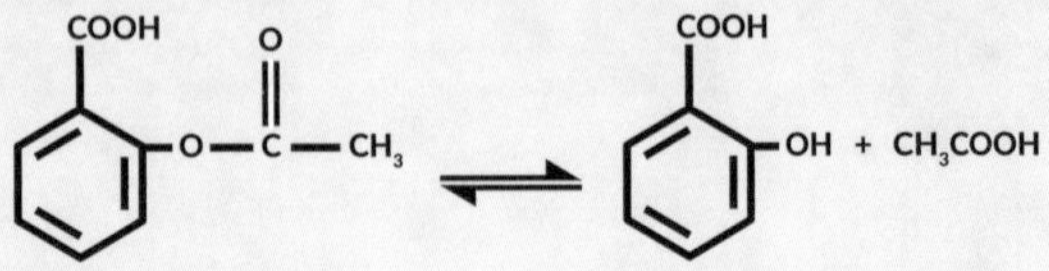

Asprin - acetylsalicylic acid   salicylic acid   acetic acid

How Can Hydrolysis be Prevented?

To reduce hydrolysis, the compound should be protected from moisture (water) exposure and other factors that favor degradation, including light exposure, metal ions and changes in temperature and pH.

Light-Protection	Amber glass, UV light-blocking containers (e.g., plastic) that close tightly to provide maximum protection against UV light, light-protective plastic, IV sleeves for IV bags, IV lines and syringes.
Adsorbent (desiccant)	To adsorb any moisture that enters the container.
Lyophilize solution	Drugs can be stored as a lyophilized (freeze-dried) powder instead of in solution.
Chelating agent	Chelating agents can limit exposure to metal ions that can catalyze hydrolysis.
Hygroscopic salt	With some formulations, a salt form of the drug can be chosen that is less hygroscopic (water-absorbing) than an alternative salt form.
Prodrug formulation	Prodrugs that release the active drug by a hydrolysis reaction can be formulated [e.g., acetylsalicylic acid (aspirin) is hydrolyzed to salicylic acid (the analgesic) and acetic acid].
Control temperature	Control the temperature in which the product is stored; hydrolysis occurs more rapidly at higher temperatures.
Control pH	Maintain pH with a buffer; see pH discussion that follows.

PHOTOLYSIS

What is Photolysis?

Many drugs are sensitive to UV light exposure, which causes photolysis (breakage) of covalent bonds, which will degrade the drug.

Which Compounds are Likely to Become Degraded by Light Exposure?

Compounds that are sensitive to light include ascorbic acid, folic acid, and many other drugs that require light protection, including nitroprusside, phytonadione injection, and other IV drugs (see Learning IV Drugs chapter).

How can Photolysis be Prevented?

Light-protection	With amber glass and plastic containers that seal out light, and light-protective sleeves (bags) for IV bags, IV lines and syringes.

ADDITIONAL PROCESSES THAT DEGRADE DRUGS

Other reactions that degrade drugs include:

- Isomerization, when a compound changes into a form with the same atoms but in an inactive structure.
- Epimerization occurs when a compound changes into an isomer that differs only in the configuration of the atoms. The two compounds are stereoisomers. Epimerization creates a chiral counterpart. The epimer can be inactive, or active (e.g., doxorubicin is active, and epirubicin, the epimer, is also active).
- Decarboxylation is another method of drug degradation that can happen to compounds with dissolved carboxylic acids. When heated, the carbon dioxide is lost from the carboxyl group. Drugs at risk of decarboxylation can be kept refrigerated.

EXCIPIENTS

MAJOR EXCIPIENTS	PURPOSE AND NOTES	EXAMPLES
Binders 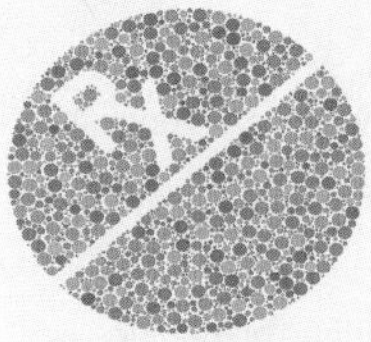	Binders add cohesion to powders to allow tablets to stick together, but permits the contents to be released once ingested, with or without a disintegrant.	Acacia, starch paste, sucrose syrup
Diluents and fillers 	Diluents (to make something more dilute) and fillers (to bulk up a small amount) add size to very small dosages. In liquids, the diluent also helps suspend the drug and facilitates disintegration, which is required for absorption (see disintegrants, next).	Dry products, like tablets and capsules: fillers include lactose and other sugars (e.g., mannitol, sorbitol), starches (many, including corn, rice, wheat), calcium salts, gelatin, bentonite Powdered cellulose is a common filler and thickener, and is used for many purposes in compounding, including as an adsorbent, disintegrant and as a suspending agent. Liquid fillers include water, glycerin and alcohol Fillers for topical products like creams and ointments include mineral oil, petrolatum, lanolin and various waxes
Disintegrants 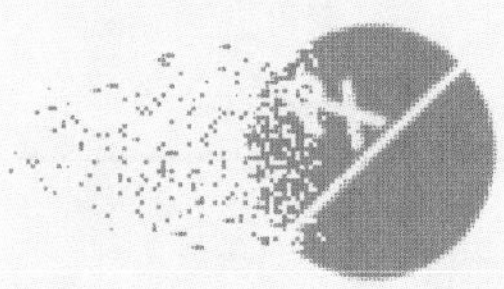	Facilitates the breakup of a tablet after oral administration. Oral products have to be dissolved in order to be absorbed in the small intestine, where most drugs are absorbed. Alginates absorb water, causing the tablet to swell and burst. Cellulose is from plants, or is synthetic, and also absorbs water well.	Alginic acid, polacrilin potassium (e.g., *Amberlite*), various cellulose products, starches, compressible sugar (e.g., *Nu-Tab*)

Flavorings and Coloring Agents 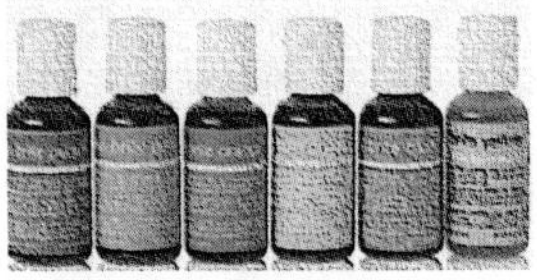	Flavorings and Coloring Agents: make the product look and taste better. Salty or sweet tastes mask a bitter flavor. Mint and spices mask poor flavor. Acids (such as citric acid) enhance fruit flavors. The color sometimes correlates with the flavor (e.g., cherry-flavored, with red color).	Coloring Agents D&C Red No. 3, Yellow No. 6, caramel, ferric oxide (red) Flavorings, Sweetening Agents: Sugar-free, artificial: aspartame, saccharin Glycerin, dextrose, lactose, mannitol, sorbitol, phenylalanine, stevia, xylitol aspartame, erythritol, maltilol, mannitol, monk fruit extract, phenylalanine, saccharin, stevia, sucralose Flavorings: are available in many flavors, including fruits, nuts (almond), etc.
Lubricants Also called: glidants or anti-adherents  	Lubricants help keep ingredients from sticking to each other and to equipment. This can be useful for tablet molds and punches, suppository molds and for capsule filling. Magnesium stearate is a common anti-adherent, and is used to improve powder flowability. See How to Prepare Suppositories section of chapter.	Magnesium stearate, calcium PEG, glycerin, mineral oil Stearic acid, talc Glidants, to improve the flow of powder in tablet and capsule formulations by reducing interparticle friction: magnesium stearate, colloidal silica
Preservatives 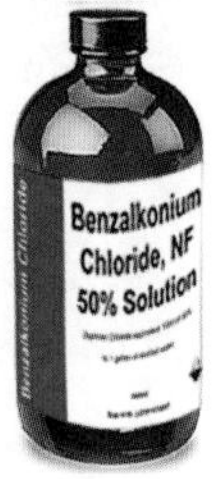 	Preservatives slow or prevent microorganism growth. Required in most preparations to control microbial growth), except if sterile and used immediately or if sealed in single-use preparations. Preservatives commonly have "benz" (like benzalkonium chloride), "cetyl" (like cetylpyridinium chloride), "phenyl/ols" and "parabens" in the name. Parabens are esters of para-hydroxybenzoic acid.	Do not use preservatives in neonates. Chlorhexidine is used as a preservative and is also used as an alcohol-based antiseptic for surgical scrubs and as a dental rinse *(Hibiclens, Biotene).* Topical/nasal: various alcohols, acids, chlorhexidine
	Oral	Oral: parabens, sodium benzoate, benzoic acid, cetylpyridinium chloride (often in mouthwashes, lozenges)
	Ophthalmic Eye drops need a preservative if they are multi-dose containers. Single-dose containers may not have a preservative.	QACs, e.g., benzalkonium chloride, EDTA, sodium benzoate, benzoic acid, Sorbic acid/potassium sorbate, chlorhexidine, biguanides (e.g., thimerosal (contains a small amount of mercury, used in some vaccines)
	Oral	Methyl, ethyl, propyl parabens Sodium benzoate/benzoic acid
Buffers 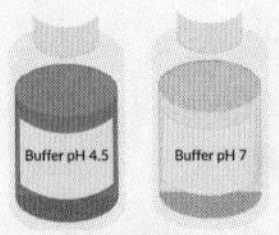 	The pKa determines how much is ionized versus how much is nonionized when placed into a solution with a set pH. Ionized compounds are more polar, which makes compounds more water-soluble. The pH of a buffer system can be calculated with the Henderson-Hasselbalch equation (see Calculations IV and Compounding III chapters).	Buffers can be purchased in prepared formulations that keep the pH within a narrow range. Common buffers include: ■ Potassium phosphate/metaphosphate ■ Sodium acetate/citrate ■ Hydrochloric acid/sodium hydroxide ■ Boric acid/potassium chloride ■ Potassium (biphthalate or phosphate)/water

Solvents Dissolve or Suspend the Ingredients

Hydrophilic Solvents

Water Water is commonly used as a solvent, as a delivery vehicle, for cleaning equipment and tools, and for other uses. Potable water (tap/drinking water) is safe to drink and is used for hand washing and initial equipment cleaning. 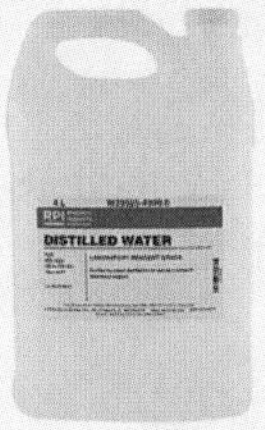	Water is the most commonly used solvent. As a delivery vehicle, water is used for oral liquid formulations (e.g., solutions, suspensions, emulsions), topicals (e.g., creams and lotions), in all types of injectable medications, sometimes used at the beginning of the compounding process for topicals, including ointments and creams, to dissolve the drug prior to adding it to the delivery vehicle. This helps avoid a gritty consistency in the final product.	USP specifies that purified water should be used in compounding, unless otherwise specified. Purified water has been treated to remove chemicals and contaminants. Types of purification include distillation, deionization, reverse osmosis, and carbon filtration. Distilled water is used often for reconstitution [i.e., adding water to lyophilized (freeze-dried) powder] to prepare oral suspensions and in non-sterile compounding preparations. Sterile water is required for sterile preparations; see next section.
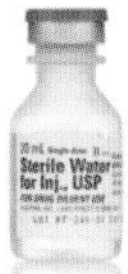	**Sterile water for injection (SWFI)**	For preparation and reconstitution of sterile drugs. The requirements for sterile water must be met plus SWFI must be devoid of bacterial endotoxins, because end otoxins (pyrogens) are produced by microorganisms that inhabit water.
	**Bacteriostatic water for injection**	SWFI, with antimicrobial preservatives
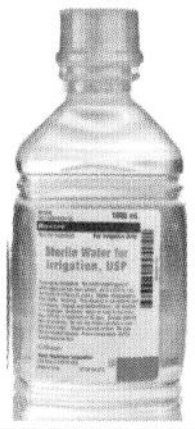	**Sterile water for irrigation (left)**	Similar to other sterile waters, in appropriately sized (larger) containers.

Hydrophobic Solvents

Alcohols **Alcohol USP** Ethanol (grain alcohol, ethyl alcohol or drinking alcohol), can be used as an alternative to fomepizole for methanol or ethylene glycol toxicity **Methanol—toxic** Fuel, used to make many chemicals **Ethylene glycol—toxic** Antifreeze **Isopropyl alcohols (see right column)**	Alcohols have high miscibility (mixes easily) with water, used to dissolve solutes that would be insoluble in water alone. Isopropyl alcohol is used as a disinfectant. **Isopropyl alcohols:**  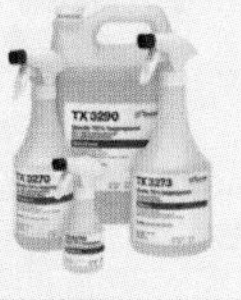	Isopropyl alcohols are used as disinfectants on equipment or on skin and can be used as solvents when compounding topical preparations. Isopropyl alcohol (IPA) is a skin disinfectant (e.g., on an alcohol swab for skin disinfection prior to a needle prick) and to disinfect equipment. IPA 70% is the preferred disinfectant in sterile compounding.

Oils and Fats Oils are hydrocarbon liquids derived from plants, animals or petroleum (i.e., petrolatum (*Vaseline* petroleum jelly). Oils are immiscible in water; they are hydrophobic, lipophilic compounds.	Oils are used as delivery vehicles, for therapeutic or nutritional use, and some are used as scents and flavorings.	Almond, borage, canola, castor coconut, mineral oils, others Omega-3 (alpha-linolenic fatty acids, DHA/EPA) Omega-6 (gamma-linoleic fatty acids)
Glycols Polyethylene glycol (PEG) is a long, synthetic polymer. The size/molecular weight depends on the number of times the structure inside the parentheses repeats: H–(O–CH2–CH2)n–OH PEG is a common excipient that is useful for many purposes. It has low toxicity and low systemic absorption. *Carbowax*, a similar product, is methoxy-polyethylene glycol (MPEG). PEG is used as a surfactant, solvent, plasticizer, suppository base, ointment base, lubricant and troche base. It is water-soluble and water-miscible (mixes well with water into a homogenous mixture). *Polybase* is a PEG mixture that is commonly used as a suppository base—it is a good delivery vehicle and slides out of molds without the need for a lubricant. It is also a good emulsifier.	**Glycols are very useful in compounding (e.g., polyethylene glycol, or PEG) or (with some glycols) are not used at all due to toxicity (ethylene glycol, which is antifreeze).** **Glycols have a low freezing point (which makes antifreeze possible), a high boiling point, and are water soluble.**	Glycerin Propylene glycol: use only in small quantities as a solvent (large quantities are toxic). PEGs are numbered based on the molecular weight, e.g., PEG 400 and PEG 3350. See first column. PEG 400 is used commonly in compounding and PEG 3350 is used commonly as a laxative. PEG linked to a protein drug (pegylated), such as PEG-filgrastim, increases the half-life by helping the drug escape the immune system and decreasing the renal clearance. Emollient products include ointments, creams, lotions, bath oils and soap substitutes.

Emollients (Moisturizers)

Prior to reviewing the emollients on the next page, it is helpful to note the differences between emollients. An emollient refers to a product that softens and soothes the skin.

Occlusive ointments, including petroleum jelly (i.e., white petrolatum), theobroma oil (i.e., cocoa butter), beeswax, paraffin and other waxes form a protective barrier to prevent the loss of water molecules from the top layer of the skin (epidermis). They work well, but feel greasy. They help fill in cracks in the skin, and help to keep very dry skin from cracking.

Humectants are put into many emollient formulations to pull in water from the atmosphere to moisturize the skin. They can be sticky-feeling, and are combined with other more soothing ingredients. Humectants include glycerin or glycerol, propylene glycol, PEG, urea, hyaluronic acid.

Selecting a moisturizer can be guided by the water content, since less water provides a stronger barrier to water loss, but a less comfortable (i.e., greasier) emollient.

Ointments have from 80-100% oil, with 0-20% water, and are best for extremely dry skin and thick skin, such as on elbows and feet.

Creams are usually about half oil, half water (minimally greater than 20% water and up to 50% oil) and are best for normal and dry skin.

Lotions have the most water, and are best for oily skin.

Ointments Provide a barrier to water-loss from the skin and are used as vehicles for topical drug delivery. Petrolatum, lanolin, mineral oil and dimethicone are common emollients. In some products the emollient components are mixed with humectants, which draw water into the skin, and make the product less greasy. Common combination products *Polybase:* PEG 400, PEG 8000, polysorbate 80 Water-soluble, water-miscible, commonly used in compounding. Can be used for compounding, or purchased OTC: *Aquaphor*: 41% petrolatum, with mineral oil, lanolin, glycerin + other ingredients. (Mineral oil is derived from petroleum, and is also called baby oil.) Semi-occlusive barrier, greasy but less than petrolatum. *Aquabase:* similar to *Aquaphor*.	Ointments are defined as semisolids, with 0- 20% water, with hydrocarbons, waxes, and/or polyols (compounds with multiple OH groups). USP separates ointments into 4 groups. Some contain water and some do not, which is important in determining the BUD; see Compounding III chapter. Four ointment groups: Hydrocarbon Bases, called "oleaginous" ointments (oil-containing, no water) Good for drug delivery and forming a protective barrier, difficult to wash off/ greasy. Absorption Bases Can be used to form water-in-oil emulsion, useful as emollients. Water-Removable Bases Are hydrophilic, oil-in-water emulsions. Per USP, are more correctly called creams. They are more easily diluted, and wash more easily off the skin. Water-Soluble Bases Does not contain petrolatum. Per USP, are more correctly called gels.	**Emollients** Hydrocarbon Bases White ointment, white petrolatum (e.g., *Vaseline* petroleum jelly) Forms occlusive barrier, feels greasy. Absorption Bases Hydrophilic petrolatum, lanolin Water-Removable Bases Are oil-in-water emulsions, which are hydrophilic. Water-Soluble Bases Polyethylene glycol ointment

Creams More water than ointments	Creams are semi-solid preparations that have a soft, spreadable consistency. Most creams are water-in-oil or oil-in-water emulsions. Water-in-oil creams feel more greasy.	*Lipoderm* cream *Eucerin*: water, petrolatum, mineral oil, ceresin, lanolin + other ingredients *Cetaphil*: water, glycerin, petrolatum, dimethicone, benzyl alcohol, PEG + other ingredients
Lotions More water than creams, which makes them more fluid. Lotions are sometimes poured from a container, which is not feasible with creams.	Lotions are used to refer to solutions although technically, lotions are emulsions Lotions can be aqueous or hydroalcoholic, with a small amount of alcohol added to solubilize ingredients, or to hasten evaporation of the solvent from the skin.	*Versabase* lotion
Gels Poloxamers contain a hydrophobic chain of polyoxypropylene with two hydrophilic chains of polyoxyethylene. This formulation makes it viable to use poloxamer gel for hydrophobic or hydrophilic drug delivery.	Gels (or jellies) are semisolid preparations of small inorganic particles or large organic molecules interpenetrated by a liquid. If the gel has small discrete particles in it, is classified as a two-phase system, which are also called a magma.	Poloxamer 407NF Poloxamer *(Pluronic)* Lecithin Organogel (PLO) gel Aqueous solutions of poloxamers are liquid when refrigerated and form a gel at room temperature, in a reversible process. The commonly used PLO gel is used often because of this property; compounds are easily mixed into the liquid (when taken from the refrigerator), which then forms a gel when stored at room temperature (see comic on the next page).
Pastes	Pastes contain powder in an ointment base.	Zinc oxide paste, used for diaper rash; zinc oxide is a desiccant (to draw water from the baby's bottom) placed into an ointment base.
Suppository bases, made of various fats and glycols	Suppository bases have to stay intact for insertion, and melt once inserted. Theobroma oil (cocoa butter) used to be a common base for suppositories until newer bases began to be used because it melts too easily.	Cocoa butter (theobroma oil), hydrogenated vegetable oils (palm, palm kernel, and coconut oils), PEG polymers, glycerinated gelatin

Additional Excipients

OTHER EXCIPIENTS	PURPOSE AND NOTES	EXAMPLES
Adsorbents	To keep powders dry, to prevent hydrolysis reactions	Magnesium oxide/carbonate, kaolin
Anti-foaming agent	Breaks up and inhibits the formation of foams.	Simethicone, dimethicone
Coatings (regular)	Prevent degradation due to oxygen, light, moisture, mask unpalatable taste.	Shellac, gelatin, gluten (food grade)
Enteric-coating	Most drugs dissolve in the stomach and are absorbed in the small intestine. Some drugs would be destroyed by stomach acid and require an acid-resistant (enteric-coated) protective layer to prevent dissolution in the stomach. The coating can also be used to mask poor taste.	Cellulose acetate phthalate Shellac (a natural polymer resin, from insects)
Gelling (thickening) agent, stabilizer	Increases the viscosity of a substance; can stabilize the mixture. Gelatin, cellulose and bentonite are used commonly; they swell well when mixed with water. Cetyl alcohol is not water-soluble.	Agar, alginates, various gums [guar, xantham, acacia (a natural gum)], gelatins, bentonite (a type of clay), carbomer, cellulose (spongy, from plants), starches, tragacanth, acrylates, cetyl alcohol, magnesium aluminum silicate (Veegum), poloxamer (pluronic) gels, polyvinyl alcohol (eye lubricant)
Humectant	Prevents preparations from becoming dry and brittle, when put into emollients, draws water into the skin to moisturize.	Glycerin or glycerol, propylene glycol, PEG, lecithin, urea, hyaluronic acid.
Levigating (wetting) agent	Liquid used in the process of reducing the particle size to reduce the surface tension.	Mineral oil, glycerin, glycols, PEG, propylene glycol

EXCIPIENTS TO BE AVOIDED IN SOME PATIENTS

EXCIPIENT	AVOID IN	ALTERNATIVE
Gelatin, used to form capsule shells	Vegetarians and vegans, anyone who wishes to avoid pork	Hypromellose capsule shells are made from cellulose and are vegan (no meat or dairy) and vegetarian (no meat).
Gluten, used as a starch (filler). Gluten is in wheat, barley and rye. Gluten as a starch in drugs is primarily from wheat.	Celiac disease, anyone who wishes to avoid gluten	Starch can come from non-gluten sources (e.g., corn, potato, tapioca).
Lactose, used as a sweetener, to compress tablets, filler, diluent	Lactose intolerance or lactose allergy	Lactose content may/may not cause symptoms (with intolerance) as the amount in compounded products can be small. Select an alternative (with lactose allergy, and possibly with lactose intolerance), depending on the purpose.
Phenylalanine, used as a sweetener Aspartame is a precursor to phenylalanine, causes same symptoms to a lesser extent	Phenylketonuria (PKU), not able to metabolize phenylalanine	Select alternative sweeteners; see excipient table.
Sorbitol, used as a sweetener	Irritable Bowel Syndrome (IBS); sorbitol can cause GI distress in IBS	Select alternative sweeteners; see excipient table.
Sucrose (table sugar), used as a sweetener and coating	Diabetes	The amount used may/may not cause the blood glucose to increase. Select alternative sweeteners; see excipient table.
Xylitol, used as a sweetener	Do not use in dogs, who are susceptible to xylitol toxicosis, with hypoglycemia and liver damage. Xylitol can cause GI upset in some humans.	Select alternative sweeteners; see excipient table.

CHAPTER CONTENT

Documentation ... 267
Non-Sterile Preparations ... 267
- Master Formula ... 268
- Compounding Record ... 269
- Preparation Steps ... 270
- Initial Steps ... 270
- Compounding Steps ... 270
- Completion Steps ... 270

Preparing Powders ... 271
- Reducing Particle Size ... 271
- Reducing Particle Size & Cake Baking ... 271
- Mixing Ingredients ... 272
- Compounding Ingredients ... 273

Dosage Forms ... 273
- Solutions, Suspensions and Emulsions ... 274
- Powders ... 274
- Capsules ... 275
- Tablets ... 275
- Lozenges/Troches ... 276
- Creams ... 276
- Lotions ... 276
- Ointments ... 276
- Pastes ... 276
- Gels ... 276
- Suppositories ... 276
- Suppositories ... 277

Compounding Kits ... 277
Non-Sterile Quality Assurance ... 277
Selecting the Beyond Use Date ... 277
Applying Product and Auxiliary Labels ... 278
Patient Counseling ... 278
Sterile Preparations ... 278
- Physiochemical Considerations ... 278
- Work Flow for CSP Preparation ... 280
- How To Set Up Items in the PEC ... 280
- How To Transfer Solutions and Inject Into IV Bags ... 280
- Visual Inspection ... 281
- Terminal Sterilization ... 281

Label Requirements ... 281
Pyrogen (Bacterial Endotoxin) Testing ... 281
Sterile Preparation and Risk ... 281
- Low-Risk Sterile Compounding ... 282
- Lyophilized Sterile IV Drugs ... 282
- Medium-Risk Sterile Compounding ... 282
- High-Risk Sterile Compounding ... 282

CSP Quality Assurance ... 282
- How to Choose a Beyond Use Date ... 283
- Determining the BUD For CSPs ... 284

Recalls ... 284
Osmolarity and Intravenous Drugs ... 284
- Osmolarity and Tonicity ... 284

Resisting Changes In pH with Buffer Systems ... 285
Test Your Knowledge with Puzzles! ... 286

CONTENT LEGEND

(💡) = Study Tip Gal

CHAPTER 17
COMPOUNDING III: DOCUMENTATION & PREPARATION

DOCUMENTATION

Two very important records that each compounded product must have are the master formulation record and the compounding record. The master formulation record is the recipe that is followed to compound a preparation. The compounding log (or record) is the log book of all products made at the pharmacy (see images on the following pages).

The documentation in the compounding log must be detailed enough that another trained person can replicate the steps involved in the preparation, evaluate if the procedure was correct, and trace the origin of all components.

The pharmacy must also keep records of steps and processes that relate to the compounded product. These include the equipment cleaning, calibration and maintenance, temperature logs for the refrigerator, freezer and room (ambient) air and records of chemicals, bulk drugs, drug products, and any other component.

NON-STERILE PREPARATIONS

Cautionary Note on Preparation of Non-Sterile HDs

Non-sterile HDs should preferably be compounded in a C-PEC. This option is not always available, and efforts must be made to protect the staff with techniques to reduce exposure (e.g., splitting tablets while enclosed in a sealed plastic bag). All equipment used for HDs, including counting trays and spatulas, must be dedicated for HDs only, and sanitized after use.

The final formulations, when possible, should be placed into single unit-dose, sealed packaging, and placed into a plastic bag labeled with a cytotoxic label (see image).

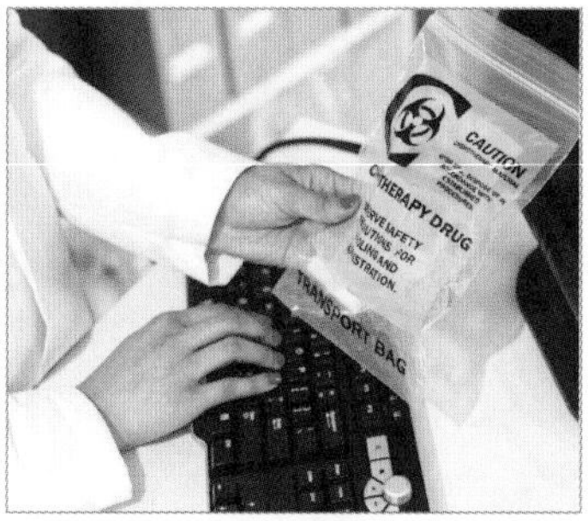

© Teva Canada Limited

MASTER FORMULA #3755
IBUPROFEN 200mg SUPPOSITORIES

Formula:			
Ibuprofen 200mg Suppositories			
Strength:	200mg	**Quantity:**	1
Ingredients:			**Quantity:**
Ibuprofen			0.2 gm
Silica Gel			0.02 gm
Base MBK (Fatty Acid Base)			Calculate
Procedure:			
Note: Calculations should be made to make an excess amount of 10% of what is needed for the lot.			
1. Calculate and weigh ingredients to prepare 10 Ibuprofen 200mg suppositories in the blue mold which is calibrated to 1.28 gm of Base MBK per suppository. Use the Suppository, general formula worksheet.			
2. Melt Base MBK at 50 degrees C using a hot water bath.			
3. Using a mortar and pestle, triturate Ibuprofen and Silic a gel together to a fine powder.			
4. Sift the powder from Step 3 into the melted Base MBK while stirring. The use of a strainer helps to insure small particle size.			
5. Turn off heat and stir until mixture is looks consistently suspended.			
6. Pour into molds (may use a large temperature.			
7. Package in universal sleeve and l			
Recommended Expiration:	18		
Recommended Storage/Auxiliary L			
Notes:			

MASTER FORMULA #3755
Compound's Official or Assigned Name
Strength, Dosage Form

Calculations
Ingredients, with Quantities

Stability & Compatibility Data, with references
Equipment
Preparation/Mixing Instructions
Labeling Information
Packaging/Storage Requirements
QC Procedures, with Expected Results
BUD, Recommended
Description of Final Product

What you SHOULD do

Formula # 3755

Raindrop Compounding Pharmacy
COMPOUNDING RECORD

PRODUCT

Drug Name and Strength	Use/Dosage Form	Quantity	Control/Rx #	Date
Ibuprofen 200 mg	Suppositories	#10	37-865	4-7-19

INGREDIENTS

Ingredient	NDC or Manufacturer #	QTY	LOT	EXP
Ibuprofen powder USP	IB100-25, Spectrum	2 g	A3472-19	3/24
Silica gel	S1935, Spectrum	0.2 g	S1008-19	12/23
MBK base	30-156, PCCA	12.8 g	1234-18	2/21
Disposable supp molds	Apothecary			

COMPOUNDING DIRECTIONS & PROCEDURES

1. Calcs: Ibuprofen 0.2 g x 10 = 2 g, Silica 0.02 g x 10 = 0.2 g, MBK base 1.28 g x 10 = 12.8 g
2. Weighed 12.8 g MBK base
3. Placed base in beaker, heat in hot-water bath at warm temp of 50 °C

COMPOUNDING RECORD OR LOG

Compound's Official Name or Assigned Name
Reference # for the Master Formula
Strength, Dosage Form

Specific to this preparation

Ingredients (including manufacturer/sources, lot numbers & exp. dates)

Steps followed

QC results

BUD, actual (assigned)

Description of the final preparation

The product's assigned control or prescription number—a duplicate prescription label can be attached to the log

Staff involved with the preparation

(1) Compounder, (2) Person who did QC, (3) RPh who approved final product, with dates

What you DID

Image above: Modified from www.totalpharmacysupply.com

PREPARATION STEPS

Prior to preparing to compound, the pharmacist will need to evaluate the prescription and determine if it is appropriate for the patient, and whether the proposed formulation is reasonable (e.g., is the formulation likely to have acceptable stability and palatability?)

When ready to compound, the initial steps will be similar for most formulations, such as calibrating equipment and weighing ingredients.

The final steps will be similar, and include packaging and performing quality control (QC).

What changes most are the steps in between, which depend on the type of formulation to be prepared.

Quality ingredients are needed for a quality product, as reviewed in the Compounding II chapter. Always review the material safety data sheets (MSDS) for each bulk ingredient to determine safety procedures for the staff who will compound the preparation, including the recommended personal protective equipment (PPE).

The Formulation Determines the Type of Garb

Minimally, PPE (i.e., garb) should include a clean lab coat and gloves when preparing non-sterile, non-hazardous preparations. The MSDS will provide information if other PPE is needed. For example, the MSDS for benzalkonium chloride recommends using gloves, a gown and eye/face protection. Benzalkonium chloride should not be exposed to skin or mucus membranes, and the MSDS provides instructions to manage exposure, such as steps to take if the compound is inhaled.

PPE is reviewed in the Compounding I chapter.

INITIAL STEPS

1. Calculate the quantities needed for each component.
2. Gather all the components and the equipment needed.
3. Wash equipment, if needed, and calibrate.
4. Perform hand hygiene and garb.

COMPOUNDING STEPS

The product is made according to the Master Formulation Record.

- Most formulations will require common techniques, such as trituration or levigation, and geometric dilution.
- Other steps are unique to the formulation type, such as calculating the density factor to make suppositories.

COMPLETION STEPS

1. Package the product and apply the container label and any needed auxiliary labels. A duplicate container label can be placed on the compounding record.

2. Perform QC: validate the weight, check the product for mixing adequacy, color, clarity, odor, consistency and pH. Enter the measurements and observations in the compounding record.

3. Counsel the patient, and if any subsequent ADRs are reported, add them to the compounding record.

Unit-Dose Repackaging

A unit-dose refers to a small package that contains one dose of a medication. Unit-dose preparations can come from the manufacturer or a repackaging company, or a pharmacy can repackage multi-dose containers into unit-dose packages.

If a pharmacy repackages clopidogrel 75 mg from a multidose container of #100 tablets, each unit-dose package will contain one 75 mg tablet, which is the usual dose of the medication.

Repackaging multi-dose medication containers into unit-dose packages is not traditional compounding, but has some commonalities, including the assignment of a beyond use date (BUD) by the pharmacy staff, and can have other requirements, such as safety measures if repackaging HDs.

BUDs for repackaged drugs should be the manufacturer's expiration date from the original container or 1-year from the repackaging date, whichever is earlier.

In both community and hospital settings, different categories of medications are kept separate (e.g., recalled, experimental, expired and repackaged unit-dose medications).

PREPARING POWDERS

REDUCING PARTICLE SIZE

When compounding with dry ingredients, the goal is to make an evenly-distributed, fine powder mixture of the ingredients. Comminution means to reduce particle size by grinding, crushing, milling, vibrating or other processes (manual or mechanical).

Packing an ointment

Initially, the compounder likely starts off with coarse granules or broken tablet pieces. Powders will be finely ground into particles that range in size from 0.1 – 10 microns. After the powder has been ground, it is placed into a sieve.

Sieves, which are sifters, are used after the powder has been ground in order to ensure that the particle size is uniform. The powder is put into the sieve and sifted through the mesh. Once placed into the sieve, the powder is stirred with a sieve brush or a plastic spatula to force the particles through the mesh. A high mesh size has many wires that make many holes, and only a fine powder will get through the mesh. The sieve number is based on the number of holes per inch; e.g., #100 sieve has 100 openings/inch.

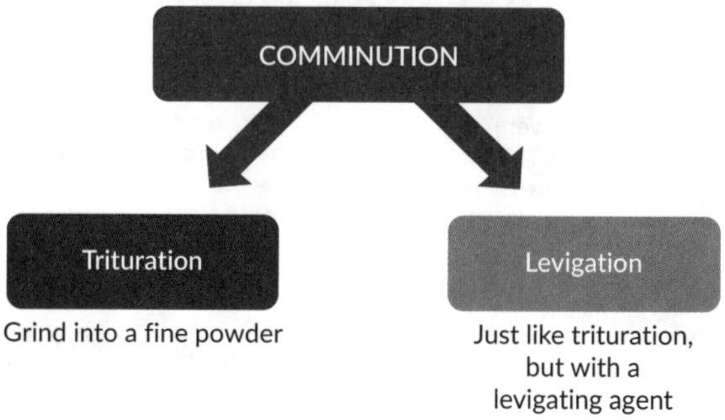

The three main methods of comminution include:

- Trituration: a general term used to mean "mix thoroughly" (or make the product homogenous). Pharmacists most commonly associate trituration with grinding tablets in a mortar with a pestle until a fine powder is achieved, but the term can describe liquids (e.g., triturating an emulsion by shaking it).
- Levigation and spatulation:
  - Levigation involves triturating the powder with a mortar and pestle by incorporating a small amount of liquid (called a levigating agent or wetting agent) to help with the grinding process. Levigation will turn the solid into a uniform paste.
  - Spatulation is similar to levigation, but performed on an ointment slab with a spatula (instead of in a mortar with a pestle).
- Pulverization by intervention is used for crystalline powders that will not crush easily. The crystals are dissolved with an intervening solvent and mixed until the solvent evaporates. When the powder recrystallizes, the particles are finer and easier to work with.

The calculations required for compounding will often require unit conversions, percentage and ratio strengths, basic algebra and changing concentrations with Q1C1 = Q2C2 and alligation.

Example:
What is the percentage strength (w/w) of ketamine in the compounded topical pain gel? (Round to the nearest WHOLE number.)

TOPICAL PAIN GEL	
Ketamine HCl	20g
Amitriptyline	10g
Baclofen	2.5g
Glycerin	15g
Tween 85	7.5g
Potassium sorbate	200 mg
Poloxamer F 127 30%	qs ad 90g

Percentage Strength:

$\frac{20\ g}{90\ g} = \frac{X\ g}{100\ g}$ x = 22.222 g or 22%

REDUCING PARTICLE SIZE & CAKE BAKING

A baker wishes to make a smooth, uniform cake, without any lumps.

1. Select finely-ground cake flour.
2. Mix a small amount of ingredients with a mixing spoon until the mixture is smooth and uniform. Add in more ingredients, repeat. This process makes the ingredients uniformly distributed and prevents a lumpy cake.

A compounding pharmacist wishes to make a smooth, evenly-distributed mixture of ingredients.

1. The pharmacist needs a fine powder too. Comminution methods are used.
2. Ingredients are mixed using geometric dilution to ensure thorough, even mixing of ingredients.

Capsules, tablets, ointments, creams - and cakes - come out smooth and uniform.

MIXING INGREDIENTS

Geometric dilution is a method of mixing ingredients to ensure that the ingredients are evenly distributed in a diluent or delivery vehicle. Typically, the drug is a fine powder. A small amount of the drug powder will be mixed into an equal amount of the diluent (e.g., into an ointment base). After the initial small amount is thoroughly mixed, another equal amount of the remaining ingredients is mixed in. This is repeated until all the ingredients are mixed together. Geometric dilution can be used with dry powder ingredients alone, or when making a paste.

When using multiple ingredients, begin with the ingredient that has the smallest quantity, followed by the ingredient with the next smallest quantity, and up until each has been added. With each addition, the amount should be roughly doubled, as shown in the comic below.

Geometric Dilution is used to Prepare Homogenous Preparations

COMPOUNDING INGREDIENTS

APIs and Excipients

The Compounding II chapter reviewed organizations that provide monographs and other sources to evaluate and identify ingredients that are high-quality. It is worth repeating prior to preparing a formulation, because a formulation cannot be high quality if any of the ingredients are low quality. This includes the drug/s, which are the active pharmaceutical ingredients, or APIs) and the excipients, which are everything else in the formulation.

- Excipients do not produce therapeutic effect, but are needed to make the dosage form stable, functional, palatable and pleasing to the patient.

High-quality ingredients ensure the purity and safety of the formulation. Ingredients that are acceptable for use will be listed in either:

- The USP National Formulary (USP-NF), or
- The Food Chemicals Codex (FCC) list of substances.

Quality Ingredients for a Quality Product

Preferably, the approved substances should be manufactured at an FDA-registered facility.

If any substance comes from a non-FDA registered facility, a Certificate of Analysis (CoA) should be obtained that confirms the specification and quality requirements.

If any component is moved to a different container, the new container should be labeled with the component name, original supplier, lot or control number, transfer date and expiration date. Ingredients deteriorate, and expiration dates are important.

If there is a component without an expiration date, the pharmacist will assign a conservative (cautious) date that is no more than 3 years from the date of receipt (the day the pharmacy received the item). The label should contain both the date of receipt and the assigned expiration date.

DOSAGE FORMS

SOLUTIONS, SUSPENSIONS AND EMULSIONS

	A **SOLUTION** is a solute dissolved in a solvent (such as NaCl, dissolved in water). Solutions are homogenous (consistent, uniform throughout). If the solute concentration is too high, it can lead to unwanted precipitation (see below). Solutions are usually for oral use. Lotions are topical solutions.	**Types of Solutions** Syrups are oral solutions with sucrose or other sugars or artificial sugars. Elixirs are sweet hydroalcoholic solutions used for drugs that would be insoluble in a purely aqueous formulation. Hydroalcohol is a mixture of alcohol and water. Tinctures are plant or animal extracts dissolved in alcohol or hydroalcohol. Spirits are alcohol or hydroalcohol of volatile, aromatic compounds such as camphor. Volatile means the compound vaporizes (evaporates) easily.
	A **SUSPENSION** is a solid dispersed in a liquid. It is a two-phase heterogeneous mixture. A wetting agent/levigating agent is a type of surfactant used to incorporate an insoluble drug into a liquid, which makes a suspension. A desirable suspension does not have rapid precipitation of the solids; particles can be re-dispersed easily by shaking.	
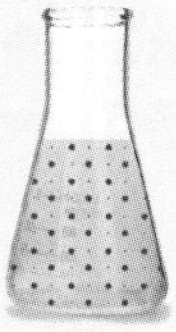	An **EMULSION** is a liquid dispersed in a liquid. It is a two-phase heterogeneous mixture. Emulsions are oil-in-water (oil droplets in an aqueous vehicle) or water-in-oil.* Water and oil normally are immiscible (do not mix). An emulsifier is a type of surfactant that is used to reduce the surface tension between oil and water. The emulsifier allows the two phases to come closer together. To make the emulsion, the emulsifier will need to be carefully chosen, according to the hydrophilic-lipophilic balance (HLB) number (see Compounding II chapter).	**EMULSIFIERS** Acacia, agar, carbomers, glyceryl monostearate, pectin, PEG, sodium lauryl sulfate, sorbitan lipophilic esters (Arlacel, Span), sorbitan hydrophilic esters (Myrj, Tween) **The phase that is present as droplets is the dispersed, internal phase or discontinuous phase, and the phase in which the droplets are suspended is the continuous or external phase.*
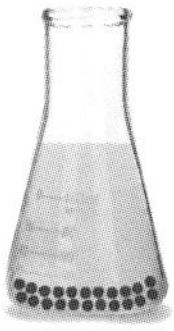	**PRECIPITATION/SEDIMENTATION** is when the dispersed phase settles (clumps) together. This can happen with suspensions and emulsions. The process of a solid settling on the bottom of a container is sedimentation. Shake or gently roll to re-disperse. This happens less commonly with solutions, but with some, such as insulin, the solid can settle to the bottom and must be re-dispersed prior to use.	

How to Prepare Solutions

Prepare the ingredients, and reduce the particle size of the drug/s to form a fine powder. The initial step in preparing any solution will be to determine if the solute will dissolve in the solution. The drug should remain soluble at different temperatures that may be encountered, including during refrigeration, if required for stability. If the drug is not soluble (e.g., will not dissolve in water) a suspension or a different solvent may be preferable. The dissolution rate can be used to determine the time it will take for the solute to dissolve. The dissolution rate is calculated using Fick's First Law of Diffusion. A larger surface area (i.e., smaller particles), stirring the preparation and using heat will increase the dissolution rate.

Determine if the solution will be stable at the desired temperature. A buffer system may be needed to resist changes in pH (see end of this chapter). A preservative may be needed to protect against microbial growth, including bacteria, fungi and yeast. Flavorings, sweeteners and coloring agents can be added. Package the solution and apply appropriate auxiliary labels. An oral solution prepared with water as a solvent can receive a maximum BUD of 14 days, and should be refrigerated.

How to Prepare Suspensions

Prepare the ingredients, and reduce the particle size of the drug/s to form a fine powder. Wet the powder, and levigate to form a paste. Continue to add liquid in portions. Add a surfactant to help keep the suspension dispersed. Transfer the mixture into a conical graduate or the container in which it will be dispensed, and QS to the final volume. A homogenizer will help make a uniform suspension. A preservative may be needed to protect against microbial growth, including bacteria, fungi and yeast. Flavorings, sweeteners and coloring agents can be added. Package the suspension and apply a beyond use date (BUD). An oral suspension prepared with water can receive a maximum BUD of 14 days, and should be refrigerated.

Even with surfactants used as suspending agents, suspensions are inherently unstable, and will need to be redispersed (i.e., shaken) prior to use.

How to Prepare Emulsions

Emulsions can be prepared with either the Continental gum or the English gum method. The Continental gum (also called the dry gum method) method uses oil, water, and an emulsifier in a 4:2:1 mixture in the order OWE: 4 parts oil, 2 parts water and 1 part emulsifier. Acacia, or another gum-type emulsifier is used. The gum is levigated with oil, then the water is added all at once. The mixture is triturated by shaking it until a cracking sound is heard and the mixture looks creamy white. Add other ingredients by dissolving them first in solution, and adding a quantity of water sufficient to make (QS) up to the final volume. Homogenize (i.e., with a homogenizer machine) to make the emulsion uniform.

The English gum method (also called the wet gum method)uses the same 4:2:1 oil, water and emulsifier mixture, with different preparation steps. Triturate the gum (emulsifier) and water to form a mucilage, then add the oil slowly, while triturating (shaking) to form the emulsion. Finish the same as in the previous method. *Remember: It rains a lot in England (wet) and the oil is added slowly because you cannot drive too fast in the rain. The continent is dry, and you can add the water quickly (all at once).*

POWDERS

Powders are fine particles of a solid. A dose of medication can be given as the dry powder (put into liquid or a small amount of soft food) for someone who is not able to swallow capsules or tablets, such as a small child or an elderly person with dysphagia. Powders are used to prepare tablets, capsules, inhalations, suspensions, ointments, creams and other topical treatments. The powder itself can consist of only the active drug, or include excipients. The excipients listed here are specific to the powder part of the preparation, and the examples are commonly used for the purpose stated:

- Glidant/lubricant to improve the flowability of a powder: magnesium stearate.
- Surfactant to neutralize the static charge and keep the powder from floating away: sodium lauryl sulfate.

Melting Point Order

For any formulation, if melting ingredients, melt the ingredient with the lowest melting point prior to adding the ingredient/s with higher melting points.

- Line up the ingredients by the melting temperature, and melt in that order, starting with the lowest melting point.

Eutectic Mixtures

A eutectic mixture means that the combination of the ingredients (when mixed together) will melt at a lower temperature than either of the individual component's melting temperatures (see comic on following page).

- A eutectic mixture can be useful by providing a lower melting point but can also create difficulty. If a pharmacist is not aware that the components form a eutectic mixture, the hot plate can be set on too high a temperature, and the mixture can burn.
- Another potential problem involves mixing powders that form a eutectic mixture when combined. If the components are solid powders at room temperature, the mixture of the powders can melt and turn the mixture into a sticky mess, and ruin the (previously) dry preparation.

An adsorbent powder (magnesium oxide, magnesium carbonate or kaolin) can be used to keep the powder dry.

How to Prepare Powders

Reduce the size of the powder. This may require breaking down tablets with a grinder, followed by trituration or levigation. Sift the powder through a sieve (pictured previously) onto glassine paper.

If the amount of powder per dose is very small, it will be necessary to add an inert filler (diluent). A filler could also be needed to provide a minimum weighable quantity if using a torsion balance (see previous description). A common diluent is lactose. Add the filler and other excipients using geometric dilution.

CAPSULES

Capsules are soluble shells of gelatin (an animal product) or hypromellose (a vegetable product), which are filled with the active drug, diluents (fillers) and any other excipients. Hard-shell capsules are used most commonly in compounding, and are filled with powders. Soft-shell capsules are used mostly for oils. Glycerol and sorbitol are used as plasticizers to make the capsules less brittle and more flexible.

The compounding space is separate from the dispensing space.

Common capsule sizes range from largest (size 000, ~1 inch long) to smallest (size 5, ~0.4 inches long).

- Capsule bodies can be filled by hand (for a small number) or with a capsule-filling machine (for larger amounts).
- In addition to using a capsule filling machine to add a powder formulation, liquids can be added to upright capsule bodies with a pipette or dropper.

How to Prepare Capsules

Capsules are made by first triturating the dry ingredients and geometrically mixing with the fillers/other excipients. The powder is put into the capsules by either hand filling (also known as the "punch method") or by using a capsule-filling machine (see the Molds, Presses and Packaging Equipment section).

Hand filling: To begin, the powder is placed on powder paper or on an ointment slab. The pile of powder is smoothed with a spatula to a height about a third of the length of the capsule. The open end of the capsule is repeatedly "punched" into the pile of powder until the capsule is filled. When the base is filled, it is fitted with the cap.

Manual capsule-filling machine: These are small devices that help the pharmacist quickly load 50, 100 or 300 capsules. Plates sort the capsule bodies to stand upright and hold them in place. The powder is put above the capsules on to a plastic sheet where a plastic spreader and tamper is used to move the powder into the capsules. The comb and spreader are used repeatedly until the powder is packed into the capsules. Then, the caps are put over the capsule bodies.

TABLETS

There are many types of tablets, including molded tablets, sublingual tablets, buccal tablets, orally disintegrating tablets, chewable tablets, effervescent tablets and compressed tablets. The molded tablet is the most common tablet type made in compounding, and the compressed tablet is the most common type made in manufacturing.

Tablets contain the active drug and excipients, including diluents, binders, disintegrants, lubricants, coloring agents, and flavoring agents.

How to Prepare Molded Tablets

The first step to compound a molded tablet is to triturate the dry ingredients and mix by geometric dilution. Alcohol and/or water is added to moisten the powder. The powder mixture should have a pasty consistency, which can be molded into tablets (using tablet molds), and allowed to dry. If the tablet is a lozenge (see next), flavoring can be added. Coloring and coating may be added.

LOZENGES/TROCHES

Lozenges (also referred to as troches) are hard, soft or chewable oral tablets that slowly dissolve in the mouth or are easily chewed and swallowed. This dosage form is generally used to deliver a medication that acts locally in the mouth. A commercially available example is a clotrimazole troche for treatment of oral thrush.

A lozenge contains the active drug in a base of sucrose or syrup for hard lozenges, PEG for soft lozenges, and glycerin or gelatin for chewable lozenges. Flavoring agents and coloring agents are added. The base is melted, mixed with the API and excipients, placed into a mold, and allowed to cool back into a solid.

CREAMS

Creams, lotions, ointments, pastes and gels are delivery vehicles, and are described in more detail in Chapter II. Creams are semi-solid formulations intended for topical use. They contain more than 20% water and up to 50% oil. They spread easily and are reasonably hydrating. Creams are packaged in tubes, and sometimes in tubs.

LOTIONS

Lotions contain the most water, are more fluid than creams, and can be poured. They absorb quickly and are easy to spread on the skin. Since lotions contain a lot of water, they can be delivered in pumps.

OINTMENTS

Ointments contain the least water, from 0–20%, with the remainder oil-based product/s. Ointments are a good delivery vehicle to evenly deliver medication over a period of time, they provide a barrier to exposure (e.g., organisms, sun) and they prevent moisture loss to foster burn and scar healing. Ointments are packaged in tubes or tubs.

See Compounding II chapter for types of ointments.

How to Prepare Ointments

Powders should be triturated well, using a levigating agent. The levigating agent must be miscible with the base, which means they can mix together well (mixing "like with like" is a common compounding principle). The powder will be mixed into the ointment base, using geometric dilution.

Certain ointments will require heat in order to mix the components together well. This is called the fusion method. Always use the lowest temperature possible. First, melt the ingredients with the highest melting point, then add the others, according to their decreasing melting points. Otherwise, undesired chemical reactions could occur. A water bath used to heat the ointment components will help prevent over-heating.

PASTES

The ingredients in pastes are similar to ointments, but they are made thicker by adding more solid ingredients. They provide a protective barrier because they do not melt significantly at body temperature.

GELS

Gels are semisolids interpenetrated by a liquid. The active ingredient and other excipients are added to the gel. Pluronic lecithin organogel ("PLO gel") can be used for transdermal drug administration. It has an organic (lipophilic) ingredient (lecithin) combined in a water-based solution of poloxamer polymers (Pluronic). The drug can be dissolved in either phase, depending on solubility. The aqueous phase (poloxamer) is liquid at low temperatures, but forms a gel at room temperature. Pre-mixed PLO gel can be purchased.

SUPPOSITORIES

A suppository base is either oil-soluble (oleaginous) or water-soluble. Oil-soluble bases include cocoa butter (also called theobroma oil) and hydrogenated vegetable oils (palm, palm kernel and coconut oils). Water-soluble bases include polyethylene glycol (PEG) polymers and glycerinated gelatin. If a drug powder is added to a base, the powder should be triturated to a fine consistency.

- If the preparation softens or melts easily, such as with some suppository bases (including theobroma oil (cocoa butter), the molds will need to be stored in the refrigerator. The melting point of theobroma oil is slightly below human body temperature. When theobroma oil is used as a suppository base, the suppository will start to melt when held in the hand. It is not possible to insert a melting suppository. Storing it in the refrigerator will make the suppository hard, and easier to insert. Storing it in the mold in which it was formed would be preferable.

The API (the drug) will displace part of the base. If the drug has the same density as the base, it will displace an equal amount of volume. If the density is greater, it will displace less, and if lower, it will displace more. To calculate the amount of base displaced, the density factor of the drug is needed. The density factor can be found in compounding references, or calculated with the Paddock Method:

$$\text{Density Factor} = \frac{B}{A - C + B}$$

A = weight of the suppository blank, B = weight of medication per suppository, and C = weight of medicated suppository.

How to Prepare Suppositories

There are three methods to prepare a suppository:

Hand molding can be used when only a few suppositories are to be prepared, using a cocoa butter base. The cocoa butter is not melted. It is grated and then mixed with the drug/s in a mortar and pestle or on a pill tile with a spatula. The mass is rolled into a cylinder, which is cut into suppository-size pieces. A tip is formed on one end to make insertion easier.

In the commonly-used fusion molding method, the base is gently heated, the ingredients are added, and the mixture is poured into room temperature molds, and left to harden. If the base is poured into a cold mold, it can cause the suppository to crack and split. If the suppository does not harden, the molds can be refrigerated. Disposable plastic molds can be used for molding. Often, the suppositories are dispensed in the mold; suppositories are soft, and easily damaged. They are stored in the mold until needed.

In the compression molding method, the pharmacist will need to know the weight of each mold, and the drug's density factor (see above). The amount of base required to fill each mold is calculated, the base is grated, mixed with the drug, and put into a cold compression mold.

Lubricants can be applied to the mold so the suppositories can be removed more easily. If a lubricant is used it must be opposite of the suppository base in terms of solubility. The goal is to reduce friction. For example: glycerin or propylene glycol (both water-soluble) are good lubricants for suppositories made with oil-soluble suppository bases, while mineral oil or vegetable oil spray (oil-soluble) are good lubricants for water-soluble bases.

SUPPOSITORIES

Vaginal suppositories are used to treat conditions inside the vagina or a condition related to the female reproductive system.

Vaginal suppositories can be used to treat *Candida* infections (including OTC suppositories), dryness or vaginal pain, menopausal symptoms (including local pain, dryness and hot flashes), and for contraception (spermicides come in OTC suppositories). Compounding pharmacies make hormone replacement suppositories that are tailored to a woman's individual requirements.

Rectal suppositories are used either to treat a local condition (such as a hemorrhoid, local infection, rectal pain, distal ulcerative colitis) where the condition is close to the end of the GI tract, or to treat a systemic condition, such as pain and fever in a patient who cannot take oral medication (e.g., acetaminophen suppository). Suppositories bypass the oral route and largely avoid first-pass metabolism.

Suppository bases must be hard enough to be briefly handled, but soft enough to melt easily once inserted.

COMPOUNDING KITS

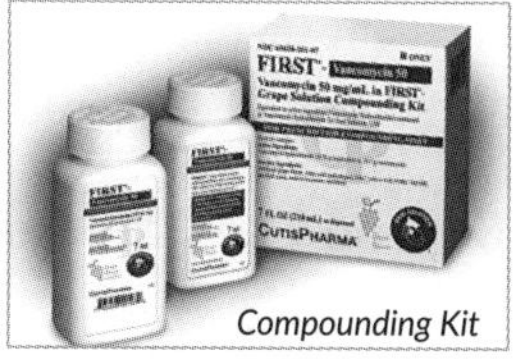

Compounding Kit

There are some companies that package pre-measured ingredients for a compounded product into "compounding kits". If the pharmacy does not receive many prescriptions for a certain product, it can be cost-effective (and easier) to purchase compounding kits (as needed) instead of purchasing the bulk ingredients.

NON-STERILE QUALITY ASSURANCE

A quality assurance (QA) plan outlines the steps and actions that ensure the maintenance of proper standards for the compounded preparations. The QA plan includes the Standard Operating Procedures (SOPs), which are itemized steps on how to perform routine and expected tasks in the pharmacy.

The QA plan must be reviewed and updated regularly. Properly maintained and implemented SOPs result in quality preparations and less errors.

The QA program should include periodic testing of the finished compounded preparations. A pharmacy may do some QA testing in-house (such as confirming weight and consistency) and outsource others (such as sending some of the compounded products to an outside company to conduct sterility or stability testing).

QA records need to include the names of the staff that are involved with compounding, including their orientation and training records.

SELECTING THE BEYOND USE DATE

The table provides the default BUDs for non-sterile compounded preparations that are packaged in tight, light-resistant containers.

USP specifies refrigeration for water-containing oral formulations only. Individual product stability information may specify refrigeration, which will override the USP-provided BUD.

FORMULATION	BEYOND USE DATE
Nonaqueous Formulations (such as a drug in petrolatum)	Not later than the time remaining until the earliest expiration date of any API or 6 months, whichever is earlier. Store at room temperature.
Water-Containing Oral Formulations (such as an oral suspension)	Not later than 14 days when stored at controlled cold temperatures. Store in refrigerator.
Water-Containing Topical/ Dermal and Mucosal Liquid and Semisolid Formulations (such as a cream or lotion)	Not later than 30 days. Store at room temperature.

In some cases, the default BUD is not used. Here are the exceptions:

1. If any ingredients decompose easily, select a shorter BUD.
2. If any ingredient expires before the BUD, use the earlier expiration date.
3. BUDs can be extended if stability data is obtained that determines the drug is stable for a longer period.

Beyond Use Date Examples

PREPARATION	KEYS	MAXIMUM BUD
Metronidazole topical solution prepared with propylene glycol and distilled water	Topical, aqueous	30 days
Acetaminophen, diphenhydramine and hydroxyzine oral suspension prepared in lemon syrup (citric acid, purified water, lemon flavoring)	Oral, aqueous	14 days, refrigerated
Topical preparation of zinc oxide in white petrolatum	Non-aqueous	180 days
Nystatin in a strawberry-flavored popsicle with an 80% sorbitol solution made with sorbitol and purified water	Water, oral	14 days, refrigerated
Polymyxin and hydrocortisone prepared in a commercial emulsion cream for skin rash	Topical, aqueous	30 days
Ciprofloxacin and dexamethasone in Versabase lotion	Topical, aqueous	30 days
Albuterol powder, ephedrine and lorazepam capsules	Non-aqueous	180 days
Estradiol powder, black cohosh powder and soybean oil preparation in hypromellose capsules	Non-aqueous	180 days
Morphine powder with stevia sweetener in a PEG lozenge	Non-aqueous	180 days
Progesterone suppository in an oleaginous base	Non-aqueous	180 days
Calamine powder prepared with glycerin in 70% isopropyl alcohol for poison ivy	Topical, aqueous	30 days
Lidocaine and diphenhydramine in poloxamer gel with lecithin/isopropyl palmitate	Topical, aqueous	30 days
Diclofenac powder in propylene glycol	Non-aqueous	180 days
Lidocaine, alcohol USP and distilled water buccal dental gel	Topical, aqueous	30 days

APPLYING PRODUCT AND AUXILIARY LABELS

The labeling of all compounded products must include the BUD and storage and handling information.

There should be a label indicating that it is a compounded product:

All hazardous drugs should be labeled appropriately:

Certain formulations may need additional auxiliary labels (see below).

Topical products: 

Emulsions, suspensions: 

Suppositories, some troches, some suspensions: 

PATIENT COUNSELING

The pharmacist must counsel the patient or caregiver about the proper use of a compounded product, with similar information as required for prescription drugs. ADRs resulting from a compounded product should be reported to the pharmacy, and the pharmacist will need to record the ADR in the compounding record. The patient's profile should include the ADR. Depending on the reaction, further action may be necessary.

STERILE PREPARATIONS

PHYSIOCHEMICAL CONSIDERATIONS

IV solutions should be isotonic (osmotic pressure matches to human blood by having the same number of particles in solution), measured in milliosmoles (mOsm) per liter (L). Human blood has an osmolarity of 285 mOsm/L. This prevents fluid transfer across the biological semipermeable membranes. The pH should be close to neutral (pH of 7); blood is slightly alkaline at a pH of 7.35 – 7.45. Non-PVC bags should be used for medications that have leaching or sorption issues (refer to the IV Drug Compatibility, Administration & Degradation chapter). The IV set must be sterile and nonpyrogenic.

BY TYPE

Ampules: ampules are small, sealed glass containers that contain medication. The neck is long. The ampule is broken by snapping the neck. This will introduce glass particles into the drug solution. A filter needle or straw will be required to filter out the glass. In the figure, the score mark is where the ampule is broken. The glass is weaker at that area and will snap off.

Vials that contain liquids: a volume of drug is drawn up in a syringe, which can then be added to an IV bag.

The compounder usually injects a volume of air equal to the volume of non-hazardous drug that is withdrawn. This is not done for hazardous drugs, such as chemotherapeutic drugs.

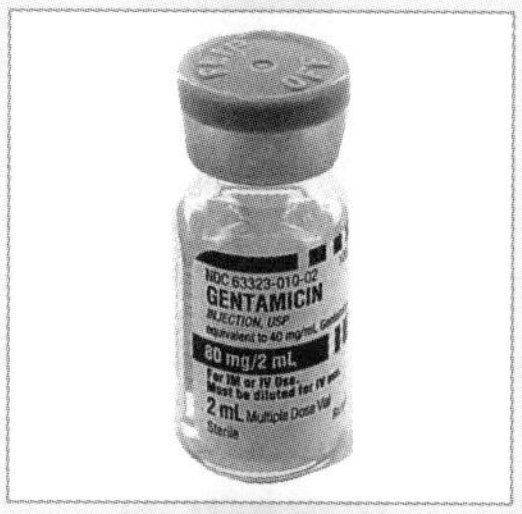

Vials that contain lyophilized or freeze-dried powder: the powder needs to be reconstituted by adding sterile water for injection, bacteriostatic water for injection, or a diluent supplied by the manufacturer. Drugs may be commercially available as powders because they are unstable as a solution.

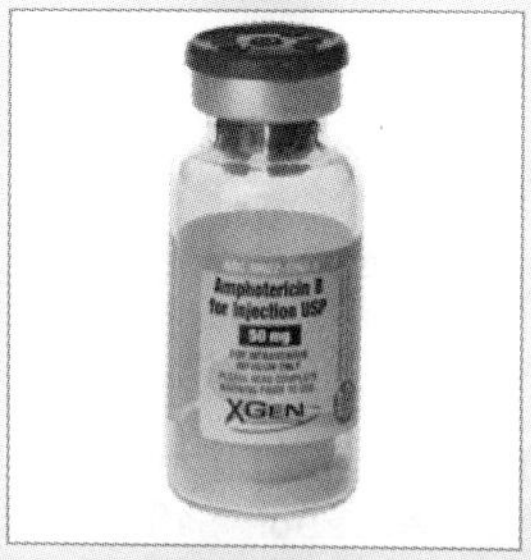

BY VOLUME

Small volume parenteral (SVP): SVPs are IV containers (IV bags) that are usually 50 or 100 mL of normal saline (NS) or 5% dextrose in water (D5W). These are the two smaller bags in the front of the figure. Another common SVP is prefilled syringes. Bags and syringes can be sent to the floor for floor stock or labeled for a specific patient.

The SVPs are often "piggybacked" off the LVP. These are called IVPBs; see figure. This reduces the need to have multiple lines running into the patient. The drugs will mix together in the line; the drugs must be compatible in the line.

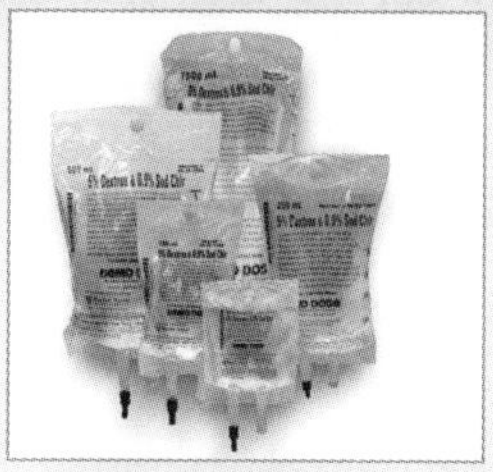

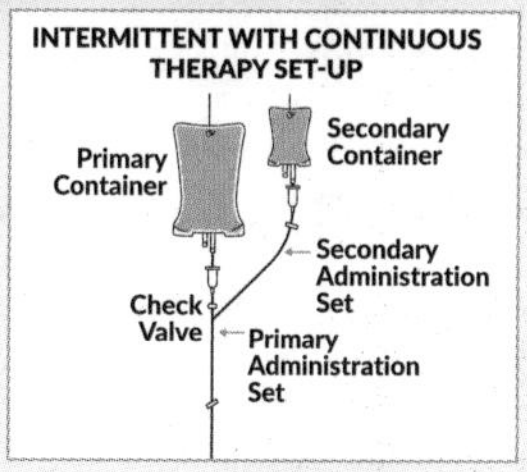

Syringes: SVPs that are used for IV and oral medications.

Caution: oral syringes must be labeled (preferably over the opening to avoid being missed) if they are for oral use or they can be mistakenly injected into an IV line, which can be fatal.

IV Syringes

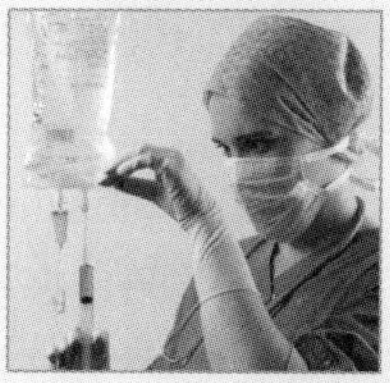

Large volume parenteral (LVP): IV containers that are larger; see figure.

1 liter bags are commonly used for fluids, which are given in a variety of formulations: NS, 1/2NS, D5W, D51/2NS, D5NS, lactated ringers (LR) and (less commonly) as many others, including D10NS, D2.51/2NS, D51/3NS, D51/4NS

Parenteral nutrition (PN) for adults is prepared in a LVP.

The yellow "banana" bag contains multivitamins, which causes the yellow color. The creamy colored bag contains lipids.

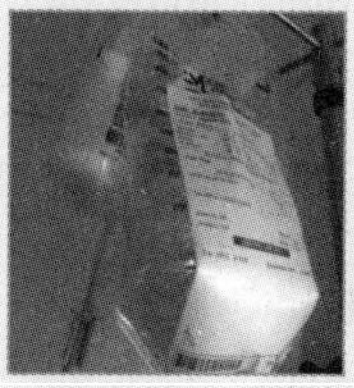

READY-TO-USE STERILE MEDICATIONS

Ready-to-use (RTUs): are available as prepared IV bags or prefilled syringes. The pharmacy staff opens the outer container and applies the patient label. These do not have a CSP risk level, as they are not compounded. The BUD is provided by the manufacturer, and is on the packaging.

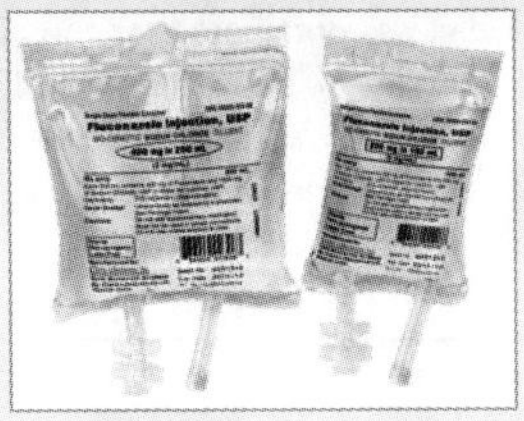

Ready-to-use vial/bag systems (*Add-Vantage*, others): come with the drug vial attached to the IV bag. At the bedside, the nurse squeezes the drug into the bag. These do not have a CSP risk level, as they are not compounded. The BUD is provided by the manufacturer, and is on the packaging.

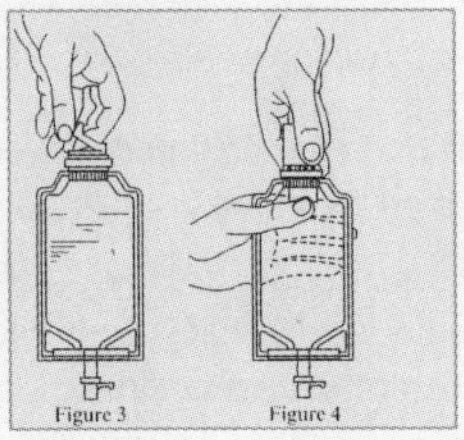

WORK FLOW FOR CSP PREPARATION

- Pharmacist reviews the order.
- Gather and inspect all materials.
- Clean hood. Place only needed items in the hood.
- Prepare CSPs with aseptic technique.
- Properly dispose of syringes and needles into the sharps container. See the Medication Safety & Quality Improvement chapter.
- Visually inspect all finished CSPs. If high-risk, complete terminal sterilization.

HOW TO SET UP ITEMS IN THE PEC

- Only required items can be placed in the hood. No paper, pens, labels, calculators or trays.
- All work must be done at least six inches within the hood, not near the front of the hood where the hood air and room air mingle. Work in the center and place critical items reasonably close to the air source.
- Place all items in the hood side-by-side. Occasionally, items can be placed behind each other (e.g., IV bags for batch preparation). If so, place the smaller items closest to the air filter. Items should not be closer than six inches from the back of the hood.
- Nothing should be between the sterile object and the HEPA filter in a horizontal airflow hood or above a sterile object in a vertical airflow hood. Hazardous drugs must be prepared in a vertical flow PEC (BSC in a PEC, or a CACI; see Compounding I chapter for space requirements).
- Do not tear open components. Open along the seal within the hood. Do not touch the syringe tip or plunger, even with gloved hands.

HOW TO TRANSFER SOLUTIONS AND INJECT INTO IV BAGS

- For greatest accuracy, use the smallest syringe that can hold the desired amount of solution. The syringe should not be larger than twice the volume to be measured.
- Powders are reconstituted by introducing a diluent such as sterile water for injection, bacteriostatic water for injection (which is sterile) or a diluent provided by the manufacturer. In some cases, dilution is done with saline or dextrose solution.
- Swab the rubber top (or ampule neck) with 70% IPA, and wait for it to air-dry; do not blow on or wave over it to dry faster.
- Prior to withdrawing any liquid from a vial, first inject a volume of air equal to the volume of fluid to be removed. Exception: do not inject air prior to removing cytotoxic drugs from vials or CSTDs..
- Puncture the rubber top of the vial with the needle bevel up. Then bring the syringe and needle straight up, penetrate the stopper, and depress the plunger of the syringe, emptying the air into the vial. Invert the vial with the attached syringe. Draw up from the vial the amount of liquid required. Withdraw the needle from the vial. In the case of a multi-dose vial, the rubber cap will close, sealing the contents of the vial.
- The volume of solution drawn into a syringe is measured at the point of contact between the rubber piston and the side of the syringe barrel.
- Coring occurs when a small piece of rubber from the stopper is aspirated into the needle, and is put into the solution in the vial. The rubber piece can get injected into a patient. Look for small cored pieces floating near the top of the solution during the visual inspection of the CSP.

- If the medication is in a glass ampule, open the ampule by forcefully snapping the neck away from you, then tilt the ampule, place the needle bevel of a filter needle or tip of a filter straw in the corner near the opening, and withdraw the medication. Use a needle equipped with a filter for filtering out any tiny glass particles, fibers, or paint chips that may have fallen into the ampule. Before injecting the contents of a syringe into an IV, the needle must be changed to avoid introducing glass or particles into the admixture. A standard needle could be used to withdraw the drug from the ampule; it is then replaced with a filter device before the drug is pushed out of the syringe.

Protect the Work Surface from HDs

- A plastic-backed preparation mat should be placed on the work surface in the PEC. The mat catches spills and drops from compounding.
- The equipment used for HDs is only for HDs.

VISUAL INSPECTION

- The supervising pharmacist should verify that the correct volume of product is in the syringe before the compounding personnel continues compounding. This is the preferred method because the pharmacist can see the actual volume in the syringe. The "syringe pull-back method" is a common method to verify IV admixtures, but not recommended by ISMP nor addressed by USP. This is when the pharmacist would verify that the correct volumes were added after the compounding is done; the compounding personnel would "pull-back" the plunger of the syringe to the volume of product he/she believes was added into the IV admixture and place the empty syringe next to the vial. This method is not recommended; it relies on the staff's memory and the pharmacist would have to verify an empty syringe, which is not reasonable.
- Finished CSPs are visually inspected immediately after preparation, against a dark background, for particulates, cored pieces, precipitates and cloudiness. The container should be lightly squeezed to check for leakage.

TERMINAL STERILIZATION

Terminal sterilization is required for high-risk CSPs. Terminal sterilization methods include steam sterilization (with an autoclave), dry-heat sterilization (depyrogenation), gas sterilization, ionizing radiation, and unidirectional aseptic processing. Do not use heat on heat-sensitive drugs (e.g., proteins, including hormones).

Bubble-Point Test and Filter Integrity

CSPs that are heat-labile (e.g., hormones, other proteins) can be sterilized with filtration using a 0.22 micron filter. If filtering is used, the bubble-point test must be performed. This test uses pressure to force liquid to "bubble" out of the filter to test the filter integrity.

LABEL REQUIREMENTS

The labels of CSPs must have the names and amounts or concentrations of ingredients, the total volume, the BUD, the route of administration, the storage requirements, and other information for safe use.

All chemotherapy preparations must have a label that reads "Chemotherapy - dispose of properly" or something similar.

Auxiliary labels should be placed on CSPs that are not refrigerated, if a filter is required and if light protection is required.

High-alert medications are drugs that have a heightened risk of causing significant patient harm when used incorrectly. High-alert medications should have appropriate auxiliary labels such as "Contains Potassium" or "Warning: Paralyzing drug."

Certain high-risk level CSPs and CSPs intended for use beyond the recommended BUD must have sterility testing. The sterility testing should use either tryptic soy broth (TSB) or fluid thioglycollate medium (FTM), and include bacterial endotoxin (pyrogen) testing prior to use.

PYROGEN (BACTERIAL ENDOTOXIN) TESTING

Endotoxins are produced by both Gram-positive and Gram-negative bacteria and fungi. Endotoxins from Gram-negative bacteria are more potent and represent a serious threat to patient safety. Pyrogens can come from using equipment (such as glassware and utensils) that has been washed with tap water. To avoid this issue, glassware and utensils should be rinsed with sterile water and depyrogenated using dry-heat (steam) sterilization with an autoclave.

Certain CSPs must be tested for endotoxins. The reagent for the bacterial endotoxins test (BET) is called the Limulus Amebocyte Lysate (LAL).

STERILE PREPARATION AND RISK

It is important to review the risk involved with sterile compounding because the risk level assigned to sterile drugs depends on the process, the ingredients and the equipment that is used in the compounding process. Ingredients and equipment are reviewed in this chapter.

The Risk Level Determines the BUD

The risk level is used to determine the BUD, as seen in the upcoming table. "Risk" in sterile compounding refers to the risk for contamination. A sterile product that is contaminated with microorganisms or any other type of contaminant is high-risk for severe illness and death. Sterile drugs are classified as low, medium or high-risk.

LOW-RISK STERILE COMPOUNDING

The majority of the compounding prepared by pharmacists is in a cleanroom set-up (i.e., a PEC, contained within an SEC) and is low-risk. Low-risk sterile compounding uses 1 to 3 additives that are supplied as sterile from the manufacturer. The sterile additives are injected into sterile fluid contained in an IV bag, or into a sterile syringe. The drug/s usually come in solution, and are ready to be withdrawn from the vial and used.

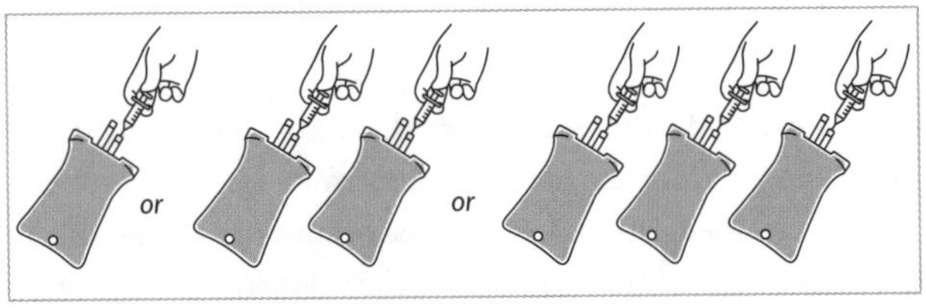

[A drug or other compound (e.g., potassium, insulin) added to an IV bag is called an additive.] Low-risk sterile drugs have the lowest contamination risk, and the longest BUD.

LYOPHILIZED STERILE IV DRUGS

Most drugs that are used at the pharmacy to prepare IV drugs come in solution. A minority of IV drugs are lyophilized (i.e., freeze-dried into a powder). The lyophilized drugs are those that would be unstable if left in solution for a long period. The powder will need to be reconstituted (put into solution) prior to use. A sterile diluent will be added to the powder, such as sterile water for injection (SWFI).

MEDIUM-RISK STERILE COMPOUNDING

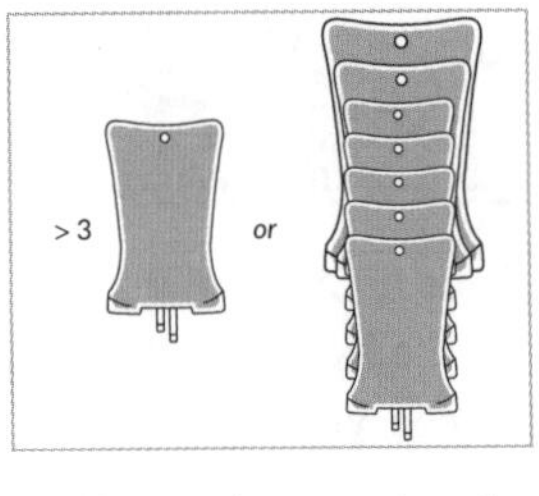

Medium risk sterile compounding is similar to low-risk in terms of ingredients; both contain only sterile ingredients. If more than 3 additives are injected into the IV bag, the compounded sterile product (CSP) that is made will be medium-risk. The contamination risk increases each time the bag is entered (i.e., with a syringe, to place in an additive). Parenteral nutrition preparation requires many additives (see image) including dextrose, lipids, amino acids, multivitamins, minerals, electrolytes, insulin...others), and each of the additives is sterile. This would be medium-risk. Another type of medium-risk compounding is making a batch of drugs; for example, preparing ten IV bags of cefazolin in 50 mL D5W to prepare for the ten total knee arthroplasty surgeries scheduled that day.

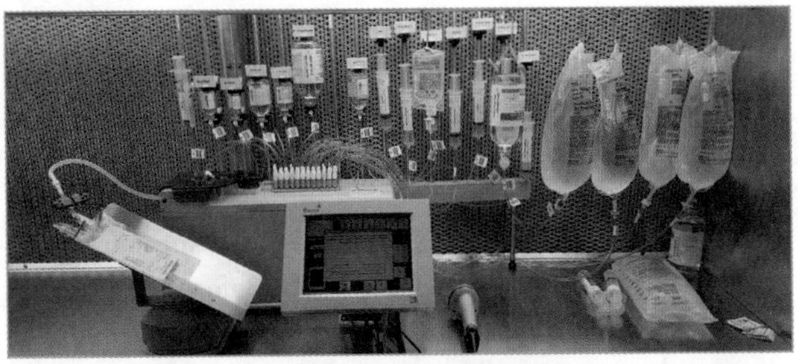

HIGH-RISK STERILE COMPOUNDING

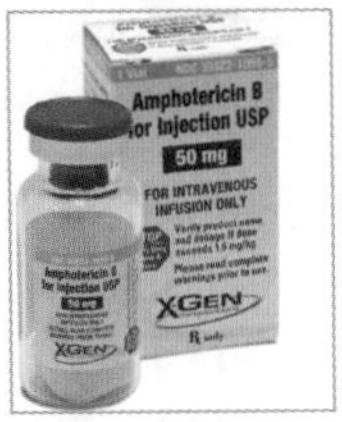

High-risk sterile compounding uses non-sterile ingredients and equipment, including some of the equipment on the following pages that is normally used for non-sterile compounding only. High-risk sterile compounding is not common in most practice settings. Consequently, the end product will need to be made sterile (i.e., sterilized) prior to use. High-risk sterile drugs have the highest contamination risk, and the shortest BUD, with the exception of immediate-use CSPs. These are CSPs prepared in emergency situations in which there is inadequate time to prepare the CSP aseptically, such as on a code blue, and have the shortest BUD.

USP Guidelines for Assigning BUD

USP categorizes CSPs by the risk of contamination, which is based on the compounding area, the ingredients, the equipment, and the complexity of the preparation. The risk levels are low, medium and high. Low-risk and medium-risk CSPs are commonly prepared by pharmacy staff. There are two other special categories: low with less than 12-hour BUD and immediate use. The risk levels are used to determine an appropriate BUD.

CSP QUALITY ASSURANCE

Every facility that prepares CSPs must have a quality assurance (QA) plan that evaluates, corrects and improves the quality processes. The plan should minimally include:

- Personnel training and assessment
- Environmental monitoring
- Equipment calibration and maintenance

Every process must be documented and follow-up actions identified that have assigned personnel responsible for each item, with expected dates of completion. If a problem has been identified or a medication error or safety issue has occurred, the analysis should be started as soon as possible with a root cause analysis, discussed in the Medication Safety chapter. A failure mode and effects analysis of new techniques can help to identify problems with new procedures in advance Standard Operating Procedures (SOPs), described earlier, should be developed, followed and periodically reviewed to determine if revisions are needed.

CSP RISK LEVEL	COMPOUNDING AREA	CHARACTERISTICS	EXAMPLES
Low	ISO 5 PEC ISO 7 buffer area ISO 8 ante area (non-HD) ISO 7 ante area (HD)	■ Use only sterile ingredients ■ Use only sterile equipment ■ No more than 3 ingredients ■ No more than 2 entries into any 1 sterile container or device ■ Use only closed or sealed systems ■ Limited to transferring, measuring, and mixing manipulations	Reconstituting a single-dose vial of antibiotic with sterile water and transferring it to a normal saline IV bag.
Low, non-HD Low & medium HD, < 12-hr BUD	ISO 5 PEC in a SCA	■ Non-hazardous, low-risk ■ Hazardous, low- and medium-risk	See examples for low-risk and medium-risk.
Medium	ISO 5 PEC ISO 7 buffer area ISO 8 ante area (non-HD) ISO 7 ante area (HD)	■ Multiple individual or small doses of sterile products combined to prepare a CSP for multiple patients or for one patient on multiple occasions ■ More than 3 ingredients ■ Complex aseptic manipulations	Using a multi-dose vial of antibiotic and transferring single-doses to several normal saline IV bags for multiple patients. This process is called batch preparation. Preparing total parenteral nutrition.
High	ISO 5 PEC ISO 7 buffer room ISO 8 ante area (non-HD) ISO 7 ante area (HD)	■ Non-sterile ingredients ■ Non-sterile equipment	CSPs from bulk drug containers, preparations that require sterilization, and products made with non-sterile components.
Immediate-use	Clean, uncluttered, functionally separate area	■ Only intended for emergency administration. ■ Must be for administration within 1 hour.	Providing stat IV administration in a medical setting or ambulance.

Ready-To-Use IV CSPs do not have CSP Risk Levels

Commercially available IV medications that are prepared according to manufacturer's directions are not considered CSPs and do not have CSP risk levels. These include ready-to-use (RTU) IVs and vial-bag systems. There is no compounding involved.

HOW TO CHOOSE A BEYOND USE DATE

The BUD is the date or time after which the CSP should not be used. The BUD is determined by USP 797 standards and the stability/expiration date of the individual ingredients, whichever is shorter. A sterility test can be performed to determine if a longer BUD is possible.

The BUD is determined by the CSP risk level and the storage temperature.

CSP RISK LEVEL	BUD ROOM TEMP	BUD FRIDGE TEMP	BUD FREEZER TEMP
Low	48 hours	14 days	45 days
Low non-HD Low/medium HD < 12-hr BUD	12 hours	12 hours	N/A
Medium	30 hours	9 days	45 days
High	24 hours	3 days	45 days
Immediate-use	1 hour	N/A	N/A

BUDs for Single Dose Containers (SDC) and Multi-Dose Containers (MDC)

The BUDs in this table are for the vials, bags, bottles, syringes and ampules that contain the drugs, electrolytes, and other items that are being put into the CSPs. For example, a single-dose 1 g vial of vancomycin, once opened, can be used for up to 6 hours if the vial was opened in the PEC, which has ISO 5 air.

DETERMINING THE BUD FOR CSPs

BUDs are determined by the risk of contamination.

The lower the risk, the longer the BUD.

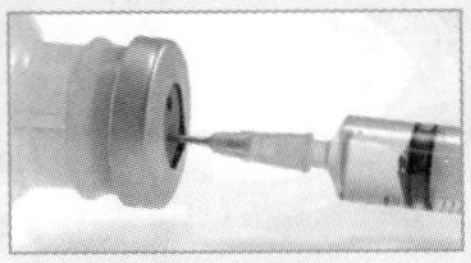

Drawing up a sterile drug with a sterile syringe, and putting the drug into an IV bag of sterile fluid (in a sterile hood), is all low risk. If refrigerated, the BUD is 14 days.

DOSE	BUD
SDC - vial, bag, bottle, syringe Outside an ISO 5 environment	1 hour from the time of puncture or opening
SDC - vial , bag, bottle, syringe Inside an ISO 5 environment	Up to 6 hours from the time of puncture or opening
SDC - ampule	1 hour from the time of puncture or opening; any contents leftover in the ampule cannot be stored; any unused must be discarded
MDC	Up to 28 days from time of puncture or opening, unless otherwise specified by the manufacturer

RECALLS

When high-risk level CSPs are dispensed before receiving the results of their sterility tests, there must be a written procedure requiring daily observation of the incubating test specimens and immediate recall of the dispensed CSPs if there is evidence of microbial growth. All patients and physicians who received the recalled CSPs are notified of the potential risk.

If sterility test results come back positive, there should be an investigation of aseptic technique, environmental control, and other sterility assurance controls to determine the source of contamination and improve the methods or processes.

Recalls are discussed further in RxPrep's MPJE Course.

CLASS	DESCRIPTION
Class I Recall	A situation in which there is a reasonable probability that the use or exposure will cause serious adverse health consequences or death. For example, microbial growth is observed in an intrathecal injection.
Class II Recall	A situation in which use or exposure can cause temporary or reversible adverse health consequences or where the probability of harm is remote. For example, ketorolac injections have been recalled in 2010 and 2015 due to the possibility of particles in the vials.
Class III Recall	A situation in which use or exposure is not likely to cause adverse health consequences. For example, the coloring on tablets may have been applied inconsistently.

OSMOLARITY AND INTRAVENOUS DRUGS

OSMOLARITY AND TONICITY

Osmolarity and tonicity are related terms; both are used to express the solute concentration in solution. Osmolarity includes all solutes and tonicity includes only the solutes that do not cross the vasculature (i.e., the biological membrane).

Osmolarity in Enteral Formulations

Providing optimal enteral nutrition to elderly or critically ill patients can require a calorie dense formula that is more concentrated (i.e., hyperosmolar) than the gastrointestinal fluids. As a result, the patient can experience osmolarity-induced vomiting and diarrhea when water is released by the cells, in an attempt by the body to dilute the preparation.

If a patient is intolerant of a hyperosmolar enteral preparation, the formula can be diluted to decrease the osmolarity. The Q1C1 = Q2C2 formula can be used to dilute the concentration.

There is an example of this type of dilution in Calculations II.

Osmolarity in Intravenous Formulations

Saline concentrations greater than 0.9% is referred to as hypertonic saline rather than hyperosmotic saline because it refers to the concentration in blood. Hypertonic saline injections, given erroneously, can be an unfortunate cause of patient fatality.

Intravenous formulations must be prepared that are not hypertonic or hypotonic, in order to avoid potentially fatal consequences.

Hypertonic saline is used for various indications in the acute care setting, such as treating hyponatremia and for use in preparing parenteral nutrition. When hypertonic saline is administered into a peripheral vein, the high concentration of solutes relative to the concentration in blood will cause water to move out of the red blood cells (RBCs), in an attempt to dilute the solute concentration. This will cause the RBCs to become shriveled and dysfunctional.

To avoid this series of unfortunate events, hypertonic saline (and very hypertonic saline, such as 23.4%) is often restricted to areas in the hospital where safe use is more likely, such as in the critical care unit and pharmacy.

The highest osmolarity acceptable for peripheral IV administration is ~900 mOsmol/L. Solutions with higher osmolarity should be administered via a central line (i.e., not by peripheral administration) to avoid damaging the vein (i.e., phlebitis). The central line delivers intravenous medications and fluids into a larger blood volume, which quickly dilutes the solution.

On the other extreme, when a preparation has lower osmolarity than blood (i.e., it is hypotonic), the RBCs will absorb fluid. This can cause hemolysis (i.e., the RBCs will burst), which can also cause fatality.

In general, ½ normal saline (0.45%), which has an osmolarity of 154 mOsm/L, is the lowest osmolarity that should be administered intravenously.

RESISTING CHANGES IN PH WITH BUFFER SYSTEMS

As stated earlier, the blood must remain slightly alkaline with a pH of 7.35–7.45. Tissues and cells are very sensitive to changes in pH. The body uses the carbonic acid-bicarbonate buffer system to resist changes in pH in both directions:

- When the pH rises, the blood becomes more basic. Hydrogen ions (protons) will be released from carbonic acid, which causes the pH of the blood to shift to the left. The blood becomes more acidic.
- When the pH falls, the blood becomes more acidic. Hydrogen ions get picked up (more bicarbonate binds with protons), which causes the pH of the blood to shift to the right. The blood becomes more basic.

The above scenario is referring to the carbonic acid-bicarbonate buffer system. There are two other buffer systems that resist changes in pH; the phosphate buffer system and the protein buffer system. Each is important; tissue cells, including in the eyes, nose, skin and elsewhere, are very sensitive to even the slightest change in pH.

Preparations that are administered in sensitive tissue (e.g., eye drops, injections) must be formulated to keep the pH within a narrow range to avoid damaging the tissue and causing pain.

In addition to providing acceptable formulations for patient care, the pH will be an important consideration to provide stability for the drug in the solution.

Similar to human blood, compounding preparations that require a narrow pH range will need a buffer system that can resist changes in pH. Buffer systems, similar to the buffer systems in the body, consist of an acid and its salt. For example, hydrochloric acid (HCl) is used with Na-hydroxide (its salt) in a common buffer system:

- HCl, with a pH of 1-3, serves as the proton donor, to shift the pH to the left.
- Na-hydroxide, with a pH of 11-13, serves as the proton acceptor, to shift the pH to the right.

In the Calculations IV chapter, the Henderson-Hasselbalch equation was used to calculate the pH of a solution when the molar (M) concentrations of the buffer components were provided. A variation of the Henderson-Hasselbalch can be used to determine the amount of buffer required.

TEST YOUR KNOWLEDGE WITH PUZZLES!

More Questions on Compounding in the RxPrep Test Banks

ACROSS

4. Sodium lauryl (fill in this word) is a good surfactant to neutralize electrical charge in powders
5. The maximum number of hours of a BUD for CSPs made in a compounding isolator in an SCA
6. The word before stearate of the excipient that increases flowability of powders
9. Number of days for a BUD for water containing topical preparation, such as a lotion or cream
10. Ganciclovir and finasteride are classified as hazardous drugs by this group
13. Creams have more water than this (greasy feeling) but good skin protectant
15. When two ingredients melt at a lower temperature than either individual ingredient
16. Chop and grind up tablets in this type of mortar
17. The method of making an emulsion (also called Dry Gum) that adds the water all at once
19. Make an emulsion with this method by triturating gum with water, then adding in the oil slowly and shaking well
20. Triturate powder in this type of mortar

DOWN

1. Possible consequence from a drug that required a Class I recall
2. Lotions have more water than this topical delivery vehicle or moisturizer
3. A levigating agent for a water-soluble (hydrophilic) delivery vehicle
5. Number of days of a BUD for a topical preparation of PLO gel with ketamine and lidocaine
7. A levigating agent for oil-soluble (lipophilic) delivery vehicle
8. What state is poloxamer or PLO gel in when stored in the refrigerator?
9. The media-fill test is passed if this does not appear in 14 days
11. Number of months for a BUD of a rash ointment made with white petrolatum and calamine powder
12. Number of days for a BUD for water containing oral preparation, such as a strawberry-flavored suspension
14. The first word of a two-word technique used to mix ingredients into a uniform, homogenous preparation
18. Don this after hand washing for sterile compounding

Answers

Across
4 Sulfate
5 Twelve
6 Magnesium
9 Thirty
10 NIOSH
13 Ointment
15 Eutectic
16 Wedgwood
17 Continental
19 English
20 Porcelain

Down
1 Death
2 Cream
3 Glycerin
5 Thirty
7 Mineral oil
8 Liquid
9 Turbidity
11 Six
12 Fourteen
14 Geometric
18 Gown

ACROSS

7. Low-risk CSPs can be kept at room temperature for 48 hours or kept refrigerated for this number of days
11. Use this percentage of isopropyl alcohol when disinfecting the sterile gloves being worn, the PEC surfaces and other surfaces
12. The type of water that contaminates glassware and equipment with pyrogens
13. This compound or 2% bleach (sodium hypochlorite) are useful for both deactivating and decontaminating HDs
14. This oil, used as a suppository base, is also called cocoa butter
16. The SR divided by 0.05 gives the minimum amount that can be accurately weighed on this type of balance
18. An HLB of 15 would indicate that this type of excipient is a useful choice for an oil-in-water emulsion (also called emulsifier, or emulgent)
19. Do not block this type of air, the cleanest air, that comes directly from the HEPA filter
21. ISO level in the PEC
22. The media-fill test indicates the compounder can prepare this type of CSPs
23. Ophthalmics and this type of nutrition preparation (and some others) are medium-risk sterile compounding

DOWN

1. The sterile gloves used for preparing CSPs cannot have this coating (makes it easier to slip gloves on and off)
2. Another name for bacterial endotoxins, which are bad, bad bugs
3. ISO level in the SEC
4. The equipment that kills pyrogens with steam heat
5. Sodium citrate and sorbic acid make this type of system to keep the pH in a narrow range
6. This type of non-sterile compounding can filter the air through more than one (redundant) HEPA filter if external exhaust is not feasible
8. Lactose, starch, gelatin, sorbitol are all used for this purpose (excipient category)
9. The days in a BUD for frozen low-risk CSPs
10. The type of sterile compounding that requires negative pressure with external exhaust
15. Minimum number of air changes required in the C-SEC
17. The gloved-fingertip test indicates proper hand hygiene/garbing technique if this number of CFUs grow on all six plates
20. Prepare CSPs at least this many inches into the PEC

Answers

Across
7 Fourteen
11 Seventy
12 Tap
13 Peroxide
14 Theobroma
16 Torsion
18 Surfactant
19 First
21 Five
22 Aseptic
23 Parenteral

Down
1 Powder
2 Pyrogens
3 Seven
4 Autoclave
5 Buffer
6 Hazardous
8 Binders
9 Forty-five
10 Hazardous
15 Thirty
17 None
20 Six

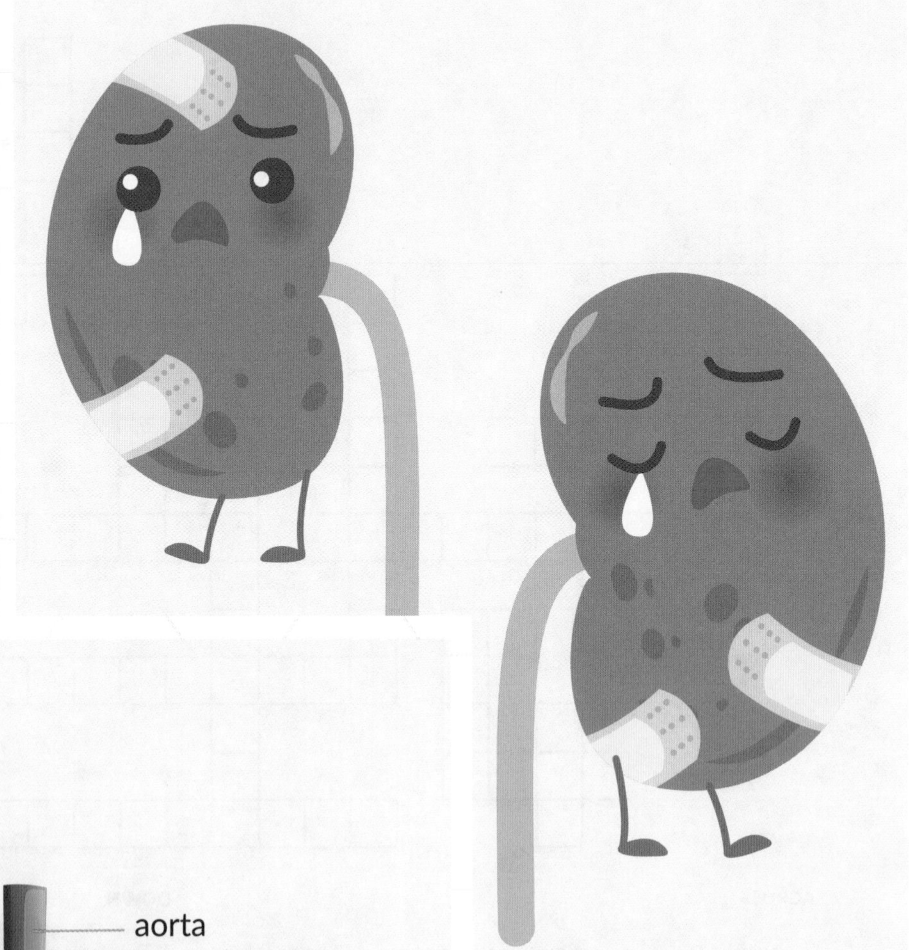

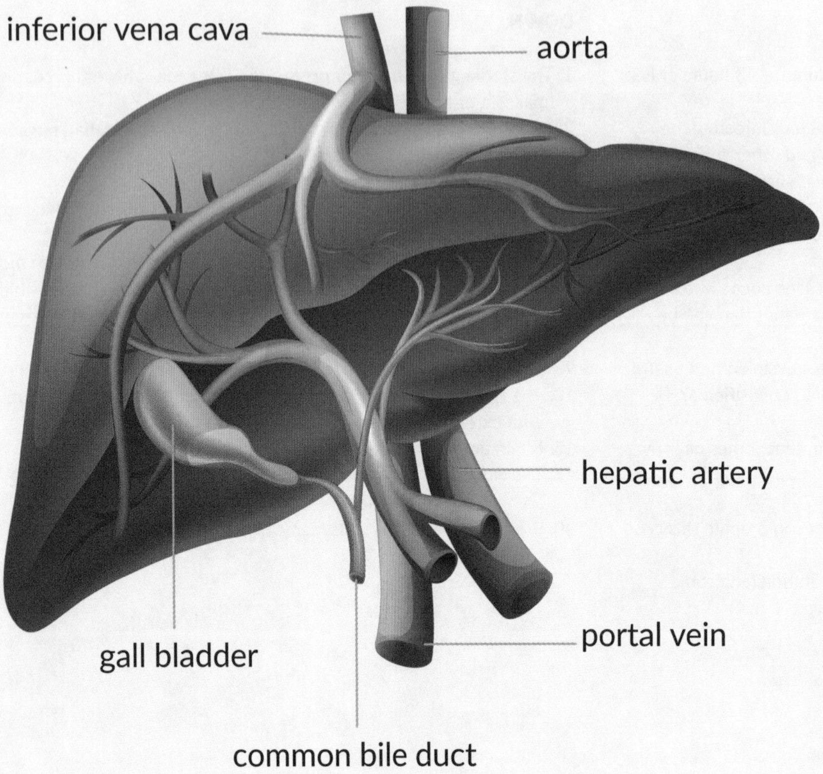
inferior vena cava
aorta
hepatic artery
portal vein
gall bladder
common bile duct

RENAL & LIVER DISEASE

CONTENTS

CHAPTER 18
RENAL DISEASE | **290**

CHAPTER 19
HEPATITIS & LIVER DISEASE | **302**

CHAPTER CONTENT

Background ... 290
Renal Physiology ... 290
Glomerulus ... 291
Proximal Tubule ... 291
Loop of Henle ... 291
Distal Convoluted Tubule ... 291
Collecting Duct ... 291
Drug-Induced Kidney Disease ... 291
Select Drugs that Cause Kidney Disease ... 292
Estimating Kidney Function ... 292
Creatinine Clearance ... 292
CrCl vs. GFR ... 292
GFR and Albuminuria for Staging Kidney Disease ... 292
ACE Inhibitors and ARBs in Chronic Kidney Disease ... 293
ACE Inhibitors and ARBs for Albuminuria ... 293
Modifying Drug Therapy ... 294
Select Drugs that Require ↓ Dose or ↑ Interval in CKD ... 294
Select Drugs that are Contraindicated in CKD ... 294
Complications of Chronic Kidney Disease ... 295
CKD Mineral and Bone Disorder ... 295
Hyperphosphatemia ... 295
Vitamin D Deficiency & Secondary Hyperparathyroidism ... 297
Anemia of CKD ... 298
Hyperkalemia ... 298
Select Drugs that Raise Potassium Levels ... 298
Steps for Treating Severe Hyperkalemia ... 299
Metabolic Acidosis ... 300
Dialysis ... 301
Factors Affecting Drug Removal During Dialysis ... 301

DEFINITIONS

Acute Kidney Injury (AKI)
A sudden loss of kidney function due to a non-renal condition (e.g., drugs). Often reversible (temporary), but can be permanent if the precipitating condition is not corrected. A common cause is dehydration (can present with BUN:SCr ratio > 20:1 plus decreased urine output, dry mucus membranes, tachycardia).

Chronic Kidney Disease (CKD)
A progressive loss of kidney function over months or years. The degree of kidney function is measured by the glomerular filtration rate (GFR) or creatinine clearance (CrCl), and by how much albumin is in the urine.

End-Stage Renal Disease (ESRD)
Total and permanent kidney failure. Fluid and waste accumulates. Dialysis (or transplant) is needed to assume the functions of the kidneys.

CONTENT LEGEND

= Study Tip Gal   = Key Drug Guy

CHAPTER 18
RENAL DISEASE

BACKGROUND

Approximately 30 million U.S. adults (more than one in seven) have chronic kidney disease (CKD). The risk is highest in African-Americans, Hispanics, American Indians and Asians. The most common causes are diabetes and hypertension; controlling blood glucose and blood pressure can prevent renal damage and delay progression to end-stage renal disease (ESRD).

Less common causes of CKD include polycystic kidney disease, some types of infections, renal artery stenosis (a blocked artery that prevents blood flow to the kidney) and drug-induced kidney disease (caused by nephrotoxic medications).

Pharmacists can assess the degree of kidney impairment in CKD patients and ensure safe and effective medication dosage adjustments. They can recognize and recommend treatment for related disorders, such as anemia, hypertension, acid-base and electrolyte disturbances and disorders of bone and mineral metabolism (e.g., management of parathyroid hormone, phosphate, calcium and vitamin D levels).

RENAL PHYSIOLOGY

The nephron is the functional unit of the kidney. Its primary function is to control the concentration of sodium and water. The nephrons reabsorb what is needed back into the blood and the remainder is excreted in the urine. This regulates blood volume, and in turn, blood pressure. The major parts of the nephron include Bowman's capsule, the glomerulus, the proximal tubule, the loop of Henle, the distal convoluted tubule and the collecting duct (see the figure on the following page). There are roughly one million nephrons in each kidney.

GLOMERULUS

The afferent arteriole delivers blood into the glomerulus, a large filtering unit that is located within Bowman's capsule. Substances with a molecular weight < 40,000 daltons, including most drugs, can pass through the glomerular capillaries into the filtrate (inside the lumen, or tube, of the nephron) and are excreted in the urine. If the glomerulus is healthy, larger substances (e.g., proteins and protein-bound drugs) are not filtered and stay in the blood (exiting the nephron via the efferent arteriole). If the glomerulus is damaged, some albumin passes into the urine. The amount of albumin in the urine is used, along with the glomerular filtration rate (GFR), to assess the severity of kidney disease (also called nephropathy). See the GFR and Albuminuria for Staging Kidney Disease section for further discussion.

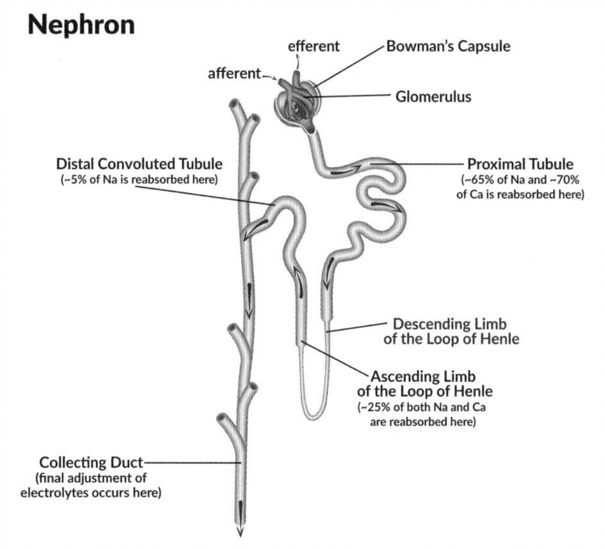

PROXIMAL TUBULE

Proximal means "close to." The proximal tubule is closest to Bowman's capsule (the entry point of the nephron). Much of the sodium (Na), chloride (Cl), calcium (Ca) and water that are initially filtered out of the blood are reabsorbed back into the bloodstream here. Blood pH is regulated by the exchange of hydrogen and bicarbonate ions.

LOOP OF HENLE

As filtrate moves down the loop of Henle (the descending limb), water is reabsorbed into the blood, but Na and Cl ions are not, which increases the concentration of Na and Cl in the filtrate. As the filtrate moves up the loop of Henle (the ascending limb), Na and Cl ions are reabsorbed back into the blood, but water is not. If antidiuretic hormone (ADH), also called vasopressin) is present, water passes through the walls of the ascending limb and is reabsorbed into the blood; less water is then excreted in the urine (anti-diuresis).

The ascending limb of the loop of Henle is the site of reabsorption for about 25% of the filtered Na. When loop diuretics inhibit the Na-K pump in the ascending limb of the loop of Henle, less Na is reabsorbed back into the blood. There is a significant increase in the concentration of Na in the filtrate, causing less water to be reabsorbed (more stays in the filtrate and is excreted in the urine along with Na). By blocking the pump, loop diuretics cause less Ca reabsorption back into the blood, leading to Ca depletion. Long-term use of loop diuretics can decrease bone density because of this.

DISTAL CONVOLUTED TUBULE

Distal means "farther away." The distal convoluted tubule is the farthest point away from entry into the nephron. It is involved in regulating K, Na, Ca and pH. Thiazide diuretics inhibit the Na-Cl pump in the distal convoluted tubule. Only about 5% of Na is reabsorbed at this point, making thiazides weaker diuretics than loops. Thiazides increase Ca reabsorption at the Ca pump in the distal convoluted tubule. Unlike loop diuretics, the long-term use of thiazide diuretics has a protective effect on bones.

COLLECTING DUCT

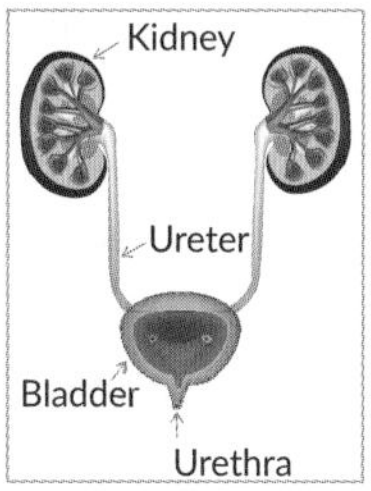

The collecting duct is a network of tubules and ducts that connect the nephrons in each kidney to a ureter. The urine filtrate passes from the ureters into the bladder and then out of the body via the urethra (see figure). The collecting duct is involved with water and electrolyte balance, which is affected by levels of ADH and aldosterone. Aldosterone works in the distal convoluted tubule and collecting duct to increase Na and water reabsorption and decrease K reabsorption. When aldosterone antagonists like spironolactone or eplerenone block aldosterone, more Na and water is excreted in the urine and serum K increases.

DRUG-INDUCED KIDNEY DISEASE

Drug-induced kidney disease (DIKD) is linked to numerous medications; it can be acute and reversible if the medication is stopped, but it can be irreversible and progress to CKD. DIKD is especially common in the hospital setting and contributes to morbidity and mortality. Risk factors include reduced renal blood flow (e.g., preexisting kidney disease, chronic or acute heart failure, dehydration, hypotension), increased age, use of multiple nephrotoxic medications at the same time, frequent use of nephrotoxic medications or use of large doses of them.

SELECT DRUGS THAT CAUSE KIDNEY DISEASE

Aminoglycosides	NSAIDs
Amphotericin B	Polymyxins
Cisplatin	Radiographic contrast dye*
Cyclosporine	Tacrolimus
Loop diuretics	Vancomycin

**Sometimes called contrast media or contrast agent; used during imaging tests (e.g., angiography, MRI, CT, positron emission tomography [PET]).*

ESTIMATING KIDNEY FUNCTION

Two common laboratory markers used to estimate kidney function are blood urea nitrogen (BUN) and serum creatinine (SCr). BUN measures the amount of nitrogen in the blood that comes from urea, a waste product of protein metabolism. As kidney function declines, BUN increases. BUN is not used alone to estimate kidney function because other factors besides renal impairment can increase the BUN (primarily dehydration).

Creatinine, a waste product of muscle metabolism, is mostly filtered by the glomerulus and is easily measured. As kidney function declines, creatinine increases (similar to BUN). The normal range of SCr is ~0.6 – 1.3 mg/dL. Any creatinine that is not filtered is secreted into the nephron tubules. The amount secreted increases as renal function declines and less creatinine is filtered (a compensatory mechanism).

CREATININE CLEARANCE

The Cockcroft-Gault equation for CrCl is the most commonly used equation to estimate kidney function when dosing medications. The accuracy of creatinine-based estimation equations is decreased when a patient has very low muscle mass, which is often the case in frail elderly patients (low muscle mass = low SCr). This can lead to an overestimation of CrCl and inappropriate drug dosing for the patient's true kidney function.

Obesity, liver disease, pregnancy, high muscle mass and other conditions associated with abnormal muscle turnover can affect the estimation of kidney function using measured SCr. The Cockcroft-Gault formula is not preferable in very young children, in ESRD or in unstable renal function (e.g., SCr is fluctuating or changing over a short period of time).

Drug dosing recommendations are generally based on CrCl (calculated using the Cockcroft-Gault formula). A few specific drugs use GFR for dosing adjustment purposes, including the SGLT2 inhibitors and metformin.

CrCl vs. GFR

CrCl

- Cockcroft-Gault equation

$$\text{CrCl (mL/min)} = \frac{140 - \text{(patient age)}}{72 \times \text{SCr}} \times \text{weight (kg)} \times 0.85 \text{ (if female)}$$

- Use actual body weight if less than IBW, use IBW if normal weight (by BMI), use adjusted body weight if overweight (by BMI)*
- Medication contraindications and dosing adjustments are typically based on CrCl calculated using the Cockcroft-Gault equation

GFR

- Not commonly calculated by pharmacists, but may be reported with a basic metabolic panel (BMP) laboratory result
  - CKD-EPI and MDRD equations are used
- Used for staging kidney disease and for dosing select drugs (e.g., metformin, SGLT2 inhibitors)
- For the exam, if GFR is not provided, CrCl provides a close estimate to determine contraindications and dosing adjustments

**See the Calculations IV chapter for more information on weights and CrCl.*

GFR AND ALBUMINURIA FOR STAGING KIDNEY DISEASE

GFR is calculated using the Modification of Diet in Renal Disease (MDRD) and Chronic Kidney Disease Epidemiology Collaboration (CKD-EPI) equations. Albumin is the primary protein that is measured in the urine to assess kidney disease; albuminuria is sometimes referred to as proteinuria.

The KDIGO and KDOQI guidelines recommend using the GFR and degree of albuminuria (level of albumin present in the urine), along with the cause of CKD, to determine the degree/stage of renal impairment. The two tables on the following page show how the GFR and degree of albuminuria are used to assess the severity of kidney disease. In the first table, the GFR value is used to determine the severity of renal impairment. The degree of albuminuria is classified according to the second table, where the 1st and 2nd columns are measurements of albumin (in different units) and the 3rd column contains an interpretation of these measurements.

The values in these tables, on the following page, do not need to be memorized, but it is important for the exam to recognize that a GFR < 60 mL/min/1.73 m^2 and/or albuminuria (ACR or AER ≥ 30) indicates that the patient has CKD and specific treatments are warranted to prevent progression of disease (see the ACE inhibitors and ARBs for Chronic Kidney Disease section).

GFR Categories

GFR (mL/min/1.73 m²)	TERMS	GFR CATEGORY (KDIGO 2012)	CKD STAGE (KDOQI 2002)
≥ 90 + kidney damage*	Normal or high	G1	Stage 1
60-89 + kidney damage*	Mild decrease	G2	Stage 2
45-59	Mild to moderate decrease	G3a	Stage 3
30-44	Moderate to severe decrease	G3b	
15-29	Severe decrease	G4	Stage 4
< 15 or dialysis dependent	Kidney failure	G5	Stage 5

**Markers of kidney damage include a history of kidney transplant, structural abnormalities on imaging, presence of albuminuria and other factors.*

Degree of Albuminuria

ACR (mg/g) or AER (mg/24 hr)	ACR (mg/mmol)	TERMS	ALBUMINURIA CATEGORY (KDIGO 2012)
< 30	< 3	Normal to mild increase (previously called normoalbuminuria)	A1
30-300	3-30	Moderate increase (previously called microalbuminuria)	A2
> 300	> 30	Severe increase (previously called macroalbuminuria)	A3

ACR: albumin to creatinine ratio; AER: albumin excretion rate

ACE INHIBITORS AND ARBS IN CHRONIC KIDNEY DISEASE

Uncontrolled blood pressure and diabetes are important risk factors for the progression of CKD. Chronic elevations in blood glucose and/or blood pressure can cause a decrease in renal function and an increase in the amount of albumin in the urine. ACE inhibitors or ARBs are first-line drugs to prevent progression of disease in patients with CKD, diabetes and/or hypertension if albuminuria is present.

The KDIGO guideline recommends a goal BP < 140/90 mmHg (with no proteinuria) or < 130/80 mmHg (with proteinuria). When starting treatment with an ACE inhibitor or ARB, the baseline SCr can increase by up to 30%. This is expected, and treatment should not be stopped. If the SCr increases by > 30%, the treatment should be discontinued and the patient will generally be referred to a nephrologist.

ACE inhibitors and ARBs should never be used together. They increase potassium, which can result in hyperkalemia. The serum creatinine and potassium should be monitored 1 – 2 weeks after initiating an ACE inhibitor or ARB. Patients should be counseled to avoid potassium supplements and salt substitutes (with KCl). It is important to maximize the dose of the ACE inhibitor or ARB for renal protection. ACE inhibitors and ARBs are discussed in more detail in the Hypertension and Chronic Heart Failure chapters.

ACE INHIBITORS AND ARBS FOR ALBUMINURIA

Who?
Recommended in all patients with albuminuria

Why?
To prevent kidney disease progression

How?
Inhibit renin-angiotensin-aldosterone system (RAAS), causing efferent arteriolar dilation

What?
Reduce pressure in the glomerulus, decrease albuminuria and provide cardiovascular protection

MODIFYING DRUG THERAPY

Common scenarios related to medications and kidney disease include:

- The drug is eliminated through the kidneys and the dose requires modification to avoid accumulation and side effects/toxicity. The dose is reduced and/or the dosing interval is extended.
- The drug can cause or worsen kidney disease (it is nephrotoxic).
- The drug becomes less effective as kidney function declines (e.g., thiazide diuretics, nitrofurantoin).
- The drug is contraindicated at a specific level of kidney impairment because drug accumulation is unsafe (e.g., increased bleeding risk with some anticoagulants), the drug can cause further kidney damage (e.g., NSAIDs) or the drug may cause more harmful effects than usual when kidney function is reduced (e.g., hyperkalemia with aldosterone receptor antagonists).

Remember the basic principles of medication dosing in patients with impaired renal function. Dose adjustments may be necessary when CrCl is < 60 mL/min; when CrCl is ≤ 30 mL/min, additional adjustments may be needed or the drug may be contraindicated.

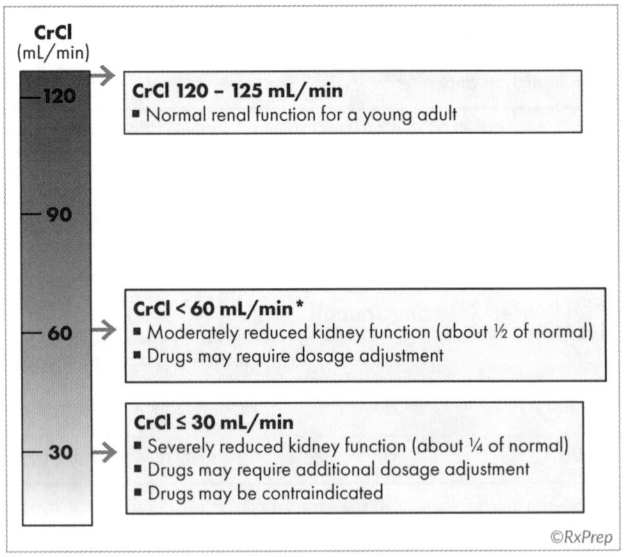

*Check package labeling for individual drug requirements.

SELECT DRUGS THAT REQUIRE ↓ DOSE OR ↑ INTERVAL IN CKD

KEY DRUGS

Anti-Infectives
Aminoglycosides (↑ dosing interval primarily)
Beta-lactam antibiotics (most)
Fluconazole
Quinolones (except moxifloxacin)
Vancomycin

Cardiovascular Drugs
LMWHs (enoxaparin)
Rivaroxaban* (for AFib)

Gastrointestinal Drugs
H2RAs (famotidine, ranitidine)
Metoclopramide

Other
Bisphosphonates*
Lithium

Others:

Anti-Infectives
Amphotericin B
Anti-tuberculosis medications (ethambutol, pyrazinamide)
Antivirals (acyclovir, valacyclovir, ganciclovir, valganciclovir, oseltamivir)
Aztreonam
NRTIs, including tenofovir
Polymyxins
Sulfamethoxazole/Trimethoprim

Cardiovascular Drugs
Antiarrhythmics (digoxin, disopyramide, dofetilide, procainamide, sotalol*)
Apixaban* (for AFib)
Dabigatran* (for AFib)
Statins (most)

Pain/Gout Drugs
Allopurinol
Colchicine
Gabapentin, pregabalin
Morphine and codeine
Tramadol ER

Others
Cyclosporine
Tacrolimus
Topiramate

*Medication has indication-specific recommendations.

SELECT DRUGS THAT ARE CONTRAINDICATED IN CKD

KEY DRUGS

CrCl < 60 mL/min
Nitrofurantoin

CrCl < 50 mL/min
Tenofovir disoproxil fumarate containing products (e.g., *Stribild***, *Complera*, *Atripla*, *Symfi*, *Symfi Lo*)
Voriconazole IV (due to the vehicle)

CrCl < 30 mL/min
Tenofovir alafenamide containing products (e.g., *Genvoya*, *Biktarvy*, *Descovy*, *Odefsey*, *Symtuza*)
NSAIDs
Dabigatran* (DVT/PE)
Rivaroxaban* (DVT/PE)

GFR < 30 mL/min/1.73 m^2
SGLT2 inhibitors (canagliflozin, dapagliflozin, empagliflozin)
Metformin

Other***
Meperidine

Others:

CrCl < 30 mL/min
Avanafil
Bisphosphonates*
Duloxetine
Fondaparinux
Potassium-sparing diuretics
Tadalafil*
Tramadol ER

Others***
Dofetilide
Edoxaban
Glyburide
Sotalol* (*Betapace AF*)

*Medication has indication-specific recommendations.

** For treated patients; contraindicated to start treatment if CrCl < 70 mL/min.

***Not specified or another CrCl cut-off is used.

COMPLICATIONS OF CHRONIC KIDNEY DISEASE

See the figure illustrating the common complications of chronic kidney disease (exam studies should focus on the treatments).

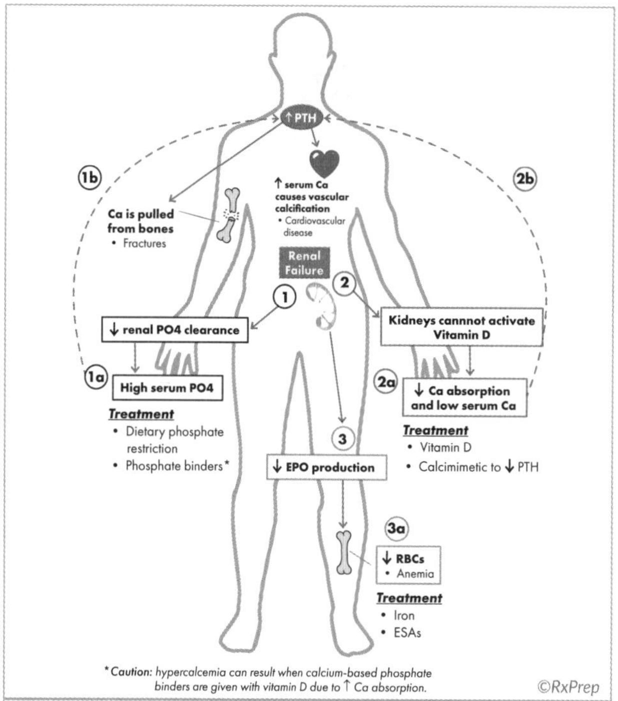

The interactions of Ca, PO_4 and vitamin D in CKD are complex. **1)** PO4 levels increase (because the kidneys cannot eliminate excess PO4 absorbed from the diet). **2)** Vitamin D cannot be activated by the kidney, causing dietary calcium absorption to decrease. Both high PO_4 **(1a)** and low Ca **(2a)** cause increased release of PTH. In a patient with healthy kidneys, PTH would cause the kidneys to increase Ca reabsorption, but in CKD this is not possible and Ca is pulled from the bones, leading to bone demineralization and increased fractures. Normally, when Ca levels return to normal, PTH release is shut down, but the chronically high PO_4 levels continue to stimulate PTH release and hypercalcemia can persist, causing calcification and cardiovascular disease. **3)** In CKD, the kidneys produce less erythropoietin (EPO), resulting in decreased RBC production in the bone marrow which causes anemia.

CKD MINERAL AND BONE DISORDER

CKD mineral and bone disorder (CKD-MBD) is common in patients with renal impairment and affects almost all patients receiving dialysis. CKD-MBD is associated with fractures, cardiovascular disease and increased mortality. Patients with advanced kidney disease require monitoring of parathyroid hormone (PTH), phosphorus (phosphate, PO4), Ca and vitamin D levels.

Hyperphosphatemia

Hyperphosphatemia contributes to chronically elevated PTH levels (secondary hyperparathyroidism) and must be treated to prevent bone disease and fractures. Treatment is initially focused on restricting dietary phosphate (e.g., avoid dairy products, cola, chocolate and nuts). As CKD progresses, phosphate binders are often required. Phosphate binders block the absorption of dietary PO4 by binding to it in the intestine. If a dose is missed (and the food is absorbed), the phosphate binder should be skipped, and the patient should resume normal dosing at the next meal or snack. There are three types of phosphate binders: 1) aluminum-based, 2) calcium-based and 3) aluminum-free, calcium-free drugs.

Phosphate Binders

DRUG	DOSE	SAFETY/SIDE EFFECTS/MONITORING
Aluminum-based: potent phosphate binders, but rarely used due to the risk of aluminum accumulation (which can cause nervous system and bone toxicity). Treatment duration is limited to 4 weeks.		
Aluminum hydroxide Suspension	300-600 mg PO TID with meals	**SIDE EFFECTS** Aluminum intoxication, "dialysis dementia," osteomalacia, constipation, nausea **MONITORING** Ca, PO4, PTH, s/sx of aluminum toxicity
Calcium-based: first-line.		
Calcium acetate (*Phoslyra, PhosLo**, others) Tablet, capsule, solution	1,334 mg PO TID with meals, titrate based on PO4 levels	**SIDE EFFECTS** Hypercalcemia, constipation, nausea **MONITORING** Ca, PO4, PTH **NOTES** Calcium acetate binds more dietary phosphorus on an elemental calcium basis compared to calcium carbonate Hypercalcemia is especially problematic with concomitant use of vitamin D (due to increased calcium absorption)
Calcium carbonate (*Tums*, others) Tablet, chewable tablet	500 mg PO TID with meals (can vary with formulation used), titrate based on PO4 levels Total daily dose of elemental calcium should be < 2,000 mg (from diet and supplements)	

DRUG	DOSE	SAFETY/SIDE EFFECTS/MONITORING
Aluminum-free, calcium-free: no aluminum accumulation, less hypercalcemia, but more expensive.		
Sucroferric oxyhydroxide *(Velphoro)* Chewable tablet	500 mg PO TID with meals, titrate based on PO4 levels	**WARNINGS** Iron absorption occurs with ferric citrate; dosage reduction of IV iron may be necessary; store out of reach of children to prevent accidental overdose **SIDE EFFECTS** Diarrhea, constipation, discolored (black) feces **MONITORING** Iron, ferritin, TSAT (only with ferric citrate), PO4, PTH **NOTES** Absorption is minimal with sucroferric oxyhydroxide
Ferric citrate *(Auryxia)* Tablet	2 tablets (420 mg) PO TID with meals, titrate based on PO4 levels	
Lanthanum carbonate *(Fosrenol)* Chewable tablet, powder	500 mg PO TID with meals, titrate based on PO4 levels Must chew tablet thoroughly to reduce risk of severe GI adverse effects Use powder if unable to chew tablets	**CONTRAINDICATIONS** GI obstruction, fecal impaction, ileus **WARNINGS** GI perforation **SIDE EFFECTS** N/V/D, constipation, abdominal pain **MONITORING** Ca, PO4, PTH
Sevelamer: a non-calcium, non-aluminum based phosphate binder that is not systemically absorbed.		
Sevelamer carbonate *(Renvela)* Tablet, powder **Sevelamer hydrochloride *(Renagel)*** Tablet	800-1,600 mg PO TID with meals, titrate based on PO4 levels	**CONTRAINDICATIONS** Bowel obstruction **WARNINGS** Can reduce dietary absorption of vitamins D, E, K and folic acid; consider vitamin supplementation **SIDE EFFECTS** N/V/D (all > 20%), dyspepsia, constipation, abdominal pain, flatulence **MONITORING** Ca, PO4, HCO3, Cl, PTH **NOTES** Can lower total cholesterol and LDL by 15 – 30%. Sevelamer carbonate can maintain bicarbonate concentrations

**Brand discontinued but name still used in practice.*

Phosphate Binder Drug Interactions

- Phosphate binders are designed to "bind" and because of this have many drug interactions. Separate administration from levothyroxine and antibiotics that chelate (e.g., quinolones, tetracyclines).
- Calcium-based phosphate binders interact with many drugs, including quinolones, tetracyclines, oral bisphosphonates and thyroid products.
- Sucroferric oxyhydroxide and ferric citrate are iron-based phosphate binders. Doxycycline should be taken one hour before both products. Ciprofloxacin should be separated by two hours from ferric citrate. Levothyroxine should not be used with sucroferric oxyhydroxide.
- Lanthanum carbonate can bind to aluminum-, calcium- or magnesium-containing antacids; administration of these products should be separated from the lanthanum dose by two hours. Quinolone antibiotics should be given one hour before or four hours after lanthanum. Separate levothyroxine by at least two hours.
- Sevelamer can decrease the absorption of some medications. Quinolone antibiotics should be given two hours before or six hours after the sevelamer dose. Mycophenolate, tacrolimus and levothyroxine serum concentrations can be decreased and doses of these medications should be given several hours before sevelamer.

Vitamin D Deficiency & Secondary Hyperparathyroidism

After controlling hyperphosphatemia, elevations in PTH are treated primarily with vitamin D. Vitamin D deficiency occurs when the kidney is unable to hydroxylate vitamin D to its final active form, 1,25-dihydroxy vitamin D. Vitamin D deficiency worsens bone disease, impairs immunity and increases the risk of cardiovascular disease.

Vitamin D occurs in two primary forms: vitamin D3 (or cholecalciferol), which is synthesized in the skin after exposure to ultraviolet light (e.g., the sun), and vitamin D2 (or ergocalciferol), which is produced from plant sterols and is the primary dietary source of vitamin D. Supplementation with oral ergocalciferol or cholecalciferol may be necessary, especially in patients with early CKD (e.g., stage 3 and 4).

The vitamin D analogs are used in patients with later stages of CKD, or ESRD, to increase calcium absorption from the gut, raise serum calcium concentrations and inhibit PTH secretion. Calcitriol *(Rocaltrol)* is the active form of vitamin D3. Newer vitamin D analogs, such as paricalcitol and doxercalciferol, are alternatives that cause less hypercalcemia than calcitriol.

Another method of inhibiting PTH release is by increasing the sensitivity of the calcium receptor on the parathyroid gland. Cinacalcet *(Sensipar)* is a "calcimimetic" which mimics the actions of calcium on the parathyroid gland and causes a further reduction in PTH. It is only used in dialysis patients.

Drugs for the Treatment of Secondary Hyperparathyroidism

DRUG	DOSING	SAFETY/SIDE EFFECTS/MONITORING
Vitamin D analogs: ↑ intestinal absorption of Ca, which provides negative feedback to the parathyroid gland.		
Calcitriol *(Rocaltrol)* Capsule, solution, injection	CKD: 0.25-0.5 mcg PO daily Dialysis: 0.25-1 mcg PO daily or 0.5-4 mcg IV 3x weekly	**CONTRAINDICATIONS** Hypercalcemia, vitamin D toxicity **WARNINGS** Digitalis toxicity potentiated by hypercalcemia **SIDE EFFECTS** Hypercalcemia, hyperphosphatemia, N/V/D (> 10%) **MONITORING** Ca, PO4, PTH, 25-hydroxy vitamin D (calcifediol) **NOTES** Take with food or shortly after a meal to ↓ GI upset (calcitriol) Calcifediol is a prodrug of calcitriol
Calcifediol *(Rayaldee)* ER capsule	CKD Stage 3 or 4: 30 mcg PO QHS	
Doxercalciferol *(Hectorol)* Capsule, injection	CKD: 1-3.5 mcg PO daily Dialysis: 10-20 mcg PO 3x weekly or 4-18 mcg IV 3x weekly	
Paricalcitol *(Zemplar)* Capsule, injection	CKD: 1-2 mcg PO daily or 2-4 mcg PO 3x weekly Dialysis: 2.8-7 mcg IV 3x weekly	
Calcimimetic: ↑ sensitivity of the calcium-sensing receptor on the parathyroid gland, which causes ↓ PTH, ↓ Ca, ↓ PO4.		
Cinacalcet *(Sensipar)*	Dialysis: 30-180 mg PO daily with food Take tablet whole, do not crush or chew	**CONTRAINDICATIONS** Hypocalcemia **WARNING** Caution in patients with a history of seizures **SIDE EFFECTS** Hypocalcemia, N/V/D, paresthesia, HA, fatigue, depression, anorexia, constipation, bone fracture, weakness, arthralgia, myalgia, limb pain, URTIs **MONITORING** Ca, PO4, PTH
Etelcalcetide *(Parsabiv)*	Dialysis: 2.5-15 mg IV 3x weekly	**WARNINGS** Hypocalcemia, worsening HF, GI bleeding, decreased bone turnover **SIDE EFFECTS** Muscle spasms, paresthesia, N/V/D **MONITORING** Ca, PO4, PTH

ANEMIA OF CKD

Anemia is defined as a hemoglobin level < 13 g/dL. It is common in CKD and is due to a combination of factors. The primary problem is a lack of erythropoietin (EPO), which is normally produced by the kidneys and travels to the bone marrow to stimulate the production of red blood cells (RBCs). RBCs (which contain hemoglobin) are released into the blood where they transport oxygen.

As kidney function declines, EPO production decreases. This leads to reduced hemoglobin levels and symptoms of anemia (e.g., fatigue, pale skin). These processes are exacerbated by CKD causing an inflammatory state, which contributes to decreased EPO production. Anemia of CKD is sometimes referred to as anemia of chronic disease.

Erythropoiesis stimulating agents (ESAs) can prevent the need for blood transfusions. ESAs include epoetin alfa *(Procrit, Epogen, Retacrit)* and the longer-lasting formulation darbepoetin alfa *(Aranesp)*. ESAs have risks, including elevated blood pressure and thrombosis. They should only be used when the hemoglobin is < 10 g/dL. The dose should be held or discontinued if the hemoglobin exceeds 11 g/dL, as the risk for thromboembolic disease (DVT, PE, MI, stroke) is increased with higher hemoglobin levels.

ESAs are only effective if adequate iron is available to make hemoglobin. It is important to assess an iron panel (iron, ferritin and TSAT) and provide supplementation to prevent iron deficiency. In ESRD, iron levels can be low due to reduced GI absorption and blood loss from dialysis treatments. Intravenous (IV) iron is given at the dialysis center. See the Anemia chapter for more information on identifying different types of anemia and use of ESAs and IV iron.

HYPERKALEMIA

A normal potassium level is 3.5 – 5 mEq/L. Hyperkalemia can be defined as a potassium level > 5.3 or > 5.5 mEq/L (ranges vary), though clinicians will be concerned with any level > 5 mEq/L.

Potassium is the most abundant intracellular cation and is essential for life. Humans obtain potassium through the diet from many foods, including meats, beans and fruits. Normal daily intake through the GI tract is about 1 mEq/kg/day. Excess intake is excreted, primarily via the kidneys and partially via the gut. Renal potassium excretion is increased by the hormone aldosterone, diuretics (loops > thiazides), by a high urine flow (via osmotic diuresis) and by negatively charged ions in the distal tubule (e.g., bicarbonate).

High dietary potassium intake does not typically cause hyperkalemia unless there is significant renal damage. With normal kidney function, the acute rise in potassium from a meal would be offset by the release of insulin, which causes potassium to shift into the cells.

The most common cause of hyperkalemia is decreased renal excretion due to kidney failure. The risk can be increased with a high dietary potassium intake or use of drugs that interfere with potassium excretion.

Patients with diabetes are at a higher risk for hyperkalemia, as insulin deficiency reduces the ability to shift potassium into the cells, and many patients with diabetes take ACE inhibitors or ARBs. Hospitalized patients are at higher risk of hyperkalemia than outpatients, primarily due to the concurrent use of drugs and IV solutions. Rarely, acute hyperkalemia can be due to tumor lysis, rhabdomyolysis or succinylcholine administration.

A patient with an elevated potassium level may be asymptomatic. When symptoms are present, they can include muscle weakness, bradycardia and fatal arrhythmias. If the potassium is high or the heart rate/rhythm is abnormal, the patient is usually monitored with an ECG. The risk for severe, negative outcomes increases as the potassium level increases.

SELECT DRUGS THAT RAISE POTASSIUM LEVELS

KEY DRUGS

- ACE inhibitors
- Aldosterone receptor antagonists
- Aliskiren
- ARBs
- Canagliflozin
- Drospirenone-containing COCs
- Sulfamethoxazole/trimethoprim
- Transplant drugs (cyclosporine, everolimus, tacrolimus)

Others:

- Glycopyrrolate
- Heparin (chronic use)
- NSAIDs
- Potassium-containing IV fluids (including parenteral nutrition)
- Potassium supplements
- Pentamidine

Treatment of Hyperkalemia

All potassium sources must be discontinued. If hyperkalemia is severe, there is an urgent clinical need to stabilize the myocardial cells (to prevent arrhythmias) and to rapidly shift potassium intracellularly or induce elimination from the body.

The table below lists the medication options for management of hyperkalemia. Several medications move potassium from the extracellular to the intracellular compartment. One or more of these methods are used in severe hyperkalemia. These drugs work quickly, but they do not lower total body potassium. Interventions to enhance potassium elimination can be used. These methods take longer to reduce potassium and are only used alone in less severe situations; they are mostly used in combination with a drug that shifts potassium intracellularly.

STEPS FOR TREATING SEVERE HYPERKALEMIA

1. Stabilize the heart

Prevent arrhythmias

2. Move it

Shift excess K intracellularly

3. Remove it

Enhance K elimination

MECHANISM	INTERVENTION	ROUTE OF ADMINISTRATION	ONSET	NOTES
Stabilize the heart	Calcium gluconate	IV	1-2 minutes	Does not decrease potassium. Stabilizes myocardial cells to prevent arrhythmias.
Move it Shift K intracellularly	Regular insulin	IV	30 minutes	Co-administered with glucose or dextrose to prevent hypoglycemia.
	Dextrose	IV	30 minutes	Stimulates insulin secretion, but does not shift K intracellularly on its own.
	Sodium bicarbonate	IV	30 minutes	Used when metabolic acidosis is present.
	Albuterol	Nebulized	30 minutes	Monitor for tachycardia and chest pain.
Remove it Eliminate K from the body	Furosemide	IV	5 minutes	Eliminates K in the urine. Monitor volume status.
	Sodium polystyrene sulfonate	Oral or rectal	1 hour; do not use oral for acute emergencies	Binds K in the GI tract. Oral may take hours to days to work. Rectal route has a faster onset and can be used in acute (emergency) treatment.
	Patiromer	Oral	~7 hours	Binds K in the GI tract. Not for acute or emergency use due to delayed onset.
	Sodium zirconium cyclosilicate	Oral	1 hour	Binds K in the GI tract. Not for acute or emergency use due to delayed onset.
	Hemodialysis		Immediate, once started	Removes K from the blood. It takes several hours to set up/complete dialysis. Other methods are generally used in conjunction.

Drugs for Treatment of Hyperkalemia

DRUG	DOSE	SAFETY/SIDE EFFECTS/MONITORING
Sodium polystyrene sulfonate (*SPS, Kayexalate,** *Kionex)* Powder, oral suspension, rectal suspension Non-absorbed cation exchange resin	Oral: 15 grams 1-4 times/day Rectal: 30-50 grams Q6H	**WARNINGS** Electrolyte disturbances (hypernatremia, hypokalemia, hypomagnesemia, hypocalcemia), fecal impaction, GI necrosis (↑ risk when administered with sorbitol; do not use together) Can bind other oral medications (check for drug interactions and separate administration) **SIDE EFFECTS** N/V, constipation or diarrhea **MONITORING** K, Mg, Na, Ca **NOTES** Do not mix oral products with fruit juices containing K
Patiromer *(Veltassa)* Powder for oral suspension Non-absorbed cation exchange polymer	8.4 grams PO once daily; max dose is 25.2 grams once daily Instructions: measure 1/3 cup of water and pour half into an empty cup; empty the *Veltassa* packet contents into the water and stir well; add the remaining water to the mixture and stir well (the mixture will be cloudy); drink the mixture right away (if powder remains in the cup, add additional water and drink; repeat as needed)	**WARNINGS** Can worsen GI motility, hypomagnesemia Binds to many oral drugs; separate by at least 3 hours before or 3 hours after **SIDE EFFECTS** Constipation, N/D **MONITORING** K, Mg **NOTES** Delayed onset of action; not for emergency use Store powder in the refrigerator (must be used within 3 months if stored at room temperature)
Sodium zirconium cyclosilicate *(Lokelma)* Powder for oral suspension Non-absorbed cation exchange polymer	10 g PO TID for up to 48 hours Instructions: empty packet contents into a cup with at least 3 tablespoons of water; stir well and drink immediately (if powder remains in the cup, add additional water and drink; repeat as needed)	**WARNINGS** Can worsen GI motility, edema, contains sodium (may need to adjust dietary sodium intake) Can bind other drugs; separate by at least 2 hours before or 2 hours after **SIDE EFFECTS** Peripheral edema **NOTES** Delayed onset of action; not for emergency use Store at room temperature

**Brand discontinued but name still used in practice.*

METABOLIC ACIDOSIS

The ability of the kidney to reabsorb bicarbonate decreases as CKD progresses. This can result in the development of metabolic acidosis. In the ambulatory care setting, treatment of metabolic acidosis is initiated when the serum bicarbonate concentration is < 22 mEq/L. Drugs to replace bicarbonate include:

- Sodium bicarbonate *(Neut)*
  - Sodium load can cause fluid retention.
  - Monitor sodium level and use caution in patients with hypertension or cardiovascular disease.
- Sodium citrate/citric acid solution *(Cytra-2, Oracit, Shohl's solution)*
  - Monitor sodium level.
  - Metabolized to bicarbonate by the liver; may not be effective in patients with liver failure.

DIALYSIS

If CKD progresses to failure (stage 5 disease), dialysis is required in all patients who do not receive a kidney transplant. The two primary types of dialysis are hemodialysis (HD) and peritoneal dialysis (PD). In HD, the patient's blood is pumped to the dialyzer (dialysis machine) and runs through a semipermeable dialysis filter which, using a concentration gradient, removes waste products, electrolytes and excess fluid. HD is a 3 - 4 hour process, several times per week (usually three times). Patients who do HD at home can do it more frequently (e.g., 5 - 6 times per week).

In PD, a dialysis solution (usually containing glucose) is pumped into the peritoneal cavity (the abdominal cavity surrounding the internal organs). The peritoneal membrane acts as the semipermeable membrane (i.e., as the dialyzer). The solution is left in the abdomen to "dwell" for a period of time, then is drained. This cycle is repeated throughout the day, every day. PD is performed by the patient at home.

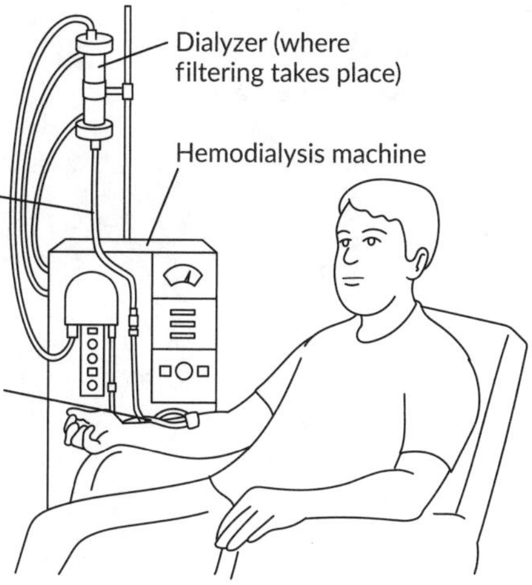

FACTORS AFFECTING DRUG REMOVAL DURING DIALYSIS

When a patient receives dialysis, the pharmacist must consider the amount of medication cleared during dialysis in order to recommend the correct dose and interval. Medications that are removed during dialysis (including many antibiotics) must be given after dialysis or may require a supplemental dose following dialysis. Drug removal during dialysis depends primarily on the factors below.

FACTOR	EFFECT
Drug Characteristic	
Molecular weight/size	Smaller molecules are more readily removed by dialysis
Volume of distribution	Drugs with a large Vd are less likely to be removed by dialysis
Protein-binding	Highly protein-bound drugs are less likely to be removed by dialysis
Dialysis Factors	
Membrane	High-flux (large pore size) and high-efficiency (large surface area) HD filters remove more substances than conventional/low-flux filters
Blood flow rate	Higher dialysis blood flow rates increase drug removal over a given time interval

Select Guidelines/References

Kidney Disease: Improving Global Outcomes (KDIGO) CKD Work Group.
KDIGO 2012 Clinical Practice Guideline for the Evaluation and Management of Chronic Kidney Disease.
Kidney Inter., Suppl. 2013;3:1-150.

CHAPTER CONTENT

Hepatitis ... 302
Background ... 302
Hepatitis A, B and C ... 302
Comparison of Hepatitis Viruses ... 303
Drug Treatment for Hepatitis C ... 303
Direct Acting Antivirals (DAAs) ... 303
DAA Mechanisms and Regimens ... 303
DAA Drug Interactions ... 305
DAA Counseling ... 305
Ribavirin ... 306
Interferon Alfa ... 307
Drug Treatment for Hepatitis B ... 307
Interferon Alfa ... 307
Interferons ... 307
Nucleoside/Tide Reverse Transcriptase Inhibitors (NRTIs) ... 307
Liver Disease and Cirrhosis ... 308
Background ... 308
Clinical Presentation ... 308
Objective Criteria ... 309
Lab Tests for Liver Disease ... 309
Assessing Severity of Liver Disease ... 309
Natural Products ... 309
Drug-Induced Liver Injury ... 309
Select Drugs with Boxed Warning for Liver Damage ... 310
Alcoholic Liver Disease ... 309
Treatment ... 310
Complications of Liver Disease and Cirrhosis ... 310
Portal Hypertension and Variceal Bleeding ... 310
Hepatic Encephalopathy ... 312
Ascites ... 313
Spontaneous Bacterial Peritonitis ... 313
Hepatorenal Syndrome ... 313

CONTENT LEGEND

= Study Tip Gal = Key Drug Guy

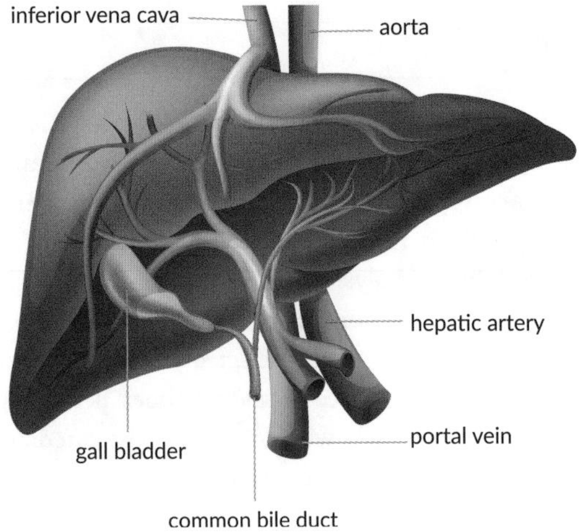

CHAPTER 19
HEPATITIS & LIVER DISEASE

HEPATITIS

BACKGROUND

Hepatitis means inflammation of the liver. Hepatitis viruses are the most common cause, but alcohol, certain drugs, autoimmune diseases and other viruses/infections can cause hepatitis. Viruses that damage the liver include hepatitis A through E (most cases of viral hepatitis are caused by hepatitis A, B and C), along with herpesvirus, CMV, Epstein-Barr virus and adenoviruses. Symptoms and treatment differ depending on the cause of hepatitis and extent of liver damage (see discussion of cirrhosis in this chapter). Many patients with hepatitis B and C do not know they are infected.

HEPATITIS A, B AND C

Hepatitis A virus (HAV) causes an acute, self-limiting illness in most patients. Transmission is primarily via the fecal-oral route through improper hand washing after exposure to an infected person or via contaminated food/water. Symptoms are generally mild and non-specific.

Hepatitis B virus (HBV) and hepatitis C virus (HCV) can cause acute illness and can lead to chronic infection, cirrhosis of the liver, liver cancer, liver failure and death. Transmission occurs from contact with infectious blood or other body fluids (e.g., having sex with an infected person), sharing contaminated needles to inject drugs or from an infected mother to her newborn (perinatal transmission). See Study Tip Gal on the following page for a comparison of the hepatitis viruses.

Comparison of Hepatitis Viruses

	HEPATITIS A	HEPATITIS B	HEPATITIS C
Acute vs Chronic	Acute	Both	Both
Transmission	Fecal-oral	Blood, body fluid	Blood, body fluid
Vaccine	Yes*	Yes*	No
First-Line Treatment	Supportive	PEG-INF or NRTI (tenofovir or entecavir)	Treatment naïve: DAA combination
Other Treatments for Select Patients			DAA combination + RBV or DAA combination + RBV + PEG-INF**

**See Immunizations chapter; DAA = direct acting antivirals, PEG-INF = pegylated interferon, RBV = ribavirin*
***HCV guidelines no longer routinely recommend interferon alfa (see text for discussion)*

DRUG TREATMENT FOR HEPATITIS C

There are six different HCV genotypes (1 – 6) and various subtypes (e.g., 1a or 1b). Treatment options and duration of therapy depend on the genotype, presence of cirrhosis and whether the patient has been treated before. Preferred HCV regimens for treatment naïve patients without cirrhosis consist of 2 – 3 direct acting antivirals (DAAs) with different mechanisms, usually for 12 weeks. Some regimens can be as short as eight weeks in appropriate patients. Some combinations include ritonavir, which is not active for HCV, but is used to boost (increase) levels of HCV protease inhibitors used with it.

Ribavirin can be added to DAA therapy as an alternative treatment option. Interferon is no longer recommended in combination regimens, but could play a role when DAAs are contraindicated or too expensive. Because treatment of HCV is rapidly changing, drug selection is typically handled by specialists. Healthcare providers should consult the AASLD website for the most up-to-date recommendations (www.hcvguidelines.org).

DIRECT ACTING ANTIVIRALS (DAAS)

DAAs have revolutionized the treatment of HCV, almost entirely eliminating older, poorly tolerated treatments (e.g., interferon and ribavirin) and offering a cure for most patients. Treatment of HCV is approached much like HIV, with regimens consisting of combinations of drugs that target different phases of the HCV life cycle. DAAs include NS3/4A protease inhibitors, NS5A replication complex inhibitors and NS5B polymerase inhibitors (see Study Tip Gal). Many DAAs are available only in combination products.

DAA MECHANISMS AND REGIMENS

Preferred HCV regimens include 2-3 DAAs with different mechanisms of action (often in one tablet)

MECHANISM	NAME CLUE	EXAMPLES
NS3/4A Protease Inhibitor	-previr P for PI	Grazo*previr* Parita*previr* Sime*previr* Voxila*previr*
NS5A Replication Complex Inhibitor	-asvir A for NS5A	Daclat*asvir* Ledip*asvir* Ombit*asvir* Pibrent*asvir* Velpat*asvir*
NS5B Polymerase Inhibitor	-buvir B for NS5B	Dasa*buvir* Sofos*buvir*

Be able to recognize appropriate and inappropriate combinations.

Example:

Daclat*asvir* + sofos*buvir*: preferred regimen combining 2 different MOAs.

Dasa*buvir* + sofos*buvir*: two DAAs with the same MOA; should not be used together in a combination regimen.

What do the protease inhibitors used for HIV and HCV have in common? They are taken with food.

Remember: **P**rotease **I**nhibitors & **G**rub (**PIG**) **Take With Food***

**Exception: elbasvir/grazoprevir (Zepatier) (without regard to food) and fosamprenavir oral susp (without food in adults)*

DRUG	DOSING	SAFETY/SIDE EFFECTS/MONITORING
All DAAs		**BOXED WARNING (FOR ENTIRE CLASS)** Risk of reactivating HBV; test all patients for HBV before starting a DAA **WARNING (FOR SOFOSBUVIR-CONTAINING REGIMENS)** Serious symptomatic bradycardia has been reported when amiodarone is taken with a sofosbuvir-containing regimen. Do not use amiodarone with sofosbuvir. **SIDE EFFECTS** Well-tolerated; HA, fatigue, diarrhea, nausea **MONITORING** LFTs (including bilirubin), HCV-RNA
Sofosbuvir (*Sovaldi*) Tablet	400 mg daily with or without food	**WARNINGS** Potentially serious drug interactions (see drug interactions) **NOTES** Sofosbuvir monotherapy is not effective and not recommended *Sovaldi, Harvoni, Epclusa, Vosevi*: protect from moisture; dispense in original container ***Harvoni, Epclusa* and *Vosevi*** Acid suppressive therapy should be avoided or minimized during therapy (see drug interactions) **Pan-Genotypic (approved for all 6 HCV genotypes) for Treatment Naïve** *Epclusa* and *Mavyret* **Approved for Salvage Therapy (failed previous therapy)** *Vosevi* and *Mavyret* (select patients) **Approved for 8-Week Course of Therapy (select patients)** *Mavyret* **Approved for HCV/HIV Co-Infection** *Epclusa, Harvoni* and *Mavyret* **Approved for Children ≥ 12 years old with certain genotypes** *Sovaldi* and *Harvoni*
Sofosbuvir/ledipasvir (*Harvoni*) Tablet	1 tablet daily with or without food	
Sofosbuvir/velpatasvir (*Epclusa*) Tablet	1 tablet daily with or without food	
Sofosbuvir/velpatasvir/ voxilaprevir (*Vosevi*) Tablet	1 tablet daily with food	
Glecaprevir/pibrentasvir (*Mavyret*) Tablet	3 tablets once daily with food	
Daclatasvir (*Daklinza*) Tablet	60 mg daily in combination with sofosbuvir Adjust dose with strong 3A4 inhibitors or moderate inducers	**CONTRAINDICATIONS** Use with strong CYP450 3A4 inducers **NOTES** Daclatasvir monotherapy is not effective and not recommended Consider screening for NS5A polymorphism if patient has HCV genotype 1a with cirrhosis
Paritaprevir/ritonavir/ ombitasvir (*Technivie*) Tablet	2 tablets once daily in the morning with a meal	**CONTRAINDICATIONS** Moderate-severe hepatic impairment (Child Pugh B or C), concomitant use with drugs highly dependent on CYP3A4 for elimination (if ↑ levels, can cause serious events) and moderate-strong inducers of CYP3A4, all contraindications to ribavirin apply when used in combination regimens *Viekira Pak* and *Viekira XR*: above contraindications apply; also contraindicated with strong inducers or inhibitors of CYP2C8 **WARNINGS** Hepatic decompensation and hepatic failure in patients with cirrhosis, risk of ↑ LFTs (> 5 x ULN) within 4 wks of treatment (female patients taking ethinyl estradiol products are at ↑ risk), significant drug interaction potential, risk of HIV protease inhibitor resistance **SIDE EFFECTS** Insomnia, pruritus
Paritaprevir/ ritonavir/ombitasvir + dasabuvir (*Viekira Pak*, *Viekira XR*) Tablet *Viekira Pak*: paritaprevir/ ritonavir/ombitasvir fixed dose combination tablet copackaged with dasabuvir (250 mg) tablets	*Viekira Pak:* 2 tablets of paritaprevir/ritonavir/ ombitasvir once daily in the morning and 1 dasabuvir tablet twice daily with meals *Viekira XR:* 3 tablets once daily with a meal	
Elbasvir/grazoprevir (*Zepatier*) Tablet	1 tablet daily with or without food	**CONTRAINDICATIONS** Moderate-severe hepatic impairment (Child Pugh B or C); use with strong inducers of CYP3A4, OATP1B1/3 inhibitors and efavirenz; all contraindications to ribavirin apply when used in combination regimens **WARNINGS** Risk of ↑ LFTs (> 5 x ULN) within 4 weeks of treatment, significant drug interaction potential **NOTES** Screening for NS5A polymorphism is recommended when treating HCV genotype 1a

DAA DRUG INTERACTIONS

All of the DAAs have significant drug interaction potential. This summary is not all-inclusive. Consult the package labeling of each agent for additional detail.

All DAAs

- All DAAs are contraindicated with strong inducers of CYP3A4 (e.g., carbamazepine, oxcarbazepine, phenobarbital, phenytoin, rifampin, rifabutin and St. John's wort).
- Most DAAs ↑ concentration of statins and ↑ risk of myopathy.

Harvoni, Epclusa and *Vosevi*

Interactions for sofosbuvir apply to these medications and:

- Antacids, H2RAs and PPIs can ↓ concentrations of ledipasvir and velpatasvir.
    - Separate from antacids by four hours.
    - Take H2RAs at the same time or separated (~12 hours) and use ≤ famotidine 40 mg BID or equivalent.
    - Using PPIs with *Epclusa* is not recommended. For *Harvoni* and *Vosevi*, specific recommendations are offered in the package labeling.

Technivie and *Viekira*

- Monitoring is required because of the potential for numerous drug-drug interactions (consult the product labeling for a complete list). See HIV chapter for additional ritonavir drug interactions.
- *Technivie* and *Viekira Pak* are substrates (major) and inhibitors (strong) of CYP3A4 and P-gp; avoid use with drugs highly dependent on CYP3A4 for elimination (if ↑ levels can cause serious events) and avoid moderate-strong CYP3A4 inducers due to ↓ efficacy of HCV therapy.
    - Drugs contraindicated with *Technivie* and *Viekira* include: strong inducers of CYP3A4 (above) and alfuzosin, colchicine, ranolazine, dronedarone, lurasidone, pimozide, ergotamine derivatives, ethinyl estradiol-containing products, cisapride, lovastatin, simvastatin, efavirenz, sildenafil (dosed for PAH), triazolam and oral midazolam.
- Dasabuvir (component of *Viekira*) is a substrate (major) of CYP2C8; avoid strong inducers or inhibitors of CYP2C8 (e.g., gemfibrozil).

Zepatier

- Contraindicated with efavirenz, HIV protease inhibitors (specifically atazanavir, darunavir, lopinavir, saquinavir, tipranavir) and cyclosporine. *Zepatier* is not recommended with nafcillin, ketoconazole, bosentan, tacrolimus, etravirine, *Stribild*, *Genvoya* and modafinil.

Mavyret

- Contraindicated with efavirenz, HIV protease inhibitors (specifically atazanavir, darunavir, lopinavir, ritonavir), ethinyl estradiol-containing products and cyclosporine.

DAA COUNSELING

Technivie and *Viekira*

- This medication can cause increases in liver function blood tests. Get immediate medical help if you develop any of the following: yellowing of the white part of your eyes or yellowing of your skin, dark-colored urine, light colored stool or bad stomach pain with severe nausea.
- *Technivie* and *Viekira (Pak* or *XR):* certain medications cannot be used with this medication. Ethinyl estradiol-containing medicines must be stopped before starting it. Use another method of birth control during treatment and for about two weeks after. Examples of ethinyl estradiol products include:
    - Combination oral contraceptive pills or patches like *Lo Loestrin FE, Norinyl, Ortho Tri-Cyclen Lo, Xulane.*
    - Hormonal vaginal rings like *NuvaRing.*
    - Hormone replacement therapy like *femhrt.*
- *Viekira Pak* contains two different types of tablets. You must take both types of tablets exactly as prescribed to treat your chronic hepatitis C virus (HCV) infection.
    - The pink tablet contains the medicines ombitasvir, paritaprevir and ritonavir (take once daily).
    - The beige tablet contains the medicine dasabuvir (take twice daily).
- *Viekira XR:* take with a meal; swallow the tablets whole and do not consume alcohol within four hours of taking *Viekira XR*.

RIBAVIRIN

Ribavirin (RBV) is an oral antiviral agent that inhibits replication of RNA and DNA viruses. It is indicated for HCV in combination with other agents (DAAs and/or interferon alfa), but never as monotherapy. Aerosolized ribavirin has been used for respiratory syncytial virus (RSV) (see Pediatric Conditions chapter).

DRUG	DOSING	SAFETY/SIDE EFFECTS/MONITORING
Ribavirin (*Ribasphere*, *Moderiba, Rebetol, Ribasphere RibaPak*) Capsule, tablet, solution (oral) *Virazole* for RSV	400-600 mg BID, varies based on indication, patient weight and genotype ↑ tolerability if given with food When Hgb < 10 g/dL, ↓ dose (avoid if Hgb < 8.5 g/dL) Capsule should not be crushed, chewed, opened, or broken	**BOXED WARNINGS** Significant teratogenic effects; not effective for monotherapy of HCV; hemolytic anemia (primary toxicity of oral therapy mostly occurring within 4 weeks of therapy); inhalation can precipitate in ventilated patients **CONTRAINDICATIONS** Pregnancy, women of childbearing age who will not use contraception reliably, male partners of pregnant women, hemoglobinopathies, CrCl < 50 mL/min (*Ribasphere, Rebetol*), autoimmune hepatitis, concomitant use with didanosine **SIDE EFFECTS** Hemolytic anemia (can worsen cardiac disease and lead to MIs; do not use in unstable cardiac disease), fatigue, HA, insomnia, N/V/D, anorexia, myalgias, hypothyroidism **MONITORING** CBC with diff, PLTs, electrolytes, LFTs/bili, HCV-RNA, TSH, monthly pregnancy tests **NOTES** Avoid pregnancy in females and female partners of male patients during therapy and 6 months after completion. At least 2 reliable forms of effective contraception required during treatment and in the 6-month post-treatment follow-up period.

Ribavirin Drug Interactions

- Do not use with didanosine due to cases of fatal hepatic failure, peripheral neuropathy and pancreatitis.
- Ribavirin can ↑ hepatotoxic effects of all NRTIs; lactic acidosis can occur.
- Zidovudine can ↑ risk and severity of anemia from ribavirin.

Ribavirin Counseling

- Ribavirin can cause birth defects or death of an unborn child. The MedGuide given to you describes the risks.
- Female patients: do not take ribavirin if you are pregnant or plan to become pregnant. You must not become pregnant during therapy and for six months after you have stopped therapy. During this time, you must use two forms of birth control and have pregnancy tests that show that you are not pregnant.
- Male patients: do not take ribavirin if your partner is pregnant or plans to become pregnant. Your female sexual partner must not become pregnant during treatment and for six months after treatment has stopped. Two forms of birth control must be used during this time.
- If you or a female sexual partner becomes pregnant, tell your healthcare provider immediately. There is a Ribavirin Pregnancy Registry that collects confidential information about pregnancy outcomes in female patients and female partners of male patients exposed to ribavirin.
- If using the oral solution, wash the measuring cup or spoon to avoid swallowing of the medicine by someone other than the person to whom it was prescribed.
- This medicine can cause a dangerous drop in your red blood cell count, called anemia. Your healthcare provider will check your red blood cell count before you start therapy and often during the first four weeks of therapy. Your red blood cell count may be checked more often if you have any heart or breathing problems.
- Do not take ribavirin alone to treat hepatitis C infection. It is used in combination with other medications.

INTERFERON ALFA

Interferons are naturally-produced cytokines that have antiviral, antiproliferative and immunomodulatory effects. Interferon alfa (INF-alfa) is approved for treatment of HBV and HCV. The pegylated forms (PEG-INF-alfa) have polyethylene glycol added, which prolongs the half-life, reducing dosing to once weekly. INF-alfa monotherapy and combination therapy have been used to treat HCV. Combination therapy for HCV consists of INF + RBV or INF + RBV + DAA/s. HCV guidelines no longer recommend interferon products, but they will continue to be used when other treatments are contraindicated or too costly. Interferons have toxicities and lab abnormalities that limit their use.

DRUG	DOSING	SAFETY/SIDE EFFECTS/MONITORING
Interferon-alfa-2b (*Intron A*) – for HBV, HCV, many cancers Pegylated interferon-alfa-2a (*Pegasys*) – for HBV and HCV Pegylated interferon-alfa-2b (*PegIntron, Sylatron*) – for HCV	SC dosing varies by indication and product: *Intron A:* 3 times weekly *Pegasys* and *PegIntron:* weekly	**BOXED WARNINGS** Can cause or exacerbate neuropsychiatric, autoimmune, ischemic or infectious disorders; if used with ribavirin, teratogenic/anemia risk **CONTRAINDICATIONS** Autoimmune hepatitis, decompensated liver disease in cirrhotic patients, infants/neonates (*Pegasys*) **WARNINGS** Neuropsychiatric, cardiovascular events, endocrine disorders (hypo/hyperthyroidism, hypo/hyperglycemia), visual disorders (retinopathy, decrease in vision), pancreatitis, myelosuppression, skin reactions **SIDE EFFECTS** CNS effects (fatigue, depression, anxiety, weakness), GI upset, ↑ LFTs (5-10x ULN during treatment), myelosuppression, mild alopecia Flu-like syndrome (fever, chills, HA, malaise); pre-treat with acetaminophen and an antihistamine **MONITORING** CBC with differential and platelets, LFTs, uric acid, SCr, electrolytes, TGs, thyroid function tests, serum HBV-DNA or HCV-RNA levels

INTERFERONS

- Alfa: HBV, HCV and some cancers
- Beta: Multiple sclerosis (MS)

Interferons do not provide a cure and are hard to take. A flu-like syndrome after the injection is common. The list of boxed warnings and warnings is long.

DRUG TREATMENT FOR HEPATITIS B

INTERFERON ALFA

Interferon alfa (see previous discussion) is approved as monotherapy for HBV.

NUCLEOSIDE/TIDE REVERSE TRANSCRIPTASE INHIBITORS (NRTIs)

These agents inhibit HBV replication by inhibiting HBV polymerase resulting in DNA chain termination. The NRTIs listed below are approved as monotherapy options for HBV. Prior to starting HBV therapy, all patients should be tested for HIV. Antivirals used for HBV can have activity against HIV and if a patient is co-infected with both HIV and HBV, it is important that the chosen therapy is appropriate for both viruses to minimize risk of HIV antiviral resistance.

DRUG	DOSING	SAFETY/SIDE EFFECTS/MONITORING
All HBV NRTIs	CrCl < 50 mL/min: ↓ dose or frequency Exception: *Vemlidy* (see below)	**BOXED WARNINGS (FOR ALL HBV NRTIs)** Lactic acidosis and severe hepatomegaly with steatosis, which can be fatal (downgraded from boxed warning to warning for both tenofovir formulations and lamivudine) Exacerbations of HBV can occur upon discontinuation, monitor closely Can cause HIV resistance in HBV patients with unrecognized or untreated HIV infection (downgraded from boxed warning to warning for both tenofovir formulations) See HIV chapter for further information

DRUG	DOSING	SAFETY/SIDE EFFECTS/MONITORING
Tenofovir disoproxil fumarate (TDF) ***(Viread)*** Tablet, powder (oral) 1st line agent	300 mg daily	**WARNINGS** Renal toxicity including acute renal failure and/or Fanconi syndrome, osteomalacia and ↓ bone mineral density **SIDE EFFECTS** TDF: N/V/D, HA, depression, renal impairment, ↓ bone mineral density, ↑ LFTs, ↑ CPK *Vemlidy:* HA, abdominal pain, fatigue, cough, nausea, ↓ bone mineral density, ↑ LFTs **NOTES** *Viread* tablets and *Vemlidy:* protect from moisture; dispense only in original container Tenofovir alafenamide (TAF) is associated with ↓ renal and bone toxicity compared to TDF *Vemlidy* is approved only for treating HBV; see HIV chapter for tenofovir combination products used for HIV
Tenofovir alafenamide (TAF) ***(Vemlidy)*** Tablet	25 mg daily with food CrCl < 15 ml/min: not recommended	
Entecavir *(Baraclude)* Tablet, oral solution 1st line agent	Nucleoside-treatment naïve: 0.5 mg daily Lamivudine-resistant: 1 mg daily Take on empty stomach	**SIDE EFFECTS** Peripheral edema, pyrexia, ascites, ↑ LFTs, hematuria, nephrotoxicity, ↑ SCr **NOTES** Food reduces AUC by 18-20%; take on an empty stomach (2 hours before or after a meal)
Adefovir *(Hepsera)* Tablet	10 mg daily	**BOXED WARNING** Caution in patients with renal impairment or those at risk of renal toxicity (including concurrent nephrotoxic agents or NSAIDs) **SIDE EFFECTS** HA, weakness, abdominal pain, hematuria, rash, nephrotoxicity
Lamivudine *(Epivir HBV)* Tablet, oral solution	100 mg daily 150 mg BID or 300 mg daily if co-infected with HIV	**BOXED WARNING** Do not use *Epivir HBV* for treatment of HIV (contains lower dose of lamivudine); can result in HIV resistance **SIDE EFFECTS** HA, N/V/D, fatigue, insomnia, myalgias, ↑ LFTs

NRTI Drug Interactions

- Ribavirin can ↑ hepatotoxic effects of all NRTIs; lactic acidosis can occur.
- Lamivudine: SMX/TMP can ↑ lamivudine levels due to ↓ excretion.
- Tenofovir disoproxil fumarate: avoid concomitant treatment with didanosine or adefovir due to ↑ risk of virologic failure and potential for ↑ side effects.
- Tenofovir alafenamide is a P-gp substrate; avoid use with oxcarbazepine, phenytoin, phenobarbital, rifampin and St. John's wort.

NRTI Counseling

- *Epivir HBV* tablets and oral solution are not interchangeable with *Epivir* tablets and solution (which have higher doses).
- Entecavir: food ↓ the absorption of this drug; take on an empty stomach (take two hours before or after a meal).
- Some people (rarely) have developed a serious condition called lactic acidosis (a buildup of an acid in the blood). Lactic acidosis is a medical emergency and must be treated in the hospital. See your healthcare provider right away if you feel very weak or tired, have unusual muscle pain, have trouble breathing, have stomach pain with nausea and vomiting, and/or feel dizzy or lightheaded.
- Lamivudine: some people (rarely) have developed pancreatitis, which is a medical emergency and must be treated in the hospital. See your healthcare provider right away if you have upper abdominal pain that radiates to your back, or abdominal pain that feels worse after eating with or without nausea or vomiting.

LIVER DISEASE AND CIRRHOSIS

BACKGROUND

Cirrhosis is advanced fibrosis (scarring) of the liver that is usually irreversible. There are many causes, but the most common in the U.S. are hepatitis C and alcohol consumption. As scar tissue replaces the healthy liver tissue, blood flow through the liver is impaired, leading to numerous complications including portal hypertension, varices, ascites and hepatic encephalopathy.

CLINICAL PRESENTATION

Symptoms can include nausea, loss of appetite, vomiting, diarrhea, malaise, pain in the upper right quadrant of the abdomen, yellowed skin and yellowed whites of the eyes (jaundice), darkened urine and/or lightened color (white or clay-colored) stool caused by low bile in the stool due to decreased production or a blocked bile duct.

OBJECTIVE CRITERIA

Cirrhosis is definitively diagnosed with a liver biopsy, but certain labs can suggest cirrhosis or liver damage (see Study Tip Gal). Aspartate aminotransferase (AST) and alanine aminotransferase (ALT) are liver enzymes. The normal range for both AST and ALT is 10 – 40 units/L. There is some slight variance in these ranges on different lab reports. In general, the higher the values, the more active (acute) the liver disease. Clinical signs of liver disease, in addition to ↑ ALT and ↑ AST, include ↓ albumin (protein produced by the liver; normal range 3.5 – 5.5 g/dL), ↑ alkaline phosphatase (Alk Phos or ALP), ↑ total bilirubin (Tbili), ↑ lactate dehydrogenase (LDH), and ↑ in prothrombin time (PT). Albumin and PT/INR are markers of synthetic (production ability) liver function and are likely to be altered in chronic liver disease (particularly cirrhosis). Liver disease can be classified as hepatocellular (↑ ALT and ↑ AST), cholestatic (↑ Alk Phos and ↑ Tbili), or mixed (↑ AST, ALT, Alk Phos and Tbili). See the Learning Lab Values & Drug Monitoring chapter for additional information.

LAB TESTS FOR LIVER DISEASE

Specific lab abnormalities can help distinguish between types of liver disease.

Acute liver toxicity, including from drugs
- ↑ AST/ALT

Chronic liver disease (e.g., cirrhosis)
- ↑ AST/ALT, Alk Phos, Tbili, LDH, PT/INR
- ↓ Albumin

Alcoholic liver disease
- ↑ AST > ↑ ALT (AST will be about double the ALT), Gamma-glutamyl transpeptidase (GGT)

Hepatic encephalopathy
- ↑ Ammonia

ASSESSING SEVERITY OF LIVER DISEASE

It is important to assess the severity of the liver disease as it serves as a predictor of patient survival, surgical outcomes, and the risk of complications such as variceal bleeding. The Child-Turcotte-Pugh (CPT) or Child Pugh classification system is widely used and online calculators are available. The score ranges from 0 – 15. Class A (mild disease) is defined as a score < 7; Class B (moderate disease) is a score of 7 – 9, and Class C (severe disease) is a score of 10 – 15. The model for end-stage liver disease (MELD) is another scoring system that ranges from 0 – 40. Higher numbers indicate a greater risk of death within three months. Noninvasive tests are increasingly used to predict fibrosis and cirrhosis.

Unlike drug dosing in renal failure, information to guide drug dosing of hepatically cleared agents in patients with liver failure is not as widely available. It is becoming more common to see package labeling for medications make specific recommendations based on Child Pugh class. In general, caution is advised when using hepatically cleared agents in severe liver disease (Class C) and, in select cases, dose adjustment could be necessary. In general, for drugs that are extensively hepatically metabolized, it is best to start at lower doses and titrate to clinical effect.

NATURAL PRODUCTS

Milk thistle, an extract derived from a member of the daisy family, is sometimes used by patients with liver disease. There is limited data to demonstrate efficacy for alcoholic liver disease, hepatitis B or C. Milk thistle does not appear to be harmful. A possible side effect is mild diarrhea and there are concerns for possible drug interactions with milk thistle and antiviral hepatitis C medications. Kava, comfrey, flavocoxid (*Limbrel*, a medical food) are known hepatotoxins.

DRUG-INDUCED LIVER INJURY

Many drugs can cause liver damage. The primary treatment (in most cases) is to stop the drug. Hepatotoxic drugs are typically discontinued when the LFTs are ≥ 3 times the upper limit of normal (> 150 units/L of ALT or AST), but clinical judgment is warranted. Rechallenging with the potential agent can be considered if clinically necessary. An excellent reference for drug-induced liver injury (DILI) is http://livertox.nih.gov.

Acetaminophen is a known hepatotoxic agent and can cause severe injury. Acetaminophen can be used by patients with cirrhosis, for limited periods of time and at lower dosages. Patients with alcoholic cirrhosis who are actively drinking and/or malnourished are more susceptible to further liver damage. NSAIDs should be avoided in patients with cirrhosis because these agents can lead to decompensation, including bleeding.

ALCOHOLIC LIVER DISEASE

Alcohol-induced liver disease is the most common type of drug-induced liver disease. Risk increases with the amount of alcohol consumed and duration, and women have higher risk than men. Alcoholic liver disease can include fatty liver, alcoholic hepatitis, and chronic hepatitis with hepatic fibrosis or cirrhosis. Chronic alcohol ingestion over a long period of time causes "steatosis" or fatty liver, due to fat deposition in the hepatocytes. This can be reversible and self-limited (if drinking is stopped) or can lead to fibrosis and cirrhosis. Some patients develop alcoholic hepatitis, an acute process with poor short-term survival. Of all chronic heavy drinkers, only 15 – 20% develop hepatitis or cirrhosis.

SELECT DRUGS WITH BOXED WARNING FOR LIVER DAMAGE

KEY DRUGS

- Acetaminophen (high doses, acute or chronic)
- Isoniazid
- Ketoconazole (oral)
- Methotrexate
- Nefazodone
- Nevirapine
- NRTIs
- Propylthiouracil
- Tipranavir
- Valproic acid

Others:

- Amiodarone
- Bosentan
- Felbamate
- Flutamide
- Leflunomide and teriflunomide
- Lomitapide
- Maraviroc
- Mipomersen
- Tolcapone

Chronic consumption of alcohol results in the secretion of pro-inflammatory cytokines (TNF-alpha, IL-6 and IL-8), oxidative stress, lipid peroxidation and acetaldehyde toxicity. These factors cause inflammation, apoptosis (cell death) and eventually fibrosis of liver cells. Drinking habits of patients need to be assessed routinely. If the patient stops drinking, the liver can possibly regenerate to some extent.

TREATMENT

The most important part of treatment is alcohol cessation. Maintenance of abstinence is essential to improving outcomes and should include the use of drug treatment to control cravings. Treatment programs use mainly benzodiazepines for alcohol withdrawal in inpatients whereas anticonvulsants are used for outpatients. Naltrexone (formerly *ReVia)*, acamprosate (formerly *Campral)* and disulfiram *(Antabuse)* are used to prevent relapses. There are a few off-label treatments. An alcohol rehabilitation program and a support group whose members share common experiences and problems are extremely helpful in breaking the addiction to alcohol. Proper nutrition is essential to help the liver recover. Vitamins and trace minerals, including vitamin A, vitamin D, thiamine (vitamin B1), folate, pyridoxine (vitamin B6) and zinc can help reverse malnutrition. Thiamine is used to prevent and treat Wernicke-Korsakoff syndrome. Wernicke's encephalopathy and Korsakoff syndrome are different conditions that are both due to brain damage caused by a lack of vitamin B1. Lastly, hepatotoxic drugs should be avoided if possible or doses should be adjusted as appropriate.

COMPLICATIONS OF LIVER DISEASE AND CIRRHOSIS

PORTAL HYPERTENSION AND VARICEAL BLEEDING

Portal hypertension (increased blood pressure in the portal vein) can cause further complications including the development and bleeding of esophageal varices (enlarged veins in the lower part of the esophagus). When blood flow through the liver is blocked by scar tissue, it backs up and flows into smaller blood vessels. These vessels can balloon out and bleed if they break open.

Acute variceal bleeding can be fatal. Patients are stabilized by providing supportive therapy such as blood volume resuscitation/blood products, mechanical ventilation, correction of coagulopathy, and attempts to stop the bleeding and preventing rebleeding. Band ligation (putting a band around the vessel) or sclerotherapy (injecting a solution into the vessel to make it collapse and close) are recommended first-line treatments for bleeding varices. These procedures are performed by a physician using endoscopy. Medications that vasoconstrict the splanchnic (GI) circulation can stop or minimize the bleeding. Octreotide is selective for the splanchnic vessels whereas vasopressin is non-selective. Surgical interventions can be considered if the patient is not responding to treatment or to prevent future rebleeding episodes. Common surgical procedures include balloon tamponade (can help control current bleeding) or transjugular intrahepatic portosystemic shunt (TIPS), in which a stent is placed in the liver to allow blood to flow directly from the portal vein to the hepatic vein (bypassing the scarred liver tissue). Short-term antibiotic prophylaxis (ceftriaxone or quinolone for up to 7 days) should be given to cirrhotic patients with a variceal bleed to reduce bacterial infections and mortality. Non-selective beta-blockers should be added after resolution of variceal bleeding for secondary prevention of variceal bleeding recurrence.

Esophageal Varices

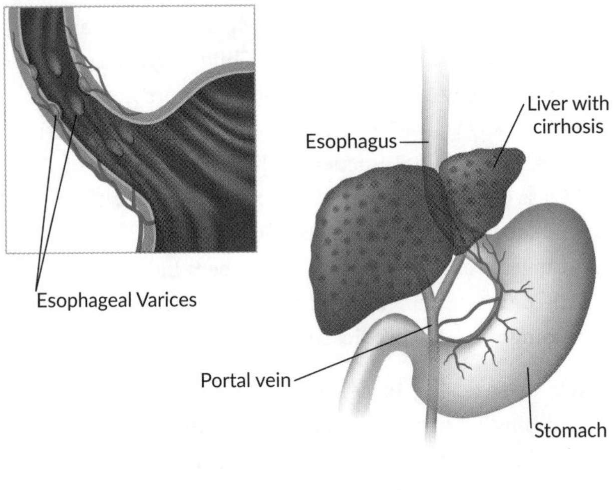

DRUG	DOSING	SAFETY/SIDE EFFECTS/MONITORING
Octreotide *(Sandostatin)* Analog of somatostatin with greater potency and longer duration of action	Bolus: 25-100 mcg IV (usual 50 mcg), can repeat in 1 hr if hemorrhage not controlled Infusion: followed by 25-50 mcg/hr continuous IV infusion x 2-5 days	**SIDE EFFECTS** Bradycardia, chest pain, fatigue, HA, pruritus, hyperglycemia, hypoglycemia (highest risk in type 1 diabetes), N/V/D, hypothyroidism, abdominal pain, malaise, fever, dizziness, flatulence, cholelithiasis, biliary sludge, constipation, injection site pain, arthropathy, myalgias, URTIs **MONITORING** Blood glucose, HR, ECG
Vasopressin *(Vasostrict)* Antidiuretic hormone analog Not first-line (usually used with nitroglycerin IV to prevent myocardial ischemia)	Infusion: 0.2-0.4 units/min IV (max 0.8 units/min), max duration 24 hours	**SIDE EFFECTS** Arrhythmias, chest pain, MI, ↓ cardiac output, ↑ BP, N/V **MONITORING** BP, HR, ECG, fluid balance

Non-selective beta-blockers (e.g., nadolol and propranolol) or endoscopic variceal ligation (EVL) are used for primary prevention of variceal bleeding. Beta-blockers reduce portal pressure by reducing portal venous inflow by two mechanisms: 1) decreased cardiac output (via beta-1 blockade), and 2) decreased splanchnic blood flow by vasoconstriction (via beta-2 blockade and unopposed alpha activity). The beta-blocker is titrated to the maximal tolerated dose (target HR 55 – 60 BPM) and continued indefinitely.

DRUG	DOSING	SAFETY/SIDE EFFECTS/MONITORING
Nadolol *(Corgard)*	Initial: 40 mg PO daily	Refer to the Hypertension chapter for a complete review of beta-blockers. **BOXED WARNING** Do not withdraw beta-blockers abruptly (particularly in patients with CAD), gradually taper over 1-2 weeks to avoid acute tachycardia, HTN and/or ischemia **CONTRAINDICATIONS** Sinus bradycardia, 2nd or 3rd degree heart block, sick sinus syndrome (unless patient has a functioning artificial pacemaker) or cardiogenic shock. Do not initiate in patients with active asthma exacerbation. **WARNING** Non-selective agents are used for portal hypertension; use extreme caution with asthma or severe COPD or peripheral vascular disease and Raynaud's disease (a condition with vasospasms in the extremities) Can mask signs of hyperthyroidism and aggravate psychiatric conditions; use caution in patients with diabetes particularly with recurrent hypoglycemia **MONITORING** HR and BP
Propranolol *(Inderal*, others)	Initial: 20 mg PO BID	

HEPATIC ENCEPHALOPATHY

Hepatic encephalopathy (HE) is caused by acute or chronic hepatic insufficiency. Symptoms include musty odor of the breath and/or urine, changes in thinking, confusion, forgetfulness, mood changes, poor concentration, drowsiness, disorientation, worsening handwriting, hand tremor (asterixis), sluggish movements and risk of coma. The symptoms of HE result from an accumulation of gut-derived nitrogenous substances in the blood (such as ammonia, glutamate). These substances would normally be cleared by the liver, but when the liver is not functioning properly, blood is shunted through collateral vessels that empty directly into the circulation instead. Treatment includes identifying and treating precipitating factors and reducing blood ammonia levels through diet (limiting the amount of animal protein) and drug therapy.

Patients should have a daily protein intake of 1 – 1.5 g/kg. Vegetable and dairy sources of protein are preferred to animal sources due to the lower calorie to nitrogen ratio. Branched-chain amino acids (BCAAs) (e.g., leucine, isoleucine, valine) are favored over aromatic amino acids (AAAs); they interfere with AAAs ability to cross the blood-brain barrier and increase hepatocyte growth factor synthesis.

Drug therapy consists of nonabsorbable disaccharides (such as lactulose) and antibiotics (rifaximin, neomycin, others) for acute and chronic therapy. Lactulose is first-line therapy for both acute and chronic (prevention) therapy, followed by rifaximin. Lactulose works by converting ammonia produced by intestinal bacteria to ammonium, which is polar and therefore cannot readily diffuse into the blood. Lactulose also enhances diffusion of ammonia into the colon for excretion. Antibiotics work by inhibiting the activity of urease-producing bacteria, which decreases the ammonia production. Zinc (220 mg PO BID) may be used; it can serve as a cofactor for enzymes of the urea cycle and further decrease ammonia concentrations and correct a zinc deficiency.

DRUG	DOSING	SAFETY/SIDE EFFECTS/MONITORING
Lactulose ***(Enulose,*** *Constulose, Generlac, Kristalose)* Oral solution and packet	Treatment: 30-45 mL (or 20-30 grams) PO every hour until evacuation; then 30-45 mL (20-30 grams) PO 3-4 times/day titrated to produce 2-3 soft bowel movements daily Enema: Q4-6H PRN Prevention: 30-45 mL (or 20-30 grams) PO 3-4 times/day titrated to produce 2-3 soft bowel movements daily	**SIDE EFFECTS** Flatulence, diarrhea, dyspepsia, abdominal discomfort, dehydration, hypernatremia, hypokalemia **MONITORING** Mental status, bowel movements, ammonia, fluid status, electrolytes
Rifaximin *(Xifaxan)* Tablet	Treatment (off-label): 400 mg PO Q8H x 5-10 days Prevention: 550 mg PO BID	**SIDE EFFECTS** Peripheral edema, dizziness, fatigue, nausea, ascites, flatulence, headache **MONITORING** Mental status, ammonia
Neomycin	4-12 g daily divided Q4-6H x 5-6 days	**BOXED WARNINGS** Neurotoxicity, (hearing loss, vertigo, ataxia); nephrotoxicity (particularly in renal impairment or with concurrent use of other nephrotoxic drugs); can cause neuromuscular blockade and respiratory paralysis especially when given soon after anesthesia or with muscle relaxants **SIDE EFFECTS** GI upset, ototoxicity, nephrotoxicity, irritation/soreness of mouth/rectal area **MONITORING** Mental status, renal function, hearing, ammonia
Metronidazole *(Flagyl, Flagyl ER, Metro)*	250 mg PO Q6-12H	**NOTES** Do not use long term due to peripheral neuropathies See Infectious Diseases I chapter for additional information

ASCITES

Ascites is fluid accumulation within the peritoneal space that can lead to the development of spontaneous bacterial peritonitis (SBP) and hepatorenal syndrome (HRS).

There are many treatment approaches to managing ascites, which are chosen based on the severity. Patients with ascites due to portal hypertension should restrict dietary sodium intake to < 2 grams/day, avoid sodium-retaining medications (including NSAIDs), and use diuretics to increase fluid loss. Restriction of fluid is recommended only in patients with symptomatic severe hyponatremia (serum Na < 120 mEq/L).

Diuretic therapy for ascites can be initiated with either spironolactone monotherapy or with a combination of furosemide and spironolactone. Furosemide by itself is ineffective. Spironolactone is initiated at a single daily dose of 50 – 100 mg and increased to a maximum of 400 mg per day. When used in combination, the drugs should be titrated to a maximal weight loss of 0.5 kg/day with a ratio of 40 mg furosemide to 100 mg spironolactone to maintain potassium balance, if possible. The FDA-approved spironolactone oral suspension *(CaroSpir)* is not therapeutically equivalent to *Aldactone*. The approved dose for treating edema associated with cirrhosis is 20 – 75 mg (4 – 15 mL) in single or divided doses (see Chronic Heart Failure and Hypertension chapters for additional information).

All patients with cirrhosis and ascites should be considered for liver transplantation. In severe cases, abdominal paracentesis is needed to directly remove ascitic fluid. Large volume paracentesis (removal of > 5 L) is associated with significant fluid shifts and the addition of albumin (6 – 8 grams per liter of fluid removed) is recommended to prevent paracentesis-induced circulatory dysfunction and progression to hepatorenal syndrome.

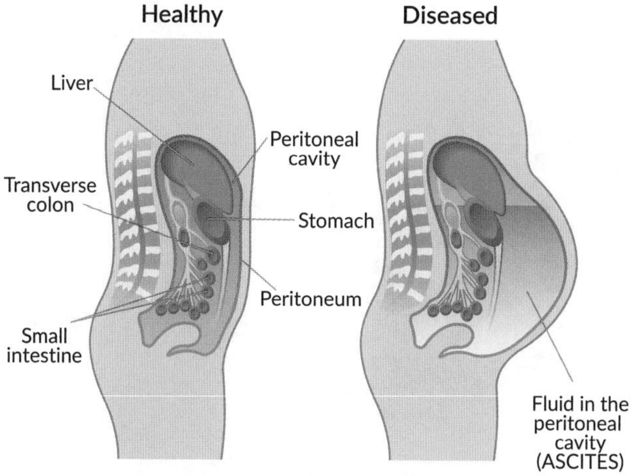

SPONTANEOUS BACTERIAL PERITONITIS

Spontaneous bacterial peritonitis (SBP) is an acute infection of the ascitic fluid. Diagnosis is guided by cell and microbiologic analysis. Targeting *Streptococci* and enteric Gram-negative pathogens with ceftriaxone (or equivalent) for 5 – 7 days is recommended. The addition of albumin (1.5 grams/kg of body weight on day 1 and 1 gram/kg on day 3) can improve survival in some patients. Patients who have survived an episode of SBP should receive secondary prophylaxis with oral ciprofloxacin or sulfamethoxazole/trimethoprim.

HEPATORENAL SYNDROME

Hepatorenal syndrome (HRS) is the development of renal failure in patients with advanced cirrhosis. HRS is the result of renal vasoconstriction, mediated by activation of the renin-angiotensin-aldosterone system (RAAS) and the sympathetic nervous system (SNS) through a feedback mechanism known as hepatorenal reflex. Appropriately treating the various stages and complications of cirrhosis, and avoiding nephrotoxins and renal hypoperfusion help prevent progression to HRS. HRS can be directly treated with albumin, octreotide and midodrine, but prevention is critical given the difficulty in managing HRS in this patient population.

Select Guidelines/References

AASLD-IDSA. Recommendations for Testing, Managing, and Treating Hepatitis C. https://www.hcvguidelines.org (accessed 2019 Apr 2).

AASLD Practice Guidelines. Alcoholic Liver Disease. https://www.aasld.org/sites/default/files/guideline_documents/AlcoholicLiverDisease1-2010.pdf (accessed 2019 Apr 2).

20

21

IMMUNIZATIONS & TRAVELERS

CONTENTS

CHAPTER 20
IMMUNIZATIONS | **316**

CHAPTER 21
TRAVELERS | **333**

CHAPTER CONTENT

Background 316
Vaccine Resources 316
Vaccine Safety Concerns 317
Autism 317
Gelatin 317
Immunity 317
Types of Vaccines 317
Inactivated Vaccines 318
Live Vaccines 318
Timing and Spacing of Vaccines 318
Simultaneous Administration 318
Vaccines Given in a Series 318
Live Vaccines and Antibody 318
Live Vaccines and the TB Skin Test 319
Vaccine Timing & Spacing 319
Vaccine Adverse Reactions 319
Local Reactions 319
Systemic Reactions 319
Management of Severe Allergic Reactions 320
Vaccine Contraindications and Precautions 320
Screening Prior to Vaccine Administration 320
Invalid Contraindications to Vaccination 320
Vaccinations for Specific Conditions/Populations 322
Vaccinations for Special Groups 322
Vaccinations for Adults 323
Routine Vaccines 324
Diphtheria Toxoid-, Tetanus Toxoid- and acellular Pertussis-Containing Vaccines 324
Haemophilus influenzae type b (Hib)-Containing Vaccines 324
Hepatitis-Containing Vaccines 324
Human Papillomavirus Vaccines 325
Influenza Vaccines 325
Influenza Vaccine Tips 325
Measles, Mumps and Rubella-Containing Vaccines 326
Meningococcal Vaccines 327
Pneumococcal Vaccines 327
Pneumococcal Vaccine Indications, Sequence and Intervals 328
Poliovirus-Containing Vaccines 329
Rotavirus Vaccines 329
Varicella-Containing Vaccines 329
Non-Routine Vaccines 330
Storage 331
Vaccine Storage Requirements 331
Administration 332
Routes of Administration 332
Administration Technique 332
Immunization Registries 332

CONTENT LEGEND

(💡) = Study Tip Gal

CHAPTER 20
IMMUNIZATIONS

BACKGROUND

Vaccines prevent patients from acquiring serious or potentially fatal diseases. Childhood diseases that used to be common (e.g., diphtheria, meningitis, polio, tetanus) are now rare because children are vaccinated to prevent the illness, or are protected by herd immunity (vaccinated people protect the unvaccinated and make them less likely to become infected). If vaccination rates drop below 85% – 95%, vaccine-preventable diseases can become a threat, as demonstrated by U.S. pertussis and measles outbreaks in recent years.

VACCINE RESOURCES

- The FDA approves vaccinations based on the safety and efficacy for the indication.
- The Advisory Committee on Immunization Practices (ACIP) provides the recommendations for vaccine administration in children and adults (i.e., who gets what vaccine and when).
- The Centers for Disease Control and Prevention (CDC) approves the ACIP recommendations and publishes them in the CDC's Morbidity and Mortality Weekly Report (MMWR) and The Pink Book (Epidemiology and Prevention of Vaccine-Preventable Diseases).
- Other helpful resources for pharmacists related to immunizations are available on the following websites:
  - American Pharmacists Association (www.pharmacist.com/immunization-center).
  - Immunization Action Coalition (www.immunize.org).

Reliable Vaccine Information for Patients

Pharmacists can provide patients with credible sources of information to counter erroneous information found on the internet and in the media. Vaccine Information Statements (VISs) are prepared by the CDC for each vaccine, to explain the benefits and risks. Federal law requires that the VIS be handed to the patient (or parent) before the vaccination is given.

VACCINE SAFETY CONCERNS

AUTISM

Some people believe that vaccines cause autism. The causes of autism are not fully understood, but there is no evidence that autism is caused by vaccines. Parents often first notice the behaviors of autism at an age when most childhood vaccine series are near completion (18 – 24 months). Abnormal brain structure that is present in children with autism can be identified in the prefrontal and temporal cortical tissue before a child is born, prior to receiving vaccines. Genetics play an important role, with high rates of autism among identical and fraternal twins, and within families.

Thimerosal

Thimerosal, a mercury-containing preservative used in some vaccines, was alleged to be contributing to the increase in autism, since mercury has been linked to some brain disorders. There is no evidence that thimerosal poses a risk for autism. Thimerosal was removed from childhood vaccines in 2001, and the rates of autism have continued to increase. Thimerosal is contained in some multi-dose flu vaccines; parents may request a single-dose flu vaccine which does not contain a preservative, or a multi-dose vaccine without thimerosal.

GELATIN

Gelatin is used in some vaccines as a stabilizer. It is porcine-derived (from pigs). For observant Muslims, Jews and Seventh-Day Adventists who follow dietary rules that prohibit pork products, most religious leaders permit the use of gelatin-containing vaccines because the gelatin is injected, not ingested, and the end-product has been rendered pure.

IMMUNITY

The purpose of the immune system is to identify self substances (normal body parts/components) and non-self (foreign) substances, which are called antigens. Antibodies are produced naturally to provide immunity against antigens. When an antigen is detected, the body produces antibodies and destroys the antigen. Immunoglobulin is the medical term for antibody.

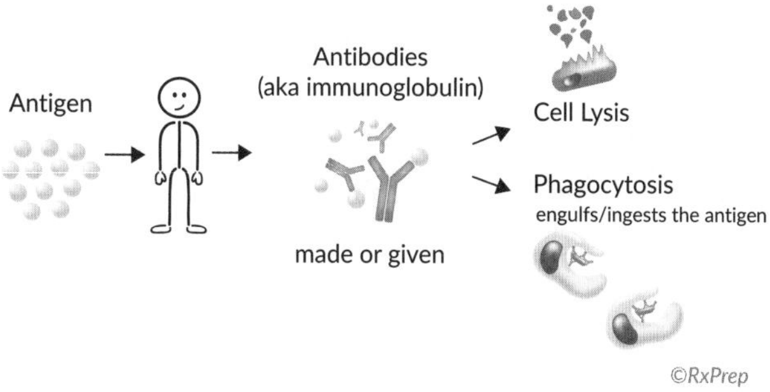

Immunity is acquired actively or passively. Active immunity develops when the person's own immune system produces antibodies to fight an infection or in response to vaccine administration. Passive immunity is acquired when antibodies are provided from someone else (see below). The CDC's Pink Book is a useful resource for details regarding immunology and immunizations.

Active Immunity

From the person's own immune system (from vaccines or fighting an infection). Lasts a long time, often a lifetime.

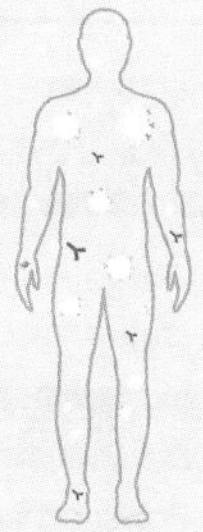

Passive Immunity

Received from someone else, such as receiving immunoglobulins (Ig) that are pooled from other people, or through transfer from a mother to her baby.

Mother gives baby a copy of her immunoglobulins shortly before birth. These decrease over time as the child's own antibody production (immunity) increases.

Intravenous immunoglobulin (IVIG) provides already made antibodies, and can be used for quick immunity after exposure to an antigen. For example, a person who is bitten by a rabid animal will quickly receive the rabies vaccine (which will take time to work) and rabies immunoglobulin, to help the patient fight the rabies organism right away.

TYPES OF VACCINES

Live attenuated (weakened) vaccines are produced by modifying a disease-producing ("wild") virus or bacterium in a laboratory; they have the ability to replicate (grow) and produce immunity, but usually do not cause illness. Live attenuated vaccines are most similar to the actual disease and produce a strong immune response to the vaccine; they are contraindicated in immunocompromised and pregnant patients since uncontrolled replication of the pathogen can occur.

Inactivated vaccines can be composed of either a whole virus or bacterium, or fractions of either. Immunity resulting from an inactivated vaccine can diminish with time and supplemental doses may be required to increase, or "boost," immunity.

INACTIVATED VACCINES

Inactivated vaccines use the killed version of a wild virus or bacteria that causes the disease. Inactivated vaccines cannot replicate (and cause disease). They are less affected by circulating antibody than live vaccines*.

Limitation: immunity is not as strong as with live vaccines; boosters may be required for ongoing immunity.

See the Live Vaccines and Antibody section

Polysaccharide, Conjugate and Recombinant Vaccines

Targets a section of the organism, such as a protein, sugar, or capsid (outer casing).

Polysaccharide Vaccines

Polysaccharide (sugar) molecules are taken from the outside layer of encapsulated bacteria (such as pneumococcal serotypes; each serotype matches to a circulating strain of the organism). Polysaccharide vaccines do not produce a good immune response in children < 2 years of age.

Ex: Pneumococcal Polysaccharide Vaccine *(Pneumovax 23)*

Conjugate Vaccines

Conjugate vaccines use polysaccharide (sugar) molecules from the outside layer of encapsulated bacteria and join the molecules to carrier proteins. Conjugation increases the immune response in infants, and the antibody booster response to multiple doses of vaccine.

Ex: Pneumococcal Conjugate Vaccine *(Prevnar 13)*, Meningococcal Conjugate *(Menactra, Menveo)*

Recombinant Vaccines

A gene segment of a protein from the organism is inserted into the gene of another cell, such as a yeast cell, where it replicates.

Ex: Human Papillomavirus Vaccine *(Gardasil 9)*, Influenza Vaccine, Recombinant *(FluBlok Quadrivalent)*

Toxoid Vaccines

The vaccine targets a toxin produced by the disease.

Ex: Diptheria Toxoid vaccine, Tetanus Toxoid vaccine

LIVE VACCINES

Live vaccines are most similar to the actual disease and provide a strong, long-lasting immune response.

Limitations: 1) Patients who are immunocompromised may not be able to halt replication; vaccination could cause the disease. 2) Circulating antibody can interfere with vaccine replication*.

Live Vaccines: **C**holera, **O**ral Typhoid, **Z**oster *(Zostavax)*, **Y**ellow Fever; **I**ntranasal Influenza, **V**aricella; **R**otavirus, **M**MR

Remember: **COZY IV RM**

See the Live Vaccines and Antibody section

TIMING AND SPACING OF VACCINES

SIMULTANEOUS ADMINISTRATION

Most common live or inactivated vaccines can be administered simultaneously (on the same day or at the same visit) without decreasing the antibody response or increasing the risk of adverse reactions (see Study Tip Gal on the following page). Simultaneous administration of all vaccines for which a child is eligible is very important in childhood vaccination. Every effort should be made to provide all necessary vaccinations at one visit, to improve compliance and increase the probability that a child will be fully immunized at the appropriate age. Combination vaccines help accomplish this with less injections.

VACCINES GIVEN IN A SERIES

Increasing the interval between doses of vaccine given in a series does not diminish the effectiveness of the vaccine after completion of the series. It may delay more complete protection. Decreasing the interval between doses of vaccine can interfere with antibody response and protection. In a few cases, the interval can be shortened for high-risk patients (e.g., between doses of the two pneumococcal vaccines in an immunocompromised patient).

LIVE VACCINES AND ANTIBODY

Antibodies, in some blood products and intravenous immunoglobulins (e.g., IVIG), can interfere with live vaccine replication and a separation period may be required (see Study Tip Gal on the following page). This is a concern with live vaccines because replication is required to produce an immune response.

The interval between an antibody-containing product and Measles, Mumps and Rubella-containing vaccine (MMR) or varicella-containing vaccine (*Varivax* or MMRV) is a minimum of 3 months and can be up to 11 months. The specific product and dose determines the separation time. The CDC's Pink Book can be consulted for recommendations.

Maternal antibodies are passed from the mother to the baby before birth, and will reduce the baby's response to live vaccines. Live vaccines are withheld until the child is 12 months of age; at this time, the mother's antibodies will be depleted.

Inactivated vaccines can be given at any time. Inactivated vaccines are started when a baby is two months old, except for the hepatitis B vaccine series, which is started at birth.

LIVE VACCINES AND THE TB SKIN TEST

The tuberculin skin test (TST), also called a purified protein derivative (PPD) test, is used to determine if a person has latent tuberculosis (TB). Live vaccines can cause a false negative result. Options to reduce the risk of a false negative TST result include:

1. Give the live vaccine on the same day as the skin test.
2. Wait 4 weeks after a live vaccine to perform the skin test.
3. Administer the skin test first, wait 48 – 72 hours to get the result, then give the live vaccine.

VACCINE TIMING & SPACING

General Rules for All Vaccines

- Vaccines can usually be given at the same time (same visit or same day).*
- Multiple live vaccines can be given on the same day or (if not given on the same day) spaced 4 weeks apart.**
- If a vaccine series requires > 1 dose, the intervals between doses can be extended without restarting the series, but they cannot be shortened in most cases.

Live Vaccines and Antibody

- MMR and varicella-containing vaccines (not zoster) require separation from antibody-containing products (e.g., blood transfusions, IVIG). The recommended spacing is:
  - Vaccine → 2 weeks → antibody-containing product
  - Antibody-containing product → 3 months or longer → vaccine
- Simultaneous administration of vaccine and antibody (in the form of immunoglobulin) is recommended for post-exposure prophylaxis of certain diseases (e.g., hepatitis A and B, rabies and tetanus).

**Exception: in patients with asplenia, Prevnar and Menactra should be separated by 4 weeks.*
***Exception: no separation is required for oral rotavirus vaccines.*

VACCINE ADVERSE REACTIONS

All vaccines have the potential to cause an adverse reaction. Reactions can range from local (e.g., soreness, redness, itching) to severe and life-threatening (e.g., anaphylaxis).

Patients are screened for precautions and contraindications before vaccine administration to reduce the risk of severe reactions (see the Screening Prior to Vaccine Administration section). The patient should be monitored for at least 15 minutes after vaccination (to watch for an allergic reaction, syncope, dizziness or falls).

Pharmacists who administer vaccines need a plan (protocol) that covers emergency management of severe reactions until emergency medical help arrives (see the Management of a Severe Reaction section). Adverse reactions that require some type of assistance should be reported to the FDA's Vaccine Adverse Event Reporting System (VAERS).

LOCAL REACTIONS

Local reactions occur at or near the injection site. These are common, more so with inactivated vaccines, and include pain, swelling and redness. Rarely, local reactions may be very exaggerated or severe.

SYSTEMIC REACTIONS

Systemic reactions are less common than local reactions. They include fever, malaise, myalgias (muscle pain), headache, loss of appetite or a mild illness that has similarities to the disease being prevented, such as a few chickenpox vesicles after receiving the varicella vaccine. Patients who have experienced systemic symptoms after a flu shot might think (incorrectly) that the vaccine caused the flu. The flu shot is inactivated (killed) vaccine and cannot cause the flu.

With live vaccines, mild systemic reactions can occur 3 – 21 days after the vaccine is given (i.e., after an incubation period). Intranasal flu vaccine can replicate in the upper airways (nose and throat) and can cause mild cold-like symptoms, such as a runny nose.

True Allergic Reactions

These are uncommon, and can be caused by the vaccine or a component of the vaccine, such as a stabilizer, preservative or antibiotic present in the vaccine (used to inhibit bacterial growth). Minor allergic reactions will resolve quickly and can be treated with diphenhydramine (OTC) or hydroxyzine (prescription). A minor reaction is not a contraindication to future vaccination.

Severe allergic reactions are very rare (< 1 in 500,000 doses). A severe reaction with anaphylaxis can be life-threatening if not managed correctly. Anaphylactic reactions are IgE-mediated, and occur within minutes of receiving the vaccine. Symptoms can include urticaria (hives), swelling of the mouth and throat, difficulty breathing, wheezing, abdominal cramping and hypotension or shock.

The protocol for emergency management (see below) will include the use of epinephrine, which must be available to quickly reverse breathing difficulty.

MANAGEMENT OF SEVERE ALLERGIC REACTIONS

All providers who administer vaccines must have emergency protocols and supplies to treat anaphylaxis. If symptoms are severe, a second person should activate the emergency medical system (EMS), by calling 911. The primary healthcare provider should remain with the patient, assessing the airway, breathing, circulation and level of consciousness.

Care should be provided until EMS arrives:

- Administer aqueous epinephrine 1:1,000 (1 mg/mL) dilution intramuscularly, 0.01 mg/kg, up to a 0.5 mg maximum per dose. Most pharmacies use prefilled epinephrine auto-injectors. At least three adult (0.3 mg) auto-injectors should be available. Most adults will require 1 – 3 doses administered every 5 – 15 minutes.
- Diphenhydramine can be given to reduce swelling and pruritus. Drugs cannot be given orally if airway swelling is present, due to a risk of choking.
- The patient should be placed in a supine position (flat on the back), unless there is breathing difficulty. Elevating the head will help breathing, but caution must be taken to keep the blood pressure adequate. If the blood pressure is low, elevate the legs only. Monitor the blood pressure and pulse every 5 minutes.
- Provide cardiopulmonary resuscitation (CPR), if necessary. Immunizing pharmacists need current basic life support (BLS or CPR) certification.
- Record all vital signs and administered medications.

The reaction should be reported to the patient's primary care physician and to the FDA's VAERS.

VACCINE CONTRAINDICATIONS AND PRECAUTIONS

There are specific circumstances when vaccines should not be given. Most precautions are temporary, and the vaccine can be given at a later time. For example, if the patient has a moderate or severe acute illness, vaccine administration should be delayed until it resolves. Mild acute illness is not a precaution and the vaccine can be administered.

A contraindication is a condition that significantly increases the potential of a serious adverse reaction. Pregnancy and immunosuppression are two important contraindications to the use of live vaccines. Live vaccine administration must be timed carefully in patients who have recently received an antibody-containing blood product, as previously described. A severe or anaphylactic reaction following a dose of vaccine is a contraindication to any subsequent doses of that vaccine.

SCREENING PRIOR TO VACCINE ADMINISTRATION

Use a screening form to rule out specific contraindications and precautions to the vaccine in adults. Note that a "yes" response to some of these questions will indicate a type of vaccine to use, rather than a contraindication to all formulations (e.g., if a person has an allergy to thimerosal, then a single-dose vial or prefilled syringe may be required to avoid the preservative).

1. Are you sick today?
2. Do you have allergies to medications, food, a vaccine component or latex?
3. Have you ever had a serious reaction after receiving a vaccine?
4. Do you have a long-term health problem with heart disease, lung disease, asthma, kidney disease, metabolic disease (e.g., diabetes), anemia or other blood disorder?
5. Do you have cancer, leukemia, AIDS or any other immune system problem?
6. Do you take cortisone, prednisone, other steroids, anticancer drugs, or have you had radiation treatments?
7. Have you ever had a seizure or nervous system problem?
8. During the past year, have you received a transfusion of blood or blood products, or been given immune (gamma) globulin or an antiviral drug?
9. For women: are you pregnant or could you become pregnant during the next month?
10. Have you received any vaccinations in the past 4 weeks?

INVALID CONTRAINDICATIONS TO VACCINATION

Vaccinations may be given, if indicated, in the following situations:

- Mild acute illness (slight fever, mild diarrhea)
- Current antimicrobial treatment (some exceptions: see varicella, zoster and oral typhoid vaccines)
- Previous local skin reaction (mild/moderate) from a vaccine
- Allergies: bird feathers, penicillin, allergies to products not in the vaccine
- Pregnancy (except live vaccines), breastfeeding, preterm birth
- Recent tuberculin skin test (see text for timing and spacing with live vaccines only)
- Immunosuppressed person in the household, recent exposure to the disease, or convalescence
- Family history of adverse events to the vaccine

Vaccine Contraindications and Precautions

VACCINE	CONTRAINDICATIONS	PRECAUTIONS
All vaccines	Severe allergic reaction (e.g., anaphylaxis) to a vaccine or vaccine component after a previous dose.	Illness: If a child or adult has only a mild illness (such as a cold), vaccines should be given (see Study Tip Gal on the previous page). Treatment with antibiotics is not a valid reason to delay vaccines. If the person has a moderate or severe acute illness (regardless of antibiotic use) it is reasonable to delay vaccines until the condition has improved.
Live vaccines	Pregnancy (do not attempt pregnancy until 4 weeks after receiving a live vaccine). Immunosuppression (see the Vaccinations for Specific Conditions/Populations chart on the following page).	Recent administration of an antibody-containing blood product (see the section on Live Vaccines and Antibody).
Diphtheria, tetanus and pertussis vaccines	For pertussis-containing vaccines: encephalopathy (e.g., coma, decreased level of consciousness, prolonged seizures) that is not attributable to another cause within 7 days of receiving the vaccine.	Guillain-Barré syndrome (GBS) within 6 weeks of a previous diphtheria, tetanus and/or pertussis vaccine. For DTaP and Tdap only: infantile spasms, uncontrolled seizures.
Hepatitis B vaccines	Hypersensitivity to yeast.	
Influenza vaccines	Live, attenuated influenza vaccine (LAIV): severe egg allergy (e.g., anaphylaxis), use of aspirin-containing products (children and adolescents), use of influenza antiviral medications in the past 48 hrs, children age 2-4 years with asthma or a wheezing episode in the last 12 months, close contact with an immunosuppressed person.	All influenza vaccines: history of GBS within 6 weeks of a previous influenza vaccination. LAIV: asthma in any patient age ≥ 5 years, underlying conditions that predispose to influenza complications (e.g., chronic lung, heart, renal, hepatic, neurologic, hematologic and metabolic disorders, including diabetes). Inactivated influenza vaccine (IIV): egg allergy other than hives (e.g., angioedema, respiratory distress, recurrent emesis or required emergency medical intervention) – give IIV (injection) only under the supervision of a healthcare provider who can manage severe allergic reactions.
Recombinant zoster vaccine (RZV) Zoster vaccine live (ZVL)	RZV only: lactation. ZVL only: history of severe allergic reaction (e.g., anaphylaxis) to gelatin or neomycin. RZV and ZVL: pregnancy.	ZVL only: use of acyclovir, famciclovir or valacyclovir in the 24 hours before vaccination; avoid these antiviral drugs for 14 days after vaccination.
Varicella vaccines	History of severe allergic reaction (e.g., anaphylaxis) to gelatin or neomycin.	Use of acyclovir, famciclovir or valacyclovir in the 24 hours before vaccination; avoid these antivirals for 14 days after vaccination.
Rotavirus vaccines	History of intussusception (part of the intestine slides into an adjacent part of the intestine, blocking food/fluids).	Chronic gastrointestinal disease.
Yellow fever vaccine	Severe allergic reaction (e.g., anaphylaxis) to eggs.	
Latex present on vial stoppers and in prefilled syringes	Most latex sensitivities are a contact-type allergy, which does not prohibit vaccine administration; if the reaction to latex is severe (e.g., anaphylactic) , avoid vaccines with latex.	

VACCINATIONS FOR SPECIFIC CONDITIONS/POPULATIONS

VACCINATIONS FOR SPECIAL GROUPS

**An annual influenza vaccine is recommended for all special groups (age ≥ 6 months).*

Infants and Children

- 3-dose Hepatitis B vaccine started at birth
- Other vaccine series start at age 2 months, including: *Prevnar 13*, DTaP, Hib, Polio, Rotavirus
- Live vaccines series generally start at age ≥12 mo, including: MMR, Varicella
- No polysaccharide vaccines before age 2 years

Healthcare Professionals
—including pharmacists, nurses, physicians

- Annual influenza vaccine is usually required (with proof/documentation of vaccination)
- Hepatitis B: if there is no evidence of vaccine series completion or a blood test showing immunity
- Tdap: 1 dose, if not up-to-date, then Td every10 years
- Varicella: if there is no history of vaccination or chickenpox infection
- MMR: if there is no history of vaccination or a blood test showing immunity

Adolescents and Young Adults

- Meningococcal vaccine (MCV4; *Menactra* or *Menveo*)
  - ❑ 2 doses: 1 dose at age 11-12 years and 1 dose at age 16 years
  - ❑ First-year college students in residential housing (if not previously vaccinated): 1 dose
- Human papillomavirus vaccine
  - ❑ Recommended at age 11-12 years
  - ❑ 2 or 3 doses (depending on age of start)
- Tdap: first dose at age > 11 years

Sickle Cell Disease & Other Causes of Asplenia (Damaged/Missing Spleen)
—the spleen contains T-cells and B-cells; a damaged or missing spleen (e.g., splenectomy) causes a type of immunodeficiency

- *H. influenzae* type b (Hib) vaccine
- Pneumococcal vaccines (*Prevnar 13* and *Pneumovax 23*)
  - ❑ Before age 65 years: 1 dose of *Prevnar 13* (if not received previously) and 2 doses of *Pneumovax 23*
  - ❑ Give *Prevnar 13* 1st, then the 1st *Pneumovax 23* ≥ 8 weeks later; give the 2nd *Pneumovax 23* ≥ 5 years after the 1st dose
- Meningococcal vaccines
  - ❑ Meningococcal conjugate vaccine (*Menactra* or *Menveo*)
  - ❑ Serogroup B meningococcal vaccine (*Bexsero* or *Trumenba*)

Pregnancy

- Live vaccines are contraindicated
- Influenza vaccine, inactivated (not live), can be given in any trimester
- Tdap x 1 with each pregnancy (weeks 27-36, optimally)*

**It's not just Mom who needs Tdap x 1 to protect the infant from pertussis; vaccinate others in close contact with the infant (e.g., father, grandparents, child-care providers), if not up-to-date.*

Diabetes

- Pneumococcal vaccine
  - ❑ Before age 65 years: 1 dose of *Pneumovax 23*
- Hepatitis B: age 19-59 years (or at age ≥ 60 years per healthcare provider discretion)

Immunodeficiency
—called altered immunocompetence, immunosuppresion or immunocompromise; caused by drugs or conditions**

- Live vaccines are contraindicated
- Pneumococcal vaccines (*Prevnar 13* and *Pneumovax 23*)
  - ❑ Before age 65 years: 1 dose of *Prevnar 13* (if not received previously) and 2 doses of *Pneumovax 23*
  - ❑ Give *Prevnar 13* 1st, then the 1st *Pneumovax 23* ≥ 8 weeks later; give the 2nd *Pneumovax 23* ≥ 5 years after the 1st dose
- HIV (CD4 count < 200 cells/mm^3)
  - ❑ Meningococcal conjugate vaccine (*Menactra* or *Menveo*)
  - ❑ Hepatitis B vaccine

**Causes of Immunodeficiency:
- Chemotherapy/bone marrow transplant drugs cause myelosuppression (↓ **WBC**, RBC, platelets)
- Strong immunosuppressant drugs used for autoimmune disease (e.g., etanercept, infliximab) or transplant (e.g., tacrolimus, cyclosporine)
- HIV with a CD4 count < 200 cells/mm^3 (AIDS)
- Systemic steroids for ≥ 14 days (does not include inhaled, topicals, intraarticular) at ≥ 20 mg or 2 mg/kg prednisone daily, or an equivalent steroid dose
- Chronic renal failure

Older Adults

- Herpes zoster vaccine
  - ❑ *Shingrix*: age ≥ 50 years, 2 doses, 2-6 months apart
  - ❑ *Zostavax* (not preferred): age ≥ 60 years
- Pneumococcal vaccines (age ≥ 65 years)
  - ❑ *Prevnar 13* x 1 if not received previously
  - ❑ *Pneumovax 23* x 1 (wait at least 1 year after *Prevnar 13* and at least 5 years after any prior doses of *Pneumovax 23*)

VACCINATIONS FOR ADULTS*

*Does not include routine childhood vaccines.

Influenza

Annually for all patients ≥ 6 months old

Tdap, Td

Tdap x 1 if not received previously
Td every 10 years

Shingles
2 VACCINES

Shingrix is preferred; vaccinate all adults ≥ 50 years, even if they have had chickenpox or shingles

Shingrix: 2-dose series, with second dose given 2-6 months after the first dose; wait ≥ 8 weeks after *Zostavax*

Alternate: *Zostavax* x 1 dose at age ≥ 60 years

Human Papilloma Virus (HPV)

Females ≤ 26 years and males ≤ 21 years who did not complete the HPV series*

*Indicated for up to age 45 years

Pneumococcal
2 VACCINES

Pneumovax 23
All adults ≥ 65 years
Patients 2-64 years old: 1 dose if heart, lung, liver disease, diabetes, alcoholic abuse, smokers
Patients 2-64 years old: 2 doses if immunocompromised

Prevnar13 (if not received before)
All adults ≥ 65 years
Patients 6-64 years old who are immunocompromised

Meningococcal
2 VACCINES, ADULTS NEED 1 OR BOTH

Serogroup B vaccines *(Bexsero, Trumenba):* give if complement component deficiency, taking eculizumab *(Soliris)*, asplenia, microbiologist with exposure to *Neisseria meningitidis*, serogroup B meningococcal disease outbreak exposure

Conjugate vaccines *(Menactra, Menveo):* same groups as above, plus: HIV, travelers/residents to countries in which the disease is common, military recruits, first year college students living in dorms, if not up-to-date

Hepatitis B

Sexually active adults who are not in a long-term, monogamous relationship, patients with diabetes age 19-59 years (or ≥ 60 years per healthcare provider discretion), household contact with an infected person, IV drug abusers (IVDAs), patients with HIV or chronic liver disease

Give alone *(Engerix-B, Recombivax, Heplisav-B)* or with hepatitis A vaccine *(Twinrix)*

Hepatitis A

Adults traveling to countries outside of the U.S. (except for developed countries), household members and other close contacts of adopted children newly arriving from countries with moderate-high infection risk, liver disease, hemophilia, men who have sex with men, IVDAs, homeless individuals

Give alone *(Havrix, VAQTA)* or with hepatitis B vaccine *(Twinrix)*

ROUTINE VACCINES

VACCINE	ADMINISTRATION RECOMMENDATIONS	STORAGE/ADMINISTRATION
Diphtheria Toxoid-, Tetanus Toxoid- and acellular Pertussis-Containing Vaccines The pediatric formulations (with the upper-case D, as in DTaP) have 3-5 times as much of the diphtheria component than the adult formulations. The adult formulations have a lower case d (Tdap or Td).		
DTaP: *Daptacel, Infanrix* DTaP-IPV: *Kinrix, Quadracel* **DTaP-HepB-IPV: *Pediarix*** DTaP-IPV/Hib: *Pentacel* DTaP-IPV/Hib/HepB: *Vaxelis* DT Td: *Tenivac* **Tdap: *Adacel, Boostrix***	**DTaP** A routine childhood vaccine series; 5 doses given at ages 2, 4, 6, 12-18 months and 4-6 years. For children younger than 7 years of age. **DT** Used for routine vaccine series in infants and children < 7 years old who have a contraindication to the acellular pertussis antigen in DTaP. **Td** Routine booster given every 10 years in patients age ≥ 7 years. Wound prophylaxis: for deep or dirty wounds, revaccinate with Td if it has been more than 5 years since the last dose. Tetanus immunoglobulin (TIG) may be required if no previous tetanus vaccines have been given. Can use Tdap x 1 if never received (see below). **Tdap** 1x booster at age ≥ 11 years (with no previous record of Tdap). Recommended in: 1) Pregnant or postpartum women, with each pregnancy (see Vaccinations for Specific Conditions/Populations). 2) Close contacts of infants younger than age 12 months (e.g., father, grandparents and child-care providers), if not up-to-date. 3) Healthcare personnel with direct patient contact, if not up-to-date. 4) Children age 7-10 years who did not get fully vaccinated with the DTaP series; give a single dose of Tdap instead of DTaP.	Store in the refrigerator. Do not freeze. Shake the prefilled syringe or vial before use. Give IM.
***Haemophilus influenzae* type b (Hib)-Containing Vaccines**		
Hib: *ActHIB, Hiberix, PedvaxHIB* DTaP-IPV/Hib: *Pentacel* DTaP-IPV/Hib/HepB: *Vaxelis*	Hib: a routine childhood vaccine series given between ages 2-15 months. *ActHIB* and *Hiberix* are 4-dose series, *PedvaxHIB* is a 3-dose series. Given to adults with asplenia.	Store in the refrigerator. Do not freeze. Shake the prefilled syringe or vial before use. Give IM.
Hepatitis-Containing Vaccines		
Hepatitis A: *Havrix*, VAQTA **Hepatitis B: *Engerix-B, Heplisav-B, Recombivax HB*** High-dose *Recombivax HB* (40 mcg/mL) is indicated for dialysis patients Hepatitis A and B: *Twinrix* **DTaP-HepB-IPV: *Pediarix*** DTaP-IPV/Hib/HepB: *Vaxelis*	**Hepatitis A** Children: a routine childhood vaccine series; 2 doses given at age 12 months and then 6-18 months later. Adults: men who have sex with men, illicit drug users, chronic liver disease, homeless individuals, clotting factor disorders, travelers to countries with high hepatitis A incidence, or anyone else who wants it. **Hepatitis B** Children: routine childhood vaccine series started within 24 hours after birth; 3 doses given at age 0, 1-2 and 6-18 months. Adults: healthcare workers, patients with ESRD (on dialysis), chronic liver disease (including HCV), HIV, diabetes (age 19-59 yrs, or ≥ 60 years at healthcare provider discretion), IV drug abusers, men who have sex with men, anyone with multiple sex partners, incarcerated people, some travelers. *Engerix-B* and *Recombivax HB*: 3-dose series given at month 0, 1 and 6 (can be completed in 4 months if necessary, but requires a booster at 1 year if the series is accelerated). *Heplisav-B* (age ≥ 18 years): 2-dose series given at month 0 and 1. Do not use in pregnant women. **Hepatitis A and B** 3-dose series given at months 0, 1 and 6.	Store in the refrigerator. Do not freeze. Shake the vial or prefilled syringe before use. Give IM.

VACCINE	ADMINISTRATION RECOMMENDATIONS	STORAGE/ADMINISTRATION
Human Papillomavirus Vaccines Prevents ~90% of cervical cancers, as well as vulvar, vaginal, oropharyngeal, penile and anal cancers, and genital warts.		
HPV9 (9-Valent): ***Gardasil 9***	**Females Age 9-26 Years*** Recommended age: 11-12 years (may be started at age 9**). **Males Age 9-21 Years (up to 26 years in select patients)*** Recommended age: 11-12 years (may be started at age 9**); can give up to age 21 years in most males and up to age 26 years in immunocompromised patients (including HIV) and men who have sex with men (vaccination for other men age 22-26 years is optional). **Regimens** If started before age 15 → 2 doses (at month 0 and 6-12 months later) If started at age 15 or older, or if immunocompromised → 3 doses (at months 0, 1-2 and 6) **FDA-approved up to age 45 years, ACIP recommendations have not changed.* ***Start at age 9 years in anyone with a history of sexual abuse.*	Store in refrigerator. Do not freeze. Shake the prefilled syringe or vial before use. Give IM. Caution for fainting (incidence is similar to other vaccines); administer to seated patient and monitor after vaccination.

INFLUENZA VACCINES

Influenza (the flu) is the most common vaccine preventable illness in the U.S. Influenza A and B are the two types of influenza viruses that cause epidemic human disease. Influenza A virus has subtypes based on the two surface antigens, hemagglutinin and neuraminidase. Immunity to the surface antigens reduces the likelihood of infection, and severity of disease if infection occurs.

The influenza vaccine is given annually. The vaccine changes every year to account for antigenic drift, which causes variations in the virus. More dramatic antigenic changes, or shifts, occur approximately every 30 years and can result in the emergence of a novel influenza virus, with the potential to cause a pandemic.

The virus spreads from person to person, primarily through respiratory droplet transmission. This can happen when an infected person coughs or sneezes in close proximity to an uninfected person. Influenza illness has an abrupt onset of symptoms (fever, myalgia, headache, malaise, nonproductive cough, sore throat and rhinitis). In children, otitis media, nausea and vomiting are commonly reported.

Uncomplicated influenza illness typically resolves after 3 – 7 days, though cough and malaise can persist for more than 2 weeks. In some people, influenza can exacerbate underlying medical conditions (e.g., pulmonary or cardiac disease) and lead to secondary bacterial pneumonia or primary influenza viral pneumonia (as with elderly or immunocompromised patients). Hospitalization and death are more common in people age < 5 years, ≥ 65 years or those with comorbid conditions. See the Infectious Diseases III chapter for treatment of influenza with antiviral medications. See the Study Tip Gal to the right for important details about influenza vaccines.

**If there is a vaccine shortage, the highest risk patients will be vaccinated first. The CDC website will provide information on who is at highest risk.*

INFLUENZA VACCINE TIPS

RECOMMENDED ANNUALLY*

All patients age ≥ 6 months, unless contraindicated.

Any vaccine can be used within the FDA indications (ACIP does not give preference to any one type of influenza vaccine).

All brand names have **FLU** in the name (e.g., *A**flu**ria*, ***Flu**zone*, ***Flu**Mist*).

SPECIFIC PATIENT CONSIDERATIONS

- **Age 6 months to 8 years (not previously vaccinated)**
  - Give 2 doses (4 weeks apart).
- **Patients with an egg allergy**
  - Can receive any age-appropriate inactivated influenza vaccine (see the drug table for details), even if severe allergy symptoms (e.g., wheezing, requiring epinephrine, hypotension or cardiovascular changes).
  - Administration should be supervised by a healthcare provider who is able to recognize and treat severe allergic reactions. No additional observation period is recommended (beyond the required 15 minutes).
  - *Flublok* (an egg-free product) is approved for age ≥ 18 years only.
  - Do not administer the live influenza vaccine (*FluMist*).
- **Pregnant patients**
  - Can receive any age-appropriate inactivated influenza vaccine (see the drug table for details). Do not administer the live influenza vaccine (*FluMist*).
- **Indicated only for patients age ≥ 65 years**
  - *Fluzone High-Dose* and *Fluad* (adjuvanted influenza vaccine).

VACCINE	ADMINISTRATION RECOMMENDATIONS	STORAGE/ADMINISTRATION
Influenza Vaccines There are many formulations of influenza vaccine. Key differences between them include the number of strains (3-trivalent or 4-quadrivalent), whether the virus is inactivated (IIV) or live attenuated (LAIV), the route (IM, intradermal, intranasal), the antigen dose or the presence of adjuvant. Inactivated influenza vaccines (IIV) are produced using eggs unless otherwise noted.		
Trivalent Inactivated Influenza Vaccines (IIV3) ■ ***Afluria, Fluvirin***: approved for various ages ■ ***Fluzone High-Dose:*** approved for age ≥ 65 years ■ ***Fluad*** (adjuvanted): approved for age ≥ 65 years **Quadrivalent Inactivated Influenza Vaccines (IIV4)** ■ ***Afluria*** *Quadrivalent*, ***Fluarix*** *Quadrivalent*, ***FluLaval*** *Quadrivalent*, ***Fluzone*** *Quadrivalent:* approved for various ages ■ ***Flucelvax Quadrivalent*** (grown in cell culture): approved for age ≥ 4 years ■ *Flublok Quadrivalent* (recombinant inactivated vaccine, RIV, egg-free): approved for age ≥ 18 years ■ *Fluzone Intradermal Quadrivalent:* approved for age 18-64 years **Quadrivalent Live Attenuated Influenza Vaccine (LAIV4)** ■ ***FluMist*** *Quadrivalent:* approved for healthy people age 2-49 years	Seasonal influenza vaccine recommendations are updated annually and can be found at www.cdc.gov. **Trivalent vs. Quadrivalent** Trivalent flu vaccines protect against three influenza viruses: two influenza A's (H1N1 and H3N2) and one influenza B. The quadrivalent flu vaccines protect against two influenza A's and two influenza B's. **Vaccine Timing** Give vaccine as soon as it is available, even if it arrives in late summer. It is preferable to administer the vaccine before October, but individuals should still be vaccinated later in the season. Outbreaks usually peak by February. **Live Attenuated Vaccine** LAIV4 is indicated for healthy patients age 2-49 years. See the previous table with vaccine contraindications and precautions for details. Do not use in pregnancy or if immunocompromised. **Egg Allergy** See Study Tip Gal on the previous page.	Store in the refrigerator. Do not freeze. **Administer IM Except:** *Fluzone Intradermal Quadrivalent* *FluMist Quadrivalent* (intranasal) **Product Notes:** *Fluzone High-Dose* contains 4x the antigen dose of standard dose IM vaccines, to increase antibody production. *Fluad* contains an oil-in-water emulsion of MF59 (an adjuvant), to increase antibody production. *Flucelvax* is grown in cell culture, but could still contain miniscule amounts of egg protein. *Fluzone Intradermal* uses a smaller needle, but causes more local reactions (redness, swelling, itching). *Afluria*: can be given with a needle-free jet injector. *FluMist Quadrivalent* is given as 0.2 mL, divided between the two nostrils.
Measles, Mumps and Rubella-Containing Vaccines (Live Attenuated)		
MMR: *M-M-R II* **MMRV** (MMR + Varicella): ***ProQuad***	Children: a routine vaccination series; 2 doses given at age 12-15 months and age 4-6 years. *ProQuad*: indicated for patients age 12 months-12 years. Adults: 1-2 doses if no evidence of immunity. Give 2 doses (4 weeks apart) to: healthcare workers, HIV patients with a CD4 count ≥ 200 cells/mm^3 for at least 6 months, nonpregnant women of childbearing age (with no evidence of immunity to rubella), international travelers, household contacts of immunocompromised people and students in postsecondary educational institutions. Do not use in pregnancy or if immunocompromised. Adults born before 1957 are generally considered immune to measles and mumps.	MMR: store in the refrigerator or freezer. MMRV: store vaccine in the freezer only due to the varicella component. Store diluents at room temperature or in the refrigerator. Give SC.

VACCINE	ADMINISTRATION RECOMMENDATIONS	STORAGE/ADMINISTRATION
Meningococcal Vaccines Quadrivalent meningococcal conjugate vaccines (MCV4) include serogroups A, C, W and Y. Serogroup B (MenB) is available in a separate vaccine.		
MCV4 (Conjugate Vaccines) ***Menactra:*** for age 9 months-55 years ***Menveo:*** for age 2 months-55 years Can be used in adults ≥ 56 years, if needed	**Routine Vaccination:** Adolescents: 2-dose series given at age 11-12 years and at age 16 years (booster dose). **Special Populations at High Risk:** Travelers to certain countries, such as the meningitis belt in Sub-Saharan Africa. Age 2 months and older with: HIV, asplenia/sickle cell disease, complement component deficiencies or eculizumab use. Lab workers with *N. meningitidis* exposure. 1st year college students (age ≤ 21 years) living in resident housing, if not up-to-date. Military recruits. The number of doses and timing (intervals) will depend on age and specific risk. People with ongoing risk of meningococcal disease should be revaccinated every 5 years.	Store in the refrigerator. Give IM. *Menveo:* both vials (the powder and the liquid) contain vaccine; use only the supplied liquid for reconstitution. ACWY vaccine is required by Saudi Arabia for travel to the Hajj and Umrah pilgrimages; proof of vaccination is required.
MenB *Bexsero:* for age 10-25 years *Trumenba:* for age 10-25 years	**Patients Age ≥ 10 Years with High Risk:** Asplenia/sickle cell disease, complement component deficiencies or eculizumab use. Lab workers with *N. meningitidis* exposure. During an outbreak. *Bexsero:* 2 doses (given 1 month apart). *Trumenba:* 2 doses (given 6 months apart). If high risk of meningococcal disease or during an outbreak: give 3 doses (at months 0, 1-2 and 6). Optional for patients age 16-23 years who are not at high risk but want the vaccine (if given, the preferred age is 16-18 years).	Store in the refrigerator. Give IM. *Bexsero* and *Trumenba* cover the serogroup B strain and are used in addition to the quadrivalent meningococcal conjugate vaccines.

PNEUMOCOCCAL VACCINES

The bacteria *S. pneumoniae*, called pneumococcus, is the most common cause of otitis media, pneumonia, meningitis and bloodstream infections in children. Adults age 65 years and older and those with altered immunocompetence are at increased risk of pneumococcal disease. As you learn the complex pneumococcal vaccine recommendations, keep in mind some key concepts:

- There are two pneumococcal vaccines: a conjugate vaccine, PCV13 *(Prevnar 13)*, and a polysaccharide vaccine, PPSV23 *(Pneumovax 23)*.
- Children age < 5 years receive PCV13 *(Prevnar 13)* as part of routine childhood vaccinations. This is because young children (< 2 years) do not produce an adequate antibody response to polysaccharide vaccines.
- Adults age 65 years and older, who have had no previous pneumococcal vaccines, receive one dose of both vaccines, first PCV13, then PPSV23 12 months later. This allows vaccines to be coordinated with annual check-ups.
- Some patients age 2 – 64 years will require one or two doses of PPSV23. Some patients age 6 – 64 years will require one dose of PCV13 (if not received as a child).
    - The pneumococcal vaccine recommendations and spacing varies based on patient risks. The usual interval between PCV13 and PPSV23 vaccines is 12 months. A shorter interval (8 weeks) is used in immunocompromised patients, to provide protection more quickly. Multiple doses of PPSV23 are separated by at least 5 years.

VACCINE	ADMINISTRATION RECOMMENDATIONS	STORAGE/ADMINISTRATION
Pneumococcal Vaccines		
13-Valent Conjugate Vaccine (PCV13): *Prevnar 13*	All children age < 5 years: 4-dose series given at age 2, 4, 6 and 12-15 months.* Patients age 6-64 years with risk factors (see Study Tip Gal below): 1 dose if never received before. All adults ≥ 65 years: 1 dose if never received before.	Store in the refrigerator. Do not freeze. Shake the vial or prefilled syringe prior to use. **PCV13** Give IM. **PPSV23** Give IM or SC.
23-Valent Polysaccharide Vaccine (PPSV23): *Pneumovax 23*	Patients age 2-64 years with risk factors (see Study Tip Gal below): 1 or 2 doses. All adults ≥ 65 years: 1 dose.	

**PCV13 initial pediatric dose is given as a series of three. After that series is complete, a patient should not get it again. Otherwise given as a one-time dose.*

Pneumococcal Vaccine Indications, Sequence and Intervals

INDICATIONS

PREVNAR 13 **(PCV13)**	***PNEUMOVAX 23*** **(PPSV23)**
Note: patients should receive PCV13 only once in their lifetime.*	Note: patients may receive 1, 2 or 3 doses in their lifetime.
Give 1 dose (if never received): ■ **Immunocompromised patients age 6-64 years** (e.g., sickle cell disease, asplenia, HIV, chronic renal failure, malignancy, transplant, immunosuppressive drugs, including steroids) ■ **Patients age ≥ 65 years**	**Give 1 dose before age 65 years:** ■ **Immunocompetent patients age 2-64 years** (diabetes, heart, lung or liver disease, alcohol abuse, smokers) **Give 2 doses before age 65 years:** ■ **Immunocompromised patients age 2-64 years** (e.g., sickle cell disease, asplenia, HIV, chronic renal failure, malignancy, transplant, immunosuppressive drugs, including steroids) **Give 1 dose at age ≥ 65 years** ■ All patients (whether 0, 1 or 2 doses were received before age 65 years)

SEQUENCE AND INTERVALS

Note: if both PCV13 and PPSV23 are required, PCV13 is given first; remember 13 comes before 23.

Immunocompetent patients

- Patients age ≥ 65 years: give *Prevnar 13* x 1 (if never received before), then 1 year later give *Pneumovax 23* x 1 (must be spaced at least 5 years from any previous *Pneumovax 23* dose).

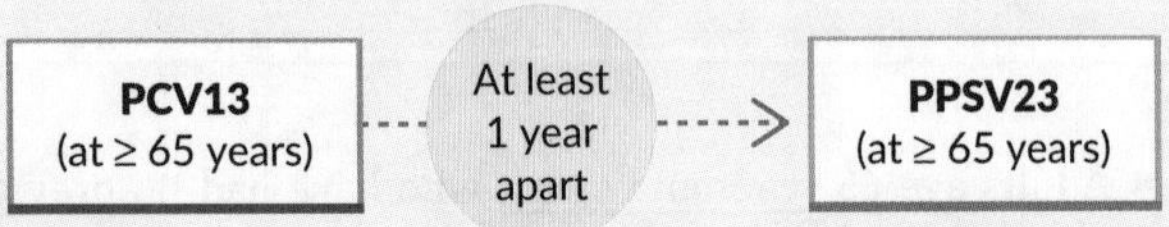

- Age 2-64 years with select indications (see above): give 1 dose of *Pneumovax 23*, then complete needed vaccinations at age ≥ 65 years (above).
  - In adults (age > 18 years): if *Pneumovax 23* was given first, wait 1 year to give *Prevnar 13* (delays protection).

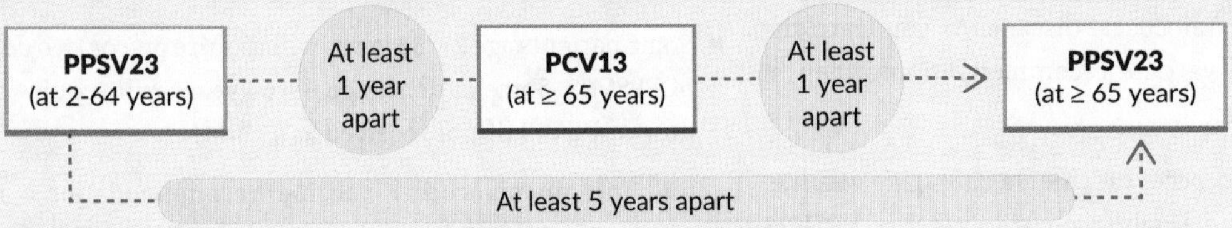

Immunocompromised patients

- Age ≥ 65 years: give *Prevnar 13* x 1 (if never received before), then 8 weeks later give *Pneumovax 23* x 1 (must be spaced at least 5 years from any previous *Pneumovax 23* dose).
- Age 6-64 years: give 1 dose of *Prevnar 13** (if never received before) plus 2 doses of *Pneumovax 23*, then complete needed vaccinations at age ≥ 65 years (above)

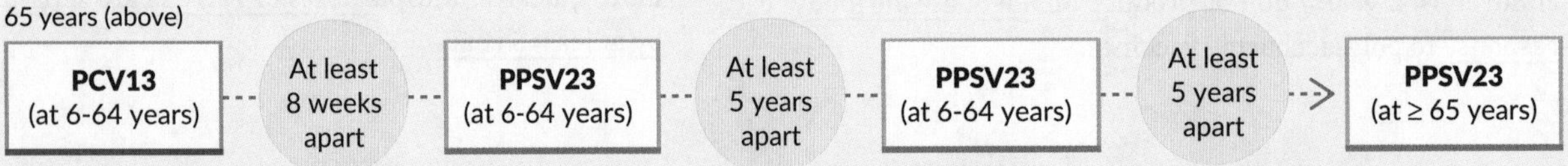

Recommendations above are abridged. For a summary of recommendations, see https://www.cdc.gov/vaccines/vpd/pneumo/hcp/who-when-to-vaccinate.html.
Complete adult recommendations are available at: https://www.cdc.gov/vaccines/vpd/pneumo/downloads/pneumo-vaccine-timing.pdf.
**Pediatric dosing requires a series of PCV13.*

VACCINE	ADMINISTRATION RECOMMENDATIONS	STORAGE/ADMINISTRATION
Poliovirus-Containing Vaccines **Only inactivated poliovirus vaccine (IPV) is available in the U.S. Oral polio vaccine (live attenuated) may be administered in other countries.**		
IPV: *IPOL* DTaP-IPV: *Kinrix, Quadracel* **DTaP-HepB-IPV: *Pediarix*** DTaP-IPV/Hib: *Pentacel* DTaP-IPV/Hib/HepB: *Vaxelis*	A routine childhood vaccine series; 4 doses given at age 2, 4, 6-18 months and 4-6 years.	Store in the refrigerator. Do not freeze. Shake the prefilled syringe or vial before use. IPV (*IPOL*): give IM or SC.
Rotavirus Vaccines (Live Attenuated)		
RV1: ***Rotarix*** RV5: ***RotaTeq***	Given to all infants. Do not initiate the series after age 15 weeks. *Rotarix:* 2 doses at age 2 and 4 months. *RotaTeq:* 3 doses at age 2, 4 and 6 months.	Store in the refrigerator. Do not freeze. Give orally.
Varicella-Containing Vaccines **Varicella virus-containing vaccines and the *Zostavax* brand of zoster vaccine are live attenuated vaccines. The *Shingrix* brand of zoster vaccine is a recombinant (non-live) vaccine.**		
Varicella Virus Vaccine (for chickenpox): *Varivax* **MMRV: *ProQuad*** **Zoster Virus Vaccines (for herpes zoster/shingles): *Shingrix, Zostavax***	**Varicella Virus Vaccine:** *Varivax:* a routine childhood vaccine series; 2 doses given at age 12-15 months and 4-6 years. Anyone without evidence of immunity to varicella should receive 2 doses of *Varivax*. Do not use in pregnancy or if immunocompromised. **Zoster Virus Vaccines:** *Shingrix* is preferred. ACIP recommends routine vaccination (2 doses given at month 0 and month 2-6) in patients age ≥ 50 years, including those who previously received varicella virus vaccine or *Zostavax* (wait at least 8 weeks after *Zostavax* before starting the 2-dose series of *Shingrix*). Vaccinate even if the patient has a history of zoster infection, since recurrence is possible. *Zostavax* (if used) is recommended in patients age ≥ 60 years (1 dose). Zoster vaccines are indicated for the prevention of shingles (not for treatment of an active case). They can reduce complications, such as the severity of postherpetic neuralgia following infections. Some antivirals (e.g., acyclovir, valacyclovir, famciclovir) can interfere with the live vaccines (*Varivax* and *Zostavax*). Stop 24 hours before vaccine administration and do not take for 14 days after vaccination.	***Varivax* and *Zostavax*** Store vaccine in the freezer. Store the diluent in the refrigerator or at room temperature. Reconstitute immediately upon removal from the freezer and inject; short stability (30 minutes). Do not give if there is a hypersensitivity to gelatin or neomycin. Give SC. ***Shingrix*** Store vaccine and adjuvant liquid in the refrigerator. Do not freeze. Give IM.

NON-ROUTINE VACCINES

DRUG	ADMINISTRATION RECOMMENDATIONS	STORAGE/ADMINISTRATION
Rabies Vaccine: ***RabAvert,*** *Imovax*	Give preventively for high risk exposure (e.g., animal handlers, traveling to a high risk area). Prevention: 3 doses. Give after a possible rabies exposure. Post-exposure (with previous vaccination): 2 doses. Post-exposure (without previous vaccination): 4 doses; 1 dose of rabies immune globulin (RIG) should be given with the first vaccine dose.	Store in the refrigerator. Reconstitute with the provided diluent. Give IM.
Typhoid Vaccine: *Vivotif* (live vaccine) Oral *Typhim Vi* (inactivated polysaccharide vaccine) Injection	To prevent typhoid fever caused by *Salmonella typhi* (see the Travelers chapter for disease information). Oral: take 1 capsule PO on alternate days (day 0, 2, 4 and 6). Complete at least 1 week prior to possible exposure. Give every 5 years if continued risk or exposure. Injection: give 1 dose at least 2 weeks prior to possible exposure. Give every 2 years if continued risk or exposure.	Oral capsules: store in the refrigerator. Take on an empty stomach (1 hour before a meal) with cold or lukewarm water. Injection: store in the refrigerator. Do not freeze. Injection: give IM.
Japanese Encephalitis Virus Vaccine: *Ixiaro*	Give if spending ≥ 1 month in endemic areas during transmission season, especially if travel will include rural areas. Give 2 doses, 28 days apart. Complete at least 1 week prior to potential exposure (see the Travelers chapter for disease information).	Store in the refrigerator. Do not freeze. Give IM.
Tuberculosis Bacille Calmette-Guerin (BCG) Vaccine Live vaccine	Not used often in the U.S. Given to infants and small children in countries with higher TB incidence. Provides weak protection for pulmonary TB.	Can cause a positive reaction to the TB skin test (see the Infectious Diseases II chapter).
Yellow Fever Vaccine: *YF-VAX* Live vaccine	Give to those who travel to, or live in areas of risk, and to travelers to countries that require vaccination (see the Travelers chapter). Contraindicated with a severe (life-threatening) allergy to eggs or gelatin, immunosuppression, age < 6 month or breastfeeding. Avoid donating blood for 2 weeks after receiving the vaccine. The International Certificate of Vaccination (yellow card) is provided and is valid for 10 years, starting 10 days after vaccination. It may be required to enter endemic areas.	Store in the refrigerator. Reconstitute with the provided diluent; swirl, do not shake. Give SC.
Cholera vaccine: *Vaxchora* Live vaccine	Give to people age 18-64 years who are traveling to an area of active toxigenic *Vibrio cholerae* transmission. Give 1 oral dose ≥ 10 days prior to exposure.	Store the packet for reconstitution in the freezer. Remove no more than 15 minutes prior to reconstitution. Dissolve the buffer packet in 100 mL of cold or room temperature water, then add the active component packet; stir for 30 seconds and drink within 15 minutes.

STORAGE

Vaccines should be properly stored and kept in the original packaging (box) until use. Some vaccines require protection from light. Vaccines should be stored in the refrigerator or freezer units designed for storing biologics (including vaccines) or in separate, free-standing freezer and refrigerator units. Household freezer units or dormitory-style refrigerators should not be used for vaccine storage. Vaccines should be stored on the shelves away from the walls; never place vaccines in the doors of the freezer or the refrigerator as the temperature there is unstable. Rotate stock so vaccines and diluents with the earliest expiration date are used first.

The CDC recommends a calibrated thermometer or a digital data logger be connected to a buffered temperature probe in the refrigerator and freezer. An example of a buffered probe is one immersed in a vial of liquid (e.g., glycol). This prevents false readings due to the rapid changes in air temperature that occur when refrigerator doors are opened. Read and document refrigerator and freezer temperatures at least twice each workday (in the morning and before the end of the workday). Maintain a consistent power source. Keep temperature logs for 3 years (or longer, as required by individual states).

Staff can easily confuse the vaccines within the storage unit. Use labels and separate containers.

VACCINE STORAGE REQUIREMENTS

- Most vaccines are stored in the refrigerator (between 36°F and 46°F, or 2°C and 8°C).
- Vaccines that should be stored in the freezer (between –58°F and +5°F, or –50°C and –15°C) include: varicella vaccine, *Zostavax*, MMRV and oral cholera vaccine.
- MMR is stored either in the refrigerator or freezer.

Diluents

- Some vaccines require reconstitution with a diluent before use. The diluents that come with varicella, *Zostavax*, MMR, and MMRV vaccines can be stored in the refrigerator or at room temperature.
- Vaccines that are reconstituted should be used shortly after preparation.

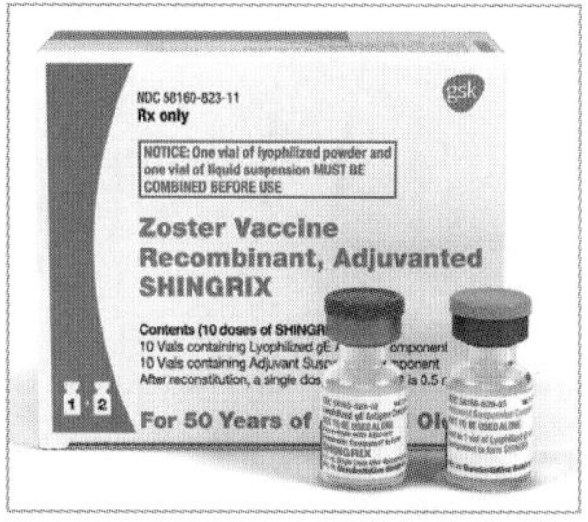

Shingrix Vaccine
Requires reconstitution, diluent included

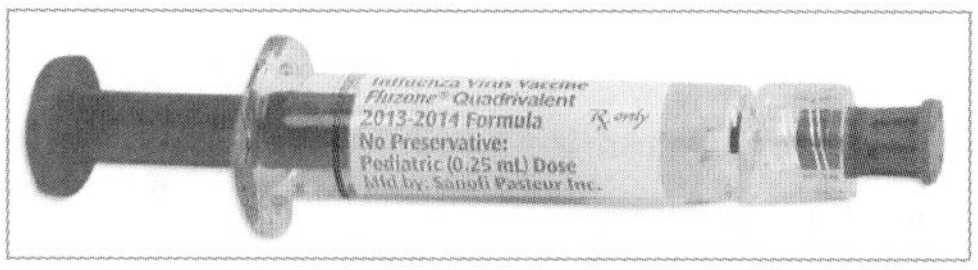

Fluzone Vaccine

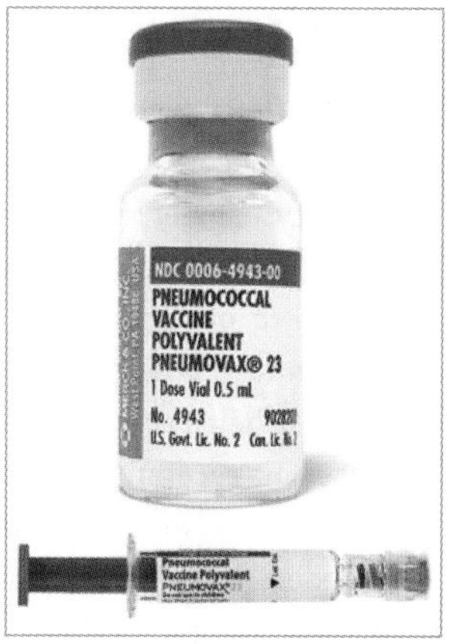

Pneumovax 23 Vaccine
Available as a vial or syringe

ADMINISTRATION

ROUTES OF ADMINISTRATION

IM ONLY	SC ONLY	IM OR SC	INTRADERMAL	INTRANASAL	PO
Most vaccines are given IM. The vaccines listed in the following sections of the table are exceptions.	MMR, MMRV, Varicella, *Zostavax*, Yellow Fever	PPSV23, IPV *(IPOL)*	*Fluzone Intradermal Quadrivalent* (Inactivated Influenza Vaccine)	*FluMist Quadrivalent* (Live Attenuated Vaccine)	Typhoid *(Vivotif)* capsules Oral solutions: Cholera *(Vaxchora)* and Rotavirus *(Rotateq, Rotarix)*

ADMINISTRATION TECHNIQUE

- SC: use a 23 – 25 gauge, 5/8" needle at a 45 degree angle. Adults: inject into the fatty tissue over the triceps. Infants: inject into the anterolateral mid-thigh muscle.
- IM: use a 22 – 25 gauge needle. Inject at a 90 degree angle. Adults: inject into the deltoid muscle above the level of the armpit and below the shoulder joint. Infants: inject into the anterolateral mid-thigh muscle. IM needle length: 1" in adults.
    - Exceptions: weight < 130 pounds, use a 5/8 – 1" needle and males > 260 pounds or females > 200 pounds, use a 1½" needle.
- Intradermal: typically uses a smaller, 30-gauge, 1.5 mm needle. Inject into the deltoid at a 90 degree angle.
- Never mix vaccines in the same syringe.
- Use of acetaminophen before vaccine administration, to prevent adverse effects, is not recommended. It can be given if symptoms occur.

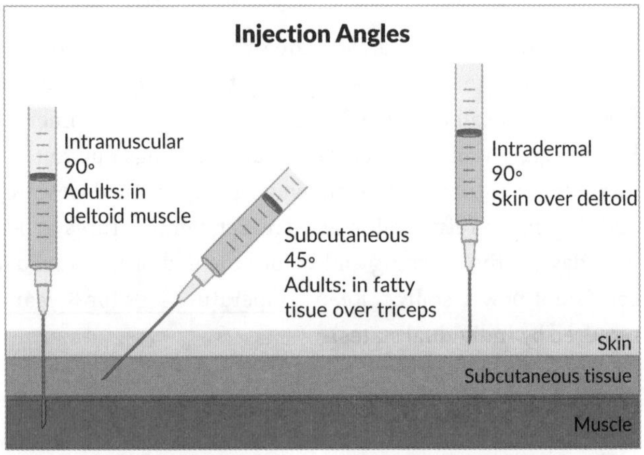

Intramuscular (IM) injection site for children and adults

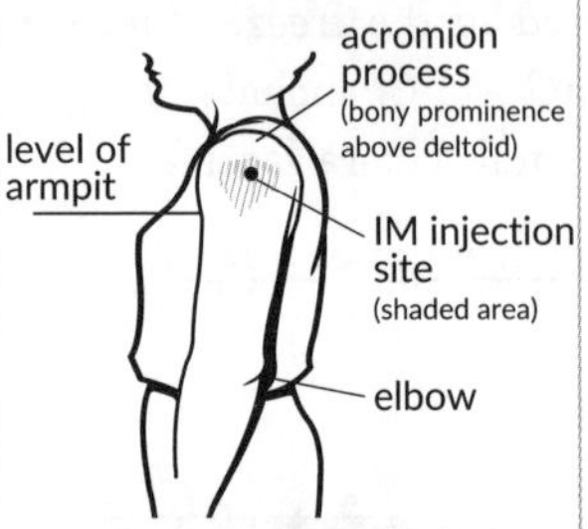

Give in the central and thickest portion of the deltoid muscle – above the level of the armpit and approximately 2-3 fingerbreadths (~2") below the acromion process. See the diagram. To avoid causing an injury, do not inject too high (near the acromion process) or too low.

Subcutaneous (Subcut) injection site for children (after the 1st birthday) and adults

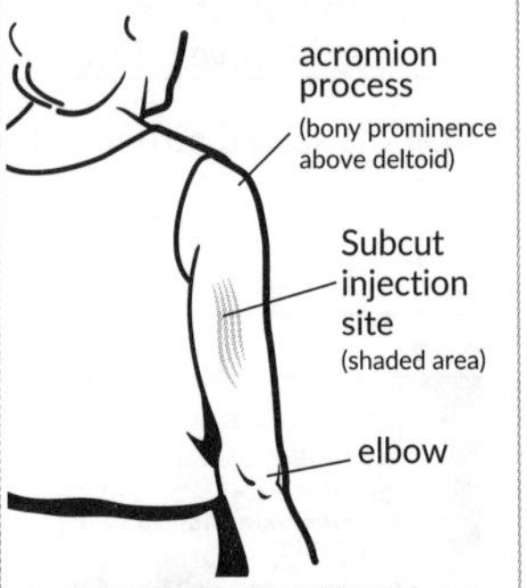

Insert needle at a 45° angle into the fatty tissue overlying the triceps muscle. Make sure you pinch up on the subcutaneous tissue to prevent injection into the muscle.

IMMUNIZATION REGISTRIES

Immunization registries are computerized information systems that collect vaccination histories and help ensure correct and timely immunizations, especially for children. They are useful for healthcare providers, who can use the registries to obtain the patient's history, produce vaccine records and manage vaccine inventories, among other benefits. It helps the community at-large to identify groups who are not receiving vaccines in order to target outreach efforts. Some systems are able to notify patients if vaccines are needed. Where allowed, pharmacists should strive to report all vaccines administrated to their state or local registry.

Select Guidelines/References

CDC Vaccine and Immunization websites: https://www.cdc.gov/vaccines, https://www.cdc.gov/vaccines/hcp/acip-recs/index.html and https://www.cdc.gov/travel (accessed 2019 Feb 17). The pediatric and adult schedules are updated annually and published in January.

The CDC's Pink Book, Epidemiology and Prevention of Vaccine Preventable Diseases (published every 2 years). https://www.cdc.gov/vaccines/pubs/pinkbook/index.html (accessed 2019 Feb 17).

CHAPTER CONTENT

Background 333
Diseases Transmitted through Contaminated Food and Water 333
Travelers' Diarrhea 334
Drugs for Travelers' Diarrhea 335
Typhoid Fever 335
Cholera 335
Polio 335
Travel Vaccines 336
Hepatitis A 336
Diseases Transmitted Through Blood and Bodily Fluids 336
Hepatitis B 336
Meningococcal Meningitis 336
Diseases Transmitted by Insect Bites 336
Dengue 337
Malaria 337
Japanese Encephalitis 338
Yellow Fever 338
Zika Virus 339
Additional Concerns for Traveling Individuals 339
Venous Thromboembolism Prevention 339
Altitude Sickness and Motion Sickness 339
The Returned Traveler 339

CONTENT LEGEND

= Study Tip Gal   = Key Drug Guy

CHAPTER 21
TRAVELERS

BACKGROUND

In 2017, U.S. residents made more than 78 million trips with at least one night outside the United States. Pharmacists assist travelers by providing formal advice, travel vaccines, malaria prophylaxis and other medications prior to travel. Consultative services provided by pharmacists can include educational awareness of country-specific risks, and ways to prevent and address them.

Travelers should carry with them a list of all their medical conditions and medications (prescription and OTC). Prescription medications should be stored in the original prescription containers. Medications and medical supplies should be packed in carry-on luggage. Travel health information, including travel health insurance recommendations, is available on the CDC's travel website where the "Yellow Book" (the CDC's standard resource on travel information) is located. Travel advisories and visa requirements can be checked on the U.S. State Department website.

When preparing a patient for travel, healthcare professionals should consider: 1) diseases spread through food and water, 2) diseases spread through blood and bodily fluids, and 3) diseases transmitted by insects. A traveler's risk for contracting disease is assessed based upon travel duration, destination-specific risks, itinerary, and patient-specific health concerns.

DISEASES TRANSMITTED THROUGH CONTAMINATED FOOD AND WATER

Contaminated food and water cause many travel-related illnesses. Many international travel destinations (especially developing countries) vary in the availability of clean water, plumbing and refrigeration. These factors can lead to unsafe food handling practices and the contamination of food and water with fecal matter, leading to increased risk of illness.

TRAVELERS' DIARRHEA

Travelers' diarrhea (TD) is the most common travel-related illness, occurring in 30 – 70% of travelers, depending on the destination and season. Areas of highest risk include most of Asia, the Middle East, Africa, Mexico, and Central and South America. TD is the sudden onset of abnormally loose or liquid, frequent stools. If blood is mixed in with the stool, it is classified as dysentery, which is often accompanied by more severe systemic symptoms such as fever. Severity is assessed by the patient as mild, moderate or severe, and this determines initial treatment (see Study Tip Gal on the following page). Dysentery is classified as severe.

Symptoms usually begin within 6 – 72 hours if caused by a bacterial or viral pathogen. More than 80 – 90% of TD cases are bacterial and *E. coli* is the primary pathogen, followed by *Campylobacter jejuni, Shigella* species, and *Salmonella* species. Untreated bacterial diarrhea can last 3 – 7 days and some pathogens can cause invasive infections outside the GI tract. Persistent TD, defined as diarrhea lasting ≥ 14 days, is more likely to occur with certain bacterial and protozoal pathogens and requires additional testing.

TD Prevention

Safe food and water habits can reduce, but do not eliminate, risk of TD. The rule "boil it, cook it, peel it, or forget it" is helpful when discussing food safety. These food and water precautions can be recommended:

- Eat only food that is cooked and served hot. Avoid food that has been sitting on a buffet.
- Eat raw fruits and vegetables only if washed in clean water or peeled (e.g., oranges).
- Use bottled water or boil for approximately one minute before drinking or using to brush teeth. Avoid ice.
- Eating at well-known restaurants can help reduce risk. Poor hygiene practice in small, local restaurants or food stands can increase risk of contracting TD.
- Keep hands clean and out of the mouth. Wash hands often with soap and water, especially after using the bathroom and before eating. If soap and water are not available, use an alcohol-based hand sanitizer.

Prophylaxis with bismuth subsalicylate (BSS), the active ingredient of *Pepto-Bismol*, reduces the incidence of TD by ~50%. Do not use BSS in patients with an aspirin allergy, pregnancy, renal insufficiency, gout, or in anyone taking anticoagulants, probenecid or methotrexate. Taking BSS with aspirin or other salicylates can cause salicylate toxicity. BSS is FDA-approved for OTC use in children ≥ 12 years old, but has been used off-label in younger children (≥ 3 years old) as long as they have had no recent or current viral infections (due to the risk of Reye's syndrome). BSS tablets or liquid can be recommended as prophylaxis in any appropriate traveler. Antibiotic prophylaxis is not routinely recommended, but should be used in patients who are at high risk of developing health-related complications of TD, including immunosuppressed patients or those with travel for performance reasons (e.g., a professional athlete). If antibiotic prophylaxis is indicated, quinolones can be used (if resistance is low) or rifaximin. Per the International Society of Travel Medicine guidelines, rifaximin is the preferred drug.

TD Treatment

Hydration (with increased fluid and salt intake) is essential for all TD cases. In an elderly patient with severe diarrhea or in any traveler with prolonged watery (cholera-like) diarrhea or vomiting, oral rehydration solution is preferred for fluid replacement. The packets are available in pharmacies throughout the world. They are easy to prepare: mix one packet with one liter of boiled, purified water.

Medical treatment is not required in patients with non-severe, non-cholera-like diarrhea. OTC anti-diarrheal drugs have been shown to reduce the number of stools passed in cases of diarrhea, allowing travelers to continue their planned itinerary. See the Constipation & Diarrhea and Infectious Diseases I and II chapters for additional information.

The primary antimotility drug used for treatment of acute diarrhea is loperamide *(Imodium A-D)*. Loperamide decreases the frequency and urgency of bowel movements, making it easier for a person with diarrhea to continue travel activities (e.g., ride on a bus or airplane). The dosage is 4 mg after the first loose stool and 2 mg after each subsequent loose stool, up to a maximum dose of 16 mg/day by prescription or 8 mg/day OTC. Loperamide can be used for up to two days. It should not be used in children < 2 years old (< 6 years old if OTC) or in patients with bloody diarrhea.

BSS is another treatment option. The salicylate portion of BSS has antisecretory, anti-diarrheal properties and can reduce stools passed by ~40%. See the Constipation & Diarrhea chapter for specific information on contraindications and side effects, such as black tongue/stools, risk of Reye's syndrome in pediatric patients and salicylate toxicity.

Compared with BSS, loperamide showed greater reduction in the number of diarrheal stools passed and has been shown to shorten the duration of acute diarrhea in both children and adults.

Antibiotics shorten the duration of moderate-to-severe TD to a little over 24 hours. Macrolides, quinolones, or rifaximin are preferred (typically a single dose regimen), depending on the patient presentation and antibiotic resistance patterns. Azithromycin is preferred for severe TD and dysentery. Quinolones, rifaximin or rifamycin can be used for severe TD if no dysentery is present. Rifaximin and rifamycin cannot be used to treat infections in which invasive pathogens (e.g., *Campylobacter jejuni, Salmonella* species) are suspected. Rifamycin (*Aemcolo*) was approved for treatment of TD caused by noninvasive strains of *E. coli* in adults on November, 2018.

DRUGS FOR TRAVELERS' DIARRHEA

Prophylaxis

- Bismuth subsalicylate tablets/liquid at a dose of 524-1050 mg PO 4 times daily (with meals and at bedtime)
  - Consider in any patient without contraindications (e.g., use with or an allergy to salicylates, ulcer, coagulopathy, black/bloody stool)
- Antibiotics (quinolones if low resistance, or rifaximin/rifamycin)
  - Limit use to patients at high risk of developing complications as a result of TD

Treatment

- Mild TD: loperamide as needed (antibiotics are not recommended)
- Moderate TD: loperamide as needed +/- antibiotics
- Severe TD (including dysentery): antibiotics are recommended (azithromycin 1,000 mg x 1 dose is preferred) +/- loperamide

TYPHOID FEVER

Typhoid fever is caused by the bacterium *Salmonella typhi*. The disease can be life-threatening. The highest areas of risk for contracting typhoid fever include East and Southeast Asia, Africa, the Caribbean, and Central and South America.

Humans are the only source for this bacteria, and disease is spread through food or water contaminated by the feces of someone with either an acute infection or from a chronic, asymptomatic carrier. The incubation period of typhoid fever and paratyphoid fever (a similar illness) is 6 – 30 days. Patients present with fatigue and increasing fever over 3 – 4 days. Headache, malaise and anorexia, along with enlargement of the liver and spleen are common, and rash can occur. Intestinal hemorrhage or perforation can occur 2 – 3 weeks later and can be fatal.

Typhoid vaccines are recommended but are only 50 – 80% effective; even vaccinated travelers should follow safe food and water precautions and wash their hands frequently. These precautions are the only prevention method for paratyphoid fever, because there is not a vaccine available.

Typhoid vaccines include *Vivotif*, an oral, live, attenuated vaccine and *Typhim Vi*, an inactivated, intramuscular injection. The oral vaccine regimen should be completed ≥ 1 week prior to travel. It should not be used in children < 6 years old, or if a patient is on antibiotics or has an extremely sensitive stomach. The intramuscular vaccine must be given ≥ 2 weeks before the expected exposure, and is not recommended for children < 2 years old. Revaccination is recommended every five years for *Vivotif* and every two years for *Typhim Vi* in patients who remain at risk.

CHOLERA

Cholera is a bacterial infection caused by *Vibrio cholerae*. The disease is very rare in the U.S., but still occurs in many places, including Africa, Southeast Asia and Haiti. The infection is often mild or asymptomatic, but in severe cases, it can present with profuse diarrhea and vomiting, and eventual dehydration that can be life threatening. The most common symptom includes watery diarrhea, which is referred to as "rice-water stools."

In addition to food and water precautions, a live-attenuated vaccine (*Vaxchora*), is recommended for those traveling to a region with active cholera transmission. *Vaxchora* is administered as a single, oral liquid dose at least 10 days before travel and is approved for use in adults age 18 through 64 years.

POLIO

Most people in the U.S. received the polio vaccine in childhood, but the virus is not eradicated worldwide. Many countries remain endemic and have had an active spread of poliovirus in the recent past. These include Afghanistan, Burma (Myanmar), Guinea, Laos, Nigeria, Madagascar, Pakistan and Ukraine. The CDC recommends a single lifetime booster dose of inactivated poliovirus vaccine at least four weeks prior to travel for adults who have previously completed a poliovirus vaccine series and who are traveling to regions where poliovirus is circulating. Travelers might be required to show proof of polio vaccination when leaving a polio-infected country. Vaccination should be documented on an International Certificate of Vaccination or Prophylaxis (ICVP), which also records Yellow Fever vaccine.

TRAVEL VACCINES

Inactivated Vaccines

Hepatitis A *(Havrix, VAQTA)*

Hepatitis B *(Engerix-B, Recombivax HB)*

Hepatitis A/B *(Twinrix)*

Japanese encephalitis *(Ixiaro)*

Meningococcus *(Menveo, Menactra)*

Polio *(IPOL)*

Typhoid-IM *(Typhim Vi)*

Live Vaccines

Cholera-PO *(Vaxchora)*

Typhoid-PO *(Vivotif)*

Yellow fever-SC *(YF-VAX)*

HEPATITIS A

Hepatitis A is a common vaccine-preventable infection among international travelers. People from developed countries who travel to developing countries are at highest risk. The infected patient can be asymptomatic or might have symptoms that include fever, malaise, jaundice, nausea and abdominal discomfort that can last up to six months. Vaccination should be considered for travelers to most parts of the world, except Canada, Western Europe and Scandinavia, Japan, New Zealand and Australia.

DISEASES TRANSMITTED THROUGH BLOOD AND BODILY FLUIDS

HEPATITIS B

Hepatitis B is transmitted through contact with contaminated blood or other body fluids. The risk for travelers who do not participate in high risk behaviors is low. Hepatitis B has an incubation period of about 90 days. Infection can present as malaise, jaundice, nausea and abdominal discomfort. Chronic infection with Hepatitis B can result in chronic liver disease and liver cancer.

Hepatitis B vaccination is extremely important for travelers who plan to receive medical care, volunteer to provide medical work or have unprotected sexual encounters with new partners. Piercings and tattoos can also transmit the virus and should be avoided. The 3-dose vaccine series takes six months to complete. If a traveler is unable to receive all three doses before departure, administer as many doses as possible before departure and complete the series upon return. In instances of high risk, an accelerated series can be administered; when the accelerated series is used, a booster dose is required at one year for long-term immunity.

MENINGOCOCCAL MENINGITIS

Bacterial meningitis involving *N. menigitidis* has a high mortality rate and is a medical emergency. Patients with symptoms of fever, severe and unrelenting headache, nausea, stiff neck (nuchal rigidity) and mental status changes require urgent treatment to avoid the risk of permanent neurological damage and death. Diagnosis is made by a lumbar puncture (LP). See ID 2: Bacterial Infections chapter.

Meningitis is spread by respiratory secretions, and is widespread in many parts of the world. Vaccination is recommended for people who travel to or reside in countries where *N. meningitidis* is hyperendemic or epidemic, particularly if spending a long time in contact with the local population. High risk regions include the meningitis belt of Africa during the dry season (December – June). The meningococcal vaccine is required by the government of Saudi Arabia for travel during the period of the annual Hajj and Umrah pilgrimages. Current recommendations include only the quadrivalent vaccines (*Menactra and Menveo*) which contain four bacterial types: ACWY. There are no recommendations to use the serogroup B meningococcal vaccines for travelers.

DISEASES TRANSMITTED BY INSECT BITES

Insects that transmit disease are vectors; a vector carries an organism to an individual, causing infection. A reservoir is any place (such as an animal, insect, soil or plant) in which the disease lives and can multiply. The primary insects that transmit infections to travelers are mosquitoes, which transmit Japanese encephalitis, yellow fever, dengue, malaria and Zika virus. The following strategies should be employed to avoid insect bites as much as possible:

- Stay and sleep in screened or air-conditioned rooms and use a bed net, which can be pre-treated with mosquito repellent, such as those listed below.
- Cover exposed skin by wearing long-sleeved shirts, long pants and hats.
- Use proper application of mosquito repellents containing 20% – 50% DEET as the active ingredient on exposed skin. DEET also provides protection against ticks. Other insect repellents that can be used topically for mosquitoes (but not for ticks) are picaridin, oil of lemon, eucalyptus or IR3535.
- Use permethrin to treat clothing, gear and bed nets but do not apply directly to the skin.

DENGUE

Dengue is transmitted by *Aedes aegypti* and *Aedes albopictus* mosquitoes. In many parts of the tropics and subtropics, dengue is endemic; it occurs every year, usually during a season when mosquito populations are high and rainfall is optimal for breeding. An estimated 75% of infections are asymptomatic, but up to 5% of patients develop severe, life-threatening disease. Severe dengue can include shock, severe bleeding or organ failure. Treatment is supportive, as there are no specific medications to treat dengue infection. *Dengvaxia* is a live attenuated recombinant vaccine, not yet available in the U.S., recommended only to those with a past dengue infection. Protection from mosquito bites is essential.

MALARIA

Malaria is transmitted by the *Anopheles* mosquito. Once in a human host, it multiplies first in the liver and then moves into the red blood cells, multiplying and destroying them. Classic symptoms of malaria include shaking, chills, high fever and flu-like illness; these should not be ignored in a patient with recent travel. Malaria is endemic in Asia, Latin America, North Africa, Eastern Europe and the South Pacific. *Plasmodium vivax* is the most common of four human malaria species (*P. falciparum, P. malariae, P. ovale,* and *P. vivax*). *P. vivax* causes 50% of malaria cases in India and is becoming increasingly resistant to malaria drugs. *P. falciparum* is the most deadly species. About 1,700 cases of malaria are diagnosed in the U.S. annually, mostly in returned travelers. Even with treatment, malaria can be fatal, so prophylactic medications are recommended for travelers to certain regions. The CDC website features maps of malaria presence by country, the species of malaria, and resistance patterns. All of this information is incorporated into the CDC's region-specific prophylaxis medication recommendations. Recommendations can change year-to-year.

Malaria Prophylaxis Regimens

Malaria prophylaxis must be started prior to travel and continue after returning (see following page for specific requirements). Malaria drugs cause nausea; taking with sufficient water, food or milk decreases nausea.

Quick Starts

Daily regimens

Avoid these in pregnancy

Cause nausea; to decrease, take with food, milk, or water

DRUG	DOSING	SAFETY/SIDE EFFECTS/NOTES
These medications are initiated just 1-2 days prior to travel, which makes them ideal when traveling with little advance notice		
Atovaquone/Proguanil (*Malarone*) Good coverage, all area	Stop: 1 week after travel Taken daily	**Not used in:** Pregnancy Breastfeeding Severe renal impairment
Doxycycline (*Doryx, Vibramycins*) Also prevents rickettsial infections and leptospirosis, so preferred in hiking/camping	Stop: 4 weeks after travel Taken daily	Causes photosensitivity* **Not used in:** Pregnancy Children < 8 years old (due to tooth development/discoloration)
Primaquine Most effective drug against *P. vivax*	Stop: 1 week after travel Taken daily	**Not used in:** G6PD-deficiency (CDC requires screening prior to use due to risk of hemolytic anemia) Pregnancy Breastfeeding (unless infant is tested for G6PD-deficiency)

**Use broad-spectrum sunscreen (protects against UVA and UVB rays) with Sun Protection Factor (SPF) 30 or higher, plus water resistant. Other strategies: seek shade, wear protective clothing, avoid mid-day sun.*

Advance Starts

Weekly regimens

Safe in children, pregnancy

Choice depends on resistance in the region

DRUG	DOSING	SAFETY/SIDE EFFECTS/NOTES
These medications must be started 1-2 weeks prior to travel		
Chloroquine Resistance issues with *P. falciparum* and *P. vivax*	Start: 1-2 weeks before travel Stop: 4 weeks after travel Taken weekly Patients taking chronic hydroxychloroquine are covered (depending on resistance)	**SIDE EFFECTS** Exacerbation of psoriasis, serious skin rash (rare), retinal toxicity/visual changes, blue-gray skin pigmentation (rare with short-term use) Contraindicated for prophylaxis if underlying retinal or visual changes **Not used in:** Area of chloroquine or mefloquine resistance
Mefloquine *(Lariam)*	Start: ≥ 2 weeks before travel Stop: 4 weeks after travel Taken weekly	**Not used in:** Underlying psychiatric conditions Seizures Arrhythmias Areas of mefloquine resistance
Tafenoquine *(Arakoda)* May be used for up to 6 months of continuous dosing	Loading dose: 3 days before travel, taken daily Maintenance dose: 7 days after last dose of loading regimen Taken weekly Terminal dose: Single dose after the last dose of the loading regimen	**Not used in:** G6PD-deficiency (CDC requires screening prior to use due to risk of hemolytic anemia) Pregnancy Breastfeeding (unless infant is tested for G6PD-deficiency) Underlying psychiatric conditions

JAPANESE ENCEPHALITIS

The Japanese Encephalitis (JE) virus is transmitted by mosquitoes. Infection is usually asymptomatic, but can develop into encephalitis (swelling around the brain), with rigors, risk of seizures, coma and death. Travelers are most likely to become infected when visiting rural agricultural areas. The best prevention is to reduce exposure to mosquitoes. The JE vaccine is sometimes recommended with travel to Asia and parts of the western Pacific. The vaccine *(Ixiaro)* is recommended for travelers older than two months of age who are planning extended exposure to the outdoors (e.g., campers) or who plan to spend at least one month in endemic areas during the JE virus transmission season. There is an accelerated schedule available for those traveling with little notice.

YELLOW FEVER

Yellow fever is caused by a virus and transmitted by mosquitoes found in tropical and subtropical areas in Africa and Central and South America. Reducing mosquito exposure is essential. Most infections are asymptomatic. If symptoms develop, the initial illness presents with influenza-like symptoms. Most patients will improve, but ~15% progress to a more toxic form of the disease with risk of shock, bleeding and organ failure. There is no specific treatment for acute infection except symptomatic relief with fluids, analgesics and antipyretics. Aspirin and other NSAIDs cannot be used due to an increased risk of bleeding.

A live-attenuated vaccine *(YF-VAX)* is available to prevent yellow fever and stop transmission. After vaccination, patients are provided an ICVP, sometimes called the "yellow card," which is required as a condition of entry for some countries. The card is valid only if the vaccination is completed 10 days before arrival. In 2015, the CDC Advisory Committee on Immunization Practices (ACIP) approved a new recommendation that a single dose of yellow fever vaccine provides life-long protection and is adequate for most travelers. Healthcare providers should review the entry requirements for destination countries, as some countries continue to require a booster vaccine dose every 10 years (as previous guidelines recommended).

The vaccine is contraindicated with hypersensitivity to eggs. Due to risks of serious adverse effects, vaccination is recommended only in travelers at a high risk of exposure or who require proof of vaccination to enter a country. Mild adverse effects are common (occurring in 10 – 30% of patients) and include low grade fever and headache lasting for 5 – 10 days. In rare cases, severe adverse effects occur, such as yellow fever vaccine-associated neurologic disease.

ZIKA VIRUS

The Zika virus is transmitted primarily by the *Aedes* species mosquito. Sexual and possible blood transfusion-associated transmission have been reported. Most Zika virus infections are asymptomatic. Symptomatic infections are generally mild with symptoms consisting of fever, maculopapular rash, arthralgia (joint pain) and conjunctivitis (red eyes).

The most pressing concern with Zika virus arose in 2015 when Brazil observed a marked increase in the number of infants born with microcephaly, a birth defect that can cause significant disability and can be life-threatening in severe cases. Zika virus RNA was subsequently identified in tissues from infants with microcephaly and from fetal losses in women who were infected during pregnancy. Zika infection during pregnancy can cause birth defects of the brain and eyes, hearing deficits and impaired growth. Reports of Guillain-Barré syndrome, an uncommon sickness of the nervous system, have also increased in areas affected by Zika.

No vaccine is available yet for the Zika virus. Avoiding mosquito bites and using condoms during sexual contact with people with possible Zika virus infection reduces transmission risk.

The CDC recommends against pregnant women traveling to any area with ongoing transmission of Zika virus. Women who are trying to become pregnant should consult with their healthcare provider prior to travel. Men who have a pregnant partner and have traveled to an area with Zika should use condoms or should avoid sex during the pregnancy. These recommendations might change as more data about the Zika virus become available.

ADDITIONAL CONCERNS FOR TRAVELING INDIVIDUALS

VENOUS THROMBOEMBOLISM PREVENTION

Travelers are at increased risk for deep vein thrombosis (DVT) and pulmonary embolism (PE) due to limited movement with long air travel. Wearing compression stockings during long trips reduces risk; these are sold in pharmacies. Travelers should be instructed to get up and walk and to perform lower leg exercises when sitting. Patients should know the symptoms of a DVT and PE and be instructed to seek immediate medical care if suspected. DVT risk factors, symptoms and treatment are discussed in the Anticoagulation chapter.

ALTITUDE SICKNESS AND MOTION SICKNESS

Acute mountain sickness (AMS) occurs when people climb rapidly to a high altitude. It occurs commonly above 8,000 feet and is more likely in individuals who live close to sea level and those who have had the condition previously. Symptoms include dizziness, headache, tachycardia and shortness of breath. The primary prophylactic medication is acetazolamide *(Diamox)* 125 mg twice daily, started the day before (preferred) or on the day of ascent. Higher doses are used for treatment. This can improve breathing, but is not without side effects (polyuria, taste alteration, risk of dehydration, photosensitivity, urticaria and a possibility of severe skin rashes). Acetazolamide is contraindicated with a sulfa allergy. Sun protection and hydration are recommended. In acute cases of altitude sickness, oxygen, inhaled beta-agonists and dexamethasone are given to reduce cerebral edema.

Motion sickness is common among travelers and is discussed in the Motion Sickness chapter.

THE RETURNED TRAVELER

It is imperative that travelers who are ill upon returning home see a healthcare provider. It is important for patients to communicate travel specifics to the healthcare provider, including the travel itinerary, the trip duration, accommodations (where they stayed), travel activities and any precautions that were taken to reduce infection risk, including vaccination history prior to leaving the U.S.

Some diseases have longer incubation periods and symptoms might not appear for weeks or months. Travelers often return home before their symptoms begin. This can lead to epidemics and the spread of disease from country to country. An example of this is the 2014 outbreak of Ebola virus in West Africa, the largest Ebola outbreak in history. Ebola is transmitted by direct contact with blood or bodily fluids of a symptomatic person. Symptoms (fever, headache, diarrhea, and hemorrhaging) can appear from 2 – 21 days after exposure. Due to the potentially long incubation, an infected person could be asymptomatic when returning to the U.S. and could spread the disease before a diagnosis is made. Isolation upon return can reduce transmission.

Another example of this is illustrated by the Zika outbreak discussed previously in this chapter. In 2015, the Zika virus was identified for the first time in the Western hemisphere with large outbreaks reported in Brazil. Since then, the virus has spread throughout much of the Americas and is still a concern for travelers, especially for those who are pregnant or are planning pregnancy in the near future.

Select Guidelines/References

Centers for Disease Control (CDC) Center on Travelers Health. Available at http://wwwnc.cdc.gov/travel (accessed 2019 Jan 15).

International Society of Travel Medicine (ISTM), Pharmacist Professional Group of the ISTM. Available at www.istm.org (accessed 2019 Jan 15).

Riddle MS, Connor BA, Beeching, NJ, et al. Guidelines for the prevention and treatment of travelers' diarrhea: a graded expert panel report. *J Travel Med* 2017; 24(Suppl 1):S63-S80.

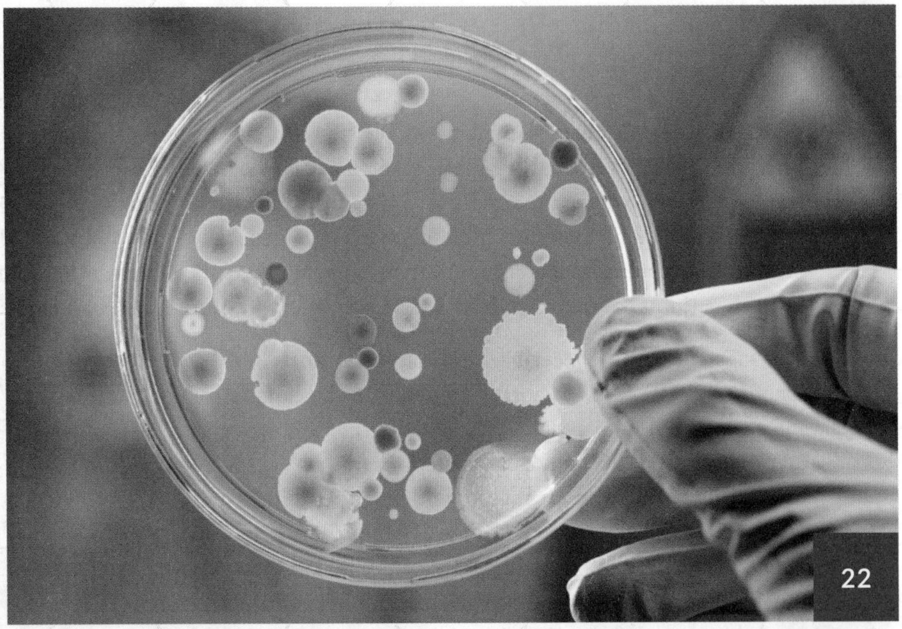

22

23

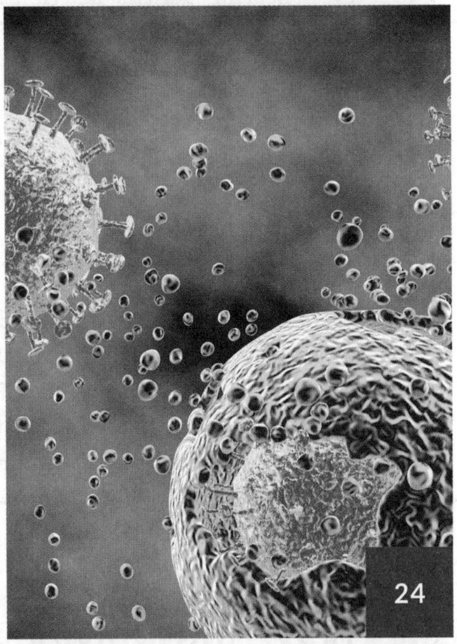

24

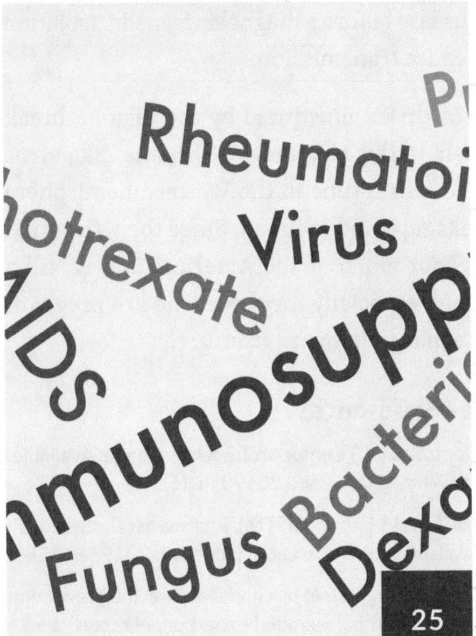

25

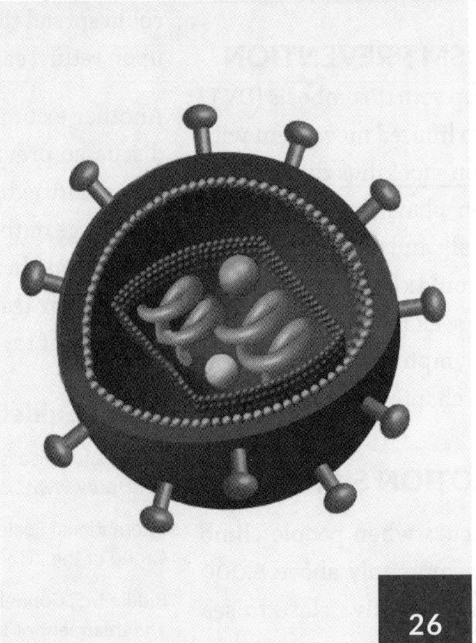

26

INFECTIOUS DISEASES

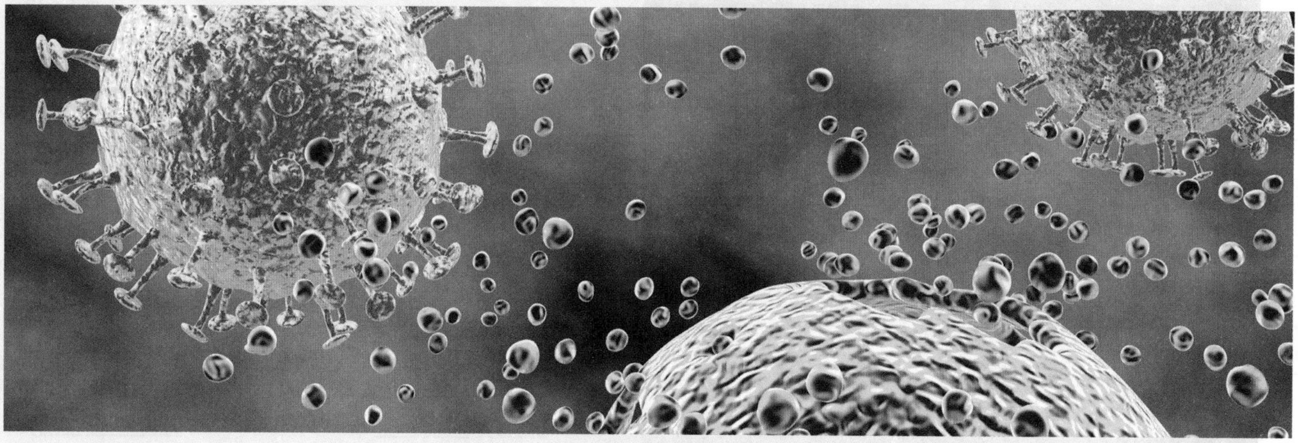

CONTENTS

CHAPTER 22
ID I: BACKGROUND & ANTIBACTERIALS BY DRUG CLASS | **342**

CHAPTER 23
ID II: BACTERIAL INFECTIONS | **375**

CHAPTER 24
ID III: ANTIFUNGALS & ANTIVIRALS | **398**

CHAPTER 25
ID IV: OPPORTUNISTIC INFECTIONS | **412**

CHAPTER 26
HUMAN IMMUNODEFICIENCY VIRUS | **415**

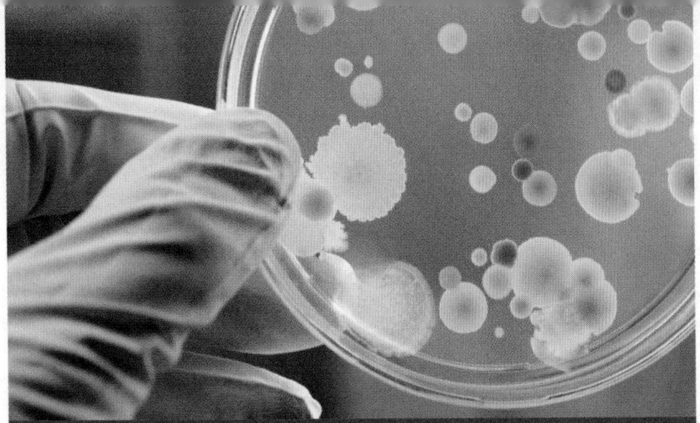

CHAPTER CONTENT

Background 342
How to Approach Infectious Diseases 342
Bacterial Organism Identification and Antibiotic Selection 343
Gram-Stain 343
Culture and Susceptibility 344
Antibiogram 345
Antibiotic Resistance 346
Common Resistant Pathogens ... 346
Collateral Damage: *Clostridium difficile* Infections 346
Antimicrobial Stewardship Programs 346
Antibiotic Mechanisms of Action .. 347
Antibiotic Pharmacokinetics and Pharmacodynamics 347
Hydrophilic and Lipophilic Drugs 347
Dose Optimization 348
Beta-Lactam Antibiotics 348
Penicillins 348
Key Features of Penicillins 350
Cephalosporins 350
Key Features of Cephalosporins 352
Carbapenems 353
Key Features of Carbapenems .. 353
Monobactam 354
Aztreonam 354
Spectrum of Activity Summary 354
Aminoglycosides 355
Aminoglycosides: Good News, Bad News 355
Traditional Dosing: Target Drug Concentrations 356
Extended Interval Dosing Nomogram 356
Quinolones 357
Key Features of Quinolones 358
Macrolides 358
Key Features of Macrolides 359
Tetracyclines 359
Key Features of Tetracyclines 360
Sulfonamides 360
Key Features of Sulfamethoxazole/Trimethoprim 361
Antibiotics for Gram+ Infections .. 361
Vancomycin 361
Lipoglycopeptides 362
Daptomycin 363
Oxazolidinones 363
Quinupristin/Dalfopristin 364
Tigecycline 364
Additional Broad-Spectrum Drugs 365
Polymyxins 365
Chloramphenicol 365
Miscellaneous Antibiotics 366
Clindamycin 366
Metronidazole and Related Drugs 366
Fidaxomicin 367
Rifaximin 367
Urinary Agents 368
Fosfomycin 368
Nitrofurantoin 368
Key Features of Nitrofurantoin 368
Topical Decolonization 368
Mupirocin Nasal Ointment 368
Summary Tables 369
Drugs of Choice/Active Drugs for Specific Pathogens 369
Storage Requirements: Liquid Oral Antibiotics 370
Storage Requirements: IV Antibiotics 370
Drug-Laboratory Interactions 370
Renal Dose Adjustments 370
No Renal Dose Adjustment Required 370
Special Requirements 371
Take With/Without Food 371
1:1 IV to Oral Dosing 371
Light Protection 371
Diluent Compatibility Requirements 371
Patient Counseling 372

CONTENT LEGEND

= Study Tip Gal
= Key Drug Guy

CHAPTER 22
INFECTIOUS DISEASES I: BACKGROUND & ANTIBACTERIALS BY DRUG CLASS

BACKGROUND

An infectious disease is caused by one or more pathogens [viruses, bacteria, fungi, protozoa, parasites and/or infectious proteins (prions)]. Infectious diseases (ID) are transmitted through various mechanisms, including physical contact with an infected individual or their body fluids, consuming contaminated food or water or by touching contaminated objects. Some conditions are transmitted by airborne inhalation and others are spread by a vector (carrier). Transmissible diseases that are spread from person to person are referred to as communicable or contagious.

HOW TO APPROACH INFECTIOUS DISEASES

ID is organized into four chapters: ID I covers the principles of infectious diseases and provides summaries of antibacterial drugs by class; ID II discusses treatment of specific bacterial infections; ID III reviews antifungals, antivirals and selected diseases; and ID IV examines prophylaxis and treatment of opportunistic infections in immunocompromised patients.

Three primary factors impact treatment decisions in infectious disease: the bug (pathogen), the drug (antibiotic) and the patient (host). Important patient-specific information includes medication allergies, immune function and chronic diseases that put a patient at risk for certain types of infections or require a change in the treatment approach (e.g., the presence of renal failure may require a change in the drug or the dose).

Do not be tempted to think of bugs, drugs and infectious diseases as separate sections to memorize. Tie together the infection, the typical pathogens involved and the antimicrobial spectrum of coverage as you progress through the chapters.

HOW DO I START?

- Recognize common organisms and groups of organisms
- Focus on resistant organisms and the drugs that treat them
- Learn the basic spectrum of coverage for antimicrobial classes
- Use bolded drugs, underlined information and Study Tip Gals to identify important points (think about how to assess the patient profile on the exam)

EXAM SCENARIO

When studying the carbapenems, think of how you would approach a case on the exam in which one of the answer choices is *Invanz* 1 gram IV Q24H. How can you decide if this is the best answer choice? Assess the following, using the underlined information in the carbapenems drug table:

- Allergies: if the patient has a penicillin allergy, there is likely a better answer choice because of the possibility of cross-reactivity.
- Culture and susceptibility: if the culture is growing ESBL-positive *E. coli*, ertapenem may be a good choice. If *Pseudomonas* is growing, you can rule out this answer choice, based on ertapenem's coverage.
- Past medical history and medication profile: if the patient has a history of seizures or takes a seizure drug, such as phenytoin, there is likely a better choice than a carbapenem, which has a risk of seizures.

BACTERIAL ORGANISM IDENTIFICATION AND ANTIBIOTIC SELECTION

GRAM-STAIN

Patient specimens (e.g., lung secretions, urine, blood, tissue from a wound or fluid from an abscess) are taken from the infection site and sent to the microbiology lab. The first step in bacterial identification is the Gram stain. Bacteria stain differently based on the composition of their cell wall.

- Gram-positive organisms: have a thick cell wall and stain dark purple or bluish from the crystal violet stain.
- Gram-negative organisms: have a thin cell wall and take up the safranin counterstain, resulting in a pink or reddish color.
- Atypical organisms: do not have a cell wall and do not stain well.

The Gram stain outlines the organism, so it can be categorized by shape (or morphology). Gram stain results (e.g., Gram-positive cocci in pairs) can help determine the appropriate empiric antibiotic regimen, which is based on a best-guess of the likely organism/s causing the infection. Empiric treatment is usually broad-spectrum, which means it covers several different types of bacteria. After identification of the organism (see the Culture and Susceptibility section), antibiotic streamlining occurs, which is the process of converting from a broad-spectrum regimen to a treatment that is targeted to the organism (narrow- spectrum).

The figure below is designed to provide a framework to classify the organisms by their Gram-stain description and shape, and can serve as a reference as you review the coverage of specific antibiotics.

Selected Bacterial Organisms

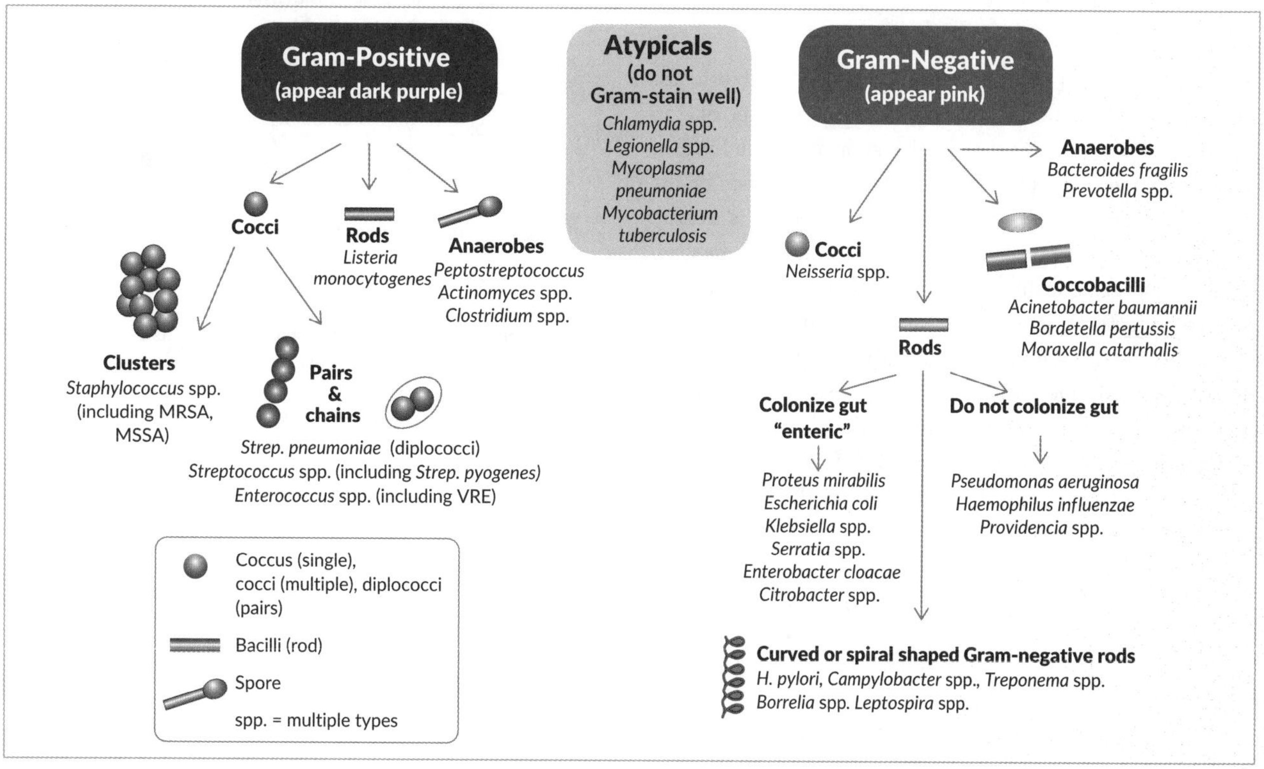

MSSA = methicillin-susceptible Staphylococcus aureus; MRSA = methicillin-resistant Staphylococcus aureus; CA-MRSA = community-associated methicillin-resistant Staphylococcus aureus; VRE = vancomycin-resistant Enterococcus

Common groups of organisms: PEK = Proteus, E. coli, Klebsiella; HNPEK = Haemophilus, Neisseria, Proteus, E. coli, Klebsiella; CAPES = Citrobacter, Acinetobacter, Providencia, Enterobacter, Serratia; mouth flora (anaerobes) = Peptostreptococcus, Actinomyces

CULTURE AND SUSCEPTIBILITY

The microbiology lab uses various methods to determine exactly which organism is present; for example, some Gram-negative bacteria (e.g., *E. coli*) break down lactose (a sugar) in a unique way and some do not (e.g., *Pseudomonas*). Lactose can be used to help determine the types of bacteria that may be present.

Once the organism has been identified, susceptibility testing is performed to determine which antibiotics are useful for treatment. The bacteria is cultured (grown on an agar plate), and is then exposed to varying concentrations of select drugs. The lab identifies the minimum inhibitory concentration (MIC) and compares it to the susceptibility breakpoint, which is the usual drug concentration that inhibits bacterial growth [and is determined by the Clinical & Laboratory Standards Institute (CLSI)]. An interpretation is made as to which drugs inhibit growth (and at what concentration) and which drugs do not (see the table to the right).

A report of susceptible (S), sometimes called sensitive, means that the drug inhibits the organism and is likely an effective treatment option. Drugs listed as intermediate (I) may be effective under specific circumstances (e.g., higher doses, extended infusions), but usually would not be selected over a drug that is reported as susceptible. Resistant (R) means the drug is unlikely to be effective and is not a treatment option. An example of a culture and susceptibility (C & S) report is shown on the following page.

Synergy

An infection could require more than one antibiotic for successful treatment. The effect of two antibiotics can be additive (an effect equal to the sum of the individual drugs) or synergistic (an effect greater than the sum of the individual drugs). In certain infections, synergy is useful. For example, aminoglycosides and beta-lactams can be used together synergistically to treat certain invasive Gram-positive infections (e.g., infective endocarditis); the beta-lactam allows the aminoglycoside to reach its intracellular target (the ribosome), where it causes lethal damage to the bacteria. Without the beta-lactam, aminoglycosides cannot penetrate the cell wall at safe doses. This synergy permits a lower dose of aminoglycoside and clears the bloodstream infection more quickly.

SELECTING AN ANTIBIOTIC USING THE BREAKPOINT AND MIC

- The minimum inhibitory concentration (MIC) is used to determine if the organism is susceptible (S), intermediate (I) or resistant (R) to the antibiotics tested.
- MICs are specific to each antibiotic and organism and should not be compared among different antibiotics.

STEPS:

Identify the organism causing the infection

1. The specimen is collected from a patient (e.g., from a wound, urine, blood, sputum).
2. A Gram-stain is performed, then the organism is grown in a culture and identified.

Susceptibility testing

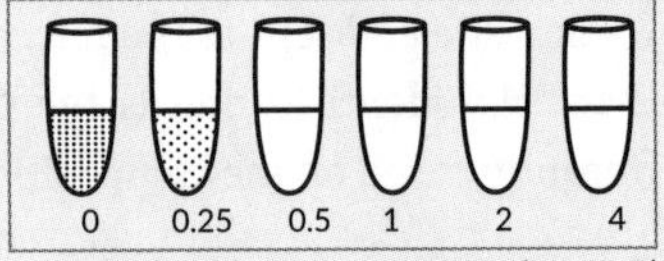

Antibiotic concentration (mcg/mL)

1. The bacteria (from the patient specimen) is added to antibiotic solutions of increasing concentrations.*
2. The solutions are incubated and observed for visible growth (solutions with bacteria will be turbid or cloudy).
3. The lowest concentration with no growth (clear) is the MIC.
4. The MIC (determined by the lab) is compared to the breakpoint (from CLSI).
5. If the MIC is ≤ the breakpoint, the bacteria is susceptible to the antibiotic and it can be used.**

Example

A sputum culture is taken from a female patient with pneumonia. The Gram-stain reveals Gram-positive diplococci and the culture is positive for *S. pneumoniae*.

S. pneumoniae (from the patient) is tested with increasing ceftriaxone concentrations (mcg/mL).

Susceptible	MIC	Breakpoint	Intermediate	Resistant
0.25	(0.5)	(1)	2	4
Ceftriaxone concentrations (doubling) →				

Interpretation: the MIC was 0.5 mcg/mL. It is susceptible (S), as it falls below the breakpoint (1 mcg/mL). A *S. pneumoniae* with an MIC = 2 mcg/mL would be considered intermediate. If the MIC was ≥ 4 mcg/mL, it would be resistant.

*There are other methods of susceptibility testing; this describes broth dilution.

**The antibiotic must penetrate the infection site and the drug must be appropriate for the patient (e.g., not allergic, no contraindications).

Selecting Treatment

Refer to the sample C & S report to the right to see how the MIC and interpretation are used when selecting an antibiotic. The goal is to pick a susceptible drug with a narrow spectrum. Recall that the MIC is specific to each antibiotic and organism and should not be compared among different antibiotics. While meropenem has the lowest MIC and is susceptible (i.e., it would treat the infection), it is the broadest-spectrum antibiotic and should not be selected.

In addition to the susceptibility interpretation and the MIC, the choice of antibiotic depends on the site of infection, plus patient-specific characteristics and cost (e.g., for the C & S report shown, nitrofurantoin or a first-generation cephalosporin might be good choices if the patient has no allergies and normal renal function).

ANTIBIOGRAM

An antibiogram combines the C & S data from individual patients at an institution into one chart (such as all Gram-positive organisms cultured at that hospital). This provides the susceptibility patterns at the hospital over a specific time period (generally 1 year). On the left side, the bacteria are listed. Along the top, the drugs are listed, and below is the percent susceptibility of each organism to that drug.

Antibiograms aid in selecting empiric treatment (for example, if a patient has a Gram-positive cocci lung infection, a drug with a high percentage of susceptibility for the likely organism can be chosen from the antibiogram). Antibiograms are used to monitor resistance trends over time.

Sample Culture and Susceptibility Report

BACTERIA
MICRO NUMBER: 053098898
TEST STATUS: FINAL
SPECIMEN SOURCE: URINE
SPECIMEN COMMENTS: AMBER, CLOUDY
RESULT: 100,000 CFU/ML E. COLI

DRUG	MIC INTERPRETATION	MIC (mg/L)
Ampicillin	R	> 32
Ampicillin/Sulbactam	S	< 2
Cefazolin-UTI	S	< 16
Cefepime	S	< 1
Ceftriaxone	S	< 1
Ciprofloxacin	S	1
Gentamicin	S	< 1
Piperacillin/Tazobactam	S	< 4
Meropenem	S	< 0.25
Nitrofurantoin	S	< 32
Tobramycin	S	< 1
Sulfamethoxazole/ Trimethoprim	R	> 76/4

S = Susceptible I = Intermediate R = Resistant

CASE EXAMPLE

A 77-year-old female is admitted to the ICU from home with confusion, cough, temperature = 101.9°F, respiratory rate = 32 breaths per minute and oxygen saturation = 88% on room air. Her chest X-ray is consistent with pneumonia and a sputum Gram stain shows Gram-positive cocci in pairs. The pharmacist is asked to choose a beta-lactam (in addition to azithromycin) for empiric treatment. After reviewing the institutional antibiogram (see example), the pharmacist recommends ceftriaxone. Local susceptibility patterns are consistent with national guidelines, showing that third generation cephalosporins are highly active against the likely pathogen (*S. pneumoniae*).

Hospital Antibiogram Example (Abridged)

JANUARY-DECEMBER	# OF ISOLATES	PENICILLIN	OXACILLIN	AMPICILLIN	CEFTRIAXONE	CLINDAMYCIN	ERYTHROMYCIN	GENTAMICIN	LEVOFLOXACIN	LINEZOLID	TETRACYCLINE	SMX/TMP	VANCOMYCIN
Gram-Positive Organisms (All Isolates)		REPORTED AS % SUSCEPTIBLE											
Staphylococcus aureus	1360												
MSSA	830	–	100	–	–	88	78	98§	87	100	93	98	100
MRSA	530	–	–	–	–	78	10	92§	15	100	93	92	100
Streptococcus pneumoniae	42	91* 83**	–	–	100* 92**	–	79	–	97	–	85	80	100
Enterococcus spp.	663	–	–	93	–	–	–	69§	–	99	–	–	100
Enterococcus faecalis	99	–	–	98	–	–	–	62§	–	99	–	–	87
Enterococcus faecium	164	–	–	10	–	–	–	90§	100	99	–	–	15
Urine Isolates													
Enterococcus spp.	153	–	–	79	–	–	–	–	61	100	–	–	81

*Non-meningitis; **Meningitis; §Synergy only

ANTIBIOTIC RESISTANCE

Antibiotic resistance is the ability of an organism to multiply in the presence of a drug that normally limits its growth or kills it. The CDC estimates that there are ~2,000,000 infections a year where the causative organism is resistant to the usual treatment. These infections are difficult to treat and often require drugs that are costly and/or toxic.

Common mechanisms of resistance include:

- Intrinsic resistance: the resistance is natural to the organism. For example, *E. coli* is resistant to vancomycin because this antibiotic is too large to penetrate the bacterial cell wall of *E. coli*.
- Selection pressure: resistance occurs when antibiotics kill off susceptible bacteria, leaving behind more resistant strains to multiply. For example, normal GI flora includes *Enterococcus*. When antibiotics (e.g., vancomycin) eliminate susceptible *Enterococci*, vancomycin-resistant *enterococcus* (VRE) can become predominant.
- Enzyme inactivation: enzymes produced by bacteria break down the antibiotic.
  - Bacteria that produce beta-lactamases break down beta-lactams (e.g., penicillins) before they can bind to their site of activity. Beta-lactamase inhibitors (clavulanate, sulbactam, tazobactam, avibactam) are combined with some beta-lactams to preserve or increase their spectrum of activity.
  - Extended-spectrum beta-lactamases (ESBLs) are beta-lactamases that can break down all penicillins and most cephalosporins. Organisms that produce ESBLs can be difficult to kill, and serious infections involving these organisms are treated with carbapenems or newer cephalosporin/beta-lactamase inhibitors.
  - Carbapenem-resistant *Enterobacteriaceae* (CRE) are multidrug-resistant (MDR) Gram-negative organisms (e.g., *Klebsiella* spp., *E. coli)* that produce enzymes (e.g., carbapenemase) capable of breaking down penicillins, most cephalosporins and carbapenems. CRE infections typically require treatment with a combination of antibiotics that include drugs such as the polymyxins, an older drug class with high risk for toxicities (see the Polymyxins drug table). Newer, costly drugs, such as ceftazidime/avibactam *(Avycaz)* are also used.

COMMON RESISTANT PATHOGENS

Klebsiella pneumoniae (ESBL, CRE)
Escherichia coli, (ESBL, CRE)
Acinetobacter baumannii
Enterococcus faecalis, Enterococcus faecium (VRE)
Staphylococcus aureus (MRSA)
Pseudomonas aeruginosa
Remember: **K**ill **E**ach **A**nd **E**very **S**trong **P**athogen

ESBL = extended-spectrum beta-lactamase
CRE = carbapenem-resistant Enterobacteriaceae
VRE = vancomycin-resistant Enterococcus

COLLATERAL DAMAGE: *CLOSTRIDIUM DIFFICILE* INFECTIONS

Collateral damage refers to the unintended consequences of antibiotic use. Antibiotics kill normal, healthy GI flora along with the pathogens they are targeting. This results in overgrowth of organisms that are resistant to the drug and can lead to superinfections, such as *C. difficile* infections (CDI). Inactive *C. difficile* spores are present in normal GI flora. When an antibiotic kills off the normal flora, *C. difficile* spores can become activated and infectious.

Activated spores produce toxins that inflame the GI mucosa. Symptoms can be mild (loose stools and abdominal cramping) to severe (pseudomembranous colitis that can require colonectomy and can be fatal). In recent years, *C. difficile* infections have become more common, more severe and more difficult to treat. All antibiotics have a warning for the risk of CDI. Certain antibiotic classes are associated with a high risk for CDI, such as clindamycin, which has a boxed warning. When appropriate, antibiotic treatments are streamlined or discontinued to reduce CDI risk.

ANTIMICROBIAL STEWARDSHIP PROGRAMS

Antimicrobial stewardship programs (ASPs) involve efforts to 1) improve patient safety and outcomes, 2) curb resistance, 3) reduce adverse effects and 4) promote cost-effectiveness.

ASPs consist of collaborative teams of ID physicians, ID pharmacists and personnel from the microbiology lab, infection prevention and control and information technology departments. ASPs use guidelines, along with local antibiogram data, to establish antibiotic guidance for their facility. Most ASPs conduct audits of prescribing habits and provide education to change suboptimal prescribing habits and improve care.

Examples of ASP interventions are 1) pharmacokinetic monitoring of aminoglycosides and vancomycin to optimize doses and minimize toxicities, 2) rapid identification of pathogens, and shortened time to starting effective treatment, through use of specialized computer software (e.g., clinical decision support programs) that integrate rapid diagnostic test results with patient information, 3) preauthorization of select antimicrobials and 4) timely transitions from IV to PO antibiotics.

ANTIBIOTIC MECHANISMS OF ACTION

Knowledge of the mechanism of action (MOA) can help distinguish what types of organisms can be treated with a given antibiotic. The major targets of antibacterials are outlined in the following diagram.

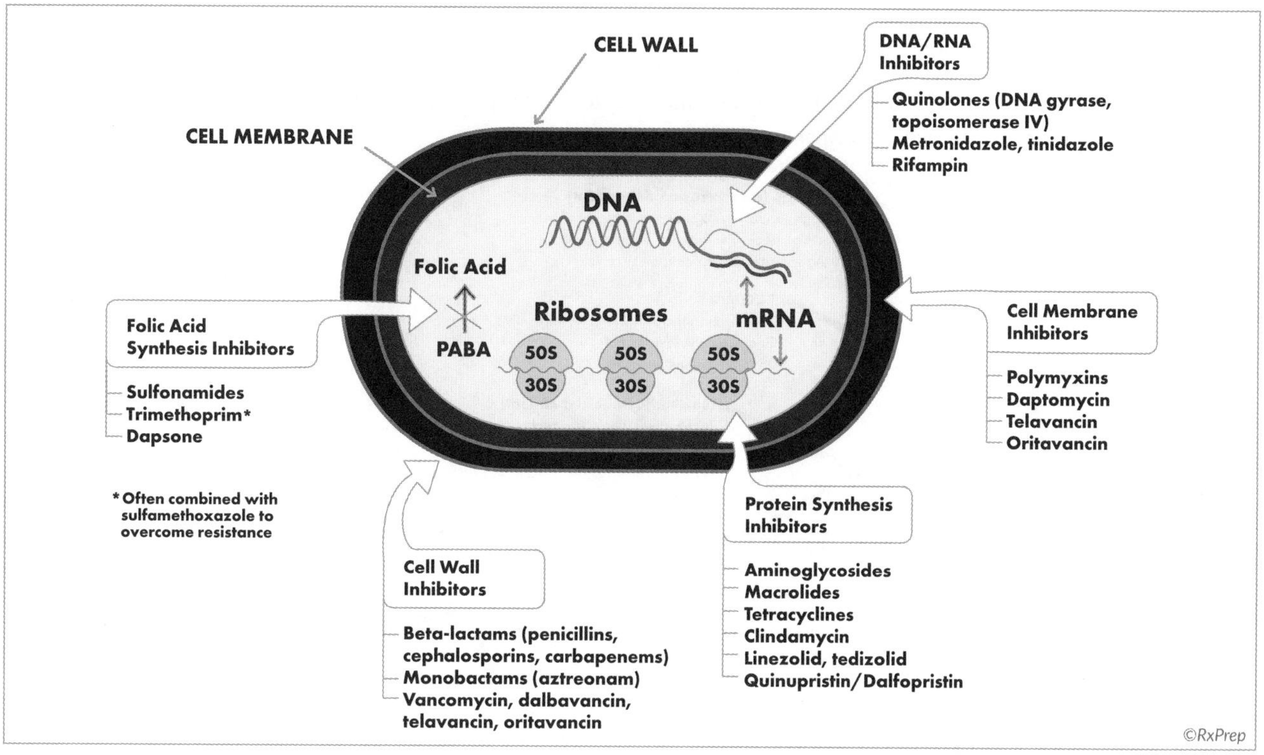

ANTIBIOTIC PHARMACOKINETICS AND PHARMACODYNAMICS

Appropriate selection of an antibiotic regimen requires an understanding of the pharmacokinetic (PK) principles of antibiotics (absorption, distribution, metabolism and excretion – refer to the Pharmacokinetics chapter) and the pharmacodynamic principles of antibiotics (concentration-dependent or time-dependent killing).

HYDROPHILIC AND LIPOPHILIC DRUGS

Hydrophilicity or lipophilicity of the antibiotic can be used to predict a number of PK parameters (see the figure below).

HYDROPHILIC AGENTS	
Beta-lactams Aminoglycosides Glycopeptides Daptomycin Polymyxins	1) Small volume of distribution → Poor tissue penetration 2) Renal elimination → Nephrotoxicity or accumulation of drug 3) Low intracellular concentrations → Not active against atypical (intracellular) pathogens 4) Increased clearance and/or distribution in sepsis → Consider loading doses and aggressive dosing in sepsis 5) Poor-moderate bioavailability → Not used PO or IV:PO ratio is not 1:1

LIPOPHILIC AGENTS	
Quinolones Macrolides Rifampin Linezolid Tetracyclines	1) Large volume of distribution → Excellent tissue penetration— including bone, lung and brain tissues. 2) Hepatic metabolism → Hepatotoxicity and DDI 3) Achieve intracellular concentrations → Active against atypical (intracellular) pathogens 4) Clearance/distribution is changed minimally in sepsis → Dose adjustments generally not needed in sepsis 5) Excellent bioavailability → IV:PO ratio is often 1:1

PO = oral, IV = intravenous, DDI = drug-drug interactions

DOSE OPTIMIZATION

The pharmacodynamics of select antibiotics are displayed in the figure below. Drugs with concentration-dependent killing (such as aminoglycosides) can be dosed less frequently and in higher doses to maximize the concentration above the MIC. Drugs with time-dependent killing (such as beta-lactams) can be dosed more frequently or administered for a longer duration to maximize the time above the MIC. Examples include extending the infusion time of beta-lactam antibiotics (e.g. from 30 minutes to 4 hours) or administering the drug as a continuous infusion. Studies have documented that extended/continuous infusions of beta-lactams reduce hospital length of stay, mortality and costs, particularly when treating pneumonia caused by MDR Gram-negative pathogens like *Pseudomonas*.

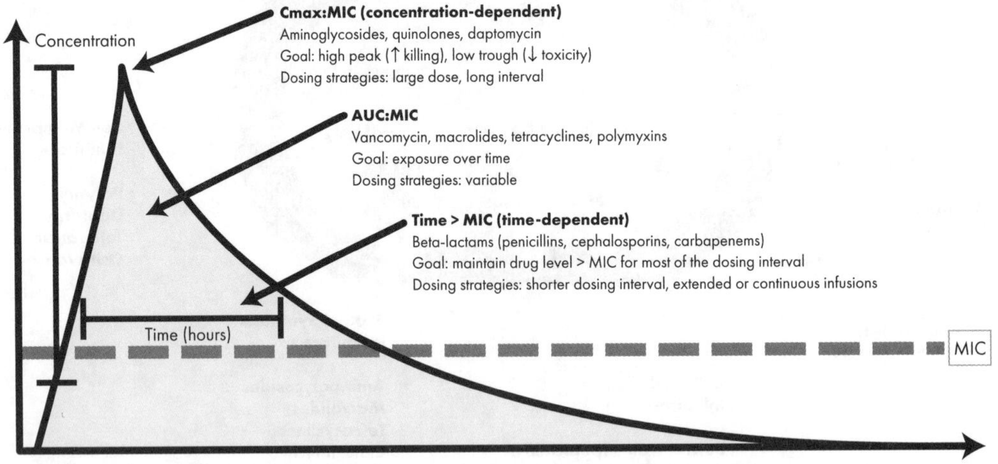

AUC = area under the concentration-time curve, Cmax = maximum plasma concentration, MIC = minimum inhibitory concentration

BETA-LACTAM ANTIBIOTICS

Beta-lactam antibiotics (penicillins, cephalosporins and carbapenems) have a chemical structure that is characterized by a beta-lactam ring. They inhibit bacterial cell wall synthesis by binding to penicillin-binding proteins (PBPs). This prevents the final step of peptidoglycan synthesis in bacterial cell walls. Refer to the Learning Basic Science Concepts chapter for details.

PENICILLINS

Coverage varies by subgroup, or type, of penicillin. As a class, they are not active against MRSA or atypical organisms.

- Natural penicillins are active against Gram-positive cocci *(Streptococci* and *Enterococci*; they do not cover *Staphylococci)* and Gram-positive anaerobes (mouth flora). They have little Gram-negative activity.
- Aminopenicillins cover *Streptococci, Enterococci* and Gram-positive anaerobes (mouth flora) plus (with the addition of the amino group) the Gram-negative bacteria *Haemophilus, Neisseria, Proteus, E. coli* and *Klebsiella* (HNPEK).
  - Aminopenicillins combined with beta-lactamase inhibitors (clavulanate, sulbactam and tazobactam) have added activity against MSSA, more resistant strains of Gram-negative bacteria (HNPEK) and Gram-negative anaerobes *(B. fragilis)*.
- Extended-spectrum penicillins, combined with a beta-lactamase inhibitor (e.g., piperacillin/tazobactam), have broad-spectrum activity. They cover the same organisms as aminopenicillin/beta-lactamase inhibitor combinations [Gram-positive bacteria *(Streptococci,* MSSA, *Enterococci)*, Gram-positive anaerobes (mouth flora), more resistant strains of HNPEK, Gram-negative anaerobes *(B. fragilis)*] plus have expanded coverage of other Gram-negative bacteria, including *Citrobacter, Acinetobacter, Providencia, Enterobacter, Serratia* (CAPES) and *Pseudomonas aeruginosa*.
- Antistaphylococcal penicillins cover *Streptococci* and have enhanced activity against methicillin-susceptible *Staphylococcus aureus* (MSSA), but they lack activity against *Enterococcus*, Gram-negative pathogens and anaerobes.

Select Penicillins

DRUG	DOSING
Natural Penicillins	
Penicillin V Potassium *(Pen VK*)* Tablet, suspension	PO: 125-500 mg Q6-12H on an empty stomach
Penicillin G Aqueous *(Pfizerpen-G)* Injection	IV: 2-4 million units Q4-6H
Penicillin G Benzathine *(Bicillin L-A)* Penicillin G Benzathine and Penicillin G Procaine *(Bicillin C-R)*	IM: 1.2-2.4 million units x 1 (frequency varies)
Aminopenicillins	
Amoxicillin *(Moxatag*)* Tablet, capsule, chewable, suspension	PO: dosing varies with formulation; 24-hr ER tablet is taken once daily
Amoxicillin/Clavulanate *(Augmentin*, *Augmentin ES-600)* Tablet, chewable, suspension	PO: dosing varies with formulation; XR tablet is taken Q12H with food
Ampicillin Injection, capsule, suspension	PO: 250-500 mg Q6H on an empty stomach 1 hr before or 2 hrs after meals IV/IM: 1-2 grams Q4-6H
Ampicillin/Sulbactam *(Unasyn)* Injection	IV: 1.5-3 grams Q6H
Extended-Spectrum Penicillins	
Piperacillin/Tazobactam *(Zosyn)* Injection	IV: 3.375 grams Q6H or 4.5 grams Q6-8H Prolonged or extended infusions: 3.375-4.5 grams IV Q8H (each dose infused over 4 hours)
Antistaphylococcal Penicillins	
Dicloxacillin Capsule	PO: 125-500 mg Q6H
Nafcillin Injection	IV/IM: 1-2 grams Q4-6H
Oxacillin Injection	IV: 250-2,000 mg Q4-6H

SAFETY/SIDE EFFECTS/MONITORING

BOXED WARNING

Penicillin G benzathine: not for IV use; can cause cardio-respiratory arrest and death

CONTRAINDICATIONS

Augmentin and *Unasyn:* history of cholestatic jaundice or hepatic dysfunction associated with previous use

Severe renal impairment (CrCl < 30 mL/min): do not use extended-release oral forms of amoxicillin and amoxicillin/clavulanate *(Augmentin XR)*, or 875 mg strength of amoxicillin/clavulanate

SIDE EFFECTS

Seizures (with accumulation), GI upset, diarrhea, rash (including SJS/TEN)/allergic reactions/anaphylaxis, hemolytic anemia, renal failure, myelosuppression with prolonged use, ↑ LFTs

MONITORING

Renal function, symptoms of anaphylaxis with 1st dose, CBC and LFTs with prolonged courses

NOTES

Aminopenicillins

Ampicillin PO is rarely used due to poor bioavailability; amoxicillin is preferred if switching from IV ampicillin

Amoxicillin/clavulanate: use a 14:1 ratio to ↓ diarrhea caused by the clavulanate component

IV ampicillin and ampicillin/sulbactam must be diluted in NS only

Extended-Spectrum Penicillins

Piperacillin/tazobactam contains 65 mg Na per 1 gram of piperacillin

Antistaphylococcal Penicillins

Preferred for MSSA soft tissue, bone and joint, endocarditis and bloodstream infections

No renal dose adjustments

Nafcillin is a vesicant – administration through a central line is preferred; if extravasation occurs, use cold packs and hyaluronidase injections

**Brand discontinued but name still used in practice.*

See lab interactions, storage requirements and renal dosage information near the end of this chapter.

Penicillin Drug Interactions

- Probenecid can ↑ the levels of beta-lactams by interfering with renal excretion. This combination is sometimes used intentionally in severe infections to ↑ antibiotic levels.
- Beta-lactams (except nafcillin and dicloxacillin) can enhance the anticoagulant effect of warfarin by inhibiting the production of vitamin K-dependent clotting factors.
- Penicillins can ↑ the serum concentration of methotrexate; they can ↓ the serum concentration of mycophenolate active metabolites due to impaired enterohepatic recirculation.

KEY FEATURES OF PENICILLINS

CLASS EFFECTS

- All penicillins should be avoided in patients with a beta-lactam allergy (exception: pregnant patients with syphilis)
- All penicillins increase the risk of seizures if accumulation occurs (e.g., with renal failure)

OUTPATIENT (ORAL)

Penicillin VK

- A first-line treatment for strep throat and mild nonpurulent skin infections (no abscess)

Amoxicillin *(Moxatag)*

- First-line treatment for acute otitis media (80-90 mg/kg/day)
- Drug of choice for infective endocarditis prophylaxis before dental procedures (2 grams PO x 1, 30-60 minutes before procedure)
- Used in *H. pylori* treatment*

Amoxicillin/Clavulanate *(Augmentin)*

- First-line treatment for acute otitis media (90 mg/kg/day) and for sinus infections (if an antibiotic is indicated)
- Use the lowest dose of clavulanate to ↓ diarrhea

INPATIENT (PARENTERAL)

Penicillin G Benzathine *(Bicillin L-A)*

- Drug of choice for syphilis (2.4 million units IM x1)
- Not for IV use; can cause death

Piperacillin/Tazobactam *(Zosyn)*

- Only penicillin active against *Pseudomonas*
- Extended infusions (4 hours) can be used to maximize T > MIC

Nafcillin, Oxacillin and Dicloxacillin

- Cover MSSA only (no MRSA)
- No renal dose adjustment needed

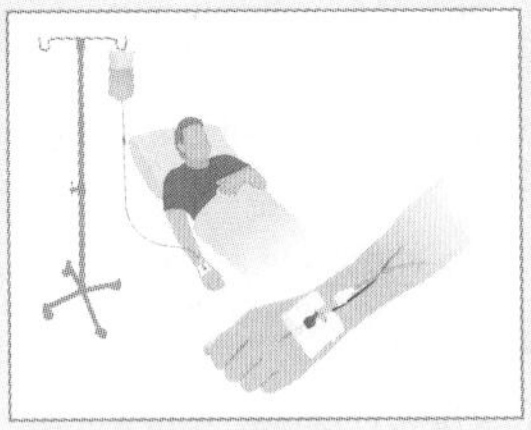

**See the Gastroesophageal Reflux Disease & Peptic Ulcer Disease chapter*

CEPHALOSPORINS

Coverage varies by cephalosporin generation. As a class, they are not active against *Enterococcus* spp. or atypical organisms.

- First generation: excellent coverage of Gram-positive cocci (e.g., *Streptococci* and *Staphylococci)* and preferred when a cephalosporin is used for MSSA infections. They have some activity against the Gram-negative rods *Proteus, E. coli* and *Klebsiella* (PEK), but in general, Gram-negative activity is decreased compared to 2nd, 3rd and 4th generation cephalosporins.
- Second generation: there are two types. Drugs such as cefuroxime cover *Staphylococci*, more resistant strains of *S. pneumoniae* plus *Haemophilus, Neisseria, Proteus, E. coli* and *Klebsiella* (HNPEK). Cefotetan and cefoxitin have added coverage of Gram-negative anaerobes *(B. fragilis)*.
- Third generation: there are two groups.
  - Group 1: includes ceftriaxone, cefotaxime and oral drugs, which cover more resistant *Streptococci* (*S. pneumoniae* and viridans group *Streptococci)*, *Staphylococci* (MSSA), Gram-positive anaerobes (mouth flora) and more resistant strains of HNPEK.
  - Group 2: includes ceftazidime, which lacks Gram-positive activity but covers *Pseudomonas*, and the newer beta-lactamase inhibitor combinations, ceftazidime/avibactam and ceftolozane/tazobactam, which have added activity against MDR *Pseudomonas* and other MDR Gram-negative rods.
- Fourth generation: only includes cefepime, which has broad Gram-negative activity (HNPEK, CAPES and *Pseudomonas)*, and Gram-positive activity similar to ceftriaxone.
- Fifth generation: only includes ceftaroline, which has Gram-negative activity similar to ceftriaxone, but broad Gram-positive activity; it is the only beta-lactam that covers MRSA.

DRUG	DOSING	SAFETY/SIDE EFFECTS/MONITORING
1st Generation		**CONTRAINDICATIONS** Ceftriaxone: hyperbilirubinemic neonates (causes biliary sludging, kernicterus); concurrent use with calcium-containing IV products in neonates ≤ 28 days old **WARNINGS** Anaphylaxis/hypersensitivity reactions Some drugs can ↑ INR in patients taking warfarin Cross sensitivity (< 10%) with PCN allergy – do not use in patients who have a type 1 PCN allergy (swelling, angioedema, anaphylaxis) Cefotetan contains a side chain [N-methylthiotetrazole (NMTT or 1-MTT)] which can ↑ the risk of bleeding and cause a disulfiram-like reaction with alcohol ingestion **SIDE EFFECTS** Seizures (with accumulation), GI upset, diarrhea, rash/allergic reactions/anaphylaxis, acute interstitial nephritis, myelosuppression with prolonged use, ↑ LFTs, drug fever, serious skin reactions (SJS/TEN) **MONITORING** Renal function, signs of anaphylaxis with 1st dose, CBC, LFTs **NOTES** Ceftriaxone – no renal adjustment Cefixime available in a chewable tablet Ceftazidime/avibactam covers some carbapenem-resistant *Enterobacteriaceae* (CRE)
Cefazolin (*Ancef**)	IV/IM: 1-1.5 grams Q8H	
Cephalexin ***(Keflex)***	PO: 250-500 mg Q6-12H	
Cefadroxil	PO: 1-2 grams Q12-24H	
2nd Generation		
Cefuroxime (*Ceftin**)	PO/IV/IM: 250-1,500 mg Q8-12H	
Cefotetan ***(Cefotan)***	IV/IM: 1-2 grams Q12H	
Cefaclor	PO: 250-500 mg Q8H	
Cefoxitin	IV/IM: 1-2 grams Q6-8H	
Cefprozil	PO: 250-500 mg Q12-24H	
3rd Generation Group 1		
Cefdinir (*Omnicef**)	PO: 300 mg Q12H or 600 mg daily	
Ceftriaxone (*Rocephin**)	IV/IM: 1-2 grams Q12-24H	
Cefotaxime	IV/IM: 1-2 grams Q4-12H	
Cefditoren (*Spectracef*)	PO: 200-400 mg Q12H with food	
Cefixime (*Suprax*)	PO: 400 mg divided Q12-24H	
Cefpodoxime	PO: 100-400 mg Q12H	
Ceftibuten	PO: 400 mg daily on an empty stomach	
3rd Generation Group 2		
Ceftazidime ***(Fortaz,*** *Tazicef*)	IV/IM: 1-2 grams Q8-12H	
Ceftazidime/Avibactam (*Avycaz*)	IV: 2.5 grams Q8H	
Ceftolozane /Tazobactam (*Zerbaxa*)	IV: 1.5 gram Q8H	
4th Generation		
Cefepime ***(Maxipime)***	IV/IM: 1-2 grams Q8-12H	
5th Generation		
Ceftaroline fosamil ***(Teflaro)***	IV: 600 mg Q12H	

**Brand discontinued but name still used in practice.*
See lab interactions, storage requirements and renal dosage information near the end of this chapter.

Cephalosporin Drug Interactions

- Drugs that decrease stomach acid can decrease the bioavailability of some cephalosporins. Cefuroxime, cefpodoxime, cefdinir and cefditoren should be separated by two hours from short-acting antacids. H2RAs and PPIs should be avoided.

KEY FEATURES OF CEPHALOSPORINS

CLASS EFFECTS

- Due to a small risk (< 10%) of cross-reactivity, do not choose a cephalosporin on the exam if the patient has a penicillin allergy (exception: pediatric patients with acute otitis media)
- Risk of seizures if accumulation occurs (e.g., with renal failure)

OUTPATIENT (ORAL)

1st Generation: Cephalexin *(Keflex)*

- Common uses: skin infections (MSSA), strep throat

2nd Generation: Cefuroxime

- Common uses: acute otitis media, community-acquired pneumonia (CAP), sinus infection (if an antibiotic is indicated)

3rd Generation: Cefdinir

- Common uses: CAP, sinus infection (if an antibiotic is indicated)

INPATIENT (PARENTERAL)

1st Generation: Cefazolin

- Common use: surgical prophylaxis

2nd Generation: Cefotetan and Cefoxitin

- Anaerobic coverage *(B. fragilis)*
- Common use: surgical prophylaxis (colorectal procedures)
- Cefotetan can cause a disulfiram-like reaction with alcohol ingestion

3rd Generation: Ceftriaxone and Cefotaxime

- Common uses: CAP, meningitis, spontaneous bacterial peritonitis, pyelonephritis
- Ceftriaxone
  - No renal dose adjustment
  - Do not use ceftriaxone in neonates (age 0-28 days)

Ceftazidime (3rd Generation) and Cefepime (4th Generation)

- Active against *Pseudomonas*

Ceftolozane/Tazobactam and Ceftazidime/Avibactam

- Used for MDR Gram-negative organisms (including *Pseudomonas)*

Ceftaroline

- Only beta-lactam active against MRSA

CARBAPENEMS

Carbapenems are very broad-spectrum antibiotics that are generally reserved for MDR Gram-negative infections. They are active against most Gram-positive, Gram-negative (including ESBL-producing bacteria) and anaerobic pathogens. They provide no coverage of atypical pathogens, MRSA, VRE, *C. difficile* and *Stenotrophomonas*.

Ertapenem is different from other carbapenems as it has no activity against *Pseudomonas, Acinetobacter* or *Enterococcus*.

DRUG	DOSING	SAFETY/SIDE EFFECTS/MONITORING
Doripenem Injection	IV: 500 mg Q8H CrCl ≤ 50 mL/min: dose adjustment required	**CONTRAINDICATIONS** Anaphylactic reactions to beta-lactam antibiotics **WARNINGS** CNS adverse effects, including states of confusion and seizures Doripenem: do not use for the treatment of pneumonia, including healthcare-associated pneumonia (HAP) and ventilator-associated pneumonia (VAP) Do not use in patients with PCN allergy; cross-reactivity has been reported to be as high as 50%, but more recent studies show rates < 10% **SIDE EFFECTS** Diarrhea, rash/severe skin reaction (DRESS), seizures with higher doses and in patients with impaired renal function (mainly imipenem), bone marrow suppression with prolonged use, ↑ LFTs **MONITORING** Renal function, symptoms of anaphylaxis with 1st dose, CBC, LFTs **NOTES** Imipenem is combined with cilastatin to prevent drug degradation by renal tubular dehydropeptidase
Imipenem/Cilastatin *(Primaxin I.V.)* Injection	IV: 250-1,000 mg Q6-8H CrCl ≤ 70 mL/min: dose adjustment required	
Meropenem *(Merrem)* Meropenem/Vaborbactam *(Vabomere)* Injection *Vabomere* approved only for complicated UTI (including pyelonephritis)	IV: 500-1,000 mg Q8H IV: 4 grams Q8H CrCl ≤ 50 mL/min: dose adjustment required	
Ertapenem *(Invanz)* Injection	IV/IM: 1 gram daily CrCl ≤ 30 mL/min: dose adjustment required Stable in NS only	As above plus **NOTES** No coverage of *Pseudomonas, Acinetobacter* or *Enterococcus* Commonly used for diabetic foot infections

See lab interactions, storage requirements and renal dosage information near the end of this chapter.

Carbapenem Drug Interactions

- Carbapenems can ↓ serum concentrations of valproic acid, leading to a loss of seizure control.
- Use with caution in patients at risk for seizures, or in combination with other drugs known to lower the seizure threshold (e.g., ganciclovir, quinolones, bupropion, tramadol). See the Seizures/Epilepsy chapter for a complete list.

KEY FEATURES OF CARBAPENEMS

Class effects:
- All cover ESBL-producing organisms
- All except ertapenem cover *Pseudomonas*
- Do not use with penicillin allergy
- Seizure risk (with higher doses, renal failure, or use of imipenem/cilastatin)

Remember what they do not cover:
- Atypicals, VRE, MRSA, *C. difficile, Stenotrophomonas*
- Ertapenem does not cover *Pseudomonas, Acinetobacter* or *Enterococcus* (**ErtAP**enem does not cover **PEA)**

Common uses:
- Polymicrobial infections (e.g., moderate-severe diabetic foot infection)
- Empiric therapy when resistant organisms are suspected
- Resistant *Pseudomonas* or *Acinetobacter* infections (except ertapenem)

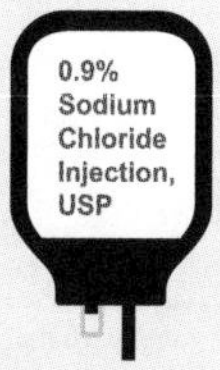

All are IV only. Ertapenem must be diluted in normal saline.

MONOBACTAM

AZTREONAM

Aztreonam has a mechanism of action similar to beta-lactams; it inhibits bacterial cell wall synthesis by binding to penicillin-binding proteins (PBPs), which prevents the final step of peptidoglycan synthesis in bacterial cell walls. The monobactam structure makes cross-reactivity with a beta-lactam allergy unlikely. Aztreonam is primarily used when a beta-lactam allergy is present.

Aztreonam covers many Gram-negative organisms, including *Pseudomonas*. It has no Gram-positive or anaerobic activity.

DRUG	DOSING	SAFETY/SIDE EFFECTS/MONITORING
Aztreonam (*Azactam*) Injection *Cayston* – inhaled, for cystic fibrosis	IV: 500-2,000 mg Q6-12H CrCl < 30 mL/min: dose adjustment required	**SIDE EFFECTS** Similar to penicillins, including rash, N/V/D, ↑ LFTs **NOTES** Can be used with a penicillin allergy

See lab interactions, storage requirements and renal dosage information near the end of this chapter.

SPECTRUM OF ACTIVITY SUMMARY

The chart below provides a visual representation of the spectrum of activity for beta-lactams and aztreonam. It can be used to identify common coverage, including which drugs have unique coverage (e.g., drugs active against *Pseudomonas* or MRSA), or where coverage is lacking (e.g., drugs that do not cover *Enterococcus*).

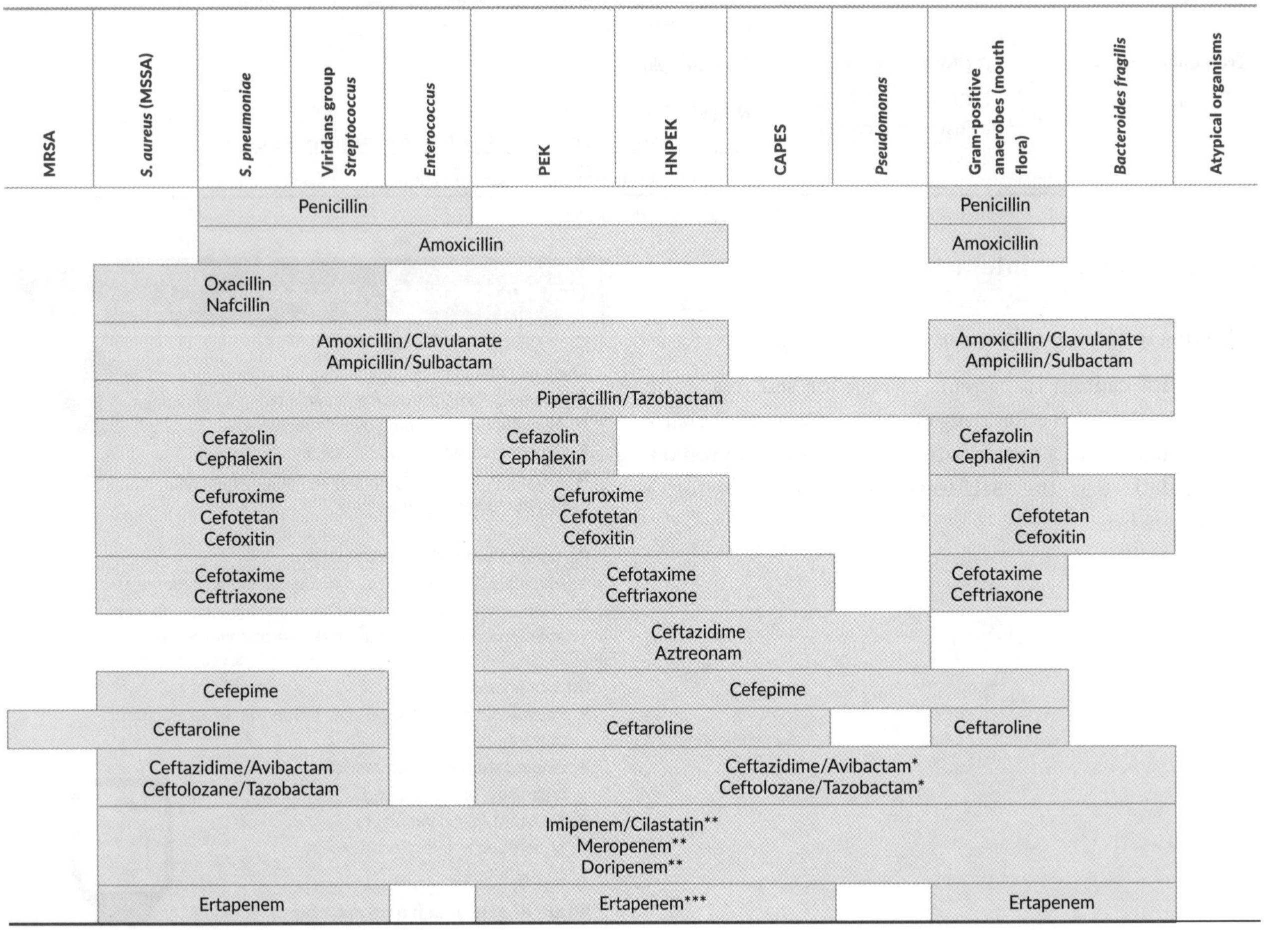

*Must be given with metronidazole for adequate anaerobic coverage

**E. faecalis only

***No Acinetobacter coverage

AMINOGLYCOSIDES

Aminoglycosides bind to the ribosome, which interferes with bacterial protein synthesis and results in a defective bacterial cell membrane. They primarily cover Gram-negative bacteria (including *Pseudomonas*); gentamicin and streptomycin are used for synergy, in combination with a beta-lactam or vancomycin, when treating Gram-positive infections (e.g., enterococcal endocarditis). Streptomycin and amikacin are used as second-line treatment for *Mycobacterial* infections. Plazomicin, a newer drug in the class, is only indicated for complicated UTI and pyelonephritis when there are no alternative treatment options.

There are two dosing strategies for aminoglycosides; traditional dosing uses lower doses more frequently (e.g., Q8H if renal function is normal). Extended interval dosing uses higher doses (to attain higher peaks) less frequently (e.g., once daily if renal function is normal). With extended interval dosing there is less accumulation of drug. This dosing strategy has been shown to decrease nephrotoxicity and decrease cost, but it is not clinically superior to traditional dosing. See Study Tip Gal for more on aminoglycosides.

AMINOGLYCOSIDES: GOOD NEWS, BAD NEWS

GOOD NEWS
Aminoglycosides kill Gram-negatives fast, are synergistic with beta-lactams for some organisms, and have low resistance and drug cost.

Aminoglycosides demonstrate concentration-dependent activity and have a post-antibiotic effect; the bacterial killing continues after the serum level drops below the MIC.

BAD NEWS
They have notable toxicities: renal damage and ototoxicity (hearing loss/tinnitus/balance problems) and require monitoring.

SMART IDEA
Take advantage of the concentration-dependent kinetics → give larger doses less frequently → this gives the kidneys time to recover between doses.

DRUG	DOSING	SAFETY/SIDE EFFECTS/MONITORING
Gentamicin IV, IM, ophthalmic, topical	If underweight (< ideal body weight): use total body weight for dosing If not obese or underweight: ideal body weight or total body weight can be used for dosing (follow the hospital protocol)	**BOXED WARNINGS** Nephrotoxicity, ototoxicity, (hearing loss, vertigo, ataxia); avoid use with other neurotoxic/nephrotoxic drugs; neuromuscular blockade and respiratory paralysis; fetal harm if given in pregnancy
Tobramycin IV, IM, ophthalmic, inhaled Tobramycin inhalation for CF *(TOBI, TOBI Podhaler, Bethkis, Kitabis Pak)*	If obese, use adjusted body weight for dosing (see Notes) **Traditional IV Dosing** Gentamicin and tobramycin: 1-2.5 mg/kg/dose; lower doses are used for Gram-positive infections; higher doses are used for Gram-negative infections Amikacin: 5-7.5 mg/kg/dose Q8H	**WARNINGS** Use caution in patients with impaired renal function, in the elderly, and those taking other nephrotoxic drugs (amphotericin B, cisplatin, polymyxins, cyclosporine, loop diuretics, NSAIDs, radiocontrast dye, tacrolimus and vancomycin) **SIDE EFFECTS** Nephrotoxicity (acute tubular necrosis), hearing loss (early toxicity associated with high-pitched sounds), vestibular toxicity (resulting in balance deficits)
Amikacin IV, IM	**Renal Dose Adjustments (Traditional Dosing)** CrCl ≥ 60 mL/min: Q8H CrCl 40-60 mL/min: Q12H CrCl 20-40 mL/min: Q24H CrCl < 20 mL/min: 1x dose, then dose per levels	**MONITORING** Drug levels, renal function, urine output, hearing tests Traditional dosing: draw a trough level right before (or 30 minutes before) the 4th dose; draw a peak level 30 minutes after the end of the 30-minute drug infusion for the 4th dose (see the table on the following page for target peaks and troughs)
Streptomycin IM	**Extended Interval IV Dosing (Gentamicin/Tobramycin)** Gentamicin and tobramycin: 4-7 mg/kg/dose (commonly 7 mg/kg) Frequency (dosing interval) is determined by a nomogram (see the example on the following page)	Extended interval dosing: draw a random level per the timing on the nomogram (see the example on the following page) Plazomicin: measure trough concentration 30 minutes before the 2nd dose; goal trough < 3 mcg/mL
Plazomicin *(Zemdri)* IV (for complicated UTI; use only when there are no alternative treatment options)	Contraindications: pregnancy, ascites, burns, cystic fibrosis, CrCl < 30 mL/min (including end-stage renal disease on dialysis) or when using for synergy in endocarditis **Other Dosing** Plazomicin 15 mg/kg IV Q24H (dose adjustments required if CrCl < 60 mL/min)	**NOTES** Amikacin has the broadest spectrum of activity The clinical definition of obesity varies; for exam purposes, obesity will be obvious, and may be stated in the question, indicating that adjusted body weight should be used for weight-based dosing (see the Calculations IV chapter for more information on weight-based dosing)

See lab interactions, storage requirements and renal dosage information near the end of this chapter.

TRADITIONAL DOSING: TARGET DRUG CONCENTRATIONS

When peak and trough levels are drawn with the 4th aminoglycoside dose (see the Monitoring section of the drug table), the levels are compared to the goal peaks and troughs to determine if dose adjustments are needed. Hospitals have protocols that guide dose adjustments. See Pharmacokinetics chapter for details.

DRUG	PEAK	TROUGH
Gentamicin Gram-negative infection	5-10 mcg/mL	≤ 2 mcg/mL
Gentamicin Gram-positive infection (synergy)	3-4 mcg/mL	< 1 mcg/mL
Tobramycin	5-10 mcg/mL	≤ 2 mcg/mL
Amikacin	20-30 mcg/mL	< 5 mcg/mL

Organism-specific peak goals are typically ≥ 10 times the MIC of the bacteria causing the infection.

EXTENDED INTERVAL DOSING NOMOGRAM

With extended interval dosing nomograms, a random level is drawn after the first dose (the timing depends on the nomogram; the Hartford nomogram shown below uses a window of 6 – 14 hours after the start of the infusion). The nomogram is used to plot the patients level and determine the appropriate dosing interval. If the level plots on a line, round up to the next dosing interval to avoid potential toxicity.

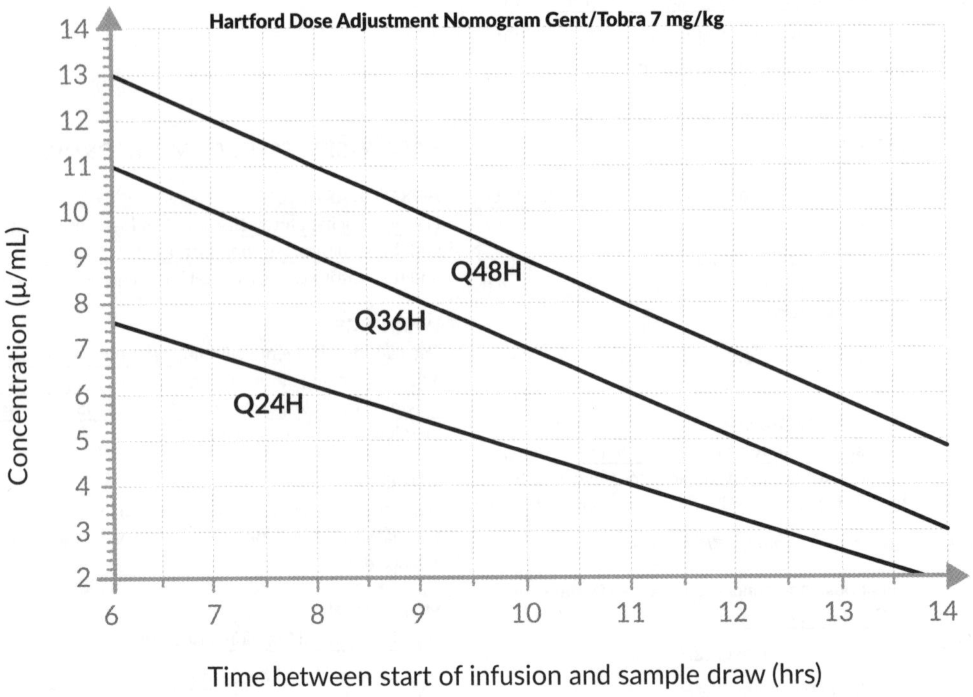

© Nicolau DP, Freeman CD, et al. Antimicrob Agents and Chemother 1995;39:650-655.

QUINOLONES

Quinolones inhibit bacterial DNA topoisomerase IV and DNA gyrase (topoisomerase II) inside the bacteria. This prevents supercoiling of DNA and promotes breakage of double-stranded DNA. Quinolones have concentration-dependent antibacterial activity and a broad-spectrum of activity against a variety of Gram-negative, Gram-positive and atypical pathogens. Some notable distinctions in the class include:

- Gemifloxacin, levofloxacin and moxifloxacin are referred to as respiratory quinolones due to enhanced coverage of *S. pneumoniae* and atypical coverage.
- Ciprofloxacin and levofloxacin have enhanced Gram-negative activity, including coverage of *Pseudomonas*. They are typically used in combination with another agent (e.g., a beta-lactam) when treating *Pseudomonas* infections empirically.
- Moxifloxacin has enhanced Gram-positive and anaerobic activity and can be used alone for mixed infections (e.g., intra-abdominal infections). Moxifloxacin is the only quinolone that cannot be used to treat urinary tract infections.
- Delafloxacin, a newer quinolone approved for skin infections, is active against MRSA. Other quinolones are noted in some resources to have activity against MRSA, but because of high rates of resistance, they should generally be avoided.

DRUG	DOSING
Ciprofloxacin (*Cipro*, *Cipro XR, Ciloxan* eye drops, *Cetraxal* and *Otiprio* ear drops) Tablet, suspension, injection, ointment, ophthalmic, otic + dexamethasone **(*Ciprodex*** ear drops) + fluocinolone (*Otovel* ear drops) + hydrocortisone (*Cipro HC* ear drops)	PO: 250-750 mg Q12H IV: 200-400 mg Q8-12H CrCl 30-50 mL/min: Q12H CrCl < 30 mL/min: Q18-24H
Delafloxacin (*Baxdela*) Tablet, injection Approved only for skin infections	PO: 450 mg Q12H IV: 300 mg Q12H CrCl < 15-29 mL/min: dose adjustment required (IV only) CrCl < 15 mL/min: not recommended (IV or PO)
Gatifloxacin (*Zymaxid* eye drops)	No oral formulation
Gemifloxacin Tablet	PO: 320 mg daily CrCl ≤ 40 mL/min: dose adjustment required
Levofloxacin (*Levaquin*) Tablet, solution, injection, ophthalmic	PO/IV: 250-750 mg daily CrCl < 50 mL/min: extend dosing interval (Q48H) and/or ↓ dose; adjustment varies based on indication and renal function
Moxifloxacin (*Avelox*, *Moxeza* and *Vigamox* eye drops) Tablet, injection, ophthalmic	IV/PO: 400 mg Q24H No dose adjustment in renal impairment
Ofloxacin (***Ocuflox*** eye drops) Tablet, ophthalmic, otic	PO: 200-400 mg Q12H CrCl < 30 mL/min: dose adjustment required

SAFETY/SIDE EFFECTS/MONITORING

BOXED WARNINGS

Tendon inflammation and/or rupture (often in the Achilles tendon) within hours/days of starting, or up to several months after completion of treatment; ↑ risk with concurrent use of systemic steroids, in organ transplant patients, and age > 60 years. Discontinue immediately if symptoms occur (see Patient Counseling section).

Peripheral neuropathy; can last months to years after the drug has been discontinued and may become permanent. Discontinue immediately if symptoms occur (see Patient Counseling section).

CNS effects [seizures, tremor, restlessness, confusion, hallucinations, depression (and suicidal thoughts), paranoia, nightmares, insomnia,↑ intracranial pressure (including pseudotumor cerebri)]. Use caution in patients with CNS disorders or with drugs that cause seizures or lower the seizure threshold (see the Seizures/Epilepsy chapter).

Avoid in patients with myasthenia gravis (may exacerbate muscle weakness).

Use last-line (only if no other possible treatments) for: acute bacterial sinusitis, acute exacerbation of chronic bronchitis and uncomplicated UTI (except moxifloxacin).

CONTRAINDICATIONS

Ciprofloxacin: concurrent administration of tizanidine.

WARNINGS

QT prolongation (highest risk with moxifloxacin); avoid in patients with known QT prolongation, or those with additive risks (hypokalemia, use of other drugs that prolong the QT interval, including Class Ia and Class III antiarrhythmics – see the Arrhythmias chapter).

Hypoglycemia and hyperglycemia; hypoglycemia can lead to coma.

Psychiatric disturbances (agitation, disorientation, lack of attention, nervousness, memory impairment and delirium).

Avoid systemic quinolones in children and in pregnancy/breastfeeding due to the risk of musculoskeletal toxicity (exception: for anthrax exposure, the benefit outweighs the risk).

Other: photosensitivity/phototoxicity, aortic aneurysm and dissection, hepatotoxicity, crystalluria (must stay hydrated).

SIDE EFFECTS

Nausea/diarrhea, headache, dizziness, serious skin reactions (SJS/TEN).

NOTES

Cipro oral suspension – shake vigorously for 15 seconds before each use. Do not put through a NG or other feeding tube (the oil-based suspension adheres to the tubing).

Cipro – can crush immediate-release tablets, mix with water and give via a feeding tube. Hold tube feedings at least 1 hour before and 2 hours after the dose.

Moxifloxacin does not reach adequate concentrations in the urine and should not be used for UTIs.

See lab interactions, storage requirements and renal dosage information near the end of this chapter.

Quinolone Drug Interactions

- Antacids and other polyvalent cations (e.g., magnesium, aluminum, calcium, iron, zinc), multivitamins, sucralfate, and bile acid resins can chelate and inhibit quinolone absorption. See the Patient Counseling section for more information.
- Lanthanum carbonate (*Fosrenol*) and sevelamer (*Renvela*) can ↓ the serum concentration of oral quinolones; separate administration by at least two hours before, and at least two hours after (with lanthanum) or six hours after (with sevelamer).
- Quinolones can ↑ the effects of warfarin.
- Quinolones can ↑ the effects of sulfonylureas, insulin and other hypoglycemic drugs.
- Caution with CVD, ↓ potassium and magnesium and with other QT-prolonging drugs (e.g., azole antifungals, antipsychotics, methadone, macrolides).
- Probenecid and NSAIDs can ↑ quinolone levels.
- Ciprofloxacin is a P-glycoprotein substrate, a strong CYP1A2 inhibitor and a weak CYP3A4 inhibitor; ciprofloxacin can ↑ the levels of caffeine and theophylline by reducing metabolism.

KEY FEATURES OF QUINOLONES

Respiratory Quinolones
- Levofloxacin, moxifloxacin, gemifloxacin
- Used for pneumonia (reliable *S. pneumoniae* activity)

Antipseudomonal Quinolones
- Ciprofloxacin, levofloxacin
- Used for *Pseudomonas* infections (including pneumonias), UTIs, intra-abdominal infections, travelers' diarrhea (without dysentery)

Moxifloxacin
- Only quinolone that is not renally adjusted
- Do not use to treat UTIs

IV to PO Ratio 1:1
- Levofloxacin and moxifloxacin

Profile Review Tips
- Caution with CVD, ↓ K/Mg and with other QT-prolonging drugs (e.g., azole antifungals, antipsychotics, methadone, macrolides)
- Avoid in patients with a seizure history or if using seizure drugs
- Avoid in children
- Watch for tendon rupture, neuropathy, CNS or psychiatric side effects

Counseling
- Avoid sun exposure, separate from cations, monitor blood glucose (DM)

MACROLIDES

Macrolides bind to the 50S ribosomal subunit, resulting in inhibition of RNA-dependent protein synthesis. They have excellent coverage of atypicals (*Legionella, Chlamydia, Mycoplasma* and *Mycobacterium avium* complex) and *Haemophilus*. Macrolides are treatment options for community-acquired upper and lower respiratory tract infections and certain sexually transmitted infections (e.g., chlamydia, gonorrhea), but utility against *S. pneumoniae, Haemophilus, Neisseria* and *Moraxella* can be limited due to increasing resistance.

DRUG	DOSING	SAFETY/SIDE EFFECTS/MONITORING
Azithromycin (*Zithromax, Z-Pak,* *Zithromax Tri-Pak, AzaSite* eye drops) Tablet, suspension, injection, ophthalmic Better Gram-negative coverage than erythromycin	*Z-Pak*: 500 mg on day 1, then 250 mg on days 2-5 *Tri-Pak*: 500 mg daily for 3 days Dosing regimens vary depending on indication IV: 250-500 mg daily No dose adjustment in renal impairment	**CONTRAINDICATIONS** History of cholestatic jaundice/hepatic dysfunction with prior use Clarithromycin and erythromycin: do not use with lovastatin or simvastatin, pimozide, ergotamine or dihydroergotamine Clarithromycin: concurrent use with colchicine in patients with renal or hepatic impairment; history of QT prolongation or ventricular arrhythmia **WARNINGS** QT prolongation (highest risk with erythromycin); avoid in patients with known QT prolongation, or those with additive risks (hypokalemia, use of other drugs that prolong the QT interval, including Class Ia and Class III antiarrhythmics – see the Arrhythmias chapter) Hepatotoxicity; use caution in patients with liver disease Exacerbation of myasthenia gravis Clarithromycin: caution in patients with CAD (↑ mortality has been documented at ≥ 1 year after the end of a 2-week course of treatment) **SIDE EFFECTS** GI upset (diarrhea, abdominal pain and cramping), taste perversion, ototoxicity (reversible and rare), severe (but rare) skin reactions (SJS/TEN/DRESS)
Clarithromycin (*Biaxin,* *Biaxin XL*) Tablet, suspension Better Gram-positive coverage	PO: 250-500 mg Q12H or 1 gram (*Biaxin XL*) daily CrCl < 30 mL/min: dose adjustment required	
Erythromycin (*E.E.S., Ery-Tab, Erythrocin,* *EryPed, Ery* and *Erygel* topical) Capsule, tablet, suspension, injection, ophthalmic, topical E.E.S = erythromycin ethylsuccinate	Dosing varies by product E.E.S 400 mg = 250 mg erythromycin base or stearate Erythromycin lactobionate is the IV form No dose adjustment in renal impairment	

See lab interactions, storage requirements and renal dosage information near the end of this chapter.

Macrolide Drug Interactions

- Erythromycin and clarithromycin are major substrates of CYP3A4 and are CYP3A4 inhibitors (moderate for erythromycin and strong for clarithromycin). Medications metabolized by CYP3A4 may need to be avoided (e.g., simvastatin and lovastatin) and others may require close monitoring, or should be used with caution in combination with erythromycin and clarithromycin. Some examples include apixaban, colchicine, dabigatran, rivaroxaban, theophylline and warfarin. Refer to the Learning Drug Interactions chapter for more information.
- Azithromycin is a minor substrate of CYP3A4 and a weak inhibitor of CYP1A2 and P-gp; it has fewer clinically significant drug interactions.
- All macrolides: use caution with CVD, ↓ potassium and magnesium and with other QT-prolonging drugs (e.g., azole antifungals, antipsychotics, methadone, quinolones).

KEY FEATURES OF MACROLIDES

Common Uses

- All macrolides: CAP, and as an alternative to a beta-lactam for strep throat
- Azithromycin: COPD exacerbations, monotherapy for chlamydia, combination therapy for gonorrhea, and prophylaxis for MAC; it is the drug of choice for severe travelers' diarrhea (including dysentery, diarrhea with bloody stools)
- Clarithromycin: used for treatment of *H. pylori* (see the Gastroesophageal Reflux Disease & Peptic Ulcer Disease chapter)
- Erythromycin causes the most GI upset due to ↑ gastric motility

Common Azithromycin Dosing *(Z-Pak)*

- Two 250 mg tablets PO x1, then 250 mg PO daily x 4 days

QT Prolongation

- Caution with CVD, ↓ K/Mg and other QT-prolonging drugs (e.g., azole antifungals, antipsychotics, methadone, quinolones)

Drug Interactions

- Clarithromycin and erythromycin are strong CYP3A4 inhibitiors; lovastatin and simvastatin are contraindicated (↑ risk of muscle toxicity)

TETRACYCLINES

Tetracyclines inhibit bacterial protein synthesis by reversibly binding to the 30S ribosomal subunit. They cover many Gram-positive bacteria (*Staphylococci, Streptococci, Enterococci, Nocardia, Bacillus, Propionibacterium* spp.), Gram-negative bacteria, including respiratory flora (*Haemophilus, Moraxella,* atypicals) and other unique pathogens (e.g., spirochetes, *Rickettsiae, Bacillus anthracis, Treponema pallidum*).

Doxycycline has broader indications, including respiratory tract infections (e.g., CAP), tick-borne/rickettsial diseases, spirochetes and sexually transmitted infections (chlamydia and gonorrhea). Doxycycline is an option for the treatment of mild skin infections, caused by CA-MRSA, and VRE urinary tract infections. Minocycline is often preferred for skin infections, including acne.

DRUG	DOSING	SAFETY/SIDE EFFECTS/MONITORING
Doxycycline (*Vibramycin*, *Doryx, Morgidox, Oracea, Acticlate,* others) Capsule, tablet, suspension, syrup, injection	PO/IV: 100-200 mg daily in 1-2 divided doses Take with food to ↓ GI irritation (except take *Oracea* on an empty stomach, 1 hr before or 2 hrs after meals) No dose adjustment in renal impairment	**WARNINGS** Children < 8 years of age, pregnancy and breastfeeding (suppresses bone growth and skeletal development, and permanently discolors teeth) Photosensitivity, tissue hyperpigmentation, severe skin reactions (DRESS/SJS/TEN), exfoliative dermatitis Gastrointestinal inflammation/ulceration (see Notes section) Minocycline: drug-induced lupus erythematosus (DILE) **SIDE EFFECTS** N/V/D, rash **MONITORING** LFTs, renal function, CBC **NOTES** IV:PO ratio is 1:1 (doxycycline, minocycline) Tablets and capsules should be taken with 8 oz of water; with doxycycline, sit upright for at least 30 minutes to avoid esophageal irritation
Minocycline (*Minocin*, *Solodyn*, *CoreMino, Ximino)* Capsule, tablet, injection	PO:/IV: 200 mg x 1, then 50-100 mg Q12H CrCl < 80 mL/min: max 200 mg/day	
Eravacycline *(Xerava)* Injection	1 mg/kg IV Q12H Only approved for complicated intra-abdominal infections	
Omadacycline *(Nuzyra)* Tablet, injection	Dose based on indication; FDA-approved for community-acquired pneumonia and skin infections	
Sarecycline *(Seysara)* Tablet	Dose based on body weight; approved for moderate-severe acne vulgaris	
Tetracycline Capsule	PO: 250-500 mg Q6H on an empty stomach CrCl ≤ 50 mL/min: dose adjustment required	

See lab interactions, storage requirements and renal dosage information near the end of this chapter.

Tetracycline Drug Interactions

- Antacids and other polyvalent cations (e.g., magnesium, aluminum, calcium, iron, zinc), multivitamins, sucralfate, bismuth subsalicylate and bile acid resins can chelate and inhibit tetracycline absorption. Separate doses (1 – 2 hours before or four hours after). Dairy products should be avoided 1 hour before or two hours after tetracycline.
- Doxycycline and minocycline can be taken with food to reduce GI upset. Dairy products are less of a concern than with tetracycline.
- Lanthanum carbonate (*Fosrenol*) can ↓ the concentration of tetracycline derivatives; take tetracycline at least 2 hours before or after lanthanum.
- Tetracycline is a major substrate of CYP3A4 and a moderate CYP3A4 inhibitor. Use caution with CYP3A4 inhibitors, which ↑ levels, and CYP3A4 inducers, which ↓ levels.
- Tetracyclines can enhance the effects of warfarin and neuromuscular blocking drugs.

KEY FEATURES OF TETRACYCLINES

Common Uses

- Doxycycline and minocycline: CA-MRSA skin infections, acne
- Doxycycline: first line for Lyme disease, Rocky Mountain Spotted Fever (tick-borne illnesses), CAP, COPD exacerbations, sinusitis (if an antibiotic is indicated), VRE UTI, monotherapy for chlamydia, combination therapy for gonorrhea
- Tetracycline: used in *H. pylori* treatment (see the Gastroesophageal Reflux Disease & Peptic Ulcer Disease chapter)

Do not use in pregnancy, breastfeeding or children age < 8 years

SULFONAMIDES

Sulfamethoxazole (SMX) inhibits dihydrofolic acid formation from para-aminobenzoic acid, which interferes with bacterial folic acid synthesis. Trimethoprim (TMP) inhibits dihydrofolic acid reduction to tetrahydrofolate, resulting in inhibition of the folic acid pathway.

Sulfamethoxazole/trimethoprim covers *Staphylococci* (including MRSA and CA-MRSA); *S. pneumoniae* and Group A Strep coverage is unreliable. Activity against Gram-negative bacteria is broad, and includes *Haemophilus, Proteus, E. coli, Klebsiella, Enterobacter, Shigella, Salmonella* and *Stenotrophomonas*. Coverage includes some opportunistic pathogens (*Nocardia, Pneumocystis, Toxoplasmosis*), but *Pseudomonas, Enterococci*, atypicals and anaerobes are not covered.

DRUG	DOSING	SAFETY/SIDE EFFECTS/MONITORING
Sulfamethoxazole/ Trimethoprim (*Bactrim, Bactrim DS*, others) Tablet, suspension, injection **Single Strength (SS)** 400 mg SMX/80 mg TMP **Double Strength (DS)** 800 mg SMX/160 mg TMP	Dose (including weight-based dosing) is based on the TMP component **Severe Infections** PO/IV: 10-20 mg TMP/kg/day, divided Q6-8H (e.g., 2 DS tablets BID-TID) **Uncomplicated UTI** 1 DS tablet PO BID x 3 days ***Pneumocystis* Pneumonia (PCP) Prophylaxis** 1 DS or SS tablet daily **PCP Treatment** IV/PO: 15-20 mg TMP/kg/day divided Q6H CrCl 15-30 mL/min: dose adjustment required CrCl < 15 mL/min: not recommended	**CONTRAINDICATIONS** Sulfa allergy, pregnancy (at term), breastfeeding, anemia due to folate deficiency, marked renal or hepatic disease, infants < 2 months of age **WARNINGS** Blood dyscrasias, including agranulocytosis and aplastic anemia Skin reactions: SJS/TEN, thrombotic thrombocytopenic purpura (TTP) G6PD deficiency; do not use with known deficiency and discontinue drug if hemolysis occurs Embryofetal toxicity **SIDE EFFECTS** Photosensitivity, ↑ K, hemolytic anemia (identified with a positive Coombs test), crystalluria (take with 8 oz of water), N/V/D, anorexia, skin rash, ↓ folate, myelosuppression with prolonged use, false elevations in SCr (due to inhibition of tubular secretion of creatinine), renal failure **MONITORING** Renal function, electrolytes, CBC, folate **NOTES** See ID II chapter for a discussion on use for UTIs during pregnancy

See lab interactions, storage requirements and renal dosage information near the end of this chapter.

Sulfonamide Drug Interactions

- SMX/TMP is a moderate-strong inhibitor of CYP2C8 and CYP2C9 and can cause significantly ↑ INR. Caution should be used in combination with warfarin (see the Learning Drug Interactions chapter for more information).
- Levels of SMX/TMP can be ↓ by CYP2C8 and CYP2C9 inducers.
- The therapeutic effects of SMX/TMP can be diminished by the use of leucovorin or levoleucovorin.
- The risk for hyperkalemia will ↑ if used in combination with ACE inhibitors, ARBs, aliskiren, aldosterone receptor antagonists (ARAs), potassium-sparing diuretics, NSAIDs, cyclosporine, tacrolimus, drospirenone-containing oral contraceptives or canagliflozin.

KEY FEATURES OF SULFAMETHOXAZOLE/ TRIMETHOPRIM

Common Uses

- CA-MRSA skin infections, UTI, *Pneumocystis* pneumonia (PCP)

5:1 Ratio of SMX/TMP (Dose by TMP)

- Single strength (SS) tablet contains 80 mg TMP
- Double strength (DS) tablet contains 160 mg TMP – usual dose is 1 tablet BID

Sulfa Allergy

- Most sulfa allergies occur with SMX/TMP (rash/hives are common)
- Rarely, severe skin reactions (e.g., SJS or TEN) can occur; if rash is accompanied by a fever or systemic symptoms, seek emergency care

INR ↑ when used with warfarin. Use alternative antibiotic when possible.

ANTIBIOTICS FOR GRAM-POSITIVE INFECTIONS

VANCOMYCIN

Vancomycin is a glycopeptide that inhibits bacterial cell wall synthesis by binding to the D-alanyl-D-alanine cell wall precursor and blocking peptidoglycan polymerization. Vancomycin only covers Gram-positive bacteria, including *Staphylococci* (MRSA), *Streptococci, Enterococci* (not VRE) and *C. difficile* (using the PO route only).

DRUG	DOSING	SAFETY/SIDE EFFECTS/MONITORING
Vancomycin (*Vancocin*, *Firvanq* oral solution*)* Capsule, oral solution, injection First-line treatment for MRSA infections Consider alternative drug when MRSA MIC ≥ 2 mcg/mL	**Systemic infections (IV only)** IV: 15-20 mg/kg Q8-12H Dose based on total body weight CrCl 20-49 mL/min: Q24H CrCl < 20 mL/min: give 1 dose, then dose per levels Peripheral IV infusions should not exceed 5 mg/mL ***C. difficile* infections (PO only)** PO: 125-500 mg QID x 10 days (upper end used for severe, complicated disease) No dose adjustment in renal impairment	**WARNINGS** Ototoxicity and nephrotoxicity; caution with use of other nephrotoxic or ototoxic drugs or with prolonged high serum concentrations (dose adjustment required in renal impairment) PO is used only for *C. difficile* colitis and enterocolitis, not for systemic infections Infusion reaction/red man syndrome (maculopapular rash, hypotension, flushing and chills from too rapid of an infusion rate – do not infuse faster than 1 gram per hour) **SIDE EFFECTS** Abdominal pain, nausea (oral route), phlebitis (irritation to vein), myelosuppression (neutropenia/thrombocytopenia), drug fever, severe skin reactions (SJS/TEN) **MONITORING** Renal function, trough serum concentration at steady state (generally 30 minutes before the 4th or 5th dose), WBC Goal trough: 15-20 mcg/mL – pneumonia, endocarditis, osteomyelitis, meningitis, bacteremia Goal trough: 10-15 mcg/mL – other infections

See lab interactions, storage requirements and renal dosage information near the end of this chapter.

Vancomycin Drug Interactions

- The risk of nephrotoxicity is ↑ when used with other nephrotoxic drugs (e.g., aminoglycosides, amphotericin B, cisplatin, polymyxins, cyclosporine, tacrolimus, loop diuretics, NSAIDs and radiographic contrast dye). Vancomycin can ↑ the risk of ototoxicity when used with other ototoxic drugs (e.g., aminoglycosides, cisplatin, loop diuretics).

LIPOGLYCOPEPTIDES

Lipoglycopeptides (with the generic name suffix "-vancin") inhibit bacterial cell wall synthesis by 1) binding to the D-alanyl-D-alanine portion of the cell wall, blocking polymerization and cross-linking of peptidoglycan, and 2) disrupting bacterial membrane potential and changing cell permeability (due to the presence of a lipophilic side chain). They have concentration-dependent antibacterial activity and have similar coverage to vancomycin (with the exception that they only come in IV form and cannot be used to treat *C. difficile* infections).

DRUG	DOSING	SAFETY/SIDE EFFECTS/MONITORING
Telavancin (*Vibativ*) Injection Approved for complicated skin and soft-tissue infections (SSTI) and hospital-acquired and ventilator-associated pneumonia	IV: 10 mg/kg daily CrCl ≤ 50 mL/min: dose adjustment required Infuse over 60 minutes to prevent infusion reaction	**BOXED WARNINGS** Fetal risk – obtain pregnancy test prior to starting therapy; nephrotoxicity; ↑ mortality with pre-existing moderate-to-severe renal impairment (CrCl ≤ 50 mL/min) when compared to vancomycin in pneumonia trials **CONTRAINDICATIONS** Concurrent use of IV unfractionated heparin (UFH) **WARNINGS** Can falsely ↑ coagulation tests (e.g., aPTT/PT/INR), but does not ↑ bleeding risk; red man syndrome with rapid IV administration (give over ≥ 60 minutes); QT prolongation **SIDE EFFECTS** Metallic taste, N/V, ↑ SCr, foamy urine **MONITORING** Renal function, pregnancy status
Oritavancin (*Orbactiv*) Injection Approved for SSTI	Single-dose IV regimen: 1,200 mg Infuse over 3 hours CrCl < 30 mL/min: has not been studied, use with caution	**CONTRAINDICATIONS** Oritavancin: use of IV UFH for 120 hours (5 days) after oritavancin administration due to interference (false elevations) with aPTT laboratory results **WARNINGS** Can cause falsely ↑ PT/INR for up to 12 hours and aPTT for up to 120 hours after a dose Oritavancin: use a different antibiotic if osteomyelitis is confirmed or suspected Dalbavancin: infusion reactions (red man syndrome) with rapid IV administration; ↑ ALT > 3x the upper limit of normal **SIDE EFFECTS** Infusion reaction (red man syndrome), N/V/D, headache, rash **MONITORING** Signs of osteomyelitis (oritavancin), LFTs, renal function **NOTES** Extremely long half-life allows a single-dose regimen for both
Dalbavancin (*Dalvance*) Injection Approved for SSTI	Single-dose IV regimen: 1,500 mg Two-dose IV regimen: 1,000 mg x 1, then 500 mg one week later Infuse over 30 minutes CrCl < 30 mL/min (not on dialysis): dose adjustment required	

See lab interactions, storage requirements and renal dosage information near the end of this chapter.

Telavancin/Oritavancin Drug Interactions

- Avoid telavancin in patients with congenital long QT syndrome, known QT prolongation or uncompensated heart failure. Use caution with other medications known to prolong the QT interval (see the Arrhythmias chapter).
- Oritavancin is a weak inhibitor of CYP2C9 and CYP2C19, and a weak inducer of CYP3A4 and CYP2D6. Use caution when coadministered with drugs metabolized by these enzymes (including warfarin).

DAPTOMYCIN

Daptomycin is a cyclic lipopeptide. It binds to cell membrane components, causing rapid depolarization; this inhibits all intracellular replication processes, including protein synthesis, and causes cell death. Daptomycin has concentration-dependent antibacterial activity against most Gram-positive bacteria, including *Staphylococci* (MRSA) and *Enterococci* (both species of VRE, *E. faecium* and *E. faecalis)*.

DRUG	DOSING	SAFETY/SIDE EFFECTS/MONITORING
Daptomycin (*Cubicin, Cubicin RF*) Injection Approved for complicated skin and soft-tissue infections (SSTI) and *S. aureus* (MRSA) bloodstream infections, including right-sided endocarditis Do not use to treat pneumonia; drug is inactivated in the lungs by surfactant	SSTI: 4 mg/kg IV daily Bacteremia/right-sided endocarditis: 6 mg/kg IV daily CrCl < 30 mL/min: dose adjustment required	**WARNINGS** Eosinophilic pneumonia – generally develops 2-4 weeks after treatment initiation Myopathy and rhabdomyolysis – discontinue in patients with s/sx and CPK > 1,000 units/L (5x ULN), or in asymptomatic patients with a CPK ≥ 2,000 units/L (10x ULN); consider temporarily withholding other drugs that can cause muscle damage (e.g., statins) during treatment Can falsely ↑ PT/INR, but does not ↑ bleeding risk Peripheral neuropathy **SIDE EFFECTS** ↑ CPK, abdominal pain, pruritus, chest pain, edema, hypertension, acute kidney injury **MONITORING** CPK level weekly (more frequently if on a statin or with renal impairment); muscle pain/weakness, s/sx of neuropathy, dyspnea **NOTES** *Cubicin:* compatible with NS and LR (no dextrose) *Cubicin RF:* compatible with NS (no dextrose) but must use only sterile or bacteriostatic water for injection to reconstitute the lyophilized powder (before diluting further with NS)

See lab interactions, storage requirements and renal dosage information near the end of this chapter.

Daptomycin Drug Interactions

- Daptomycin can have additive risk of muscle toxicity when used in conjunction with statins.

OXAZOLIDINONES

Linezolid and tedizolid bind to the 50S subunit of the bacterial ribosome, inhibiting translation and protein synthesis. They have coverage similar to vancomycin, but also cover VRE *(E. faecium* and *E. faecalis)*.

DRUG	DOSING	SAFETY/SIDE EFFECTS/MONITORING
Linezolid (*Zyvox*) Tablet, suspension, injection	PO/IV: 600 mg Q12H No dose adjustment in renal impairment IV:PO ratio is 1:1	**CONTRAINDICATIONS** Do not use with or within 2 weeks of MAO inhibitors **WARNINGS** Duration-related myelosuppression (thrombocytopenia, anemia, leukopenia), peripheral and optic neuropathy when used > 28 days, serotonin syndrome, hypoglycemia – caution with insulin or other hypoglycemic drugs, seizures, lactic acidosis; ↑ BP – use caution and monitor BP in patients with uncontrolled hypertension and untreated hyperthyroidism **SIDE EFFECTS** ↓ platelets, ↓ Hgb, ↓ WBC, HA, nausea, diarrhea, ↑ LFTs **MONITORING** HR, BP, BG (DM), weekly CBC, visual function **NOTES** Do not shake linezolid suspension
Tedizolid (*Sivextro*) Tablet, injection Approved for SSTI	PO/IV: 200 mg daily for 6 days Infuse over 1 hour, stable in NS No dose adjustment in renal impairment IV:PO ratio is 1:1	**WARNINGS** Consider alternative treatment in patients with neutropenia **SIDE EFFECTS** Nausea, diarrhea, paresthesias, hypertension, visual impairment, blurred vision (less GI side effects and myelosuppresion compared to linezolid)

See lab interactions, storage requirements and renal dosage information near the end of this chapter.

Linezolid/Tedizolid Drug Interactions

- Linezolid and tedizolid are reversible monoamine oxidase inhibitors. Avoid tyramine-containing foods and serotonergic drugs (see the Learning Drug Interactions chapter).
- Linezolid can exacerbate hypoglycemic episodes; use caution in patients receiving insulin or oral hypoglycemic drugs (e.g., sulfonylureas).

QUINUPRISTIN/DALFOPRISTIN

This drug is a streptogramin; it binds to the 50S ribosomal subunit inhibiting protein synthesis. Quinupristin/dalfopristin covers most Gram-positive bacteria, including *Staphylococci* (MRSA) and *Enterococcus faecium* (VRE, but not *E. faecalis*). It is approved for complicated skin and soft-tissue infections, but is not well-tolerated; use is typically limited to vancomycin-resistant *E. faecium* infections.

DRUG	DOSING	SAFETY/SIDE EFFECTS/MONITORING
Quinupristin/ Dalfopristin (*Synercid*) Injection	IV: 7.5 mg/kg Q8-12H Infuse over 60 minutes No dose adjustment in renal impairment	**SIDE EFFECTS** Arthralgias/myalgias (up to 47% of patients), infusion reactions, including edema and pain at infusion site (up to 44% of patients), phlebitis (up to 40% of patients), hyperbilirubinemia (up to 35% of patients), CPK elevations, GI upset, ↑ LFTs **NOTES** Dilute in D5W only Administer via central line, such as a peripherally inserted central catheter (PICC), to avoid phlebitis

See lab interactions, storage requirements and renal dosage information near the end of this chapter.

Quinupristin/Dalfopristin Drug Interactions

- Quinupristin/dalfopristin is a weak CYP3A4 inhibitor; it can ↑ levels of CCBs, cyclosporine, dofetilide and others.

TIGECYCLINE

Tigecycline is a glycylcycline. It binds to the 30S ribosomal subunit inhibiting protein synthesis; structurally, it is related to the tetracyclines. Tigecycline has a broad-spectrum of activity against Gram-positive bacteria, including *Staphylococci* (MRSA) and *Enterococci* (VRE), Gram-negative bacteria, anaerobes and atypical organisms. Among the Gram-negatives, it has no activity against the "3 P's": *Pseudomonas, Proteus, Providencia* species. Tigecycline is approved for complicated skin and soft-tissue infections, intra-abdominal infections and community-acquired pneumonia; use is limited (see Boxed Warning).

DRUG	DOSING	SAFETY/SIDE EFFECTS/MONITORING
Tigecycline (*Tygacil*) Injection Derivative of minocycline	IV: 100 mg x 1 dose, then 50 mg Q12H Severe hepatic impairment: dose adjustment required No adjustment in renal impairment	**BOXED WARNING** ↑ risk of death, use only when alternative treatments are not suitable **WARNINGS** Hepatotoxicity, pancreatitis, photosensitivity, teeth discoloration in children < 8 years old (avoid use) Lower cure rates in ventilator-associated pneumonia **SIDE EFFECTS** N/V/D, headache, dizziness, ↑ LFTs, rash/severe skin reactions (SJS) **NOTES** Do not use for bloodstream infections; it does not achieve adequate concentrations in the blood since it is lipophilic (drug distributes quickly out of the blood into tissues) Reconstituted solution should be yellow-orange; discard if not this color

See lab interactions, storage requirements and renal dosage information near the end of this chapter.

Tigecycline Drug Interactions

- Tigecycline can ↑ the INR in patients taking warfarin.

ADDITIONAL BROAD-SPECTRUM DRUGS

POLYMYXINS

The polymyxin class consists of two drugs, colistimethate (sometimes referred to as colistin) and polymyxin B. Colistimethate is an inactive prodrug that is hydrolyzed to colistin. Colistin acts as a cationic detergent and damages the bacterial cytoplasmic membrane, causing leaking of intracellular substances and cell death. Polymyxins cover Gram-negative bacteria, such as *Enterobacter* spp., *E. coli, Klebsiella pneumoniae* and *Pseudomonas aeruginosa* (they do not cover *Proteus* spp.). Due to the risk of toxicities, they are used primarily for MDR Gram-negative pathogens in combination with other antibiotics.

DRUG	DOSING	SAFETY/SIDE EFFECTS/MONITORING
Colistimethate sodium (*Coly-Mycin M*) Injection (can be used for inhalation administration)	IV/IM: 2.5-5 mg/kg/day in 2-4 divided doses Dose is expressed in terms of colistin base activity CrCl < 80 mL/min: dose adjustment required Solutions for inhalation must be mixed immediately prior to administration	**WARNING** Dose-dependent nephrotoxicity (monitor renal function and electrolytes), neurotoxicity (dizziness, headache, tingling, oral paresthesia, vertigo) **NOTES** Colistimethate sodium is a prodrug that is converted to colistin (the active form); assess dose carefully, as it can be represented in units of colistimethate sodium, mg of colistimethate sodium, or mg of colistin base activity Avoid use with other nephrotoxic medications Neurotoxicity can result in respiratory paralysis from neuromuscular blockade
Polymyxin B sulfate Injection	IV: 15,000-25,000 units/kg/day divided every 12 hours CrCl < 80 mL/min: dose adjustment required	**BOXED WARNINGS** Nephrotoxicity (dose-dependent) Neurotoxicity (dizziness, tingling, numbness, paresthesia, vertigo) Safety in pregnancy is not established Should only be administered to hospitalized patients Avoid concurrent or sequential use of other neurotoxic or nephrotoxic drugs Neurotoxicity can result in respiratory paralysis from neuromuscular blockade **MONITORING** Renal function **NOTES** 1 mg = 10,000 units polymyxin B

See lab interactions, storage requirements and renal dosage information near the end of this chapter.

Polymyxin Drug Interactions

- Other nephrotoxic drugs can enhance the nephrotoxic effects (refer to the Aminoglycoside section).

CHLORAMPHENICOL

Chloramphenicol reversibly binds to the 50S subunit of the bacterial ribosome inhibiting protein synthesis. It covers Gram-positives, Gram-negatives, anaerobes and atypical organisms.

DRUG	DOSING	SAFETY/SIDE EFFECTS/MONITORING
Chloramphenicol Injection Rarely used due to adverse effects	IV: 50-100 mg/kg/day in divided doses Q6H (max 4 grams/day) No adjustment in renal impairment, but use with caution	**BOXED WARNING** Serious and fatal blood dyscrasias (aplastic anemia, pancytopenia – may be irreversible) **WARNINGS** Gray syndrome with high serum levels – circulatory collapse, cyanosis, acidosis, abdominal distention, myocardial depression, coma and death **MONITORING** CBC at baseline and every 2 days during therapy, LFTs, renal function, serum drug concentrations

See lab interactions, storage requirements and renal dosage information near the end of this chapter.

MISCELLANEOUS ANTIBIOTICS

CLINDAMYCIN

Clindamycin is a lincosamide which reversibly binds to the 50S subunit of the bacterial ribosome inhibiting protein synthesis. It covers most anaerobes and Gram-positive bacteria (including some community-associated MRSA). It does not cover *Enterococcus* or Gram-negative pathogens.

DRUG	DOSING	SAFETY/SIDE EFFECTS/MONITORING
Clindamycin *(Cleocin)* Injection, capsule, suspension Topical: foam, gel, lotion, kit, solution, swab ***(Cleocin-T, Clindagel,*** *Clindacin ETZ, Clindacin Pac, Clindacin-P, Evoclin)* Vaginal: cream, suppository *(Clindesse, Cleocin)*	PO: 150-450 mg Q6H IV: 600-900 mg Q8H No dose adjustment in renal impairment	**BOXED WARNING** Colitis (*C. difficile*) **WARNING** Severe or fatal skin reactions (SJS/TEN/DRESS) **SIDE EFFECTS** N/V/D, rash, urticaria, ↑ LFTs (rare) **NOTES** An induction test (D-test) should be performed on *S. aureus* that is susceptible to clindamycin but resistant to erythromycin; a flattened zone between the disks (positive D-test) indicates inducible clindamycin resistance and clindamycin should not be used Common uses: purulent and non-purulent skin infections, beta-lactam alternative for dental abscesses

See lab interactions, storage requirements and renal dosage information near the end of this chapter.

METRONIDAZOLE AND RELATED DRUGS

These antibiotics cause a loss of helical DNA structure and strand breakage resulting in inhibition of protein synthesis. Metronidazole has activity against anaerobes and protozoal infections. It is effective for bacterial vaginosis, trichomoniasis, giardiasis, amebiasis, *C. difficile* and is used in combination regimens for intra-abdominal infections.

Tinidazole is structurally related to metronidazole, but activity is limited to protozoa (giardiasis, amebiasis), trichomoniasis and bacterial vaginosis organisms. Secnidazole, a newer drug in the class, is only indicated for bacterial vaginosis.

DRUG	DOSING	SAFETY/SIDE EFFECTS/MONITORING
Metronidazole *(Flagyl,* *Metro)* Tablet, capsule, injection Topical: *MetroCream, Metrogel, MetroLotion, Noritate, Rosadan* Vaginal: *MetroGel-Vaginal, Nuvessa, Vandazole*	PO/IV: 500-750 mg Q8-12H or 250-500 mg Q6-8H No dose adjustment in renal impairment Take immediate-release tablets with food to ↓ GI upset IV:PO ratio is 1:1	**BOXED WARNING** Possibly carcinogenic based on animal data **CONTRAINDICATIONS** Pregnancy (1st trimester), use of alcohol or propylene glycol-containing products during treatment or within 3 days of treatment discontinuation (disulfiram reaction) Metronidazole: use of disulfiram within the past 2 weeks Tinidazole: breastfeeding **WARNINGS** CNS effects: seizures, peripheral neuropathy Metronidazole: aseptic meningitis, encephalopathy, optic neuropathy
Tinidazole *(Tindamax)* Tablet	2 grams PO daily Take with food to minimize GI effects No adjustment in renal impairment	**SIDE EFFECTS** Metallic taste, HA, nausea, furry tongue, darkened urine, dizziness, rash/severe skin reactions (SJS/TEN) **NOTES** See the ID II chapter for a discussion on use for STIs in pregnancy
Secnidazole *(Solosec)* Granule packet Approved only for bacterial vaginosis	PO: 2 gram single dose Sprinkle contents of 1 packet onto applesauce, yogurt, or pudding and consume within 30 minutes; do not chew the granules	**WARNINGS** Possibly carcinogenic (based on animal data with structurally similar drugs) **SIDE EFFECTS** Vulvovaginal candidiasis, HA, N/D

See lab interactions, storage requirements and renal dosage information near the end of this chapter.

Metronidazole and Tinidazole Drug Interactions

- Metronidazole is a weak inhibitor of CYP3A4 and CYP2C9. Tinidazole is a minor substrate of CYP3A4.
- Metronidazole and tinidazole should not be used with alcohol (during and for 3 days after discontinuation of treatment) due to a potential disulfiram-like reaction (abdominal cramping, nausea/vomiting, headaches, and flushing).
- Metronidazole, and potentially tinidazole, can ↑ INR in patients taking warfarin.

FIDAXOMICIN

Fidaxomicin inhibits RNA polymerase, resulting in inhibition of protein synthesis and cell death. It is used for *C. difficile* infections.

DRUG	DOSING	SAFETY/SIDE EFFECTS/MONITORING
Fidaxomicin *(Dificid)* Tablet	PO: 200 mg BID x 10 days No dose adjustment in renal impairment	**WARNINGS** Not effective for systemic infections – absorption is minimal **SIDE EFFECTS** N/V, abdominal pain, GI bleeding, anemia

See lab interactions, storage requirements and renal dosage information near the end of this chapter.

RIFAXIMIN

Rifaximin inhibits bacterial RNA synthesis by binding to bacterial DNA-dependent RNA polymerase. It is structurally related to rifampin. It covers *E. coli*.

DRUG	DOSING	SAFETY/SIDE EFFECTS/MONITORING
Rifaximin *(Xifaxan)* Tablet	**Travelers' diarrhea:** PO: 200 mg TID x 3 days **Reduction of hepatic encephalopathy recurrence:** PO: 550 mg BID **Irritable bowel syndrome w/diarrhea (IBS-D):** PO: 550 mg TID x 14 days No dose adjustment in renal impairment	**SIDE EFFECTS** Peripheral edema, dizziness, headache, flatulence, nausea, abdominal pain, rash/pruritus **NOTES** Not effective for systemic infections (< 1% absorption) Used as salvage treatment in patients with *C. difficile* infection

See lab interactions, storage requirements and renal dosage information near the end of this chapter.

URINARY AGENTS

FOSFOMYCIN

Inhibits bacterial cell wall synthesis by inactivating the enzyme pyruval transferase, which is critical in the synthesis of cell walls. It covers *E. coli* (including ESBLs) and *E. faecalis* (including VRE). A single-dose regimen is used for uncomplicated UTI (cystitis only).

DRUG	DOSING	SAFETY/SIDE EFFECTS/MONITORING
Fosfomycin (*Monurol*) 1 packet granules = 3 grams	**Female, uncomplicated UTI** 3 grams PO x 1, mixed in 3-4 oz of cold water	**SIDE EFFECTS** Headache, diarrhea, nausea

See lab interactions, storage requirements and renal dosage information near the end of this chapter.

NITROFURANTOIN

Nitrofurantoin is a bacterial cell wall inhibitor. It is used for uncomplicated UTI (cystitis only). It covers *E. coli, Klebsiella, Enterobacter, S. aureus,* and *Enterococcus* (VRE).

DRUG	DOSING	SAFETY/SIDE EFFECTS/MONITORING
Nitrofurantoin (*Macrobid, Macrodantin,* *Furadantin)* Capsule, suspension	*Macrodantin:* PO: 50-100 mg QID x 3-7 days; 50-100 mg QHS for prophylaxis *Macrobid:* PO: 100 mg BID x 5 days The macrocrystal formulation (*Macrobid*) dissolves more slowly and is given BID	**CONTRAINDICATIONS** Renal impairment (CrCl < 60 mL/min*) – inadequate urine concentrations and risk for accumulation of neurotoxins; previous history of cholestatic jaundice/hepatic dysfunction, pregnancy (at term) **WARNINGS** Optic neuritis, hepatotoxicity, peripheral neuropathy, pulmonary toxicity, hemolytic anemia (use caution in patients with G6PD deficiency) **SIDE EFFECTS** GI upset (take with food), headache, rash, brown urine discoloration (harmless)

**Per package labeling. Some sources (e.g., Beer's Criteria) recommend use if CrCl > 30 mL/min.*
See lab interactions, storage requirements and renal dosage information near the end of this chapter.

KEY FEATURES OF NITROFURANTOIN

Drug of choice for uncomplicated UTI
- See the ID II chapter for a discussion on use in pregnancy

Do not use
- Contraindicated when CrCl < 60 mL/min

Dosing
- Macro**bid** is BID
- Macrodantin is QID

Counseling
- Take with food to prevent nausea, cramping
- Can discolor the urine (brown)

TOPICAL DECOLONIZATION

MUPIROCIN NASAL OINTMENT

Mupirocin is a topical antimicrobial ointment used to eliminate *Staphylococci* (MRSA) colonization of the nares. See the Common Skin Conditions chapter for a discussion regarding topical mupirocin use for infected skin lesions.

DRUG	DOSING	SAFETY/SIDE EFFECTS/MONITORING
Mupirocin Nasal (*Bactroban* Nasal) 1 g tubes	**Decolonization:** ½ tube in each nostril BID x 5 days	**SIDE EFFECTS** Headache, burning, localized irritation, rhinitis, pharyngitis

See lab interactions, storage requirements and renal dosage information near the end of this chapter.

SUMMARY TABLES

DRUGS OF CHOICE/ACTIVE DRUGS FOR SPECIFIC PATHOGENS

Community-associated methicillin-resistant *Staphylococcus aureus* (CA-MRSA) skin & soft tissue infections (SSTIs)
SMX/TMP
Doxycycline, minocycline
Clindamycin*
Linezolid

For more severe SSTIs requiring IV treatment or hospitalization (cover MRSA and *Streptococci*)
Vancomycin (consider using alternative if MIC ≥ 2)
Linezolid, tedizolid
Daptomycin
Ceftaroline
Telavancin
Oritavancin
Dalbavancin
Quinupristin/Dalfopristin
Tigecycline

Nosocomial MRSA
Vancomycin (consider using alternative if MIC ≥ 2)
Linezolid
Daptomycin (not in pneumonia)
Rifampin (select infections, never used alone)
Telavancin

VRE *(E. faecalis)*
Pen G or ampicillin
Linezolid
Daptomycin
Tigecycline
Cystitis only: nitrofurantoin, fosfomycin, doxycycline

VRE *(E. faecium)*
Daptomycin
Linezolid
Quinupristin/Dalfopristin
Tigecycline
Cystitis only: nitrofurantoin, fosfomycin, doxycycline

Pseudomonas aeruginosa
Piperacillin/Tazobactam
Cefepime
Ceftazidime
Ceftazidime/Avibactam
Ceftolozane/Tazobactam
Carbapenems (except ertapenem)
Ciprofloxacin, levofloxacin
Aztreonam
Aminoglycosides
Colistimethate, polymyxin B

Acinetobacter baumannii
Carbapenems (except ertapenem)
Ampicillin/Sulbactam
Minocycline
Tigecycline
Quinolones
SMX/TMP
Colistimethate, polymyxin B

Extended spectrum beta-lactamase producing Gram-negative rods (ESBL GNR) – *E. coli, K. pneumoniae, P. mirabilis*
Carbapenems
Ceftolozane/Tazobactam
Ceftazidime/Avibactam
Cefepime (high-dose)
Aminoglycosides
Cystitis only: fosfomycin

Carbapenem-resistant Gram-negative rods (CRE)
Ceftazidime/Avibactam
Colistimethate, polymyxin B

Bacteroides fragilis
Metronidazole
Beta-lactam/beta-lactamase inhibitor
Cefotetan, cefoxitin
Carbapenems
Tigecycline
Others (reduced activity): clindamycin, moxifloxacin

***C. difficile* Infection**
Vancomycin (oral)
Fidaxomicin
Metronidazole

Atypical Organisms
Azithromycin, clarithromycin
Doxycycline, minocycline
Quinolones

HNPEK
Beta-lactam/beta-lactamase inhibitor
Amoxicillin (if beta-lactamase negative)
Cephalosporins (except 1st generation)
Carbapenems
SMX/TMP
Aminoglycosides
Quinolones

**A D-test must be performed before using clindamycin.*

STORAGE REQUIREMENTS: LIQUID ORAL ANTIBIOTICS

REFRIGERATION REQUIRED AFTER RECONSTITUTION

Penicillin VK	Cefadroxil	Cefaclor
Ampicillin	Cefpodoxime	Ceftibuten
Amoxicillin/Clavulanate *(Augmentin)*	Cefprozil	Vancomycin oral *(Firvanq)*
Cephalexin *(Keflex)*	Cefuroxime	Valganciclovir *(Valcyte)**

REFRIGERATION RECOMMENDED

Amoxicillin – improves taste

DO NOT REFRIGERATE

Cefdinir (formerly *Omnicef*)	Ciprofloxacin *(Cipro)*	Acyclovir *(Zovirax)**
Azithromycin	Levofloxacin *(Levaquin)*	Fluconazole *(Diflucan)**
Clarithromycin *(Biaxin)* – bitter taste, thickens/gels	Clindamycin *(Cleocin)* – thickens, may crystallize	Posaconazole *(Noxafil)**
Doxycycline *(Vibramycin)*	Linezolid *(Zyvox)*	Voriconazole *(Vfend)**
	Sulfamethoxazole/Trimethoprim *(Sulfatrim)*	Nystatin*

STORAGE REQUIREMENTS: IV ANTIBIOTICS

Most IV medications are refrigerated; the list below represents a few that are not.

DO NOT REFRIGERATE

Metronidazole *(Flagyl)*	Sulfamethoxazole/Trimethoprim *(Sulfatrim)*
Moxifloxacin *(Avelox)*	Acyclovir *(Zovirax)** – refrigeration causes crystallization

**Discussed in the ID III chapter.*

DRUG-LABORATORY INTERACTIONS

Some antimicrobials can cause abnormalities in laboratory values, necessitating a change in treatment (e.g., a positive Coombs test in combination with bleeding indicates that a patient could be experiencing drug-related hemolysis and the antibiotic should be discontinued). Some medications can interfere with the result of the test, even if there are no clinical effects (e.g., daptomycin can cause a falsely elevated INR, but does not cause bleeding). In other cases, a drug should not be started in patients with certain laboratory test results (e.g., primaquine in patients with G6PD deficiency).

See the Learning Lab Values & Drug Monitoring chapter for a complete list of drugs (antibiotics and other drugs) that interfere with lab tests. Refer to the Anemia chapter for a complete discussion on hemolytic anemia and drugs that can cause hemolysis and/or should be avoided with G6PD deficiency.

RENAL DOSE ADJUSTMENTS

Many antibiotics are cleared through the kidneys and require dose adjustments based on renal function. This includes most beta-lactams and quinolones. See Key Drugs Guy for antibiotics that do not require renal adjustment.

NO RENAL DOSE ADJUSTMENT REQUIRED

KEY DRUGS

- Antistaphylococcal penicillins (e.g., dicloxacillin, nafcillin)
- Ceftriaxone
- Clindamycin
- Doxycycline
- Macrolides (azithromycin and erythromycin only)
- Metronidazole
- Moxifloxacin
- Linezolid

Others:

- Chloramphenicol
- Fidaxomicin
- Select tetracyclines (e.g., eravacycline, seracycline, omacycline)
- Quinupristin/Dalfopristin
- Rifaximin
- Rifampin*
- Tedizolid
- Tigecycline
- Tinidazole
- Vancomycin (PO only)

**This agent is discussed in the ID II chapter.*

SPECIAL REQUIREMENTS

TAKE WITH/WITHOUT FOOD

Most antibiotics can be taken with food to decrease GI upset; except these drugs, which are different.

Take within one hour of finishing a meal: amoxicillin ER

Take on an empty stomach: ampicillin oral capsules and suspension, ceftibuten suspension, levofloxacin oral solution, penicillin VK, rifampin*, isoniazid*, itraconazole solution*, voriconazole*

1:1 IV TO ORAL DOSING

For these drugs, the oral and IV dose is the same.

Levofloxacin, moxifloxacin

Doxycycline, minocycline

Sulfamethoxazole/Trimethoprim

Linezolid, tedizolid

Metronidazole

Fluconazole*, isavuconazonium*, posaconazole* (oral tablets and IV), voriconazole*

LIGHT PROTECTION DURING ADMINISTRATION

See the Learning IV Medications chapter for a complete list of drugs (including antibiotics and other drugs) that require specific light protection.

Doxycycline

Micafungin*

Pentamidine*

DILUENT COMPATIBILITY REQUIREMENTS

See the Learning IV Medications chapter for a complete list of drugs (including antibiotics and other drugs) that require specific diluents.

Compatible with dextrose only

Dalbavancin, oritavancin

Pentamidine*

Quinupristin/Dalfopristin

Sulfamethoxazole/Trimethoprim

Amphotericin B* (conventional, *Abelcet*, *Ambisome*)

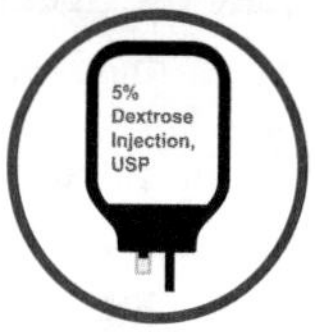

Compatible with saline only

Ampicillin

Ampicillin/Sulbactam

Ertapenem

Daptomycin (*Cubicin RF* – see the daptomycin drug table for reconstitution requirements prior to dilution)

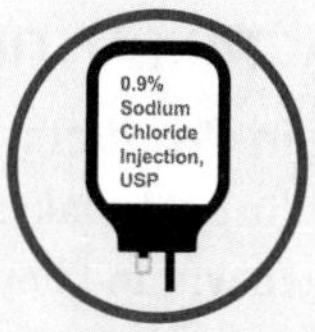

Compatible with NS/LR only

Caspofungin*

Daptomycin (*Cubicin*)

These drugs are discussed in the ID II-IV chapters.

PATIENT COUNSELING

ALL ANTIBIOTICS

- Antibiotics only treat bacterial infections. They do not treat viral infections, such as the common cold.
- Skipping doses or not completing the full course of treatment can ↓ the effects, cause the infection to return, and increase the likelihood that this medication will not work for you in the future. If your symptoms worsen, contact your healthcare provider.
- Many antibiotics can cause rash. If you experience a rash, contact your healthcare provider.
- Many antibiotics can cause GI upset. Taking the medication with food can help, but some antibiotics need to be taken on an empty stomach.
- Measure liquid doses carefully using the measuring device/syringe that comes with the medication. Ask your pharmacist if you do not have one. Household spoons should not be used, as they often do not deliver the correct dose.
- Contact your healthcare provider if you have watery diarrhea several times a day, with or without abdominal cramping. This can occur during treatment, or weeks after the antibiotic treatment has finished. You should not self-treat with anti-diarrheal medication.
- Some oral liquid and chewable dosage forms contain phenylalanine. Let your healthcare provider know if you have phenylketonuria (inability to metabolize phenylalanine).

BETA-LACTAM ANTIBIOTICS

Amoxicillin Products

- Amoxicillin can be taken with or without food. Amoxicillin ER is taken within 1 hour of finishing a meal. *Augmentin* is taken with food to ↑ what your body absorbs and ↓ stomach upset.
- Suspensions should be refrigerated (especially important for *Augmentin*).

Cephalexin *(Keflex)*, Cefuroxime, Cefdinir (formerly *Omnicef)*

- Cephalexin: take this medication by mouth, with or without food, every six hours. The suspension should be refrigerated.
- Cefuroxime: take this medication by mouth, with food, every 12 hours. The suspension should be refrigerated.
- Cefdinir: can be taken with or without food. The suspension should not be refrigerated.

Penicillin VK

- Take this medication by mouth one hour before or two hours after a meal, usually every six hours.
- The suspension should be refrigerated.

QUINOLONES

- Antacids, didanosine *(Videx)*, sucralfate *(Carafate)*, bile acid resins, magnesium, aluminum, calcium, iron, zinc and multivitamins can bind to quinolones and prevent them from working properly. Take:
  - Ciprofloxacin two hours before or six hours after these drugs.
  - Levofloxacin two hours before or two hours after these drugs.
  - Moxifloxacin four hours before or eight hours after these drugs.
- Dairy products can decrease how well these antibiotics work. Avoid consuming calcium-rich foods (dairy products) with the dose.
- Drink plenty of fluids to prevent crystals from forming in the urine.
- This medication can cause tendon inflammation (tendinitis) or tendon rupture. It is rare, but if you hear or feel a pop, or notice pain/swelling in the back of the ankle (Achilles), shoulder, hand or other site, stop the medication and contact your healthcare provider immediately. This occurs more frequently if you are age ≥ 60 years, have had an organ transplant, or use steroid medications, such as prednisone.
- This medication can increase your risk for seizures. This is rare, but you should not take this medication if you have a history of seizures. Other effects include restlessness, anxiousness, trouble sleeping/nightmares, lightheadedness, dizziness, headaches or depression.
- This medication can make your skin more sensitive to the sun, and you can burn more easily. Use sunscreen, wear protective clothing and avoid sun exposure.
- Do not take this medication if you have myasthenia gravis. Breathing problems can occur.
- This medication can cause weakness or tingling/painful sensations in the arms and legs. If this occurs, contact your healthcare provider immediately.
- If you use blood sugar-lowering medications, your blood sugar may get unusually low. Check your blood sugar level more frequently and treat low blood sugar if it occurs.

Ciprofloxacin *(Cipro)*

- Do not use this medication if you take a different medication called tizanidine *(Zanaflex)*.
- The liquid suspension should not be refrigerated.

Levofloxacin *(Levaquin)*

- Take this medication once daily, with or without food. The suspension is taken one hour before or two hours after eating.
- The liquid formulation should not be refrigerated.

MACROLIDES

Azithromycin *(Zithromax)*

- Common dosing is two tablets on day 1, followed by one tablet daily on days 2 – 5.
- The tablets and immediate release oral suspension can be taken with or without food.
- The suspension should be stored at room temperature and should not be refrigerated.

Clarithromycin *(Biaxin)*

- Common side effects include abnormal (metallic) taste, diarrhea and GI upset.
- The tablets and oral suspension are taken twice daily, with or without food or with milk. *Biaxin XL* tablets should be taken with food.
- The liquid suspension should not be refrigerated.

TETRACYCLINES

Doxycycline *(Vibramycin*, Others)

- This medication can make your skin more sensitive to the sun, and you can burn more easily. Use sunscreen, wear protective clothing and avoid the sun.
- Take with a full glass of water and stay upright for 30 minutes to avoid GI irritation.
- This medication should be taken twice daily, 1 – 2 hours before, or 4 – 6 hours after antacids, vitamins, magnesium, calcium, iron, zinc, dairy products, or bismuth subsalicylate.
- *Oracea* should be taken on an empty stomach (one hour before or two hours after meals).
- Do not use this medication if you are pregnant, if you could become pregnant, or if you are breastfeeding.
- The liquid suspension should not be refrigerated.

Minocycline *(Minocin, Solodyn)*

- Take this medication with or without food, 1 – 2 times daily. Swallow the tablet or capsule whole with a full glass of water to decrease GI irritation.
- Do not use this medication if you are pregnant, if you could become pregnant, or if you are breastfeeding.

SULFAMETHOXAZOLE AND TRIMETHOPRIM *(BACTRIM)*

- Do not use this medication if you have an allergy to sulfa.
- Take with a full glass of water to prevent crystal formation in the urine. Take with or without food. If stomach upset occurs, take with food or milk.
- Do not use this medication if you are pregnant, if you could become pregnant, or if you are breastfeeding.
- This medication can make your skin more sensitive to the sun, and you can burn more easily. Use sunscreen, wear protective clothing, and avoid the sun.
- Shake the suspension prior to use. The suspension should not be refrigerated and it should be protected from light.

CLINDAMYCIN *(CLEOCIN)*

- Take by mouth, with or without food, 3 – 4 times a day. Take with a full glass of water to avoid GI irritation.
- The liquid suspension should not be refrigerated.

METRONIDAZOLE *(FLAGYL)*

- Common side effects include nausea and an unusual (metallic) taste in the mouth.
- Do not use any alcohol products while using this medication, and for at least three days afterward.
- Immediate-release tablets and capsules may be taken with food to minimize stomach upset.

NITROFURANTOIN *(MACRODANTIN, MACROBID)*

- Take this medication with food to help it get into the body and ↓ side effects. Swallow the medication whole.
- Nausea and headache may occur.
- This medication can cause your urine to turn dark yellow or brown in color. This is a harmless, temporary effect and will disappear when the medication is stopped. Dark brown urine can be a sign of liver damage. Seek immediate medical attention if you notice dark urine with any of the following: persistent nausea or vomiting, pale stools, unusual fatigue or if your skin and whites of your eyes become yellow.
- This medication can cause very serious (possibly fatal) lung problems. This is rare, but can occur within the first month of treatment or after long-term use of the drug (generally for 6 months or longer). Seek immediate medical attention if you develop symptoms of lung problems, including: persistent cough, chest pain, shortness of breath/trouble breathing, joint/muscle pain or bluish/purplish skin.

MUPIROCIN OINTMENT *(BACTROBAN NASAL)* 1 GRAM TUBE

- Place ½ the ointment from the tube into one nostril and the other ½ into the other nostril. Press the nostrils at the same time and let go; do this many times (for about 1 minute) to spread the ointment into the nose.
- Wash your hands after use.
- The most common side effects are burning and itching.

Select Guidelines/References

Guidelines available at the Infectious Diseases Society of America website (www.idsociety.org)

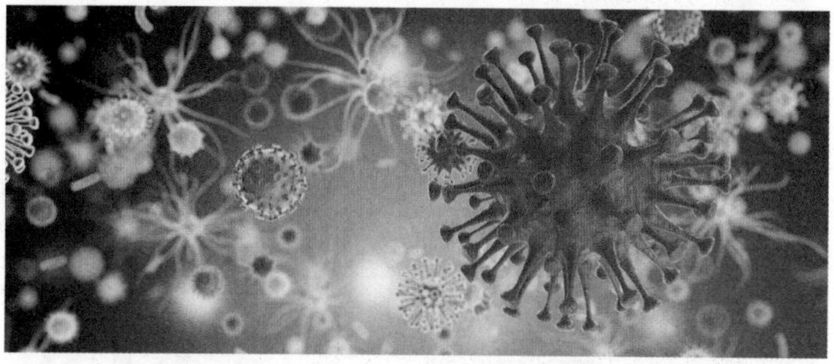

CHAPTER CONTENT

Background **375**
- Antibiotic Selection Principles 375
- Common Bacterial Pathogens for Selected Sites of Infection 376
- Assessment of Treatment 377

Perioperative Antibiotic Prophylaxis **377**
- Timing of Perioperative Antibiotics 377
- Perioperative Antibiotic Selection 377

Meningitis **378**
- Acute Bacterial Meningitis Treatment (Community-Acquired) 378

Upper Respiratory Tract Infections **379**
- Acute Otitis Media (AOM) 379
- AOM Treatment in Kids: When to Consider Observation 379
- Overview of Non-AOM Upper Respiratory Tract Infection Management 380

Lower Respiratory Tract Infections **380**
- Bronchitis 380
- Community-Acquired Pneumonia 381
- CAP Patient Assessment (Stepwise Approach) 382
- Hospital-Acquired and Ventilator-Associated Pneumonias 383
- Tuberculosis 384
- RIPE Therapy for TB 386

Infective Endocarditis **386**
- Infective Endocarditis (IE) Treatment 387
- IE Dental Prophylaxis 387

Intra-Abdominal Infections **387**
- Management of Secondary Peritonitis and Cholangitis 388

Skin and Soft-Tissue Infections (SSTIs) **388**
- Outpatient Treatment of *Staphylococci* (MSSA, MRSA) and *Streptococci* SSTIs 389
- Severe Skin and Soft Tissue Infections 390

Diabetic Foot Infections **390**
- Treatment of Moderate-Severe (Life or Limb-Threatening) Diabetic Foot Infections 391

Urinary Tract Infections (UTIs) **391**
- UTI Treatment 392
- Bacteriuria and Pregnancy 393

Travelers' Diarrhea **393**

***Clostridium difficile* Infection** **394**
- *C. difficile* Guideline Recommendations 394

Sexually Transmitted Infections **395**
- Symptoms of Common STIs 395
- Treatment of Sexually Transmitted Infections 395
- Gonorrhea & Chlamydia: They Often Go Together 396
- Penicillin Pregnancy Puzzler 396

Rickettsial Diseases and Related Infections **397**
- Lyme Disease or Ringworm? 397

CONTENT LEGEND

= Study Tip Gal

CHAPTER 23
INFECTIOUS DISEASES II: BACTERIAL INFECTIONS

BACKGROUND

Infectious Diseases I should be reviewed before this chapter, to gain a working knowledge of bacterial pathogens, microbiology reports, bacterial resistance and antimicrobial (antibiotic) drugs, including their coverage (spectrum of activity) and pharmacokinetic/pharmacodynamic properties that play an important role in selecting optimal treatment for infections.

ANTIBIOTIC SELECTION PRINCIPLES

- The presence of an infection is determined by signs and symptoms. For example, a positive urine culture does not determine the presence of an infection. The diagnosis must initially be made based on symptoms (e.g., dysuria, urgency, leukocytosis, fever) and a urinalysis. Once the diagnosis of infection is made, the culture helps guide an appropriate antibiotic choice.
- Infection characteristics include infection site, infection severity and whether it is community- or hospital-acquired. Infections that are hospital-acquired often involve multidrug-resistant (MDR) organisms.
- Antibiotic characteristics include the spectrum of activity and ability to penetrate the site of infection. Lipophilic antimicrobials have better tissue penetration. Antibiotics that are cleared hepatically may not achieve adequate drug concentrations in the urine.
- Patient characteristics impact treatment choices. These include age, body weight, renal and hepatic function, allergies, recent antibiotic use, colonization with resistant bacteria, recent environmental exposure, vaccination status, pregnancy status, immune function and comorbid conditions.
- A broad-spectrum regimen is often used empirically to ensure adequate coverage of the likely pathogens. Local resistance patterns and antibiotic use guidelines should be considered when selecting empiric treatment.
- When culture and susceptibilities are available, empiric antibiotics can be streamlined to narrower-spectrum treatment in order to limit collateral damage associated with broad-spectrum agents (e.g., *C. difficile* infections).

COMMON BACTERIAL PATHOGENS FOR SELECTED SITES OF INFECTION

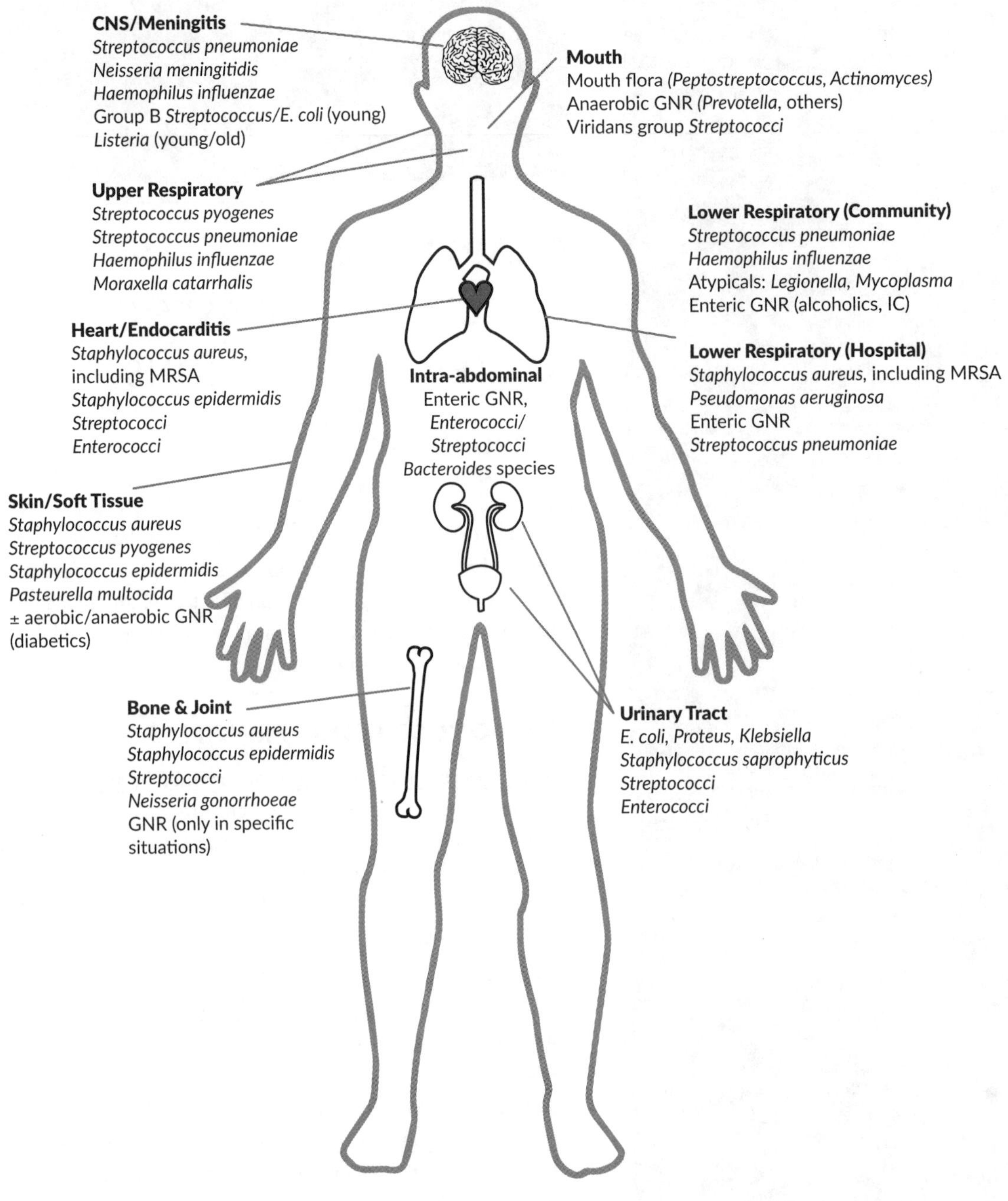

CNS = central nervous system, IC = immunocompromised, GNR = Gram-negative rods, Enteric GNR = *Proteus, E. coli, Klebsiella, Enterobacter*

Empiric Treatment

Select an empiric drug based on the likely organisms at the infection site. Is the patient at risk for MRSA? MDR bacteria? If yes, provide coverage. It is preferable to have the Culture and Susceptibility (C & S) report to select antibiotics, but this may not be complete in time. Typically, the Gram-stain and shape of the organism/s are available first.

Streamline

C & S available: streamline to narrow-spectrum antibiotics as soon as possible; if > 1 organism is present, attempt to cover multiple organisms with the same drug/s.

Is the patient eating normally? Is there an oral form of the drug that is able to penetrate the infection site? Consider IV:PO conversion.

Assess the Patient

Throughout treatment, monitor for improvement. The patient's condition can override the culture information; perhaps an identified organism is not the cause of the illness. With all antibiotics, set the duration of treatment; do not let antibiotics continue until discharge if not necessary.

ASSESSMENT OF TREATMENT

MONITORING TREATMENT RESPONSE	REASONS FOR LACK OF RESPONSE
Clinical status of the patient: 1. Fever trend (and other vital signs) 2. WBC trend 3. Reduction in signs and symptoms of infection Radiographic findings (such as CXR) Repeat cultures negative Decreased pain/inflammation – markers of inflammation include procalcitonin levels (more specific to bacterial infection), C-reactive protein (CRP) and erythrocyte sedimentation rate (ESR)	**Antibiotic factors** Inadequate spectrum and/or dose, poor tissue penetration, drug-drug interactions, non-adherence, inadequate duration of treatment **Microbiologic factors** Resistance, superinfection (*C. difficile*), alternative etiology (viral, fungal, noninfectious cause) **Host factors** Uncontrolled source of infection (e.g., abscess or fluid collection), immunocompromised

PERIOPERATIVE ANTIBIOTIC PROPHYLAXIS

When a surgeon cuts into the skin during an operative (surgical) procedure, organisms that live on the surface of the skin (primarily *Staphylococci* and *Streptococci)* can cause an infection. Intravenous (IV) antibiotics are given prior to surgery to reduce this risk. Cefazolin, a first-generation cephalosporin (or cefuroxime, a second-generation agent), are the preferred drugs for prophylaxis. In colorectal surgeries, the prophylactic antibiotic needs to cover skin flora plus broad Gram-negative and anaerobic organisms. Appropriate prophylactic options for colorectal surgery include cefotetan or cefoxitin. Alternatives, including options for patients with beta-lactam allergies, are shown in the table below. Vancomycin provides coverage for methicillin-resistant *S. aureus* (MRSA), methicillin-sensitive *S. aureus* (MSSA), *Streptococci* and *Enterococci* (but not vancomycin-resistant *Enterococcus*, referred to as VRE). The start time for antibiotics is important to achieve adequate tissue penetration at the start of surgery. See Study Tip Gal to the right for details on timing of antibiotics, when to give an additional dose and duration of antibiotics after surgery.

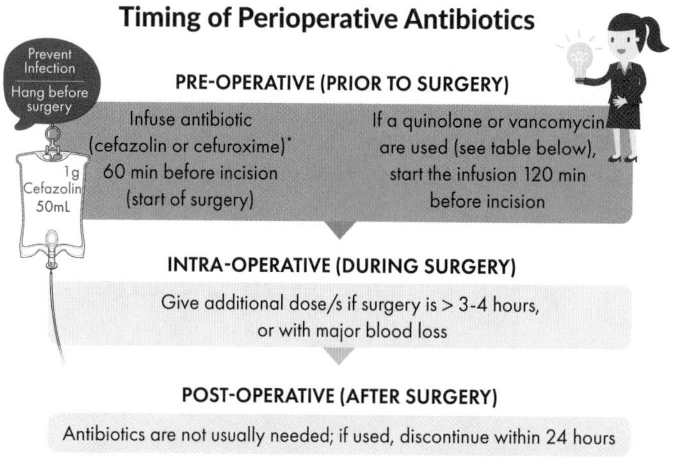

**Use vancomycin if there is a risk for MRSA (or if a beta-lactam allergy is present). For surgeries involving the bowel, or with risk for an anaerobic infection, provide broader Gram-negative and anaerobic coverage (see table below).*

PERIOPERATIVE ANTIBIOTIC SELECTION

SURGICAL PROCEDURE	RECOMMENDED ANTIBIOTICS*	IF BETA-LACTAM ALLERGY
Cardiac or vascular surgeries	Cefazolin or cefuroxime	Vancomycin or clindamycin
Hip fracture repair/ total joint replacement	Cefazolin	Vancomycin or clindamycin
Colon (colorectal)	Cefotetan, cefoxitin, ampicillin/sulbactam, ertapenem, or Metronidazole + (cefazolin or ceftriaxone)	Clindamycin + (aminoglycoside or quinolone or aztreonam), or Metronidazole + (aminoglycoside or quinolone)
Hysterectomy	Cefotetan, cefoxitin, cefazolin or ampicillin/ sulbactam	Clindamycin or vancomycin + (aminoglycoside or quinolone or aztreonam), or Metronidazole + (aminoglycoside or quinolone)

** For procedures and/or patients where MRSA is a likely pathogen, consider using vancomycin as routine prophylaxis.*

MENINGITIS

Meningitis is inflammation of the meninges (membranes) that cover the brain and spinal cord. The meninges swell, causing three classic symptoms: severe headache, nuchal rigidity (stiff neck) and altered mental status. Other symptoms could include chills, vomiting and photophobia. Meningitis symptoms must be quickly recognized and treated to avoid severe complications, including death.

Diagnosis is made with a lumbar puncture (LP), which takes a sample of cerebral spinal fluid (CSF) and analyzes it to help guide drug selection before the culture and susceptibility results are available. Some patients will need a computed tomography (CT) scan prior to the LP. It is preferable to get the LP prior to starting antibiotics; however, antibiotics should be given quickly, even when the LP is delayed.

Meningitis is mostly caused by viral infections, but can be due to bacteria or fungi. The most common bacteria causing meningitis are *Streptococcus pneumoniae, Neisseria meningitidis* and *Haemophilus influenzae*. The risk of meningitis caused by these pathogens can be decreased with vaccinations (see the Immunizations chapter for a detailed discussion). *Listeria monocytogenes* is prevalent in select patient groups (neonates, patients age > 50 years and immunocompromised patients) and requires additional treatment (with ampicillin). Recent surgery increases the risk of MRSA and MDR organisms, and will require different antibiotics.

ACUTE BACTERIAL MENINGITIS TREATMENT (COMMUNITY-ACQUIRED)

- Empiric antibiotic selection depends on age and risk factors (see the table below).
- Antibiotic durations are pathogen-dependent: 7 days for *N. meningitidis* and *H. influenzae*, 10 – 14 days for *S. pneumoniae* and 21 days for *Listeria monocytogenes*. Antibiotic dosages are aggressive (high) to penetrate the CNS.
- Dexamethasone can be given 15 – 20 min prior to or with the 1st antibiotic dose to prevent neurological complications. The adult dose is 0.15 mg/kg (rounded to 10 mg) IV Q6H. Steroid treatment should be continued for 4 days.

	AGE < 1 MONTH	AGE 1-23 MONTHS	AGE 2-50 YEARS	AGE > 50 YEARS OR IMMUNOCOMPROMISED

EMPIRIC TREATMENT	Ampicillin (for *Listeria* coverage) + Cefotaxime (no ceftriaxone*) or Gentamicin	Ceftriaxone or cefotaxime + Vancomycin	Adult doses: Ceftriaxone 2 grams IV Q12H or cefotaxime 2 grams IV Q4-6H + Vancomycin 30-45 mg/kg/day in divided doses	Ceftriaxone or cefotaxime + Vancomycin + Ampicillin (for *Listeria* coverage)
COMMON PATHOGENS	*S. agalactiae* *E. coli* *Listeria monocytogenes* *Klebsiella* spp.	*S. pneumoniae* *N. meningitidis* *S. agalactiae* *H. influenzae* *E. coli*	*S. pneumoniae* *N. meningitidis*	*S. pneumoniae* *N. meningitidis* *L. monocytogenes* Aerobic gram-negative bacilli
If severe PCN allergy: quinolone (moxifloxacin or levofloxacin) + vancomycin (± SMX/TMP 10-20 mg TMP/kg/day IV divided Q6-12H for *Listeria* coverage)				

**Neonates should not be given ceftriaxone due to the increased risk of biliary sludging (solids that precipitate from bile) and kernicterus (brain damage from high bilirubin).*

UPPER RESPIRATORY TRACT INFECTIONS

ACUTE OTITIS MEDIA (AOM)

Acute otitis media (AOM) is the most common childhood infection in the United States requiring antibiotic treatment. Signs and symptoms often have a rapid onset and can include bulging tympanic (eardrum) membranes, otorrhea (middle ear effusion/fluid), otalgia (ear pain), fever, crying and tugging or rubbing the ears.

- Systemic drugs are preferred for pain (acetaminophen or ibuprofen), rather than topical anesthetic drops.
- Most AOM is viral and antibiotics will be ineffective.
- Observation without antibiotics, for 48 – 72 hours, is an option for non-severe AOM, depending on age and the extent of infection. Severe symptoms include moderate-severe otalgia > 48 hours or temperature > 102.2°F. The decision for observation should involve both the pediatrician and the caregiver (see Study Tip Gal).

AOM TREATMENT IN KIDS: WHEN TO CONSIDER OBSERVATION

Try observation for 2-3 days if symptoms are non-severe (mild otalgia < 48 hrs or temperature < 102.2°F) and:

- Age 6-23 months: symptoms in one ear only.
- Age ≥ 2 years: symptoms in one or both ears.

If the symptoms do not improve or worsen, use antibiotics.

Example

A physician gives a prescription for amoxicillin to a parent whose son has non-severe AOM on the right-side only, and advises the parent:

"Don't fill it right away; hold on to it for a couple of days and see if he improves without medicine, which is likely. If he does not get any better, go ahead and get the medicine for him."

What does Mom or Dad usually do with the prescription?

Most often, they fill it and give it to their child.

Acute Otitis Media: Antibiotic Treatment

FIRST-LINE DRUGS AND DOSES	ALTERNATIVE TREATMENT (IF PENICILLIN ALLERGY)	TREATMENT FAILURE*
Amoxicillin: 80-90 mg/kg/day in 2 divided doses or Amoxicillin/Clavulanate**: 90 mg/kg/day of amoxicillin with 6.4 mg/kg/day of clavulanate, in 2 divided doses Amoxicillin to clavulanate ratio is 14:1	Cefdinir 14 mg/kg/day in 1 or 2 doses	Amoxicillin/Clavulanate**: 90 mg/kg/day of amoxicillin with 6.4 mg/kg/day of clavulanate, in 2 divided doses
	Cefuroxime 30 mg/kg/day in 2 divided doses	Ceftriaxone 50 mg/kg IM/IV daily for 3 days
	Cefpodoxime 10 mg/kg/day in 2 divided doses	
	Ceftriaxone 50 mg/kg IM/IV daily for 1 or 3 days	

*Not improved after 48-72 hours of initial treatment.
**May be considered in patients who have received amoxicillin in the past 30 days.*

- First-line treatment is high-dose amoxicillin (80 – 90 mg/kg/day divided Q12H) or amoxicillin/clavulanate (90 mg/kg/day of amoxicillin, divided Q12H). This amoxicillin dose covers most *S. pneumoniae*.
- With high-dose amoxicillin/clavulanate, the formulation with the least amount of clavulanate should be used, as it is less likely to cause diarrhea. *Augmentin ES-600* (amoxicillin 600 mg and clavulanate 42.9 mg per 5 mL) has a lower ratio of amoxicillin/clavulanate than other formulations.
- In children with a non-severe penicillin allergy, the American Academy of Pediatrics (AAP) recommends a cephalosporin. Although there is some risk of cross-reactivity, it is thought to be much lower than old estimates and is negligible with second- and third- generation cephalosporins (cefuroxime, cefdinir, cefpodoxime and ceftriaxone). Non-beta-lactam antibiotics that are suitable for use in children (e.g., azithromycin) have limited efficacy against the typical pathogens, due to resistance.
- Ceftriaxone (50 mg/kg) is given by IM or IV injection only, and is used in children who cannot swallow (NPO), those who have nausea and vomiting or when initial treatment fails. It is given once daily for 1 or 3 days (initial treatment) or for 3 days (treatment failure).
- The treatment duration for first- and second-line oral drugs is 10 days for children < 2 years, 7 days for ages 2 – 5 years and 5 – 7 days for ages ≥ 6 years.

Acute Otitis Media: Prevention

The pneumococcal conjugate vaccine (PCV13, *Prevnar 13*) series is recommended for all children starting at 2 months of age. The pneumococcal polysaccharide vaccine (PPSV23, *Pneumovax 23*) is recommended in select patients (see the Immunizations chapter for detailed information). Annual influenza vaccine should be given to all patients age ≥ 6 months. Prophylactic antibiotics should not be prescribed to reduce the frequency of AOM.

OVERVIEW OF NON-AOM UPPER RESPIRATORY TRACT INFECTION MANAGEMENT

The majority of upper respiratory tract infections are viral and antibiotics are not beneficial. With pharyngitis and sinusitis, antibiotics can be used if symptoms are severe or chronic and/or if there is microbiologic/diagnostic evidence of a bacterial infection.

	COMMON COLD	INFLUENZA	PHARYNGITIS	SINUSITIS

Typical Etiology	Respiratory viruses (rhinovirus, coronavirus)	Influenza virus	Respiratory viruses *S. pyogenes*	Respiratory viruses, *S. pneumoniae, H. influenzae* and *M. catarrhalis*; *Staphylococci*, anaerobes and Gram-negative rods can also be present in chronic sinusitis
Clinical Presentation	Congestion, headache, sore throat, cough, mild (low-grade) fever and runny nose; generally clears up in a few days	Sudden onset of fever, chills, fatigue, body aches, dry cough, sore throat and headache; symptoms are more severe than the common cold	"Strep throat" often presents with sore throat, fever, headache, swollen lymph nodes and white patches on the tonsils; there is an absence of cough or runny nose	Nasal congestion, purulent nasal discharge, facial pain/pressure, ear pain/pressure, dental pain, fever, headache and fatigue
Criteria for Anti-Infective Treatment	None	< 48 hours since symptom onset Severe illness (e.g., hospitalized) Symptoms plus risk factors for influenza complications Prophylaxis (for those at high risk of influenza complications or during an outbreak scenario)	Positive rapid antigen diagnostic test or positive *S. pyogenes* culture	≥ 10 days of symptoms or ≥ 3 days of severe symptoms (fever > 102°F, face pain, purulent nasal discharge) or Worsening symptoms after initial improvement
Anti-Infective options	None	Treatment: Oseltamivir x 5 days Baloxavir marboxil x 1 dose Zanamivir x 5 days Peramivir (IV) x 1 dose	Penicillin, amoxicillin or 1st/2nd generation cephalosporin If beta-lactam allergy: clarithromycin, azithromycin or clindamycin Treat for 10 days, except with azithromycin (5 days)	**First-Line** Amoxicillin/Clavulanate **Second-Line (failure of first-line treatment)** Oral 2nd or 3rd generation cephalosporin + clindamycin, doxycycline or a respiratory quinolone (levofloxacin, moxifloxacin, gemifloxacin) Treatment duration varies

LOWER RESPIRATORY TRACT INFECTIONS

BRONCHITIS

Bronchitis is an inflammation of the mucous membranes of the bronchi. It is classified as acute or chronic. Chronic bronchitis is treated with supportive measures, including fluids and analgesics; antibiotics are used only when exacerbations occur.

Acute Bronchitis

- Symptoms of acute bronchitis are usually self-limited and can include: cough lasting more than 5 days (up to 3 weeks) with or without sputum production, fatigue, headache and watery eyes. Systemic symptoms, such as fever, are rare.
- Acute bronchitis is primarily caused by respiratory viruses, including respiratory syncytial virus (RSV), adenovirus, rhinovirus, coronavirus, influenza virus and parainfluenza virus.

- In severe cases, a bacterial cause can be considered. Common pathogens include *Mycoplasma pneumoniae, H. influenzae, Bordetella pertussis* and *Chlamydophila pneumoniae.*
- Diagnosis is usually made by ruling out other causes of acute cough (e.g., common cold, acute asthma, pneumonia). Cultures are not routinely performed.

Acute Bacterial Exacerbation of Chronic Bronchitis

- Acute bacterial exacerbation of chronic bronchitis (ABECB) is primarily due to COPD, which is often diagnosed in older patients who smoke (or have a long history of smoking). ABECB can be referred to as a COPD exacerbation. It can flare repeatedly, which impacts quality of life for the patient. Most exacerbations are triggered by infections (bacterial or viral), pollution, pulmonary embolism or an unknown cause.
- ABECB is diagnosed based on the patient's presentation. The Global Initiative for Chronic Obstructive Lung Disease (GOLD) guideline defines an acute exacerbation as an acute increase in symptoms (e.g., dyspnea, increased sputum volume or purulence, cough or wheeze) beyond normal day-to-day variation that necessitates a change in COPD medications. Supportive treatment is often adequate, but if there is increased sputum purulence and/or volume, increased dyspnea or if mechanical ventilation is required, antibiotics should be given for 5 – 10 days.

BRONCHITIS: NOTES & TREATMENT

Acute Bronchitis (not COPD exacerbation)
Mild-to-Moderate Disease

↓

Supportive treatment (e.g., fluids to prevent dehydration, antipyretics for fever, antitussive agents, vaporizers)

↓

Pneumonia suspected?

↓

Check chest X-ray and consider antibiotics (see Community-Acquired Pneumonia section)

Confirmed or probable *Bordetella pertussis* (whooping cough)?

↓

Use antibiotics:
- Azithromycin 500 mg x 1, then 250 mg daily on days 2-5
- Clarithromycin 500 mg BID or 1 gram ER daily x 7 days
- SMX/TMP DS 1 tablet BID x 14 days

COPD patient with Acute Bacterial Exacerbation of Chronic Bronchitis (ABECB)

↓

Supportive treatment (e.g., oxygen, short-acting inhaled bronchodilators, IV or PO steroids)

↓

Use antibiotics if:
- Mechanically ventilated, or
- Purulent sputum* + ≥ 1 additional symptom, or
- All 3 of the following: ↑ dyspnea, ↑ sputum volume and ↑ sputum purulence

↓

Preferred antibiotics:
- Amoxicillin/clavulanate, or
- Azithromycin, or
- Doxycycline

Duration of treatment: 5-7 days

**Purulent sputum is thick and is often yellow or green. If sputum is purulent, only 1 additional symptom is needed to justify antibiotic treatment. Without purulent sputum, all 3 primary symptoms are needed to justify antibiotic treatment.*

COMMUNITY-ACQUIRED PNEUMONIA

Community-acquired pneumonia (CAP) is contracted outside of healthcare facilities and is one of the most common types of pneumonia. CAP can be bacterial, viral or fungal (rare). When symptoms are mild (e.g., the patient is not confined to bed, hospitalized or unable to complete daily activities), it can be termed "walking pneumonia." Most bacterial cases are caused by *S. pneumoniae, H. influenzae, M. pneumoniae* and possibly *C. pneumoniae*. Patients often present with fever, productive cough with purulent sputum and pleuritic chest pain. Rales (crackling noises) can be heard over the infected lobe on auscultation. A chest X-ray is the gold standard for the diagnosis of CAP; findings of "infiltrates," "opacities" or "consolidations" on a chest x-ray indicate pneumonia.

The antibiotic recommendations for CAP are designed to provide reliable empiric coverage of *S. pneumoniae*, atypical bacteria and, if risk factors are identified, additional pathogens such as *Pseudomonas aeruginosa* and MRSA. Coverage must be considered by specific antibiotic, rather than using class trends (e.g., ciprofloxacin is not used for CAP; it is not a respiratory quinolone because it does not reliably cover *S. pneumoniae*).

Outpatient CAP Treatment

Outpatient treatment of CAP requires an assessment of patient comorbidities and risk factors for drug-resistant *S. pneumoniae*. Outpatients who have not recently received antibiotics and who are otherwise healthy can receive a single-drug regimen with a macrolide or doxycycline. Patients with a history of recent antibiotic use, comorbidities or immunosuppression require broader coverage due to the possibility of drug-resistant *S. pneumoniae* (DRSP). This typically requires treatment with two drugs. Monotherapy with a respiratory quinolone is an option, but requires a careful review of the patient profile. Quinolones have many safety warnings and the risk of side effects is substantial (see the ID I chapter).

CAP PATIENT ASSESSMENT (STEPWISE APPROACH)

Step 1: check for a history of antibiotic use within the past 3 months

Step 2: look for comorbidities or immunosuppression

Step 3: decide whether the patient falls into Category 1 or Category 2 (see below)

Step 4: choose one option within the category. Be sure to look for allergies, drug-disease interactions (e.g., quinolones and seizures), drug-drug interactions (e.g., QT prolongation) and culture results (if available)

PATIENT CHARACTERISTICS	RECOMMENDED EMPIRIC REGIMEN
Category 1 **No antibiotic use within the past 3 months and previously healthy**	**Option 1** ■ Macrolide (azithromycin, clarithromycin, erythromycin) **Option 2** ■ Doxycycline
Category 2 **Risk for drug-resistant *S. pneumoniae* or comorbidities:** ■ Antibiotic use within the previous 3 months ■ Chronic diseases: heart, lung, liver or renal disease; diabetes mellitus; alcoholism; malignancies; asplenia ■ Immunocompromised or use of immunosuppressant drugs	**Option 1** ■ Beta-lactam + macrolide or doxycycline ❑ Amoxicillin (high-dose), amoxicillin/clavulanate, cefpodoxime, cefdinir, cefuroxime, ceftriaxone plus ❑ Macrolide or doxycycline **Option 2** ■ Respiratory quinolone monotherapy ❑ Moxifloxacin, gemifloxacin or levofloxacin

CLINICAL SCENARIO

RP is a 46-year-old female who presents to the urgent care clinic with shortness of breath, productive cough and a temperature of 100.2°F. A chest X-ray reveals a left lower lobe infiltrate. Her past medical history (PMH) includes back pain and schizophrenia. Her scheduled medications include *Geodon* 40 mg PO BID and trazodone 50 mg PO QHS. Which empiric antibiotic regimen should RP receive for pneumonia?

Stepwise approach: RP reports no recent antibiotic use and her PMH does not include immunosuppression or any of the chronic comorbidities listed in Category 2. She is not at risk for drug-resistant *S. pneumoniae* and can be treated per Category 1. The choice is between a macrolide, such as azithromycin, or doxycycline. Macrolides can prolong the QT interval. Since *Geodon* and trazodone can prolong the QT interval, doxycycline would be the best choice in this outpatient with CAP.

Inpatient CAP Treatment

Treatment for patients who are ill enough to require hospitalization for CAP is more complex and monotherapy with a macrolide or doxycycline is not recommended. Patients who are not in the ICU can be treated with IV or PO antibiotics. IV antibiotics are preferred for initial therapy in ICU patients. Treatment duration is typically 5 – 7 days. Regimens include:

- Beta-lactam + macrolide or doxycycline
  - Preferred beta-lactams: ceftriaxone, cefotaxime, ampicillin (IV) plus
  - Macrolide (azithromycin, clarithromycin, erythromycin) or doxycycline
- Respiratory quinolone monotherapy (due to safety risks, reserve quinolones for when a beta-lactam allergy is present)
  - Moxifloxacin, gemifloxacin or levofloxacin (IV or PO)
- If the patient has risk factors for *Pseudomonas*, the regimen must cover both *S. pneumoniae* and *Pseudomonas*. Options include: piperacillin/tazobactam, cefepime, imipenem/cilastatin or meropenem, plus either levofloxacin or an aminoglycoside and azithromycin. If MRSA is a concern, add vancomycin or linezolid.

HOSPITAL-ACQUIRED AND VENTILATOR-ASSOCIATED PNEUMONIAS

Hospitalized patients who develop pneumonia are at risk for infection with nosocomial pathogens (see the Common Pathogens in HAP and VAP section below). Hospital-acquired pneumonia (HAP) has an onset > 48 hours after hospital admission and occurs in non-mechanically ventilated patients. HAP is the leading infectious cause of death in ICU patients.

Mechanically ventilated patients are at especially high-risk of developing pneumonia. Ventilator-associated pneumonia (VAP) occurs > 48 hours after the start of mechanical ventilation and can negatively impact patient outcomes (e.g., prolonging duration of ventilation and hospitalization). The rate of VAP can be reduced by proper hand-washing, elevating the head of the bed by ≥ 30 degrees, weaning off the ventilator as soon as possible, removing nasogastric (NG) tubes when possible and discontinuing unnecessary stress ulcer prophylaxis.

Common pathogens in HAP and VAP

Nosocomial pathogens occur more commonly in HAP and VAP. MRSA is a common Gram-positive nosocomial pathogen. Gram-negative nosocomial pathogens include *P. aeruginosa, Acinetobacter* spp. and other Gram-negative rods (e.g., *Enterobacter* spp., *E. coli* and *Klebsiella* spp.).

Current guidelines recommend a careful assessment of patient risk for MDR pathogens (see the Risk Factors box to the right). These risk factors, along with the risk for patient mortality, are used to select the empiric antibiotic regimen. Coverage of MRSA and double coverage of *P. aeruginosa* are required in specific situations (see the table below).

RISK FACTORS FOR MDR PATHOGENS

Risk factors for MRSA, MDR *Pseudomonas* or other MDR pathogens in HAP/VAP

- IV antibiotic use within 90 days
- High prevalence of MRSA in the hosptial unit
- Positive MRSA nasal swab (indicates colonization)

Risk factors for MDR pathogens in VAP

- Hospitalization for ≥ 5 days prior to VAP
- Septic shock at the time of VAP onset
- Acute respiratory distress syndrome (ARDS) prior to VAP
- Acute renal replacement therapy (i.e., hemodialysis) prior to VAP onset

Treatment of HAP and VAP

RISK ASSESSMENT	RECOMMENDED EMPIRIC REGIMEN	
Target *Pseudomonas* and MSSA if the patient has: ■ HAP without a high risk of mortality and with a low MRSA risk ■ VAP without risk factors for MDR pathogens or MRSA	**Select one drug** Piperacillin/tazobactam Cefepime Levofloxacin Imipenem/cilastatin or meropenem	
Target *Pseudomonas* and MRSA if the patient has: ■ HAP without a high risk of mortality, but with MRSA risk ■ VAP without risk factors for MDR pathogens, but with risk for MRSA	**Select one drug (single coverage of *Pseudomonas*)** Piperacillin/tazobactam Cefepime or ceftazidime Levofloxacin or ciprofloxacin Imipenem/cilastatin or meropenem Aztreonam	**Plus an anti-MRSA drug (choose one)** Vancomycin Linezolid
Target MDR *Pseudomonas* and MRSA if the patient has: ■ HAP with a high risk of mortality, or received antibiotics in the past 90 days ■ VAP with risk factors for MDR pathogens or > 10% resistance to monotherapy drug	**Select two drugs; avoid two beta-lactams (double coverage of *Pseudomonas*)** Piperacillin/tazobactam Cefepime or ceftazidime Levofloxacin or ciprofloxacin Imipenem/cilastatin or meropenem Aztreonam Tobramycin, gentamicin or amikacin* Colistimethate* or polymyxin B*	

**These agents are always used in combination with another antipseudomonal drug.*

Duration of Treatment

Treat for 7 days. Shorter or longer treatment durations may be indicated based on clinical, radiologic and laboratory parameters.

TUBERCULOSIS

Tuberculosis (TB) is caused by *Mycobacterium tuberculosis* (an aerobic, non-spore forming bacillus). It primarily infects the lungs, but can disseminate (spread) to other organs. TB can be fatal if not treated properly and the incidence of MDR strains continues to increase. The disease has two phases: latent and active.

With latent disease, the immune system is able to contain the infection and the patient lacks symptoms. Active pulmonary TB is transmitted by aerosolized droplets (e.g., sneezing, coughing, talking) and is highly contagious. It most often presents with cough/hemoptysis (coughing up blood), purulent sputum, and fever/night sweats. Hospitalized patients with active pulmonary TB are isolated in a single negative pressure room; healthcare workers caring for the patient must wear a respirator mask (e.g, an N95 face mask).

Latent Tuberculosis Diagnosis

Latent disease can be diagnosed using the tuberculin skin test (TST), also called a purified protein derivative (PPD) test. The solution is injected intradermally and the area is inspected for induration (a raised area) 48 – 72 hours later. A false positive TST can occur in those who have received the bacille Calmette-Guerin (BCG) vaccine (used in areas of the world with high TB rates). A diagnostic blood test, the interferon-gamma release assay (IGRA) for latent tuberculosis, is available and preferred over TST in some groups. It is simpler in that it does not require a follow-up visit and can be used in patients who have received the BCG vaccine. If an IGRA is not available, TST is acceptable.

DIAGNOSIS OF LATENT TB: CRITERIA FOR POSITIVE TB SKIN TEST (TST) RESULTS

≥ 5 mm induration
Close contacts of recent TB cases
Significant immunosuppression
(e.g., HIV, taking transplant medications)

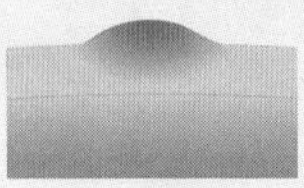

≥ 10 mm induration
Recent immigrants
IV drug users
Moderate immunosuppression
Residents/employees of "high-risk" congregate settings (e.g., prison inmates, healthcare workers)

≥ 15 mm induration
Patients with no risk factors

Induration = raised area

Latent Tuberculosis Treatment

Treatment of latent TB with one of the following regimens greatly reduces the risk of developing active disease:

- Isoniazid (INH) 300 mg PO daily (or 15 mg/kg PO twice weekly; max single dose is 900 mg) for 9 months. These regimens are preferred for HIV+ patients, pregnant women and children.
- Rifampin 600 mg daily for 4 months, if INH-resistant infection or patient does not tolerate INH.
- INH and rifapentine once weekly for 12 weeks (not recommended in HIV+ patients, children < 2 years old, pregnancy or presumed INH- or rifampin-resistant TB).

Rifampin + pyrazinamide is no longer recommended due to the risk of hepatotoxicity.

Active Tuberculosis Diagnosis

Active TB is a public health issue because it is highly contagious and can be difficult to treat. A positive TST is likely with active TB, but the diagnosis must be confirmed with a sputum culture. *M. tuberculosis* (MTB) is an acid-fast bacilli (AFB) and can be detected using an AFB stain in the laboratory. The acid-fast test is not specific to MTB and definitive diagnosis must be made using polymerase chain reaction (PCR) testing or culture results. MTB is a slow-growing organism; the final culture and susceptibility results can take up to 6 weeks.

Active Tuberculosis Treatment

Active TB treatment is divided into two phases (intensive and continuation). To avoid resistance, the preferred intensive phase regimen consists of four drugs: rifampin, isoniazid, pyrazinamide and ethambutol for two months (this regimen is known as "RIPE").

In the continuation phase, treatment can be scaled back to two drugs, depending on the drug susceptibility of the isolate, and continued for four months. The continuation phase is extended to seven months if: 1) there is evidence of cavitary pulmonary TB and the sputum culture remains positive after two months of treatment, 2) if intensive phase treatment did not include pyrazinamide or 3) if the patient is being treated with once weekly INH and rifapentine and has a positive sputum culture at the end of the intensive phase.

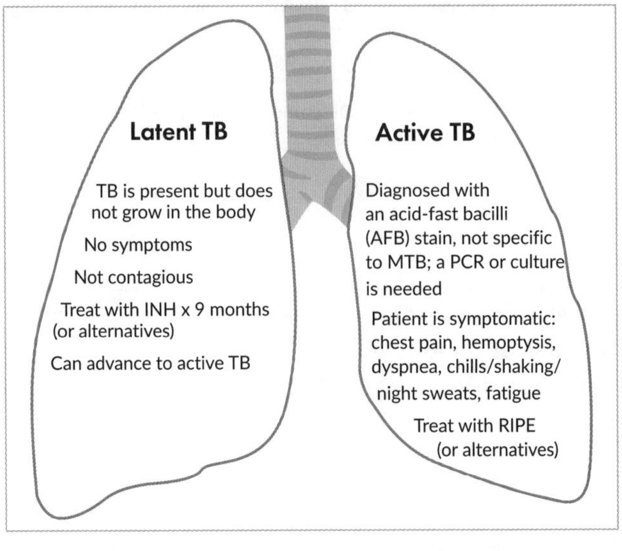

Use of Directly Observed Treatment (DOT) is used to increase medication adherence, and is preferred in select populations (homeless, drug resistant disease, adherence issues, positive sputum smears and delayed culture positivity). Alternate dosing regimens (2 – 3x per week) can be used in this setting. Daily dosing regimens are strongly encouraged if DOT is not possible.

TB can be resistant to INH and/or rifampin; if TB is resistant to both, it is called multidrug-resistant TB (MDR-TB). Resistant TB requires use of second-line agents and longer durations of treatment (up to 24 months). While many agents can be used, preferred drugs include quinolones (moxifloxacin or levofloxacin) or injectables (streptomycin, amikacin or kanamycin). Streptomycin given IM is an alternative agent to ethambutol, but it has toxicities and resistance is increasing. In extremely drug-resistant TB (XDR-TB), bedaquiline (*Sirturo*) can be used, but it has boxed warnings for QT prolongation and an increased risk of death compared to placebo.

Active TB Treatment Regimens

PREFERRED REGIMEN (TOTAL TREATMENT DURATION: 6 MONTHS)	
Intensive Phase	
Take all 4 drugs for 2 months (until cultures and susceptibilities are available)	RIPE: Rifampin (RIF) + Isoniazid (INH) + Pyrazinamide (PZA) + Ethambutol* Duration: 8 weeks
Continuation Phase	
Take 2 drugs for 4 months (based on culture and susceptibility results)	INH and RIF daily or 3x per week (if susceptible to INH and RIF) Duration: 18 weeks

**Ethambutol can be discontinued if culture and susceptibility results demonstrate susceptibility to first-line drugs.*

RIPE Therapy for Active TB

DRUG	DOSING	SAFETY/SIDE EFFECTS/MONITORING
Rifampin (*Rifadin*) + isoniazid (*Rifamate*) + isoniazid + pyrazinamide (*Rifater*)	10 mg/kg (max 600 mg) PO daily or 2-3x/week Doses differ for other indications Take on an empty stomach	**CONTRAINDICATIONS** Concurrent use with protease inhibitors (PIs) **SIDE EFFECTS** ↑ LFTs, orange-red discoloration of body secretions, positive Coombs test, flu-like syndrome, GI upset, rash/pruritus **NOTES** Orange-red discoloration of body secretions (sputum, urine, sweat, tears) - can stain contact lenses and clothing Rifabutin dosed 5 mg/kg/day (300 mg) can replace rifampin to avoid significant drug-drug interactions (e.g., HIV patient taking protease inhibitors)
Isoniazid (INH) + rifampin (*Rifamate*) + pyrazinamide + rifampin (*Rifater*)	5 mg/kg (max 300 mg) PO daily or 15 mg/kg (max 900 mg) 2-3x/week Take on an empty stomach Use pyridoxine 25 mg PO daily to ↓ the risk of INH-associated peripheral neuropathy	**BOXED WARNING** Severe (and fatal) hepatitis **CONTRAINDICATIONS** Active liver disease, previous severe adverse reaction to INH **WARNINGS** Peripheral neuropathy is rare, but occurs more commonly in patients predisposed to neuropathy (e.g., diabetes, HIV, renal failure, alcoholism, elderly and malnutrition); pyridoxine supplementation is recommended for these patients and patients who are pregnant or breastfeeding **SIDE EFFECTS** ↑ LFTs (usually asymptomatic), drug-induced lupus erythematosus (DILE), risk for hemolytic anemia (detected with a positive Coombs test), agranulocytosis, aplastic anemia, hyperglycemia, headache, GI upset, pancreatitis, severe skin reactions (SJS/DRESS), optic neuritis **NOTES** Store oral solution at room temperature
Pyrazinamide + rifampin + isoniazid (*Rifater*)	20-25 mg/kg PO daily (max daily doses vary based on weight) CrCl < 30 mL/min: extend interval	**CONTRAINDICATIONS** Acute gout, severe hepatic damage **SIDE EFFECTS** ↑ LFTs, hyperuricemia/gout, GI upset, malaise, arthralgias, myalgias, rash

DRUG	DOSING	SAFETY/SIDE EFFECTS/MONITORING
Ethambutol *(Myambutol)*	15-20 mg/kg (max 1.6 grams) PO daily or 25-30 mg/kg (max 2.4 grams) 3x/week or 50 mg/kg (max 4 grams) 2x/week Take without regard to meals CrCl < 50 mL/min: extend interval	**CONTRAINDICATIONS** Optic neuritis (risk vs. benefit decision); use in young children, unconscious patients or any patient who cannot discern and report visual changes **SIDE EFFECTS** Optic neuritis (dose-related), ↑ LFTs, ↓ visual acuity, partial loss of vision/blind spot and/or color blindness (usually reversible), rash, headache, confusion, hallucinations, N/V

Tuberculosis Agents Drug Interactions

- Rifampin is a potent inducer of CYP450 1A2, 2C8, 2C9, 2C19, 3A4 and P-glycoprotein. It can significantly ↓ the concentration and therapeutic effect of many other drugs (100+ are documented). Some notable interactions include ↓ serum concentrations of protease inhibitors (substitute rifabutin) and warfarin (a very large ↓ in INR is common), and ↓ efficacy of oral contraceptives. Apixaban, edoxaban, rivaroxaban and dabigatran should be avoided with rifampin. It is important to screen the medication profile for drug interactions with rifampin due to its extremely high potential for drug-drug interactions (DDIs). See the Learning Drug Interactions chapter.
- INH is a weak inhibitor of CYP1A2, 2C9 and 3A4, and a moderate inhibitor of CYP2C19 and 2D6. Use of INH can ↑ the levels of many other drugs, which can lead to toxicity. Enzyme inhibition can decrease the activation of other drugs that require conversion to an active metabolite. INH has MAO inhibitor activity; tyramine- and histamine-containing foods should be avoided.

RIPE THERAPY FOR TB

MONITOR INFECTION
Sputum sample, for culture
Chest X-ray (are lungs clear or clearing up?)

DRUG-SPECIFIC KEY POINTS

All RIPE Drugs
↑ LFTs, including total bilirubin – monitor

Rifampin
Orange bodily secretions
Strong CYP450 inducer (can use rifabutin if unacceptable DDIs)
Flu-like symptoms

Isoniazid (INH)
Peripheral neuropathy – give with pyridoxine 25 mg PO daily
Monitor for symptoms of DILE

Rifampin and INH
Take on an empty stomach
Risk for hemolytic anemia (identified by a positive Coombs test)

Pyrazinamide
↑ uric acid – do not use with acute gout

Ethambutol
Visual damage (requires baseline and monthly vision exams)
Confusion/hallucinations

Pyrazinamide and Ethambutol
↑ dosing interval with renal impairment

INFECTIVE ENDOCARDITIS

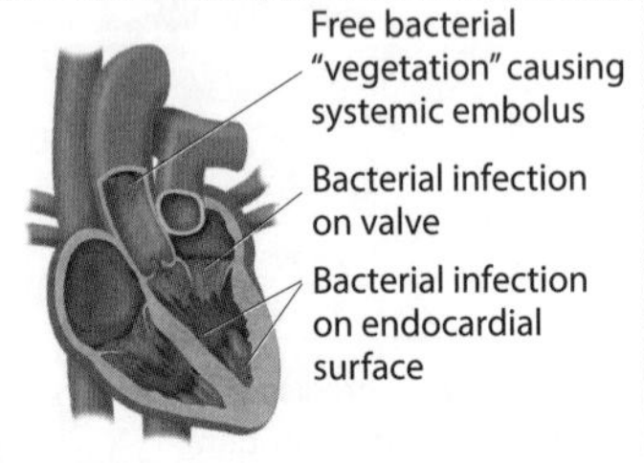

An infection of the inner tissue of the heart, typically the heart valves, is called infective endocarditis (IE). Patients who have prosthetic heart valves, chronic IV access, IV drug abuse or frequent and chronic healthcare exposure are some of those who are most at risk. The majority of patients present with fever, with or without a heart murmur. IE is diagnosed using the Modified Duke Criteria, which includes an echocardiogram to visualize the vegetation and positive blood cultures. The three most common species of organisms that cause IE are *Staphylococci, Streptococci* and *Enterococci*.

IE is generally fatal if left untreated. Empiric treatment often includes vancomycin and ceftriaxone. Definitive treatment, and antibiotic duration for IE, are dependent on the pathogen, the type of infected valve (native or prosthetic) and the susceptibility results. Gentamicin is added to primary antimicrobial therapy for synergy, when the infection is more difficult to eradicate, such as with prosthetic valve infections or when treating more resistant organisms. In some cases the risk of additive nephrotoxicity outweighs the benefit and it is left off of the regimen (e.g., when vancomycin is used for streptococcal endocarditis in patients with a beta-lactam allergy).

In general, 4 – 6 weeks of IV antibiotic treatment is required; when prosthetic valves and/or more resistant organisms are involved, treatment durations are at the upper end of this range or longer. The duration of gentamicin synergy varies from 2 – 6 weeks, depending on the organism being treated and the presence or absence of a prosthetic valve. When gentamicin is used for synergy, traditional dosing is used to target peak levels of 3 – 4 mcg/mL and trough levels < 1 mcg/mL. Extended interval dosing of aminoglycosides is less common when treating IE.

Some bacteria can form a biofilm (slime layer), especially on prosthetic valves. This is difficult for some antibiotics to penetrate. Rifampin is used in cases of staphylococcal prosthetic valve endocarditis, due to its ability to treat organisms in a biofilm.

INFECTIVE ENDOCARDITIS (IE) TREATMENT

ORGANISM	PREFERRED ANTIBIOTIC REGIMEN
Viridans group *Streptococci*	Penicillin or ceftriaxone (± gentamicin) If beta-lactam allergy, use vancomycin monotherapy
Staphylococci (MSSA)	Nafcillin or cefazolin (+ gentamicin and rifampin if prosthetic valve) If beta-lactam allergy, use vancomycin* (+ gentamicin and rifampin if prosthetic valve)
Staphylococci (MRSA)	Vancomycin* (+ gentamicin and rifampin if prosthetic valve)
Enterococci	Penicillin or ampicillin + gentamicin (for both native and prosthetic valve IE) If beta-lactam allergy, use vancomycin + gentamicin If VRE, use daptomycin or linezolid

**Daptomycin monotherapy is an alternative for MSSA and MRSA IE when the patient has a beta-lactam allergy and no prosthetic valve*

IE DENTAL PROPHYLAXIS

The mouth contains bacteria that can enter the blood during dental procedures and travel to the heart, where they can settle on the myocardial lining, a heart valve or a blood vessel. IE after dental procedures is rare, but risk is increased with certain cardiac conditions. In patients at high risk for IE, antibiotics should be used before all dental procedures that involve manipulation of gingival tissue (gums), the periapical region (near the root of the tooth) or perforation of the oral mucosa. See the following table for the risk criteria and recommended prophylaxis regimens.

PATIENTS AT HIGH RISK FOR IE	ADULT PROPHYLAXIS REGIMENS*
Dental work needed, such as a root canal **+** **Select cardiac conditions, including:** ▪ Artificial (prosthetic) heart valve or heart valve repaired with artificial material ▪ History of endocarditis ▪ Heart transplant with abnormal heart valve function ▪ Certain congenital heart defects including heart/heart valve disease 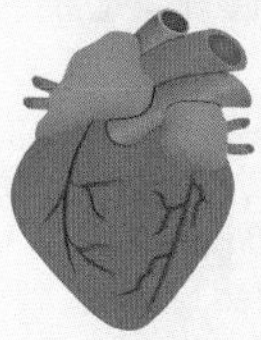	**Oral:** Amoxicillin 2 grams 30-60 min before dental procedure **If unable to take oral medication:** Ampicillin 2 grams IM/IV, or Cefazolin 1 gram IM/IV **If able to take oral medication but allergic to penicillins:** Cephalexin or cefadroxil** 2 grams, or Clindamycin 600 mg, or Azithromycin or clarithromycin 500 mg **If unable to take oral medication and allergic to penicillins:** Cefazolin or ceftriaxone** 1 gram IM/IV Clindamycin 600 mg IM/IV

**In pediatric patients, use weight-based doses of the same antibiotics.*

***Cephalosporins should not be used in an individual with a history of anaphylaxis, angioedema or urticaria with penicillins or ampicillin.*

INTRA-ABDOMINAL INFECTIONS

Intra-abdominal infections are a common cause of hospital admission and the second most common cause of infectious mortality in ICU patients. They are usually polymicrobial and can occur in any intra-abdominal organ or space. Types of infections include: primary, secondary and tertiary peritonitis, and biliary tract infections (cholecystitis and cholangitis).

Primary peritonitis, referred to as spontaneous bacterial peritonitis (SBP), is an infection of the peritoneal space that often occurs in patients with liver disease (e.g., cirrhosis). The most likely pathogens are *Streptococci*, enteric Gram-negative organisms (*Proteus*, *E. Coli* and *Klebsiella*, or PEK) and, rarely, anaerobes. The drug of choice is ceftriaxone for 5 – 7 days. Alternative treatments include ampicillin, gentamicin or a quinolone. SMX/TMP, ofloxacin and/or ciprofloxacin can be used for primary or secondary prophylaxis of SBP.

Secondary peritonitis is caused by a traumatic event (e.g., ulceration, ischemia, obstruction or surgery). Abscesses are common and should be drained, and damaged tissue may require surgery. The most likely pathogens are *Streptococci*, enteric Gram-negatives and anaerobes (*Bacteroides fragilis*). In more severe cases (critically ill patients in the ICU), coverage of *Pseudomonas* and CAPES organisms may be necessary.

Cholecystitis is an acute inflammation of the gallbladder due to an obstructive stone. It is usually managed surgically with a cholecystectomy. Infection may not be the precipitating factor, but is present in 50% of cases. If infection is present, likely pathogens and antimicrobial selection are similar to primary peritonitis. Cholangitis is an infection of the common bile duct and is generally managed with bile decompression and antimicrobial therapy. Likely pathogens and antimicrobial selection are similar to secondary peritonitis.

Treatment of intra-abdominal infections (with the exception of primary peritonitis) consists of selecting one or more antibiotics that will cover the likely pathogens, including anaerobes. This is accomplished with a single drug in some cases. If the antibiotic selected does not have anaerobic coverage, an additional antibiotic (usually metronidazole) must be added (see the ID I chapter for a detailed discussion of antibiotic coverage). Duration of treatment is 4 – 7 days for mild to moderate cases. Longer courses (7 – 14 days) may be needed in more severe cases. If an intra-abdominal abscess is present, ≥ 14 days of treatment may be required.

MANAGEMENT OF SECONDARY PERITONITIS AND CHOLANGITIS

MILD-TO-MODERATE INFECTIONS	HIGH-SEVERITY INFECTIONS (ICU PATIENT)
Cover PEK, anaerobes, *Streptococci* ± *Enterococci*	Cover PEK, CAPES, *Pseudomonas*, anaerobes, *Streptococci* ± *Enterococci*
Possible regimens include:	Possible regimens include:
Cefoxitin	Carbapenem (except ertapenem)
Ertapenem	Piperacillin/Tazobactam
Moxifloxacin	(Cefepime or ceftazidime) + metronidazole
(Cefazolin, cefuroxime or ceftriaxone) + metronidazole	(Ciprofloxacin or levofloxacin) + metronidazole
(Ciprofloxacin or levofloxacin) + metronidazole	(Aztreonam or aminoglycoside) + metronidazole

CAPES (nosocomial GNRs) = Citrobacter, Acinetobacter, Providencia, Enterobacter, Serratia; ICU = intensive care unit; PEK (enteric GNRs) = Proteus, E. coli, Klebsiella

SKIN AND SOFT-TISSUE INFECTIONS (SSTIs)

Skin and soft-tissue infections (SSTIs) can involve any or all layers of the skin (epidermis, dermis and subcutaneous fat), fascia and muscle. SSTIs usually result from the introduction of bacteria through breaks in the skin barrier, and less frequently from an infection that spreads from the bloodstream to the skin. Minor local trauma (small cuts, insect bites) can be the provoking event and can progress to a deeper infection.

SSTI CLASSIFICATIONS

Mild infection - Systemic signs* absent

Moderate infection - Systemic signs* present

Severe infection - Failed incision and drainage (I&D), if purulent + oral antibiotics, or signs of a deeper infection (fluid-filled blisters, skin sloughing, hypotension or evidence of organ dysfunction) or patient is immunocompromised

**Systemic signs: temperature > 100.4°F, heart rate > 90 BPM, WBC > 12,000 or < 4000 cells/mm³*

Measures to prevent bacterial skin infections include:

- Wash hands often.
- Cover open/draining wounds with clean bandages.
- Avoid water, including hot tubs, swimming pools and rivers/ocean if open wound/skin infection.
- Follow first aid measures (see the Common Skin Conditions chapter).

SSTIs can be broadly divided into infections that are superficial (impetigo, furuncles and carbuncles), nonpurulent infections that penetrate the subcutaneous tissues (cellulitis) and purulent infections (abscesses). Each is further categorized as mild, moderate or severe, which impacts the choice of antibiotics and the route (topical, PO or IV). Common antibiotics used for outpatient treatment of mild-moderate infections are listed in the following table. The list is not all-inclusive, but represents commonly used oral antibiotics.

OUTPATIENT TREATMENT OF *STAPHYLOCOCCI* (MSSA, MRSA) AND *STREPTOCOCCI* SSTIs

INFECTION	PRESENTATION	TREATMENT/COMMENTS
Superficial Infections		
Impetigo *Strep.* spp., *S. aureus* (most often MSSA) 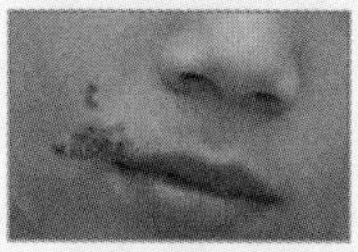	Common in children. A blister-like rash found anywhere on the skin, usually around the nose, mouth, hands and arms. Blisters produce a thick yellowish clear fluid that dries and forms honey-colored crusts over the area.	Use warm, wet compresses to help remove dried crusts. Apply a topical antibiotic, typically mupirocin *(Bactroban)*. Retapamulin *(Altabax)* and ozenoxacin *(Xepi)* are alternative treatments approved for impetigo. **If numerous lesions, use systemic antibiotics (cover MSSA):** ■ Cephalexin *(Keflex)* 250 mg PO QID
Folliculitis/furuncles/ carbuncles *S. aureus*, including community-acquired MRSA (CA-MRSA) 	Folliculitis: a hair follicle infection that looks like a red pimple. Furuncle (boil): an infection in the hair follicle and surrounding tissue. Carbuncle: a group of infected furuncles.	Folliculitis and furuncles may require only warm compresses to ↓ inflammation and help with drainage. Carbuncles require I&D to drain pus. **If systemic signs, use antibiotics for MSSA:** ■ Cephalexin *(Keflex)* 500 mg PO QID **If non-responsive to initial treatment, change to a drug with CA-MRSA coverage:** ■ SMX/TMP DS 1-2 tablets BID ■ Doxycycline 100 mg PO BID Occasionally, folliculitis is due to a fungal infection and can be treated with ketoconazole cream.
Cellulitis (Non-Purulent Infections)		
Mild infection *Streptococci*, including *S. pyogenes* (Group A Strep, GAS), *S. aureus* 	Mild symptoms: localized pain, swelling, redness, warmth. Often occurs on the legs.	**Oral antibiotics must be active against *Streptococci* (± MSSA):** ■ Cephalexin *(Keflex)* 500 mg PO QID ■ Clindamycin 300 mg PO QID (if beta-lactam allergy) Other antibiotics that cover *Streptococcus* can be used (e.g., penicillin VK, dicloxacillin). Duration of treatment: 5 days (longer if no improvement within 5 days). Moderate to severe infections require IV treatment; refer to chapter text for severity classification.
Abscess (Purulent Infections)		
Mild to moderate purulent infection Commonly caused by CA-MRSA 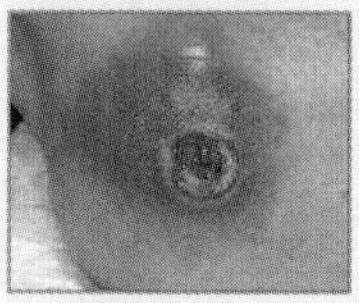	Initially appears as a fluid collection (abscess). Recurrent MRSA infections: consider nasal decolonization with nasal mupirocin, and skin decolonization with chlorhexidine or dilute bleach. Contagious; to avoid spreading, keep the lesion covered, do not share personal towels and wash sheets/towels/clothing in hot water.	Single abscess, no systemic signs (mild infection): primary treatment is I&D. **If systemic signs or multiple sites (moderate infection), perform I&D, culture fluid and use oral antibiotics that cover CA-MRSA:** ■ SMX/TMP DS 1-2 tablets BID ■ Doxycycline 100 mg PO BID ■ Minocycline 200 mg PO x 1, then 100 mg PO BID ■ Clindamycin 300 mg PO QID Linezolid also covers CA-MRSA, but is more expensive. If cultures show MSSA, use cephalexin *(Keflex)*.

**Mupirocin (Bactroban) topical cream or ointment can be used for superficial S. aureus and S. pyogenes infections.*

SEVERE SKIN AND SOFT TISSUE INFECTIONS

Severe purulent infections or those in more complicated patients (e.g., failed initial treatment, immunocompromised) require IV antibiotics initially. Drugs that are active against MRSA should be selected. Once the patient is stable and pathogen/s have been identified, it is often possible to transition to oral antibiotics to complete treatment.

INFECTION	NOTES	TREATMENT
Severe purulent SSTI	Duration of therapy: 7-14 days Animal or human bite infections require broader coverage of aerobic Gram-negatives (including *Pasteurella* spp. for animal bites), Gram-positives and anaerobes (e.g., ampicillin/sulbactam, amoxicillin/clavulanate).	Use antibiotics with MRSA (including CA-MRSA) activity: Vancomycin (goal trough 10-15 mg/L) Daptomycin Linezolid Telavancin Ceftaroline Tedizolid Dalbavancin Oritavancin Once clinically stable, transition to PO antibiotics.
Necrotizing fasciitis *S. pyogenes* (Group A Strep, GAS) is common, as well as some other bacteria, like *Clostridium* spp.	Fast moving type of skin infection that rapidly destroys tissue and can quickly penetrate down to the muscle, causing sepsis. Presentation: intense pain/tenderness over affected skin and underlying muscle, with reddish or purplish skin discoloration, edema and systemic signs. Refer for emergency treatment in a hospital with a surgical ICU.	Empiric therapy is broad: Vancomycin + beta-lactam (piperacillin/tazobactam, imipenem/cilastatin or meropenem).

DIABETIC FOOT INFECTIONS

Patients with diabetes are at high risk for foot infections because of neuropathic damage and compromised blood flow to the lower extremities. Foot infections are the most common cause of amputation in diabetic patients. Ulcers are evaluated for the presence of inflammation and purulence, and then classified by severity, which guides management (e.g., surgery and/or antibiotics). *Staphylococcus* spp. and *Streptococcus* spp. are the predominant pathogens in diabetic foot infections. Since infections can be polymicrobial, broad-spectrum empiric treatment is usually necessary. Cultures should be performed in order to narrow therapy whenever possible. Knowledge of antibiotics that cover common MDR pathogens (e.g., MRSA, *Pseudomonas*) and anaerobic organisms is important for identifying appropriate treatment on the exam.

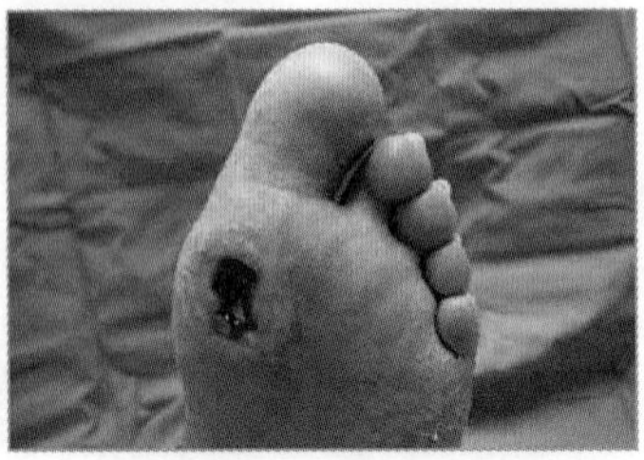

Most common cause of amputations.

Starts in soft tissue, can spread into bone (osteomyelitis).

Proper foot care is crucial to avoid infections.

It is imperative that patients follow proper foot care and evaluation, as discussed in the Diabetes chapter. If a deeper infection is present, such as osteomyelitis, longer courses of antibiotics (often IV) are required.

ETIOLOGY	GRAM-POSITIVE	GRAM-NEGATIVE
Aerobic	*S. aureus* (including MRSA) Group A *Streptococcus* Viridans group *Streptococci* *S. epidermidis*	*E. coli* *Klebsiella pneumoniae* *Proteus mirabilis* *Enterobacter cloacae* *Pseudomonas aeruginosa*
Anaerobic	*Peptostreptococcus* *Clostridium perfringens*	*Bacteroides fragilis* and others

TREATMENT OF MODERATE-SEVERE (LIFE OR LIMB-THREATENING) DIABETIC FOOT INFECTIONS

TYPE OF REGIMEN	TREATMENT	DURATION OF TREATMENT
Monotherapy options (when no MRSA coverage needed)	Ampicillin/sulbactam, piperacillin/tazobactam*, a carbapenem (imipenem/cilastatin*, meropenem*, ertapenem), tigecycline** or moxifloxacin	7-14 days More severe, deep tissue infection: 2-4 weeks Severe, limb-threatening or bone/joint infection: 4-6 weeks Osteomyelitis: requires longer courses of therapy and may require chronic suppressive therapy
Combination therapy options (when MRSA and *Pseudomonas* coverage needed)	Vancomycin plus one of the following: Ceftazidime*, cefepime*, piperacillin/tazobactam*, aztreonam* or a carbapenem* (except ertapenem) Note: consider adding anaerobic coverage (metronidazole) if ceftazidime, cefepime or aztreonam are selected Vancomycin alternatives: daptomycin or linezolid	

**Has Pseudomonas coverage.*
***Tigecycline is overly broad (covers MRSA) and should only be used when all other alternatives have been exhausted (see the ID I chapter).*

URINARY TRACT INFECTIONS (UTIS)

Most urinary tract infections (UTIs) occur in the lower urinary tract, which includes the bladder (cystitis) and the urethra. More severe infections can occur in the kidneys (pyelonephritis), or the upper urinary tract. UTIs are more common in females than males, as the female urethra provides a shorter route for organisms to travel up into the bladder. Sexual intercourse can facilitate this movement; women who commonly develop UTIs after intercourse may be prescribed prophylactic antibiotics.

UTIs are classified as uncomplicated or complicated. Uncomplicated UTIs are those that occur in non-pregnant, premenopausal women who have no urologic abnormalities or comorbidities. An infection in males is considered to be complicated because it is likely due to some type of abnormality or obstruction, such as an enlarged prostate. Complicated infections can also result from a neurogenic bladder (e.g., spinal cord injury, stroke, multiple sclerosis), an obstruction (e.g., a stone) or the presence of an indwelling catheter. All patients with catheters are at risk for catheter-associated infections (see the Medication Safety & Quality Improvement chapter for a discussion of ways to reduce this common, and often preventable, infection).

A urinalysis is considered positive when there is evidence of pyuria (positive leukocyte esterase or > 10 WBC/mm^3) and bacteriuria (≥ 10^5 bacteria/mL in asymptomatic patients, ≥ 10^3 bacteria/mL in symptomatic males and ≥ 10^2 bacteria/mL in symptomatic females and catheterized patients).

UTI SYMPTOMS

UTI (cystitis)
- Urgency and frequency (the feeling of needing to go often and quickly), including overnight (nocturia)
- Dysuria (painful urination, burning)
- Suprapubic heaviness
- Hematuria (blood in the urine)

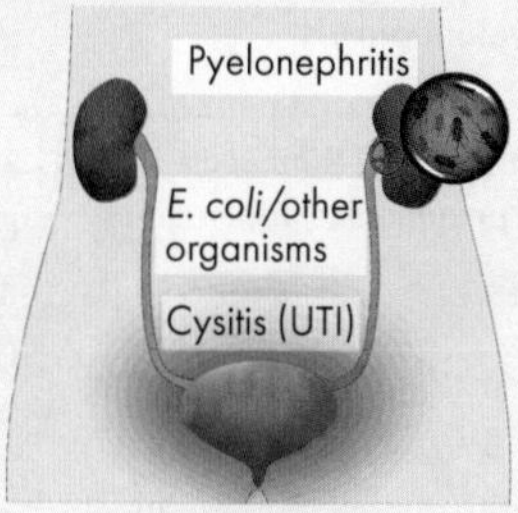

Upper UTI (pyelonephritis)
- Flank/costovertebral angle pain
- Abdominal pain, nausea and vomiting
- Fever and malaise

Vaginal *Candida albicans* (fungal infection)
- Extremely itchy with white, thick discharge (see the Common Skin Conditions chapter)

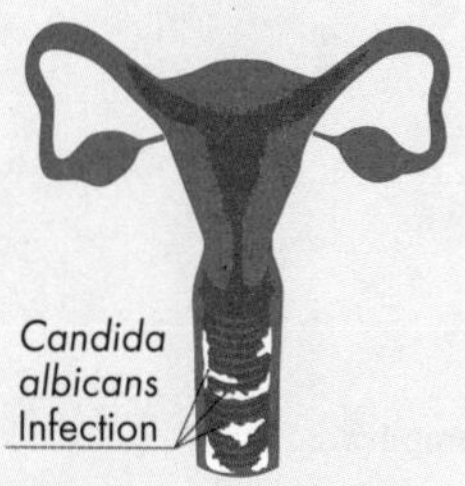

UTI TREATMENT

DIAGNOSIS	DRUGS OF CHOICE	COMMENTS
Acute uncomplicated cystitis Occurs in females of child bearing age (~15-45 years) Common pathogens: *Proteus, E. coli* (vast majority) and *Klebsiella* (PEK), *S. saprophyticus, Enterococci*	Nitrofurantoin (*Macrobid*) 100 mg PO BID with food x 5 days (contraindicated if CrCl < 60 mL/min) or SMX/TMP DS 1 tablet PO BID x 3 days (not with sulfa allergy or ≥ 20% *E. coli* resistance rate) or Fosfomycin 3 grams x 1 dose (inferior efficacy) **Alternative Options:** Beta-lactam (amoxicillin/clavulanate or cephalosporin) x 3-7 days or Ciprofloxacin 250 mg PO BID (or *Cipro ER* 500 mg PO daily) x 3 days* or Levofloxacin 250 mg PO daily x 3 days* *Quinolones: do not use in children, pregnant patients or those with seizures, neuropathy or QT prolongation risk; watch for tendinitis/rupture and BG changes (especially in patients with diabetes). Pregnancy: Cephalexin Amoxicillin Fosfomycin (if beta-lactam allergy) Treat asymptomatic pregnant women for 3-7 days. Pregnant women with acute cystitis (symptomatic) should be treated for 7 days.	Usually treated empirically as an outpatient. If no response with a 3 day course, check a urine culture and treat accordingly. Do not use moxifloxacin for UTIs (does not reach high levels in the urine) or gemifloxacin (limited activity against normal UTI pathogens). Prophylaxis: if ≥ 3 episodes in 1 year, can use SMX/TMP SS 1 tablet daily, nitrofurantoin 50 mg PO daily, or SMX/TMP DS 1 tablet after sexual intercourse. Can add phenazopyridine (*Pyridium*) 200 mg PO TID x 2 days to relieve dysuria.
Acute uncomplicated pyelonephritis Common pathogens: *E. coli, Enterococci, P. mirabilis, K. pneumoniae, P. aeruginosa*	**Moderately ill outpatient (PO)** If local quinolone resistance ≤ 10%: Ciprofloxacin 500 mg PO BID (or ciprofloxacin ER 1,000 mg daily) x 7 days Levofloxacin 750 mg PO daily x 5 days If local quinolone resistance > 10%: Ceftriaxone 1 gram IV x 1 or aminoglycoside extended-interval dose IV x 1, then continue with a quinolone (as above) x 5-7 days SMX/TMP x 14 days Beta-lactam (amoxicillin/clavulanate, cefdinir, cefaclor or cefpodoxime) x 10-14 days **Severely ill hospitalized patient (IV)** Initial: ciprofloxacin or levofloxacin; gentamicin (± ampicillin;, ceftriaxone or piperacillin/tazobactam (± gentamicin); a carbapenem Step down to oral treatment options based on culture & susceptibility results. Treatment duration: 14 days total (including IV and PO).	If risk for or documented *Pseudomonas* infection, consider piperacillin/ tazobactam or meropenem ± aminoglycoside.
Complicated UTI Common pathogens: *E.coli, Klebsiella, Enterobacter, Serratia, Pseudomonas, Enterococci, Staphylococci*	Similar options as noted above for pyelonephritis. If ESBL-producing bacteria are present, use a carbapenem. Treat for 7 days if there is prompt symptom relief. Treat for 10-14 days if there is a delayed response.	Urinalysis, urine and blood cultures are required. May be due to an obstruction or catheterization – remove or change catheter if possible. Plazomicin (*Zemdri*) is a newer aminoglycoside approved for use when there are no other treatment options for complicated UTI.

Urinary Analgesic

Phenazopyridine can help with dysuria (pain/burning with urination). Appropriate antibiotics will resolve symptoms promptly.

DRUG	DOSING	SAFETY/SIDE EFFECTS/MONITORING
Phenazopyridine (*Pyridium*, *Azo*, *Uristat* others) OTC and Rx 	200 mg PO TID x 2 days (max) Take with 8 oz of water, with or immediately following food, to minimize stomach upset	**CONTRAINDICATIONS** Do not use in patients with renal impairment or liver disease  *orange urine color* **SIDE EFFECTS** Headache, dizziness, stomach cramps, body secretion discoloration **NOTES** Can cause red-orange coloring of the urine and other body fluids; contact lenses/clothes can be stained Hemolytic anemia with G6PD deficiency (discontinue if hemolysis occurs)

BACTERIURIA AND PREGNANCY

Bacteriuria (≥ 10^5 bacteria/mL on a urinalysis) in pregnant women must be treated even if asymptomatic. If not treated, bacteriuria can lead to pyelonephritis, premature birth and neonatal meningitis.

- Beta-lactams are preferred (amoxicillin ± clavulanate or an oral cephalosporin).
- Nitrofurantoin and SMX/TMP can be used in patients with a beta-lactam allergy. The American College of Obstetricians and Gynecologists (ACOG) states that they should be avoided in the 1st trimester, if possible, and there are safety risks when used later in pregnancy (SMX/TMP can cause hyperbilirubinemia and kernicterus in the newborn if used close to delivery, and nitrofurantoin should be avoided in the 3rd trimester due to the possibility of hemolytic anemia in the infant).
- Fosfomycin can be considered for use in pregnant patients who have drug allergies.
- Quinolones should be avoided due to cartilage toxicity and arthropathies (see the ID I chapter for more information).

TRAVELERS' DIARRHEA

Travelers' diarrhea (TD) is a common travel-related illness and is primarily caused by ingestion of contaminated food or water. Bacteria causes 80% of TD cases, including enterotoxigenic *Escherichia coli, Campylobacter jejuni, Shigella* spp. and *Salmonella* spp. Viral diarrhea can involve a number of pathogens, most commonly norovirus and rotavirus. Protozoa, including *Giardia, Entamoeba histolytica, Cryptosporidium* and *Cyclospora*, are less common causes of TD.

Patients present with a sudden onset of symptoms, including loose stools, abdominal cramps/pain, fever, vomiting or dysentery (bloody diarrhea). These symptoms limit traveler activity. Protozoal diarrhea (e.g., caused by *Giardia* or *E. histolytica)* generally has a more gradual onset of low-grade symptoms, with 2 – 5 loose stools per day.

Azithromycin is preferred if dysentery is present. Quinolones (for 1 – 3 days) or rifaximin (for 3 days) can be used when invasive diarrhea is not present. Travel destination can impact the preferred treatment; in practice, always consult specific guidance. Adjunctive treatment, including antimotility agents (loperamide), provide symptomatic relief but should be avoided for bloody diarrhea or for patients with a fever (see Travelers and Constipation & Diarrhea chapters for information on prevention and symptomatic treatment).

TRAVELERS' DIARRHEA TREATMENT

Preferred treatment if fever or blood in stools, or if patient is pregnant or pediatric:

Azithromycin 1,000 mg PO x 1 or 500 mg PO daily x 1-3 days

Otherwise, choose one:

Ciprofloxacin 750 mg PO x 1 or 500 mg PO BID x 3 days

Levofloxacin 500 mg PO x1 or daily x 1-3 days

Ofloxacin 400 mg PO x1 or BID x 3 days

Rifaximin 200 mg PO TID x 3 days

Metronidazole, tinidazole and nitazoxanide should be reserved for TD caused by Protozoa (e.g., Giardia or Cryptosporidia).

CLOSTRIDIUM DIFFICILE INFECTION

The GI tract contains > 1,000 species of organisms as part of the normal flora. Antibiotics eliminate much of the "healthy" bacteria, allowing an overgrowth of *Clostridium difficile* (a Gram-positive, obligate anaerobic, spore-forming rod). Some types of *C. difficile* release toxins (toxin A and B) that attack the intestinal lining, causing inflammation of the colon (colitis). Symptoms of *C. difficile* infection (CDI) include abdominal cramps, profuse diarrhea (can be bloody) and fever. Inflammation of the colon can lead to pseudomembranous colitis, which can progress to toxic megacolon and result in colectomy or death. Rates of CDI have increased in recent years due to overuse of antibiotics. Other risk factors include recent healthcare exposure, use of proton pump inhibitors, advanced age, immunocompromised state, obesity and previous CDI.

CDI Treatment

Treatment recommendations vary based on whether it is the first infection or a recurrence. Review the profile to determine the recommended treatment. Probiotics are not beneficial for treatment; they may be useful for prophylaxis.

C. DIFFICILE GUIDELINE RECOMMENDATIONS

- If suspected (e.g., multiple loose stools), discontinue antibiotics as soon as possible
- Do not use anti-diarrheal medication (e.g., *Pepto-Bismol, Imodium, Lomotil)*
- Isolate patients (in a single room with a dedicated bathroom; use contact precautions – gown and gloves)
- After patient care/visits: wash hands with soap and water (do not use alcohol-containing hand sanitizers)
- Diagnosis: positive *C. difficile* stool toxin (enzyme immunoassay combined with a glutamate dehydrogenase test) or positive *C. difficile* culture

1ST EPISODE
Non Severe* or Severe*
VAN 125 mg PO QID x 10 days, or
FDX 200 mg PO BID x 10 days
If above treatments are not available and episode is non-severe*:
use MET 500 mg PO TID x 10 days

Fulminant/ Complicated Disease
VAN 500 mg PO/NG/PR QID +
metronidazole 500 mg IV Q8H

2nd EPISODE (1st Recurrence)
If MET used for initial episode:
VAN 125 mg PO QID x 10 days
If VAN used for initial episode:
FDX 200 mg PO BID x 10 days
If VAN or FDX used for initial episode:
VAN tapered** and pulsed regimen

SUBSEQUENT EPISODES
VAN tapered and pulsed regimen, or
VAN 125 mg PO QID x 10 days, then rifaximin 400 mg TID x 20 days, or
FDX 200 mg PO BID x 10 days, or
Fecal microbiota transplant

VAN = vancomycin; FDX = fidaxomicin (Dificid); MET = metronidazole

**Non-severe = WBC ≤ 15,000 cells/mm³ and SCr < 1.5 mg/dL; severe = WBC ≥ 15,000 cells/mm³ or SCr > 1.5 mg/dL; fulminant/complicated disease = significant systemic toxic effects present (e.g., hypotension, shock, ileus or toxic megacolon).*

*** Example vancomycin tapered and pulsed regimen = 125 mg PO QID x 10 days, BID x 1 week, daily x 1 week, then 125 mg every 2-3 days for 2-8 weeks.*

SEXUALLY TRANSMITTED INFECTIONS

Sexually transmitted infections (STIs) are acquired through sexual activity. Safer sex practices and education are important for prevention. Condoms (male and female) can help decrease transmission of STIs. Oral sex has a much lower risk of HIV transmission than vaginal or anal sex, but still carries risk for herpes, syphilis, hepatitis B, gonorrhea and HPV. The *Sheer Glyde* dental dam is FDA-approved for safer sex; it blocks passage of infectious organisms during oral contact.

Screening and prevention counseling should be performed for timely diagnosis of STIs and prevention of complications, including cervical cancer, infertility or transmission to partners. Sexual partners should be treated concurrently to prevent re-infection, except in bacterial vaginosis. See Study Tip Gal for usual symptoms of common STIs and the table below for treatment recommendations (refer to ID III for a discussion of herpes simplex virus).

SYMPTOMS OF COMMON STIs

Chlamydia: genital discharge or no symptoms

Gonorrhea: genital discharge or no symptoms

Syphilis: painless, smooth genital sores (chancre)

HPV: genital warts or no symptoms

Females only

Bacterial vaginosis: vaginal discharge (clear, white or gray) that has a "fishy" odor and pH > 4.5; little or no pain

Trichomoniasis: yellow/green frothy vaginal discharge; soreness, pain with intercourse

TREATMENT OF SEXUALLY TRANSMITTED INFECTIONS

INFECTION	DOC	DOSING/DURATION	ALTERNATIVES/NOTES
Syphilis *Treponema pallidum*, a spirochete Primary, secondary or early latent (< 1 year duration)	Penicillin G benzathine (*Bicillin L-A*, do not substitute with *Bicillin C-R*)	2.4 million units IM x 1	Doxycycline 100 mg PO BID or tetracycline 500 mg PO QID x 14 days Pregnant patients allergic to PCN should be desensitized and treated with *Bicillin L-A* (see Study Tip Gal on next page) Syphilis is diagnosed using the rapid plasma reagin (RPR) or the Venereal Diseases Research Lab (VDRL) blood test
Syphilis Late latent (> 1 year or unknown duration) or tertiary syphilis	As above	2.4 million units IM weekly x 3 weeks (7.2 million units total)	Doxycycline 100 mg PO BID or tetracycline 500 mg PO QID x 28 days Pregnant patients allergic to PCN should be desensitized and treated with *Bicillin L-A* (see Study Tip Gal on next page)
Neurosyphilis (including ocular syphilis) and **congenital syphilis**	Penicillin G aqueous crystalline		Penicillin G procaine
Gonorrhea *Neisseria gonorrhoeae*, a Gram-negative diplococcus Urethral, cervical, rectal, pharyngeal	Ceftriaxone plus either Azithromycin (preferred) or Doxycycline	250 mg IM x 1 1 gram PO x 1 100 mg PO BID x 7 days	Monotherapy is not recommended due to resistance Treatment covers co-infection with *Chlamydia* Ceftriaxone is most effective for pharyngeal infections If ceftriaxone is not available, use cefixime *(Suprax)* 400 mg PO x 1 + azithromycin (or doxycycline) with a test for cure in 1 week If severe cephalosporin allergy, use azithromycin (+ gemifloxacin or gentamicin) with a test for cure in 1 week
Chlamydia *Chlamydia trachomatis*, an intracellular obligate Gram-negative organism	Azithromycin or Doxycycline	1 gram PO x 1 100 mg PO BID x 7 days	Erythromycin base 500 mg PO QID x 7 days, or Levofloxacin 500 mg PO daily x 7 days, or Ofloxacin 300 mg PO BID x 7 days Pregnancy: azithromycin (preferred) or amoxicillin

INFECTION	DOC	DOSING/DURATION	ALTERNATIVES/NOTES
Bacterial Vaginosis Many different organisms	Metronidazole or Metronidazole 0.75% gel or Clindamycin 2% cream	500 mg PO BID x 7 days 1 applicatorful intravaginally daily or BID x 5 days 1 applicatorful intravaginally at bedtime x 3-7 days	Clindamycin 300 mg PO BID x 7 days (or clindamycin ovules* 100 mg intravaginally at bedtime x 3 days), or Tinidazole 2 g PO daily x 2 days (or 1 g PO daily x 5 days), or Secnidazole 2 g PO x 1 dose Females with bacterial vaginosis should not douche
Trichomoniasis *Trichomonas vaginalis*, a flagellated protozoan	Metronidazole or Tinidazole	2 grams PO x 1 2 grams PO x 1	Metronidazole 500 mg PO BID x 7 days Pregnancy: metronidazole (per package labeling) is contraindicated in the 1st trimester, but based on additional safety data, the CDC recommends metronidazole for trichomoniasis in all trimesters
Genital Warts *Human papillomavirus* (HPV)	Imiquimod cream (*Aldara, Zyclara*) *Aldara* also approved for superficial basal cell carcinoma and actinic keratosis	Apply topically to entire treatment area before bedtime, wash off after 8 hours. Apply 3x/week until cleared (or 16 weeks)	Treatment not required if asymptomatic. *Gardasil* vaccine protects against HPV strains that cause most genital warts and reduces risk of cervical and other cancers. See Immunizations chapter.

**Clindamycin ovules use a base that can weaken latex or rubber products (i.e., condoms); alternative contraception methods should be used within 72 hours of clindamycin ovules.*

GONORRHEA & CHLAMYDIA: THEY OFTEN GO TOGETHER

Gonorrhea treatment

Ceftriaxone 250 mg IM

+

Azithromycin 1 gram or doxycycline 100 mg BID x 7 days

THESE TREAT CHLAMYDIA TOO.

PENICILLIN PREGNANCY PUZZLER

Penicillin is the only treatment for syphilis during pregnancy.
Syphilis must be treated during pregnancy.

What if a pregnant female has syphilis and a penicillin allergy?

Per the CDC, follow these steps:

1. Confirm the allergic reaction with a skin test.
2. Desensitize the patient with an approved desensitization protocol.
3. Treat with IM penicillin G benzathine (*Bicillin L-A*)

Penicillin is also recommended for syphilis treatment in HIV-infected patients.

RICKETTSIAL DISEASES AND RELATED INFECTIONS

Rickettsial infections are caused by a variety of bacteria that are carried by many ticks, fleas and lice. The rickettsial diseases caused in humans are listed in the table below, along with the recommended treatments. Rocky Mountain spotted fever is the most common and most fatal rickettsial illness in the U.S. Initial signs and symptoms include fever, headache and muscle pain, followed by the development of a rash.

DISEASE	ORGANISM	TREATMENT
Rocky Mountain Spotted Fever	*Rickettsia rickettsii* Gram-negative obligate intracellular bacteria	Doxycycline 100 mg PO/IV BID x 5-7 days (also the drug of choice in pediatric patients)
Typhus	*Rickettsia typhi* Gram-negative obligate intracellular bacteria	Doxycycline 100 mg PO/IV BID x 7 days
Lyme Disease	*Borrelia burgdorferi, Borrelia mayonii* Spirochetes	Doxycycline 100 mg PO BID x 10-21 days, or Amoxicillin 500 mg PO TID x 14-21 days, or Cefuroxime 500 mg PO BID x 14-21 days
Ehrlichiosis	*Ehrlichia chaffeensis* Obligate intracellular bacteria	Doxycycline 100 mg PO/IV BID x 7-14 days
Tularemia	*Francisella tularensis* Aerobic Gram-negative coccobacilli	Gentamicin or tobramycin 5 mg/kg/day IV divided Q8H x 7-14 days

Select Guidelines/References

Bratzler DW, Dellinger EP, Olsen KM, et al. Clinical practice guidelines for antimicrobial prophylaxis for surgery. *Am J Health-Syst Pharm.* 2013;70:195-283.

Lieberthal AS, Carroll AE, Chonmaitree T, et al. The diagnosis and management acute otitis media. *Pediatrics.* 2013;31:e964-e999.

Mcdonald LC, Gerding DN, Johnson S, et al. Clinical practice guidelines for Clostridium difficile Infection in Adults and Children 2017 Update by the Infectious Diseases Society of America (IDSA) and Society for Healthcare Epidemiology of America (SHEA). *Clinical Infectious Diseases.* 2017;66:e1-e48.

Workowski KA, Golan GA. Sexually Transmitted Diseases Treatment Guidelines, 2015. *MMWR Recomm Rep* 2015;64(No. RR-3):1-137.

Guidelines available at the Infectious Diseases Society of America website (www.idsociety.org).

LYME DISEASE OR RINGWORM?

Lyme Disease

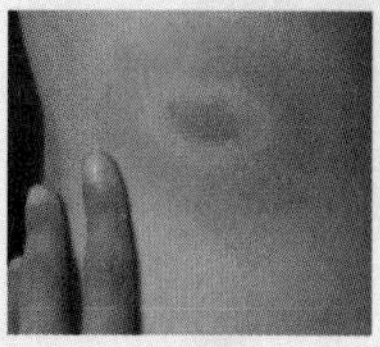

Bacterial (spirochete) infection
Borrelia burgdorferi and
Borrelia mayonii, spread by ticks

Bullseye rash (round, red), achy joints, fever

Diagnosis: ELISA test (identifies antibodies)
Treatment: doxycycline 100 mg BID PO/IV

Ringworm

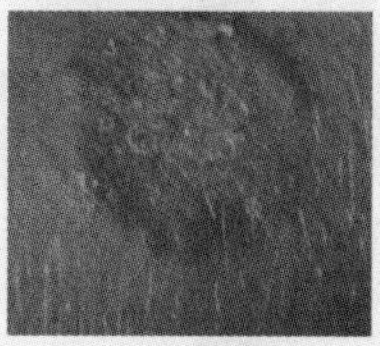

Fungal infection
Tinea corporis

1+ reddish, raised rings, can be itchy
Treatments: clotrimazole or another topical antifungal

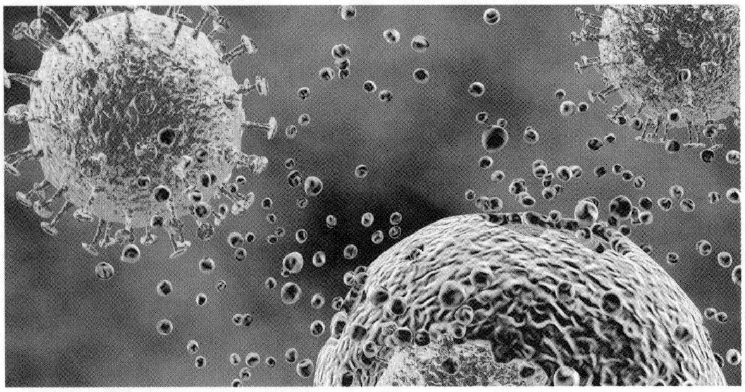

CHAPTER 24
INFECTIOUS DISEASES III: ANTIFUNGALS & ANTIVIRALS

CHAPTER CONTENT

Systemic Fungal Infections ... 398
Amphotericin B Deoxycholate and Lipid Formulations ... 399
Flucytosine ... 399
Azole Antifungals ... 400
Key Issues with Azole Antifungals ... 400
Echinocandins ... 402
Other Antifungal Agents ... 403
Treatment Recommendations for Selected Fungal Pathogens ... 404
Antifungal Patient Counseling ... 404
Viral Infections ... 405
Influenza ... 405
Herpes Viruses ... 406
Antivirals for Herpes Simplex Virus and Varicella Zoster Virus ... 407
Herpes Simplex Labialis (Cold Sores) ... 407
Genital Herpes ... 408
Invasive HSV Infections ... 409
Varicella Zoster Virus and Herpes Zoster ... 409
Cytomegalovirus ... 410
Epstein-Barr Virus ... 411
Antiviral Patient Counseling ... 411

SYSTEMIC FUNGAL INFECTIONS

Fungal infections cause a wide spectrum of disease, from mild infections such as nail bed infections, to severe infections such as meningitis or pneumonia. Invasive fungal infections are associated with high morbidity and mortality. Candidemia, the 4th most common cause of nosocomial bloodstream infections in the U.S., has a mortality rate up to 20%. Diagnosis of fungal infections can be made by culture, serologic studies, or histologic features of a tissue specimen.

Fungi are classified as either yeasts, molds, or dimorphic (see box). Dimorphic fungi exist as mold forms at lower temperatures and yeast forms at higher temperatures ("mold in the cold, yeast in the heat"). *Zygomycetes* refers to a class of fungi which includes *Mucor* species and *Rhizopus* species; invasive disease with this group is commonly referred to as "mucormycosis."

FUNGAL CLASSIFICATIONS

Yeasts	Molds
Candida species	*Aspergillus* species
C. albicans	*Zygomycetes* (*Mucor* and *Rhizopus* species)
C. tropicalis	**Dimorphic fungi**
C. parapsilosis	*Histoplasma capsulatum*
C. glabrata	*Blastomyces dermatitidis*
C. krusei	*Coccidioides immitis*
Cryptococcus neoformans	

Certain types of fungi (including yeasts such as *Candida*) can colonize body surfaces and are considered to be normal flora in the intestine. They do not normally cause serious infections unless they infect a normally sterile space (e.g., the blood), or if the immune system is weakened by drugs or diseases (e.g., chemotherapy, HIV). See Infectious Diseases (ID) IV for more information on opportunistic infections.

Some fungi reproduce by spreading microscopic spores. These spores are often present in the air, where they can be inhaled or come into contact with the skin, causing lung and skin infections and in some cases central nervous system infections. Long-term, systemic antifungals are necessary for certain invasive fungal infections (e.g., *Cryptococcus, Coccidioides*) in someone who is chronically immunosuppressed.

C. albicans is the most susceptible of the *Candida* species to drug treatment. *C. glabrata* and *C. krusei* tend to be more difficult to treat, due to resistance to certain azole antifungals. Of the molds, *Aspergillus* and *Zygomycetes* require the use of specific agents with adequate spectrum of activity.

CONTENT LEGEND

(💡) = Study Tip Gal

AMPHOTERICIN B DEOXYCHOLATE AND LIPID FORMULATIONS

Amphotericin B is a broad-spectrum agent. It binds to ergosterol, altering cell membrane permeability and causing cell death. Amphotericin B deoxycholate (the conventional form) has many toxicities. Lipid formulations are a complex of the active medication and a lipid component. They are used clinically because they are associated with fewer toxicities. Amphotericin B products are active against yeasts, molds and dimorphic fungi. They are used as initial treatment for many invasive infections, including *Cryptococcal* meningitis, histoplasmosis and mucormycosis.

FORMULATIONS	DOSING	SAFETY/SIDE EFFECTS/MONITORING
Conventional Formulation		**BOXED WARNINGS** Medication errors confusing the lipid-based forms of amphotericin (*AmBisome* and *Abelcet*) and conventional amphotericin B have resulted in death. Conventional amphotericin B for injection doses should not exceed 1.5 mg/kg/day; verify product name and dosage if dose exceeds 1.5 mg/kg/day. Overdose can result in cardiopulmonary arrest. **SIDE EFFECTS** Infusion-related: fever, chills, HA, malaise, rigors, hypotension/hypertension, thrombophlebitis, N/V. Other: ↓ K, ↓ Mg, nephrotoxicity, anemia. There have been rare reports of severe back/chest pain with the first dose of *AmBisome*. **MONITORING** Renal function, LFTs, electrolytes (especially K and Mg), CBC. **NOTES** Amphotericin B deoxycholate (conventional formulation) requires pre-medication to reduce infusion-related reactions. Give the following 30-60 minutes prior to infusion: ■ Acetaminophen or NSAID. ■ Diphenhydramine and/or hydrocortisone. ■ NS boluses to ↓ risk of nephrotoxicity. ■ ± meperidine to ↓ duration of severe rigors. Lipid formulations have ↓ infusion reactions and ↓ nephrotoxicity compared to conventional formulation; choice of formulation will depend on the site of infection and patient specific factors (e.g., renal dysfunction). Both formulations are yellow-orange in color. Lipid-based products are opaque.
Amphotericin B Deoxycholate Injection	0.1-1.5 mg/kg/day	
Lipid Formulations		
Amphotericin B Lipid Complex (*Abelcet*) Injection	5 mg/kg/day	
Liposomal Amphotericin B (*AmBisome*) Injection	3-6 mg/kg/day	

Amphotericin B Drug Interactions

- Additive risk of nephrotoxicity when used with other nephrotoxic agents such as aminoglycosides, cisplatin, colistimethate, cyclosporine, flucytosine, loop diuretics, NSAIDs, radiocontrast dye, tacrolimus and vancomycin.
- Can ↑ risk of digoxin toxicity due to hypokalemia. Use caution with any agent that ↓ potassium or magnesium since amphotericin decreases both. Scheduled replacement of potassium or magnesium should be considered.

FLUCYTOSINE

Flucytosine works by penetrating fungal cells where it is converted to fluorouracil, which competes with uracil, interfering with fungal RNA and protein synthesis. Due to development of resistance when used alone, flucytosine is recommended for use in combination with amphotericin B for treatment of invasive *Cryptococcal* (meningitis) or *Candida* infections.

DRUG	DOSING	SAFETY/SIDE EFFECTS/MONITORING
Flucytosine, 5-FC (*Ancobon*) Spectrum: covers yeasts, including *Candida* and *Cryptococcus*	50-150 mg/kg/day, divided Q6H PO CrCl < 40 mL/min: adjustment required	**BOXED WARNING** Use with extreme caution in patients with renal dysfunction. Closely monitor hematologic, renal and hepatic status. **SIDE EFFECTS** Dose-related myelosuppression (anemia, neutropenia, thrombocytopenia), ↑ SCr, ↑ BUN, hepatitis, ↑ bilirubin, many CNS effects, hypoglycemia, ↓ K, aplastic anemia **NOTES** Avoid use as monotherapy due to rapid resistance.

AZOLE ANTIFUNGALS

Azole antifungals decrease ergosterol synthesis and cell membrane formation. Azoles are inhibitors of the fungal CYP450 system (mainly CYP450 3A4), resulting in significant drug interactions as a class. The coverage and indications of azoles vary widely. Ketoconazole was the first azole, but due to toxicities and many significant drug interactions it is now most often used topically. Fluconazole has reliable activity against *C. albicans* and *C. tropicalis*. Itraconazole can be used as an alternative to fluconazole in some cases, as it is active against *C. albicans, C. tropicalis* and *Cryptococcus neoformans*, but use is often limited by drug interactions, lack of available data and expense. The primary uses for itraconazole are for the dimorphic fungi *Blastomycosis* and *Histoplasmosis* and for nail bed infections (onychomycosis). See the Common Skin Conditions chapter for treatment of non-invasive fungal infections, including onychomycosis.

KEY ISSUES WITH AZOLE ANTIFUNGALS

CLASS EFFECTS

- All can cause ↑ LFTs
- All have a risk for QT prolongation (except isavuconazonium)

DRUG SPECIFIC EFFECTS

Fluconazole

- The only azole that requires renal dose adjustment
- Narrower spectrum, covers *C. albicans* well
- Useful for vaginal candidiasis (non-pregnant)
- *C. glabrata* can be resistant and *C. krusei* is inherently resistant

Voriconazole

- Drug of choice for Aspergillus
- Monitor for visual changes, phototoxicity

Posaconazole and isavuconazonium

- Active against molds including *Aspergillus* and *Zygomycetes*
- Posaconazole: tablet dose ≠ suspension dose (due to different bioavailability)

DRUG	DOSING	SAFETY/SIDE EFFECTS/MONITORING
Ketoconazole *(Nizoral, Nizoral A-D, Extina, Xolegel* – all brand names are topicals) Tablet, cream, foam, gel, shampoo Used off-label to treat Cushing disease and advanced prostate cancer due to anti-androgenic activity (different dosing)	200-400 mg PO daily No adjustment in renal impairment	**BOXED WARNINGS** **Ketoconazole** Hepatotoxicity which has led to liver transplantation and/or death QT prolongation: use with cisapride, dofetilide, pimozide, and quinidine is contraindicated due risk of life-threatening ventricular arrhythmias such as torsades de pointes Use oral tablets only when other effective antifungal therapy is unavailable or not tolerated and the benefits outweigh risks (hepatotoxicity, adrenal insufficiency, drug interactions) **Itraconazole** Contraindicated for treatment of onychomycosis in patients with ventricular dysfunction or a history of heart failure Itraconazole can cause ↑ plasma concentrations of certain drugs and can lead to QT prolongation and ventricular tachyarrhythmias, including torsades de pointes. Coadministration with methadone, disopyramide, dofetilide, dronedarone, quinidine, ergot alkaloids, irinotecan, lurasidone, oral midazolam, pimozide, triazolam, felodipine, nisoldipine, ranolazine, eplerenone, cisapride, lovastatin, simvastatin and, in subjects with renal or hepatic impairment, colchicine, is contraindicated. **WARNINGS** Liver dysfunction, hepatotoxicity Fluconazole: not recommended in pregnancy, exfoliative skin disorders **SIDE EFFECTS** ↑ LFTs, QT prolongation, headache, N/V, abdominal pain, rash/pruritus, ↑ triglycerides, ↓ K, hypertension, edema, dizziness, hair loss (or possible hair growth) and altered hair texture with ketoconazole shampoo **NOTES** All azoles are cleared hepatically except fluconazole, which requires renal dose adjustment Fluconazole and voriconazole penetrate the CNS adequately to treat fungal meningitis (see voriconazole drug table next)
Fluconazole *(Diflucan)* Tablet, suspension, injection Spectrum: yeasts (including *C. albicans, C. tropicalis, Cryptococcus)* and *Coccidioides* Limited efficacy for *C. glabrata* due to resistance *C. krusei* is considered fluconazole-resistant	50-800 mg PO/IV daily Vaginal candidiasis: 150 mg PO x 1 CrCl ≤ 50 mL/min: ↓ dose by 50%	
Itraconazole *(Sporanox, Sporanox PulsePak, Tolsura)* Tablet, capsule, solution Spectrum: yeasts (*C. albicans, C. tropicalis*), dimorphic fungi, *Aspergillus*	200 mg PO daily-BID *Tolsura:* 130 mg PO daily-BID Capsules and oral solution are not interchangeable; oral solution is better absorbed Solution is taken without food; capsule and tablet are taken with food Limited data on use in renal impairment (use with caution)	

DRUG	DOSING	SAFETY/SIDE EFFECTS/MONITORING
Voriconazole *(Vfend, Vfend IV)* Tablet, suspension, injection Spectrum similar to itraconazole but better coverage of *Aspergillus* species, *C. glabrata* and *C. krusei*, compared to itraconazole/fluconazole No activity against *Zygomycetes (Mucor, Rhizopus)* Drug of choice for Aspergillosis	Loading dose: 6 mg/kg IV Q12H x 2 doses Maintenance dose: 4 mg/kg IV Q12H or 200 mg PO Q12H Hepatic impairment: reduce maintenance dosage by 50% (mild to moderate), only use if benefit outweighs risk, monitor closely (severe) CrCl < 50 mL/min: the intravenous vehicle SBECD (sulfobutyl ether beta-cyclodextrin) accumulates; oral voriconazole is preferred. If IV is used, monitor SCr and change to oral voriconazole when possible Therapeutic Range: Trough levels: 1-5 mcg/mL	**CONTRAINDICATIONS** Coadministration with astemizole, barbiturates (long-acting), carbamazepine, efavirenz (≥ 400 mg/day), ergot alkaloids, pimozide, quinidine, rifabutin, rifampin, ritonavir (≥ 800 mg/day), sirolimus, St. John's wort or terfenadine **WARNINGS** Liver damage, visual disturbances (optic neuritis and papilledema), phototoxicity (malignancy has been reported in patients with prior photosensitivity reactions on long-term voriconazole), avoid in pregnancy, QT prolongation (correct K, Ca, and Mg prior to initiating treatment), infusion-related reactions, serious skin reactions (SJS/TEN), skeletal adverse effects (fluorosis, periostitis) **SIDE EFFECTS** Visual changes (~20% - blurred vision, photophobia, altered color perception, altered visual acuity), ↑ LFTs, ↑ SCr, CNS toxicity (hallucinations, headache, dizziness), rash (SJS/TEN), photosensitivity, ↓ K, ↓ Mg, skeletal pain **MONITORING** LFTs, renal function, electrolytes, visual function (for > 28 days), CBC, trough concentrations **NOTES** Caution driving at night due to vision changes Avoid direct sunlight Hold tube feedings for 1 hour before and 1 hour after doses Suspension – shake for 10 seconds before each use. Do not refrigerate.
Posaconazole *(Noxafil)* Tablet, suspension, injection Spectrum similar to voriconazole plus *Zygomycetes (Mucor* and *Rhizopus)*	Suspension: 200 mg TID or 400 mg BID Give with a full meal (during or within 20 minutes following a meal) Tablets: 300 mg PO BID on day 1, then 300 mg PO daily with food (can range from 100-400 mg/day, divided in 1-3 doses) IV: 300 mg BID x 1 day, then 300 mg daily eGFR < 50 mL/min/1.73m^2: the IV vehicle SBECD (sulfobutyl ether beta-cyclodextrin) can accumulate and worsen renal function. Oral treatment is preferred.	**CONTRAINDICATIONS** Coadministration with sirolimus, ergot alkaloids, pimozide, quinidine, atorvastatin, lovastatin, simvastatin, pimozide or quinidine **WARNINGS** QT prolongation – correct K, Ca, and Mg prior to initiating therapy Prescribing and dispensing errors: suspension and tablet are not interchangeable as dosing regimens differ (tablet is better absorbed) Neurotoxicity with vincristine due to increased vincristine levels (seizures, peripheral neuropathy, SIADH, paralytic ileus) **SIDE EFFECTS** N/V/D, fever, headache, ↑ LFTs, rash, ↓ K, ↓ Mg, hyperglycemia **MONITORING** LFTs, renal function, electrolytes, CBC
Isavuconazonium sulfate *(Cresemba)* Capsules, injection Prodrug of isavuconazole Similar spectrum to posaconazole	IV/PO: 372 mg Q8H for 6 doses, then 372 mg daily No adjustment for renal dysfunction, use with caution in severe hepatic impairment Swallow capsules whole, do not crush or open; can be taken without regard to food	**CONTRAINDICATIONS** Use with strong CYP3A4 inhibitors or inducers, familial short QT syndrome **WARNINGS** Hepatic adverse drug reactions, infusion reaction (discontinue infusion if occurs), hypersensitivity reactions (anaphylaxis, SJS/TEN), embryofetal toxicity, drug interactions, particulates (undissolved drug) **SIDE EFFECTS** N/V/D, HA, infusion reactions (hypotension, dyspnea, chills, dizziness, tingling and numbness), peripheral edema, ↓ K, ↑ LFTs **MONITORING** LFTs, electrolytes **NOTES** Requires a filter (0.2-1.2 micron) during administration due to possible particulates Causes QT shortening (not prolongation) Capsules must be protected from moisture; original container has a desiccant

Azole Antifungals Drug Interactions

- All azoles are moderate-strong CYP3A4 inhibitors. In addition:
  - Itraconazole is an inhibitor of P-gp.
  - Ketoconazole inhibits P-gp.
  - Fluconazole inhibits CYP2C9 (strong) and 2C19 (strong).
  - Voriconazole inhibits CYP2C9 (moderate) and 2C19 (moderate).
  - Isavuconazonium inhibits CYP3A4 (moderate), and induces CYP2B6 (weak).
- Absorption of itraconazole and ketoconazole is pH-dependent; ↑ pH will ↓ absorption. Separate antacids two hours from doses. If PPIs and H2RAs must be used during antifungal therapy, administer itraconazole or ketoconazole with 8 oz. non-diet cola to provide an acidic environment for absorption.
- PPIs and cimetidine can decrease absorption of posaconazole suspension and should be stopped during therapy to avoid treatment failure.
- Voriconazole is metabolized by CYP2C19, 2C9 and 3A4; the voriconazole concentration can ↑ dangerously when given with drugs that inhibit voriconazole's metabolism or with small dose increases – it exhibits first-order, followed by zero-order (non-linear), kinetics.
- Avoid use of voriconazole with the following drugs: barbiturates (long-acting), carbamazepine, efavirenz (≥ 400 mg/day), ergot alkaloids, pimozide, quinidine, rifabutin, rifampin, ritonavir (≥ 800 mg/day), cobicistat, sirolimus and St. John's wort.
- Avoid use of isavuconazonium with strong CYP3A4 inhibitors or inducers.
- All azoles can ↑ INR in patients on warfarin – greatest risk with fluconazole, ketoconazole and voriconazole. Monitor INR.
- Strong CYP3A4 inhibitors can ↑ concentrations of apixaban and rivaroxaban. Monitor for s/sx of bleeding.

ECHINOCANDINS

Echinocandins inhibit synthesis of beta (1,3)-D-glucan, an essential component of the fungal cell wall. They are effective against most *Candida* species, including non-albicans strains that are resistant to azoles (e.g., *C. glabrata* and *C. krusei*). Activity includes *Aspergillus* species, but other medications are generally preferred for aspergillosis. They should be used as part of a combination regimen if used for *Aspergillus* species. Echinocandins are generally well-tolerated and are not associated with significant renal or hepatic toxicity. Echinocandins are available only as injections.

DRUG	DOSING	SAFETY/SIDE EFFECTS/MONITORING
Caspofungin ***(Cancidas)*** Injection	70 mg IV on day 1, then 50 mg IV daily Moderate hepatic impairment: 70 mg IV on day 1, then 35 mg IV daily ↑ dose to 70 mg IV daily when used in combination with rifampin or other strong enzyme inducers	**WARNINGS** Histamine-mediated symptoms (rash, pruritus, facial swelling, flushing, hypotension) have occurred; anaphylaxis **SIDE EFFECTS** ↑ LFTs, headache, hypotension, ↑ or ↓ K, ↓ Mg, fever, N/V/D, hyperglycemia, anemia, ↑ SCr, rash Severe skin reactions, including SJS/TEN (caspofungin) **MONITORING** LFTs **NOTES** All are given once daily and do not require dose adjustment in renal impairment Very few drug interactions
Micafungin ***(Mycamine)*** Injection	**Candidemia** 100 mg IV daily **Esophageal Candidiasis** 150 mg IV daily	
Anidulafungin *(Eraxis)* Injection	**Candidemia** 200 mg IV on day 1, then 100 mg IV daily **Esophageal Candidiasis** 100 mg IV on day 1, then 50 mg daily	

OTHER ANTIFUNGAL AGENTS

Systemic medications are considered second-line for treatment of superficial fungal infections. Topical products are preferred (see Common Skin Conditions chapter for topical antifungals). Griseofulvin is a less favorable agent, as it has a narrow antifungal spectrum, is less effective than other systemic agents (e.g., itraconazole or terbinafine), and requires prolonged courses. Nystatin suspension and clotrimazole troches/lozenges are useful for treating mild, localized *Candida* infections (e.g., thrush). Systemic treatment (e.g., fluconazole, micafungin) is required in patients with HIV and in moderate-severe infections, including esophageal candidiasis.

DRUG	DOSING	SAFETY/SIDE EFFECTS/MONITORING
Griseofulvin Tablet (microsize, ultramicrosize), suspension (microsize) Griseofulvin binds to keratin precursor cells which prevents fungal invasion; indicated for dermatomycosis and tinea infections of skin, hair and nails	Microsize: 500-1,000 mg/day in 1-2 divided doses Ultramicrosize: 375-750 mg/day in 1-2 divided doses	**CONTRAINDICATIONS** Severe liver disease, porphyria, pregnancy **SIDE EFFECTS** Photosensitivity, ↑ LFTs, HA, rash, urticaria, dizziness, leukopenia, severe skin reactions **MONITORING** LFTs, renal function, CBC **NOTES** Cross reaction possible with PCN allergy Take with a fatty meal to ↑ absorption or with food/milk to avoid GI upset Duration of therapy depends on site of infection. Tinea corporis: 2-4 weeks. Tinea pedis: 4-8 weeks
Terbinafine *(Lamisil*)* Tablet, topical Topical forms (Rx, OTC) Inhibits squalene epoxidase, a key enzyme in fungi sterol biosynthesis, resulting in a deficiency of ergosterol and buildup of squalene within the cell wall, leading to cell death	250 mg/day in 1-2 divided doses without regards to meals	**CONTRAINDICATIONS** Chronic or active liver disease **WARNINGS** Hepatotoxicity, taste/smell disturbance (including loss of taste or smell that can be permanent), depression, neutropenia, thrombotic thrombocytopenic purpura (TTP), hemolytic uremic syndrome (HUS), serious skin reactions (SJS/TEN/DRESS/erythema multiforme) Can cause or exacerbate systemic lupus erythematosus Confirm fungal infection prior to use for onychomycosis or dermatomycosis **SIDE EFFECTS** HA, ↑ LFTs, skin rashes, abdominal pain, pruritus, diarrhea, dyspepsia, taste disturbance **MONITORING** CBC, LFTs
Clotrimazole 10 mg troche/lozenge Topical and vaginal forms (*Mycelex*, multiple brand names)	**Oral Candidiasis** Prophylaxis: 10 mg 3x/day Treatment: 10 mg 5x/day x 14 days Allow troche to dissolve slowly over 15-30 minutes	**SIDE EFFECTS** ↑ LFTs, nausea, dysgeusia **MONITORING** LFTs
Nystatin *(Bio-Statin)* Suspension, tablet Topical forms (*Nyamyc, Nystop*)	**Oral Candidiasis** Suspension: 400,000-600,000 units 4 times/day; swish in the mouth and retain for as long as possible (several minutes) before swallowing **Intestinal infections** Oral tablets: 500,000-1,000,000 units Q8H	**SIDE EFFECTS** N/V/D, stomach pain Minimal GI absorption, low systemic risk

**Brand discontinued but name still used in practice.*

Drug Interactions

- Griseofulvin: can ↑ metabolism of hormonal (estrogen and progestin) contraceptives which can lead to contraceptive failure. Use a nonhormonal form of contraception.
- Terbinafine is a strong CYP2D6 inhibitor and a weak/moderate CYP3A4 inducer.

TREATMENT RECOMMENDATIONS FOR SELECTED FUNGAL PATHOGENS

PATHOGEN	FIRST-LINE TREATMENT
Candida albicans	**Oropharyngeal infection (thrush)** ■ Mild disease: topical antifungals (clotrimazole, nystatin) ■ If HIV+ or moderate-to-severe disease: fluconazole (PO) preferred **Esophageal infection** ■ Fluconazole or echinocandin **Bloodstream or other invasive infection** ■ If patient is not neutropenic: echinocandin (preferred), fluconazole (alternative) ■ If patient is neutropenic: echinocandin (preferred), amphotericin B or fluconazole (alternatives)
Candida glabrata or *Candida krusei*	Echinocandins or amphotericin B
Aspergillus	Voriconazole (preferred), liposomal amphotericin B, isavuconazonium
Cryptococcus neoformans	Induction in serious infections (meningitis): amphotericin B + flucytosine (5-FC) Consolidation: fluconazole (prolonged)
Coccidioides immitis	Fluconazole, itraconazole or amphotericin B
Histoplasma capsulatum	Liposomal amphotericin B followed by itraconazole
Zygomycetes class (*Rhizopus, Mucor*, etc.)	Amphotericin B ± posaconazole, isavuconazonium
Dermatophytes	Nail bed infections: itraconazole, terbinafine, or fluconazole (confirm fungal infection prior to treatment); see the Common Skin Conditions chapter

ANTIFUNGAL PATIENT COUNSELING

Azole Antifungals

- Common side effects include headache, nausea and abdominal pain.
- This drug can (rarely) damage the liver. Get immediate medical help if you develop any of the following: yellowing of the white part of your eyes or yellowing of your skin, dark-colored urine, light colored stool or severe stomach pain with nausea.
- There are many interactions with this drug and other medicines.

Ketoconazole *(Nizoral)* and Itraconazole *(Sporanox)*

- With ketoconazole and itraconazole: do not use with antacids. These medicines will reduce the amount of the antifungal medicine that gets into your system.
- Itraconazole tablets and capsules should be taken with food.
- Itraconazole solution should be taken on an empty stomach.

Voriconazole *(Vfend)*

- Avoid driving at night because this medication can cause vision problems like blurry vision. If you have any change in your eyesight, avoid all driving or using dangerous machinery. Vision changes are temporary and reversible.
- Avoid sunlight. Your skin can burn more easily. Your eyes can hurt in bright sunlight.
- Take this medication by mouth on an empty stomach, at least one hour before or one hour after meals, usually every 12 hours or as directed.
- The liquid suspension should not be refrigerated.
- This medication can cause harm to a baby if taken during pregnancy. Use effective contraception during treatment.

Posaconazole *(Noxafil)*

- Posaconazole tablets should be taken with food; posaconazole suspension should be administered during or within 20 minutes following a full meal or oral liquid nutritional supplement to maximize absorption.

Nystatin

- If you are using the suspension form of this medication, shake well before using. Be sure to swish the medication around in your mouth for several minutes before swallowing.

Terbinafine *(Lamisil)*

- The most common side effect is headache.
- Terbinafine is used to treat certain types of fungal infections (e.g., fingernail or toenail). It works by stopping the growth of fungus.
- Take this medication by mouth with or without food, usually once a day. Dosage and length of treatment depend on the location of the fungus and the response to treatment.
- It can take several months after you finish treatment to see the full benefit of this drug. It takes time for your new healthy nails to grow out and replace the infected ones.
- Skipping doses or not completing the full course of therapy can decrease the effectiveness of treatment, cause the infection to return, and increase the likelihood that this medication will not work for you in the future.
- This drug can (rarely) damage the liver. Get immediate medical help if you develop any of the following: yellowing of the white part of your eyes or yellowing of your skin, dark-colored urine, light colored stool, or bad stomach pain with severe nausea.

VIRAL INFECTIONS

Viruses depend on the host cell's metabolic processes for survival; for that reason they are sometimes referred to as obligate intracellular parasites. Many viral infections have no effective drug treatment. Medications are available to treat influenza virus, herpes simplex virus [genital herpes, herpes labialis (cold sores) and systemic herpes virus infections], varicella-zoster virus (VZV) and cytomegalovirus (CMV).

Treatments for viral infections work by either directly inhibiting viruses (antiviral agents) or augmenting or modifying host defenses to the viral infection (immunomodulating agents). Antivirals target critical steps in the viral life cycle, such as entry into the cell or replication. As viruses depend on hosts for metabolism/replication, antivirals can injure or destroy the host cells.

INFLUENZA

Influenza is a respiratory virus that affects 3 – 11% of the U.S. population annually, with peak activity typically occurring between late November and March. Influenza A and B are the strains that commonly infect humans. Both can cause severe illness, leading to hospitalization and death, particularly in at-risk patients (e.g., pregnant women, children age < 5 years, adults age ≥ 65 years, immunocompromised patients and those with comorbid conditions such as diabetes, asthma or cardiovascular disease). Influenza spreads via respiratory droplets generated by coughing and sneezing. A person with influenza can be contagious one day prior to developing symptoms and for up to 5 – 7 days after becoming ill. Influenza commonly presents with symptoms that include fever, chills, fatigue, body aches, non-productive cough, sore throat and headaches. The seasonal influenza vaccine is the most effective prevention for influenza infection and is recommended for all patients age ≥ 6 months who have no contraindications. See the Immunizations chapter for details.

Antivirals for Influenza

The Centers for Disease Control and Prevention (CDC) provides annual updates to the antiviral treatment recommendations based on the type of circulating virus each influenza season. Neuraminidase inhibitors (oseltamivir, zanamivir and peramivir) reduce the amount of virus in the body by inhibiting the enzyme which enables release of new viral particles from infected cells. They are active against both influenza A and B and decrease the duration of symptoms by about one day and reduce complications from influenza. To be most effective, neuraminidase inhibitors should be started within 48 hours of illness onset. In hospitalized, severely ill patients and those at high risk of complications, neuraminidase inhibitors should still be started > 48 hours after symptom onset. There is less benefit if started later, after the virus has already caused damage to respiratory epithelial cells.

A new class of antivirals, the endonuclease inhibitors, was recently approved for treatment of influenza. Baloxavir marboxil *(Xofluza)* is the first drug in this class. The most appropriate use for this drug is not yet well defined, but it has the advantage of a single dose regimen. It should be started within 48 hours of symptom onset. Adamantanes (rimantadine and amantadine) are only effective for influenza A, and in recent years have not been recommended as monotherapy due to resistance.

Neuraminidase Inhibitors

DRUG	DOSING	SAFETY/SIDE EFFECTS/MONITORING
Oseltamivir *(Tamiflu)* 30, 45, 75 mg capsules 6 mg/mL (60 mL) suspension 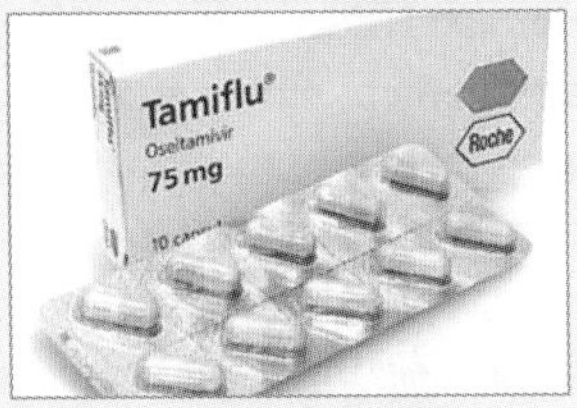	**Treatment, age > 12 years:** 75 mg BID x 5 days **Prophylaxis, age > 12 years:** 75 mg daily x 10 days **Pediatric patients:** dose is based on body weight **CrCl ≤ 60 mL/min: adjustment required**	**WARNINGS** Neuropsychiatric events (sudden confusion, delirium, hallucinations, unusual behavior, or self-injury), serious skin reactions (SJS/TEN), anaphylaxis **SIDE EFFECTS** Headache, nausea, vomiting, diarrhea, abdominal pain **NOTES** Preferred in pregnancy over other neuraminidase inhibitors
Zanamivir *(Relenza Diskhaler)* 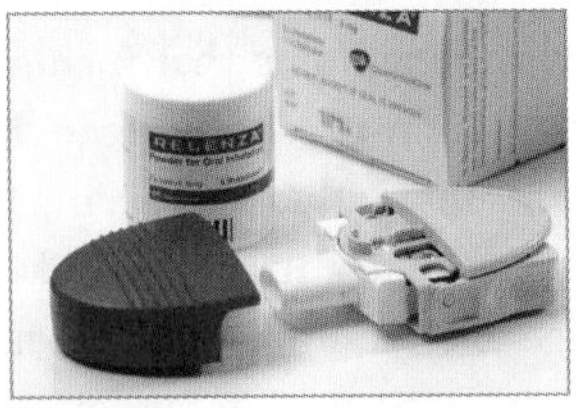	**Treatment, age ≥ 7 years:** 10 mg (two 5 mg inhalations) BID x 5 days **Prophylaxis, age ≥ 5 years:** 10 mg (two 5 mg inhalations) once daily x 10 days (household setting) or 28 days (community outbreak)	**WARNINGS** Neuropsychiatric events, bronchospasm (do not use in asthma/COPD or with any breathing problems); stop the drug if wheezing or breathing problems develop **SIDE EFFECTS** Headache, throat pain, cough
Peramivir *(Rapivab)* Injection	**Treatment (adult):** 600 mg IV as a single dose CrCl < 50 mL/min: adjustment required	**WARNINGS** Neuropsychiatric events, serious skin reactions (SJS/TEN), anaphylaxis, hepatic or renal impairment **SIDE EFFECTS** Hypertension, insomnia, increased blood glucose, diarrhea, constipation, neutropenia, ↑ AST/ALT

Endonuclease Inhibitors

DRUG	DOSING	SAFETY/SIDE EFFECTS/MONITORING
Baloxavir marboxil *(Xofluza)* Capsule	Treatment, age ≥ 12 years: 40 - < 80 kg: 40 mg PO x 1 dose within 48 hrs of symptom onset ≥ 80 kg: 80 mg PO x 1 dose within 48 hrs of symptom onset Use with caution in renal or hepatic impairment (limited data)	**SIDE EFFECTS** Diarrhea **NOTES** Avoid administration with dairy products, calcium, antacids or other supplements containing polyvalent cations (e.g., magnesium, selenium, zinc) Store in original blister packaging

Adamantanes

DRUG	DOSING	SAFETY/SIDE EFFECTS/MONITORING
Rimantadine *(Flumadine)* Tablet Amantadine – not recommended for influenza prophylaxis and treatment of influenza A due to resistance. Used for Parkinson Disease (see the Parkinson Disease chapter).	Treatment/Prophylaxis: 100 mg BID CrCl < 30 mL/min: adjustment required Hepatic impairment: use with caution	**WARNINGS** Seizures – use with caution in patients with a history of seizure disorder Psychosis – avoid use **SIDE EFFECTS** N/V, loss of appetite, dry mouth, insomnia, impaired concentration

HERPES VIRUSES

There are hundreds of herpes viruses in existence, but not all are responsible for causing human disease. Clinically significant herpes viruses include: herpes simplex viruses 1 and 2 (HSV-1, HSV-2), varicella-zoster virus (VZV), cytomegalovirus (CMV), Epstein-Barr virus (EBV), HHV-6, HHV-7 and Kaposi sarcoma associated herpes virus (HHV-8).

Both HSV-1 and HSV-2 can cause a variety of infections, including orofacial infection, genital infection, eye infections, encephalitis, esophagitis and pulmonary infections. HSV-1 is most commonly associated with oropharyngeal disease. HSV-2 is associated more closely with genital disease. Each virus is capable of causing infections clinically indistinguishable at both anatomic sites.

Infection with varicella zoster virus is commonly called chickenpox. After an occurrence of varicella zoster infection, the virus lies dormant in the nerve root and can later cause herpes zoster infection, often referred to as shingles.

Antivirals for Herpes Simplex Virus and Varicella Zoster Virus

DRUG	SAFETY/SIDE EFFECTS/MONITORING
**Acyclovir *(Zovirax,* *Sitavig)* Capsule, tablet, buccal tablet, suspension, injection, topical *Zovirax* cream, *Sitavig* – for cold sores (herpes simplex labialis)	**WARNINGS** Thrombocytopenic purpura/hemolytic uremic syndrome (TTP/HUS) has been reported in immunocompromised patients Caution in patients with renal impairment, the elderly, and/or those receiving nephrotoxic agents, infuse acyclovir over at least 1 hour and maintain adequate hydration to reduce risk of renal tubular damage **SIDE EFFECTS** Malaise, headache, N/V/D, rash, pruritus, ↑ LFTs, neutropenia, ↑ seizures (especially with IV acyclovir, famciclovir), transient burning or stinging with topical formulation Anaphylaxis (famciclovir) ↑ SCr/BUN with crystal nephropathy (IV acyclovir) **MONITORING** Renal function, LFTs, CBC **NOTES** Acyclovir dose is based on IBW; even in obese patients (see the Calculations IV chapter) Infuse acyclovir over 1 hour to prevent renal damage ↓ dose and/or extend interval in renal impairment In general, 5 mg/kg IV acyclovir = 1,000 mg PO valacyclovir
Valacyclovir *(Valtrex)* Tablet Prodrug of acyclovir	
Famciclovir *(Famvir)* Tablet Prodrug of penciclovir	

Herpes Simplex Labialis (Cold Sores)

Cold sores are ubiquitous and are highly contagious. Children often pick up the infection from family members. Infection is usually due to HSV-1 in children, but can be caused by HSV-2 when older due to oral/genital sex. Virus can be shed when asymptomatic, but is most commonly spread with active lesions; kissing and sharing drinks should be avoided when lesions are oozing. Sore eruption is preceded by prodromal symptoms (tingling, itching, soreness). In most patients the sore appears in the same location repeatedly. The most common site is the junction between the upper and lower lip. Triggers that cause sore outbreaks include stress/fatigue, stress to the skin (e.g., sun exposure, acid peels) and dental work. Patients should identify their own trigger/s and attempt to avoid them. The prodromal period is the optimal time to apply topical or take oral medication to reduce blister duration. If recurrences are frequent (> 4 times/year), chronic suppression can be taken daily. OTC and Rx topicals shorten the duration by up to one day; oral (systemic) antivirals shorten the duration by up to two days.

Topical Treatment for Herpes Labialis

DRUGS	DOSING	NOTES
Docosanol *(Abreva)* – OTC Cream	Apply 5x daily at first sign of outbreak, continue until healed.	Systemic antivirals are more effective. 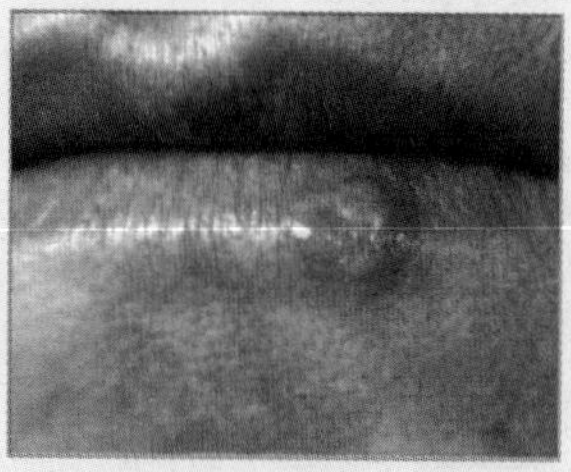
Acyclovir *(Zovirax)* – Rx Topical cream	Apply 5x daily for 4 days (can be used on genital sores).	
Acyclovir *(Sitavig)* – Rx Buccal tablet	Apply 50 mg tablet as a single dose to the upper gum region.	
Penciclovir *(Denavir)* – Rx Cream	Apply every 2 hours during waking hours for 4 days.	

Systemic Treatment of Herpes Labialis

HSV INFECTION	ACYCLOVIR	VALACYCLOVIR	FAMCICLOVIR
Initial episode	200-400 mg PO 5x daily or 400 mg TID x 7-10 days	2 grams PO BID x 1 day	
Recurrent episode	200-400 mg PO 5x daily x 5 days or 400 mg PO TID x 5 days or 800 mg PO BID x 5 days	2 grams PO BID x 1 day	1.5 grams PO x 1 dose
Chronic suppression	400 mg PO BID		

Genital Herpes

Genital herpes is a chronic, life-long viral infection. One in six people in the U.S. have HSV-2. The first episode of genital herpes usually begins within 2 – 14 days after exposure, but up to 50% of patients are asymptomatic. Symptoms of the first episode can include flu-like symptoms, fever, headache, malaise, myalgia, and development of pustular or ulcerative lesions on external genitalia. Lesions usually begin as papules or vesicles that rapidly spread. Clusters of lesions form, crust, and then re-epithelialize. Lesions are painful. Itching, dysuria, and vaginal or urethral discharge are common symptoms. Recurrent infections are not associated with systemic manifestations. Symptoms are localized to the genital area, milder, and of shorter duration. Patients typically experience a prodrome (symptoms that occur hours to days before lesions appear) which can consist of mild tingling or shooting pain in the legs, hips, thighs or buttocks.

Treatment must be initiated during the prodrome or within one day of lesion onset. Acyclovir *(Zovirax)* is the least expensive regimen, but, it must be dosed up to five times per day. Valacyclovir *(Valtrex)* is a prodrug of acyclovir that results in higher concentrations than with oral acyclovir and less frequent dosing that can enhance adherence. If the virus is found to be resistant to acyclovir, it will be resistant to valacyclovir. Famciclovir *(Famvir)* is a pro-drug of penciclovir. Strains resistant to acyclovir are generally resistant to famciclovir. Infections caused by acyclovir-resistant HSV are treated with foscarnet until the lesions heal.

Suppressive therapy (antivirals taken chronically) reduces the frequency of genital herpes recurrences by 70 – 80%. It is recommended for patients who have frequent recurrences (e.g., > 6 recurrences/year) and many report no symptomatic outbreaks. Viral transmission is also reduced.

Treatment of Genital Herpes In Non-HIV Patients

HSV INFECTION	ACYCLOVIR	VALACYCLOVIR	FAMCICLOVIR
Initial episode*	400 mg PO TID x 7-10 days or 200 mg PO 5x daily x 7-10 days	1 gram PO BID x 7-10 days	250 mg PO TID x 7-10 days
Recurrent episodes	400 mg PO TID x 5 days or 800 mg PO BID x 5 days or 800 mg PO TID x 2 days	500 mg PO BID x 3 days or 1 gram PO daily x 5 days	125 mg PO BID x 5 days or 500 mg PO x 1, then 250 mg PO BID x 2 days or 1 gram PO BID x 1 day
Chronic suppression	400 mg PO BID	500 - 1,000 mg PO daily	250 mg PO BID

**Treatment can be extended if healing is incomplete after 10 days of therapy*

Invasive HSV Infections

HSV is the most commonly identified cause of viral encephalitis in U.S. (10 – 20% of all cases). Cases of HSV encephalitis occur more frequently in young patients (ages 5 – 30) and older adults (age > 50 years). Hallmark symptoms include acute onset of fever, focal neurologic symptoms and altered mental status. HSV encephalitis is treated with IV acyclovir 10 mg/kg/dose Q8H x 14 – 21 days. Other invasive infections (e.g., esophagitis and pneumonitis) occur infrequently, typically in the immunosuppressed population, and are treated with IV acyclovir 5 mg/kg/dose Q8H.

Varicella Zoster Virus and Herpes Zoster

Most adults in the U.S. have had varicella zoster virus (chickenpox) infection during childhood. The virus can lie dormant in the nerve for decades without causing any symptoms. The recurrence of viral symptoms is called herpes zoster or shingles. The risk of herpes zoster increases with age, and older patients are more likely to experience postherpetic neuralgia, non-pain complications, hospitalizations and interference with activities of daily living. An outbreak can occur as the patient ages, and is often due to acute stress. Although herpes zoster can occur at any age, adults > 60 years old are most often affected. The shingles rash is distinctive - it can be itchy or tingly, is very painful and often manifests unilaterally (on only one side of the body). Pharmacists should be able to recognize a shingles rash and inform patients to see a physician; refer to the image.

Antiviral therapy should be initiated at the earliest sign or symptom of shingles and is most effective when started within 72 hours of the onset of zoster rash. Pain can be treated with topical agents (*Lidoderm* patch, lidocaine viscous gel), neuropathic pain agents (antiepileptic drugs, antidepressants), and NSAIDs or opioids. Most patients recover without long-term effects; 5 – 10% have chronic pain (called postherpetic neuralgia), which can be debilitating.

Shingles vaccines (*Shingrix, Zostavax*) can prevent shingles and shingles-related complications. *Shingrix* is recommended by the Advisory Committee on Immunization Practices (ACIP) over *Zostavax* in patients > 50 years of age as it has improved efficacy and duration of effect over time. Patients previously vaccinated with *Zostavax* should be re-vaccinated with *Shingrix* for this reason. *Zostavax* is still available, but only recommended by ACIP for patients ≥ 60 years of age. Vaccines should be used in patients who have experienced a previous shingles outbreak to decrease the likelihood of recurrence and severity of postherpetic neuralgia. See the Immunizations chapter.

Herpes Zoster (Shingles) Treatment

DRUG	DOSING	DESCRIPTION
Acyclovir *(Zovirax)*	800 mg PO 5x daily for 7days (or 10 days)	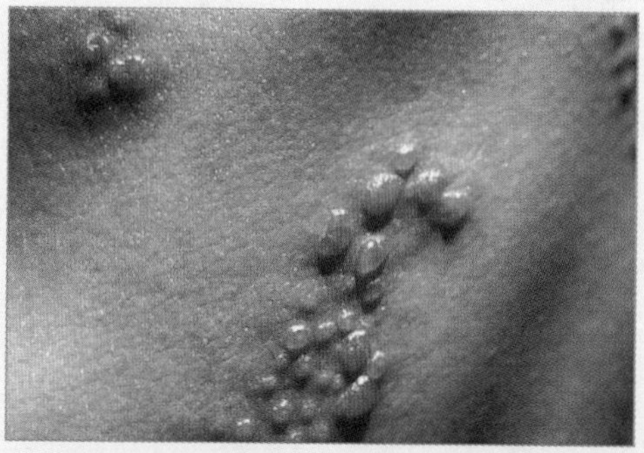 A cluster of fluid-filled blisters, often in a band around one side of the waist, on one side of the forehead, around an eye or on the neck (less common on other areas of the body)
Valacyclovir *(Valtrex)*	1 gram PO TID for 7 days	
Famciclovir *(Famvir)*	500 mg PO TID for 7 days	

Cytomegalovirus

Cytomegalovirus (CMV) is a double-stranded DNA virus within the herpes virus family (HHV-5). It occurs in severely immunocompromised states (e.g., AIDS, transplant recipients) and most commonly causes retinitis, colitis or esophagitis. Ganciclovir and valganciclovir are the treatments of choice for CMV disease. Foscarnet and cidofovir should be reserved for refractory cases of CMV infection, treatment limiting toxicities due to ganciclovir, and/or when the CMV strain is found to be resistant to (val)ganciclovir. Secondary prophylaxis (also called maintenance) is necessary in some patients (e.g., HIV patients with CMV retinitis and CD4+ counts < 50 cells/mm^3); valganciclovir is preferred. Letermovir *(Prevymis)*, a non-nucleoside CMV inhibitor, is FDA-approved for the prophylaxis of CMV in patients receiving a hematopoietic stem cell transplant who screen positive for CMV.

DRUG	DOSING	SAFETY/SIDE EFFECTS/MONITORING
Ganciclovir **(*Cytovene*** injection, *Zirgan* ophthalmic gel)	Treatment: 5 mg/kg IV BID Maintenance/secondary prophylaxis: 5 mg/kg IV daily ↓ dose and extend interval when CrCl < 70 mL/min Prepare in sterile water, not bacteriostatic (ganciclovir) Hazardous agents: special handling required	**BOXED WARNINGS** Myelosuppression; carcinogenic and teratogenic effects and inhibition of spermatogenesis in animals **SIDE EFFECTS** Fever, N/V/D, anorexia, thrombocytopenia, neutropenia, leukopenia, anemia, ↑ SCr, seizures (rare), retinal detachment (valganciclovir) **MONITORING** CBC with differential, PLT, SCr, retinal exam (valganciclovir) **NOTES** Patients of reproductive potential: females should use contraception during treatment and for 30 days after, males for 90 days IV ganciclovir 5 mg/kg = PO valganciclovir 900 mg Ganciclovir and valganciclovir are the drugs of choice for CMV disease Suspension: refrigerate; discard after 49 days
Valganciclovir ***(Valcyte)*** Tablet, suspension Prodrug of ganciclovir with good bioavailability	Treatment: 900 mg PO BID x 21 days Maintenance/secondary prophylaxis: 900 mg PO daily ↓ dose and extend interval when CrCl < 60 mL/min Hazardous agents: special handling required	
Cidofovir Injection CMV retinitis in HIV patients only	5 mg/kg/wk IV x 2 weeks, then 5 mg/kg once every 2 weeks Hazardous agent: special handling required Renal impairment: ↓ dose or discontinue based on level of SCr increase (also see Contraindications)	**BOXED WARNINGS** Dose-dependent nephrotoxicity, neutropenia, carcinogenic/teratogenic **CONTRAINDICATIONS** SCr > 1.5 mg/dL, CrCl ≤ 55 mL/min, urine protein ≥ 100 mg/dL (> 2+ proteinuria), sulfa allergy, use with or within 7 days of other nephrotoxic drugs, direct intraocular injection **SIDE EFFECTS** Similar to ganciclovir with risk of nephrotoxicity; lower risk for myelosuppression, metabolic acidosis **NOTES** Patient should receive hydration before each dose Can decrease tenofovir clearance
Foscarnet *(Foscavir)* Injection CMV retinitis, resistant HSV	Induction: 90 mg/kg IV Q12H or 60 mg/kg Q8H x 2-3 weeks Maintenance: 90-120 mg/kg IV daily Resistant HSV infection: 40 mg/kg Q8-12H x 2-3 weeks Renal impairment: ↓ dose and extend interval	**BOXED WARNINGS** Renal impairment occurs to some degree in majority of patients; seizures due to electrolyte imbalances (some leading to status epilepticus or death) **SIDE EFFECTS** Electrolyte abnormalities (↓ K, ↓ Ca, ↓ Mg, ↓ Phos), ↑ SCr, ↑ BUN, QT prolongation **NOTES** Vesicant (central line preferred)

Epstein-Barr Virus

Epstein-Barr Virus (EBV), is a member of the herpes virus family. Infectious EBV is called mononucleosis or "mono" and most people get infected with EBV at some point in their lives. It is transmitted through bodily fluids, primarily saliva, and can spread by kissing, sharing drinks or food, or contact with an object that has been in the mouth of an infected person (e.g., child's toys). Common symptoms are fatigue, fever, sore throat and swollen lymph nodes. They usually resolve in 2 – 4 weeks. No drug treatment or vaccine exists for mononucleosis.

Amoxicillin or ampicillin treatment in a child with EBV can cause a non-pruritic (i.e., non-itchy) rash that appears similar to an allergic reaction; it is not, and should not be included as an "allergy" in the medical record.

ANTIVIRAL PATIENT COUNSELING

Oseltamivir *(Tamiflu)*

- Treatment should begin within two days of onset of influenza symptoms.
- The most common side effects are headache, nausea and vomiting. Take with or without food. There is less chance of stomach upset if you take it with a light snack, milk, or a meal.
- Your risk of self-injury and confusion can be increased shortly after taking this medication. Closely monitor for signs of unusual behavior. Contact your healthcare provider immediately if you or your loved ones show any signs of unusual behavior.
- *Tamiflu* can decrease the effectiveness of intranasal influenza vaccine. Contact your health provider if you received this vaccine in the past two weeks.

Acyclovir *(Zovirax)*

- This medication works best within the first day of symptoms of an outbreak.
- The most common side effects are malaise (a generally ill feeling), headache, nausea and diarrhea.
- Take this medication by mouth with or without food, usually 2 to 5 times daily, as directed. The intervals should be evenly spaced.
- Drink plenty of fluids while taking this medication.
- The topical cream can cause temporary burning or stinging.

Valacyclovir *(Valtrex)*

- The most common side effects are tiredness and headache.
- *Valtrex* is used daily to manage herpes simplex, and when used along with the following safer sex practices can lower the chances of passing genital herpes to your partner.
  - ❑ Do not have sexual contact when you have any symptom or outbreak of genital herpes.
  - ❑ Use a condom made of latex or polyurethane whenever you have sexual contact.
- This medication does not cure herpes infections (cold sores, chickenpox, shingles, or genital herpes).
- This medication can be taken with or without food. If stomach upset occurs, take with meals.
- Start treatment within 24 hours of the onset of symptoms. This medication is less helpful if you start treatment too late.

Select Guidelines/References

Patterson TF, Thompson GR 3rd, Denning DW, et al. Practice Guidelines for the Diagnosis and Management of Aspergillosis: 2016 Update by IDSA. *Clin Infect Dis.* 2016;63:e1-e60.

Pappas PG, Kauffman CA, Andes DR, et al. Clinical Practice Guideline for Management of Candidiasis: 2016 Update by IDSA. *Clin Infect Dis.* 2016;62:409-17.

Uyeki TM, Bernstein HH, Bradley JS, et al. Clinical Practice Guidelines by the Infectious Diseases Society of America: 2018 Update on Diagnosis, Treatment, Chemoprophylaxis, and Institutional Outbreak Management of Seasonal Influenza. *Clin Infect Dis.* 2018;48:1003-1032.

CHAPTER CONTENT

Background ...412
Primary Prophylaxis in Patients with Malignancies ...413
Primary Prophylaxis in Patients with HIV ...413
Treatment of Opportunistic Infections ...414

CHAPTER 25
INFECTIOUS DISEASES IV: OPPORTUNISTIC INFECTIONS

BACKGROUND

Immunocompromised patients are predisposed to infections with a variety of pathogens, including bacteria, fungi, viruses and protozoa. These are called opportunistic infections (OIs) because they occur when the immune system is unable to respond normally. The risk can be related to a disease or to a drug treatment that suppresses the immune system. Immunocompromised states include:

- Diseases that destroy key components of the immune response (primarily HIV patients with a CD4+ T lymphocyte count < 200 cells/mm^3).
- Use of systemic steroids for 14 days or longer at a prednisone dose (or prednisone equivalent dose) ≥ 20 mg/day or ≥ 2 mg/kg/day.
- Asplenia (lack of a functioning spleen), as with sickle cell disease or following a splenectomy.
- Use of immunosuppressants for autoimmune conditions or transplant (e.g., TNF-alpha inhibitors).
- Use of cancer chemotherapy agents that destroy white blood cells.

OIs can be prevented with antibiotics, antifungals or antivirals; this is referred to as chemoprophylaxis, or simply prophylaxis.

PRIMARY PROPHYLAXIS IN PATIENTS WITH MALIGNANCIES

Patients with malignancies undergoing chemotherapy are at high risk for opportunistic infections, which contributes to morbidity and mortality. Severe neutropenia (ANC < 500 cells/mm³) is a major risk factor for developing infections. Effective strategies to anticipate, prevent, and manage infectious complications can greatly improve outcomes. Without neutrophils, patients are highly susceptible to Gram-negative pathogens, fungal infections and viral infections. Antimicrobials are used for the duration of neutropenia to prevent infectious diseases. Antibiotic regimens are chosen based on malignancy type, anticipated duration of neutropenia and risk for a particular infection. Antibiotic prophylaxis often consists of a quinolone (primarily levofloxacin) or 3rd generation cephalosporin. Antifungal prophylaxis commonly involves fluconazole or an echinocandin. In higher risk patients where mold/*Mucor* coverage is necessary, voriconazole, posaconazole or amphotericin are used. Antivirals targeting herpes simplex virus (HSV) and/or varicella zoster virus (VZV) are used for patients at intermediate-to-high risk of infection, and typical agents include acyclovir, valacyclovir and famciclovir. Patients who develop a fever while neutropenic receive presumptive treatment with specific antimicrobial regimens based on current guidelines.

PRIMARY PROPHYLAXIS IN PATIENTS WITH HIV

HIV-infected patients not taking antiretroviral therapy (ART) are at risk for developing OIs with progressive immunosuppression. Patients are at higher risk as CD4+ counts decline. The table below outlines select OIs, the CD4+ count at which the patient becomes at risk for the infection, and the primary prophylaxis regimen that should be initiated to prevent the infection. Oropharyngeal/esophageal *Candida* infections (also called thrush) can occur when the CD4+ count is < 200 cells/mm³. These infections resolve quickly with fluconazole treatment. No prophylaxis (primary or secondary) is recommended for candidiasis.

INFECTION	INDICATION	PRIMARY PROPHYLAXIS REGIMEN	CRITERIA FOR DISCONTINUING PRIMARY PROPHYLAXIS
Pneumocystis pneumonia (PCP)	CD4+ count ≤ 200 cells/mm³ or oropharyngeal candidiasis or other AIDS-defining illness	Preferred: SMX/TMP DS tab PO daily or SS PO daily Alternative: SMX/TMP DS 3x/week or dapsone or dapsone + pyrimethamine + leucovorin* or atovaquone or Inhaled pentamidine	CD4+ count ≥ 200 cells/mm³ for ≥ 3 months on ART
Toxoplasma gondii encephalitis (commonly called Toxo)	Toxoplasma IgG positive patients with CD4+ count ≤ 100 cells/mm³	Preferred: SMX/TMP DS tab PO daily Alternative: SMX/TMP DS 3x/week or 1 SS PO daily or dapsone + pyrimethamine + leucovorin* or atovaquone or atovaquone + pyrimethamine + leucovorin*	CD4+ count > 200 cells/mm³ for > 3 months on ART
Mycobacterium avium complex (MAC) infection	Primary prophylaxis not recommended for patients with HIV who immediately start antiretroviral therapy (ART). Initiate in patients not taking ART and CD4+ count ≤ 50 cells/mm³ Must rule out active disseminated MAC disease.	Preferred: azithromycin 1,200 mg PO weekly Alternative: azithromycin 600 mg PO twice weekly or clarithromycin 500 mg PO BID	Taking fully suppressive ART

* *Leucovorin added as rescue therapy to reduce risk for myelosuppression associated with pyrimethamine.*

TREATMENT OF OPPORTUNISTIC INFECTIONS

Treatment for each infection remains the same, regardless of the cause of immunosuppression. Newly diagnosed patients with HIV and an OI should be monitored closely for immune reconstitution inflammatory syndrome (IRIS) when antiretroviral therapy (ART) is started (see Human Immunodeficiency Virus chapter). The following table lists select OIs and the recommended medications for treatment. After completing initial treatment for the infection, secondary prophylaxis is given to prevent recurrence of the infection, in patients who continue to be at risk.

When treating oropharyngeal candidiasis (thrush) in patients with HIV, even with mild disease, systemic treatment is preferred (rather than localized agents such as clotrimazole, miconazole or nystatin).

INFECTION	PREFERRED REGIMEN	ALTERNATIVE REGIMEN	SECONDARY PROPHYLAXIS
Candidiasis (oropharyngeal/esophageal)	Fluconazole	Itraconazole, posaconazole	None
Cryptococcal meningitis	Induction therapy: Amphotericin B (deoxycholate or liposomal) + flucytosine	Fluconazole ± flucytosine	Fluconazole (low dose)
Cytomegalovirus (CMV)	Valganciclovir or Ganciclovir	If toxicities to ganciclovir or resistant strains: foscarnet, cidofovir	No drugs recommended Maintain CD4+ count > 100 cells/mm^3
Mycobacterium avium complex (MAC) infection	(Clarithromycin or azithromycin) + ethambutol	Add a 3rd or 4th agent using rifabutin, amikacin or streptomycin, moxifloxacin or levofloxacin	Same as treatment regimens
Pneumocystis pneumonia (PCP)	SMX/TMP ± prednisone or methylprednisolone Duration: 21 days	Atovaquone or clindamycin + primaquine or pentamidine IV or dapsone + trimethoprim**	SMX/TMP or dapsone or dapsone + pyrimethamine + leucovorin* or atovaquone or inhaled pentamidine
Toxoplasmosis gondii encephalitis (commonly called Toxo)	Pyrimethamine + leucovorin* + sulfadiazine	SMX/TMP or (either clindamycin or azithromycin) + pyrimethamine + leucovorin* or atovaquone or atovaquone + sulfadiazine or atovaquone + pyrimethamine + leucovorin*	Same as treatment; reduced doses

**Leucovorin added as rescue therapy to reduce risk for myelosuppression associated with pyrimethamine.*

*** Selection of alternative therapy for PCP depends on severity of illness and patient specific factors (e.g., allergies and G6PD deficiency). For example, atovaquone, clindamycin + primaquine or pentamidine are all potential options in the setting of sulfa allergy; however, only atovaquone (mild-to-moderate disease) and pentamidine (moderate-severe disease) are available options in the setting of G6PD deficiency.*

Select Guidelines/References

Panel on Opportunistic Infections in HIV-Infected Adults and Adolescents. Guidelines for the Prevention and Treatment of Opportunistic Infections in HIV-Infected Adults and Adolescents: Recommendations from the Centers for Disease Control and Prevention, the National Institutes of Health, and the HIV Medicine Association of the Infectious Diseases Society of America. Available at https://aidsinfo.nih.gov/guidelines/html/4/adult-and-adolescent-opportunistic-infection/392/whats-new. (accessed 2019 Feb 20).

National Comprehensive Cancer Network (NCCN) Clinical Practice Guidelines in Oncology. Prevention and Treatment of Cancer-Related Infections. Version 1.2019. http://www.nccn.org/professionals/physician_gls/pdf/infections.pdf. (accessed 2019 Feb 20).

CHAPTER CONTENT

Background **415**
Transmission **415**
Screening and Diagnosis **415**
Over-the-Counter HIV Testing 416
HIV Replication Stages and Antiretroviral Sites of Action .. **417**
Initial Evaluation and Monitoring **417**
Antiretroviral Therapy **418**
Recommended Initial Regimens 418
INSTI-Based Regimen (INSTI + 2 NRTIs) 418
Regimens for Antiretroviral-Naïve Pregnant Women . 419
Combination Products **419**
Single Tablet Regimens 419
Other Combination Products 420
Nucleoside/Nucleotide Reverse Transcriptase Inhibitors .. **420**
Key Features of NRTIs 420
Non-Nucleoside Reverse Transcriptase Inhibitors **423**
Key Features of NNRTIs 423
Protease Inhibitors/Pharmacokinetic Boosters **425**
Key Features of PIs 425
Pharmacokinetic Boosters 429
PI and PK Booster Drug Interactions 429
Integrase Strand Transfer Inhibitors **430**
Key Features of INSTIs 430
CCR5 Antagonist **431**
Fusion Inhibitor **432**
CD4-Directed Post-Attachment HIV-1 Inhibitor **432**
Select Complications of ART **432**
Therapies for HIV Complications 433
HIV Prevention Strategies **433**
Treatment as Prevention 433
Pre-Exposure Prophylaxis (PrEP) 433
Nonoccupational Post-Exposure Prophylaxis (nPEP) . 434
Occupational Post-Exposure Prophylaxis (PEP) 434
Summary Tables and Tips **434**
Administration (Food) Requirements 434
ART Adverse Effects by Class and Agent 435
Patient Counseling **436**
Dispense in Original Container 436
Fill In The Antiretroviral **439**

CONTENT LEGEND

= Study Tip Gal   = Key Drug Guy

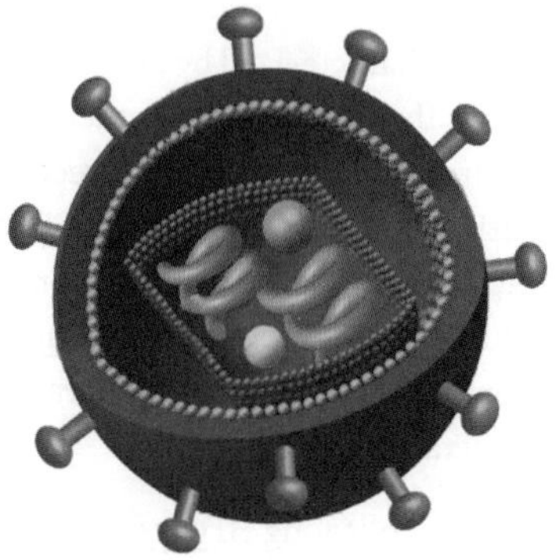

CHAPTER 26
HUMAN IMMUNODEFICIENCY VIRUS

BACKGROUND

The first cases of Human Immunodeficiency Virus (HIV)/Acquired Immunodeficiency Syndrome (AIDS) were reported in 1981. The Centers for Disease Control and Prevention now estimates that there are more than 1.1 million people in the United States living with HIV infection, and about 1 out of every 7 persons is unaware that they are infected. HIV is a single-stranded RNA retrovirus that attacks the immune system, mainly the CD4+ T-helper cells, causing a progressive decrease in CD4+ T cell count. Once CD4+ counts fall below 200 cells/mm^3, the person becomes more susceptible to opportunistic infections (OIs) and certain malignancies due to the loss of cell-mediated immunity. HIV has two viral subtypes, HIV-1 and HIV-2. HIV-1 accounts for the vast majority of infections worldwide. It is the predominant subtype in the United States and will be referred to as simply "HIV" throughout the Course Book.

TRANSMISSION

HIV can be spread through infected blood, semen and vaginal secretions. Unprotected intercourse and sharing needles with HIV-infected individuals are the two most common means of transmission. Transmission via sexual exposure may be facilitated through the presence of sores or cuts in the vagina, penis, rectum or mouth. Vertical transmission (from mother to child) may also occur, either during pregnancy, at birth or through breastfeeding.

SCREENING AND DIAGNOSIS

The CDC recommends routine HIV screening for patients 13 – 64 years old in all healthcare settings (unless the patient declines testing). Pregnant women and patients initiating treatment for tuberculosis or sexually transmitted infections should also be tested for HIV. Persons at high risk for HIV (e.g., injection drug users, persons with high-risk sexual behaviors) should be tested for HIV at least annually.

An acute HIV infection is characterized by an initial burst of viremia (virus in the blood). Persons with acute HIV infection may experience non-specific flu-like symptoms, such as fever, fatigue/malaise, myalgias/arthralgias, lymphadenopathy (swollen lymph nodes) and rash. Many persons do not recognize that they have developed an acute HIV infection since symptoms, if present, are self-limiting. Anti-HIV antibodies (HIV Ab) are undetectable at this time, however, HIV RNA and HIV p24 antigen will be present (typically at 2 weeks post infection). Following this acute phase of the infection, the HIV Ab test will usually become positive about 4 – 8 weeks after contracting the disease; for some individuals, it may take up to 3 – 6 months for HIV Ab to be detected. The term "recent infection" generally refers to the phase up to 6 months after the onset of the infection during which HIV Ab are detectable.

The CDC recommends the following HIV testing algorithm:

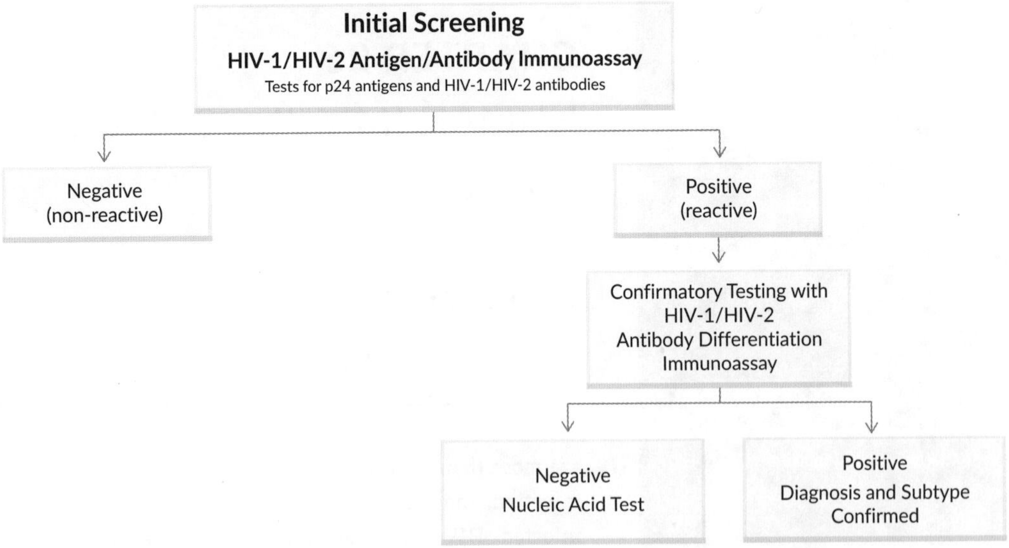

If this algorithm cannot be implemented, alternative testing includes using the HIV immunoassay screening test [referred to as HIV ELISA (enzyme-linked immunosorbent assay)] as an initial screening. This tests only for the presence of HIV Ab in the blood sample. Alternative confirmatory tests include the HIV RNA viral load and the Western Blot. Regardless of the test used, a positive HIV screening test may not always represent true infection (due to the rare chance of false-positive tests). All positive screening tests must be followed by a supplemental confirmatory test. Diagnosis of HIV is confirmed when both the HIV immunoassay screening and supplemental confirmatory tests are positive.

OVER-THE-COUNTER HIV TESTING

There is now only one over-the-counter (OTC) HIV test that patients can do at home. The *Home Access Express HIV Test System* was a fingerstick blood test, but is no longer available. The *OraQuick In-Home HIV Test* is an oral swab test that offers results in 20 – 40 minutes. This test detects the presence of HIV Ab, which may take up to 6 months after onset of infection to develop. Individuals with a positive OTC HIV home test result must follow-up with their healthcare provider for a confirmatory HIV laboratory-based test.

Use of the *OraQuick In-Home HIV Test* involves swabbing a test stick along the upper gums once and the lower gums once, then inserting the stick into a test tube with liquid. After 20 minutes, the test stick can be read (see picture below for interpretation). The tests should be used ≥ 3 months from the possible exposure; testing sooner than 3 months can lead to a false negative result.

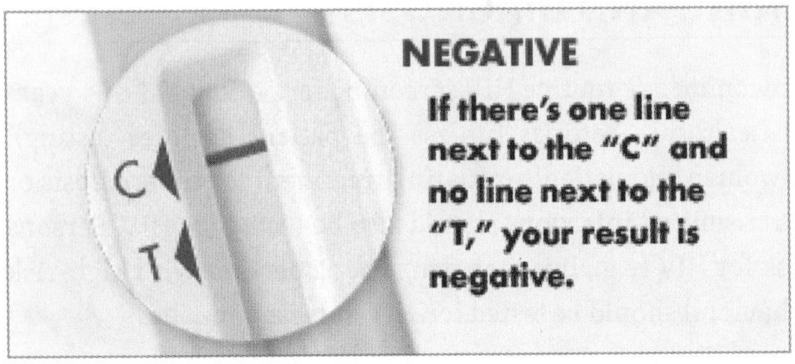

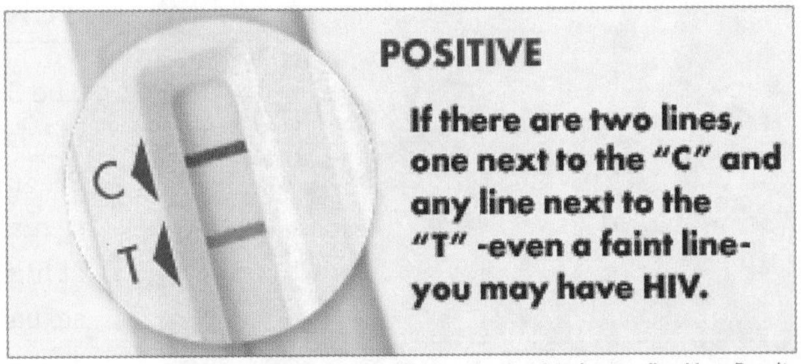

© http://www.oraquick.com/Taking-the-Test/Understanding-Your-Results

HIV REPLICATION STAGES AND ANTIRETROVIRAL SITES OF ACTION

It is very important to understand the steps (or stages) involved in HIV viral replication and know where each drug class works. See following description and diagram.

STAGE	DESCRIPTION OF STAGE	DRUG CLASS TARGETING THIS STAGE
Stage 1: Binding/Attachment	HIV attaches to a CD4 receptor and the co-receptors (CCR5 and/or CXCR4) on the surface of the CD4+ host cell. The virus must bind/attach to both a CD4 receptor and a co-receptor for the next step of viral replication to occur.	CCR5 Antagonist (blocks only the CCR5 co-receptor, not the CXCR4 co-receptor) CD4-Directed Post-Attachment HIV-1 Inhibitor (binds to CD4 receptors and blocks HIV entry into host cell)
Stage 2: Fusion	Fusion of the HIV viral envelope with the CD4+ host cell membrane allows HIV to enter the host cell, where uncoating of the virus releases HIV RNA and viral proteins and enzymes needed for HIV replication into the host cell's cytoplasm.	Fusion Inhibitors
Stage 3: Reverse Transcription	Once inside the cell, single-stranded HIV RNA is converted to double-stranded HIV DNA by reverse transcriptase.	Nucleoside/Nucleotide Reverse Transcriptase Inhibitors (NRTIs) and Non-Nucleoside Reverse Transcriptase Inhibitors (NNRTIs)
Stage 4: Integration	HIV DNA is transported across the host cell nuclear membrane and is integrated into the host cell's DNA.	Integrase Strand Transfer Inhibitors (INSTIs)
Stage 5: Transcription and Translation	HIV DNA is transcribed and translated into new HIV RNA as well as new viral proteins (envelope proteins and non-functional long-chain proteins).	
Stage 6: Assembly	New HIV RNA, viral envelope proteins and non-functional long-chain viral proteins migrate to the host cell surface to begin forming new, immature HIV virus. Protease enzyme is also incorporated into this newly forming HIV virus.	
Stage 7: Budding and Maturation	Newly formed, immature HIV virus buds off from the host cell. During the maturation process, protease cleaves the long-chain viral proteins into smaller, functional viral proteins and enzymes. The mature HIV virus is now able to move on to infect other CD4+ host cells.	Protease Inhibitors (PIs)

INITIAL EVALUATION AND MONITORING

Initial evaluation for patients with HIV is extensive. Vaccinations may be indicated based on the CD4+ count; see the Immunizations chapter. The following laboratory parameters are recommended for all HIV-infected individuals:

- CD4+ count – quantifies the CD4+ cells in the blood. It is the major laboratory indicator of immune function and serves as a key factor in determining the need for opportunistic infection (OI) prophylaxis. CD4+ counts should be measured at baseline, every 3 – 6 months and any time clinical failure is suspected. The treatment goal is a normal CD4+ count (800 – 1200 cells/mm^3).
- HIV viral load – quantifies the copies of HIV RNA in the blood. It is the most important indicator of response to antiretroviral therapy (ART) and is used to assess for possible problems with medication adherence or drug resistance. HIV viral load should be measured at baseline, 2 – 8 weeks post ART initiation or modification, then every 3 – 6 months thereafter. The treatment goal is to have an undetectable HIV viral load.

HIV Life Cycle

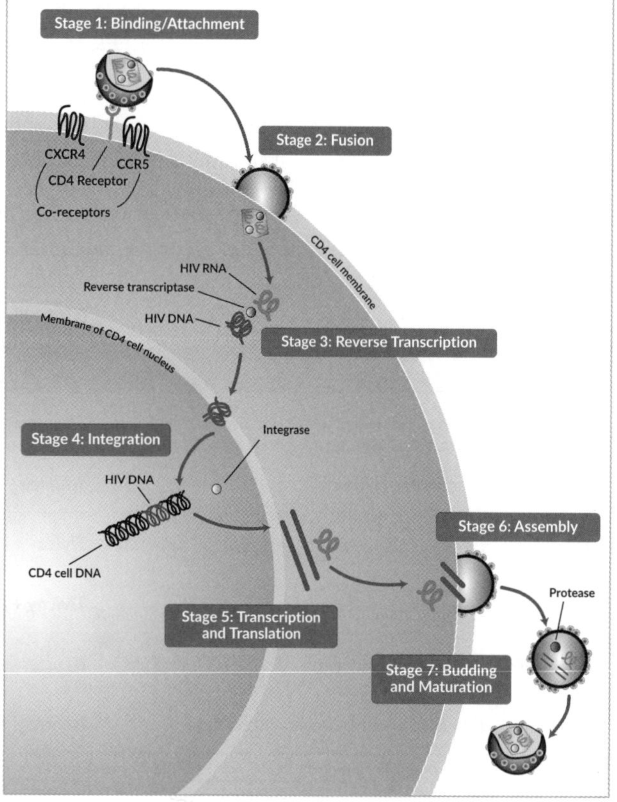

- Drug resistance testing – genotypic testing that determines the specific genetic mutations of the virus and reports susceptibility information for individual antiretroviral medications. Testing is performed at entry to care, at ART initiation or modification, or if treatment failure is suspected.
- Comprehensive metabolic panel (includes SCr, glucose, LFTs), CBC with differential, lipid panel and urinary analysis prior to ART initiation and every 6 – 12 months thereafter.
- Hepatitis B and C testing – perform at baseline.
- Pregnancy testing – perform at baseline.
- Drug specific testing when required – HLA-B*5701 for abacavir and tropism testing for maraviroc.

ANTIRETROVIRAL THERAPY

Treatment for HIV requires combination antiretroviral therapy (ART). ART has dramatically reduced HIV-associated morbidity and mortality and, although not curative, has transformed HIV disease into a chronic, manageable condition. Without treatment, the vast majority of HIV-infected individuals will eventually develop progressive immunosuppression (as evident by low CD4+ count), leading to OIs and premature death. The primary goals of ART are to restore and preserve the immune system, suppress HIV viral load to undetectable levels, reduce HIV-associated morbidity, prolong survival and prevent HIV transmission.

ART is recommended in all HIV-infected individuals to reduce risk of disease progression and, in combination with safer sex/behavior risk reduction practices, to prevent transmission of HIV to non-HIV-infected individuals. On a case-by-case basis, ART may be deferred due to clinical and/or psychosocial factors, but therapy should be initiated as soon as is feasible. Patients starting ART should be willing and able to commit to treatment and understand the benefits and risks of therapy and the importance of adherence. Patients need to be advised that they must have an adherence rate of 95% or higher in order for their ART regimen to be effective long-term. An example of 95% or higher adherence is no more than 1 missed dose per month for a patient taking a once daily regimen.

RECOMMENDED INITIAL REGIMENS

Selection of an ART regimen should be individualized based on efficacy, toxicity, pill burden, dosing frequency, drug interaction potential, resistance test results and comorbid conditions. Recommended initial regimens have optimal and durable efficacy, favorable tolerability and toxicity profile and ease of use. INSTI-based regimens are recommended as initial therapy for most patients with HIV. An INSTI-based regimen combines an INSTI with 2 NRTIs (called the "NRTI backbone") (see Study Tip Gal for the currently recommended regimens).

INSTI-based regimens have better tolerability and viral suppression than PI- or NNRTI-based regimens, which can be used as initial regimens in certain clinical situations (e.g., resistance, comorbidities, drug interactions).

The regimens are listed below in alphabetical order, not by order of preference. HIV treatment guidelines are updated frequently. Check for guideline updates at: http://aidsinfo.nih.gov.

REGIMENS	BRAND NAME	COMMENTS
INSTI-BASED REGIMEN (INSTI + 2 NRTIs)		
Bictegravir/emtricitabine/tenofovir alafenamide	***Biktarvy***	■ Use of abacavir requires testing for HLA-B*5701 allele. If positive, do not use abacavir. ■ Tenofovir disoproxil fumarate should be used with caution in patients with renal insufficiency. ■ Single tablet regimens have no flexibility in renal dosing of the individual components; contraindications are specific to baseline CrCl: ❏ *Triumeq:* do not start if CrCl < 50 mL/min. ❏ *Biktarvy:* do not start if CrCl < 30 mL/min. ■ Lamivudine and emtricitabine are interchangeable.
Dolutegravir/abacavir/lamivudine	***Triumeq***	
Dolutegravir + emtricitabine/tenofovir disoproxil fumarate	***Tivicay + Truvada***	
Dolutegravir + emtricitabine/tenofovir alafenamide	***Tivicay + Descovy***	
Raltegravir + emtricitabine/tenofovir disoproxil fumarate	***Isentress + Truvada***	
Raltegravir + emtricitabine/tenofovir alafenamide	***Isentress + Descovy***	

See summary tables of combination products, food and storage requirements and important adverse effects later in the chapter.

REGIMENS FOR ANTIRETROVIRAL-NAÏVE PREGNANT WOMEN

Regimen should include 2 NRTIs plus either a boosted-PI or INSTI. Preferred drugs are listed. Choose one line from the first column, then add one line from the second or third column.

If a woman with HIV becomes pregnant while on effective ART, then the effective ART regimen should be continued Dolutegravir should be avoided due to a risk of neural tube defects.

NRTI COMBINATIONS	PI	INSTI
Abacavir/lamivudine	Atazanavir + ritonavir	Raltegravir
Tenofovir disoproxil fumarate/emtricitabine (or lamivudine)	Darunavir + ritonavir (BID regimen only)	

COMBINATION PRODUCTS

Combination products increase convenience (lower pill burden) and improve adherence. Some ARTs are not available in combination products due to differences in dosing schedule (e.g., raltegravir) or formulation requirements (e.g., ritonavir). Single tablet regimens are increasingly common. Proper storage and administration is important to treatment success (see summary tables at the end of the chapter).

SINGLE TABLET REGIMENS

GENERIC NAME	BRAND	NOTES
Complete Regimens (1 tablet once daily)		
INSTI-based		
Elvitegravir / cobicistat / emtricitabine / tenofovir disoproxil fumarate	***Stribild***	With food, original container Do not start if CrCl < 70 mL/min
Elvitegravir / cobicistat / emtricitabine / tenofovir alafenamide	***Genvoya***	With food, original container Do not start if CrCl < 30 mL/min
Bictegravir / emtricitabine / tenofovir alafenamide	***Biktarvy***	Original container
Dolutegravir / abacavir / lamivudine	***Triumeq***	Original container
Dolutegravir / lamivudine	*Dovato*	Complete regimen with only 2 drugs; for initial treatment.*
Dolutegravir / rilpivirine	*Juluca*	With food, original container. Complete regimen with only 2 drugs; not for initial treatment.
NNRTI-based		
Doravirine / lamivudine / tenofovir disoproxil fumarate	*Delstrigo*	Original container
Efavirenz / emtricitabine / tenofovir disoproxil fumarate	***Atripla***	Without food, original container
Efavirenz / lamivudine / tenofovir disoproxil fumarate	*Symfi*	Without food, original container
Efavirenz / lamivudine / tenofovir disoproxil fumarate	*Symfi Lo*	Without food, original container
Rilpivirine / emtricitabine / tenofovir disoproxil fumarate	***Complera***	With food, original container
Rilpivirine / emtricitabine / tenofovir alafenamide	***Odefsey***	With food, original container
PI-based		
Darunavir / cobicistat / emtricitabine 200 mg / tenofovir alafenamide	*Symtuza*	With food, original container

**Not yet included in treatment guidelines.*

OTHER COMBINATION PRODUCTS
(MUST BE USED WITH ADDITIONAL ARTs TO MAKE A COMPLETE REGIMEN)

GENERIC NAME	BRAND	DOSE/NOTES
NRTI Combination Products (1 tablet daily unless noted)		
Abacavir / lamivudine	***Epzicom***	
Abacavir / lamivudine / zidovudine	*Trizivir*	1 tab BID
Emtricitabine / tenofovir alafenamide	***Descovy***	Original container
Emtricitabine / tenofovir disoproxil fumarate	***Truvada***	Original container
Lamivudine / zidovudine	*Combivir*	1 tab BID
Lamivudine / tenofovir disoproxil fumarate	*Cimduo*	Original container
Common PI Combination Products (1 tablet daily)		
Atazanavir / cobicistat	*Evotaz*	With food
Darunavir / cobicistat	*Prezcobix*	With food

NUCLEOSIDE/NUCLEOTIDE REVERSE TRANSCRIPTASE INHIBITORS

Nucleoside/nucleotide reverse transcriptase inhibitors (NRTIs) are structurally similar to naturally occurring nucleosides/nucleotides needed to synthesize viral DNA. NRTIs competitively bind to the enzyme reverse transcriptase, blocking HIV viral RNA-dependent DNA polymerase. This results in DNA chain termination and stops further viral DNA synthesis (see Stage 3 in the HIV life cycle diagram). All NRTIs have a warning for lactic acidosis and severe hepatomegaly with steatosis, sometimes fatal (especially didanosine, stavudine and zidovudine). If a patient is suspected to have lactic acidosis or hepatotoxicity, a healthcare provider should be contacted for recommendations and the NRTI-containing regimen should be stopped.

KEY FEATURES OF NRTIs

Renal dose adjustment required (except abacavir).

No CYP450 drug interactions.

Take without regard to meals (except didanosine).

Warning: lactic acidosis and hepatomegaly with steatosis (zidovudine, stavudine, didanosine > other NRTIs). This remains a boxed warning for some of the older NRTIs.

Abacavir – hypersensitivity reactions; test for HLA-B*5701.

Tenofovir toxicities – nephrotoxicity, osteoporosis, Fanconi syndrome. Thought to be ↓ with tenofovir alafenamide.

DRUG	DOSING	SAFETY/SIDE EFFECTS/MONITORING
Abacavir, ABC *(Ziagen)* Tablet, oral solution (20 mg/mL)	300 mg BID or 600 mg daily No renal dose adjustments required	**BOXED WARNINGS** Screen for the HLA-B*5701 allele before starting abacavir therapy; if positive, use is contraindicated due to ↑ risk for hypersensitivity reactions. Record as abacavir allergy in patient record and do not use Serious, sometimes fatal, hypersensitivity reactions [fever, rash, fatigue, malaise, GI symptoms (N/V/D, abdominal pain), and/or respiratory symptoms (dyspnea, cough)]; discontinue drug and do not re-challenge regardless of HLA-B*5701 status **CONTRAINDICATIONS** Previous hypersensitivity to abacavir, moderate to severe hepatic impairment **WARNINGS** Caution in CVD due to possible ↑ risk of MI, lactic acidosis and severe hepatomegaly with steatosis **SIDE EFFECTS** N/V, HA, rash, ↑ LFTs, hyperlipidemia **NOTES** Caution with alcohol (↑ abacavir AUC) Warning card (summarizing symptoms of hypersensitivity) required Abacavir/lamivudine with either efavirenz or atazanavir + ritonavir should not be used in patients with pre-treatment HIV viral load > 100,000 copies/mL

DRUG	DOSING	SAFETY/SIDE EFFECTS/MONITORING
Lamivudine, 3TC **(*Epivir*)** Tablet, oral solution (10 mg/mL)	150 mg BID or 300 mg daily CrCl < 50 mL/min: ↓ dose	**BOXED WARNINGS** Do not use *Epivir-HBV* for treatment of HIV (contains lower dose of lamivudine); can result in HIV resistance. Severe acute exacerbation of hepatitis B (HBV) can occur when drug is discontinued in patients with HBV infection **WARNINGS** Lactic acidosis and severe hepatomegaly with steatosis **SIDE EFFECTS** HA, N/V/D, fatigue, insomnia, myalgias, ↑ LFTs **MONITORING** LFTs, renal function, HBV status prior to initiation **NOTES** Avoid combining with emtricitabine; antagonistic interaction as both are cytosine analogs: FTC and 3TC Has activity against HBV. In HIV/HBV co-infection, must dose lamivudine at the higher, HIV treatment dose found in *Epivir* and *Symfi* (*Epivir* is not equivalent to *Epivir-HBV*)
Emtricitabine, FTC (*Emtriva*) Capsule, oral solution (10 mg/mL)	Cap: 200 mg daily Soln: 240 mg daily (refrigerate; stable for 3 months at room temp) CrCl < 50 mL/min: ↓ dose or frequency	**BOXED WARNINGS** Severe acute exacerbation of hepatitis B (HBV) can occur when drug is discontinued in patients with HBV infection *Truvada* for pre-exposure prophylaxis (PrEP): only for patients confirmed to be HIV negative prior to initiating and every 3 months during use **WARNINGS** Lactic acidosis and severe hepatomegaly with steatosis **SIDE EFFECTS** N/V/D, rash, dizziness, HA, insomnia, hyperpigmentation primarily of palms and/or soles (mainly in children), ↑ CPK, ↑ LFTs **MONITORING** LFTs, renal function, HBV status prior to initiation **NOTES** Avoid combining with lamivudine; antagonistic interaction as both are cytosine analogs: FTC and 3TC (e.g., avoid giving with *Triumeq, Epivir, Epivir-HBV*) Capsule and oral solution are not bioequivalent
Tenofovir disoproxil fumarate, TDF **(*Viread*)** Tablet, oral powder (40 mg/g) **Tenofovir alafenamide** (TAF) Tablet No single agent for HIV *Vemlidy* for hepatitis B	300 mg daily CrCl < 50 mL/min: ↓ frequency 25 mg in *Odefsey, Descovy, Biktarvy* 10 mg in *Genvoya, Symtuza* CrCl < 15 mL/min and not on hemodialysis: avoid use	**BOXED WARNINGS** All tenofovir-containing products: severe acute exacerbation of hepatitis B (HBV) can occur when drug is discontinued in patients with HBV infection **WARNINGS** Renal toxicity including acute renal failure and/or Fanconi syndrome, osteomalacia and ↓ bone mineral density; lactic acidosis and severe hepatomegaly with steatosis **SIDE EFFECTS** Tenofovir disoproxil-containing products: N/V/D, HA, depression, renal impairment, ↓ bone mineral density, ↑ LFTs, ↑ CPK Tenofovir alafenamide-containing products: nausea, ↓ bone mineral density **MONITORING** LFTs, CBC, renal function, CPK, urinalysis, Ca, PO4, bone density (long-term), HBV status prior to initiation **NOTES** Dispense in original containers Avoid use with didanosine due to resistance/virologic failure and ↑ didanosine concentration Consider vitamin D and calcium supplementation **Tenofovir disoproxil fumarate** Approved for treatment of chronic HBV (same treatment dose as HIV infection) Powder should be mixed with 2-4 oz of soft food (applesauce, yogurt) to avoid bitter taste. Do not mix powder with liquid **Tenofovir alafenamide** Newer form of tenofovir; achieves ↑ intracellular concentrations with ↓ blood levels, resulting in presumably ↓ rates of renal and bone toxicity compared to tenofovir disoproxil fumarate

DRUG	DOSING	SAFETY/SIDE EFFECTS/MONITORING
Zidovudine, ZDV or AZT ***(Retrovir)*** Capsule, tablet, oral solution (10 mg/mL), injection	PO: 300 mg BID IV: 1 mg/kg Q4H CrCl < 15 mL/min: ↓ dose and/or change frequency Take without regard to food (although better tolerated when taken with food)	**BOXED WARNINGS** Hematologic toxicities (neutropenia and anemia) especially in advanced HIV Prolonged use has been associated with symptomatic myopathy and myositis Lactic acidosis and severe hepatomegaly with steatosis **SIDE EFFECTS** N/V, anorexia, HA, insomnia, skin/nail hyperpigmentation (blue), myopathy, macrocytic anemia, lipoatrophy, ↑ LFTs, insulin resistance/diabetes, hyperlipidemia **MONITORING** CBC, LFTs, lipids, blood glucose, MCV (if the MCV is not ↑, there is likely an adherence problem) **NOTES** Erythropoietin is indicated to manage zidovudine-induced anemia Lipoatrophy: stavudine > zidovudine > other NRTIs IV zidovudine should be administered in the setting of labor for HIV-infected pregnant women, with HIV viral load > 1,000 copies/mL (or unknown HIV viral load)
Stavudine, d4T *(Zerit)* Capsule, oral solution (1 mg/mL)	≥ 60 kg: 40 mg Q12H < 60 kg: 30 mg Q12H CrCl ≤ 50 mL/min: ↓ dose and/or frequency Oral soln: stable for 30 days in refrigerator. Shake vigorously before use	**BOXED WARNINGS** Pancreatitis (sometimes fatal) has occurred during combination therapy with didanosine Lactic acidosis and severe hepatomegaly with steatosis **WARNINGS** Neurologic symptoms including motor weakness (mimics Guillian-Barrè syndrome) and hepatotoxicity **SIDE EFFECTS** N/V/D, peripheral neuropathy (can be irreversible), ↑ LFTs, hyperbilirubinemia, lipoatrophy, pancreatitis, HA, insulin resistance/diabetes, hyperlipidemia **NOTES** Lipoatrophy: stavudine > zidovudine > other NRTIs
Didanosine, ddI *(Videx, Videx EC)* Capsule, solution (10 mg/mL)	≥ 60 kg: 400 mg daily < 60 kg: 250 mg daily CrCl < 60 mL/min: ↓ dose Oral soln: stable for 30 days if refrigerated	**BOXED WARNING** Pancreatitis (sometimes fatal); lactic acidosis and severe hepatomegaly with steatosis **CONTRAINDICATIONS** Concurrent use with allopurinol or ribavirin **WARNINGS** Noncirrhotic portal hypertension, retinal changes and optic neuritis **SIDE EFFECTS** N/V/D, peripheral neuropathy (potentially irreversible), ↑ amylase, ↑ LFTs, pruritus/rash

NRTI Drug Interactions

NRTIs do not undergo hepatic transformation via the CYP450 metabolic pathway, therefore, they have fewer significant drug interactions compared to PIs and NNRTIs. Some NRTIs have other mechanisms of drug interactions (e.g., P-glycoprotein, overlapping toxicities). A few notable drug interactions include:

- Avoid concurrent use of ribavirin with didanosine (↑ risk of liver failure, pancreatitis), and ribavirin with zidovudine (significantly ↑ risk and severity of anemia).
- Avoid emtricitabine and lamivudine combination (antagonistic interaction as both are cytosine analogs: FTC and 3TC).
- Avoid didanosine (ddI) and stavudine (d4T) combination due to ↑ risk of peripheral neuropathy, pancreatitis and lactic acidosis.
- Avoid didanosine and tenofovir combination due to resistance and virologic failure as well as increased didanosine concentration.
- Allopurinol can ↑ didanosine levels; contraindicated.
- Avoid zidovudine and stavudine (antagonistic interaction as both are thymidine analogs: d4T and AZT).
- Methadone can ↑ zidovudine levels; monitor for zidovudine toxicity.
- Caution when using sofosbuvir/ledipasvir with *Stribild* due to ↑ tenofovir disoproxil fumarate levels; monitor renal function closely.
- Tenofovir alafenamide is a P-gp substrate; avoid rifampin and St. John's wort with *Descovy, Genvoya, Odefsey* and *Symtuza.*

NON-NUCLEOSIDE REVERSE TRANSCRIPTASE INHIBITORS

Non-nucleoside reverse transcriptase inhibitors (NNRTIs) work by non-competitive binding to reverse transcriptase and blocking the RNA-dependent and DNA-dependent DNA polymerase activities including HIV replication (see Stage 3 in the HIV life cycle diagram). None of the currently recommended ART regimens for treatment-naïve patients contain an NNRTI.

KEY FEATURES OF NNRTIs

No renal dose adjustment needed (avoid *Atripla* and *Complera* if CrCl < 50 mL/min)

Primarily CYP450 inducers (exceptions: efavirenz is an inducer > inhibitor; rilpivirine, doravirine are substrates)

Hepatotoxicity and rash, including SJS/TEN (nevirapine > other NNRTIs)

- Monitor for erythema, facial edema, skin necrosis, blisters and tongue swelling

Food requirements:

- With food – etravirine, rilpivirine
- Without food – efavirenz

Efavirenz – CNS effects; ↓ by giving at bedtime, empty stomach

Rilpivirine – QT prolongation, depression suicidality

DRUG	DOSING	SAFETY/SIDE EFFECTS/MONITORING
Efavirenz, EFV ***(Sustiva)*** Capsule, tablet	600 mg daily Capsule contents may be sprinkled onto 1-2 tsp of food	**WARNINGS** Serious psychiatric symptoms (suicidal ideation, depression), CNS symptoms (generally resolve in 2-4 weeks), convulsions, QT prolongation, hepatotoxicity, fetal toxicity **SIDE EFFECTS** CNS effects (impaired concentration, abnormal dreams, confusion, dizziness), rash, HA, N/V, fatigue, insomnia **MONITORING** Lipids, CNS and psychiatric effects, LFTs, ECG **NOTES** Package insert states to avoid in 1st trimester; based on additional data, guidelines recommend no restrictions on use in pregnancy May cause false positive for cannabinoid and benzodiazepine on drug screening tests Efavirenz should not be used with abacavir/lamivudine (or emtricitabine) in patients with pre-treatment HIV viral load > 100,000 copies/mL
Rilpivirine, RPV *(Edurant)* Tablet	25 mg daily with a meal Requires acidic environment for absorption: do not use with PPIs. Separate from H2RAs and antacids.	**CONTRAINDICATIONS** Concurrent use with PPIs, rifampin, rifapentine, carbamazepine, oxcarbazepine, phenobarbital, phenytoin, St. John's wort and dexamethasone (more than a single dose) **WARNINGS** QT prolongation, serious skin reactions, multiorgan hypersensitivity reactions (DRESS), depressive disorders, hepatotoxicity **SIDE EFFECTS** Depressive disorders, mood changes, insomnia, HA, rash **MONITORING** LFTs, rash, lipids, CNS effects, QT **NOTES** Higher rates of failure if viral load > 100,000 copies/mL and/or CD4+ counts < 200 cells/mm^3 at treatment initiation Protein supplement drinks should not be substituted for normal to high calorie meal (does not increase rilpivirine absorption)
Doravirine, DOR *(Pifeltro)*	100 mg daily	**CONTRAINDICATIONS** Concurrent use with rifampin, rifapentine, carbamazepine, oxcarbazepine, phenobarbital, phenytoin and St. John's wort **SIDE EFFECTS** ↑ LFTs, fatigue, insomnia, HA, rash

DRUG	DOSING	SAFETY/SIDE EFFECTS/MONITORING
Nevirapine, NVP *(Viramune, Viramune XR)* Tablet, oral suspension (10 mg/mL)	200 mg daily x 14 days, then 200 mg BID *(Viramune)* or 400 mg daily *(Viramune XR)* Requires 14 day lead-in period (may ↓ risk of rash, hepatotoxicity) If treatment is interrupted > 2 weeks, re-initiate titration.	**BOXED WARNINGS** Hepatotoxicity (liver failure, death) – risk highest during the first 6 weeks of therapy but may be seen later; more common in women and with higher CD4+ counts as noted below Serious skin reactions (SJS/TEN) – risk highest during the first 18 weeks of therapy and intensive monitoring is required **CONTRAINDICATIONS** Moderate-to-severe hepatic impairment, use in post-exposure prophylaxis regimens **SIDE EFFECTS** Rash (SJS/TEN), nausea, diarrhea, ↑ LFTs **NOTES** Do not initiate therapy in women with CD4+ counts > 250 cells/mm^3 or in men with CD4+ counts > 400 cells/mm^3 due to ↑ risk of hepatotoxicity
Etravirine, ETR *(Intelence)* Tablet	200 mg BID after meals Tablets may be dispersed in water to ease administration	**SIDE EFFECTS** Nausea, rash (including SJS/TEN), ↑ cholesterol, ↑ LDL, ↑ TGs, hyperglycemia, ↑ LFTs, peripheral neuropathy **NOTES** Typically used in patients who are treatment-experienced and have resistance to first line ART regimens

NNRTI Drug Interactions

All NNRTIs are cleared non-renally and metabolized in the liver via the CYP450 system; they have many drug interactions. They are all CYP3A4 substrates and may also be an inducer (nevirapine), or both inducer and inhibitor (efavirenz and etravirine). Many of the NNRTIs inhibit other isoenzymes. Always run a drug interaction check for patients receiving NNRTIs. Below are some notable drug interactions:

- Class interactions: avoid with St. John's wort, avanafil, *Viekira Pak* and *Viekira XR*
- Efavirenz: moderate inducer and substrate of CYP3A4 and 2B6. Avoid with carbamazepine, flibanserin, itraconazole, ketoconazole, midazolam (PO), posaconazole, *Zepatier*, others. If used with voriconazole, both drugs require dose adjustment.
- Etravirine: moderate inhibitor of CYP2C9 and CYP2C19; moderate inducer of CYP3A4; and major substrate of CYP3A4, 2C9 and 2C19. Avoid concurrent use with carbamazepine, clopidogrel, flibanserin, phenobarbital, phenytoin, rifampin, *Zepatier*, others.
- Nevirapine: weak CYP3A4 inducer and major CYP3A4 substrate. Avoid concurrent use with carbamazepine, itraconazole, ketoconazole, rifampin, others.
- Rilpivirine: major substrate of CYP3A4. Contraindicated with strong CYP3A4 inducers (carbamazepine, oxcarbazepine, phenobarbital, phenytoin, rifampin, systemic dexamethasone (> 1 dose) and PPIs. Caution with other acid suppressants: separate from H2RAs and antacids (product-specific timing recommendations).
- Methadone levels can be ↓ by efavirenz and nevirapine. Monitor for signs and symptoms of possible methadone withdrawal.
- Hormonal contraceptive levels can be ↓ by efavirenz and nevirapine and result in unintended pregnancy. Patients should be counseled to use alternative or additional contraception.

PROTEASE INHIBITORS/PHARMACOKINETIC BOOSTERS

Protease inhibitors (PIs) work by inhibiting HIV protease and rendering the enzyme incapable of cleaving the Gag-Pol polyprotein, resulting in non-functional viral proteins and preventing the assembly and maturation of HIV virions (see Stage 7 in the HIV life cycle diagram). The PIs are effective even with multiple gene mutations (more resistant viruses).

It is recommended that all PIs be "boosted." Boosting takes advantage of a pharmacokinetic interaction to increase the drug levels and efficacy of PIs. All PIs are substrates of CYP3A4 and when given concurrently with a strong CYP3A4 inhibitor, the PI competes for metabolism and this results in increased PI drug levels. PIs should rarely, if at all, be given unboosted (except nelfinavir). The boosting agent is not considered one of the three required drugs to make an effective ART regimen. Boosting agents include low dose ritonavir and cobicistat. See Pharmacokinetic Booster comparison chart for differences between the agents.

KEY FEATURES OF PIs

- The generic names end in "-navir"
- Primarily CYP450 inhibitors (always check for drug interactions; also see PI Drug Interactions section)
- No renal dose adjustment needed for PIs, but may be used as part of a regimen with renal restrictions
- Hepatotoxicity (highest risk with tipranavir)
- Taken with a pharmacokinetic booster (ritonavir or cobicistat) to increase levels of the PI
- Metabolic abnormalities such as hyperlipidemia, lipohypertrophy (atazanavir, darunavir < other PIs), insulin resistance/hyperglycemia (highest risk with indinavir, lopinavir/ritonavir)
- Increased CVD risk (lowest with atazanavir and darunavir)
- GI upset (N/V/D); take with food to decrease GI side effects (exceptions: fosamprenavir and lopinavir/ritonavir)
- Bleeding events (in patients with hemophilia)
- ECG changes (especially saquinavir/ritonavir, lopinavir/ritonavir and atazanavir/ritonavir)
- Rash (including SJS/TEN)

DRUG	DOSING	SAFETY/SIDE EFFECTS/MONITORING
Darunavir, DRV ***(Prezista)*** Tablet, oral suspension (100 mg/mL)	Treatment naïve: 800 mg + 100 mg ritonavir daily or 150 mg cobicistat Treatment-experienced: 600 mg + 100 mg ritonavir BID Swallow whole If CrCl < 70 mL/min, do not give *Prezcobix* as part of a regimen that includes tenofovir disoproxil fumarate	**CONTRAINDICATIONS** Use with narrow therapeutic index drugs that are highly dependent on CYP3A4 for clearance (darunavir + ritonavir) **WARNINGS** Drug-induced hepatitis, serious skin reactions (SJS/TEN), use caution in patients with a sulfa allergy **SIDE EFFECTS** N/V/D, rash, ↑ LFTs, HA, hyperglycemia, ↑ SCr (with *Prezcobix*) **MONITORING** LFTs, rash, blood glucose, lipids, SCr (with *Prezcobix*) **NOTES** Must be given with ritonavir or cobicistat (cobicistat only FDA-approved with darunavir daily dose) Less likely to cause lipodystrophy and affect blood glucose/lipids than other PIs

DRUG	DOSING	SAFETY/SIDE EFFECTS/MONITORING
Atazanavir, ATV ***(Reyataz)*** Capsule, oral powder	300 mg + 100 mg ritonavir daily (or 150 mg cobicistat) 400 mg daily if therapy-naïve, not on tenofovir, and unable to tolerate ritonavir If CrCl < 70 mL/min, do not give *Evotaz* as part of a regimen that includes tenofovir disoproxil fumarate	**WARNINGS** PR interval prolongation, severe skin reactions, hyperbilirubinemia, hepatotoxicity, nephrolithiasis and cholelithiasis **SIDE EFFECTS** Indirect hyperbilirubinemia (jaundice or scleral icterus – think "bananavir" – reversible), cholelithiasis, HA, N/V/D, severe skin reactions, depression, myalgia, hyperglycemia, ↑ SCr (with *Evotaz*), kidney stones **MONITORING** ECG in at-risk patients, LFTs (including bilirubin), blood glucose, lipids, SCr (with *Evotaz*) **NOTES** Compared to other PIs, less likely to cause lipodystrophy or affect blood glucose and lipids Caution with acid-suppressive drugs as they can ↓ the absorption of atazanavir **With H2RAs** Atazanavir alone (unboosted): Take at least 2 hours before or 10 hours after H2RA Atazanavir with ritonavir: Take together or at least 10 hours after H2RA **With Antacids** Take atazanavir at least 2 hours before or 1 hour after antacids **With PPIs** Atazanavir with ritonavir: Take at least 12 hours after PPIs. The dose should not be > 20 mg of omeprazole (or equivalent) per day (PPIs are not recommended if atazanavir unboosted or in treatment-experienced patients)
Fosamprenavir, FPV *(Lexiva)* Tablet, oral suspension (50 mg/mL)	Treatment naïve: 1,400 mg ± 100-200 mg ritonavir daily or 700 mg + 100 mg ritonavir BID Treatment-experienced: 700 mg + 100 mg ritonavir BID Oral suspension: take without food (adults) Tablets: take without regard to meals (unboosted); take with food (boosted with ritonavir)	**WARNINGS** Use caution in patients with a sulfa allergy, nephrolithiasis, hemolytic anemia, hypersensitivity reactions (SJS/TEN) **SIDE EFFECTS** N/V/D, HA, rash, hyperlipidemia (especially TG) **MONITORING** LFTs, GI symptoms, blood glucose, lipids **NOTES** Prodrug of amprenavir Caution when dispensing: Potential for medication error among *Lexiva*, *Lexapro*, and *Levitra* Unboosted fosamprenavir not recommended due to inferior potency compared to boosted PIs
Indinavir, IDV *(Crixivan)* Capsule	Without ritonavir: 800 mg every 8 hours. Take on empty stomach (1 hour before or 2 hours after a meal) With ritonavir: 800 mg + 100-200 mg ritonavir BID. Take with food due to ritonavir component and with 48 oz. of water Swallow whole; do not break, crush, or chew	**WARNINGS** Nephrolithiasis/urolithiasis, hyperbilirubinemia, hemolytic anemia **SIDE EFFECTS** Nephrolithiasis, N/V/D, HA, ↑ LFTs, rash, metallic taste, abdominal pain **MONITORING** LFTs (including bilirubin), urinalysis, CBC, blood glucose, lipids **NOTES** Compared to other PIs, indinavir (and lopinavir/ritonavir) have highest risk of causing hyperglycemia, including insulin resistance/diabetes Avoid high fat/high calorie meal as indinavir absorption is decreased

DRUG	DOSING	SAFETY/SIDE EFFECTS/MONITORING
Lopinavir + ritonavir, LPV/r *(Kaletra)* Tablet, oral solution (80 mg lopinavir + 20 mg ritonavir/mL)	Treatment naïve: 800 mg lopinavir/200 mg ritonavir daily or 400/100 mg BID Treatment-experienced: 400/100 mg BID Tablets: take without regard to meals. Swallow whole; do not break, crush, or chew. Store at room temperature Solution: take with food. Refrigerate; stable for 2 months at room temp. Contains 42% alcohol	**WARNINGS** Pancreatitis, hepatotoxicity, QT and/or PR interval prolongation, caution in patients with CVD due to increased risk of MIs **SIDE EFFECTS** N/V/D, abdominal pain, hyperlipidemia (especially TG), hyperglycemia **MONITORING** LFTs, blood glucose, lipids, ECG in at-risk patients **NOTES** Compared to other PIs, lopinavir/ritonavir (and indinavir) have highest risk of causing hyperglycemia, including insulin resistance/diabetes Avoid once daily dosing with carbamazepine, phenytoin, phenobarbital and in pregnant women
Nelfinavir, NFV *(Viracept)* Tablet	750 mg TID or 1,250 mg BID	**SIDE EFFECTS** Diarrhea (up to 20% in adults), flatulence, nausea, rash, ↑ LFTs **MONITORING** LFTs, GI symptoms (and electrolytes, hydration status if diarrhea), blood glucose, lipids **NOTES** Boosting with ritonavir not recommended (achieves adequate concentrations on its own) If difficulty with swallowing, tablets may be dissolved in small amount of water and consumed immediately Do not use with PPIs
Saquinavir, SQV *(Invirase)* Capsule, tablet	1,000 mg + ritonavir 100 mg BID Must be given with ritonavir	**CONTRAINDICATIONS** Severe hepatic impairment, congenital or acquired QT prolongation, complete AV block or at high-risk for AV block, and refractory hypokalemia or hypomagnesemia **WARNINGS** PR and QT interval prolongation (avoid use if QT > 450 msec), photosensitivity reaction **SIDE EFFECTS** Nausea, vomiting, diarrhea, HA, abdominal pain, fatigue, hyperglycemia **MONITORING** ECG (baseline and ongoing),electrolytes (esp K, Mg), blood glucose, lipids **NOTES** Capsules may be opened and mixed with syrup or jam immediately before taking
Tipranavir, TPV *(Aptivus)* Capsule, oral solution (100 mg/mL)	500 mg + ritonavir 200 mg BID Swallow whole; do not break, crush, or chew Must be given with ritonavir Capsules: refrigerate; can store at room temp up to 60 days; need to discard 60 days after opening bottle Solution: store at room temp; need to discard 60 days after opening bottle	**BOXED WARNINGS** Clinical hepatitis and hepatic decompensation (sometimes fatal) and intracranial hemorrhage **CONTRAINDICATIONS** Moderate or severe hepatic impairment **WARNINGS** Use caution in patients with a sulfa allergy, intracranial hemorrhage (caution in those with bleeding risk) **SIDE EFFECTS** N/V/D, HA, ↑ CPK, hyperlipidemia (especially TG) **MONITORING** LFTs, blood glucose, lipids **NOTES** Capsules contain 7% alcohol Oral solution contains vitamin E; additional vitamin supplements should be avoided

PI Drug Interactions

All PIs are metabolized in the liver via the CYP450 system; they have many drug interactions. All PIs are CYP3A4 substrates and most are strong inhibitors of CYP3A4. The drug interaction list below highlights the most important interactions and contraindications; it is not all-inclusive.

- Avoid with PIs:
  - CYP3A4 inducers (e.g., rifampin and St. John's wort): they can lower PI concentrations.
  - Antiarrhythmics: dronedarone (contraindicated with all PIs), amiodarone (contraindicated with some), use caution with all antiarrhythmics.
  - Anticoagulants/antiplatelets: apixaban, edoxaban, rivaroxaban, ticagrelor and vorapaxar.
  - Direct-acting antivirals (DAA) for HCV: many DAAs interact; check for interactions when initiating.
  - Other drugs that are contraindicated or should be avoided with all PIs: alfuzosin, cisapride, colchicine (in patients with hepatic or renal impairment), eplerenone, ergot derivatives, flibanserin, ivabradine, lurasidone, midazolam (PO), pimozide, salmeterol, suvorexant, triazolam and voriconazole.
- PIs can alter the INR (mainly ↓) in patients taking warfarin due to CYP2C9 induction; the INR should be closely monitored.
- Anticonvulsants: carbamazepine, phenytoin and phenobarbital (avoid with darunavir/ritonavir, atazanavir/ritonavir and cobicistat). These anticonvulsants are CYP inducers that compete with the boosters, decreasing PI concentrations.
- Hormonal contraceptives (especially those containing ethinyl estradiol and norethindrone): ritonavir may ↓ levels via CYP induction. Check for drug-specific recommendations (variable among PIs/contraceptives) and counsel on use of additional/alternative contraceptive methods as appropriate.
- Methadone: ritonavir may ↓ levels (via CYP induction). Monitor for possible methadone withdrawal.
- Phosphodiesterase-5 inhibitors (PDE-5 inhibitors): PIs can ↑ levels of PDE-5 inhibitors and ↑ risk of toxicity. Initiate PDE-5 inhibitors at lowest dose and extend the dosing interval. Sildenafil (used chronically for PAH) is contraindicated.
- Statins: PIs can ↑ statin levels. Lovastatin and simvastatin are contraindicated with PIs. Rosuvastatin and atorvastatin are preferred statins with PIs. Start statin therapy with a low dose and titrate to response. Monitor closely for statin toxicity.
- PIs ↑ the levels of trazodone and many tricyclic antidepressants. Start with low doses and then titrate antidepressant doses based upon clinical response.
- Atazanavir: caution with the use of acid-suppression. See specific information in the drug table.
- Do not use nelfinavir with PPIs.
- Elbasvir/grazoprevir (*Zepatier*): do not use with darunavir/ritonavir or lopinavir/ritonavir. Lopinavir inhibits OATP1/B1.

PHARMACOKINETIC BOOSTERS

Ritonavir is a protease inhibitor, but it is currently used only for its potent CYP3A4 inhibition to increase, or boost, the level of other PIs. Cobicistat *(Tybost)* is a strong CYP3A4 inhibitor and FDA-approved to pharmacokinetically enhance, or boost, levels of atazanavir and darunavir. Cobicistat itself is not a protease inhibitor and is not interchangeable with ritonavir.

PI AND PK BOOSTER DRUG INTERACTIONS

Protease inhibitors, ritonavir and cobicistat have many significant drug interactions and contraindications due to enzyme and transporter interactions.

Be sure to look for them on a patient profile.

Know which formulations/combinations contain these medications to be able to identify interactions.

	RITONAVIR *(Norvir)*	COBICISTAT *(Tybost)*
Boxed Warning	Interacts with many medications, including antiarrhythmics, ergot alkaloids and sedatives/hypnotics, resulting in potentially serious and/or life-threatening adverse events	None
Dose	100 to 400 mg PO daily (in 1-2 divided doses)	150 mg PO daily with darunavir or atazanavir
Antiretroviral activity	Yes	No
Enzyme activity	Strong inhibitor: CYP3A4, 2C8 Also inhibits: CYP2D6, 2C9, 2C19, BCRP Inducer: CYP2C9 (weak/moderate)	Strong inhibitor: CYP3A4 Also inhibits: CYP2D6, BCRP, OATP1B1, OATP1B3
P-glycoprotein inhibition	Strong	Weak
Adverse effects	N/V/D, paresthesias, arthralgias, ↑ CPK, lipid abnormalities	Increase in SCr (average 0.4), without affecting glomerular filtration function
Additional considerations	Take with food Capsules and tablets are not bioequivalent (higher peak concentrations with the tablet may cause more GI side effects) Tablets: do not break, crush or chew Capsules: refrigerate; stable at room temperature for up to 30 days Solution: 43% alcohol; shake well Powder: 100 mg packet can be mixed with soft food or liquid. Take within 2 hours. Must be given in 100 mg increments only. Difficult to co-formulate with other ARVs	Take with food Can be co-formulated *(Stribild, Genvoya, Prezcobix, Evotaz, Symtuza)*
Contraindicated with both	Alfuzosin, amiodarone, carbamazepine, cisapride, colchicine (with renal or hepatic impairment), dronedarone, ergot derivatives, flecainide, lovastatin, lurasidone, midazolam (PO), phenobarbital, phenytoin, pimozide, propafenone, quinidine, ranolazine, rifampin, simvastatin, sildenafil (used for PAH), St. John's wort, triazolam Any narrow therapeutic index drug that is highly dependent on CYP3A4 for clearance	

INTEGRASE STRAND TRANSFER INHIBITORS

Integrase strand transfer inhibitors (INSTIs) block the integrase enzyme needed for viral DNA to integrate with the host cell DNA/human genome (see Stage 4 in the HIV life cycle diagram).

KEY FEATURES OF INSTIs

The generic names end in "-tegravir"

No renal dose adjustment needed

- Do not start *Stribild* if CrCl < 70 mL/min
- Do not start *Genvoya* or *Biktarvy* if CrCl < 30 mL/min

No major CYP450 interactions (combination products will have interactions based on the non-INSTI components)

↑ CPK (raltegravir > other INSTIs)

Headache, insomnia

Interaction with polyvalent cations – must separate

DRUG	DOSING	SAFETY/SIDE EFFECTS/MONITORING
Elvitegravir, EVG No single agent	*Stribild:* 1 tablet daily CrCl < 70 mL/min: do not start CrCl < 50 mL/min: discontinue *Genvoya:* 1 tablet daily CrCl < 30 mL/min: do not start Boosting with cobicistat allows once daily dosing	**BOXED WARNING** Acute exacerbation of HBV can occur when drug is discontinued in patients with HBV (specific for emtricitabine and tenofovir) **CONTRAINDICATIONS** Concurrent use of alfuzosin, cisapride, ergot derivatives, lovastatin, midazolam (oral), pimozide, rifampin, sildenafil (when used for pulmonary arterial hypertension), simvastatin, St. John's wort and triazolam **WARNINGS** Lactic acidosis with severe hepatomegaly with steatosis, new onset or worsening renal impairment, ↓ bone density **SIDE EFFECTS** Proteinuria, ↑ SCr, nausea and diarrhea, hyperlipidemia, HA, insomnia **MONITORING** CPK, LFTs, renal function
Bictegravir No single agent	*Biktarvy:* 1 tablet daily CrCl < 30 mL/min: do not start	**BOXED WARNING** Acute exacerbation of HBV can occur when drug is discontinued in patients with HBV (specific for emtricitabine and tenofovir) **CONTRAINDICATIONS** Coadministration with dofetilide or rifampin **WARNINGS** Lactic acidosis with severe hepatomegaly with steatosis, new onset or worsening renal impairment, potentially significant drug interactions **SIDE EFFECTS** Diarrhea, nausea, HA **MONITORING** LFTs, renal function
Dolutegravir, DTG ***(Tivicay)*** Tablet	For patients ≥ 40 kg only 50 mg PO daily 50 mg PO BID (for treatment-experienced patients, those with INSTI resistance or those taking certain UGT1A or CYP3A4 inducers)	**CONTRAINDICATION** Coadministration with dofetilide **SIDE EFFECTS** Insomnia, HA, diarrhea, rash, ↑ CPK, ↑ LFTs among hepatitis B/C patients, ↑ SCr without affecting GFR **MONITORING** CPK, LFTs (especially in patients with hepatitis B or C)
Raltegravir, RAL ***(Isentress, Isentress HD)*** Tablet (including chewable), powder packet for oral suspension	400 mg BID HD: 1,200 mg daily (two 600 mg tablets) Oral suspension: Keep in original container, do not open foil packet until ready for reconstitution and use	**SIDE EFFECTS** Nausea, HA, insomnia, fatigue, ↑ CPK, myopathy and rhabdomyolysis **MONITORING** CPK (if symptomatic), LFTs

INSTI Drug Interactions

- INSTIs should be taken 2 hours before or 6 hours after cation-containing antacids or laxatives, sucralfate, iron or calcium supplements or buffered medications. Exception: no dose separation needed for raltegravir and calcium carbonate. H2RAs and PPIs do not pose an interaction with INSTIs.
- Elvitegravir: major CYP3A4 substrate and an inducer of CYP2C9 (weak/moderate). It may ↓ the plasma concentrations of CYP2C9 substrates. Multiple interactions with DAAs used for HCV. Avoid with rifampin.
- Bictegravir: substrate for CYP3A4 and UGT1A1. Contraindicated with dofetilide and rifampin. Not recommended with strong CYP3A4 inducers (e.g., anticonvulsants and St. John's wort). *Biktarvy* can be taken on an empty stomach 2 hours before antacids with aluminum, magnesium or calcium. Routine administration of these antacids at the same time or 2 hrs after *Biktarvy* is not recommended. *Biktarvy* can be taken with supplements containing calcium or iron together with food.
- Cobicistat-containing INSTI products: interactions are very similar to ritonavir interactions (see Boosters table following the PIs). Cobicistat is an inhibitor of CYP3A4 (strong), CYP2D6 (weak) and is contraindicated with a number of medications.
- Raltegravir: metabolized by the UGT1A1-mediated glucuronidation pathway. Rifampin, a strong inducer of UGT1A1, will ↓ levels of raltegravir. When given concurrently with rifampin, use raltegravir 800 mg BID. PPIs can ↑ levels of raltegravir although dosage adjustment is not needed. Rifampin is contraindicated with raltegravir HD.

CCR5 ANTAGONIST

Maraviroc inhibits binding to the CCR5 co-receptor on the CD4+ cells and prevents HIV from entering the cell (see Stage 1 in the HIV life cycle diagram). Unlike the other antiretroviral drug classes, the CCR5 antagonist does not directly target the HIV cell; it blocks the human host cell receptor.

DRUG	DOSING	SAFETY/SIDE EFFECTS/MONITORING
Maraviroc, MVC (*Selzentry*) Tablet, solution	300 mg BID Adjust dose if concurrent CYP3A4 inhibitor or inducer; see contraindications for renal impairment. Prior to starting therapy, patients must undergo a tropism test. Maraviroc will only work in patients with CCR5-tropic disease (patient must be negative for CXCR4- or dual/mixed-tropic disease)	**BOXED WARNING** Hepatotoxicity, may occur with severe rash or other allergic type features **CONTRAINDICATIONS** Patients with severe renal impairment (CrCl < 30 mL/min) taking potent CYP3A4 inhibitors/inducers **WARNINGS** Hypersensitivity reactions (including SJS), CV events (including MI), orthostatic hypotension in patients with renal impairment **SIDE EFFECTS** URTIs, fever, cough, rash, abdominal pain, dizziness **MONITORING** Tropism testing prior to initiation, LFTs, s/sx of infection, skin reactions **NOTES** Swallow tablets whole; do not chew, break, or crush

CCR5 Antagonist Drug Interactions

Maraviroc is a P-gp and major CYP3A4 substrate. Maraviroc concentrations can be significantly ↑ in the presence of strong CYP3A4 inhibitors and ↓ with CYP3A4 inducers, and maraviroc dosage is determined by the presence of drug interactions. Avoid use with St. John's wort.

FUSION INHIBITOR

Fusion inhibitors block the fusion of the HIV virus with the CD4+ cells by blocking the conformational change in gp41 required for membrane fusion and entry into CD4+ cells (see Stage 2 in the HIV life cycle diagram).

DRUG	DOSING	SAFETY/SIDE EFFECTS/MONITORING
Enfuvirtide, T20 *(Fuzeon)* Powder for injection	90 mg SC BID Reconstituted solution should be refrigerated and used within 24 hours	**WARNINGS** ↑ risk of bacterial pneumonia, hypersensitivity reaction **SIDE EFFECTS** Local injection site reactions in 98% of patients (pain, erythema, nodules and cysts, ecchymosis), diarrhea, nausea, fatigue **NOTES** Patient should be counseled regarding proper reconstitution and injection technique and to rotate injection sites Typically used in patients who are treatment-experienced with resistance to multiple other ART

CD4-DIRECTED POST-ATTACHMENT HIV-1 INHIBITOR

Ibalizumab-uiyk *(Trogarzo)* is the first of a new class of monoclonal antibodies for HIV. It binds to domain 2 of CD4 and blocks entry of HIV into host cells without causing immunosuppression. It is approved for use with other ARTs in patients who are heavily treatment-experienced (with multidrug resistant HIV, or MDR-HIV) who are failing their current ART regimen.

DRUG	DOSING	SAFETY/SIDE EFFECTS/MONITORING
Ibalizumab-uiyk *(Trogarzo)* Injection	Loading dose: 2,000 mg IV x 1 Maintenance dose: 800 mg/250 mL normal saline IV every 2 weeks	**WARNING** Risk for immune reconstitution inflammatory syndrome (IRIS) **SIDE EFFECTS** Infusion-related reactions, diarrhea, dizziness, nausea, rash **NOTES** Once diluted, the product should be administered immediately Observe patient for infusion-related reactions for 1 hour after the first infusion

SELECT COMPLICATIONS OF ART

- Lipodystrophy: changes in fat distribution in the body. Further subcategorized as lipoatrophy (fat loss or wasting) or lipohypertrophy (fat accumulation).
  - Lipoatrophy: loss of subcutaneous fat in the face, arms, legs and buttocks. Most commonly associated with NRTIs, specifically stavudine (and zidovudine to a lesser extent).
  - Lipohypertrophy: fat accumulation in the upper back and neck ("buffalo hump"), abdominal area and breast area in both men and women. Most commonly associated with PIs. Breast enlargement with efavirenz has been reported.
- Immune reconstitution inflammatory syndrome (IRIS): paradoxical worsening of a preexisting OI or malignancy when ART is initiated. Since ART leads to an improvement in immune function, an inflammatory reaction may occur at the site of the preexisting infection. Patients with low CD4+ counts and high viral loads are at highest risk. IRIS generally develops within 1 – 3 months of ART initiation. Common pathogens include *M. tuberculosis*, *M. avium*, *Pneumocystis jiroveci* pneumonia (PCP), herpes simplex virus (HSV), herpes zoster, cytomegalovirus (CMV), *Cryptococcus* and HBV. Management of IRIS consists of the following:
  - Start or continue therapy for the underlying opportunistic pathogen or malignancy.
  - Continue ART (if already taking). Among patients newly diagnosed with HIV with OI, ART may be intentionally delayed while treating the OI to minimize risk for IRIS. ART should be started within 2 weeks of OI treatment initiation for the majority of OIs with the exception of cryptococcal meningitis and *M. tuberculosis*.
  - In select circumstances, the addition of systemic steroids may be appropriate.

- Lactic acidosis and severe hepatomegaly with steatosis: stop treatment in any patient who develops clinical or laboratory findings suggestive of lactic acidosis or hepatotoxicity (↑ LFTs may accompany hepatomegaly and steatosis). Most commonly associated with NRTIs.
- Diarrhea: diarrhea is a common side effect of ART. All ARTs have been associated with GI toxicity, however, PIs are generally the most problematic (especially nelfinavir and lopinavir/ritonavir).

THERAPIES FOR HIV COMPLICATIONS

DRUG	INDICATION
Poly-L-Lactic Acid, injection	Lipoatrophy (facial)
Calcium hydroxylapatite *(Radiesse, Radiesse Plus)*, injection	Lipoatrophy (facial)
Tesamorelin *(Egrifta)*, injection	HIV-associated lipodystrophy (specifically reduction of excess abdominal fat)
Crofelemer *(Mytesi)*, tablet	Non-infectious diarrhea due to ART
Megestrol *(Megace ES)*, tablet, suspension	Anorexia or cachexia associated with AIDS (increases appetite)
Dronabinol *(Marinol, Syndros)*, capsule, oral solution	AIDS-related anorexia

HIV PREVENTION STRATEGIES

Various prevention strategies are utilized to reduce the number of new HIV infections. Prevention strategies include pre-exposure prophylaxis, treatment as prevention and post-exposure prophylaxis (occupational and nonoccupational). These strategies are often utilized in combination and coupled with continued community education on HIV transmission and risk factors.

TREATMENT AS PREVENTION

The risk of transmitting HIV to another individual is directly proportional to the HIV viral load. Treatment as Prevention aims to treat the HIV infected individual with effective ART to reduce the HIV viral load thus reducing the risk of transmitting HIV to another person.

PRE-EXPOSURE PROPHYLAXIS (PrEP)

Pre-exposure prophylaxis (PrEP) is an HIV prevention method in which people who do not have HIV take emtricitabine/tenofovir *(Truvada)* 1 tab PO daily, in combination with safer sex/behavior risk reduction practices, to reduce their risk of becoming infected. The effectiveness of PrEP is directly related to medication adherence. PrEP is recommended for both homosexual and heterosexual individuals who are at very high risk for sexual exposure to HIV as well as for active intravenous drug users.

Before Initiating PrEP

- Confirm HIV negative status through HIV antibody test
- Confirm CrCl ≥ 60 mL/min
- Confirm patient very high risk for acquiring HIV
- Screen for hepatitis B and STIs

Once PrEP is initiated, follow-up visits are needed at least every 3 months with the following recommendations during each visit:

- HIV test and document negative result
- Provide no more than 90-day supply at a time (renew Rx only once HIV negative status is confirmed)
- Pregnancy test (for non-HIV-infected women taking PrEP)
- Counseling on PrEP adherence and safe sex/behavior risk reduction practices
- Every 6 months, check SCr and calculate CrCl, and test for bacterial STIs (regardless of symptoms)

NONOCCUPATIONAL POST-EXPOSURE PROPHYLAXIS (nPEP)

Nonoccupational exposure is the use of ART prophylaxis after sexual, injection drug use, or some other nonoccupational exposure to HIV. Regardless of whether or not nPEP is prescribed, the exposed patient should be tested for HIV Ab at baseline, 4 – 6 weeks, 3 months and 6 months after the exposure event.

REGIMENS	CRITERIA TO QUALIFY	DURATION
INSTI-BASED (PREFERRED) Emtricitabine + tenofovir disoproxil fumarate *(Truvada)* 1 tablet daily + Raltegravir 400 mg PO BID or Dolutegravir 50 mg PO daily **PI-BASED (ALTERNATIVE)** Emtricitabine + tenofovir disoproxil fumarate *(Truvada)* 1 tablet daily + Darunavir 800 mg + ritonavir 100 mg daily	As soon as possible but within 72 hours since exposure Known HIV (+) status of source (if HIV status unknown, then case-by-case determination) Exposed patient is HIV (–) or being tested for HIV Type of exposure is also factored into decision to initiate nPEP	28 days

OCCUPATIONAL POST-EXPOSURE PROPHYLAXIS (PEP)

Occupational exposure typically refers to exposure of health care personnel to blood or body fluids that are potentially contaminated with HIV. ART prophylaxis for occupational exposure is generally only recommended if the source of contaminated blood or body fluid is known to be HIV infected. If the source patient's HIV status is unknown, the HIV status should be determined, if possible, to guide need for HIV PEP. Therapy should be started right away, ideally within 72 hours, when treatment is indicated. Per the 2013 updated guideline, a three drug regimen including raltegravir *(Isentress)* + emtricitabine/tenofovir *(Truvada)* for a 4-week course is the preferred regimen. The exposed health care personnel should be tested for HIV Ab at baseline, 4 – 6 weeks, 3 months and 6 months after the exposure event. If PEP is initiated, then CBC, renal and liver function should be tested at baseline and repeated at 2 weeks post-exposure.

SUMMARY TABLES AND TIPS

ADMINISTRATION (FOOD) REQUIREMENTS

With food

Protease Inhibitors (except fosamprenavir suspension)

- Atazanavir and *Evotaz*
- Darunavir and *Prezcobix*
- Indinavir (boosted)
- *Kaletra* oral soln
- Nelfinavir
- Ritonavir
- Saquinavir
- Tipranavir

Genvoya

Stribild

Rilpivirine (and all combos that contain it)

Complera, Juluca, Odefsey

Etravirine (after meals)

Symtuza

Tenofovir powder (to avoid bitter taste)

Cobicistat

Without food

Atripla

Efavirenz (small amount of non-fatty food is okay) and combos that contain it:

Symfi and *Symfi Lo*

Fosamprenavir (oral suspension, in adults)

Didanosine

Indinavir (unboosted)

ART ADVERSE EFFECTS BY CLASS AND AGENT

This table is a summary of important adverse effects of ART drug classes and individual drugs covered throughout the chapter.

ART	COMMON ADVERSE EFFECT
NRTIs Class Effect: Lactic acidosis	
Abacavir	Hypersensitivity and possible ↑ risk of MI
Didanosine	Pancreatitis and peripheral neuropathy
Emtricitabine	Headache
Lamivudine	Headache
Stavudine	Pancreatitis and peripheral neuropathy
Tenofovir (TDF, TAF)	Renal toxicity (Fanconi syndrome) and ↓ bone mineral density
Zidovudine	Macrocytic anemia and myopathy
NNRTIs Class Effect: Rash	
Efavirenz	CNS effects (impaired concentration, abnormal dreams, confusion)
Nevirapine	Hepatotoxicity and hypersensitivity reaction
Etravirine	SJS/TEN
Doravirine	Hepatotoxicity
Rilpivirine	Depression and insomnia
PIs Class Effects: Metabolic abnormalities (hyperlipidemia, hyperglycemia, lipohypertrophy) and N/V/D	
Darunavir	Headache
Atazanavir	Nephrolithiasis and indirect hyperbilirubinemia
Fosamprenavir	Rash
Indinavir	Nephrolithiasis and urolithiasis
Lopinavir/ritonavir	Hypertriglyceridemia
Nelfinavir	Diarrhea
Ritonavir	N/V/D
Saquinavir	Nausea
Tipranavir	Intracranial hemorrhage
INSTIs	
Bictegravir	Headache
Raltegravir	↑ CPK, myopathy and rhabdomyolysis
Elvitegravir	Headache and insomnia
Dolutegravir	↑ SCr without affecting GFR

PATIENT COUNSELING

All HIV Medications

- This medication is not a cure for HIV and should be used along with other practices to prevent the spread of HIV to others. Avoid sharing needles or personal items that may have blood on them (e.g., razors or toothbrushes) and do not have unprotected sex.
- It is very important to continue taking this medication (and other HIV medications in your regimen) exactly as prescribed by your healthcare provider. Do not skip doses or stop taking any part your HIV medication regimen even for a short time unless directed to do so by your healthcare provider. Skipping or stopping your medication, or taking only some but not all of the HIV medications in your full regimen, may cause the amount of HIV virus to increase and make the infection more difficult to treat (resistant). Refill all HIV medications before you run out.
- If you are taking HIV medications for the first time, you may experience symptoms of an old infection. This can happen as your immune system begins to work better. Contact your healthcare provider immediately if you notice any new occurrence of the following symptoms: fever, cough, trouble breathing, vision problems, headaches or skin problems.
- Rarely, this medication can cause severe liver problems. Tell your healthcare provider immediately if you develop symptoms such as persistent nausea/vomiting, loss of appetite, stomach/abdominal pain, pale stools, dark urine, yellowing eyes/skin or unusual tiredness.
- This medication can cause changes in body fat, such as increased fat in the upper back and neck, breasts and belly areas, and loss of fat from legs, arms and face. These symptoms occur after you have been on the medication for a long time.
- Do not breastfeed. HIV can be passed on to your baby through your breastmilk.
- HIV is always treated with more than one medication. Some combination medicines are available to decrease the amount of pills you take each day.

NRTIs Patient Counseling

- Take this medication with or without food.
- Rarely, this medication can cause a build-up of acid in your blood; report any symptoms such as stomach pain, nausea, vomiting, troubled breathing, weakness or muscle pain.
- If you have hepatitis B and are taking a regimen containing lamivudine, emtricitabine and/or tenofovir, your hepatitis symptoms may become suddenly worse if you stop taking any of these medications. This can lead to death. Talk with your healthcare provider before stopping the medication/s. Tell your healthcare provider immediately if you develop symptoms of worsening liver problems.

DISPENSE IN ORIGINAL CONTAINER

Many HIV medications (most of the newer ones) must be protected from moisture and dispensed only in the original container.

Atripla	*Odefsey*	Doravirine
Biktarvy	*Stribild*	Etravirine
Cimduo	*Symfi and Symfi Lo*	Indinavir
Complera	*Symtuza*	Nelfinavir
Descovy	*Triumeq*	Raltegravir
Delstrigo	*Truvada*	Ritonavir (tabs)
Genvoya	Darunavir	Rilpivirine
Juluca	Dolutegravir (10 mg tabs only)	Tenofovir disoproxil fumarate

Abacavir

- Read the MedGuide that has been given to you. Carry the Warning Card (which lists the symptoms of a serious allergic reaction) with you at all times and contact your healthcare provider if you develop the following symptoms: fever, rash, nausea, vomiting, diarrhea, severe stomach pain, extreme tiredness or aches, generalized ill feeling, shortness of breath, cough or sore throat, as you may need to stop taking products that contain abacavir.
- If you have an allergic reaction while taking an abacavir-containing product, you should dispose of any remaining medication. If exposed to abacavir again, a life-threatening reaction can occur.

Lamivudine

- If you have Hepatitis B and HIV, your healthcare provider will prescribe a higher dose of lamivudine than is present in *Epivir-HBV*, because a higher dose is required to treat HIV.

Emtricitabine

- Headaches are a common side effect of this medication.
- This medication can cause darkening skin color on palms of hands and on soles of feet.
- This medication may cause rash in some people who take it. If you develop a rash, notify your healthcare provider as soon as possible.

Tenofovir disoproxil fumarate and tenofovir alafenamide

- Tell your healthcare provider immediately if any of these rare but serious side effects occur: signs of kidney problems such as a change in the amount of urine, unusual thirst or muscle cramps/weakness.
- Bone problems, including bone pain, softening or thinning of the bones, can happen in some people who take this medication. Your healthcare provider may order extra tests to check your bones.
- Tenofovir disoproxil fumarate powder: This medication comes with a dosing scoop; use only the dosing scoop to measure the oral powder. Mix the oral powder with soft foods that can be swallowed without chewing (e.g., applesauce, baby food or yogurt). Do not mix with liquid as the powder may float to the top even after stirring. Give the entire dose right away after mixing to avoid a bad taste.

NNRTIs Patient Counseling

- This medication may cause a rash in some people who take it. It may go away, but if you develop a rash, notify your healthcare provider. If the rash is very severe, accompanied with a fever, or you develop skin blistering, seek care immediately.
- This medication interacts with many other medications. Tell your healthcare provider about all the medications you are taking, including any over-the-counter medications and herbal supplements. Do not start, stop or change the dosage of any medication before checking with your healthcare provider or pharmacist first.

Efavirenz

- Take this medication on an empty stomach, usually once daily at bedtime. Taking efavirenz with food, especially fatty foods, can increase the blood level of this medication, which may increase your risk of certain side effects.
- Headache, nausea, vomiting and diarrhea may occur.
- Dizziness, drowsiness, abnormal dreams/nightmares, trouble sleeping, tiredness/fatigue and trouble concentrating may occur. These side effects often begin 1 – 2 days after starting this medication and usually go away in 2 – 4 weeks. They are also reduced by taking efavirenz on an empty stomach at bedtime. If any of these effects persist or worsen, tell your healthcare provider promptly.
- Efavirenz may cause confusion, make it difficult to concentrate, or slow down your reactions. Use caution when driving or performing tasks that requires you to be awake and alert. Avoid drinking alcohol.
- Serious psychiatric symptoms have been reported during efavirenz treatment, especially in people who have mental health conditions. Tell your healthcare provider immediately if any of these unlikely but serious side effects occur: mental/mood changes such as depression, thoughts of suicide, nervousness, angry behavior or hallucinations.
- This medication may decrease the effectiveness of hormonal birth control pills, patches, or rings which can result in pregnancy. To reduce the risk of unintended pregnancy, and also the risk of spreading HIV to others, use barrier protection during all sexual activity.
- If you take efavirenz during pregnancy, your baby has a higher and unknown risk for some birth defects. Do not use efavirenz without your healthcare provider's consent if you are pregnant or planning to get pregnant. Use two forms of birth control, including a barrier form (such as a condom and diaphragm with spermicide gel) while you are taking efavirenz, and for at least 12 weeks after your treatment ends. Tell your healthcare provider if you become pregnant during treatment.

Rilpivirine

- This medication may cause depression and trouble sleeping. If you notice changes in your mood, such as feeling sad, hopeless, anxious or have thoughts of suicide, contact your healthcare provider.
- It is very important to take this medication with a full meal as this helps ensure that your body is absorbing enough of the medication to work against the virus. Ideally, your meal should be at least 500 calories. A protein drink should not be used in place of a meal.

STRATEGIES TO IMPROVE ADHERENCE TO ANTIRETROVIRAL THERAPY

Multidisciplinary team approach (e.g., nurses, social workers, pharmacists, psychologists, physicians)

Accessible, non-judgmental health care team, establish trusting relationship with patient

Evaluate patient's knowledge of HIV disease, prevention and treatment, and provide information as needed; establish patient readiness to start ART and involve in ART regimen selection

Identify potential barriers to adherence (e.g., psychosocial or cognitive issues, substance abuse, low literacy, busy daily schedule, lack of prescription coverage and/or social support)

Assess adherence at every clinic visit, and simplify ART regimen when possible; provide positive reinforcement to foster adherence success

Identify non-adherence and reasons for non-adherence (e.g., adverse effects from medications, complex regimen, difficulty swallowing large pills, forgetfulness, pill fatigue, food requirements, stigma, change or lapse of insurance coverage)

Provide resources (e.g., referrals for mental health and/or substance abuse treatment, prescription drug assistance programs, pillboxes, reminder tools, medication lists or calendars)

- Medications that reduce stomach acid can significantly affect the absorption of this medication and result in failure of HIV treatment. Talk with your healthcare provider or pharmacist before starting any acid suppressant medications.

PI Patient Counseling

- Diarrhea, nausea, vomiting, heartburn, stomach pain, headache, dizziness, fatigue, weakness or changes in taste may occur. If any of these effects persist or worsen, tell your healthcare provider or pharmacist promptly.
- A mild rash (redness and itching) may occur within the first few weeks after the medicine is started and usually goes away within 2 weeks with no change in treatment. If a severe rash develops with symptoms of fever, body or muscle aches, mouth sores, shortness of breath or swelling of the face, contact your healthcare provider immediately.
- Before using this medication, tell your healthcare provider your medical history, especially if you have: diabetes, heart problems (coronary artery disease, heart attack), hemophilia, high cholesterol/triglycerides, gout/high uric acid in the blood, liver problems (such as hepatitis B or hepatitis C), kidney problems and/or pancreatitis.
- Some patients taking this medication have increased blood sugar levels. If you have diabetes, check your blood sugar levels regularly as directed by your healthcare provider. Tell your healthcare provider immediately if you have symptoms of high blood sugar, such as increased thirst, increased urination, confusion, drowsiness, flushing, rapid breathing or fruity breath odor.
- This medication interacts with many other medications. Tell your healthcare provider about all the medications you are taking, including any over-the-counter medications and herbal supplements. Do not start, stop or change the dosage of any medicine before checking with your healthcare provider or pharmacist first.
- Seek immediate medical attention if any of these rare but serious side effects occur: symptoms of a heart attack (such as chest/jaw/left arm pain, shortness of breath or profuse sweating), change in heart rhythm, dizziness, lightheadedness, severe nausea or vomiting, severe stomach pain, extreme weakness or trouble breathing.

Atazanavir

- Take this medication once daily with food. If you are also prescribed ritonavir, make sure to take both atazanavir and ritonavir at the same time.
- Acid-lowering medications for indigestion, heartburn or ulcers (e.g., prescription or over-the-counter medications such as antacids, famotidine or omeprazole) can significantly decrease the amount of atazanavir that gets in your system and result in failure of your HIV treatment. Ask your healthcare provider or pharmacist how to use these medications together with atazanavir safely.
- May cause skin or the whites of eyes to turn yellow. This is usually not a dangerous side effect, however, if this becomes bothersome, talk with your healthcare provider. If you develop yellowing of skin/eyes along with severe abdominal pain and/or nausea/vomiting, contact your healthcare provider immediately as these could be signs of liver problems.
- Although rare, some patients have developed gallstones or kidney stones while on this medication. Take this medication with plenty of water to reduce chances of developing kidney stones. Seek immediate care if you notice signs of a kidney stone (e.g., pain in side/back/abdomen, painful urination or blood in the urine).

Darunavir

- Take darunavir with ritonavir at the same time(s) each day with food.
- Headaches are a common side effect of this medication.
- This medication may cause rash in some people, which is usually mild and will resolve on its own over time. If you develop a severe, bothersome rash, contact your healthcare provider immediately. If you have a sulfa allergy, tell your healthcare provider or pharmacist right away.

INSTI Patient Counseling

- This medication can interact with antacids, multivitamins, iron and other supplements. Talk with your healthcare provider before taking these two medications together. Generally, you should separate this HIV medication at least 2 hours before or 6 hours after the antacids.
- May cause rash in some people. Notify your healthcare provider if it becomes bothersome. If you develop severe rash, accompanied with fever and/or difficulty breathing, seek medical attention immediately.
- May cause muscle pain, tenderness or weakness. Inform your healthcare provider if you notice these symptoms, especially if you develop these out of proportion to your actual level of activity.
- May cause headache or difficulty sleeping.
- Rarely, may cause kidney or liver problems. Your healthcare provider will be checking your labs from time to time to monitor your kidneys and liver.

Dolutegravir

- Take this medication with or without food.
- Follow the dosing instructions as prescribed by your healthcare provider (once vs. twice a day).

- Do not take this medication if you are also taking dofetilide for a heart rhythm problem. Contact your healthcare provider to discuss alternative HIV therapy options.

Raltegravir

- This medication is to be taken twice a day with or without food.
- Rarely this medication can cause muscle problems. Report any new muscle pain, weakness or extreme tiredness.

Elvitegravir

- This medication should be taken with food.

***Stribild* and *Genvoya* (also see emtricitabine and tenofovir disoproxil fumarate counseling points)**

- This medication contains 4 medications in one pill: elvitegravir, cobicistat, emtricitabine and tenofovir.
- Take this medication once a day with food. Keep the medication in the original container.
- If you have hepatitis B, it's very important that you do not suddenly stop this medication unless instructed to do so by your healthcare provider. Abruptly stopping this medication may result in worsening of your hepatitis symptoms.
- This medication interacts with many medications. Tell your healthcare provider and pharmacist about all the medications you are taking, including any over-the-counter medications and herbal supplements. Do not start, stop or change the dosage of any medication before checking with your healthcare provider or pharmacist first.

FILL IN THE ANTIRETROVIRAL

Test yourself on the names and ingredients of selected products for HIV. Write in the missing information below.

BRAND NAME	INGREDIENTS	TAKE WITH FOOD? (Y / N / EITHER)
Truvada		
	Emtricitabine/tenofovir alafenamide	
Genvoya		
	Darunavir	
	Elvitegravir/cobicistat/emtricitabine/tenofovir disoproxil fumarate	
Triumeq		
	Emtricitabine/tenofovir disoproxil fumarate/rilpivirine	
Tivicay		
	Raltegravir	
Odefsey		

Select Guidelines/References

Panel on Antiretroviral Guidelines for Adults and Adolescents. Guidelines for the use of antiretroviral agents in HIV-1-infected adults and adolescents. Department of Health and Human Services. Available at: http://aidsinfo.nih.gov/contentfiles/lvguidelines/adultandadolescentgl.pdf. (accessed 2019 Feb 27)

Panel on treatment of HIV-infected pregnant women and prevention of perinatal transmission. Recommendations for use of antiretroviral drugs in pregnant HIV-1-infected women for maternal health and interventions to reduce perinatal HIV transmission in the United States. Available at: http://aidsinfo.nih.gov/contentfiles/lvguidelines/perinatalgl.pdf. (accessed 2019 Feb 27)

Panel on opportunistic infections in HIV-infected adults and adolescents. Guidelines for the prevention and treatment of opportunistic infections in HIV-infected adults and adolescents: recommendations from the Centers for Disease Control and Prevention, the National Institutes of Health, and the HIV Medicine Association of the Infectious Diseases Society of America. Available at: http://aidsinfo.nih.gov/contentfiles/lvguidelines/adult_oi.pdf. (accessed 2019 Feb 27)

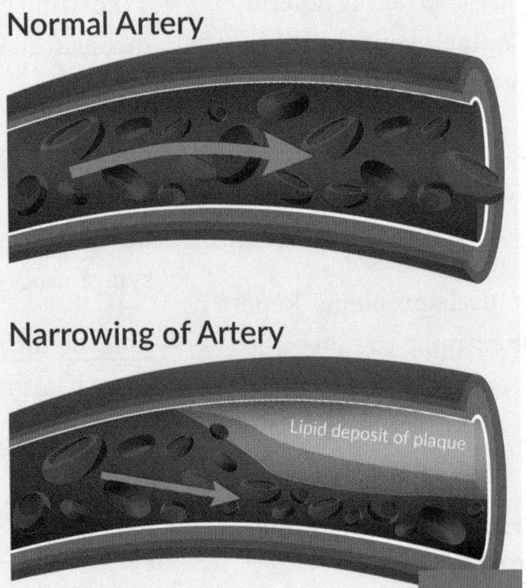

27

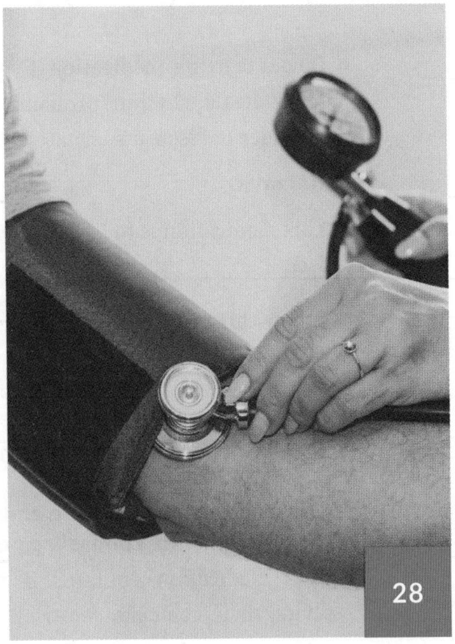
28

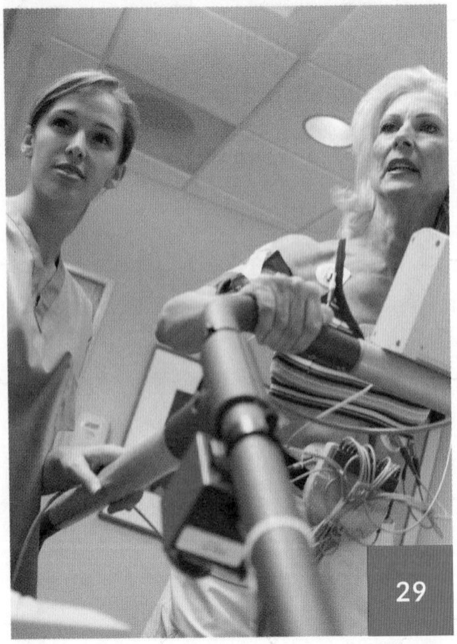
29

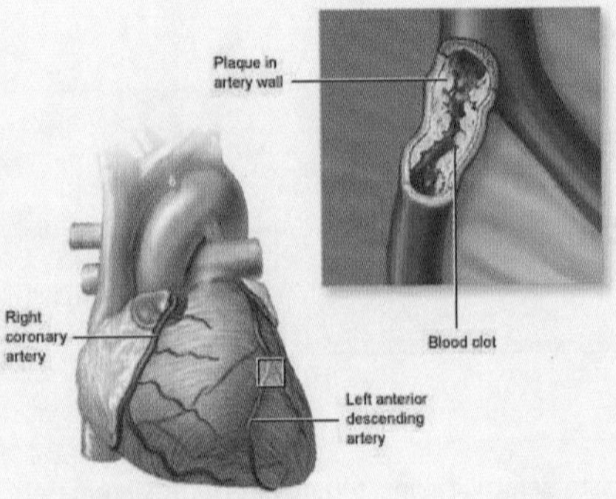

30

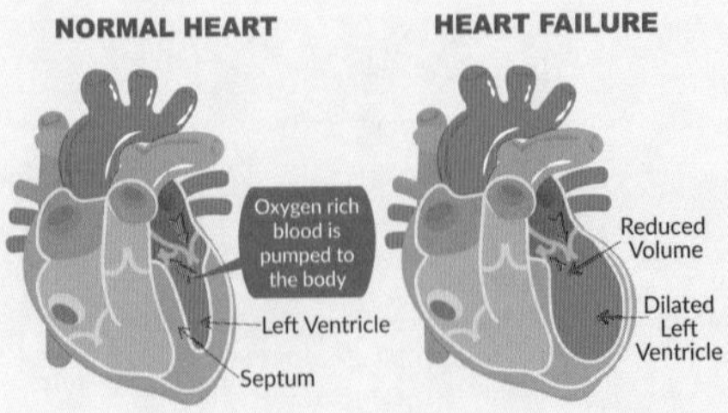

31

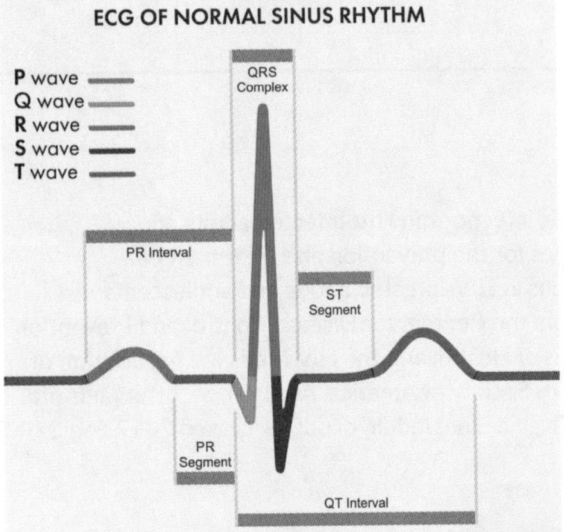

32

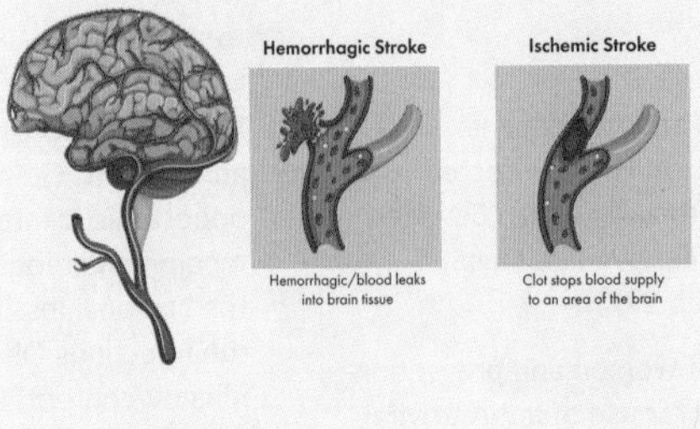

33

CARDIOVASCULAR CONDITIONS

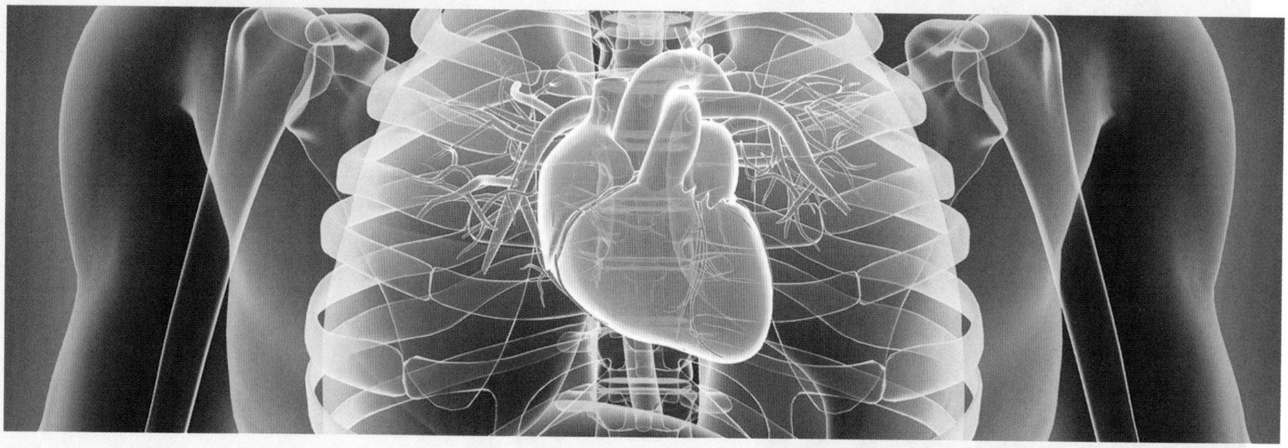

CONTENTS

CHAPTER 27
DYSLIPIDEMIA | **442**

CHAPTER 28
HYPERTENSION | **458**

CHAPTER 29
ISCHEMIC HEART DISEASE | **474**

CHAPTER 30
ACUTE CORONARY SYNDROMES | **481**

CHAPTER 31
CHRONIC HEART FAILURE | **489**

CHAPTER 32
ARRHYTHMIAS | **505**

CHAPTER 33
STROKE | **517**

CHAPTER CONTENT

Background 442
Classification of Dyslipidemia 443
Primary (or Familial) 443
Secondary (or Acquired) 443
Select Drugs/Conditions that Can Raise LDL and/or Triglycerides 443
Cholesterol (Lipoprotein) Types and Normal Values .. 443
Friedewald Equation 443
Non-Drug Treatment 444
Natural Products 444
Treatment Principles 444
Statin Treatment 444
Non-Statin Treatments 445
Calculating ASCVD Risk 445
Determining Statin Treatment Intensity Based on Patient Risk 445
Drug Treatment 446
Statins 446
Statin Equivalent Doses 446
Managing Myalgias 446
Determining Add-On Treatment Based on Patient Risk 448
Ezetimibe 449
Proprotein Convertase Subtilisin Kexin Type 9 Inhibitors 450
Bile Acid Sequestrants/Bile Acid Binding Resins 451
Fibrates 452
Niacin 453
Fish Oils 454
Specialty Drugs: Lomitapide and Mipomersen 455
Patient Counseling 456

CONTENT LEGEND

= Study Tip Gal = Key Drug Guy = Required Formula

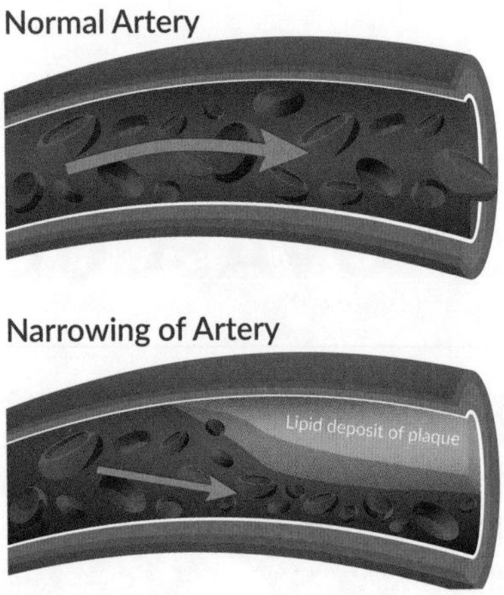

CHAPTER 27

DYSLIPIDEMIA

BACKGROUND

Cholesterol is required for good health. It is a structural component of cells, a precursor in hormone synthesis and used in the production of bile acids by the liver. The bile acids travel from the liver through the bile ducts (with free cholesterol and waste products) and into the small intestine. Bile acids in the small intestine are needed to absorb fat. The acidic environment in the intestine converts the bile acids into bile salts, which are recycled from the intestine and returned to the liver. This process involves the gut (enteric system) and the liver (hepatic), and is referred to as enterohepatic recycling (see Learning Drug Interactions chapter for details).

The recycling system decreases the liver's need for new cholesterol. Cholesterol exits the body either as free cholesterol or as bile acid. If the absorption of free cholesterol is blocked in the intestine (such as with ezetimibe) or the enterohepatic recirculation of bile salts is blocked (by bile acid sequestrants, such as colesevelam), the end result is a decrease in cholesterol.

Cholesterol cannot dissolve in the blood; it is transported in lipoproteins (lipid + a protein carrier). The three major types of lipoproteins are low-density lipoproteins (LDL), high-density lipoproteins (HDL) and very-low density lipoproteins (VLDL), which serve as a carrier for triglycerides (TG). Total cholesterol (TC) accounts for cholesterol in all of the different lipoproteins.

Non-HDL is the difference between the TC and the HDL concentration: non-HDL = TC – HDL. Non-HDL includes atherogenic (increased risk of fatty plaques in the arteries) cholesterol such as LDL, intermediate density lipoproteins (IDL), VLDL, chylomicron remnants and lipoprotein(a). Apolipoprotein B (apoB) is a high-risk marker and an indicator of the progression of atherosclerosis, which begins when an apoB particle becomes trapped within the vascular wall.

Elevations in non-HDL, LDL and TG place a patient at an increased risk for atherogenic disease, including coronary, cerebrovascular and peripheral artery disease. With each of these conditions, fatty deposits accumulate in the arteries (atherosclerosis). Non-HDL cholesterol has emerged as a stronger predictor of atherosclerotic cardiovascular disease (ASCVD) than LDL. It is helpful to identify areas of risk (e.g., coronary or cerebral arteries), but it is also important to realize that atherosclerosis is systemic (can occur in whole body). Elevated TG can cause acute pancreatitis.

CLASSIFICATION OF DYSLIPIDEMIA

Abnormal lipoprotein levels are called dyslipidemias and can include ↑ TC, ↑ LDL, ↑ TG and/or ↓ HDL. Dyslipidemias can be inherited, which are called primary or familial, but are most often a result of poor diet, lifestyle, medications or other secondary causes.

PRIMARY (OR FAMILIAL)

Familial dyslipidemias are classified according to the Fredrickson classification. Familial hypercholesterolemias (FH) are genetic defects resulting in severe cholesterol elevations and increased risk of premature ASCVD. FHs include heterozygous familial hypercholesterolemia (HeFH) and homozygous familial hypercholesterolemia (HoFH).

SECONDARY (OR ACQUIRED)

Common causes of secondary dyslipidemia are shown in the Key Drugs Guy on this page. Severe elevations (including LDL ≥ 190 mg/dL and TG ≥ 500 mg/dL) must be evaluated and treated appropriately. When dyslipidemia is due to diet and lifestyle, improving eating habits, exercising regularly and, if required, using medications can correct the dyslipidemia.

CHOLESTEROL (LIPOPROTEIN) TYPES AND NORMAL VALUES

Many clinicians recommend checking lipoprotein levels after a 9 – 12 hour fast. If the patient is not fasting, the TG level can be falsely elevated resulting in an incorrect LDL calculation. If it is not reported, LDL may need to be calculated using the Friedewald equation:

$$LDL = TC - HDL - \frac{TG}{5}$$

This formula is not used when the TG are > 400 mg/dL. Non-HDL and apoB do not require fasting for accurate assessment.

SELECT DRUGS/CONDITIONS THAT CAN RAISE LDL AND/OR TRIGLYCERIDES

KEY DRUGS

↑ LDL and TG:
Protease inhibitors

Steroids, diuretics

Immunosuppressants (e.g., cyclosporine, tacrolimus)

↑ LDL Only:
Fibrates, SGLT2 inhibitors

↑ TG Only:
IV lipid emulsions, propofol, beta-blockers, atypical antipsychotics

Conditions:
Obesity, poor diet

Hypothyroidism

Alcoholism, smoking

Diabetes

Renal/liver disease, nephrotic syndrome

Others

↑ LDL and TG:
Retinoids

↑ LDL Only:
Anabolic steroids, progestins

↑ TG Only:
Estrogen, tamoxifen, clevidipine, bile acid sequestrants

Conditions:
Pregnancy

Polycystic ovarian syndrome

Anorexia

CLASSIFICATION OF CHOLESTEROL AND TG LEVELS (MG/DL)

NON-HDL*

< 130	Desirable
130-159	Above desirable
160-189	Borderline high
190-219	High
≥ 220	Very high

LDL

< 100	Desirable
100-129	Above desirable
130-159	Borderline high
160-189	High
≥ 190	Very high

HDL

< 40 (men)	Low
< 50 (women)	Low

Triglycerides

< 150	Normal
150-199	Borderline high
200-499	High
≥ 500	Very high†

HDL = high-density lipoprotein cholesterol, LDL = low-density lipoprotein cholesterol, non-HDL = non-high-density lipoprotein cholesterol

**Non-HDL = total cholesterol minus HDL*

†Severe hypertriglyceridemia is another term used for very high triglycerides in pharmaceutical product labeling.

EXAM SCENARIO

JS is a 47-year-old male with dyslipidemia and type 2 diabetes. He stopped taking his simvastatin over 5 months ago due to muscle aches. His cholesterol panel has the following values: TC 202 mg/dL, HDL 36 mg/dL, and TG 280 mg/dL.

Calculate the patient's LDL cholesterol:
LDL is calculated using the Friedewald equation LDL = TC - HDL - (TG/5)

$$202 - 36 - \frac{280}{5} = 110$$

EXAM SCENARIO

AL is a 62-year-old female with history of smoking, obesity and hypertension. Her cholesterol panel has the following values: TC 260 mg/dL, HDL 28 mg/dL, and TG 480 mg/dL.

Calculate the patient's LDL cholesterol:
This formula cannot be used to estimate the LDL if the TGs are > 400 mg/dL; in this case, the LDL must be measured directly.

NON-DRUG TREATMENT

Lifestyle modifications are an important part of management. The following recommendations apply to adults with and without ASCVD and should be emphasized, monitored and reinforced:

- Consume a diet based on individual calorie requirements, personal preferences, and other medical conditions, to maintain a healthy weight (BMI 18.5 – 24.9 kg/m^2).
  - Diet should be rich in vegetables, fruits, whole grains and high-fiber foods.
  - Consume fish, especially fish with high fat content (rich in omega-3 fatty acids).
  - Limit intake of saturated fat, *trans* fat (partially hydrogenated) and cholesterol by choosing lean meats, non-meat alternatives and low-fat dairy products. Aim for 5 – 6% of calories from saturated fat.
  - Limit intake of added sugars and salt.
- Engage in aerobic physical activity 3 – 4 times per week, lasting 40 minutes/session (decreases LDL 3 – 6 mg/dL).
- Avoid tobacco products and limit alcohol consumption.

NATURAL PRODUCTS

Red yeast rice is the product of yeast grown on rice that contains naturally occurring HMG-CoA reductase inhibitors, and is similar in efficacy to low-dose statins. The *Natural Medicines Database* recommends against the use of red yeast rice products. Some contain too little drug, some contain too much and some contain contaminants that have caused renal damage. Plant stanols, sterols, fibrous foods (found in psyllium, barley, oat bran) and a specific type of artichoke extract are each effective in lowering LDL to various extents. OTC fish oils can be used to lower TG. They can increase LDL in some patients. Garlic used to be recommended for this purpose but the effect is not significant. Fish oils and niacin are discussed later in this chapter. See Dietary Supplements, Natural & Complementary Medicine chapter.

TREATMENT PRINCIPLES

The 2018 American College of Cardiology and the American Heart Association guidelines (ACC/AHA) on cholesterol management provide consensus recommendations from a large number of organizations including the National Lipid Association (NLA). It combines elements from previous 2013 ACC/AHA and NLA individual guidelines. The recommendations in this chapter primarily reflect the 2018 ACC/AHA guidelines. Treatment is important as lowering LDL by 1% reduces the risk of heart disease and stroke also by 1%. Recommendations for managing cholesterol in certain populations are addressed in disease specific guidelines (e.g., diabetes and the ADA guidelines).

STATIN TREATMENT

The statin-benefit patient groups, in which a statin of appropriate intensity should be considered, originally appeared in the 2013 ACC/AHA guidelines and remain in the 2018 ACC/AHA guidelines but with the addition of specific LDL values. For example, in a patient at very high-risk of ASCVD on a maximally tolerated statin dose, add-on treatment is recommended if LDL is > 70 mg/dL.

KEY POINT: ACC/AHA

Statins (primarily), dosed at the appropriate intensity, are used in patients with ASCVD and patients at risk for ASCVD. Non-statins are considered if LDL remains above a defined threshold on maximally tolerated statins.

NON-STATIN TREATMENTS

Non-statins are recommended if additional LDL-lowering is needed in those on maximally tolerated statins or if statins are not tolerated. The 2018 ACC/AHA guidelines recommend adding a PCSK9 inhibitor or ezetimibe if goal LDL reduction is not met (e.g., LDL remains > 70mg/dL in very high-risk ASCVD). Ezetimibe is preferred due to cost.

CALCULATING ASCVD RISK

The global risk assessment tool is used to provide an estimate of an individual's risk of having a first cardiovascular event (e.g., MI, stroke or death) during the next 10 years. This is called the 10-year ASCVD risk. Healthcare providers can use the estimated risk to determine whether they should prescribe risk-reducing treatments, including statins and antihypertensives. An elevated risk level can also motivate the patient to address modifiable risk factors. The online calculator is used to determine a patient's risk (http://tools.acc.org/ASCVD-Risk-Estimator-Plus/). The clinician inputs the patient's gender, age (20 – 79 years), race, TC, HDL, systolic blood pressure, whether antihypertensive treatment is used, the presence of diabetes and smoking status. A 10-year ASCVD risk of ≥ 7.5% is an indication to start statin therapy for primary prevention in individuals age 40 – 75 years if discussion of treatment options favors starting a statin. This risk assessment should be repeated every 4 – 6 years in those who are found to be at a low 10-year risk (< 7.5%). Note that the risk score is not needed for patients who have clinical ASCVD, diabetes, or LDL ≥ 190 mg/dL as all patients in these groups should be started on a statin.

If a risk-based treatment decision is still uncertain after a quantitative risk assessment, additional risk-enhancing factors should be considered to assist with decision making. These factors include: very high LDL, family history of premature ASCVD, metabolic syndrome, chronic kidney disease, history of preeclampsia or premature menopause, chronic inflammatory disorders, high CRP, high coronary artery calcium score (CAC) and abnormal ankle brachial index. The CAC measurement is helpful in deciding if statins should be initiated in those with intermediate risk assessment (e.g., 10-year ASCVD 7.5-19.9%). A CAC score ≥ 100 Agatston units indicates statins should be initiated.

Determining Statin Treatment Intensity Based on Patient Risk

STATIN BENEFIT GROUPS	PATIENT CRITERIA	STATIN TREATMENT
Secondary Prevention		
Clinical ASCVD	Includes CHD*, stroke, TIA or peripheral arterial disease thought to be of atherosclerotic origin	High-intensity**
Primary Prevention		
Primary elevation of LDL ≥ 190 mg/dL	Primary elevation of LDL ≥ 190 mg/dL	High-intensity**
Diabetes and age 40-75 years with LDL between 70-189 mg/dL	Multiple ASCVD risk factors	High-intensity**
	Regardless of 10-year ASCVD risk	Moderate-intensity
Ages 40-75 years with LDL between 70-189 mg/dL	10-year ASCVD risk ≥ 20%	High-intensity**
	10-year ASCVD risk 7.5- 19.9% + risk-enhancing factors	Moderate-intensity

**CHD = coronary heart disease, which includes: ACS, S/P MI, stable or unstable angina, coronary or other arterial revascularization*

***Consider moderate-intensity statin if not a candidate for high-intensity or patient ≥ 75 years with LDL 70-189 mg/dL*

Statin Treatment Intensity Definitions and Selection Options

HIGH-INTENSITY	MODERATE-INTENSITY	LOW-INTENSITY
Daily dose ↓ LDL ≥ 50%	**Daily dose ↓ LDL 30% – 49%**	**Daily dose ↓ LDL < 30%**
Atorvastatin 40-80 mg daily	Atorvastatin 10-20 mg daily	Simvastatin 10 mg daily
Rosuvastatin 20-40 mg daily	Rosuvastatin 5-10 mg daily	Pravastatin 10-20 mg daily
	Simvastatin 20-40 mg daily	Lovastatin 20 mg daily
	Pravastatin 40-80 mg daily	Fluvastatin 20-40 mg daily
	Lovastatin 40 mg daily	Pitavastatin 1 mg daily
	Fluvastatin XL 80 mg daily	
	Fluvastatin 40 mg BID	
	Pitavastatin 2-4 mg daily	

DRUG TREATMENT

Statins are the drugs of choice in treating elevated non-HDL and LDL. Although statins increase the risk of diabetes and myalgias, they are still recommended given their reduction in cardiovascular disease and mortality. If a patient is completely statin intolerant or needs additional LDL lowering, it is reasonable to use other cholesterol-lowering drugs. Guidelines focus on the use of ezetimibe and PCSK9 inhibitors over other non-statin drugs because of the clinical benefits shown.

Many of the cholesterol-lowering drugs can cause liver damage (niacin, fibrates, ezetimibe and potentially statins). Liver enzymes should be monitored and the drug stopped if the AST (10 – 40 units/L) or ALT (10 – 40 units/L) is ≥ 3 times the upper limit of normal. Increases in liver enzymes in patients using statins are similar to that of the population not using statins; however, LFTs should be monitored at baseline and periodically thereafter.

Metreleptin *(Myalept)* is not discussed in the drug tables. This is a recombinant human leptin analog, used as an adjunct to diet, to treat leptin deficiency with lipodystrophy. The drug may be a breakthrough for some patients with leptin deficiency, but has safety issues, including the development of leptin antibodies and lymphoma risk. It is a REMS drug with restricted use.

STATINS

Statins inhibit the enzyme 3-hydroxy-3-methylglutaryl coenzyme A (HMG-CoA) reductase, which prevents the conversion of HMG-CoA to mevalonate. This is the rate-limiting step in cholesterol synthesis. Evidence supports the use of statin treatment to decrease ASCVD risk, in those most likely to benefit (i.e., statin benefit groups). It is important to recognize the statin doses (intensity) that are necessary to provide patients with the most benefit from these drugs, and the expected percentage reduction of LDL.

STATIN EQUIVALENT DOSES

- Pitavastatin 2 mg
- Rosuvastatin 5 mg
- Atorvastatin 10 mg
- Simvastatin 20 mg
- Lovastatin 40 mg
- Pravastatin 40 mg
- Fluvastatin 80 mg

Remember: **P**harmacists **R**ock **At S**aving **L**ives and **Pr**eventing **F**atty-deposits

EXAM SCENARIO

TM is a 57-year-old male with dyslipidemia and is currently taking simvastatin 40 mg. His physician would like to switch to an equivalent atorvastatin dose.

Calculate the equivalent dose of atorvastatin:

$$\frac{\text{Atorvastatin 10 mg}}{\text{Simvastatin 20 mg}} = \frac{\text{Atorvastatin x mg}}{\text{Simvastatin 40 mg}} \quad x = 20 \text{ mg}$$

Muscle Damage from Statins

One of the biggest adverse effects of statin drugs is muscle damage. This generally presents as muscle soreness, tiredness or weakness that is symmetrical (on both sides of the body) in large adjacent muscle groups in the legs, back or arms. Symptoms usually occur within six weeks of starting treatment, but can develop at any point (even after years of therapy). The severity of these muscle effects can present in a variety of ways, including:

- Myalgias: muscle soreness and tenderness
- Myopathy: muscle weakness +/– CPK elevations
- Myositis: muscle inflammation
- Rhabdomyolysis: muscle symptoms with very high CPK (> 10,000) + muscle protein in the urine (myoglobinuria), which leads to acute renal failure

Patients may attempt to self-treat with natural products (e.g., Coenzyme Q10 and vitamin D supplements), but evidence of benefit is limited. Prompt recognition and management is important to decrease lasting effects (see Study Tip below).

MANAGING MYALGIAS

REDUCE THE RISK

Avoid drug interactions, including OTC products.

Do not use simvastatin 80 mg/day.

Do not use gemfibrozil + statin.

MANAGING MYALGIAS

Hold statin, check CPK, investigate other possible causes.

After 2-4 weeks: re-challenge with same statin at same or ↓ dose. Most patients who did not tolerate a statin will tolerate it when re-challenged, or will tolerate a different statin.

If myalgias return, discontinue statin. Once muscle symptoms resolve, use a low dose of a different statin; gradually ↑ dose.

Statins

<table>
<tr><th>DRUG</th><th>DOSING</th><th>SAFETY/SIDE EFFECTS/MONITORING</th></tr>
<tr><td>Atorvastatin (Lipitor)
+ amlodipine (Caduet)</td><td>10-80 mg daily</td><td rowspan="7">CONTRAINDICATIONS
Active liver disease (including any unexplained ↑ LFTs), pregnancy, breastfeeding, concurrent use of strong CYP3A4 inhibitors (simvastatin and lovastatin), concurrent use with cyclosporine (pitavastatin)

WARNINGS
Skeletal muscle effects (e.g., myopathy, rhabdomyolysis) – risk ↑ with higher doses, advanced age (≥ 65 years), CYP3A4 inhibitors, niacin, uncontrolled hypothyroidism and renal impairment

Diabetes: ↑ A1C and fasting blood glucose; benefits of statin therapy far outweigh the risk of hyperglycemia

Hepatotoxicity, ↑ LFTs (rare)

Immune-mediated necrotizing myopathy (IMNM) can occur in rare cases

Rosuvastatin: proteinuria, hematuria – usually transient

Atorvastatin: hemorrhagic stroke in patients with recent stroke or TIA; benefits outweigh the risk

SIDE EFFECTS
Myalgias, arthralgias, myopathy, diarrhea, cognitive impairment

MONITORING
LFTs at baseline and as clinically indicated thereafter; lipid panel at baseline, 4-12 weeks after initiation or up titration of treatment to assess for medication adherence, then every 3-12 months thereafter

NOTES
Can take Crestor, Lipitor, Livalo, Lescol XL and Pravachol at any time of day

For CrCl < 30 mL/min, use lower starting doses of lovastatin, simvastatin and rosuvastatin
For CrCl < 60 mL/min, use lower starting dose of pitavastatin

Rosuvastatin exposures are 2 times higher in Asian patients – consider 5 mg starting dose

Lipid Effects
↓ LDL ~20-55%, ↑ HDL ~5-15%, ↓ TG ~10-30%</td></tr>
<tr><td>Fluvastatin (Lescol*, Lescol XL)</td><td>20-80 mg

Lescol is taken in the evening

Lescol XL is taken daily</td></tr>
<tr><td>Lovastatin (Altoprev, Mevacor*)</td><td>20-80 mg

Lovastatin (immediate release) is taken with evening meal

Altoprev (extended release) is taken at bedtime</td></tr>
<tr><td>Pitavastatin (Livalo, Zypitamag)</td><td>1-4 mg daily</td></tr>
<tr><td>Pravastatin (Pravachol)</td><td>10-80 mg daily</td></tr>
<tr><td>Rosuvastatin (Crestor)</td><td>5-40 mg daily</td></tr>
<tr><td>Simvastatin (Zocor)

Tablet, suspension

+ ezetimibe (Vytorin)</td><td>10-40 mg daily in the evening

Do not initiate 80 mg dose</td></tr>
</table>

**Lescol and Mevacor brands discontinued but names still used in practice.*

Statin Drug Interactions

- Simvastatin and lovastatin are contraindicated with strong CYP450 3A4 inhibitors, conivaptan and gemfibrozil.
- ↑ risk of myopathies when used with fibrates (avoid statins with gemfibrozil) and niacin products containing ≥ 1 gram.
- Myopathy, including rhabdomyolysis, has been reported when coadministered with colchicine.
- May enhance anticoagulant effect of vitamin K receptor antagonists (warfarin). Monitor PT/INR after initiation/dose change.
- Rosuvastatin and pravastatin generally have less drug interactions compared to other statins (see interactions box).

DRUG	SIGNIFICANT DRUG INTERACTIONS*
Simvastatin CYP3A4 substrate (major), inhibits 2C8 (weak), 2C9 (weak)	Max 10 mg/day – verapamil, diltiazem, dronedarone Max 20 mg/day – amiodarone, amlodipine, lomitapide, ranolazine Max 40 mg/day – ticagrelor
Lovastatin CYP3A4 substrate (major), P-gp substrate, inhibits 2C9 (weak)	Max 20-40 mg/day - danazol, diltiazem, dronedarone, verapamil, amlodipine, amiodarone, ticagrelor
Atorvastatin CYP3A4 substrate (major), P-gp substrate	Avoid cyclosporine, gemfibrozil, tipranavir + ritonavir Max 20-40 mg/day – clarithromycin, itraconazole, cobicistat and cobicistat-containing drugs, darunavir + ritonavir, fosamprenavir ± ritonavir, saquinavir + ritonavir ↑ levels of norethindrone and ethinyl estradiol
Rosuvastatin CYP3A4 and 2C9 substrate (minor), BCRP substrate	Max 5 mg/day – cyclosporine Max 10 mg/day – gemfibrozil, atazanavir + ritonavir, lopinavir + ritonavir

**Other statins (pravastatin, fluvastatin and pitavastatin) are not as commonly used, but can have similar drug interactions.*

STRONG CYP3A4 INHIBITORS - AVOID WITH SIMVASTATIN AND LOVASTATIN			
Itraconazole	Voriconazole	HIV protease inhibitors	Cyclosporine
Ketoconazole	Erythromycin	Cobicistat-containing regimens	Danazol (with simvastatin)
Posaconazole	Clarithromycin	Nefazodone	Grapefruit juice

Determining Add-On Treatment Based on Patient Risk

PATIENT CRITERIA	NON-STATIN TREATMENT
Very-high risk and LDL remains ≥ 70 mg/dL*	Ezetimibe or PCSK9 inhibitors**
Primary hypercholesterolemia (LDL ≥ 190 mg/dL) and LDL remains ≥ 100 mg/dL*	Ezetimibe or PCSK9 inhibitors*

**On max-tolerated statin*

***Ezetimibe is preferred add-on due to cost*

EZETIMIBE

Inhibits absorption of cholesterol in the small intestine. The IMPROVE-IT study showed that the addition of ezetimibe to moderate-intensity statin therapy in stable patients with recent ACS, and who had LDL cholesterol levels within guideline recommendations, further lowered the risk of cardiovascular events.

DRUG	DOSING	SAFETY/SIDE EFFECTS/MONITORING
Ezetimibe *(Zetia)* + simvastatin *(Vytorin)*	10 mg daily If CrCl < 60 mL/min, do not exceed simvastatin 20 mg/day when using combination product *(Vytorin)*	**CONTRAINDICATIONS** *Vytorin*: statin contraindications apply; active liver disease (including any unexplained ↑ in LFTs), pregnancy/breastfeeding **WARNINGS** Avoid use in moderate-or-severe hepatic impairment Skeletal muscle effects (e.g., myopathy, rhabdomyolysis), risk ↑ when combined with a statin **SIDE EFFECTS** Myalgias, diarrhea, URTIs, arthralgias, pain in extremities, sinusitis **MONITORING** When used with a statin and/or fibrate, obtain LFTs at baseline and as clinically indicated thereafter **NOTES** **Lipid effects with ezetimibe monotherapy** ↓ LDL 18-23%, ↑ HDL 1-3%, ↓ TG 5-10%

Ezetimibe Drug Interactions

- When ezetimibe and cyclosporine are given together, the concentration of both can ↑; monitor levels of cyclosporine.
- Concomitant bile acid sequestrants ↓ ezetimibe; give ezetimibe two hours before or four hours after bile acid sequestrants.
- Can ↑ risk of cholelithiasis when used with fenofibrate; avoid use with gemfibrozil.

PROPROTEIN CONVERTASE SUBTILISIN KEXIN TYPE 9 INHIBITORS

Alirocumab and evolocumab are human monoclonal antibodies that bind to proprotein convertase subtilisin kexin type 9 (PCSK9). PCSK9 binds to the LDL receptors and promotes LDL receptor degradation. The LDL receptor is the primary receptor that clears circulating LDL; therefore, the decrease in LDL receptor levels by PCSK9 results in higher blood levels of LDL. By inhibiting the binding of PCSK9 to LDL receptors, these drugs increase the number of LDL receptors available to clear LDL, which lowers LDL levels. Both medications are indicated for heterozygous familial hypercholesterolemia (HeFH) or ASCVD as an adjunct to diet and maximally tolerated statin therapy (or other therapies in HeFH) when additional LDL lowering is required. Evolocumab specifically is indicated to reduce the risk of MI, stroke and coronary revascularization in patients with established cardiovascular disease. Evolocumab is also indicated for primary hyperlipidemia and as an adjunct in homozygous familial hypercholesterolemia (HoFH).

<table>
<tr><th>DRUG</th><th>DOSING</th><th>SAFETY/SIDE EFFECTS/MONITORING</th></tr>
<tr><td>Alirocumab
(Praluent)

75 mg/mL, 150 mg/mL prefilled syringes or pen-injector</td><td>HeFH or ASCVD
75-150 mg SC once every 2 weeks or 300 mg (150 mg x 2 sites) SC monthly</td><td rowspan="2">WARNING
Allergic reactions

SIDE EFFECTS
Injection site reactions, nasopharyngitis, influenza, URTIs, UTI, back pain (evolocumab), ↑ LFTs (alirocumab)

MONITORING
LDL-C at baseline and at 4-8 weeks to assess response

NOTES
Special storage and handling required (see Patient Counseling)

Expensive: ~$14,000/yr

Lipid Effects
↓ LDL ~60%, ↓ non-HDL ~35%, ↓ apoB ~50%, ↓ TC ~36%</td></tr>
<tr><td>Evolocumab
(Repatha, Repatha SureClick, Pushtronex)

140 mg/mL prefilled syringe or autoinjector

420 mg/3.5mL prefilled cartridge</td><td>HeFH or ASCVD
140 mg SC once every 2 weeks or 420 mg monthly

HoFH
420 mg SC once monthly

The 420 mg dose is given as three 140 mg injections consecutively within 30 minutes or as a 420 mg single injection</td></tr>
</table>

BILE ACID SEQUESTRANTS/BILE ACID BINDING RESINS

These drugs bind bile acids in the intestine, forming a complex that is excreted in the feces. This non-systemic action results in a partial removal of the bile acids from the enterohepatic circulation, preventing their reabsorption.

DRUG	DOSING	SAFETY/SIDE EFFECTS/MONITORING
Cholestyramine *(Prevalite, Questran, Questran Light)* Also approved for pruritus due to increased levels of bile acids, and regression of arteriolosclerosis 4 gram powder packet	Initial: 4 grams daily or BID Maintenance: 8-16 grams/day divided BID with meals (max 24 grams/day)	**CONTRAINDICATIONS** Cholestyramine – complete biliary obstruction Colesevelam – bowel obstruction, TG > 500 mg/dL, history of hypertriglyceridemia-induced pancreatitis **WARNINGS** Cholestyramine "light" formulations and colesevelam granules contain phenylalanine and should not be used in patients with PKU ↑ bleeding tendency due to vitamin K deficiency **SIDE EFFECTS** Constipation (may need dose reduction or laxative), abdominal pain, cramping, bloating, gas, ↑ TG, ↑ LFTs, dyspepsia, nausea, esophageal obstruction **NOTES** Not recommended when TG are ≥ 300 mg/dL Cholestyramine packet – mix powder with 2-6 oz. water or non-carbonated liquid; sipping or holding the resin suspension in the mouth for prolonged periods may lead to changes in the surface of the teeth resulting in discoloration, erosion of enamel or decay; good oral hygiene should be maintained Colesevelam packet – empty 1 packet into a glass; add 4-8 oz. of water, fruit juice, or a diet soft drink and mix well Colestipol packet – empty 1 packet into at least 3 oz. of liquid and stir until completely mixed Colesevelam can be considered as an option in a pregnant patient **Lipid Effects** ↓ LDL ~10-30%, ↑ HDL ~3-5%, no change or ↑ TG ~5%
Colesevelam *(Welchol)* 625 mg tablet, 3.75 gram granule packet Also approved for glycemic control in type 2 DM (↓ A1C ~0.5%)	Tablets/granules: 3.75 grams daily or in divided doses with a meal and liquid	
Colestipol *(Colestid)* 1 gram tablet, 5 gram packet and granules	Tablets: 2 grams daily or BID (max 16 grams/day) Packet and granules: 5 grams daily or BID (max 30 grams/day)	

Bile Acid Sequestrants Drug Interactions

- Colesevelam has less drug interactions than the other two bile acid sequestrants and is more commonly used. For cholestyramine or colestipol, take all other drugs at least 1 – 4 hours before or 4 – 6 hours after the bile acid sequestrants.
- The following medications should be taken four hours prior to colesevelam: cyclosporine, glimepiride, glipizide, glyburide, levothyroxine, olmesartan, phenytoin, and oral contraceptives containing ethinyl estradiol and norethindrone. Colesevelam ↑ levels of metformin ER.
- With warfarin, monitor INR frequently during initiation and after dose change.
- Bile acid sequestrants can ↓ absorption of fat-soluble vitamins (A, D, E, K), folate and iron. Separate administration times with multivitamin.

FIBRATES

Fibrates are peroxisome proliferator receptor alpha (PPARα) activators, which upregulate the expression of apolipoprotein C2 (apoC-II) and apolipoprotein A1 (apoA-I). ApoC-II increases lipoprotein lipase activity leading to increased catabolism of VLDL particles. This will decrease TG significantly, but in the setting of high TG (increased VLDL particles) fibrate therapy can lead to an increase of LDL particles and subsequently increase LDL cholesterol. The decreased TG can lead to an increase in HDL cholesterol. The ACCORD Lipid Study showed no significant difference in experiencing a major cardiac event between patients treated with fenofibrate plus simvastatin compared with simvastatin alone.

DRUG	DOSING	SAFETY/SIDE EFFECTS/MONITORING
Fenofibrate, Fenofibric Acid ***(Antara, Tricor, Trilipix,** Fenoglide, Fibricor, Lipofen, Triglide, generics)*	*Antara* (micronized capsule): 30-90 mg daily Fenofibrate (micronized): 43-130 mg daily *Antara*, micronized (brand) and fenofibrate, micronized (generic) have slightly different dosing regimens for treatment of hypertriglyceridemia *Fenoglide:* 40-120 mg daily with meals *Fibricor:* 35-105 mg daily *Lipofen:* 50-150 mg daily with meals *TriCor:* 48-145 mg daily *Triglide:* 160 mg daily *Trilipix:* 45-135 mg daily	**CONTRAINDICATIONS** Severe liver disease including primary biliary cirrhosis Severe renal disease (CrCl < 30 mL/min) Gallbladder disease Nursing mothers (fenofibrate derivatives only) Concurrent use with repaglinide or simvastatin (gemfibrozil only) **WARNINGS** Myopathy, ↑ risk when coadministered with a statin particularly in the elderly, diabetes, renal failure or hypothyroidism Cholelithiasis Reversible ↑ SCr (> 2 mg/dL); clinical significance unknown **SIDE EFFECTS** Dyspepsia, ↑ LFTs (dose-related), abdominal pain, ↑ CPK, URTIs **MONITORING** LFTs, renal function **NOTES** Reduce dose if CrCl 30-80 mL/min (fenofibrates) **Lipid Effects** ↓ TG ~20-50%, ↑ HDL ~15%, ↓ LDL ~5-20% (can ↑ LDL when TG are high)
Gemfibrozil *(Lopid)*	600 mg BID, 30 minutes before breakfast and dinner	

Fibrate Drug Interactions

- Fibrates (especially gemfibrozil) can ↑ the risk of myopathies and rhabdomyolysis. Gemfibrozil should not be given with ezetimibe or statins.
- Colchicine can ↑ the risk of myopathy when coadministered with fenofibrate.
- Gemfibrozil is contraindicated with repaglinide as it can ↑ hypoglycemic effects.
- Fibrates can ↑ the effects of sulfonylureas and warfarin.

NIACIN

Niacin decreases the rate of hepatic synthesis of VLDL (decreases TG) and LDL; can also increase the rate of chylomicron TG removal from plasma. It alters the binding of HDL particles to scavenger receptor B-1 in the liver, which removes the cholesterol inside, but does not take up the HDL particle which leaves it free to return to the circulation for reverse cholesterol transport. Niacin is also known as nicotinic acid or vitamin B3, although doses for cholesterol reduction are much higher than doses found in multivitamin products.

<table>
<tr><th>DRUG</th><th>DOSING</th><th>SAFETY/SIDE EFFECTS/MONITORING</th></tr>
<tr><td>Immediate-release (crystalline) niacin (Niacor)

Generics OTC</td><td>250 mg with evening meal

Can ↑ every 4-7 days to max dose of 3 grams daily in 3 divided doses</td><td rowspan="3">CONTRAINDICATIONS
Active liver disease, active PUD, arterial bleeding

WARNINGS
Use with caution in patients with unstable angina or in the acute phase of an MI

Rhabdomyolysis with niacin doses ≥ 1 gram/day combined with statins

Hepatotoxicity

SIDE EFFECTS
Flushing, pruritus (itching), N/V/D, ↑ BG, hyperuricemia (or gout), cough, orthostatic hypotension, hypophosphatemia, ↓ platelets

MONITORING
Check LFTs at the start (baseline), every 6-12 weeks for the first year, and then ~ every 6 months; blood glucose (if have diabetes); uric acid (if have gout); INR (if on warfarin), lipid profile

NOTES
Immediate-release niacin has poor tolerability due to flushing/itching

Controlled- and sustained-release forms (CR and SR) have less (but still significant) flushing but more hepatotoxicity

The best clinical choice is extended-release Niaspan, with less flushing and less hepatotoxicity (compared to other CR and SR formulations) – but it is the most expensive

To reduce flushing: take aspirin 325 mg (or ibuprofen 200 mg) 30-60 minutes before the dose; take with food, but avoid spicy food and hot beverages (which can worsen flushing)

Formulations of niacin (IR vs. ER) are not interchangeable

Flush-free niacins (inositol hexaniacinate or hexanicotinate), niacinamide or nicotinamide are not effective

Lipid Effects
↓ LDL 5-25%, ↑ HDL 15-35%, ↓ TG 20-50%</td></tr>
<tr><td>Extended-Release Niacin (Niaspan)

500, 750, 1,000 mg</td><td>500 mg nightly x 4 weeks

Can ↑ to a max dose of 2 grams daily</td></tr>
<tr><td>Controlled- or Sustained- Release Niacin (Slo-Niacin, OTC)

250, 500, 750 mg</td><td>250-750 mg daily</td></tr>
</table>

Niacin Drug Interactions

- Monitor for other concurrent drugs that are potentially hepatotoxic.
- Take niacin 4 – 6 hours after bile acid sequestrants.

FISH OILS

The mechanism is not completely understood; may reduce hepatic synthesis of TG. These are indicated as an adjunct to diet when TG ≥ 500 mg/dL. Fish oil is also known as omega-3 fatty acids.

DRUG	DOSING	SAFETY/SIDE EFFECTS/MONITORING
Omega-3 Acid Ethyl Esters *(Lovaza)* 1 gram capsule contains 465 mg eicosapentaenoic (EPA) acid and 375 mg docosahexaenoic acid (DHA)	4 capsules daily or 2 capsules BID	**WARNINGS** Use with caution in patients with known hypersensitivity to fish and/or shellfish *Lovaza* and *Epanova* can ↑ levels of LDL; monitor Monitor LFTs (in patients with hepatic impairment) and LDL periodically during therapy There is a possible association between *Lovaza* and more frequent recurrences of symptomatic atrial fibrillation or flutter in patients with paroxysmal or persistent atrial fibrillation, particularly within the first months of initiating therapy
Icosapent ethyl *(Vascepa)* Contains 0.5 or 1 gram of icosapent ethyl, an ethyl ester of omega-3 fatty acid EPA	0.5 gram capsules- 4 BID with food or 1 gram capsules- 2 BID with food	**SIDE EFFECTS** Eructation (burping), dyspepsia, taste perversions *(Lovaza, Epanova)*, arthralgias *(Vascepa)*, vomiting, flatulence *(Epanova)* **NOTES** There are many OTC omega-3 fatty acid products marketed as dietary supplements; only prescription medications *Epanova, Lovaza* and *Vascepa* are FDA approved for TG lowering, in addition to diet, when TG ≥ 500 mg/dL
Omega-3-carboxylic acids *(Epanova)* 1 gram capsule contains omega-3-carboxylic acids with 850 mg of polyunsaturated fatty acids (mostly EPA + DHA)	2-4 capsules daily	Stop prior to elective surgeries due to increased risk of bleeding **Lipid Effects** ↓ TG up to 45%, ↑ HDL ~9% Can ↑ LDL (up to 44% with *Lovaza*, 15% with *Epanova*); no ↑ seen with *Vascepa*

Fish Oil Drug Interactions

- Omega-3-fatty acids can prolong bleeding time, use with caution with other medications that can↑ bleeding risk (e.g., antiplatelets, anticoagulants). Monitor INR if patients are taking warfarin at dose initiation or dose change.

SPECIALTY DRUGS: LOMITAPIDE AND MIPOMERSEN

Lomitapide and mipomersen are specialty drugs that work by decreasing apoB, which is the main component of LDL and VLDL (the precursor to LDL). Lomitapide binds to and inhibits microsomal triglyceride transfer protein (MTP), which prevents the assembly of apoB containing lipoproteins. Mipomersen is an oligonucleotide inhibitor of apoB synthesis. Both medications are approved for use in patients with homozygous familial hypercholesterolemia (HoFH).

DRUG	DOSING	SAFETY/SIDE EFFECTS/MONITORING
Lomitapide (*Juxtapid*) Capsule Due to the risk of hepatotoxicity, this agent is only available through a *Juxtapid* Risk Evaluation and Mitigation Strategy (REMS) program.	5-60 mg daily Hepatic impairment or ESRD: dosage adjustment required. Take whole, with water, but without food, at least two hours after the evening meal.	**BOXED WARNING** Hepatotoxicity (↑ LFTs, steatosis) **CONTRAINDICATIONS** Active liver disease (including unexplained ↑ LFTs), moderate or severe hepatic impairment Lomitapide: pregnancy, concomitant use with moderate or strong CYP3A4 inhibitors **SIDE EFFECTS** N/V/D, dyspepsia, abdominal pain, constipation, flatulence, ↑ LFTs, chest pain, back pain, fatigue, weight loss, influenza, nasopharyngitis Mipomersen: Injection site reactions, flu-like symptoms, antibody formation **MONITORING** LFTs (including total bilirubin), alkaline phosphatase, lipids Lomitapide: pregnancy test in females of reproductive potential at baseline **NOTES** Drug interactions involving CYP3A4 and P-glycoprotein (see Learning Drug Interactions chapter) Expensive: ~$433,000 - $440,000/yr
Mipomersen (*Kynamro*) Prefilled syringe Due to the risk of hepatotoxicity, this agent is only available through a *Kynamro* REMS program.	200 mg SC once weekly Maximal LDL reduction seen after ~6 months	

PATIENT COUNSELING

ALL CHOLESTEROL MEDICATIONS

- For all cholesterol medicines: your healthcare provider should recommend lifestyle changes including heart healthy eating habits and exercise.

Statins

- Contact your healthcare provider right away if you have muscle weakness, tenderness, aching, cramps, stiffness or pain that happens without a good reason, especially if you also have a fever or feel more tired than usual. These may be symptoms of muscle damage.
- Contact your healthcare provider right away if you are passing brown or dark-colored urine, have pale stools, feel more tired than usual or if your skin and/or whites of your eyes become yellow. These may be symptoms of liver damage.
- Take *Zocor* and fluvastatin IR in the evening, lovastatin IR with the evening meal, and *Altoprev* at bedtime. All other statins can be taken at any time of day.
- Grapefruit and grapefruit juice can interact with this medication. This could lead to higher amounts of the drug in your body. Do not consume grapefruit products without discussing with your healthcare provider (for lovastatin, simvastatin or atorvastatin).
- Do not use if pregnant or nursing or if you think you may be pregnant. This drug can harm your unborn baby. If you become pregnant, stop statin therapy and call your healthcare provider right away.

Ezetimibe

- Contact your healthcare provider right away if you are passing brown or dark-colored urine, have pale stools, feel more tired than usual or if your skin and/or whites of your eyes become yellow. These may be symptoms of liver damage.
- Contact your healthcare provider right away if you have muscle weakness, tenderness, aching, cramps, stiffness or pain that happens without a good reason, especially if you also have a fever or feel more tired than usual. These may be symptoms of muscle damage.
- Take this medication once daily, with or without food.

PCSK9 Inhibitors

- The most common side effects include runny nose, sore throat, symptoms of the common cold or flu, back pain, and redness, pain or bruising at the injection site.
- This medication can cause an allergic reaction. Seek emergency medical care right away if you develop symptoms of rash, redness, severe itching, a swollen face or trouble breathing.
- Prior to administration, allow prefilled pen/syringe to warm to room temperature (30 to 45 minutes) and inspect visually for particulate matter and discoloration.
- Do not freeze, expose to extreme heat or shake.
- Rotate the injection sites. Do not inject into areas that are injured, tender, bruised, red, firm or hot. Avoid scars, visible veins or stretch marks.
- If you miss a dose, inject the missed dose as soon as you remember, within seven days of your missed dose. Then, take the next dose two weeks from the missed dose. If the missed dose is not given within seven days, skip the dose and wait until the next scheduled dose.

Alirocumab

- Administer by subcutaneous injection into the thigh, abdomen or upper arm using a single-dose prefilled pen/syringe. It can take up to 20 seconds to inject all contents of the pen.
- Store in the refrigerator in the outer carton in order to protect from light. This drug should be used as soon as possible after it has warmed up (it should not be out of the refrigerator for > 24 hours).

Evolocumab

- Given as an injection under the skin (subcutaneously), every two weeks or one time each month.
- Available as a single-use prefilled autoinjector, a single use on-body infusor or as a single-use prefilled syringe.
- Store in the refrigerator. Can be kept at room temperature (up to 77°F) in the original carton; it must be used within 30 days if removed from refrigerator.
- If your healthcare provider prescribes the monthly dose, you will give yourself three separate injections in a row, using a different syringe or autoinjector for each injection. Give all of these injections within 30 minutes and alternate the injection site.
- If your healthcare provider prescribes the *Pushtronex* system, you can give the once monthly injection as one injection. This is available as an on-body infusor with a cartridge that will infuse the dose over nine minutes. Do not inject together with other medications at the same injection site.

Bile Acid Sequestrants

- See Notes section in drug table for instructions regarding food and fluid intake for specific agents.
- Take this medication at mealtimes with plenty of water or other liquid. Never take dry.
- This medication can cause constipation, your pharmacist can recommend a laxative (senna) or stool softener (docusate). Drink plenty of water and eat food with fiber such as fruits, vegetables and grains.
- Separate the dose of this medication from multivitamins, due to ↓ absorption of vitamins A, D, E and K (mostly K), folate and iron. You may need to take a multivitamin (especially women and children) while taking this medication.

Fibrates

- *Antara, Fibricor, Triglide* and *Trilipix*: take once daily, with or without food.
- *Fenoglide, TriCor* and *Lipofen*: Take once daily, with food.
- *Lopid*: Take twice daily, 30 minutes before breakfast and dinner.
- Do not crush or chew.
- Contact your healthcare provider if you experience muscle aches.
- Contact your healthcare provider right away if you experience abdominal pain, nausea or vomiting. These may be signs of inflammation of the gallbladder or pancreas.
- Contact your healthcare provider right away if you are passing brown or dark-colored urine, feel more tired than usual or if your skin and/or whites of your eyes become yellow. These may be signs of liver damage.

Niacin

- *Niaspan*: take at bedtime after a low-fat snack. Other niacins: take with food.
- Do not crush or chew long-acting formulations.
- Contact your healthcare provider right away if you are passing brown or dark-colored urine, feel more tired than usual or if your skin and/or whites of your eyes become yellow. These may be symptoms of liver damage.
- Flushing (warmth, redness, itching and/or tingling of the skin) is a common side effect that may subside after several weeks of consistent use. Taking 325 mg of aspirin (or 200 mg of ibuprofen) 30 – 60 minutes before the dose (for a few weeks) can help ↓ flushing. With *Niaspan*, flushing will occur mostly at night; use caution if awakened due to dizziness.
- Avoid drinking alcohol or hot beverages or eating spicy foods around the time of taking this medicine to help reduce flushing.
- If you have diabetes, check your blood sugar when starting this medication because there may be a mild increase.

Fish Oil

- *Lovaza* can be taken once daily, or split BID. *Epanova* is taken once daily.
- Take *Vascepa* with food. Take *Epanova* and *Lovaza* with or without food.
- Take whole; do not break, crush, dissolve or chew.
- This medication does not usually cause side effects, but can cause indigestion (stomach upset), burping or abnormal sense of taste (*Lovaza*) or joint pain (*Vascepa*).

Select Guidelines/References

Grundy SM, Stone NJ, Bailey AL, et al. 2018 AHA/ACC/AACVPR/AAPA/ABC/ACPM/ADA/AGS/APhA/ASPC/NLA/PCNA guideline on the management of blood cholesterol: a report of the American College of Cardiology/American Heart Association Task Force on Clinical Practice Guidelines. *Circulation*. 2018;000:e000–e000. DOI: 10.1161/CIR.0000000000000625.

CHAPTER CONTENT

Background ... 458
Etiology and Pathophysiology ... 458
Compensatory Mechanisms in Hypertension ... 459
Screening and Diagnosis ... 460
Blood Pressure Monitoring ... 460
Lifestyle Management ... 460
Drugs that Can Increase Blood Pressure ... 460
Natural Products ... 461
Treatment Principles (ACC/AHA) ... 461
Hypertension Guideline Recommendations ... 461
Pregnancy and Hypertension ... 461
Combination Blood Pressure Drugs ... 462
Thiazide-Type Diuretics ... 462
Calcium Channel Blockers ... 464
Dihydropyridine CCBs ... 464
Non-Dihydropyridine CCBs ... 465
Renin-Angiotensin Aldosterone System Inhibitors ... 466
Angiotensin-Converting Enzyme Inhibitors ... 466
Angiotensin Receptor Blockers ... 467
Direct Renin Inhibitor ... 467
RAAS Inhibitor Drug Interactions ... 467
Additional Agents For Treating Hypertension ... 468
Potassium-Sparing Diuretics ... 468
Beta-Blockers ... 469
Centrally-Acting Alpha-2 Adrenergic Agonists ... 471
Direct Vasodilators ... 471
Alpha Blockers ... 472
Hypertensive Crises: Urgencies and Emergencies ... 472
Key IV Hypertension Medications ... 472
Patient Counseling ... 472

CONTENT LEGEND

= Study Tip Gal   = Key Drug Guy

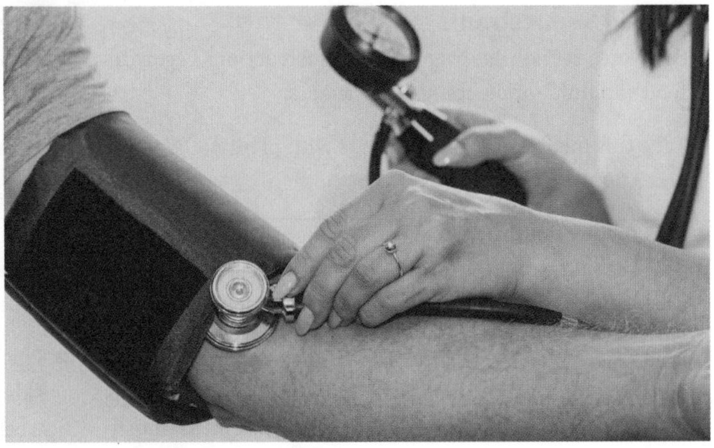

CHAPTER 28
HYPERTENSION

BACKGROUND

Hypertension, or high blood pressure (BP), affects one in three American adults and is a common disease managed in primary care. Hypertension is largely asymptomatic, which can delay diagnosis and can contribute to medication non-adherence in treated patients. Medication side effects, cost and pill burden can also lead to discontinuation of treatment. Uncontrolled hypertension places the patient at greater risk for heart disease, stroke and kidney disease. Pharmacists play a vital role by screening and monitoring patients, and providing counseling about the importance of lifestyle management (e.g., healthy diet, sodium restriction, physical activity, smoking cessation) and medication adherence. Patient self-monitoring of blood pressure at home can improve motivation and success of therapy.

ETIOLOGY AND PATHOPHYSIOLOGY

Most patients (~95%) have primary, or essential, hypertension. The cause is unknown, but a combination of risk factors (e.g., obesity, sedentary lifestyle, excessive salt intake, smoking, family history, diabetes, dyslipidemia) is usually present. Secondary hypertension can be caused by renal disease (e.g., chronic kidney disease), adrenal disease (e.g., excess aldosterone secretion), obstructive sleep apnea or drugs (see Key Drugs Guy later in the chapter). There is increased activity of the sympathetic nervous system (SNS) and the renin-angiotensin-aldosterone system (RAAS), leading to increased levels of neurohormones (e.g., norepinephrine, angiotensin II, aldosterone) that can increase blood pressure. Most medications used to treat hypertension target these neurohormonal pathways (see the Compensatory Mechanisms in Hypertension flow diagram on next page).

COMPENSATORY MECHANISMS IN HYPERTENSION

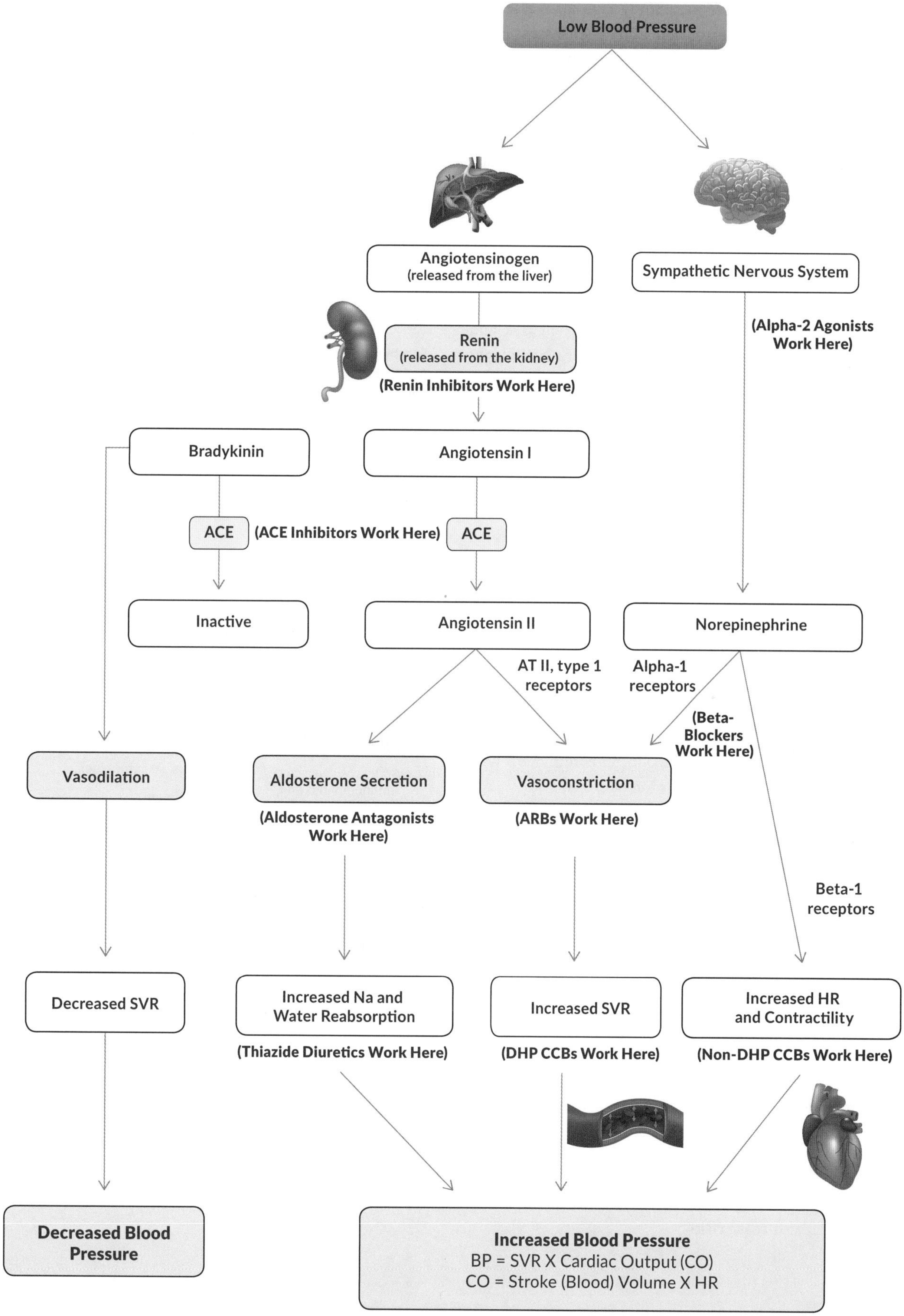

SCREENING AND DIAGNOSIS

Accurate measurement of BP (see Study Tip Gal) is essential for the diagnosis of hypertension and when assessing if titration of medication is needed. BP readings in the same individual can vary during the day, due to stress, exercise, medications, eating and other activities of daily living. BP usually decreases during the night and increases again in the early morning. BP assessments should be based on an average of at least two readings on two separate occasions, preferably standardized to the timing of medication administration.

Self-monitoring of BP, using an automated home or ambulatory monitoring device is preferred. BP readings in a clinical office setting tend to be higher, which can lead to inaccurate clinical decisions related to patient risk and treatment needed. The American College of Cardiology/ American Heart Association (ACC/AHA) has defined four categories of BP in adults, based on systolic BP (SBP) and/or diastolic BP (DBP) readings:

- Normal: SBP < 120 mmHg and DBP < 80 mmHg
- Elevated: SBP 120 – 129 mmHg and DBP < 80 mmHg
- Hypertension:
    - Stage 1: SBP 130 – 139 mmHg or DBP 80 – 89 mmHg
    - Stage 2: SBP ≥ 140 mmHg or DBP ≥ 90 mmHg

LIFESTYLE MANAGEMENT

Lifestyle interventions are essential to prevent hypertension (in patients with normal or elevated blood pressure) and during the treatment of hypertension, in conjunction with medications. Proven interventions include:

- Weight loss (1 kg of weight loss decreases BP by ~1 mmHg)
- A heart-healthy diet [e.g., the DASH eating plan (Dietary Approaches to Stop Hypertension)] that is high in fruits, vegetables, fiber and low-fat dairy products, and low in saturated fats and sugar
- Adequate dietary potassium intake or supplementation, unless contraindicated (e.g., chronic kidney disease)
- Reducing sodium intake to < 1,500 mg daily
- Routine physical activity
- Limiting alcohol consumption to one drink daily for women and two drinks daily for men
- Tobacco cessation
- Controlling blood glucose and cholesterol to reduce cardiovascular disease risk

BLOOD PRESSURE MONITORING

Correct use of your blood pressure monitoring device

DO	DON'T
Go to the restroom and empty the bladder	Talk
Sit in a chair (both feet on floor) and relax for at least 5 minutes	Sit or lie down on an examination table
Use the correct cuff size	Drink caffeine, exercise or smoke for 30 minutes prior
Support the arm at heart level (e.g., resting on a desk)	Use a finger or wrist monitor (less accurate)
Wait 1-2 minutes in between measurements	

Self-monitoring: bring device and BP reading log to clinic visits
Ambulatory BP monitoring devices: wear during daily activities; obtains readings every 15-60 minutes, day and night

Home BP monitoring devices: record the average of 2-3 readings in the morning and/or evening before eating or taking any medications

DRUGS THAT CAN INCREASE BLOOD PRESSURE

KEY DRUGS

- Amphetamines and ADHD drugs
- Cocaine
- Decongestants (e.g., pseudoephedrine, phenylephrine)
- Erythropoiesis-stimulating agents
- Immunosuppressants (e.g., cyclosporine)
- NSAIDs
- Systemic steroids

Others:

- Alcohol (excessive)
- Appetite suppressants (e.g., phentermine)
- Caffeine
- Herbals (e.g., Ma Huang, licorice, yohimbine)
- Oral contraceptives
- Select oncology agents (e.g., bevacizumab, tyrosine kinase inhibitors)
- Antidepressants (e.g., TCAs, SNRIs, MAO inhibitors)

NATURAL PRODUCTS

In addition to fiber and potassium consumed in a heart-healthy diet, some patients may supplement drug treatment with natural medicines. Although not recommended by guidelines, fish oil, coenzyme Q10, L-arginine, garlic, fiber and potassium have some evidence for reducing blood pressure and overall cardiovascular risk.

TREATMENT PRINCIPLES (ACC/AHA)

- Emphasize lifestyle modifications throughout treatment.
- Once daily regimens are preferred for increased medication adherence.
- Four preferred drug classes are recommended for initial and/or titration of treatment before selecting medications from alternate drug classes:
  - ACE inhibitors, ARBs, CCBs or thiazide diuretics (see Study Tip Gal for initial drug selection based on patient-specific criteria).
  - Do not use ACE inhibitors and ARBs in combination.
- Most patients will require ≥ two drugs (see Combination Blood Pressure Drugs table).
- When titrating medications, adding a second drug before reaching maximum doses of the first medication can be more effective and cause less side effects.
- Patients with hypertension and comorbid conditions (e.g., heart failure, ischemic heart disease) should be treated according to the specific disease-state guideline recommendations. Refer to Course Book chapters as appropriate.

HYPERTENSION GUIDELINE RECOMMENDATIONS

WHEN TO START TREATMENT

- Stage 2 HTN:
  - SBP ≥ 140 mmHg or DBP ≥ 90 mmHg
- Stage 1 HTN (SBP 130-139 mmHg or DBP 80-89 mmHg) and:
  - Clinical CVD (stroke, heart failure or coronary heart disease)
  - 10-year ASCVD risk ≥ 10%*

BP GOALS

- All patients: < 130/80 mmHg**

INITIAL DRUG SELECTION

- Non-black: thiazide, CCB, ACE inhibitor or ARB
- Black: thiazide or CCB
- CKD*** (all races): ACE inhibitor or ARB (to slow progression to ESRD)
- Diabetes with albuminuria (all races): ACE inhibitor or ARB
- Start 2 first-line drugs (from preferred drug classes) in Stage 2 HTN when average SBP and DBP > 20/10 mmHg above goal (e.g., 150/90 mmHg)

MONITORING

- Check BP every month and titrate medication if not at goal

ASCVD = atherosclerotic cardiovascular disease; risk can be assessed using an online tool (http://tools.acc.org/ASCVD-Risk-Estimator/)

**The ADA recommends a goal BP < 130/80 mmHg for patients with diabetes and high ASCVD risk and < 140/90 mmHg for patients at lower risk (see Diabetes chapter); exam questions should specify which guideline to follow*

***CKD: stage 3 (eGFR < 60 mL/min/1.73 m^2) and/or albuminuria (urine albumin ≥ 300 mg/day or albumin:creatinine ratio ≥ 300 mg/g)*

PREGNANCY AND HYPERTENSION

Planning for pregnancy includes the discontinuation of teratogenic drugs that can cause fetal harm. If pregnancy is detected, ACE inhibitors, ARBs and the direct renin inhibitor aliskiren should be discontinued immediately as there is a boxed warning for fetal toxicity in pregnant patients. When making antihypertensive treatment recommendations in pregnancy, it must first be determined if the patient is experiencing preeclampsia or chronic hypertension, as these are treated differently. Preeclampsia occurs after week 20 of the pregnancy and is evident by elevated blood pressure and proteinuria in the majority of cases. It is more common in women who are overweight, and/or have pre-existing hypertension, renal disease or diabetes.

Pregnant patients with chronic hypertension should receive drug treatment if SBP is ≥ 160 mmHg or DBP is ≥ 105 mmHg. Recommended first-line agents, according to the American College of Obstetricians and Gynecologists (ACOG), include labetalol, nifedipine extended-release and methyldopa. BP should be maintained between 120 – 160 mmHg systolic and 80 – 105 mmHg diastolic.

COMBINATION BLOOD PRESSURE DRUGS

Tip: the brand names of many diuretic combinations end in HCT, -ide or -etic

ACE INHIBITOR OR ARB + DIURETIC

Lisinopril/Hydrochlorothiazide *(Zestoretic)*

Losartan/Hydrochlorothiazide *(Hyzaar)*

Olmesartan/Hydrochlorothiazide *(Benicar HCT)*

Valsartan/Hydrochlorothiazide *(Diovan HCT)*

Azilsartan/Chlorthalidone *(Edarbyclor)*

Benazepril/Hydrochlorothiazide *(Lotensin HCT)*

Candesartan/Hydrochlorothiazide

Captopril/Hydrochlorothiazide

Enalapril/Hydrochlorothiazide *(Vaseretic)*

Fosinopril/Hydrochlorothiazide

Irbesartan/Hydrochlorothiazide *(Avalide)*

Moexipril/Hydrochlorothiazide

Quinapril/Hydrochlorothiazide *(Accuretic)*

Telmisartan/Hydrochlorothiazide *(Micardis HCT)*

ACE INHIBITOR OR ARB + CCB

Benazepril/Amlodipine *(Lotrel)*

Valsartan/Amlodipine *(Exforge)*

Olmesartan/Amlodipine *(Azor)*

Perindopril/Amlodipine *(Prestalia)*

Telmisartan/Amlodipine *(Twynsta)*

Trandolapril/Verapamil *(Tarka)*

DIRECT RENIN INHIBITOR + DIURETIC

Aliskiren/Hydrochlorothiazide *(Tekturna HCT)*

ALPHA-2 AGONIST + DIURETIC

Methyldopa/Hydrochlorothiazide

BETA BLOCKER + DIURETIC

Atenolol/Chlorthalidone *(Tenoretic)*

Bisoprolol/Hydrochlorothiazide *(Ziac)*

Metoprolol Tartrate/Hydrochlorothiazide *(Lopressor HCT)*

Metoprolol Succinate/Hydrochlorothiazide *(Dutoprol)*

Nadolol/Bendroflumethiazide

Propranolol/Hydrochlorothiazide

BETA BLOCKER + ARB

Nebivolol/Valsartan *(Byvalson)*

K-SPARING + THIAZIDE-TYPE DIURETIC

Triamterene/Hydrochlorothiazide *(Maxzide, Maxzide-25, Dyazide)*

Amiloride/Hydrochlorothiazide

Spironolactone/Hydrochlorothiazide *(Aldactazide)*

TRIPLE COMBINATIONS

Olmesartan/Amlodipine/Hydrochlorothiazide *(Tribenzor)*

Valsartan/Amlodipine/Hydrochlorothiazide *(Exforge HCT)*

THIAZIDE-TYPE DIURETICS

Thiazide-type diuretics are inexpensive, effective and have mild side effects in most patients. They are one of four drug classes that can be considered initially. Loop diuretics are used primarily in heart failure (see Chronic Heart Failure chapter).

Thiazides and thiazide-type diuretics inhibit sodium reabsorption in the distal convoluted tubules (see Nephron diagram), causing increased excretion of sodium, chloride, water and potassium.

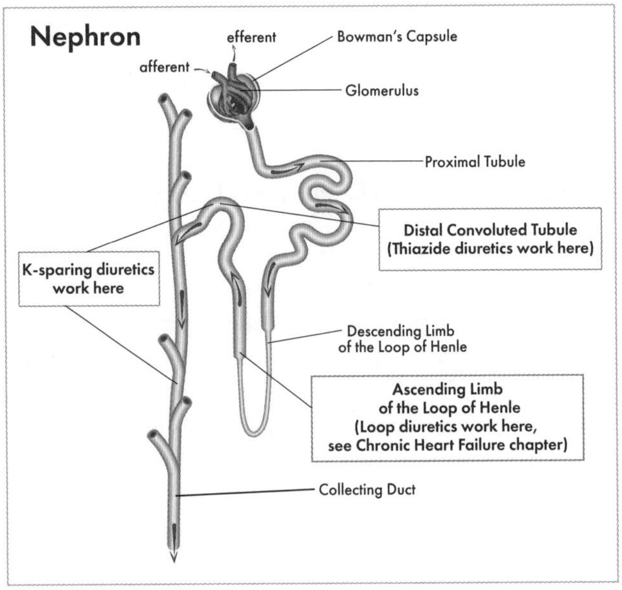

DRUG	DOSING	SAFETY/SIDE EFFECTS/MONITORING
Chlorothiazide *(Diuril)* Tablet, oral suspension, injection	500-2,000 mg daily in 1-2 divided doses	**CONTRAINDICATIONS** Hypersensitivity to sulfonamide-derived drugs (not likely to cross-react – see Drug Allergies & Adverse Drug Reactions chapter); anuria **WARNINGS** Sulfa allergy (see above), progressive liver disease (fluid and electrolyte changes may precipitate hepatic coma), can precipitate or exacerbate other conditions [e.g., gout, diabetes, systemic lupus erythematosis (SLE), CKD] **SIDE EFFECTS** Hypokalemia (↓ K), hypomagnesemia (↓ Mg), hyponatremia (↓ Na), hypercalcemia (↑ Ca), hyperuricemia (↑ UA), elevated lipids (↑ LDL, ↑ TG), hyperglycemia (↑ BG), dizziness, photosensitivity, rash, hypochloremic alkalosis (rare) **MONITORING** BP, electrolytes, renal function, fluid status (input and output, weight), BG (in patients with diabetes) **NOTES** Chlorthalidone has better evidence than hydrochlorothiazide and is preferred by some clinicians (but if a patient is doing well on hydrochlorothiazide, do not switch) Thiazides are not effective when CrCl < 30 mL/min (except metolazone, which may work in patients with reduced renal function or diuretic resistance) Take early in the day to avoid nocturia Chlorothiazide is the only medication in this class available IV Hypokalemia can be avoided with regular intake of potassium rich foods or potassium supplements
Chlorthalidone Tablet	12.5-25 mg daily (max dose is 100 mg daily but doses > 25 mg/day have limited clinical benefit)	
Hydrochlorothiazide *(Microzide*)* Tablet, capsule	12.5-50 mg daily (max dose is 100 mg daily but doses > 50 mg/day have limited clinical benefit and ↑ risk of adverse effects)	
Indapamide Tablet	1.25-5 mg daily	
Metolazone Tablet	2.5-5 mg daily	

* *Brand discontinued but name still used in practice*

Thiazide-Type Diuretic Drug Interactions

- All antihypertensives can enhance the blood pressure lowering effects of other drugs; carefully monitor blood pressure when adding on treatment.
- Avoid drugs that can cause sodium and water retention (e.g., NSAIDs), as they can decrease the effectiveness of antihypertensive medications.
- Thiazide diuretics can ↓ lithium renal clearance and ↑ the risk of lithium toxicity. Avoid if possible.
- Thiazide diuretics can ↑ dofetilide serum concentrations leading to an ↑ risk of QT prolongation; do not use in combination.

CALCIUM CHANNEL BLOCKERS

There are two types of CCBs, dihydropyridines (DHP) and non-dihydropyridines (non-DHP). Nifedipine (a DHP CCB) and diltiazem (a non-DHP CCB) have many long-acting formulations. Not all generic products are therapeutically equivalent to the brand name products. If the pharmacist is substituting a generic product for a brand name product, they should check the FDA Orange Book and choose a generic product that is AB-rated to the brand product.

DIHYDROPYRIDINE CCBs

DHP CCBs have generic names that end in "-pine"; they are used for hypertension, chronic stable angina and Prinzmetal's angina (see Ischemic Heart Disease chapter). They inhibit Ca ions from entering vascular smooth muscle and myocardial cells; this causes peripheral arterial vasodilation (which ↓ SVR and BP) and coronary artery vasodilation. The peripheral vasodilation leads to common side effects of reflex tachycardia, headache, flushing and peripheral edema.

DRUG	DOSING	SAFETY/SIDE EFFECTS/MONITORING
Amlodipine *(Norvasc)*	2.5-10 mg daily	**WARNINGS** Hypotension (especially in patients with severe aortic stenosis); worsening angina and/or MI has occurred with initiation or dosage titration (due to reflex tachycardia); severe hepatic impairment (start low and titrate slowly); use caution in heart failure (see Notes) Nifedipine IR: do not use for chronic hypertension or acute BP reduction in non-pregnant adults (profound hypotension, MI and/or death has occurred) **SIDE EFFECTS** Peripheral edema, flushing, headache, palpitations/tachycardia, gingival hyperplasia, dizziness, fatigue **MONITORING** BP, HR, peripheral edema **NOTES** Amlodipine and felodipine are considered the safest if a CCB must be used to lower BP in patients with heart failure with reduced ejection fraction Nifedipine ER is a drug of choice in pregnancy *Adalat CC* and *Procardia XL*: OROS/gel matrix formulations (see Learning Drug Formulations chapter) can leave a ghost tablet (empty shell) in the stool
Felodipine ER	2.5-10 mg daily	
Isradipine	2.5-10 mg BID	
Nifedipine ER *(Adalat CC, Procardia XL)* Nifedipine IR *(Procardia)*	30-90 mg daily	
Nisoldipine ER *(Sular)*	8.5-34 mg daily	
Nisoldipine ER (original formulation)	10-60 mg daily	
Nicardipine IR Nicardipine SR **Nicardipine IV *(Cardene IV)*** Capsule, injection	IR: 20-40 mg TID SR: 30-60 mg BID IV: 5 mg/hr, ↑ by 2.5 mg/hr every 5-15 minutes to max dose of 15 mg/hr	
Clevidipine *(Cleviprex)* Injection	1-21 mg/hr	**CONTRAINDICATIONS** Allergy to soybeans, soy products or eggs; defective lipid metabolism (e.g., lipoid nephrosis, hyperlipidemia with acute pancreatitis); severe aortic stenosis **WARNINGS** Hypotension, reflex tachycardia, hypertriglyceridemia, infections (see Notes) **SIDE EFFECTS** Headache, atrial fibrillation, nausea, fever **MONITORING** BP, HR **NOTES** A lipid emulsion (provides 2 kcal/mL); it is milky-white in color Use strict aseptic technique due to infection risk; maximum time of use after vial puncture is 12 hours

EXAM SCENARIO

TW is a 54-year-old female admitted to the medical ICU with a hypertensive emergency. She is receiving clevidipine 50 mg/100 mL at a rate of 3 mg/hr. The bottle has 52 mL remaining at 1400.

- **How many calories per day is TW receiving from clevidipine?**
  Calculate using the flow rate, product concentration and known kcal/mL provided.

$$\frac{3\text{ mg}}{\text{hr}} \times \frac{24\text{ hrs}}{\text{day}} \times \frac{100\text{ mL}}{50\text{ mg}} \times \frac{2\text{ kcal}}{\text{mL}} = 288\text{ kcal/day}$$

- **At what time should the bottle of clevidipine be removed and replaced?**
  48 mL of clevidipine have been used. First, calculate how long the bottle has been hanging.

$$48\text{ mL} \times \frac{50\text{ mg}}{100\text{ mL}} \times \frac{1\text{ hr}}{3\text{ mg}} = 8\text{ hrs}$$

The bottle needs to be removed and replaced every 12 hours (in other words, in 4 more hours). It is currently 1400. A new bottle should be hung at 1800.

- **What other drugs may require similar calculations?**
  Propofol *(Diprivan)* is another lipid emulsion that provides calories (1.1 kcal/mL) and requires tubing/vial changes every 12 hours (refer to the Acute & Critical Care Medicine chapter for more information).

NON-DIHYDROPYRIDINE CCBs

The non-DHP CCBs, verapamil and diltiazem, are primarily used to control HR in certain arrhythmias (e.g., atrial fibrillation), and are sometimes used for hypertension and angina. They inhibit Ca ions from entering vascular smooth muscle and myocardial cells, but they are more selective for the myocardium than the DHP CCBs. The decrease in BP produced by non-DHP CCBs is due to negative inotropic (↓ force of ventricular contraction) and negative chronotropic (↓ HR) effects.

DRUG	DOSING	SAFETY/SIDE EFFECTS/MONITORING
Diltiazem *(Cardizem, Cardizem CD, Cardizem LA, Cartia XT, Tiazac,* *others)* IR tablet, ER tablet (24-HR), ER capsule (12-HR), ER capsule (24-HR), injection	120-360 mg daily; max dose varies with product IR tablet: daily dose given in 4 divided doses ER capsule (12-HR): daily dose given in 2 divided doses	**CONTRAINDICATIONS** Hypotension (SBP < 90 mmHg) or cardiogenic shock; 2nd or 3rd degree AV block or sick sinus syndrome (unless the patient has a functioning artificial ventricular pacemaker); acute MI and pulmonary congestion **WARNINGS** Hypotension, heart failure (may worsen symptoms), bradycardia, AV block (1st, 2nd or 3rd),↑ LFTs **SIDE EFFECTS** Edema, constipation (more with verapamil), gingival hyperplasia, headache, dizziness **MONITORING** BP, HR, ECG, LFTs **NOTES** IV:PO dose conversions are not 1:1
Verapamil *(Calan, Calan SR,* *Verelan, Verelan PM)* IR tablet, ER tablet, ER capsule (24-HR), injection	240-480 mg daily IR tablet: daily dose given in 3 divided doses *Calan SR:* daily dose can be given in 2 divided doses (QAM and QPM) *Verelan PM:* daily dose given QHS	

Calcium Channel Blocker Drug Interactions

- Watch for additive effects when administering other drugs that ↓ HR, including beta-blockers, digoxin, clonidine, amiodarone and dexmedetomidine *(Precedex)*.
- All CCBs, both DHP and non-DHP, are major substrates of CYP450 3A4. Strong CYP3A4 inducers and inhibitors should be used with caution, and in some cases, avoided in combination with CCBs. Check for drug interactions when initiating a CCB or when other medications are added to a CCB. Grapefruit juice should be avoided.
- Diltiazem and verapamil are substrates of P-gp and moderate inhibitors of CYP3A4. They can increase the concentration of many other drugs. Patients who take statins should use lower doses of simvastatin or lovastatin (see Dyslipidemia chapter) or use a statin that is not metabolized by CYP3A4 (e.g., pitavastatin, pravastatin, rosuvastatin).

RENIN-ANGIOTENSIN ALDOSTERONE SYSTEM INHIBITORS

Angiotensin II (Ang II) causes vasoconstriction and increased release of aldosterone, resulting in sodium and water retention. RAAS inhibitors decrease BP by inhibiting the effects of Ang II. Some agents (ACE inhibitors and ARBs) have been shown to slow the progression of kidney disease in patients with albuminuria (e.g., due to diabetes, hypertension). Ang II constricts the efferent arterioles of the nephron (see Nephron diagram), causing increased workload in the glomeruli; over time, this results in kidney damage. Blocking Ang II causes efferent arteriole vasodilation and decreases glomerular filtration pressure. In heart failure, ACE inhibitors and ARBs protect the myocardium from the remodeling effects of Ang II.

RAAS inhibitors should not be used in combination (e.g., ACE inhibitor ± ARB ± aliskiren ± ARNI) due to an increased risk for adverse effects (see RAAS Inhibitor Drug Interactions). Angioedema is a potentially fatal adverse effect that can occur with use of any agent. It is more common with ACE inhibitors, than with ARBs or aliskiren, and black patients have a higher risk. For testing purposes, if a patient develops angioedema with any RAAS inhibitor, other agents in the class should be avoided.

ANGIOTENSIN-CONVERTING ENZYME INHIBITORS

ACE inhibitors end in "-pril". They block the conversion of angiotensin I to Ang II, resulting in ↓ vasoconstriction and ↓ aldosterone secretion, and they block the degradation of bradykinin, which is thought to contribute to the vasodilatory effects (and side effects of cough and angioedema).

DRUG	DOSING	SAFETY/SIDE EFFECTS/MONITORING
Benazepril *(Lotensin)*	5-40 mg daily	**BOXED WARNING** Can cause injury and death to the developing fetus when used in the 2nd and 3rd trimesters; discontinue as soon as pregnancy is detected **CONTRAINDICATIONS** History of angioedema, use with aliskiren in patients with diabetes, use within 36 hours of an angiotensin receptor and neprilysin inhibitor [ARNI (sacubitril/valsartan)] **WARNINGS** Angioedema, hyperkalemia, hypotension (↑ risk if salt- or volume-depleted), renal impairment, bilateral renal artery stenosis (avoid use) **SIDE EFFECTS** Cough, dizziness, headache, rash **MONITORING** BP, K, renal function, s/sx of angioedema **NOTES** Once daily agents can be used BID if needed
Captopril	12.5-100 mg BID	
Enalapril *(Vasotec,* *Epaned* powder for oral solution) **Enalaprilat *(Vasotec IV)***	PO: 5-20 mg daily or BID IV (enalaprilat): 0.625-5 mg Q6H	
Fosinopril	10-40 mg daily	
Lisinopril *(Prinivil, Zestril,* *Qbrelis* oral solution)	5-40 mg daily	
Moexipril	3.75-30 mg daily	
Perindopril	4-16 mg daily	
Quinapril *(Accupril)*	5-40 mg daily	
Ramipril *(Altace)*	2.5-20 mg daily	
Trandolapril	1-8 mg daily	

ANGIOTENSIN RECEPTOR BLOCKERS

ARBs end in "-sartan." They block Ang II from binding to the angiotensin II type-1 (AT1) receptor on vascular smooth muscle, preventing vasoconstriction.

DRUG	DOSING	SAFETY/SIDE EFFECTS/MONITORING
Azilsartan *(Edarbi)*	40-80 mg daily	Same as ACE inhibitors except: Less cough and angioedema, no washout period required with neprilysin inhibitor Additional safety issues unique to ARBs include: **WARNINGS** Olmesartan: sprue-like enteropathy – severe, chronic diarrhea with substantial weight loss; can occur months to years after drug initiation **NOTES** Azilsartan: keep in original container to protect from light and moisture
Candesartan *(Atacand)*	8-32 mg daily in 1-2 divided doses	
Eprosartan	400-800 mg daily in 1-2 divided doses	
Irbesartan *(Avapro)*	75-300 mg daily	
Losartan *(Cozaar)*	25-100 mg daily in 1-2 divided doses	
Olmesartan *(Benicar)*	10-40 mg daily	
Telmisartan *(Micardis)*	40-80 mg daily	
Valsartan *(Diovan,* *Prexxartan* oral solution)	80-320 mg daily	

DIRECT RENIN INHIBITOR

Aliskiren directly inhibits renin, which is responsible for the conversion of angiotensinogen to angiotensin I (Ang I). A decrease in the formation of Ang I results in a decrease in the formation of Ang II.

DRUG	DOSING	SAFETY/SIDE EFFECTS/MONITORING
Aliskiren *(Tekturna)*	150-300 mg daily Take with or without food but be consistent in administration with regard to meals Avoid high fat foods (reduces absorption)	Same as ACE inhibitors and ARBs except: **CONTRAINDICATIONS** Do not use with ACE inhibitors or ARBs in patients with diabetes **SIDE EFFECTS** Diarrhea **NOTES** *Tekturna:* tablets must be protected from moisture *Tekturna HCT* (see the Combination Blood Pressure Drugs table): the original container contains a dessicant

RAAS INHIBITOR DRUG INTERACTIONS

- All RAAS inhibitors ↑ the risk of hyperkalemia. Other medications that increase potassium (e.g., potassium-sparing diuretics) should be used cautiously. Patients should avoid salt substitutes that contain potassium chloride (instead of sodium chloride).
- Avoid using more than one RAAS inhibitor together (ACE inhibitor ± ARB ± aliskiren) due to an ↑ risk of renal impairment, hypotension and hyperkalemia. The use of aliskiren in combination with an ACE inhibitor or ARB is specifically contraindicated in patients with diabetes.
- ACE inhibitors and ARBs should not be used in combination with *Entresto* (sacubitril/valsartan). If switching from an ACE inhibitor to *Entresto*, or vice versa, a 36 hour washout period is required. See the Chronic Heart Failure chapter for additional information.
- ACE inhibitors and ARBs can ↓ lithium renal clearance and ↑ the risk of lithium toxicity.

ADDITIONAL AGENTS FOR TREATING HYPERTENSION

POTASSIUM-SPARING DIURETICS

The potassium-sparing diuretics triamterene and amiloride have minimal BP lowering effects and are most commonly used in combination with hydrochlorothiazide (e.g., *Maxzide, Dyazide*) to counteract the mild potassium losses seen with thiazide diuretics. The aldosterone receptor antagonists, spironolactone and eplerenone, are the preferred add-on drugs in patients with resistant hypertension (uncontrolled BP despite maximum tolerated doses of a CCB + thiazide diuretic + ACE inhibitor or ARB) and they are commonly used in heart failure.

Spironolactone is a non-selective aldosterone receptor antagonist (also blocks androgen), while eplerenone is a selective aldosterone receptor antagonist that does not exhibit endocrine side effects. These agents compete with aldosterone at receptor sites in the distal convoluted tubule and collecting ducts of the nephron (see Nephron diagram), increasing sodium and water excretion and conserving potassium.

DRUG	DOSING	SAFETY/SIDE EFFECTS/MONITORING
Amiloride	5-10 mg daily, max dose is 20 mg daily	**BOXED WARNINGS** Amiloride and triamterene: hyperkalemia (K > 5.5 mEq/L) – more likely in patients with diabetes, renal impairment, or elderly patients **CONTRAINDICATIONS** Hyperkalemia (K > 5.5 mEq/L), anuria, renal impairment, co-administration of potassium supplements or other potassium sparing diuretics, Addison's disease or other conditions that ↑ K Eplerenone: type 2 diabetes with microalbuminuria, SCr > 2 mg/dL in males or > 1.8 mg/dL in females, CrCl < 50 mL/min, co-administration of strong CYP3A4 inhibitors (see Learning Drug Interactions chapter) **SIDE EFFECTS** Spironolactone: gynecomastia, breast tenderness, impotence, irregular menses, amenorrhea Eplerenone: hypertriglyceridemia All: dehydration, hyponatremia, dizziness, hyperchloremic metabolic acidosis (rare) **MONITORING** BP, electrolytes (check K before starting and frequently thereafter), renal function, fluid status (input and output, weight) **NOTES** *CaroSpir* suspension (also approved for use in heart failure and edema due to cirrhosis) is not therapeutically equivalent to *Aldactone* and dosing recommendations differ; doses > 100 mg can cause unexpectedly high concentrations; use a different formulation in this case
Eplerenone (*Inspra*)	50 daily or BID	
Spironolactone (*Aldactone*, *CaroSpir* oral suspension)	25-100 mg daily in 1-2 divided doses	
Triamterene (*Dyrenium*) **+ HCTZ (*Maxzide, Maxzide-25, Dyazide*)**	100-300 mg daily in 1-2 divided doses + HCTZ: 37.5 mg/25 mg daily or BID + HCTZ: 75 mg/50 mg daily	

Potassium-Sparing Diuretic Drug Interactions

- Potassium-sparing diuretics ↑ the risk of hyperkalemia. Additive potassium accumulation can occur when these agents are used with other potassium-sparing drugs (see Learning Drug Interactions chapter).
- Diuretics can ↓ lithium renal clearance and ↑ the risk of lithium toxicity.
- Eplerenone is a major substrate of CYP3A4; use with strong CYP3A4 inhibitors (e.g., ketoconazole, itraconazole, clarithromycin, ritonavir) is contraindicated.

BETA-BLOCKERS

Beta-blockers mostly end in "-olol." They are no longer recommended first-line for uncomplicated hypertension unless the patient has a comorbid condition for which beta-blockers are recommended first-line (e.g., post-MI, stable ischemic heart disease, heart failure). For most conditions, any beta-blocker can be selected, but bisoprolol, carvedilol or metoprolol succinate should be used if treating chronic heart failure.

Beta-blockers decrease BP by competitively blocking beta-1 and/or beta-2 adrenergic receptors resulting in decreases in HR and myocardial contractility. Some drugs in the class have alpha-1 blocking properties, which decreases peripheral vasoconstriction as another mechanism of lowering BP. Beta-blockers with intrinsic sympathomimetic activity (ISA) partially stimulate beta receptors while blocking the effects of catecholamines such as norepinephrine; because they do not decrease HR to the same degree as beta-blockers without ISA, they are not recommended in post-MI patients. Acebutolol, penbutolol, and pindolol are the beta-blockers with ISA.

<table>
<tr><th>DRUG</th><th>DOSING</th><th>SAFETY/SIDE EFFECTS/MONITORING</th></tr>
<tr><th colspan="3">Beta-1 Selective Blockers</th></tr>
<tr><td>Acebutolol</td><td>200-800 mg daily in 1-2 divided doses</td><td rowspan="7">BOXED WARNING
Do not discontinue abruptly (particularly in patients with CAD/IHD); gradually taper dose over 1-2 weeks to avoid acute tachycardia, hypertension, and/or ischemia

CONTRAINDICATIONS
Severe bradycardia; 2nd or 3rd degree AV block or sick sinus syndrome (unless a permanent pacemaker is in place); overt cardiac failure or cardiogenic shock
Esmolol: pulmonary hypertension; use of IV non-DHP CCBs

WARNINGS
Caution in patients with diabetes (can worsen hyperglycemia or hypoglycemia and mask hypoglycemic symptoms – see Diabetes chapter); can mask signs of hyperthyroidism (e.g., tachycardia); use caution with bronchospastic diseases (e.g., asthma, COPD), peripheral vascular disease, pheochromocytoma and heart failure; may exacerbate CNS depression

SIDE EFFECTS
↓ HR, hypotension, fatigue, dizziness, depression, ↓ libido, impotence

MONITORING
HR (↓ dose if HR < 55 BPM), BP

NOTES
Oral agents: titrate doses every 1-2 weeks (as tolerated), take without regard to meals (except Lopressor and Toprol XL should be taken with or immediately following food)
Metoprolol tartrate IV is not equivalent to PO (IV:PO ratio is 1:2.5)
When switching from metoprolol tartrate to metoprolol succinate, the same total daily dose of metoprolol should be used
Kapspargo Sprinkle should be swallowed whole; for patients with difficulty swallowing, the capsule can be opened and the contents sprinkled on 1 teaspoonful of soft food (e.g., applesauce, yogurt or pudding) – the mixture must be swallowed within 60 minutes
Toprol XL can be split in half
For beta-1 selective drugs, remember: "AMEBBA" – Atenolol, Metoprolol, Esmolol, Bisoprolol, Betaxolol, Acebutolol</td></tr>
<tr><td>Atenolol (Tenormin)</td><td>25-100 mg daily</td></tr>
<tr><td>Betaxolol
Betoptic-S – ophthalmic solution</td><td>5-20 mg daily</td></tr>
<tr><td>Bisoprolol</td><td>2.5-20 mg daily</td></tr>
<tr><td>Esmolol (Brevibloc)
Injection</td><td>0.5-1 mg/kg IV bolus followed by 50-150 mcg/kg/min via continuous IV infusion, titrate as needed to a maximum of 300 mcg/kg/min</td></tr>
<tr><td>Metoprolol tartrate (Lopressor)
Tablet, injection
Metoprolol succinate extended release (Toprol XL, Kapspargo Sprinkle)
Tablet, capsule sprinkle</td><td>IR: 100-450 mg daily in 2-3 divided doses
XL: 25-100 mg daily; max dose is 400 mg daily</td></tr>
<tr><th colspan="3">Beta-1 Selective Blocker with Nitric Oxide-Dependent Vasodilation</th></tr>
<tr><td>Nebivolol (Bystolic)</td><td>5-10 mg daily; max dose is 40 mg daily
CrCl < 30 mL/min or moderate liver impairment, start at 2.5 mg daily</td><td>Same as above plus:

CONTRAINDICATIONS
Severe liver impairment (Child-Pugh > class B)

SIDE EFFECTS
Nausea, diarrhea, ↑ TGs, ↓ HDL

NOTES
Nitric oxide causes peripheral vasodilation</td></tr>
</table>

DRUG	DOSING	SAFETY/SIDE EFFECTS/MONITORING
Beta-1 and Beta-2 Blockers (Non-Selective)		
Nadolol (*Corgard*)	40-320 mg daily	Same as for beta-1 selective blockers plus: **NOTES** Propranolol has high lipid solubility (lipophilic) and crosses the blood-brain barrier; it may be associated with more CNS side effects but this makes it useful for other conditions (e.g., migraine prophylaxis, essential tremor)
Pindolol	5-30 mg BID	
Propranolol (*Inderal LA, Inderal XL*, *InnoPran XL, Hemangeol*) Tablet, ER capsule, oral solution, injection	IR: 40-160 mg BID, max dose is 640 mg daily LA: 80-160 mg daily, same max dose as IR XL: 80 mg daily; max dose is 120 mg daily	
Timolol *Timoptic* – ophthalmic solution	10-30 mg BID	
Non-Selective Beta-Blocker and Alpha-1 Blockers		
Carvedilol (*Coreg, Coreg CR*) Tablet, ER capsule	IR: 6.25-25 mg BID CR: 20-80 mg daily	Same as for beta-1 selective and non-selective blockers plus: **CONTRAINDICATIONS** Severe hepatic impairment **WARNINGS** Intraoperative floppy iris syndrome has occurred in cataract surgery patients who were on or were previously treated with an alpha-1 blocker **SIDE EFFECTS** Edema, weight gain, ↑ TGs, ↓ HDL **NOTES** Take all forms of carvedilol with food to ↓ the rate of absorption and the risk of orthostatic hypotension Carvedilol CR has less bioavailability than carvedilol IR; dosing conversions are not 1:1 (e.g., *Coreg* 3.125 mg BID = *Coreg CR* 10 mg daily)
Labetalol Tablet, injection	PO: 100-1,200 mg BID	Same as above for carvedilol plus: **NOTES** Drug of choice in pregnancy Injection is commonly used in the hospital setting and can be administered by repeated IV push or slow continuous infusion

Beta-Blocker Drug Interactions

- Beta-blockers can enhance the hypoglycemic effects of insulin and sulfonylureas and can mask some of the symptoms of hypoglycemia (e.g., shakiness, palpitations, anxiety); sweating and hunger are symptoms that are not masked. Beta-blockers can ↓ insulin secretion causing hyperglycemia. Monitor blood glucose in patients with diabetes.
- Watch for additive effects when administering other drugs that ↓ HR, including diltiazem, verapamil, digoxin, clonidine, amiodarone and dexmedetomidine (*Precedex*).
- Carvedilol, propranolol and metoprolol are major substrates of CYP2D6 and nebivolol is a minor substrate of CYP2D6. Monitor for drug interactions.
- Carvedilol and propranolol are inhibitors of P-gp and may increase the serum concentration of P-gp substrates (e.g., cyclosporine, dabigatran, digoxin, ranolazine).

CENTRALLY-ACTING ALPHA-2 ADRENERGIC AGONISTS

These drugs decrease BP by stimulating alpha-2 adrenergic receptors in the brain and reducing sympathetic outflow of norepinephrine, which decreases SVR and HR. Clonidine is commonly used for resistant hypertension and in patients who can not swallow (e.g., due to dysphagia, dementia) since it is available as a patch formulation. Since the patch is changed weekly, it can help with adherence.

DRUG	DOSING	SAFETY/SIDE EFFECTS/MONITORING
Clonidine (*Catapres, Catapres-TTS patch,* *Duraclon* inj) ***Kapvay*** – for ADHD Tablet, patch, injection	0.1-0.2 mg PO BID, max dose is 2.4 mg daily **Weekly patch** *Catapres-TTS-1* = 0.1 mg/24 hr *Catapres-TTS-2* = 0.2 mg/24 hr *Catapres-TTS-3* = 0.3 mg/24 hr	**CONTRAINDICATIONS** Methyldopa: active liver disease and concurrent use with MAO inhibitors **WARNINGS** Do not discontinue abruptly (can cause rebound hypertension, sweating, anxiety, tremors); must taper gradually over 2-4 days Methyldopa: risk for hemolytic anemia (detected by a positive Coombs test), hepatic necrosis **SIDE EFFECTS** Dry mouth, somnolence, fatigue, dizziness, constipation, ↓ HR, hypotension, headache, depression, behavioral changes, sexual dysfunction Clonidine patch: skin rash, pruritus, erythema, contact dermatitis Methyldopa: edema or weight gain (control with diuretics), hypersensitivity reactions [myocarditis, drug-induced fever, drug-induced lupus erythematosus (DILE)], ↑ prolactin levels **MONITORING** BP, HR, mental status **NOTES** Clonidine patch: apply weekly; remove before MRI Methyldopa is a drug of choice in pregnancy
Guanfacine IR (*Tenex**) Guanfacine ER (*Intuniv*) – for ADHD	1-2 mg QHS	
Methyldopa Tablet, injection	250 mg BID-TID; max dose is 3 grams daily	

**Brand discontinued but name still used in practice.*

DIRECT VASODILATORS

These drugs cause direct vasodilation of arterioles, with little effect on veins. The result is a decrease in SVR and a reduction in BP.

DRUG	DOSING	SAFETY/SIDE EFFECTS/MONITORING
Hydralazine Tablet, injection	PO: 10-50 mg QID, max dose is 300 mg daily IV: 10-20 mg Q4-6H PRN	**CONTRAINDICATIONS** Mitral valvular rheumatic heart disease, CAD **WARNING** Drug-induced lupus erythematosus (DILE – dose and duration related) **SIDE EFFECTS** Headache, hypotension, reflex tachycardia, palpitations, peripheral neuritis **MONITORING** HR, BP, ANA titer
Minoxidil *Men's Rogaine, Women's Rogaine* – OTC topical for hair growth	5-40 mg daily in 1-2 divided doses, max dose is 100 mg daily	**BOXED WARNING** Potent antihypertensive – can cause pericardial effusion and angina exacerbations; administer with a beta-blocker and loop diuretic **CONTRAINDICATION** Pheochromocytoma **SIDE EFFECTS** Fluid retention, tachycardia, hair growth

ALPHA BLOCKERS

Alpha blockers (e.g., doxazosin, prazosin, terazosin) bind to alpha-1 adrenergic receptors which results in peripheral vasodilation of arterioles and veins. They are not recommended for hypertension but may be used in men who have hypertension and benign prostatic hypertrophy (see Benign Prostatic Hypertrophy chapter).

HYPERTENSIVE CRISES: URGENCIES AND EMERGENCIES

A hypertensive crisis is defined as a rapidly accelerating BP (generally ≥ 180/120 mmHg). The two types of crises are:

- Hypertensive emergency: patient has acute target organ damage that may be life-threatening (e.g., encephalopathy, stroke, acute kidney injury, acute coronary syndrome, aortic dissection, acute pulmonary edema).
  - Treat with IV medications (see Key Drugs Guy).
  - Decrease BP by no more than 25% (within the first hour), then if stable, decrease to ~160/100 mmHg in the next 2 – 6 hours.
- Hypertensive urgency: no evidence of acute target organ damage.
  - Treat with any oral medication that has a short onset of action (e.g., 15 – 30 minutes).
  - Decrease BP gradually over 24 – 48 hours.

PATIENT COUNSELING

ALL HYPERTENSION MEDICATIONS

- You may not feel that you have high blood pressure, as often there are no obvious symptoms. It is important that you continue using this medication, even if you feel well. You may need to use blood pressure medication for the rest of your life to prevent serious complications, such as kidney damage, stroke and heart attack.
- If you miss a dose, take the missed dose as soon as you remember. If it is almost time for your next dose, skip the missed dose and take the medication at the next regularly scheduled time. Do not take extra medication to make up the missed dose.
- To be sure this medication is helping your condition, your blood pressure will need to be checked on a regular basis. You may have been instructed to check your blood pressure at home. Record the measurements in a notebook and bring them to your appointments for your provider to see.
- This medication is only one part of a complete treatment program for your high blood pressure; it is important that you follow the recommended diet, exercise and weight control plans closely.

KEY IV HYPERTENSION MEDICATIONS

Chlorothiazide	Metoprolol tartrate
Clevidipine	Nicardipine
Diltiazem	Nitroglycerin*
Enalaprilat	Nitroprusside*
Esmolol	Propranolol
Hydralazine	Verapamil
Labetalol	

**Vasodilators (discussed in the Acute & Critical Care Medicine chapter)*

DIURETICS

- This medication will cause you to urinate more throughout the day. If you need to take the medication twice daily, be sure to take your second dose no later than 4 P.M. to avoid getting up at night to go to the bathroom.
- This medication can make you feel dizzy and lightheaded when getting up from a sitting or lying position. Get up slowly. Let your feet hang over the bed for a few minutes before getting up. Hang on to the bed or nearby dresser when standing from a sitting position.
- This medication can decrease the amount of potassium in your body. Potassium supplements may be needed while you are on this medication to ensure you have enough potassium for your heart.
- If you have diabetes, your blood sugar may need to be monitored more frequently when you start this medication as it can affect increase your blood sugar.

CALCIUM CHANNEL BLOCKERS

- This medication can cause a few side effects, including swelling of the ankles, feeling tired, dizziness, headache, a hot or warm feeling in your face and palpitations.
- Other medications can alter how this drug works. Do not start any new medications, including over-the-counter drugs or supplements, unless you check with your healthcare provider first. Avoid eating grapefruit or drinking grapefruit juice while using this medication.
- *Adalat CC:* should be taken on an empty stomach.
- *Adalat CC* and *Procardia XL:* this medication can leave an empty shell in your stool. If you see the tablet in your stool, it is nothing to worry about.

ACE INHIBITORS, ARBS AND ALISKIREN

- This medication can cause birth defects if taken during pregnancy. Use an effective form of birth control while taking this medication. If you become pregnant during treatment, stop using this medication and tell your healthcare provider right away.
- This medication can increase the amount of potassium in your body. Do not use salt substitutes or potassium supplements while taking this medication, unless your healthcare provider has told you to do so.
- Get emergency medical help if you have any of these signs of an allergic reaction: hives, difficulty breathing, or swelling of your face, lips, tongue, and/or throat.
- ACE inhibitors: tell your healthcare provider if you develop a dry, hacking cough that is bothersome while taking this medication.

BETA-BLOCKERS

- Take this medication at the same time every day. Do not abruptly discontinue your medication without consulting your healthcare provider as stopping suddenly can make your condition worse.
- This medication can cause a few side effects, including dizziness, fatigue, and rarely, sexual problems. If these side effects bother you, let your healthcare provider know.
- If you have diabetes, this medication can cause you to miss some of the symptoms of low blood sugar (e.g., shakiness, palpitations, anxiety). You will still experience sweating and hunger if your blood sugar is low.
- Non-selective beta-blockers: contact your healthcare provider if you experience any difficulty breathing while taking this medication.
- *Coreg/Coreg CR*: take this medication with food.
- *Lopressor/Toprol XL:* take with or immediately after meals.

CLONIDINE

- Do not stop clonidine suddenly; this can cause your blood pressure to become dangerously high. Make sure you do not run out of medication.
- Clonidine can cause a variety of side effects, including drowsiness, dizziness, fatigue, dry mouth, depression and sexual dysfunction. If the side effects bother you, let your healthcare provider know but do not stop taking this medication suddenly.
- Apply the clonidine patch *(Catapres-TTS)* weekly to a hairless area of the skin on the upper outer arm or chest. Change the patch every seven days. The white adhesive cover can be applied over the patch to keep it in place. Do not place the patch on broken or irritated skin. After seven days, remove the used patch and apply a new patch to a different area than the previous site to avoid skin irritation. When removing the patch, be sure to discard it safely, away from the reach of any children or pets. The patch will need to be removed before an MRI to prevent a potential burn.

Select Guidelines/References

2017 ACC/AHA/AAPA/ABC/ACPM/AGS/APhA/ASH/ASPC/NMA/PCNA guideline for the prevention, detection, evaluation, and management of high blood pressure: a report of the American College of Cardiology/American Heart Association Task Force on Clinical Pactice Guidelines. *Hypertension* 2018;71:e13-e115.

CHAPTER CONTENT

Background 474
Pathophysiology 474
Diagnosis 475
Non-Drug Treatment 475
Drug Treatment 475
Treatment Approach for Stable Ischemic Heart Disease 475
Antiplatelet Agents 476
Aspirin 476
Clopidogrel 476
Antianginal Treatment 477
Beta-Blockers 477
Calcium Channel Blockers 477
Nitrates 477
Patient Counseling 479

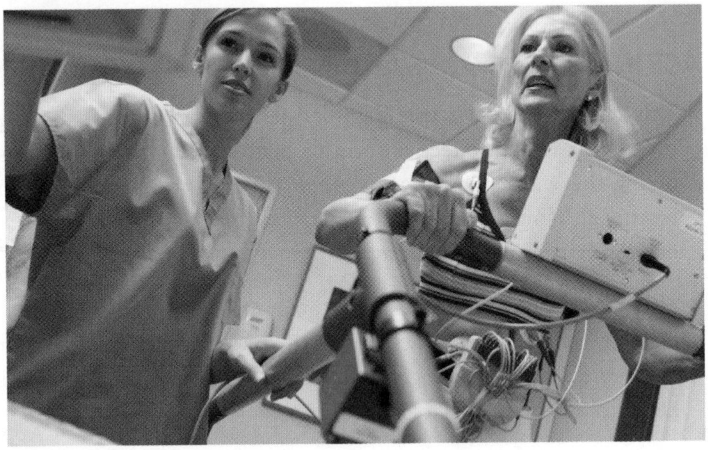

CHAPTER 29
ISCHEMIC HEART DISEASE

BACKGROUND

Angina is chest pain, pressure, tightness or discomfort, usually caused by ischemia of the heart muscle or spasm of the coronary arteries. The chest pain is described as "squeezing," "grip-like," "heavy," or "suffocating," and typically does not vary with position or respiration. Stable angina, also known as stable ischemic heart disease (SIHD), is associated with predictable chest pain, often brought on by exertion or emotional stress and relieved within minutes by rest or with nitroglycerin. Unstable angina (UA) is a type of acute coronary syndrome (ACS); this is a medical emergency where the chest pain increases (in frequency, intensity or duration) and is not relieved with nitroglycerin or rest (see Acute Coronary Syndromes chapter).

Some patients (women, elderly and those with diabetes) may not experience the classic symptoms of SIHD; they may not recognize the need for medical attention or they may be misdiagnosed with another condition (e.g., GERD).

When chest pain is caused by vasospasm of the coronary arteries, it is called Prinzmetal's (variant or vasospastic) angina. This type of angina can occur at rest and is often caused by illicit drug use, particularly cocaine.

ANGINAL PRESENTATIONS

Stable Ischemic Heart Disease
Chest pain that is predictable; it occurs with activity or stress and is relieved promptly by rest or nitroglycerin; usual underlying cause is atherosclerosis (CAD)

Prinzmetal's Angina
Chest pain due to vasospasm of coronary arteries; it is unpredictable and can occur at rest but is not usually associated with underlying CAD

Acute Coronary Syndromes
Acute chest pain that is severe and not relieved by rest or nitroglycerin; acute medical care is needed (includes UA, NSTEMI and STEMI – see Acute Coronary Syndromes chapter)

Silent Ischemia
Transient myocardial ischemia without symptoms of chest pain

PATHOPHYSIOLOGY

Chest pain occurs when there is an imbalance between myocardial oxygen demand (workload) and supply (blood flow). In SIHD, myocardial oxygen supply is often decreased due to plaque build up (atherosclerosis) within the inner walls of the coronary arteries. This is known as coronary artery disease (CAD), and it causes narrowing of the arteries and reduced blood flow to the heart. Myocardial oxygen demand increases when the heart is working harder, due to an increased heart rate, contractility or left ventricular wall tension [caused by increased preload (volume of blood returning to the heart) and/or afterload (systemic vascular resistance, or SVR)].

CONTENT LEGEND

= Study Tip Gal

DIAGNOSIS

A cardiac stress test is performed to assess the likelihood of CAD and diagnose SIHD. The cardiac stress test increases myocardial oxygen demand, by exercising on a treadmill or pedaling a stationary exercise bicycle. When disabilities or medical conditions limit exercise, intravenous pharmacological stimulation is used, with either dipyridamole, adenosine *(Adenoscan)*, regadenoson *(Lexiscan)* or dobutamine. As myocardial oxygen demand increases, the patient is monitored for the development of symptoms (e.g., chest pain, dyspnea, lightheadedness), changes in heart rate and blood pressure and transient rhythm disturbances or ST segment abnormalities on an ECG.

When the diagnosis of SIHD is certain, stress testing can be used to determine if coronary angiography should be performed to assess the extent of atherosclerosis and need for revascularization.

EVALUATION OF SIHD
History and physical
CBC, CK-MB, troponins (I or T), aPTT, PT/INR, lipid panel, glucose
ECG (at rest and during chest pain)
Cardiac stress test/stress imaging
Cardiac catheterization/angiography

NON-DRUG TREATMENT

Multiple risk factors for heart disease, vascular disease and stroke are typically present in patients with SIHD, including hypertension, smoking, dyslipidemia, diabetes, obesity and physical inactivity. Patients should be encouraged to follow a heart healthy diet (e.g., saturated fats < 7% and *trans* fats < 1% of total calories, adequate intake of fresh fruits and vegetables, low-fat dairy products), maintain a BMI of 18.5 – 24.9 kg/m^2, and maintain a waist circumference < 35 inches in females and < 40 inches in males.

Patients should engage in 30 – 60 minutes of moderate-intensity aerobic activity 5 – 7 days per week, supplemented by an increase in daily lifestyle activities (e.g., walking breaks at work, gardening). Medically supervised programs, such as cardiac rehabilitation, are encouraged for at-risk patients at first diagnosis.

Patients who smoke should quit, and secondhand smoke should be avoided. Alcohol intake should be limited to 1 drink/day (4 oz wine, 12 oz beer, or 1 oz of spirits) for women and 1 – 2 drinks/day for men.

DRUG TREATMENT

The treatment goals for SIHD are to improve function (by eliminating anginal pain episodes), prevent future cardiovascular events (e.g., MI, heart failure) and reduce the risk of cardiovascular death. An antiplatelet agent and an antianginal regimen are used together. Aspirin is the recommended antiplatelet agent; clopidogrel *(Plavix)* is used in patients with an allergy or other contraindication to aspirin, or in combination with aspirin in select patients (see Dual Antiplatelet Therapy section).

Antianginal treatment decreases myocardial oxygen demand or increases myocardial oxygen supply (see Antianginal Treatment table). Beta-blockers are first-line; calcium channel blockers (CCBs), both dihydropyridines and non-dihydropyridines, or long-acting nitrates should be used when beta-blockers are contraindicated or when additional symptomatic relief is needed. Ranolazine can also be used as a substitute for, or in addition to, beta-blockers. Short-acting nitroglycerin, as a sublingual (SL) tablet, powder or translingual (TL) spray, is recommended for immediate relief of angina in all patients.

SIHD is one of the atherosclerotic cardiovascular diseases (ASCVD). Patients should be treated with a high-intensity statin (see Dyslipidemia chapter). Patients with hypertension, heart failure and diabetes should be aggressively managed with the guideline-driven treatments for each of these conditions. An annual influenza vaccine is recommended; pneumococcal vaccines *(Prevnar 13* and *Pneumovax 23)* should be administered per ACIP recommendations (see Immunizations chapter). Rivaroxaban *(Xarelto)* in combination with low-dose aspirin is FDA-approved to reduce the risk of cardiovascular events in patients with CAD or peripheral artery disease (PAD).

TREATMENT APPROACH FOR STABLE ISCHEMIC HEART DISEASE

A – Antiplatelet and antianginal drugs (beta-blockers, CCBs and nitrates)

B – Blood pressure and beta-blockers

C – Cholesterol (statins) and cigarettes (cessation)

D – Diet and diabetes

E – Exercise and education

ANTIPLATELET AGENTS

Aspirin binds irreversibly to cyclooxygenase-1 and 2 (COX-1 and 2) enzymes which results in decreased prostaglandin (PG) and thromboxane A2 (TXA2) production. TXA2 is a potent vasoconstrictor and inducer of platelet aggregation. Aspirin has antiplatelet, antipyretic, analgesic and anti-inflammatory properties. Clopidogrel is a prodrug that irreversibly inhibits P2Y12 ADP-mediated platelet activation and aggregation.

DRUG	DOSING	SAFETY/SIDE EFFECTS/MONITORING
Aspirin (*Bayer, Bufferin, Ecotrin,* *Ascriptin, Durlaza,* others) + omeprazole (*Yosprala*) OTC: tablet, chewable tablet, enteric-coated tablet, suppository Rx: ER capsule (*Durlaza*), delayed-release tablet (*Yosprala*) See Pain chapter for more information on aspirin products	75-162 mg daily *Yosprala*: 81 mg/40 mg daily	**CONTRAINDICATIONS** NSAID or salicylate allergy; children and teenagers with viral infection (due to risk of Reye's syndrome) patients with rhinitis, nasal polyps or asthma (due to risk of urticaria, angioedema, or bronchospasm) **WARNINGS** Bleeding (including GI bleed/ulceration) – risk increased with heavy alcohol use or other drugs that ↑ bleeding risk (e.g., NSAIDs, anticoagulants, other antiplatelet agents) **SIDE EFFECTS** Dyspepsia, heartburn, nausea, tinnitus (in toxicity) **MONITORING** Bleeding, bruising **NOTES** Shown to ↓ incidence of MI, CV events and death; used in all SIHD patients indefinitely (unless contraindicated) *Yosprala* is indicated for patients who require aspirin but are at risk of developing aspirin-associated gastric ulcers Non-enteric coated, chewable aspirin is preferred in ACS; if only enteric coated aspirin is available, it should be chewed (325 mg) *Durlaza* and *Yosprala* should not be used when rapid onset is needed (e.g., ACS, pre-PCI)
Clopidogrel (*Plavix*) Tablet	75 mg daily	**BOXED WARNING** Clopidogrel is a prodrug. Effectiveness depends on the conversion to an active metabolite, mainly by CYP450 2C19. Poor metabolizers of CYP2C19 exhibit higher cardiovascular events than patients with normal CYP2C19 function. Tests to check CYP2C19 genotype can be used as an aid in determining a therapeutic strategy. Consider alternative treatments in patients identified as CYP2C19 poor metabolizers. Refer to the Pharmacogenomics chapter. **CONTRAINDICATIONS** Serious bleeding (e.g., GI bleed, intracranial hemorrhage) **WARNINGS** ↑ bleeding risk, stop 5 days prior to elective surgery (e.g., CABG); avoid use with omeprazole or esomeprazole (see Drug Interactions section); premature discontinuation (↑ risk of thrombosis); thrombotic thrombocytopenic purpura (TTP) has been reported **SIDE EFFECTS** Gastrointestinal hemorrhage, hematoma, pruritus **MONITORING** Symptoms of bleeding, Hgb/Hct as necessary **NOTES** Used in SIHD patients with a contraindication to aspirin; may be used in combination with aspirin (see Dual Antiplatelet Therapy section)

Dual Antiplatelet Therapy

Monotherapy with aspirin or clopidogrel is used in the vast majority of patients with SIHD. In 2016, the ACC/AHA released a guideline update on dual antiplatelet therapy (DAPT). The primary benefit in SIHD is after placement of a bare metal stent (DAPT for at least one month), a drug-eluting stent (DAPT for at least 6 months), or post-CABG (DAPT for 12 months). When using DAPT in SIHD, clopidogrel is the only P2Y12 inhibitor recommended and the dose of aspirin should be 81 mg daily; aspirin, at doses of 75 – 162 mg, should be continued indefinitely after the course of DAPT has been completed.

Antiplatelet Drug Interactions

- Most drug interactions are due to additive effects with other agents that can ↑ bleeding risk (see the Learning Drug Interactions chapter).
- Aspirin: use caution in combination with other ototoxic drugs (see the Learning Drug Interactions chapter).
- Clopidogrel: avoid in combination with omeprazole and esomeprazole (other PPIs interact less) and use caution with other CYP2C19 inhibitors.

ANTIANGINAL TREATMENT

DRUG	MECHANISM OF CLINICAL BENEFIT	CLINICAL NOTES
Beta-Blockers Used 1st line in SIHD See the Hypertension chapter for a complete review of these agents	Reduce myocardial oxygen demand: ↓ HR, ↓ contractility and ↓ left ventricular wall tension	Start low, go slow; titrate to resting HR of 55-60 BPM; avoid abrupt withdrawal All agents are equally effective; can be used as monotherapy or in combination with DHP CCBs, long-acting nitrates, and/or ranolazine Provide mortality reduction and symptom improvement More effective than nitrates and CCBs in silent ischemia; avoid in Prinzmetal's angina
Calcium Channel Blockers Preferred agents for Prinzmetal's (variant) angina See the Hypertension chapter for a complete review of these agents	Reduce myocardial oxygen demand: non-DHPs ↓ HR and contractility; DHPs ↓ SVR (afterload) Increase myocardial oxygen supply: all CCBs ↑ blood flow through coronary arteries	Can be used in SIHD when beta-blockers are contraindicated or as add-on therapy to beta-blockers for continued symptoms Slow-release or long-acting DHPs and non-DHPs are effective; avoid short-acting DHPs (e.g., nifedipine IR) DHPs are preferred when CCBs are used in combination with beta-blockers (due to the risk of excessive bradycardia when non-DHPs are used with beta-blockers)
Nitrates	Reduce myocardial oxygen demand: ↓ preload (free radical nitric oxide produces vasodilation of veins more than arteries) Increases myocardial oxygen supply: ↑ blood flow through collateral (non-atherosclerotic) arteries	**SL tablets, SL powder or TL spray** Recommended for all patients for fast relief of angina; call 911 if chest pain does not go away after the first dose of SL tablet, SL powder or TL spray; nitrate tolerance does not develop with SL/TL products **Long-acting nitrates** Long-acting nitrates are used when beta-blockers are contraindicated or as add-on therapy for treatment of symptoms; a nitrate-free interval is required to prevent tolerance (see the Nitroglycerin Formulations table on the next page)
Ranolazine (*Ranexa*)	Selectively inhibits the late phase Na current and ↓ intracellular Ca; may decrease myocardial oxygen demand by decreasing ventricular tension and oxygen consumption	**CONTRAINDICATIONS** Liver cirrhosis, use in combination with strong CYP3A4 inhibitors and inducers **WARNINGS** Can cause QT prolongation Acute renal failure has been observed in some patients with CrCl < 30 mL/min **SIDE EFFECTS** Dizziness, headache, constipation, nausea **MONITORING** ECG, K, renal function **NOTES** Can use in place of beta-blockers or as add-on therapy for treatment of symptoms Has little to no clinical effects on HR or BP Do not crush, break or chew

Nitroglycerin Formulations Used in SIHD

<table>
<tr><th>FORMULATIONS*</th><th>SAFETY/SIDE EFFECTS/MONITORING</th></tr>
<tr><td>Short-Acting Nitrates</td><td rowspan="9">CONTRAINDICATIONS
Hypersensitivity to organic nitrates, use in combination with PDE-5 inhibitors or riociguat (see the Drug Interactions section)
SL tablets, powder and spray: ↑ intracranial pressure, severe anemia, circulatory failure and shock (SL powder only)

WARNINGS
Hypotension, headache, tachyphylaxis (↓ effectiveness/tolerance), may aggravate angina caused by hypertrophic cardiomyopathy

SIDE EFFECTS
Headache, flushing, syncope, dizziness, lightheadedness

MONITORING
BP, HR, chest pain

NOTES

Short-acting nitrates
Used PRN for immediate relief of chest pain; all patients with SIHD should have a short-acting product available and be familiar with use in urgent or emergent situations (see the Patient Counseling section)
Keep nitroglycerin SL tablets in the original amber glass bottle; discard 6 months after opening

Long-acting nitrates
Long-acting or scheduled products require a 10-12 hour nitrate-free period to ↓ tolerance (some products require a longer nitrate-free interval)
Ointment: dosed BID (6 hours apart with a 10-12 hour nitrate-free interval)
Patch: wear on for 12-14 hours, off for 10-12 hours; rotate sites; dispose of safely, away from children and pets
Isosorbide mononitrate: use IR product BID, at least 7 hours apart (e.g., 8 AM and 3 PM), and ER product QAM
Isosorbide dinitrate: IR product is dosed BID-TID; when used TID, take at 8 AM, 12 PM and 4 PM for a 14 hour nitrate-free interval (or similar); take SR/ER product daily in the morning or divided BID with an 18 hour nitrate-free interval
Isosorbide dinitrate is the preferred formulation for systolic HF (in combination with hydralazine)</td></tr>
<tr><td>Nitroglycerin SL tablet (Nitrostat)
0.3 mg, 0.4 mg, 0.6 mg</td></tr>
<tr><td>Nitroglycerin translingual spray (NitroMist, Nitrolingual Pump Spray)
0.4 mg/spray</td></tr>
<tr><td>Nitroglycerin SL powder (GoNitro)
0.4 mg/packet</td></tr>
<tr><td>Long-acting nitrates</td></tr>
<tr><td>Nitroglycerin ointment 2% (Nitro-BID)</td></tr>
<tr><td>Nitroglycerin transdermal patch (Nitro-Dur, Minitran)
0.1, 0.2, 0.3, 0.4, 0.6, 0.8 mg/hr</td></tr>
<tr><td>Isosorbide mononitrate IR/ER tablet (Monoket, Imdur**)
IR: 10 mg, 20 mg
ER: 30 mg, 60 mg, 120 mg</td></tr>
<tr><td>Isosorbide dinitrate IR/ER (Dilatrate-SR, Isordil Titradose)
IR: 5 mg, 10 mg, 20 mg, 30 mg, 40 mg
ER: 40 mg</td></tr>
</table>

**IV nitroglycerin is discussed in the Acute & Critical Care Medicine chapter*
***Brand discontinued but name still used in practice.*

Nitrate Drug Interactions

- Avoid use of long-acting nitrates in combination with PDE-5 inhibitors and riociguat; use caution with other antihypertensive medications and alcohol, as these combinations can cause a significant decrease in BP.
  - If a patient does not use long-acting nitrates but has short-acting nitroglycerin available for immediate relief of angina, it should not be used if the patient has recently taken a PDE-5 inhibitor (avanafil in the past 12 hours, sildenafil or vardenafil in the past 24 hours, or tadalafil in the past 48 hours). Occasionally, and with careful monitoring, nitrates may be used in an acute emergency in a patient who has recently taken a PDE-5 inhibitor.

Ranolazine Drug Interactions

- Ranolazine is a major substrate of CYP3A4 and a minor substrate of CYP2D6 and P-gp. It is a weak inhibitor of CYP3A4, 2D6 and P-gp. Do not use with strong CYP3A4 inhibitors or inducers. Limit the dose to 500 mg BID in patients taking moderate CYP3A4 inhibitors (e.g., diltiazem, verapamil). Limit simvastatin to 20 mg/day if used together.

PATIENT COUNSELING

ANTIPLATELET AGENTS

- This medication helps prevent platelets from sticking together and forming a clot that can block an artery. Do not stop taking it without talking to your healthcare provider as you could be at risk of developing a clot which can be life-threatening.
- If you miss a dose, take it as soon as you remember. If it is almost time for your next dose, skip the missed dose and take the next dose at your regularly scheduled time. Do not take two doses at the same time unless instructed by your healthcare provider.
- You may bleed and bruise more easily while taking this medication, even from a minor scrape. It may take longer to stop bleeding. Call your healthcare provider at once if you have black or bloody stools, or if you cough up blood or vomit that looks like coffee grounds. These could be signs of serious bleeding in the stomach or intestines.
- Your risk of bleeding in the stomach or intestines may be increased if you drink alcohol, have a history of stomach ulcers or take other medications that increase the risk of bleeding (e.g., blood thinners or ibuprofen). Do not take other over-the-counter pain relievers without consulting your healthcare provider.

Aspirin

- Stop taking this medication and tell your healthcare provider right away if you develop signs of an allergic reaction (e.g., hives, swelling in the face, wheezing), ringing in the ears or loss of hearing.

Clopidogrel

- Thrombotic thrombocytopenic purpura (TTP) is a rare, but serious, side effect of this medication. Seek prompt medical attention if you experience any of these symptoms: fever, weakness, extreme skin paleness, purplish spots or skin patches (called purpura), yellowing of the skin or eyes (jaundice) or mental status changes.
- If you need to have any type of surgery or dental work, tell the surgeon or dentist ahead of time that you are using clopidogrel. You may need to stop using the medication for at least five days before having major surgery, to prevent excessive bleeding.
- Some acid-reducing medications can decrease the beneficial effects of clopidogrel. Do not take heartburn medications without consulting your healthcare provider.

ALL NITROGLYCERIN PRODUCTS

- Do not use this medication with: sildenafil *(Viagra, Revatio)*, tadalafil *(Cialis, Adcirca)*, vardenafil *(Levitra, Staxyn)*, avanafil *(Stendra)* and riociguat *(Adempas)*. A dangerous drop in blood pressure could occur.
- Side effects of this medication can include headache, dizziness, lightheadedness, redness/mild warmth (flushing) or nausea. Headache is often a sign that this medication is working. Flushing and headache should become less bothersome as your body gets used to the medication. Your healthcare provider may recommend treating headaches with acetaminophen. If headaches continue or become severe, tell your healthcare provider.
- To reduce the risk of dizziness and lightheadedness with this medication, get up slowly when rising from a sitting or lying position. Hold onto the side of the bed or chair to avoid falling. Limit alcoholic beverages.

NITROGLYCERIN SUBLINGUAL TABLETS, POWDER AND TRANSLINGUAL SPRAY

- At the first sign of chest pain: take one dose immediately (one SL tablet, one SL powder packet or one TL spray). Call 911 immediately if chest pain persists after the first dose. Continue to take two additional doses at five minute intervals while waiting for the ambulance to arrive. Do not take more than three doses within 15 minutes.
- This medication may be taken 5 – 10 minutes before activities that bring on chest pain.

Nitroglycerin SL Tablets

- Nitroglycerin SL tablets should not be chewed, crushed or swallowed. Place the tablet under the tongue, or in the area between the inside of the cheek and the gums/teeth, and let it dissolve.
- You may feel a slight burning or tingling sensation with SL tablets. This is not a sign of how well the medication is working. Do not use more medication because you do not feel these sensations.
- Keep nitroglycerin SL tablets tightly capped in the original amber glass bottle, and store at room temperature. Shake out one tablet only; do not let the other tablets get wet.

Nitroglycerin SL Powder

- Empty the contents of a packet under the tongue, close your mouth and breath normally through your nose. Let the powder dissolve without swallowing. Do not rinse the mouth or spit for five minutes after the dose.

Nitroglycerin TL Spray

- The pump must be primed before first use (five sprays for *Nitrolingual Pump Spray* and ten sprays for *NitroMist*). If not used within six weeks, prime the pump with one spray (*Nitrolingual Pump Spray*) or two sprays (*NitroMist*) before use.
- Do not shake. Press the button firmly with the forefinger to release the spray onto or under the tongue. Close your mouth after the spray. Do not inhale the spray and try not to swallow too quickly afterwards. Do not spit or rinse the mouth for 5 – 10 minutes after the dose.

NITROGLYCERIN OINTMENT

- Measure the dose of ointment with the dose measuring applicator supplied with the tube. Place the applicator on a flat surface, printed side down. Squeeze the needed amount of ointment onto the applicator, and place the applicator (ointment side down) on the chest or other desired area of the skin.
- Spread the ointment, using the dose measuring applicator, lightly onto the skin. Do not rub into the skin. Tape the applicator into place.
- This medication can stain clothing. Care should be taken to completely cover the dose measuring applicator.

NITROGLYCERIN PATCHES

- Remove the patch from its pouch and remove the protective clear liner. Apply the patch to a clean, dry, and hairless area of the skin and press it firmly in place with the palm of your hand. Any area may be selected except the extremities below the knees or elbows; the chest is the preferred site. Hair in the area may be clipped, but not shaved. Avoid areas with cuts or irritation. Do not apply the patch immediately after bathing or showering; wait until your skin is completely dry. You may bathe, shower, and swim while wearing the patch.
- Apply one new patch each morning and wear for 12 – 14 hours. For the medication to work well, there must be a 10 – 12 hour "patch free" interval where the patch is left off.
- To reduce skin irritation, apply each new patch to a different area of skin.
- After removing the old patch, fold it in half with the sticky sides together, and discard out of the reach of children and pets.

RANOLAZINE

- Ranolazine is used to decrease the number of times you get chest pain. It works differently than other drugs for chest pain, so it can be used with your other medications (beta-blockers, nitrates and calcium channel blockers).
- Take this medication by mouth twice daily with or without food. Swallow the tablet whole. Do not crush or chew the tablets.
- Use this medication regularly to get the most benefit from it. Take it at the same times each day. It should not be used to treat chest pain when it occurs. Use other medications (e.g., SL nitroglycerin) to relieve chest pain, as directed by your healthcare provider.
- Dizziness, headache, lightheadedness, nausea and constipation can occur. If any of these effects persist or worsen, notify your healthcare provider promptly.
- Ranolazine can cause a condition that affects the heart rhythm (QT prolongation). This heart rhythm can infrequently result in serious fast/irregular heartbeat and other symptoms (such as severe dizziness, fainting) that require immediate medical attention. The risk is increased if you are taking other drugs that can affect the heart rhythm. Check with your healthcare provider before using any herbal or OTC medications.
- Other drugs may interfere with this medication. Avoid grapefruit and grapefruit juice. Inform your healthcare provider and pharmacist that you are taking this medication before starting new drugs.

Select Guidelines/References

2014 ACC/AHA/AATS/PCNA/SCAI/STS focused update of the guideline for the diagnosis and management of patients with stable ischemic heart disease. *Circulation.* 2014;130:1749-1767.

2012 ACCF/AHA/ACP/AATS/PCNA/SCAI/STS guideline for the diagnosis and management of patients with stable ischemic heart disease. *Circulation.* 2012;126(25):e354-e471.

CHAPTER CONTENT

Background 481
Signs and Symptoms 481
Diagnosis 482
Comparing UA, NSTEMI and STEMI 482
Drug Treatment 482
Drug Treatment of ACS 482
Drugs for ACS (MONA-GAP-BA) 483
P2Y12 Inhibitors 484
Glycoprotein IIB/IIIA Receptor Antagonists 486
Fibrinolytics 487
Protease-Activated Receptor-1 Antagonist 487
Secondary Prevention After ACS 488
Drugs for Secondary Prevention After ACS 488
Other Considerations 488
Patient Counseling 488

CONTENT LEGEND

= Study Tip Gal

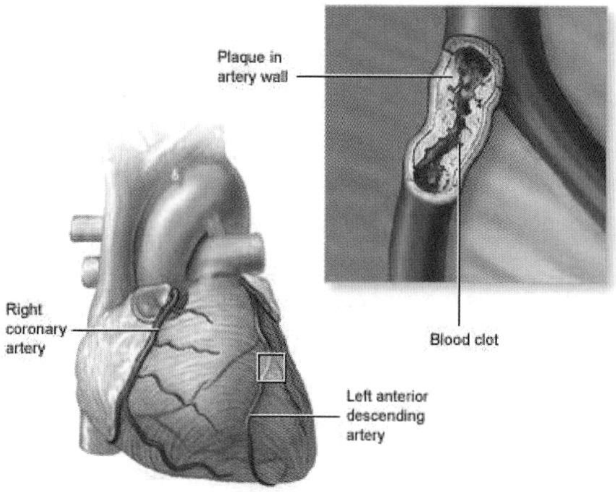

CHAPTER 30
ACUTE CORONARY SYNDROMES

BACKGROUND

Acute coronary syndrome (ACS) results from plaque buildup in the coronary arteries (coronary atherosclerosis) that causes sudden, reduced blood flow and an imbalance between myocardial oxygen supply and demand. The plaques are made up of fatty deposits that cause the arteries to narrow, making blood flow more difficult. The surface of the plaque can rupture, leading to clot formation and an acute reduction in blood flow (ischemia). Ischemia may ultimately lead to cardiac muscle cell death (myocyte necrosis).

ACS encompasses non-ST segment elevation acute coronary syndromes (NSTE-ACS) and ST segment elevation myocardial infarction (STEMI). NSTE-ACS describes both unstable angina (UA) and non-ST segment elevation myocardial infarction (NSTEMI), since patients are indistinguishable upon presentation and the term emphasizes the continuum between UA and NSTEMI.

SIGNS AND SYMPTOMS

The classic symptoms of ACS include chest pain ("pain" includes symptoms of discomfort, pressure and squeezing) lasting ≥ 10 minutes, severe dyspnea, diaphoresis, syncope/presyncope and/or palpitations. The pain can radiate to the arms, back, neck, jaw or epigastric area. Female, elderly and diabetic patients are less likely to experience the classic symptoms. Symptoms can occur at rest, with minimal exertion, or may be precipitated by exercise, cold weather, extreme emotions, stress or sexual intercourse. ACS is a medical emergency. Patients with a prescription for sublingual nitroglycerin (NTG) should use one dose every five minutes for up to three doses for relief of chest pain. If the chest pain or discomfort is not improved or is worse five minutes after the first dose, 911 should be called immediately.

DIAGNOSIS

A 12-lead ECG should be performed and evaluated within ten minutes at the site of first medical contact (which could be in an ambulance). Patients with an acute MI (STEMI or NSTEMI) should be urgently transported to a hospital with percutaneous coronary intervention (PCI) capability, if possible. If the ECG is not diagnostic, but the patient remains symptomatic, serial ECGs should be performed every 15 – 30 minutes during the first hour to detect ischemic changes.

Biochemical markers are released into the bloodstream when myocardial cells die. The measurement of these cardiac enzymes helps establish the diagnosis. The cardiac troponins I and T (TnI and TnT) are the most sensitive and specific biomarkers for ACS. They are detectable in the blood within 2 – 12 hours (depending on the assay) after myocardial necrosis and can remain detectable for up to 5 – 14 days. Creatine kinase myocardial isoenzyme (CK-MB) and myoglobin are less sensitive markers than troponins, but may still be monitored in clinical practice. Cardiac troponin I or T levels should be obtained at presentation and 3 – 6 hours after symptom onset in all patients with ACS symptoms. B-type natriuretic peptide (BNP) or N-terminal pro-B-type natriuretic peptide (NT-proBNP) levels may be obtained to assess risk.

RISK FACTORS

- Age (men > 45 years of age, women > 55 years of age or with early hysterectomy)
- Family history (1st degree relative) of coronary event before 55 years of age (men) or 65 years of age (women)
- Smoking
- Hypertension
- Dyslipidemia
- Diabetes
- Chronic angina
- Known coronary artery disease
- Lack of exercise
- Excessive alcohol

COMPARING UA, NSTEMI AND STEMI

	UA	NSTEMI	STEMI
Symptoms	Chest pain (described in text)		
Cardiac Enzymes	Negative	Positive	Positive
ECG Changes	None or transient ischemic changes*		ST segment elevation**
Blockage	Partial blockage		Complete blockage

**ST segment depression or prominent T-wave inversion*
***Meeting defined criteria and in ≥ 2 contiguous leads (e.g., leads looking at the same area of the heart)*

DRUG TREATMENT

Treatment is selected for the patient depending on the diagnosis and symptom severity. In NSTE-ACS, patients may be treated with medications alone (referred to as medical management) or with PCI (referred to as an early invasive strategy). PCI is a coronary revascularization procedure that involves inflating a small balloon inside a coronary artery to widen it and improve blood flow. Usually metal mesh, called a stent, is placed into the artery afterward to keep the artery open.

A STEMI results from complete blockage of one or more coronary arteries, and the blocked arteries need to be opened as quickly as possible. In most U.S. cities the fastest way to do this is with PCI, making PCI the preferred approach. PCI should be performed within 120 minutes (2 hours) of first medical contact. If first medical contact occurs at a hospital that cannot perform PCI, a decision must be made to transfer the patient to another facility or use a fibrinolytic drug (see fibrinolytic section of this chapter). Patients may also go directly for urgent coronary artery bypass graft (CABG) surgery if there is significant multi-vessel disease within the coronary arteries.

DRUG TREATMENT OF ACS

MONA-GAP-BA

Morphine	GPIIb/IIIa antagonists	Beta-blockers
Oxygen	Anticoagulants	ACE inhibitors
Nitrates	P2Y12 inhibitors	
Aspirin		

- NSTE-ACS: MONA-GAP-BA +/- PCI
- STEMI: MONA-GAP-BA + PCI or fibrinolytic (PCI preferred)

Colors correspond with the drug summary table on the next page

Acute treatment is aimed at providing immediate relief of ischemia and preventing MI expansion and death. Drug treatment includes the use of antianginal, antiplatelet and anticoagulant therapy (see Study Tip Gal and summary table). High-intensity statin therapy should be initiated or continued in all patients, if there are no contraindications to use, per the NSTE-ACS and STEMI guidelines. An MI is considered atherosclerotic cardiovascular disease (ASCVD) according to the 2018 ACC/AHA Guideline on the Treatment of Blood Cholesterol (refer to Dyslipidemia chapter).

DRUGS FOR ACS (MONA-GAP-BA)

DRUG	MOA OF CLINICAL BENEFIT	CLINICAL COMMENTS
GIVE THESE IMMEDIATELY (as needed)		
Morphine	Produces arterial and venous dilation; leading to a ↓ in myocardial O2 demand; provides pain relief	Morphine sulfate (2-5 mg IV repeated at 5- to 30-minute intervals PRN) may be used in patients with ongoing chest discomfort despite NTG therapy. Side effects: hypotension, bradycardia, N/V, sedation and respiratory depression. See Pain chapter for additional information.
Oxygen		Administer to patients with arterial oxygen saturation < 90% (SaO2 < 90%) or those in respiratory distress.
Nitrates	Dilate coronary arteries and improve collateral blood flow; ↓ cardiac O2 demand by ↓ preload, ventricular wall tension and afterload (modestly)	Sublingual NTG (0.3-0.4 mg) if not already administered. Start IV NTG (start at 10 mcg/min, titrate as needed) for persistent ischemic pain, hypertension or heart failure. Do not use NTG if SBP < 90 mmHg, HR < 50 BPM or if patient is experiencing a right ventricular infarction. NTG should not be administered with PDE-5 inhibitors for erectile dysfunction. See Ischemic Heart Disease and Sexual Dysfunction chapters for additional details.
Aspirin	Inhibits platelet aggregation/clot formation by inhibiting production of thromboxane A2 (TXA2) via irreversible COX-1 and COX-2 inhibition	Non-enteric-coated, chewable aspirin (162-325 mg) should be given to all patients immediately, if no contraindications are present (do not use extended-release aspirin products). A maintenance dose of aspirin 81-162 mg daily should be continued indefinitely. If intolerant to aspirin, may use clopidogrel or ticagrelor (discussed later in this chapter).
GIVE THESE NEXT [choice of agent/s relates to plan (PCI vs. CABG vs. medical management)]		
Glycoprotein (GP) IIb/IIIa receptor antagonists	Block fibrinogen from binding to the GPIIb/IIIa receptors on platelets, preventing platelet aggregation	Drugs include abciximab, eptifibatide and tirofiban. Option for medical management (eptifibatide or tirofiban) or for patients going for PCI +/- stent (all agents). If used in PCI, they are given concurrently with heparin.
Anticoagulants	Inhibit clotting factors and can reduce infarct size	Drugs include LMWHs, UFH and bivalirudin (preferred for STEMI). See Anticoagulation chapter.
P2Y12 Inhibitors	Inhibit P2Y12 receptor on platelets, preventing platelet aggregation	Drugs include clopidogrel, prasugrel and ticagrelor. Ticagrelor or clopidogrel can be given in medical management as well as with PCI (ticagrelor given preference per guidelines). Prasugrel should only be given if the patient is going for PCI. Administer the loading dose followed by a maintenance dose. Do not give a P2Y12 inhibitor if patient is going for urgent CABG surgery.
GIVE WITHIN 24 HOURS (as needed); CONTINUE AS AN OUTPATIENT		
Beta-Blockers	↓ O2 demand by ↓ BP, HR, and contractility; ↓ ischemia, reinfarction, and arrhythmias; prevent cardiac remodeling; ↑ long-term survival	An oral, low dose beta-blocker (beta-1 selective blocker without intrinsic sympathomimetic activity preferred) should be started within the first 24 hours in patients who do not have any of the following: 1) signs of HF, 2) evidence of a low-output state, 3) ↑ risk for cardiogenic shock, 4) other contraindications to beta-blockade [e.g. severe bradycardia (usually defined as HR < 45 BPM in ACS)]. If the patient has concomitant HFrEF that is stable, choose 1 of the 3 beta-blockers used in HFrEF (bisoprolol, metoprolol succinate or carvedilol; see Chronic Heart Failure chapter). IV beta-blocker therapy may be reasonable in STEMI patients, especially if ongoing ischemia or hypertension is present. If beta-blockers and nitrates are ineffective, oral long-acting nondihydropyridine calcium channel blockers (verapamil or diltiazem) are reasonable to use for recurrent ischemia, if there are no contraindications. See Hypertension chapter.
ACE Inhibitors	Inhibit angiotensin converting enzyme and block the production of angiotensin II; prevent cardiac remodeling; ↓ preload and afterload	An oral ACE inhibitor should be started within the first 24 hours and continued indefinitely in all patients with left ventricular ejection fraction (LVEF) < 40%, those with HTN, DM or stable CKD unless contraindicated (use ARB if patient is ACE inhibitor intolerant). Use in other patients may be reasonable. Do not use an IV ACE inhibitor within the first 24 hours due to the risk of hypotension. See Hypertension chapter.

Medications to Avoid in the Acute Setting

- NSAIDs (except for aspirin), whether nonselective or COX-2-selective, should not be administered during hospitalization due to ↑ risk of mortality, reinfarction, hypertension, cardiac rupture, renal insufficiency and heart failure associated with their use.
- Immediate-release nifedipine should not be used due to ↑ risk of mortality.

P2Y12 INHIBITORS

P2Y12 inhibitors bind the adenosine diphosphate (ADP) P2Y12 receptor on the platelet surface which prevents ADP-mediated activation of the GPIIb/IIIa receptor complex, thereby reducing platelet aggregation. Clopidogrel and prasugrel are structurally similar and classified as thienopyridines; they are prodrugs that irreversibly bind to the receptor. Ticagrelor is not a prodrug and has reversible binding to the receptor. P2Y12s are associated with bleeding and there is no antidote. They are commonly used with aspirin after an ACS, which is called dual antiplatelet therapy (DAPT).

DRUG	DOSING	SAFETY/SIDE EFFECTS/MONITORING
Clopidogrel *(Plavix)* Tablet Indicated for ACS, recent MI, stroke and PAD	LD: 300-600 mg PO (600 mg for PCI) MD: 75 mg PO daily If patient received fibrinolytic therapy for STEMI and is > 75 years of age, omit the loading dose and start 75 mg daily	**BOXED WARNING** Clopidogrel is a prodrug. Effectiveness depends on the conversion to an active metabolite, mainly by CYP450 2C19. Poor metabolizers of CYP2C19 exhibit higher cardiovascular events than patients with normal CYP2C19 function. Tests to check CYP2C19 genotype can be used as an aid in determining a therapeutic strategy. Consider alternative treatments in patients identified as CYP2C19 poor metabolizers. Refer the to Pharmacogenomics chapter **CONTRAINDICATIONS** Serious bleeding (e.g., GI bleed, intracranial hemorrhage) **WARNINGS** Bleeding risk, avoid with omeprazole or esomeprazole (inhibit CYP 2C19, see boxed warning), premature discontinuation (↑ risk of thrombosis), thrombotic thrombocytopenic purpura (TTP) **SIDE EFFECTS** Bleeding, hematoma, pruritus **NOTES** Stop 5 days prior to elective surgery (e.g., CABG)
Prasugrel *(Effient)* Tablet Indicated for patients with ACS who are to be managed with PCI	LD: 60 mg PO (no later than 1 hour after PCI) MD: 10 mg PO daily with ASA (5 mg daily if patient weighs < 60 kg) Once PCI is planned, give the dose promptly and no later than 1 hour after the PCI Protect from moisture; dispense in original container	**BOXED WARNING** Significant, sometimes fatal, bleeding Do not initiate if CABG likely, stop at least 7 days prior to elective surgery **CONTRAINDICATIONS** Serious bleeding; history of TIA or stroke **WARNINGS** Bleeding risk, premature discontinuation (↑ risk of thrombosis), thrombotic thrombocytopenic purpura (TTP) **SIDE EFFECTS** Bleeding (more than clopidogrel) **NOTES** Not recommended in patients ≥ 75 years due to high bleeding risk, unless patient is considered high risk (DM or prior MI)

DRUG	DOSING	SAFETY/SIDE EFFECTS/MONITORING
Ticagrelor *(Brilinta)* Tablet Indicated for patients with ACS	LD: 180 mg MD: 90 mg PO BID for 1 year, then 60 mg BID Tablets can be crushed and mixed with water to be swallowed or given via NG tube	**BOXED WARNINGS** Significant, sometimes fatal, bleeding Maintenance doses of aspirin above 100 mg reduce the effectiveness of ticagrelor and should be avoided; after any initial aspirin dose, maintenance aspirin dose should not exceed 100 mg daily Avoid use when CABG likely, stop 5 days before any surgery **CONTRAINDICATIONS** Serious bleeding, history of intracranial hemorrhage **WARNINGS** Bleeding risk, severe hepatic impairment, bradyarrhythmias **SIDE EFFECTS** Bleeding, dyspnea (> 10%), ↑ SCr, ↑ uric acid
Cangrelor *(Kengreal)* Injection Indicated as adjunct to PCI to ↓ risk of periprocedural MI, repeat revascularization and stent thrombosis in patients who are P2Y12 inhibitor naïve and are not receiving a GP IIb/IIIa inhibitor	30 mcg/kg IV bolus prior to PCI, then 4 mcg/kg/min IV infusion for 2 hours or duration of procedure (whichever is longer)	**CONTRAINDICATIONS** Significant active bleeding **SIDE EFFECTS** Bleeding **NOTES** Effects are gone 1 hour after drug discontinuation Transition to oral P2Y12 inhibitor after PCI: ticagrelor 180 mg given during or immediately after stopping cangrelor infusion; prasugrel 60 mg or clopidogrel 600 mg immediately after stopping cangrelor infusion (do not give prior to stopping cangrelor)

LD = loading dose, MD = maintenance dose

P2Y12 Inhibitor Drug Interactions

- All P2Y12 inhibitors: most drug interactions are due to additive effects with other drugs that can ↑ bleeding risk. If an ACS patient experiences bleeding while on a P2Y12 inhibitor, it should be managed without discontinuing the P2Y12 inhibitor, if possible. Stopping the P2Y12 inhibitor (particularly within the first few months after ACS) ↑ the risk of subsequent cardiovascular events.
    - NSAIDs, warfarin, SSRIs and SNRIs increase risk of bleeding. See Learning Drug Interactions chapter.
- Avoid clopidogrel in combination with omeprazole and esomeprazole (other PPIs interact less) and use caution with other CYP2C19 inhibitors.
- Ticagrelor is a CYP3A4 (major) substrate; avoid use with strong CYP3A4 inhibitors and inducers. See Learning Drug Interactions chapter for more information. Avoid simvastatin and lovastatin doses greater than 40 mg/day. Monitor digoxin levels with initiation of or any change in ticagrelor dose.
- Clopidogrel increases the effects of repaglinide, which can lead to hypoglycemia. Use in combination should be avoided.
- Opioids delay and reduce absorption, leading to reduced exposure to metabolites. Consider a parenteral antiplatelet in ACS setting.

GLYCOPROTEIN IIB/IIIA RECEPTOR ANTAGONISTS

Glycoprotein IIb/IIIa receptor antagonists block the platelet glycoprotein IIb/IIIa receptor, which is the binding site for fibrinogen, von Willebrand factor and other ligands. Inhibition of binding at this final common receptor blocks platelet aggregation and prevents further thrombosis. Eptifibatide and tirofiban have reversible blockade and abciximab has irreversible blockade.

DRUG	DOSING	SAFETY/SIDE EFFECTS/MONITORING
Abciximab *(ReoPro)* Injection	LD: 0.25 mg/kg IV bolus MD: 0.125 mcg/kg/min (max 10 mcg/min) IV infusion for 12 hrs (PCI, STEMI with PCI) or 18-24 hrs (NSTE-ACS unresponsive to conventional medical therapy with planned PCI within 24 hrs) Not recommended for medical management (NSTE-ACS without PCI)	**CONTRAINDICATIONS** Thrombocytopenia (platelets < 100,000/mm^3) History of bleeding diathesis (predisposition) Active internal bleeding Severe uncontrolled HTN Recent major surgery or trauma (within past 4 weeks for tirofiban, past 6 weeks for abciximab/eptifibatide) History of stroke within 2 years (abciximab); history of stroke within 30 days or any history of hemorrhagic stroke (eptifibatide)
Eptifibatide *(Integrilin)* Injection	LD: 180 mcg/kg IV bolus (max 22.6 mg), repeat bolus in 10 mins if undergoing PCI MD: 2 mcg/kg/min (max 15 mg/hour) IV infusion started after the first bolus. Continue for 18-24 hours after PCI or for 12-72 hours if PCI was not performed CrCl < 50 mL/min: same LD, reduce MD to 1 mcg/kg/min (max 7.5 mg/hour)	**For abciximab** Recent (within 6 weeks) GI or GU bleeding of clinical significance ↑ prothrombin time Hypersensitivity to murine proteins Intracranial neoplasm, arteriovenous malformation or aneurysm **For eptifibatide** Dependency on renal dialysis
Tirofiban *(Aggrastat)* Injection	LD: 25 mcg/kg IV bolus over 5 min or less MD: 0.15 mcg/kg/min IV infusion for up to 18 hours CrCl ≤ 60 mL/min: same LD, reduce MD to 0.075 mcg/kg/min	**SIDE EFFECTS** Bleeding, thrombocytopenia (especially abciximab), hypotension **MONITORING** Hgb, Hct, platelets, s/sx of bleeding, renal function **NOTES** Do not shake vials upon reconstitution Must filter abciximab Platelet function returns in ~24-48 hours after discontinuing abciximab and ~4-8 hours after stopping eptifibatide/tirofiban

LD = loading dose, MD = maintenance dose

FIBRINOLYTICS

These medications cause fibrinolysis (clot breakdown) by binding to fibrin in a thrombus (clot) and converting entrapped plasminogen to plasmin. Fibrinolytics are used only for STEMI. Once a STEMI is confirmed on a 12-lead ECG, timing is critical. The blocked artery or arteries must be opened as quickly as possible with either PCI or fibrinolytic therapy. PCI is preferred if it can be performed within 90 minutes (optimal door-to-balloon time) or within 120 minutes of first medical contact (which could be in an ambulance). If PCI is not possible within 120 minutes of first medical contact, fibrinolytic therapy is recommended and should be given within 30 minutes of hospital arrival (door-to-needle time). Survival is better when fibrinolytics are given promptly. The European Society of Cardiology (ESC) recommends that fibrinolytics be given within 10 minutes of STEMI diagnosis. In the absence of contraindications and when PCI is not available, fibrinolytic therapy is reasonable in STEMI patients who are still symptomatic within 12 – 24 hours of symptom onset.

DRUG	DOSING	SAFETY/SIDE EFFECTS/MONITORING
Alteplase *(Activase)* Recombinant tissue plasminogen activator (tPA, rtPA)* *Cathflo Activase* (single-use 2 mg vial) used to restore function of potentially clotted central lines and devices	Accelerated Infusion > 67 kg: 100 mg IV over 1.5 hrs; given as 15 mg bolus, 50 mg over 30 min, 35 mg over 1 hr (max 100 mg total) ≤ 67 kg: 15 mg bolus, 0.75 mg/kg (max 50 mg) over 30 min, 0.5 mg/kg (max 35 mg) over 1 hr (max 100 mg total)	**CONTRAINDICATIONS** Active internal bleeding or bleeding diathesis History of recent stroke Any prior intracranial hemorrhage (ICH) Recent intracranial or intraspinal surgery or trauma (last 2-3 months) Intracranial neoplasm, arteriovenous malformation, or aneurysm Severe uncontrolled hypertension (unresponsive to emergency therapy) **SIDE EFFECTS** Bleeding (including ICH), hypotension **MONITORING** Hgb, Hct, s/sx of bleeding **NOTES** Door-to-needle time should be < 30 minutes Contraindications and dosing differ for alteplase in ischemic stroke (refer to Stroke chapter) *The abbreviation "tPa" is prone to errors; not recommended by ISMP, but used commonly
Tenecteplase *(TNKase)*	Single IV bolus dose: < 60 kg: 30 mg 60-69 kg: 35 mg 70-79 kg: 40 mg 80-89 kg: 45 mg ≥ 90 kg: 50 mg	
Reteplase *(Retavase)*	2 dose regimen: 10 units IV, followed by 10 units IV given 30 minutes later	

PROTEASE-ACTIVATED RECEPTOR-1 ANTAGONIST

Vorapaxar is a reversible antagonist of the protease-activated receptor-1 (PAR-1) expressed on platelets, but its long half-life makes it effectively irreversible. Vorapaxar is indicated in patients with a history of MI or with peripheral arterial disease (PAD) to reduce thrombotic cardiovascular events (CV death, MI, stroke and urgent coronary revascularization). This drug was used in addition to aspirin and/or clopidogrel in clinical trials. It has not yet been incorporated into clinical guidelines.

DRUG	DOSING	SAFETY/SIDE EFFECTS/MONITORING
Vorapaxar *(Zontivity)* Tablet	2.08 mg (one tablet) PO daily	**BOXED WARNING** Bleeding risk (including ICH and fatal bleeding); contraindicated in patients with history of stroke, TIA, ICH or active serious bleeding **WARNING** Do not use in severe liver impairment **SIDE EFFECTS** Bleeding, anemia **NOTES** No antidote

Vorapaxar Drug Interactions

- Vorapaxar is a substrate of CYP3A4 and inhibitor of P-gp. Avoid concomitant use with strong CYP3A4 inhibitors and strong CYP3A4 inducers.

SECONDARY PREVENTION AFTER ACS

Taking the right medications after an ACS can reduce the risk of complications (e.g., heart failure) or future events. Many of the recommended medications will be taken indefinitely (forever) after an ACS event (see Study Tip gal).

DRUGS FOR SECONDARY PREVENTION AFTER ACS

Aspirin
- Indefinitely (81 mg per day), unless contraindicated

P2Y12 Inhibitor
- Medical Therapy Patients (fibrinolytics): ticagrelor or clopidogrel with aspirin 81 mg for at least 12 months
- PCI-Treated Patients (including any type of stent): clopidogrel, prasugrel or ticagrelor with aspirin 81 mg for at least 12 months
  - Continuation of DAPT beyond 12 months may be considered in patients who are tolerating DAPT and are not at high risk of bleeding following coronary stent placement

Nitroglycerin
- Indefinitely (SL tabs or spray PRN)

Beta-Blocker
- 3 years; continue indefinitely if HF or if needed for management of HTN

ACE Inhibitor
- Indefinitely if EF < 40%, HTN, CKD or diabetes; consider for all MI patients with no contraindications

Aldosterone Antagonist (see Chronic Heart Failure chapter)
- Indefinitely if EF ≤ 40% and either symptomatic HF or DM receiving target doses of an ACE inhibitor and beta-blocker
- Contraindications: significant renal impairment (SCr > 2.5 mg/dL in men, SCr > 2 mg/dL in women) or hyperkalemia (K > 5 mEq/L)

Statin (see Dyslipidemia chapter)
- High-intensity statin therapy
- Patients ≥ 75 years of age: consider moderate- or high-intensity statin therapy

OTHER CONSIDERATIONS

- Pain relief: patients with chronic musculoskeletal pain should use acetaminophen, nonacetylated salicylates, tramadol or small doses of narcotics before considering the use of NSAIDs. If these options are insufficient, it is reasonable to use nonselective NSAIDs such as naproxen (lowest CV risk). COX-2 selective agents have high CV risk and should be avoided.
- Warfarin use: if patients require warfarin (e.g., patients with AFib) along with aspirin and a P2Y12 inhibitor, it may be reasonable to lower the INR goal to 2 – 2.5. Use this triple combination for the shortest time possible to limit the risk of bleeding. Clopidogrel is the preferred P2Y12 for triple therapy. Proton pump inhibitors should be prescribed in any patient with a history of GI bleeding while taking triple antithrombotic therapy.
- Lifestyle counseling should include smoking cessation, managing chronic conditions (such as HTN, DM), avoiding excessive alcohol intake, encouraging physical exercise and a healthy diet.

PATIENT COUNSELING

Refer to the Ischemic Heart Disease chapter for patient counseling on aspirin, nitrates and clopidogrel.

Select Guidelines/References

2017 ESC Guidelines for the Management of Acute Myocardial Infarction in Patients Presenting with ST-Segment Elevation. https://academic.oup.com/eurheartj/article/39/2/119/4095042 (accessed 2019 Mar 4).

2016 ACC/AHA Guideline Focused Update on Duration of Dual Antiplatelet Therapy in Patients With Coronary Artery Disease. http://www.onlinejacc.org/content/68/10/1082 (accessed 2019 Mar 4).

2014 AHA/ACC Guideline for the Management of Patients with Non-ST-Elevation Acute Coronary Syndromes. http://www.onlinejacc.org/content/64/24/e139 (accessed 2019 Mar 4).

2013 ACCF/AHA Guideline for Management of ST-Elevation Myocardial Infarction. http://www.onlinejacc.org/content/61/4/e78 (accessed 2019 Mar 4).

CHAPTER CONTENT

Background ... 489
Diagnosis ... 489
Ejection Fraction ... 490
Classification Systems ... 490
Signs and Symptoms of Systolic Heart Failure ... 490
Pathophysiology ... 491
Terminology ... 491
Compensatory Mechanisms ... 491
Lifestyle Management ... 491
Drugs That Cause or Worsen Heart Failure ... 492
Select Drugs that Cause or Worsen Heart Failure ... 491
Drug Treatment ... 492
Treatment of Chronic Systolic Heart Failure ... 492
Loop Diuretics ... 493
ACE Inhibitors and Angiotensin Receptor Blockers ... 494
Angiotensin Receptor and Neprilysin Inhibitor ... 495
Beta-Blockers ... 496
Aldosterone Receptor Antagonists ... 497
Hydralazine/Nitrate ... 498
Digoxin ... 499
Ivabradine ... 500
Potassium Oral Supplementation ... 501
Heart Failure Exacerbations and Quality Improvement ... 501
Congestive Heart Failure Management/Action Plan ... 502
Patient Counseling ... 503

CONTENT LEGEND

= Study Tip Gal   = Key Drug Guy

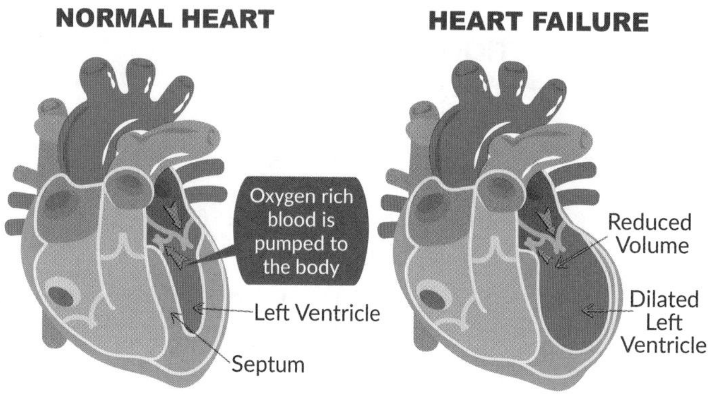

CHAPTER 31
CHRONIC HEART FAILURE

BACKGROUND

Heart failure (HF) is a common condition in the U.S., especially in older adults. It is the primary diagnosis in over 1 million hospitalizations each year. Heart "failure" occurs when the heart is not able to supply sufficient oxygen-rich blood to the body, because of impaired ability of the ventricle to either fill or eject blood. HF is commonly classified as either ischemic (due to decreased blood supply, such as from an MI) or non-ischemic, such as from long-standing uncontrolled hypertension. Other less common causes include valvular disease, excessive alcohol intake or illicit drug use, congenital heart defects, viral infections, diabetes and cardiotoxic drugs/chest radiation. In the U.S., most cases are due to damage from an MI or from long-standing hypertension.

DIAGNOSIS

Symptoms of HF are usually related to fluid overload; shortness of breath (SOB) and edema are very common (see Study Tip Gal on next page). Symptoms can occur due to problems with systolic (contraction) or diastolic (relaxation) functions of the heart. Patients cycle through periods of stability and exacerbation (increased symptoms). Exacerbations frequently result in hospitalization and negatively impact the patient's quality of life.

An ultrasound of the heart (echocardiography or ECHO) is performed when HF is suspected. It provides an estimate of left ventricular ejection fraction (LVEF). LVEF is a measurement of how much blood is pumped out of the left ventricle (the main pumping chamber of the heart) with each contraction. The term LVEF is used interchangeably with ejection fraction (EF). An EF < 40% indicates systolic dysfunction, or heart failure with reduced ejection fraction (HFrEF); this type of heart failure is the focus of this chapter, since it is most widely studied and has well-defined treatment guidelines. Other types of HF are described in the table. Many patients have components of both systolic and diastolic dysfunction.

EJECTION FRACTION

EF	TERM	PRIMARY PROBLEM
55-70%	Normal	Normal
≥ 50%	Heart Failure with Preserved EF (HFpEF) Diastolic Dysfunction	Impaired ventricular relaxation and filling during diastole
40-49%	Heart Failure with Mid-Range EF (HFmrEF)	Likely mixed systolic and diastolic dysfunction
< 40%	Heart Failure with Reduced EF (HFrEF) Systolic Dysfunction	Impaired ability to eject blood during systole

CLASSIFICATION SYSTEMS

Two classification systems are currently recommended for HFrEF. The American College of Cardiology and the American Heart Association (ACC/AHA) recommend categorizing patients by the HF stage (see table). The staging system is used to guide treatment in order to slow progression in asymptomatic patients (stages A and B) or in symptomatic patients (stages C and D). HF patients can also be classified by the level of limitation in physical functioning using the New York Heart Association (NYHA) classification system. Many drug therapies were studied based on the NYHA functional classification of the patients, so this remains extremely relevant to drug therapy decisions.

ACC/AHA STAGING SYSTEM		NYHA FUNCTIONAL CLASS	
A	At high risk for development of HF, but without structural heart disease or symptoms of HF (e.g., patients with HTN, CAD, DM, obesity, metabolic syndrome)	No corresponding category	
B	Structural heart disease present, but without signs or symptoms of HF (e.g., LVH, low EF, valvular disease, previous MI)	I	No limitations of physical activity. Ordinary physical activity does not cause symptoms of HF (e.g., fatigue, palpitations, dyspnea)
Clinical Diagnosis of HF			
C	Structural heart disease with prior or current symptoms of HF (e.g., patients with known structural heart disease, SOB and fatigue, reduced exercise tolerance)	I	No limitations of physical activity. Ordinary physical activity does not cause symptoms of HF
		II	Slight limitation of physical activity. Comfortable at rest, but ordinary physical activity results in symptoms of HF
		III	Marked limitation of physical activity. Comfortable at rest but minimal exertion (e.g., bathing, dressing) causes symptoms of HF
D	Advanced structural heart disease with symptoms of HF at rest despite maximal medical treatment (refractory HF requiring specialized interventions)	IV	Unable to carry on any physical activity without symptoms of HF, or symptoms of HF at rest

SIGNS AND SYMPTOMS OF SYSTOLIC HEART FAILURE

Labs

↑ BNP (B-type natriuretic peptide): normal is < 100 pg/mL

↑ NT-proBNP (N-terminal pro B-type natriuretic peptide): normal is < 300 pg/mL

BNP and proBNP are used to distinguish between cardiac and non-cardiac causes of dyspnea

Left-Sided Signs and Symptoms

Orthopnea: SOB when lying flat

Paroxysmal nocturnal dyspnea (PND): nocturnal cough and SOB

Bibasilar rales: crackling lung sounds heard on lung exam

S3 gallop: abnormal heart sound

Hypoperfusion (renal impairment, cool extremities)

General Signs and Symptoms

Dyspnea (SOB at rest or upon exertion)

Cough

Fatigue, weakness

Reduced exercise capacity

Right-Sided Signs and Symptoms

Peripheral edema

Ascites: abdominal fluid accumulation

Jugular venous distention (JVD): neck vein distention

Hepatojugular reflux (HJR): neck vein distention from pressure placed on the abdomen

Hepatomegaly: enlarged liver due to fluid congestion

PATHOPHYSIOLOGY

TERMINOLOGY

Cardiac output (CO) is the volume of blood that is pumped by the heart in one minute. CO is a function of the heart rate (HR) and the stroke volume (SV), or the volume of blood ejected from the left ventricle during one complete heartbeat (cardiac cycle). SV depends on preload, afterload and contractility. The cardiac index (CI) relates the CO to the size of the patient, and is calculated by dividing the CO by the body surface area (BSA).

CO = HR x SV

CI = CO / BSA

COMPENSATORY MECHANISMS

During low cardiac output states (the main problem in HFrEF), neurohormones are released that increase the blood volume or increase the force or speed of contractions. This might temporarily increase CO, but chronic neurohormonal activation causes damage to the myocytes and produces changes in the size, composition and shape of the heart (e.g., hypertrophy, dilatation). This is called cardiac remodeling.

The three main pathways activated in heart failure are: the renin angiotensin aldosterone system (RAAS), sympathetic nervous system (SNS) and vasopressin (see Drug Treatment in this chapter and diagram of the RAAS in the Hypertension chapter). Briefly, renin splits angiotensinogen to produce angiotensin I. Angiotensin I is further converted into angiotensin II (Ang II) by the angiotensin-converting enzyme (ACE). There are also non-ACE pathways for the formation of Ang II. Ang II causes blood vessel constriction (vasoconstriction), and stimulates the release of aldosterone (from the adrenal gland) and vasopressin (from the pituitary gland). Aldosterone causes sodium and water retention, and increases potassium excretion. Vasopressin causes vasoconstriction and water retention. Activation of the SNS results in the release of norepinephrine (NE) and epinephrine (EPI), which increases heart rate, contractility (positive inotropy) and vasoconstriction. Each pathway potentiates the others, contributing to the vicious cycle of chronic neurohormonal activation. Importantly, the neurohormones that normally balance these systems (e.g., natriuretic peptides) are insufficient.

LIFESTYLE MANAGEMENT

Patients with heart failure should be instructed to:

- Monitor and document body weight daily, in the morning after voiding and before eating.
- Notify the provider when weight ↑ by 2 – 4 pounds in one day or 3 – 5 pounds in one week, or when the symptoms have worsened (↑ SOB with activity, ↑ swelling in the feet/ankles/legs or others listed in the Study Tip Gal on the previous page). A HF action plan should be provided and explained to the patient (see example at end of chapter).
- Maintain sodium restriction of < 1,500 mg/day in stage A and B HF (maintain some degree of sodium restriction in other patients).
- Maintain fluid restriction (1.5 – 2 L/day) in stage D, especially in patients with hyponatremia.
- Stop smoking. Limit alcohol intake. Avoid illicit drug use.
- Obtain recommended vaccines: Influenza (annually), pneumococcal vaccines if 65 years of age or older and any patient-specific requirements.
- Consider weight reduction to BMI < 30 kg/m^2 to reduce the heart's workload and preserve function.
- Exercise training (or regular physical activity) is recommended in patients who are able to participate.

OTC and Alternative Medications

- Omega-3 fatty acid supplementation is reasonable to use as adjunctive therapy in patients with NYHA Class II – IV symptoms to ↓ mortality and cardiovascular hospitalizations. The optimal dose has not been established but 1 gram daily is commonly used.
- Hawthorn and coenzyme Q10 may improve HF symptoms based on small studies.
- Avoid the use of products containing ephedra (ma huang) or ephedrine. Patients should consult with their healthcare provider prior to the use of sympathomimetics (stimulants), such as decongestants.

KEY DRUGS

Remember: It's the **D**rug **I**nformation **NATION**

Dipeptidyl peptidase 4 inhibitors (DPP-4 inhibitors)
Alogliptin, saxagliptin

Immunosuppressants
TNF inhibitors (etanercept, rituximab) and interferons

Nondihydropyridine CCBs
Diltiazem and verapamil (specifically in systolic HF)

Antiarrhythmics
Avoid Class I agents (e.g., procainamide, quinidine, flecainide) in HF

Amiodarone and dofetilide have less risk of worsening HF

Thiazolidinediones
↑ risk of edema

Itraconazole

Oncology agents
Anthracyclines (doxorubicin, daunorubicin)

NSAIDs
All (including celecoxib)

SELECT DRUGS THAT CAUSE OR WORSEN HEART FAILURE

Others:

Systemic steroids

Amphetamines, other sympathomimetics (stimulants), illicit drugs (e.g., cocaine)

Triptans: contraindicated with history of CVD or uncontrolled HTN

Oncology drugs: some tyrosine kinase inhibitors (lapatinib, sunitinib) and drugs that cause fluid retention (e.g., trastuzumab, imatinib, docetaxel)

Excessive alcohol

DRUGS THAT CAUSE OR WORSEN HEART FAILURE

Most drugs that cause or worsen HF do so by causing fluid retention/edema, by increasing blood pressure or via negative inotropic effect. See the Key Drugs Guy on previous page.

DRUG TREATMENT

Most patients with heart failure are treated with a combination of an ACE inhibitor, ARB or angiotensin receptor and neprilysin inhibitor (ARNI) with a beta-blocker and a loop diuretic (for example: lisinopril + carvedilol + furosemide). An aldosterone receptor antagonist is usually added next. The following diagram reviews the pathophysiology and current treatment recommendations are summarized below (see Study Tip Gal).

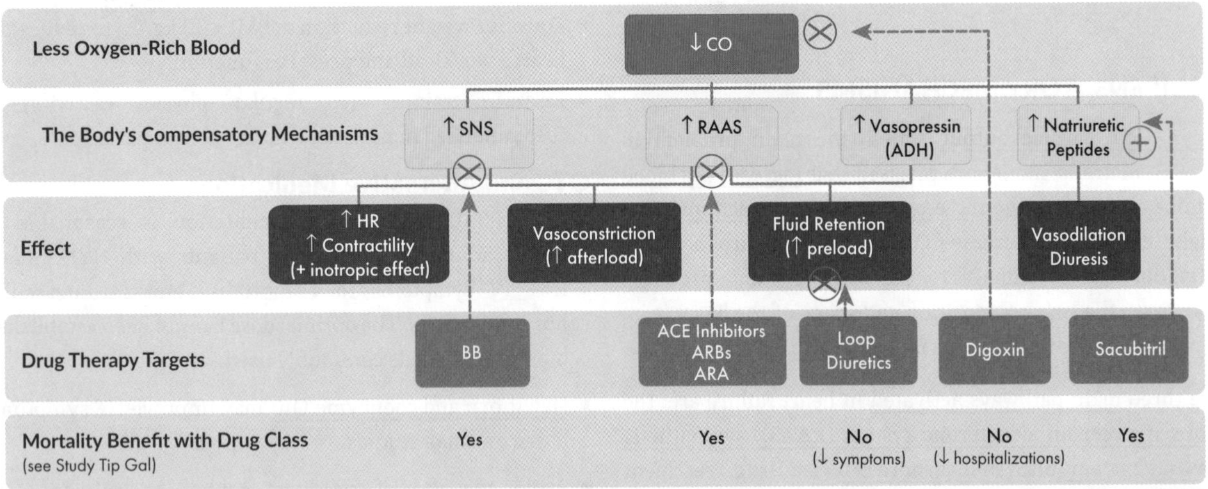

TREATMENT OF CHRONIC SYSTOLIC HEART FAILURE

Medications that ↓ mortality; recommended for all patients without contraindications

- **ACE inhibitors or angiotensin receptor blockers (ARBs)**
  - Block neurohormonal activation of the RAAS, resulting in vasodilation and improved EF
- **Angiotensin receptor and neprilysin inhibitor (ARNI)**
  - Sacubitril/valsartan *(Entresto)* ↓ the risk of CV death and hospitalization for HF in NYHA Class II-IV patients who have a decreased EF
  - In patients with chronic symptomatic HF (NYHA Class II-III) who tolerate an ACE inhibitor or ARB, an ARNI is preferred to an ACE inhibitor/ARB to further reduce morbidity and mortality
- **Beta-blockers (BB)**
  - Block the SNS activation by blocking EPI and NE; also provide benefit in controlling heart rate and reducing arrhythmia risk
- **Aldosterone receptor antagonists (ARAs)**
  - Provide added diuresis; improve symptoms and EF
  - ↓ morbidity and mortality in NYHA Class II-IV

Medications that ↓ mortality for select patients

- **Hydralazine and nitrates *(BiDil)***
  - ↓ morbidity and mortality in black patients with NYHA Class III-IV when added to optimal therapy with an ACE inhibitor/ARB and BB or in other patients who cannot tolerate an ACE inhibitor or ARB

Medications that improve other aspects of HF (not proven to ↓ mortality)

- **Loop diuretics**
  - Reduce blood volume, which ↓ edema and congestion; most HF patients need a loop diuretic for symptom relief
- **Digoxin**
  - Provides a small increase in cardiac output, improves symptoms and decreases cardiac hospitalizations
- **Ivabradine *(Corlanor)***
  - ↓ risk of hospitalization in patients with stable NYHA Class II-III HF in normal sinus rhythm with a resting heart rate ≥ 70 BPM

LOOP DIURETICS

Loop diuretics are used to ↓ fluid volume to make it easier for the heart to pump. Loop diuretics block sodium and chloride reabsorption in the thick ascending limb of the loop of Henle, interfering with the chloride-binding co-transport system. They ↑ excretion of sodium, potassium, chloride, magnesium, calcium and water. They are used to reduce congestive symptoms (reduce preload) and restore euvolemia (or "dry" weight). Loop diuretics have not been shown to alter the survival of stable heart failure patients, but most patients require them for symptom control. Care must be taken not to over-diurese patients, which can lead to hypotension or renal impairment; the lowest effective dose should be used. If the response to the loop is poor, a combination with a thiazide-type diuretic, such as metolazone, can be useful. Loops can be used for BP reduction in patients with renal impairment when other options are not adequate.

DRUG	DOSING	SAFETY/SIDE EFFECTS/MONITORING
Furosemide (*Lasix*) Tablet, injection	Oral: 20-40 mg daily or BID Max 600 mg/day	**BOXED WARNING** Can lead to profound diuresis resulting in fluid and electrolyte depletion **CONTRAINDICATIONS** Anuria **WARNINGS** Sulfa allergy (not likely to cross-react – see cautionary statement in Drug Allergies & Adverse Drug Reactions chapter); this warning does not apply to ethacrynic acid **SIDE EFFECTS** ↓ K, ↓ Na, ↓ Mg, ↓ Cl, ↓ Ca (different than thiazides which ↑ Ca), ↑ HCO3/metabolic alkalosis, hyperuricemia (↑ UA), hyperglycemia (↑ BG), ↑ TGs, ↑ total cholesterol, orthostatic hypotension, photosensitivity, ototoxicity (more with ethacrynic acid) including hearing loss, tinnitus and vertigo **MONITORING** Renal function, fluid status (input and output, weight), BP, electrolytes, audiology testing with high doses or rapid IV administration, s/sx of HF **NOTES** Take early in the day to avoid nocturia Store furosemide injection at room temp (refrigeration causes crystals to form, which may dissolve upon warming). Do not use furosemide solutions if they are yellow in color; must be clear Furosemide and bumetanide are light-sensitive (in amber bottles); IV admixtures do not require light protection **Dose Conversions** Oral equivalent dosing: furosemide 40 mg = bumetanide 1 mg = torsemide 20 mg = ethacrynic acid 50 mg Furosemide IV:PO ratio 1:2 (furosemide 20 mg IV = furosemide 40 mg PO) Bumetanide, torsemide and ethacrynic acid IV:PO ratio 1:1
Bumetanide (*Bumex*) Tablet, injection	Oral: 0.5-1 mg daily or BID Max 10 mg/day	
Torsemide (*Demadex*) Tablet	Oral: 10-20 mg daily Max 200 mg/day	
Ethacrynic Acid (*Edecrin*) Tablet, injection	Oral: 50-200 mg daily or divided Max 400 mg/day	

Loop Diuretic Drug Interactions.

- Avoid NSAIDs (including COX-2 inhibitors) in patients with HF. NSAIDs ↑ sodium and water retention, which ↓ the effect of the loop diuretics and can lead to renal impairment.
- Can acutely ↓ blood pressure; risk for additive hypotension with other drugs that lower blood pressure.
  - Combining loop diuretics with ACE inhibitors or ARBs can cause severe hypotension and worsening renal function. Monitor BP and renal function carefully.

EXAM SCENARIO

A patient was being treated with furosemide 40 mg IV BID for an acute HF exacerbation. She is now ready for discharge and the team wants to send her home on bumetanide. What would be an equivalent oral dose of bumetanide?

First, determine the equivalent oral dose for the current total daily dose of IV furosemide.

$$\frac{80 \text{ mg IV}}{X \text{ mg PO}} = \frac{1}{2}$$

X = 160 mg PO furosemide

Then, determine the equivalent dose for bumetanide.

$$\frac{160 \text{ mg PO furosemide}}{X \text{ mg PO bumetanide}} = \frac{40}{1}$$

X = 4 mg PO bumetanide

ACE INHIBITORS AND ANGIOTENSIN RECEPTOR BLOCKERS

ACE inhibitors block the conversion of angiotensin I to Ang II resulting in ↓ vasoconstriction and ↓ aldosterone secretion (refer to the Hypertension chapter). They block the degradation of bradykinin, which may contribute to the vasodilatory effects (and the side effects of cough and angioedema). ARBs block Ang II from binding to the angiotensin II type-1 (AT1) receptor. Overall, these agents ↓ RAAS activation (a major compensatory mechanism in HF), resulting in decreased preload and afterload. They ↓ cardiac remodeling, improve left ventricular function and ↓ morbidity and mortality. The clinical benefits appear to be a drug class effect. An ACE inhibitor (or ARB if intolerant to ACE inhibitors) is recommended for all HF patients (NYHA Class I – IV) regardless of symptoms. Other important points include:

- The target doses for these medications for HF are the doses used in clinical trials demonstrating their benefit or the maximum tolerated dose for a given patient. Titrate the drug to the target dose (if possible). Titrate to reduce symptoms, not BP.
- The combination of an ACE inhibitor and ARB has been shown to ↓ hospitalizations for HF, but it is more common to combine either one with an aldosterone receptor antagonist (ARA). Triple combination of ACE inhibitor + ARB + ARA is not recommended due to a higher risk of hyperkalemia and renal insufficiency.
- Angioedema occurs more frequently with ACE inhibitors (than with ARBs or aliskiren) and in black patients. For testing purposes, if a patient develops angioedema with any of these medications, the others should be avoided.

DRUG	DOSING	SAFETY/SIDE EFFECTS/MONITORING
ACE Inhibitors – only those mentioned in the guidelines (see complete list in Hypertension chapter)		
Captopril *(Capoten)*	Start 6.25 mg TID, 1 hr before meals Target dose: 50 mg TID	**BOXED WARNING** Can cause injury and death to the developing fetus when used in the 2nd and 3rd trimesters; discontinue as soon as pregnancy is detected **CONTRAINDICATIONS** History of angioedema, use with aliskiren in patients with diabetes, use within 36 hours of a neprilysin inhibitor (sacubitril/valsartan) **WARNINGS** Angioedema, hyperkalemia, hypotension (↑ risk if salt- or volume-depleted), renal impairment, bilateral renal artery stenosis (avoid use) **SIDE EFFECTS** Cough, dizziness, HA, rash **MONITORING** BP, K, renal function, s/sx of HF and angioedema
Enalapril *(Vasotec,* *Epaned* powder for oral solution) **Enalaprilat *(Vasotec IV)***	Start 2.5 mg PO BID Target dose: 10-20 mg PO BID	
Fosinopril	Start 5-10 mg daily Target dose: 40 mg daily	
Lisinopril *(Prinivil, Zestril,* *Qbrelis* oral solution)	Start 2.5-5 mg daily Target dose: 20-40 mg daily	
Perindopril	Start 2 mg daily Target dose: 8-16 mg daily	
Quinapril *(Accupril)*	Start 5 mg BID Target dose: 20 mg BID	
Ramipril *(Altace)*	Start 1.25-2.5 mg daily Target dose: 10 mg daily	
Trandolapril	Start 1 mg daily Target dose: 4 mg daily	
ARBs – only those mentioned in the guidelines (see complete list in Hypertension chapter)		
Candesartan *(Atacand)*	Start 4-8 mg daily Target dose: 32 mg daily	Same as above except: Less cough and angioedema, no washout period required with neprilysin inhibitor
Losartan *(Cozaar)* Benefit in clinical trials but no FDA indication for HF	Start 25-50 mg daily Target dose: 50-150 mg daily	
Valsartan *(Diovan)*	Start 40 mg BID Target dose: 160 mg BID	

ANGIOTENSIN RECEPTOR AND NEPRILYSIN INHIBITOR

Entresto is a combination of a neprilysin inhibitor (sacubitril) and an ARB (valsartan). Neprilysin is the enzyme responsible for degradation of several beneficial vasodilatory peptides, including natriuretic peptides, adrenomedullin, substance P and bradykinin. These peptides counteract the effects of RAAS activation and produce vasodilation. An ARNI is indicated in NYHA Class II – IV patients to reduce HF hospitalizations and cardiovascular death, and is recommended as a potential first-line option (in place of an ACE inhibitor or ARB as monotherapy) in select symptomatic HF patients (NYHA Class II – III) who tolerate an ACE inhibitor or ARB to further improve morbidity and survival. The ARNI is usually added to other HF therapies (e.g., beta-blocker, loop diuretic) in place of an ACE inhibitor or other ARB.

DRUG	DOSING	SAFETY/SIDE EFFECTS/MONITORING
Sacubitril/Valsartan ***(Entresto)*** Tablet	Start: 50-100 mg BID Target dose: 200 mg BID eGFR < 30 mL/min/1.73m^2 = 50 mg BID The dose is the sum of the two components: 50 mg = 24/26 mg sacubitril/valsartan 100 mg = 49/51 mg sacubitril/valsartan 200 mg = 97/103 mg sacubitril/valsartan	**BOXED WARNING** Can cause injury and death to the developing fetus when used in the 2nd and 3rd trimesters; discontinue as soon as pregnancy is detected **CONTRAINDICATIONS** Use with ACE inhibitors or ARBs, history of angioedema, use with aliskiren in patients with diabetes **WARNINGS** Angioedema, renal impairment, hyperkalemia, hypotension (↑ risk if salt- or volume-depleted), bilateral renal artery stenosis (avoid use) **SIDE EFFECTS** Cough, dizziness **MONITORING** BP, K, renal function, s/sx of HF **NOTES** Do not use with an ACE inhibitor or another ARB. Must have 36 hour wash-out period between stopping an ACE inhibitor and starting sacubitril/valsartan.

ACE Inhibitor, ARB and ARNI Drug Interactions

- Risk of hyperkalemia. Other medications that ↑ potassium (e.g., potassium-sparing diuretics) should be used cautiously. Avoid using salt substitutes (which contain KCl rather than NaCl) or OTC potassium supplements. Monitor K and renal function frequently.
- ↑ risk of renal impairment, hypotension and hyperkalemia when multiple RAAS inhibitors are used. Avoid using ACE inhibitor ± ARB ± aliskiren and the triple combination of ACE inhibitor, ARB and ARA. The use of aliskiren in combination with an ACE inhibitor, ARB or ARNI is specifically contraindicated in patients with diabetes or when eGFR is < 60 mL/min. Combining an ACE inhibitor or ARB (not both) with an ARA is very common in HF.
- Additive antihypertensive effects with other drugs that ↓ BP; monitor BP.
- Use with NSAIDs (especially in patients who are elderly, volume depleted or with compromised renal function) can worsen renal function.
- ACE inhibitors and ARBs can ↓ lithium renal clearance and ↑ risk of lithium toxicity.

BETA-BLOCKERS

Beta-adrenergic receptor antagonists, or simply beta-blockers, antagonize the effects of catecholamines (especially NE) at the beta-1 and beta-2 adrenergic receptors. Beta-blockers ↓ vasoconstriction, improve cardiac function and ↓ morbidity and mortality; they are recommended for all HF patients. Unlike ACE inhibitors (or ARBs), the clinical benefits of beta-blockers are not considered a class effect. Only bisoprolol, carvedilol (IR and ER) and metoprolol succinate ER are recommended in the guidelines. The target doses for these agents are the doses used in clinical trials demonstrating their benefit, or the maximum tolerated dose for a given patient. Beta-blockers with intrinsic sympathomimetic activity (ISA) should be avoided. Beta-blockers should only be stopped in ADHF if hypotension or hypoperfusion is present.

DRUG	DOSING	SAFETY/SIDE EFFECTS/MONITORING
Beta-Blockers – only those mentioned in the guidelines (see complete list in Hypertension chapter)		
Bisoprolol Benefit in clinical trials, but not FDA-approved for HF	Start 1.25 mg daily Target dose: 10 mg daily Titrate every 2 weeks as tolerated	**BOXED WARNING** Do not discontinue abruptly (particularly in patients with CHD/IHD); gradually taper over 1-2 weeks to avoid acute tachycardia, HTN, and/or ischemia **CONTRAINDICATIONS** Severe bradycardia, 2nd or 3rd degree heart block or sick sinus syndrome (unless patient has a functioning artificial pacemaker) or cardiogenic shock **WARNING** Caution in patients with diabetes (can worsen hyperglycemia or hypoglycemia and mask hypoglycemic symptoms); can mask signs of hyperthyroidism; use caution with bronchospastic diseases (e.g., asthma, COPD), peripheral vascular disease and Raynaud's disease; may aggravate psychiatric conditions
Metoprolol succinate extended release (*Toprol XL*, *Kapspargo Sprinkle*) Metoprolol tartrate (*Lopressor*) is not recommended in HF guidelines	Start 12.5-25 mg/day Target dose: 200 mg daily Titrate every 2 weeks as tolerated	**SIDE EFFECTS** ↓ HR, hypotension, fatigue, dizziness, depression, ↓ libido, impotence, ↑ TGs, ↓ HDL; weight gain and edema especially with carvedilol **MONITORING** HR (↓ dose if HR < 55 BPM), BP, s/sx of HF **NOTES** Metoprolol IV is not equivalent to PO (IV:PO ratio 1:2.5) *Toprol XL* can be cut at the score line; preferably taken with or immediately after meals *Kapspargo Sprinkle* should be swallowed whole; for patients with difficulty swallowing, the capsule can be opened and the contents sprinkled on 1 teaspoonful of soft food (e.g., applesauce, yogurt or pudding) – the mixture must be swallowed within 60 minutes
Non-Selective Beta-Blocker and Alpha-1 Blocker		
Carvedilol (*Coreg*, *Coreg CR*)	**Immediate release** Start 3.125 mg BID Target dose: ≤ 85 kg: 25 mg BID > 85 kg: 50 mg BID **Controlled release** Start 10 mg daily Target dose: 80 mg daily Titrate every 2 weeks as tolerated	Same as above **CONTRAINDICATION** Severe hepatic impairment **WARNING** Intraoperative floppy iris syndrome has occurred in cataract surgery patients who were on or were previously treated with an alpha-1 blocker **NOTES** Take with food (all forms) to ↓ the rate of absorption and the risk of orthostatic hypotension Carvedilol CR has reduced bioavailability compared to carvedilol IR; dosing conversions are not 1:1 (e.g., *Coreg* 3.125 mg BID = *Coreg CR* 10 mg daily)

Beta-Blocker Drug Interactions

- Beta-blockers can enhance the hypoglycemic effects of insulin and sulfonylureas and can mask some of the symptoms of hypoglycemia (e.g., shakiness, palpitations, anxiety). Monitor blood glucose in patients with diabetes.
- Use caution with other drugs that ↓ HR (e.g., digoxin, verapamil, diltiazem).
- CYP450 2D6 inhibitors can ↑ carvedilol levels and rifampin can ↓ carvedilol levels.
- Carvedilol is an inhibitor of P-gp and can ↑ concentrations of P-gp substrates (e.g., digoxin, cyclosporine, dabigatran, ranolazine).

ALDOSTERONE RECEPTOR ANTAGONISTS

Aldosterone is a mineralocorticoid, with receptors in the kidneys, as well as on the heart, brain, vasculature, adipose tissue and immune cells; it causes retention of Na and water. Aldosterone receptor antagonists (ARAs), also referred to as mineralocorticoid receptor antagonists (MRAs), compete with aldosterone at receptor sites in the distal convoluted tubule and collecting ducts. Spironolactone is a non-selective ARA (also blocks androgen), while eplerenone is a selective ARA that does not exhibit endocrine side effects. ARAs reduce sodium and water retention, cardiac remodeling (especially myocardial fibrosis) and the risk of sudden cardiac death. ARAs reduce morbidity and mortality and should be added to standard treatment in patients with NYHA Class II – IV.

DRUG	DOSING	SAFETY/SIDE EFFECTS/MONITORING
Spironolactone (*Aldactone* tablet, *CaroSpir* oral suspension)	Start 12.5-25 mg daily Target dose: 25 mg daily or BID *CaroSpir:* start 20 mg (4 mL) daily for eGFR > 50 mL/min/1.73m^2	**CONTRAINDICATIONS** Hyperkalemia, anuria, significant renal impairment (CrCl ≤ 30 mL/min), Addison's disease or other conditions that ↑ K **WARNINGS** Do not initiate treatment in heart failure patients with K > 5 mEq/L, eGFR < 30 mL/min/1.73 m^2 or SCr > 2.0 mg/dL (females) or SCr > 2.5 mg/dL (males) **SIDE EFFECTS** Hyperkalemia, ↑ SCr, dizziness, hyperchloremic metabolic acidosis (rare) Spironolactone: gynecomastia, breast tenderness, impotence, irregular menses, amenorrhea Eplerenone: ↑ TGs **MONITORING** BP, electrolytes (check K before starting and frequently thereafter), renal function; fluid status (input and output, weight), s/sx of HF **NOTES** *CaroSpir* suspension (also approved for use in hypertension and edema in cirrhosis) is not therapeutically equivalent to *Aldactone.* Doses > 100 mg of *CaroSpir* can cause unexpectedly ↑ concentrations. Use a different formulation in this case.
Eplerenone (*Inspra*) Tablet	Start 25 mg daily Target dose: 50 mg daily, titrate based on K level	

ARA Drug Interactions

- ARAs ↑ the risk of hyperkalemia. Monitor for additive hyperkalemia with drugs that ↑ potassium. Monitor K and renal function frequently.
- The triple combination of ACE inhibitor, ARB and ARA is not recommended due to a higher risk of hyperkalemia and renal insufficiency.
- Additive antihypertensive effects with other drugs that ↓ BP; monitor BP.
- Use with NSAIDs in patients with impaired renal function can cause severe hyperkalemia and ↓ antihypertensive effect.
- Diuretics can ↓ lithium's renal clearance and ↑ risk of lithium toxicity.
- Eplerenone is a major substrate of CYP3A4; use with strong CYP3A4 inhibitors is contraindicated.

HYDRALAZINE/NITRATE

Hydralazine is a direct arterial vasodilator which ↓ afterload. Nitrates ↑ the availability of nitric oxide which causes venous vasodilation and ↓ preload. Hydralazine also decreases the development of nitrate tachyphylaxis (tolerance). The combination improves the survival of patients with heart failure, although not as much as ACE inhibitors. It is used as alternative treatment for patients who cannot tolerate ACE inhibitors or ARBs due to poor renal function, angioedema or hyperkalemia. The combination product, *BiDil*, is indicated in self-identified black patients with NYHA Class III or IV who are symptomatic despite optimal treatment with ACE inhibitors and beta-blockers. Hydralazine or oral nitrates may be used as monotherapy for other indications; they have not individually been shown to affect HF outcomes. Isosorbide dinitrate was the oral nitrate used in clinical trials; there are no data with isosorbide mononitrate, although it is used in practice. As with ACE inhibitors or ARBs, the target doses are those shown to be beneficial in clinical trials.

DRUG	DOSING	SAFETY/SIDE EFFECTS/MONITORING
Hydralazine Tablet, injection **+ isosorbide dinitrate *(BiDil)***	Start 25-50 mg TID-QID Target dose: 300 mg/day in divided doses	**CONTRAINDICATION** Mitral valve rheumatic heart disease, CAD **WARNING** Drug-induced lupus erythematosus (DILE – dose and duration related) **SIDE EFFECTS** Headache, hypotension, reflex tachycardia, palpitations, fluid retention, peripheral neuritis **MONITORING** HR, BP, s/sx of HF, CBC, ANA titer
Isosorbide dinitrate IR/ER *(Dilatrate SR, Isordil Titradose)* Preferred formulation for systolic HF Isosorbide mononitrate *(Monoket, Imdur*)* Not listed in HF guidelines	Dinitrate: Start 20-30 mg TID-QID Target dose: 120 mg daily in divided doses	**CONTRAINDICATIONS** Use with PDE-5 Inhibitors and riociguat **SIDE EFFECTS** Hypotension, headache, dizziness, lightheadedness, flushing, tachyphylaxis (need 10-12 hour nitrate-free interval), syncope **MONITORING** HR, BP, s/sx of HF
Isosorbide dinitrate + hydralazine *(BiDil)*	Start 20/37.5 mg TID (1 tab TID) Target dose: 40/75 mg TID (2 tabs TID) No nitrate tolerance	**NOTES** Refer to Ischemic Heart Disease and Acute & Critical Care Medicine chapters for further discussion of nitrates for other indications

**Brand discontinued but name still used in practice.*

BiDil Drug Interactions

- Do not use in patients taking PDE-5 inhibitors (e.g., avanafil, sildenafil, tadalafil, vardenafil) or riociguat. The combination can cause severe hypotension. Refer to the Sexual Dysfunction chapter for further discussion.

DIGOXIN

Digoxin inhibits the Na/K ATPase pump which results in a positive inotropic effect (↑ in CO). It also exerts a parasympathetic effect which provides a negative chronotropic effect (↓ HR). Digoxin is added in patients who remain symptomatic despite receiving standard treatment of an ACE inhibitor (or ARB) with a beta-blocker. Digoxin improves symptoms, exercise tolerance and quality of life. Digoxin does not improve survival of heart failure patients, but it does reduce hospitalizations for heart failure. Dosing should take into account the patient's renal function, body size, age and gender (lower dose for renal insufficiency, smaller, older, female), with the majority of patients taking no more than 0.125 mg daily. Serum digoxin concentrations for HF should be kept < 1 ng/mL (range 0.5 – 0.9 ng/mL). Patients on digoxin should maintain a serum potassium between 4 – 5 mEq/L and magnesium > 2 mEq/L.

DRUG	DOSING	SAFETY/SIDE EFFECTS/MONITORING
Digoxin *(Digitek, Digox, Lanoxin)* Tablet, solution, injection	Available as 0.0625, 0.125, 0.1875, 0.25 mg Typical dose: 0.125-0.25 mg daily Loading doses not used in HF Therapeutic range for HF = 0.5-0.9 ng/mL (higher range for AFib) CrCl < 50 mL/min; ↓ dose or frequency ↓ dose by 20-25% when going from PO to IV Antidote: *DigiFab*	**CONTRAINDICATIONS** Ventricular fibrillation **WARNINGS** 2nd/3rd degree heart block without a pacemaker, Wolff-Parkinson-White syndrome (WPW) with AFib, vesicant (avoid extravasation) **SIDE EFFECTS** Dizziness, mental disturbances, headache, N/V/D **MONITORING** ECG, HR, BP, electrolytes, renal function and digoxin level (drawn optimally 12-24 hrs after dose) **TOXICITY** Initial s/sx of toxicity are N/V, loss of appetite and bradycardia. Severe s/sx of toxicity include yellow/green vision, blurriness, halos (around lights or objects), abdominal pain, confusion, delirium, prolonged PR interval, arrhythmias **NOTES** Digoxin is mostly renally cleared and partially cleared hepatically; ↓ renal function requires a ↓ digoxin dose, and in acute renal failure, digoxin is held

Digoxin Drug Interactions

- Monitor for bradycardia when administered with other drugs that ↓ HR (e.g., beta-blockers, ivabradine, non-DHP calcium channel blockers, others).
- Digoxin is a P-gp and CYP3A4 substrate (minor). Digoxin levels ↑ with amiodarone, dronedarone, quinidine, verapamil, erythromycin, clarithromycin, itraconazole, cyclosporine, propafenone and many other drugs. Reduce digoxin dose by 50% if patient is on amiodarone or dronedarone.
- Hypokalemia, hypomagnesemia, and hypercalcemia ↑ risk of digoxin toxicity.
- Hypothyroidism can ↑ digoxin levels.

IVABRADINE

High resting heart rate is associated with increased morbidity and mortality in heart failure. Ivabradine is an inhibitor of the "funny" current (I_f) in the sinus node and belongs to a class of drugs known as hyperpolarization-activated cyclic nucleotide-gated channel blockers (HCN blockers). Inhibition of this current results in a reduction in sinus rate and hence heart rate. Ivabradine reduces the risk of hospitalizations for worsening heart failure, but does not affect mortality. It is recommended as a potential adjunctive therapy to reduce HF hospitalizations in symptomatic stable chronic HF patients (NYHA Class II – III), with EF ≤ 35% who are treated with all appropriate first-line medications, are in sinus rhythm and have a resting HR ≥ 70 BPM.

DRUG	DOSING	SAFETY/SIDE EFFECTS/MONITORING
Ivabradine *(Corlanor)* Indicated in patients with: ■ stable, symptomatic chronic HF ■ LVEF ≤ 35% ■ sinus rhythm with resting heart rate ≥ 70 BPM ■ on maximally tolerated doses of beta-blockers or have a contraindication to beta-blocker use	Starting dose: 5 mg PO twice daily; after two weeks, adjust dose based on heart rate Maintenance dose: 2.5-7.5 mg PO twice daily Target: resting heart rate between 50-60 BPM	**CONTRAINDICATIONS** Acute decompensated HF; BP < 90/50 mmHg; sick sinus syndrome, sinoatrial block or 3rd degree AV block unless patient has a functioning pacemaker; resting heart rate < 60 BPM prior to treatment; severe hepatic impairment; pacemaker dependence (heart rate maintained exclusively by the pacemaker); use in combination with strong CYP3A4 inhibitors **WARNINGS** ↓ HR and bradycardia which can ↑ risk of QT prolongation and ventricular arrhythmias, fetal toxicity (females should use effective contraception as drug can cause fetal harm); monitor for atrial fibrillation, not recommended in patients with 2nd degree AV block unless patient has a functioning pacemaker **SIDE EFFECTS** Bradycardia, hypertension, atrial fibrillation, luminous phenomena (phosphenes - seeing flashes of light) **MONITORING** HR, ECG, BP

Ivabradine Drug Interactions

- Ivabradine is a substrate of CYP3A4 and is contraindicated with strong CYP3A4 inhibitors. Ivabradine should be avoided in patients taking strong CYP3A4 inducers and moderate CYP3A4 inhibitors.
- Monitor for bradycardia when used with other drugs that ↓ HR (digoxin, non-DHP calcium channel blockers, amiodarone). Bradycardia can ↑ risk of QT prolongation, especially in patients taking QT prolonging drugs.

POTASSIUM ORAL SUPPLEMENTATION

Potassium supplementation is an important aspect of managing HF because loop diuretics cause ↓ K while other HF drugs (RAAS inhibitors, ARAs) ↑ K. Maintenance of potassium levels is essential to reduce the proarrhythmic risk of digoxin, especially as HF ↑ arrhythmia risk. There are different formulations (tablets, capsules and liquids) which also vary by salt form (acetate, bicarbonate, citrate, chloride, gluconate and phosphate). The salt used depends on patient factors including acid-base status and deficiency of other electrolytes such as phosphate. Potassium chloride is used most commonly.

Frequency of monitoring serum potassium depends on renal function (and stability), medication regimen and clinical status. Check potassium levels if the renal function changes, and after any change in diuretic, ACE inhibitor, ARB or ARA dose. Magnesium deficiency aggravates hypokalemia. The magnesium level should be checked and corrected (as needed) prior to correcting the potassium level.

The usual range of K is 3.5 – 5 mEq/L. Supplementation may not be needed in patients who are able to supplement their intake of potassium through dietary sources (e.g., bananas, potatoes, orange juice, beans, dark leafy greens, apricots, peaches, avocados, white mushrooms, tomatoes and some varieties of fish).

DRUG	DOSING	SAFETY/SIDE EFFECTS/MONITORING
Potassium chloride (*Klor-Con, Klor-Con 10, Klor-Con M20, Micro-K*, *Klor-Con M10, Klor-Con M15, K-Tab, Kaon-Cl, others*) ER tablet and capsule, oral solution, injection, packet Potassium bicarbonate and potassium citrate (*Effer-K, Klor-Con/EF*) Effervescent tablet	**Prevention of hypokalemia:** 20-40 mEq/day in 1-2 divided doses **Treatment of mild hypokalemia:** 40-100 mEq/day in 2-5 divided doses; adjust dose according to laboratory values No more than 20-25 mEq should be given as a single dose to avoid GI discomfort	**CONTRAINDICATIONS** Severe renal impairment, hyperkalemia Oral solid dosage forms are contraindicated in patients with delayed or obstructed passage through the GI tract **WARNINGS** Caution in patients with mild-moderate renal impairment, patients with disorders that alter K (untreated Addison's disease, heat cramps, severe tissue trauma/burns) and in patients taking other medications that ↑ K **SIDE EFFECTS** N/V/D, abdominal pain, flatulence, hyperkalemia **MONITORING** K, Mg, Cl, pH, urine output **NOTES** KCl 10% = 20 mEq/15 mL Take with meals and a full glass of water or other liquid to minimize the risk of GI irritation *Micro-K*: capsules can be opened and contents sprinkled on a spoonful of applesauce or pudding and immediately swallowed without chewing *K-Tab, Klor-Con*: swallow whole; do not crush, cut, chew, or suck on tablet *Klor-Con M*: swallow whole; do not crush, chew, or suck on tablet; tablet can also be cut in half and swallowed separately, or can dissolve the whole tablet in 4 oz. of water – stir for 2 mins. and drink immediately *Effer-K*: dissolve tablet completely in 3-4 oz. cold water and drink immediately. Can further dilute if GI upset occurs.

HEART FAILURE EXACERBATIONS AND QUALITY IMPROVEMENT

HF is the most common condition causing hospitalization in patients greater than 65 years old. HF admissions are caused by either new-onset HF (known as acute HF) or worsening HF (known as acute decompensated HF, or ADHF). ADHF presents with either worsening congestion and/or hypoperfusion. Treatment consists of IV loop diuretics, vasodilators and/or inotropes, which are discussed in the Acute & Critical Care Medicine chapter. Many HF hospitalizations are due to nonadherence with medications and/or lifestyle recommendations.

Avoidable HF admissions are a major cause of increased healthcare costs. Medicare now penalizes hospitals for excessive readmissions due to HF exacerbations. Pharmacists are actively involved in quality improvement initiatives directed at decreasing hospital readmissions, such as medication optimization (making sure the right medications are being used and harmful medications are not being used) and medication adherence strategies. Despite all of this, up to 25% of HF patients do not fill one or more discharge medications, and ~34% stop taking one or more medications within a month of discharge. Lifestyle adherence is essential (discussed at the beginning of the chapter), including healthy eating and sodium restriction. Patients need to know what steps to take if symptoms worsen. The steps are outlined in the sample HF action plan on the next page.

CONGESTIVE HEART FAILURE MANAGEMENT/ACTION PLAN

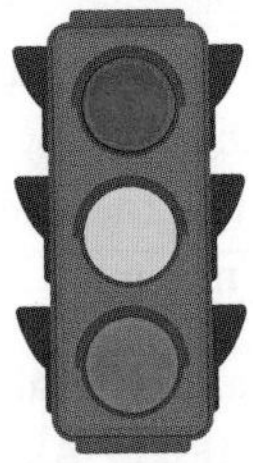

1. GREEN MEANS GO. FOLLOW MEDICATION, WEIGHT AND DIET ADVICE

2. YELLOW MEANS CAUTION. YOU MAY NEED TO CHANGE YOUR MEDICINES

3. RED MEANS DANGER. GET HELP FROM A DOCTOR TODAY. CALL 911.

1. GREEN – GO

- No shortness of breath
- Usual amount of swelling in legs
- No weight gain
- No chest pain
- No change in usual activity

Bring all your medicines to every appointment

Weigh yourself every day

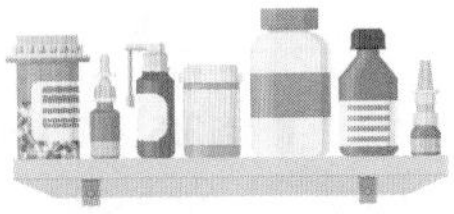

Take all your medicines

Eat a low salt diet

Go to your doctor appointments

2. YELLOW – CAUTION

Weight gain of:
- 2-4 pounds in 1 day
- 3-5 pounds in a week

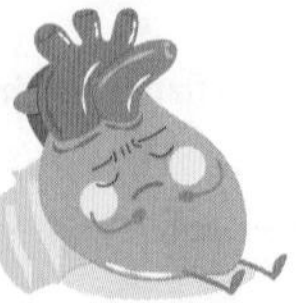

Increased number of pillows to sleep

You may need to change your medicines

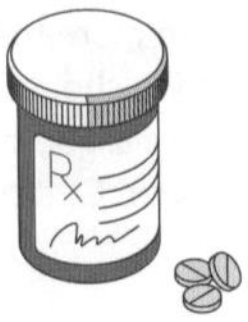

Increased swelling or coughing

Shortness of breath with activity

Call your doctor for instructions

3. RED – DANGER

Weight gain of more than 5 pounds in 1 week

Dizziness or falling

Call your doctor <u>today</u> to report symptoms and request an appointment

Waking at night due to shortness of breath

Shortness of breath at rest, chest tightness or wheezing

<u>Call 911 if having severe chest pain</u>

Adapted from www.ccwjc.com

PATIENT COUNSELING

All Heart Failure Patients

- Monitor body weight daily, in the morning before eating and after using the restroom. Weight should be recorded.
- Follow the steps in your HF action plan or contact your healthcare provider if your symptoms worsen or if you gain weight (2 – 4 pounds in one day or 3 – 5 pounds in one week).
- Follow a sodium restricted diet. Foods high in sodium include:
  - Prepared sauces and condiments (such as soy sauce, BBQ sauce, Worcestershire sauce or salsa)
  - Canned vegetables and soups
  - Frozen dinners
  - Deli meats (sandwich meats, bacon, ham, hot dogs, sausage or salami)
  - Salty foods (pickles, olives, cheese, nuts, chips or crackers)
- Take nutrition classes and learn to read nutrition labels. Choose "no sodium added" or "low sodium" options. Healthy ways of cooking include broiling, baking, poaching and steaming without added salt.
- Stop smoking. Do not use any illegal drugs; they can badly damage the heart. Alcohol, including beer and wine, should be avoided or limited to one drink per day for females and two drinks per day for males.
- Avoid pain medicines like ibuprofen (NSAIDs) without checking with a healthcare provider. Also, do not use nutritional supplements, vitamins or herbals for HF without discussing with the pharmacist if they are safe to use.
- Take your medications as directed. Discuss with your healthcare provider if the medications are too expensive. Not taking the medications and not following the food and salt recommendations will usually cause worsening of the HF symptoms and possible hospitalization.

Loop Diuretics

- This medicine helps your body remove extra fluid. Taking it consistently (even if you feel better) will help with shortness of breath and swelling.
- It is best to take the medicine early in the day so you won't have to get up in the middle of the night to go to the bathroom.
- You might feel dizzy if you stand up quickly. Get up slowly if you have been sitting or lying down.
- Follow all recommendations from your healthcare provider regarding salt and water intake. Have your labs checked as directed.

Beta-Blockers

- Do not stop taking the medication unless your healthcare provider tells you to do so.
- If you miss a dose, take your dose as soon as you remember, unless it is time to take your next dose. Do not double the dose.
- This medication can cause you to feel dizzy, tired or faint. Do not drive a car, use machinery or do anything that requires you to be alert until you adjust to the medication and the symptoms subside. These effects will go away in a few days. However, call your healthcare provider if the symptoms feel severe or you have weight gain or increased shortness of breath.
- This medication can cover up some of the signs and symptoms of low blood sugar (hypoglycemia); make sure to test your blood sugar often and take a fast-acting sugar source if needed.
- Medications used to treat severe allergic reactions may not work as well while taking this medication.

Toprol XL

- If you have been told to cut the *Toprol XL* or its generic equivalent tablet in half, you must use a pill cutter and cut only at the score line. Otherwise, the medicine will enter your body too quickly. Swallow the ½ tablet whole. The tablets cannot be crushed or chewed and should be taken preferably with or following a meal.

Coreg CR

- Take with food, to help reduce dizziness.
- Swallow *Coreg CR* capsules whole. Do not chew or crush the capsules.
- If you have trouble swallowing *Coreg CR* whole, the capsule can be carefully opened and the beads sprinkled over a spoonful of applesauce which should be taken right away. The applesauce should not be warm. Only use applesauce.

Digoxin

- This medicine helps make the heart beat stronger. Keep taking as directed, even if you feel well.
- Do not stop taking this medicine without talking to your healthcare provider. Stopping this medication suddenly may make your condition worse.
- Avoid becoming overheated or dehydrated as an overdose can easily occur if you are dehydrated.
- Symptoms of overdose include poor or no appetite, nausea, vomiting, diarrhea, vision changes (such as blurred or yellow/green vision), uneven heartbeats and feeling like you might pass out. If any of these occur, see a healthcare provider right away.
- There are many medications that can interact with digoxin. Check with your physician or pharmacist before starting any new medicines, including over the counter, vitamin and/or herbal products.
- To be sure that this medication is not causing harmful effects, your blood may need to be tested on a regular basis. Your kidney function will also need to be monitored.

Sacubitril/Valsartan *(Entresto)*

- This medication is used with other heart failure therapies, in place of an ACE inhibitor or other ARB therapy.
- Do not take this medication if you have had an allergic reaction including swelling of your face, lips, tongue, throat or trouble breathing while taking a type of medicine called an angiotensin-converting enzyme (ACE) inhibitor or angiotensin II receptor blocker (ARB).
- This medication cannot be used for at least 36 hours after stopping an ACE inhibitor.
- Do not take this medication if you have diabetes and take a medicine that contains aliskiren.
- Tell your healthcare provider if you are pregnant, plan to become pregnant or are breastfeeding or plan to breastfeed.
- Tell your healthcare provider about all the medications that you take, especially if you take potassium supplements or salt substitutes, non-steroidal anti-inflammatory drugs (NSAIDs), lithium or other medications for high blood pressure or heart problems.

Ivabradine

- This medication can cause an abnormal heart rhythm. Tell your healthcare provider if you have symptoms of an irregular heartbeat, such as feeling that your heart is pounding or racing (palpitations), chest pressure or pain, or worsened shortness of breath.
- This medication can cause a low heart rate. Contact your healthcare provider if you have symptoms such as dizziness, fatigue, lack of energy, or have low blood pressure.
- Tell your healthcare provider if you are pregnant, plan to become pregnant or are breastfeeding or plan to breastfeed.
- Avoid drinking grapefruit juice and taking St. John's wort during treatment with ivabradine. Tell your pharmacist all the medications, herbals and OTC medications you are taking.

Select Guidelines/References

2017 ACC/AHA/HFSA Focused Update of the 2013 ACCF/AHA Guideline for the Management of Heart Failure. http://circ.ahajournals.org/content/early/2017/04/26/CIR.0000000000000509 (accessed 2019 Mar 6).

2016 ACC/AHA/HFSA Focused Update on New Pharmacological Therapy for Heart Failure: An Update of the 2013 ACCF/AHA Guideline for the Management of Heart Failure. http://www.onlinejacc.org/content/68/13/1476 (accessed 2019 Mar 6).

CHAPTER CONTENT

Background 505
The Heart's Natural Pacemaker and Arrhythmias 505
Normal Sinus Rhythm 506
The Cardiac Conduction Pathway 506
Electrical Signaling: The Cardiac Action Potential 507
Arrhythmias 507
Supraventricular Arrhythmias 507
Ventricular Arrhythmias 508
QT Prolongation & Torsade De Pointes 508
Select Drugs that Can Increase or Prolong the QT Interval 508
Antiarrhythmic Drugs 509
Vaughan Williams Classification 509
Classifying Drugs with Vaughan Williams 508
Rate Control 509
Rhythm Control 509
AFib: Rate vs. Rhythm Control 509
Antiarrhythmics Mechanisms of Action 510
Common Antiarrhythmics 511
Other Antiarrhythmics 513
Patient Counseling 516

CONTENT LEGEND

= Study Tip Gal = Key Drug Guy

ECG OF NORMAL SINUS RHYTHM

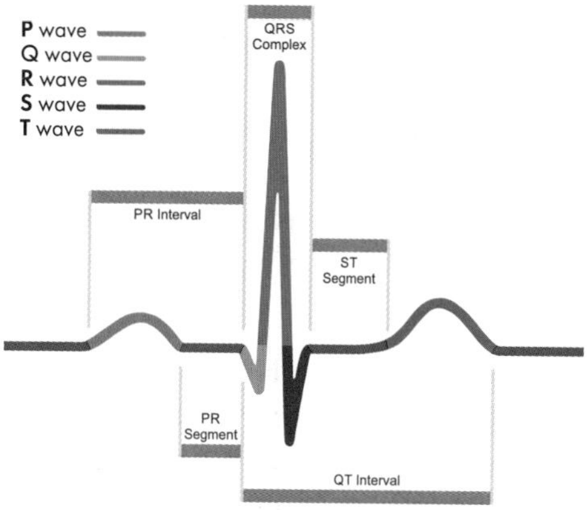

CHAPTER 32
ARRHYTHMIAS

BACKGROUND

The term conduction means to transmit electrical charges (or heat) through a substance. The cardiac conduction system is the electrical signaling system that causes the ventricles to contract. The "lub-dub" sounds heard through auscultation (listening to the heart by placing a stethoscope on the chest) are made by the closing of heart valves that occur in sequence with each heartbeat. Blood flows in one direction, from chamber to chamber, or to the lungs (to pick up oxygen) or to the body (to provide oxygen and nutrients). The first heart sound (S1) signals the beginning of ventricular systole (systole means to contract) and the second heart sound (S2) signals the end of ventricular systole. A normal heart beats with a relatively steady rate and a regular, coordinated rhythm. Sounds other than S1 and S2 are abnormal (e.g., S3, which is more common in heart failure and murmurs). Murmurs are caused by turbulent blood flow or regurgitation (i.e., blood flowing in the wrong direction).

An arrhythmia is an abnormal heart rhythm, which can cause the heart to beat too slow (bradycardia) or too fast (tachycardia). Any change from the normal sequence of electrical impulses can cause an arrhythmia. When the electrical impulses are too fast, too slow, or erratic, the heart cannot pump blood efficiently, and symptoms can develop.

THE HEART'S NATURAL PACEMAKER AND ARRHYTHMIAS

The rate and rhythm of the heartbeat is set by the rapidly firing cells in the sinoatrial (SA, or sinus) node. The SA node is called the heart's natural pacemaker.

An arrhythmia is caused by a disruption somewhere in the conduction (electrical signaling) system:

- The SA node can be firing at an abnormal rate or rhythm.
- Scar tissue from a prior heart attack can block and divert signal transmission.
- Another part of the heart may be acting as the pacemaker.

A small percentage of arrhythmias are silent (asymptomatic), and might be detected during a medical exam. With most arrhythmias, patients can feel that the heart is beating very fast, or feel a "fluttering" in their chest or think that their heart was "skipping a beat." Symptoms can include dizziness, shortness of breath, fatigue, lightheadedness and chest pain. In severe cases, arrhythmias can lead to syncope, heart failure and death.

An electrocardiogram (ECG) is used to diagnose arrhythmias. An ECG machine records the heart's electrical activity using electrodes placed on the skin. An ECG recorded in a medical office will pick up an arrhythmia only when it is present at the time the ECG is being conducted.

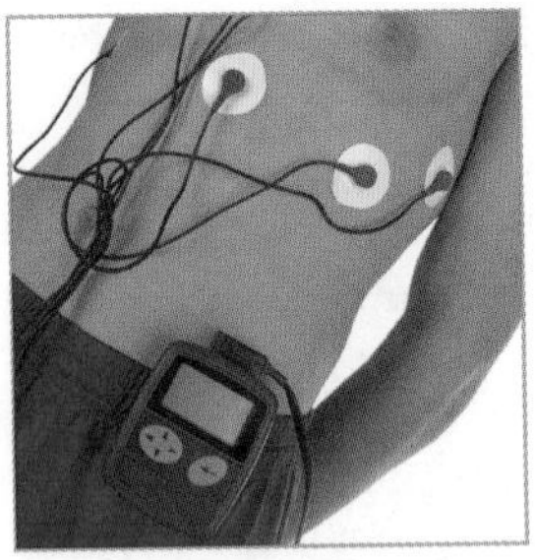

A Holter monitor (see figure on left) is an ambulatory ECG device that records the heart's electrical activity for 24–48 hours. It is used to detect arrhythmias that are intermittent [i.e., the heart goes in and out of normal sinus rhythm (NSR).]

NORMAL SINUS RHYTHM

A NSR is the normal heart rhythm, with a normal heart rate (between 60 to 100 BPM). A NSR originates (begins) in the sinoatrial (SA, or sinus) node. The SA node is called the heart's natural pacemaker; this is where the electrical signal for a heartbeat begins, and the frequency of the signals determines the pace, or heart rate.

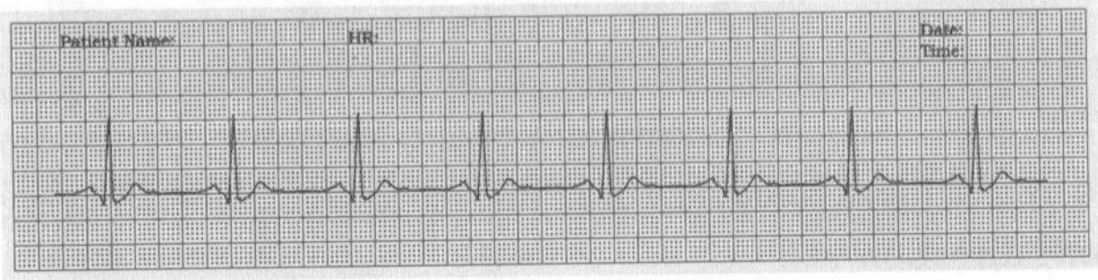

A normal rhythm on an ECG is seen with the characteristic appearance of consecutive heartbeats shown on an ECG printout (see above figure).

THE CARDIAC CONDUCTION PATHWAY

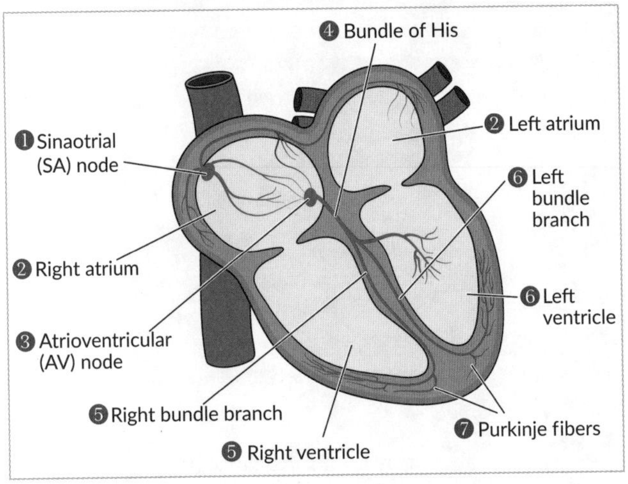

The cardiac conduction pathway consists of a group of specialized cardiac cells (myocytes) that send electrical impulses (signals) to the heart muscle, causing it to contract. The main components include the SA node, AV node, bundle of His, bundle branches and Purkinje fibers. The conduction pathway can be traced by following the numbers in the above image.

The SA node is a cluster of cells located at the junction of the superior vena cava and the right atrium. The electrical impulse begins in the SA node (1) and travels through the right and left atria (2), which cause the atria to contract. When the signal reaches the atrioventricular (AV) node (3), the electrical conduction slows down before traveling through the bundle of His (4) and into the ventricles. The bundle of His divides into the right bundle branch for the right ventricle (5) and into the left bundle branch for the left ventricle (6). The signal spreads through the ventricles via the Purkinje fibers (7), which causes the ventricles to contract.

Any disruption in the normal sequence of impulse conduction can result in an arrhythmia (see Study Tip Gal on previous page).

ELECTRICAL SIGNALING: THE CARDIAC ACTION POTENTIAL

The cardiac action potential refers to the movement of ions through channels in the myocytes that cause the electrical impulses in the cardiac conduction pathway. In essence, the action potentials provide the electricity needed to power the heart. The SA (pacemaker) cells have automaticity, which means that unlike other myocytes, the pacemaker cells initiate their own action potential; they do not require external stimulation. The cells spontaneously depolarize. The action potential is triggered when a threshold voltage is reached. This occurs in 5 phases (labeled as Phases 0, 1, 2, 3, and 4).

- Phase 0: rapid ventricular depolarization initiates a heartbeat in response to an influx of Na; this causes ventricular contraction (represented by the QRS complex on the ECG)
- Phase 1: early rapid repolarization; Na channels close
- Phase 2: plateau in response to an influx of Ca and efflux of K
- Phase 3: rapid ventricular repolarization in response to an efflux of K (represented by the T wave on the ECG)
- Phase 4: resting membrane potential; atrial depolarization occurs (represented by the P wave on the ECG)

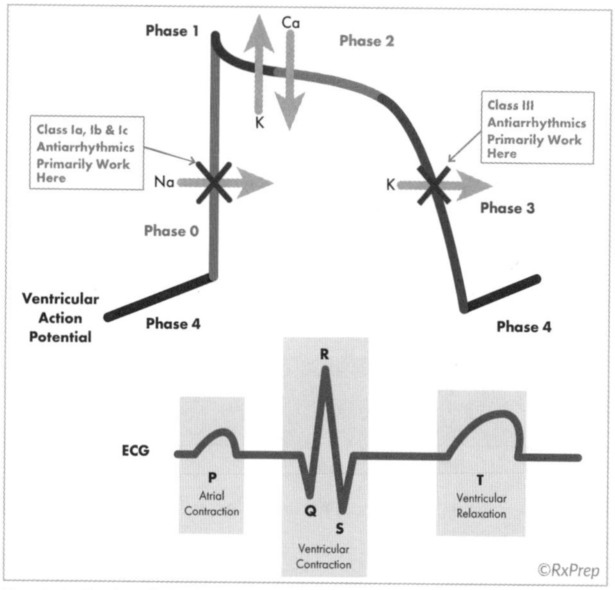

Depolarization/repolarization of cardiac cells must be properly sequenced and coordinated to produce the net ECG effects shown.

ARRHYTHMIAS

Abnormalities of the heart or its conduction system can alter the cardiac action potential and lead to arrhythmias. The most common cause of arrhythmias is myocardial ischemia or infarction. Other conditions resulting in damage to cardiac tissue can cause arrhythmias, including heart valve disorders, hypertension and heart failure. Non-cardiac conditions can trigger or predispose a patient to arrhythmias. These include electrolyte imbalances (especially potassium, magnesium, sodium and calcium), elevated sympathetic states (e.g., hyperthyroidism, infection) and drugs (including illicit drugs and antiarrhythmics).

Arrhythmias are generally classified into two categories based on their location of origin: supraventricular (originating above the AV node) and ventricular (originating below the AV node). Arrhythmias originating in or just below the atrioventricular node are called junctional rhythms, which are less common.

SUPRAVENTRICULAR ARRHYTHMIAS

Supraventricular tachyarrhythmias include sinus tachycardia, atrial fibrillation, atrial flutter, focal atrial tachycardias and supraventricular re-entrant tachycardias (formerly known as paroxysmal supraventricular tachycardias or PSVTs). Many patients have ongoing supraventricular arrhythmias (especially atrial fibrillation), without realizing it.

Atrial fibrillation (AFib) is the most common type of arrhythmia. AFib results from multiple waves of electrical impulses in the atria, resulting in an irregular (and usually rapid) ventricular response. The rapid ventricular rate can result in hypotension and worsen underlying ischemia and heart failure. Due to the disorganized depolarization of the atria, the atria are not able to adequately contract. This results in blood stagnation in the atria, which increases the risk of clot formation. A clot can embolize to the brain (blocking blood in an artery in the brain), which causes a stroke. To reduce clotting risk, patients with AFib may require anticoagulants; see the Anticoagulation chapter.

Atrial flutter is usually more organized and regular than AFib. This arrhythmia occurs most often with heart disease, and in the first week after heart surgery. Atrial flutter often leads to AFib.

VENTRICULAR ARRHYTHMIAS

Common ventricular arrhythmias include premature ventricular contractions (PVCs), ventricular tachycardia and ventricular fibrillation. PVCs are relatively common and occur in people both with and without heart disease. They are referred to as a skipped heartbeat. PVCs are generated from within the ventricular tissue. In some people, it can be related to stress or too much caffeine, nicotine or exercise.

A series of PVCs in a row, resulting in a heart rate of greater than 100 BPM, is known as ventricular tachycardia (VT). VT is further classified based on the presence or absence of a detectable peripheral pulse. VT with a pulse is treated with antiarrhythmics, whereas pulseless VT is a medical emergency, and advanced cardiac life support (ACLS) should be initiated. Untreated VT can degenerate into ventricular fibrillation (completely disorganized electrical activation of the ventricles) which is always a medical emergency.

SELECT DRUGS THAT CAN INCREASE OR PROLONG THE QT INTERVAL

KEY DRUGS

Antiarrhythmics
Class I (especially Class Ia) and Class III

Antibiotics
Quinolones and macrolides

Azole antifungals
All except isavuconazonium

Antidepressants
Tricyclics (e.g., amitriptyline, clomipramine, doxepin)

SSRIs (e.g., citalopram, escitalopram); sertraline is preferred in cardiac patients

SNRIs, mirtazapine and trazodone

Antiemetic agents
5-HT3 receptor antagonists, droperidol and phenothiazines

Antipsychotics (most)
Chlorpromazine, clozapine, haloperidol, olanzapine, paliperidone, quetiapine, risperidone, thioridazine, ziprasidone

Other drugs
Donepezil, fingolimod, methadone, tacrolimus

Others:

Antibiotics:
Foscarnet, telavancin and others

Oncology drugs: Arsenic, bortezomib, bosutinib, ceritinib, crizotinib, dasatinib, lapatinib, nilotinib, sorafenib, sunitinib

HIV drugs:
Protease inhibitors (atazanavir, saquinavir) and rilpivirine

Other drugs:
Alfuzosin, apomorphine, atomoxetine, buprenorphine, chloroquine, diphenhydramine, ezogabine, galantamine, mirabegron, pentamidine, propofol, quinine, ranolazine, sevoflurane, solifenacin, tizanidine

QT PROLONGATION & TORSADE DE POINTES

The QT interval is measured from the beginning of the QRS complex to the end of the T wave on an ECG. It reflects ventricular depolarization and repolarization. The QT interval varies with the heart rate, so a QT interval corrected for heart rate (QTc) is reported. A QTc interval is considered prolonged when it is > 440 milliseconds (msec), but is more worrisome when markedly prolonged (> 500 msec). Prolongation of the QT interval is a risk factor for Torsade de Pointes (TdP), a particularly lethal ventricular tachyarrhythmia which can cause sudden cardiac death.

Drugs Can Cause QT Prolongation

See the Key Drugs Guy for drugs that can prolong the QT interval. The risk of drug-induced QT prolongation increases with:

- Higher doses (the risk is concentration-dependent).
- Multiple QT-prolonging drugs (additive effect).
- Reduced drug clearance (e.g., with renal or liver disease).
- Drug interactions that decrease clearance (with enzyme inhibitors).
- With low potassium (hypokalemia) and/or low magnesium (hypomagnesemia).
- Other cardiac conditions; cardiac damage is a risk for arrhythmias, including TdP.

QT Risk Requires Assessment

In addition to recognizing the drugs that prolong the QT interval, an assessment of the patient's risk for TdP will be required. For example, if low-dose amitriptyline is being used for neuropathic pain, the dose is not particularly risky; but if the same patient is admitted to the hospital with hypokalemia and started on fluconazole and ondansetron, the level of concern would be heightened.

CLASSIFYING DRUGS WITH VAUGHAN WILLIAMS

CLASS I
Ia: **D**isopyramide, **Q**uinidine, **P**rocainamide
Ib: **L**idocaine, **M**exiletine
Ic: **F**lecainide, **P**ropafenone

CLASS II
Beta-blockers

CLASS III
Dronedarone, **D**ofetilide, **S**otalol, **I**butilide, **A**miodarone

CLASS IV
Verapamil, **D**iltiazem

Remember:

Double **Q**uarter **P**ounder, **L**ettuce, **M**ayo, **F**ries **P**lease!
Because **D**ieting **D**uring **S**tress **I**s **A**lways **V**ery **D**ifficult

ANTIARRHYTHMIC DRUGS

Antiarrhythmic drugs work by affecting the electrical currents in the cells of the heart. By blocking the movement of ions in different phases of the cardiac action potential (discussed previously), select drugs can reduce conduction velocity and/or automaticity, or prolong the refractory period, which can slow or terminate the abnormal electrical activity causing the arrhythmia. They can also occasionally worsen the existing arrhythmia or cause other arrhythmias.

Ventricular arrhythmias are managed in hospital settings. AFib is managed inpatient and outpatient, and most pharmacists will be assisting patients with AFib. This overview reviews the guideline-recommended treatment of AFib, which involves two main strategies: rate control and rhythm control (see the Study Tip Gal to the right).

AFIB: RATE VS RHYTHM CONTROL

Rate Control

- Patient remains in AFib and takes medications to control ventricular rate (HR).
  - Beta-blockers or non-DHP CCBs (sometimes digoxin).

Rhythm Control

- The goal is to restore and maintain NSR.
  - Class Ia, Ic or III antiarrhythmic or electrical cardioversion.
- If AFib is permanent, avoid rhythm-control antiarrhythmic drugs (risk > benefit).

Stroke Prophylaxis (see Anticoagulation chapter)

- Clots can form when a patient is in AFib, which can embolize (causing stroke) when the patient returns to NSR.
- For many patients, it is safer to remain in AFib with rate control than to try to restore NSR. A rate control strategy may require anticoagulation (indefinitely) for stroke prevention.
- When a rhythm control strategy is chosen, restoration and maintenance of NSR is not guaranteed. Long-term anticoagulation decisions depend on the patient's clot risk.

VAUGHAN WILLIAMS CLASSIFICATION

The Vaughan Williams classification system is the most commonly used classification system for antiarrhythmic drugs. The drugs are split into categories based on their dominant electrophysiological effect. It has the virtue of simplicity, although many drugs overlap into more than one category. See Study Tip Gal on the previous page.

RATE CONTROL

The goal resting HR is < 80 BPM in patients with symptomatic AFib; however, a more lenient rate-control strategy of < 110 BPM may be reasonable in patients who are asymptomatic and have preserved left ventricular function. Beta-blockers (preferred) or non-dihydropyridine (non-DHP) calcium channel blockers (CCB) are recommended for controlling ventricular rate in patients with AFib. Of note, patients with heart failure with reduced ejection fraction (HFrEF) should not receive a non-DHP CCB. Digoxin is not first-line for ventricular rate control, but can be added for refractory patients or used in those who are not able to tolerate beta-blockers or CCB.

RHYTHM CONTROL

Rhythm control consists of 1) methods for conversion to NSR and 2) maintenance of NSR. Conversion to NSR is most effective with direct current cardioversion. Medications can be used as well and include amiodarone (oral and IV), dofetilide, flecainide, ibutilide and propafenone.

For maintenance of NSR, recommended options include dofetilide, dronedarone, flecainide, propafenone or sotalol. Due to toxicities, amiodarone is recommended only when other agents have failed or are contraindicated (e.g., amiodarone is used in heart failure). Despite this, amiodarone is the top-selling antiarrhythmic in the U.S. Prior to starting any drug for a non-life-threatening arrhythmia, electrolytes and a toxicology screen should be checked to identify reversible causes.

TYPE OF AFIB	DEFINITION
Paroxysmal	AFib that terminates spontaneously or with intervention within 7 days of onset; episodes may recur with variable frequency
Persistent	Continuous AFib that is sustained > 7 days
Long-standing Persistent	Continuous AFib of > 12 months
Permanent	Term used when a joint decision has been made by the clinician and patient to cease further attempts to restore and/or maintain NSR; this is a treatment choice rather than a characteristic of the arrhythmia itself
Valvular	AFib with moderate to severe mitral stenosis or with a mechanical heart valve; long-term anticoagulation with warfarin is indicated
Non-valvular	AFib without moderate to severe mitral stenosis or a mechanical heart valve

Cardioversion

Cardioversion is an attempt to return the heart to NSR. Cardioversion is done with drugs or with a medical procedure that delivers a high-energy shock through the chest wall. The shock breaks the incorrect cycle, stops the arrhythmia and allows the sinus node to begin firing again with a NSR. The most common arrhythmia treated with the procedure is AFib.

AFib has a high rate of thromboembolism. If the patient is not already using therapeutic anticoagulation, it should be started at least three weeks before cardioversion, and continued for at least four weeks after successful cardioversion to NSR. If using warfarin, the INR should be at the therapeutic level (2-3).

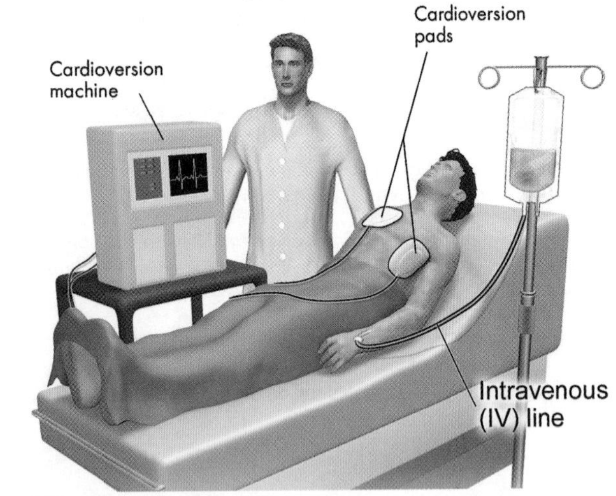

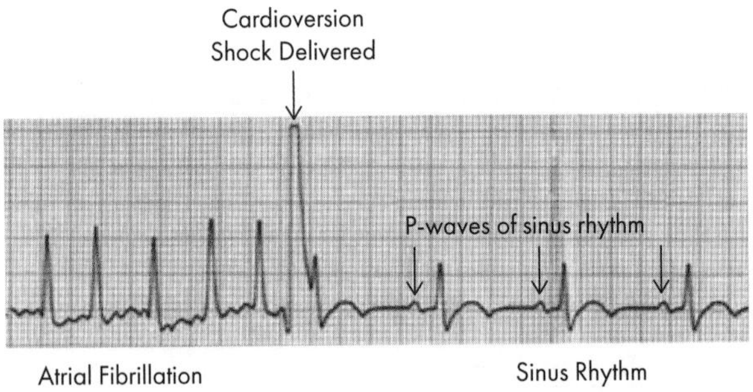

ANTIARRHYTHMICS MECHANISMS OF ACTION

CLASS	MECHANISM	CONSEQUENCE
Class I	Na-channel blockers	Reduces the speed of ion conduction through the sodium channels. Proarrhythmic (higher risk of arrhythmia). Negative inotrope potential, which ↓ the force of the heart's contraction.
Class II	Beta-blockers	Blocks the sympathetic activity that can trigger an arrhythmia; indirectly blocks calcium channels, which ↓ ion conduction speed. Used primarily to slow the rate in ventricular tachyarrhythmias.
Class III	K-channel blockers, primarily	Amiodarone and dronedarone block K-channels (primarily) and block alpha & beta adrenergic receptors, and Ca & Na channels. Amiodarone is useful for different types of arrhythmias, including AFib, the most common arrythmia, and is preferentially used in HF. Sotalol blocks K-channels and is a beta-blocker.
Class IV	Ca-channel blockers, non-dihydropiridines (non-DHP)	Used primarily to slow the rate in ventricular tachyarrhythmias (rate control). Negative inotropic effect (↓ contraction force), which can cause cardiac decompensation; do not use verapamil or diltiazem with heart failure and reduced ejection fraction (HFrEF).
Digoxin	Na-K-ATPase blocker	Blocking the Na-K-ATPase pump will ↑ force of cardiac conduction (positive inotrope) and ↓ heart rate (negative chronotrope).
Adenosine	Activates adenosine receptors to ↓ AV node conduction	Used for paroxysmal supraventricular tachyarrythmias (PSVTs).

COMMON ANTIARRHYTHMICS

Commonly used antiarrhythmics include amiodarone, the non-DHP CCB (diltiazem and verapamil), digoxin and beta-blockers. Common beta-blockers used for HF (metoprolol XL, carvedilol) will treat HF and ↓ HR (see Chronic Heart Failure chapter). The other antiarrhythmics are used less commonly, but many have toxicities that require careful attention [e.g., cinchonism (another name for quinine or quinidine toxicity) with quinidine, DILE with procainamide], which are underlined in the Other Antiarrhythmics section.

Class III Antiarrhythmics: Block Potassium Channels

DRUG	DOSING	SAFETY/SIDE EFFECTS/MONITORING
Amiodarone ***(Nexterone, Pacerone)*** Tablet, injection	Pulseless VT/VF: 300 mg IV push x 1, may repeat 150 mg x 1 if needed VT with pulse: 150 mg IV bolus, then 1 mg/min x 6 hours, then 0.5 mg/min x 18 hours or longer Ventricular arrhythmias: 800-1,600 mg/day x 1-3 weeks, then 600-800 mg/day x 4 weeks, then 400 mg/day AFib – cardioversion (off label): 600-800 mg/day PO for a 10 gram loading dose, followed by 200 mg daily AFib – maintenance of NSR (off label): 400-600 mg/day for 2-4 weeks; then 100-200 mg daily t½ = 40-60 days	**BOXED WARNINGS** Pulmonary toxicity and hepatotoxicity. Use only for life-threatening arrhythmias due to toxicities. Proarrhythmic; patients should be hospitalized when loading dose is given. **CONTRAINDICATIONS** Iodine hypersensitivity, severe sinus-node dysfunction causing marked ↓ HR, 2nd/3rd degree heart block (unless patient has artificial pacemaker), ↓ HR that is causing syncope, cardiogenic shock. **WARNINGS** Hyper- and hypo-thyroidism (hypo is more common) - amiodarone partially inhibits peripheral conversion of T4 to T3, optic neuropathy (visual impairment), photosensitivity (slate-blue skin discoloration), neurotoxicity (peripheral neuropathy), severe skin reactions (SJS/TEN). **SIDE EFFECTS** Hypotension, bradycardia, corneal microdeposits, dizziness, ataxia, N/V, constipation, tremor, skin photosensitivity, drug-induced lupus erythematosus (DILE). **MONITORING** ECG, BP, HR, electrolytes, pulmonary function (including chest X-ray) at baseline and annually, LFTs at baseline and every 6 months, thyroid function at baseline and every 3-6 months, eye exams. **NOTES** Avoid in pregnancy or women who are breastfeeding. Infusions longer than 2 hours must be administered in a non-polyvinyl chloride (PVC) container such as polyolefin or glass. Premixed *Nexterone* comes in GALAXY containers (non-PVC and non-DEHP) that can be stored up to 24 months at room temperature. PVC tubing is fine to use. Use a 0.22 micron filter. Incompatible with heparin (flush with saline). Premixed IV bag advantages: longer stability, non-PVC, comes in common concentrations. Slow the infusion rate or discontinue if hypotension or bradycardia occurs. Recommended as antiarrhythmic drug of choice in patients with heart failure. Oral and IV amiodarone can provide rate control (due to beta-blocking properties) when other measures are unsuccessful or contraindicated. Amiodarone (chemical structure of drug) contains iodine (thyroid hormones also contain iodine).

Amiodarone Drug Interactions

- Amiodarone is often given with drugs that it interacts with, including warfarin, digoxin and statins. Common interactions with cardiovascular drugs are reviewed in the Learning Drug Interactions chapter.
- Amiodarone can increase the level of many other drugs; it is an inhibitor of CYP450 2C9 (moderate), 2D6 (moderate), 3A4 (weak) and P-gp.
- Amiodarone is a substrate of CYP3A4, 2C8 and P-gp. Strong/moderate inhibitors of these enzymes will ↑ amiodarone and strong/moderate inducers will ↓ amiodarone.
- When starting amiodarone, ↓ digoxin by 50% and ↓ warfarin by 30 - 50%. Do not exceed 20 mg/day of simvastatin or 40 mg/day of lovastatin; statin levels will increase. Consider use of alternative statin.
- Additive effect with other drugs that decrease HR, including non-DHP CCB, digoxin, beta-blockers, clonidine and dexmedetomidine *(Precedex)*.
- Sofosbuvir can enhance the bradycardic effect of amiodarone; do not use together.

Class IV Antiarrhythmics: Block Calcium Channels

DRUG	DOSING	SAFETY/SIDE EFFECTS/MONITORING
Diltiazem *(Cardizem, Cardizem CD, Cardizem LA, Tiazac,* *Cartia XT, Dilt-XR, Diltzac, Taztia XT)* Tablet, capsule, injection	120-360 mg PO daily	**CONTRAINDICATIONS** Severe hypotension (SBP < 90 mmHg), 2nd/3rd degree heart block/sick sinus syndrome (unless the patient has a pacemaker), cardiogenic shock, HFrEF, Wolff-Parkinson-White syndrome with AFib. **WARNINGS** Hypotension, heart failure (may worsen symptoms), 1st degree AV block with sinus bradycardia, ↑ LFTs. **SIDE EFFECTS** Edema, arrhythmias, constipation (more with verapamil), gingival hyperplasia, HA, dizziness. **MONITORING** ECG, BP, HR, electrolytes, LFTs. **NOTES** Only non-DHP CCBs are used as antiarrhythmics.
Verapamil *(Calan,* *Calan SR, Verelan, Verelan PM)* Tablet, capsule, injection	180-480 mg PO daily	

Verapamil & Diltiazem Drug Interactions

- Additive effect with other drugs that decrease HR, including amiodarone, digoxin, beta-blockers, clonidine and dexmedetomidine *(Precedex)*.
- All CCBs, DHP and non-DHP, are CYP3A4 substrates. Use strong CYP3A4 inducers/inhibitors with caution, and in some cases, avoid. Check for drug interactions when starting a CCB and do not use grapefruit with any CCB.
- Diltiazem and verapamil are substrates of P-gp, and inhibitors of CYP3A4. They can increase the concentration of many other drugs. Patients who take statins should use lower doses of simvastatin or lovastatin (see Dyslipidemia chapter) or use a statin that is not metabolized by CYP3A4 (e.g., pitavastatin, pravastatin, rosuvastatin).

Digoxin: Blocks Na-K-ATPase Pump

DRUG	DOSING	SAFETY/SIDE EFFECTS/MONITORING
Digoxin *(Digitek, Digox, Lanoxin)* Tablet, solution, injection Tablet strengths: 0.0625, 0.125, 0.1875, 0.25 mg	Typical dose: 0.125-0.25 mg PO daily Loading dose [called total digitalizing dose (TDD)] is: 8-12 mcg/kg. Give ½ of the TDD as the initial dose, followed by ¼ of the TDD in 2 subsequent doses at 4-8 hour intervals. Alternatively, give 0.25 mg IV and repeat dosing to a max of 1.5 mg over 24 hours Therapeutic range = 0.8-2 ng/mL for AFib (lower range for HF) When CrCl < 50 mL/min, ↓ dose or ↓ frequency. Hold in acute renal failure ↓ dose by 20-25% when going from oral to IV	**CONTRAINDICATIONS** Ventricular fibrillation. **WARNINGS** 2nd/3rd degree heart block without a pacemaker, Wolff-Parkinson-White syndrome with AFib, vesicant-avoid extravasation. **SIDE EFFECTS** Dizziness, mental disturbances, headache, N/V/D. **MONITORING** ECG, HR, BP, electrolytes, renal function and digoxin level (drawn 12-24 hrs after dose). **Toxicity** Initial s/sx of toxicity are N/V, loss of appetite and bradycardia. Severe s/sx of toxicity include blurred/double vision, altered color perception, greenish-yellow halos around lights or objects, abdominal pain, confusion, delirium, prolonged PR interval, arrhythmias. **NOTES** Not usually given alone for rate control (used in combination with a beta-blocker or CCB). Antidote: *DigiFab*

Digoxin Drug Interactions

- Additive effect with other drugs that decrease HR, including amiodarone, non-DHP CCB, beta-blockers, clonidine and dexmedetomidine *(Precedex)*.
- Hypokalemia, hypomagnesemia and hypercalcemia ↑ the risk of digoxin toxicity.
- Hypothyroidism can ↑ digoxin levels.
- Digoxin is a substrate of P-gp. Digoxin levels ↑ with inhibitors, including amiodarone, dronedarone, quinidine, verapamil, erythromycin, clarithromycin, itraconazole, propafenone and many other drugs. With amiodarone or dronedarone, ↓ digoxin dose by 50%.

OTHER ANTIARRHYTHMICS

DRUG	DOSING	SAFETY/SIDE EFFECTS/MONITORING
Class Ia: block sodium and potassium channels		
Disopyramide *(Norpace, Norpace CR)*	400-600 mg/day Take on an empty stomach	**BOXED WARNING** Reserve use for patients with life-threatening ventricular arrhythmias. **CONTRAINDICATIONS** 2nd/3rd degree heart block (unless patient has a functional artificial pacemaker), cardiogenic shock, congenital QT syndrome, sick sinus syndrome. **WARNINGS** Proarrhythmic, hypotension, HF, BPH/urinary retention/narrow-angle glaucoma, myasthenia gravis (due to anticholinergic effects). **SIDE EFFECTS** Anticholinergic effects (e.g., dry mouth, constipation, urinary retention), hypotension.
Quinidine Tablet, injection	IR: 400 mg PO Q6H ER: 300-648 mg PO Q8-12H Take with food or milk to ↓ GI upset Different salt forms are not interchangeable (267 mg of gluconate = 200 mg of sulfate form)	**BOXED WARNING** May ↑ mortality in treatment of AFib or atrial flutter; control AV conduction before initiating. **CONTRAINDICATIONS** Concurrent use of quinolones that prolong the QT interval or ritonavir; 2nd/3rd degree heart block or idioventricular conduction delays (unless patient has a functional artificial pacemaker), thrombocytopenia, thrombotic thrombocytopenic purpura (TTP), myasthenia gravis. **WARNINGS** Proarrhythmic, hepatotoxicity, hemolysis risk (avoid in G6PD deficiency), can cause positive Coombs test. **SIDE EFFECTS** Drug-induced lupus erythematosus (DILE), diarrhea (35%), stomach cramping (22%), lightheadedness, N/V, cinchonism (e.g., overdose; symptoms include tinnitus, hearing loss, blurred vision, headache, delirium), rash. **NOTES** Avoid changes in Na intake; ↓ Na intake can ↑ quinidine levels. Alkaline foods/alkaline urine ↑ quinidine levels and can lead to toxicity.
Procainamide Tablet, injection	Active metabolite, N-acetyl procainamide (NAPA), is renally cleared; ↓ dose when CrCl < 50 mL/min **Therapeutic levels:** Procainamide: 4-10 mcg/mL NAPA: 15-25 mcg/mL Combined: 10-30 mcg/mL Draw level 6-12 hrs after IV infusion has started	**BOXED WARNINGS** Potentially fatal blood dyscrasias (e.g., agranulocytosis); monitor patient closely in the first 3 months and periodically thereafter. Long-term use leads to positive antinuclear antibody (ANA) in 50% of patients, which can result in drug-induced lupus erythematosus (DILE) in 20-30% of patients. Reserve use for patients with life-threatening ventricular arrhythmias. **WARNINGS** Proarrhythmic. **SIDE EFFECTS** Hypotension, rash,
Class Ib: block sodium channels. Useful for ventricular arrhythmias only (no efficacy in AFib)		
Lidocaine *(Xylocaine)* Used for refractory VT/cardiac arrest		**BOXED WARNINGS** Mexiletine: reserve use for patients with life-threatening ventricular arrhythmias, abnormal liver function seen in patients with CHF or ischemia. **CONTRAINDICATIONS** 2nd/3rd degree heart block (unless patient has a functional artificial pacemaker). Lidocaine: Wolff-Parkinson-White syndrome, Adam-Stokes syndrome, allergy to corn or corn-related products or amide type anesthetic. Mexiletine: cardiogenic shock. **WARNINGS** Caution in the elderly, hepatic impairment and in patients with HF. Mexiletine: blood dyscrasias, severe skin reactions (DRESS).
Mexiletine Capsule	200 mg PO Q8H; max 1.2 g/day Take with food	

Class Ic: block sodium channels		
Flecainide Tablet	50-100 mg PO Q12H; max 400 mg/day Store in tight, light-resistant container	**BOXED WARNINGS** When treating atrial flutter, 1:1 atrioventricular conduction may occur; pre-emptive negative chronotropic therapy (e.g., digoxin, beta-blockers) can ↓ the risk. Proarrhythmic effects especially in AFib, do not use in chronic AFib. Reserve use for patients with life-threatening ventricular arrhythmias. **CONTRAINDICATIONS** 2nd/3rd degree heart block (unless patient has a functional artificial pacemaker), cardiogenic shock, structural heart disease (e.g., heart failure, myocardial infarction), concurrent use of ritonavir. **WARNINGS** Avoid use in severe hepatic impairment. **SIDE EFFECTS** Dizziness, visual disturbances, dyspnea.
Propafenone *(Rythmol SR)* Capsule, tablet		**BOXED WARNINGS** Reserve use for patients with life-threatening ventricular arrhythmias. **CONTRAINDICATIONS** Sinoatrial and atrioventricular disorders (unless patient has a functional artificial pacemaker), sinus bradycardia, cardiogenic shock, hypotension, structural heart disease (e.g., heart failure, myocardial infarction), bronchospastic disorders. **WARNINGS** Proarrhythmic. **SIDE EFFECTS** Taste disturbance (metallic), dizziness, visual disturbances, N/V. **NOTES** Propafenone has significant beta-adrenergic receptor blocking effects, negative inotropic and proarrhythmic properties (contraindicated in HF).
Class III: primarily block potassium channels		
Dronedarone *(Multaq)*	400 mg PO Q12H Prior to initiation, class I or III antiarrhythmics or strong CYP3A inhibitors must be stopped	**BOXED WARNINGS** Increased risk of death, stroke and HF in patients with decompensated HF (NYHA Class IV or any class with a recent hospitalization due to HF) or permanent AFib. **CONTRAINDICATIONS** Pregnancy, 2nd/3rd degree heart block (unless patient has a pacemaker), symptomatic HF, HR < 50 bpm, concurrent use of strong CYP3A4 inhibitors and QT-prolonging drugs, QTc ≥ 500 msec, PR interval > 280 msec, lung or liver toxicity from previous use, hepatic impairment, nursing mothers. **WARNINGS** Hepatic failure (especially in the first 6 months), pulmonary disease (including pulmonary fibrosis and pneumonitis), marked ↑ SCr, prerenal azotemia and ARF (usually in the setting of heart failure or hypovolemia), ↓ magnesium and ↓ potassium with administration of potassium-depleting diuretics. **SIDE EFFECTS** QT prolongation, ↑ SCr, N/V/D, abdominal pain, diarrhea, bradycardia, asthenia. **NOTES** Unlike amiodarone, dronedarone does not contain iodine, and has little effect on thyroid function. Dronedarone is a moderate inhibitor of CYP2D6, 3A4 and P-gp and a major substrate of CYP3A4. Avoid use with strong inhibitors and inducers of CYP3A4 and with drugs that prolong the QT interval. ↓ digoxin dose 50%. Use low doses of statins metabolized by CYP3A4, or use alternate statin. Monitor INR if on warfarin.

Sotalol *(Betapace AF, Betapace, Sotylize, Sorine)* Oral, injection Non-selective beta-blocker	CrCl < 60 mL/min: ↓ frequency CrCl < 40 mL/min: varies by formulation	**BOXED WARNINGS** Initiation (or reinitiation) and dosage increases should be done in a hospital with continuous ECG monitoring and experienced staff. Adjust dosing interval based on CrCl to ↓ risk of proarrhythmia; QT prolongation is directly related to sotalol concentration. **CONTRAINDICATIONS** 2nd/3rd degree heart block (unless patient has a functional artificial pacemaker), congenital or acquired long QT syndrome, sinus bradycardia, uncontrolled HF, cardiogenic shock, asthma. For *Betapace AF, Sotylize*, sotalol injection: QTc > 450 msec, bronchospastic conditions, CrCl < 40 mL/min, K < 4 mEq/L, sick sinus syndrome. **SIDE EFFECTS** Bradycardia, palpitations, chest pain, dizziness, fatigue, dyspnea, N/V, TdP, HF, bronchoconstriction. **NOTES** *Betapace* should not be substituted with *Betapace AF* since *Betapace AF* is distributed with educational information specifically for patients with AFib/Atrial flutter.
Ibutilide *(Corvert)* Injection		**BOXED WARNING** Proarrhythmic; confirm that benefits of maintaining NSR outweigh the risks. **SIDE EFFECTS** Ventricular tachycardias (e.g., TdP), headache, hypotension, QT prolongation. **NOTES** Correct hypokalemia and hypomagnesemia prior to use and throughout treatment.
Dofetilide *(Tikosyn)*	CrCl < 60 mL/min: ↓ dose CrCl < 20 mL/min: contraindicated	**BOXED WARNING** Must be initiated (or reinitiated) in a setting with continuous ECG monitoring, experienced staff and ability to assess CrCl for a minimum of 3 days; proarrhythmic, with QT prolongation. **CONTRAINDICATIONS** Patients with congenital or acquired long QT syndromes; concurrent use of cimetidine, dolutegravir, hydrochlorothiazide, itraconazole, ketoconazole, megestrol, prochlorperazine, trimethoprim, verapamil; HR < 50, QTc > 440 msec. **SIDE EFFECTS** Headache, dizziness, ventricular tachycardias (e.g., TdP), ↑ QT interval.
Drugs Not Included in Vaughan Williams Classification		
Adenosine *(Adenocard)*	6 mg IV push (may increase to 12 mg if not responding) t½: less than 10 sec Used in paroxysmal supraventricular tachycardia (PSVTs); do not use for converting AFib/Atrial flutter or ventricular tachycardia	**CONTRAINDICATIONS** 2nd/3rd degree heart block, sick sinus syndrome or symptomatic bradycardia (except in patients with a functional pacemaker), bronchospastic lung disease. **SIDE EFFECTS** Transient new arrhythmia, facial flushing, chest pain/pressure, neck discomfort, dizziness, headache, GI distress, transient ↓ in blood pressure, dyspnea.

PATIENT COUNSELING

Amiodarone Patient Counseling

- This medication can cause severe lung or liver problems in rare instances. Get immediate medical help if you experience any of these serious side effects: cough, fever, chills, chest pain, difficult or painful breathing, coughing up blood, severe stomach pain, nausea, vomiting, fatigue, yellowing eyes or skin, or dark-colored urine and new shortness of breath. Your blood will need to be checked, and a chest X-ray, during treatment.
- This medication is used to treat certain types of serious (possibly fatal) irregular heartbeat problems called arrhythmias. It is used to restore and maintain the normal heart rhythm and keep a regular, steady heartbeat. Amiodarone works by blocking certain electrical signals in the heart that can cause an irregular heartbeat. This medication has not been shown to help people with these arrhythmias live longer.
- Take this medication by mouth, usually once or twice daily or as directed by your healthcare provider. If stomach upset occurs, take the medication with food.
- Like other medications used to treat irregular heartbeats, amiodarone can infrequently cause them to become worse. Seek immediate medical attention if your heart continues to pound or skips a beat.
- This drug may infrequently cause serious vision changes. Tell your healthcare provider immediately if you develop any vision changes (such as seeing halos or blurred vision). You will need to have your eyes checked before and during the time you are taking amiodarone.
- You may develop "pins and needles" or numbness in your legs, hands and feet, or muscle weakness or trouble walking. Discuss with your healthcare provider if this happens.
- This drug can change how your thyroid gland works and may cause your metabolism to speed up or slow down. Tell your healthcare provider if you develop any symptoms of low or overactive thyroid including cold or heat intolerance, unexplained weight loss/gain, thinning hair, unusual sweating, nervousness, irritability or restlessness. Discuss this with your healthcare provider; tests can be ordered to check your thyroid function.
- This drug may cause your skin to be more sensitive to the sun. Stay out of the sun during mid-day and use protective clothing and broad spectrum sunscreen. Infrequently, this medication has caused the skin to become a blue-gray color. This effect is not harmful and usually goes away months after the drug is stopped.
- Avoid eating grapefruit or drinking grapefruit juice while using this medication. Grapefruit will cause too much of the medication to get into your body.
- This drug can interact with other medications. Before starting a new medication, including any over-the-counter medications, discuss with your healthcare provider if it is safe to use with amiodarone.

Digoxin Patient Counseling

- This medicine helps the heart beat with a more regular rate. Keep taking as directed, even if you feel well.
- Do not stop taking this medicine without talking to your healthcare provider. Stopping suddenly may make your condition worse.
- Avoid becoming overheated or dehydrated as an overdose can occur more easily if you are dehydrated.
- Symptoms of overdose may include nausea, vomiting, diarrhea, loss of appetite, vision changes (such as blurred or yellow/green vision), confusion, hallucinations and feeling like you might pass out. If any of these occur, see your healthcare provider right away.
- There are many medications that can interact with digoxin. Check with your healthcare provider before starting any new medications, including over the counter, vitamin and/or herbal products.
- To be sure that this medication is not causing harmful effects, your blood may need to be tested on a regular basis. Your kidney function will also need to be monitored.

Select Guidelines/References

2019 AHA/ACC/HRS Focused Update of the 2014 AHA/ACC/HRS Guideline for the Management of Patients With Atrial Fibrillation. *J Am Coll Cardiol.* 2019; doi.org/10.1016/j.jacc.2019.01.011.

2014 AHA/ACC/HRS Guideline for the Management of Patients With Atrial Fibrillation: A Report of the American College of Cardiology/American Heart Association Task Force on Practice Guidelines and the Heart Rhythm Society. *J Am Coll Cardiol.* 2014; 64(21):2246-80.

CHAPTER CONTENT

Background 517
Presentation and Diagnosis 518
Signs and Symptoms of Stroke 518
Ischemic Stroke: Acute Management 518
Alteplase 518
Other Treatments 519
Ischemic Stroke: Secondary Prevention 520
Treatment of Modifiable Risk Factors 520
Antiplatelet Treatment 520
Hemorrhagic Stroke 522
Intracerebral Hemorrhage (ICH) 522
Mannitol 522
Acute Subarachnoid Hemorrhage (SAH) 523
Nimodipine 523

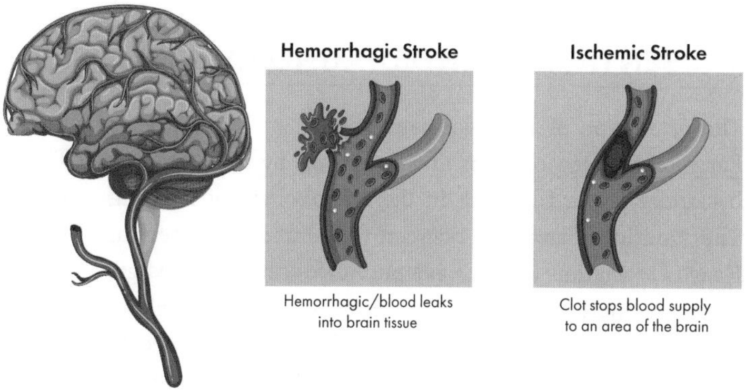

CHAPTER 33
STROKE

BACKGROUND

A stroke, or cerebrovascular accident (CVA), occurs when blood flow to an area of the brain is interrupted. There are a few different types of stroke. Acute ischemic stroke can be caused by a thrombus that forms during a cerebral atherosclerotic infarction (similar to a myocardial infarction, but in the brain). This is sometimes referred to as a non-cardioembolic stroke, to indicate the origin of disease as being in the brain, not the heart.

A cardioembolic stroke is an ischemic stroke that occurs when an embolus (i.e., a clot) forms in the heart and travels to the brain. A common cause of cardioembolic stroke is atrial fibrillation (see the Arrhythmias and Anticoagulation chapters). Intracerebral hemorrhage (ICH), subarachnoid hemorrhage (SAH) and subdural hematoma are all hemorrhagic strokes (bleeding in the brain due to a ruptured blood vessel).

Approximately 87% of all strokes are ischemic and 13% are hemorrhagic. When a stroke occurs, ischemia kills brain cells in the immediate area of injury. When brain cells die, they release chemicals that set off a chain reaction; cells in the larger, surrounding area of brain tissue can die and the functions controlled by that area can be lost or impaired.

There are numerous risk factors for stroke, many of which are modifiable (see box). Some people recover completely from less serious strokes (e.g., transient ischemic attacks, or TIAs), while others face chronic disability or loss of life.

RISK FACTORS FOR STROKE

- Hypertension – most important
- Atrial Fibrillation
- Gender (females > males)
- Ethnicity (highest risk in African Americans)
- Age ≥ 55 years
- Atherosclerosis
- Diabetes
- Prior Stroke or TIA
- Smoking
- Dyslipidemia
- Patent Foramen Ovale (PFO)
- Sickle Cell Disease

CONTENT LEGEND

= Study Tip Gal
= Key Drug Guy

PRESENTATION AND DIAGNOSIS

The evaluation of a stroke patient must be done quickly. Early recognition of signs and symptoms by the patient or bystander is the first link in the stroke chain of survival. The American Stroke Association (ASA) and the American Heart Association (AHA) have public education campaigns aimed to increase early recognition (see the box below). Promptly calling 9-1-1 and activating the emergency medical system is essential, as brain tissue is rapidly lost as the stroke progresses (commonly stated as "time is brain").

SIGNS AND SYMPTOMS OF STROKE

ACT F.A.S.T.

Face:
Ask the person to smile. Does one side of the face droop or is it numb? Is the smile uneven?

Arms:
Ask the person to raise both arms. Does one arm drift downward?

Speech:
Ask the person to repeat a simple sentence. Are the words slurred? Is the sentence repeated correctly?

Time:
If the person shows any of these symptoms, even if they go away, call 9-1-1 immediately!

Once in the care of healthcare professionals, a clinical assessment (e.g., history, physical exam, laboratory tests) and a neurological assessment, using stroke scales such as the National Institutes of Health Stroke Scale (NIHSS), help determine the severity of the stroke and guides treatment.

Supportive cardiac and respiratory care, and quickly identifying whether the stroke is ischemic or hemorrhagic, is critical. Agents used to treat ischemic stroke can increase the risk of bleeding and can be harmful, or even fatal, in cases of hemorrhagic stroke. Brain imaging using computed tomography (CT) is ideally performed within 20 minutes of arrival to the emergency department. Less commonly, magnetic resonance imaging (MRI) is performed.

ISCHEMIC STROKE: ACUTE MANAGEMENT

The immediate goal of treatment is to restore blood flow to the ischemic area of the brain to obtain complete neurological recovery. Intracranial pressure (ICP), cerebral perfusion pressure (CPP) and blood pressure (BP) should be monitored and controlled. Restoring blood flow requires mechanical removal of a clot (e.g., with stent retrievers) or the clot can be dissolved with intravenous fibrinolytic therapy if the patient arrives at the hospital in a timely manner after symptom onset.

ALTEPLASE

Alteplase is recombinant tissue plasminogen activator (tPA or rtPA). It binds to fibrin in a thrombus (clot) and converts plasminogen to plasmin, resulting in fibrinolysis. Alteplase is the only fibrinolytic agent that is used in acute ischemic stroke. Patients are candidates for alteplase if a clot is confirmed on brain imaging, there are no contraindications to use (see drug table on the next page) and the following criteria are met:

- It can be administered within three hours of symptom onset (FDA-approved time line).
- It can be administered within 4.5 hours of symptom onset in select patients (guideline recommendation; not FDA-approved).
- It can be administered within 60 minutes of hospital arrival (door-to-needle time).
- BP is < 185/110 mmHg; if the only contraindication to treatment is a BP > 185/110 mmHg, then BP should be safely lowered so alteplase can be administered.

DRUG	DOSING	SAFETY/SIDE EFFECTS/MONITORING
Alteplase (*Activase*) Must exclude intracranial hemorrhage before use	0.9 mg/kg (maximum dose 90 mg); give 10% of the dose as a bolus over 1 minute then infuse the remainder over 60 minutes Dosing is different for MI and pulmonary embolism indications	**CONTRAINDICATIONS** **Absolute (per package labeling)** Active bleed (including ICH, SAH, internal bleeding); recent (within the past 3 months) serious head injury, intracranial or intraspinal surgery; intracranial conditions that can increase the risk of bleeding (e.g., intracranial neoplasm, ateriovenous malformation, aneurysm); bleeding diathesis; severe uncontrolled BP (> 185/110 mmHg) **Additional Exclusion Criteria (per AHA/ASA guidelines)** Stroke within the past 3 months; previous ICH; INR > 1.7, aPTT > 40 seconds, platelet count < 100,000/mm^3, received a treatment dose of LMWH within the previous 24 hours, current use of a direct thrombin inhibitor or direct factor Xa inhibitor with elevated anticoagulation tests (e.g., aPTT, PT/INR, factor Xa activity assays) or use within 48 hours; blood glucose < 50 mg/dL **WARNINGS** Major bleeding (e.g., ICH), angioedema, cholesterol embolization (rare) **MONITORING** Neurological assessments and BP measurements every 15 minutes during the infusion and for 2 hours after, then every 30 minutes for the next 6 hours, then hourly until 24 hours after treatment Obtain follow-up brain imaging (e.g., head CT) 24 hrs after treatment, before starting anticoagulants or antiplatelet agents **NOTES** Must keep BP < 180/105 mmHg for at least the first 24 hours after treatment If severe headache, acute hypertension, nausea, vomiting or worsening neurological function occurs, discontinue the infusion and obtain an emergency head CT Contraindications to use of alteplase in ACS may be different The abbreviation "tPa" is prone to errors; not recommended by ISMP, but used commonly

Alteplase Drug Interactions

- There is a risk for additive effects when used in combination with other drugs that can ↑ bleeding risk. See the Learning Drug Interactions chapter for further discussion.

OTHER TREATMENTS

Aspirin

Aspirin 162 – 325 mg PO within 24 – 48 hours after stroke onset is recommended to prevent early recurrent stroke. Aspirin should not be given within 24 hours of fibrinolytic therapy.

Hypertension Management

Antihypertensives (e.g., IV labetalol, nicardipine or clevidipine) should be used to lower BP to < 185/110 mmHg prior to giving alteplase, and to maintain BP < 180/105 mmHg for at least 24 hours after the infusion. Patients who do not receive alteplase may not require treatment unless BP is severely elevated (≥ 220/120 mmHg). If treated, a 15% reduction in BP during the first 24 hours after stroke onset is considered safe. Once neurologically stable, antihypertensive medications may be restarted in patients with preexisting hypertension (or newly diagnosed hypertension). See the Secondary Prevention section for further discussion.

Hyperglycemia Management

Maintain blood glucose levels in the range of 140 – 180 mg/dL and closely monitor to prevent hypoglycemia.

Deep Vein Thrombosis (DVT) Prevention

DVT prophylaxis with intermittent pneumatic compression (IPC) devices is recommended. If subcutaneous anticoagulants (unfractionated heparin or LMWH) are used, they should not be started within 24 hours of receiving alteplase.

ISCHEMIC STROKE: SECONDARY PREVENTION

The recommendations below reflect secondary prevention measures after a first occurrence of stroke or TIA. Many of the same recommendations also apply to primary prevention of stroke.

TREATMENT OF MODIFIABLE RISK FACTORS

- Hypertension – blood pressure lowering treatment can be initiated after the first several days of stroke if BP is > 140/90 mmHg. ACE inhibitors and thiazide-type diuretics have the best evidence for stroke risk reduction, even in patients without a history of hypertension or with a baseline BP < 140/90 mmHg. BP goals should be individualized; a goal BP < 130/80 mmHg is recommended per the 2017 ACC/AHA Guideline for the Management of High Blood Pressure (see the Hypertension chapter). Lifestyle modifications are an important part of hypertension management (see below).
- Dyslipidemia – treat according to the 2018 ACC/AHA Guideline on the Treatment of Blood Cholesterol (see the Dyslipidemia chapter).
- Diabetes – patients with no established history should be screened for diabetes in the post stroke period; an A1C is the preferred test. Treat diabetes according to the most recent ADA guidelines (see the Diabetes chapter).
- Atrial fibrillation – cardioembolic stroke due to atrial fibrillation requires anticoagulation to prevent future strokes (see the Anticoagulation chapter).
- Lifestyle modifications – patients should be screened for obesity and counseled on lifestyle modifications for hypertension and cardiovascular risk reduction (e.g., smoking cessation, diet, exercise, weight loss).
  - Nutrition – sodium restriction to < 2.4 grams/day, or < 1.5 grams/day for greater blood pressure reduction, and a Mediterranean-type diet (emphasizing vegetables, fruits, whole grains, low-fat dairy products, poultry, legumes and olive oil) is recommended.
  - Physical activity – if capable, patients should engage in moderate-vigorous intensity exercise (at least 30 – 40 minutes most days of the week).
  - Weight reduction – maintain a BMI 18.5 – 24.9 kg/m^2 and a waist circumference < 35 inches for women and < 40 inches for men.
  - Alcohol intake – limit to ≤ 2 drinks/day for males and ≤ 1 drink/day for females.

ANTIPLATELET TREATMENT

For patients with non-cardioembolic ischemic stroke or TIA, an antiplatelet agent, rather than oral anticoagulation, is recommended to reduce the risk of recurrent stroke, MI or death. Aspirin is recommended within 24 – 48 hours after onset. Other antiplatelets (e.g., clopidogrel) should be used in patients who have a contraindication to aspirin.

The combination of aspirin and clopidogrel can be initiated within 24 hours of a minor ischemic stroke and continued for 21 days. This combination should not be used long-term for secondary prevention of stroke or TIA as it increases the risk of hemorrhage. This is different than the recommendations for dual antiplatelet therapy in heart disease (see the Ischemic Heart Disease and Acute Coronary Syndromes chapters).

For patients who have an ischemic stroke or TIA while taking aspirin, there is no added benefit to increasing the aspirin dose. Alternative antiplatelet agents are often considered, though no single agent or combination has been adequately studied in patients who have had an event while receiving aspirin.

Antiplatelet Drugs

Aspirin binds irreversibly to cyclooxygenase-1 and 2 (COX-1 and 2) enzymes, resulting in decreased prostaglandin (PG) and thromboxane A2 (TXA2) production; TXA2 is a potent vasoconstrictor and inducer of platelet aggregation. Aspirin has antiplatelet, antipyretic, analgesic and anti-inflammatory properties. Aspirin plus extended-release dipyridamole is another option; dipyridamole inhibits the uptake of adenosine into platelets and increases cAMP levels, which inhibits platelet aggregation. Clopidogrel is a prodrug that irreversibly inhibits P2Y12 ADP-mediated platelet activation and aggregation.

DRUG	DOSING	SAFETY/SIDE EFFECTS/MONITORING
Aspirin *(Bayer, Bufferin, Ecotrin,* *Ascriptin, Durlaza*, others) + omeprazole *(Yosprala)* OTC: tablet, chewable tablet, enteric-coated tablet, suppository Rx: ER capsule *(Durlaza)*, delayed-release tablet *(Yosprala)* See Pain chapter for more information on aspirin products	50-325 mg daily *Yosprala:* 81 mg/ 40 mg or 325 mg/ 40 mg daily Do not crush enteric-coated, delayed-release or ER products	**CONTRAINDICATIONS** NSAID or salicylate allergy; children and teenagers with viral infection (due to risk of Reye's syndrome) patients with rhinitis, nasal polyps or asthma (due to risk of urticaria, angioedema, or bronchospasm) **WARNINGS** Bleeding (including GI bleed/ulceration, others) – risk increased with heavy alcohol use or other drugs that ↑ bleeding risk (e.g., NSAIDs, anticoagulants, other antiplatelet agents) **SIDE EFFECTS** Dyspepsia, heartburn, nausea, tinnitus (in toxicity) **MONITORING** Bleeding, bruising **NOTES** *Yosprala* is indicated for patients who require aspirin but are at risk of developing aspirin-associated gastric ulcers
Extended-release dipyridamole/aspirin *(Aggrenox)* Capsule	200 mg/25 mg BID Intolerable headache: 200 mg/25 mg QHS (+ low-dose aspirin daily in the morning), then resume BID dosing within 1 week	As above for aspirin component plus: **WARNINGS** Hypotension and chest pain (in patients with coronary artery disease) can occur due to the vasodilatory effects of dipyridamole **SIDE EFFECTS** Headache, diarrhea **NOTES** Not interchangeable with the individual components of aspirin and dipyridamole Amount of aspirin provided is not adequate for prevention of cardiac events (e.g., MI)
Clopidogrel *(Plavix)* Tablet	75 mg daily	**BOXED WARNING** Clopidogrel is a prodrug. Effectiveness depends on the conversion to an active metabolite, mainly by CYP450 2C19. Poor metabolizers of CYP2C19 exhibit higher cardiovascular events than patients with normal CYP2C19 function. Tests to check CYP2C19 genotype can be used as an aid in determining a therapeutic strategy. Consider alternative treatments in patients identified as CYP2C19 poor metabolizers. Refer to the Pharmacogenomics chapter. **CONTRAINDICATIONS** Serious bleeding (e.g., GI bleed, intracranial hemorrhage) **WARNINGS** ↑ bleeding risk, stop 5 days prior to elective surgery (e.g., CABG); avoid use with omeprazole or esomeprazole (see Drug Interactions section); premature discontinuation (↑ risk of thrombosis); thrombotic thrombocytopenic purpura (TTP) has been reported **SIDE EFFECTS** Gastrointestinal hemorrhage, hematoma, pruritus **MONITORING** Symptoms of bleeding, Hgb/Hct as necessary **NOTES** Drug of choice in stroke/TIA patients with a contraindication or allergy to aspirin; do not use in combination with aspirin long-term for stroke prevention

Antiplatelet Drug Interactions

- Most drug interactions are due to additive effects with other agents that can ↑ bleeding risk (see the Learning Drug Interactions chapter).
- Clopidogrel: avoid in combination with omeprazole and esomeprazole (other PPIs interact less) and use caution with other CYP2C19 inhibitors.

HEMORRHAGIC STROKE

Hemorrhagic strokes result in a significant amount of morbidity and mortality. Treatment is largely supportive and includes airway management, establishing hemostasis, prevention or management of seizures, assessment for dysphagia, DVT prophylaxis and control of blood pressure and blood glucose. Hospitalized patients with hemorrhagic stroke should use IPC devices on the legs to prevent DVT; anticoagulants should not be used while the patient is bleeding.

INTRACEREBRAL HEMORRHAGE (ICH)

There is a high risk for rapid neurological deterioration in the early hours of an ICH, due to ongoing bleeding and enlargement of the hematoma in the brain. Patients with a severe coagulation factor deficiency or severe thrombocytopenia should receive appropriate factor replacement therapy or platelet infusions. In patients with ICH who are anticoagulated, reversal of the anticoagulant effects should be considered (see the Anticoagulation chapter for information on reversal agents). If there is clinical evidence of seizures, they should be treated, but prophylactic anticonvulsant medication should not be used.

Increased intracranial pressure (ICP) is the primary complication in ICH. Measures should be taken to lower the ICP; these include elevating the head of the bed by 30 degrees and using mannitol or hypertonic saline.

Mannitol

Mannitol produces an osmotic diuresis by increasing the osmotic pressure of the glomerular filtrate in the kidneys. This inhibits tubular reabsorption of water and electrolytes and increases urinary output. Mannitol reduces ICP by withdrawing water from the brain parenchyma and excreting it in the urine.

DRUG	DOSING	SAFETY/SIDE EFFECTS/MONITORING
Mannitol *(Osmitrol)*	5%, 10%, 15%, 20%, 25% Mannitol 20%: 0.25-1 grams/kg/dose IV Q6-8H PRN	**CONTRAINDICATIONS** Severe renal disease (anuria), severe dehydration, progressive heart failure, pulmonary edema or congestion **WARNINGS** Can accumulate in the brain (causing rebound increases in ICP) if used for long periods of time as a continuous infusion; intermittent boluses preferred **SIDE EFFECTS** Fluid and electrolyte loss, dehydration, hyperosmolar-induced hyperkalemia, acidosis, ↑ osmolar gap, extravasation (vesicant) **MONITORING** Renal function, daily fluid intake and output, serum electrolytes, serum and urine osmolality, CPP, ICP **NOTES** Maintain serum osmolality < 300-320 mOsm/kg

ACUTE SUBARACHNOID HEMORRHAGE (SAH)

SAH is bleeding that occurs in the space between the brain and the surrounding membrane (subarachnoid space). SAH usually results from the rupture of a cerebral aneurysm and presents with severe headache, often described as the worst headache the patient has ever experienced. Surgical clipping or endovascular coiling, to completely remove the aneurysm, is performed when feasible to prevent rebleeding. Cerebral artery vasospasm can occur 3 – 21 days after the bleed, causing delayed cerebral ischemia. Oral nimodipine is used to prevent vasospasm. The use of prophylactic anticonvulsants may be considered in the immediate post-hemorrhagic period to prevent seizures. The routine use of long-term anticonvulsants is not recommended, but may be considered for patients with known risk factors for delayed seizure disorder (e.g., prior seizure, intracerebral hematoma).

Nimodipine

Nimodipine is a dihydropyridine calcium channel blocker that is more selective for cerebral arteries due to increased lipophilicity.

DRUG	DOSING	SAFETY/SIDE EFFECTS/MONITORING
Nimodipine (*Nymalize*) Capsule, oral solution	60 mg PO Q4H for 21 days Start within 96 hours of SAH onset Swallow capsules whole; administer on an empty stomach, at least 1 hour before or 2 hours after meals Patients with cirrhosis: 30 mg PO Q4H for 21 days (closely monitor)	**BOXED WARNING** Do not administer nimodipine IV or by other parenteral routes; death and serious life-threatening adverse events have occurred (including cardiac arrest, cardiovascular collapse, hypotension and bradycardia) when the contents of nimodipine capsules have been inadvertently injected parenterally (see Notes) **CONTRAINDICATIONS** ↑ risk of significant hypotension when used in combination with strong inhibitors of CYP3A4 (see Drug Interactions section) **SIDE EFFECTS** Hypotension, bradycardia, headache, nausea, edema **MONITORING** CPP, ICP, BP, HR, neurological checks **NOTES** If capsules cannot be swallowed, contents may be withdrawn with a parenteral syringe, then transferred to an oral syringe that cannot accept a needle and that can only administer medication orally or via nasogastric tube; label oral syringes "For Oral Use Only" or "Not for IV Use"; the medication should be drawn up in the pharmacy to reduce medication errors

Nimodipine Drug Interactions

- Nimodipine is a major substrate of CYP3A4; strong CYP3A4 inhibitors (e.g., clarithromycin, protease inhibitors, azole antifungals) are contraindicated. Avoid grapefruit juice. Strong CYP3A4 inducers (e.g., rifampin, carbamazepine, phenytoin, St. John's wort) can decrease the levels of nimodipine and should be avoided.

Select Guidelines/References

2018 Guidelines for the early management of patients with acute ischemic stroke. AHA/ASA. *Stroke.* 2018;49:e46-e99.

Guidelines for the prevention of stroke in patients with stroke and transient ischemic attack. AHA/ASA. *Stroke.* 2014;45:2160-2236.

Guidelines for the management of spontaneous intracerebral hemorrhage. AHA/ASA. *Stroke.* 2015;41:2108-2129.

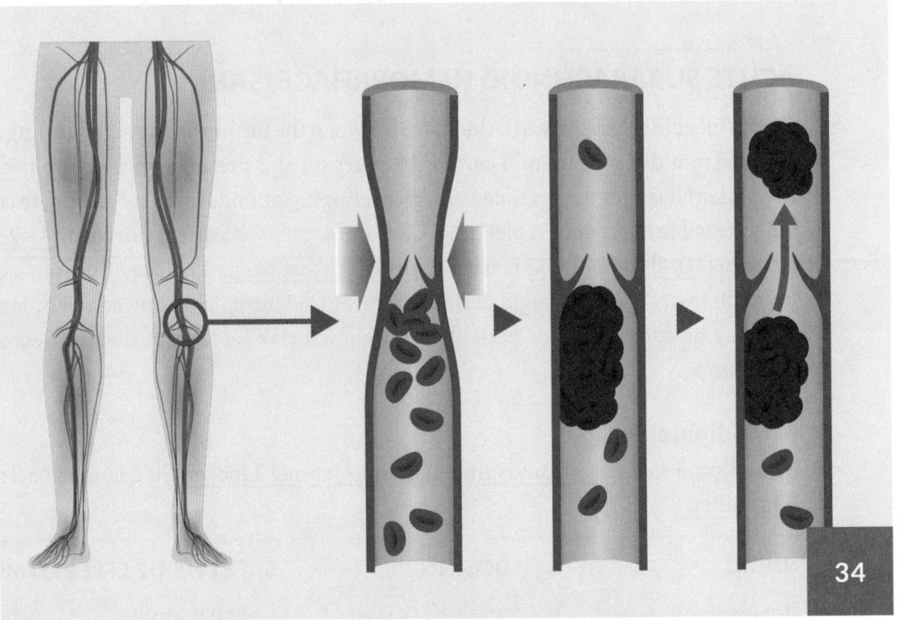

34

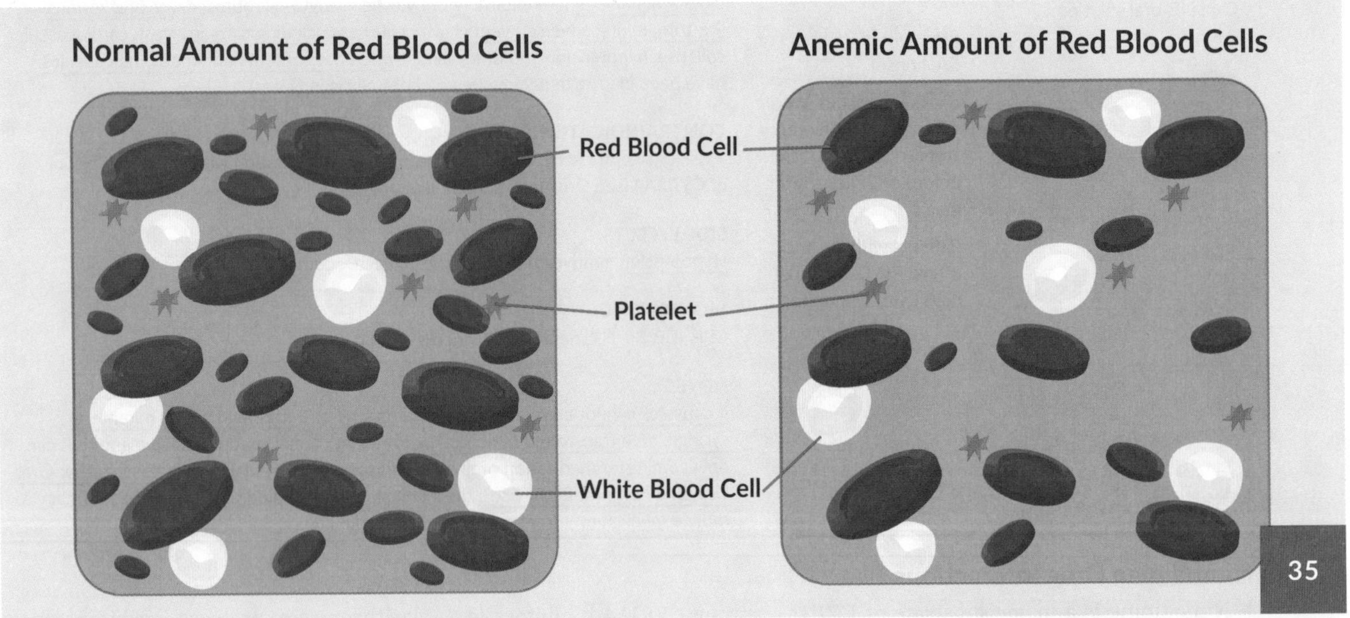

Normal Amount of Red Blood Cells
Anemic Amount of Red Blood Cells
Red Blood Cell
Platelet
White Blood Cell

35

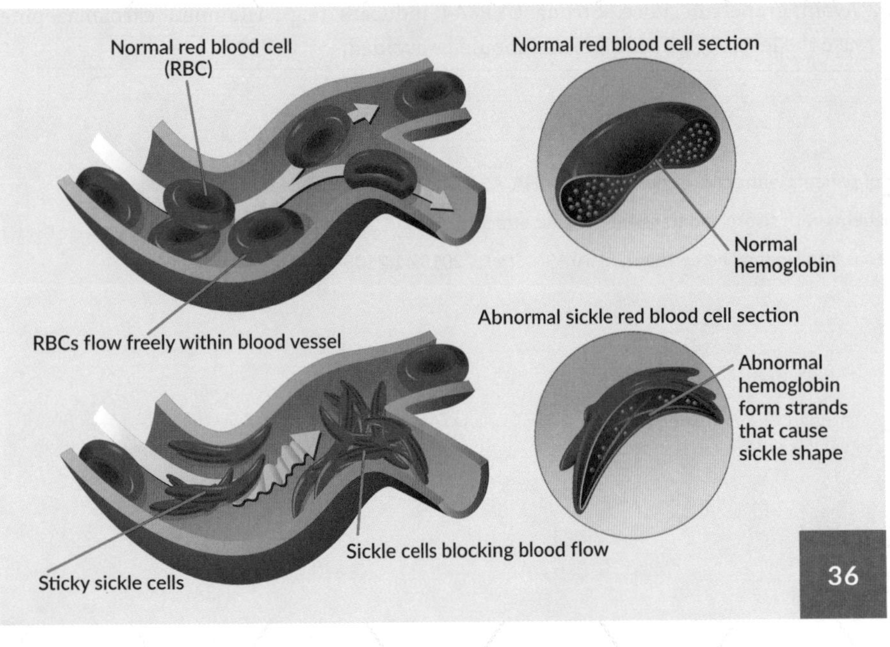

Normal red blood cell (RBC)
Normal red blood cell section
Normal hemoglobin
RBCs flow freely within blood vessel
Abnormal sickle red blood cell section
Abnormal hemoglobin form strands that cause sickle shape
Sickle cells blocking blood flow
Sticky sickle cells

36

ANTICOAGULATION & BLOOD DISORDERS

CONTENTS

CHAPTER 34
ANTICOAGULATION | **526**

CHAPTER 35
ANEMIA | **542**

CHAPTER 36
SICKLE CELL DISEASE | **550**

CHAPTER CONTENT

Background ... 526
Clot Formation ... 526
- Anticoagulants are for Blood Clots ... 526
- Coagulation Cascade ... 527

Drug Treatment ... 527
- Vitamin K Antagonism ... 527
- Factor Xa Inhibition ... 527
- Thrombin Inhibition ... 528
- High Alert Medications ... 528

Unfractionated Heparin ... 528
Low Molecular Weight Heparins ... 529
Heparin-Induced Thrombocytopenia Overview ... 530
- Management of HIT Complicated by Thrombosis (HITT) ... 530

Factor Xa Inhibitors ... 530
- Conversion Between Anticoagulants ... 532

Direct Thrombin Inhibitors ... 533
- Dabigatran Drug Interactions ... 534

Warfarin ... 534
- Warfarin Drug Interactions ... 535
- Warfarin Use – Key Points ... 535
- Warfarin Tablet Colors ... 535

Antidotes For Reversal ... 536
- Warfarin Reversal ... 538

Perioperative Management of Patients on Warfarin ... 538
Venous Thromboembolism (VTE) ... 538
- Diagnosis ... 538
- VTE Prophylaxis ... 538
- VTE Treatment ... 539

Atrial Fibrillation/Flutter ... 539
Anticoagulation in Pregnancy ... 540
Patient Counseling ... 540

CONTENT LEGEND

(💡) = Study Tip Gal

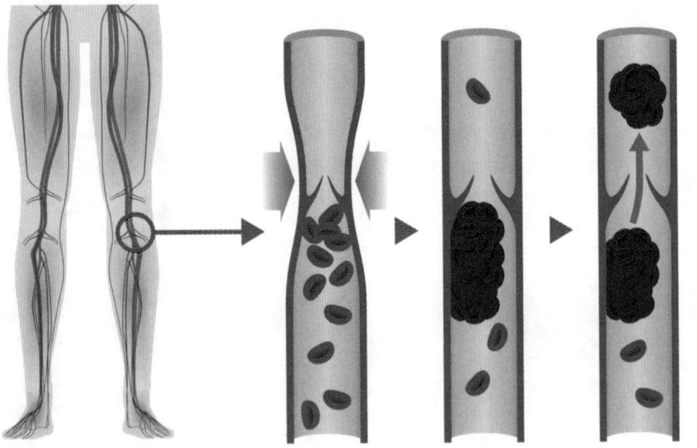

CHAPTER 34

ANTICOAGULATION

BACKGROUND

Anticoagulants are used to prevent blood clots from forming and to keep existing clots from becoming larger. They do not break down clots (like thrombolytics). Anticoagulants are commonly used for acute coronary syndrome (ACS), prevention of cardioembolic stroke and prevention/treatment of venous thromboembolism (VTE), which refers to deep vein thrombosis (DVT) and/or pulmonary embolism (PE) (see Study Tip Gal). The most common side effect from anticoagulants is bleeding, which can be fatal. Anticoagulants are high-risk medications for this reason.

CLOT FORMATION

Coagulation is the process by which blood clots form. A number of factors can lead to activation of the coagulation process such as blood vessel injury, blood stasis (stopping or slowing of blood flow) and pro-thrombotic conditions. Coagulation involves activation of platelets and the clotting cascade. All of the clotting factors have an inactive and an active form. Once activated, a clotting factor will activate the next clotting factor in the sequence until fibrin is formed. The coagulation cascade has two pathways which lead to fibrin formation: the contact activation pathway (or the intrinsic pathway) and the tissue factor pathway (or the extrinsic pathway). Anticoagulants inhibit the coagulation cascade and prevent (or reduce) clot formation.

ANTICOAGULANTS ARE FOR BLOOD CLOTS

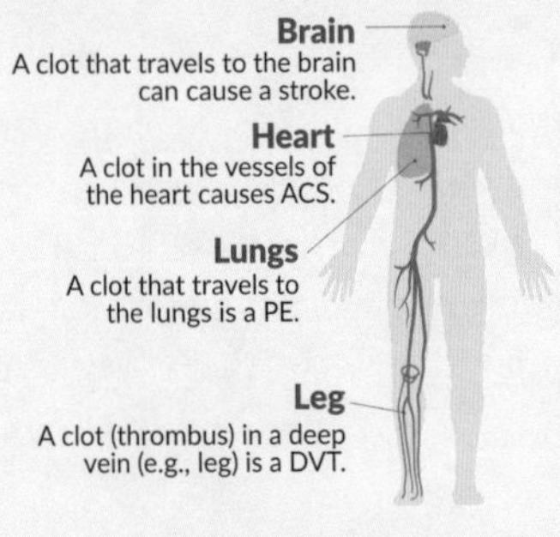

Blood clots can form anywhere in the body and cause serious conditions that can be fatal. If the clot (or a piece of it) travels to another location it is called an embolus. Anticoagulants are used to treat all of these conditions

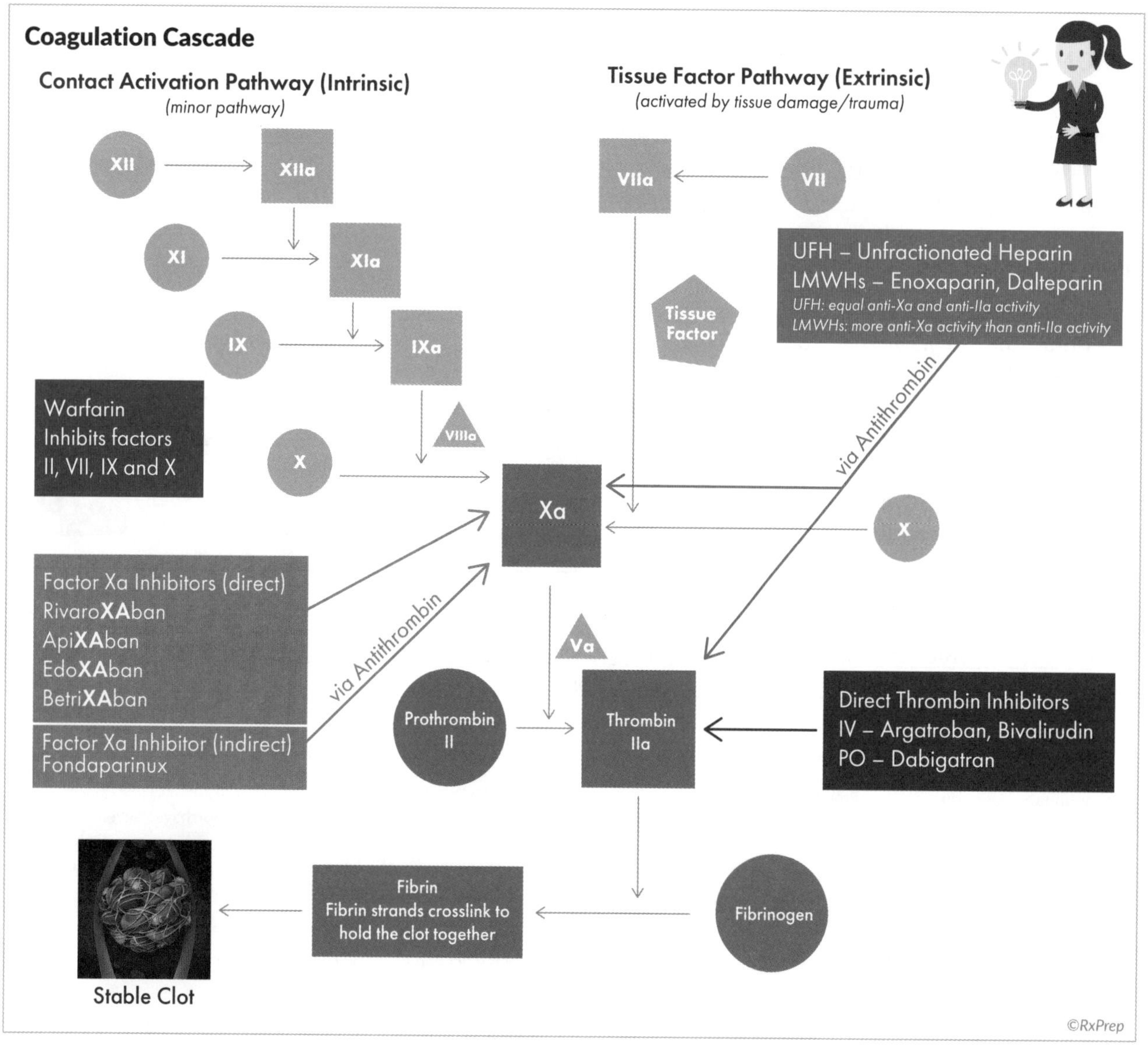

DRUG TREATMENT

Anticoagulants work by various mechanisms (see Study Tip Gal above). Injectable anticoagulants are used for ACS and VTE (treatment and prevention), while oral anticoagulants are used mainly for VTE (treatment and prevention) and stroke prevention in patients with AFib. An overview of these clinical conditions is included at the end of the chapter.

VITAMIN K ANTAGONISM

Warfarin is a vitamin K antagonist. Vitamin K is required for the carboxylation (activation) of clotting factors II, VII, IX and X. Without adequate vitamin K, the liver produces the clotting factors, but they have reduced coagulant activity. Warfarin has a narrow therapeutic range and requires careful monitoring of the international normalized ratio (INR), which is affected by many drugs and changes in dietary vitamin K.

FACTOR Xa INHIBITION

Unfractionated heparin (UFH), low molecular weight heparins (LMWHs) and fondaparinux work by binding to antithrombin (AT) causing a conformational change which increases AT activity 1,000-fold. AT inactivates thrombin and other proteases like factor Xa involved in blood clotting. LMWHs inhibit factor Xa more specifically than unfractionated heparin. Fondaparinux *(Arixtra)* requires AT binding to selectively inhibit Factor Xa. Apixaban *(Eliquis)*, betrixaban *(Bevyxxa)*, edoxaban *(Savaysa)* and rivaroxaban *(Xarelto)*, work by inhibiting factor Xa directly. These oral agents are taken once or twice daily and require no laboratory monitoring for efficacy.

THROMBIN INHIBITION

UFH and LMWH inhibit thrombin, and Factor Xa, through antithrombin binding. Direct thrombin inhibitors (DTIs) block thrombin directly, decreasing the amount of fibrin available for clot formation. The intravenous DTIs are important clinically since they do not cross-react with heparin-induced thrombocytopenia (HIT) antibodies. Once HIT develops in the hospital setting, the injectable DTI argatroban is the drug of choice. Dabigatran (*Pradaxa*) is an oral DTI.

HIGH ALERT MEDICATIONS

All anticoagulants can cause significant bleeding and are classified as "high-alert" medications by the Institute for Safe Medication Practices (ISMP). Bleeding events with anticoagulants put patients at increased risk for death. The Joint Commission's National Patient Safety Goals require policies and protocols to properly initiate and manage anticoagulant therapy. Patients receiving anticoagulants should receive individualized care through a defined process that includes standardized ordering, dispensing, administration, monitoring and patient/caregiver education (for treatment doses). Refer to the Medication Safety & Quality Improvement chapter for additional information. When pharmacists are involved in managing anticoagulants, patient care and outcomes are improved and costs are decreased.

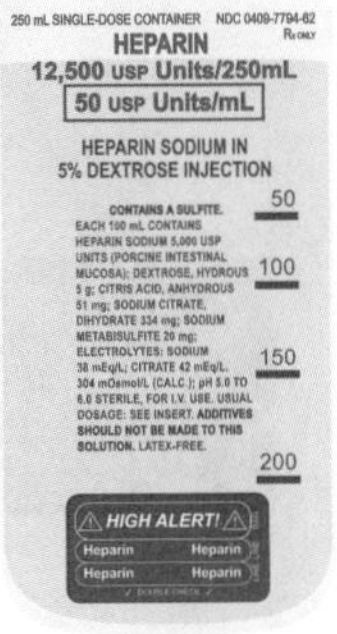

UNFRACTIONATED HEPARIN

UFH binds to antithrombin (AT), which then inactivates thrombin (Factor IIa) and Factor Xa (as well as factors IXa, XIa, XIIa and plasmin) and prevents the conversion of fibrinogen to fibrin.

DRUG	DOSING	SAFETY/SIDE EFFECTS/MONITORING
Unfractionated Heparin Injection **Anticoagulation Treatment/ Prophylaxis** Treatment infusion: 25,000 units in 250 mL (concentration: 100 units/mL) in D5W, ½ NS or NS Many strengths and volumes (ranging 1 unit/mL to 20,000 units/mL), including total units of 5,000, 10,000, 12,500, 20,000, 25,000 & others **Line Flush** 10 units/mL, 100 units/mL syringes (in 1, 2, 2.5, 3, 5, 10, 30 mL), others	**Prophylaxis of VTE** 5,000 units SC Q8-12H **Treatment of VTE** 80 units/kg IV bolus; 18 units/kg/hr infusion or 5,000 units IV bolus; 1,000 units/hr infusion. If outpatient, 333 units/kg x 1 dose SC; 250 units/kg SC Q12H **Treatment of ACS/STEMI** 60 units/kg IV bolus (max 4,000 units); infuse 12 units/kg/hr (max 1,000 units/hr) Use total body weight for dosing Onset: IV: immediate; SC: 20-30 min t½ = 1.5 hrs HIT antibodies have cross-sensitivity with LMWHs	**CONTRAINDICATIONS** Uncontrolled active bleed (intracranial hemorrhage), severe thrombocytopenia, history of HIT, hypersensitivity to pork products. Some products contain benzyl alcohol as a preservative (do not use in neonates, infants, pregnancy and breastfeeding) **WARNING** Fatal medication errors: verify the correct concentration is chosen **SIDE EFFECTS** Bleeding (epistaxis, ecchymosis, gingival, GI), thrombocytopenia, HIT, alopecia, hyperkalemia and osteoporosis (with long-term use) **MONITORING** aPTT or anti-Xa level aPTT taken 6 hours after initiation and every 6 hrs until therapeutic range of 1.5-2.5 x control (patient's baseline), then every 24 hrs aPTT after every dosage change Platelets, Hgb, Hct at baseline and daily (↓ in platelets > 50% from baseline suggests possible HIT) **NOTES** Antidote: protamine (see Antidotes and Reversal section) Unpredictable anticoagulant response (has variable and extensive binding to plasma proteins and cells) Continuous IV infusions are common for treating VTE and ACS because heparin has a very short half-life Do not give IM due to hematoma risk Heparin lock-flushes (*HepFlush*) are only used to keep IV lines open. Fatal errors, especially in neonates, occurred when the incorrect heparin strength (higher dose) was chosen. Heparin injection 10,000 units/mL and flushes 10 or 100 units/mL look and sound alike.

LOW MOLECULAR WEIGHT HEPARINS

LMWHs bind to AT, which inactivates Factor Xa and Factor IIa. The anti-factor Xa activity is much greater then the anti-factor IIa activity.

DRUG	DOSING	SAFETY/SIDE EFFECTS/MONITORING
Enoxaparin (*Lovenox*) Multidose vial (300 mg/3 mL) and prefilled syringes: 30 mg/0.3 mL 40 mg/0.4 mL 60 mg/0.6 mL 80 mg/0.8 mL 100 mg/mL 120 mg/0.8 mL 150 mg/mL 1 mg = 100 units anti-Xa activity	**Prophylaxis of VTE** 30 mg SC Q12H or 40 mg SC daily CrCl < 30 mL/min: 30 mg SC daily **Treatment of VTE and UA/NSTEMI** 1 mg/kg SC Q12H (or 1.5 mg/kg SC daily only for inpatient VTE treatment) CrCl < 30 mL/min: 1 mg/kg SC daily Use total body weight for dosing **Treatment for STEMI** Patients < 75 years: 30 mg IV bolus plus a 1 mg/kg SC dose followed by 1 mg/kg SC Q12H (max 100 mg for the first two SC doses only) CrCl < 30 mL/min: 30 mg IV bolus plus a 1 mg/kg SC dose, followed by 1 mg/kg SC daily Patients ≥ 75 years: 0.75 mg/kg SC Q12H (no bolus – max 75 mg for the first two SC doses only) CrCl < 30 mL/min: 1 mg/kg SC daily (no bolus) Patients managed with percutaneous coronary intervention (PCI): if the last SC dose was given 8-12 hours before balloon inflation, give 0.3 mg/kg IV bolus	**BOXED WARNING** Patients receiving neuraxial anesthesia (epidural, spinal) or undergoing spinal puncture are at risk of hematomas and subsequent paralysis **CONTRAINDICATIONS** History of HIT, active major bleed, hypersensitivity to pork **SIDE EFFECTS** Bleeding, anemia, ↑ LFTs, thrombocytopenia, hyperkalemia, injection site reactions (bruising) **MONITORING** Platelets, Hgb, Hct, SCr Anti-Xa level monitoring is recommended in pregnancy Monitoring may be done in obesity, low body weight, pediatrics, elderly or renal insufficiency aPTT is not used Obtain peak anti-Xa levels 4 hours post SC dose **NOTES** More predictable anticoagulant response than UFH; does not require anti-Xa level monitoring in most cases. This makes LMWH more cost effective, even though the actual drug costs more than UFH Antidote: protamine (see Antidotes and Reversal section) Do not expel air bubble from syringe prior to injection (can cause loss of drug) Do not administer IM Store at room temperature
Dalteparin (*Fragmin*)	**Prophylaxis of VTE** 2,500-5,000 units SC daily **Treatment of UA/NSTEMI** 120 units/kg (max 10,000 units) SC Q12H	

UFH/LMWH Drug Interactions

- Most drug interactions are due to additive effects with other drugs that can ↑ bleeding risk (other anticoagulants, antiplatelet drugs, some herbals, NSAIDs, SSRIs, SNRIs, thrombolytics). See the Learning Drug Interactions chapter.

KEY POINTS

When studying the Anticoagulation, Acute Coronary Syndrome, Ischemic Heart Disease and Stroke chapters, it can be difficult to determine when a fibrinolytic, antiplatelet or anticoagulant would be appropriate.

- Fibrinolytics break down existing clots, but are associated with very high risk of bleeding. They are used for STEMI and acute ischemic stroke, when the patient could die without rapid restoration of blood flow.
- Antiplatelet agents (aspirin, clopidogrel) are used mainly for ACS and to prevent stroke/TIA. Dual antiplatelet therapy (DAPT) refers to using both aspirin and a P2Y12 inhibitor (e.g., clopidogrel) together, which is very common in patients who have had an ACS. Antiplatelet agents are not sufficient for treating DVT/PE.
- Oral anticoagulants are used mainly in AFib (for stroke prevention) and for DVT/PE (treatment and prevention). Oral medications like *Xarelto* or *Eliquis* are not indicated for ACS when platelet aggregation is the main target of drug therapy.

HEPARIN-INDUCED THROMBOCYTOPENIA OVERVIEW

Heparin-induced thrombocytopenia (HIT) is an immune-mediated IgG drug reaction that has a high risk of venous and arterial thrombosis (clot). The immune system forms antibodies against heparin bound to platelet factor 4 (PF 4), the antibodies then join with heparin and PF 4 to create a complex, and this complex binds to the Fc receptors on platelets. This causes platelet activation and a release of pro-coagulant microparticles. If left untreated, HIT can lead to a prothrombotic state causing many complications including heparin-induced thrombocytopenia and thrombosis (HITT). HITT leads to amputations, post-thrombotic syndrome and/or death. The estimated incidence of HIT is ~3% of those patients exposed to heparin for more than four days. It is lower with a shorter duration of treatment. The typical onset of HIT occurs 5 – 14 days after the start of heparin or within hours if a patient has been exposed to heparin within the past three months. A diagnosis is made by a compatible clinical picture, an unexplained drop in platelet count (defined as > 50% drop from baseline) and laboratory confirmation of antibodies (ELISA test and confirmatory serotonin release assay) or platelet activation by heparin. Thrombocytopenia is the most common sign of HIT. A thrombosis can come before thrombocytopenia in up to 25% of patients with HIT.

MANAGEMENT OF HIT COMPLICATED BY THROMBOSIS (HITT)

- If HIT is suspected or confirmed, stop all forms of heparin and LMWH including heparin flushes (can use regional citrate) and heparin-coated catheters. If the patient is on warfarin and diagnosed with HIT, the warfarin should be discontinued and vitamin K should be administered. Although the patient is at a high-risk of thrombosis, warfarin use with a low platelet count has a high correlation with warfarin-induced limb gangrene and necrosis.
- In patients with HIT, non-heparin anticoagulants are recommended (in particular, argatroban) over heparin, LMWH or vitamin K antagonists.
- Do not start warfarin therapy until the platelets have recovered to ≥ 150,000/mm^3. Warfarin should be initiated at lower doses (5 mg maximum). Overlap warfarin with a non-heparin anticoagulant for a minimum of five days and until the INR is within target range for 24 hours. Argatroban can increase the INR, value must be interpreted cautiously.
- If urgent cardiac surgery or PCI is required, bivalirudin is the preferred anticoagulant.

FACTOR Xa INHIBITORS

Apixaban *(Eliquis)*, betrixaban *(Bevyxxa)*, edoxaban *(Savaysa)* and rivaroxaban *(Xarelto)* are direct Factor Xa inhibitors that are available orally. Fondaparinux *(Arixtra)* is an injectable synthetic pentasaccharide that selectively inhibits Factor Xa via antithrombin (AT), making it an indirect inhibitor of Factor Xa. Fondaparinux is used off-label in practice for HIT.

DRUG	DOSING	SAFETY/SIDE EFFECTS/ MONITORING
Oral Direct Factor Xa Inhibitors		
Apixaban *(Eliquis)* Tablet Missed Dose: Take immediately on the same day and twice daily administration should be resumed. The dose should not be doubled to make up for a missed dose.	**Nonvalvular AFib (stroke prophylaxis)** 5 mg BID Unless patient has at least 2 of the following: age ≥ 80 years, body weight ≤ 60 kg, or SCr ≥ 1.5 mg/dL, then give 2.5 mg BID **Treatment of DVT/PE** 10 mg PO BID x 7 days, then 5 mg PO BID **Prophylaxis for DVT (after knee/hip replacement)** 2.5 mg PO BID (for 12 days after knee or 35 days after hip replacement surgery). Give first dose 12-24 hours after surgery **Reduction in the Risk of Recurrence of DVT and PE** 2.5 mg PO BID after at least 6 months of treatment for DVT or PE	**BOXED WARNINGS** All: patients receiving neuraxial anesthesia (epidural, spinal) or undergoing spinal puncture are at risk of hematomas and subsequent paralysis Apixaban, edoxaban and rivaroxaban: premature discontinuation ↑ risk of thrombotic events Edoxaban only: reduced efficacy in nonvalvular AFib patients with CrCl > 95 mL/min; do not use **CONTRAINDICATIONS** Active pathological bleeding **WARNINGS** Not recommended with prosthetic heart valves, avoid in patients with moderate to severe hepatic impairment **SIDE EFFECTS** Bleeding, anemia Edoxaban: rash, ↑ LFTs **MONITORING** Hgb, Hct, SCr, LFTs; no monitoring of efficacy required **NOTES** Antidote for apixaban and rivaroxaban: andexanet alfa *(Andexxa)* Can be crushed and put on applesauce (apixaban, edoxaban, rivaroxaban); crushed and mixed in water, D5W or apple juice (apixaban) or suspended in water to administer by NG tube (apixaban, edoxaban, rivaroxaban) Betrixaban is not approved for treating DVT/PE or nonvalvular AFib **Elective Surgery** Discontinue 24 hours prior to elective surgery (rivaroxaban, edoxaban) Discontinue 48 hours prior to elective surgery with moderate-high bleeding risk or 24 hours prior with a low bleeding risk (apixaban)
Rivaroxaban *(Xarelto)* Tablet *Xarelto Starter Pack:* 30-day blister pack containing 15 mg and 20 mg tablets (for ease of prescribing for DVT/PE treatment) Missed Dose: Administer the dose as soon as possible on the same day as follows: If taking 15 mg twice daily: take immediately to ensure intake of 30 mg/day. In this particular instance, two 15 mg tablets may be taken at once. Then resume regular schedule on the following day If taking 10, 15 or 20 mg once daily: take immediately on the same day; otherwise skip	Doses ≥ 15 mg must be taken with food; 10 mg dose can be taken without regard to meals **Nonvalvular AFib (stroke prophylaxis)** CrCl > 50 mL/min: 20 mg PO daily with evening meal CrCl 15-50 mL/min: 15 mg PO daily with evening meal CrCl < 15 mL/min: avoid use **Treatment of DVT/PE** 15 mg PO BID x 21 days, then 20 mg PO daily CrCl < 30 mL/min: avoid use **Prophylaxis for DVT (after knee/hip replacement)** 10 mg PO daily (for 12 days after knee or 35 days after hip replacement surgery). Give first dose 6-10 hours after surgery CrCl < 30 mL/min: avoid use **Reduction in the Risk of Recurrence of DVT and PE (after 6 months of standard treatment)** 10 mg PO daily CrCl < 30 mL/min: avoid use **Reduction in the Risk of Major CVD events in CAD/PAD** 2.5 mg PO BID in combination with low-dose aspirin	
Edoxaban *(Savaysa)* Tablet Missed Dose: Take immediately on the same day. The dose should not be doubled to make up for a missed dose	**Nonvalvular AFib (stroke prophylaxis)** CrCl > 95 mL/min: do not use CrCl 51-95 mL/min: 60 mg daily CrCl 15-50 mL/min: 30 mg daily CrCl < 15 mL/min: not recommended **Treatment of DVT/PE** 60 mg daily, start after 5-10 days of parenteral anticoagulation CrCl 15-50 mL/min or body weight ≤ 60 kg or on certain P-gp inhibitors: 30 mg daily CrCl < 15 mL/min: not recommended	
Betrixaban *(Bevyxxa)* Capsule Missed Dose: Take immediately on the same day. The dose should not be doubled to make up for a missed dose	**Prophylaxis of VTE in adult patients hospitalized for medical illness** 160 mg x 1, then 80 mg PO daily with food; recommended duration: 35-42 days CrCl ≥ 15 to < 30 mL/min: 80 mg x 1, then 40 mg PO daily with food	

DRUG	DOSING	SAFETY/SIDE EFFECTS/MONITORING
Injectable Indirect Factor Xa Inhibitor (SC)		
Fondaparinux (*Arixtra*) Prefilled syringes: 2.5 mg/0.5 mL, 5 mg/0.4 mL, 7.5 mg/0.6 mL, 10 mg/0.8 mL Store at room temperature	**Prophylaxis of VTE** ≥ 50 kg: 2.5 mg SC daily < 50 kg: contraindicated **Treatment of VTE** < 50 kg: 5 mg SC daily 50-100 kg: 7.5 mg SC daily > 100 kg: 10 mg SC daily **Both indications** CrCl 30-50 mL/min: use caution CrCl < 30 mL/min: contraindicated	**BOXED WARNING** Patients receiving neuraxial anesthesia (epidural, spinal) or undergoing spinal puncture are at risk of hematomas and subsequent paralysis **CONTRAINDICATIONS** Severe renal impairment (CrCl < 30 mL/min), active major bleed, bacterial endocarditis, thrombocytopenia with positive test for anti-platelet antibodies in presence of fondaparinux **SIDE EFFECTS** Bleeding (epistaxis, ecchymosis, gingival, GI, etc.), anemia, local injection site reactions (rash, pruritus, bruising), thrombocytopenia, hypokalemia, hypotension **MONITORING** Anti-Xa levels (3 hrs post-dose), platelets, Hgb, Hct, SCr **NOTES** Do not expel air bubble from syringe prior to injection No antidote Do not administer IM

Factor Xa Inhibitor Drug Interactions

- Avoid using with other anticoagulants (unless benefit outweighs risk). Monitor for additive effects with other drugs that can ↑ bleeding risk (antiplatelet drugs, some herbals, NSAIDs, SSRIs, SNRIs, thrombolytics). See the Learning Drug Interactions chapter.
- Apixaban is a substrate of CYP450 3A4 (major) and P-gp. Avoid use with strong dual inducers of CYP3A4 and P-gp (e.g., carbamazepine, phenytoin, rifampin, St. John's wort). For patients receiving doses > 2.5 mg BID, the dose of apixaban should be decreased by 50% when coadministered with drugs that are strong dual inhibitors of CYP3A4 and P-gp (e.g., clarithromycin, itraconazole, ketoconazole, or ritonavir). For patients taking 2.5 mg BID, avoid these strong dual inhibitors.
- Rivaroxaban is a substrate of CYP3A4 (major) and P-gp. Avoid use with drugs that are combined P-gp and strong CYP3A4 inducers (e.g., carbamazepine, phenytoin, rifampin, St. John's wort) or combined P-gp and strong CYP3A4 inhibitors (e.g., ketoconazole, itraconazole, lopinavir/ritonavir, ritonavir, indinavir, and conivaptan). The benefit must outweigh the potential risks in these situations: CrCl 15 – 80 mL/min who are receiving combined P-gp and moderate CYP3A4 inhibitors (e.g., diltiazem, verapamil, dronedarone, erythromycin).
- Betrixaban is a substrate of P-gp. Reduce the dose when used with P-gp inhibitors (amiodarone, verapamil, ketoconazole, clarithromycin). Avoid betrixaban in patients with severe renal impairment receiving P-gp inhibitors.
- Edoxaban is a substrate of P-gp; avoid use with rifampin. When treating DVT/PE, reduce dose to 30 mg daily with verapamil, macrolides (azithromycin, clarithromycin, erythromycin) and oral itraconazole or ketoconazole.
- *Stribild, Genvoya* (each containing cobicistat) and *Tybost* can increase exposure to the factor Xa inhibitors. Rivaroxaban should not be used with any of these medications. Recommendations are product-specific for the other anticoagulants.

CONVERSION BETWEEN ANTICOAGULANTS

- From warfarin to another oral anticoagulant*. Stop warfarin and convert to:
  - **R**ivaroxaban when INR is < 3
  - **E**doxaban when INR is ≤ 2.5
  - **A**pixaban when INR is < 2
  - **D**abigatran when INR is < 2

Remember: **READ**

**Converting from warfarin to betrixaban should not be required because they do not have the same indications.*

- From oral Xa inhibitors (apixaban, edoxaban and rivaroxaban) to warfarin:
  - Overlap Xa inhibitor with warfarin until INR therapeutic.
  - Stop Xa inhibitor. Start parenteral anticoagulant and warfarin at next scheduled dose. Refer to warfarin initiation later in this chapter. Refer to package labeling for other conversion recommendations.
- From dabigatran to warfarin:
  - Start warfarin 1-3 days before stopping dabigatran (determined by renal function). Refer to dabigatran labeling for specifics.

DIRECT THROMBIN INHIBITORS

These agents directly inhibit thrombin (Factor IIa); they bind to the active thrombin site of free and clot-associated thrombin.

DRUG	DOSING	SAFETY/SIDE EFFECTS/MONITORING
Oral Direct Thrombin Inhibitor		
Dabigatran *(Pradaxa)* Capsules Missed Dose: Take immediately unless it is within 6 hours of next scheduled dose; the dose should not be doubled to make up for a missed dose	**Nonvalvular AFib (stroke prophylaxis)** 150 mg BID CrCl 15-30 mL/min: 75 mg BID CrCl < 15 mL/min: no recommendations **Treatment of DVT/PE and Reduction in the Risk of Recurrence of DVT and PE** 150 mg BID, start after 5-10 days of parenteral anticoagulation CrCl ≤ 30 mL/min: no recommendations **Prophylaxis of DVT/PE following hip replacement surgery** 110 mg on day 1, then 220 mg daily CrCl ≤ 30 mL/min: no recommendations	**BOXED WARNINGS** Patients receiving neuraxial anesthesia (epidural, spinal) or undergoing spinal puncture are at risk of hematomas and subsequent paralysis Premature discontinuation ↑ risk of thrombotic events **CONTRAINDICATIONS** Active pathological bleeding, treatment of patients with mechanical prosthetic heart valve/s **SIDE EFFECTS** Dyspepsia, gastritis-like symptoms, bleeding (including more GI bleeding) **MONITORING** Hgb, Hct, SCr; no monitoring of efficacy required **NOTES** Antidote: idarucizumab *(Praxbind)* Protect from moisture; dispense in original container and discard 4 months after opening Blister packs are good until the date on the pack Swallow capsules whole (do not break, chew, crush or open); do not administer by NG tube Can ↑ aPTT, PT/INR Discontinue if undergoing invasive surgery (1-2 days before if CrCl ≥ 50 mL/min, 3-5 days before if CrCl < 50 mL/min)
Injectable Direct Thrombin Inhibitors (IV or SC)		
Argatroban Injection Indicated for HIT and in patients undergoing PCI who are at risk for HIT **Bivalirudin *(Angiomax)*** Injection Indicated for patients with ACS undergoing PCI and are at risk for HIT	**HIT** Argatroban: initial: 2 mcg/kg/min – titrate to target aPTT. Max: 10 mcg/kg/min **PCI** IV drugs given as a bolus followed by an infusion; all are weight-based Used in patients at risk for HIT Argatroban – ↓ dose in hepatic impairment Bivalirudin – ↓ dose when CrCl < 30 mL/min	**CONTRAINDICATIONS** Active major bleeding **SIDE EFFECTS** Bleeding, anemia, hematoma **MONITORING** aPTT and/or ACT (for bivalirudin), platelets, Hgb, Hct, renal function **NOTES** Safe for patients with history of HIT; no cross-reaction with HIT antibodies No antidote Argatroban can ↑ INR; if starting on warfarin concurrently do not use a loading dose of warfarin; dose cautiously
Desirudin *(Iprivask)* Injection Indicated for VTE prevention after hip arthroplasty	15 mg SC Q12H CrCl < 60 mL/min: ↓ dose	**BOXED WARNING** Patients receiving neuraxial anesthesia (epidural, spinal) or undergoing spinal puncture are at risk of hematomas and subsequent paralysis **MONITORING** aPTT, renal function, CBC **NOTES** No antidote

DABIGATRAN DRUG INTERACTIONS

- Avoid using with other anticoagulants (unless benefit outweighs risk). Monitor for additive effects with other drugs that can ↑ bleeding risk (antiplatelet drugs, some herbals, NSAIDs, SSRIs, SNRIs, thrombolytics).
- Dabigatran is a substrate of P-gp; avoid use with rifampin.
- Nonvalvular AFib: if CrCl 30 – 50 mL/min and patient is taking P-gp inhibitors (dronedarone or systemic ketoconazole), reduce dose to 75 mg BID. In severe renal impairment (CrCl 15 – 30 mL/min), avoid use with any P-gp inhibitors.
- Other indications: avoid use with P-gp inhibitors in patients with CrCl < 50 mL/min.
- *Stribild, Genvoya* (each containing cobicistat) and *Tybost* with atazanavir can increase exposure to dabigatran. Recommendations depend on renal function and indication for dabigatran.

WARFARIN

Warfarin competitively inhibits the C1 subunit of the multi-unit vitamin K epoxide reductase (VKORC1) enzyme complex, thereby reducing the regeneration of vitamin K epoxide and causing depletion of active clotting factors II, VII, IX and X and proteins C and S.

DRUG	DOSING	SAFETY/SIDE EFFECTS/MONITORING
Warfarin (*Coumadin, Jantoven*) Tablet Racemic mixture of R- and S- enantiomers with the S- enantiomer being 2.7-3.8 times more potent **Missed Dose** Take immediately on the same day. Do not double the dose the next day to make up for a missed dose	Healthy outpatients: 10 mg daily for first 2 days, then adjust dose per INR values Lower doses (≤ 5 mg) for elderly, malnourished, taking drugs which can ↑ warfarin levels, liver disease, heart failure, or have a high risk of bleeding Take at the same time each day Highly protein bound (99%) See Study Tip Gal for tablet colors	**BOXED WARNING** Major or fatal bleeding **CONTRAINDICATIONS** Pregnancy (except with mechanical heart valves at high risk for thromboembolism), hemorrhagic tendencies, blood dyscrasias, uncontrolled hypertension, noncompliance, recent or potential surgery of the eye or CNS, major regional lumbar block anesthesia or traumatic surgery resulting in large open surfaces, pericarditis or pericardial effusion, bacterial endocarditis, (pre-)eclampsia, possible miscarriage **WARNINGS** Tissue necrosis/gangrene, HIT (contraindicated as monotherapy in the initial treatment of active HIT), systemic atheroemboli and cholesterol microemboli, presence of CYP2C9*2 or *3 alleles and/or polymorphism of VKORC1 gene may increase bleeding risk (routine genetic testing is not currently recommended; see Pharmacogenomics chapter) **SIDE EFFECTS** Bleeding, skin necrosis, purple toe syndrome **MONITORING** Goal INR is 2-3 (target 2.5) for most indications (DVT, AFib, bioprosthetic mitral valve, mechanical aortic valve, antiphospholipid syndrome) and should be 2.5-3.5 for some high-risk indications such as a mechanical mitral valve or 2 mechanical heart valves Begin INR monitoring after the initial 2 or 3 doses, or if on a chronic, stable dose of warfarin, monitor at intervals every 4-12 weeks Hct, Hgb, signs of bleeding **NOTES** Antidote: vitamin K (see Antidotes and Reversal section for details) Dental cleanings and single tooth extraction do not generally require a change in warfarin dosing, if INR is in therapeutic range

WARFARIN DRUG INTERACTIONS

Pharmacokinetic Interactions

- Warfarin is a substrate of CYP2C9 (major), 1A2 (minor), 2C19 (minor) and 3A4 (minor) and an inhibitor of CYP2C9 (weak) and CYP2C19 (weak). Avoid use with tamoxifen.
- CYP2C9 inducers can ↓ INR; these include aprepitant, bosentan, carbamazepine, phenobarbital, phenytoin, primidone, rifampin (large ↓ INR), licorice and St. John's wort.
- CYP2C9 inhibitors can ↑ INR; these include amiodarone, azole antifungals (e.g., fluconazole, ketoconazole, voriconazole), capecitabine, etravirine, fluvastatin, fluvoxamine, macrolide antibiotics, metronidazole, tigecycline, TMP/SMX and zafirlukast. See Learning Drug Interactions chapter.
  - When starting amiodarone, ↓ the dose of warfarin by 30 – 50%.
- Other antibiotics: penicillins, including amoxicillin, some cephalosporins, quinolones and tetracyclines ↑ anticoagulant effect of warfarin - monitor INR.
- Check for CYP1A2, 2C19 and 3A4 interactions; these occur, but usually have less of an effect on INR.

Pharmacodynamic Drug Interactions

- The most common pharmacodynamic interactions are with NSAIDs, antiplatelet agents, other anticoagulants, SSRIs and SNRIs. These interactions ↑ bleeding risk, but the INR may not be increased.
- Drugs that ↑ clotting risk (e.g., estrogen and SERMs) should be discontinued if possible.

Dietary Supplements/Food Interactions

- Monitor the INR closely if patients are taking natural products with warfarin, but understand that some natural products contain plant salicylates (e.g., willow bark) which increase the risk of bleeding without increasing the INR.
  - ↑ bleeding risk with warfarin: "the 5 G's" (garlic, ginger, ginkgo, ginseng, glucosamine), bromelain, dong quai, vitamin E, evening primrose oil, high doses of fish oils, goldenseal, grapefruit, policosanol, willow bark and wintergreen oil.
  - ↓ effectiveness of warfarin: alfalfa, green tea, coenzyme Q10 and St. John's wort. American ginseng may decrease the effects of warfarin, but there is evidence that both American and Panax ginseng inhibit platelet aggregation (listed above), which potentially has the opposite effect.
- Any additions of vitamin K will ↓ the INR. Check any nutritional products (including enteral nutrition) for vitamin K content. Stay consistent with the amount of vitamin K in the diet (see foods high in vitamin K box). Tube feeds should be held one hour before and after warfarin.

WARFARIN TABLET COLORS

Pink (1 mg)	**P**each (5 mg)
Lavender (2 mg)	**T**eal (6 mg)
Green (2.5 mg)	**Y**ellow (7.5 mg)
Brown/Tan (3 mg)	**W**hite (10 mg)
Blue (4 mg)	

Remember:

Please **L**et **G**reg **B**rown **B**ring **P**eaches **T**o **Y**our **W**edding

FOODS HIGH IN VITAMIN K

Broccoli	Collard greens	Parsley
Brussel sprouts	Coriander	Soybean oil
Cabbage	Endive	Spinach
Canola oil	Green kale	Swiss chard
Cauliflower	Lettuce (red leaf or butterhead)	Tea (green or black)
Chickpeas	Mustard greens	Turnip greens
Cole slaw		Watercress

WARFARIN USE – KEY POINTS

- In healthy outpatients, the initial starting dose of warfarin should be 10 mg daily for the first two days, then adjust per INR values.
- In patients with acute DVT/PE, start warfarin on the same day as the parenteral anticoagulant (e.g., enoxaparin or UFH) and continue both anticoagulants for a minimum of 5 days and until the INR is ≥ 2 for at least 24 hours. Both criteria must be met.
- Routine pharmacogenomic testing is not recommend.
- Routine use of vitamin K supplementation is not recommended in patients taking warfarin.
- For patients with stable therapeutic INRs presenting with a single subtherapeutic (low) INR value, routinely bridging with UFH or LMWH is not recommended.
- For patients with previously stable therapeutic INRs who present with a single out-of-range INR of ≤ 0.5 below or above the therapeutic range, continue current dose and obtain another INR within 1 – 2 weeks.
- For patients with consistently stable INRs on warfarin therapy, INR testing can be done up to every 12 weeks rather than every 4 weeks.
- Warfarin is highly protein bound. Caution is advised with other highly protein bound drugs that may displace warfarin such as phenytoin, valproic acid and others.

ANTIDOTES FOR REVERSAL

Bleeding is the major adverse effect of anticoagulants. Bleeding can be serious and fatal. Anticoagulation needs to be reversed if a patient experiences life-threatening bleeding or requires surgery.

Protamine combines with strongly acidic heparin to form a stable salt complex neutralizing the anticoagulant activity of UFH and LMWH. Other drug-specific antidotes include: phytonadione (vitamin K), *Praxbind* and *Andexxa*. *Kcentra* is indicated for the urgent reversal of warfarin. Prothrombin complex concentrates (PCCs) are sometimes used (off-label) for reversal of factor Xa inhibitors. If PCCs are used in this manner, monitoring clotting tests (PT, PTT, INR, anti-Xa) to assess reversal is not useful and is not recommended.

ANTIDOTE	DOSING	SAFETY/SIDE EFFECTS/MONITORING
For UFH/LMWH reversal		
Protamine sulfate Injection 10 mg/mL (5 mL, 25 mL)	**For IV UFH Reversal** 1 mg protamine will reverse ~100 units of heparin. Since UFH has a very short half-life, reverse the amount of heparin given in the last 2-2.5 hours; max dose: 50 mg **For LMWH Reversal** Enoxaparin given within the last 8 hours: 1 mg protamine per 1 mg of enoxaparin (can neutralize ~60% of the anti-Xa activity of LMWH) Enoxaparin given > 8 hours ago: 0.5 mg protamine per 1 mg of enoxaparin Dalteparin: 1 mg protamine for each 100 anti-Xa units of dalteparin	**BOXED WARNING** Hypersensitivity: hypotension, cardiovascular collapse, non-cardiogenic pulmonary edema, pulmonary vasoconstriction **SIDE EFFECTS** Hypotension, bradycardia, flushing, anaphylaxis **MONITORING** aPTT, anti-Xa levels, cardiac monitoring required (ECG, BP, HR) **NOTES** Rapid IV infusion causes hypotension Administer slow IV push (50 mg over 10 minutes) Inject without further dilution over 1-3 minutes
For dabigatran reversal		
Idarucizumab (*Praxbind*) Injection 2.5 g/50 mL single-use vial	5 grams IV (given as 2 separate 2.5 gram doses no more than 15 minutes apart) Do not confuse with IDArubicin	**WARNINGS** Thromboembolic risk, risk of serious adverse reactions due to sorbitol excipient **SIDE EFFECTS** HA, ↓ K, delirium, constipation, fever
For reversal of the Factor Xa inhibitors apixaban and rivaroxaban		
Andexanet alfa (*Andexxa*) Injection	Bolus, followed by infusion. Dosing is specific to the Xa inhibitor, the dose and when the last Xa inhibitor dose was taken	**BOXED WARNING** Thromboembolic risks, ischemic events, cardiac arrest, sudden death **SIDE EFFECTS** Injection site reaction, DVT, ischemic stroke, UTI, pneumonia **NOTES** Not indicated for reversal of Factor Xa inhibitors other than apixaban and rivaroxaban

ANTIDOTE	DOSING	SAFETY/SIDE EFFECTS/MONITORING
For warfarin reversal		
Vitamin K or phytonadione *(Mephyton)* 5 mg tablets 1 mg/0.5 mL, 10 mg/mL injection	1-10 mg PO/IV If given IV, infuse slowly; rate of infusion should not exceed 1 mg/min To ↓ risk of anaphylaxis, dilute dose in a minimum of 50 mL of compatible solution and administer using an infusion pump over at least 20 minutes	**BOXED WARNINGS** Severe reactions resembling hypersensitivity reactions (e.g., anaphylaxis) have occurred rarely during or immediately after IV administration (even with proper dilution and rate of administration); some patients had no previous exposure to phytonadione **SIDE EFFECTS** Anaphylaxis, flushing, rash, dizziness **NOTES** Requires light protection during administration SC route not recommended due to variable absorption; IM route not recommended due to risk of hematoma Orlistat and mineral oil ↓ absorption of oral vitamin K See specific recommendations in Warfarin Reversal section
Four Factor Prothrombin Complex Concentrate (Human) *(Kcentra)* Injection Factors II, VII, IX, X, Protein C, Protein S	IV dose is based on patient's INR and body weight Do not repeat dose	**BOXED WARNING** Arterial and venous thromboembolic complications have been reported **CONTRAINDICATIONS** Disseminated intravascular coagulation (DIC) and known HIT (contains heparin) **WARNINGS** Made from human blood and may carry risk of transmitting infectious agents **SIDE EFFECTS** HA, N/V/D, arthralgia, hypotension, ↓ K, thrombotic events **NOTES** Administer with vitamin K Do not let drug back-up into line; will clot Refrigerate; allow to reach room temp prior to administration
Three Factor Prothrombin Complex Concentrates (Human) *(Bebulin, Profilnine)* Off-label	Weight-based dosing given IV slowly Given with fresh frozen plasma (FFP) or factor VIIa	**WARNINGS** *Bebulin* and *Profilnine* contain Factors II, IX and X but low or nontherapeutic levels of factor VII and should not be confused with Prothrombin Complex Concentrate (Human) [(Factors II, VII, IX, X), Protein C, Protein S] *(Kcentra)* which contains therapeutic levels of factor VII. Made from human blood and may carry risk of transmitting infectious agents (e.g., viruses) **SIDE EFFECTS** Chills, fever, flushing, nausea, headache, risk of thrombosis **NOTES** Slow infusion and give antihistamine to minimize side effects Administer vitamin K concurrently
Factor VIIa Recombinant *(NovoSeven RT)* Off-label	10-20 mcg/kg IV bolus over 5 minutes	**BOXED WARNING** Serious thrombotic events are associated with the use of factor VIIa outside labeled indications

WARFARIN REVERSAL

Variable INRs are common in clinical practice. Elevated INRs are concerning due to increased risk of bleeding. Vitamin K is used to reverse warfarin (to ↓ INR quickly); it can be used by itself or with other agents for life-threatening bleeding. Bleeding (regardless of the INR), will warrant more serious intervention.

Oral formulations of vitamin K (generally at doses of 2.5 – 5 mg) are preferred for reversal in patients without significant or major bleeding. Vitamin K given subcutaneous (SC) has a slow onset and a variable response; SC injections should be avoided. The intramuscular (IM) route should also be avoided due to the risk of hematoma formation. Intravenous vitamin K should be used only when the patient is experiencing serious bleeding. IV injection is reported to cause anaphylaxis in 3 of out 100,000 patients, so infuse slowly.

Use of Vitamin K for Overanticoagulation

SYMPTOMS/INR VALUE	WHAT TO DO
INR above therapeutic range but < 4.5 without bleeding	Reduce or skip warfarin dose. Monitor INR. Resume warfarin when INR therapeutic. Dose reduction may not be needed if only slightly above therapeutic range.
For patients with a supratherapeutic INR of 4.5-10 without bleeding	Routine use of vitamin K is not recommended if no evidence of bleeding. Hold 1-2 doses of warfarin. Monitor INR. Resume warfarin at lower dose when INR therapeutic. Vitamin K can be used if urgent surgery needed (≤ 5 mg, with additional 1-2 mg in 24 hours if needed) or bleeding risk is high (1-2.5 mg).
For patients with INR > 10 without bleeding	Hold warfarin. Give oral vitamin K 2.5-5 mg even if not bleeding. Monitor INR. Resume warfarin at a lower dose when INR is therapeutic.
For patients with major bleeding from warfarin	Hold warfarin therapy. Give vitamin K 5-10 mg by slow IV injection and four-factor prothrombin complex concentrate (PCC). PCC suggested over fresh frozen plasma (FFP) due to risks of allergic reactions, infection transmission, longer preparation time, slower onset and higher volume.

PERIOPERATIVE MANAGEMENT OF PATIENTS ON WARFARIN

- Stop warfarin therapy approximately five days before major surgery. In patients with a mechanical heart valve, AFib or VTE at high risk for thromboembolism, bridging therapy with LMWH or UFH is recommended (bridging means stopping the warfarin and using anticoagulant doses of the LMWH or UFH for a short period to prevent clotting). Discontinue therapeutic-dose SC LMWH 24 hours before surgery (stop the UFH IV therapy 4 – 6 hours before surgery). Patients at low risk for thromboembolism do not require bridging; stop the warfarin and restart after surgery when hemostasis is achieved.
- If INR is still elevated 1 – 2 days before surgery, give low-dose vitamin K (1 – 2 mg).
- If reversal of warfarin is needed in a patient requiring an urgent surgical procedure, give low-dose (2.5 – 5 mg) IV or oral vitamin K.
- Resume warfarin therapy 12 – 24 hours after the surgery, when there is adequate hemostasis.

VENOUS THROMBOEMBOLISM (VTE)

DIAGNOSIS

Symptoms of a DVT include pain in the affected limb and unilateral lower extremity swelling. DVTs can be diagnosed with an ultrasound (or MRI or venography, in some cases). A D-dimer (a lab test) can aid in the diagnosis. If a PE is suspected, it is diagnosed with a pulmonary CT angiogram.

VTE PROPHYLAXIS

Risk factors for the development of VTE are shown below. The CHEST guidelines provide specific recommendations for the prevention of VTE depending on the patient's level of risk. UFH, LMWHs, fondaparinux, rivaroxaban, apixaban, betrixaban and dabigatran are all approved for VTE prophylaxis (refer to the recommended doses in the drug tables). If patients have a contraindication to anticoagulants (such as an active bleed) or have a high risk for bleeding, they will need non-drug alternatives to prevent VTE. These options include intermittent pneumatic compression (IPC) devices or graduated compression stockings (GCS).

RISK FACTORS FOR THE DEVELOPMENT OF VENOUS THROMBOEMBOLISM

Surgery	Inherited or acquired thrombophilia (e.g., antithrombin deficiency, Factor V Leiden, antiphospholipid syndrome, Protein C or Protein S deficiency)
Major trauma or lower extremity injury	Acute medical illness
Immobility	Venous compression (tumor, hematoma, arterial abnormality)
Cancer or chemotherapy	Inflammatory bowel disease
Previous VTE Pregnancy and postpartum period	Nephrotic syndrome
Estrogen-containing medications or selective estrogen receptor modulators	Myeloproliferative disorders
Erythropoiesis-stimulating agents	Paroxysmal nocturnal hemoglobinuria
Increasing age	Central venous catheterization
Obesity	

For long distance travelers at risk for VTE (previous VTE, recent surgery or trauma, active malignancy, pregnancy, estrogen use, advanced age, limited mobility, severe obesity, or known thrombophilic disorder), the following recommendations will ↓ VTE risk: frequent ambulation, calf muscle exercise, sitting in an aisle seat and using graduated compression stockings with 15 – 30 mmHg of pressure at the ankle during travel. Aspirin or anticoagulants should not be used.

VTE TREATMENT

Any VTE that is caused by surgery or a reversible risk factor should be treated for three months. If the VTE is unprovoked (unknown cause), extending therapy longer than three months is recommended, as long as the patient's bleeding risk is low-to-moderate. If the risk of bleeding is high, limit the treatment to three months. If a patient has two unprovoked VTE episodes, long-term treatment can be considered. Estrogen-containing medications and selective estrogen receptor modulators (SERMs) are contraindicated in patients with history of, or current, VTE and should be discontinued.

- For patients without cancer, dabigatran and the oral factor Xa inhibitors (rivaroxaban, apixaban and edoxaban) are preferred over warfarin for the first three months of treatment for a DVT in the leg or a PE.
- For patients with cancer, LMWH is preferred over all oral anticoagulants (including warfarin).
- In patients with an unprovoked DVT or PE who are stopping anticoagulation, aspirin is recommended to prevent recurrence (if there are no contraindications).

ATRIAL FIBRILLATION/FLUTTER

Patients with atrial fibrillation or atrial flutter (AFib/AFlutter) can form clots in the heart. Clots that are ejected from the heart and travel to the brain can cause a stroke (cardioembolic stroke) or transient ischemic attack (TIA). Stroke prevention is an important goal in patients with AFib/AFlutter (see Arrhythmias chapter).

AFib and AFlutter are common in patients with heart valve problems. Some of these patients require valve replacement surgery. This involves replacing the damaged valve with a mechanical (prosthetic) or animal (sometimes called a bioprosthetic) valve. Patients with mechanical heart valves have the highest risk for clotting/strokes and are treated with warfarin only. None of the Factor Xa inhibitors or DTIs are approved for this population.

ANTICOAGULATION FOR PATIENTS WITH AFIB WHO WILL UNDERGO CARDIOVERSION

- AFib > 48 hours or unknown duration: anticoagulation (if warfarin, target INR 2-3) for at least 3 weeks prior to and 4 weeks after cardioversion (regardless of method - electrical or pharmacologic) when normal sinus rhythm is restored.
- AFib ≤ 48 hours duration undergoing elective cardioversion: start full therapeutic anticoagulation at presentation, do cardioversion, and continue full anticoagulation for at least 4 weeks while patient is in normal sinus rhythm.
- For patients staying in AFib, chronic anticoagulation therapy may be needed for stroke prevention. Treatment depends on the number of risk factors present. See text.

The majority of patients with AFib/AFlutter do not have heart valve involvement (called nonvalvular AFib), but they still require evaluation of their stroke risk. The 2018 American College of Chest Physicians (CHEST) guidelines use the CHA_2DS_2-VASc scoring system to estimate risk of stroke in AFib/AFlutter and guide therapy. In previous guidelines the simpler $CHADS_2$ scoring system was used but this did not take into account additional factors such as vascular disease, age and sex.

CHA_2DS_2-VASc Scoring Systems (CHEST Guideline)

Count the number of risk factors the patient has, then select the recommended therapy. The higher the score, the greater the stroke risk and the more intensive the anticoagulant recommendations.

CHA_2DS_2-VASc SCORING SYSTEM

Add up the total number of risk factors for a given patient.

C - CHF	1
H - HTN	1
A - Age ≥ 75 years	2
D - Diabetes	1
S_2 - Prior Stroke/TIA	2
V - Vascular Disease (prior MI, PAD, aortic plaque)	1
A - Age 65-74 years	1
S - Sex category, female	1

RISK CATEGORY	RECOMMENDED THERAPY
CHA_2DS_2-VASc Score = 0 (males) Score = 1 (females)	No anticoagulation recommended.
CHA_2DS_2-VASc Score ≥ 1 (males) Score ≥ 2 (females)	Oral anticoagulation may be considered.
CHA_2DS_2-VASc Score ≥ 2 (males) Score ≥ 3 (females)	Oral anticoagulation is recommended. Non-vitamin K oral anticoagulant (NOAC*) is recommended over warfarin.

**NOAC: apixaban, rivaroxaban, edoxaban, dabigatran*

ANTICOAGULATION IN PREGNANCY

For prevention and treatment of VTE in pregnant women, LMWH is preferred over UFH. Pneumatic compression devices can be used alone or with LMWH in select patients. Since warfarin is teratogenic, women who require chronic warfarin therapy for mechanical heart valves or inherited thrombophilias are generally converted to LMWH during pregnancy. They may be switched back to warfarin after the 13th week of pregnancy, then back to LMWH close to delivery. When LMWH is used in pregnancy, anti-Xa levels are recommended to monitor therapy. The oral factor Xa inhibitors and direct thrombin inhibitors have not been adequately studied in pregnancy and are not recommended.

PATIENT COUNSELING

For All Anticoagulants

- This medication is very important for your health, but it can cause serious and life-threatening bleeding problems. Call your healthcare provider right away if you develop any of these signs or symptoms of serious bleeding:
    - Red or black stools that look like tar
    - Coughing or vomiting up blood or blood clots (often described as looking like coffee grounds)
    - Unexpected pain, swelling, or discomfort
    - Headaches, dizziness, or weakness
    - Unusual bruising that develops without known cause
    - Frequent nose bleeds
    - Unusual bleeding gums
    - Bleeding from cuts that take longer than normal to stop
    - Menstrual bleeding or vaginal bleeding that is much heavier than normal
    - Pink or brown urine
- Tell physicians and dentists that you are using this medication before any surgery is performed.
- Call your healthcare provider right away if you fall or injure yourself, especially if you hit your head.
- Alcoholic drinks should be avoided.
- This medication can interact with many other drugs. Check with your healthcare provider before taking any other medication, including over the counter medications, vitamins, or herbal products.
- Do not start, stop, or change any medicine without talking with your healthcare provider.

Enoxaparin

- Wash and dry hands.
- Sit or lie in a comfortable position so you can see your abdomen. Choose an area on the right or left side of your abdomen, at least two inches from the belly button. (see picture below)
- Clean the injection site with an alcohol swab and allow the site to dry.
- Remove the needle cap by pulling it straight off the syringe and discard it in a sharps collector. Do not twist the cap off as this can bend the needle.
- Hold the syringe like a pencil in your writing hand.
- Do not expel the air bubble in the syringe prior to injection unless your healthcare provider has advised you to do so.
- With your other hand, pinch an inch of the cleansed area to make a fold in the skin. Insert the full length of the needle straight down – at a 90 degree angle – into fold of skin.
- Press the plunger with your thumb until the syringe is empty.
- Pull the needle straight out at the same angle that it was inserted, and release the skin fold.
- Point the needle down and away from yourself and others, and push down on the plunger to activate the safety shield.
- Do not rub the site of injection as this can lead to bruising. Place the used syringe in the sharps collector.

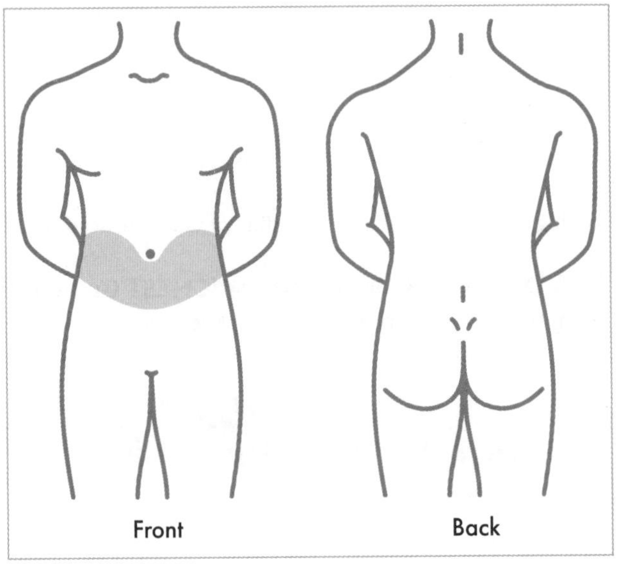

Dabigatran

- Do not stop taking dabigatran without talking to your prescriber. Stopping dabigatran increases your risk of developing a clot.
- Take with a full glass of water and swallow the capsules whole. Do not break, chew, or empty the pellets from the capsule. It is fine to take with or without food.
- Common side effects of dabigatran include indigestion, upset stomach or stomach burning and/or pain.
- Only open one bottle of dabigatran at a time. Finish your opened bottle of dabigatran before opening a new bottle. After opening a bottle of dabigatran, use within four months.
- Keep dabigatran in the original bottle or blister package to keep it dry and protect the capsules from moisture. Do not put dabigatran in pill boxes or pill organizers.
- Tightly close your bottle of dabigatran right after you take your dose.
- If you miss a dose of dabigatran, take it as soon as you remember. If your next dose is less than six hours away, skip the missed dose. Do not take two doses of dabigatran at the same time.

Rivaroxaban

- Rivaroxaban is not for patients with artificial heart valves.
- If you take rivaroxaban for atrial fibrillation: Take rivaroxaban once daily with your evening meal.
  - If you miss a dose of rivaroxaban, take it as soon as you remember on the same day. Take your next dose at your regularly scheduled time.
- If you take rivaroxaban for blood clots in the veins of your legs or lungs: take rivaroxaban once or twice daily as prescribed with food at the same time each day.
  - If you miss a dose of rivaroxaban and take rivaroxaban twice daily: take rivaroxaban as soon as you remember on the same day. You may take 2 doses at the same time to make up for the missed dose. Take your next dose at your regularly scheduled time.
  - If you miss a dose of rivaroxaban and take rivaroxaban once daily: take rivaroxaban as soon as you remember on the same day. Take your next dose at your regularly scheduled time.
- If you take rivaroxaban for hip or knee replacement surgery: take rivaroxaban once daily with or without food.
  - If you miss a dose of rivaroxaban, take it as soon as you remember on the same day. Take your next dose at your regularly scheduled time.

Warfarin

- Take warfarin at the same time every day as prescribed by your doctor. You can take warfarin either with food or on an empty stomach.
- Ask your pharmacist if your tablet looks different.
- Warfarin lowers the chance of blood clots forming in your body.
- If you miss a dose, take the dose as soon as possible on the same day. Do not take a double dose the next day to make up for a missed dose.
- You will need to have your blood tested frequently to monitor your response to this medication. This test is called an INR. Your dose may be adjusted to keep you INR in a target range.
- Do not make changes in your diet, such as eating large amounts of green, leafy vegetables. Be consistent with the amount of leafy green vegetables and other foods rich in vitamin K.
- Avoid drinking alcohol.
- Other side effects besides bleeding include purple toe syndrome that can cause your toes to become painful and purple in color. Also, death of skin tissue can occur. Report any unusual changes or pain immediately to your healthcare provider.

Select Guidelines/References

Antithrombotic Therapy for VTE Disease: CHEST Guideline Expert Panel Report. https://journal.chestnet.org/article/S0012-3692(15)00335-9/pdf (accessed 2019 Feb 1).

Antithrombotic Therapy for Atrial Fibrillation: CHEST Guideline Expert Panel Report. https://journal.chestnet.org/article/S0012-3692(18)32244-X/pdf (accessed 2019 Feb 1).

CHAPTER CONTENT

Background ... 542
Symptoms of Anemia ... 542
Types of Anemia ... 543
Iron Deficiency Anemia ... 543
Diagnosis and Treatment of Iron Deficiency Anemia ... 544
Assessing and Treating Iron Deficiency Anemia ... 544
Oral Iron ... 544
Parenteral Iron ... 545
Macrocytic Anemia ... 546
Diagnosis of Macrocytic Anemia ... 546
Treatment of Macrocytic Anemia ... 546
Vitamin B12 and Folic Acid Products ... 546
Normocytic Anemia ... 547
Anemia of Chronic Kidney Disease ... 547
Erythropoiesis-Stimulating Agents (ESAs) ... 547
Aplastic Anemia ... 548
Hemolytic Anemia ... 548
Select Drugs that Can Cause Hemolytic Anemia ... 549

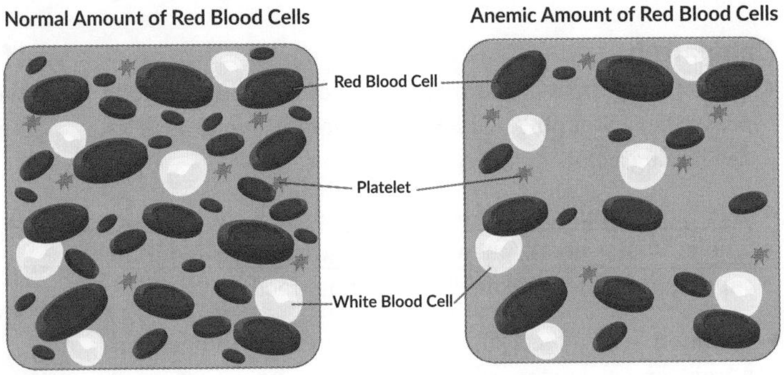

CHAPTER 35
ANEMIA

BACKGROUND

Anemia is the most common blood disorder worldwide and it affects approximately 3.5 million Americans. Anemia is a decrease in hemoglobin (Hgb) and hematocrit (Hct) concentrations below the normal range for age and gender. Hgb is an iron-rich protein found in red blood cells (RBCs); its main purpose is to carry oxygen from the lungs to the tissues. RBCs are formed in the bone marrow, where they take up Hgb and iron before being released into the circulation as immature RBCs, known as reticulocytes. After 1 – 2 days, the reticulocytes mature into erythrocytes, which have a lifespan of about 120 days. Erythrocytes are removed from circulation by macrophages, mainly in the spleen.

Anemia can occur due to impaired RBC production, increased RBC destruction (hemolysis) or blood loss. A decrease in Hgb or RBC volume results in decreased oxygen carrying capacity of the blood. Diagnosis of the underlying cause is essential. Anemia can result from nutritional deficiencies (e.g., iron, folate, vitamin B12) or it can occur as a complication of another medical disorder, such as chronic kidney disease (CKD) or a malignancy.

SYMPTOMS OF ANEMIA

Most patients with mild or early stage anemia are asymptomatic. If anemia becomes severe and/or prolonged, the lack of oxygen in the blood can lead to classic symptoms of fatigue, weakness, shortness of breath, exercise intolerance, headache, dizziness, anorexia and/or pallor. If sudden blood loss occurs, the patient can experience acute symptoms, such as chest pain, fainting, palpitations and tachycardia. Glossitis (an inflamed, sore tongue), koilonychias (thin, concave, spoon-shaped nails) or pica (craving and eating non-foods such as chalk or clay) can develop with iron deficiency anemia. Patients with vitamin B12 (cobalamin) deficiency can present with neurologic symptoms, including peripheral neuropathies, visual disturbances and/or psychiatric symptoms.

CONTENT LEGEND

= Study Tip Gal = Key Drug Guy

A decreased oxygen supply can cause ischemic damage to many organs. In chronic anemia, the heart tries to compensate for low oxygen levels by pumping faster (tachycardia). This can increase the mass of the ventricular wall (hypertrophy) and lead to heart failure.

TYPES OF ANEMIA

The type and cause of anemia cannot be determined based on signs and symptoms alone. The mean corpuscular volume (MCV), which reflects the size or average volume of RBCs, can help determine the type of anemia and the possible underlying cause. A low MCV means that RBCs are smaller than normal (microcytic) and a high MCV means that RBCs are larger than normal (macrocytic). These findings correlate with different causes of anemia. Certain genetic conditions can cause anemia due to dysfunctional RBCs (see the Sickle Cell Disease chapter).

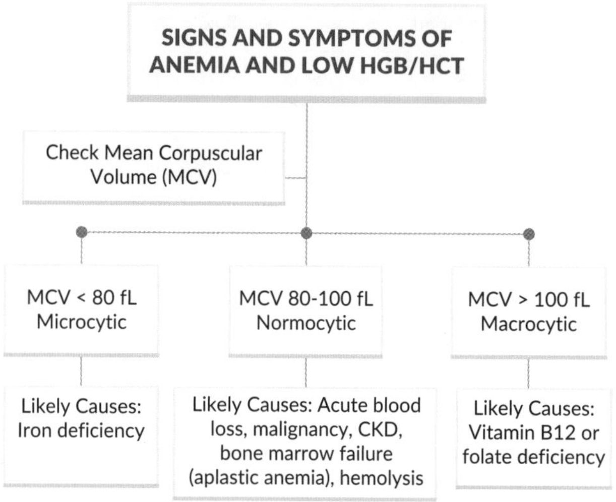

Laboratory tests used to determine the type and cause of anemia are shown in the table below.

- Iron studies further evaluate microcytic anemia; they include serum iron (bound to transferrin), serum ferritin (iron stores), transferrin saturation (amount of transferrin binding sites occupied by iron) and total iron binding capacity (amount of transferrin binding sites available to bind iron or unbound sites).
- Vitamin B12 and folate levels further evaluate macrocytic anemia. Vitamin B12 is required for enzyme reactions involving methylmalonic acid and homocysteine, making these tests potentially useful in confirming a diagnosis.
- Reticulocyte counts are a measure of RBC production, which is usually impaired in anemia.

COMMON LABORATORY TESTS IN ANEMIA*

Relevant CBC Components	**Iron Studies**
Hemoglobin (Hgb)	Serum Iron
Hematocrit (Hct)	Serum Ferritin
Red Blood Cell (RBC) Count	Total Iron Binding Capacity (TIBC)
Reticulocyte Count	Transferrin Saturation (TSAT)
RBC Indices	**Additional Tests**
Mean Corpuscular Volume (MCV)	Serum Folate
Mean Corpuscular Hemoglobin (MCH)	Serum Vitamin B12
Mean Corpuscular Hemoglobin Concentration (MCHC)	Methylmalonic Acid
Red Blood Cell Distribution Width (RDW)	Homocysteine

**Refer to the Learning Lab Values & Drug Monitoring chapter for normal laboratory ranges in adults.*

IRON DEFICIENCY ANEMIA

Iron deficiency is the most common nutritional deficiency in the United States. Common causes are shown in the box below. Dietary iron is available in two forms: heme iron (found in meat and seafood) and non-heme iron (found in nuts, beans, vegetables and fortified grains, such as cereals). Heme iron is more readily absorbed than non-heme iron, which is affected by gastric pH and other foods being consumed. Meat, seafood, poultry and ascorbic acid increase the absorption of non-heme iron, while foods that contain phytate and polyphenols (e.g., grains, beans, cereals and legumes) can decrease non-heme iron absorption. This is particularly important for patients who follow a vegetarian diet, since they are more likely to consume foods with a less absorbable form of iron along with foods that decrease the absorption of iron. Vegetarians may require iron supplementation, even if dietary intake of iron seems adequate.

CAUSES OF IRON DEFICIENCY

Inadequate Dietary Intake

- Iron-poor diets (e.g., vegetarian, vegan), malnutrition, disease-related (e.g., dementia, psychosis)

Blood Loss

- Acute (e.g., GI hemorrhage), chronic (e.g., heavy menses, blood donations, peptic ulcer disease, inflammatory bowel disease) or drug-induced (e.g., NSAIDs, steroids, antiplatelets, anticoagulants)

Decreased Iron Absorption

- High gastric pH (e.g., PPIs), GI diseases (e.g., celiac disease, inflammatory bowel disease, gastrectomy, gastric bypass)

Increased Iron Requirements

- Pregnancy, lactation, infants*, rapid growth (e.g., adolescence)

**See the Dietary Supplements, Natural & Complimentary Medicine chapter for infant iron requirements.*

Preventative measures can be used for some of the at-risk patient populations. For example, women who use hormonal contraception may experience less bleeding during menstrual periods and their risk of developing iron deficiency may be lower. The CDC recommends low-dose iron supplementation (30 mg/day) for all pregnant women, beginning at the first prenatal visit; this is usually provided in the prenatal vitamin. Larger doses of iron are required if iron deficiency anemia (IDA) is diagnosed in pregnancy.

DIAGNOSIS AND TREATMENT OF IRON DEFICIENCY ANEMIA

The Study Tip Gal below summarizes the laboratory findings that are consistent with a diagnosis of IDA as well as important treatment information.

ASSESSING AND TREATING IRON DEFICIENCY ANEMIA

LABORATORY FINDINGS
- ↓ Hgb, MCV < 80 fL, ↓ RBC production (low reticulocyte count)
- ↓ serum iron, ferritin and TSAT
- ↑ TIBC

TREATMENT: ORAL IRON THERAPY
- Recommended dose: 100 – 200 mg elemental iron per day*
- Take iron on an empty stomach**
- Avoid H2RAs and PPIs; separate from antacids
- Sustained- release or enteric-coated formulations cause less GI irritation but are not recommended for initial therapy

% ELEMENTAL IRON IN ORAL PRODUCTS	
Ferrous gluconate	12%
Ferrous sulfate	20%
Ferrous sulfate, dried	30%
Ferrous fumarate	33%
Carbonyl iron	100%
Polysaccharide iron complex	100%

GOALS
- ↑ in serum Hgb by 1 g/dL every 2-3 weeks; continue treatment for 3-6 months after anemia has resolved until iron stores return to normal

**One oral formulation is not better than another if dosed appropriately based on elemental iron needs.*
***1 hr before or 2 hrs after meals; can be taken with food if GI upset occurs.*

Oral Iron

Oral iron supplementation can adequately treat most patients with IDA; parenteral iron therapy is typically reserved for select patient populations due to a higher risk of side effects, cost and burden of administration (see the Parenteral Iron Therapy section).

DRUG	DOSING	SAFETY/SIDE EFFECTS/MONITORING
Ferrous sulfate (*FeroSul, Fer-In-Sol,* many OTC multivitamins with iron) Tablet, elixir, oral solution, syrup	325 mg (65 mg elemental iron) PO daily to TID Most commonly prescribed and the least expensive	**BOXED WARNING** Accidental overdose of iron-containing products is a leading cause of fatal poisoning in children under 6; keep iron out of the reach of children; in the case of an accidental overdose, go to the emergency department or call a poison control center immediately (even if asymptomatic) **CONTRAINDICATIONS** Hemochromatosis, hemolytic anemia, hemosiderosis **SIDE EFFECTS** Constipation (dose-related), dark and tarry stools, nausea, stomach upset **MONITORING** Hgb, iron studies, RBC indices, reticulocyte count **NOTES** Other dosing regimens are available in addition to those listed A stool softener such as docusate is often recommended to prevent iron-induced constipation The antidote for iron overdose is deferoxamine (*Desferal*)
Ferrous sulfate, dried (*Slow Fe, Slow Iron*) ER tablet	160 mg (50 mg elemental iron) PO daily to TID	
Ferrous fumarate (*Ferretts, Ferrimin 150, Hemocyte*)	324 mg (106 mg elemental iron) PO daily to TID	
Ferrous gluconate (*Ferate*)	324 mg (38 mg elemental iron) PO daily to TID	
Carbonyl iron (*FerraPlus 90, Ferralet 90, Iron Chews*)	90 mg (90 mg elemental iron) PO daily or as directed	
Polysaccharide iron complex (*Ferrex 150,* others) Capsules, liquid	150 mg PO daily	

Oral Iron Drug Interactions

- Antacids, H2RAs and PPIs ↓ iron absorption by ↑ gastric pH. Patients should take iron 2 hours before or 4 hours after taking antacids. H2RAs and PPIs raise gastric pH for up to 24 hours; separating the administration of these agents from iron supplements does not improve absorption.
- Iron is a polyvalent cation that can ↓ the absorption of other drugs by binding with them in the GI tract to form nonabsorbable complexes. Separate administration of iron supplements from the following agents (consult prescribing information for exact details):
  - Quinolone and tetracycline antibiotics (less of a concern with doxycycline and minocycline): take iron two hours before or 4 – 8 hours after these agents.
  - Bisphosphonates: take iron 60 minutes after oral ibandronate or 30 minutes after alendronate/risedronate.
  - Cefdinir, dolutegravir, levothyroxine, levodopa and methyldopa - separate from iron by 2 - 4 hours.
- Vitamin C ↑ the absorption of iron (by providing an acidic environment). Giving iron with ascorbic acid (vitamin C 200 mg) may enhance the absorption to a minimal extent.

Oral Iron Patient Counseling

- This medication is used to treat a condition called anemia, which is caused by low levels of iron in your body. It needs to be taken for a few months for your symptoms to improve.
- Take this medication on an empty stomach. If stomach upset occurs, it can be taken with food, but avoid cereals, tea, coffee, eggs, milk and high fiber products, as these decrease iron absorption.
- Iron can cause dark stools, which is expected. If you develop constipation, your healthcare provider can recommend a stool softener (e.g., docusate sodium).

Parenteral Iron

Parenteral iron provides elemental iron and avoids the issues with iron absorption. These factors make it more effective and result in faster increases in Hgb levels than oral iron. The total dose needed to replenish iron stores (e.g., 1,000 mg) can be provided in a single infusion, if desired. Due to the risk of more severe adverse reactions, as well as the cost of therapy, IV iron administration is typically restricted to the following patients:

- CKD on hemodialysis (most common use of IV iron).
- CKD receiving erythropoiesis-stimulating agents (ESAs).
- Unable to tolerate oral iron or failure of oral therapy (e.g., IBD, celiac disease, certain gastric bypass procedures, achlorhydria and bacterial overgrowth syndromes such as *H. pylori*).
- Losing iron too fast for oral replacement.
- As an alternative when blood transfusions are not accepted by the patient (e.g., for religious reasons).

Intravenous (Parenteral) Iron Therapy

DRUG	SAFETY/SIDE EFFECTS/MONITORING
Iron sucrose *(Venofer)*	**BOXED WARNING (IRON DEXTRAN AND FERUMOXYTOL)** Serious and sometimes fatal anaphylactic reactions have occurred with the use of iron dextran or ferumoxytol; all patients receiving iron dextran should be given a test dose prior to the first full therapeutic dose; fatal reactions have occurred even in patients who tolerated the test dose; a history of drug allergy or multiple drug allergies may ↑ this risk
Ferumoxytol *(Feraheme)*	
Iron dextran complex *(INFeD)*	**SIDE EFFECTS** Muscle aches, flushing, hypotension, hypertension, tachycardia, chest pain and peripheral edema All parenteral iron products carry a risk for hypersensitivity reactions (including anaphylaxis)
Sodium ferric gluconate *(Ferrlecit)*	**MONITORING** Hgb, iron studies, reticulocyte count, vital signs, signs and symptoms of anaphylaxis
Ferric carboxymaltose *(Injectafer)*	**NOTES** Give by slow IV injection or infusion to ↓ the risk of hypotension
Ferric pyrophosphate citrate *(Triferic)*	All agents are stable in NS; *Feraheme* is stable in NS or D5W *Triferic* is only indicated for iron replacement in patients with hemodialysis-dependent CKD; it should be added to the bicarbonate concentrate of the hemodialysate for patients receiving hemodialysis

MACROCYTIC ANEMIA

Macrocytic anemia is caused by vitamin B12 or folate deficiency, or both. Pernicious anemia, the most common cause of vitamin B12 deficiency, occurs due to a lack of intrinsic factor, which is required for adequate vitamin B12 absorption in the small intestine. Pernicious anemia can be diagnosed using the Schilling test and requires lifelong parenteral vitamin B12 replacement. Other causes of macrocytic anemia include alcoholism, poor nutrition, gastrointestinal disorders (e.g., Crohn's disease, celiac disease) and pregnancy. The long term use (≥ 2 years) of metformin, H2RAs or PPIs can decrease the absorption of vitamin B12.

Vitamin B12 deficiency can result in serious neurologic dysfunction, including cognitive impairment and peripheral neuropathies. If vitamin B12 deficiency goes undiagnosed for more than three months, neurologic symptoms can become irreversible. Folic acid deficiency does not result in neurologic symptoms; it causes ulcerations of the tongue and oral mucosa, and changes to skin, hair and fingernail pigmentation.

DIAGNOSIS OF MACROCYTIC ANEMIA

In addition to low Hgb and high MCV, reticulocyte counts and serum levels of vitamin B12 and/or folate will be low. Since vitamin B12 is required for enzyme reactions involving methylmalonic acid and homocysteine, they accumulate when vitamin B12 is deficient. Homocysteine levels can also be elevated in folate deficiency.

TREATMENT OF MACROCYTIC ANEMIA

The initial treatment of vitamin B12 deficiency typically involves vitamin B12 injections, to bypass absorption barriers, followed by oral supplements, if appropriate. Vitamin B12 injections are recommended first line for anyone with a severe deficiency or neurological symptoms.

Vitamin B12 and Folic Acid Products

DRUG	DOSING	SAFETY/SIDE EFFECTS/MONITORING
Cyanocobalamin, vitamin B12 *(B-12 Compliance, Nascobal, Physicians EZ Use B-12*, oral generics) Injection, lozenge, tablets (including ER and SL forms), SL liquid, nasal solution	IM or deep SC: 100-1,000 mcg daily/weekly/monthly (varies depending on severity of deficiency) Oral/sublingual: 1,000-2,000 mcg daily *Nascobal*: 500 mcg in one nostril once weekly	**CONTRAINDICATIONS** Allergy to cobalt or vitamin B12 (an intradermal test dose is recommended for any patient suspected of vitamin B12 sensitivity prior to intranasal or injectable administration) **WARNINGS** Parenteral products may contain aluminum (which can accumulate and cause CNS and bone toxicity if renal function is impaired) or benzyl alcohol (which can cause fatal toxicity and "gasping syndrome" in neonates) **SIDE EFFECTS** Pain with injection Rash, polycythemia vera, pulmonary edema (all rare) **MONITORING** Hgb, Hct, vitamin B12, reticulocyte count
Folic acid, folate, vitamin B9 *(FA-8)* Tablet, capsule, injection	0.4-1 mg daily	**WARNINGS** As above for cyanocobalamin **SIDE EFFECTS** Bronchospasm, flushing, rash, pruritus, malaise (all rare) **MONITORING** Hgb, Hct, folate, reticulocyte count

Vitamin B12 and Folic Acid Drug Interactions

- Chloramphenicol can ↓ the efficacy of vitamin B12. Colchicine can ↓ the absorption of vitamin B12.
- The efficacy of raltitrexed (a chemotherapeutic agent) can be ↓ by folic acid; avoid combination.
- Folic acid can ↓ the serum concentration of fosphenytoin, phenytoin, primidone and phenobarbital.
- Green tea and sulfasalazine may ↓ the serum concentration of folic acid.

NORMOCYTIC ANEMIA

ANEMIA OF CHRONIC KIDNEY DISEASE

Anemia of chronic kidney disease (CKD) is primarily due to a deficiency in erythropoietin (EPO), a hormone produced by the kidneys that stimulates the bone marrow to produce RBCs. Iron therapy and erythropoiesis-stimulating agents (ESAs) are the treatments for anemia of CKD.

IV iron is first-line for hemodialysis (HD) patients. Non-HD CKD patients with anemia can be treated with oral iron supplements. The KDIGO (Kidney Disease Improving Global Outcomes) guidelines recommend iron therapy in both non-HD and HD patients if TSAT is ≤ 30% and ferritin levels are ≤ 500 ng/mL. The KDOQI (Kidney Disease Outcomes Quality Initiative) guidelines recommend iron therapy if TSAT is ≤ 20% (non-HD and HD patients) and ferritin levels are ≤ 100 ng/mL in non-HD patients and ≤ 200 ng/mL in HD patients. These criteria are important when using ESAs. ESAs help maintain Hgb levels and reduce the need for blood transfusions, but they are ineffective if iron stores are low.

Erythropoiesis-Stimulating Agents (ESAs)

DRUG	DOSING	SAFETY/SIDE EFFECTS/MONITORING
Epoetin alfa ***(Epogen, Procrit,*** *Retacrit*-biosimilar) IV, SC Single dose and multidose vials	**Chronic Kidney Disease** 50-100 units/kg IV or SC 3x/week Initiate when Hgb < 10 g/dL ↓ or interrupt dose when Hgb approaches or exceeds 11 g/dL (CKD on HD), or > 10 g/dL (CKD not on HD) **Cancer (taking chemotherapy)** 150 units/kg SC 3x/week or 40,000 units SC weekly Initiate when Hgb < 10 g/dL and when at least 2 additional months of chemotherapy are planned **All Indications:** Titrate dose up or down based on Hgb levels; do not ↑ the dose more frequently than once every 4 weeks	**BOXED WARNINGS** ↑ risk of death, MI, stroke, VTE, thrombosis of vascular access and tumor progression or recurrence Use the lowest effective dose to reduce the need for blood transfusions **Chronic Kidney Disease** ↑ risk of death, serious cardiovascular events, and stroke when Hgb level > 11 g/dL **Cancer** Shortened overall survival and/or ↑ risk of tumor progression or recurrence in clinical studies of patients with some cancers Not indicated when the anticipated outcome is cure; discontinue when chemotherapy completed **Perisurgery** DVT prophylaxis is recommended due to ↑ risk of DVT **CONTRAINDICATIONS** Uncontrolled hypertension, pure red cell aplasia (PRCA) that begins after treatment Epoetin alfa: multidose vials contain benzyl alcohol (contraindicated in neonates, infants, pregnancy and lactation) **WARNINGS** Hypertension, seizures, serious allergic reactions Epoetin alfa: contains albumin from human blood (remote risk for transmission of viral diseases) **SIDE EFFECTS** Arthralgia/bone pain, fever, headache, pruritus/rash, N/V, cough, dyspnea, edema, injection site pain, dizziness **MONITORING** Hgb, Hct, TSAT, serum ferritin, BP **NOTES** IV route is recommended for patients on hemodialysis Store in the refrigerator; protect from light; discard multidose vials 21 days after initial entry
Darbepoetin ***(Aranesp)*** IV, SC Single dose vial Single dose prefilled syringe (needle included)	**Chronic Kidney Disease** HD: 0.45 mcg/kg IV or SC weekly or 0.75 mcg/kg IV or SC every 2 weeks Non-HD: 0.45 mcg/kg IV or SC every 4 weeks **Cancer (taking chemotherapy)** 2.25 mcg/kg SC weekly or 500 mcg SC every 3 weeks **All Indications:** Initiation and titration criteria is the same as for epoetin alfa The darbepoetin t½ is 3-fold longer than epoetin alfa (it can be given weekly)	

ESA Patient Counseling

- This medication is used to treat a condition called anemia, which is when your body is not producing enough red blood cells. It can help reduce your need for a blood transfusion.
- This medication can increase your risk of life-threatening conditions, including heart attack, heart failure, stroke or blood clots. Seek emergency medical help if you have symptoms such as: chest pain, shortness of breath, leg pain (with or without swelling), a cool or pale arm or leg, sudden confusion, trouble speaking, numbness or weakness on one side of your body (e.g., face, arm or leg), trouble seeing or loss of consciousness.
- For people with cancer: this medication can make your tumor grow faster. Talk with your healthcare provider about your individual risk.
- This medication can cause other serious side effects such as high blood pressure, seizures or serious allergic reactions (causing rash, shortness of breath, wheezing, fainting, sweating and/or facial swelling). Stop the medication and contact your healthcare provider right away if you have any of these symptoms.
- This medication comes in a single dose vial and must be drawn up into a syringe (*Aranesp* also comes in a pre-filled syringe). Instructions for use include (read the complete instructions for use provided before administration):
  - ❑ Do not shake the vial or syringe; this will ruin the medication and it will not work.
  - ❑ Do not use the medication if it has changed color or has any particles in it.
  - ❑ Recommended sites for injection into the skin include the outer areas of the upper arms, the abdomen (except for two inches around the navel), the front of the middle thighs and the upper outer area of the buttocks. See figure.
  - ❑ Rotate injections sites; do not inject into an area that is tender, red, bruised, hard or has scars or stretch marks.
  - ❑ Throw away used needles and syringes in a puncture-proof container with a tight fitting lid.

ESA Injection Sites

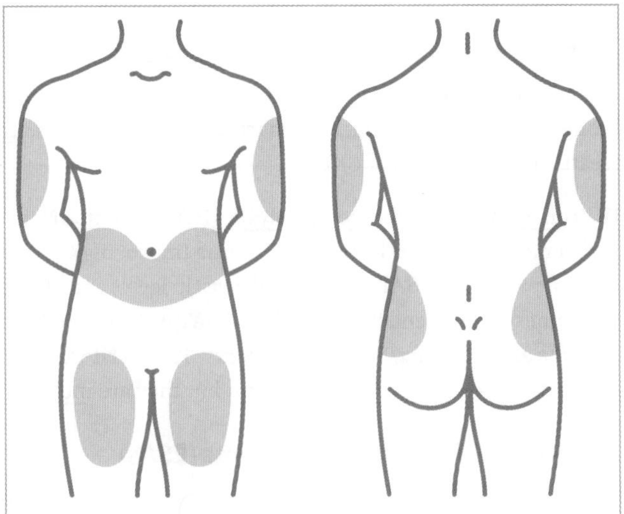

APLASTIC ANEMIA

Aplastic anemia (AA) occurs when the bone marrow fails to make enough RBCs, WBCs and platelets. It can be caused by drugs, infectious diseases, hereditary conditions or autoimmune disorders. In many cases, the cause is unknown. Patients with AA are at risk for life-threatening infections or bleeding. Treatment can include immunosuppressants, blood transfusions or a stem cell transplant. Eltrombopag (*Promacta*), a thrombopoietin nonpeptide agonist, increases platelet counts and is approved for the treatment of severe aplastic anemia in patients who are unresponsive to immunosuppressive therapy.

HEMOLYTIC ANEMIA

Hemolytic anemia develops when RBCs are destroyed and removed from the bloodstream before their normal lifespan of 120 days. This type of anemia can be acquired (e.g., drug-induced or associated with an immune disorder) or inherited (e.g., sickle cell disease, G6PD deficiency). There is more than one mechanism of drug-induced hemolytic anemia, but most often the medication binds to the RBC surface and triggers the development of antibodies that attack the RBC. The direct Coombs test is used to detect antibodies that are stuck to the surface of RBCs. See the Key Drugs Guy for medications that can cause acquired or inherited hemolytic anemia.

Glucose-6-phosphate dehydrogenase (G6PD) deficiency is an X-linked inherited disorder that most commonly affects persons of African, Asian, Mediterranean, or Middle Eastern descent. The G6PD enzyme protects RBCs from harmful substances (e.g., reactive oxygen species). Without sufficient levels of the enzyme, RBCs hemolyze (break apart) 24 - 72 hours after exposure to oxidative stress. Infections, certain foods (e.g., fava beans), severe stress, and certain drugs are factors that can increase the risk of hemolysis in a patient with G6PD deficiency. Most individuals do not need treatment but should be instructed to avoid certain high-risk medications (see Key Drugs Guy), foods or other known triggers. Medications that can cause acquired, drug-induced, hemolysis are not prohibited in patients with G6PD deficiency but, if used, they should be monitored closely and discontinued if hemolysis develops.

SELECT DRUGS THAT CAN CAUSE HEMOLYTIC ANEMIA

KEY DRUGS

- Dapsone
- Methylene Blue
- Primaquine
- Pegloticase
- Rasburicase
- Valproic acid

Others:

- Cephalosporins
- Levodopa
- Methyldopa
- Nitrofurantoin
- Penicillins
- Quinidine
- Quinine
- Rifampin

Select Guidelines/References

Short MW, Domaglaski JE. Iron deficiency anemia: evaluation and management. *Am Fam Physician.* 2013:87:98-104.

Kidney Disease: Improving Global Outcomes (KDIGO) Anemia Work Group. KDIGO Clinical Practice Guideline for Anemia in Chronic Kidney Disease. Kidney Int Suppl. 2012;2:279-335.

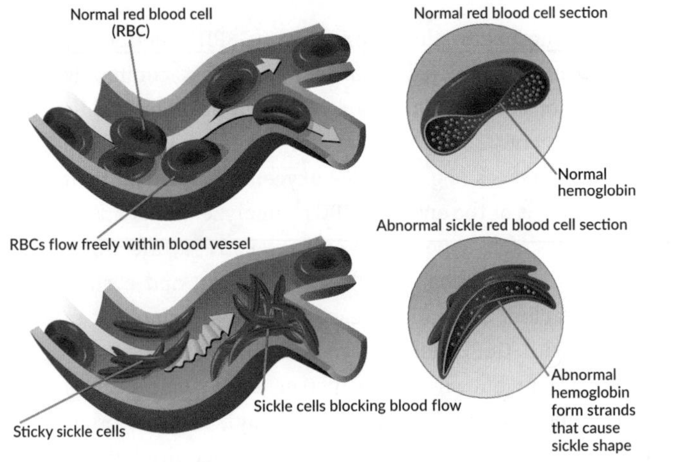

CHAPTER CONTENT

Background 550
Acute and Chronic Complications 550
Infection Risk 551
Non-Drug Treatment 551
Drug Treatment 551
Immunizations and Antibiotics 551
Key Vaccines in Sickle Cell Disease 551
Analgesics 552
Hydroxyurea 552
L-Glutamine *(Endari)* 553
Iron Chelation Treatment 553

CONTENT LEGEND

= Key Drug Guy

CHAPTER 36
SICKLE CELL DISEASE

BACKGROUND

Red blood cells (RBCs) contain adult hemoglobin (HgbA) and are shaped like a donut (without the hole). They have the flexibility to move through large and small blood vessels to deliver oxygen to the tissues. RBCs have a lifespan of 90 – 120 days.

Sickle cell disease (SCD) is a group of inherited RBC disorders resulting from a genetic mutation in the genes that encode hemoglobin (see the Pharmacogenomics chapter for a discussion on genetic inheritance). Patients with homozygous inheritance of the sickle cell gene (i.e., they have two copies of the mutated gene) have RBCs that contain abnormal hemoglobin, called hemoglobin S (i.e., HgbS or sickle hemoglobin). This causes RBCs to be rigid with a concave "sickle" shape. Sickled RBCs burst (hemolyze) after 10 – 20 days, which causes anemia and fatigue. SCD most commonly affects the African American population.

The irregularly shaped RBCs are unable to transport oxygen effectively and they stick together, blocking smaller blood vessels (vascular occlusion) and causing a wide array of complications. Symptoms of SCD develop approximately 2 – 3 months after birth. This is because a fetus and young infants have RBCs with fetal hemoglobin (HgbF), which blocks the sickling of RBCs. A hemoglobin electrophoresis test can measure the amount of each Hgb (A, F and S) in the blood.

ACUTE AND CHRONIC COMPLICATIONS

Vascular occlusion prevents oxygen from reaching the tissues, causing them to become ischemic. This can lead to different types of sickle cell crises (see the box on the following page), the most common of which is vasoocclusive crisis (VOC), or acute pain crisis. VOC most commonly occurs in the lower back, legs, hips, abdomen and chest, and can last for days or weeks. If the pain is in the chest and there is evidence of a pulmonary infection, it is called acute chest syndrome. Acute chest syndrome is life-threatening and is the leading cause of death in SCD. Due to the risk of acute stroke, females with SCD should not use estrogen; progestin-only contraceptives, levonorgestrel intrauterine devices (IUDs) and barrier methods are preferred for contraception.

The most common chronic complications of SCD are chronic pain, avascular necrosis (bone death), pulmonary hypertension and renal impairment.

INFECTION RISK

A healthy spleen has several physiologic roles, including the removal of old or damaged RBCs. It aids in immune function, making and storing white blood cells and clearing some types of bacterial pathogens from the body, particularly the encapsulated organisms *Streptococcus pneumoniae*, *Haemophilus influenzae* and *Neisseria meningitidis*. In SCD, the spleen becomes fibrotic and shrinks in size due to repetitive sickling and infarctions. This causes functional asplenia (decreased or absent spleen function), typically within the first year of life. Patients with functional asplenia are at an increased risk for serious infections; they require immunizations and prophylactic antibiotics, and should seek medical attention when temperature is > 101.3°F.

SICKLE CELL DISEASE COMPLICATIONS

Acute	Chronic
Acute chest syndrome	Avascular necrosis (bone death)
Anemia	Leg ulcers
Cholecystitis (gallbladder infection)	Gallstones
Infection	Pain
Multiorgan failure (kidneys, liver, lung)	Pregnancy complications (including fetal death)
Priapism (painful and prolonged erection)	Pulmonary hypertension
Spleen sequestration	Renal impairment
Stroke	Retinopathy
Vasoocclusive crisis (acute pain crisis)	Recurrent priapism

NON-DRUG TREATMENT

Blood transfusions protect against many of the life-threatening complications of SCD by providing RBCs with HgbA. Stroke, acute chest syndrome and severe anemia are acute complications that warrant treatment with blood transfusions. When administering chronic (monthly) blood transfusions, the goal Hgb level should be no higher than 10 g/dL post-infusion. One of the risks of blood transfusions is iron overload, which can lead to hemosiderosis (excess iron that impairs organ function). Chelation therapy to remove excess iron is discussed later in the chapter.

The only cure for SCD is bone marrow transplantation. Due to the high risks involved with such invasive treatment, as well as the substantial cost, it is not a widely used approach. Children are more likely to tolerate bone marrow transplantation than adults, who have accumulated organ damage. Gene therapy, by providing an antisickling gene and allowing for production of normal RBCs, is under investigation.

DRUG TREATMENT

The primary drug classes used in SCD are immunizations and antibiotics to reduce infection risk, analgesics to control pain, hydroxyurea or L-glutamine to prevent or reduce the frequency of acute and chronic complications, and chelation therapy to manage iron overload from blood transfusions.

IMMUNIZATIONS AND ANTIBIOTICS

Infections are a major cause of death, especially in children < 5 years of age. Sepsis and meningitis, due to *S. pneumoniae*, *H. influenzae*, *N. meningitidis* and *Salmonella* spp., can occur. The risk of infections caused by atypical organisms (*Chlamydophila* and *Mycoplasma pneumoniae*) is increased. Vaccinations are essential to prevent infection (see the Key Drugs Guy).

Prophylactic penicillin, given orally, reduces the risk of death from invasive pneumococcal infections in young children. Infants who screen positive for SCD at birth should be initiated on twice daily penicillin and treated until age five years. If a patient undergoes surgical removal of the spleen, or if invasive pneumococcal infection develops despite penicillin prophylaxis, it should be continued indefinitely.

KEY VACCINES IN SICKLE CELL DISEASE

Routine Childhood Series

- *Haemophilus influenzae* type B (Hib)
- Pneumococcal conjugate (PCV13, *Prevnar*)

Additional Vaccines For Functional Asplenia

- Meningococcal conjugate series plus routine boosters
- Meningococcal serogroup B (*Bexsero, Trumenba*)*
- Pneumococcal polysaccharide (PPSV23, *Pneumovax 23*)**
- Pneumococcal conjugate (PCV13, *Prevnar*) x 1 in any patient ≥ 6 years of age, if never received as a part of routine childhood series

**At age ≥ 10 years*
***At age ≥ 2 years, booster 5 years later and at age ≥ 65 years*

ANALGESICS

Mild to moderate pain can often be managed at home with rest, fluids, application of warm compresses to affected areas and the use of NSAIDs or acetaminophen. For severe pain and VOC, management must be guided by the patient's self-reported pain severity. Outpatient analgesic use should be reviewed and a treatment plan initiated within 30 minutes of triage. Patients with severe pain and VOC will require IV administration of opioids or patient-controlled analgesia (PCA). Refer to the Pain chapter for a detailed discussion of analgesics.

HYDROXYUREA

Hydroxyurea is a disease-modifying agent that stimulates production of HgbF. Long-term use of hydroxyurea reduces the frequency of acute pain crises, episodes of acute chest syndrome and the need for blood transfusions. It is indicated for adults with ≥ 3 moderate – severe pain crises in one year, or patients with severe or recurrent acute chest syndrome, chronic symptomatic anemia or disability. Use should be considered in all children > 9 months of age regardless of disease severity.

DRUG	DOSE	SAFETY/SIDE EFFECTS/MONITORING
Hydroxyurea (*Droxia, Hydrea, Siklos*) Capsule	Start: *Droxia:* 15 mg/kg/day as a single dose *Siklos:* 20 mg/kg/day as a single dose ↑ by 5 mg/kg/day every 8-12 weeks to a goal absolute neutrophil count (ANC) of 2,000-4,000/mm^3 Max: 35 mg/kg/day Use IBW or TBW, whichever is less, when calculating daily dose Round doses up to the nearest capsule size CrCl < 60 mL/min: adjustment required	**BOXED WARNINGS** Myelosuppression (↓ WBCs and platelets), malignancy (leukemia, skin cancer) **WARNINGS** Fetal toxicity, avoid live vaccinations, skin ulcers, macrocytosis Increased risk of pancreatitis, hepatotoxicity and peripheral neuropathy when used with antiretroviral drugs **SIDE EFFECTS** ↑ LFTs, uric acid, BUN and SCr; mouth ulcers, N/V/D, alopecia, hyperpigmentation or atrophy of skin and nails, low sperm counts (males) **MONITORING** CBC with differential every 2-4 weeks during treatment initiation and titration, then every 2-3 months once a stable dose is achieved; if toxicity occurs (ANC < 2,000/mm^3, platelets < 80,000/mm^3), hold hydroxyurea until the bone marrow recovers, then restart at a dose 5 mg/kg/day lower HgbF, uric acid, renal function, LFTs, baseline pregnancy test **NOTES** Contraception required during treatment and after discontinuation (6 months for females, 12 months for males) Hazardous agent – wear gloves when dispensing and wash hands before and after contact (see the Compounding chapters) Folic acid supplementation is recommended to prevent macrocytosis Clinical response can take 3-6 months

Hydroxyurea Drug Interactions

- There is a higher risk for potentially fatal pancreatitis, hepatotoxicity, hepatic failure and severe peripheral neuropathy when used in combination with antiretrovirals (especially didanosine and stavudine). Avoid hydroxyurea in combination with pimecrolimus, tacrolimus (topical) and other drugs that cause myelosuppression (e.g., clozapine, deferiprone, leflunomide, natalizumab, tofacitinib).

Hydroxyurea Patient Counseling

- Anyone handling the capsules (patient or caregiver) should wear disposable gloves to reduce the risk of exposure. Wash hands before and after handling. The capsules should not be opened.
- If you accidentally spill any of the contents, immediately wipe them up with a damp cloth and throw the cloth away in a sealed plastic bag. Then clean the area three times with detergent solution followed by clean water.
- For males and females of reproductive age:
  - This medication can decrease sperm count in men.
  - Avoid getting pregnant while taking this medication as it can harm an unborn baby. Discuss effective birth control and family planning with your healthcare provider.
  - Effective contraception should be used during and after stopping this medication (at least one year for males and six months for females).

- Wear sun protection, as this medication can increase the risk of skin cancer.
- Hydroxyurea can lower your body's ability to fight infection and make you more prone to illness or bleeding. Call your healthcare provider immediately if you experience fever, chills, body aches, severe sore throat, mouth sores, cough, shortness of breath, painful or difficult urination, easy bruising/bleeding, purple or red pinpoint spots under the skin, pale skin, rash, rapid heart rate and/or confusion.

L-GLUTAMINE *(ENDARI)*

L-glutamine oral powder *(Endari)* is FDA-approved for adults and children age ≥ 5 years with SCD. L-glutamine is an amino acid shown to reduce acute complications of SCD (e.g., number of pain crises requiring parenteral analgesics, number and duration of hospitalizations and occurrence of acute chest syndrome). The mechanism of action is not fully known, but it is thought to decrease oxidative stress, which can damage sickled RBCs.

DRUG	DOSE	SAFETY/SIDE EFFECTS/MONITORING
L-glutamine *(Endari)* Oral powder (5 grams per package)	TBW < 30 kg: 5 grams twice daily TBW 30-65 kg: 10 grams twice daily TBW > 65 kg: 15 grams twice daily	**SIDE EFFECTS** Constipation, nausea, headache, pain (abdominal, extremities, back, chest), cough **NOTES** Mix each dose in 8 oz. of a cold or room temperature beverage (e.g., water, milk or apple juice), or 4-6 oz. of food (e.g., applesauce or yogurt); medication does not have to be completely dissolved prior to administration

IRON CHELATION TREATMENT

Chronic blood transfusions cause iron overload, which damages the liver, heart and other organs. Chelation therapy is used to remove excess iron stores from the body. Historically, deferoxamine (the antidote for iron toxicity) was used, but it has significant toxicities, is not available in oral formulation and requires slow, prolonged infusions over 8 – 12 hours when administered by IV or SC routes. Oral chelating agents, such as deferasirox *(Exjade, Jadenu)* and deferiprone *(Ferriprox)*, are now more commonly used. Due to the side effect profile of both agents, treatment is typically prescribed, dispensed and monitored by specialty clinics and pharmacies.

Select Guidelines/References

National Heart, Lung, and Blood Institute. Evidence-based management of sickle cell disease. Expert panel report, 2014. https://www.nhlbi.nih.gov/sites/default/files/media/docs/sickle-cell-disease-report%20020816_0.pdf (accessed 2019 Jan 15).

37

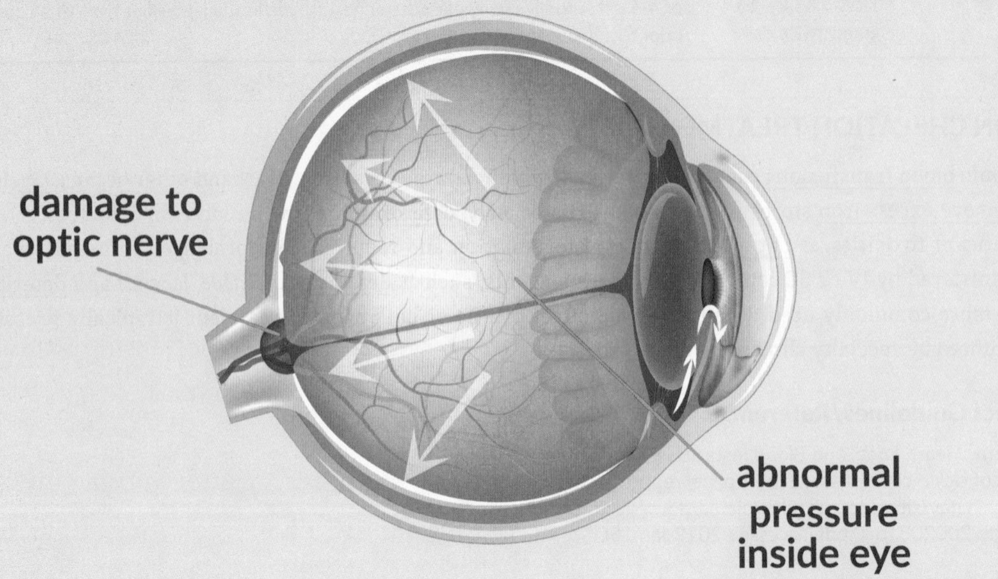
damage to
optic nerve
abnormal
pressure
inside eye

38

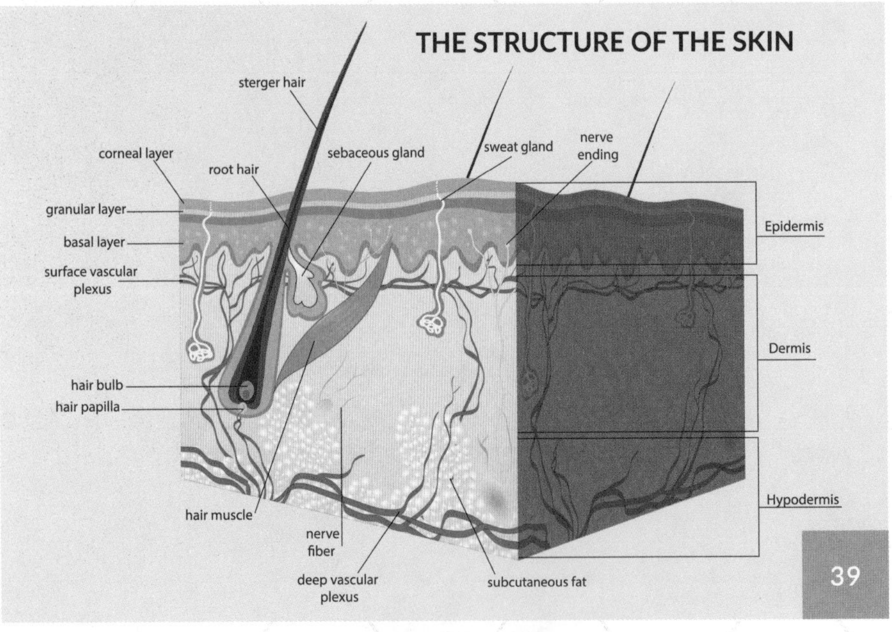
THE STRUCTURE OF THE SKIN
sterger hair
corneal layer
root hair
sebaceous gland
sweat gland
nerve
ending
granular layer
basal layer
surface vascular
plexus
Epidermis
Dermis
hair bulb
hair papilla
Hypodermis
hair muscle
nerve
fiber
deep vascular
plexus
subcutaneous fat

39

EYES, EARS, NOSE & SKIN CONDITIONS

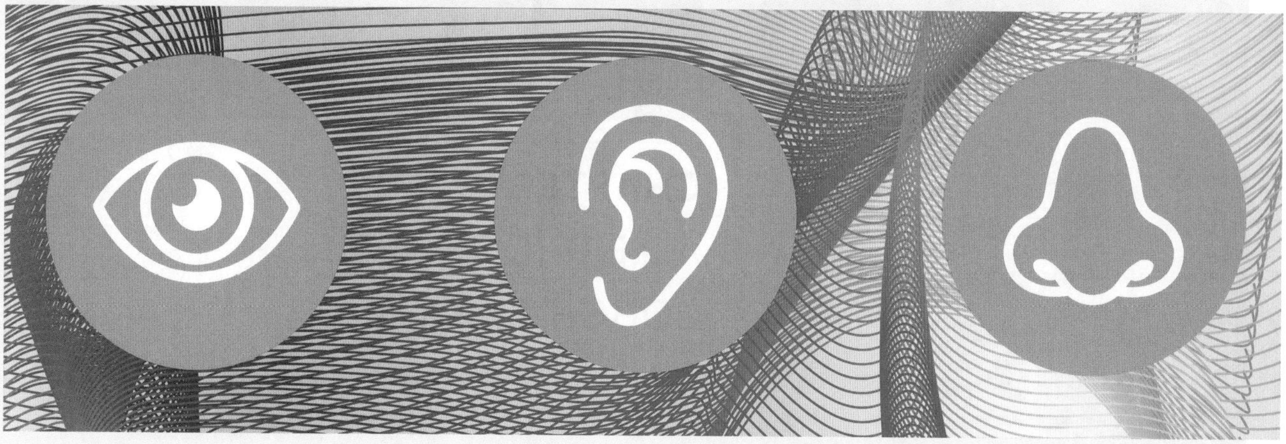

CONTENTS

CHAPTER 37
ALLERGIC RHINITIS, COUGH & COLD | **556**

CHAPTER 38
COMMON CONDITIONS OF THE EYES AND EARS | **566**

CHAPTER 39
COMMON SKIN CONDITIONS | **573**

CHAPTER CONTENT

Allergic Rhinitis 556
Background 556
Non-Drug Treatment 557
Nasal Irrigation and Wetting Agents 557
Drug Treatment 557
Intranasal Steroids 558
Antihistamines 559
Diphenhydramine In Pharmacy; It's Everywhere 559
Decongestants 560
Additional Allergy Medications 561
Cough and Cold 562
Background 562
Drug Treatment 562
Natural Products Used for Colds 562
Expectorants 563
Cough Suppressants 563
Decongestants 564
Analgesics/Antipyretics 564
Select Cough and Cold Combination Products 564
Cough and Cold Combo Products: What's in a Name? . 565
Cough and Cold Products in Children 564
Pediatric Cough and Cold Treatment - Caution Needed . 564
Patient Counseling: Flonase and Nasacort 24 HR 565

CONTENT LEGEND

= Study Tip Gal

CHAPTER 37
ALLERGIC RHINITIS, COUGH & COLD

ALLERGIC RHINITIS

BACKGROUND

Allergic rhinitis, commonly called hay fever or simply "allergies," causes cold-like symptoms [congestion, rhinorrhea (runny nose), sneezing, sinus pressure and itchy eyes]. Colds are caused by a virus; allergic rhinitis is caused by exposure to an allergen (e.g., pollen, dust, pet dander). Refer to the figure below that distinguishes between colds and allergic rhinitis. Allergic rhinitis can be easily spotted when a person has a few quick sneezes in succession (due to an exposure to an allergen), with watery, itchy red eyes, itchy nose and throat.

Allergic rhinitis symptoms can be intermittent (e.g., exposure to animal dander when visiting a friend's home) or chronic (e.g., symptoms that last for months whenever the pollen count is elevated).

Allergic rhinitis can cause misery, missed days at school and work and lost productivity. Untreated symptoms can lead to chronic sinusitis, otitis media (in children) and asthma exacerbations.

Many patients with asthma have allergic rhinitis; both are inflammatory over-reactions to some type of trigger.

COLDS VS. ALLERGIES
The symptoms of the common cold and allergies are very similar, which can make it difficult to tell the difference between the two.

COLD	ALLERGY
Sneezing	Sneezing
Runny Nose	Runny Nose
Thick, dark mucus	Thin, clear mucus
Sore throat	Wheezing
Body aches	Red, watery eyes
Symptoms take about three days to appear and usually last for about a week	Symptoms can last for days or months after contact with allergens

NON-DRUG TREATMENT

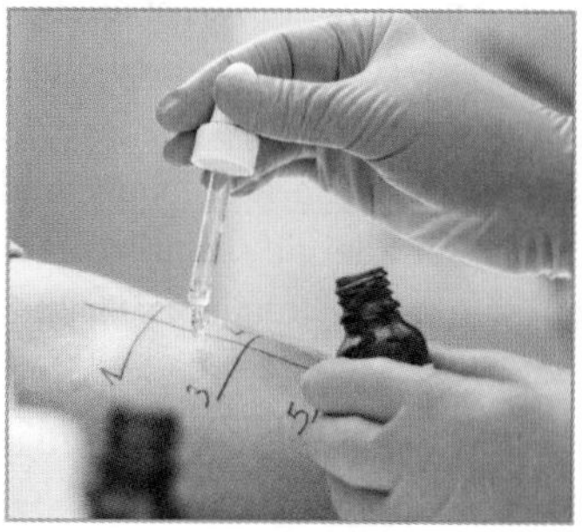

Avoiding exposure to known or suspected allergens (if possible) will reduce symptoms (i.e., it might be possible to avoid triggers from dust mites, but it may not be possible to avoid chronic exposure to air pollution). An IgE-mediated skin prick test (see figure) or blood test can determine patient-specific allergens.

Common allergens include:

- Pollens from trees, grasses and weeds
- Molds, both indoor and outdoor
- Dust mites that live in bedding, carpeting and other items that hold moisture
- Animal dander from furred animals such as cats, dogs, horses and rabbits

Ventilation systems with high-efficiency particulate air (HEPA) filters reduce some allergens (pollen, mold), but these systems can be expensive and are not effective for everyone.

Vacuuming carpets, drapes and upholstery with a HEPA vacuum cleaner often (at least weekly) reduces allergens. Dust mites can be reduced by removing carpets and upholstered furniture, encasing pillows, mattresses and box springs in allergen-impermeable covers and washing bedding and soft toys in hot water weekly.

When air pollutants are triggers, outdoor activities may need to be limited when air is unhealthy. The air quality index (AQI) rates the local air as good to hazardous. The AQI is useful for other conditions in which the air quality can affect breathing, including asthma, other types of lung disease and heart disease.

Pollen counts can be monitored when pollen is a trigger. When the pollen count is high, it is best to have patients stay indoors, with the windows closed and with the air conditioner on.

When children are raised in an overly-clean environment they lose the chance to build a healthy immune system. Parents should attempt to reach a balance between healthy and unhealthy levels of exposure.

NASAL IRRIGATION AND WETTING AGENTS

Nasal wetting agents (e.g., saline, propylene and polyethylene glycol sprays) or nasal irrigation with warm saline [isotonic (0.9%) or hypertonic (2 – 3.5%)] can reduce symptoms. Nasal irrigation rinses out allergens and mucus, increases ciliary function and reduces swelling. A popular product, the *"neti pot,"* looks like a small genie lamp or teapot. It is used to hold saline solution that is poured into one nostril and drained out of the other nostril.

Nasal irrigation is safe for children and pregnant women. Instruct patients to use only boiled (then cooled to room temperature) or distilled water (not directly from the faucet). Tap water contains organisms that are safe to ingest orally (killed by stomach acid), but can cause infections when used for nasal irrigation. The most common side effects are nasal burning, stinging, pain or irritation, which are increased with higher concentrations of saline. The pots or bottles should be rinsed with safe water after every use and left to air dry. Pots and bottles should never be shared with others. Nasal gels with petrolatum *(Allergen Block)* can be applied around the nostrils to physically block pollens and allergens from entering the nose.

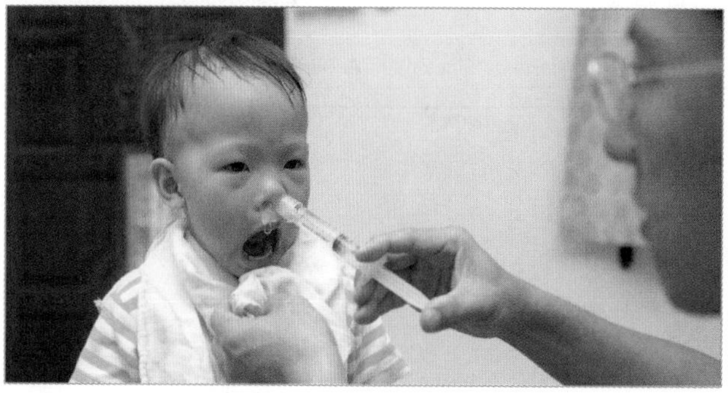

DRUG TREATMENT

Selecting appropriate medication treatment depends on the severity of illness and symptoms. Intranasal steroids are first-line for chronic, moderate-to-severe rhinitis. Milder, intermittent symptoms can be treated with oral antihistamines. Decongestants are used for congestion (if present) and come in nasal and oral formulations. Opthalmic medications for red, itchy eyes can be found in the Common Conditions of the Eyes & Ears chapter.

Intranasal Steroids

Intranasal steroids work by decreasing inflammation. They are considered first-line treatment for moderate-severe rhinitis. They are especially effective in reducing the nasal symptoms of allergic rhinitis (e.g., sneezing, itching, rhinorrhea, congestion). Several come OTC [e.g., triamcinolone (*Nasacort Allergy 24HR*), fluticasone (*Flonase Allergy Relief*) and budesonide (*Rhinocort Allergy*)]. Take note that steroids used to treat chronic allergic rhinitis have different brand names and delivery than steroids used to treat asthma. For example, fluticasone for allergic rhinitis comes in a nasal inhaler as *Flonase* ("-nase" for nasal), and for asthma comes in an oral inhaler as *Flovent*.

DRUG	DOSING	SAFETY/SIDE EFFECTS/MONITORING
Budesonide ***(Rhinocort Allergy OTC)*** Rx (generics) and OTC	Adult: 1 spray per nostril daily (max 4 sprays per nostril daily) Age ≥ 6 yrs: 1 spray per nostril daily (max 2 sprays per nostril daily)	**WARNINGS** Avoid use in patient with recent nasal septal ulcers, nasal surgery, or recent nasal trauma due to delayed wound healing High doses for prolonged periods can cause: adrenal suppression, ↓ growth velocity (pediatrics) and immunosuppression Use caution in patients with cataracts and/or glaucoma; ↑ intraocular pressure, open-angle glaucoma and cataracts have occurred with prolonged use **SIDE EFFECTS** Headache, dry nose, epistaxis (nose bleeds), unpleasant taste, localized infection **MONITORING** Growth (pediatrics), ocular changes, signs/symptoms of oral thrush and/or adrenal suppression If using regularly for several months, recommend periodic nasal exams to evaluate for nasal septal perforation or ulcers **NOTES** Can take up to one week to get full relief Budesonide is the preferred nasal steroid in pregnancy Shake bottle well before each use Discard device after total number of estimated doses, even if the bottle does not feel completely empty
Fluticasone ***(Flonase Allergy Relief, Flonase Sensimist, Children's Flonase,*** *Ticaspray, Xhance)* Rx and OTC OTC products: *Flonase Allergy Relief, Flonase Sensimist* + azelastine (*Dymista, Ticalast*)	Adult: 1-2 sprays per nostril daily (*Flonase Allergy Relief, Flonase Sensimist*) Age 4-11 yrs: 1 spray per nostril daily (*Flonase Allergy Relief*) Age ≥ 2 yrs: 1-2 sprays per nostril daily (*Sensimist*)	
Triamcinolone *(Nasacort Allergy 24HR OTC,* *Nasal Allergy 24HR OTC)* OTC	Adult and children age ≥ 6 yrs: 1-2 sprays per nostril daily Age 2-5 yrs: 1 spray per nostril daily	
Beclomethasone *(Beconase AQ, Qnasl, Qnasl Childrens)*	Adult: 1-2 sprays per nostril BID (*Beconase AQ*); 2 sprays per nostril daily (*Qnasl*)	
Ciclesonide *(Omnaris, Zetonna)*	Adult: 2 sprays per nostril daily (*Omnaris*); 1 spray per nostril daily (*Zetonna*)	
Flunisolide	Adult: 2 sprays per nostril BID or TID	
Mometasone (*Nasonex, Sinuva*)	Adult: 2 sprays per nostril daily	

Antihistamines

Oral antihistamines are commonly used for mild-moderate disease. They are effective in reducing symptoms of itching, sneezing, rhinorrhea and other types of immediate hypersensitivity reactions, but have little effect on nasal congestion. Antihistamines work by blocking histamine at the histamine-1 (H1) receptor site. The second-generation agents are generally preferred since they cause less sedation and cognitive impairment. Antihistamines can help if symptoms of allergic conjunctivitis (e.g., itchy, red eyes) are present.

DIPHENHYDRAMINE IN PHARMACY; IT'S EVERYWHERE

Diphenhydramine is a first-generation antihistamine, but it is used for many indications, such as:

- Treatment of acute allergic reactions (+/- epinephrine, depending on severity)
- Prevention of allergic reactions (included in most premedication regimens for high-risk drugs)
- Allergic rhinitis
- Cough (has antitussive properties)
- Sleep (sedating)
- Dystonic reactions (anticholinergic properties)
- Motion sickness

Because of the wide range of effects, it can also worsen some disease states (e.g., BPH, constipation, dementia, glaucoma)

DRUG	DOSING	SAFETY/SIDE EFFECTS/MONITORING
Select First-Generation Oral Antihistamines		
Diphenhydramine HCl (*Benadryl*, many others) Capsule, tablet, chewable, elixir, strip, syrup, suspension, injection, cream, gel, solution, stick Rx and OTC 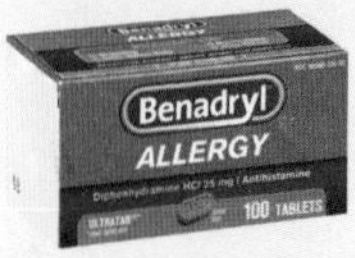	Adult: 25-50 mg PO Q4-6H (max 300 mg/day) Age 6-11 yrs: 12.5-25 mg PO Q4-6H (max 150 mg/day) Age < 6 yrs: do not use for self care	**CONTRAINDICATIONS** Newborns or premature infants, lactating women, acute asthma, use with MAO inhibitors **WARNINGS** Avoid use in the elderly (due to strong anticholinergic effects; Beers criteria) and in children < 2 years Can cause CNS depression/sedation Use with caution in patients with cardiovascular disease, prostate enlargement, glaucoma, asthma, pyloroduodenal obstruction and thyroid disease **SIDE EFFECTS** Somnolence, cognitive impairment, strong anticholinergic effects (dry mouth, blurred vision, urinary retention, constipation) and seizures/arrhythmias in higher doses **NOTES** First-generation antihistamines should not be taken by lactating women; second-generation agents preferred Should be discontinued ≥ 72 hours prior to allergy skin testing Can cause photosensitivity; use sunscreens and wear protective clothing while taking
Clemastine (*Dayhist Allergy 12 HR Relief*) Tablet, syrup OTC	Adult: 1.34-2.68 mg Q8-12H (max 8.04 mg/day)	
Carbinoxamine (*Karbinal ER, RyVent*) Tablet, liquid	**IR** (adult): 4-8 mg Q6-8H **ER** (adult): 6-16 mg Q12H	
Chlorpheniramine (*Aller-Chlor, Chlor-Trimeton,* others) Tablet, liquid, syrup OTC	**IR** (adult): 4 mg Q4-6H (max 24 mg/day) **ER** (adult): 12 mg Q12H (max 24 mg/day)	

DRUG	DOSING	SAFETY/SIDE EFFECTS/MONITORING
Second-Generation Oral Antihistamines		
Cetirizine (*Zyrtec*, *All Day Allergy*, others) Capsule, tablet, solution, syrup, chewable, ODT OTC **+ pseudoephedrine (*Zyrtec D*)** 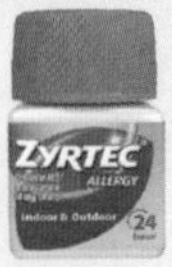 	Adult: 5-10 mg PO daily (max 5 mg daily in elderly) ≥ 6 yrs: use adult dose 2-5 yrs: 2.5-5 mg PO daily	**CONTRAINDICATIONS** Levocetirizine: end-stage renal disease (CrCl < 10 mL/min), hemodialysis, infants and children 6 months to 11 years of age with renal impairment **WARNINGS** Can cause CNS depression/sedation, especially when used with other sedating drugs Use with caution in the elderly and in renal or hepatic impairment **SIDE EFFECTS** Somnolence can still be seen (more with cetirizine and levocetirizine), headache **NOTES** Fexofenadine: take with water (not juice due to ↓ absorption); avoid administration with aluminum or magnesium-containing products Should be discontinued ≥ 72 hours prior to allergy skin testing If using in pregnancy, loratadine and cetirizine are considered low risk Cetirizine and levocetirizine have a fast onset and may work best for some patients More sedating: cetirizine, levocetirizine, hydroxyzine and meclizine Less sedating: fexofenadine and loratadine
Levocetirizine (*Xyzal Allergy 24HR OTC*) Tablet, solution OTC	Adult: 5 mg PO QHS 6-11 yrs: 2.5 mg PO QHS 6 mos-5 yrs: 1.25 mg PO QHS	
Fexofenadine (*Allegra 24HR*, *Allegra Allergy, Allegra Allergy Childrens, Mucinex Allergy*) Tablet, suspension, ODT Rx and OTC **+ pseudoephedrine (*Allegra D*)**	Adult: 60 mg PO BID or 180 mg daily 2-11 yrs: 30 mg PO BID	
Loratadine (*Claritin OTC*, *Alavert OTC, Claritin RediTabs OTC*) Tablet, capsule, chewable, solution, syrup, ODT OTC **+ pseudoephedrine (*Claritin D*)**	Adult: 10 mg PO daily or 5 mg PO BID (*RediTabs*) Age ≥ 6 yrs: use adult dose 2-5 yrs: 5 mg PO daily	
Desloratadine (*Clarinex*) Tablet, syrup, ODT	Adult: 5 mg PO daily	
Intranasal Antihistamines		
Azelastine (*Astelin, Astepro*) + fluticasone (*Dymista, Ticalast*)	Adult: 1-2 sprays per nostril BID	**SIDE EFFECTS** Bitter taste, headache, somnolence, nasal irritation, epistaxis, sinus pain **NOTES** Helps with nasal congestion; can be combined with intranasal steroid (increases cost and risk for side effects)
Olopatadine (*Patanase*)	Adult: 2 sprays per nostril BID	

Decongestants

Decongestants are effective in reducing sinus and nasal congestion. Decongestants are alpha-adrenergic agonists (sympathomimetics) that work by causing vasoconstriction that decreases sinus vessel engorgement and mucosal edema. If a product contains a D after the name (such as *Mucinex D* or *Robitussin D*), it usually contains a decongestant such as phenylephrine or pseudoephedrine (see Study Tip Gal on combination products). Phenylephrine has poor oral absorption. It comes as a nasal inhaler, but lasts for a shorter time and causes more side effects than the popular oxymetazoline inhalers. Pseudoephedrine is an effective systemic decongestant; pseudoephedrine is a precursor to methamphetamine, and has restricted distribution (see box later in chapter).

DRUG	DOSING	SAFETY/SIDE EFFECTS/MONITORING
Systemic (Oral)		
Phenylephrine HCl ***(Sudafed PE**, others)* Tablet, liquid, solution, injection OTC	Adult: 10 mg PO Q4H PRN (max 60 mg/day) 6-11 yrs: 5 mg PO Q4H PRN (max 30 mg/day) 4-5 yrs: 2.5 mg PO Q4H PRN (max 15 mg/day)	**CONTRAINDICATIONS** Do not use within 14 days of MAO inhibitors **WARNINGS** Avoid in children < 2 years (FDA), < 4 years (package labeling) Use with caution in patients with CV disease and uncontrolled hypertension (can ↑ BP), hyperthyroidism (can worsen), diabetes (can ↑ BG), bowel obstruction, glaucoma (can ↑ IOP), BPH (can cause urinary retention) and in the elderly **SIDE EFFECTS** Cardiovascular stimulation (tachycardia, palpitations, ↑ BP), CNS stimulation (anxiety, tremors, insomnia, nervousness, restlessness, fear, hallucinations), dizziness, headache, anorexia **NOTES** Phenylephrine has low bioavailability (≤ 38%); pseudoephedrine is more effective Onset of 15-60 minutes
Pseudoephedrine *(Sudafed, Nexafed, Zephrex-D*, others) Tablet, liquid, syrup Available behind the counter (see box on following page)	Adult: 60 mg PO Q4-6H PRN, or 120 mg PO ER Q12H, or 240 mg PO ER daily (max 240 mg/day) 6-11 yrs: 30 mg PO Q4-6H PRN (max 120 mg/day) 4-5 yrs: 15 mg PO Q4-6H PRN (max 60 mg/day)	
Topicals (Intranasal)		
Oxymetazoline 0.05% ***(Afrin**, Neo-Synephrine 12-Hour, Vicks Sinex, Zicam Extreme Congestion Relief)* OTC	Adult: 2-3 sprays per nostril Q12H PRN ≥ 6 yrs: use adult dose	**CONTRAINDICATIONS** Oxymetazoline: do not use for more than 3 days **WARNINGS** Do not use with MAO inhibitors, or if patient has closed angle glaucoma Use with caution in patients with CV disease and uncontrolled hypertension, thyroid disease, diabetes and BPH **SIDE EFFECTS** Nasal stinging, burning and dryness (vehicle-related), sneezing, trauma from the tip of the device, rhinitis medicamentosa (rebound congestion if used longer than 3 days) **NOTES** Fast onset (5-10 minutes)
Phenylephrine 0.125%, 0.25%, 0.5%, 1% *(Neo-Synephrine*, Little Noses Decongestant Drops*, others) OTC	Adult: 2-3 sprays of 0.25% to 1% per nostril Q4H PRN	
Tetrahydrozoline 0.05%, 0.1%	Adult: 3-4 sprays of 0.1% per nostril Q3-4H PRN or 2-4 drops per nostril Q3-4H PRN	

**Brand discontinued but name still used in practice.*

Additional Allergy Medications

Intranasal Cromolyn *(Nasalcrom)* - OTC

Cromolyn is a mast cell stabilizer used for treatment and prophylaxis of allergic rhinitis. It must be started at the onset of allergy season and used regularly (not PRN) to be effective. Symptoms will start to improve in 3 – 7 days, but maximal effect can take ≥ 2 – 4 weeks of continued use. Although generally not as effective as other agents, it is used in children ≥ 2 years old and in pregnancy due to its safety profile.

Intranasal Ipratropium Bromide

This drug is effective for decreasing rhinorrhea by causing nasal dryness (not effective for other nasal symptoms).

Oral Antileukotrienes: Montelukast *(Singulair)*

Montelukast has similar efficacy to antihistamines or pseudoephedrine, and can be recommended for adjunctive relief. See the Asthma chapter for more information.

Immunotherapy

Immunotherapy is a preventative treatment for allergies, either through subcutaneous (SC) injections or sublingual (SL) treatments. They work by slowly increasing exposure to the allergen, making the immune system becomes less sensitive to the substance. Long-term immunotherapy can improve the underlying allergic disease and relieve symptoms even after stopping treatment. It is recommended to treat for a minimum of three years.

SC allergy shots are the traditional method of treatment, which must be given in a physician office. An alternative option is SL treatment. There are four FDA-approved SL treatments for allergic rhinitis that are tailored to specific allergens. The first dose must be given in the doctor's office with all of these agents, but subsequent doses can be taken at home. The patient must be monitored for at least 30 minutes for signs of allergic reactions (boxed warning) and the patient should have an epinephrine auto-injector.

- *Oralair* contains five different grass pollen extracts. Place one SL tablet under the tongue daily; initiate treatment four months before and during grass pollen season.
- *Grastek* contains timothy grass pollen extract. Place one SL tablet under the tongue daily; initiate treatment three months before and during grass pollen season.
- *Ragwitek* contains ragweed pollen extract. Place one SL tablet under the tongue daily; initiate treatment three months before and during pollen season.
- *Odactra* contains house dust mite allergen extract. Place one SL tablet under the tongue daily.

COUGH AND COLD

BACKGROUND

The common cold, a viral infection of the upper respiratory tract, is caused by over 200 viruses including rhinoviruses and coronaviruses. It is transmitted by mucus secretions (via patient's hands) or by the air (from coughing or sneezing). Coughing or sneezing into the elbow or into a tissue is preferable over coughing into a hand, which can then touch surfaces and spread illness. Frequent hand cleansing with soap or soap substitutes (e.g., hand sanitizer) should be encouraged. Refer to the Medication Safety & Quality Improvement chapter for correct hand washing technique, and to the Infectious Diseases II chapter for a table of common upper and lower respiratory infections. Colds are usually self-limiting, but they are the leading cause of absenteeism in work and school due to bothersome symptoms.

DRUG TREATMENT

Treatment of cough and cold is based on the presenting symptoms; each patient will present differently and require different treatment. The goal of treatment is to reduce duration and frequency of symptoms to allow the patient to feel better and return to normal activities.

Natural Products used for Colds

Zinc, in various formulations including lozenges, is used for cold prevention and treatment. Zinc lozenges or syrup might decrease cold duration if used correctly (taken every two hours while awake, starting within 24 hours of symptom onset). For this purpose zinc supplements are rated as "possibly effective" by the *Natural Medicines Database*. Zinc lozenges can cause mouth irritation, a metallic taste and nausea. They should not be used for more than five to seven days, as long term use can cause copper deficiency. Due to loss of smell, zinc nasal formulations were removed from the market.

COMBAT METHAMPHETAMINE EPIDEMIC ACT 2005

The sale of non-prescription pseudoephedrine is restricted as part of the "Combat Methamphetamine Epidemic Act" (CMEA) to crack down on the methamphetamine epidemic. The act applies to any non-prescription product containing pseudoephedrine, phenylpropanolamine and ephedrine, all of which can be converted rather easily into methamphetamine.

These products must be kept behind the counter or in a locked cabinet. They often are, but do not need to be, located in the pharmacy. Stores must keep a logbook of any sale more than a single dose package (maximum of 60 mg). For any sale above this amount, the customer must show a government-issued photo ID (e.g., driver's license, ID card or US passport).

Customers record their name, date and time of sale and signature in the logbook. The store staff must verify that the name matches the photo ID and that the date and time are correct. The store staff must also record the address; some stores can swipe the driver's license electronically to do this. The store staff must record what the person received as well as the quantity purchased. Under federal law the maximum amount allowed for purchase is 3.6 grams per day, and 9 grams in a 30-day period. The logbook must be kept for a minimum of 2 years and must be kept secured and readily available upon request by board inspectors or law enforcement. The logbook cannot be shared with the public.

Many states now have their own restrictions in addition to the federal restriction, such as age restrictions, prescription required or stricter limits.

Vitamin C (ascorbic acid) supplements are commonly used, but they have little to no efficacy for cold prevention. Some data has shown a decrease in the duration of the cold by 1 – 1.5 days at doses of 1 – 3 grams/day. There might also be a dose-dependent response; doses of at least 2 grams/day appear to work better than 1 gram/day. Vitamin C is rated as "possibly effective" for cold treatment by the *Natural Medicines Database*. High doses of vitamin C (4 g/day or greater) can cause diarrhea and possibly kidney stones in male patients. Echinacea is rated as "possibly effective" for cold treatment.

With any of these products it is important to use the correct dose from a reputable manufacturer. *Airborne* and *Emergen-C Immune+* are popular products that contain a variety of ingredients, including vitamins C, vitamin E, zinc and echinacea.

Expectorants

Cough associated with colds is usually nonproductive (i.e., a dry cough). If productive cough is present, expectorants can be used to decrease phlegm viscosity in the lower respiratory tract and increase secretions in the upper respiratory tract to help move phlegm upwards and out.

DRUG	DOSING	SAFETY/SIDE EFFECTS/MONITORING
Guaifenesin *(Mucinex, Robitussin Mucus + Chest Congestion, Robafen)* Tablet, caplet, liquid, syrup, granule OTC	200-400 mg Q4H PRN, or 600-1,200 mg ER Q12H (max 2.4 g/day) Age 6-11 yrs:1,200 mg/day (max) Age 4-5 yrs: 600 mg/day (max)	**SIDE EFFECTS** Nausea (dose-related), vomiting, dizziness, headache, rash, diarrhea, stomach pain **NOTES** OTC: do not use ER tablets in children < 12 years of age Some formulations contain phenylalanine

Cough Suppressants

Cough suppressants are used for dry, unproductive cough, or to suppress productive cough at night to allow for restful sleep. Dextromethorphan (DM) and codeine have a high affinity for several regions of the brain, including the medullary cough center, suppressing the cough reflex. Benzonatate suppresses cough by topical anesthetic action on the respiratory stretch receptors.

Both DM and codeine have abuse potential. DM acts as a serotonin reuptake inhibitor. At usual antitussive doses, it does not have addictive properties, but at high doses it acts as an NMDA-receptor blocker leading to euphoria and hallucinations similar to PCP, termed "robo-tripping." Due to its abuse potential, California became the first state to ban the sale of DM to minors < 18 years of age. A few other states have followed, some with more stringent requirements. Codeine products scheduled as C-V drugs must contain one or more non-codeine active ingredients and no more than 200 mg of codeine/100 mL. Codeine is commonly abused, particularly in combination with promethazine, known by the street names "purple drank" and "lean."

DRUG	DOSING	SAFETY/SIDE EFFECTS/MONITORING
Dextromethorphan *(Delsym,* *DayQuil Cough)* Capsule, liquid, lozenge, strips OTC	10-20 mg Q4H PRN, or 30 mg Q6-8H PRN, or 60 mg ER Q12H PRN (max 120 mg/day) Age 6-12 yrs: 60 mg/day max Age 4-6 yrs: 30 mg/day max	**CONTRAINDICATIONS** All dextromethorphan-containing products should not be used within 14 days of MAO inhibitor use **SIDE EFFECTS** N/V, drowsiness, serotonin syndrome if co-administered with other serotonergic drugs **NOTES** If the product name has DM at the end, such as *Robitussin DM*, it contains dextromethorphan Additive CNS depression can occur
Codeine C-II	Adults: 10-20 mg Q4-6H PRN (max 120 mg/day)	**BOXED WARNING** Respiratory depression and death have occurred in children who received codeine following tonsillectomy and/or adenoidectomy and had evidence of being ultra-rapid metabolizers of codeine due to a CYP450 2D6 polymorphism; deaths have also occurred in nursing infants after being exposed to high concentrations of morphine because the mothers were ultra-rapid metabolizers **CONTRAINDICATIONS** Children < 12 years **NOTES** In January 2018, the FDA changed the labeling for all prescription cough and cold medications that contain codeine or hydrocodone; they are no longer indicated in patients < 18 years old. See Pain chapter and Pediatrics chapter for more information
Benzonatate *(Tessalon Perles)*	100-200 mg TID PRN (max 600 mg/day)	**WARNINGS** Do not use in children < 10 years of age; accidental ingestion and fatal overdose has been reported **SIDE EFFECTS** Somnolence, confusion, hallucinations
Diphenhydramine *(Benadryl)* Rx and OTC	25 mg Q4H PRN (max 150 mg/day)	See First-Generation Oral Antihistamine table

Decongestants

Systemic and nasal decongestants are used to relieve congestion and rhinorrhea. These agents are discussed in the previous section.

Analgesics/Antipyretics

Analgesics and antipyretics such as acetaminophen and ibuprofen are used to relieve sore throat, body malaise and fever. They are often added to combination products for cough/cold. Use caution not to exceed the maximum daily dosing for acetaminophen or ibuprofen if multiple medications are being used. See Pain chapter for more information, and the Study Tip Gal on the following page to help with recognizing ingredients in a product.

Select Cough and Cold Combination Products

The following cough and cold combination products are all available by prescription only. See the Study Tip Gal on the next page for methods to help recognize the ingredients in combination products.

DRUG	ADULT DOSING
Dextromethorphan/promethazine	15 mg/6.25 mg per 5 mL; 5 mL Q4-6H PRN (max 30 mL/day)
Brompheniramine/pseudoephedrine/ dextromethorphan *(Bromfed DM)*	2 mg/30 mg/10 mg per 5 mL; 10 mL Q4H PRN (max 60 mL/day)
Promethazine/codeine C-V	6.25 mg/10 mg per 5 mL; 5 mL Q4-6H PRN (max 30 mL/day)
Promethazine/phenylephrine/codeine (Promethazine VC/Codeine) C-V	6.25 mg/5 mg/10 mg per 5 mL; 5 mL Q4-6H PRN (max 30 mL/day)
Guaifenesin/codeine *(Robafen AC, Virtussin A/C, G Tussin AC)* C-V	100 mg/10 mg per 5 mL; 10 mL PO Q4H PRN (max 60 mL/day)
Guaifenesin/codeine/pseudoephedrine *(Coditussin DAC, Virtussin DAC)* C-V	100 mg/10 mg/30 mg per 5 mL; 10 mL Q4H PRN (max 40 mL/day)
Chlorpheniramine/hydrocodone ***(Tussionex,** TussiCaps)* C-II	8 mg/10 mg ER per 5 mL; 5 mL Q12H PRN (max 10 mL/day)
Chlorpheniramine/codeine *(Tuzistra XR)* C-III (ER suspension)	10 mL PO Q12H PRN (max 20 mL/day)

Cough and Cold Products in Children

In 2008, the FDA warned that OTC cough and cold products should not be used in children under 2 years old due to safety concerns. Later that same year, many manufacturers voluntarily re-labeled these cough and cold products to state: "do not use in children under 4 years of age." The American Academy of Pediatrics (AAP) has recommended against their use in children under 6 years old, due to inadequate data on efficacy and the potential for errors and adverse effects (see Study Tip Gal). These cough and cold products include any product containing decongestants and the antihistamines diphenhydramine, brompheniramine or chlorpheniramine.

Do not use promethazine in any form in children less than 2 years old. Codeine products are contraindicated in children < 12 years of age, and in those < 18 years after the most common childhood surgeries (tonsillectomy/adenoidectomy) due to the risk of respiratory depression. In January 2018, the FDA changed the labeling for all prescription cough and cold medications that contain codeine or hydrocodone; they are no longer indicated in patients < 18 years old.

PEDIATRIC COUGH AND COLD TREATMENT - CAUTION NEEDED

CHILDREN < 12 YEARS
Avoid codeine-containing products (FDA)

CHILDREN < 6 YEARS
Avoid all OTC cough and cold products (AAP)

CHILDREN < 4 YEARS
Avoid many OTC cough and cold products (package labeling)

CHILDREN < 2 YEARS
Avoid OTC cough and cold products (FDA)

Avoid promethazine (FDA)

Avoid topical menthol and camphor (package labeling)

If a young child has a cold, it is safe and useful to recommend proper hydration, nasal bulbs for gentle suctioning, saline drops/sprays (*Ocean* and generics), vaporizers/humidifiers and ibuprofen and acetaminophen, if needed for fever or pain. Do not use aspirin in children due to the risk of Reye's syndrome. Symptoms of the common cold usually resolve in a few days (up to 2 weeks). If the child is a small infant, seems seriously ill or if symptoms worsen or do not go away, the child should be seen by a pediatrician.

Acetaminophen or ibuprofen can be used to reduce fever, aches and pains. OTC infant drops for fever come with a calibrated dropper or oral syringe; only this device should be used. Advise against using kitchen teaspoons to measure out medication since these come in different sizes. If under the age of 2 years, a pediatrician should be consulted prior to OTC treatment.

- Acetaminophen infants' or children's liquid suspensions (both 160 mg/5 mL): 10-15 mg/kg/dose Q4-6H PRN, max 75 mg/kg/day.
- Ibuprofen infants' drops (50 mg/1.25 mL) or children's liquid suspensions (100 mg/5 mL): 5- 10 mg/kg/dose Q6-8H PRN. Max daily dose 40 mg/kg/day for both formulations.

Some doctors recommend alternating ibuprofen with acetaminophen at each dosing interval to avoid acetaminophen toxicity or ibuprofen-induced GI discomfort.

Menthol and camphor used topically, such as in *Vick's VapoRub*, do not work well and should not be used in children less than 2 years old. Menthol can result in aspiration or cardiac and CNS toxicity if ingested. Camphor is generally considered safe but lacks sufficient data. *Vick's BabyRub* contains petrolatum, eucalyptus oil, lavender oil, rosemary oil and aloe extract and is considered relatively safe but lacks sufficient efficacy data.

PATIENT COUNSELING: *FLONASE* AND *NASACORT 24 HR*

BEFORE USING

- Shake the bottle gently, then remove the dust cover/cap.
- Prime the pump before the first use or when you have not used it for awhile (seven days for *Flonase*, 14 days for *Nasacort*). To prime, point the bottle away from you; press down and release the pump a few times until a fine spray appears. The pump is now ready for use.
- Blow your nose to clear your nostrils.

COUGH AND COLD COMBO PRODUCTS: WHAT'S IN A NAME?

The name of a combination cough/cold product can tell you what it contains. This is based on either the symptom it treats (e.g., *Robitussin Cough + Chest Congestion DM* contains dextromethorphan, a cough suppressant, + guaifenesin, an expectorant for congestion) or the abbreviation. Some commonly used abbreviations are:

D = decongestant (e.g., phenylephrine or pseudoephedrine); example: *Mucinex D* = guaifenesin + pseudoephedrine

PE = **p**henyl**e**phrine; example: *Sudafed PE* = phenylephrine

DM = **d**extro**m**ethorphan; example: *Robafen DM* = guaifenesin + dextromethorphan

AC = contains codeine; example: *Robafen AC* = guaifenesin + codeine

Guaifenesin is a mucolytic (thins out mucus); single agent is *Mucinex*.

Analgesics in combination cough and cold products are usually acetaminophen.

Antihistamines (e.g., diphenhydramine, chlorpheniramine, brompheniramine) are common and cause sedation. The night-time products, and some anytime products, contain an antihistamine.

USING THE SPRAY

- Close one nostril. Keeping the bottle upright, carefully insert the nasal applicator into the other nostril.
- Start to breathe in through your nose, and press firmly and quickly down once on the applicator to release the spray. Avoid spraying in eyes or toward the middle of the nose.
- Breathe out through your mouth. If a second spray is needed in that nostril, repeat the above three steps. Repeat the above three steps in the other nostril.
- Wipe the nasal applicator with a clean tissue and replace with dust cover.
- Do not use the bottle for more than the labeled number of sprays even if it is not completely empty.
- Do not blow your nose right after using the nasal spray. Clean the nasal applicator tip regularly (at least once a week for *Flonase*, after every use for *Nasacort*) by gently pulling it off and rinsing it under warm water. Let it air dry before replacing back onto the bottle.

Select Guidelines/References

Seidman MD, Gurgel RK, Lin SY et al. Clinical Practice Guideline: Allergic Rhinitis. *Otolaryngology-Head and Neck Surgery.* 2015;152(IS):S1-S43.

Krinsky DL, Berardi RR, Ferreri SP, eds. Handbook of Nonprescription Drugs. 18th ed. Washington DC: APhA; 2015:172-208.

CHAPTER CONTENT

Background 566
Eye & Ear Prescription Interpretation 566
Glaucoma 567
Drugs that Can Increase IOP 567
Drug Treatment 567
Glaucoma Treatment Goal: Decrease IOP 567
Conjunctivitis 569
Treatment of Conjunctivitis by Type 569
Blepharitis (Eyelid Inflammation) 570
Other Ocular Conditions 570
Symptom-Based Ophthalmic Treatments 570
Medication Induced Ophthalmic Issues 570
Eye Drop Patient Counseling 571
Common Drugs Known to Cause Vision Changes or Damage 571
Common Ear Conditions 572
Otitis Externa 572
Ear Wax (Cerumen) Blockage 572
Ear Drop Patient Counseling 572

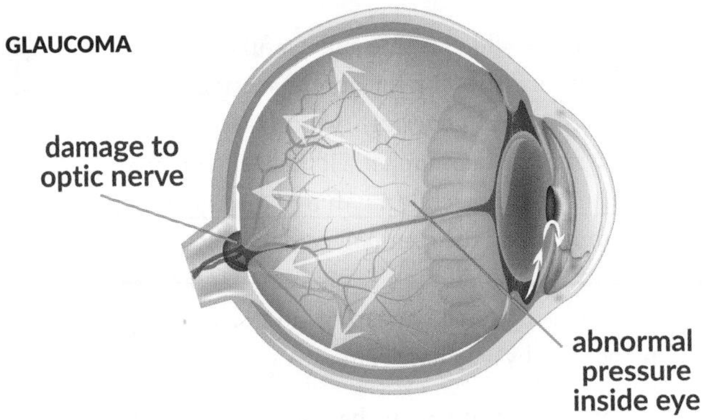

CHAPTER 38
COMMON CONDITIONS OF THE EYES AND EARS

BACKGROUND

Many eye and ear conditions can be treated with topical medications that are applied directly to the eye or ear. By applying the medication directly to the specific location, instead of systemically, adverse effects are minimized.

The various formulations of topical eye and ear medications are shown in the box. The eyes are more sensitive than the ears. Eye drops can be used in the ear, but never use ear drops in the eyes. The ear drops may not have an appropriate pH, may not be isotonic and may not be sterile. Correct administration technique is key for each medication to work.

EYE & EAR PRESCRIPTION INTERPRETATION

ABBREV.	MEANING	CAUTION
AD AS AU	Right Ear Left Ear Each Ear	These abbreviations can be mistaken (interchanged) for each other and can mean other things; know how to interpret them, but it is safer to write them out (e.g., use right eye instead of OD)
OD OS OU	Right Eye Left Eye Each Eye	
Memory tip: A is from the Latin for ear (auris), O is for eye (oculus), D is for right (dextra) and S is for left (sinistra)		

EYE AND EAR FORMULATIONS

- Solutions: 1 drop = 0.05 mL.
- Suspensions: shake well.
- Ointments: apply to the conjunctival sac or over lid margins (for blepharitis). Ointments can make vision blurry. Do not use with contact lenses.
- Gels: with cap on, invert and shake once to get the medication into the tip before instilling into the eye.

CONTENT LEGEND

= Study Tip Gal   = Key Drug Guy

GLAUCOMA

Glaucoma is a disease of the eye that results in damage to the optic nerve and loss of the visual field (e.g., the vision straight ahead and the peripheral vision, measured by the visual field test). In most cases, the intraocular pressure (IOP) is above the normal range of 12 – 22 mmHg. IOP can be increased from genetics, age and medications (see Key Drugs Guy). The goal of treatment is to reduce IOP. Patients can be asymptomatic, or they can experience eye pain, headache and decreased vision.

DRUGS THAT CAN INCREASE IOP

- Anticholinergics (e.g., oxybutynin, tolterodine, benztropine, trihexyphenidyl, TCAs)
- Cough, cold and motion sickness medications (e.g., antihistamines, scopolamine)
- Chronic steroids, especially eye drops such as prednisolone *(PredForte)*
- Topiramate *(Topamax)*

There are two main forms of glaucoma. The more common type, open-angle glaucoma, is treated with eye drops that lower IOP or surgery. Angle-closure, or closed-angle glaucoma, is a sharp, sudden increase in IOP due to a blockage. This type of glaucoma is a medical emergency that is treated surgically.

DRUG TREATMENT

Glaucoma treatments decrease IOP by targeting the aqueous humor (fluid in the eye) in two main ways (see Study Tip Gal). Prostaglandin (PG) analogs are used commonly as initial treatment. PG analogs are the most effective drugs at decreasing IOP (~30%); they are safe and are used once daily. Ophthalmic beta-blockers (e.g., timolol), another common class of drugs, decrease IOP by ~22%. A beta-blocker is preferable if the pressure is high in one eye only. The iris-darkening/eyelash thickening seen with PG analogs is not desirable in one eye. If monotherapy does not sufficiently decrease IOP, consider switching to a different medication or using combination therapy.

Adequate treatment requires good eye drop technique and a high level of adherence. The correct way to administer eye drops is described later in this chapter. Because glaucoma often presents with no symptoms, adherence can be a major issue. Counseling on proper administration technique and the importance of adherence is critical.

GLAUCOMA TREATMENT GOAL: DECREASE IOP

Options:

- Make less fluid (with beta-blockers, like timolol)
- Move fluid out (with prostaglandin analogs, like latanoprost)
- Or, do both: often achieved with the add-on treatment brimonidine

DRUG	DOSING	SIDE EFFECTS/CLINICAL CONCERNS
Prostaglandin Analogs: increase aqueous outflow		
Bimatoprost *(Lumigan)* **Latanoprost *(Xalatan, Xelpros)*** **Travoprost *(Travatan Z)*** Latanoprostene bunod *(Vyzulta)* Tafluprost *(Zioptan)* **Bimatoprost *(Latisse)*** is indicated for eyelash hypotrichosis (to ↑ eyelash growth); do not use with prostaglandin analogs indicated for glaucoma	1 drop QHS The preservative benzalkonium chloride (BAK) can absorb into contact lenses and discolor them – remove lenses before use and wait 15 min after eye drop administration to re-insert lenses (most given QHS)	**WARNINGS** Ocular effects: darkening of the iris, eyelid skin and eyelashes; eyelash length and number can increase; long-term consequences to the eye are not known; contamination of multiple-dose ophthalmic solutions can cause bacterial keratitis **SIDE EFFECTS** Blurred vision, stinging, increased pigmentation of the iris/eyelashes, eyelash growth/thickening, foreign body sensation **NOTES** *Travatan Z* and *Xelpros* do not contain BAK (have a different preservative); can be used in patients with a past reaction to BAK or dry eye *Zioptan* comes as 10 single-use, preservative free containers in a foil pouch; discard each container after use Store unopened bottles of latanoprost, bottles of latanoprostene bunod and pouches of *Zioptan* in the refrigerator

DRUG	DOSING	SIDE EFFECTS/CLINICAL CONCERNS
Beta-Blockers: reduce aqueous humor production		
Timolol 0.25% and 0.5% *(Timoptic, Timoptic-XE, Istalol,* *Timolol GFS, Betimol, Timoptic Ocudose)* **+ dorzolamide *(Cosopt, Cosopt PF)*** + brimonidine *(Combigan)* Betaxolol *(Betoptic S)* Carteolol *(Ocupress)* Levobunolol *(Betagan)* Metipranolol *(OptiPranolol)*	*Timolol:* 1 drop daily or BID *Timoptic-XE, Timolol GFS* (gels): daily Gels: shake once before use; wait 10 minutes after administering other eye drops before inserting gel Select products contain the preservative BAK; remove contact lenses before use	**CONTRAINDICATIONS** Sinus bradycardia; heart block > 1st degree (except in patients with a pacemaker); cardiogenic shock; uncompensated cardiac failure; bronchospastic disease **SIDE EFFECTS** Burning, stinging, itching of the eyes or eyelids, changes in vision, increased sensitivity of the eyes to light, bradycardia, bronchospasm with non-selective agents, fatigue **NOTES** All are non-selective beta-blockers except betaxolol *Cosopt PF* (the PF stands for "preservative free") is packaged in single-use containers Some products contain sulfites, which can cause allergic reactions
Cholinergics (Miotics): increase aqueous outflow		
Carbachol *(Isopto Carbachol, Miostat)*	1-2 drops up to TID	**SIDE EFFECTS** Corneal clouding, poor vision at night (due to pupil constriction), burning (transient), irritation, hypotension, bronchospasm, abdominal cramps/GI distress **NOTES** Use with caution in patients with a history of retinal detachment or corneal abrasion
Pilocarpine *(Isopto Carpine, Pilopine HS)*	Solution: 1-2 drops up to 4 times per day Select products contain the preservative BAK; remove contact lenses before use	
Carbonic Anhydrase Inhibitors: reduce aqueous humor production		
Dorzolamide *(Trusopt)* **+ timolol *(Cosopt, Cosopt PF)*** Brinzolamide *(Azopt)* + brimonidine *(Simbrinza)* Acetazolamide – oral Methazolamide *(Neptazane)* - oral	*Trusopt:* 1 drop TID *Cosopt:* 1 drop BID *Azopt:* 1 drop TID Acetazolamide 250 mg PO 1-4 times per day, or 500 mg ER PO BID Select ophthalmic products contain the preservative BAK; remove contact lenses before use	**WARNINGS** Sulfonamide allergy: caution due to the risk of systemic exposure and cross reactivity (especially with oral formulations) **SIDE EFFECTS** Eye drops: burning, blurred vision, blepharitis, dry eye Oral (acetazolamide): CNS effects (ataxia, confusion), photosensitivity/ skin rash (including risk of SJS and TEN), anorexia, nausea, risk of hematological toxicities **NOTES** Acetazolamide oral capsules are infrequently used for glaucoma; they are used for the prevention and treatment of acute mountain (altitude) sickness
Adrenergic Alpha-2 Agonists: increase aqueous outflow, reduce aqueous humor production		
Brimonidine *(Alphagan P)* + timolol *(Combigan)* + brinzolamide *(Simbrinza)* Apraclonidine *(Iopidine)* Brimonidine *(Lumify)* is OTC and indicated for ocular redness	*Alphagan* and *Iopidine* are dosed TID Select products contain the preservative BAK; remove contact lenses before use	**WARNINGS** CNS depression: caution with heavy machinery, driving **SIDE EFFECTS** Sedation, burning/stinging/itchy eyes, dry mouth, dry nose
Rho Kinase Inhibitors: increase aqueous outflow		
Netarsudil *(Rhopressa)*	1 drop daily in the evening Contains the preservative BAK; remove contact lenses before use	**SIDE EFFECTS** Burning/eye pain, corneal disease, conjuctival hemorrhage and conjuctival hyperemia (excess blood vessels) **NOTES** Store in the refrigerator before opening; once opened, store at room temperature for ≤ 6 weeks

CONJUNCTIVITIS

Conjunctivitis, also known as "pink eye," occurs in one or both eyes. Symptoms include swelling, itching, burning, and redness of the conjunctiva, the protective membrane that lines the eyelids and covers the white part of the eye (the sclera). Conjunctivitis can be due to a virus, a bacteria, an allergen, or some type of ocular irritant, such as a chemical or contact lenses. In most cases, conjunctivitis causes only mild discomfort, does not harm vision and will clear without medical treatment. In some cases, treatment is required.

Viral and bacterial conjunctivitis occur mostly in young children and are highly contagious. Infected children should stay at home and only return to school once treatment begins, unless there are systemic symptoms. To prevent the spread of the infection, any patient with viral or bacterial conjunctivitis should be instructed to:

- Not touch their eyes.
- Use proper hand hygiene and wash their hands thoroughly and frequently.
- Change towels and washcloths daily, and do not share towels with others.
- Discard eye cosmetics, particularly mascara.

Chemical conjunctivitis has no specific drug treatment and is not described in the following table. The irritant should be flushed out of the eyes with saline, and inflammation can be reduced with an NSAID or a steroid eye drop. If contact lenses caused the irritation, they should not be used until the condition clears. It might be helpful to change the type of contact lenses or the brand of disinfectant solution. If the condition is severe, such as a burn, or the chemical is dangerous or unknown, the patient should be referred for emergency care.

TREATMENT OF CONJUNCTIVITIS BY TYPE

Conjunctivitis is usually viral and self-limiting. With bacterial or allergic conjunctivitis, treatments are helpful. Antibiotics are only indicated for bacterial conjunctivitis. If antibiotics are used, the full treatment course should be completed. These treatments can be combined with symptomatic treatment (see Symptom-Based Ophthalmic Treatments on the following page).

TYPE	CAUSES	TREATMENT
Viral	Adenovirus (most common), other viruses Most infections are mild, but some can be severe (e.g., caused by zoster virus or HIV)	No topical treatment for common viral conjunctivitis; the infection runs its course over several days to 2-3 weeks
Bacterial	*Staphylococcus aureus*, *Streptococcus pneumoniae*, *Haemophilus influenzae*, *Moraxella catarrhalis* More severe cases caused by *Neisseria gonorrhoeae* or *Chlamydia*, which requires systemic treatment	Select topical antibiotic eye drops or ointments: **Moxifloxacin *(Vigamox,* *Moxeza)*** **Neomycin/Polymyxin B/Dexamethasone *(Maxitrol)*** **Ofloxacin *(Ocuflox)*** **Trimethoprim/Polymyxin B *(Polytrim)*** Azithromycin *(AzaSite)* – store in the refrigerator, stable for 14 days at room temperature Besifloxacin *(Besivance)* Ciprofloxacin *(Ciloxan)* Erythromycin Gentamicin *(Gentak)* Neomycin/Bacitracin/Polymyxin B *(Neo-Polycin)* Tobramycin *(Tobrex)* Tobramycin/Dexamethasone *(TobraDex, TobraDex ST)* Sulfacetamide *(Bleph-10)*
Allergic	Common allergens include pollen, dust mites, animal dander, molds	**MAST CELL STABILIZERS** Alcaftadine *(Lastacaft)* Cromolyn Lodoxamide *(Alomide)* Nedocromil *(Alocril)* **ANTIHISTAMINES** **Azelastine** **Olopatadine *(Patanol, Pataday, Pazeo)*** Cetirizine *(Zerviate)* Epinastine *(Elestat)* Ketotifen *(Alaway* OTC)

BLEPHARITIS (EYELID INFLAMMATION)

Blepharitis most commonly involves the part of the eyelid where the eyelashes come out of the skin. In many patients the condition is chronic and difficult to treat and in others, it is an acute, short-term condition. The primary symptoms are inflamed, irritated and itchy eyelids. The preferred treatment includes application of a warm compress over the eye for a few minutes to loosen the crusty deposits, then use of a warm, moist washcloth (water plus a few drops of baby shampoo) to wipe away the debris. In some cases, antibiotic ointments, steroid eye drops and/or artificial tears are helpful.

OTHER OCULAR CONDITIONS

SYMPTOM-BASED OPHTHALMIC TREATMENTS

Symptoms can accompany the diseases previously discussed (e.g., conjunctivitis) or they can occur independently. Common ophthalmic symptoms include inflammation, dry eye and eye redness. Inflammation can be reduced with a cold compress and either an NSAID eye drop (if mild) or a steroid eye drop (if severe). Artificial tears can help with a "gritty" feeling and alleviate dryness. Chronic dry eye requires more aggressive treatment. Instruct patients to return for follow-up if they do not recover within a few days.

SYMPTOM	EXAMPLES OF TREATMENT	USAGE NOTES
Inflammation	**STEROIDS** **Prednisolone *(Omnipred, Pred Forte, Pred Mild)*** Dexamethasone *(Maxidex, Ozurdex)* Fluorometholone *(Flarex, FML Forte, FML Liquifilm* suspension, ointment) Loteprednol *(Alrex, Lotemax* suspension, ointment, gel) **NSAIDS** **Ketorolac *(Acular,*** *Acular LS, Acuvail)* Nepafenac *(Ilevro, Nevanac)* Bromfenac Diclofenac Flurbiprofen	Steroid eye drops should be used short-term due to risk of ↑ IOP
Dryness	*Liquifilm* ***Refresh*** ***Systane*** Others	Often referred to as Artificial Tears Contain common lubricants – mineral oil, glycerin, propylene glycol, dextran, hypromellose Administered multiple times daily, as needed
Chronic Dry Eye Syndrome	**Cyclosporine Emulsion Eye Drops *(Restasis)*** Lifitegrast *(Xiidra)*	For keratoconjunctivitis sicca (severe, chronic dry eye syndrome)
Redness	Brimonidine *(Lumify)* **Naphazoline *(Clear Eyes Redness Relief)*** **Tetrahydrozoline *(Visine)***	

MEDICATION INDUCED OPHTHALMIC ISSUES

Medications can cause ocular adverse effects. Most disappear once the drug is discontinued (such as blurry vision from an anticholinergic). In other cases, the damage can be permanent (such as vision loss with a PDE-5 inhibitor). Patients must be instructed to report visual changes immediately; in most cases the damage is reversible if the medication is stopped quickly. See the Key Drugs Guy to the right for specific medications and their effects.

EYE DROP PATIENT COUNSELING

All Eye Drops

- Wash your hands before and after using eye drops.
- Before you open the bottle, shake it a few times. Gels should be inverted and shaken once prior to use (to help the medication reach the tip).
- Bend your neck back so that you are looking up. Use one finger to pull down your lower eyelid. It is helpful, at least initially, to use a mirror.
- Without letting the tip of the bottle touch your eye or eyelid, release one drop of the medication by either squeezing the bottle or pushing on the bottom of the bottle. The drop should go into the space between your eye and your lower eyelid. If you squeeze in more than one drop, you are wasting medication.
- After you squeeze the drop of medication into your eye, close your eye. Press a finger between your eye and the top of your nose. Press for at least one full minute so more of the medication stays in your eye and you are less likely to have side effects. Blot extra solution from the eyelid with a tissue.
- If you need to take more than one glaucoma medication:
  - If there are two drops of the same medication being given at the same time, wait five minutes between drops (do not administer two drops at once).
  - Wait at least 5 - 10 minutes to put a second medication in your eye. If administering a gel, wait 10 minutes after the other eye medication before use.
- If your eye drop contains a preservative called benzalkonium chloride (BAK) and you wear soft contact lenses, remove the lenses prior to administration (wait 15 minutes to reinsert).

Prostaglandin Analog Counseling

- Remove contact lenses before using this medication because it contains a preservative that can be absorbed by the lenses, causing them to become discolored. Wait at least 15 minutes after use before putting your lenses back in.
- You can experience an increase in brown coloring of the iris and gradual changes in eye color (for this reason, this drug is not usually given to patients with light eyes who have glaucoma in one eye only). Eyelash growth and darkening of eyelashes can increase. The skin on the eyelids and around the eyes can darken.
- This medication is well tolerated, but occasionally a patient can experience excessive tearing, eye pain or lid crusting. If this occurs, please discuss with your optometrist or ophthalmologist.

COMMON DRUGS KNOWN TO CAUSE VISION CHANGES OR DAMAGE

Retinal changes/retinopathy
Chloroquine
Hydroxychloroquine

Optic neuropathy
Amiodarone (plus corneal deposits)
Ethambutol
Linezolid

Floppy iris syndrome; causes difficulty in cataract surgery
Alpha blockers (e.g., doxazosin)

Color discrimination
Digoxin (with toxicity) – yellow/green vision
PDE-5 inhibitors (e.g., sildenafil) – greenish tinge around objects
Voriconazole - color vision changes

Vision loss/abnormal vision
Digoxin (with toxicity) – blurriness, halos
PDE-5 inhibitors – vision loss in one or both eyes (can be permanent)
Isotretinoin – ↓ night vision which can be permanent, dry eyes irritation
Vigabatrin – permanent vision loss (high risk)
Voriconazole - abnormal vision, photophobia

- Tafluprost (*Zioptan*) is kept refrigerated. Once opened the pouch of 10 single-use containers is good at room temperature for 28 days.
- Do not use this medication (without the approval of your optometrist or ophthalmologist) if you are using bimatoprost (*Latisse*), to increase eyelash growth. *Latisse* can reduce the effectiveness of the glaucoma medication.

Bimatoprost *(Latisse)* Counseling

- Wash the face thoroughly, remove make-up and remove contact lenses prior to use (wait 15 minutes to reinsert lenses).
- Remove an applicator from the tray and hold it horizontally. Place one drop of medication on the area closest to the tip (not on the tip). Do not allow the bottle or applicator to touch fingers or any other unintended surface.
- Apply the medication by drawing a line with the applicator along the skin of the eyelid, just above the eyelash line. Apply on the top eyelid only, never the lower lid. Discard the applicator after use.
- Use a tissue or cotton pad to blot away excess medication below the eyelid.
- Using a new applicator, repeat the same process on the other eye. Discard the applicator after use.

Timolol *(Timoptic)* Counseling

- Common side effects include burning/stinging or itching of the eyes, and possible light sensitivity.
- Timolol is a beta-blocker. Although proper application should keep most of the medication in the eye, it can worsen other conditions if it gets into your body. If you have asthma, COPD, chronic bronchitis, emphysema or advanced cardiac disease, discuss if this medication is safe to use with your healthcare provider.
- If dispensing drops using the *Ocudose* preservative-free, single-use dispenser: open the cap by turning it as indicated by the arrows on the top. Do not pull the cap directly up and away from the bottle; this will prevent your dispenser from working properly. Use immediately upon opening; discard after use.
- Invert the bottle, and press lightly with the thumb or index finger over the "Finger Push Area" until a single drop is dispensed into the eye.
- If using the gel *(Timoptic XE, Timolol GFS)*: turn the container upside down once and shake the contents prior to use. The gel is used once daily. If using other eye drops beforehand, wait at least 10 minutes before using the gel.

COMMON EAR CONDITIONS

Common conditions treated in the ear include pain, such as from an outer ear infection (otitis externa) and ear wax (cerumen) impaction. Tinnitus (ringing, roaring or buzzing sounds) is caused by drug toxicity (e.g., salicylates), noise exposure, or it can be idiopathic. There is no effective drug treatment for tinnitus.

OTITIS EXTERNA

Ear drops with antibiotics can be used for outer ear infections. Pain can be treated with systemic analgesics (e.g., ibuprofen, acetaminophen). During treatment, patients should stay out of the water, avoid flying due to the pressure changes, and avoid the use of headphones and ear plugs. A few common antibiotic products include:

- Ciprofloxacin and dexamethasone *(Ciprodex)*
- Ciprofloxacin and hydrocortisone *(Cipro HC)*
- Neomycin, colistin, hydrocortisone and thonzonium *(Coly-Mycin S)*

EAR WAX (CERUMEN) BLOCKAGE

Ear blockage occurs when wax (cerumen) accumulates in the ear or becomes too hard to wash away naturally. It is removed in a medical office. If the condition is chronic, ear wax removal medication [carbamide peroxide *(Debrox)*, triethanolamine] can be used every 4 – 8 weeks as a preventive measure. Instruct the patient to tilt the head sideways (see counseling section) and instill 5 – 10 drops twice daily for up to four days.

EAR DROP PATIENT COUNSELING

- If cold, gently shake the bottle or roll it in your hands for 1 – 2 minutes to warm the solution. Do not drop in cold medication. Ear drops that are too cold are uncomfortable and can cause dizziness.
- Lie down or tilt the head so that the affected ear faces up.
- Gently pull the earlobe up and back for adults (down and back for children < 3 years) to straighten the ear canal.
- Administer the prescribed number of drops into the ear canal. Keep the ear facing up for about five minutes to allow the medication to coat the ear canal.
- Do not touch the dropper tip to any surface. To clean, wipe with a clean tissue.

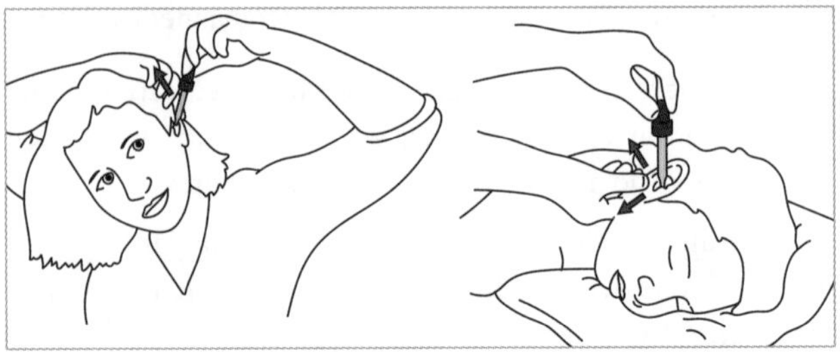

Select Guidelines/References

American Academy of Ophthalmology Glaucoma Panel. Preferred Practice Pattern Guidelines. Primary Open-Angle Glaucoma. 2016. https://www.aao.org/preferred-practice-pattern/primary-open-angle-glaucoma-ppp-2015 (accessed 2019 Feb 4).

CHAPTER CONTENT

Background 573
Natural Products 573
Acne 574
Acne Treatment Summary 574
Cold Sores 576
Dandruff 576
Alopecia (Hair Loss) 577
Eczema (Atopic Dermatitis) 578
Hyperhidrosis 578
Fungal Infections: Skin 579
Athlete's Foot *(Tinea Pedis)* 579
Jock Itch *(Tinea Cruris)* 579
Ringworm *(Tinea Corporis)* 579
Cutaneous (Skin) *Candida* Infections 579
Fungal Treatments for the Skin 579
Fungal Infections: Toenail & Fingernail 580
Fungal Infections: Vaginal 580
Diaper Rash 581
Hemorrhoids 582
Pinworm *(Vermicularis)* 582
Lice and Scabies 583
Minor Wounds 584
Cuts, Lacerations and Abrasions 584
Bites 584
Burns 585
Poison Ivy, Oak and Sumac 585
Inflammation and Rash 586
Sunscreens and Sun Protection 587
Time to Burn (TTB) 587
Potencies of Topical Steroids 588

CONTENT LEGEND

= Study Tip Gal   = Key Drug Guy

THE STRUCTURE OF THE SKIN

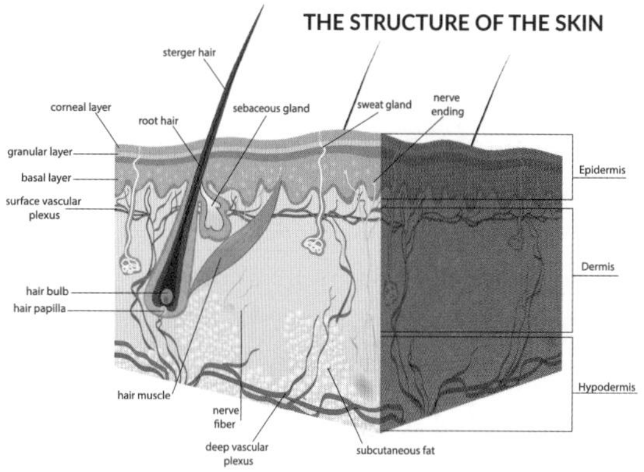

CHAPTER 39
COMMON SKIN CONDITIONS

BACKGROUND

Patients in the community setting ask pharmacists for recommendations for a variety of skin conditions. Identifying the cause of a rash or sore can be simple, or challenging. *The Handbook of OTC Drugs* has pictures of common conditions, and many more are available at www.dermnet.com. If recommending OTC treatment, the patient should be counseled to seek further help if the condition does not improve or worsens. A pharmacist should be able to identify certain skin conditions, such as a blemish that could be skin cancer (see the Oncology I chapter), or the discoloration of skin and secretions caused by certain medications (see box below).

NATURAL PRODUCTS

Aloe is a natural product produced from the aloe vera plant that is used for many skin conditions, including sunburn and psoriasis. It has little proven efficacy but if used as a gel or lotion it may provide a soothing effect. Tea tree oil is used for a variety of skin conditions, such as acne. It may be helpful for onychomycosis symptoms (depending on the dose and application schedule), but is not useful in eradicating the infection in most patients. Lysine, taken as a tablet, capsule or applied topically, is used for cold sore *(herpes simplex labialis)* prevention and treatment. Biotin is a vitamin used for hair loss and brittle nails. Topical vitamin D is used in skin conditions, such as diaper rash and psoriasis.

DRUGS THAT CAN DISCOLOR SKIN AND SECRETIONS

Brown
Entacapone
Levodopa
Methyldopa

Brown/Black/Green
Iron (black stool)
Methocarbamol

Brown/Yellow
Nitrofurantoin
Metronidazole
Tinidazole
Riboflavin (B2)

Purple/Orange/Red
Chlorzoxazone

Orange/Yellow
Sulfasalazine

Yellow-Green
Propofol
Flutamide

Red-Orange
Phenazopyridine
Rifampin
Rifapentine

Red
Anthracyclines
Deferasirox (urine)

Blue
Methylene blue
Mitoxantrone

Blue-Gray
Amiodarone
Chloroquine

ACNE

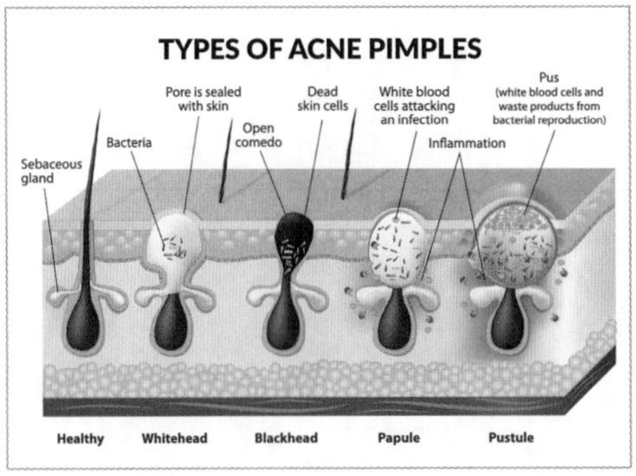

Most people develop acne at some point, including infants to adults. It primarily develops in adolescents during puberty. Androgens (male sex hormones) are the primary determinant of acne along with presence of the bacteria, *P. acnes*, and fatty acids (sebum) present in oil (sebaceous) glands. Acne mainly appears on the face, chest, shoulders and back. Diets with a high glycemic index or dairy can worsen acne.

Acne lesions are classified as whiteheads, blackheads, small bumps, cysts and nodules. Treatment is determined by severity: mild (few, occasional pimples), moderate (inflammatory papules) or severe (nodules and cysts). Acne is treated with these primary groups of agents: OTC benzoyl peroxide and salicylic acid, retinoids, topical or systemic (oral) antibiotics and systemic isotretinoin (see Study Tip Gal).

- Benzoyl peroxide (BPO) is the most effective OTC agent. It is also available by prescription, including in combination with hydrocortisone, the retinoid adapalene or with the antibiotics erythromycin or clindamycin.
- Salicylic acid is a mildly useful OTC agent, and is primarily used in "medicated pads" for facial cleansing.
- Retinoids, primarily topical tretinoin and derivatives are the usual Rx drug of choice and are also used to reduce wrinkles.
  - Retinoids are teratogenic. They must be avoided in pregnancy or breastfeeding (see Drug Use in Pregnancy and Lactation chapter).
  - Retinoids are vitamin A derivatives. The mechanism is primarily to reduce adherence of the keratinocytes (outer skin cells) in the oil gland.
  - They are well-tolerated when used topically, with mild skin irritation (redness, drying) and photosensitivity possible. Use daily at night with the correct (pea sized) amount. Can decrease to every other night if irritation occurs. Use moisturizer each morning, followed by sunscreen.
  - Retinoids take 4 – 12 weeks to work and acne can worsen initially. An antibiotic (often minocycline) together with retinoids can help. Tazarotene often works better than tretinoin; it is used for difficult cases.
  - The oral retinoid isotretinoin has many safety considerations and is reserved for severe nodular acne only. Cholesterol and pregnancy tests are required, among other monitoring.
- Some women find benefit with oral contraceptive pills, especially if the acne occurs around the menstrual cycle, or if irregular menses or symptoms of androgenic excess are present.
- Spironolactone is an aldosterone receptor antagonist with antiandrogen effects. It is not FDA-approved for acne, but is recommended as a useful treatment for some females.
- Azelaic acid *(Azelex, Finacea)* is a topical dicarboxylic acid cream or gel available OTC and Rx for acne and rosacea. Oxymetazoline hydrochloride 1% cream *(Rhofade)* is approved for erythema associated with rosacea.

ACNE TREATMENT SUMMARY

Acne treatment is determined by acne severity and success of past treatments.

	MILD	MODERATE	SEVERE
FIRST-LINE TREATMENT	Topicals: BPO and/or retinoid	Topicals: combination* or PO antibiotic + BPO + topical retinoid (+/– topical antibiotic)	Topicals: combination* + PO antibiotic or Oral: isotretinoin
ALTERNATIVE TREATMENT	Add topical retinoid or BPO, switch to another retinoid or topical dapsone	Other combination,* switch PO antibiotic, add combined OCP or spironolactone (females) or PO isotretinoin	Switch PO antibiotic, add combined OCP or spironolactone (females) or PO isotretinoin (if not previously tried)

**Topical combination therapy includes the following combinations: BPO + topical antibiotic, BPO + retinoid or BPO + retinoid + topical antibiotic.*

DRUGS	NOTES	SAFETY/COUNSELING
Topical Retinoids		
Tretinoin *(Atralin, Renova, Retin-A, Retin-A Micro,* *Altreno, Avita, Refissa, Tretin-X)* Rx: cream, gel, lotion And many other products, such as clindamycin + tretinoin gel *(Ziana)* **Adapalene *(Differin)*** OTC: gel *(Differin gel 0.1%)* Rx: Adapalene + BPO gel *(Epiduo, Epiduo Forte)* Tazarotene Rx: cream *(Tazorac, Avage),* foam *(Fabior)*, gel *(Tazorac)*	Slower-release, less skin irritation with: microsphere gel ***(Retin-A Micro)*** and polymerized cream or gel *(Avita)* *Altreno* 0.05% is first lotion form of tretinoin, which is less irritating *Fabior* foam is stronger, more irritating Tazarotene is contraindicated in pregnancy Topical retinoids should be avoided in pregnancy	Limit sun exposure. Apply daily, usually at bedtime, about 20 minutes after washing face. If irritation, use lower strength, or every other night. May need to reduce contact initially (wash off if skin is irritated). A pea-sized amount is sufficient (for facial application); it should be divided into 4 equal parts and smoothed over the entire surface of the face, not just on acne. Avoid salicylic acid scrubs or astringents while starting a retinoid; this will worsen irritation. Wash only with mild soap twice daily. Takes 4 – 12 weeks to see response; may worsen acne initially.
BENZOYL PEROXIDE (BPO) OTC: many products including *Benoxyl, Benzac, Clearasil* OTC: BPO + hydrocortisone *(Vanoxide-HC)* **TOPICAL ANTIBIOTICS AND COMBINATIONS** Rx: Erythromycin + BPO *(Benzamycin)*, Clindamycin + BPO *(Acanya, BenzaClin, Duac, Neuac)* **OTHERS** OTC: **Salicylic acid** *(Clearasil*, and others) Rx: **Azelaic acid** cream, gel, lotion *(Azelex* 15%, *Finacea* 20%) OTC: **Azelaic acid** lower strengths *(Paula's Choice, The Ordinary*, and others) Rx: Dapsone gel *(Aczone)*	*Benzamycin* and *BenzaClin* Add indicated amount of purified water to the vial (70% ethyl alcohol for *Benzamycin)* and immediately shake to completely dissolve medication. If needed, add additional purified water to bring level up to the mark. Add the solution in the vial to the gel and stir until homogenous in appearance (1 to 1.5 minutes). *Benzamycin* is kept refrigerated. *BenzaClin* is kept at room temp. Place a 3 month expiration date on the label following mixing. 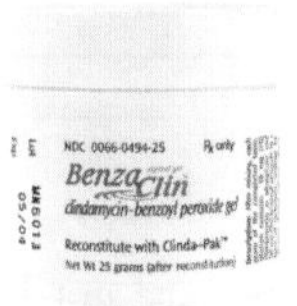	BPO: can bleach clothing, hair. Start with 2.5-5% BPO, which is generally adequate and less irritating than the higher strengths. Limit sun exposure as skin will burn more easily. *Duac*: dispense with 60 day expiration. Apply QHS to affected areas. Can store at room temp, do not freeze. Limit sun exposure. Clindamycin topicals: clean face, shake (if lotion), apply a thin layer once or twice daily. Avoid contact with eyes; if contact, rinse with cold water. Takes 2-6 weeks for effect and up to 12 weeks for full benefit. Dapsone gel: avoid in G6PD deficiency.
Oral Retinoids		
ORAL RETINOIDS **Isotretinoin *(Absorica,*** *Amnesteem, Claravis, Myorisan)* Rx: capsules 0.5-1 mg/kg/day, divided BID with food for 15-20 weeks.	Only for severe refractory nodular acne Female patients must sign patient information/ informed consent form about birth defects that contains warnings about the risk of potential birth defects if the fetus is exposed to isotretinoin. Must have had 2 negative pregnancy tests prior to starting treatment. Cannot get pregnant for 1 month before, while taking the drug, or for 1 month after the drug is stopped. Do not breastfeed or donate blood until at least 1 month has passed after the drug is stopped. Do not use with vitamin A supplements, tetracyclines, steroids, progestin-only contraceptives or St. John's wort. Must swallow capsule whole, or puncture and sprinkle on applesauce or ice cream – this may irritate esophagus.	**BOXED WARNING** Birth defects have been documented; must not be used by women who are pregnant or may become pregnant Can only be dispensed by a pharmacy registered and activated with the pregnancy REMS (iPLEDGE) program. 1-month Rx at a time, fill within 7 days with yellow sticker attached. **WARNINGS** Arthralgias, skeletal hyperostosis (calcification of ligaments that attach to the spine), osteoporosis, psychiatric issues (depression, psychosis, risk of suicide), decreased night vision (may be permanent), difficulty wearing contact lens (dry eyes/irritation), dry skin, chapped lips, ↑ cholesterol (TG) and BG. **Counseling**: contraception and behaviors associated with risk of pregnancy must be repeated on a monthly basis. 2 forms of birth control are required (cannot use a progestin-only pill). Carry bottled water, eye drops and lip balm.
Oral Antibiotics Used for Acne		
Minocycline *(Minocin, Solodyn,* *CoreMino, Minolira, Ximono)* ≥ 12 years,dosed by weight Sarecycline *(Seysara)* Rx: capsule, tablet	Doxycycline and minocycline are more effective than tetracycline in eradicating *P. acnes*. Sulfamethoxazole/trimethoprim is also used. Erythromycin is used less commonly due to resistance. Sarecycline is a new tetracycline derivative for non-nodular moderate to severe acne.	Photosensitivity, rash in susceptible patients, dizziness, diarrhea, somnolence. Like other tetracyclines, can cause fetal harm if administered during pregnancy. May cause permanent discoloration in teeth if used when teeth are forming (up to 8 years of age).

COLD SORES

- Cold sores (herpes simplex labialis) are common and are highly contagious. Infection is usually due to herpes simplex virus type 1 (HSV-1), but can be caused by HSV-2 when due to oral/genital sex. The virus spreads mostly with active lesions. Kissing and sharing drinks can transmit the infection.
- Sore eruption is preceded by prodromal symptoms (e.g., tingling, itching, soreness). In most patients, the sore appears in the same location repeatedly. The most common site is the junction between the upper and lower lip. Triggers that instigate sore outbreaks include fatigue, stress, stress to the skin (sun exposure, acid peels) and dental work.
- The prodromal period is the optimal time to apply topical or take oral medication to reduce blister duration. If recurrences are frequent (> 4 times/year), chronic suppression, taken daily, can be used. OTC and Rx topicals shorten the duration by up to one day; oral (systemic) antivirals shorten the duration by up to two days.
- The natural product lysine is used commonly for cold sore prevention and treatment.

DRUGS	NOTES	SAFETY/COUNSELING
OTC **Docosanol *(Abreva)*** **Rx** **Acyclovir topical cream/ointment *(Zovirax)*** Acyclovir buccal tablets *(Sitavig)* Penciclovir topical cream *(Denavir)*	Oral antivirals can be used, are more effective, and are discussed in the Infectious Diseases III chapter. 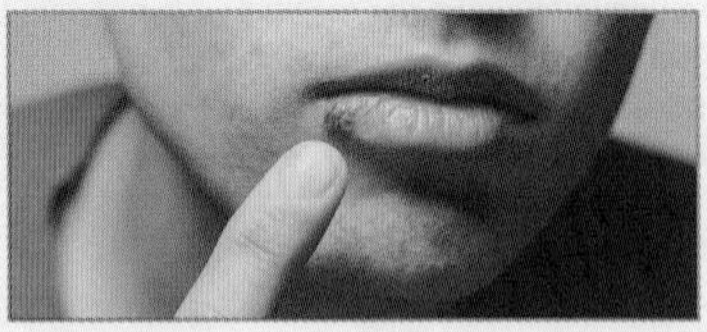	*Abreva* cream: apply 5x daily at first sign of outbreak, continue until healed. *Zovirax* cream: apply 5 times daily for 4 days (can be used on genital sores). *Sitavig* tablet: apply one 50 mg tablet as a single dose to the upper gum region. *Denavir* cream: apply every 2 hours during waking hours for 4 days.

DANDRUFF

- Dandruff occurs when the scalp is itchy and/or scaling with white oily flakes (dead skin) in the hair and on the shoulders, back or clothing.
- Dandruff can be due to either eczema or fungal (yeast) overgrowth, and is worsened by hormones, the weather or shampoo. Seborrheic dermatitis is a common form of eczema that causes flaking, itchy skin on the face, back, chest or head. If it is on the scalp it is commonly referred to as dandruff.
- Patients are not likely to know the cause of dandruff. A store-brand, inexpensive dandruff shampoo can be tried first, and if this is ineffective, the ketoconazole antifungal shampoo can be used.

DRUGS	NOTES	SAFETY/COUNSELING
OTC **Ketoconazole 1% shampoo *(Nizoral A-D)*, selenium sulfide *(Selsun*,** *Dandrex, Tersi)*, **pyrithione zinc *(Head & Shoulders)***, coal tar shampoos ***(T/Gel)***, *Suave* or store brands "dandruff" shampoos **Rx** **Ketoconazole 2% shampoo *(Nizoral)*** Ketoconazole topical comes in many formulations for dandruff or seborrheic dermatitis (see notes above): cream, foam, gel & shampoo		Rub shampoo in well, leave in for 5 minutes, then rinse out. Shampoo daily. If the shampoo stops working, switch products. ***Nizoral A-D*** Apply twice weekly, for up to 8 weeks. Do not use if open sores on scalp. Can cause skin irritation.

ALOPECIA (HAIR LOSS)

As people age, hair tends to gradually thin. Other causes of hair loss include hormonal factors, medical conditions and medications.

- The most common cause of hair loss is hereditary male-pattern baldness, and less commonly, female-pattern baldness.
- Hormonal changes in women that can result in hair loss are usually associated with pregnancy, childbirth or menopause.
- Medical conditions that cause hair loss include hypothyroidism, alopecia areata (an autoimmune condition), scalp infections and some other conditions, including lupus.
- Drugs that can contribute to alopecia include various chemotherapeutics (primarily because hair cells are rapidly dividing and are affected by the treatment) and infrequently with the following: valproate, spironolactone heparin, warfarin, clomiphene, hydroxychloroquine, interferons, lithium, some types of oral contraceptives, levonorgestrel and procainamide.
- Zinc and vitamin D deficiency can contribute to hair loss.
- Medications work modestly for hair loss; many people will seek surgical intervention.

DRUGS	NOTES	SAFETY/COUNSELING
Finasteride *(Propecia)* Rx: tablet Finasteride is a 5-alpha reductase type 2 inhibitor also approved for BPH. 1 mg daily, at least 3 months duration to begin to see effect	Must be used indefinitely or condition reappears Do not dispense to patients taking finasteride ***(Proscar)*** for BPH	**CONTRAINDICATION** Pregnancy **WARNING** Hazardous drug for females of childbearing age – can damage male fetus **SIDE EFFECTS** Lower dose than *Proscar*; lower risk of sexual side effects; see Overactive Bladder chapter for further details
Minoxidil topical *(Rogaine*, others) OTC: 5% foam, 2% and 5% solution	Minoxidil tablets (Rx) indicated for hypertension (very rarely used) 5% strength is more effective, but causes more facial hair growth	For men and women Must be used indefinitely or condition reappears
Bimatoprost *(Latisse)* Rx: solution For thinning eyelashes (hypotrichosis) 	Do not use with PG analogs used for glaucoma (IOP may increase)	May cause itchy eyes and/or eye redness. Eyelid skin darkening may occur, may be reversible Hair growth may occur in other skin areas that the solution frequently touches Apply nightly, with applicator brush, to the skin at the base of the upper eyelashes only (do not apply to the lower lid). Blot any excess. Repeat on other eye. Dispose the applicator after one use. If stopped, lashes will return to previous appearance

ECZEMA (ATOPIC DERMATITIS)

Eczema is a general term for many types of skin inflammation, and is used interchangeably with the term atopic dermatitis.

- Eczema is most common in young children and infants, but can occur at any age.
- Eczema presents as skin rashes, which become crusty and scaly; blisters can develop. The rash is itchy, red, dry and sore.
- Common sites affected include the elbows, behind the knees/ears, face (often the cheeks), buttocks, hands and feet.
- Patients should avoid "triggers" such as environmental irritants, allergens (soaps, perfumes), pollution, stress or weather changes.
- Hydration is essential to reduce disease severity. Use moisturizers. Maintain humidity in the home.
- Treatment can include topical steroids (occasional oral courses, if needed), antihistamines (for itching), or immunosuppressant calcineurin inhibitors, if topical steroids with hydration are not adequate.
- In severe, refractory cases, oral immunosuppressants (cyclosporine, methotrexate) or monoclonal antibody drugs can be used. Dupilumab *(Dupixent)* is approved for moderate to severe eczema and is administered by subcutaneous injection every other week; others used off-label are discussed in the Systemic Steroids & Autoimmune Conditions chapter.

DRUGS	NOTES	SAFETY/COUNSELING
OTC Moisturizers with petrolatum, lanolin *(Aquaphor, Eucerin, Keri* or store brands) **Rx** Treat first with topical steroids (see Inflammation and Rash and Potencies of Topical Steroids in this chapter). Only use the agents below if steroids failed: **Topical Calcineurin Inhibitors** Tacrolimus *(Protopic)* – ointment Pimecrolimus *(Elidel)* – cream **Topical Phosphodiesterase-4 Inhibitor** Crisaborole *(Eucrisa)* – 2% ointment **Monoclonal Antibody (IL-4 antagonist)** Dupilumab *(Dupixent)* – injection	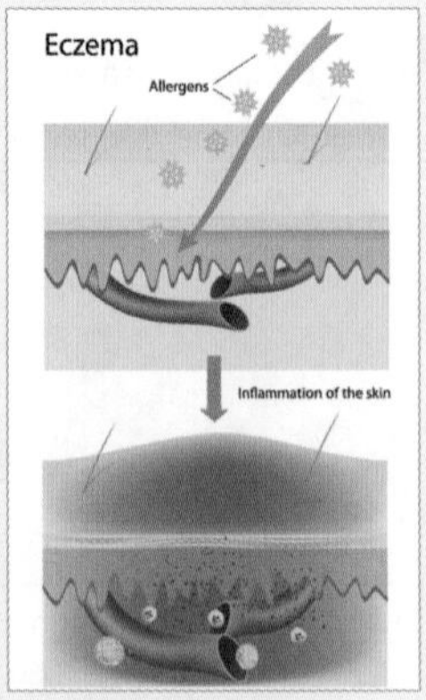	Do not use *Elidel* or *Protopic* in children < 2 years of age Topical calcineurin inhibitors: associated with lymphoma and skin cancer; use only as second-line agents for short-term, intermittent treatment Apply a thin layer only to the affected skin twice a day Use the smallest amount needed to control symptoms Takes weeks to work; continue to apply Wash hands after application Topical calcineurin inhibitors: side effects can include headache, skin burning, itching, cough, flu-like symptoms Dupilumab: injection site reactions

HYPERHIDROSIS

Hyperhidrosis is excessive sweating. Diagnosis is based on physical exam and thorough medical history. Treatment depends on where the excessive sweating on the body is noticed (e.g., underarms, hands, feet).

DRUGS	NOTES	SAFETY/COUNSELING
OTC Antiperspirants *(Secret Clinical Strength, Certain Dri* and others) **Rx** Glycopyrronium topical *(Qbrexza)*	*Qbrexza* is a topical anticholinergic.	Patients with medical conditions that can be exacerbated by anticholinergics (e.g., glaucoma, UC, myasthenia gravis) should avoid *Qbrexza.* *Qbrexza*: remove a single-use cloth and apply to clean dry skin on the underarm area. Wash hands with soap and water afterwards.

FUNGAL INFECTIONS: SKIN

Tinea pedis, cruris, corporis and topical *Candida* infections are covered here. For vaginal infections, onychomycosis and diaper rash, see separate sections in this chapter.

ATHLETE'S FOOT *(TINEA PEDIS)*

- A fungal infection of the foot caused by various fungi (commonly *trichophyton rubrum*).
- Symptoms are feet itching, peeling, redness, mild burning and sometimes sores. This is a common infection, particularly among those using public pools, showers and locker rooms.
- Diagnosis is usually by symptoms, but if unclear (psoriasis and other conditions can cause itchy skin), the skin can be scraped off and viewed under a microscope.
- It is treated topically with antifungals, except in severe cases.

JOCK ITCH *(TINEA CRURIS)*

- Affects the genitals, inner thighs and buttocks.
- The rash is red, itchy and can be ring-shaped.
- Jock itch is not very contagious, but can be spread person-to-person with close contact.
- Keep the skin dry (use a clean towel after showering) and treat with an antifungal topical. Creams work best.
- Change underwear at least daily.

RINGWORM *(TINEA CORPORIS)*

- Not a worm, but a skin fungal infection.
- Ringworm can appear anywhere on the body and typically looks like circular, red, flat sores (one or more, may overlap), usually with dry, scaly skin. Occasionally the ring-like presentation is not present – just itchy red skin. The outer part of the sore can be raised while the skin in the middle appears normal.
- It can spread person-to-person or by contact with infected animals.
- Most cases are treated topically.
- Tinea capitis is "ringworm" on the scalp. This affects primarily young children, mostly in crowded, lower-income situations and requires systemic therapy, with the same drugs used for onychomycosis.

CUTANEOUS (SKIN) *CANDIDA* INFECTIONS

- Topical *Candida* infections cause red, itchy rashes, most commonly in the groin, armpits or anywhere the skin folds.
- These are more likely in obese persons because they will have more skin with folds; the infection can be in unusual places, such as under the breasts, if the skin is moist. Diabetes is another risk factor.
- Occasionally, fungal infections appear in the corner of nails (on the skin, not in the nailbed). If this is a suspected bacterial infection, OTC antibiotic topicals or mupirocin (*Bactroban* – excellent gram positive coverage) can be used.
- *Candida* can cause diaper rash in infants (discussed under diaper rash).

FUNGAL TREATMENTS FOR THE SKIN

DRUGS	NOTES	SAFETY/COUNSELING
OTC **Terbinafine (*Lamisil AT*** cream, gel, spray) **Butenafine (*Lotrimin Ultra*** cream) **Clotrimazole (*Lotrimin AF***, *Pro-Ex Antifungal, Shopko Athletes Foot* cream) **Miconazole (*Lotrimin AF***, *Cruex, Desenex Jock Itch* powder and spray) Miconazole + petrolatum *(Baza)* – for moisture barrier, used in geriatrics **Tolnaftate (*Tinactin*** powder, cream, spray) **Undecylenic acid (*Fungi-Nail***, others) **Rx** **Betamethasone/Clotrimazole (*Lotrisone*)**: popular for tinea with inflammation/itching **Ketoconazole:** cream, foam *(Extina)* Luliconazole *(Luzu)* 1% cream	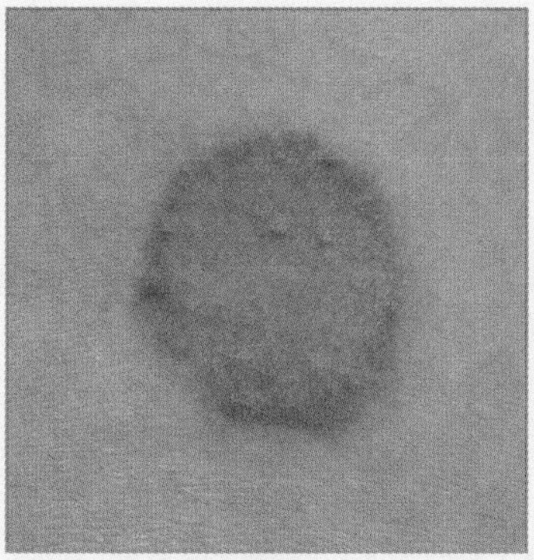 Tinea corporis (ringworm) – the name "ringworm" is a misnomer; this is a fungal infection. The rings can be single or overlap	Terbinafine and butenafine are highly effective Topical antifungals come in creams, ointments, gels and solutions Creams work best and are used in most cases Solutions can be easier to apply in hairy areas Powders do not work well for treatment but may be used for prevention, such as in shoes after a gym workout; use cotton socks Apply medicine 1-2 inches beyond the rash Use for at least 2-4 weeks, even if it appears healed Reduce moisture to the infected area If foot infection, do not walk barefoot (to avoid spreading it); wear sandals in public showers (to avoid catching it) Note the same name in OTC products *(Lotrimin AF)* can refer to different active ingredients; be careful with recommendations to avoid mix-ups

FUNGAL INFECTIONS: TOENAIL & FINGERNAIL

- Onychomycosis, a fungal infection of the nail, often caused by tinea unguium, can cause pain, discomfort and disfigurement and lead to physical limitations (e.g., difficulty standing, walking). Discoloration and disfigurement can lead to self-esteem and psychological issues.
- Topical agents are limited to mild cases and patients who cannot tolerate systemic therapies, in combination with systemic treatment or as prophylaxis. They are not potent enough to cure most infections.
- Itraconazole and terbinafine are approved for this use and most commonly used; fluconazole and posaconazole are used off-label. Griseofulvin is rarely used.
- It takes a long time for the nail bed to look better - sometimes up to a year in toenails. Toenails take longer to treat than fingernails, and are more commonly infected.
- Pulse therapy (intermittent) can be used to reduce costs and possibly toxicity, but may not be as effective.
- A 20% potassium hydroxide (KOH) smear is essential for diagnosis as other conditions can produce a similar presentation.

DRUGS	NOTES	SAFETY/COUNSELING
Rx **Terbinafine *(Lamisil)*** – oral (topical is *Lamisil AT;* used for fungal skin infections) 250 mg PO daily for 6 weeks (fingernail) or 12 weeks (toenail) Itraconazole *(Sporanox)* Dose 200 mg daily x 12 weeks or "pulse-dosing" (fingernails only): 200 mg BID x 1 week, 3 weeks off then repeat 1-week course Ciclopirox *(Penlac, Loprox)* -topical, used QHS Tavaborole *(Kerydin)* - topical oxaborole antifungal Efinaconazole *(Jublia)* - topical azole antifungal	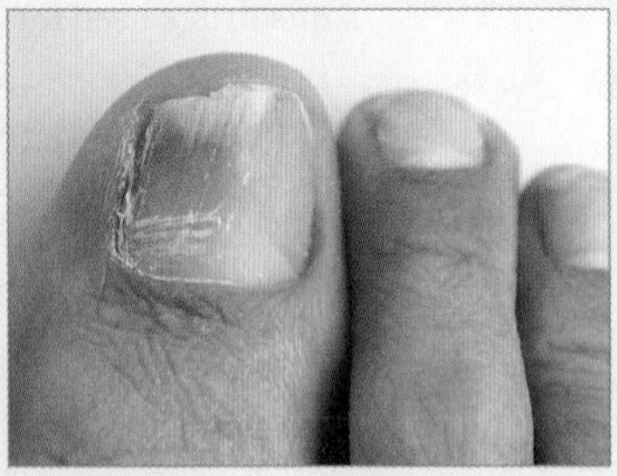 Ciclopirox (*Penlac, Loprox*) – used in combination with orals; poor efficacy when used alone Tavaborole (*Kerydin*) – applied topically x 48 weeks Efinaconazole (*Jublia*) – applied topically x 48 weeks	For systemic azoles, refer to Infectious Diseases III chapter. Systemic drugs used for nail fungal infections are hepatotoxic (monitor LFTs), QT prolonging (avoid in QT risk) and CYP450 3A4 substrates & inhibitors (there are many drug interactions). Nausea and diarrhea are common. Itraconazole (*Sporanox*): boxed warning to avoid use in heart failure. Requires gastric acid for absorption; cannot use with strong acid suppressing agents. Terbinafine (*Lamisil*) – oral: primarily headache, rash, nausea, risk of hepatotoxicity. Recurrence is common. Practice proper foot care and keep the nails dry. Keep blood glucose controlled. Do not smoke.

FUNGAL INFECTIONS: VAGINAL

Vaginal fungal infections are common, ~75% of women will have at least one episode (and half of these women will have recurrence). In a small percentage of women infections occur chronically. Fungal vaginal infections are uncommon before a female begins menstruating, as they occur most commonly during the week prior to menstruation, making treatment decisions around the menses important. Women can begin treatment during menses, or wait until the bleeding stops. Tampons should not be used when medication is applied.

- Vaginal fungal infections are common during pregnancy. Pregnant patients should consult their physician. Longer (7 – 10 day) treatment is required.
- Symptoms are primarily itching, with possible soreness and pain (burning) during urination or sex. Some women have a cottage-cheese like discharge (white, thick, clumpy).
- Diagnosis can be confirmed with either a vaginal culture to check for fungal growth or, via a pH test: a pH > than 4.5 indicates the presence of either a *Candida* or trichomoniasis infection. OTC test kits are available (e.g., *Vagisil Screening Kit*) to test vaginal pH.
- Testing is not necessary if the woman has been seen by a physician for the initial infection and is able to recognize the symptoms. Self-treatment with OTC products is appropriate.
- If there are more than four infections in a year, or if symptoms recur within two months, refer to the physician to rule-out an underlying condition that could be causative (e.g., diabetes, HIV, receiving steroids or other immune-suppressing agents, pregnancy, or irritation from repeated douching or use of lubricants).
- Women taking high-dose estrogen, hormone replacement therapy or antibiotics are at elevated risk. Antibiotic use can wipe out the normal flora and lead to fungal overgrowth.

- Lactobacillus or yogurt with active cultures is thought to reduce infection occurrence; however, this is rated as "possibly ineffective" by the *Natural Medicines Database.*
- If self-treating, counsel that condoms and diaphragms do not provide adequate pregnancy protection; the oil in OTC antifungals weakens the latex.
- To avoid future infections, keep the vaginal area clean, wipe from front to back, use cotton underwear, avoid tight-fitting clothing (including pantyhose), change pads/tampons often, change out of wet swimsuits or clothing quickly and recommend against use of vaginal douches, sprays and deodorant tampons (these can alter the vaginal pH and contribute to infection).

DRUGS	NOTES	SAFETY/COUNSELING
Mild-moderate, infrequent infection 1, 3 or 7 day treatment, with vaginal cream, ointment or vaginal suppository/tab **OTC, topical** **Butoconazole *(Gynazole-1***, others) **Clotrimazole *(Gyne-Lotrimin***, others) **Miconazole *(Monistat* 3**, others) **Terconazole *(Terazol 7***, others) **Rx, oral** **Fluconazole *(Diflucan)*** 150 mg PO x 1 Complicated infections, pregnancy: 7–10 days treatment, or refer to healthcare provider	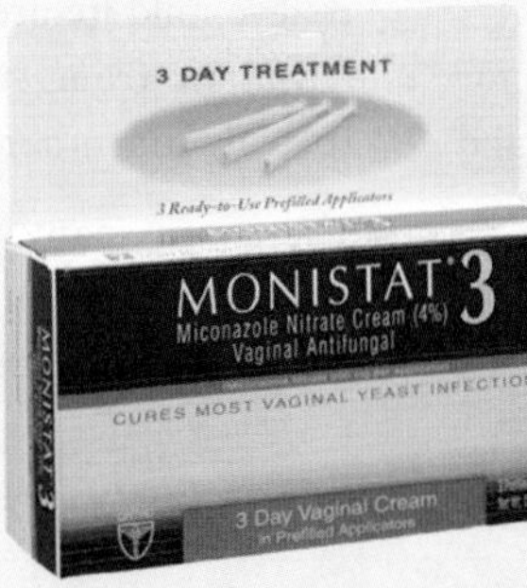 Always counsel on ways to avoid future infections (see above) The male sexual partner can be tested if female partner's infections are recurrent (not common)	Counseling for OTC antifungals: Prior to using the product, wash the vagina with mild soap and water, and pat dry with a towel Insert applicator, suppository or vaginal tab at night before bed. Lying down immediately after insertion helps retain the medicine inside the vagina; a protective pad can be used. The creams and suppositories are oil-based medications that can weaken latex condoms and diaphragms; avoid sexual intercourse If you get your menstrual cycle during treatment, continue the treatment, otherwise wait until menstrual cycle is over before starting treatment if desired (this is not necessary) Do not use tampons during treatment Complete entire course of treatment Medical care is warranted if symptoms persist/return within 2 months after using an OTC product, or if > 4/year

DIAPER RASH

Diaper rash is very comon in babies. The skin is sensitive, and when exposed to urine and stools, and a diaper moving back and forth, a rash appears. Once the skin is damaged it is susceptible to bacteria and yeast overgrowth.

Prevention

- Change diapers often; do not cover diapers with plastic.
- Wipe well with unscented wipes or plain water.
- Leave the diaper off, when possible, to let the skin air-dry.
- Use a skin protectant:
    - Petrolatum ointment (*A & D Ointment*, store brands) is a good preventative ointment containing vitamins A & D.
    - Petrolatum with zinc oxide (a desiccant, used to dry out the skin) may be preferable for babies prone to rash.

Treatment

- Clotrimazole, miconazole, nystatin: for stubborn rashes, if yeast is thought to be involved.
- Hydrocortisone 0.5-1% cream can be applied twice a day, but not for more than several days at a time. Combinations of the above are used.

DRUGS	SAFETY/COUNSELING
OTC Petrolatum + zinc oxide ***(Desitin**, Butt Paste, Triple Paste)* Plain petrolatum ***(A&D Ointment)***, and others **Rx** miconazole + zinc oxide + petrolatum *(Vusion)*	Infants should be referred to the physician (especially if under 6 months) and older babies if condition appears serious or worsens. Diaper rashes can have more than one contributing organism. Topical antibiotics can be needed if bacterial involvement is suspected. Topical antifungals can be needed if fungal involvement is suspected. Topical steroids, low potency, may be used short-term.

HEMORRHOIDS

Hemorrhoids are swollen blood vessels in the lower rectum. They are often the result of constipation and straining to have a bowel movement. Rectal tissue is sensitive with a rich blood vessel supply making it susceptible to engorgement. Common symptoms are pruritus, burning and rectal bleeding. The blood is usually bright red.

- If dietary fiber is not optimum, increasing fiber intake can help reduce straining. Products such as psyllium will mix with the stool to make it easier to push out. A stool softener (such as docusate) will reduce straining.
- Phenylephrine (*Preparation H*, others) is a vasoconstrictor that shrinks the hemorrhoid and reduces burning and itching.
- Hydrocortisone (*Anusol-HC, Preparation H Hydrocortisone*, others) comes in anal suppositories and various topicals including creams and wipes. These reduce itching and inflammation.
- Witch hazel (*Tucks pads*) is a mild astringent that can relieve mild itching. Barriers (skin protectants) to reduce irritation from stool/urine are helpful in some cases (petrolatum, others – see Diaper Rash section).
- There are many combination products. Some contain mineral oil (skin protectant), zinc oxide (desiccant) or pramoxine (anesthetic).

DRUGS	NOTES	SAFETY/COUNSELING
OTC **Phenylephrine topical (*Preparation H*,** *Anusol**, *Anu-Med*, and others)	 Recommend suppositories for internal hemorrhoids and topical creams/ointments/wipes for external symptoms.	Clean the skin first with mild soap and warm water. Gently pat dry. Apply ointment externally up to 5 times daily. For suppository: hold wrapped suppository container with rounded end up, separate the foil tabs and slowly peel apart, remove from the wrapper, insert into the rectum up to 4 times daily, especially at night and after bowel movements.

**Brand name discontinued but still used in practice.*

PINWORM *(VERMICULARIS)*

Pinworm infection most commonly occurs in children and presents as anal itching. Anthelmintics, such as mebendazole, pyrantel pamoate and albendazole, are active against *Enterobius vermicularis.* The "tape" test is used to identify eggs: stick a piece of tape around the anus in the morning prior to voiding/defecating. It can take up to three morning tape tests to identify the eggs. Pinworms are often resistant to treatment; reinfection is common. Wash hands frequently and treat the entire household.

DRUGS	NOTES	SAFETY/COUNSELING
OTC **Pyrantel pamoate** (*Reese's Pinworm Medicine*) Previously *Pamix* and *Pin-X* were popular. Patients may still ask for these. **Rx** Albendazole (*Albenza*) Mebendazole	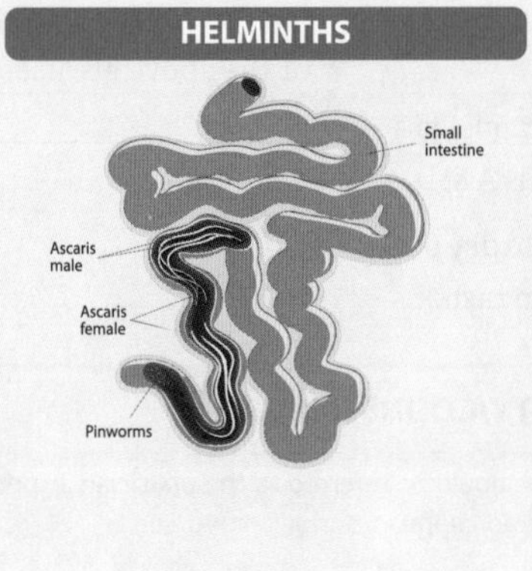	Pyrantel causes headache and dizziness. OTC requires 3 treatments separated by 3 weeks. Mebendazole can be crushed, chewed, and mixed with food. Albendazole tablets can be crushed or chewed, then follow with water. Mebendazole and albendazole cause headache, nausea and are hepatotoxic. Albendazole can be used for other serious systemic infections (e.g., neurocysticercosis). In those cases only, it is used with antiepileptic drugs and high-dose steroids to decrease CNS inflammation and must be taken with a high-fat meal.

LICE AND SCABIES

This section largely discusses lice; scabies (mites) are treated with some of the same medications. Scabies are primarily spread through close body and skin contact. The primary treatment for scabies is permethrin in a cream formulation *(Elimite)* and the prescription drug ivermectin *(Stromectol)*, two oral doses, taken one week apart. Ivermectin, when taken orally, can be difficult to tolerate due to lymph node enlargement, arthralgias, skin tenderness, pruritus and fever. Ivermectin is available in a topical formulation for lice called *Sklice*. Ivermectin is not first-line for lice and is only used in difficult-to-treat cases. Oral ivermectin requires a body weight of at least 15 kg.

- Lice, *Pediculus humanus capitis*, occurs most commonly in elementary school age children.
- Topical pyrethrins and permethrin are the OTC drugs of choice; can be used in infants as young as 2 months. Avoid with chrysanthemums or ragweed allergy.
- Malathion lotion 0.5% *(Ovide)* is an organophosphate. Only for use on persons 6 years of age and older. Can irritate the skin and is flammable; do not smoke or use electrical heat sources, including hair dryers, curlers, and curling or flat irons, when applying and while the hair is wet.
- Benzyl alcohol lotion *(Ulesfia* 5% lotion) kills live lice but not nits. Can irritate the skin and eyes; avoid eye contact.
- Lindane shampoo 1% (previously branded as *Kwell*) is no longer recommended due to neurotoxicity and is reserved for refractive cases, and never in pregnancy, on irritated skin, in infants, children or the elderly.
- If the same medication has been used several times, it may not be working.
- Repeating the procedure, and removing the nits from hair, bedding and elsewhere is essential:
  - Wash clothes and bedding in hot water, followed by a hot dryer.
  - If something cannot be washed, seal it in an air-proof bag for two weeks or dry clean. Vacuum the carpet well. Soak combs and brushes in hot water for 10 minutes. Make sure to check other children in the household.
  - Do not use a combination shampoo/conditioner, or conditioner before using lice medicine. Do not re-wash the hair for 1 – 2 days after treatment.
  - After each treatment, check the hair and use a nit comb to remove nits and lice every 2 – 3 days. Continue to check for 2 – 3 weeks to be sure all lice and nits are gone.
  - Re-treatment is needed for OTC and prescription products (except *Sklice*) on days 7 – 10 (they vary; check the product) in order to kill any surviving hatched lice before they produce new eggs.

DRUGS	NOTES	SAFETY/COUNSELING
LICE **OTC** **Permethrin *(Nix)***, ages 2 + months **Pyrethrin/Piperonyl butoxide *(RID*,** *LiceMD)*, ages 2 + months **Rx** Spinosad *(Natroba)*, ages 4 + yrs Malathion *(Ovide)*, ages 6 + years Benzyl Alcohol Lotion *(Ulesfia)*, ages 6 + months Ivermectin lotion *(Sklice)*, ages 6 + months **SCABIES** **Rx** Permethrin cream *(Elimite)* Ivermectin oral *(Stromectol)*		DOC for lice: permethrin or pyrethrin/piperonyl butoxide. Repeat treatment on day 9. Malathion: flammable, do not use near heat source or organophosphate. Spinosad: works well, expensive. In addition to OTC treatment, remove the live lice and nits by inspecting the hair in 1-inch segments and using a lice comb. Without removing live lice and nits, the OTC product will not work. Nits are "cemented" to the hair shaft and do not fall off after treatment. Nit removal requires multiple efforts, which should be continued for 2 weeks after treatment. See above. Only in resistant/difficult cases use *Sklice* (topical ivermectin), or can use oral ivermectin *(Stromectol)* in those weighing at least 15 kg. Lindane (previously *Kwell*, others) is no longer routinely recommended; high risk neurotoxicity/seizures – more commonly used for scabies (mites).

MINOR WOUNDS

The basic types of minor wounds are cuts, abrasions, bites and burns. Some can be effectively treated with simple first aid and others, depending on the severity, may need more medical attention than first aid can provide. Puncture wounds should be referred to a medical provider. Make sure tetanus vaccine is current (every 10 years, after series has been completed). If the wound is dirty a repeat tetanus vaccine may be required if it is > 5 years since vaccination. If wounds lead you to suspect abuse, contact authorities.

Some chronic wounds (e.g., pressure ulcers) require management by wound care providers. Debridement of chronic wounds is often needed to remove the dead, devitalized or contaminated tissue that prevents healing. There are several methods of debridement, but the most common method is enzymatic debridement, which is done with the application of collagenase ointment *(Santyl)*. Other debridement methods, including surgical debridement, are considered for more complicated wounds.

CUTS, LACERATIONS AND ABRASIONS

- Lacerations are defined as irregular wounds with ragged edges, with the potential for deeper skin damage and bruising under the skin.
- A cut is different than a laceration because the edges will be more uniform or regular.
- After cleaning, if the bleeding does not stop, or it extends far below the surface layers of the skin, seek medical attention because it may require stitching to get the wound to close. If not, regular bandaging should close the wound over time.
- Antibiotic ointment can be applied prior to bandaging.
- Tissue adhesives *(Band-Aid Liquid Bandage, Nexcare Skin Crack Care*, others) create a polymer layer, which binds to the skin, keeping the wound clean and keeping moisture out. Some contain topical analgesics.
- *Seal-On* is a topical sponge (dressing) that can absorb blood and is used for nosebleeds and minor bleeds.
- Abrasions are minor injuries to the top layer of skin and are primarily treated with simple first aid.
- Abrasions such as a skinned knee should be cleaned thoroughly; apply antibiotic ointment and allow to air heal.

BITES

- Bites (except minor insect bites) should never be treated with only first aid, because of the high risk of infection, especially with animal or human bites.
- Certain spider bites in the U.S. can be deadly such as the brown recluse, the black widow and the hobo spider. Spiders tend to stay hidden and are not aggressive. See Emergency Preparedness, Toxicology & Antidotes chapter.
- Spider bites can usually be avoided by inspecting and shaking out clothing or equipment prior to use, and wearing protective clothing. If bitten, stay calm, identify the type of spider if possible, wash with soap and cold water, apply cold compress with ice, elevate extremity and get emergency medical care.
- Minor, harmless insect bites can be treated with a topical steroid or oral antihistamine (such as diphenhydramine) to reduce itching.

BURNS

- Burns are characterized as first degree (red/painful, minor swelling), second degree (thicker, very painful, produce blisters) and third degree (damage to all layers of skin, appears white or charred).
- Burns from a chemical exposure, or in immunosuppressed patients should be referred for emergency medical care.
- If the burn is first or second degree, OTC treatment is acceptable if the area is less than two inches in diameter and not located on the face, over a major joint or on the feet or genitals. In diabetes a burn on a foot, even mild, could lead to an amputation. Vigilance is required.
- Minor burns should be treated first by running the burn under cool water or soaking in cool water for 5 – 20 minutes.
- Do not apply ice as it can further damage injured skin. Bandages should be applied if the skin is broken, or if blisters pop.
- Burned skin itches as it heals; the fingernails of children may need to be cut short and filed, or covered. The skin that has been burned will be more sensitive to the sun for up to a year.
- Ointments (80% oil / 20% water, such as *Aquaphor*) should be used for skin protection over a minor burn to hold in moisture and reduce scarring risk.
- Silver sulfadiazine (*Silvadene; SSD*) can be used topically to reduce infection risk and promote healing, although it has not been shown to be very effective. If the skin is broken systemic toxicity could occur. Do not use with sulfa allergy or G6PD deficiency (due to hemolysis risk).

DRUGS	NOTES	SAFETY/COUNSELING
OTC **Polymyxin/bacitracin/neomycin**, triple antibiotic ointment ***(Neosporin Original***, store brands) For neomycin allergy, use *Polysporin* (bacitracin and polymyxin) or bacitracin alone. Either is sufficient **Rx** **Mupirocin *(Bactroban)*** is an antibiotic cream or ointment; very good staph and strep coverage, including MRSA; can be used for nasal MRSA colonization *(Bactroban nasal)* **Bacitracin/neomycin/polymyxin B/ hydrocortisone *(Cortisporin*** ointment) is a popular Rx topical used for superficial skin infections Collagenase *(Santyl)* – topical debriding agent for chronic wounds	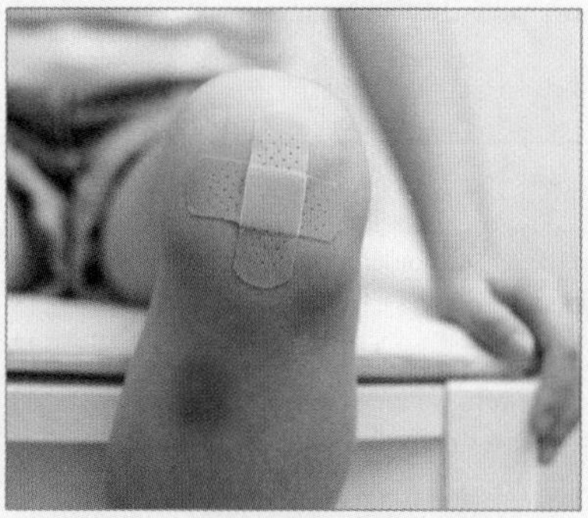 If the wound is not in an area that will get dirty or be rubbed by clothing, it does not need to be covered. Leaving a wound uncovered helps it stay dry and helps it heal.	**Application of topical antibiotic** Clean the affected area and apply a small amount of medication (an amount equal to the surface area of the tip of a finger) to the affected area 1 to 3 times daily. If area can get dirty (such as a hand) or be irritated by clothing, cover with an adhesive strip (e.g., *Band-Aid)* or with sterile gauze and adhesive tape +/- antibiotic ointment. Change daily. Burns require a moist (but not wet) environment by applying either ointment or a bandage designed for burns.

POISON IVY, OAK AND SUMAC

- Poison ivy, oak or sumac poisoning is an allergic reaction that results from touching the sap of these plants, which contain the toxin uroshiol.
- See the image below for the appearance of each of the leaves. Poison oak and ivy are known for leaves in clusters of three.
- The sap may be on the plant, in the ashes of burned plants, on an animal or on other objects that came in contact with the plant (e.g., clothing, garden tools and sports equipment).
- Small amounts of uroshiol can remain under a person's fingernails for days unless removed with good cleaning.

DRUGS	NOTES	SAFETY/COUNSELING
OTC Aluminum acetate solution *(Burow's, Boro-Packs, Domeboro Soothing Soak)* Colloidal oatmeal *(Aveeno)* Calamine lotion + pramoxine (anesthetic): *Caladryl, IvaRest* *Zanfel* works by binding urushiol (this is the toxin) - low evidence for efficacy	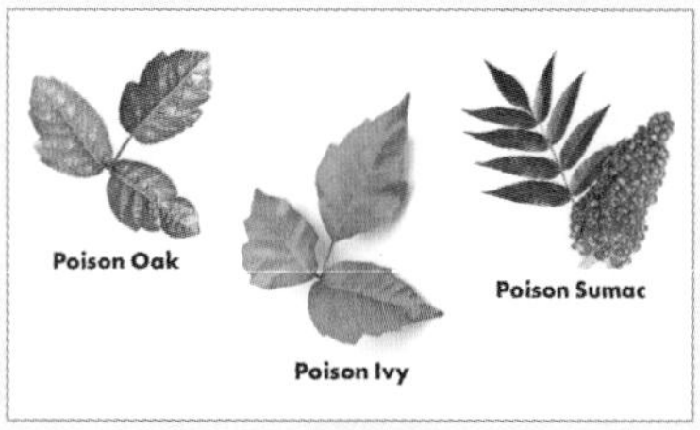 *"Leaves of three, let it be."*	Aluminum acetate is an astringent. Wash the uroshiol off with soap and water carefully, including under fingernails and on clothing. Topical or oral steroids will help (oral needed in severe rash). Cold compresses can help.

INFLAMMATION AND RASH

- The primary treatment for skin irritation is topical steroids. Two strengths of hydrocortisone (HC) are available OTC, 0.5% and 1%; all other topical steroids are prescription.
- The steroid vehicle influences the strength of the medication. Usual potency, from highest to weakest: ointment > creams > lotions > solutions > gels > sprays.
- Thin skin on the face, eyelids and genitals is highly susceptible to topical steroid side effects; low potency steroids should be used on these areas, and skin folds (armpits, groin, under the breasts) where the absorption is higher.
- Local (skin) steroid side effects, if used long-term include skin thinning, pigment changes (lighter or darker), telangectasia (i.e., spider veins, or small blood vessels visible through the skin), rosacea, perioral dermatitis and acne, increased risk skin infections, delayed wound healing, irritation/burning/peeling, and possibly contact dermatitis.
- For urticaria (hives), OTC second-generation antihistamines (e.g., cetirizine) are preferred over first-generation antihistamines (e.g., diphenhydramine) due to better tolerability. Higher doses are used. The "non-sedating" antihistamines are more sedating with higher doses. First-generation antihistamines can be given at bedtime. See the Allergic Rhinitis, Cough & Cold chapter.
- Histamine-2 receptor antagonists (e.g., famotidine) are helpful in some patients for urticaria/hives. Hydroxyzine is often prescribed (see table).

DRUGS	NOTES	SAFETY/COUNSELING
OTC Lowest potency: **Hydrocortisone** 0.5% (infants) and 1% for mild conditions, thin skin (groin area, elderly) and for children. HC 1% lotion *(Aquanil)* **Rx** Higher potency: see chart at the end of the chapter. Apply high potency Rx steroids once daily. Apply OTC/lower potency 1-2x daily. It is common to see a higher potency product, followed by a lower potency product, to treat acute inflammation.	Common topical steroids, ranked by potency, are included at the end of this chapter. Use ointments for thick or dry skin. Ointments have low water content (reduced absorption) and form a skin barrier. See Compounding chapters. Use lotions, gels and foams for hairy skin. No evidence for use of topical diphenhydramine, can use systemic but caution due to side effects. Skin should be lubricated (hydrated) with moisturizers for most conditions. The steroid vehicle can lubricate. Camphor, menthol, local anesthetics (often in combo creams with HC) can help relieve itching. Severe rash will likely require oral steroids for 1-2 weeks.	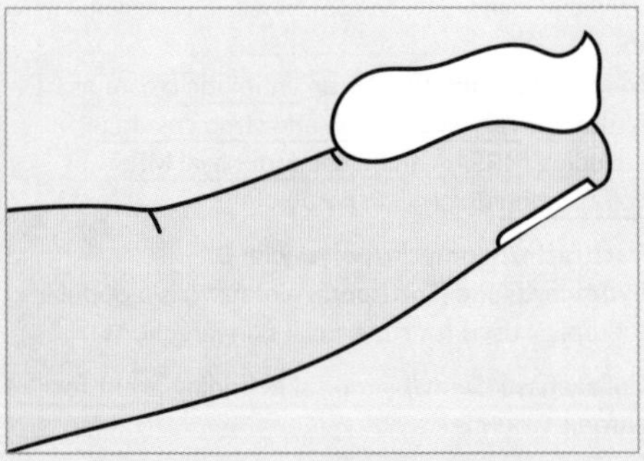 The "finger-tip" unit is used to estimate amount: from the fingertip to the 1st joint covers one adult hand (about ½ g). Encourage patient not to use more than directed as over-use has risks (see above). Do not apply for longer than 2 weeks.
Hydroxyzine *(Vistaril)*	Used for general urticaria (hives) with severe itching. Dose is 25 mg TID-QID.	Anticholinergic side effects, primarily sedation and dry mouth.

SUNSCREENS AND SUN PROTECTION

- Applying sunscreen is important due to the risk of sun damage and skin cancer. Keep in mind that sunscreen blocks vitamin D production in the skin and many Americans are vitamin D deficient.
- It is advisable to stay out of the sun when it is strongest (between 10AM – 4PM). The damaging ultraviolet (UV) rays penetrate clouds; this applies to overcast days as well. Another way to avoid the sun is to wear protective clothing.
- Where skin is exposed, sunscreen can be applied that provides both UVA (A for aging - causes damage below the skin surface) and UVB (B for burning) protection. Both UVA and UVB contribute to skin cancer. A "broad spectrum" sunscreen should be chosen that protects against both UVA and UVB. SPF stands for sun protection factor, which is a measure of how well the sunscreen deflects UVB rays.
- Some dermatologists and the American Academy of Pediatrics (AAP) recommend a minimum SPF 15 and others like the American Academy of Dermatology (AAD) recommend a minimum SPF 30. The key is to apply liberally and at least every two hours and reapply after swimming or sweating. The AAP recommends keeping babies less than 6 months old out of the sun.

TTB (with sunscreen in min) = SPF X TTB (without sunscreen)

- How SPF works: if someone would normally burn in 10 minutes, an SPF of 5 would extend the time they would burn to 50 minutes (5 x 10 = 50.) However, it is not accurate to calculate that if one normally would burn in one hour, then a sunscreen with an SPF of 10 would permit the person to stay in the sun for 10 hours (10 times longer) without burning, since the intensity of the sun varies during the day, and the sunscreen would not last more than a couple of hours.
- Sunscreen labeling is no longer permitted to use "waterproof" or "sweatproof" since they all wash off, at least partially, in the water. They can claim to be "water-resistant" but only for 40 – 80 minutes. Always reapply after swimming, or sweating.
- The AAD recommends sunscreens with any of the following ingredients: avobenzone, cinoxate, ecamsule, menthyl anthranilate, octyl methoxycinnamate, octyl salicylate, oxybenzone or sulisobenzone.
- Oxybenzone irritates some people's skin (uncommon).
- Recently, the FDA issued a warning to oral sunscreen manufacturers marketing dietary supplements for sun protection (*Sunsafe Rx, Heliocare)*. Oral sunscreen is not an effective substitute for topical sunscreen and should not be recommended.

POTENCIES OF TOPICAL STEROIDS

TREATMENT	ACTIVE INGREDIENT
Very High Potency	
***Clobex* Lotion/Spray/Shampoo, 0.05%**	**Clobetasol propionate**
Cormax Solution, 0.05%	Clobetasol propionate
Diprolene Ointment, 0.05%	Betamethasone dipropionate
***Olux* Foam, 0.05%**	**Clobetasol propionate**
Temovate Cream/Ointment/Solution, 0.05%	Clobetasol propionate
Ultravate Cream/Ointment, 0.05%	Halobetasol propionate
Vanos Cream, 0.1%	**Fluocinonide**
Psorcon Ointment, 0.05%	Diflorasone diacetate
High Potency	
***Diprolene* Cream AF, 0.05%**	**Betamethasone dipropionate**
***Elocon* Ointment, 0.1%**	**Mometasone furoate**
Florone Ointment, 0.05%	Diflorasone diacetate
Halog Ointment/Cream, 0.1%	Halcinonide
***Lidex* Ointment, 0.05%**	**Fluocinonide**
Psorcon Cream, 0.05%	Diflorasone diacetate
Topicort Cream/Ointment, 0.25%	Desoximetasone
Topicort Gel, 0.05%	Desoximetasone
High-Medium Potency	
Cutivate Ointment, 0.005%	Fluticasone propionate
***Lidex-E* Cream, 0.05%**	**Fluocinonide**
Luxiq Foam, 0.12%	Betamethasone valerate
Topicort LP Cream, 0.05%	Desoximetasone
Medium Potency	
Cordran Ointment, 0.05%	Flurandrenolide
***Elocon* Cream, 0.1%**	**Mometasone furoate**
***Kenalog* Cream/Spray, 0.1%**	**Triamcinolone acetonide**
Synalar Ointment, 0.025%	Fluocinolone acetonide

TREATMENT	ACTIVE INGREDIENT
Lower Potency	
Capex Shampoo, 0.01%	Fluocinolone acetonide
Cordran Cream/Lotion/Tape, 0.05%	Flurandrenolide
Cutivate Cream/Lotion, 0.05%	Fluticasone propionate
DermAtop Cream, 0.1%	Prednicarbate
DesOwen Lotion, 0.05%	Desonide
Locoid Cream/Lotion/Ointment/Solution, 0.1%	Hydrocortisone butyrate
Pandel Cream, 0.1%	Hydrocortisone probutate
Synalar Cream, 0.025%/0.01%	Fluocinolone acetonide
Mild Potency	
Aclovate Cream/Ointment, 0.05%	Alclometasone dipropionate
Derma-Smoothe/FS Oil, 0.01%	Fluocinolone acetonide
Desonate Gel, 0.05%	Desonide
Synalar Cream/Solution, 0.01%	Fluocinolone acetonide
Tridesilon Cream, 0.05%	Desonide
Verdeso Foam, 0.05%	Desonide
Lowest Potency	
Cetacort Lotion, 0.5%/1%	Hydrocortisone
Cortaid Cream/Spray/Ointment	**Hydrocortisone**
Hytone Cream/Lotion, 1%/2.5%	Hydrocortisone
Micort-HC Cream, 2%/2.5%	Hydrocortisone
Nutracort Lotion, 1%/2.5%	Hydrocortisone
Synacort Cream, 1%/2.5%	Hydrocortisone

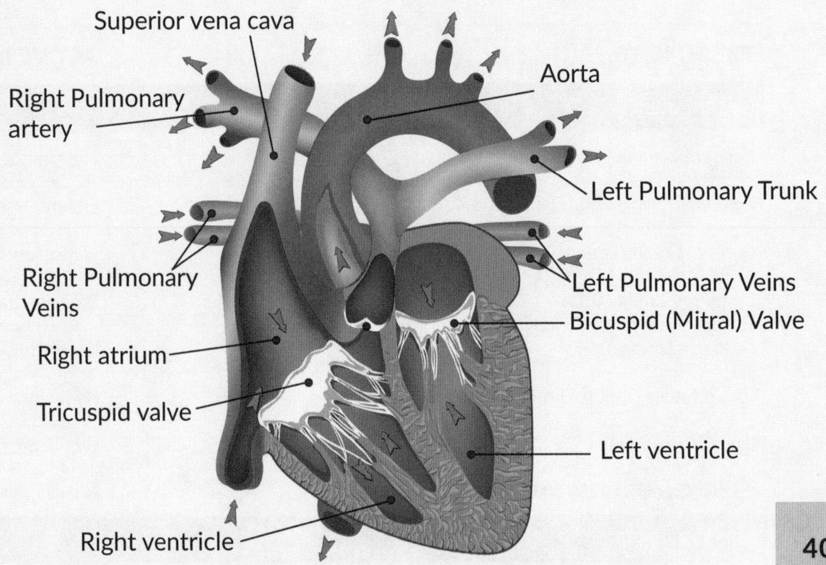
Superior vena cava
Aorta
Right Pulmonary artery
Left Pulmonary Trunk
Right Pulmonary Veins
Left Pulmonary Veins
Bicuspid (Mitral) Valve
Right atrium
Tricuspid valve
Left ventricle
Right ventricle

40

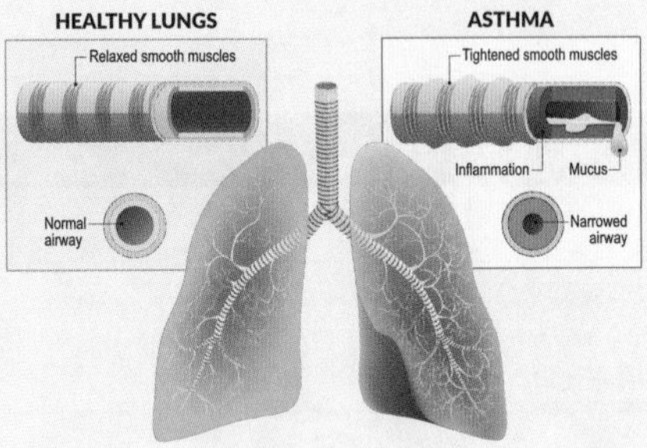
HEALTHY LUNGS
Relaxed smooth muscles
Normal airway
ASTHMA
Tightened smooth muscles
Inflammation
Mucus
Narrowed airway

41

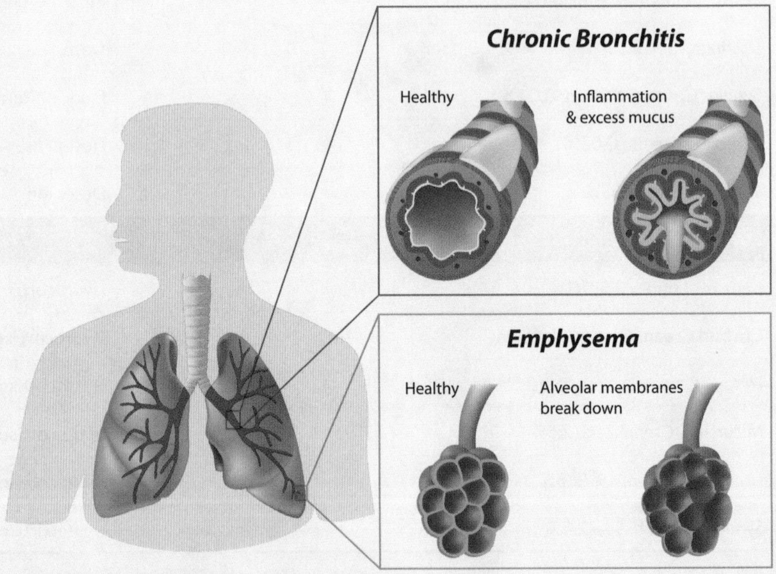
Chronic Bronchitis
Healthy
Inflammation & excess mucus
Emphysema
Healthy
Alveolar membranes break down

42

43

PULMONARY CONDITIONS & TOBACCO CESSATION

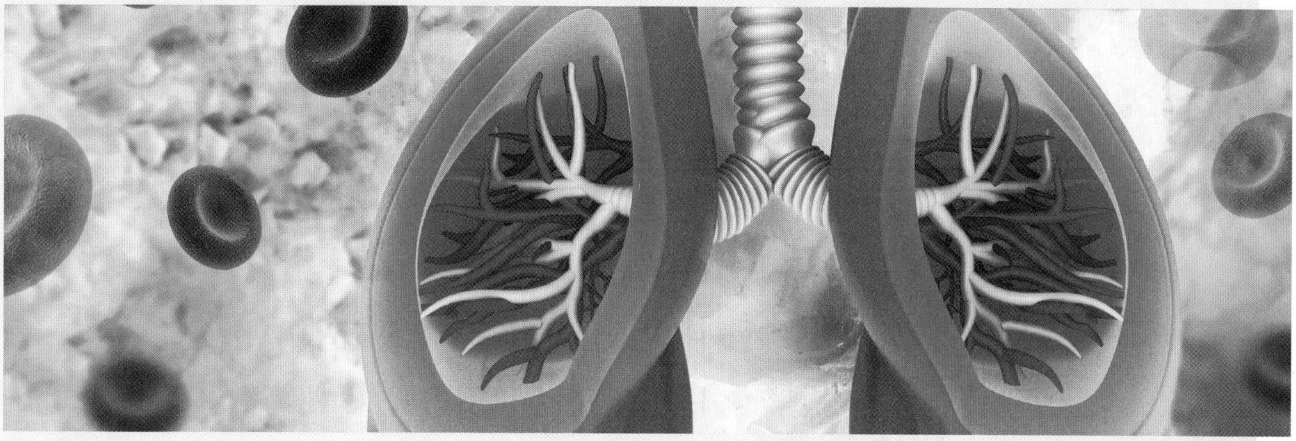

CONTENTS

CHAPTER 40
PULMONARY ARTERIAL HYPERTENSION | 592

CHAPTER 41
ASTHMA | 599

CHAPTER 42
CHRONIC OBSTRUCTIVE PULMONARY DISEASE | 617

CHAPTER 43
TOBACCO CESSATION | 629

CHAPTER CONTENT

Background 592
Classification 592
Pathophysiology 593
Non-Drug Treatment 593
Drug Treatment 593
PAH Treatment Algorithm 594
Prostacyclin Analogues (or Prostanoids) and Receptor Agonists 595
Endothelin Receptor Antagonists 596
Phosphodiesterase-5 Inhibitors 597
Soluble Guanylate Cyclase Stimulator 597
Pulmonary Fibrosis 598
Select Drugs that Can Cause Pulmonary Fibrosis 598

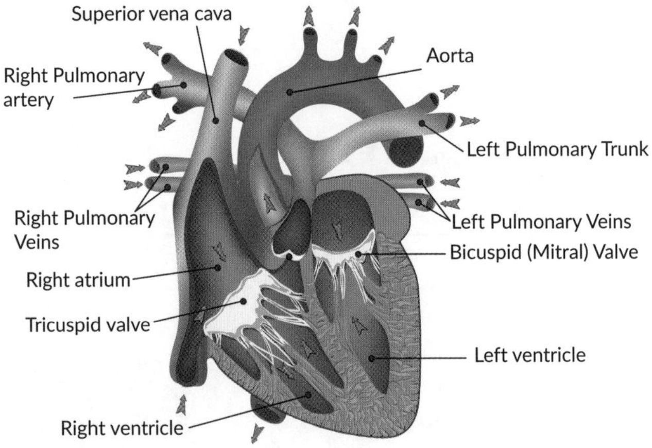

CHAPTER 40
PULMONARY ARTERIAL HYPERTENSION

BACKGROUND

Pulmonary hypertension (PH) is characterized by continuous high blood pressure in the pulmonary arteries. A normal pulmonary artery pressure (PAP) ranges from 8 – 20 mmHg when a person is resting. PH is defined as a mean PAP (mPAP) ≥ 25 mmHg in the setting of normal fluid status. Other hemodynamic parameters are affected as well.

CLASSIFICATION

PH may occur secondary to various disease states. The World Health Organization (WHO) classifies PH into five groups (see box on left). The primary focus of this chapter is Group 1, pulmonary arterial hypertension (PAH). When there is no identifiable cause, it is called primary, or idiopathic, PAH. Secondary causes include genetic inheritance, connective tissue diseases, advanced liver disease and HIV. Less commonly, medications can be the causative factor (see box below). The PH treatments discussed in this chapter are only approved for the treatment of PAH, with the exception of riociguat (*Adempas*).

WORLD HEALTH ORGANIZATION (WHO) CLINICAL CLASSIFICATION OF PULMONARY HYPERTENSION

Group 1: pulmonary arterial hypertension (PAH) – includes idiopathic, heritable, drug- and toxin-induced, disease-associated (e.g., connective tissue diseases, HIV infection, portal hypertension), and persistent pulmonary hypertension of a newborn

Group 2: pulmonary hypertension due to left heart disease

Group 3: pulmonary hypertension due to lung diseases and/or hypoxia

Group 4: chronic thromboembolic pulmonary hypertension (CTEPH)

Group 5: pulmonary hypertension with unclear or multifactorial mechanisms

SELECT DRUGS THAT CAN CAUSE PAH

Cocaine

SSRI use during pregnancy (↑ risk in newborns)

Weight loss drugs (diethylpropion, lorcaserin, phendimetrazine, phentermine)

Methamphetamines/Amphetamines

Dasatinib (*Sprycel*)

Diazoxide (*Proglycem*)

Treatment of the other PH groups is aimed at the underlying causes. Group 2 is pulmonary venous hypertension, which arises from left-sided heart disease (e.g., left ventricular systolic or diastolic dysfunction, valvular disease, congenital heart disease). Group 3 is

CONTENT LEGEND

= Key Drug Guy

PH due to hypoxia or chronic lung diseases, such as COPD, pulmonary fibrosis or emphysema. Group 4 is chronic thromboembolic PH (CTEPH), which occurs in a minority of pulmonary embolism (PE) survivors. Warfarin, with an INR goal of 2 – 3, is recommended for CTEPH; for patients who are not thrombectomy candidates, riociguat *(Adempas)* is an approved treatment. Group 5 is PH caused by conditions that do not fit in the above categories (e.g., sarcoidosis).

PATHOPHYSIOLOGY

PAH stems from an imbalance in vasoconstrictor and vasodilator substances. Vasoconstrictor substances [e.g., endothelin-1 and thromboxane A2 (TXA2)] are increased and vasodilating substances (e.g., prostacyclins) are decreased. Vasoconstriction results in reduced blood flow and high pressure within the pulmonary vasculature. In addition, there is an imbalance between cell proliferation and apoptosis (cell death) in the walls of the pulmonary arteries. The increasing amount of pulmonary artery smooth muscle cells causes pulmonary artery walls to thicken and form scar tissue (vasoproliferation). As the walls thicken and scar, the arteries become increasingly narrower. These changes make it difficult for the right ventricle to pump blood through the pulmonary arteries and into the lungs due to the increased pressure. As a result of working harder, the right ventricle becomes enlarged and right heart failure develops. Heart failure is the most common cause of death in people who have PAH.

Symptoms of PAH include fatigue, dyspnea, chest pain, syncope, edema, tachycardia and/or Raynaud's phenomenon. In Raynaud's, reduced blood supply causes discoloration and coldness in the fingers, toes and occasionally other areas. The WHO also has a functional classification system for PAH, similar to the NYHA classification used in heart failure.

There is no cure for PAH, but in the last decade, knowledge of the disease has increased significantly and many more treatment options have become available. Without treatment, life expectancy is three years. In some cases, a lung or heart-lung transplant may be an option, at least for younger patients.

NON-DRUG TREATMENT

Patients with PAH should follow a sodium-restricted diet of < 2.4 grams/day to help manage volume status, especially if they have right ventricular failure. Routine immunizations against influenza and pneumococcal pneumonia are advised. Exposure to high altitudes may contribute to hypoxic pulmonary vasoconstriction and may not be tolerated by patients. Oxygen is used when needed to maintain oxygen saturation above 90%.

DRUG TREATMENT

The biochemical changes mentioned above (↑ TXA2, ↓ prostacyclin), along with other altered pathways, lead to a pro-thrombotic state. Anticoagulation with warfarin, titrated to an INR of 1.5 – 2.5, can be considered to prevent blood clots from forming; this lower than usual INR goal is based on observational evidence and expert opinion assessing the risks and benefits of anticoagulation therapy in PAH. Other supportive therapies includes loop diuretics (for volume overload), and possibly digoxin (to improve cardiac output or control heart rate in atrial fibrillation). Patients should be referred to a PAH specialty center for further assessment and management, including right heart catheterization to confirm the PAH diagnosis and determine responsiveness to acute vasoreactivity testing. During right heart catheterization, short-acting vasodilators (e.g., inhaled nitric oxide, IV epoprostenol or IV adenosine) are administered. If the mPAP falls by at least 10 mmHg to an absolute value less than 40 mmHg, patients are considered responders and should be initiated on chronic vasodilatory treatment with calcium channel blockers (CCBs). Approximately 10% of patients are candidates for CCB therapy, though only half of these will have a sustained response. The CCBs used most frequently are long-acting nifedipine, diltiazem and amlodipine. The use of verapamil is not recommended due to its more pronounced negative inotropic effects, relative to diltiazem.

Non-responders to vasoreactivity testing, and positive responders who fail CCB therapy, need to be treated with one or more vasodilating drugs approved for PAH. These include prostacyclin analogues and receptor agonists, endothelin receptor antagonists (ERAs), phosphodiesterase-5 inhibitors (PDE-5), which are the same drugs used for erectile dysfunction but with different brand names and doses, and/or a soluble guanylate cyclase (sGC) stimulator. In most cases, drug therapy will reduce symptoms and improve exercise tolerance. Parenteral prostacyclin analogues, specifically IV epoprostenol, have been shown to decrease mortality. Some patients may benefit from combination therapy.

PAH TREATMENT ALGORITHM

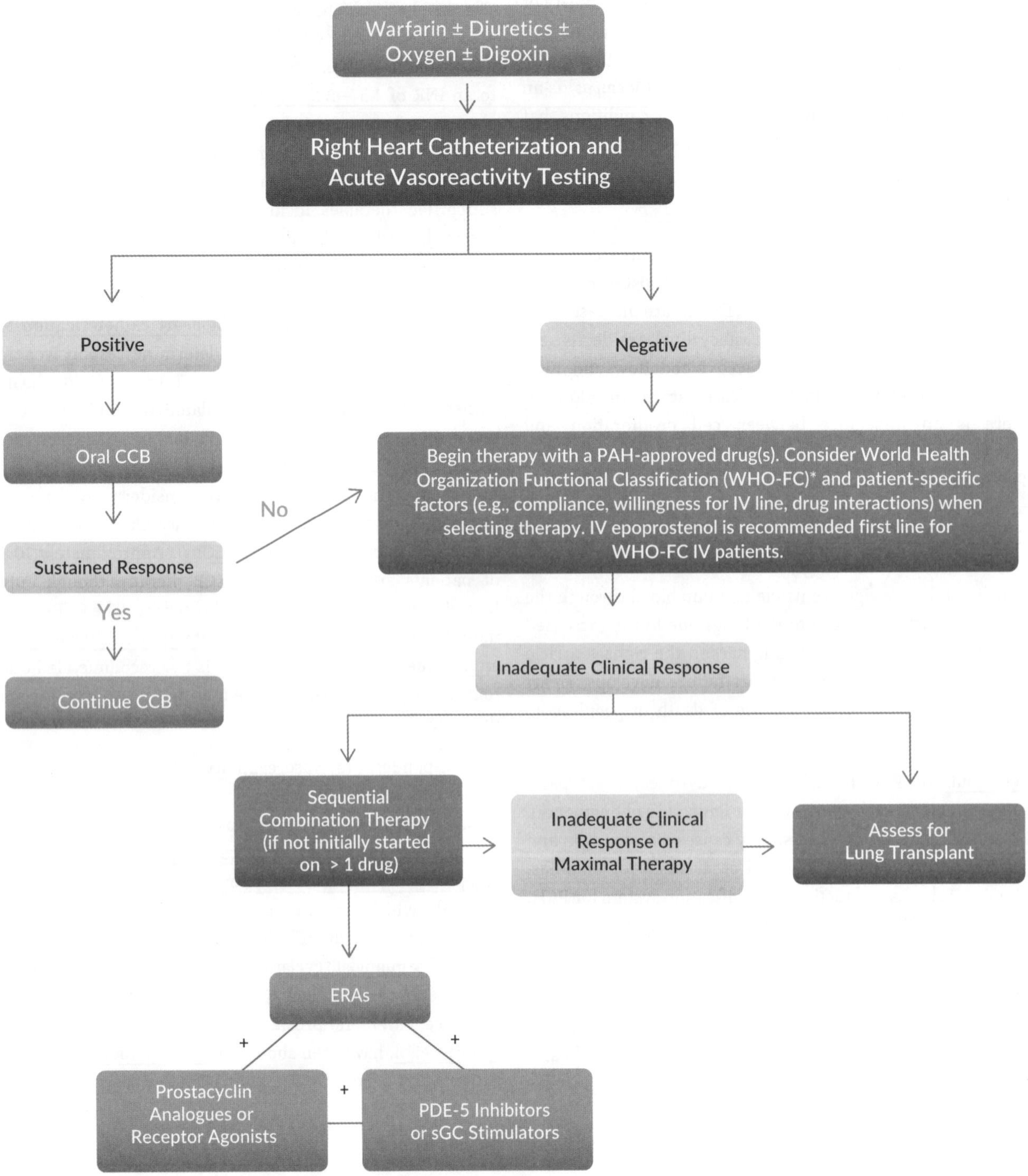

**WHO-FC: Class I = patients with PH but without limitation of physical activity; Class II = patients with PH resulting in slight limitation of physical activity (symptoms with ordinary physical activity); Class III = patients with PH with marked limitation of physical activity (symptoms with less than ordinary physical activity); Class IV = patients with PH unable to be physically active and with signs of right heart failure (symptoms may be present at rest)*

PROSTACYCLIN ANALOGUES (OR PROSTANOIDS) AND RECEPTOR AGONISTS

Prostacyclin synthase is reduced in patients with PAH, causing decreased production of prostacyclin I2 (a vasodilator with anti-proliferative effects) in pulmonary artery smooth muscle cells. Prostacyclin analogues are potent vasodilators (of both pulmonary and systemic vascular beds) and inhibitors of platelet aggregation. The prostacyclin receptor agonist selexipag *(Uptravi)* is structurally different but works similarly. Drugs which decrease prostaglandins (e.g., NSAIDs) should be avoided in patients with PAH.

DRUG	DOSING	SAFETY/SIDE EFFECTS/MONITORING
Epoprostenol *(Flolan,* *Veletri)* AKA prostacyclin Continuous IV infusion via central venous catheter	Start at 2 ng/kg/min and ↑ by 1-2 ng/kg/min in 15 minute intervals based on clinical response; usual dose is 25-40 ng/kg/min (can be higher)	**CONTRAINDICATIONS** Epoprostenol: heart failure with ↓ left ventricular ejection fraction Treprostinil (oral): severe hepatic impairment (Child-Pugh Class C) **WARNINGS** Rebound PH (do not ↓ dose or discontinue abruptly – see Notes), increased risk of bleeding Chronic IV infusions: sepsis and blood stream infections Treprostinil (oral): tablet shell does not dissolve and can lodge in diverticuli **SIDE EFFECTS** Vasodilation reactions (hypotension, headache, dizziness, flushing, N/V/D), edema, jaw pain, musculoskeletal pain (e.g., myalgias), tachycardia, flu-like syndrome, anxiety, tremor, thrombocytopenia IV/SC infusions: infusion-site pain (especially SC *Remodulin* – see Notes) Treprostinil (inhaled) and iloprost: cough and mouth/throat irritation **NOTES** Parenteral agents are considered the most potent of all PAH medications. Avoid interruptions in therapy – immediate access to a back up pump, infusion sets and medication is essential for parenteral products (particularly for epoprostenol); epoprostenol half-life is ~6 minutes and treprostinil half-life is ~4 hours Avoid large, sudden reductions in dose; decrease dose gradually if side effects occur Epoprostenol: must protect from light before reconstitution and during infusion *Flolan:* reconstituted solutions require use of ice packs for stability. *Veletri* is thermostable (no need for ice packs) *Remodulin:* infusion site pain can occur in up to 85% of patients with SC administration (may need an analgesic to tolerate); thermostable (no ice packs needed) To ↓ infections, patients must be instructed on how to care for infusion sites and use of sterile technique when preparing the drug for parenteral use Lower starting doses required with mild or moderate hepatic impairment for selexipag and treprostinil; avoid selexipag with severe hepatic impairment
Treprostinil *Remodulin:* continuous SC or IV (central venous catheter) infusion *Tyvaso:* inhalation *Orenitram*: oral, ER tablet	*Remodulin:* start at 1.25 ng/kg/min and ↑ at weekly intervals, up to 40 ng/kg/min (and possibly more) *Tyvaso:* start with 18 mcg (3 inhalations) 4 times/day and ↑ every 1-2 weeks to target of 54 mcg (9 inhalations) 4 times/day; doses should be taken Q4H during waking hours *Orenitram:* start at 0.25 mg BID or 0.125 mg TID, ↑ every 3-4 days up to the maximum tolerated dose; take with food	
Iloprost *(Ventavis)* Inhalation	2.5-5 mcg/inhalation given 6-9 times/day, no more than once every 2 hrs	
Selexipag *(Uptravi)* Tablet	Start with 200 mcg BID and ↑ at weekly intervals to maximum dose of 1600 mcg BID	

Prostacyclin Analogue and Receptor Agonist Drug Interactions

- The effects of antihypertensive, antiplatelet and anticoagulant agents can be increased.
- Treprostinil levels are increased by CYP450 2C8 inhibitors (e.g., gemfibrozil) and decreased by CYP2C8 inducers (e.g., rifampin). Strong CYP2C8 inhibitors should be avoided with selexipag.

ENDOTHELIN RECEPTOR ANTAGONISTS

Endothelin is a vasoconstrictor with cellular proliferative effects. ERAs block endothelin receptors on pulmonary artery smooth muscle cells.

<table>
<tr><th>DRUG</th><th>DOSING</th><th>SAFETY/SIDE EFFECTS/MONITORING</th></tr>
<tr><td>Bosentan (Tracleer)</td><td>< 40 kg: 62.5 mg BID
≥ 40 kg: 62.5 mg BID (for 4 wks), then 125 mg BID</td><td rowspan="3">BOXED WARNINGS
Embryo-fetal toxicity (women of childbearing potential must have a negative pregnancy test prior to initiation of therapy and monthly thereafter)
Bosentan: hepatotoxicity (↑ ALT/AST and liver failure)
Available only through individual REMS programs (Tracleer REMS Program, Letairis REMS Program and Opsumit REMS Program); prescribers, pharmacies and patients must enroll (only female patients required to be enrolled in the Letairis and Opsumit REMS programs)

CONTRAINDICATIONS
Pregnancy
Bosentan: use with cyclosporine or glyburide
Ambrisentan: idiopathic pulmonary fibrosis

WARNINGS
Hepatotoxicity, ↓ Hgb/Hct, fluid retention (e.g., pulmonary edema, peripheral edema), decreased sperm counts
Bosentan: hypersensitivity reactions (e.g., rash, angioedema, anaphylaxis, DRESS)

SIDE EFFECTS
Headache, upper respiratory tract infections (e.g., nasal congestion, cough, bronchitis), flushing, hypotension

MONITORING
LFTs, bilirubin, Hgb/Hct, pregnancy tests

NOTES
Bosentan approved for children 3 and older</td></tr>
<tr><td>Ambrisentan (Letairis)</td><td>5 mg daily, may ↑ to 10 mg daily after 4 weeks if tolerated</td></tr>
<tr><td>Macitentan (Opsumit)</td><td>10 mg daily</td></tr>
</table>

Endothelin Receptor Antagonist Drug Interactions

- Bosentan is a substrate and inducer of CYP3A4 and 2C9; monitor for drug interactions. Levels of bosentan can increase with CYP2C9 (e.g., amiodarone, fluconazole) and CYP3A4 (e.g., ritonavir) inhibitors. Concurrent use of cyclosporine or glyburide is contraindicated. Bosentan can decrease the effectiveness of hormonal contraceptives (at least one barrier method of contraception, if not two, is recommended).
- Ambrisentan is a substrate of CYP3A4 (major), CYP2C19 (minor) and P-gp. Cyclosporine can increase the serum concentration of ambrisentan; limit the dose of ambrisentan to 5 mg daily when given with cyclosporine.
- Macitentan is a substrate of CYP3A4 (major) and CYP2C19 (minor). Strong CYP3A4 inhibitors and inducers should be avoided with macitentan.

PHOSPHODIESTERASE-5 INHIBITORS

PDE-5 is responsible for the degradation of cyclic guanosine monophosphate (cGMP); increased cGMP concentrations lead to pulmonary vasculature relaxation and vasodilation.

DRUG	DOSING	SAFETY/SIDE EFFECTS/MONITORING
Sildenafil *(Revatio)* ***Viagra*** - ED Tablet, oral suspension, intravenous	IV: 2.5-10 mg TID Oral: 5-20 mg TID, taken 4-6 hours apart	**CONTRAINDICATIONS** Use with nitrates or riociguat *Revatio*: avoid taking with protease inhibitors (e.g., atazanavir, ritonavir, others) **WARNINGS** Hearing loss (with or without tinnitus and dizziness), vision loss [rare but may be due to nonarteritic anterior ischemic optic neuropathy (NAION)], priapism (seek emergency medical care if erection lasts > 4 hours), hypotension, pulmonary edema *Revatio*: not recommended for pediatric use due to increased mortality **SIDE EFFECTS** Headache, epistaxis, flushing, dyspepsia, extremity or back pain, N/D
Tadalafil *(Adcirca)* *Cialis* - ED, BPH Tablet	40 mg daily 20 mg daily if mild- mod renal or hepatic impairment CrCl < 30 mL/min: avoid use Severe hepatic impairment: avoid use	

PDE-5 Inhibitor Drug Interactions

- Do not give with other PDE-5 inhibitors used for erectile dysfunction.
- Do not use with nitrate medications (any formulation – see Ischemic Heart Disease chapter) or the sGC stimulator riociguat as the potential for excessively low blood pressure is increased. Taking nitrates is an absolute contraindication to the use of PDE-5 inhibitors; this includes the illicit drugs such as amyl nitrate and butyl nitrate ("poppers").
- Use caution with alpha blocker therapy (or other antihypertensives) as PDE-5 inhibitors can increase the hypotensive effects of these agents. When tadalafil is used for PAH, alpha 1-blockers are not recommended for the treatment of BPH. Alcohol can enhance hypotension with PDE-5 inhibitors.
- PDE-5 inhibitors are major substrates of CYP3A4; avoid use of strong CYP3A4 inhibitors and inducers.

SOLUBLE GUANYLATE CYCLASE STIMULATOR

Soluble guanylate cyclase (sGC) is a receptor for endogenous nitric oxide. Riociguat *(Adempas)* sensitizes sGC to endogenous nitric oxide and directly stimulates the receptor at a different binding site. This increases cGMP, leading to relaxation and antiproliferative effects in the pulmonary artery smooth muscle cells. Riociguat is approved for use in both PAH and CTEPH.

DRUG	DOSING	SAFETY/SIDE EFFECTS/MONITORING
Riociguat *(Adempas)*	Start with 0.5-1 mg TID, increasing by 0.5 mg TID every 2 weeks if SBP > 95 mmHg; max dose is 2.5 mg TID	**BOXED WARNING** Embryo-fetal toxicity (women of childbearing potential must have a negative pregnancy test prior to initiation of therapy and monthly thereafter) Available only through the *Adempas* REMS Program; prescribers, pharmacies and female patients must enroll **CONTRAINDICATIONS** Pregnancy, use of PDE-5 inhibitors or nitrates **WARNINGS** Hypotension, bleeding, pulmonary edema **SIDE EFFECTS** Headache, dyspepsia, dizziness, N/V/D

Riociguat Drug Interactions

- Do not use with nitrate medications (any formulation – see Ischemic Heart Disease chapter) or PDE-5 inhibitors as the potential for excessively low blood pressure is increased. Specifically, riociguat should not be administered within 24 hours of sildenafil, or within 24 hours before or 48 hours after tadalafil.
- Smoking increases riociguat clearance; the dose may need to be decreased with smoking cessation.
- Separate from antacids by > 1 hour.
- Riociguat is a major substrate of CYP3A4, 2C8 and P-gp; monitor for drug interactions and dose adjustments.

PULMONARY FIBROSIS

Pulmonary fibrosis (PF) is scarred and damaged lung tissue. The common presentation is exertional dyspnea with a nonproductive cough. As the condition worsens, breathing becomes more labored. There are a variety of causes of PF, including toxin exposure (e.g., asbestos, silica), medical conditions, and drugs (see box), among others. Often the contributing factor is not identified and the PF is called idiopathic pulmonary fibrosis (IPF).

If the condition is drug-induced, the offending drug should be discontinued. Aside from treatment with chronic oxygen supplementation, two drugs are now available for IPF. Both pirfenidone *(Esbriet)* and nintedanib *(Ofev)* slow the rate of decline in lung function. In addition to these two drugs, several of the drugs approved for PAH (particularly sildenafil) may be used off-label for PF. The prognosis of IPF is poor; five year survival is approximately 20 – 30% once diagnosed.

SELECT DRUGS THAT CAN CAUSE PULMONARY FIBROSIS

KEY DRUGS

- Amiodarone
- Bleomycin (and a few other chemo drugs)
- Dronedarone
- Methotrexate

Others:

- Nitrofurantoin
- Sulfasalazine

Select Guidelines/References

Pharmacologic therapy for pulmonary arterial hypertension in adults. *Chest*. 2014;146:449-475.

2015 ESC/ERS guidelines for the diagnosis and treatment of pulmonary hypertension. *Eur Heart J*. 2016;37:67-119.

CHAPTER CONTENT

Background ... **599**
Diagnosis and Assessment ... **599**
- Spirometry: Tests Lung Function (How Well the Lungs Work) ... 600
- Environmental Triggers and Comorbid Conditions ... 600
- Classifying Asthma Severity ... 600

Treatment Principles ... **601**
- General Approach ... 601
- Controlling Risk Factors ... 601

Drug Treatment ... **602**
- Asthma Treatment Algorithm ... 603
- Beta-2 Agonists ... 604
- Inhaled Corticosteroids ... 605
- Controller (Maintenance) Inhalers ... 606
- Recognizing and Understanding Inhaled Delivery Devices ... 607
- MDIs and DPIs ... 607
- Leukotriene Modifying Agents ... 607
- Theophylline ... 608
- Anticholinergics ... 608
- Omalizumab *(Xolair)* ... 609
- Interleukin Receptor Antagonists ... 609

Special Situations ... **609**
- Exercise-Induced Bronchospasm: *Prevent It* ... 609
- Pregnancy: *Keep Control* ... 609

Patient Self-Management and Education ... **610**
- Inhalers ... 610
- Nebulizers ... 611
- Spacers ... 611
- With a Spacer, More Drug Gets Into The Lungs ... 611
- Peak Flow Meters ... 611
- Sample Asthma Action Plan (Adult) ... 612

Patient Counseling ... **613**

CONTENT LEGEND

= Study Tip Gal

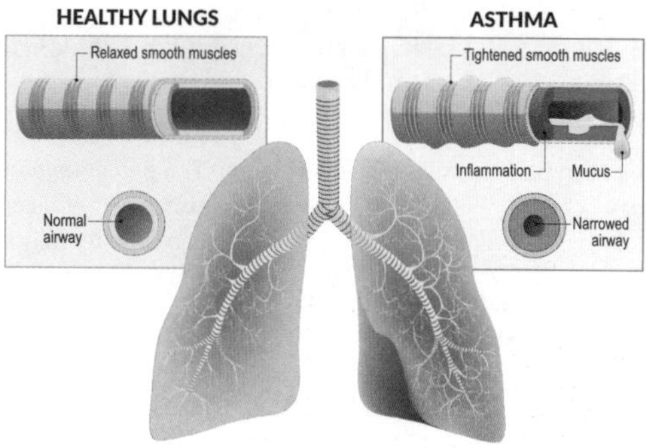

CHAPTER 41
ASTHMA

BACKGROUND

Asthma is a disease that affects the airways (bronchi) of the lungs. It is one of the most common chronic diseases among children, and the prevalence is increasing each year. Asthma is characterized by a predisposition to chronic airway inflammation and bronchoconstriction (narrowed airways). The inflammation and bronchoconstriction cause airflow obstruction, which results in expiratory airflow limitation (difficulty with exhalation). This results in recurrent episodes of wheezing, breathlessness, chest tightness and coughing, which are the classic symptoms of asthma. The symptoms can vary over time and in intensity, often occurring more frequently at night or on awakening. They can also be triggered by a variety of factors (see section on Environmental Triggers and Comorbid Conditions).

The inflammation and bronchoconstriction in asthma is reversible with medication (and sometimes spontaneously). Patients with asthma can live successful and active lives if they adhere to treatment and follow an asthma action plan. The most common complication of asthma is exacerbations, which can range from mild to severe, and in some cases can be fatal. There is no cure for asthma, but it can be controlled.

DIAGNOSIS AND ASSESSMENT

There are many types of asthma. When a patient exhibits the classic symptoms of asthma, a detailed history and physical examination can help define the type of asthma, along with triggers, environmental factors and comorbid conditions that can contribute to disease severity (see the table on the following page). Most types of asthma have activation of inflammatory mediators (e.g., histamine, leukotrienes, cytokines) and an increase in inflammatory cells (e.g., mast cells, eosinophils) contributing to the disease process. Some patients have a genetic predisposition to the development of severe allergic asthma, which is mediated by immunoglobulin E (IgE), or severe eosinophilic asthma. These cases can require specialized treatments in addition to the use of routine inhaled medications.

An asthma diagnosis is confirmed with spirometry and pulmonary function tests (see the Study Tip Gal on the following page). These should be measured at the patient's baseline, and after use of a short-acting bronchodilator (e.g., albuterol) to test for reversibility (i.e., if the FEV1 increases by more than 12% with the use of the bronchodilator). Spirometry is performed in a medical facility (not at home).

SPIROMETRY: TESTS LUNG FUNCTION (HOW WELL THE LUNGS WORK)

FEV1
How much air can be forcefully exhaled in one second.

FVC
After taking a deep breath, the maximum volume of air that is exhaled (how much air is exhaled).

FEV1/FVC
The percentage of total air capacity ("vital capacity") that can be forcefully exhaled in one second (the speed of the exhale).

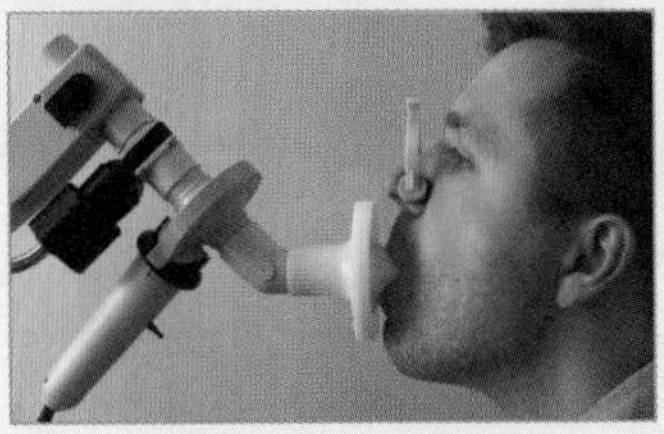

Peak expiratory flow rate (PEFR) is measured using a peak flow meter. This is typically used for monitoring asthma control as part of the asthma action plan, but it can be used at initial diagnosis to test for variability in expiratory airflow limitation. Patients will use the peak flow meter twice daily for a period of two weeks to check the PEFR; if the average daily PEFR variability is greater than 10%, this suggests a diagnosis of asthma. PEFR and peak flow meters are described in more detail later in the chapter.

ENVIRONMENTAL TRIGGERS AND COMORBID CONDITIONS

The triggers that set off an asthma attack vary; some people will have bronchoconstriction from a pet, and others do not. Patients need to learn their personal triggers and avoid them, when possible. If the trigger cannot be avoided, acute treatment may be needed. Some of the most common triggers are listed below. Coughing and laughter are other triggers that are often under-appreciated. Common comorbid conditions that can trigger an attack are listed below the triggers.

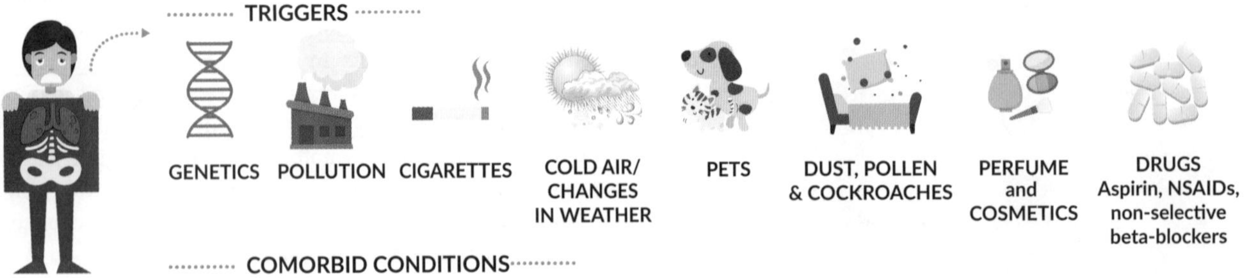

Infections (Colds and Viruses), Allergic Rhinitis, GERD, Obesity, Obstructive Sleep Apnea, Anxiety, Stress and Depression

CLASSIFYING ASTHMA SEVERITY

Classification of asthma severity guides the intensity (or step) of initial treatment. The table below describes the four key components that are assessed at diagnosis and at each follow up visit (daytime symptoms, nighttime awakenings, frequency of rescue inhaler use and activity limitations), along with lung function and exacerbation frequency. This can be used for any patient ≥ 12 years of age, though criteria are similar for younger patients.

Components of Severity		Classification of Asthma Severity			
		Intermittent	Persistent		
			Mild	Moderate	Severe
Impairment	Daytime symptoms	≤ 2 days/week	> 2 days/week but not daily	Daily	Throughout the day
	Nighttime awakenings	≤ 2x/month	3-4x/month	> 1x/week but not nightly	Often (7x/week)
	Rescue inhaler use	≤ 2 days/week	> 2 days/week, but not daily or > 1 x/day	Daily	Several times per day
	Activity limitations	None	Minor limitation	Some limitation	Extremely limited
	Lung function FEV1 (% predicted) FEV1/FVC*	> 80% Normal	> 80% Normal	60-80% Reduced 5%	< 60% Reduced 5%
Risk	Exacerbations requiring oral systemic steroids	0-1/year	≥ 2/year		
Recommended Step for Initiating Treatment (See Asthma Treatment Algorithm)		Step 1	Step 2	Step 3**	Step 4 or 5**

Adapted from NHLBI EPR 2007
**Normal FEV1/FVC by age: 8-19 years, 85%; 20-39 years, 80%; 40-59 years, 75%; 60-80 years, 70%*
***Consider a short course of oral systemic steroid*

TREATMENT PRINCIPLES

Long term asthma management should focus on reducing impairment (e.g., symptoms, frequency of rescue inhaler use, limitations to normal activity) and reducing risk (exacerbations, hospitalizations and medication adverse events). Initiating, monitoring and adjusting treatment follows a step-wise and continuous process.

GENERAL APPROACH

- Select treatment according to the initial assessment of asthma severity (see Classification of Asthma Severity Chart on previous page and Treatment Algorithm later in chapter).
- Follow up in 2 – 6 weeks. At each visit:
    - Assess adherence to medications.
    - Perform medication counseling (confirm appropriate inhaler technique and understanding of maintenance versus rescue treatment). See the detailed patient instructions on technique, priming and cleaning of select inhalers at the end of the chapter.
    - Assess control of risk factors, triggers and comorbid conditions.
    - Review the asthma action plan (see example later in the chapter).
    - Address patient concerns.
    - Assess asthma control/severity and step up, maintain or step down treatment as shown in the Treatment Algorithm. Do not step up therapy until the items above have been addressed; there might be other factors contributing to poor asthma control (e.g., incorrect inhaler technique or lack of adherence) and increasing doses of medications and/or adding other drugs can increase side effects without providing additional benefit.
- Follow up visits can decrease to 1 – 6 months once control is gained, and to every three months if a step down in treatment is planned.

CONTROLLING RISK FACTORS

Patients with asthma should avoid exposure to tobacco smoke and those who smoke should quit, or be strongly encouraged to quit at each healthcare visit. Physical activity should not be avoided, even in those with exercise-induced bronchospasm.

Identifying and avoiding triggers, when possible, is advised. Some triggers should not be avoided (e.g., laughter) and others are difficult to avoid (e.g., stress, respiratory infections). Comorbid conditions should be treated to improve asthma control.

An annual influenza vaccine is recommended in all patients with asthma ≥ 6 months of age. Patients age 2 – 64 years should receive one dose of the pneumococcal polysaccharide vaccine (PPSV23, *Pneumovax 23*). Asthma is not an indication to administer pneumococcal conjugate vaccine (PCV13, *Prevnar 13*), except in children age 6 – 18 years who require high dose oral steroids. Refer to the Immunizations chapter for more details on the criteria for pneumococcal vaccination.

Any patient with persistent asthma and a clear connection of symptoms with exposure to an allergen should have skin or in vitro testing to assess sensitivity. Treatment with subcutaneous allergen immunotherapy should be used, if indicated, based on the test results.

DRUG TREATMENT

Asthma drugs come in oral, inhaled and injectable formulations. Inhaled forms deliver drugs directly into the lungs, have reduced toxicity and are the preferred delivery vehicle. Drugs used to treat asthma long-term are classified as relievers (rescue inhalers) or controllers (maintenance drugs). The table on the following page describes the different classes of asthma medications and the primary role or place in treatment for each.

Relievers, or rescue inhalers, rapidly open airways within minutes of inhalation to make breathing easier. Frequent use (two days per week or more) indicates worsening asthma control and a need to reassess, and possibly step up, treatment. In addition to intermittent use for acute asthma symptoms, rescue inhalers can be used preventively for exercise-induced bronchospasm (EIB). Inhaled epinephrine is now FDA-approved and available OTC for mild symptoms of intermittent asthma.

Controllers, or maintenance inhalers, are taken on a chronic, daily basis to reduce inflammation and maintain asthma control. Inhaled corticosteroids (ICS) are the mainstay of treatment for patients with asthma. Doses are categorized as low, medium or high and can be escalated (either by increasing the number of inhalations per dose or by increasing to a higher strength inhaler), if indicated, based on asthma severity.

ASTHMA MEDICATION CLASS	NOTES
Relievers (Rescue Drugs)	
Inhaled low-dose ICS + formoterol	Combines an inhaled corticosteroid (ICS) and a long-acting beta-2 agonist (LABA) Used intermittently (as needed) for acute asthma symptoms Combination proven to have reduced exacerbations over SABA alone
Inhaled short-acting beta-2 agonists (SABAs)	Used intermittently (as needed) for acute asthma symptoms Quickly reverse bronchoconstriction
Systemic steroids	Injections: used during exacerbations Oral: used during exacerbations or for severe asthma that is difficult to control with other drug combinations Use should be limited as much as possible due to the risks of adverse effects (see Systemic Steroids & Autoimmune Conditions chapter)
Inhaled epinephrine	Available OTC, can be used for acute treatment of mild symptoms in intermittent asthma only Not included in asthma guidelines
Inhaled short-acting muscarinic antagonists (SAMAs) Also called inhaled anticholinergics	Can be used in combination during exacerbations
Controllers (Maintenance Drugs)	
Inhaled corticosteroids (ICS)	First-line for all patients with persistent asthma; the most effective anti-inflammatory drugs
Inhaled long-acting beta-2 agonists (LABAs)	Used in combination with ICS (should never be used alone due to increased risk of serious adverse outcomes) Preferred add-on agents to ICS
Oral leukotriene receptor antagonists (LTRAs)	Alternative option to LABA in combination with ICS; can also be added to ICS/LABA treatment Most commonly used in children
Theophylline (oral or IV)	Least desirable option for add-on treatment due to significant adverse effects, drug interactions and the need to monitor serum drug concentrations
Inhaled long-acting muscarinic antagonists (LAMAs) Also called inhaled anticholinergics	Can be used as add-on treatment in patients with a history of exacerbations despite ICS/LABA treatment
Injectable monoclonal antibodies (SC or IV)	Add-on treatment in persistent severe asthma of a specific type: Omalizumab: for severe allergic asthma Mepolizumab, reslizumab, benralizumab and dupilumab: for severe eosinophilic asthma

ASTHMA TREATMENT ALGORITHM

Assess Asthma Control at Each Follow-Up Visit

Well controlled: maintain current step (if controlled for at least 3 months, may step down treatment)
Symptoms/use of rescue inhaler ≤ 2 days/week, nighttime awakenings ≤ 2 times/month, no limitations to normal activity

Not well-controlled: step up 1 step
Symptoms/use of rescue inhaler > 2 days/week, nighttime awakenings 1-3 times/week, some limitations to normal activity

Very poorly controlled: step up 1-2 steps (consider a short course of oral steroid)
Symptoms/use of rescue inhaler several times daily, nighttime awakenings ≥ 4 days/week, normal activity extremely limited

DETERMINE TREATMENT STEP BASED ON ASTHMA SEVERITY

All patients, regardless of treatment step, should have a rescue inhaler for use as needed

Step 1 (Intermittent Asthma)

As-needed low-dose ICS + formoterol or
low-dose ICS taken whenever SABA is taken

↓ + ICS controller

Step 2 (Mild Persistent Asthma)

Daily low-dose ICS or
as-needed low-dose ICS + formoterol*

↓ + LABA or daily dosing

Step 3 (Moderate Persistent Asthma)

Low-dose ICS + LABA

↓ ↑ ICS dose

Step 4 (Severe Persistent Asthma)

Medium-dose ICS + LABA**

↓ ↑ ICS dose

Step 5 (Severe Persistent Asthma)

High-dose ICS + LABA, refer for further assessment***

**Alternative treatment: LTRA, or low-dose ICS taken whenever SABA is taken*
***Alternative treatment: high-dose ICS, add on tiotropium or LTRA*
****Consider adding: tiotropium, oral steroid, omalizumab for patients with severe allergic asthma or mepolizumab, reslizumab, benralizumab or dupilumab for patients with severe eosinophilic asthma*

BETA-2 AGONISTS

These medications bind to beta-2 receptors, causing relaxation of bronchial smooth muscle, which leads to bronchodilation. SABAs are used as needed (rescue therapy) for acute asthma symptoms. Traditionally, they were used as monotherapy in Step 1 of treatment in low-risk patients, but due to increased risk of exacerbations they are no longer recommended this way. SABAs can still be considered for use with an ICS for patients in Step 1, and as a rescue option in later steps of therapy. They can also be used for other reversible airway diseases, such as colds, allergies and bronchitis.

LABAs are used as part of maintenance therapy beginning in Step 3 of treatment and only in combination with an ICS. If not already part of the patient regimen, a LABA should be added to medium-dose ICS before increasing to high-dose ICS, as this leads to more rapid improvement in symptoms, lung function and a reduction in exacerbations.

DRUG	DOSING	SAFETY/SIDE EFFECTS/MONITORING
Short-Acting Beta-2 Agonists (SABAs)		
Albuterol (*ProAir HFA, ProAir RespiClick, Proventil HFA, Ventolin HFA,* *ProAir Digihaler*) 90 mcg/inh, 0.5% and 0.083% nebulizer solution, syrup	MDI/DPI: 1-2 inhalations Q4-6H PRN Nebulizer: 1.25-5 mg Q4-8H PRN PO forms are available but not recommended	**WARNINGS** Caution in CVD, glaucoma, hyperthyroidism, seizures, diabetes **SIDE EFFECTS** Nervousness, tremor, tachycardia, palpitations, cough, hyperglycemia, ↓ K **MONITORING** Number of days of SABA use, symptom frequency, peak flow, pulmonary function tests, BP, HR, blood glucose, K **NOTES** MDIs (HFA products): shake well before use Levalbuterol contains R-isomer of albuterol Epinephrine inhaler is FDA-approved for mild symptoms in intermittent asthma only. Not discussed in guidelines. Most albuterol inhalers contain 200 inhalations/canister; the exception is *Ventolin HFA* which is available as both a 200 inhalations/canister and 60 inhalations/canister EIB: use 2 inhalations 5 minutes prior to exercise
Levalbuterol (*Xopenex, Xopenex Concentrate, Xopenex HFA*) 45 mcg/inh, nebulizer solution	MDI: 1-2 inhalations Q4-6H PRN Nebulizer: 0.63-1.25 mg Q6-8H PRN (max = 1.25 mg three times daily)	
Racepinephrine (*Asthmanefrin Refill*) OTC	Should not be used since it is non-selective	
Epinephrine (*Primatene Mist*) OTC	MDI: 1-2 inhalations Q4H PRN (max = 8 inhalations/day)	
Long-Acting Beta-2 Agonists (LABAs)		
Salmeterol (*Serevent Diskus*) 50 mcg/inh	DPI: 1 inhalation BID	Side effects and monitoring are the same as SABAs plus: **BOXED WARNING** ↑ risk of asthma-related deaths, should only be used in asthma patients who are currently receiving but are not adequately controlled on a long-term asthma control medication (an inhaled corticosteroid) ↑ risk of asthma-related hospitalizations in pediatric and adolescent patients **NOTES** Maintenance inhaler only; not for acute bronchospasm

INHALED CORTICOSTEROIDS

Corticosteroids inhibit the inflammatory response. They block the late-phase reaction to the allergen, reduce airway hyper-responsiveness, and are potent and effective anti-inflammatory medications. ICSs reduce symptoms, increase lung function, improve quality of life and reduce the risk of exacerbations. They are used as-needed in combination with formoterol for rescue treatment with acute symptoms, and individually or in combination for maintenance/controller treatment.

DRUG	DOSING	SAFETY/SIDE EFFECTS/MONITORING
Beclomethasone *(QVAR RediHaler,* *QVAR)** 40, 80 mcg/inh	MDI: 1-4 inhalations BID	**CONTRAINDICATIONS** Primary treatment of status asthmaticus or acute episodes of asthma **WARNINGS** High doses for prolonged periods of time can cause adrenal suppression, ↑ risk of fractures, growth retardation (in children) and immunosuppression **SIDE EFFECTS (INHALED)** Dysphonia (difficulty speaking), oral candidiasis (thrush), cough, headache, hoarseness, URTIs, hyperglycemia **MONITORING** Use of SABA/rescue inhaler, symptom frequency, peak flow, growth (children/adolescents) and signs/symptoms of hypothalamic-pituitary-adrenal (HPA) axis suppression/adrenal insufficiency, signs/symptoms of oral candidiasis, bone mineral density **NOTES** To prevent oral candidiasis, rinse mouth and throat with warm water and spit out after each use, or use a spacer device if using a MDI *Alvesco* is an MDI that does not need to be shaken before use Budesonide is the only ICS available as a nebulized solution; used commonly in young children Only use *Pulmicort Respules* with a jet nebulizer machine that is connected to an air compressor; do not use an ultrasonic nebulizer *QVAR RediHaler* is a breath-activated aerosol that acts as a cross between a DPI and MDI; inhalation releases aerosolized medication - no shaking, priming, activation or spacer needed
Budesonide ***Pulmicort Flexhaler*** 90, 180 mcg/inh ***Pulmicort Respules*** nebulizer suspension **+ formoterol *(Symbicort)***	 DPI: 1-4 inhalations BID 0.25-0.5 mg daily or BID in children age 1-8 years	
Ciclesonide *(Alvesco)* 80, 160 mcg/inh	MDI: 1-2 inhalations BID	
Fluticasone ***Flovent HFA:*** 44, 110, 220 mcg/inh ***Flovent Diskus:*** 50, 100, 250 mcg/inh ***Arnuity Ellipta:*** 100, 200 mcg/inh **+ salmeterol *(Advair Diskus, Advair HFA,*** *AirDuo RespiClick, Wixela Inhub)* **+ vilanterol *(Breo Ellipta)***	 MDI: 2 inhalations BID DPI: 1-2 inhalations BID DPI: 1-2 inhalations daily	
Mometasone *Asmanex HFA:* 100, 200 mcg/inh *Asmanex Twisthaler:* 110, 220 mcg/inh **+ formoterol *(Dulera)***	 MDI: 1-2 inhalations BID DPI: 1-2 inhalations daily	

**Brand discontinued but name still used in practice.*

Categorization of Daily Dosages for Inhaled Corticosteroids

DRUG	LOW DAILY DOSE	MEDIUM DAILY DOSE	HIGH DAILY DOSE
Beclomethasone MDI 40 or 80 mcg/inh	80-240 mcg	> 240-480 mcg	> 480 mcg
Budesonide DPI 90 or 180 mcg/inh	180-540 mcg	> 600-1,080 mcg	> 1,080 mcg
Ciclesonide MDI 80, 160 mcg/inh	160-320 mcg	> 320-640 mcg	> 640 mcg
Fluticasone MDI: 44, 110, or 220 mcg/inh DPI: 50, 100, or 250 mcg/inh	 88-264 mcg 100-300 mcg	 > 264-440 mcg > 300-500 mcg	 > 440 mcg > 500 mcg
Mometasone MDI: 100 or 200 mcg/inh DPI: 110 or 220 mcg/inh	 200 mcg 110-220 mcg	 400 mcg > 220-440 mcg	 > 400 mcg > 440 mcg

CONTROLLER (MAINTENANCE) INHALERS

There are many inhaled products available to treat respiratory conditions. This can create confusion in terms of proper use for specific disease states. The table below categorizes the different classes of controller medications for asthma and chronic obstructive pulmonary disease (COPD). <u>ICS and ICS/LABA</u> combinations are <u>preferred for asthma</u>, whereas <u>LABA, LAMA or LAMA/LABA</u> combinations are <u>preferred for COPD</u>. Some ICS/LABA combinations are approved for COPD and can be used in select patients (see COPD chapter for treatment recommendations).

Combination inhalers increase adherence to treatment which improves disease control. Combination ICS/LABA products are considered to be safer for asthma, as they reduce the risk of using a LABA alone. Because of this, combination ICS/LABA inhalers do not have the boxed warning for asthma related deaths that LABA alone have. Note that this table does not include short-acting (rescue) medications.

DRUG CLASS	ASTHMA	COPD
ICS	**Beclomethasone *(QVAR RediHaler)*** **Budesonide *(Pulmicort Flexhaler)*** **Fluticasone *(Flovent HFA, Flovent Diskus, Arnuity Ellipta)*** Ciclesonide *(Alvesco)* Flunisolide *(Aerospan)* Mometasone *(Asmanex HFA, Asmanex Twisthaler)*	No single ICS product is FDA-approved for COPD
LABA	**Salmeterol** *(Serevent Diskus)*	**Salmeterol** *(Serevent Diskus)* Formoterol *(Perforomist* – nebulizer) Indacaterol *(Arcapta Neohaler)* Arformoterol *(Brovana)* Olodaterol *(Striverdi Respimat)*
LAMA	**Tiotropium** *(Spiriva Respimat* only)	**Tiotropium *(Spiriva HandiHaler, Spiriva Respimat)*** Aclidinium *(Tudorza Pressair)* Glycopyrrolate *(Seebri Neohaler, Lonhala Magnair* – nebulizer) Revefenacin *(Yupelri* – nebulizer) Umeclidinium *(Incruse Ellipta)*
ICS/LABA	**Budesonide/formoterol *(Symbicort)*** **Fluticasone/salmeterol** ***(Advair Diskus, Advair HFA,*** *AirDuo RespiClick, Wixela Inhub)* **Mometasone/formoterol *(Dulera)*** **Fluticasone/vilanterol *(Breo Ellipta)***	**Budesonide/formoterol *(Symbicort)*** **Fluticasone/salmeterol** ***(Advair Diskus,*** *Wixela Inhub)* **Fluticasone/vilanterol *(Breo Ellipta)***
LAMA/LABA	No combination LAMA/LABA products are FDA-approved for asthma	Aclidinium/formoterol *(Duaklir Pressair)* Glycopyrrolate/formoterol *(Bevespi Aerosphere)* Glycopyrrolate/indacaterol *(Utibron Neohaler)* Tiotropium/olodaterol *(Stiolto Respimat)* Umeclidinium/vilanterol *(Anoro Ellipta)*
LAMA/LABA/ ICS	No combination LAMA/LABA/ICS products are FDA-approved for asthma	Umeclidinium/vilanterol/fluticasone *(Trelegy Ellipta)*

RECOGNIZING AND UNDERSTANDING INHALED DELIVERY DEVICES

Inhaled devices come as metered-dose inhalers (MDIs) or dry powder inhalers (DPIs), including breath-actuated DPIs. Recognizing the type of inhaler is important. It impacts the technique the patient needs to use and how they should be educated (see Patient Self-Management and Education section).

MDIs AND DPIs

MDIs

- Brand name identifiers:
  - *HFA*, *Respimat* or no suffix (e.g., *Alvesco*)
- Deliver a dose of aerosolized liquid medication
- Some use a propellant (HFA)
- Administration requires a slow and deep inhalation at the same time as pressing the canister to deliver the dose
- A spacer can be used for patients who cannot coordinate breathing in at the same time they are pressing the canister
- Shake well in most cases; exceptions are:
  - *QVAR RediHaler*, *Alvesco* and *Respimat* products

DPIs

- Brand name identifiers:
  - *Diskus, Ellipta, Pressair, Handihaler, Neohaler, RespiClick, Flexhaler*
- Deliver a dose of fine powdered medication
- No propellant
- Administration requires a quick and forceful inhalation (no need to press anything at the same time)
- Spacers cannot be used, the drug is delivered by the breath and no coordination is needed
- Do not shake
- No priming needed, except for *Flexhaler* (prior to first use)

Note: QVAR RediHaler is a breath-activated aerosol, which has characteristics of both a DPI and MDI (see ICS table)

LEUKOTRIENE MODIFYING AGENTS

Leukotriene receptor antagonists (LTRAs) inhibit leukotriene mediators of airway inflammation. This reduces airway edema, constriction and inflammation. Montelukast inhibits leukotriene D4 (LTD4), while zafirlukast inhibits both LTD4 and LTE4. Zileuton, a 5-lipoxygenase inhibitor, inhibits leukotriene formation.

DRUG	DOSING	SAFETY/SIDE EFFECTS/MONITORING
Montelukast (*Singulair*) Tablet, chewable tablet, packet	10 mg daily in the evening Age 6-14 years: 5 mg daily in the evening Age 1-5 years: 4 mg daily in the evening	**CONTRAINDICATIONS** Zafirlukast and zileuton: hepatic impairment **WARNINGS** Neuropsychiatric events; monitor for signs of aggressive behavior, hostility, agitation, hallucinations, depression, suicidal thinking Systemic eosinophilia, sometimes presenting with features of vasculitis consistent with Churg-Strauss syndrome (rare) **SIDE EFFECTS** Headache, dizziness, abdominal pain, ↑ LFTs, URTIs **MONITORING** LFTs (zafirlukast and zileuton), mood or behavior changes (montelukast) **NOTES** Montelukast granules: can be administered directly in the mouth, dissolved in a small amount (5 mL) of breast milk or formula, or mixed with a spoonful of applesauce, carrots, rice or Ice cream; do not mix with anything else and use within 15 minutes of opening the packet Zafirlukast: protect from moisture and light; dispense in original container
Zafirlukast (*Accolate*)	20 mg BID Age 5-11 years: 10 mg BID Take 1 hr before or 2 hrs after meals (empty stomach)	
Zileuton (*Zyflo*, *Zyflo CR*)	*Zyflo*: 600 mg QID *Zyflo CR*: 1,200 mg BID within 1 hour after morning and evening meals (with food) Age < 12 years: not recommended	

Leukotriene Modifying Agents Drug Interactions

- Montelukast is a minor substrate of CYP450 3A4 and 2C8/9, and a weak inhibitor of CYP2C8/9. Gemfibrozil can ↑ levels of montelukast and lumacaftor can ↓ levels of montelukast.
- Zafirlukast is a major substrate of CYP2C9; it also inhibits CYP2C8 (weak) and 2C9 (moderate). Zafirlukast can ↑ levels of theophylline, warfarin and other CYP2C9 substrates. Levels of zafirlukast can be ↓ by erythromycin and theophylline.
- Zileuton is a minor substrate of CYP1A2, 2C9, and 3A4, and a weak inhibitor of CYP1A2. It can ↑ levels of pimozide, propranolol, theophylline, and warfarin.

THEOPHYLLINE

Theophylline blocks phosphodiesterase, causing an increase in cyclic adenosine monophosphate (cAMP) and release of epinephrine from adrenal medulla cells. This results in bronchodilation, but it also causes diuresis, CNS and cardiac stimulation and gastric acid secretion. Use of theophylline is limited by ↓ effectiveness, drug interactions and adverse effects.

DRUG	DOSING	SAFETY/SIDE EFFECTS/MONITORING
Theophylline *(Elixophyllin, Theo-24, Theochron)* ER Capsule, ER tablet, elixir, oral solution, injection Active metabolites are caffeine and 3-methylxanthine Aminophylline contains 80% theophylline	Oral LD: 5 mg/kg IBW (or TBW if it is less than IBW) Oral maintenance dose: 300-600 mg daily Therapeutic range: 5-15 mcg/mL (measure peak level at steady state, after 3 days of oral dosing)	**WARNINGS** Caution in patients with cardiovascular disease, hyperthyroidism, PUD and seizure disorder (use can exacerbate these conditions) **SIDE EFFECTS** Nausea, vomiting, headache, ↑ HR, insomnia, tremor and nervousness Signs of toxicity: persistent vomiting, arrhythmias, seizures **MONITORING** Theophylline levels, HR, CNS effects, use of rescue inhaler **NOTES** To convert aminophylline to theophylline, multiply by 0.8*; to convert theophylline to aminophylline, divide by 0.8 **Remember*: ATM (Aminophylline → Theophylline Multiply)

Theophylline Drug Interactions

Theophylline is a major substrate of CYP1A2 and a minor substrate of CYP3A4 and 2E1. It has saturable kinetics (first order kinetics, followed by zero order kinetics); in the higher end of the therapeutic range, small increases in dose can result in a large increase in theophylline concentration (see Pharmacokinetics chapter).

- Drugs that can ↑ theophylline levels due to CYP1A2 inhibition include: cimetidine, ciprofloxacin, fluvoxamine, propranolol, zafirlukast and zileuton.
- Drugs that can ↑ theophylline levels due to CYP3A4 inhibition include: clarithromycin and erythromycin.
- Drugs and conditions that can ↑ theophylline levels due to other mechanisms: alcohol, allopurinol, disulfiram, estrogen-containing oral contraceptives, methotrexate, pentoxifylline, propafenone, verapamil. Acute pulmonary edema, CHF, cirrhosis or liver disease, cor-pulmonale, fever, hypothyroidism and shock can decrease theophylline clearance.
- Drugs and conditions that can ↓ theophylline levels: carbamazepine, fosphenytoin, phenobarbital, phenytoin, primidone, rifampin, ritonavir, tobacco/marijuana smoking, St. John's wort, levothyroxine, high-protein diet and charbroiled meats. Hyperthyroidism and cystic fibrosis can increase theophylline clearance.
- Theophylline will ↓ lithium (by ↑ renal excretion of lithium) and will ↓ zafirlukast.

ANTICHOLINERGICS

Anticholinergics inhibit muscarinic cholinergic receptors and reduce the intrinsic vagal tone of the airway, leading to bronchodilation. Short-acting anticholinergics (e.g., ipratropium) are sometimes used in combination with SABAs in hospitalized patients experiencing an acute exacerbation. A long-acting anticholinergic, tiotropium *(Spiriva Respimat)*, is FDA-approved for asthma in patients 6 years of age and older with a history of exacerbations despite ICS/LABA therapy. Refer to the COPD chapter for more information on anticholinergics.

OMALIZUMAB *(XOLAIR)*

Omalizumab is a monoclonal antibody that inhibits IgE binding to the IgE receptor on mast cells and basophils. It is indicated for moderate to severe persistent, allergic asthma in patients 6 years of age and older if a skin test to a perennial allergen is positive and symptom control on inhaled corticosteroids is inadequate (Step 5 or 6 treatment).

DRUG	DOSING	SAFETY/SIDE EFFECTS/MONITORING
Omalizumab *(Xolair)*	Given SC every 2 or 4 weeks Dose and frequency based on pretreatment total IgE serum levels and body weight; adjust dose during treatment if significant changes in body weight occur Administer in a healthcare setting under medical supervision Doses > 150 mg should be divided over more than one injection site	**BOXED WARNING** Anaphylaxis has occurred as early as after the first dose but also has occurred beyond 1 year after beginning treatment. Closely observe patients after administration and be prepared to manage anaphylaxis that can be life-threatening **WARNINGS** Slight ↑ risk of serious cardiovascular and cerebrovascular adverse events, malignancies have been observed in clinical studies (rare) **SIDE EFFECTS** Injection site reactions, arthralgias, pain, dizziness, fatigue **MONITORING** Baseline IgE, FEV1, peak flow, s/sx of anaphylaxis and infection

INTERLEUKIN RECEPTOR ANTAGONISTS

Interleukin is a cytokine responsible for the growth, differentiation, recruitment, activation and survival of eosinophils (a cell type associated with inflammation and an important component in the cause of some types of asthma). Monoclonal antibodies can be used to inhibit interleukin from binding to receptors. Mepolizumab, reslizumab and benralizumab are IL-5 receptor antagonists, and dupilumab is an IL-4 and IL-3 receptor antagonist. All are indicated for management of severe asthma with an eosinophilic phenotype. When used, they should be added to maintenance inhaler treatment.

Mepolizumab *(Nucala)*

Mepolizumab is indicated in patients ≥ 12 years of age and given SC once every four weeks. Side effects are minor (headache and injection site reactions).

Reslizumab *(Cinqair)*

Reslizumab is indicated in adult patients only, and is given IV once every four weeks. Reslizumab has a boxed warning for anaphylaxis that can be life-threatening; after administration, patients should be observed by a healthcare professional who is able to manage anaphylaxis.

Benralizumab *(Fasenra)*

Benralizumab is indicated for patients ≥ 12 years of age and given SC once every four weeks x three doses, then every eight weeks. Side effects are minor.

Dupilumab *(Dupixent)*

Dupilumab is indicated for patients ≥ 12 years of age and given SC every other week.

SPECIAL SITUATIONS

EXERCISE-INDUCED BRONCHOSPASM: *PREVENT IT*

SABAs are preferred to prevent most EIB. They are taken 5 – 15 minutes before exercise and last 2 – 3 hours. If a longer duration of symptom control is needed, salmeterol (a LABA), can be taken 30 minutes before exercise. If the patient is using a LABA for asthma maintenance, they should not use additional doses for EIB. LABAs should never be used alone for persistent asthma.

Montelukast is taken two hours prior to exercise and lasts up to 24 hours. It is effective in only 50% of patients. Patients taking montelukast for asthma, or any another indication, should not take an additional dose to prevent EIB.

EIB is often a marker of inadequate asthma control. It might be necessary to start or increase a controller medication (e.g., increasing the ICS dose) to control the EIB.

PREGNANCY: *KEEP CONTROL*

Asthma control can worsen during pregnancy. To ensure oxygen supply to the fetus, it is safer to treat asthma with medications than to have poorly controlled asthma. Down-titration of medications is not recommended and exacerbations should be treated aggressively. A short-acting beta-agonist is a must. ICS are preferred controllers, typically budesonide.

EXAM SCENARIO
SG is a 35-year-old female with asthma. She brings a prescription for *Advair Diskus* to the pharmacy and requests a refill on her *ProAir RespiClick*. You review her medication refill history and see that she filled prescriptions for *Pulmicort Flexhaler* 3 weeks ago and *ProAir RespiClick* approximately 2 months ago.

SG tells you that she is stopping her *Pulmicort Flexhaler* and starting the *Advair Diskus* instead. She says she uses her *ProAir RespiClick* about 3 times a day, on at least 3 days of the week. She feels like she cannot have as active of a social life as she would like, due to asthma attacks.

How would you assess SG's asthma control?
SG is not well controlled, as she uses her SABA inhaler *(ProAir RespiClick)* more than 2 days a week and has limitations to normal activity.

Is the change in treatment appropriate?
A step up in treatment is needed. The change from an ICS to an ICS/LABA combination product is appropriate.

What counseling points about her treatment are important for SG?

- See specific instructions for inhaler technique later in the chapter.
- Use *Advair Diskus* twice daily to help control asthma symptoms. It is not a rescue medication.
- Rinse the mouth and spit after each dose of *Advair Diskus* to prevent thrush (an infection in the mouth).
- Use *ProAir Respiclick* as needed for shortness of breath. Using it more than twice weekly means asthma is not well controlled. If *ProAir Respiclick* is used too often, it can cause palpitations, nervousness or tremor.
- Monitor the counter on the *ProAir Respiclick* to make sure it does not run out before the next refill.
- Avoid triggers known to make asthma worse.

PATIENT SELF-MANAGEMENT AND EDUCATION

INHALERS

Most patients (up to 80%) cannot use their inhaler correctly, which results in little or no medication reaching the lungs. This contributes to poor symptom control and increased exacerbations. Patient counseling and assessing inhaler technique is essential. Up to 50% of adults and children do not take their controller medications as prescribed. Many times, this is unintentional and due to a lack of education, cost or forgetfulness. Assessing adherence is important when evaluating asthma control.

Patients should be aware of how to monitor the doses remaining in an inhaler. Some inhalers have an internal dose counter. Most controller inhalers are designed to last one month when the patient is adherent to therapy. SABA rescue inhalers can last a varying amount of time depending on use, but for a patient with good asthma control, an albuterol inhaler should last about 12 months (or 3 - 4 months for the smaller *Ventolin HFA* inhaler with 60 inhalations/canister). It is useful for patients to know when the inhaler should run out. Refer to the table below for examples of the number of days that commonly used inhalers will last.

DRUG	INHALATIONS	EXAMPLE DOSAGE	SUPPLY
Maintenance Inhalers			
Advair Diskus	60	1 inhalation BID	30 days (60/2 inhalations daily)
QVAR RediHaler	120	1-2 inhalations BID	30 days (120/4 inhalations daily)
Asmanex Twisthaler	60	2 inhalations daily	30 days (60/2 inhalations daily)
SABA Rescue Inhalers			
Albuterol MDI	200	2 inhalations per dose, used twice weekly (4 inhalations/week)	50 weeks (200/4 inhalations weekly)
Ventolin HFA	60		15 weeks (60/4 inhalations weekly)

General Guidance

If prescribed > 1 inhalation of medication at a time, the patient should wait 60 seconds between each one. If using more than one inhaler, the sequence of inhalers is important. Bronchodilators (beta-2 agonists and anticholinergics) work faster than inhaled corticosteroids. Using bronchodilators first will allow the airways to open quickly and the inhaled corticosteroid will be able to travel deeper into the lungs.

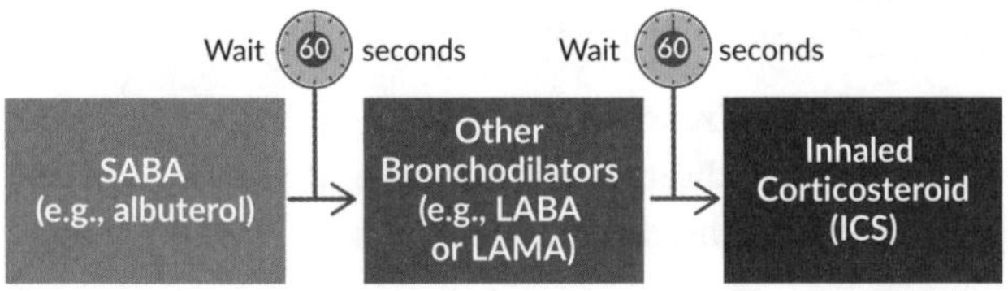

©RxPrep

NEBULIZERS

A nebulizer is a device that turns liquid medication into a fine mist. The fine mist can be inhaled through a face mask or mouthpiece and into the lungs. Nebulizers use natural breathing, making medication delivery easy for infants, children and the elderly. There are two types of nebulizers: jet nebulizers and ultrasound nebulizers. Check the medication information to see which nebulizer device is indicated.

Albuterol comes as a nebulized solution in both unit dose packaging and in a 20 mL vial. The two common concentrations are 0.083% solution, containing 2.5 mg/3 mL, and a 0.5% solution, containing 2.5 mg/0.5 mL. The 0.083% solution is a ready-to-use preparation that can be placed directly into the nebulizer; no dilution is required. The 0.5% concentrated solution must be diluted with 2.5 mL of normal saline prior to use.

SPACERS

Spacer is a generic term for different types of open tubes that are placed between the mouthpiece of an MDI and the mouth of the patient to help with medication delivery. Spacers are used for children and in anyone with dexterity issues (i.e., difficulty pressing down and breathing in at the same time with an MDI). Spacers reduce the risk of thrush (see Study Tip Gal). They should never be used with a DPI. Clean spacers at least once a week (in warm, soapy water).

WITH A SPACER, MORE DRUG GETS INTO THE LUNGS

Spacers are helpful for children and anyone that has difficulty with hand-breath coordination (e.g., pressing down on the inhaler while breathing in at the same time) with an MDI. Plus, spacers reduce the risk of thrush from steroid inhalers.

Common spacers: *AeroChamber, OptiHaler, OptiChamber*

PEAK FLOW METERS

Peak flow meters are handheld devices that measure the peak expiratory flow rate (PEFR). The PEFR is the maximum flow rate from a forceful exhalation, starting from fully inflated lungs. The patient's best PEFR is called their personal best (PB), which can be measured by spirometry. The measurement takes into account the patient's height, gender and age because the PEFR depends on the muscular strength of the patient. Patients can measure their PB themselves by taking peak flow readings twice a day (morning and evening) for 2 – 3 weeks when asthma is in good control. The highest reading that occurs most frequently is the PB.

Peak flow meters are beneficial in patients with frequent asthma exacerbations, persistent asthma (Step 3 - 6), poor perception of airflow obstruction and unexplained response to environmental factors. When used correctly, peak flow meters can identify exacerbations early (even before the patient is symptomatic), allowing treatment to begin sooner.

An asthma action plan is developed by the healthcare provider so the patient knows how to manage symptoms at home and avoid hospitalizations due to an exacerbation. This is done by taking the patient's PB and outlining "zones" of control (based on the percentage of their PB). Each "zone" is then given a specific action to follow (see example on the next page).

Peak Flow Meter Technique

- Use the peak flow meter every morning upon awakening and before the use of any asthma medications. Proper technique and best effort are essential. Less than the best effort can lead to taking unnecessary medication.
- Move the indicator to the bottom of the numbered scale. Stand up straight. Exhale comfortably.
- Inhale as deeply as possible. Place lips firmly around the mouthpiece, creating a tight seal.
- Blow out as hard and as fast as possible. Write down the PEFR.
- Repeat steps two more times, with enough rest in between. Record the highest value.
- Compare the peak flow value to your personal asthma action and follow the steps as instructed.

Peak Flow Meter Care

- Always use the same brand of peak flow meter.
- Clean at least once a week using warm water and mild soap; if you have an infection, clean the meter more frequently. Rinse gently; do not use brushes to clean the inside of the peak flow meter. Do not place peak flow meters in boiling water. Allow the meter to air dry before using again.

ZONES OF AN ASTHMA ACTION PLAN

Green zone (> 80-100% of personal best)
- Indicates "all clear" - good control
- Patients are instructed to follow routine maintenance plan

Yellow zone (50-80% of personal best)
- Indicates "caution" - worsening lung function
- Patient-specific intervention required (action plan) - usually an increase in rescue inhaler use and the addition or increase of other medications

Red zone (< 50% of personal best)
- Indicates "medical alert" - seek medical attention
- Action plan includes using rescue inhaler, possibly steroids and going to the emergency department

SAMPLE ASTHMA ACTION PLAN (ADULT)

Asthma Action Plan

For: ______________________ Doctor: ______________________ Date: ______________

Doctor's Phone Number ______________________ Hospital/Emergency Department Phone Number ______________________

GREEN ZONE

Doing Well

- No cough, wheeze, chest tightness, or shortness of breath during the day or night
- Can do usual activities

And, if a peak flow meter is used,

Peak flow: more than ________
(80 percent or more of my best peak flow)

My best peak flow is: ________

Take these long-term control medicines each day (include an anti-inflammatory).

Medicine	How much to take	When to take it

Before exercise	❐ ________	❐ 2 or ❐ 4 puffs ________	5 minutes before exercise

YELLOW ZONE

Asthma is Getting Worse

- Cough, wheeze, chest tightness, or shortness of breath, or
- Waking at night due to asthma, or
- Can do some, but not all, usual activities

-Or-

Peak flow: ________ to ________
(50 to 79 percent of my best peak flow)

First **Add: quick-relief medicine—and keep taking your GREEN ZONE medicine.**

________ (short-acting beta$_2$-agonist) ❐ 2 or ❐ 4 puffs, every 20 minutes for up to 1 hour
❐ Nebulizer, once

Second **If your symptoms (and peak flow, if used) return to GREEN ZONE after 1 hour of above treatment:**
❐ Continue monitoring to be sure you stay in the green zone.

-Or-

If your symptoms (and peak flow, if used) do not return to GREEN ZONE after 1 hour of above treatment:
❐ Take: ________ (short-acting beta$_2$-agonist) ❐ 2 or ❐ 4 puffs or ❐ Nebulizer
❐ Add: ________ (oral steroid) mg per day For ________ (3–10) days
❐ Call the doctor ❐ before/ ❐ within ________ hours after taking the oral steroid.

RED ZONE

Medical Alert!

- Very short of breath, or
- Quick-relief medicines have not helped, or
- Cannot do usual activities, or
- Symptoms are same or get worse after 24 hours in Yellow Zone

-Or-

Peak flow: less than ________
(50 percent of my best peak flow)

Take this medicine:

❐ ________ (short-acting beta$_2$-agonist) ❐ 4 or ❐ 6 puffs or ❐ Nebulizer

❐ ________ (oral steroid) mg

Then call your doctor NOW. Go to the hospital or call an ambulance if:
- You are still in the red zone after 15 minutes AND
- You have not reached your doctor.

DANGER SIGNS

- **Trouble walking and talking due to shortness of breath**
- **Lips or fingernails are blue**
- **Take ❐ 4 or ❐ 6 puffs of your quick-relief medicine AND**
- **Go to the hospital or call for an ambulance ________ (phone) NOW!**

See the reverse side for things you can do to avoid your asthma triggers.

www.nhlbi.nih.gov

EXAM SCENARIO

ES is a 29-year-old male with asthma. He comes into the pharmacy asking for help interpreting his peak flow readings. He states that he feels fine, but is worried that his peak flow readings are declining. ES is able to demonstrate appropriate use of the peak flow meter, and reports that he has been checking at the appropriate time (first thing in the morning, before medications, and taking the best of three readings). His personal best (PB) is 480 mL, and his readings from the last few days are as follows:

Monday: 400 mL (83% PB)
Tuesday: 388 mL (81% PB)
Wednesday: 420 mL (88% PB)

What zone is ES in?

ES is in the green zone. All readings fall within 80-100% of his personal best.

What steps should ES take today?

ES should be advised to follow the instructions in his specific asthma action plan. Make sure this is filled out to include his medications (rescue and maintenance) and personal range of each zone:

- Green Zone (> 80%) = > 384 mL
- Yellow Zone (50 – 80%) = 240 mL – 384 mL
- Red Zone (< 50%) = < 240 mL

Since he feels well and his peak flow readings are in the green zone, he should continue his maintenance medications. His action plan might include using albuterol prior to exercise. For anyone with asthma, it is important to avoid triggers and monitor for symptoms, regardless of peak flow readings.

PATIENT COUNSELING

SELECT METERED-DOSE INHALERS

Ventolin HFA, ProAir HFA, Symbicort, Flovent HFA, Dulera, Others

STEP 1

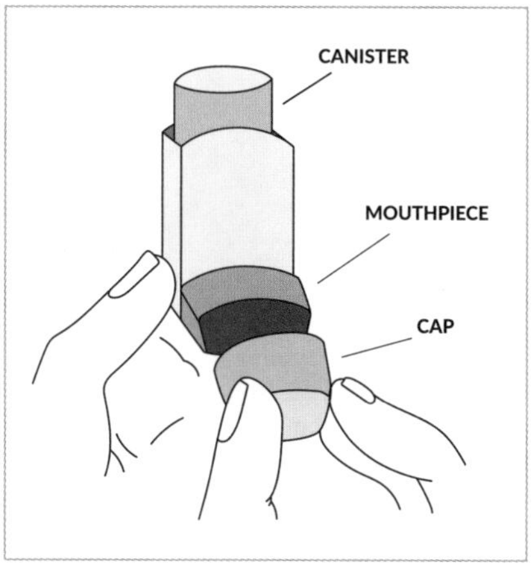

Make sure the canister is fully inserted into the actuator (if it comes separately). Always use the actuator that came with the canister. Shake the inhaler well for 5 seconds immediately before each spray (except for *QVAR RediHaler* or *Alvesco*, which do not need to be shaken). Remove cap from the mouthpiece and check mouthpiece for foreign objects prior to use.

STEP 2

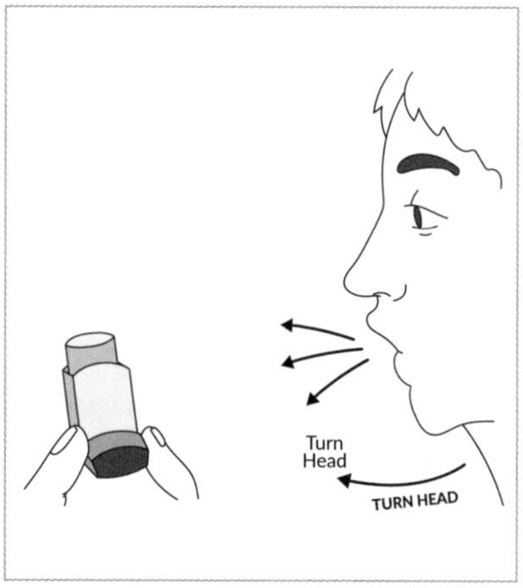

Breathe out fully through your mouth expelling as much air from your lungs as possible. Holding the inhaler upright (as shown in the picture), place the mouthpiece into your mouth and close your lips around it.

STEP 3

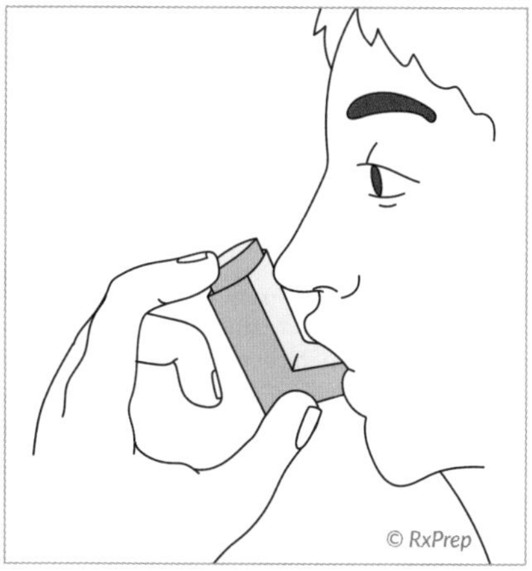

While breathing in slowly and deeply through your mouth, press the top of the canister all the way down with your index finger. Right after the spray comes out, take your finger off the canister. After you have inhaled all the way, take the inhaler out of your mouth and close your mouth. Hold your breath as long as possible, up to 10 seconds, then breathe normally. If another inhalation is needed, wait 1 minute and repeat Steps 1-3. Place cap back on the mouthpiece after use.

TO PRIME	TO CLEAN
Ventolin HFA, ProAir HFA Spray 4 times (3 for *ProAir*) away from the face, shaking between sprays. Prime again if > 14 days from last use or if you drop it.	***Ventolin HFA, ProAir HFA*** To prevent medication buildup and blockage, remove the metal canister (do not let this get wet) and rinse the mouthpiece only under warm running water for 30 seconds, then turn upside down and rinse under warm water for another 30 seconds. Shake to remove excess water and let air dry. Clean at least weekly.
Flovent HFA, Dulera Spray 4 times away from the face, shaking between sprays. Prime again with just 1 spray if > 7 days from last use (> 5 days for *Dulera*).	***Flovent HFA*** Use a clean cotton swab dampened with water to clean the small circular opening where the medication sprays out. Gently twist the swab in a circular motion to remove any medication buildup. Do not take the canister out of the plastic actuator. Wipe the inside of the mouthpiece with a damp tissue. Let air dry overnight.
Symbicort Spray 2 times away from the face, shaking between sprays. Prime again if > 7 days from last use.	***Symbicort, Dulera*** Wipe the inside and outside of the mouthpiece opening with a clean, dry cloth. Do not put into water.

SELECT DRY POWDER INHALERS

Advair Diskus

STEP 1

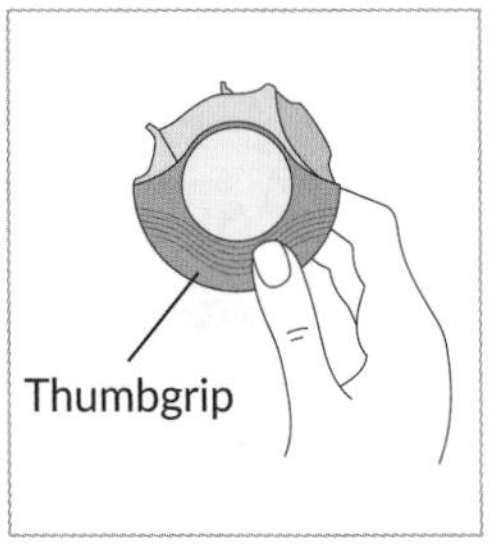

Hold the *Diskus* in your left hand and put the thumb of your right hand in the thumb grip. Push the thumb grip away from you as far as it will go until the mouthpiece appears and the *Diskus* snaps into position.

STEP 2

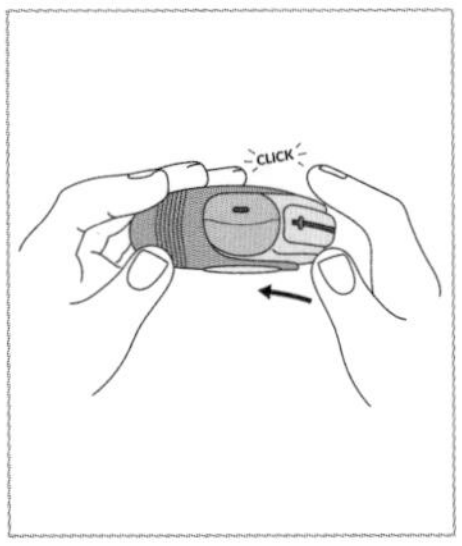

Hold the *Diskus* in a level, flat position with the mouthpiece towards you. Slide the lever away from the mouthpiece until it clicks.

STEP 3

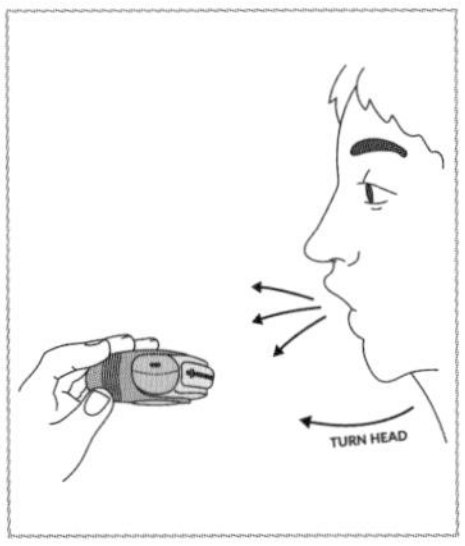

Before using, breathe out fully while holding the *Diskus* away from your mouth. Do not tilt the *Diskus*.

STEP 4

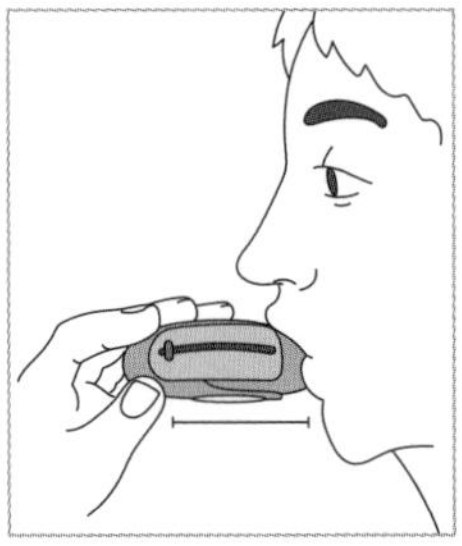

Put the mouthpiece to your lips. Breathe in quickly and deeply through the inhaler. Do not breathe in through your nose. Remove the *Diskus* from your mouth and hold your breath as long as possible, up to 10 seconds. Then, breathe out slowly.

STEP 5

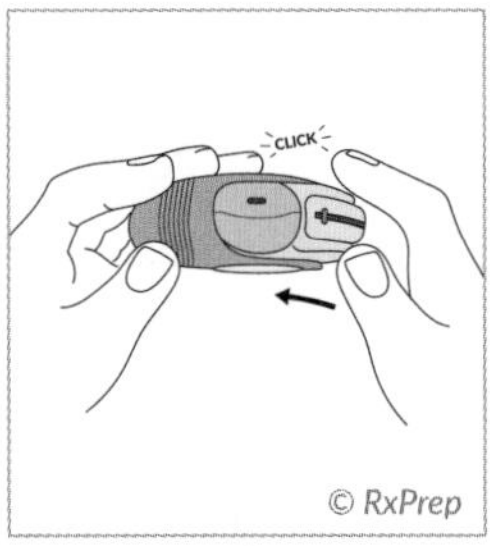

Close the *Diskus* by putting your thumb in the thumb grip and sliding it as far back towards you as it will go, until the *Diskus* clicks shut. Rinse your mouth with water and spit out the water to prevent thrush. Do not swallow the water.

TO CLEAN
Do not wash the *Diskus*. Store in a dry place.

Pulmicort Flexhaler

STEP 1

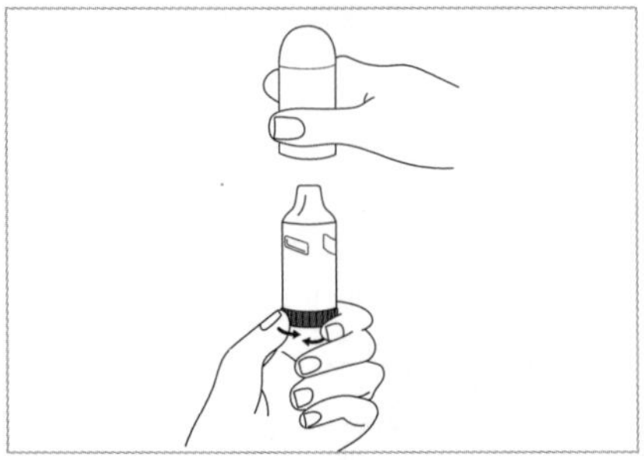

Twist off the white cover. Holding the middle of the inhaler with one hand, twist the brown base fully in one direction as far as it will go with the other hand. Twist it fully back again in the other direction as far as it will go. You will hear a "click" during one of the twisting movements. The dose is now loaded. Do not shake the inhaler after it is loaded. (Of note, only one dose is loaded at a time, no matter how often you twist the brown base, but the dose counter will continue to advance).

STEP 2

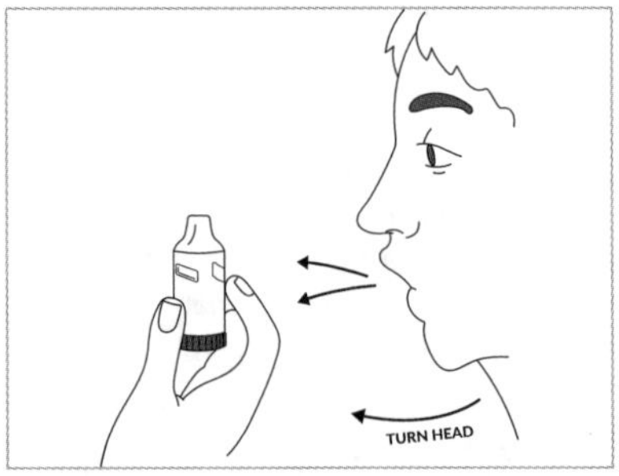

Turn your head away from the inhaler and breathe out fully.

STEP 3

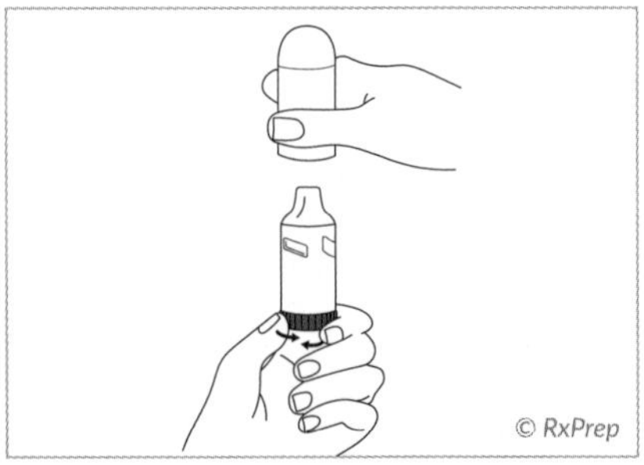

Place the mouthpiece in your mouth and close your lips around the mouthpiece. Breathe in deeply and forcefully through the inhaler. Remove the inhaler from your mouth and breathe out. Replace the white cover on the inhaler and twist shut. Rinse your mouth with water and spit out the water to prevent thrush.

TO PRIME
Twist off the white cover. Holding the inhaler upright, twist the brown base fully in one direction as far as it will go and then fully back. You will hear a click during one of the twisting motions. Repeat twisting motion again (back and forth). The inhaler is now primed and ready to load your first dose. This inhaler does not need to be primed again (even after long periods of no use).

TO CLEAN
Wipe the mouthpiece with a dry tissue weekly. Do not use water or immerse it in water.

ProAir RespiClick, AirDuo RespiClick

STEP 1

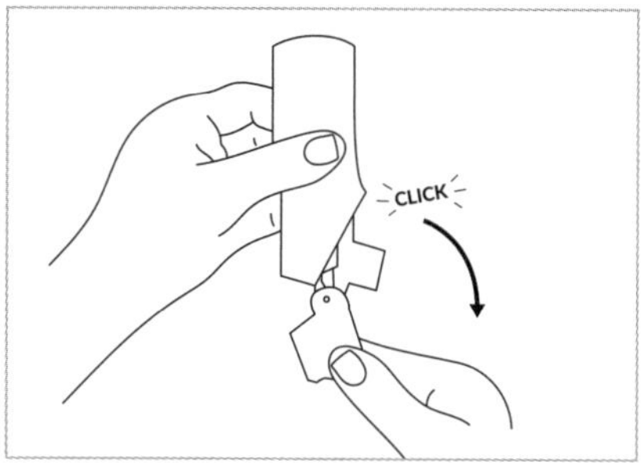

Make sure the cap is closed before each dose. Hold the inhaler upright as you open the cap fully. Open the cap all the way back until you hear a "click". Your inhaler is now ready to use. Do not open the cap unless you are taking a dose. Note: opening and closing the cap without inhaling a dose will waste medication and can damage your inhaler.

STEP 2

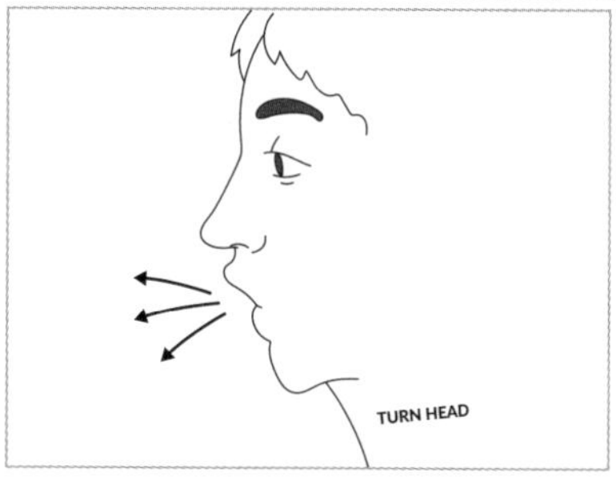

Breathe out through your mouth and push as much air from your lungs as you can. Turn your head away from the inhaler so you do not breathe into the mouthpiece.

STEP 3

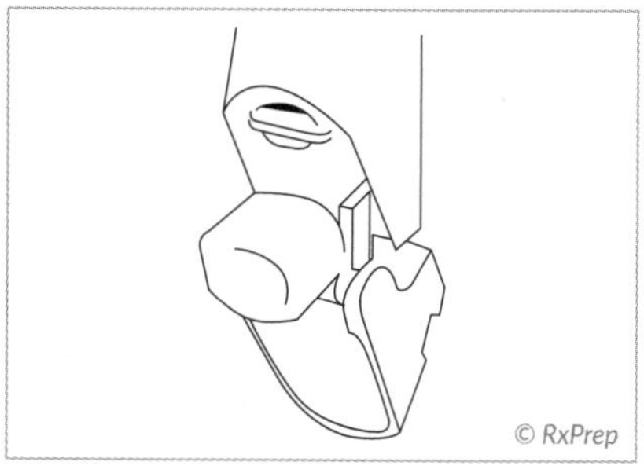

Put the mouthpiece in your mouth and close your lips around it. Breathe in deeply through your mouth, until your lungs feel completely full of air. Do not let your lips or fingers block the vent above the mouthpiece. Hold your breath for as long as possible, up to 10 seconds. Remove the inhaler from your mouth. Check the dose counter on the back of the inhaler to make sure you received the dose. Close the cap over the mouthpiece after each use of the inhaler. Make sure the cap closes firmly into place.

For *AirDuo RespiClick*: rinse your mouth with water and spit out the water to prevent thrush. Do not swallow the water.

TO PRIME
None needed.

TO CLEAN
Keep your inhaler dry and clean at all times. Do not wash or put any part of your inhaler in water. If the mouthpiece needs cleaning, gently wipe it with a dry cloth or tissue after using.

Patient Counseling for *Singulair*

For adults and children ≥ 12 months of age with asthma:

- Take this medication once a day in the evening. You can take this medication with or without food.
- Take every day for as long as your healthcare provider prescribes it, even if you have no asthma symptoms.
- If your asthma symptoms get worse, or if you need to increase the use of your rescue inhaler for asthma attacks, call your healthcare provider right away.
- Do not take this medication for immediate relief of an asthma attack. If you have an asthma attack, follow the instructions your healthcare provider gave you for treating asthma attacks. Always have your rescue inhaler with you.
- The most common side effects with this medication include: stomach pain, upper respiratory infections, headache and sinus infection.
- Rarely, this medication has been associated with behavior and mood changes, such as aggressive behavior, hostility, anxiousness, depression and/or suicidal thoughts and actions. Please report any of these symptoms to your healthcare provider immediately.
- For *Singulair* oral granules: never store any oral granules mixed with food, baby formula or breast milk for use at a later time. Give within 15 minutes of opening the packet. Throw away any unused portion. Do not mix *Singulair* oral granules with anything other than the liquids or foods shown below. They can be given:
  - ❑ Directly in the mouth.
  - ❑ Dissolved in one teaspoonful (5 mL) of baby formula or breast milk.
  - ❑ Mixed with one spoonful of applesauce, mashed carrots, rice or ice cream.

For patients 6 years of age and older for the prevention of exercise-induced asthma:

- Take this medication at least two hours before exercise.
- Always have your rescue inhaler with you for asthma attacks.
- If you are taking *Singulair* daily for chronic asthma or allergies, do not take another dose to prevent exercise-induced asthma. Talk to your healthcare provider about your treatment of exercise-induced asthma.
- Do not take an additional dose of *Singulair* within 24 hours of a previous dose.

Patient Counseling for *Pulmicort Respules*

- Take one ampule out of the sealed aluminum envelope, and record the date you opened the envelope.
- Place any unused ampules back into the envelope and store upright, protected from light, at room temperature. Keep in mind, any remaining ampules should be used within two weeks.
- Gently swirl the ampule using a circular motion, making sure to not squeeze the ampule and keeping it in an upright position.
- Twist off the top of the ampule and squeeze all the liquid into the nebulizer and use right away. If using a face mask, make sure it fits snugly.
- Turn the compressor on and continue treatment until the mist stops, generally within 5 – 10 minutes.
- Rinse your mouth with water and spit the water out after each dose. Wash your face after treatment if a face mask was used.

Select Guidelines/References

National Heart, Lung and Blood Institute. Expert Panel Report 3: Guidelines for the Diagnosis and Management of Asthma. August 2007. https://www.nhlbi.nih.gov/health-pro/guidelines/current/asthma-guidelines (accessed 2019 Apr 20).

Global Initiative for Asthma (GINA). Global Strategy for Asthma Management and Prevention, 2018. http://www.ginasthma.org (accessed 2019 Apr 20).

Global Initiative for Asthma (GINA). Global Strategy for Asthma Management and Prevention, 2019 Pocket Guide. http://www.ginasthma.org (accessed 2019 Apr 23).

CHAPTER CONTENT

Background **617**
Diagnosis **617**
COPD vs Asthma 618
COPD Assessment **618**
Degree of Airflow Limitation 618
Symptoms 618
Risk of Exacerbations 618
Comorbidities 618
Combined Assessment of COPD 618
Non-Drug Treatment **619**
Drug Treatment **619**
Inhaler Products **620**
Muscarinic Antagonists/Anticholinergics 621
Beta-2 Agonists 622
Phosphodiesterase-4 Inhibitor 622
Patient Counseling **623**
Select Metered Dose Inhalers 623
Select Dry Powder Inhalers 625

CONTENT LEGEND

= Study Tip Gal

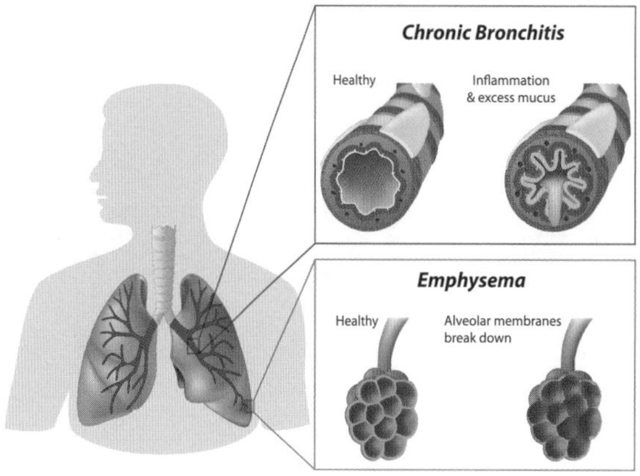

CHAPTER 42
CHRONIC OBSTRUCTIVE PULMONARY DISEASE

BACKGROUND

Chronic obstructive pulmonary disease (COPD) is a respiratory disease that causes obstructed airflow from the lungs. It is one of the leading causes of death worldwide. Symptoms include dyspnea (shortness of breath) that is chronic and progressive over time, chronic cough, sputum production and wheezing.

COPD is most commonly caused by tobacco smoke, but can be caused by other air pollutants (e.g., noxious particles, smoke from fires, cigars, pipes and marijuana). Long term exposure to these gases or particles leads to chronic inflammation in the lungs, and eventually to emphysema and/or bronchitis. Emphysema is a destruction of the small passages in the lungs, called alveoli. Bronchitis is inflammation and narrowing of the bronchial tubes, and results in mucus production and a chronic cough.

Individuals with alpha-1 antitrypsin (AAT) deficiency are at a higher risk of developing COPD, because AAT helps to protect the lungs from damage caused by inflammation.

DIAGNOSIS

COPD should be suspected in any patient with symptoms (described above) and a history of exposure to risk factors (e.g., tobacco smoke). It is important to rule out other common reasons for shortness of breath and cough, such as asthma, chronic heart failure and other pulmonary conditions (e.g., tuberculosis). Asthma is the most difficult to differentiate from COPD; key features of both conditions are shown in the Study Tip Gal on the following page.

The limitation of airflow in asthma is reversible with medication. In COPD, the limitation of airflow is not fully reversible and progresses over time, leading to gradual loss of lung function.

Spirometry is required to assess lung function and make a diagnosis of COPD. It is an objective measurement of airflow limitation and the most reproducible test available. Spirometry measures the total amount of air a person can breathe out (forced vital capacity, or FVC) and the amount of air exhaled in one second (forced expiratory volume, or FEV1). A post-bronchodilator FEV1/FVC < 0.70 confirms a diagnosis of COPD.

COPD VS. ASTHMA

COPD
- Age of onset: usually > 40 years
- Smoking history: usually > 10 years
- Sputum production: common
- Allergies: uncommon
- Symptoms: persistent
- Disease process: progressive, worsens over time
- Exacerbations: a common complication
- First-line treatment: bronchodilators

ASTHMA
- Age of onset: usually < 40 years
- Smoking history: uncommon
- Sputum production: infrequent
- Allergies: common
- Symptoms: intermittent and variable
- Disease process: stable, does not worsen over time
- Exacerbations: a common complication
- First-line treatment: inhaled corticosteroids

COPD ASSESSMENT

COPD assessment includes four aspects, described below.

- Degree of airflow limitation (disease severity)
- Symptoms
- Risk of exacerbations
- Presence of comorbidities

DEGREE OF AIRFLOW LIMITATION

The post-bronchodilator FEV1 is assessed using spirometry and helps determine disease severity. The GOLD guidelines use a grading system of 1 – 4 to classify patients based on spirometry results. The grade assignment is used to assess prognosis and disease progression.

Severity of Post-Bronchodilator Airflow Limitation

CLASSIFICATION	SEVERITY	AIRFLOW LIMITATION
In patients with FEV1/FVC < 0.70		
GOLD 1	Mild	FEV1 ≥ 80% predicted
GOLD 2	Moderate	50% ≤ FEV1 < 80% predicted
GOLD 3	Severe	30% ≤ FEV1 < 50% predicted
GOLD 4	Very Severe	FEV1 < 30% predicted

SYMPTOMS

The classic symptoms of chronic cough, sputum production and dyspnea can appear years before airflow limitation is recognized. For this reason, scoring systems are used for symptom assessment, and they are integral to selecting drug treatment. The two most commonly used scoring systems are the:

- Modified British Medical Research Council (mMRC) dyspnea scale – available at: https://www.verywell.com/guidelines-for-the-mmrc-dyspnea-scale-914740
- COPD Assessment Test (CAT) – available at: http://www.catestonline.org/images/pdfs/CATest.pdf

The mMRC dyspnea scale assesses breathlessness. Scores range from 0 (only breathless with strenuous exercise) to 4 (too breathless to leave the house or breathless with normal daily activities, such as dressing and undressing). The CAT is a comprehensive assessment of symptoms (e.g., cough, mucus production, chest tightness, energy level, breathlessness, sleep patterns, limitations to normal activity), with possible scores ranging from 0 – 40; higher scores indicate worse symptoms.

The application of these two scoring systems is shown in the Combined Assessment of COPD chart and the clinical scenarios that follow.

RISK OF EXACERBATIONS

A COPD exacerbation is an acute worsening of the patient's respiratory symptoms beyond normal day-to-day variation. If a patient has two or more exacerbations per year, they are considered to be "frequent exacerbators." The risk of exacerbations increases as airflow limitation worsens. Hospitalization for an exacerbation is associated with an increased risk of death. Taking measures to prevent and quickly treat COPD exacerbations is an important component to managing patients with COPD.

COMORBIDITIES

Comorbid conditions, such as cardiovascular diseases, osteoporosis, diabetes, depression, anxiety, skeletal muscle dysfunction and lung cancer should be monitored and treated appropriately. Poor control of comorbid conditions can independently influence mortality and hospitalizations.

COMBINED ASSESSMENT OF COPD

The combined assessment of COPD has been simplified to focus on symptom assessment and risk of exacerbations as the critical components that drive treatment. At each follow up visit, symptoms should be assessed using the mMRC

CLINICAL SCENARIOS

These examples illustrate how the different assessments are used to direct treatment.

Patient 1: a 62-year-old male with FEV1/FVC < 0.7 and FEV1 40% predicted. CAT score is 16 and he had no exacerbations in the past year. *Assessment:* confirmed diagnosis of COPD, GOLD grade 3, group B

Patient 2: a 62-year-old female with FEV1/FVC < 0.7 and FEV1 40% predicted. CAT score is 16 and she had 2 exacerbations in the past year, one of which required hospitalization. *Assessment:* confirmed diagnosis of COPD, GOLD grade 3, group D

Both patients have the same degree of disease severity and symptoms (based on FEV1 and CAT score). In both cases, better symptom control is needed, but patient 2 requires more intensive treatment due to her history of exacerbations. See the section on Initial Pharmacologic Treatment for a review of the differences in treatment recommendations for both patients.

or CAT system, and history of exacerbations should be documented. The patient is then assigned to a group (ABCD) which determines the initial treatment warranted (see Initial Pharmacologic Therapy).

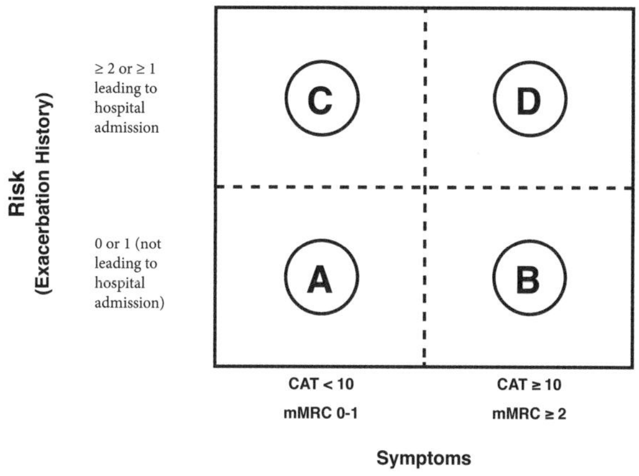

NON-DRUG TREATMENT

Smoking cessation is the only management strategy proven to slow the progression of COPD. Healthcare providers should encourage all patients who smoke to quit using proven strategies (see Tobacco Cessation chapter). Vaccinations reduce the risk of hospitalizations due to serious respiratory illness, and the risk of death. Patients with COPD should receive an annual influenza vaccine as well as pneumococcal vaccinations per ACIP recommendations (see Immunizations chapter).

To improve outcomes, it is essential to assess inhaler technique (see detailed instructions on inhaler use, priming and cleaning at the end of the chapter) and adherence routinely. Pulmonary rehabilitation programs help improve quality of life and symptoms. Long-term oxygen treatment has been shown to increase survival in patients with severe resting hypoxemia (PaO2 < 55 mmHg or SaO2 < 88%).

DRUG TREATMENT

The medications used in COPD do not modify the long-term decline in lung function or reduce mortality. They decrease symptoms and/or prevent complications, such as exacerbations and hospitalizations. Each treatment regimen should be patient-specific, based on CAT and/or mMRC score and risk of exacerbations (see the ABCD assessment tool and treatment recommendations in the table below).

Bronchodilators are the first-line treatment for all patients. A short-acting beta-2 agonist (SABA) and/or short-acting muscarinic antagonist (SAMA) can be used as needed. If regular use is required, long-acting beta-2 agonists (LABAs) and/or long-acting muscarinic antagonists (LAMAs) are preferred. Combination treatment is often required. Two bronchodilators (e.g., LABA plus LAMA) is generally preferred.

Long term monotherapy with oral steroids or ICS is not recommended. ICS can be added to LABA treatment or LAMA/LABA treatment in select patients with past exacerbations and high blood eosinophil (eos) counts (a marker of inflammation). Although there is a risk of pneumonia, adding an ICS has been shown to improve symptoms, lung function, quality of life, and reduce exacerbation frequency. ICS products are discussed in the Asthma chapter. Other less commonly used treatments include the phosphodiesterase-4 (PDE-4) inhibitor (roflumilast) and azithromycin, which are used in only the most severe cases, and theophylline, which is not recommended unless long-acting bronchodilators are unavailable or unaffordable.

Initial Pharmacologic Therapy

The ABCD assessment determines the patient's group and initial treatment.

PATIENT GROUP	RECOMMENDED TREATMENT
A	A bronchodilator: SABA* or SAMA* PRN, LABA or LAMA
B	LAMA or LABA
C	LAMA**
D	LAMA or LAMA + LABA (if highly symptomatic) or LABA + ICS (if eos ≥ 300 cells/μL)

**Combination treatment with SABA/SAMA improves FEV1 and symptoms compared to monotherapy with either agent*

***LAMAs are preferred over LABAs in group C as they have been shown to have a greater impact on exacerbation rates*

Escalation of Treatment

At each follow-up visit, an assessment of inhaler use, non-pharmacologic approaches, symptoms and exacerbations is repeated. If there was an appropriate response to initial treatment, no change is necessary. If the response was not appropriate, treatment should be escalated based on the primary concern (dyspnea or exacerbations).

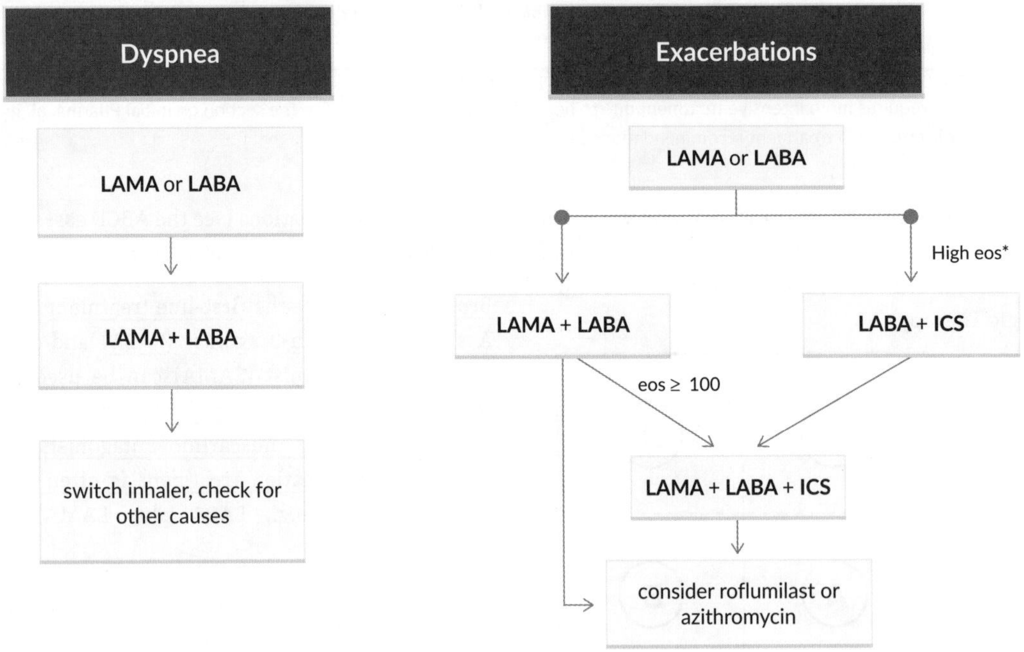

Eos = blood eosinophils (cells/ μL)
**eos ≥ 300, or eos ≥ 100 with ≥ 2 moderate exacerbations / 1 hospitalization*

COPD Exacerbations

COPD exacerbations can be caused by respiratory tract infections (viral or bacterial) or other factors, such as increased air pollution. They are typically treated with a SABA, with or without a SAMA, plus an injectable or oral systemic steroid. If there is increased sputum purulence, increased sputum volume, increased dyspnea or if mechanical ventilation is required, antibiotics should be utilized for 5 – 10 days (see the Infectious Diseases II chapter).

INHALER PRODUCTS

There are two categories of inhaler devices: metered dose inhalers (MDIs) and dry powder inhalers (DPIs). The difference between these two types is reviewed in a Study Tip Gal in the Asthma chapter. Poor adherence and incorrect use of inhalers are common concerns in the management of COPD and can lead to decreased quality of life, worsened health outcomes and increased frequency of exacerbations and hospitalizations. To improve adherence, many inhaled medications are available in combination products. Consult the Asthma chapter for a list of maintenance inhalers that are indicated in asthma vs. COPD. A comprehensive review of appropriate technique is shown for select inhalers at the end of the chapter.

MUSCARINIC ANTAGONISTS/ANTICHOLINERGICS

Muscarinic antagonists cause bronchodilation by blocking the constricting action of acetylcholine at M3 muscarinic receptors in bronchial smooth muscle. Medications in this class are generally well tolerated.

DRUG	DOSING
Short-acting muscarinic antagonist (SAMA)	
Ipratropium bromide	
Atrovent HFA 17 mcg/inh	MDI: 2 inhalations QID
Nebulizer solution 0.02%	Nebulizer: 0.5 mg TID-QID
+ albuterol	
Combivent Respimat 20 mcg ipratropium + 100 mcg albuterol/inh	MDI: 1 inhalation QID
Nebulizer solution 0.5 mg ipratropium + 2.5 mg albuterol per 3 mL	Nebulizer: 3 mL QID
Long-acting muscarinic antagonists (LAMAs), also called anticholinergics	
Aclidinium *(Tudorza Pressair)* 400 mcg/inh + formoterol *(Duaklir Pressair)*	DPI: 1 inhalation BID
Glycopyrrolate	
Seebri Neohaler 15.6 mcg/inh	DPI: 1 capsule via *Neohaler* device BID
Lonhala Magnair 25 mcg/inh nebulizer solution + formoterol *(Bevespi Aerosphere)* + indacaterol *(Utibron Neohaler)*	Nebulizer: 25 mcg BID
Revefenacin *(Yupelri)* 175 mcg/inh nebulizer solution	Nebulizer: 175 mcg (1 unit-dose vial) daily
Tiotropium	
Spiriva HandiHaler 18 mcg capsule	DPI: 1 capsule via *HandiHaler* device daily (requires 2 puffs)
Spiriva Respimat 2.5 mcg/inh + olodaterol *(Stiolto Respimat)*	MDI: 2 inhalations daily
Umeclidinium *(Incruse Ellipta)* 62.5 mcg/inh + vilanterol *(Anoro Ellipta)* + vilanterol/fluticasone *(Trelegy Ellipta)*	DPI: 1 inhalation daily

SAFETY/SIDE EFFECTS/MONITORING

WARNINGS

Use with caution in patients with narrow-angle glaucoma, myasthenia gravis, urinary retention, benign prostatic hyperplasia and bladder neck obstruction

SIDE EFFECTS

Dry mouth, upper respiratory tract infections (nasopharyngitis, sinusitis), cough, bitter taste

MONITORING

S/sx at each visit, smoking status, COPD questionnaires, annual spirometry

NOTES

Avoid spraying in the eyes

HandiHaler and *Neohaler* devices are DPIs that come with a capsule that is placed into the device; do not swallow the capsules by mouth

Tudorza Pressair is a DPI that has an indicator window that turns from green to red if the dose was inhaled properly

BETA-2 AGONISTS

These agents bind to beta-2 receptors in the lung causing relaxation of bronchial smooth muscle and bronchodilation. LABAs should be used as monotherapy for COPD only, due to the serious risks associated with use in asthma (see Boxed Warning). SABAs, which are frequently used for other reversible airway diseases, are discussed in more detail in the Asthma chapter.

DRUG	DOSING	SAFETY/SIDE EFFECTS/MONITORING
Long-acting beta-2 agonists (LABAs)		**BOXED WARNING** LABAs increase the risk of asthma-related deaths and should only be used in asthma patients who are currently on a long-term asthma control medication (inhaled corticosteroid) but are not adequately controlled **CONTRAINDICATIONS** Status asthmaticus, acute episodes of asthma or COPD, monotherapy in the treatment of asthma **SIDE EFFECTS** Nervousness, tremor, tachycardia, palpitations, hyperglycemia, ↓ K, cough **MONITORING** S/sx at each visit, smoking status, COPD questionnaires, annual spirometry **NOTES** *Neohaler* devices are DPIs that come with a capsule that is placed into the device; do not swallow the capsules by mouth Arformoterol contains the R-isomer of formoterol
Salmeterol *(Serevent Diskus)* 50 mcg/inh **+ fluticasone *(Advair Diskus,*** *Wixela Inhub)*	DPI: 1 inhalation BID	
Formoterol *(Perforomist)* 20 mcg/2 mL nebulizer solution **+ budesonide *(Symbicort)*** + aclidinium *(Duaklir Pressair)* + glycopyrrolate *(Bevespi Aerosphere)*	Nebulizer solution: 20 mcg BID	
Arformoterol *(Brovana)* 15 mcg/2 mL nebulizer solution	Nebulizer solution: 15 mcg BID	
Indacaterol *(Arcapta Neohaler)* 75 mcg capsule + glycopyrrolate *(Utibron Neohaler)*	DPI: 1 capsule via *Neohaler* device daily	
Olodaterol *(Striverdi Respimat)* 2.5 mcg/inh + tiotropium *(Stiolto Respimat)*	MDI: 2 inhalations daily	
Vilanterol (only available in combination products) **+ fluticasone *(Breo Ellipta)*** + umeclidinium *(Anoro Ellipta)* + umeclidinium/fluticasone *(Trelegy Ellipta)*		

PHOSPHODIESTERASE-4 INHIBITOR

Roflumilast is a PDE-4 inhibitor that ↑ cAMP levels, leading to a reduction in lung inflammation. This medication should always be used in combination with at least one long-acting bronchodilator; its use is reserved for patients with very severe COPD, chronic bronchitis and a history of exacerbations.

DRUG	DOSING	SAFETY/SIDE EFFECTS/MONITORING
Roflumilast *(Daliresp)* Tablet	500 mcg PO daily	**CONTRAINDICATIONS** Moderate to severe liver impairment **WARNINGS** Psychiatric events (depression, mood changes) including suicidality **SIDE EFFECTS** Diarrhea, weight loss, nausea, ↓ appetite, insomnia, HA **MONITORING** S/sx at each visit, LFTs, smoking status, COPD questionnaires, annual spirometry

Roflumilast Drug Interactions

Roflumilast is a substrate of CYP450 3A4 and 1A2. Use with strong enzyme inducers (e.g., carbamazepine, phenobarbital, phenytoin, rifampin) is not recommended. Use with CYP3A4 inhibitors or dual CYP3A4 and CYP1A2 inhibitors (e.g., erythromycin, ketoconazole, fluvoxamine, cimetidine) will ↑ roflumilast levels.

PATIENT COUNSELING

SELECT METERED DOSE INHALERS

Atrovent HFA

STEP 1	STEP 2	STEP 3
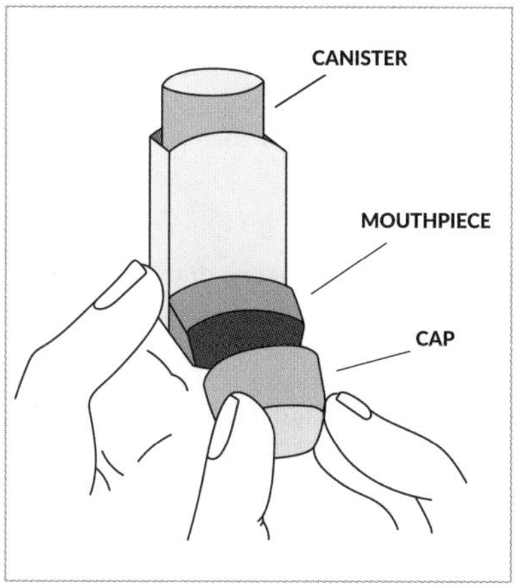	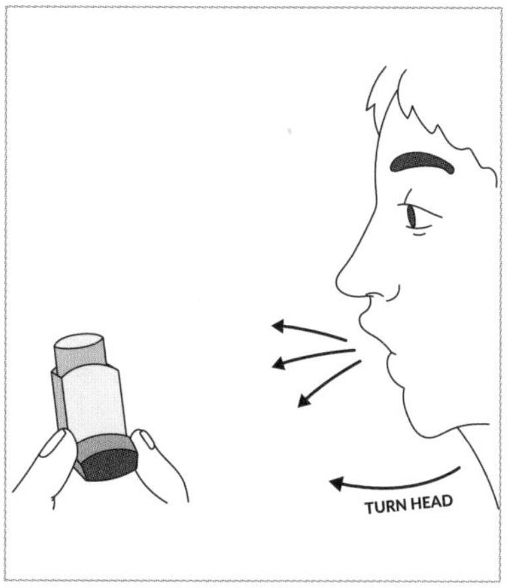	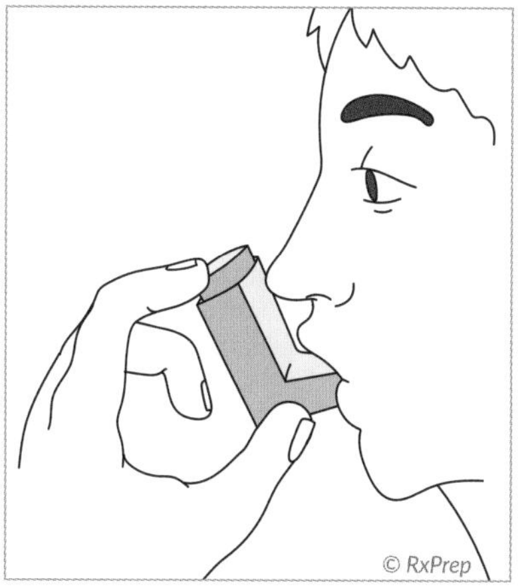
Make sure the canister is fully inserted into the actuator (if it comes separately). The *Atrovent HFA* plastic actuator should only be used with the *Atrovent HFA* canister. Remove the protective dust cap from the mouthpiece and check mouthpiece for foreign objects prior to use. You do not have to shake *Atrovent HFA* before using it.	Breathe out fully through your mouth. Holding the inhaler upright (as shown in the picture), place the mouthpiece into your mouth and close your lips around it. Keep your eyes closed so that no medication will be sprayed into your eyes.	While breathing in slowly and deeply through your mouth, press the top of the canister all the way down with your index finger. Hold your breath as long as possible, up to 10 seconds, then breathe normally. If another inhalation is needed, wait at least 15 seconds and repeat Steps 1-3. Place cap back on the mouthpiece after use.

TO PRIME
Spray 2 times away from the face. Prime again if > 3 days from last use.

TO CLEAN
To prevent medication buildup and blockage, remove the metal canister (do not let this get wet) and rinse the mouthpiece only under warm running water for 30 seconds. Shake to remove excess water and let air dry. Clean at least weekly.

Combivent Respimat, Stiolto Respimat, Striverdi Respimat

STEP 1

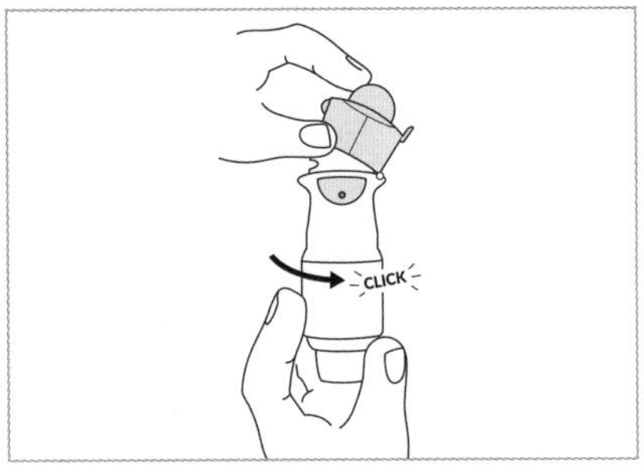

Hold the inhaler upright with the cap closed. Turn the clear base in the direction of the arrows on the label until it clicks (half a turn).

STEP 2

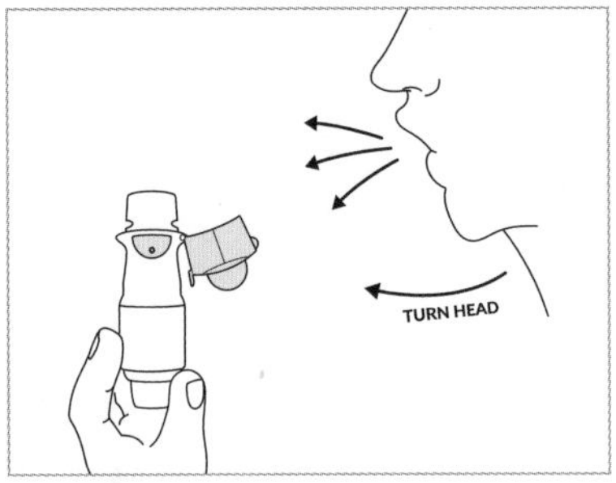

Open the cap until it snaps fully open. Turn head away from the inhaler and breathe out slowly and fully.

STEP 3

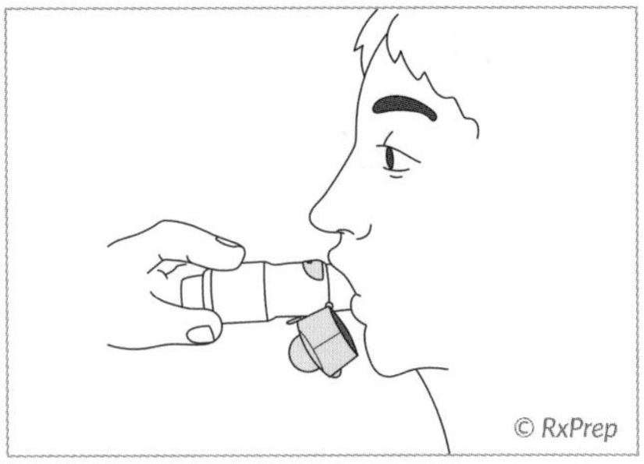

Close lips around the end of the mouthpiece without covering the air vents. While taking a slow, deep breath through your mouth, press the dose release button and continue to breathe in slowly. Hold your breath as long as possible, up to 10 seconds. Close the cap when finished.

To simplify these steps for patient counseling, think: *TOP*

T	O	P
TURN the clear base	**OPEN** the cap and close your lips around the mouthpiece	**PRESS** the dose-release button and inhale

TO ASSEMBLE DEVICE FOR FIRST USE

With the cap closed, press the safety catch while pulling off the clear base. Do not touch the piercing element located inside the bottom of the clear base. Write the discard by date on the label of the inhaler (which is 3 months from the date the cartridge is inserted).

Push the narrow end of the cartridge into the inhaler and push down firmly until it clicks into place. Put the clear base back into place until it clicks. Do not remove the clear base or the cartridge once assembled.

TO PRIME FOR FIRST USE

Hold the inhaler upright with the cap closed. Turn the clear base in the direction of the arrows on the label until it clicks (half a turn). Flip the cap until it snaps fully open.

Point the inhaler toward the ground away from your face. Press the dose release button. Close cap. Repeat these steps over again until a spray is visible. Once the spray is visible, repeat the steps 3 more times to make sure the inhaler is prepared for use. If inhaler is not used for > 3 days, release 1 spray toward the ground to prepare the inhaler. If inhaler has not been used for > 21 days, follow priming instructions above for initial use.

TO CLEAN

Clean the mouthpiece, including the metal part inside the mouthpiece, with a damp cloth or tissue weekly.

SELECT DRY POWDER INHALERS

Spiriva HandiHaler

STEP 1	STEP 2	STEP 3	STEP 4	STEP 5
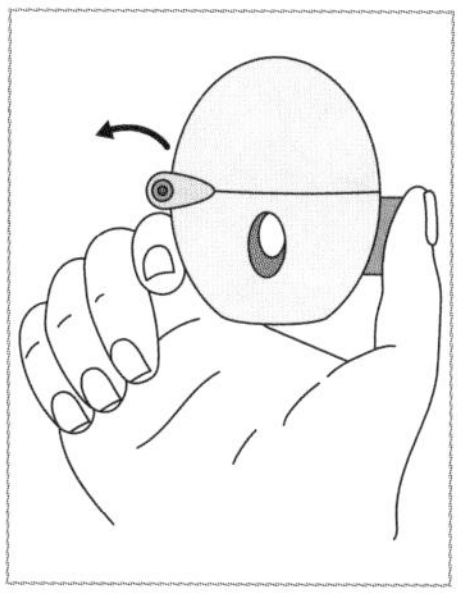	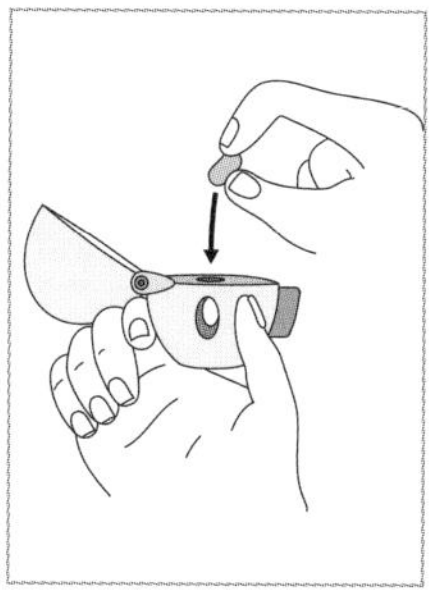	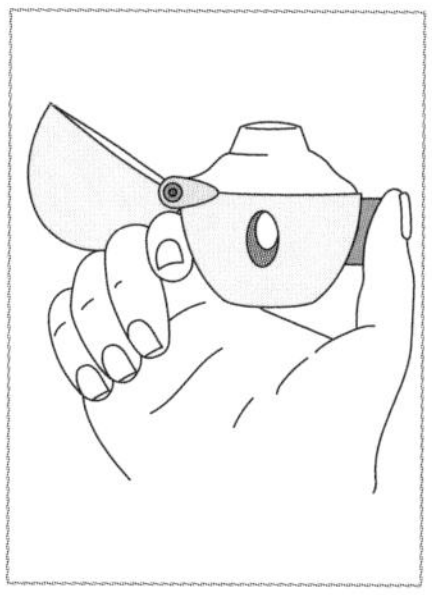	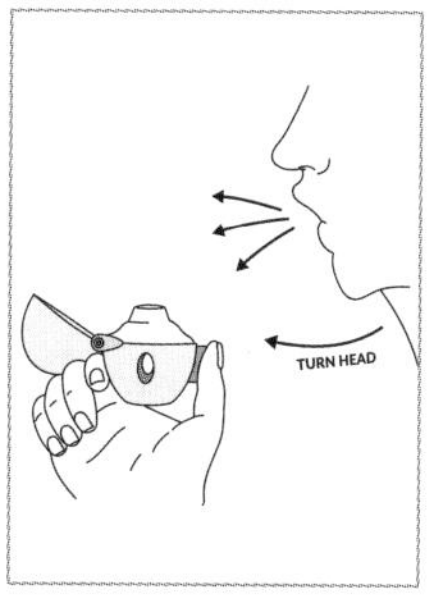	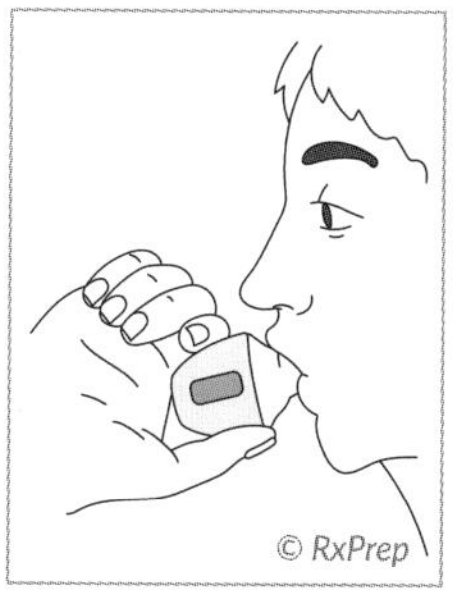
Open the *HandiHaler* device by pressing on the green button and lifting the cap upwards. Open the mouthpiece by pulling the mouthpiece ridge up and away from the base so the center chamber is showing.	Remove the *Spiriva* capsule from the blister pack and insert it into the chamber. Close the mouthpiece firmly against the gray base until you hear a click.	Press the green piercing button once until it is flat (flush) against the base, then release. Do not shake the device.	Turn head away from the inhaler and breathe out fully.	Raise the *HandiHaler* to your mouth in a horizontal position and close your lips around the mouthpiece. Breathe in deeply and fully. You should hear or feel the *Spiriva* capsule vibrate (rattle). Remove inhaler from your mouth and hold your breath for a few seconds. Breathe normally. To get the full dose, you must inhale twice from each capsule. Repeat the last two steps, breathing out fully again and breathing in deeply and fully through the inhaler. Tip out the used capsule into a trash can after 2 inhalations. Do not touch the capsule. Close the lid of the device.

TO CLEAN

Clean inhaler as needed. Rinse inhaler with warm water, pressing the green button a few times so the chamber and piercing needle are under the running water. Make sure any powder build up is removed. Let air dry. It takes 24 hours to air dry the *HandiHaler* device after it is cleaned.

Tudorza Pressair

STEP 1

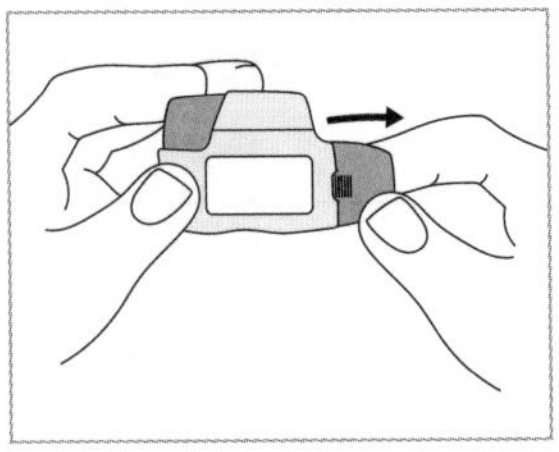

Remove the protective cap by lightly squeezing the arrows marked on each side of the cap and pulling outwards. Check the mouthpiece for foreign objects.

STEP 2

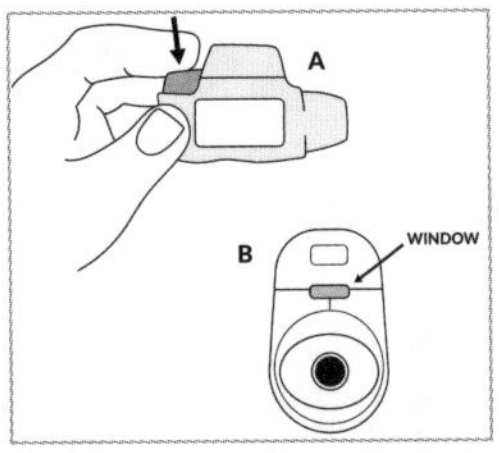

Hold the inhaler with the mouthpiece facing you and the green button straight up. Before putting into your mouth, press the green button all the way down and release.

Check the control window; the dose is ready for inhalation if it changed from red to green. Breathe out completely, away from the inhaler.

STEP 3

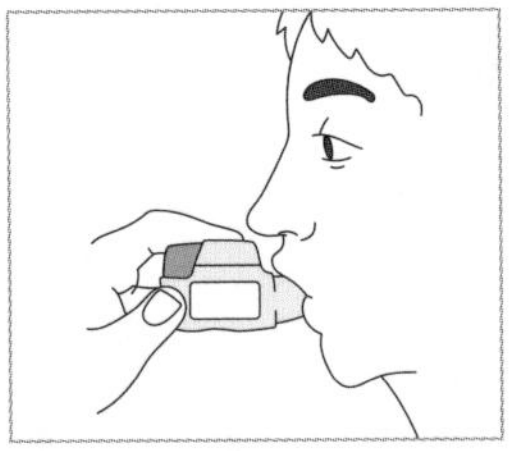

Put your lips tightly around the mouthpiece. Breathe in quickly and deeply through your mouth. Breathe in until you hear a "click" sound and keep breathing in to get the full dose.

Do not hold down the green button while breathing in.

STEP 4

Remove the inhaler from your mouth and hold your breath for as long as comfortable. Then breathe out slowly through your nose. Place the protective cap on the inhaler.

Check that the control window has turned to red which indicates the full dose has been inhaled correctly.

TO CLEAN

Routine cleaning is not required. If needed, wipe the outside of the mouthpiece with a dry tissue or paper towel.

Anoro Ellipta, Arnuity Ellipta, Breo Ellipta, Incruse Ellipta

STEP 1	STEP 2	STEP 3
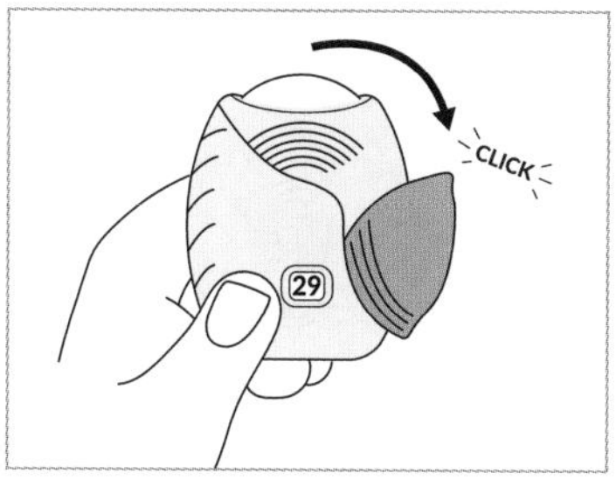	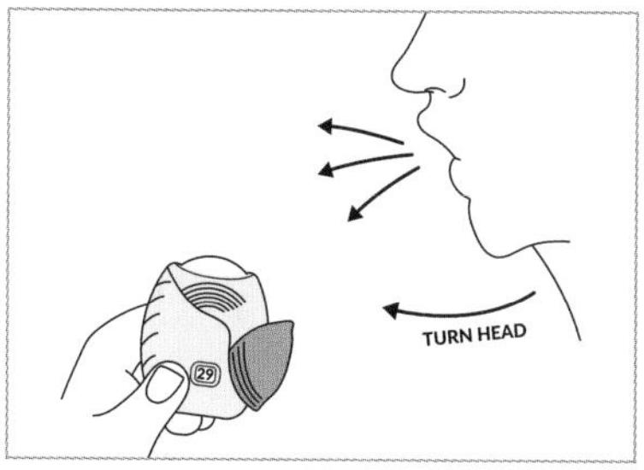	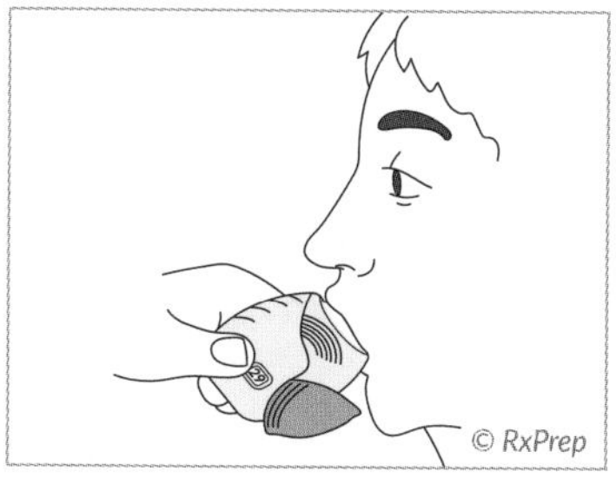
Open the cover of the inhaler by sliding the cover down to expose the mouthpiece. You should hear a "click." The counter will count down by 1 number, indicating that the inhaler is ready to use. If you open and close the cover without inhaling the medication, the dose will be lost. It is not possible to accidentally take a double dose or an extra dose in 1 inhalation.	While holding the inhaler away from your mouth, breathe out fully. Do not breathe out into the mouthpiece.	Put the mouthpiece between your lips and close your lips firmly around it. Take one long, steady, deep breath in through your mouth. Do not block the air vent with your fingers. Remove inhaler from mouth and hold your breath for 3-4 seconds or as long as comfortable. Breathe out slowly and gently. Close the inhaler. For ICS products: rinse your mouth with water and spit out the water to prevent thrush.

TO CLEAN

Routine cleaning is not required. If needed, you can clean the mouthpiece using a dry tissue, before you close the cover.

Arcapta Neohaler, Seebri Neohaler, Utibron Neohaler

STEP 1	STEP 2	STEP 3	STEP 4
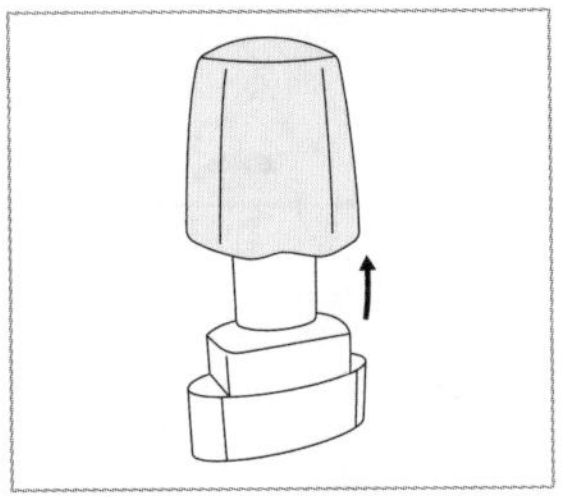	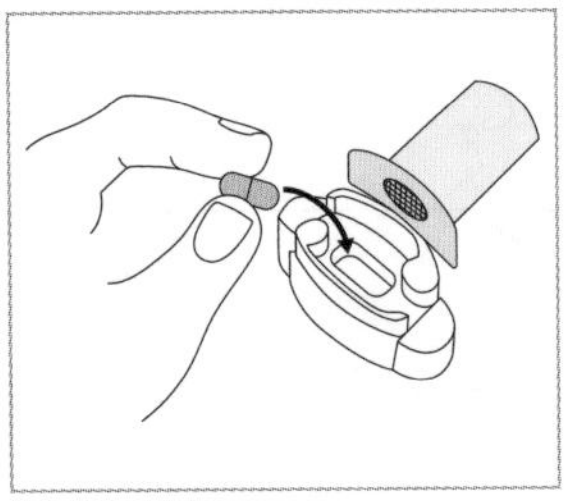	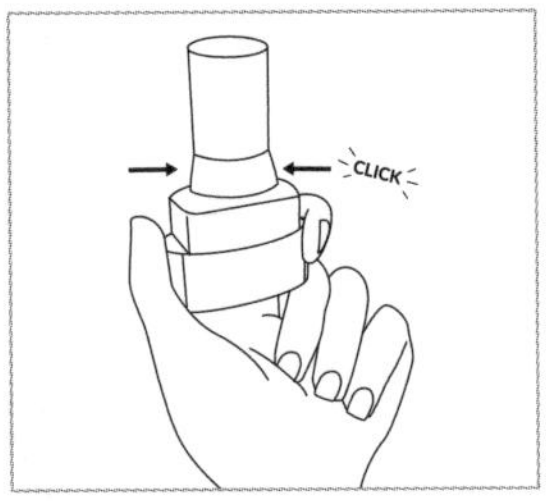	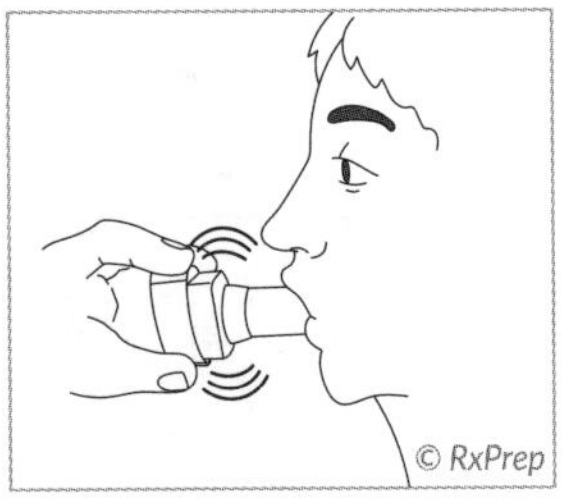
Pull off the cap.	Hold the base of the inhaler firmly and tilt the mouthpiece to open the inhaler. Remove a capsule from the blister pack and place the capsule into the capsule chamber. Close the inhaler fully, until you hear a "click" sound.	Hold the inhaler upright. Press both buttons fully one time. You should hear a "click" as the capsule is being pierced. Release the buttons fully. The inhaler is now ready to be used. Before using, breathe out fully, away from the inhaler.	Place the mouthpiece in your mouth and close your lips around the mouthpiece. Hold the inhaler with the buttons to the side (not up and down). Breathe in rapidly and deeply (you should hear a whirring sound when breathing in). Hold your breath as long as comfortable while removing the inhaler from your mouth, then breathe out. The capsule chamber should be empty of all powder. If it is not, inhale again. Remove the capsule by tipping it out then discard it. Replace the cap.

TO CLEAN

Routine cleaning is not required. If needed, a clean, dry, lint-free cloth or a clean, dry soft brush can be used to wipe the inhaler between uses.

Select Guidelines/References

Global Strategy for the Diagnosis, Management and Prevention of COPD, 2019 Report. Global Initiative for Chronic Obstructive Lung Disease (GOLD). http://www.goldcopd.org (accessed 2019 Mar 27).

CHAPTER CONTENT

Background ... **629**
Treatment Principles ... 629
Electronic Cigarettes ... 629
Smoking and Drug Interactions ... 630
Exceptions to Drug Treatment ... 630
Vaccinations in Smokers ... 630
Drug Treatment ... **630**
Nicotine Replacement Therapy (NRT) ... 630
Bupropion and Varenicline ... 631
Treatment Considerations for Tobacco Cessation ... 631
Patient Counseling ... **632**
Nicotine Patch Administration ... 632
How to Chew Nicotine Gum ... 632

THE "5 A'S" MODEL FOR TREATING TOBACCO USE AND DEPENDENCE

Ask about tobacco use
Identify and document tobacco use status for every patient at every visit.

Advise to quit
In a clear, strong and personalized manner, urge every tobacco user to quit.

Assess willingness to make a quit attempt
Is the tobacco user willing to make a quit attempt at this time (e.g., in the next month)?

Assist in quit attempt
For the patient willing to make a quit attempt, offer medication (if appropriate) and provide or refer for behavioral counseling.

For patients unwilling to quit at this time, provide motivational interventions designed to increase future quit attempts.

For the recent quitter, or any patient with remaining challenges, provide relapse prevention.

Arrange follow up
For the patient willing to make a quit attempt, arrange for follow up visits within the first week after the quit date.

For patients unwilling to make a quit attempt at this time, address tobacco dependence and willingness to quit at the next clinic visit.

CONTENT LEGEND

= Study Tip Gal

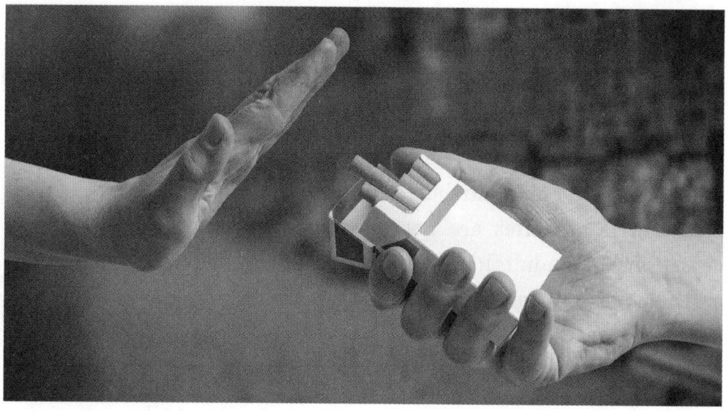

CHAPTER 43
TOBACCO CESSATION

BACKGROUND

Smoking is the leading cause of preventable death in the U.S. and a known risk factor for multiple cancers, heart disease, stroke, pregnancy complications, COPD and many other diseases. Tobacco dependence is a chronic disease that often requires repeated interventions and multiple attempts to quit. Effective treatments exist that can significantly increase the rates of long-term abstinence. It is essential for healthcare providers to ask patients about tobacco use, document the response and provide treatment. A national network of tobacco quitlines is available for patients at 1-800-QUIT-NOW (1-800-784-8669).

TREATMENT PRINCIPLES

The combination of counseling and medication is more effective than either one alone. Two counseling components that are especially effective are behavioral counseling (e.g., problem-solving skills training) and social support. There is a strong correlation between counseling intensity (length and number of counseling sessions) and quitting success.

There are several effective, first-line medications for tobacco dependence, including five nicotine replacement therapies (NRTs) and two non-nicotine therapies. Combining two of these drug treatments, such as using a long-acting nicotine patch with a short-acting formulation (e.g., gum, lozenge) or a nicotine patch with bupropion sustained release (SR), is most effective and can be used first-line. Medications reduce withdrawal symptoms, including anxiety, irritability, depression, insomnia, poor concentration, restlessness, increased appetite and an urge to smoke (cravings). Medications should be encouraged for all patients attempting to quit, except when medically contraindicated.

ELECTRONIC CIGARETTES

The risks and benefits of electronic cigarettes, also known as e-cigarettes and "electronic nicotine delivery systems" (ENDS), continues to be investigated. High nicotine variability has been found between and within brands, and there is some risk for nicotine addiction when non-smokers use them. Carcinogens and other chemicals can be present in the nicotine vapors. The attractiveness of the cartridge flavors has increased adolescent use and contributed to accidental poisonings in children. E-cigarettes are not recommended for smoking cessation. Some adults use them to quit smoking, and by doing so, their risk of tobacco-related illnesses can be reduced.

SMOKING AND DRUG INTERACTIONS

The non-nicotine chemicals in tobacco smoke induce CYP450 enzymes, primarily CYP450 1A2. Smokers who quit can experience side effects from supratherapeutic levels of caffeine, theophylline, fluvoxamine, olanzapine, clozapine and the R-isomer of warfarin (the less potent isomer of warfarin). Smoking increases the risk of bleeding with warfarin and clopidogrel. Women ≥ 35 years of age who smoke should not be taking estrogen-containing oral contraceptives due to an increased risk of cardiovascular events.

EXCEPTIONS TO DRUG TREATMENT

Treatment guidelines promote the use of behavioral counseling over drugs for the following populations: pregnant women, adolescents, smokeless tobacco users (e.g., chewing tobacco) and "light" smokers using < 10 cigarettes a day.

VACCINATIONS IN SMOKERS

Smokers age 19 – 64 years should receive the pneumococcal polysaccharide vaccine (*Pneumovax 23*) and an annual influenza vaccine. Additional immunizations depend on the patient's age and risk factors, per the ACIP recommendations. See the Immunizations chapter for further discussion.

DRUG TREATMENT

NICOTINE REPLACEMENT THERAPY (NRT)

DRUG	DOSING	SAFETY/SIDE EFFECTS/MONITORING
Nicotine patch ***(NicoDerm CQ,*** others) OTC	Initial Dose: If > 10 cigarettes/day: 21 mg patch If ≤ 10 cigarettes/day: 14 mg patch 10 Week Schedule: (see patch schedule below)	**WARNINGS** *Avoid in immediate post-MI period, life-threatening arrhythmias, severe or worsening angina, and pregnancy Inhaler/nasal spray: avoid in asthma, COPD and other chronic respiratory diseases **SIDE EFFECTS** Headache, dizziness, nervousness, insomnia, dyspepsia Patch: vivid dreams, skin irritation Inhaler: mouth and throat irritation, cough, rhinitis Nasal spray: nasal irritation, watery eyes, sneezing, transient changes in taste and smell **NOTES** The FDA prohibits sale of nicotine products to individuals < 18 years of age. Identification required to purchase. The nicotine patch has the highest adherence rate. Combination therapy with short-acting NRT and patch is the most effective (e.g., shorter-acting gum can be used to reduce cravings). The patch must be removed before an MRI. See Patient Counseling section for more information on nicotine patches. The gum and lozenge are sugar-free and have been shown to reduce or delay weight gain (4 mg strengths). The inhaler mimics the hand to mouth smoking action, providing a coping mechanism. The nasal spray has the fastest delivery and is useful for rapid relief of withdrawal symptoms. It has the highest dependence potential among NRTs.
Nicotine polacrilex **gum *(Nicorette,*** others) and **lozenge *(Nicorette, Nicorette Mini,*** others) OTC	Initial Dose for gum or lozenge: 1st cigarette > 30 min upon waking: 2 mg 1st cigarette ≤ 30 min upon waking: 4 mg 12 Week Schedule for gum or lozenge: Min (both): 9 pieces/day during first 6 wks Max (gum): 24 pieces/day Max (lozenge): 20 pieces/day	
Nicotine inhaler *(Nicotrol Inhaler)* Rx	6-16 cartridges daily for up to 12 wks, then taper frequency of use over 6-12 wks Use up to 6 months	
Nicotine nasal spray *(Nicotrol NS)* Rx	1 dose = 2 sprays (1 spray in each nostril), use 1-2 doses per hour, ↑ PRN for symptom relief Min: 8 doses/day Max: 5 doses/hr or 40 doses/day Use up to 3 months	

Patch 10 Week Schedule:

	> 10 cigarettes	≤ 10 cigarettes
Wks 1-6	21 mg	14 mg
Wks 7-8	14 mg	7 mg
Wks 9-10	7 mg	None

**Package labeling warns of NRT use in these situations but in practice the decision to use NRT is based on comparing the risks of smoking to the potential risks of NRT.*

BUPROPION AND VARENICLINE

Bupropion blocks neuronal reuptake of dopamine and/or norepinephrine resulting in reduced cravings and other withdrawal symptoms. Varenicline is a partial neuronal alpha–4 beta–2 nicotinic receptor agonist. It causes low-level stimulation of the receptor, while blocking the ability of nicotine to bind. This relieves symptoms of nicotine withdrawal and inhibits the surges of dopamine responsible for the reinforcement and reward associated with smoking. Since both drugs work by reducing cravings, they are started before the quit date. These drugs do not need to be tapered when they are discontinued.

DRUG	DOSING	SAFETY/SIDE EFFECTS/MONITORING
Bupropion SR ***(Zyban)*** Tablet *Aplenzin*, bupropion IR, *Forfivo XL*, *Wellbutrin SR*, *Wellbutrin XL*– for depression *Aplenzin*, *Wellbutrin XL* – for seasonal affective disorder (SAD)	Start at least 1 week before quit date 150 mg QAM for 3 days, then 150 mg BID Max dose: 300 mg/day Use up to 6 months	**BOXED WARNING** Risk of suicidal thinking and behavior is increased in children, adolescents, and young adults taking antidepressants **CONTRAINDICATIONS** Seizure disorder, history of anorexia/bulimia, use within 14 days of discontinuing MAO inhibitors, use in patients receiving linezolid or IV methylene blue, use in patients undergoing abrupt discontinuation of alcohol, benzodiazepines, barbiturates or antiepileptic drugs **WARNINGS** Serious neuropsychiatric events, including suicidal thinking and behavior (stop if patient becomes agitated, hostile, depressed, or has other abnormal behavior or mood changes), activation of mania/hypomania, hypertension, angle-closure glaucoma, hypersensitivity reactions [e.g., anaphylactic shock, rash (including SJS), angioedema, dyspnea] **SIDE EFFECTS** Dry mouth, insomnia, agitation, headache, nausea/vomiting, constipation, sweating, anxiety, tachycardia, tremors, dizziness, blurred vision **NOTES** Do not use with other forms of bupropion (See Depression chapter for more information) Delays weight gain To ↓ insomnia, take the 1st dose upon awakening and the 2nd dose 8 hours after the 1st dose If no significant progress by week 7, consider discontinuation
Varenicline ***(Chantix)*** Tablet	Start 1 week before quit date Days 1-3: 0.5 mg daily Days 4-7: 0.5 mg BID Day 8 (quit date) and beyond: 1 mg BID CrCl < 30 mL/min: 0.5 mg daily titrated to max 0.5 mg BID Use for 12 weeks; can use another 12 weeks to maintain success	**WARNINGS** Serious neuropsychiatric events, including suicidal thinking and behavior (stop if patient becomes agitated, hostile, depressed, or has other abnormal behavior or mood changes), seizures, ↑ effects of alcohol and risk of blackout (amnesia), somnambulism (sleepwalking), accidental injury (e.g., traffic accidents), CVD risk, angioedema, rash (including SJS) **SIDE EFFECTS** Nausea (~30%, dose-dependent), insomnia, abnormal dreams, constipation, flatulence, vomiting, headache **NOTES** To ↓ nausea, use lower dosage and take with food and a full glass of water To ↓ insomnia, take 2nd dose earlier than bedtime For patients unable to quit abruptly on day 8, the goal should be to decrease smoking by 50% in the first 4 weeks, an additional 50% in weeks 5-8, with complete cessation by week 12 Efficacy has not been determined in those < 16 years (not recommended)

TREATMENT CONSIDERATIONS FOR TOBACCO CESSATION

- All smokers should be offered medications unless it is contraindicated or if they are a pregnant female or adolescent.
- Combination of patch + gum or lozenge is more effective than patch alone

WEIGHT GAIN	DEPRESSION	DENTURES	COST	SKIN CONDITION (E.G., DERMATITIS)	ASTHMA/ COPD
Use	**Use**	**Avoid**	**Avoid**	**Avoid**	**Avoid**
Gum, lozenge and bupropion SR delay weight gain	Bupropion SR	Gum	Rx only: varenicline, bupropion SR, inhaler, spray	Patch	Inhaler or spray

PATIENT COUNSELING

NICOTINE PATCH

NICOTINE PATCH ADMINISTRATION

- At the start of each day, remove a new patch from the pouch; save the pouch to throw away used patches.
- Apply the sticky side of the patch to a clean, dry and relatively hairless area of the skin; press the patch firmly onto the skin for ~10 seconds.
- Wear the patch for 24 hours (especially if you crave cigarettes when you wake up). If you have vivid dreams or trouble sleeping, remove the patch prior to bedtime (after about 16 hours) and apply a new one in the morning.
- Discard the patch by folding the sticky ends together, place it back in the pouch and put it in a trash can with a lid to keep away from children and pets.
- Wash your hands after applying (and removing) the patch.
- Rotate patch sites and do not apply to the same site for at least one week. Skin reactions can occur but they generally go away in a few days.
- Never cut the patch or wear more than one patch at a time.

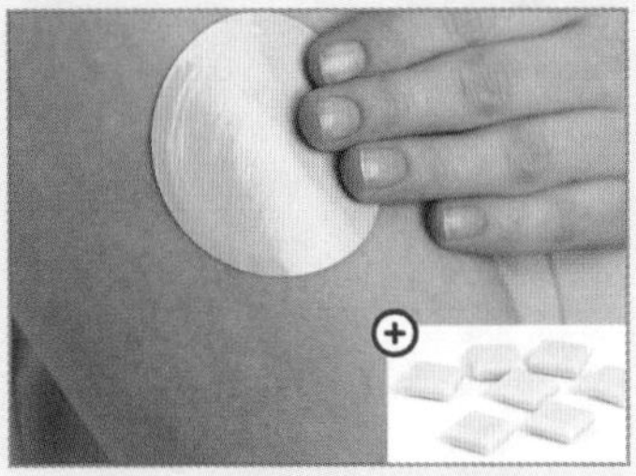

Use short-acting gum or lozenges to help with cravings while using the patch

NICOTINE LOZENGE AND INHALER

Nicotine Lozenge

- Place the lozenge in your mouth and let it dissolve slowly rather than chewing or swallowing it. You may feel a warm or tingling sensation. Move the lozenge from one side of the mouth to the other until it has completely dissolved (this could take 20 – 30 minutes).
- Do not use more than one lozenge at a time, or one lozenge after another continuously, as you may experience side effects, including hiccups, heartburn and nausea.
- Acidic beverages (e.g., coffee, juices, soft drinks) interfere with the buccal absorption of nicotine; you should wait 15 minutes after eating or drinking before use.

Nicotine Inhaler

- Puff on the inhaler in short, frequent breaths (similar to a pipe or cigar) and inhale deeply into the back of the throat.
- Each cartridge provides about 20 minutes of continuous puffing and is only good for one day after opening.
- You can develop a cough and mild irritation in the mouth and throat when you first use the inhaler. These side effects usually improve after a short time.
- Clean the mouthpiece with soap and water regularly.
- Keep the inhaler at room temperature. The amount of nicotine inhaled decreases in cold temperatures. In cold weather, keep the inhaler and cartridge in an inside pocket or other warm area.

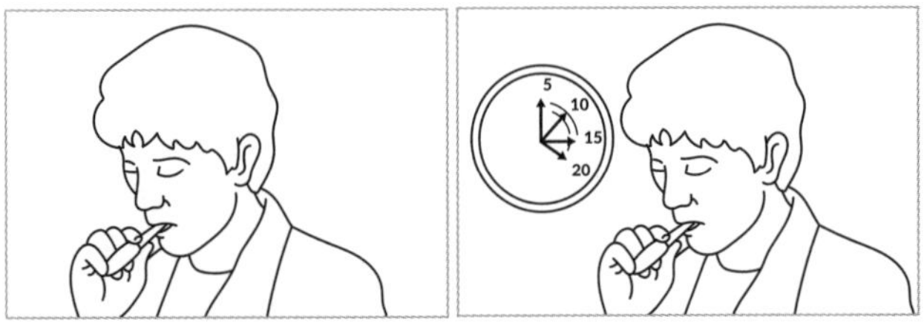

Nicotrol Inhaler (nicotine inhalation system) package insert. New York, NY: Pharmacia & Upjohn CO; 2019 Feb.

NICOTINE GUM

HOW TO CHEW NICOTINE GUM

- Chew slowly several times, until there is a "tingle" or peppery "flavor" in the mouth.
- "Park" between the cheek and gum.
- When the "tingle" or "flavor" goes away, begin chewing slowly again until it returns, then "park" the gum again.
- Repeat for a total time of about 30 minutes or until the "flavor" or "tingle" goes away completely.

NICOTINE NASAL SPRAY

- Blow your nose before use, if needed. Tilt your head back slightly and insert the tip of the bottle into the nostril. Spray once in each nostril while breathing through the mouth. Do not sniff, swallow, or inhale through the nose.
- You can experience sneezing, coughing, watery eyes, runny nose and a hot peppery feeling in the back of the throat when you first use the nasal spray. Wait five minutes after use before driving or operating heavy machinery. These side effects should lessen in a few days.

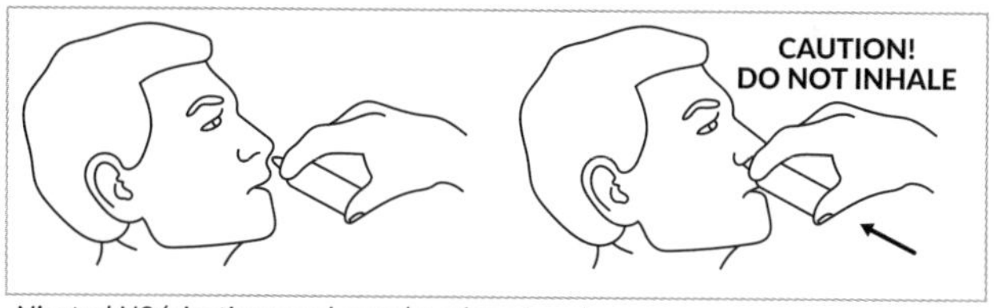

Nicotrol NS (nicotine nasal spray) package insert. New York, NY: Pharmacia & Upjohn CO; 2019 Feb.

BUPROPION AND VARENICLINE

- Start these medications at least one week before your quit date. This allows the medication to build up in the body to work. You can continue to use tobacco during this time. Try to stop using tobacco on your quit date.
- If changes in behavior or thinking are noticed, such as agitation, hostility, depressed mood or suicidal thoughts or actions, stop the medication and call your healthcare provider right away.

Bupropion

- The most common side effects are dry mouth and trouble sleeping. These are generally mild and often disappear after a few weeks.
- Do not take this medication if you have a seizure disorder, an eating disorder, take other forms of bupropion, or have taken an MAO inhibitor within the last 14 days.
- To decrease seizure risk, do not take more than prescribed. Swallow tablets whole; do not chew, cut, or crush tablets as the medication will be released into your body too quickly.
- If you are able to quit smoking with this medication, your healthcare provider may keep you on it for several months so you do not go back to smoking.

Varenicline

- The most common side effects are nausea and trouble sleeping. These are generally mild and often disappear after a few weeks. Take the second dose earlier than bedtime to decrease insomnia or a prescriber may adjust the dose.
- Take this medication after eating and with a full glass (8 ounces) of water.
- Most people will take this medication for up to 12 weeks. If you do not quit using tobacco by 12 weeks, reaffirm your motivation to quit smoking and consider another 12 weeks of therapy.
- Decrease the amount of alcohol you drink when you start this medication until you know whether it affects your tolerance. Some people have experienced increased drunkenness, unusual or sometimes aggressive behavior, and/or having no memory of things that have happened while drinking alcohol and using this medication.
- Use caution when driving or operating machinery until you know how this medication affects you.
- Some people can have serious reactions while taking this medication. It is important to stop taking *Chantix* and contact a healthcare provider if these symptoms occur:
  - ❑ Swelling of the face, mouth, tongue and neck.
  - ❑ Rash, redness, blistering and peeling of the skin.
- Not recommended to combine with other drugs that help you quit smoking.

Select Guidelines/References

Treating Tobacco Use and Dependence. 2008 Update. Content last reviewed October 2018. Agency for Healthcare Research and Quality, Rockville, MD. http://www.ahrq.gov/professionals/clinicians-providers/guidelines-recommendations/tobacco/index.html (accessed 2019 Jan 24).

44

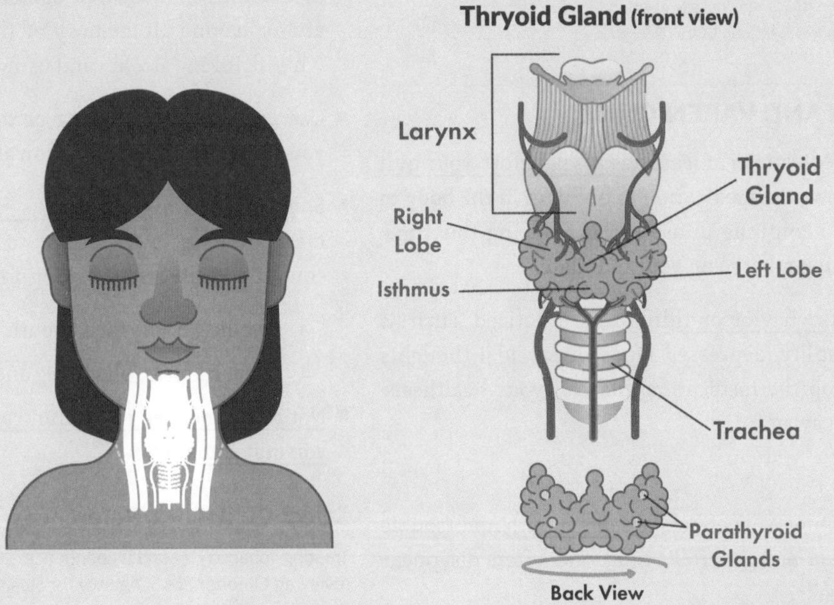

45

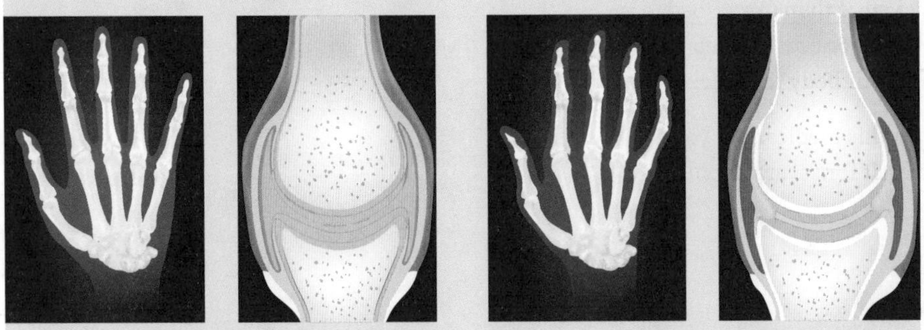

Hand normal joint

Cross section of joint

Hand with Rheumatoid arthritis

Cross section of joint with Rheumatoid arthritis

46

ENDOCRINE CONDITIONS

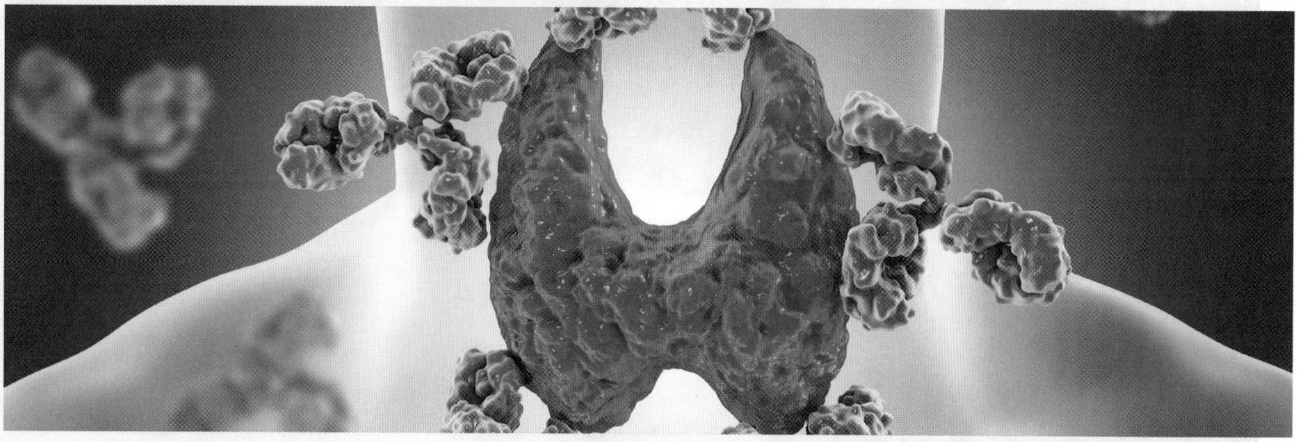

CONTENTS

CHAPTER 44
DIABETES | **636**

CHAPTER 45
THYROID DISORDERS | **664**

CHAPTER 46
SYSTEMIC STEROIDS & AUTOIMMUNE CONDITIONS | **671**

CHAPTER CONTENT

Background ... 636
Classification/Types of Diabetes ... 636
Type 1 Diabetes ... 636
Type 2 Diabetes ... 636
Prediabetes ... 637
Diabetes in Pregnancy ... 637
Risk Factors for Type 2 Diabetes ... 637
Diagnosis/Screening ... 637
Diagnostic Criteria ... 638
Non-Drug Treatment ... 638
Natural Products ... 638
Comprehensive Care ... 639
Complications of Diabetes ... 639
Antiplatelet Therapy ... 639
Cholesterol Control ... 639
Blood Pressure Control ... 639
Vaccinations ... 639
Neuropathy ... 640
Diabetic Kidney Disease ... 640
Retinopathy Screening and Treatment ... 640
Foot Care Patient Counseling ... 640
Glycemic (Blood Glucose) Control ... 641
Adult Treatment Goals (ADA) ... 641
Glycemic Targets for Non-Pregnant Adults with Diabetes ... 641
Drug-Induced Hyperglycemia ... 641
Drugs that Can Raise Blood Glucose ... 641
Treatment for Type 2 Diabetes ... 642
Treatment Algorithm ... 642
Primary Mechanisms of Action ... 642
Oral Medications For Type 2 Diabetes ... 643
Combination Products ... 643
Biguanide ... 643
Insulin Secretagogues ... 644
Thiazolidinediones ... 646
Sodium Glucose Co-Transporter 2 Inhibitors ... 647
Dipeptidyl Peptidase 4 Inhibitors ... 648
Other Oral Medications ... 648
Injectable Medications for Diabetes ... 649
Glucagon-Like Peptide 1 Agonists ... 649
Amylinomimetic (Amylin Analog) ... 652
Insulin ... 653
Concentrated Insulin Products ... 656
Insulin Dosing ... 656
Initiating Insulin in Type 1 Diabetes ... 656
Initiating Basal-Bolus Insulin ... 656
Insulin Calculations ... 656
Initiating and Adjusting Insulin in Type 2 Diabetes ... 657
Insulin Conversions ... 657
Insulin Administration Patient Counseling ... 657
Self-Monitoring Blood Glucose ... 658
Syringes and Needles ... 658
Multidose Pens (No Needle Included) ... 659
Injectable Drug Stability ... 659
Hypoglycemia ... 660
Select Drugs that Can Lower Blood Glucose ... 660
Inpatient Glucose Control ... 660
Hyperglycemic Crises ... 661
Hyperglycemic Crises Treatment ... 661
Selecting Drug Treatment ... 662
Factors to Consider When Selecting Drug Treatment ... 662

CONTENT LEGEND

= Study Tip Gal   = Key Drug Guy

CHAPTER 44
DIABETES

BACKGROUND

Diabetes is a common condition in the United States, affecting ~30 million Americans, or 9.4% of the population. Of these, 23 million are diagnosed and 7 million remain undiagnosed.

Diabetes is characterized by hyperglycemia due to decreased insulin secretion (from the pancreas), decreased insulin sensitivity (primarily in muscle cells) or both. Chronic hyperglycemia leads to many complications, including organ and nerve damage.

CLASSIFICATION/TYPES OF DIABETES

TYPE 1 DIABETES

Type 1 diabetes accounts for ~5% of all cases of diabetes. It is caused by an autoimmune destruction of the beta cells in the pancreas. These are the cells that produce insulin; once the beta cells are destroyed, insulin cannot be produced. Without insulin, glucose cannot enter muscle cells and fat is used as an alternative energy source. Fat breakdown produces ketones, and the ketones can cause diabetic ketoacidosis (DKA), which is life-threatening. Patients with type 1 diabetes must be treated with insulin and should be screened for other autoimmune disorders (e.g., thyroid disorders, celiac disease).

Type 1 diabetes usually presents in younger, thinner patients, but it can also occur in older patients; family history is the biggest risk factor. In some patients, it is difficult to distinguish between type 1 and type 2 diabetes, especially early in the disease. The C-peptide test is used to determine if the patient is still producing insulin.

TYPE 2 DIABETES

Type 2 diabetes accounts for ~95% of cases and is due to both insulin resistance (decreased insulin sensitivity) and insulin deficiency. The pancreatic beta cells produce less insulin over time as they become damaged. Hyperglycemia develops gradually and this is why the onset of type 2 diabetes is often not noticed. Type 2 diabetes is strongly associated with obesity, physical inactivity, family history and the presence of other comorbid conditions (see Risk Factors box). Type 2 diabetes is usually diagnosed in older patients and can be managed with lifestyle modifications alone (in a small minority of patients) or in combination with oral and/or injectable medication/s.

PREDIABETES

Prediabetes means that there is an increased risk of developing diabetes. Following dietary and exercise recommendations reduces the risk of progression from prediabetes to diabetes. Metformin can be used to help improve blood glucose levels, especially in patients with a BMI ≥ 35 kg/m², age < 60 years and women with a history of gestational diabetes mellitus (GDM). Annual monitoring for development of diabetes and treatment of modifiable cardiovascular disease (CVD) risk factors are recommended.

DIABETES IN PREGNANCY

Diabetes in pregnancy consists of either women who develop diabetes during pregnancy (gestational diabetes mellitus, or GDM) or women who had diabetes prior to becoming pregnant (pre-gestational diabetes). In both types, the blood glucose targets are more stringent than the targets for the non-pregnant population with diabetes (see Goals box); they are closer to normal non-diabetes levels to help keep the mother and the baby healthy. If the mother has uncontrolled diabetes in pregnancy, the baby can be large (macrosomia), will be at risk for hypoglycemia at birth, and will have a high risk for childhood obesity and type 2 diabetes. Women who develop GDM have an increased risk of developing type 2 diabetes later in life.

The first step in diabetes management during pregnancy is lifestyle modifications (diet and exercise). Frequent self-monitoring of blood glucose (SMBG) is used to assess if lifestyle modifications are adequate; if not, insulin is the preferred treatment. Metformin or glyburide can be considered, but both cross the placenta. Long-term safety in offspring is not known and glyburide is associated with higher rates of neonatal hypoglycemia and macrosomia.

GOALS FOR DIABETES IN PREGNANCY

Fasting: ≤ 95 mg/dL

1 hour post-meal: ≤ 140 mg/dL

2 hours post-meal: ≤ 120 mg/dL

RISK FACTORS FOR TYPE 2 DIABETES

Overweight (BMI ≥ 25 kg/m2 *or* ≥ 23 kg/m2 in Asian Americans*)	Physical inactivity	High-risk race/ethnicity (African American, Latino, Native American, Asian American*, Pacific Islander)
Hypertension (≥ 140/90 mmHg *or* taking medications for hypertension)	A1C ≥ 5.7%, impaired glucose tolerance *or* impaired fasting glucose on previous testing	First-degree relative with diabetes
HDL < 35 mg/dL *and/or* TG > 250 mg/dL	History of CVD	History of gestational diabetes mellitus
Women with polycystic ovary syndrome	Other clinical conditions associated with insulin resistance (e.g., severe obesity, acanthosis nigricans)	Current Smoker

**Asian Americans have a higher risk of diabetes at a lower BMI*

DIAGNOSIS/SCREENING

Signs and Symptoms

Classic symptoms of hyperglycemia include polyuria (excessive urination), polyphagia (excessive hunger or increased appetite), polydipsia (excessive thirst), blurred vision and fatigue. In type 1 diabetes, especially in children, DKA is commonly the initial presentation and is caused by a total deficiency in insulin. DKA seldom occurs in type 2 diabetes unless it is associated with the stress of another illness, such as an infection.

Screening

All asymptomatic adults should be screened for type 2 diabetes by assessing for risk factors (see Risk Factors box) or by using a risk assessment tool (e.g., www.diabetes.org/are-you-at-risk/diabetes-risk-test/). Adults who are overweight or obese (BMI ≥ 25 kg/m² or ≥ 23 kg/m² in Asian Americans), and who have one or more additional risk factors, should be tested for type 2 diabetes and prediabetes. Children and adolescents who are overweight or obese and have at least one additional risk factor should also be tested. In patients without risk factors, testing should start at 45 years of age. All pregnant women should be screened at their initial prenatal visit and at 24 - 28 weeks gestation.

Diagnosis

The criteria for diagnosis varies based on the type of test used (see Study Tip Gal); no single test is preferred over another. Diagnosis should be confirmed with repeat testing for fasting plasma glucose (FPG), oral glucose tolerance test (OGTT) and hemoglobin A1C (A1C), unless two test results are above the diagnostic threshold. Fasting is defined as no caloric intake for at least eight hours. Normal test results should be repeated at least every three years.

> **DIAGNOSTIC CRITERIA**
>
> 
>
> **Diagnosis of Prediabetes**
> - FPG 100-125 mg/dL
>
>   *or*
> - 2-hr PG of 140-199 mg/dL after a 75-g OGTT
>
>   *or*
> - A1C 5.7-6.4%
>
> **Diagnosis of Diabetes**
> - Classic symptoms of hyperglycemia or hyperglycemic crisis AND a random plasma glucose ≥ 200 mg/dL
>
>   *or*
> - FPG ≥ 126 mg/dL*
>
>   *or*
> - 2-hr PG ≥ 200 mg/dL after a 75-g OGTT*
>
>   *or*
> - A1C ≥ 6.5%*
>
> ** Diagnosis requires 2 abnormal tests from either different blood samples or the same blood sample.*

NON-DRUG TREATMENT

Lifestyle modifications should be used alone or in combination with medications when necessary to meet treatment goals. All patients who smoke should quit (see Tobacco Cessation chapter). Psychosocial assessment and emotional well-being are important components of diabetes care and self-management.

Weight Loss

Weight loss improves blood glucose, blood pressure and cholesterol levels. Overweight or obese patients should be encouraged to lose > 5% of their body weight through diet, physical activity and behavioral therapy. Reducing weekly calorie intake by 3,500 kcal will result in a one pound weight loss. Waist circumference should be < 35 inches for females and < 40 inches for males. If unable to achieve these goals with lifestyle changes alone, medications can help (see Weight Loss chapter). Surgery is recommended in patients with diabetes and BMI ≥ 40 or those with BMI 35–39.9 who do not achieve adequate weight loss and improvement in comorbidities with non-surgical methods.

Nutrition

Patients with diabetes should receive individualized medical nutrition therapy (MNT). Various diets have been shown to provide benefit, including Mediterranean-style diets, the Dietary Approaches to Stop Hypertension (DASH) plan, plant-based diets (vegan or vegetarian) and lower-fat or lower-carbohydrate diets. Low-carbohydrate diets are not recommended in pregnant or breastfeeding females, those with an eating disorder, renal disease or taking sodium glucose co-transporter 2 (SGLT2) inhibitors (due to risk of ketoacidosis). Carbohydrates from vegetables, fruits, whole grains, legumes, dairy products and those high in fiber should be selected over other carbohydrate sources, especially those that contain added fat, sugar or sodium. Increased intake of long-chain omega-3 fatty acids from foods such as fatty fish, and omega-3 linolenic acid (ALA) from foods such as flaxseed and soy, is recommended. The recommendations for saturated fat, cholesterol, *trans* fat and sodium intake are the same as that for the general population. Sugar-sweetened beverages should be avoided. Drinking alcohol increases risk of hypoglycemia in a patient with diabetes. If alcohol is consumed it should be done so in moderation (≤ 1 drink/day for females, ≤ 2 drinks/day for males).

Patients with type 1 diabetes should use the carbohydrate-counting meal planning approach, where the prandial (mealtime) insulin dose is adjusted to the carbohydrate intake. If the insulin dose is fixed (not adjusted based on the grams of carbohydrates in the meal), then the carbohydrate intake needs to be constant. A carbohydrate serving is measured as 15 grams, which is approximately one small piece of fruit, 1 slice of bread, ⅓ cup of cooked rice/pasta or ½ cup of oatmeal.

Physical Activity

Changing sedentary (long hours of sitting) habits reduces the risk of hyperglycemia. Patients should be instructed to "get up and move" every 30 minutes, at a minimum. Adults with diabetes should perform at least 150 minutes of moderate-intensity aerobic activity per week spread over at least 3 days. Resistance training, such as weight lifting, is recommended at least twice weekly. Flexibility and balance training is recommended in older adults.

Smoking Cessation

Smoking is a risk factor for developing type 2 diabetes. Tobacco use should be assessed regularly and smoking cessation encouraged with each healthcare visit (see Tobacco Cessation chapter).

NATURAL PRODUCTS

The ADA guidelines advise against the use of natural products for patients with diabetes due to a lack of evidence. Some products that have been used by patients include cinnamon, alpha lipoic acid, vitamin D, garlic, chromium and ginseng. See the Dietary Supplements, Natural & Complementary Medicine chapter for more details.

COMPREHENSIVE CARE

In addition to glycemic control, treatment in patients with diabetes is aimed at preventing long-term macrovascular and microvascular complications. ADA has the following recommendations for monitoring, preventing and treating complications of uncontrolled diabetes.

COMPLICATIONS OF DIABETES

Microvascular Disease

Retinopathy (most common)

Diabetic kidney disease (may progress to ESRD)

Peripheral neuropathy (↑ risk for foot infections and amputations)

Autonomic neuropathy (erectile dysfunction, gastroparesis, loss of bladder control/UTIs)

Macrovascular Disease (ASCVD)

Coronary artery disease (e.g., MI, stable angina)

Cerebrovascular disease (e.g., TIA/stroke)

Peripheral artery disease

Antiplatelet Therapy

- Aspirin (75–162 mg/day) should be used for secondary prevention in any patient with ASCVD. Clopidogrel 75 mg/day is recommended if there is an aspirin allergy or contraindication.
- Aspirin (75–162 mg/day) can be considered for primary prevention in patients with type 1 and type 2 diabetes who have increased ASCVD risk after discussion between provider and patient on the benefits and risks (increased risk of bleeding).
- Low-dose aspirin should also be used in pregnant patients with type 1 or type 2 diabetes to reduce the risk of preeclampsia. This should be started in the first trimester and continued until the baby is born.

Blood Pressure Control

- The BP goals from ADA differ from the 2017.
- ACC/AHA Guideline for the Management of High Blood Pressure (see Hypertension chapter). The ADA makes these recommendations:
  - Patients with diabetes, hypertension and ASCVD (or 10-year ASCVD risk > 15%) have a BP goal < 130/80 mmHg.
  - Patients with diabetes, hypertension and 10-year ASCVD risk < 15% have a BP goal < 140/90 mmHg.
- Most patients will require two or more medications to achieve BP targets; two drugs should be initiated at baseline if the BP is ≥ 160/100 mmHg.
- The ACC/AHA and ADA guidelines both recommend that one or more antihypertensive medications be taken at bedtime.

Cholesterol Control

- Fasting lipid panel should be obtained at diagnosis of diabetes, initial medical evaluation and every five years thereafter (more frequently if indicated).
- Once statin treatment is initiated, lipid panel should be obtained 4–12 weeks after drug initiation or dose change and annually thereafter.
- Patients with a fasting TG level ≥ 500 mg/dL should be evaluated for secondary causes and medical therapy should be considered to reduce the risk of pancreatitis.
- Statin therapy is indicated in most patients with diabetes, and intensity of dosing is based on ASCVD history. Treatment is guided by both the ADA guidelines and the 2018 ACC/AHA Guideline on the Treatment of Blood Cholesterol (see Dyslipidemia chapter). The ADA makes these recommendations:
  - Patients with clinical ASCVD or 10-year ASCVD risk > 20%: high-intensity statin
  - Patients without ASCVD and age 40–75 years:
    - ✓ Moderate-intensity statin
  - Patients without ASCVD and age < 40 years:
    - ✓ No ASCVD risk factors: statin not recommended
    - ✓ ASCVD risk factors: moderate-intensity statin
- Additional LDL lowering medications (PCSK9 inhibitor or preferably ezetimibe) are recommended in patients with ASCVD and LDL cholesterol ≥ 70 mg/dL on a maximally tolerated statin.

Vaccinations

- Patients with diabetes have higher rates of hepatitis B, hospitalizations and mortality from influenza and pneumococcal diseases.
- Patients with diabetes should receive all age appropriate routine vaccinations, an annual influenza vaccine (not live), hepatitis B series and the pneumococcal vaccines *Prevnar 13* and *Pneumovax 23* (see Immunizations chapter).

Neuropathy

- Patients with diabetes are at increased risk for foot ulcers and amputations due to the loss of protective sensation (LOPS) often with peripheral neuropathy and PAD.
- The 10-g monofilament and at least one additional test (pinprick, temperature or vibration sensation) should be performed annually for diabetic peripheral neuropathy.
- Signs and symptoms of autonomic neuropathy (e.g., gastroparesis, neurogenic bladder, erectile dysfunction) should be assessed in those who have peripheral neuropathy or other microvascular complications.
- A comprehensive foot exam should be performed at least annually with visual examination of the skin for dryness/cracking, signs of infection, ulcers, bunions, calluses and other deformities, such as claw toes.
- Screening for peripheral neuropathy and PAD [e.g., assessment of claudication, pedal pulses and an ankle-brachial index (ABI)] is recommended.
- Patients with sensory loss in the feet, prior amputations and ulcers should have their feet inspected at every healthcare visit. Patients who smoke, have LOPS, structural abnormalities, PAD or a prior lower-extremity complication should be referred to a foot care specialist.
- Optimizing blood glucose helps avoid and delay the progression of neuropathy.
- Pregabalin, duloxetine and tapentadol are FDA-approved treatments but the ADA guidelines recommend pregabalin, duloxetine or gabapentin first-line. Tapentadol, tramadol and opioids are not recommended due to safety and addiction concerns. Other drugs that can be considered include tricyclic antidepressants (TCAs), venlafaxine, carbamazepine and topical capsaicin.

Diabetic Kidney Disease

- Diabetic kidney disease is the leading cause of end-stage renal disease (ESRD).
- A urine test is performed annually to measure urine albumin excretion as an indicator of disease progression.
- An ACE inhibitor or ARB (but not both in combination) should be started in nonpregnant patients with a urinary albumin excretion ≥ 30 mg/24 hours [or urine albumin-to-creatinine ratio (UACR) ≥ 30 mg/g]. A level < 30 mg/24 hours is considered normal.
- Optimizing blood glucose and BP and using an ACE inhibitor or ARB helps to slow the progression of diabetic kidney disease and delay or prevent renal failure.

CLINICAL SCENARIOS

Patient with diabetes and hypertension, but no albuminuria
- Thiazide, CCB, ACE inhibitor or ARB

Patient with diabetes and albuminuria, but no hypertension
- ACE inhibitor or ARB

Patient with diabetes, hypertension and albuminuria
- ACE inhibitor or ARB (add thiazide or CCB as needed)

Retinopathy Screening and Treatment

- Diabetic retinopathy is the leading cause of blindness in adults.
- A dilated, comprehensive eye exam is performed by an ophthalmologist or optometrist at diagnosis (type 2 diabetes) or within five years of diabetes onset (type 1 diabetes). If the patient has one or more normal eye exams and blood glucose is well controlled, screening is every two years. Patients with any degree of retinopathy should have annual exams.
- Women with preexisting diabetes who become pregnant are at higher risk for development and/or progression of retinopathy. These patients should be monitored each trimester and up to one year postpartum.
- Smoking cessation and optimizing blood glucose, BP and cholesterol reduces the risk and slows the progression of retinopathy.
- Ranibizumab *(Lucentis)*, a once monthly intravitreal injection, is FDA-approved for diabetic retinopathy.

Foot Care Patient Counseling

- Wash and dry feet daily. Apply moisturizer to tops and bottoms of feet.

- Check feet daily

- Trim toenails with a nail file

- Wear socks and shoes

- Elevate feet when sitting

GLYCEMIC (BLOOD GLUCOSE) CONTROL

ADULT TREATMENT GOALS (ADA)

A1C: < 7%

Preprandial plasma glucose: 80-130 mg/dL

Peak postprandial plasma glucose: < 180 mg/dL

GLYCEMIC TARGETS FOR NON-PREGNANT ADULTS WITH DIABETES

Two primary techniques for assessing glycemic control are self-monitoring of blood glucose (SMBG), using a glucose meter to test capillary plasma glucose, and measurement of glycosylated hemoglobin (A1C). Continuous Glucose Monitoring (CGM) is used in combination with SMBG in select patients (e.g., frequent hypoglycemia, intensive insulin regimens). See SMBG section later in chapter.

The A1C should be measured quarterly in patients who are not at goal, or when treatment has recently changed, and at least twice per year if patients are at goal and have stable glycemic control. Use of point-of-care (POC) testing for A1C allows for more timely treatment changes. Some patients have an individualized A1C goal that is more stringent (e.g., < 6.5%) or less stringent (e.g., < 8%), based on patient-specific factors assessed by the healthcare provider.

While SMBG measures the blood glucose at a given moment, the A1C measures the average blood glucose over the past 2 – 3 months. Estimated average glucose (eAG) can be easier for patients to understand than A1C. Data has shown that an A1C of 6% is equivalent to an eAG of 126 mg/dL, and with each 1% increase in A1C, the eAG increases by approximately 28 mg/dL. The estimated average glucose can be quickly determined with the following formula: (A1C - 2) x 30. For example, an A1C of 7% would be roughly equivalent to 150 mg/dL [(7 - 2) x 30 = 150].

DRUG-INDUCED HYPERGLYCEMIA

When assessing glycemic control, it is important to review the full medication profile for drugs that can cause hyperglycemia (see Key Drugs Guy). In most cases, the mechanism is reduced insulin secretion or sensitivity. Use of some of these drugs is unavoidable (e.g., to control BP or cholesterol) and the benefits might outweigh the risks. Use of other drugs (e.g., steroids, antipsychotics, protease inhibitors) will require close monitoring. Patients should be counseled about the risks of hyperglycemia when using these drugs, as well as symptoms of hyperglycemia. Some medications can cause hypoglycemia or hyperglycemia (see Hypoglycemia section for further discussion).

DRUGS THAT CAN RAISE BLOOD GLUCOSE

KEY DRUGS

- Beta-blockers*
- Cough syrups (OTC and Rx)
- Diuretics (thiazides/loops)
- Immunosuppressants (e.g., cyclosporine, tacrolimus)
- Niacin
- Protease inhibitors
- Quinolones*
- Second-generation (atypical) antipsychotics (e.g., clozapine, olanzapine, quetiapine)
- Statins
- Systemic steroids

Others:

- Azole antifungals (esp. posaconazole)
- Beta-agonists
- Diazoxide
- Inteferon alfas
- Octreotide*

** Can also cause hypoglycemia (see Hypoglycemia section)*

> ***There are a lot of people with diabetes; consequently, there are a lot of drugs. At the end of the chapter is a summary page on how to pick the right drug for a patient. Get through the detail first. The summary page (Selecting Drug Treatment) will pull it all together.***

TREATMENT FOR TYPE 2 DIABETES

The goal of treatment is to maintain blood glucose levels and avoid long-term complications of hyperglycemia. The ADA guideline recommendations provide options for initial treatment, and add-on therapy, based on quarterly assessment of the A1C. Patients often require more than one medication to achieve blood glucose goals. Macrovascular complications indicate the presence of atherosclerotic cardiovascular disease (ASCVD), which is more likely to develop in patients with ASCVD risk factors (diabetes, hypertension, dyslipidemia, smoking, albuminuria and family history of premature ASCVD). ASCVD is the leading cause of morbidity and mortality in patients with diabetes. The ADA recommends specific drugs with proven cardiovascular benefit in patients with long-standing uncontrolled type 2 diabetes and established ASCVD. These specific drugs have been shown to decrease cardiovascular and all-cause mortality when added to standard treatment (see treatment algorithm for specific drugs).

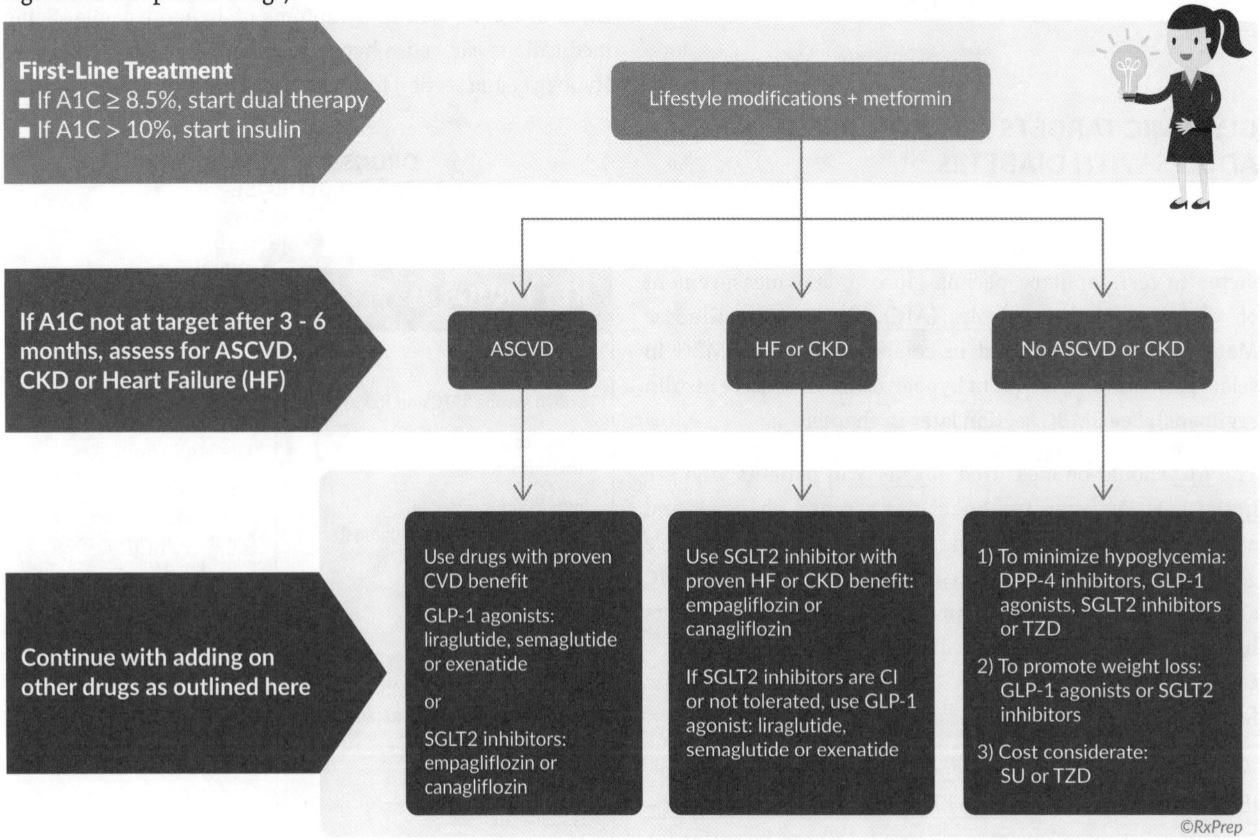

ASCVD includes: acute coronary syndromes, history of myocardial infarction, stable or unstable angina, coronary or other arterial revascularization, stroke, transient ischemic attack, or peripheral arterial disease

SU = sulfonylurea, TZD = thiazolidinediones, DPP-4 = dipeptidyl peptidase 4, SGLT2 = sodium glucose co-transporter 2, GLP-1 = glucagon-like peptide 1

PRIMARY MECHANISMS OF ACTION

When combination treatment is needed, drugs that have different mechanisms of action should be used. Medications can target insulin resistance, hormones that regulate blood glucose (insulin and glucagon), or they can increase removal of glucose from the body. Combination products (see table on following page) can help with adherence.

↑/REPLACES INSULIN SECRETION	↓ HEPATIC GLUCOSE OUTPUT	↓ GLUCAGON* WHICH ↓ GLUCOSE PRODUCTION	SLOWS GASTRIC EMPTYING (↑ SATIETY)	↑ GLUCOSE EXCRETION	↑ INSULIN SENSITIVITY
Insulin	Metformin	GLP-1 agonists	GLP-1 agonists	SGLT2 inhibitors	TZDs
SUs		DPP-4 inhibitors	Pramlintide		Metformin
Meglitinides		Pramlintide			

**Glucagon is produced by the pancreas; it stimulates the conversion of glycogen (stored glucose in the liver) to glucose*

ORAL MEDICATIONS FOR TYPE 2 DIABETES

COMBINATION DRUGS FOR DIABETES

METFORMIN + SULFONYLUREA

Metformin/glipizide

Metformin/glyburide *(Glucovance*)*

METFORMIN + THIAZOLIDINEDIONE

Metformin/pioglitazone *(Actoplus Met, Actoplus Met XR)*

METFORMIN + DPP-4 INHIBITOR

Metformin/alogliptin *(Kazano)*

Metformin/linagliptin *(Jentadueto, Jentadueto XR)*

Metformin/sitagliptin *(Janumet*, *Janumet XR)*

Metformin/saxagliptin *(Kombiglyze XR)*

METFORMIN + SGLT2 INHIBITOR

Metformin/canagliflozin *(Invokamet, Invokamet XR)*

Metformin/dapagliflozin *(Xigduo XR)*

Metformin/empagliflozin *(Synjardy, Synjardy XR)*

Metformin/ertugliflozin *(Segluromet)*

**Brand discontinued but name still used in practice.*

METFORMIN + MEGLITINIDE

Metformin/repaglinide *(PrandiMet)*

SULFONYLUREA + THIAZOLIDINEDIONE

Glimepiride/pioglitazone *(Duetact)*

DPP-4 INHIBITOR + THIAZOLIDINEDIONE

Alogliptin/pioglitazone *(Oseni)*

DPP-4 INHIBITOR + SGLT2 INHIBITOR

Linagliptin/empagliflozin *(Glyxambi)*

Saxagliptin/dapagliflozin *(Qtern)*

Sitagliptin/ertugliflozin *(Steglujan)*

GLP-1 AGONIST + LONG-ACTING INSULIN

Liraglutide/insulin degludec *(Xultophy)*

Lixisenatide/insulin glargine *(Soliqua)*

Does not include premixed insulins - see Insulin section

BIGUANIDE

Metformin primarily works by ↓ hepatic glucose production, ↓ intestinal absorption of glucose and ↑ insulin sensitivity. Metformin is first-line treatment for type 2 diabetes and can be used in prediabetes. Use of metformin is dependent on estimated glomerular filtration rate (eGFR); see Renal Disease chapter.

DRUG	DOSING	SAFETY/SIDE EFFECTS/MONITORING
Metformin *(Glucophage, Glucophage XR, Fortamet, Glumetza,* *Riomet)* IR: 500, 850, 1,000 mg ER: 500, 750, 1,000 mg *Riomet* liquid: 500 mg/5 mL	IR: 500 mg BID or 850 mg daily initially ER: 500-1,000 mg daily with dinner initially Titrate by 500 mg weekly or 850 mg every 2 weeks Max dose: 2,000-2,550 mg/day (varies by product) eGFR 30-45 mL/min/1.73 m^2: not recommended to start, consider dose ↓ 50% if already on drug eGFR < 30 mL/min/1.73 m^2: contraindicated	**BOXED WARNING** Lactic acidosis – risk ↑ with hypoxic states (e.g., acute HF, sepsis), dehydration, hepatic or renal impairment, age ≥ 65 years, intravascular iodinated contrast media, alcohol or certain drugs (see Drug Interactions) **CONTRAINDICATIONS** eGFR < 30 mL/min/1.73 m^2, acute or chronic metabolic acidosis (includes DKA), with or without coma **WARNINGS** Not recommended to initiate with eGFR 30-45 mL/min/1.73 m^2; assess benefit if already taking and eGFR falls below 45 mL/min/1.73 m^2 Vitamin B12 deficiency **SIDE EFFECTS** N/V/D, flatulence, abdominal cramping **MONITORING** BG, A1C, renal function, B12 **NOTES** ↓ A1C 1-2% Give with a meal to ↓ GI upset ER: swallow whole; do not crush, break or chew ER formulations can leave a ghost tablet (empty shell) in the stool

Metformin Drug Interactions

- Alcohol can ↑ the risk for lactic acidosis; excessive intake, acute or chronic, should be avoided.
- Intravascular iodinated contrast media (used for imaging studies) can ↑ the risk of lactic acidosis. Discontinue metformin at the time of, or before the imaging procedure, in patients with an eGFR between 30 – 60 mL/min/1.73 m^2 or a history of hepatic disease, alcoholism or heart failure. Metformin can be restarted 48 hours after the procedure if the eGFR is stable.
- The combination of metformin and topiramate can ↑ the risk of metabolic acidosis.

Metformin Patient Counseling

- Diarrhea, nausea, vomiting, abdominal discomfort and flatulence can occur. These side effects often go away with time. It is best to take this medication with food (evening meal for once daily doses).
- A very rare, life-threatening condition called lactic acidosis can develop while taking metformin. Seek emergency medical help if you have any of these symptoms: feeling weak or tired, slow or irregular heartbeat, unusual muscle pain, trouble breathing, unusual stomach pain, dizziness or feeling cold.
- If you need to have any type of procedure using a contrast dye, you likely need to temporarily stop taking metformin.
- Do not crush, chew or break extended-release tablets. Swallow the pill whole; it is made to release the medication slowly into the body. Breaking the pill releases too much of the drug at one time.
- If using *Glumetza, Fortamet* or *Glucophage XR*, you might see a shell of the medication in the stool. This is normal, the drug is in your body and the tablet is empty.
- This medication can cause low levels of vitamin B12 when used long-term. If you have anemia or peripheral neuropathy, you might need to have B12 levels checked periodically.

INSULIN SECRETAGOGUES

Sulfonylureas (SUs) and meglitinides are known as insulin secretagogues; they work by stimulating insulin secretion from the pancreatic beta cells to decrease postprandial blood glucose. Meglitinides have a faster onset (15 – 60 minutes) and a shorter duration of action compared to the SUs. They require multiple daily dosing so use is typically restricted to patients with an irregular meal schedule, those who develop late postprandial hypoglycemia with SUs or instead of SUs in patients with sulfa allergies. Older, first generation SUs (chlorpropamide, tolazamide and tolbutamide) should not be used as they can cause prolonged hypoglycemia. Meglitinide names end in "-glinide" and sulfonylurea names start with "G" and end in "-ide."

Meglitinides

DRUG	DOSING	SAFETY/SIDE EFFECTS/MONITORING
Repaglinide *(Prandin)*	0.5-2 mg before each meal (TID AC) Titrate at weekly intervals to max dose of 16 mg daily Take 15-30 minutes before meals	**CONTRAINDICATIONS** Type 1 diabetes, DKA Repaglinide: use with gemfibrozil **WARNINGS** Hypoglycemia, caution with severe liver/renal impairment **SIDE EFFECTS** Weight gain, headache, upper respiratory tract infections (URTIs) **MONITORING** BG, A1C **NOTES** ↓ A1C 0.5-1.5%
Nateglinide *(Starlix)*	60-120 mg before each meal (TID AC) Take 1-30 minutes before meals	

Sulfonylureas

DRUG	DOSING	SAFETY/SIDE EFFECTS/MONITORING
Glipizide ***(Glucotrol, Glucotrol XL,*** Glipizide XL)	IR: 5 mg daily, ↑ by 2.5-5 mg every few days; max dose = 40 mg/day; daily doses > 15 mg should be divided BID XL: 5 mg daily, titrate to a max dose of 20 mg/day	**CONTRAINDICATIONS** Type 1 diabetes, DKA, sulfa allergy (not likely to cross-react – see Drug Allergies & Adverse Drug Reactions chapter) Glyburide: use with bosentan **WARNINGS** Hypoglycemia Glimepiride: hypersensitivity reactions (e.g., anaphylaxis, angioedema, SJS) **SIDE EFFECTS** Weight gain, nausea **MONITORING** BG, A1C **NOTES** ↓ A1C 1-2% ↓ efficacy after long-term use (as pancreatic beta cell function declines) Glipizide IR is taken 30 minutes before a meal; all other products take with breakfast or the first meal of the day; may need to hold doses if NPO *Glucotrol XL* is in an OROS formulation (see Learning Drug Formulations chapter) and can leave a ghost tablet (empty shell) in the stool Glyburide has a weakly active metabolite that is renally cleared, and is not a preferred drug in patients with renal insufficiency Glyburide tablets cannot be used interchangeably with micronized tablet formulations, which have better absorption Glimepiride, glyburide and chlorpropamide are higher risk drugs in elderly, on The Beers Criteria Patients with G6PD deficiency can be at increased risk of hemolytic anemia with sulfonylureas
Glimepiride ***(Amaryl)***	1-2 mg daily, ↑ by 1-2 mg every 1-2 weeks; max dose = 8 mg/day	
Glyburide **Micronized glyburide *(Glynase)***	Glyburide: 2.5-5 mg daily, ↑ by 2.5 mg weekly; max dose = 20 mg/day *Glynase:* 1.5-3 mg daily, ↑ by 1.5 mg weekly; max dose = 12 mg/day	

Sulfonylurea and Meglitinide Drug Interactions

- Insulin in combination with either SUs or meglitinides ↑ risk of hypoglycemia and should be avoided.
- A reduction in SU or meglitinide dose might be required when a TZD, GLP-1 agonist, DPP-4 inhibitor or SGLT2 inhibitor is initiated. Use caution with other drugs that can decrease blood glucose (see Hypoglycemia section).
- Sulfonylureas are CYP450 2C9 substrates; use caution with drugs that are CYP2C9 inducers or inhibitors.
- Gemfibrozil and clopidogrel can ↑ repaglinide concentrations leading to ↓ blood glucose.
- Alcohol can ↑ the risk for delayed hypoglycemia when taking insulin or insulin secretagogues.

Sulfonylurea and Meglitinide Patient Counseling

- This medication can cause low blood sugar, which is more likely if you skip a meal, exercise too long, drink alcohol or are under stress.
- Very low blood sugar can cause seizures (convulsions), fainting or coma. Always keep a source of sugar available in case you have symptoms of low blood sugar.
- Sulfonylureas should be taken with breakfast (except glipizide IR is taken 30 minutes before meals).
- Take repaglinide 15 – 30 minutes before meals and nateglinide 1 – 30 minutes before meals. If you forget to take a dose until after eating, skip that dose and take only your next regularly scheduled dose, before a meal. If you plan to skip a meal, skip the dose for that meal.
- Keep this medication away from children, even one tablet can be dangerous.
- Do not crush, chew or break extended-release tablets. Swallow the pill whole; it is made to release the medication slowly into the body. Breaking the pill would release too much of the drug at one time.

THIAZOLIDINEDIONES

Thiazolidinediones (TZDs) are peroxisome proliferator-activated receptor gamma (PPARγ) agonists that cause ↑ peripheral insulin sensitivity (↑ uptake and utilization of glucose by the peripheral tissues, also known as insulin sensitizers). Names of TZDs end in "-glitazone."

DRUG	DOSING	SAFETY/SIDE EFFECTS/MONITORING
Pioglitazone (*Actos*)	Initial: 15-30 mg daily NYHA Class I/II heart failure: start with 15 mg daily Max dose: 45 mg daily	**BOXED WARNINGS** Can cause or exacerbate heart failure Rosiglitazone: increased risk of MI **CONTRAINDICATIONS** NYHA Class III/IV heart failure **WARNINGS** Hepatic failure, edema (including macular edema), risk of fractures Ovulation can occur in premenopausal anovulatory women, which can lead to unintended pregnancy; contraception is recommended in all premenopausal women Pioglitazone: increased risk of urinary bladder tumors; do not use in patients with active bladder cancer and consider risk in patients with a prior history of bladder cancer **SIDE EFFECTS** Peripheral edema, weight gain, URTIs, myalgia Pioglitazone: ↑ HDL, ↓ TGs and ↓ total cholesterol **MONITORING** LFTs, BG, A1C, s/sx of heart failure **NOTES** ↓ A1C 0.5-1.4% Take without regard to meals
Rosiglitazone (*Avandia*)	4-8 mg daily Max dose: 8 mg daily	

Thiazolidinedione Drug Interactions

- These medications are major substrates of CYP450 2C8; use caution with drugs that are CYP2C8 inducers (e.g., rifampin) or inhibitors (e.g., gemfibrozil).

Thiazolidinedione Patient Counseling

- Take once daily, with or without food. It can take several weeks for this medication to work.
- This drug can cause your body to keep extra fluid (water retention), which can cause swelling, weight gain and heart problems such as heart failure. Inform your healthcare provider right away if you have trouble breathing (especially when you lie down), swelling in the ankles or legs, unusual or fast weight gain or if you feel unusually tired.
- Women are more likely than men to have bone fractures while taking this medication. Talk with your healthcare provider if you are concerned about this possibility.
- Contact your healthcare provider right away if you are passing dark-colored urine, have decreased appetite, stomach pain, nausea or vomiting, feel more tired than usual or if your skin and/or whites of your eyes become yellow. These are signs of liver damage.
- Tell your healthcare provider if you have heart failure, heart disease or liver problems. For pioglitazone, tell your healthcare provider if you have or have had bladder cancer.

SODIUM GLUCOSE CO-TRANSPORTER 2 INHIBITORS

The sodium glucose co-transporter 2 (SGLT2) protein, expressed in the proximal renal tubules, is responsible for the reabsorption of filtered glucose. By inhibiting SGLT2, these drugs reduce reabsorption of glucose and ↑ urinary glucose excretion and thereby ↓ plasma glucose concentrations. SGLT2 inhibitors are dosed based on eGFR (see Renal Disease chapter). Names of SGLT2 inhibitors end in "-gliflozin."

DRUG	DOSING	SAFETY/SIDE EFFECTS/MONITORING
Canagliflozin *(Invokana)*	100 mg daily prior to the first meal of the day; can ↑ to 300 mg daily eGFR 45-59 mL/min/1.73 m²: 100 mg max dose eGFR 30-44 mL/min/1.73 m²: not recommended eGFR < 30 mL/min/1.73 m²: contraindicated	**BOXED WARNING (CANAGLIFLOZIN)** Increased risk of leg and foot amputations; evaluate risk prior to treatment (history of amputation, PAD, peripheral neuropathy and/or diabetic foot ulcers) **CONTRAINDICATIONS** Severe renal impairment (eGFR < 30 mL/min/1.73 m²), ESRD or on dialysis **WARNINGS** Ketoacidosis (including fatal cases), genital mycotic infections, urosepsis and pyelonephritis, necrotizing fasciitis of the perineum, ↑ LDL, risk of fractures (primarily seen with canagliflozin) Hypotension, acute kidney injury and renal impairment (due to intravascular volume depletion) Canagliflozin: hyperkalemia Dapagliflozin: risk of bladder cancer **SIDE EFFECTS** Weight loss, hypoglycemia, ↑ urination, ↑ thirst, ↑ Mg/PO4 **MONITORING** Renal function, BG, A1C, LDL, BP, volume status **NOTES** ↓ A1C 0.7-1% Do not monitor BG with urine glucose tests as SGLT2 inhibitors increase urinary glucose excretion Canagliflozin and empagliflozin are approved to reduce risk of cardiovascular mortality in patients with type 2 diabetes and ASCVD
Dapagliflozin *(Farxiga)*	5 mg daily in the morning; can ↑ to 10 mg daily eGFR 30-45 mL/min/1.73 m²: not recommended eGFR < 30 mL/min/1.73 m²: contraindicated	
Empagliflozin *(Jardiance)*	10 mg daily in the morning; can ↑ to 25 mg daily eGFR 30-44 mL/min/1.73 m²: not recommended eGFR < 30 mL/min/1.73 m²: contraindicated	
Ertugliflozin *(Steglatro)*	5 mg daily in the morning; can ↑ to 15 mg daily eGFR 30-59 mL/min/1.73 m²: not recommended eGFR < 30 mL/min/1.73 m²: contraindicated	

SGLT2 Inhibitor Drug Interactions

- The risk of intravascular volume depletion (causing hypotension and acute kidney injury) can be increased if used in combination with diuretics, RAAS inhibitors or NSAIDs.
- UDP-glucuronosyl transferase (UGT) inducers (e.g., rifampin, phenytoin, phenobarbital) can ↓ levels of canagliflozin; consider using 300 mg dose if used in combination and eGFR ≥ 60 mL/min/1.73 m².
- Monitor potassium levels closely in patients taking canagliflozin with other medications that can ↑ potassium (e.g., ACE inhibitors, ARBs, aldosterone antagonists).

SGLT2 Inhibitor Patient Counseling

- Take this medication in the morning (canagliflozin should be taken before the first meal).
- Genital yeast infections can occur while taking this medication; tell your healthcare provider if you develop an odor, discharge, itchiness or pain in the genital area.
- This medication can cause increased urination and dehydration resulting in dizziness, lightheadedness, weakness, fainting and thirst. This can lead to sudden injury of the kidneys; tell your healthcare provider right away if you are sick, and cannot eat or drink, or if you lose liquids due to vomiting, diarrhea or being in the sun too long.
- This medication can cause a serious condition called ketoacidosis, which can lead to death. Tell your healthcare provider right away if you develop nausea, vomiting, tiredness, trouble breathing or stomach pain.
- Infections of the urinary tract can occur while taking this medication. Tell your healthcare provider if you have burning or pain when urinating, a need to urinate frequently and urgently, have pain in the lower part of your stomach or blood in the urine, especially if you also have a fever.
- Canagliflozin can increase your risk of leg and foot amputations. Contact your healthcare provider right away if you develop new pain or tenderness, sores or ulcers or infections in your legs or feet.

DIPEPTIDYL PEPTIDASE 4 INHIBITORS

Dipeptidyl peptidase 4 (DPP-4) inhibitors prevent the enzyme DPP-4 from breaking down incretin hormones, glucagon-like peptide 1 (GLP-1) and glucose-dependent insulinotropic polypeptide (GIP). These hormones help to regulate blood glucose levels by ↑ insulin release from the pancreatic beta cells and ↓ glucagon secretion from pancreatic alpha cells. A reduction in glucagon results in ↓ hepatic glucose production. These medications enhance the effects of the body's own incretins. Names of DPP-4 inhibitors end in "-gliptin."

DRUG	DOSING	SAFETY/SIDE EFFECTS/MONITORING
Sitagliptin ***(Januvia)***	100 mg daily CrCl 30-49 mL/min: 50 mg daily CrCl < 30 mL/min: 25 mg daily	**WARNINGS** Acute pancreatitis, severe and disabling arthralgia (joint pain), hypersensitivity reactions [e.g., anaphylaxis, angioedema, severe skin reactions (SJS)], bullous pemphigoid (blisters/erosions requiring hospitalization) Risk of heart failure (especially in patients with a history of heart failure or renal impairment); seen with saxagliptin and alogliptin specifically, but warning added for entire class Alogliptin: hepatotoxicity **SIDE EFFECTS** Nasopharyngitis, URTIs, UTIs, peripheral edema, rash **MONITORING** BG, A1C, renal function **NOTES** ↓ A1C 0.5-0.8%; ↓ postprandial BG Take with or without food
Saxagliptin *(Onglyza)*	2.5-5 mg daily eGFR < 45 mL/min/1.73 m^2: 2.5 mg daily	
Linagliptin ***(Tradjenta)***	5 mg daily No renal dose adjustment	
Alogliptin *(Nesina)*	25 mg daily CrCl 30-59 mL/min: 12.5 mg daily CrCl < 30 mL/min: 6.25 mg daily	

DPP-4 Inhibitor Drug Interactions

- Saxagliptin is a major substrate of CYP450 3A4 and P-gp. Limit the dose to 2.5 mg with strong CYP3A4 inhibitors, including protease inhibitors (e.g., atazanavir, ritonavir), clarithromycin, itraconazole, ketoconazole, nefazodone.
- Linagliptin is a major substrate of CYP3A4 and P-gp. Linagliptin levels are ↓ by strong CYP3A4 inducers (e.g., carbamazepine, efavirenz, phenytoin, rifampin, St. John's wort).

DPP-4 Inhibitor Patient Counseling

- Take this medication once daily in the morning, with or without food.
- Seek immediate medical help if you develop symptoms of a severe allergic reaction: severe rash with itching, redness or swelling, swelling in your face, lips, tongue or throat, wheezing or trouble breathing or severe dizziness.
- This medication can cause pain and inflammation in your pancreas. Stop taking it and tell your healthcare provider right away if you have severe stomach pain, with or without vomiting. The pain can radiate from the abdomen through to the back.
- Saxagliptin and alogliptin: this medication can cause heart failure. Inform your healthcare provider right away if you have trouble breathing (especially when you lie down), swelling in the ankles or legs, unusual or fast weight gain, or if you feel unusually tired.

OTHER ORAL MEDICATIONS

The following classes of drugs can be used in specific situations, but given their modest efficacy, side effects and/or frequency of administration, they are not used routinely for the treatment of type 2 diabetes.

DRUG CLASS	COMMENTS
Alpha-Glucosidase Inhibitors Acarbose *(Precose)* Miglitol *(Glyset)*	MOA: inhibit the metabolism of intestinal sucrose, which delays glucose absorption. Do not cause hypoglycemia alone, but if hypoglycemia occurs due to another drug, it cannot be treated with sucrose (present in fruit juices, table sugar or candy); glucose tablets or gel need to be purchased to treat hypoglycemia. Each dose should be taken with the first bite of each meal. GI side effects are common (flatulence, diarrhea, abdominal pain).
Bile Acid Binding Resins Colesevelam *(Welchol)*	Also indicated for Dyslipidemia (see Dyslipidemia chapter). Constipation is the most common side effect. Can bind and decrease absorption of other drugs and fat-soluble vitamins (A, D, E, K).
Dopamine Agonist Bromocriptine *(Cycloset)*	Contraindicated in patients with syncopal migraines (can cause hypotension and orthostasis) and those who are breastfeeding (inhibits lactation). Should not be used with metoclopramide or other dopamine agonists.

INJECTABLE MEDICATIONS FOR DIABETES

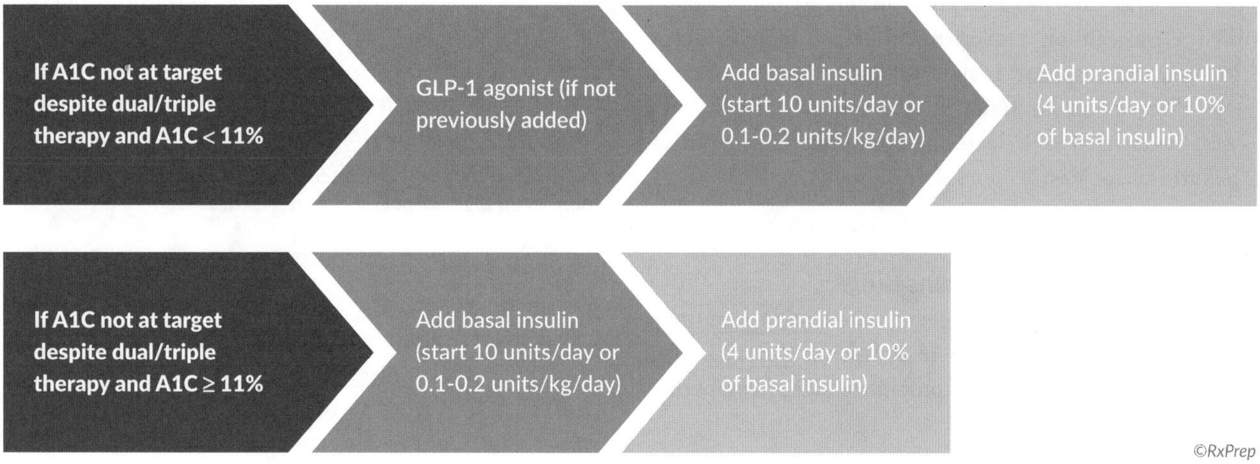

©RxPrep

GLUCAGON-LIKE PEPTIDE 1 AGONISTS

Glucagon-like peptide 1 (GLP-1) agonists are analogs of the incretin hormone GLP-1, which ↑ glucose-dependent insulin secretion, ↓ glucagon secretion, slows gastric emptying, improves satiety and can result in weight loss. They are approved for use in patients with type 2 diabetes and are available in single-dose or multidose pens (*Bydureon* is also available as a single-dose vial/tray). All are given subcutaneously, and some are available in combination with long-acting insulin. Names of GLP-1 agonists end in "-tide."

DRUG	DOSING	SAFETY/SIDE EFFECTS/MONITORING
Exenatide (*Byetta*)	Start: 5 mcg SC BID for 1 month; can ↑ to 10 mcg SC BID ESRD or CrCl < 30 mL/min: not recommended	**BOXED WARNING** All (except *Byetta* and *Adlyxin*): risk of thyroid C-cell carcinomas – seen in rats, unknown if risk applies to humans **CONTRAINDICATIONS** All (except *Byetta* and *Adlyxin*): personal or family history of medullary thyroid carcinoma (MTC) or patients with Multiple Endocrine Neoplasia syndrome type 2 (MEN 2) **WARNINGS** Pancreatitis (can be fatal, usually in patients with risk factors: history of pancreatitis, gallstones, alcoholism or ↑ TGs) Not recommended in patients with severe GI disease, including gastroparesis *Bydureon:* serious injection-site reactions (e.g., abscess, cellulitis, necrosis) with or without SC nodules *Ozempic:* ↑ complications with diabetic retinopathy **SIDE EFFECTS** Nausea (primary side effect), vomiting, diarrhea, constipation, antibodies, hypoglycemia, weight loss, injection site reactions *Trulicity:* cardiovascular effects (tachycardia, 1st degree AV block, PR interval prolongation) **MONITORING** BG, A1C, renal function **NOTES** ↓ A1C 0.5-1.5%; ↓ postprandial BG *Victoza* approved to reduce risk of cardiovascular events in patients with type 2 diabetes and ASCVD *Byetta* and *Adlyxin:* give dose within 60 minutes of meals; all others can be given without regard to meals Pen needles are not provided with *Byetta*, *Victoza*, or *Adlyxin*; provided with all others Pen injection devices should never be shared (even when the needle is changed) due to the risk for transmission of blood-borne pathogens
Exenatide extended release (*Bydureon, Bydureon BCise)*	2 mg SC once weekly ESRD or CrCl < 30 mL/min: not recommended	
Liraglutide (*Victoza*) ***Saxenda*** – for weight loss	Start: 0.6 mg SC daily x 1 week, then 1.2 mg SC daily; can ↑ to 1.8 mg SC daily	
Dulaglutide (*Trulicity*)	Start: 0.75 mg SC once weekly; can ↑ to 1.5 mg SC once weekly	
Lixisenatide (*Adlyxin*)	Start: 10 mcg SC daily x 14 days, then ↑ to 20 mcg SC daily eGFR < 15 mL/min/1.73 m^2: not recommended	
Semaglutide (*Ozempic*)	Start: 0.25 mg SC once weekly x 4 weeks, then ↑ to 0.5 mg SC once weekly; can ↑ to 1 mg SC weekly	

Albiglutide (Tanzeum) removed from list, as it was discontinued in July 2018

GLP-1 Agonist Drug Interactions

- These drugs slow gastric emptying and can reduce the extent and rate of absorption of orally administered drugs. Use caution with narrow therapeutic index drugs or medications that require threshold concentrations for efficacy (e.g., antibiotics, oral contraceptives). Take oral contraceptives at least one hour before exenatide or *Adlyxin* and at least 11 hours after *Adlyxin*.
- Can ↑ the INR in patients on warfarin, monitor INR.

GLP-1 Agonist Patient Counseling

- The most common side effects include nausea, vomiting, diarrhea and headache. These symptoms decrease over time. Talk to your healthcare provider if side effects bother you or do not go away.
- This medication can cause pain and inflammation in your pancreas. Stop taking it and tell your healthcare provider right away if you have severe stomach pain, with or without vomiting. The pain can radiate from the abdomen through to the back.
- Administer by SC injection (using a new needle) in the stomach area, upper leg (thigh) or the back of the upper arm. Rotate injection sites.

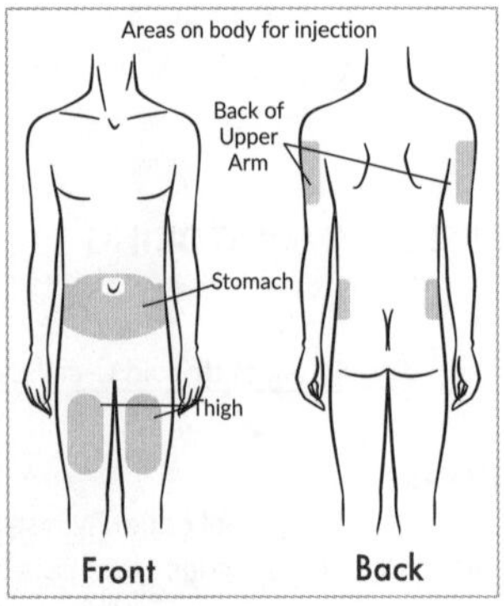

- Do not store your pen with the needle attached. Remove the needle from the pen immediately after injection; this helps prevent leaking of the medication from the pen and air bubbles from forming in the cartridge. Keep pens and needles out of the reach of children and pets. Keep refrigerated until you are ready to use your pen.
- Properly dispose of needles and single-use pens or syringes. See the Device Disposal section later in the chapter.

For all except *Byetta* and *Adlyxin*

- Do not take this medication if you or any family members have had thyroid cancer, especially medullary thyroid cancer. While taking this medication, tell your healthcare provider if you get a lump or swelling in your neck, hoarseness, have trouble swallowing, or develop shortness of breath. These might be symptoms of thyroid cancer.

Byetta

- Inject two times each day, within 60 minutes before the morning and evening meals (or before the two main meals of the day, at least six hours apart). Never inject after a meal due to the risk of low blood sugar.
- Prime each pen the first time you use it; it does not need to be primed prior to each injection.
- Insert the needle into the skin, push the inject button firmly, count to five, then remove the needle from the skin.
- Each pen contains enough drug to inject a dose twice daily for 30 days. Mark the date when you first use your pen and the date 30 days later. After 30 days, throw away the *Byetta* pen, even if it is not completely empty.

Bydureon

- *Bydureon* single-dose vial/tray requires you to mix the powder medication with a liquid in a syringe. Once mixed, it must be injected immediately otherwise clumps will form. Insert the needle into the skin, push down on the syringe plunger with your thumb until it stops, then withdraw the needle.
- *Bydureon* pen: remove one pen from the refrigerator and let it stand at room temperature for at least 15 minutes. Check the liquid inside the inspection window to make sure it is clear and free of particles. Do not use if the liquid is colored or has particles. Air bubbles are normal.
  - Screw the needle onto the pen. With the pen upright, slowly turn the knob at the end of the pen until you hear the click and the green label disappears.
  - Hold the pen by the end with the orange label and tap the pen firmly against the palm of your hand. Tap about 80 times, rotating the pen every 10 taps. When mixed, *Bydureon* (both formulations) will be a uniformly cloudy solution with no clumps.
  - Hold the pen with the needle pointing straight up and turn the white knob until the orange label disappears and the injection button is released. Insert the needle into the skin, press the injection button firmly until you hear a click, count to 10 before withdrawing the needle.
- *Bydureon BCise*: remove one pen from the refrigerator and let it stand at room temperature for at least 15 minutes.
  - Mix the medicine by holding the device with the orange cap facing up. Shake the entire device up and down for at least 15 seconds. Look at the medicine window to make sure it is fully mixed. When fully mixed, inject right away.
  - Turn the bottom knob from the locked to the unlocked position until you hear a click. You will see the plunger appear in the window.

- Unscrew the orange cap. A green shield will appear (this covers the needle). Push the edge of the green shield against your skin until you hear a click. Hold the device in place for 15 seconds. When finished, you should see an orange rod in the window. Remove the needle and discard the entire device.

Trulicity

- Remove the Base Cap from the pen and place the Clear Base flat and firmly against the skin at the injection site. Unlock the pen by turning the Lock Ring. Press and hold the green injection button; you will hear a loud click. Continue to hold the Clear Base against the skin until a second click is heard; this happens when the needle starts retracting in about 5 – 10 seconds. You will know the injection is complete when the gray plunger is visible. You can then remove the pen from your skin.

Bydureon and Trulicity

- These medications are taken once weekly. If a dose is missed, take it as soon as you remember, as long as the next regularly scheduled dose is at least three days (72 hours) later. If the next dose is < 3 days later, skip the missed dose entirely and continue with the next regularly scheduled dosing day.

- Each prefilled pen comes with one dose of medication and must be disposed of after a single use.

Victoza

- *Victoza* is taken once daily. Prime each pen the first time you use it; it does not need to be primed prior to each injection. To do this, attach your needle and turn the dose selector to the Flow Check line. Face the needle away from you and tap the pen to move air to the top. Press the injection button. You should see liquid come out of the pen. You may need to repeat these steps (up to six times) before liquid comes out.

- To take your dose, turn the dose selector on your pen until your needed dose (0.6, 1.2 or 1.8 mg) lines up with the pointer, insert the needle into the skin, press down firmly on the dose button until 0 mg lines up with the pointer, count to 6 before withdrawing the needle.

- Store your pen with the pen cap on at room temperature for up to 30 days. Discard after 30 days, even if medicine remains.

Ozempic

- Remove the pen from the refrigerator and let it stand at room temperature for 15 minutes.

- Attach a new needle for each use. Prime the needle before each use by turning the dose counter to the Flow Indicator. Turn the pen straight up and press the dose button. This should release a drop of medication at the needle tip.

- Turn the dose selector on your pen until your needed dose (0.25, 0.5 or 1 mg) lines up with the pointer, insert the needle into the skin, press down firmly on the dose button until 0 mg lines up with the pointer, count to six before withdrawing the needle.

- This medication is taken once weekly. If a dose is missed, take it as soon as you remember, as long as it is within five days. If > 5 days since the dose was missed, skip the dose entirely and continue with the next regularly scheduled dosing day.

- Each pen will be used for multiple injections. Store your opened pen with the pen cap on at room temperature or in the refrigerator for up to 56 days.

Adlyxin

- This medication is taken once daily within one hour of the first meal of the day. Each pen contains 14 doses. After 14 days, the pen must be discarded, even if there is some medication left.

- The starter pack contains two different colored pens; the green pen contains 10 mcg/dose and the burgundy pen contains 20 mcg/dose. You must start with the green pen and use all 14 doses before using the burgundy pen.

- Activate each pen the first time you use it; it does not need to be activated prior to each injection. To activate, attach a new needle and pull the injection button out. Pointing away from you, inject the dose (discard this). The window will turn from orange to white.

- Before each dose, check to make sure the activation window is white and the liquid is clear and colorless with no particles. Air bubbles are normal.

- Attach a needle then pull the injection button out firmly until it stops (the arrow in the window will now be pointing towards the needle). Insert the needle into the skin then press the injection button until you feel or hear a click, count to two then withdraw the needle.

AMYLINOMIMETIC (AMYLIN ANALOG)

Pramlintide is a synthetic analog of the human neuroendocrine hormone, amylin. Amylin is produced by pancreatic beta cells; it helps control postprandial glucose by slowing gastric emptying, suppressing glucagon secretion following a meal and increasing satiety.

DRUG	DOSING	SAFETY/SIDE EFFECTS/MONITORING
Pramlintide (*SymlinPen 60, SymlinPen 120*) Can use in type 1 and 2 diabetes	Type 1: start at 15 mcg/dose, ↑ in 15 mcg increments every 3 days (if no significant nausea) Max = 60 mcg/dose Type 2: start at 60 mcg/dose, ↑ to 120 mcg/dose after 3 days (if no significant nausea) Administer SC in abdomen or thigh prior to each major meal (≥ 250 kcal or ≥ 30 grams of carbohydrates – if consuming less than the above quantities, skip dose)	**BOXED WARNING** Severe hypoglycemia when used with insulin (usually within 3 hours following administration) **CONTRAINDICATIONS** Gastroparesis, hypoglycemia unawareness **WARNINGS** Hypoglycemia – reduce mealtime insulin by 50% when starting **SIDE EFFECTS** N/V, anorexia, headache, weight loss **MONITORING** BG, A1C **NOTES** ↓ A1C 0.5-1%

Pramlintide Drug Interactions

- Slows gastric emptying; administer oral medications at least one hour before and two hours after if rapid onset or threshold concentration is critical (e.g., analgesics, antibiotics, oral contraceptives).

INSULIN

Insulin is a hormone that has three main functions: a) it signals the liver to convert glucose into glycogen (stored glucose for later use), and prevents glycogen breakdown when blood glucose is high after a person eats; b) it is required for glucose uptake by muscle cells, which use glucose as energy, and c) it regulates fat storage in adipose tissue, converting excess glucose to fat and preventing fat breakdown for energy.

In an individual without diabetes, the pancreas releases the right amount of insulin for the body, providing a consistent level (or basal amount) of insulin at all times, then releasing more insulin when the blood glucose is elevated postprandially (after meals). In a patient with diabetes, insulin can be given to mimic the normal physiologic process. Insulin regimens can include:

- Basal Insulin: long- or intermediate-acting insulin (mostly affects fasting blood glucose)
- Bolus Insulin: rapid- or short-acting insulin, mainly used for two purposes:
  - Prandial (mealtime) in fixed doses (e.g., 6 units SC TID AC) to prevent elevations from food
  - Correction for acute elevations in response to SMBG

Insulins are high-risk medications. See the summary table comparing the properties (onset, peak and duration) of the commercially available insulins at the end of this section.

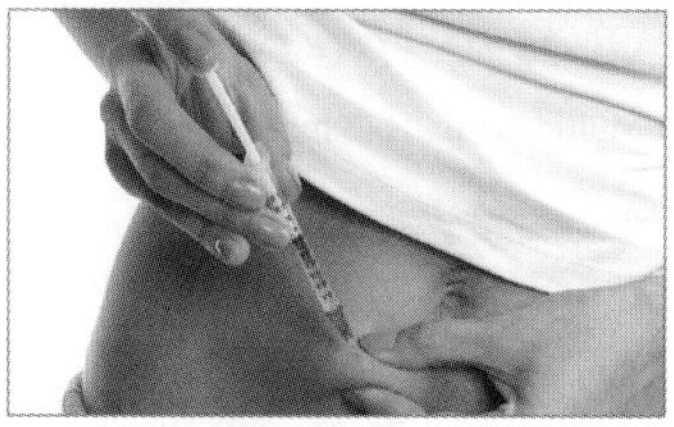

INSULIN TYPE	UNIQUE CONCERNS	SAFETY/SIDE EFFECTS/MONITORING
Rapid-Acting Insulins (commonly called prandial or mealtime insulin)		
Aspart (*Novolog, Novolog FlexPen*, *Fiasp, Fiasp FlexTouch*) Glulisine (*Apidra, Apidra SoloStar*) **Lispro (*Humalog, Humalog KwikPen*,** *Admelog, Admelog SoloStar*) All: 100 units/mL Vials (10 mL) Pens (3 mL) **Other concentrations:** *Humalog KwikPen* also comes in 200 units/mL	Faster onset and shorter duration of action than regular (short-acting) insulin (see Insulin Properties table) Give up to 15 minutes before meals or immediately after meals *Fiasp*: give at start of meals or within 20 minutes of starting meals	**CONTRAINDICATIONS** Use in acute hypoglycemia, hypersensitivity **WARNINGS** Hypoglycemia, hypokalemia (shifts K from extracellular space to intracellular space), renal/hepatic impairment (might need to ↓ dose) Pen devices should never be shared (even when the needle is changed) due to the risk for transmission of blood-borne pathogens **SIDE EFFECTS** Weight gain, lipodystrophy (thickening or thinning of adipose tissue), injection site reactions, peripheral edema, antibodies **MONITORING** BG, A1C, weight **NOTES** *Fiasp* formulated with niacinamide (vitamin B3) for faster absorption
Afrezza Oral inhalation powder Available as 4, 8, and 12 unit cartridges (single inhalation)	Inhale at the beginning of meals Has a shorter duration of action than injectable rapid-acting insulins (see Insulin Properties table)	Same as above plus: **BOXED WARNING** Acute bronchospasm in patients with chronic lung disease such as asthma or COPD – detailed medical history, physical examination, and spirometry (FEV1) required before initiation **CONTRAINDICATIONS** Asthma, COPD, other chronic lung disease **WARNINGS** Decline in pulmonary function (FEV1), lung cancer, DKA **SIDE EFFECTS** Cough, throat pain **MONITORING** Pulmonary function tests (FEV1) **NOTES** Not recommended in patients who smoke or who have recently stopped smoking Replace the inhaler every 15 days to maintain accurate drug delivery

INSULIN TYPE	UNIQUE CONCERNS	SAFETY/SIDE EFFECTS/MONITORING
Short-Acting Regular Insulins (commonly called prandial or mealtime insulin)		
Regular insulin *(Humulin R, Novolin R,* Novolin R ReliOn) 100 units/mL Vials (3 mL, 10 mL)	Give 30 minutes before meals	Same as rapid-acting injectables on previous page plus: **NOTES** Insulin of choice for IV solutions, including TPN; rapid-acting insulin can be used IV (off-label) Available without a prescription Available alone or combined with intermediate-acting insulins (NPH)
Concentrated regular insulin *(Humulin R U-500, Humulin R U-500 KwikPen)* 500 units/mL Vial (20 mL) Multidose pens (3 mL)	5 times as concentrated as regular insulin U-100; recommended when patient requires > 200 units/day of insulin Give 30 minutes before meals	Same as rapid-acting injectables above plus: **WARNINGS** The prescribed dose of *Humulin R U-500* should always be expressed in units of insulin; all patients using the U-500 insulin vial must be prescribed a U-500 insulin syringe to avoid dosing errors; each marking on the U-500 syringe represents 5 units and no dose conversions are needed) – do not use any other type of syringe **NOTES** Do not transfer insulin from the *KwikPen* into a syringe, the dose window shows the number of units Do not mix with other insulins or administer IV, IM or in an insulin pump
Intermediate-Acting Insulin (commonly called basal insulin)		
NPH insulin *(Humulin N, Humulin N KwikPen, Novolin N,* Novolin N ReliOn) 100 units/mL Vials (3 mL, 10 mL) Pens (3 mL)	Typically given once or twice daily NPH insulins are cloudy (including pre-mixed preparations)	Same as rapid-acting injectables on previous page plus: **NOTES** Available without a prescription Can mix with rapid or short-acting insulins – draw up rapid or short acting insulin first (clear before cloudy)
Long-Acting Insulins (commonly called basal insulin)		
Detemir *(Levemir, Levemir FlexTouch)* **Glargine *(Lantus, Lantus SoloStar, Toujeo SoloStar,*** *Toujeo Max SoloStar, Basaglar KwikPen)* Degludec *(Tresiba FlexTouch)* All (except *Toujeo SoloStar*): 100 units/mL Vials (10 mL) Pens (3 mL) **Other concentrations:** *Tresiba FlexTouch* also comes in 200 units/mL *Toujeo* only comes in 300 units/mL (*SoloStar*:1.5 mL pen; *Max SoloStar*: 3 mL pen)	Give once or twice daily, at the same time each day *Levemir*: if given once daily, dose with evening meal or at bedtime *Tresiba*: can be given any time of day	Same as rapid-acting injectables on previous page plus: **NOTES** Do not mix with other insulins Glargine has an acidic pH and can sting upon injecting

INSULIN TYPE	UNIQUE CONCERNS	SAFETY/SIDE EFFECTS/MONITORING
Pre-Mixed Insulins		
70% insulin aspart protamine suspension, 30% insulin aspart solution *(Novolog Mix 70/30)* 75% insulin lispro protamine suspension, 25% insulin lispro solution *(Humalog Mix 75/25)* 50% insulin lispro protamine suspension, 50% insulin lispro solution *(Humalog Mix 50/50)* 70% NPH, 30% regular ***(Humulin 70/30, Humulin 70/30 Kwikpen, Novolin 70/30)***	Typically given twice daily Timing of administration before meals is according to rapid or short-acting insulin component NPH and protamine insulins are cloudy	Same as rapid-acting injectables plus: **NOTES** *Humulin 70/30, Humulin 70/30 KwikPen* and *Novolin 70/30* are available without a prescription All mixed insulins are named as the percentage of each component, with basal first [e.g., Novolin 70/30 contains 70% NPH (basal), 30% Regular] Protamine suspensions are intermediate acting insulins All products available in vials (10 mL) and/or pens (3 mL); *Humulin 70/30* also available in 3 mL vial

Summary of Insulin Properties by Product Type

INSULIN	ONSET	PEAK	DURATION
Rapid-Acting Insulins			
Insulin aspart *(Novolog*, *Fiasp*)* Insulin glulisine *(Apidra)*	10-30 minutes	0.5-3 hours	3-5 hours
Insulin lispro *(Humalog*, *Admelog)* Inhaled insulin *(Afrezza)*	~15 minutes	~1 hour	2-3 hours
Short-Acting Insulins			
Regular *(Humulin R, Novolin R)*	15-30 minutes	2.5-5 hours	4-12 hours
Concentrated regular *(Humulin R U-500)*	15-30 minutes	4-8 hours	13-24 hours
Intermediate-Acting Insulins (Basal)			
NPH *(Humulin N, Novolin N)*	1-2 hours	4-12 hours	14-24 hours
Insulin NPH/insulin regular *(Humulin 70/30, Novolin 70/30)*	30 minutes	2-12 hours	18-24 hours
Long-Acting Insulins (Basal)			
Insulin detemir *(Levemir)*	3-4 hours	-	6-23 hours (dose-dependent)
Insulin glargine *(Lantus, Toujeo*, *Basaglar)*	3-4 hours *(Toujeo* – 6 hours)	-	≥ 24 hours
Insulin degludec *(Tresiba FlexTouch)*	1 hour	-	> 24 hours

**Fiasp is formulated with niacinamide (vitamin B3) for faster absorption. Absorbed in ~2.5 minutes.*

Insulin Drug Interactions

Many drugs can increase the risk of hypoglycemia when used in combination with insulin, especially meglitinides and SUs. When used in combination with TZDs, SGLT2 inhibitors, DPP-4 inhibitors, GLP-1 agonists, SUs, meglitinides and pramlintide, insulin doses may need to be decreased. Use caution with use of other drugs and supplements known to cause hypoglycemia (see Hypoglycemia section). TZDs also increase the risk of heart failure with insulin. Avoid the combination of rosiglitazone and insulin.

Insulin Vials, Pens and Pumps

Most insulin products contain 100 units/mL of insulin with a few exceptions (see Concentrated Insulin Products box). Most insulin vials dispensed to patients contain 10 mL, except *Humulin R U-500*, which comes in a 20 mL vial. Most insulin pen cartridges contain 3 mL, except *Toujeo SoloStar* which contains 1.5 mL. In general, pens are easier to use, especially in patients with hand tremor, arthritis or vision difficulty, and cause fewer dosing errors if used correctly. All insulin pens are multi-dose; needles must be dispensed with the pens.

All pens are dosed in units of insulin, meaning that when dialing the pen, a patient is dialing to the number of units to be given. If it is a concentrated insulin the pen simply gives less volume. For example, if 20 units of *Lantus* (or any 100 unit/mL insulin) is needed, the patient would dial the pen to 20 units and the pen would give 0.2 mL. For *Tresiba* (200 units/mL), the patient would still dial the pen to 20 units, but the pen would deliver 0.1 mL because of the concentration. This concept applies to all pens containing concentrated insulin. For vials of *Humulin R U-500*, it is essential to dose using the U-500 syringe because it measures in units of insulin. Typical syringes measure in volume and can result in dosing errors.

Insulin pumps are devices that deliver SC insulin; they consist of a pump, insulin reservoir, tubing and cannula. Only rapid acting injectable insulin or regular insulin is used in an insulin pump. The devices can be programmed to mimic the insulin secretion of the pancreas, by providing a continuous infusion (basal rate) throughout the day and boluses of rapid-acting or regular insulin as needed (e.g., mealtimes). Pumps are most often used by patients with type 1 diabetes but are increasingly used by patients with type 2 diabetes. Candidates for insulin pumps must be receiving multiple daily doses of insulin, be experienced in carbohydrate counting, be highly motivated, understand how to operate the pump and be willing to test their blood sugar frequently throughout the day. Insulin pumps are not appropriate for newly diagnosed patients.

CONCENTRATED INSULIN PRODUCTS

Rapid-Acting Insulin:
Humalog KwikPen: 200 units/mL

Regular (Short-Acting) Insulin:
Humulin R U-500: 500 units/mL

Long-Acting Insulins:
Tresiba FlexTouch (insulin degludec): 200 units/mL

Toujeo SoloStar, Toujeo Max SoloStar (insulin glargine): 300 units/mL

INSULIN DOSING

INITIATING INSULIN IN TYPE 1 DIABETES

Most people with type 1 diabetes should be treated with an insulin pump or multiple daily injections of insulin. This requires 3 – 4 injections/day between basal (long-acting or intermediate acting) and bolus/prandial (rapid- or short-acting) insulin. Patients should be educated to match the prandial insulin dose to carbohydrate intake, premeal blood glucose and anticipated activity. Rapid-acting injectable insulins and long-acting basal insulins are preferred (over short- and intermediate- acting insulins), because they have less hypoglycemia risk and better mimic the physiologic pattern of the insulin made by the body.

Insulin should be started at a total daily dose (TDD) of 0.5 units/kg/day based on total body weight (TBW). A basal-bolus strategy, using long-acting insulin and rapid-acting insulin, can be determined as shown in the Study Tip Gal. If using NPH and regular insulin (NPH/R strategy), use $2/3$ of the TDD as the NPH dose and $1/3$ as the regular insulin dose; these are generally given together twice daily, 30 minutes prior to breakfast and dinner (evening meal).

INITIATING BASAL-BOLUS INSULIN

Start a basal-bolus regimen with *Lantus* and *Humalog* in a 70 kg patient

Step 1: calculate TDD (0.6 units/kg/day using TBW)

Example: 0.6 units/kg/day x 70 kg = 42 units

Step 2: divide the TDD into 50% basal (long-acting) insulin and 50% bolus (rapid-acting) insulin

Example: 21 units Lantus and 21 units Humalog

Step 3: divide the bolus insulin among 3 meals*

Example: 7 units of Humalog TID AC

Final = 21 units *Lantus* daily plus 7 units *Humalog* TID AC

**Can divide evenly or give more insulin for larger meals and less insulin for smaller meals*

Insulin-to-Carbohydrate Ratio

Every person responds differently to insulin (some are more sensitive to the effects than others); because of this, mealtime insulin can be adjusted based on the number of carbohydrates an individual is eating with a meal. An insulin-to-carbohydrate ratio (ICR) is patient specific and helps determine the units of insulin required to cover the grams of carbohydrate included in a meal. It can be calculated using the Rule of 500 (for rapid-acting insulins) or Rule of 450 (for regular insulin): See last page of chapter for example.

Rule of 500 (Rapid-Acting Insulin)

$$\frac{500}{\text{total daily dose of insulin (TDD)}} = \text{grams of carbohydrate covered by 1 unit of rapid-acting insulin}$$

Rule of 450 (Regular Insulin)

$$\frac{450}{\text{total daily dose of insulin (TDD)}} = \text{grams of carbohydrates covered by 1 unit of regular insulin}$$

Correction dose calculation

Patients with diabetes should know how to calculate their correction dose, which is the amount of insulin needed to return their blood glucose to a normal range. For example, if the glucose is higher than desired before a meal, a correction dose of insulin can be given. The correction dose of insulin is added to the dose they normally take for that meal, in order to ensure that the patient will reach his or her glycemic target after the meal. The correction dose is determined based on an individual's correction factor, which provides the number of points (mg/dL) that each unit of insulin will decrease the glucose. See last page of chapter for example.

Correction Factor – 1,800 Rule (Rapid-Acting Insulin)

$$\frac{1{,}800}{\text{total daily dose of insulin (TDD)}} = \text{correction factor for 1 unit of rapid-acting insulin}$$

Correction Factor – 1,500 Rule (Regular Insulin)

$$\frac{1{,}500}{\text{total daily dose of insulin (TDD)}} = \text{correction factor for 1 unit of regular insulin}$$

Correction Dose

$$\frac{\text{(blood glucose now) - (target blood glucose)}}{\text{correction factor}} = \text{correction dose}$$

INITIATING AND ADJUSTING INSULIN IN TYPE 2 DIABETES

In patients with type 2 diabetes, basal insulin is often initiated when a patient fails to reach glycemic targets with multiple oral medications. Basal insulin is started at 0.1 – 0.2 units/kg/day (using TBW) or 10 units/day. This dose is titrated by 10 - 15% or 2 – 4 units once or twice weekly to reach the fasting blood glucose goal. If the A1C remains above goal, despite control of fasting blood glucose levels, the addition of one to three injections of rapid-acting mealtime insulin (basal-bolus strategy) with titration to achieve postprandial targets is recommended. Alternative strategies are to try a GLP-1 agonist with basal insulin, or use a pre-mixed insulin product twice daily.

EXAM SCENARIO

RC is a 47-year-old male with type 2 diabetes, currently treated with *Toujeo* 18 units SC QHS and *Novolog* 5 units SC TID AC. He presents with the following blood glucose log (all readings in mg/dL and taken before meals or at bedtime):

	BREAKFAST	LUNCH	DINNER	BED
Day 1	105	118	200	126
Day 2	97	115	197	122

What adjustment should be made to his regimen?
His lunchtime *Novolog* dose should be increased.

Explanation: The goal range for preprandial blood sugar is 80-130 mg/dL. His readings are all within the normal range, except for the readings before dinner. Remember to always look backwards. His high readings before dinner means he did not have enough insulin with lunch. His lunchtime dose should be increased.

Fasting blood sugar is most affected by basal insulin. If his pre-breakfast readings were high, he would require an increase in *Toujeo*. For prandial elevations, the rapid- or short-acting insulin should be adjusted.

INSULIN CONVERSIONS

Changing the type of insulin

- Usually, dose of the new insulin is the same dose of the old insulin (a 1:1 conversion)*

Exception #1

NPH dosed BID → *Lantus* or *Basaglar* dosed daily

- Use 80% of the NPH dose

Example: NPH 30 units AC breakfast and 20 units AC dinner = 50 units NPH daily

50 x 0.8 = 40 units *Lantus* or *Basaglar*

Exception #2

Toujeo → *Lantus* or *Basaglar*

- Use 80% of the *Toujeo* dose

*The dose of the new insulin might be adjusted when the BG is not controlled (e.g., using a higher dose for hyperglycemia)

INSULIN ADMINISTRATION PATIENT COUNSELING

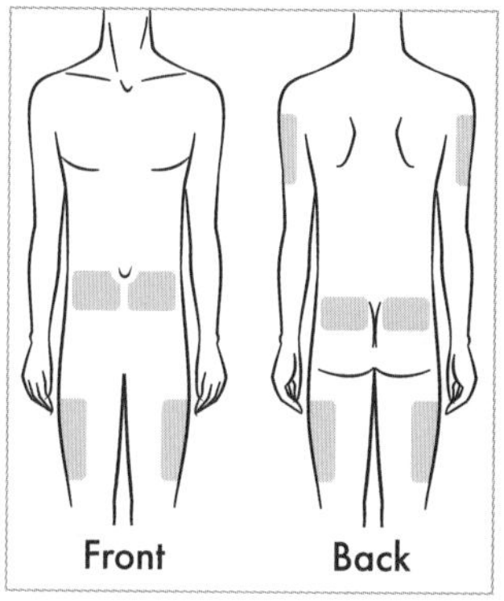

- Wash your hands and lay out all supplies.
- Check the insulin for any discoloration, crystals or particles.
- If the insulin is a suspension, roll the bottle gently between the hands (do not shake). If it is a pen, invert it 4 - 5 times.
- Clean the injection site (area of the skin) and wipe the top of the insulin vial (if using) with an alcohol swab.
- Pens:
  - Use a new needle for each injection. Prior to each injection, prime the needle by turning the knob to 2 units, facing the needle away from you and pressing the injection button.
  - Turn the dosing knob to select the correct number of units before injecting.
- Vials: inject an equal volume of air into the vial before withdrawing the insulin. Limit bubbles in the syringe.
- If mixing two types of insulin in the same syringe: the clear insulin should be drawn into the syringe before the cloudy insulin (for ease, inject air into the cloudy insulin first, then inject air into the clear insulin before withdrawing it out).
- Insulin is best absorbed in the abdomen which is the preferred injection site. Alternate sites of injection include the posterior upper arm, superior buttocks and lateral thigh area (see Diagram).

- To inject subcutaneously, gently pinch a 2 inch portion of the skin and fat between your thumb and first finger and insert the needle all the way at a 90 degree angle (or 45 degrees if you are thin). Press the injection button (pen) or plunger (syringe) all the way down to inject the insulin. Count 5 – 10 seconds before removing the needle.
- Rotate injection sites around the abdomen regularly to prevent inflammation and/or thinning of fat tissue.
- Properly dispose of needles or entire syringes (see Device Disposal section later in the chapter). Do not store pens with the needle attached.

SELF-MONITORING BLOOD GLUCOSE

Self-monitoring blood glucose (SMBG) is important to prevent hypo- and hyperglycemia and associated complications. Patients on multiple-dose insulin or insulin pump therapy should perform SMBG prior to meals and snacks, occasionally postprandially, at bedtime, prior to exercise or other critical tasks such as driving, when low blood glucose is suspected, and after treating low blood glucose, until normoglycemic. For patients on basal insulin, oral therapies or medical nutrition therapy, SMBG can be useful if part of the self-management plan.

Preparing to Test

- Some blood glucose meter devices require calibration before first use (enter correct calibration code if required). Recalibration might be needed if a new package of strips is opened, the meter is left in extreme conditions, the meter is dropped or if the level does not match how the patient is feeling.
- Read the test strip packaging to make sure the strips are compatible with the glucose meter. Do not use test strips from a damaged or expired bottle.
- Wash hands vigorously, with warm water and mild soap, to clean the site (finger) and increase circulation at the fingertips.
- Dry hands thoroughly since water can affect the blood sample and create an error or false reading.
- Allow arm to hang down at the side of the body for 30 seconds so blood can pool into the fingertips.

Testing Blood Glucose

- Use a new test strip for each test. Insert the test strip completely into the glucose meter prior to applying the blood sample.

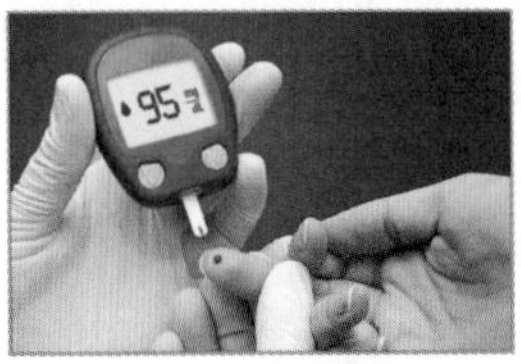

- In order to minimize pain, lance the side of the finger (where there are fewer nerves), instead of on the finger pads. Keep the hand below the level of the heart.
- Make sure there is a large enough drop of blood as directed by the meter. Allow the blood to flow freely and do not squeeze the finger.
- Apply the blood to the test strip.
- Properly dispose of lancets in a sharps container (see Device Disposal section later in the chapter).

Blood Glucose Meter Maintenance

- Clean the meter regularly and store it properly, along with supplies, away from heat and humidity.
- Test the meter regularly with the control solution. Keep extra batteries charged and ready.
- Close the lid of the strips container after every use, as air and moisture can destroy the strips and affect results.

Alternative Site Testing

- Select meters are approved for testing the forearm, palm or thigh. Always verify which sites are appropriate according to the individual meter instructions. A different end cap on the lancing device might be required for alternative site testing.
- Alternative sites, such as the forearm or thigh, can give a test result that is 20 to 30 minutes old. Alternative testing sites are not recommended in cases where the blood glucose is changing rapidly (e.g., after a meal or after exercise) or when hypoglycemia is suspected.

SYRINGES AND NEEDLES

Choosing the correct syringe when using a vial of insulin is important. The smallest syringe that will hold the dose should be used. The smaller the syringe barrel, the easier it is to read the scale markings in order to draw up an accurate dose. This is helpful for patients with vision problems.

Selecting an Insulin Syringe

- If injecting < 30 units of insulin, use a 0.3 mL syringe (markings in half-unit or 1 unit increments).
- If injecting 30 – 50 units of insulin, use a 0.5 mL syringe (markings in 1 unit increments).
- If injecting ≥ 51 units of insulin, use a 1 mL syringe (holds up to 100 units).
- If using *Humulin R U-500* insulin vials, use the U-500 syringe (markings in 5 unit increments; holds up to 250 units).

ROOM TEMPERATURE STABILITY OF INSULIN AND INJECTABLE MEDICATIONS

< 1 Week	
Afrezza – if opened	3 days
1-2 Weeks	
Afrezza – if unopened	
Humalog 50/50 and *75/25* pens	10 days
Humulin 70/30 pen	
2 Weeks	
Humulin N pen	
Novolog 70/30 pen	14 days
Trulicity and *Adlyxin* pens	
3 Weeks	
Xultophy 100/3.6 pen	21 days
~4 Weeks	
Apidra, Humalog, Novolog, Admelog, Fiasp vials & pens	
Humalog 50/50 and *75/25* vials	
Novolog 70/30 vial	
Humulin R U-500 pen	
Lantus vial and pen	28 days
Basaglar pen	
Bydureon vial and pen	
Soliqua 100/33 pen	
Symlin, Victoza, Byetta pens	30 days
Humulin R U-100, N and *70/30* vials	31 days
~6 Weeks	
Humulin R U-500 vial	40 days
Novolin R U-100, N and *70/30* vials	
Toujeo pen	42 days
Levemir vial and pen	
8 Weeks	
Tresiba pen	
Ozempic pen	56 days

MULTIDOSE PENS (NO NEEDLE INCLUDED)

Diabetes medications that are available as multidose pens do not include needles. Needles must be provided with:

Insulin Pens

FlexPen: Novolog products

KwikPen: Humalog, Humulin products and *Basaglar*

FlexTouch: Levemir, Fiasp, Tresiba

SoloStar: Lantus, Admelog, Toujeo

GLP-1 Agonists

Byetta, Victoza, Adlyxin

Pramlintide

SymlinPen

Selecting an Insulin Pen Needle

- When selecting a needle for a patient, consider the length and gauge (thickness):
  - Lengths: ½" (12.7 mm), 5/16" (8 mm), 3/16" (5 mm), 5/32" (4 mm).
  - Many users feel that shorter needles are more comfortable. Use ½" needles for obese patients or if back leakage of drug is a problem.
  - Gauges: the higher the gauge, the thinner the needle. Gauge usually ranges from 28G – 32G.
  - Common brands: *BD, Comfort EZ*, other manufacturers
- Needles are purchased separately and require a prescription in some states.
- Healthcare facilities often use needles with safety shields that are different from needles dispensed from an outpatient pharmacy. Outpatient needles have an inner cover that must be removed prior to injection. If not removed, no insulin will be injected. This has led to issues with patients incorrectly using insulin pens at home if they were taught in a facility, resulting in severe cases of hyperglycemia. Counsel patients on proper use of needles and to remove the inner cover prior to use.

Device Disposal

Used needles, syringes, single-dose pens (with needles attached) and lancets should be placed in a sharps disposal container. These containers can be taken to any proper disposal site (e.g., public health clinic or local needle exchange). If a sharps disposal container is not available, a household container with a tight fitting lid can be used (e.g., detergent bottle or empty metal coffee container). Ask the local health department for guidelines or visit www.safeneedledisposal.org. See the Medication Safety & Quality Improvement chapter for more information.

INJECTABLE DRUG STABILITY

Injectable products should be refrigerated and protected from light until first use. If refrigerated and unopened, they are stable until the expiration date on the label. Do not use the injectable medication if it is frozen, discolored, or contains particulates. Stability of the different injectable products at room temperature, including insulins, is shown in the table on the previous page.

HYPOGLYCEMIA

Normal fasting blood glucose in a person without diabetes is 70 – 99 mg/dL. Hypoglycemia is defined as a blood glucose < 70 mg/dL. The lower the level, the more symptomatic the patient. Hypoglycemic symptoms include dizziness, headache, anxiety, irritability, shakiness, diaphoresis (sweating), hunger, confusion, nausea, lack of coordination, tremors, palpitations or fast heart rate and blurred vision. Seizures, coma and death can occur with severe hypoglycemia.

All episodes of hypoglycemia are dangerous and should be reported to the prescriber. Hypoglycemia unawareness, or one or more episodes of severe hypoglycemia, should trigger re-evaluation of treatment.

Drugs That Cause Hypoglycemia

Insulin is the primary cause of drug-induced hypoglycemia. Drugs that make the body secrete more insulin, such as SUs and meglitinides (insulin secretagogues), and pramlintide (which is used with insulin at mealtimes), are also high-risk. There is a greater risk for hypoglycemia if food intake is decreased and mealtime insulin is not reduced appropriately, or if a patient continues taking mealtime insulin, SUs or meglitinides when not eating.

The GLP-1 agonists, DPP-4 inhibitors, TZDs and SGLT2 inhibitors have a low risk for hypoglycemia when used alone. When used in combination with a hypoglycemic drug (e.g., insulin or an insulin secretagogue), the risk can increase and necessitate a dose reduction. Some other non-diabetes drugs that have package insert warnings for hypoglycemia are shown in the Key Drugs Guy.

All beta-blockers can mask hypoglycemia symptoms of shakiness, palpitations and anxiety (sweating and hunger are not masked). This can prevent prompt recognition of low blood glucose and can result in more severe hypoglycemia.

SELECT DRUGS THAT CAN LOWER BLOOD GLUCOSE

KEY DRUGS

- Linezolid
- Lorcaserin *(Belviq)*
- Pentamidine
- Beta-blockers*
- Quinolones*

Others:
- Octreotide*
- Quinine

**Can also cause hyperglycemia (see Drug-Induced Hyperglycemia section)*

Hypoglycemia Treatment

Glucose is the preferred treatment of hypoglycemia, but any form of carbohydrate that contains glucose will raise blood sugar (see figure below). Added fat will slow absorption and prolong the hypoglycemia. Treat hypoglycemia with the following steps, commonly called the "rule of 15":

1. Take 15 – 20 grams of glucose or simple carbohydrates.
2. Recheck blood glucose after 15 minutes.
3. If hypoglycemia continues, repeat step #1.
4. Once blood glucose is normal, eat a small meal or snack to prevent recurrence.

Raise Blood Sugar with 15 Grams of Simple Carbs

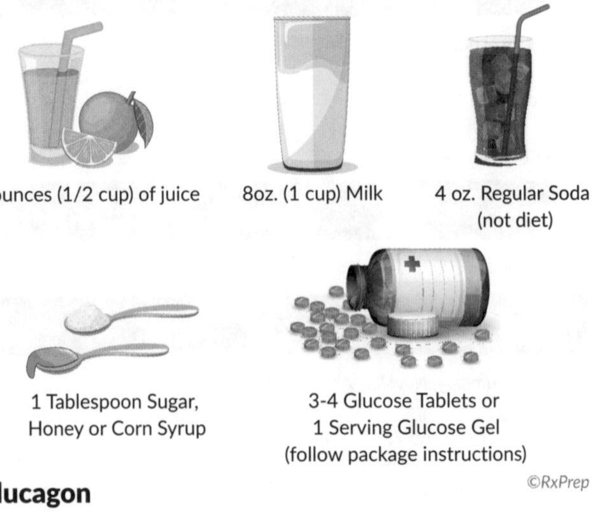

Glucagon

Glucagon should be prescribed for all patients at significant risk of severe hypoglycemia. Glucagon administration is not limited to healthcare professionals; caregivers and family members should be instructed on its administration. Glucagon *(GlucaGen)* is only used if the patient is unconscious or not conscious enough to self-treat the hypoglycemia. If using glucagon, place the patient in a lateral recumbent position (on side) to protect the airway and prevent choking when consciousness returns. Glucagon 1 mg is given by SC, IM or IV injection. Glucagon must be reconstituted prior to administration. Once conscious, administer a carbohydrate source; this can be in the form of glucose given intravenously (e.g., Dextrose 25%, Dextrose 50%).

INPATIENT GLUCOSE CONTROL

Target blood glucose for hospitalized patients is between 140 – 180 mg/dL. More stringent goals might be appropriate for select patients. The use of sliding scale insulin (SSI) alone to control blood glucose in the hospital setting is strongly discouraged. This method of administering insulin in response to elevated blood glucose levels is reactionary (treats blood glucose after it becomes elevated, rather than preventing elevated blood glucose) and leads to poor outcomes. In addition, most sliding scales used are not patient-specific (although they can be).

Guidelines recommend a proactive approach, using a physiologic insulin regimen to improve glycemic control and decrease hospital complications. This typically includes some combination of basal, bolus (prandial) and correction dose insulin. Correction dose insulin is similar to sliding scale insulin, in that a scale is used to select an insulin bolus dose in response to blood glucose levels. With correction dose regimens, the patient's insulin sensitivity (or correction factor) is used as a guide for initial scale selection which makes this strategy more patient specific.

In non-critically ill patients, a basal and correction dose strategy is recommended if the patient is not eating well (poor intake). A basal, bolus and correction dose regimen is preferred if the patient is eating adequately. Many hospitals still currently use sliding scale insulin alone to manage blood glucose. For sliding scales or correction dose insulin, regular U-100 or rapid-acting insulin are used.

SLIDING SCALE EXAMPLE

BLOOD GLUCOSE READING (MG/DL)	INSTRUCTION
< 60	Hold insulin; contact MD
150-200	Give 2 units of insulin
201-250	Give 4 units of insulin
251-300	Give 6 units of insulin
301-350	Give 8 units of insulin
351-400	Give 10 units of insulin
401-450	Call MD

HYPERGLYCEMIC CRISES

Diabetic Ketoacidosis

Diabetic ketoacidosis (DKA) is a hyperglycemic crisis that most commonly presents in patients with type 1 diabetes, but can present in type 2 diabetes. DKA occurs due to insulin non-compliance (e.g., ran out, lost medication, homeless, refused to take), subtherapeutic insulin dosing, a condition that can cause hyperglycemia (e.g., a stressor, such as infection, MI or trauma), or as the initial presentation in a patient with type 1 diabetes. Ketones are present because triglycerides and amino acids are used for energy, which produces free fatty acids (FFAs). Glucagon converts the FFAs into ketones. Insulin normally prevents this conversion, but in DKA, insulin is absent or severely lacking.

- Recognizing DKA:
  - BG > 250 mg/dL
  - Ketones (urine and serum, or picked up as "fruity" breath)
  - Anion gap metabolic acidosis (arterial pH < 7.35, anion gap > 12)

Hyperosmolar Hyperglycemic State

Hyperosmolar hyperglycemic state (HHS) is a hyperglycemic crisis that most often occurs in type 2 diabetes due to some type of severe stress (e.g., very high BG levels, severe infection). Serum ketones are negligible or not present because the patient with type 2 diabetes has enough insulin to suppress ketogenesis. The blood glucose is usually much higher at presentation because acidosis is not present and the patient can endure the symptoms longer.

- Recognizing HHS:
  - BG > 600 mg/dL
  - High serum osmolality > 320 mOsm/L
  - Extreme dehydration
  - Altered consciousness (confusion, dizziness, seizures)
  - pH > 7.3, bicarbonate > 15 mEq/L

HYPERGLYCEMIC CRISES TREATMENT

Fluids
Start with NS
When blood glucose reaches 200 mg/dL, change to D5W½NS

Regular insulin infusion (insulin of choice for IV solutions)
1) 0.1 unit/kg bolus, then 0.1 units/kg/hr continuous infusion OR
2) 0.14 units/kg/hr continuous infusion

Prevent hypokalemia (insulin shifts K into the cells)
Monitor potassium and keep serum level between 4-5 mEq/L

Treat acidosis (only if pH < 6.9)
Give sodium bicarbonate if needed

SELECTING DRUG TREATMENT

The available treatment options for the management of type 2 diabetes have expanded greatly. Metformin is first-line in most patients and selecting medications for add-on therapy has become more complex. Multiple issues must be considered:

1. What factors will affect the patient? See Study Tip Gal below.

FACTORS TO CONSIDER WHEN SELECTING DRUG TREATMENT

Biggest decrease in A1C (> 1%)

- ❑ Insulin (most), metformin, sulfonylureas, TZDs, GLP-1 agonists

Greatest hypoglycemia risk

- ❑ Insulin (most), sulfonylureas, meglitinides, pramlintide (with insulin)

Cardiac benefits (diabetes plus prior CVD event)

- ❑ Empagliflozin, canagliflozin, liraglutide, semaglutide, exenatide

Most likely to cause weight gain

- ❑ Insulin, sulfonylureas, meglitinides, TZDs

Most likely to cause weight loss

- ❑ SGLT2 inhibitors, GLP-1 agonists, pramlintide

Cheapest

- ❑ Metformin, sulfonylureas, TZDs

Injectable formulations

- ❑ Insulin, GLP-1 agonists, pramlintide

2. Which patients should not receive certain medications? See drugs/drug classes to avoid in select conditions in the table below.

DO NOT USE IF:	DRUGS/DRUG CLASSES
eGFR (mL/min/1.73 m^2) or CrCl (mL/min) < 30	Metformin, SGLT2 inhibitors, exenatide, glyburide
Heart failure	TZDs, alogliptin, saxagliptin
Peripheral neuropathy, PAD or diabetic foot ulcers	Canagliflozin
Gastroparesis or other GI disorder	GLP-1 agonists, pramlintide
Sulfa allergy	Sulfonylureas*

**Although sulfonylureas are used in clinical practice in patients with a sulfa allergy, they are considered contraindicated per package labeling.*

3. What adverse effects should be monitored for and recognized if they occur? See major risks associated with select drugs/drug classes in the table below.

MAJOR RISKS	DRUGS/DRUG CLASSES
Lactic acidosis	Metformin
Hepatotoxicity	TZDs, alogliptin
Hypotension/dehydration	SGLT2 inhibitors
UTI/genital infections	SGLT2 inhibitors
Potassium abnormalities	Canagliflozin (hyperkalemia), insulin (hypokalemia)
Pancreatitis	DPP-4 inhibitors, GLP-1 agonists
Hypersensitivity reactions	Sulfonylureas, DPP-4 inhibitors, insulin
Ketoacidosis	SGLT2 inhibitors (can occur when BG < 250 mg/dL)
Cancer	Pioglitazone, dapagliflozin (bladder cancer) GLP-1 agonists (thyroid cancer)

Select Guidelines/References

American Diabetes Association (ADA). Standards of Medical Care in Diabetes – 2019. *Diabetes Care.* 2019;42 (suppl 1):S1-S193.

Consensus Statement by the American Association of Clinical Endocrinologists and American College of Endocrinology on the Comprehensive Type 2 Diabetes Management Algorithm – *2018 Executive Summary. Endocr Pract.* 2018;24:91-120.

American Diabetes Association (ADA). Hyperglycemic Crises in Adult Patients with Diabetes. *Diabetes Care.* 2009;32 (7):1335-1343.

EXAM SCENARIO

JJ is a 35-year-old male with type 2 diabetes, currently treated with *Lantus* 50 units SC QHS and *Novolog* 15 units SC TID AC.

1. What is JJ's correction factor? 19

Explanation:
Step 1: Determine what type of insulin JJ is administering. The Rule of 1,800 is for rapid-acting insulins (e.g., *Novolog, Humalog*) and the Rule of 1,500 is used for regular insulin (e.g., *Novolin R, Humulin R*). JJ is administering rapid-acting insulin.

Step 2: Calculate Total Daily Dose of insulins (TDD). Add up all the units of insulin in a 24 hour period. JJ administers 50 units of *Lantus* along with a total of 45 units of *Novolog* each day.
TDD = 50 + 45 = 95

Step 3: Use the formula below to calculate the correction factor.
Correction factor= 5

$$\frac{1{,}800}{\text{total daily dose of insulin (TDD)}} = \text{correction factor for 1 unit of rapid-acting insulin}$$

$$\frac{1{,}800}{95} = \text{18.947, or 19 when rounded to nearest whole unit of insulin}$$

JJ has a target premeal blood glucose of 140 mg/dL. He checks his glucose before dinner and it is 200 mg/dL.

2. What dose of *Novolog* should JJ administer before dinner? 18

Explanation:
Determine the correction dose using the formula

$$\frac{\text{(blood glucose now) - (target blood glucose)}}{\text{correction factor}} = \text{correction dose}$$

$$\frac{(200) - (140)}{19} = 3$$

Add the correction dose to the number of units he usually administers before meals to get the dose he needs before dinner.

EXAM SCENARIO

AL is a 23-year-old female with type 1 diabetes, currently treated with *Lantus* 30 units SC QHS and *Novolog* 8 units SC TID AC.

1. What is AL's insulin-to-carbohydrate ratio? 9

Explanation:
Determine what type of insulin AL is administering. The Rule of 500 is for rapid-acting insulins (e.g., *Novolog, Humalog*) and the Rule of 450 is used for regular insulin (e.g., *Novolin R, Humulin R*). AL is administering rapid-acting insulin.

$$\frac{500}{\text{total daily dose of insulin (TDD)}} = \text{grams of carbohydrate covered by 1 unit of rapid-acting insulin}$$

$$\frac{500}{54} = \text{9.259, or 9 when rounded to nearest whole gram of carbs}$$

This means every 1 unit of AL's *Novolog* will cover 9 grams of carbohydrates.

2. AL is going to have a small apple (15 grams), turkey sandwich (30 grams) and one cup of skim milk (15 grams) for lunch. How many units of insulin are needed to cover this meal? 7

Explanation:
There is a total of 60 grams of carbohydrates in this meal

$$\frac{\text{60 grams}}{\text{9 grams/ 1 unit of } \textit{Novolog}} = \text{6.667, or 7 when rounded to nearest whole unit of insullin}$$

EXAM SCENARIO

CS is a 56-year-old female with hypertension, diabetes and heart failure. At her last clinic visit 3 months ago, her A1C was 8.6% despite treatment with metformin ER 2,000 mg PO daily and *Januvia* 100 mg PO daily. At that time, *Invokana* 100 mg PO daily was added to her regimen. CS also takes lisinopril, *Coreg CR*, furosemide and spironolactone for her hypertension and heart failure.

At the current visit, CS complains of dry mouth, weakness, dizziness and lightheadedness. On a couple of occasions she has nearly fainted. These symptoms began approximately 2 months ago.

What do CS's symptoms likely describe?
CS has symptoms of dehydration and hypotension.

Which medications could be associated with these symptoms?
The addition of *Invokana* (canagliflozin) to her medication regimen put CS at risk for these adverse effects. *Invokana* decreases blood glucose by excreting it in the urine; water is also excreted with glucose. The use of diuretics and antihypertensive medications could be contributing to the problem due to additive effects.

What laboratory abnormalities could occur with this combination of medications?
CS is at risk for acute kidney injury and hyperkalemia. Evaluate for elevated BUN, SCr, eGFR and potassium. Check an anion gap and ketones; if they are elevated, this is a sign of ketoacidosis, which can occur with *Invokana*.

If asked to select an alternative diabetes medication, what should be avoided?
There are a number of treatment options for diabetes management. In CS, avoid pioglitazone and rosiglitazone, due to her diagnosis of heart failure.

CHAPTER CONTENT

Background 664
Pathophysiology 664
Hypothyroidism 665
S/Sx of Hypothyroidism 665
Select Drugs and Conditions that can Cause Hypothyroidism 665
Diagnosis 665
Monitoring 665
Drug Treatment 665
Drug Interactions 667
Patient Counseling 667
Levothyroxine Tablet Colors 667
Hyperthyroidism 667
S/Sx of Hyperthyroidism 668
Drug Treatment 668
Potassium Iodide Use After Exposure to Radiation 669
Thyroid Storm 669
S/Sx of Thyroid Storm 669
Drug Treatment 669
Thyroid Disease and Pregnancy 669
Pregnancy and Hypothyroidism 669
Pregnancy and Hyperthyroidism 670

CONTENT LEGEND

= Study Tip Gal   = Key Drug Guy

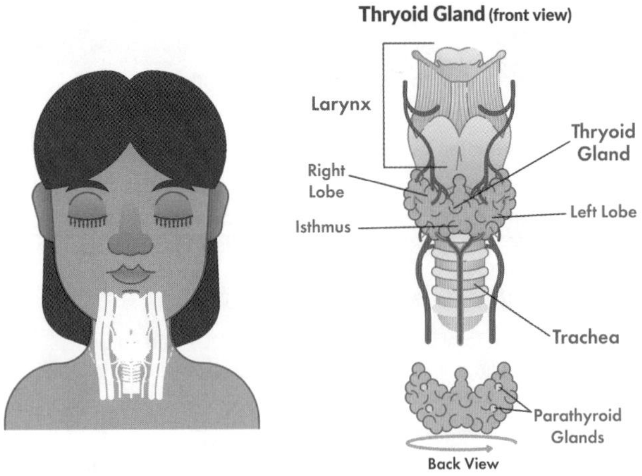

CHAPTER 45
THYROID DISORDERS

BACKGROUND

The thyroid gland sits low on the neck, below the Adam's apple and in front of the trachea (windpipe). The gland is shaped like a butterfly, with two symmetrical lobes. The lobes sit on each side of the trachea, connected by a stretch of tissue called the isthmus. The thyroid gland produces the thyroid hormones, which regulate metabolism, including the chemical processes needed to maintain life: cardiac and nervous system functions, body temperature, muscle strength, skin dryness, menstrual cycles, weight and cholesterol levels. Hyperthyroidism (overactive thyroid) and hypothyroidism (underactive thyroid) are the most common thyroid disorders.

PATHOPHYSIOLOGY

Triiodothyronine (T3)

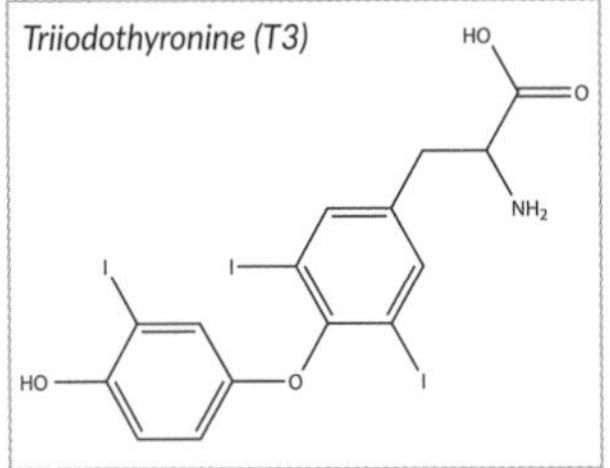

The thyroid gland produces the two thyroid hormones: triiodothyronine, which is known as T3 and thyroxine, which is known as T4. The production of both hormones requires iodine and tyrosine. The thyroid gland is the only organ that can absorb iodine, which is contained in T3 and T4 (see T3 structure). T3 is primarily formed from the breakdown of T4. A small percentage (< 20%) is produced by the thyroid gland directly. T3 is more potent than T4 but has a shorter half-life.

Thyroid hormone production is regulated by thyroid-stimulating hormone (TSH) and thyrotropin. Both hormones are secreted by the pituitary gland, which is located in the brain, and regulates growth and development.

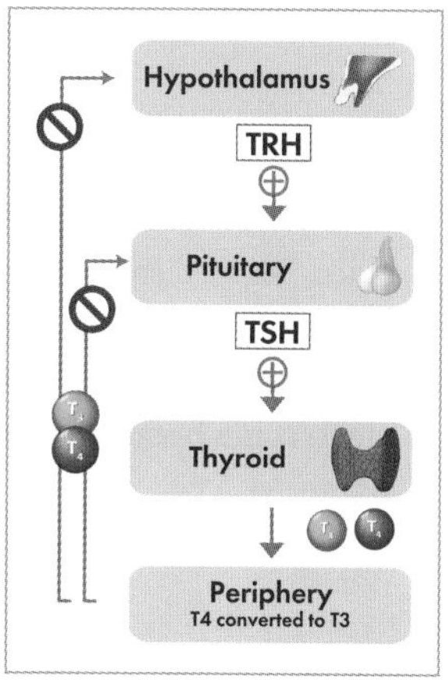

TRH = Thyrotropin Releasing Hormone
TSH = Thyroid-Stimulating Hormone

Negative Feedback Loop

Feedback loops are used to regulate the production of hormones secreted by the pituitary and thyroid glands, including T3 and T4. When the level of circulating (free) T4 increases, the circulating T4 inhibits the secretion of TSH. Less TSH will decrease T4 production.

T3 and T4 are transported in the blood and largely bound to proteins. The free T4 (FT4) is monitored; this is the unbound, active form.

HYPOTHYROIDISM

In hypothyroidism, there is a deficiency in T4, and consequently, an elevation in TSH. Hypothyroidism occurs more commonly in females (~80% of cases). The incidence increases with age. When thyroid hormone decreases, the body slows down, and the classic symptoms of low metabolism (e.g., fatigue and weight gain) appear. Other symptoms related to slow metabolism can be found in the Study Tip Gal below. The most common cause of hypothyroidism is Hashimoto's disease, an autoimmune condition in which a patient's own antibodies attack the thyroid gland. Drugs and conditions can cause hypothyroidism (see Key Drugs Guy). Hypothyroidism can cause depression, infertility and cardiovascular disease.

Myxedema coma is an uncommon, but potentially fatal complication of hypothyroidism that can occur when hypothyroidism is left untreated for a long time, or when hypothyroidism decompensates. Myxedema coma is a life-threatening emergency characterized by poor circulation, hypothermia and hypometabolism. Initial treatment for myxedema coma is IV levothyroxine.

S/SX OF HYPOTHYROIDISM

Cold intolerance/sensitivity	Myalgias
Dry skin	Weakness
Fatigue	Depression
Muscle cramps	Bradycardia
Voice changes	Coarse hair or loss of hair
Constipation	Menorrhagia (heavier than normal menstrual periods)
Weight gain	Memory and mental impairment
Goiter (possible; can be due to low iodine intake)	

SELECT DRUGS AND CONDITIONS THAT CAN CAUSE HYPOTHYROIDISM

KEY DRUGS

Remember: **I TALC**

Interferons*

Tyrosine kinase inhibitors (e.g., sunitinib)

Amiodarone*

Lithium

Carbamazepine

Conditions:
Hashimoto's Disease

Others:
Oxcarbazepine

Eslicarbazepine

Phenytoin

Conditions:
Iodine deficiency

Pituitary failure

Surgical removal of thyroid gland

Congenital hypothyroidism

Thyroid gland ablation with radioactive iodine

External irradiation

**Can also cause hyperythyroidism (see Hyperthyroidism section)*

DIAGNOSIS

A diagnosis of hypothyroidism is based off of two laboratory tests:

- Low free thyroxine (↓ FT4): normal range 0.9 – 2.3 ng/dL
- High thyroid-stimulating hormone (↑ TSH): normal range 0.3 – 3 mIU/L

Screening should be considered in patients > 60 years old.

MONITORING

TSH is the primary screening test for thyroid function (occasionally FT4 is ordered with TSH). TSH is the most reliable indicator for treatment. The TSH level and symptoms should be monitored every 4 – 6 weeks until levels are normal, then 4 – 6 months later, then yearly. It is important to monitor thyroid function as the patient ages because a dose reduction can be required. Too high of a dose of thyroid hormone replacement in elderly patients can cause atrial fibrillation and fractures. Serum FT4 is monitored, in addition to TSH, in central hypothyroidism (rare), which is a defect in pituitary production of TSH. FT4 is also monitored when treating hypothyroidism in pregnancy.

DRUG TREATMENT

The goals of treatment are to resolve symptoms, normalize TSH and avoid over-treatment; excessive doses of thyroid hormone will cause hyperthyroidism. Patients should be counseled on symptoms of both hypo- and hyperthyroidism. Levothyroxine (T4) is the drug of choice for hypothyroidism. A consistent preparation (i.e., the same formulation and manufacturer) is preferred to minimize variability from refill to refill. Some patients state they feel better using or supplementing with other thyroid hormone formulations, including liothyronine (T3, *Cytomel* and *Triostat*) or desiccated thyroid (T3 and T4, *Armour Thyroid* and *NP Thyroid*), although these are generally not recommended. Desiccated thyroid is called "natural thyroid" and is dosed in grains. It is not recommended because it can contain variable amounts of T3 and T4.

Levothyroxine should be taken with water consistently at least 60 minutes before breakfast or at bedtime (at least three hours after the last meal) for consistent absorption. Containers should be stored properly and patients should be counseled regarding drug interactions.

Iodine supplementation, including kelp or other iodine-containing functional foods, is not required in the U.S. because most of the salt has iodine added (iodized salt). This has eliminated almost all U.S. cases of iodine deficiency goiter. Individuals who are restricting salt intake can consume foods high in iodine (e.g., dairy, seafood, meat, some breads), and can take a multivitamin containing iodine.

Hypothyroidism Treatment

DRUG	DOSING	SAFETY/SIDE EFFECTS/MONITORING
Levothyroxine (T4) ***(Synthroid, Levoxyl, Unithroid,*** *Tirosint, Tirosint-SOL)* Capsule, tablet, injection, oral solution Check the therapeutic equivalence of a generic to a brand in the *Orange Book*. Not all generic levothyroxine formulations are A-rated to various brands.	Full replacement dose = 1.6 mcg/kg/day (IBW) Start with full replacement dose in otherwise healthy, young (< 50 years of age) and middle age patients with markedly ↑ TSH Start with partial replacement dose in milder hypothyroidism and those with comorbidities If known CAD, start with 12.5-25 mcg daily Elderly often need 20-25% less per kg; may require < 1 mcg/kg/day	**BOXED WARNING** Thyroid supplements are ineffective and potentially toxic when used for the treatment of obesity or for weight reduction, especially in euthyroid patients; high doses can cause serious or even life-threatening toxic effects particularly when used with some anorectic drugs (e.g., sympathomimetic amines) **CONTRAINDICATIONS** Uncorrected adrenal insufficiency **WARNINGS** ↓ dose in cardiovascular disease (chronic hypothyroidism predisposes to coronary artery disease), ↓ bone mineral density which can lead to osteoporosis **SIDE EFFECTS** If patient is euthyroid, no side effects should exist. If dose is too high, patient will experience hyperthyroid symptoms such as ↑ HR, palpitations, sweating, weight loss, arrhythmias and irritability **MONITORING** TSH levels and clinical symptoms every 4-6 weeks until levels are normal, then 4-6 months later, then yearly; serum FT4 in select patients **NOTES** Highly protein bound (> 99%) Levothyroxine is the drug of choice due to chemical stability, once-daily dosing, low cost, lack of antigenicity and more uniform potency Levothyroxine tablet colors are standard; they do not change between manufacturers (see Study Tip Gal on tablet colors) Dose reduction may be necessary as the patient ages **Levothyroxine IV** Use immediately upon reconstitution; IV to PO ratio is 0.75:1 **Oral solution** Can be given undiluted or diluted in water only; store in orginal container **Thyroid USP** Natural porcine-derived thyroid that contains both T3 and T4; less predictable potency and stability. Not preferred, but some feel better using it **Liothyronine** Shorter half-life causes fluctuations in T3 levels
Thyroid, Desiccated USP (T3 and T4) ***(Armour Thyroid,*** *Nature-Throid, NP Thyroid, Westhroid, WP Thyroid)* Tablet	Start 15-30 mg daily (15 mg in cardiac disease); titrate in 15 mg increments Usual dose is 60-120 mg daily	
Liothyronine (T3) ***(Cytomel,*** *Triostat)* Tablet, injection	Start 25 mcg daily; titrate in 12.5-25 mcg increments Usual dose is 25-75 mcg daily	
Liotrix (T3 and T4 in 1:4 ratio) *(Thyrolar)* Tablet	Start 25 mcg levothyroxine/6.25 mcg liothyronine daily Usual dose is 50-100 mcg levothyroxine/12.5-25 mcg liothyronine	

DRUG INTERACTIONS

Drugs that ↓ thyroid hormone levels

- Drugs that ↓ levothyroxine absorption:
  - Aluminum (antacids), calcium, cholestyramine, iron, magnesium, multivitamins (containing ADEK, folate, iron), orlistat *(Xenical, Alli)*, sevelamer and sucralfate: separate doses by four hours from thyroid replacement therapy.
  - Sodium polystyrene sulfate *(Kayexalate)* and patiromer *(Veltassa)*: separate doses by three hours from thyroid replacement therapy.
  - Lanthanum: separate doses by two hours from thyroid replacement therapy.
- Estrogen, SSRIs and hepatic inducers ↓ thyroid hormone levels.
- Beta-blockers, amiodarone, propylthiouracil (PTU) and systemic steroids can ↓ the effectiveness of levothyroxine by ↓ the conversion of T4 to T3.
- Thyroid hormone is highly-protein bound (> 99%). Drugs that can cause protein-binding site displacement include salicylates (> 2 g/day), heparin, phenytoin, NSAIDs and others.

Thyroid hormone can change the concentration or effect of these drugs:

- ↑ effect of anticoagulants (e.g., ↑ PT/INR with warfarin).
- ↓ levels of digoxin and theophylline; ↓ effect of antidiabetic drugs.

PATIENT COUNSELING

- Levothyroxine is a replacement for a hormone that is normally produced by your body to regulate your energy and metabolism. Levothyroxine is given when the thyroid does not produce enough of this hormone on its own.
- There are many medicines that can alter the effects of levothyroxine; tell the pharmacist about all medications you are taking, including OTC drugs, including vitamins, supplements, herbs and heartburn medications.
- Different brands of levothyroxine may not work the same. If you get a prescription refill and your new pills look different, speak to the pharmacist.
- This medicine is safe to use while you are pregnant. It is also safe to use while you are breastfeeding a baby. It does pass into breast milk, but it is not harmful to a nursing infant.
- Tell your healthcare provider if you become pregnant during treatment; it is likely that your dose will need to be increased during pregnancy or if you plan to breastfeed.
- Take this medication with water. Take it 60 minutes before breakfast or at bedtime (at least three hours after your last meal).
- If you are taking other medicines on an empty stomach first thing in the morning, discuss the best dosing with your pharmacist. Medications for your bones (osteoporosis) like *Actonel* or *Fosamax* should be taken 30 minutes before your thyroid medicine.
- Some patients will notice a slight reduction in symptoms within one to two weeks, but the full effect is often delayed for a month or two before people start to feel normal.
- Even if you feel well, you still need to take this medicine every day for the rest of your life to replace the thyroid hormone your body cannot produce.
- To be sure the dose being used is optimal for you, your blood will need to be tested on a regular basis (at least annually).

LEVOTHYROXINE TABLET COLORS

Remember: **O**rangutans **W**ill **V**omit **O**n **Y**ou **R**ight **B**efore **T**hey **B**ecome **L**arge, **P**roud **G**iants.

25 mcg - orange
50 mcg - white (no dye)
75 mcg - violet
88 mcg - olive
100 mcg - yellow
112 mcg - rose
125 mcg - brown
137 mcg - turquoise
150 mcg - blue
175 mcg - lilac
200 mcg - pink
300 mcg - green

HYPERTHYROIDISM

Hyperthyroidism (overactive thyroid or thyrotoxicosis) occurs when there is over-production of thyroid hormones. FT4 is high and TSH is low, and symptoms are nearly opposite of those seen in hypothyroidism. Hyperthyroidism can significantly accelerate metabolism, causing weight loss, and other symptoms, including agitation and heat intolerance (see Study Tip Gal on the next page).

Left untreated, hyperthyroidism can cause tachycardia, arrhythmias, heart failure and osteoporosis. No one should use thyroid hormone to lose weight; it can lead to psychiatric issues and severe cardiac complications.

Causes

The most common cause of hyperthyroidism is Graves' disease, which most commonly occurs in females ages 30 – 50 years. Graves' disease is an autoimmune disorder (like Hashimoto's) but instead of destroying the thyroid gland, the antibodies stimulate the thyroid to produce too much T4. Less common causes include thyroid nodules and thyroiditis (inflammation of the thyroid). Drug causes of hyperthyroidism include iodine, amiodarone and interferons. Iodine-induced hyperthyroidism can be due to excess iodine in the diet, exposure to radiographic contrast media or from medications. Excess iodine increases the synthesis and release of thyroid hormone in iodine-deficient patients and in older patients with pre-existing multinodular goiters. Excessive doses of thyroid hormone can cause hyperthyroidism.

S/SX OF HYPERTHYROIDISM

- Heat intolerance or increased sweating
- Weight loss (or gain)
- Agitation, nervousness, irritability, anxiety
- Palpitations and tachycardia
- Fatigue and muscle weakness
- Frequent bowel movements or diarrhea
- Insomnia
- Tremor
- Thinning hair
- Goiter (possible)
- Exophthalmos (protrusion of the eyeballs), diplopia
- Light or absent menstrual periods

DRUG TREATMENT

Treatment involves anti-thyroid medications, destroying part of the gland via radioactive iodine (RAI-131) or surgery. RAI-131 has historically been considered the preferred treatment in Graves' disease, but all three treatment options are effective and relatively safe. With any option, the patient can be treated with beta blockers first for symptom control (to reduce palpitations, tremors and tachycardia). Propylthiouracil (PTU) or methimazole can be used as a temporary measure until surgery is complete. It takes one - three months of treatment with anti-thyroid medications at high doses to control symptoms. Once symptoms are controlled, the dose should be reduced to prevent hypothyroidism from occurring.

Hyperthyroidism Treatment

DRUG	DOSING	SAFETY/SIDE EFFECTS/MONITORING
Thionamides – inhibit synthesis of thyroid hormones by blocking the oxidation of iodine in the thyroid gland; PTU also inhibits peripheral conversion of T4 to T3		
Propylthiouracil (PTU) Tablet	50-150 mg Q8H initially until euthyroid (higher doses for more severe hyperthyroidism), followed by dose reduction	**BOXED WARNING** Severe liver injury and acute liver failure (with PTU) Pregnancy: PTU preferred in 1st trimester (due to increased risk of fetal abnormalities from methimazole); methimazole often recommended for 2nd and 3rd trimesters (to decrease risk of liver toxicity from PTU) **SIDE EFFECTS** GI upset, drug-induced lupus erythematosus (DILE), headache, rash (exfoliative dermatitis, pruritus), fever, constipation, loss of taste/taste perversion, lymphadenopathy, bleeding Hepatitis, agranulocytosis (rare) **MONITORING** CBC, LFTs, PT and thyroid function tests (TSH, FT4, total T3) every 4-6 weeks until euthyroid **NOTES** PTU is preferred in thyroid storm Take with food to reduce GI upset Patient must monitor for liver toxicity (abdominal pain, yellow skin/eyes, dark urine, nausea, weakness) and infection (high fever or severe sore throat) PTU is not a first line treatment for hyperthyroidism except in patients who cannot tolerate other options or conditions where other antithyroid therapies are contraindicated
Methimazole (*Tapazole*) Tablet	Mild hyperthyroidism: 5 mg Q8H initially until euthyroid (↑ doses for more severe hyperthyroidism), then 5-15 mg daily	

DRUG	DOSING	SAFETY/SIDE EFFECTS/MONITORING
Iodides – temporarily inhibit secretion of thyroid hormones; T4 and T3 levels will be reduced for several weeks but effect will not be maintained		
Potassium iodide and iodine solution *(Lugol's Solution)* Oral solution	Preparation for thyroidectomy: 5-7 drops Q8H for 10 days prior to surgery (off-label)	**CONTRAINDICATIONS** Hypersensitivity to iodide or iodine, dermatitis herpetiformis, hypocomplementemic vasculitis, nodular thyroid condition with heart disease **SIDE EFFECTS** Rash, metallic taste, sore throat/gums, GI upset, urticaria, hypo/hyperthyroidism with prolonged use **MONITORING** Thyroid function tests, s/sx of hyperthyroidism **NOTES** Dilute in a glassful of water, juice, or milk; take with food or milk to reduce GI upset *SSKI* is also used as an expectorant
Saturated solution of potassium iodide *(SSKI, ThyroSafe)* Oral solution	Preparation for thyroidectomy: 1-2 drops Q8H for 10 days prior to surgery (off-label)	

POTASSIUM IODIDE USE AFTER EXPOSURE TO RADIATION

Potassium iodide (KI) blocks the accumulation of radioactive iodine in the thyroid gland; thus preventing thyroid cancer. Potassium iodide should be taken as soon as possible after radiation exposure on the advice of public health or emergency management personnel only. The correct dose must be used and higher doses do not offer greater protection. Refer to the CDC website for age-specific dosing based on the duration of radiation exposure (https://emergency.cdc.gov/radiation/ki.asp). Iodized salt and foods do not contain enough iodine to block radioactive iodine and are not recommended.

THYROID STORM

Thyroid storm is a life-threatening medical emergency characterized by decompensated hyperthyroidism that can be precipitated by infection, trauma, surgery, radioactive iodine treatment or non-adherence to antithyroid medication. It is important to recognize symptoms so that treatment can be implemented promptly (see Study Tip Gal).

S/SX OF THYROID STORM

- Fever (> 103°F)
- Tachycardia
- Tachypnea
- Dehydration
- Profuse sweating
- Agitation
- Delirium
- Psychosis
- Coma

DRUG TREATMENT

- Antithyroid drug therapy (PTU is preferred; 500 – 1,000 mg loading dose, then 250 mg PO Q4H)

  PLUS

- Inorganic iodide therapy such as *SSKI* 5 drops (in water or juice) PO Q6H or *Lugol's Solution* 4 – 8 drops PO Q6 – 8H

  PLUS

- Beta blocker (e.g., propranolol 40 – 80 mg PO Q6H)

  PLUS

- Systemic steroid (e.g., dexamethasone 2 – 4 mg PO Q6H

  PLUS

- Aggressive cooling with acetaminophen and cooling blankets and other supportive treatments (e.g., antiarrhythmics, insulin, fluids, electrolytes)

Antithyroid drug should be given ≥ 1 hour before iodide to block synthesis of thyroid hormone. PTU tablets can be crushed and administered through an NG tube if needed.

THYROID DISEASE AND PREGNANCY

PREGNANCY AND HYPOTHYROIDISM

Untreated maternal hypothyroidism has been associated with loss of pregnancy, low birth weight, premature birth and lower IQ in children. Levothyroxine is safe in pregnancy and is the recommended treatment. Pregnant women treated with thyroid hormone replacement will require a 30 – 50% increase in the dose throughout the course of their pregnancy and for several months after giving birth. Aggressive control of hypothyroidism in pregnancy is recommended. Treatment should ideally be started prior to the pregnancy.

PREGNANCY AND HYPERTHYROIDISM

Poor control of hyperthyroidism in pregnancy is associated with pregnancy loss, prematurity and low birth weight like hypothyroidism, as well as thyroid storm, maternal hypertension and congestive heart failure. There can also be lasting effects in the baby, including seizure disorders and neurobehavioral disorders. Pregnancy should be postponed until a stable euthyroid state is reached. If a woman with hyperthyroidism does become pregnant, she should be evaluated to see if treatment can be stopped (mild disease). If treatment is needed, it should be with antithyroid drugs based on the trimester. For the first trimester, PTU should be used (due to fetal toxicity with methimazole). After that, the decision is individualized, as both PTU and methimazole carry potential risks. Historically, the patient would be switched to methimazole for the remainder of the pregnancy.

Select Guidelines/References

2016 American Thyroid Association Guidelines for Diagnosis and Management of Hyperthyroidism and Other Causes of Thyrotoxicosis. *Thyroid.* 2016; 26(10):1343-1422.

Guidelines for the Treatment of Hypothyroidism: Prepared by the American Thyroid Association Task Force on Thyroid Hormone Replacement. *Thyroid.* 2014; 24(12): 1670-1751.

2017 Guidelines of the American Thyroid Association for the Diagnosis and Management of Thyroid Disease During Pregnancy and the Postpartum. *Thyroid.* 2017; 27(3):315-389.

CHAPTER CONTENT

Systemic Steroids **671**
Cushing's Syndrome 672
Glucocorticoids (Systemic Steroids) 673
Steroids: Least Potent to Most Potent 673
Autoimmune Conditions **674**
Immunosuppression from Steroids 674
Treatment 674
Treating Acute Inflammation with Steroids 674
Rheumatoid Arthritis **675**
Clinical Presentation 675
Non-Drug Treatment 675
Drug Treatment 675
Traditional (Non-Biologic) Disease-Modifying Antirheumatic Drugs (DMARDs) 676
Anti-TNF Biologic DMARDs 679
Other Biologic DMARDs (Non-TNF Inhibitors) 680
Systemic Lupus Erythematosus **681**
Background 681
Select Drugs That Can Cause Drug-Induced Lupus Erythematosus (DILE) 682
Clinical Presentation 682
Non-Drug Treatment 682
Drug Treatment 682
Multiple Sclerosis **683**
Background 683
Clinical Presentation 683
Treatment 683
Disease-Modifying Therapies 683
Drugs Used for Symptom Control 686
Raynaud's Phenomenon **686**
Drug-Induced Raynaud's 686
Celiac Disease **687**
Background 687
Clinical Presentation 687
Treatment 687
Myasthenia Gravis **688**
Background 688
Drugs that Can Worsen Myasthenia Gravis 688
Treatment 688
Sjögren's Syndrome **689**
Dry Eyes Treatment 689
Dry Mouth Treatment 689
Psoriasis **690**
Background 690
Non-Drug Treatment 690
Drug Treatment 690
Topical Psoriasis Treatment 690
Systemic Psoriasis Treatment 691

CONTENT LEGEND

= Study Tip Gal   = Key Drug Guy

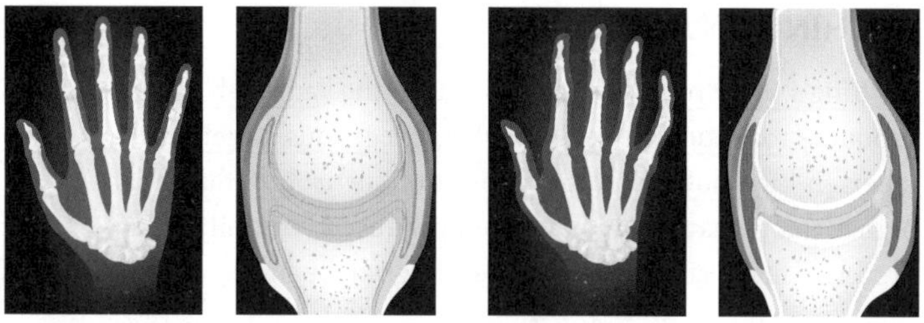

Hand normal joint | Cross section of joint | Hand with Rheumatoid arthritis | Cross section of joint with Rheumatoid arthritis

CHAPTER 46
SYSTEMIC STEROIDS & AUTOIMMUNE CONDITIONS

SYSTEMIC STEROIDS

There are several drug classes that can be used to treat inflammation, including drugs that target the chemical pathway of inflammation (e.g., various biologics), cancer drugs that have strong anti-inflammatory properties, steroids and NSAIDs. Steroids and NSAIDs are used commonly; of these two classes, steroids are stronger anti-inflammatory drugs. Both have serious adverse effects, but chronic use of NSAIDs is considered to be safer than long-term use of steroids. See the Pain chapter for a review of NSAIDs.

Steroids are used for a variety of conditions, including inflammatory conditions (e.g., rheumatoid arthritis, psoriasis, acute asthma exacerbation), immune suppression post-transplant and adrenal insufficiency [to replace endogenous (our own) steroids that the adrenal gland is not producing in adequate amounts]. The two primary endogenous steroids that can require replacement are:

- Cortisol, which can be replaced by any of the steroids.
- Aldosterone, which is replaced by giving fludrocortisone.

Fludrocortisone mimics aldosterone. It has mineralocorticoid activity, which is used to maintain a balance of water and electrolytes. This helps to keep blood pressure stable. Fludrocortisone is FDA-approved for Addison's disease but is also used off-label for orthostatic hypotension. Other commonly used steroids (e.g., prednisone, hydrocortisone) have more glucocorticoid activity, which has more anti-inflammatory effects. The rest of this section discusses only the commonly used glucocorticoids, which will be referred to simply as steroids. Systemic steroids can cause the adrenal gland to stop producing cortisol due to feedback inhibition. This is called suppression of the hypothalamic-pituitary-adrenal (HPA) axis (see diagram on the following page). When long-term steroids are discontinued, they need to be tapered off to give the adrenal gland time to resume cortisol production.

CUSHING'S SYNDROME

Cushing's syndrome develops when the adrenal gland produces too much cortisol, or when exogenous steroids are taken in high doses and the amount of cortisol produced is higher than what would have been produced naturally. This produces many adverse effects (see diagram below).

Addison's disease can be thought of as the opposite of Cushing's; in Addison's disease, the adrenal gland is not making enough cortisol. If exogenous steroids are stopped suddenly, it can cause an "Addisonian Crisis," which can be fatal.

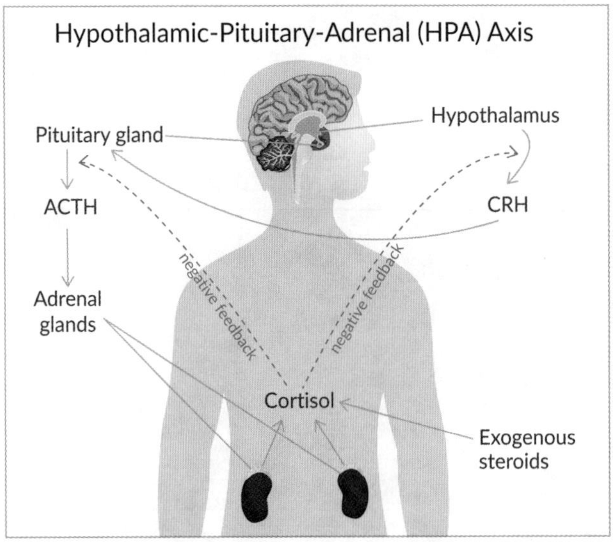

CRH = Corticotropin Releasing Hormone;
ACTH = Adrenocorticotropic Hormone, also called corticotropin

Cushing's Syndrome: High Steroid Intake or Production

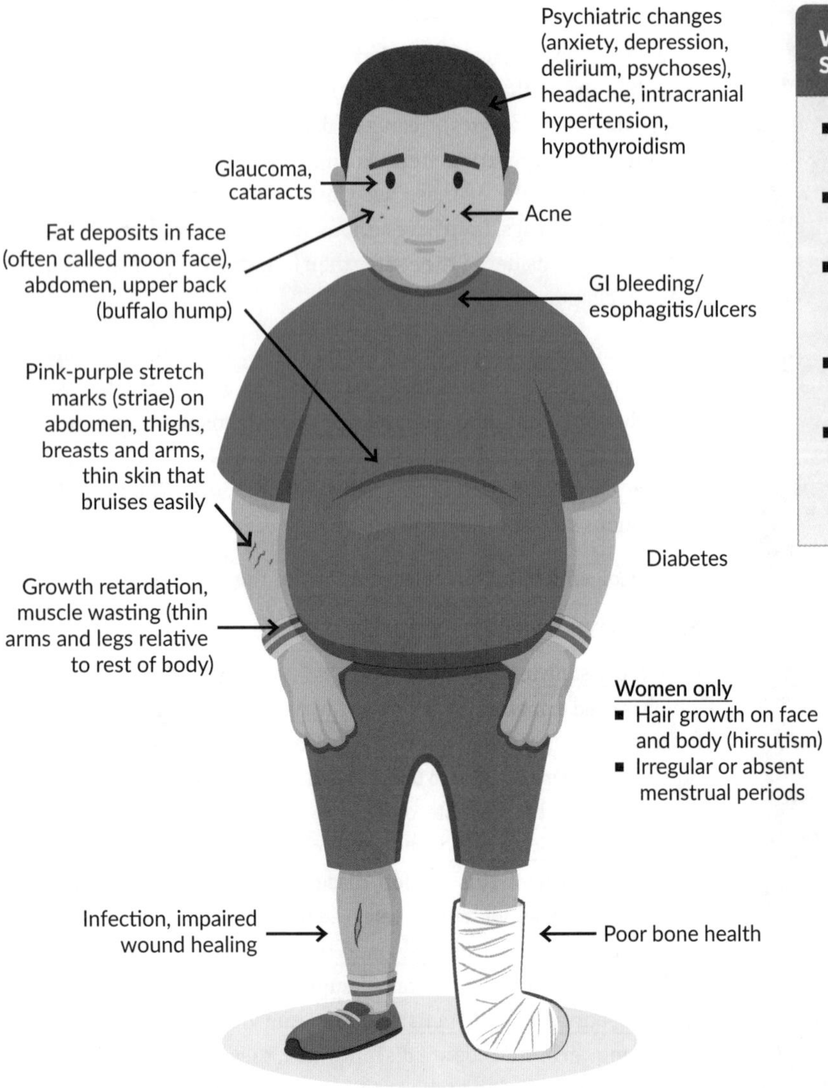

WAYS TO REDUCE SYSTEMIC STEROID RISKS

- Use alternate day dosing (skip every other day); this decreases Cushing-like side effects.
- For joint inflammation, inject into the joint so the drug stays local.
- For a condition in the gut, use a steroid with low systemic absorption, such as budesonide *(Entocort EC)*.
- For treatment of asthma, use inhaled steroids that mostly stay in the lungs.
- For conditions that require long-term steroids (e.g., transplant, or a severe autoimmune condition), use the lowest possible dose for the shortest possible time.

<table>
<tr><th colspan="3">SYSTEMIC STEROIDS (PO, IV) DOSE EQUIVALENCE</th></tr>
<tr><td>Cortisone</td><td>25 mg</td><td rowspan="2">Short-acting</td></tr>
<tr><td>Hydrocortisone</td><td>20 mg</td></tr>
<tr><td>Prednisone</td><td>5 mg</td><td rowspan="4">Intermediate-acting</td></tr>
<tr><td>Prednisolone</td><td>5 mg</td></tr>
<tr><td>Methylprednisolone</td><td>4 mg</td></tr>
<tr><td>Triamcinolone</td><td>4 mg</td></tr>
<tr><td>Dexamethasone</td><td>0.75 mg</td><td rowspan="2">Long-acting & highest potency</td></tr>
<tr><td>Betamethasone</td><td>0.6 mg</td></tr>
</table>

STEROIDS: LEAST POTENT TO MOST POTENT

Remember: **C**ute **H**ot **P**harmacists and **P**hysicians **M**arry **T**ogether & **D**eliver **B**abies

GLUCOCORTICOIDS (SYSTEMIC STEROIDS)

<table>
<tr><th>DRUG</th><th>DOSING</th><th>SAFETY/SIDE EFFECTS/MONITORING</th></tr>
<tr><td>Dexamethasone
(DexPak 6, 10 or 13 day, Decadron, Dexamethasone Intensol, DoubleDex, others)</td><td rowspan="8">Dosing varies by condition

Many formulations: liquids, ODT (children), injections [fast-acting, long-acting (for joints usually)], tablets, others

If once daily, take between 7-8 AM to mimic the natural diurnal cortisol release

Take oral doses with food to decrease GI upset

Steroid-Induced Medical Conditions
Short-term side effects can lead to:

↑ blood glucose → diabetes

↑ blood pressure → hypertension

↑ intraocular pressure → glaucoma

Emotional instability, euphoria, mood swings → psychiatric conditions</td><td rowspan="8">CONTRAINDICATIONS
Live vaccines, serious systemic infections

WARNINGS
Adrenal suppression – HPA axis suppression may lead to adrenal crisis and death; if taking longer than 14 days, must taper slowly

Immunosuppression, psychiatric disturbances, Kaposi sarcoma, can worsen other conditions (use with caution in heart failure, diabetes, hypertension, osteoporosis)

SIDE EFFECTS
Short-term side effects (used < 1 month)
↑ appetite/weight gain, emotional instability (euphoria, mood swings, irritability), insomnia, fluid retention, indigestion, bitter taste, ↑ in blood pressure and blood glucose with higher doses

Long-term side effects
See Cushing's Syndrome figure

MONITORING
BP, weight, appetite, mood, growth (children/adolescents), bone mineral density, blood glucose, electrolytes, infection, IOP if > 6 weeks

NOTES
Cortisone is a prodrug of cortisol

Prednisone is a prodrug of prednisolone

Prednisolone is used commonly in children (many formulations)</td></tr>
<tr><td>Hydrocortisone
(Solu-Cortef, Cortef)</td></tr>
<tr><td>Methylprednisolone
(Medrol, Solu-Medrol, Depo-Medrol, Medrol Therapy Pack, others)</td></tr>
<tr><td>Prednisone
(Deltasone, Prednisone Intensol, Rayos)</td></tr>
<tr><td>Prednisolone
(Millipred, Orapred ODT, Veripred)</td></tr>
<tr><td>Triamcinolone
(Kenalog, Pro-C-Dure 5, Pro-C-Dure 6, others)</td></tr>
<tr><td>Betamethasone
(Celestone Soluspan, ReadySharp Betamethasone)</td></tr>
<tr><td>Cortisone</td></tr>
</table>

EXAM SCENARIO
AS is a 30-year-old female who presented to the hospital with an acute flare of her Crohn's disease. She was started on *Solu-Medrol* 40 mg IV BID. The medical team is now ready to transition her to oral prednisone at an equivalent dose. Assuming the IV:PO ratio of *Solu-Medrol* is 1:1, what is the equivalent daily dose?

$$\frac{\text{Methylprednisolone 4 mg}}{\text{Prednisone 5 mg}} = \frac{\text{Methylprednisolone 80 mg}}{\text{Prednisone X mg}}$$

$$X = 100 \text{ mg Prednisone}$$

AUTOIMMUNE CONDITIONS

Autoimmune diseases are conditions that occur when the body's immune system attacks and destroys healthy body tissue. The immune system is a complex organization of cells and antibodies designed to "seek and destroy" invaders of the body, particularly infections. Symptoms vary based on the type of autoimmune disease and the location of the immune response. Common symptoms of most autoimmune diseases include fatigue, weakness and pain. Nonspecific laboratory blood tests that can be useful in detecting inflammation include: erythrocyte sedimentation rate (ESR), C-reactive protein (CRP), rheumatoid factor (RF) and anti-nuclear antibody (ANA).

Rheumatoid arthritis (RA), systemic lupus erythematosus (SLE), multiple sclerosis (MS), celiac disease, Sjögren's syndrome, Raynaud's, myasthenia gravis and psoriasis are discussed in this chapter. Other autoimmune diseases covered elsewhere in the book include type 1 diabetes (see the Diabetes chapter) and Hashimoto's thyroiditis and Graves disease (see the Thyroid Disorders chapter).

IMMUNOSUPPRESSION FROM STEROIDS

A patient is immunosuppressed when using ≥ 2 mg/kg/day or ≥ 20 mg/day of prednisone or prednisone equivalent (see potency table) for > 2 weeks.

Immunosuppressed patients cannot receive live vaccines and have a high risk of infection.

Due to HPA axis suppression, the steroid will need to be tapered slowly to allow the adrenal gland to resume normal cortisol production; otherwise the patient is at risk for Addisonian Crisis.

There are many ways to taper steroids; a common method is to reduce the dose by ~10-20% every few days. Tapers can last 7-14 days (or longer or shorter), depending on the condition being treated.

TREATMENT

Treatment of autoimmune diseases typically involves drugs that suppress the immune system, which decreases the immune response (see Study Tip Gal below for steroid immunosuppression overview). The use of strong immunosuppressants can increase the risk of certain conditions including:

- Re-activation of tuberculosis and hepatitis B and C (if present): testing (and treatment, if needed) must be done prior to the start of immunosuppressive drugs.
- Viruses: if the virus can be prevented by a live vaccine, the vaccine must be given prior to the start of immunosuppressive treatment.
- Lymphomas and certain skin cancers: these cancer types are normally suppressed by a competent immune system.
- Infections of various types (e.g., bacterial, fungal): this requires monitoring of symptoms (by the patient), complete blood counts (CBC), and may require infection control measures.

TREATING ACUTE INFLAMMATION WITH STEROIDS

Give a high dose initially (to quickly reduce inflammation), then taper the dose down to treat the remaining inflammation while preventing a rebound attack.

The ***Medrol Tablet Therapy Pack**** provides a tapering system that is convenient for the patient. The pack includes 21 x 4 mg tablets used in a tapered dose schedule over 6 days:

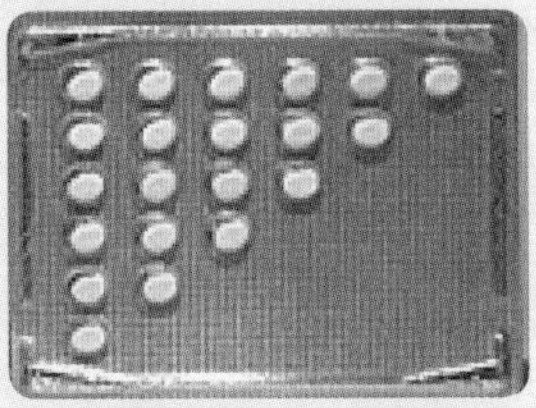

Day 1: 2 tablets before breakfast, 1 tablet after lunch, 1 tablet after dinner, 2 tablets at bedtime

Day 2: 1 tablet before breakfast, 1 tablet after lunch, 1 tablet after dinner, 2 tablets at bedtime

Day 3: 1 tablet before breakfast, 1 tablet after lunch, 1 tablet after dinner, 1 tablet at bedtime

Day 4: 1 tablet before breakfast, 1 tablet after lunch, 1 tablet at bedtime

Day 5: 1 tablet before breakfast, 1 tablet at bedtime

Day 6: 1 tablet before breakfast

**Will not be appropriate for all patients (e.g., may need a longer taper or a higher starting dose)*

RHEUMATOID ARTHRITIS

Rheumatoid arthritis (RA) is a chronic, progressive autoimmune disorder that primarily affects joints. Other organs in the body, including the kidneys, eyes, heart and lungs can be affected. Like many of the autoimmune conditions discussed in this chapter, the disease course is highly variable and some patients have much more aggressive disease than others.

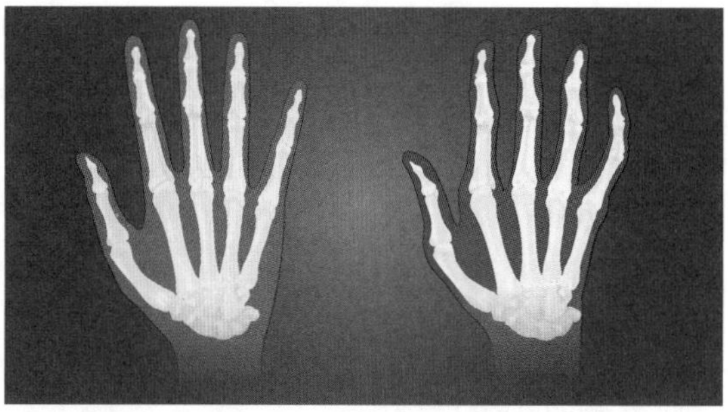

Healthy Hand   Hand with Rheumatoid Arthritis

CLINICAL PRESENTATION

RA typically results in warm, tender, swollen and painful joints. It usually presents in the smaller joints of the fingers, wrist, ankles and feet first. Bilateral, symmetrical disease is consistent with an RA diagnosis, in contrast to osteoarthritis (OA) which presents unilaterally (on one side of the body, such as the right hand).

The classic symptoms of RA are shown in the box to the right. RA is a systemic disease and has systemic symptoms, such as fever, weakness and loss of appetite. Stiffness and pain are worse after rest, which is why "morning stiffness" is a common complaint. In contrast, OA does not cause prolonged stiffness. Diagnosis will depend on a combination of signs, symptoms, lab tests and x-rays.

When a patient presents with joint pain and swelling, it can be challenging to identify the type of arthritis that is causing the symptoms. Joint erosion and rheumatoid nodules can be absent if RA is caught early. Anti-citrullinated peptide antibody (ACPA) and rheumatoid factor (RF) are useful laboratory tests in diagnosing RA (note RF has lower specificity for RA and can be positive due to another autoimmune disorder).

ARTICULAR (JOINT) SYMPTOMS OF RA	
Joint swelling	Weakness
Pain	Difficult to move
Stiffness	Edema
Bone deformity	Redness

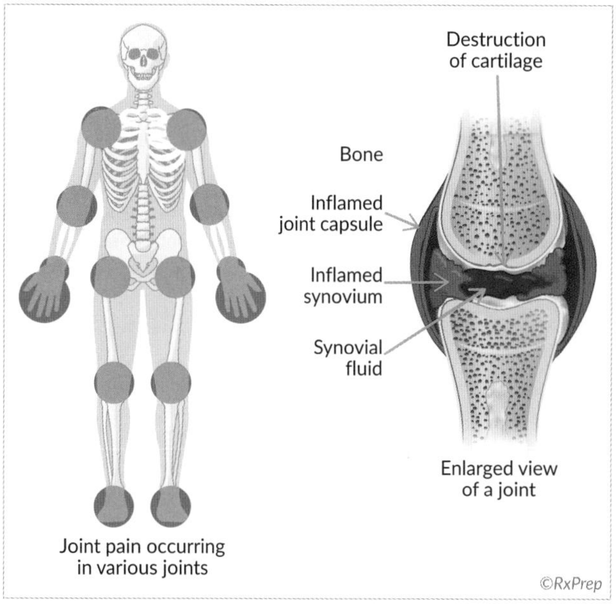

NON-DRUG TREATMENT

Non-drug treatments include rest, physical therapy, occupational therapy, exercise, diet and weight control and surgical intervention (e.g., a joint replacement).

DRUG TREATMENT

RA is classified as mild, moderate or severe. Patients with symptomatic RA should be started on a disease-modifying antirheumatic drug (DMARD), regardless of the severity of disease. DMARDs work via various mechanisms to slow the disease process and help prevent further joint damage. The treatment goal is remission of the disease (or low disease activity). Methotrexate (MTX) is the preferred initial therapy for most patients. For patients with moderate or high disease activity despite MTX (with or without a systemic steroid), a combination of DMARDs or a tumor necrosis factor (TNF) inhibitor biologic or a non-TNF biologic, with or without MTX, is recommended. Never use two biologic DMARDs in combination due to the risk of serious (fatal) infections.

Low-dose steroids (defined as ≤ 10 mg/day of prednisone or equivalent) can be added in patients with moderate or high disease activity when starting a DMARD (as a "bridging" option to provide relief while waiting for the DMARD to take effect) and in patients with DMARD failure. Steroids are commonly used in RA flares and should be used at the lowest dose and for the shortest duration possible. NSAIDs are a weaker option for bridging than steroids, but are less toxic, and are often used for this purpose; anti-inflammatory (higher) doses are required. NSAID toxicity (e.g., GI bleeds, CVD risk) must be considered.

Traditional (Non-Biologic) Disease-Modifying Antirheumatic Drugs (DMARDs)

DRUG	DOSING	SAFETY/SIDE EFFECTS/MONITORING
Methotrexate ***(Trexall,** Otrexup, Rasuvo, Xatmep)* *Trexall* is an oral tablet *Otrexup* and *Rasuvo* are single-dose (needle included) SC auto-injectors *Xatmep* is an oral solution for use in pediatric patients Injection (IV/IT) – for oncology use Irreversibly binds and inhibits dihydrofolate reductase, inhibiting folate, thymidylate synthetase and purine; has immune modulator and anti-inflammatory activity	7.5-20 mg once weekly (PO, SC, IM) Low weekly doses are used for RA; to avoid error, it is safest to take as a single dose (rather than divided oral dosages of 2.5 mg Q12H x 3 doses per week – see below) Never dose daily for RA; numerous incidences of adverse events (e.g., mouth sores, intestinal bleeding, liver damage) have occurred due to patients taking daily	**BOXED WARNINGS** Hepatotoxicity, myelosuppression, mucositis/stomatitis, pregnancy (embryo-fetal toxicity and/or fetal death), acute renal failure, pneumonitis, GI toxicity, dermatologic reactions, malignant lymphomas, potentially fatal opportunistic infections; renal and lung toxicity are more likely when using higher oncology doses **CONTRAINDICATION** Pregnancy, breastfeeding, alcoholism, chronic liver disease, blood dyscrasias, immunodeficiency syndrome **SIDE EFFECTS** Vary by route and dosage N/V/D, ↑ LFTs, stomatitis, alopecia, photosensitivity, arthralgia, myalgia **MONITORING** CBC, LFTs (at baseline, every 2-4 weeks for first 3 months or following dose increases, every 8-12 weeks for 3-6 months, then less frequently), chest X-ray, hepatitis B and C serologies (if at high risk), SCr, PFTs (if lung-related symptoms), TB test **NOTES** Folate can be given to ↓ hematological, GI and hepatic side effects; give 5 mg PO weekly on the day following MTX administration (some take 1 mg daily on non-MTX days) *Xatmep* requires no preparation; eliminates the need for needles, crushing or splitting tablets, or compounding tablets into a liquid formulation
Hydroxychloroquine ***(Plaquenil)*** Tablet +/- MTX Immune modulator	400 mg/day initially, then 300 mg/day for maintenance dose Take with food or milk	**WARNINGS** Irreversible retinopathy, loss of visual acuity/macular pigment changes, neuromuscular weakness, cardiomyopathy, bone marrow suppression (anemia, leukopenia, thrombocytopenia), hypoglycemia, caution in patients with G6PD deficiency **SIDE EFFECTS** N/V/D, abdominal pain, rash, pruritus, HA, vision changes (dose-related), pigmentation changes of the skin and hair (rare) **MONITORING** CBC and LFTs at baseline and periodically; eye exam and muscle strength at baseline and every 3 months during prolonged therapy **NOTES** Lower risk of liver toxicity than MTX, can use as an alternative when there is a concern for liver disease Monotherapy: if low disease activity and symptoms < 24 months If inadequate or no response after 6 months, consider alternative
Sulfasalazine *(Azulfidine, Azulfidine EN-tabs)* Tablet +/- MTX Immune modulator	500-1,000 mg/day initially, then 1,000 mg BID (max is 3 grams/day) Take with food and 8 oz. of water to prevent crystalluria	**CONTRAINDICATION** Patients with a sulfa or salicylate allergy, GI or GU obstruction, porphyria **WARNINGS** Blood dyscrasias, severe skin reactions (SJS/TEN), hepatic failure and pulmonary fibrosis; use caution in patients with G6PD deficiency **SIDE EFFECTS** HA, rash, anorexia, dyspepsia, N/V/D, oligospermia (reversible), folate deficiency, arthralgia, crystalluria **MONITORING** CBC and LFTs (baseline, then every other week for first 3 months, then monthly for 3 months, then once every 3 months), renal function **NOTES** Can cause yellow-orange coloration of skin/urine Impairs folate absorption, can give 1 mg/day folate supplement

DRUG	DOSING	SAFETY/SIDE EFFECTS/MONITORING
Leflunomide *(Arava)* Tablet +/- MTX Inhibits pyrimidine synthesis resulting in anti-proliferative and anti-inflammatory effects Prodrug of teriflunomide	100 mg PO x 3 days, then 20 mg PO daily (can use 10 mg PO daily if unable to tolerate 20 mg) May omit loading dose if at higher risk of liver toxicity or myelosuppression	**BOXED WARNINGS** Embryo-fetal toxicity: exclude pregnancy prior to starting therapy Hepatotoxicity: avoid in pre-existing liver disease or ALT > 2x upper limit of normal (ULN) **CONTRAINDICATION** Pregnancy, severe hepatic impairment, current teriflunomide therapy **WARNINGS** Severe infections, serious skin reactions (SJS/TEN), peripheral neuropathy, interstitial lung disease, hypertension Upon discontinuation of treatment, use accelerated drug elimination procedure (see Notes) to reduce levels of active metabolite, teriflunomide **SIDE EFFECTS** ↑ LFTs, nausea, diarrhea, respiratory infections, rash, HA **MONITORING** LFTs and CBC at baseline and monthly for first 6 months, BP at baseline and regularly, screen for TB and pregnancy prior to starting therapy **NOTES** Accelerated drug elimination options: 1. Cholestyramine 8 grams PO TID x 11 days (use 4 g if 8 g dose not tolerated) 2. Activated charcoal suspension 50 grams PO Q12H x 11 days Must have negative pregnancy test prior and use 2 forms of birth control during treatment; if pregnancy is desired, must wait 2 years after discontinuation or use accelerated drug elimination procedure
Tofacitinib *(Xeljanz, Xeljanz XR)* Tablet +/- non-biologic DMARDs (MTX), do not use with biologic DMARDs or potent immunosuppressants Inhibits janus kinase (JAK) enzymes, which stimulate immune cell function	5 mg PO BID XR: 11 mg PO daily Dose adjustments with moderate-strong CYP 450 3A4 inducers and hepatic or renal impairment Do not start if: absolute lymphocyte count < 500 cells/mm^3, Hgb < 9 g/dL, or ANC < 1,000 cells/mm^3	**BOXED WARNINGS** Serious infections including tuberculosis (TB), fungal, viral, bacterial, or other opportunistic infections; screen for active and latent TB and treat before starting Malignancy: ↑ risk for lymphomas and other malignancies **WARNINGS** GI perforation, ↑ LFTs, not studied in patients with a baseline CrCl < 40 mL/min, avoid live vaccines **SIDE EFFECTS** Upper respiratory tract infections (URTIs), urinary tract infections (UTIs), diarrhea, HA, hypertension, ↑ lipids **MONITORING** CBC (for lymphopenia, neutropenia and anemia) and lipids at baseline, then 4-8 weeks later, then every 3 months, LFTs (at baseline and periodically thereafter), new onset abdominal pain, signs of infection **NOTES** Special alert from the FDA about the risk of pulmonary embolism (PE) when a high dose was used Caution in patients of Asian descent (↑ frequency of side effects) Available through specialty/network pharmacies
Baricitinib *(Olumiant)* Tablet +/- non-biologic DMARDs (MTX), do not use with biologic DMARDs or potent immunosuppressants Inhibits Janus Kinase (JAK) enzymes, which stimulate immune cell function	2 mg PO daily GFR < 60 mL/min/1.73m^2: not recommended Do not start if: absolute lymphocyte count < 500 cells/mm^3, Hgb < 8 g/dL, or ANC < 1,000 cells/mm^3	Same as above for tofacitinib, except: **BOXED WARNINGS** Thrombosis, including DVT, PE and arterial thrombosis; many were serious and some resulted in death

Methotrexate Drug Interactions

- Methotrexate should not be taken with alcohol; this combination ↑ the risk of liver toxicity.
- Renal elimination is ↓ by aspirin/NSAIDs, beta-lactams, and probenecid, resulting in toxicity; caution if using together.
- Sulfonamides and topical tacrolimus ↑ adverse effects of methotrexate. Avoid using together.
- Methotrexate can ↓ effectiveness of loop diuretics; loop diuretics can ↑ the methotrexate concentration. Use caution if using them together.
- Methotrexate and cyclosporine levels will both ↑ when used together, leading to toxicity; avoid using together.
- Probenecid can ↑ levels of methotrexate. Avoid using together, or consider a lower methotrexate dose.

Methotrexate Patient Counseling

- Common side effects of this medication include nausea, vomiting, abdominal pain, diarrhea, mouth sores and rash.
- If you are using this medication for rheumatoid arthritis or psoriasis, the dose is usually taken once weekly. Some patients are told to divide the once weekly dose in half and take it over two consecutive days per week. Do not use this medication daily or double-up on doses. Serious side effects could occur if it is used more frequently than directed. Choose a day of the week to take your medication that you can remember.
- Methotrexate has caused birth defects and death in unborn babies. If you are pregnant or plan on becoming pregnant, you should not use this medication. Use an effective form of birth control, whether you are a man or a woman. Tell your healthcare provider if you or your sexual partner become pregnant during treatment.
- Do not use methotrexate if you are breastfeeding.
- If you have kidney problems or excess body water (ascites, pleural effusion), you must be closely monitored and your dose may be adjusted or stopped by your healthcare provider.
- Your healthcare provider will perform periodic blood tests to check your liver function. Tell your healthcare provider right away if you develop any new or worsening symptoms, including black, tarry stools or symptoms of liver damage (unusual tiredness or weakness, yellow skin or eyes or darkened urine, stomach upset or pain).
- Methotrexate (usually at high dosages) has caused severe (sometimes fatal) bone marrow suppression (decreasing your body's ability to fight infections) and stomach/intestinal disease (e.g., bleeding) when used at the same time as NSAIDs. NSAIDs should not be used with high-doses of methotrexate. Caution is also advised with aspirin. If you are using low-dose aspirin (81 – 325 milligrams per day) for heart attack or stroke prevention, continue to take it unless directed otherwise.
- Rarely, methotrexate use has resulted in serious (sometimes fatal) lung problems, such as scarring and lung infections (*Pneumocystis* pneumonia).
- For *Rasuvo* and *Otrexup* single-use auto-injectors:
  - Store at room temperature.
  - Inspect the syringe. Liquid should be yellow *(Otrexup)* to yellow-brown *(Rasuvo)*; discard if cloudy or containing particles.
  - Select an injection site on the abdomen (two inches away from the navel) or upper thigh only. Do not inject in the arms or any other areas of the body.
  - Swab with an alcohol pad and allow to dry – do not fan or blow on the area.
  - For *Otrexup*, twist the cap to break the seal and remove the safety clip. For *Rasuvo*, pull the yellow cap directly off without twisting.
  - Pinch the skin and inject at a 90° angle. Press firmly until you hear a click. Hold three seconds for *Otrexup* and five seconds for *Rasuvo*.
  - Check the viewing window to be sure the medication was given.
  - Dispose of the used injector in a sharps container (see the Medication Safety & Quality Improvement chapter).

Anti-TNF Biologic DMARDs

Tumor necrosis factor (TNF) alpha inhibitors (also called anti-TNF biologics) are used for a variety of diseases. Dosing for RA is provided below. Recommended dosing for psoriatic arthritis, plaque psoriasis, Crohn's disease, ulcerative colitis and other indications may vary. Each drug has its own pregnancy registry, due to the unknown risks to the fetus. When the anti-TNF inhibitor is supplied as a single-dose pre-filled syringe, auto-injector or vial kit for subcutaneous (SC) injection, needles are included with the device and do not require a separate purchase.

DRUG	DOSING	SAFETY/SIDE EFFECTS/MONITORING
Etanercept *(Enbrel*, *Enbrel SureClick, Erelzi*-biosimilar) Single dose pre-filled syringe or auto-injector, multidose vial starter kit (tray) +/- MTX	50 mg SC weekly	**BOXED WARNINGS** Serious infections, some fatal, including TB, fungal, viral, bacterial or opportunistic; screen for latent TB (and treat if needed) prior to therapy Lymphomas and other malignancies **CONTRAINDICATIONS** Active systemic infection, doses > 5 mg/kg in moderate-severe heart failure (infliximab), sepsis (etanercept) **WARNINGS** Can cause demyelinating disease, hepatitis B reactivation, heart failure, hepatotoxicity, lupus-like syndrome, seizures, myelosuppression and severe infections Do not use with other biologic DMARDs or live vaccines **SIDE EFFECTS** Infections and injection site reactions (redness, rash, swelling, itching, or bruising), positive anti-nuclear antibodies, headache, nausea, ↑ CPK (adalimumab) **MONITORING** TB test (prior to initiation and annually if risk factors for TB are present), signs of infection, CBC, LFTs, HBV (HBsAg and anti-HBc prior to initiation and during treatment), symptoms of heart failure, malignancies, vitals (during infliximab infusion) **NOTES** Do not shake or freeze; requires refrigeration (biologics will denature if hot); allow to reach room temperature before injecting (15-30 minutes); etanercept and adalimumab can be stored at room temperature for a maximum of 14 days; do not refrigerate once warmed MTX is used 1st line and anti-TNF biologics are add-on therapy; however, if the initial presentation is severe, they can be started as initial therapy (with or without MTX) Antibody induction can occur and will ↓ usefulness of the drug Rotate injection sites
Adalimumab *(Humira*, *Humira Pen, Amjevita*-biosimilar, *Cyltezo*-biosimilar, *Hyrimoz*-biosimilar) Single dose pre-filled syringe or pen +/- MTX	40 mg SC every other week (if not taking MTX, can ↑ dose to 40 mg SC weekly)	
Infliximab *(Remicade*, *Renflexis*-biosimilar, *Inflectra*-biosimilar, *Ixifi*-biosimilar) Injection (IV) + MTX	3 mg/kg IV at weeks 0, 2, and 6, then every 8 weeks (can ↑ dose to 10 mg/kg or treat as often as every 4 weeks based on need, but infection risk will ↑) Requires a filter and is stable in NS only Infusion reactions: hypotension, fever, chills, pruritus (can pre-medicate with acetaminophen, antihistamine, steroids) Delayed hypersensitivity reaction 3-12 days after administration (fever, rash, myalgia, HA, sore throat)	
Certolizumab pegol *(Cimzia*, *Cimzia Prefilled, Cimzia Starter Kit)* Single dose pre-filled syringe and vial starter kit +/- MTX	400 mg SC at weeks 0, 2, and 4, then 200 mg SC every other week (can consider 400 mg every 4 weeks)	
Golimumab *(Simponi*, *Simponi Aria)* Single dose pre-filled syringe or auto-injector (SC), injection (IV) + MTX	SC *(Simponi)*: 50 mg monthly IV *(Simponi Aria)*: 2 mg/kg infused over 30 minutes at weeks 0 and 4, then every 8 weeks IV golimumab requires a filter	

Patient Counseling: Subcutaneous *Adalimumab, Etanercept and Golimumab*

- Inject exactly as prescribed by your healthcare provider (once weekly for etanercept, every 1 – 2 weeks for adalimumab, monthly for golimumab).
- Common side effects include injection site reactions, such as redness, swelling, itching or pain. These symptoms usually go away within 3 – 5 days. If you have pain, redness or swelling around the injection site that does not go away or gets worse, call your healthcare provider. Other side effects can include upper respiratory infections (sinus infections), headache, dizziness or coughing.
- People taking this medication should not get live vaccines. Make sure your vaccines are up-to-date before starting this drug. You can continue receiving the annual influenza shot (but not the influenza nasal vaccine, since this is a live vaccine).
- This medication works by blocking the immune system so it lowers your ability to fight infections. This can increase the chances of getting a serious infection. Tell your healthcare provider immediately if you have any signs of infection, such as a fever of 100.5°F (38°C) or higher, chills, very bad

sore throat, ear or sinus pain, a cough, more sputum or a change in the color of your sputum.

- This medication has a possibility of causing liver damage. Call your healthcare provider right away if you have any of these symptoms: feeling very tired, yellowing of your skin or eyes, poor appetite, vomiting or pain on the right side of your stomach (abdomen).
- This medication can worsen heart failure. Notify your healthcare provider if you experience sudden weight gain or shortness of breath.
- Store the medication (single dose syringes or multidose vials) in the refrigerator with protection from light and sources of heat. Etanercept and adalimumab can be stored at room temperature for a maximum of 14 days. Allow the medication to warm to room temperature before injecting, by letting it sit at room temperature outside the carton (takes 15 – 30 minutes); do not warm any other way. Once warmed, do not return to the refrigerator. Do not shake the medication. Before using, check for particles or discoloration. If either is present, do not use.
- Before injecting each dose, clean the injection site with rubbing alcohol. Do not wave the hand over the wet area to dry. It is important to change the location of the injection site each time you use this drug. New injections should be given at least one inch (2.5 centimeters) from the last injection site. Do not inject into areas of the skin that are sore, bruised, red, broken or hard.
- For adalimumab *(Humira)*: inject SC into the abdomen or thigh. A loud click is heard when the plum-colored activator button is pressed. Continue to hold the injector against the skin until the yellow marker fully appears in the window view and stops moving (can take 10 seconds).
- For etanercept *(Enbrel)* syringe or auto-injector: inject SC into the abdomen, thigh or upper arm. A loud click is heard when the injection begins, continue to hold the injector against the skin for 15 seconds. You may hear a second click as the purple button pops back up, indicating all of the medication has been injected.
- For etanercept *(Enbrel)* vials for reconstitution: when reconstituting *Enbrel* powder from the multidose vial, some foaming is normal. The final solution should be clear and colorless with no particulate matter. After use, the window will turn yellow. If it does not, contact your healthcare provider for instructions.
- For golimumab *(Simponi)*: inject SC into the abdomen, thigh or upper arm. A loud click is heard when the injection begins, continue to hold the injector against the skin until a second click is heard (3 – 15 seconds).

Other Biologic DMARDs (Non-TNF Inhibitors)

The following drugs are biologics that affect the immune system in mechanisms other than TNF inhibition. Safety data on the use of non-TNF biologics in pregnancy is limited. Pregnant patients exposed to these drugs are encouraged to register in a pregnancy exposure registry so that pregnancy outcomes can be monitored. When the agent is supplied as a single-dose pre-filled syringe, auto-injector or vial kit for SC injection, needles are included with the device and do not require a separate purchase.

DRUG	DOSING	SAFETY/SIDE EFFECTS/MONITORING
Rituximab *(Rituxan)* Injection (IV) + MTX Depletes CD20 B cells believed to have a role in RA development and progression	1,000 mg IV on day 1 and day 15 (in combination with MTX for both doses) Can repeat treatment if needed at 16-24 weeks Pre-medicate with a steroid, acetaminophen and an antihistamine Start infusion at 50 mg/hr; can ↑ by 50 mg/hr every 30 minutes if no reaction (max 400 mg/hr) Gently invert the bag to mix the solution, do not shake	**BOXED WARNINGS** Serious, and fatal, infusion-related reactions (usually with the first infusion), progressive multifocal leukoencephalopathy (PML) due to JC virus infection (can be fatal), serious skin reactions (SJS/TEN) HBV reactivation, some cases resulting in fulminant hepatitis, hepatic failure and death; screen high risk groups for HBV and HCV prior to initiating therapy; monitor patients for clinical and laboratory signs (HBsAg and anti-HBc) several months after treatment **WARNINGS** Infections; do not give with other biologic DMARDs or live vaccines **SIDE EFFECTS** In patients treated for RA: infusion-related reactions, URTIs, UTIs, N/V/D, peripheral edema, weight gain, hypertension, HA, angioedema, fever, insomnia, pain **MONITORING** ECG, vitals, infusion reactions, CBC, SCr, electrolytes, screen for HBV before treatment

DRUG	DOSING	SAFETY/SIDE EFFECTS/MONITORING
Anakinra (*Kineret*) Single dose pre-filled syringe +/- MTX IL-1 receptor antagonist; IL-1 mediates immunologic reactions in RA; not recommended first line per guidelines	100 mg SC daily (same time each day) Give only after failure of one or more DMARDs CrCl < 30 mL/min: 100 mg SC every other day	**WARNINGS** Malignancies and serious infections, discontinue if a serious infection develops, screen for TB prior to initiating therapy, do not give with other biologics or live vaccines **SIDE EFFECTS** URTIs, HA, N/D, abdominal pain, injection site reactions, antibody development, arthralgias **MONITORING** CBC, SCr, signs of infection **NOTES** Do not shake or freeze; refrigerate and protect from light
Abatacept (*Orencia, Orencia ClickJect*) Single dose pre-filled syringe or auto-injector (SC), injection (IV) +/- MTX Inhibits T-cell activation by binding to CD80 and CD86 on antigen presenting cells (blocking interaction with CD28)	IV: 500-1,000 mg (based on TBW) at 0, 2, and 4 weeks, then every 4 weeks Infuse over 30 minutes SC: 125 mg weekly SC with IV loading dose: give first IV dose as above, then 125 mg SC within 24 hours, then 125 mg SC weekly	**WARNINGS** As above for anakinra plus: caution in patients with COPD – may worsen symptoms **SIDE EFFECTS** Headache, nausea, injection site reactions, infections, nasopharyngitis, antibody development **MONITORING** Signs of infection, hypersensitivity **NOTES** Stable in NS only Requires a filter and light protection during administration; do not shake
Tocilizumab (*Actemra*) Single dose pre-filled syringe (SC), injection (IV) +/- MTX IL-6 receptor antagonist; IL-6 mediates immunologic reactions in RA	IV: 4 mg/kg every 4 weeks given over 60 minutes (can ↑ to 8 mg/kg) Max dose per infusion: 800 mg SC: If < 100 kg: 162 mg every other week (can ↑ to weekly) If ≥ 100 kg: 162 mg weekly	**BOXED WARNING** Serious infections, discontinue if a serious infection develops, screen for TB prior to initiating therapy **WARNINGS** ↑ LFTs, neutropenia and thrombocytopenia, GI perforation, can cause demyelinating diseases, hypersensitivity reactions, lipid abnormalities, do not give with other biologic DMARDs or live vaccines **SIDE EFFECTS** URTIs, HA, hypertension, injection-site reactions, ↑ LDL and total cholesterol **MONITORING** LFTs, CBC (baseline, 4-8 weeks after start of therapy, and every 3 months thereafter), lipid panel, signs of infection **NOTES** Do not use SC injection for IV infusion; SC products contain polysorbate 80 Do not start if: ALT or AST are > 1.5 times ULN, ANC < 2,000 cells/mm^3, or platelets < 100,000 cell/mm^3
Sarilumab (*Kevzara*) Single dose pre-filled syringe +/- MTX IL-6 receptor antagonist	200 mg SC every 2 weeks	

SYSTEMIC LUPUS ERYTHEMATOSUS

BACKGROUND

Systemic lupus erythematosus (SLE) is an autoimmune disease commonly referred to as lupus. SLE primarily affects young women, with a female-to-male ratio of 10:1. The disease predominantly occurs in people age 15 – 45 years, and it is more common in women of African-American and Asian descent. Patients experience flare-ups of varying degrees, as well as periods of disease remission. Factors such as sunlight, certain drugs and viral infections are known to trigger SLE, but the underlying cause is not fully understood. As the disease progresses, symptoms can be present in almost every organ system, with the heart, lungs, kidneys and brain being most affected. Drug-induced lupus erythematosus (DILE) can have similar clinical and laboratory features as SLE, but usually resolves within weeks after drug discontinuation. A few common DILE drugs are listed in the Key Drugs Guy on the following page.

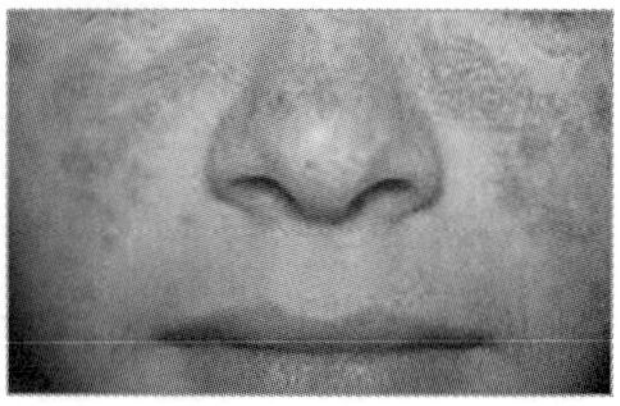

CLINICAL PRESENTATION

The most common symptoms include fatigue, depression, anorexia, weight loss, muscle pain, discoid rash, malar rash (butterfly rash), photosensitivity and joint pain and stiffness (e.g., arthritis). Over half of the people with SLE develop a characteristic red, flat, facial rash over the bridge of their nose and cheeks. It is frequently referred to as the SLE "butterfly rash" because of its shape. Usually, the rash is not painful or itchy. The facial rash, along with inflammation in other organs, can be precipitated or worsened by exposure to sunlight.

Arthritis and cutaneous manifestations are most common, but renal, hematologic and neurologic manifestations contribute largely to morbidity and mortality. Lupus nephritis (kidney disease) develops in over 50% of patients with SLE. Common laboratory findings may include positive antinuclear antibodies (ANA - with titers ≥ 1:160), positive anti-single stranded DNA (anti-ssDNA), positive anti-double stranded DNA (anti-dsDNA), positive anti-Sm, positive antiphospholipid antibodies, low complement (C3, C4, CH50) and elevated acute phase reactants (such as ESR, CRP).

SELECT DRUGS THAT CAN CAUSE DRUG-INDUCED LUPUS ERYTHEMATOSUS (DILE)

KEY DRUGS

Methimazole	**A**nti-TNF agents
Propylthiouracil	**T**erbinafine
Methyldopa	**I**soniazid
Minocycline	**Q**uinidine
Procainamide	Remember: **M**y **P**retty **M**alar **M**arking **P**robably **H**as **A** **T**rans**l**ent **Q**uality
Hydralazine (alone, and in *BiDil*)	

NON-DRUG TREATMENT

Non-drug treatment consists of rest and proper exercise to manage the fatigue. Smoking cessation is encouraged since tobacco smoke can be a trigger for disease flares. Photosensitivity is common with the condition and is also a risk with some treatments; sunscreens and sun protection/avoidance is required.

DRUG TREATMENT

Treatment approaches emphasize using a combination of drugs to minimize chronic exposure to steroids. Patients with mild disease may do well on an NSAID (dosed at anti-inflammatory doses to decrease swelling and pain), but use caution since the doses are high and these patients are more sensitive to the GI and renal side effects. Use with a proton pump inhibitor is generally recommended to reduce GI risk.

Many patients with SLE will require one or more immunosuppressants or cytotoxic agents to control the disease. Hydroxychloroquine, cyclophosphamide, azathioprine, mycophenolate mofetil and cyclosporine are all options for chronic therapy. In some cases, it may take up to six months to see maximal benefit from treatment. With the exception of hydroxychloroquine, these drugs do not have an FDA indication for SLE and are discussed in detail in other chapters (see Transplant, Oncology II and Inflammatory Bowel Disease chapters). The FDA-approval of belimumab in more recent years was an advancement in the treatment options for this disease.

DRUG	DOSING	SAFETY/SIDE EFFECTS/MONITORING
IgG1-lambda monoclonal antibody: prevents the survival of B lymphocytes by blocking the binding of soluble human B lymphocyte stimulator protein (BLyS) to receptors on B lymphocytes; this reduces the activity of B-cell mediated immunity and the autoimmune response		
Belimumab *(Benlysta)* Single dose pre-filled syringe or auto-injector (SC), injection (IV)	IV: 10 mg/kg every 2 weeks x 3 doses, then every 4 weeks thereafter; infuse over 1 hour Consider giving pre-medication for infusion reactions and hypersensitivity reactions SC: 200 mg once weekly	**WARNINGS** Serious (sometimes fatal) infections, PML, acute hypersensitivity reactions, malignancy, psychiatric events, do not give with other biologic DMARDs or live vaccines **SIDE EFFECTS** Nausea, diarrhea, fever, depression, insomnia **NOTES** Crosses the placenta - caution with use in pregnancy African American patients may have a lower response rate; use with caution

MULTIPLE SCLEROSIS

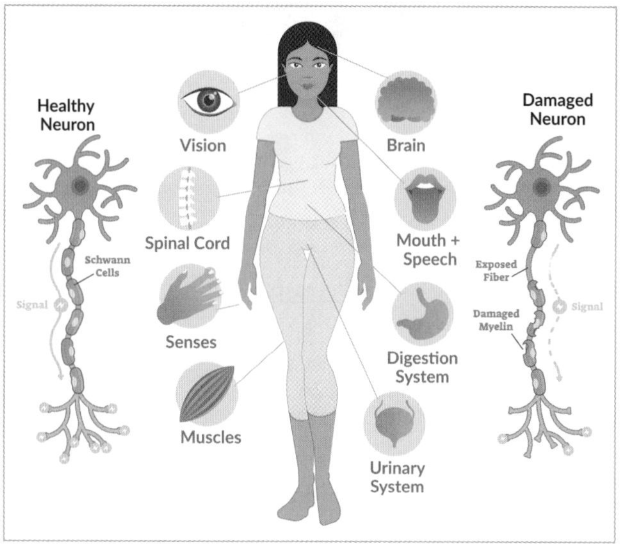

BACKGROUND

Multiple sclerosis (MS) is a chronic, progressive autoimmune disease in which the patient's immune system attacks the myelin sheath, the fatty substance that surrounds and insulates nerve fibers of the brain and spinal cord axons. As demyelination progresses, symptoms worsen because the nerves can no longer properly conduct electrical impulses. Similar to other autoimmune conditions, most patients experience periods of disease activity followed by intervals of remission.

CLINICAL PRESENTATION

The presentation of MS is highly variable, with some patients having a much more aggressive course while others have occasional discrete attacks. Early symptoms include fatigue, weakness, tingling, numbness and blurred vision. As the condition worsens, a variety of physical and psychological issues can make life very challenging, including deterioration of cognitive function, muscle spasms, pain, incontinence, depression, heat sensitivity, sexual dysfunction, difficulty walking with gait instability and visual disturbances.

If left untreated, about 30% of patients will develop significant physical disability. Up to 10% of patients have a milder phenotype in which no significant physical disability develops, although these patients may develop mild cognitive dysfunction. Male patients can have a more progressive form of the disease and generally have the worst prognosis. Symptoms are characterized as primary (muscle weakness), secondary (which result from primary symptoms, such as incontinence due to muscle impairment) and tertiary (which involve psychological and social concerns, such as depression).

MS occurs in both men and women, but as with other autoimmune conditions, it is more common in women (ratio 2:1). The typical age of onset is between 20 - 40 years of age. Various tests are performed to make a diagnosis including magnetic resonance imaging (MRI), spinal fluid analysis, and evoked potentials (tests that measure electrical conduction of the brain). A primary goal of therapy is prevention of disease progression; what is lost in neuronal function cannot be regained. The agents that can modify disease progression are costly, ranging from approximately $65,000 – $80,000/year.

TREATMENT

Promoting functional rehabilitation and emotional health are important for all stages of MS. Programs exist to support cognitive and vocational rehabilitation. Physical and occupational therapy programs are available for motor functions, speech and swallowing. Medications are used to modify disease, treat relapses and manage symptoms. Mitoxantrone *(Novantrone)* is a chemotherapeutic agent approved for MS; a review of mitoxantrone can be found in the Oncology II chapter. Steroids are used to help with relapses. Corticotropin *(HP Acthar)* can be administered SC or IM daily for 2 – 3 weeks. Remember, corticotropin is also called ACTH (see HPA axis diagram earlier in chapter). Other drugs used for various related symptoms are summarized later in the chapter.

Disease-Modifying Therapies

Interferon beta formulations *(Betaseron, Avonex, Rebif, Extavia, Plegridy)* and glatiramer acetate *(Copaxone, Glatopa)* are parenteral drugs that have been the mainstay of treatment for patients with relapsing forms of MS. Pegylated interferon beta *(Plegridy)* allows for more convenient SC dosing every 14 days. For SC injections, the site of administration should be rotated to prevent lipoatrophy and rare necrosis. When the medication is supplied as a single-dose pre-filled syringe, auto-injector or vial kit for SC injection, needles are included with the device and do not require a separate purchase.

If the drug is a powder that is reconstituted, the drug powder may require refrigeration or be kept at room temperature. If a drug is reconstituted, immediate use is necessary (at most within a few hours; a few reconstituted injections permit short storage in the refrigerator). Some of the powders that are reconstituted contain albumin and some patients will not wish to use, or cannot use, albumin-containing products.

Fingolimod *(Gilenya)* and teriflunomide *(Aubagio)* were the first oral disease-modifying agents to be approved for MS. In 2013, a third oral agent, dimethyl fumarate *(Tecfidera)* was approved. If these are not effective the monoclonal antibodies or chemotherapy drugs can be tried, but due to significant toxicities, these should be reserved for refractory cases.

DRUG	DOSING	SAFETY/SIDE EFFECTS/MONITORING
Glatiramer acetate: an immune modulator thought to induce and activate T-lymphocyte suppressor cells in relapsing forms of MS (exact mechanism is not well defined)		
Glatiramer acetate (***Copaxone,*** *Glatopa*) Pre-filled syringes 20 and 40 mg/mL concentrations are not interchangeable	20 mg SC daily or 40 mg SC 3 times per week (at least 48 hours apart) If increasing dose to 40 mg, start 48 hrs after the 20 mg dose	**WARNINGS** Immediate post-injection reaction, chest pain, lipoatrophy **SIDE EFFECTS** Injection site reactions (inflammation, erythema, pain, pruritus, residual mass), infection, pain, flushing, diaphoresis, dyspnea, weakness, anxiety, rash, nausea, nasopharyngitis, vasodilation, antibody development **NOTES** Preferred agent if treatment is necessary during pregnancy Check solution for discoloration and discard if present Can be kept at room temp for up to one month, or in the refrigerator (preferred); if cold, let it stand at room temp for 20 minutes prior to injecting

Glatiramer Counseling

- This medication is given by injection under the skin, as directed by your healthcare provider. It is available in two different doses. Depending on your dose, this medication is injected daily or three times a week at least 48 hours apart. Administer consistently on the same three days each week (e.g., a M, W, F schedule).
- Common side effects include redness, warmth and itchy skin where you inject. Other side effects include sweating, chest pain, weakness and anxiety. These should be mild; if they are not, contact your healthcare provider.
- The syringes can be kept at room temperature for up to one month. If a syringe has been in the refrigerator up until use, keep the syringe at room temperature for 20 minutes. Do not inject the medication cold because this will be painful. The liquid in the syringe should be clear and colorless to slightly yellow. If particles or discoloration are present, do not use it.
- Change the injection site daily to prevent skin problems (rotate injection sites between your arms, abdomen, hips and thighs). Keep track of your injections and do not inject into the same site for at least one week.
- After pulling out the needle, apply gentle pressure on the injection site. Do not rub the area. Discard any unused portion after a single use and put the used syringe into a sharps container (see the Medication Safety & Quality Improvement chapter).

DRUG	DOSING	SAFETY/SIDE EFFECTS/MONITORING
Interferon beta products: alter the expression and response to surface antigens, enhancing immune cell function (exact mechanism in MS is not well defined)		
Interferon beta-1a (*Avonex, Avonex Pen, Rebif, Rebif Rebidose*) Powder (for reconstitution), pre-filled syringe and pen	*Avonex*: 30 mcg IM weekly *Rebif*: 22 mcg or 44 mcg SC three times per week (at least 48 hours apart)	**WARNINGS** Psychiatric disorders (depression/suicide), injection site necrosis, myelosuppression, ↑ LFTs, thyroid dysfunction (hyper and hypo), infections, anaphylaxis, worsening cardiovascular disease, seizure risk **SIDE EFFECTS** Flu-like symptoms following administration (lasting minutes to hours); ↓ with continued treatment – can use acetaminophen or NSAIDs prior to injection or start with lower doses and titrating weekly to target dose Visual disturbances, fatigue, depression, pain, urinary tract infections, HA **MONITORING** LFTs, CBC (at 1, 3 and 6 months, then periodically); thyroid function every 6 months (in patients with thyroid dysfunction or as clinical necessary) **NOTES** Refrigerate all except *Betaseron* and *Extavia* (which can be stored at room temperature). If refrigerated, let stand at room temperature prior to injection. Do not expel the small air bubble in pre-filled syringes due to loss of dose Do not shake *Avonex, Betaseron or Extavia* Some formulations contain albumin which can increase the risk of Creutzfeldt-Jakob disease transmission (rare); avoid in albumin-sensitive patients
Interferon beta-1b (*Betaseron, Extavia*) Powder (for reconstitution), and auto-injector	SC: 0.25 mg every other day (use within 3 hrs of reconstitution)	
Peginterferon beta-1a (*Plegridy, Plegridy Starter Pack*) Pre-filled syringe and pen	SC: 63 mcg on day 1, 94 mcg on day 15, then 125 mcg every 14 days starting on day 29	

DRUG	SAFETY/SIDE EFFECTS/MONITORING
Oral immunomodulators	
Teriflunomide *(Aubagio)* Tablet Active metabolite of leflunomide	Severe hepatotoxicity and teratogenicity – contraindicated in pregnancy and with severe hepatic impairment Can use accelerated elimination to remove drug - see leflunomide
Fingolimod *(Gilenya)* Capsule	Can cause bradycardia – patient must be monitored for at least 6 hours after the first dose (ECG required at baseline and at end of initial observation period or if treatment course is interrupted); contraindicated in most patients with a history of CVD or stroke. Use caution with other drugs that slow HR MS can become much worse when treatment is stopped Other significant adverse effects: macular edema (monitor with eye exams), hepatotoxicity (monitor LFTs) and myelosuppression (monitor CBC)
Dimethyl fumarate *(Tecfidera)* Capsule NrF2 activator	Hepatotoxicity (monitor LFTs), neutropenia (reversible, but monitor CBC) Can cause flushing (prevent with aspirin 30 minutes prior to dose and administer with food) Do not crush, chew, or sprinkle capsule contents on food
Simponimod *(Mayzent)* Tablet	Contraindicated with CYP2C9*3/*3 genotype (testing required before use), some arrhythmias, or with any of the following in the past 6 months: MI, unstable angina, stroke/TIA or some HF (decompensation requiring hospitalization, or Class III/IV) Other significant adverse effects: macular edema (monitor with eye exams), ↑ BP, bradyarrhythmias, hepatotoxicity (monitor LFTs) and infections (monitor CBC)
Potassium channel blocker: may increase nerve signal conduction; indicated to improve walking	
Dalfampridine *(Ampyra)* Tablet	Contraindicated in patients with a history of seizures Takes up to 6 weeks to show efficacy; most patients do not respond
Monoclonal antibodies	
Natalizumab *(Tysabri)* Injection (IV) Monoclonal antibody that binds to the alpha-4 subunit of integrins expressed on the surface of leukocytes	See Inflammatory Bowel Disease chapter
Recombinant humanized monoclonal antibodies	
Alemtuzumab *(Lemtrada)* Injection (IV) CD52-directed cytolytic monoclonal antibody Ocrelizumab *(Ocrevus)* Injection (IV) Targets CD20+ B cells	**BOXED WARNINGS** Alemtuzumab: serious, sometimes fatal, autoimmune conditions and infusion reactions; malignancies, stroke, REMS program required **CONTRAINDICATIONS** Alemtuzumab: HIV (causes prolonged ↓ in CD4 count) Ocrelizumab: active hepatitis B infection **NOTES** Indicated when there is an inadequate response to ≥ 2 MS drugs Complete all vaccinations 6 weeks before treatment Premedicate with a steroid, an antihistamine and/or acetaminophen (varies by drug) Ocrelizumab requires a 0.22 micron in-line filter, has similar safety issues as other drugs that target CD20 (e.g., rituximab)
Oral anti-neoplastic	
Cladribine *(Mavenclad)* Tablet	Boxed warning for malignancies, teratogenicity Contraindicated in patients with current malignancy, HIV or active chronic infections Contraception must be used for men and women of reproductive potential during treatment and for 6 months after the last dose

Drugs Used for Symptom Control

Patients with MS may need a variety of medications for symptom control. The individual drugs used can be found in different chapters in this book. Drugs commonly used for symptom control in MS include anticholinergics for incontinence, laxatives for constipation (or loperamide if diarrhea), skeletal muscle relaxants for muscle spasms/spasticity, or analgesics for muscle spasms and pain. For localized pain and spasms, botulinum toxin (*Botox*) injections can provide relief for up to three months. Propranolol can help with tremor. For depression, many antidepressants can be used; if an SNRI is chosen, it may also help with neuropathic pain. Fatigue is often treated with modafinil (or similar agents), or stimulants used for ADHD, such as methylphenidate. Meclizine and scopolamine are used for dizziness and vertigo. Acetylcholinesterase inhibitors, including donepezil, are used to help cognitive function. Erectile dysfunction can be treated with the phosphodiesterase-5 inhibitors.

Notice that the drugs used for symptom control can worsen other symptoms. For example, anticholinergics can worsen cognitive function (not all of them do, it is patient-specific). Drugs for vertigo and propranolol can worsen cognitive function; propranolol has added concerns for worsening depression and causing problems with sexual performance. The SSRI and SNRI antidepressants can worsen sexual dysfunction. Opioids, if used for pain, will worsen constipation, can decrease cognition and have dependence concerns. Managing the various medications used for MS requires competent pharmacists.

RAYNAUD'S PHENOMENON

Raynaud's is a common condition which is triggered by exposure to cold and/or stress, leading to vasospasm in the extremities (most commonly in the fingers and/or toes). Drugs used for treatment are often used for other conditions and are discussed in other chapters in detail, but it is useful to know the presentation and which drugs are used for symptom relief. The vasospasm causes the skin to turn white and then blue, which is followed by painful swelling when the affected areas warm, and can result in amputation in severe cases. Laboratory findings that can signify other autoimmune conditions are generally absent. The calcium channel blocker (CCB) nifedipine is commonly used for prevention but other CCBs can be used. Additional agents used for vasodilation include iloprost, topical nitroglycerin and the phosphodiesterase-5 inhibitors. See Study Tip Gal.

DRUG-INDUCED RAYNAUD'S

↓ blood flow to fingers causes ↑ cyanosis (blue-ish fingers) and pain

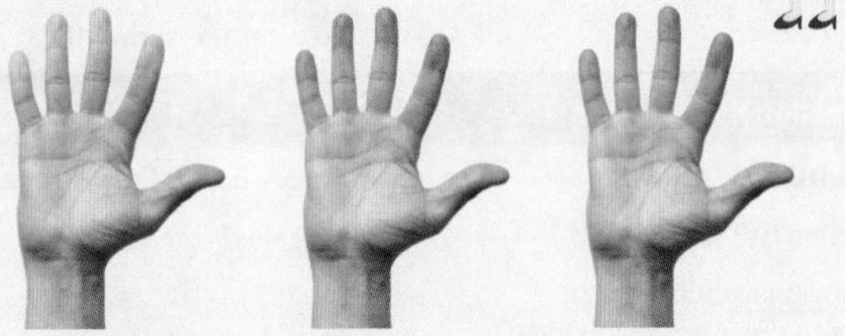

Fingers become white due to lack of blood flow. | *Fingers turn blue as vessels dilate to keep blood in tissues.* | *Fingers finally turn red as blood flow returns.*

Drugs that cause or worsen Raynaud's:

Beta-blockers

Bleomycin, cisplatin

Sympathomimetics (from vasoconstriction): amphetamines (e.g., *Concerta, Vyvanse*), pseudoephedrine and illicit drugs (e.g., cocaine and methamphetamine)

CELIAC DISEASE

BACKGROUND

Celiac disease (celiac sprue) is an immune response to eating gluten, a protein found in wheat, barley and rye. The primary and most effective treatment is to avoid gluten entirely. Gluten is present in many foods, food additives and in many drug excipients. Pharmacists can assist patients in avoiding gluten-containing drugs completely, as even a small exposure will trigger a reaction. To emphasize this point, the FDA permits food products to be labeled "gluten-free" only if the food contains less gluten than 20 parts per million.

CLINICAL PRESENTATION

The common symptoms of celiac disease are diarrhea, abdominal pain, bloating and weight loss. Constipation (rather than diarrhea) can be present, and is more common in children. In celiac disease, antibodies attack and damage the lining of the small intestine, which can lead to vitamin and nutritional deficiencies as a result of decreased absorption. Other complications include small bowel ulcers, amenorrhea and infertility, as well as an increased risk of cancer (primarily lymphomas). Ninety-five percent of cases will respond well to dietary changes, although avoiding gluten entirely is not a simple task.

Dermatitis herpetiformis is an extremely itchy, blistery skin rash with chronic eruptions that occurs in 20 – 25% of patients with celiac disease, more often in males. The rash can be present with or without overt intestinal symptoms and is often mistaken for eczema or psoriasis, which leads to a delay in diagnosis and treatment.

TREATMENT

The FDA has strict regulations regarding the active ingredients in drug formulations, but there is little oversight for the excipients included, making the identification of gluten difficult. The active drug is gluten-free, but the excipients may contain gluten. It is not safe to assume that generic formulations will contain the same excipients as the brand; and there is no legal requirement to match the excipients.

Package inserts might contain information on the excipient components. Look for the key word "starch," which will be either corn, potato, tapioca or wheat. If the package insert lists "starch" alone then the manufacturer must be consulted to find out if the starch is wheat. The manufacturer might report that they do not use gluten in the manufacturing process, but they cannot state whether the excipients purchased from outside vendors are gluten-free. The risk of cross-contamination is low, but not absent, and this information should be provided to the patient who ultimately must decide, hopefully in consult with the prescriber, whether to take the drug or not.

MYASTHENIA GRAVIS

BACKGROUND

Myasthenia gravis is an autoimmune disease that attacks the connections between nerves and muscles, resulting in weakness in skeletal muscles (e.g., muscles that control the eyes, face, neck and limbs). In most cases, the immune system targets the acetylcholine (ACh) receptor. Symptoms often include changes to the eyes/vision [e.g., double vision (diplopia), drooping eyelid (ptosis)], problems with chewing/swallowing and weakness in the neck and jaw. This condition affects women more than men, and average onset is age 28.

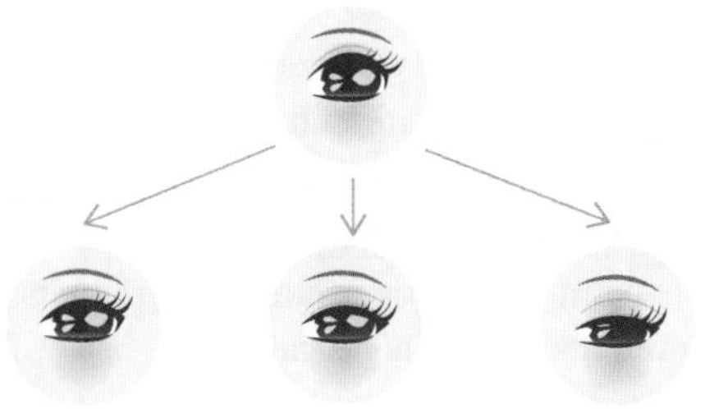

DRUGS THAT CAN WORSEN MYASTHENIA GRAVIS

Many drugs can worsen or unmask Myasthenia Gravis. This includes:

- Antibiotics: aminoglycosides and quinolones
- Magnesium salts
- Select anti-arrhythmics
- Beta-blockers and calcium channel blockers
- Select antipsychotics
- Muscle relaxants
- Local anesthetics

These drugs should be avoided in patients with the disease, or used cautiously if the benefit outweighs the risk.

TREATMENT

Cholinesterase inhibitors are the mainstay of treatment in Myasthenia Gravis, specifically pyridostigmine *(Mestinon)*. This increases ACh levels and helps to decrease the symptoms of muscle weakness. Most people also require immunosuppressant medications for sufficient symptom control. Some severe cases require treatment with plasmapheresis or intravenous immunoglobulin (IVIG), or even thymectomy (removal of the thymus gland).

DRUG	DOSING	SAFETY/SIDE EFFECTS/MONITORING
Cholinesterase inhibitors: block the breakdown of acetylcholine by acetylcholinesterase, which improves neuromuscular transmission and increases muscle strength		
Pyridostigmine *(Mestinon)* Tablet IV and IM forms used for myasthenia gravis crisis, nerve gas exposure and reversal of nondepolarizing muscle relaxants	60-1,500 mg/day (usually 600 mg/day) divided into 5-6 doses	**CONTRAINDICATIONS** Mechanical intestinal or urinary obstruction **WARNINGS** Cholinergic effects: symptoms of excess ACh can occur (e.g., salivation, lacrimation, excessive urination, diarrhea). Refer to the Learning Basic Science Content chapter CVD, glaucoma, bronchospastic respiratory disease (e.g., COPD or asthma)

SJÖGREN'S SYNDROME

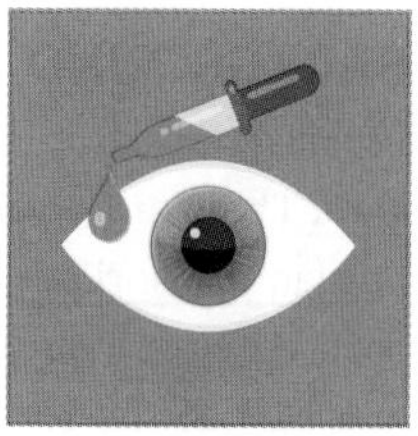

Sjögren's syndrome is an autoimmune disease most often characterized by severe dry eyes and dry mouth. Many other symptoms can be associated with Sjögren's, including thyroiditis, Raynaud's phenomenon, neuropathy and lymphadenopathy. Sjögren's syndrome can be primary or secondary (e.g., associated with another autoimmune disease, such as RA or SLE). Dry mouth and dry eyes are a source of significant morbidity for these patients and can lead to complications, such as dental caries corneal ulceration and chronic oral infections. There is no known cure for Sjögren's; treatment focuses on reducing the symptoms of dry eyes and dry mouth.

DRY EYES TREATMENT

The use of artificial teardrops is the primary treatment for dry eyes. Popular OTC artificial teardrops available are *Systane, Refresh, Clear Eyes* and *Liquifilm*. It may be necessary to try a couple of different OTC eye drops before finding one that provides the most comfort. If the preservative (e.g., benzalkonium chloride) is irritating, preservative-free artificial tear drops packaged in individual use containers are available. If the eyes dry out while sleeping, an ointment is preferable.

Cyclosporine eye drops *(Restasis)* can be used in patients who do not have satisfactory relief from other measures, including ductal occlusion (lacrimal duct plugs). *Restasis* provides benefit for a small percentage of users, but it is expensive. Patients should be instructed to monitor for a reduction in symptoms and a reduction in the use of OTC eye drops. Counsel patients to use *Restasis* properly to avoid infection, which is more likely due to the dry eye state, and that it may take up to 3 – 6 months to notice an increase in tear production. Lifitegrast *(Xiidra)*, a first in class drug, was approved in 2016 for the treatment of signs and symptoms of dry eye disease. Refer to the Common Conditions of the Eyes & Ears chapter for detailed patient counseling information for eye drops.

Eye Drops for Dry Eyes

DRUG	DOSING	SAFETY/SIDE EFFECTS/MONITORING
Cyclosporine Emulsion (*Restasis*, *Cequa)* Ophthalmic	1 drop in each eye Q12H	**SIDE EFFECTS** Burning, stinging, redness, pain, blurred vision, foreign body sensation, discharge, itching eye **NOTES** Prior to use, invert the vial several times to make the emulsion uniform
Lifitegrast *(Xiidra)* Ophthalmic	1 drop in each eye Q12H	**SIDE EFFECTS** Eye irritation, discomfort, blurred vision, unusual taste **NOTES** Store in the original foil pouch to protect from light

DRY MOUTH TREATMENT

Non-drug treatment for dry mouth includes salivary stimulation, using sugar-free chewing gum (with xylitol) or lozenges, and daily rinses with antimicrobial mouthwash. Salivary substitutes are available in lozenges, rinses, sprays and swabs *(Plax, Oralube, Salivart)*. These contain carboxymethylcellulose or glycerin. If OTC treatments do not provide sufficient relief, prescription oral muscarinic agonists, such as pilocarpine *(Salagen)* or cevimeline *(Evoxac)*, can be used. These drugs are contraindicated in patients with uncontrolled asthma and narrow-angle glaucoma, due to cholinergic properties and associated side effects.

PSORIASIS

BACKGROUND

Psoriasis is a chronic, autoimmune disease that appears on the skin. There are several types of psoriasis. The most common is plaque psoriasis, which appears as raised, red patches covered with a silvery white buildup of dead skin cells, on any part of the body. Treatments can be divided into three main types: light therapy, topical and systemic medications. Most psoriasis is treated with topical medication and UV light therapy. Soaking can also help loosen and remove the plaques.

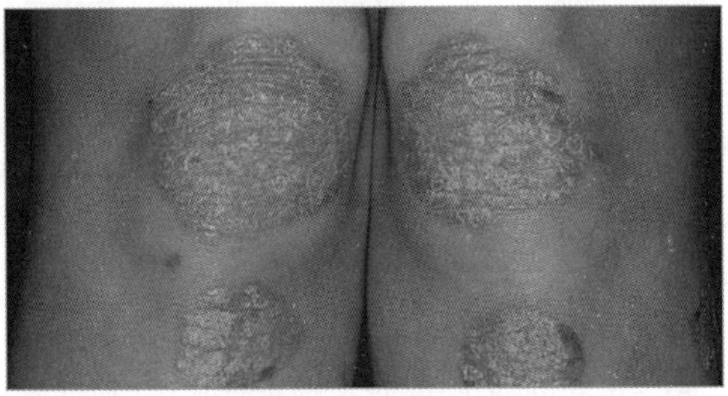

NON-DRUG TREATMENT

Ultraviolet (UV) light exposure causes activated T cells in the skin to die. This slows skin turnover and decreases scaling and inflammation. Brief, daily exposures to small amounts of sunlight can improve psoriasis, but intense sun exposure can worsen symptoms and cause skin damage. UVB phototherapy, in controlled doses from an artificial source, can improve mild to moderate psoriasis symptoms. Other non-drug treatments include photochemotherapy (ultraviolet A light with psoralen, a light sensitizer) and laser light therapy.

DRUG TREATMENT

There are many topical options for treating psoriasis, including steroids, vitamin D analogues (calcipotriene), anthralin, retinoids (some of the same drugs used for acne), salicylic acid (primarily in medicated shampoo), coal tar and moisturizers. Topical vitamin D analogues, tazarotene and salicylic acid are used in combination with topical steroids. If these fail, topical calcineurin inhibitors *(Protopic, Elidel)* can be tried; these are the preferred agents when applying to the face. Treatment for more severe symptoms can require immunosuppressants, including methotrexate, cyclosporine, hydroxyurea or immunomodulators, such as etanercept and infliximab. Newer systemic agents approved for plaque psoriasis include *Otezla* and monoclonal antibodies that have interleukin receptor antagonist actions.

Topical Psoriasis Treatment

DRUG/DRUG CLASS	COMMENTS
Steroids	Use high-potency steroids only short-term due to risk of side effects Can be used as monotherapy or with other therapies See Common Skin Conditions chapter
Tazarotene *(Tazorac)* – a topical retinoid	See Common Skin Conditions chapter
Coal Tar products (many, including *DHS Tar, Ionil-T, Psoriasin, Pentrax Gold)* + salicylic acid *(Tarsum)* Also used for dandruff and dermatitis	Coal tar products are messy, time consuming and can stain clothing and bedding, but some patients get relief at a reasonable cost There are many topical formulations available (cream, foam, emulsion, ointment, oil, shampoo), bath products (e.g., bar soap) Do not use salicylic acid products with other salicylates as systemic absorption can occur Can cause skin irritation and photosensitivity
Anthralin *(Dritho-Crème HP, Zithranol,* others)	Keratolytic containing salicylic acid with irritant potential, ↑ contact time as tolerated up to 30 min
Calcipotriene *(Calcitrene, Dovonex, Sorilux)* Cream, foam, ointment, solution + betamethasone *(Taclonex* ointment, *Taclonex* scalp suspension, *Enstilar* foam)	Vitamin D analog – contraindicated and should be avoided in hypercalcemia or vitamin D toxicity If using a suspension, shake well Do not apply to face, axillae or groin

Systemic Psoriasis Treatment

DRUG/DRUG CLASS	COMMENTS
Retinoid	
Acitretin *(Soriatane)* Tablet	Boxed warning for hepatotoxicity and pregnancy (female must sign informed consent before dispensing) Used only in severe cases when patient is unresponsive to other therapies due to numerous contraindications and side effects
Phosphodiesterase-4 inhibitor	
Apremilast *(Otezla)* Tablet	Warnings: depression, suicidal ideation and weight loss Most common side effects are diarrhea, N/V, headache
Interleukin Receptor Antagonists: monoclonal antibodies that bind to and interfere with proinflammatory cytokines	
Brodalumab *(Siliq)* Guselkumab *(Tremfya)* Ixekizumab *(Taltz)* Secukinumab *(Cosentyx)* Tildrakizumab-asmn *(Ilumya)* Ustekinumab *(Stelara)* All available in single dose pre-filled syringes, auto-injectors or vials for subcutaneous injection	Like other monoclonal antibodies, these can cause serious infections (including active TB); screen for latent TB (and treat if needed) before starting, avoid live vaccines, may exacerbate Crohn's disease, latex hypersensitivity Other common side effects include diarrhea and URTIs Brodalumab: boxed warning for suicidal ideation and behavior; REMS program required

Select Guidelines/References

2015 American College of Rheumatology Guideline for the Treatment of Rheumatoid Arthritis. https://www.rheumatology.org/Practice-Quality/Clinical-Support/Clinical-Practice-Guidelines/Rheumatoid-Arthritis (accessed 2019 Apr 1).

American College of Rheumatology Guidelines for Screening, Treatment and Management of Lupus Nephritis. https://www.rheumatology.org/Practice-Quality/Clinical-Support/Clinical-Practice-Guidelines/Lupus-Nephritis (accessed 2019 Apr 1).

American Academy of Dermatology. Psoriasis Clinical Guidelines. Section 1-6. https://www.aad.org/practicecenter/quality/clinical-guidelines/psoriasis (accessed 2019 Apr 1).

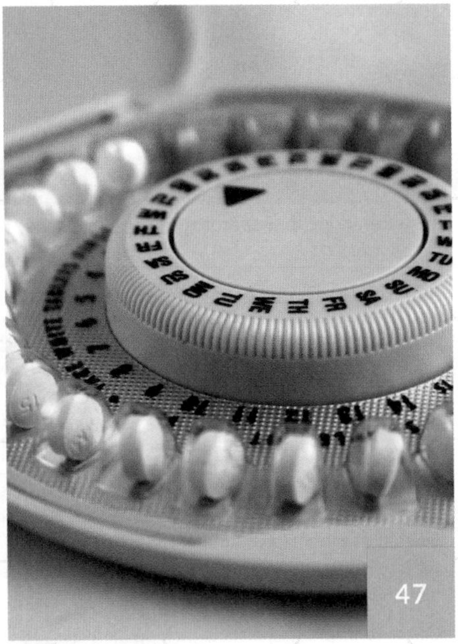

47

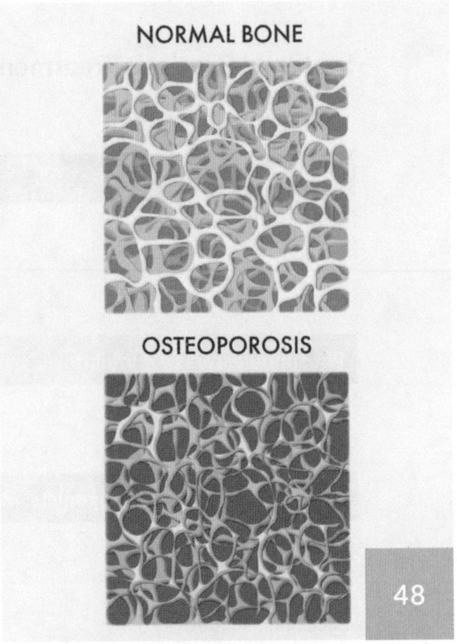

48

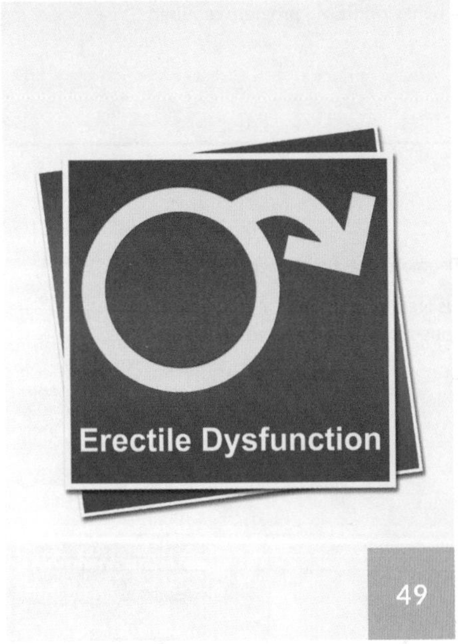

49

50

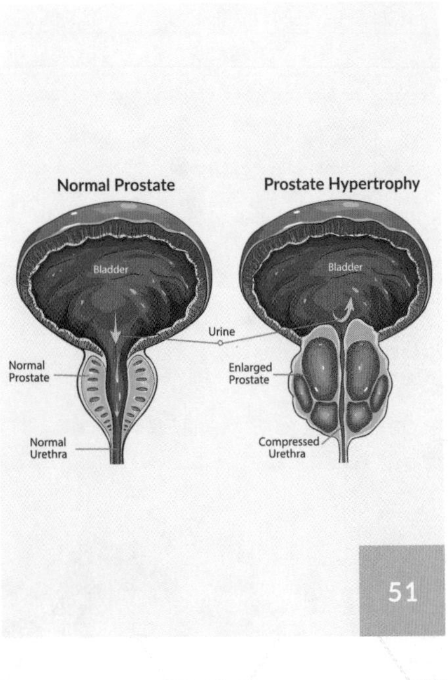

51

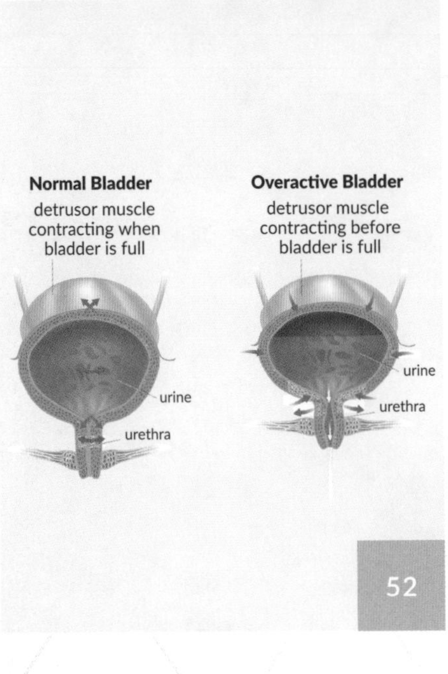

52

MALE & FEMALE HEALTH

CONTENTS

CHAPTER 47
CONTRACEPTION & INFERTILITY | **694**

CHAPTER 48
DRUG USE IN PREGNANCY & LACTATION | **707**

CHAPTER 49
OSTEOPOROSIS, MENOPAUSE & TESTOSTERONE USE | **713**

CHAPTER 50
SEXUAL DYSFUNCTION | **729**

CHAPTER 51
BENIGN PROSTATIC HYPERPLASIA (BPH) | **734**

CHAPTER 52
OVERACTIVE BLADDER | **740**

CHAPTER CONTENT

Background 694
Menstrual Cycle Phases 694
Fertility Awareness 695
Pregnancy 695
Preconception Health 695
Contraception 695
Effectiveness of Contraceptive Methods 696
Non-Pharmacologic and OTC Contraceptive Methods 696
Temperature and Cervical Mucus Methods 696
Barrier Methods 696
Other OTC Contraceptive Methods 697
Patient Counseling for OTC Contraceptive Methods 697
Hormonal Contraceptives 697
Estrogen and Progestin Combination Oral Contraceptives 697
Progestin-Only Pills 698
Non-Oral Hormonal Contraceptives 698
Contraception and Menstrual Periods 698
Select Contraceptive Types 699
Adverse Effects of Hormonal Contraceptives 700
Severe & Rare Adverse Effects of Estrogen 700
Considerations for Drug Selection 701
Drug Interactions with Hormonal Contraceptives 701
Starting Birth Control Pills 702
Late or Missed Pills – Instructions for Typical Formulations 702
COC Patient Counseling 703
Patient Counseling for Non-Oral Formulations 703
Long-Acting Reversible Contraceptives 704
Emergency Contraception (EC) 704
Levonorgestrel 705
Ulipristal Acetate *(Ella)* 705
Patient Counseling for EC 705
Infertility 706
Infertility Drugs Act Like Endogenous Hormones to Trigger Ovulation 706
Gonadotropin Drug Names 706

CONTENT LEGEND

= Study Tip Gal

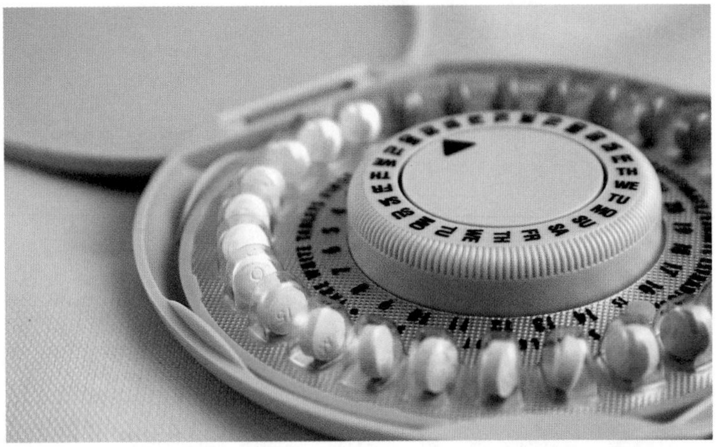

CHAPTER 47
CONTRACEPTION & INFERTILITY

BACKGROUND

There are 61 million U.S. women in their childbearing years (ages 15 – 44 years). Forty-three million of these women are sexually active and do not want to become pregnant. To achieve this goal, a woman must use contraceptives for roughly three decades of her life.

Contraception is available in many different forms, including OTC and prescription options. Proper use is essential to prevent unintended pregnancy. With so many forms of contraception available, patient-specific factors should drive decisions on which product to use. Pharmacists are in a unique position to increase appropriate use of contraceptive methods, access to contraception and prevention of unintended pregnancies.

On the other hand, many people struggle with becoming pregnant. Infertility treatments can be invasive and expensive. Pharmacists (usually in specialty settings) play an essential role in gaining access and appropriate use of infertility treatments.

MENSTRUAL CYCLE PHASES

A normal menstrual cycle ranges from 23 – 35 days (average 28 days). The start of bleeding (menses) indicates that the next cycle has begun and is counted as day 1 of the cycle; the remnants of the previous cycle (the thick, bloody endometrial lining) is sloughing off. Menstruation typically lasts a few days. Changes in hormone levels cause the events that characterize the different phases of the menstrual cycle (see next page). Menses occurs during the follicular phase, when the estrogen and progesterone levels start off low.

PHASES OF THE MENSTRUAL CYCLE

Follicular	Each follicle in an ovary contains an oocyte (immature egg). Follicle stimulating hormone (FSH) spurs follicle development and causes estrogen to surge. Estrogen peaks by the end of the phase.* The surge in estrogen causes luteinizing hormone (LH) and FSH to increase.
Ovulatory	The LH surge triggers ovulation 24-36 hours later. Ovulation is the release of the egg (ova) from the ovary.**
Luteal	The start of ovulation begins the luteal (last) phase, which lasts ~14 days. Progesterone is dominant in this phase.

Estrogen (E) and progesterone (P) cause the endometrium (the lining of the uterus) to thicken to prepare for an embryo, and P causes the cervical mucus to thicken and body temperature to increase. When E and/or P are low during the cycle, blood can drip off the lining, causing spotting (which can require an increase in E or P in birth control pills).

**Luteinizing hormone causes corpus luteum development in the ovary. LH and FSH work together in the ovulatory phase to trigger ovulation.*

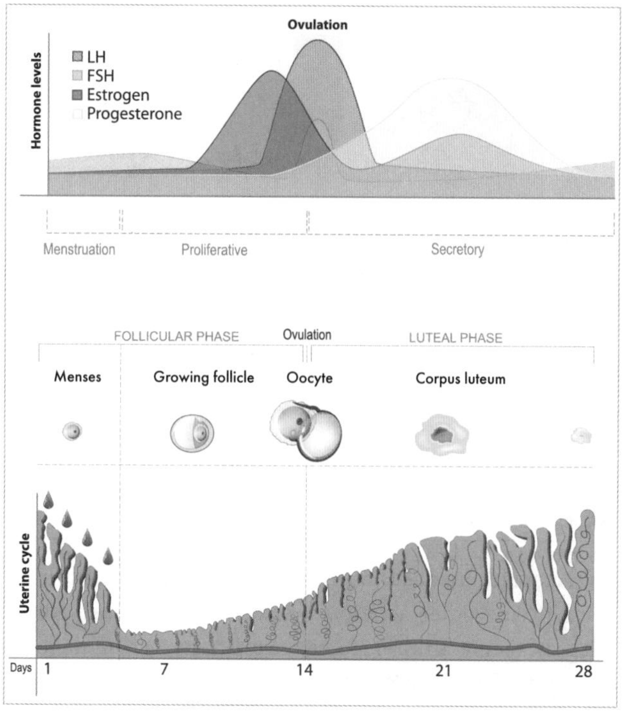

FERTILITY AWARENESS

The mid-cycle luteinizing hormone (LH) surge results in release of the oocyte (egg) from the ovary into the fallopian tube. The oocyte lives for 24 hours once released, and sperm can survive for ~3 days. Ovulation kits predict the best time for intercourse based on ovulation in order to try to conceive (get pregnant). Some kits test for LH in the urine and are positive if LH is present. A person wishing to conceive should have intercourse when the LH surge is detected, and for the following 2 days (based on sperm survival of ~3 days).

Alternative methods to test for ovulation include monitoring body temperature and cervical mucus (discussed on the next page).

PREGNANCY

Human chorionic gonadotropin (hCG) is released when a fertilized egg attaches to the lining of the uterus (called implantation). Detecting hCG in the urine or blood indicates pregnancy. A home urine test can pick up pregnancy sooner if the woman tests the first urine in the morning, when the hCG level is highest.

PRECONCEPTION HEALTH

Preconception health focuses on steps to take to protect the health of a baby in the future. Any woman planning to conceive (and all women of child bearing age) should:

- Take folic acid (folate) (400 mcg/day) to help prevent birth defects of the brain and spinal cord (neural tube defects). Folic acid can come from fortified foods, supplements or a combination of the two, and from consuming food with folate from a varied diet (e.g., dried beans, leafy green vegetables and oranges).
- Stop smoking, using illicit drugs, and drinking excessive amounts of alcohol.
- Keep vaccinations current. Attempt to avoid illnesses that will adversely affect the baby (e.g., toxoplasmosis).
- Avoid toxic chemicals, including drugs on the Hazardous Drug List developed by NIOSH; see the Compounding chapters.

The general health of the male partner is important.

CONTRACEPTION

Contraception should be used until ready to conceive. A prompt return to fertility occurs when most contraceptives are discontinued. The only reversible contraceptive method that has a delay in return to fertility is the medroxyprogesterone injection.

Contraceptive preferences vary markedly with age. For women in their teens and 20's, the pill is the leading method. Among women 35 years and older, more rely on sterilization, which is often performed immediately postpartum (following a birth). Male contraception options are limited. Presently, male condoms and vasectomy are the only options.

EFFECTIVENESS OF CONTRACEPTIVE METHODS

The figure below provides a comparison of the efficacy of contraceptive methods that are available as OTC or Rx products. Contraceptive methods, except for condoms, do not provide protection from sexually transmitted diseases (STDs). Condoms provide protection from some infections – female internal condoms provide more protection than male external condoms.

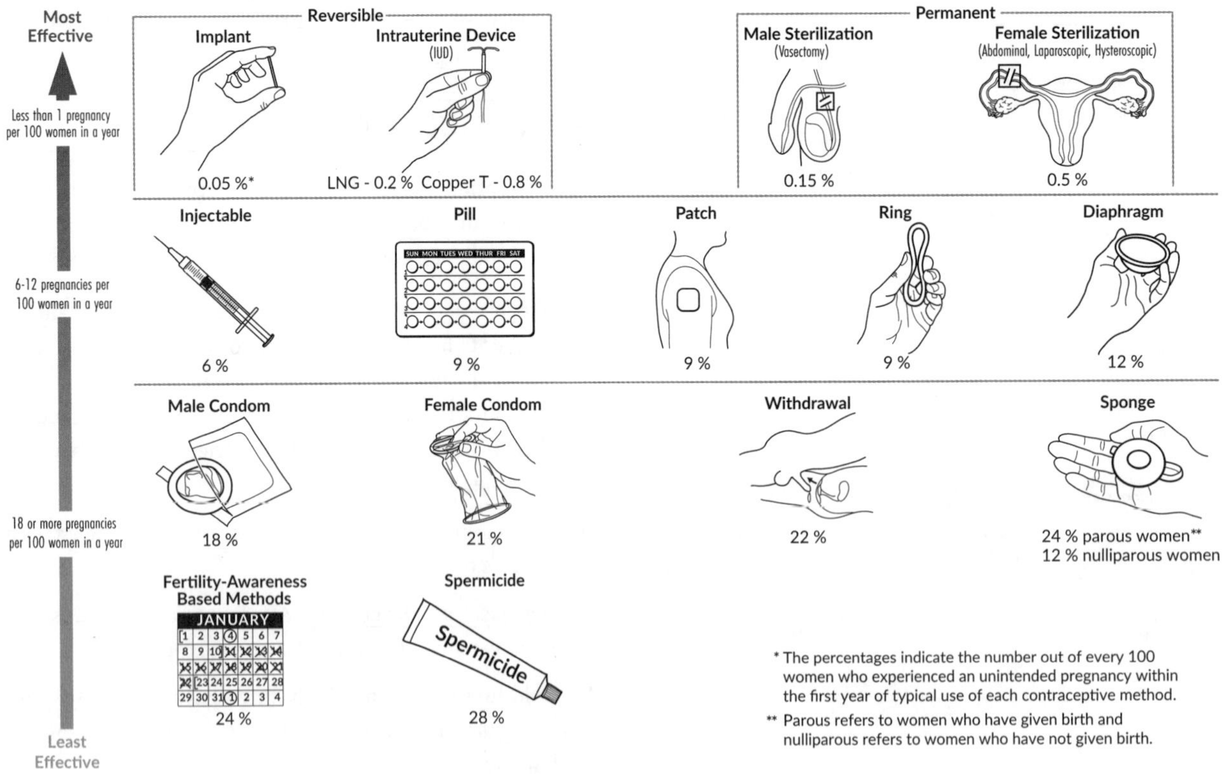

© https://www.cdc.gov/reproductivehealth/contraception/unintendedpregnancy/pdf/Contraceptive_methods_508.pdf

NON-PHARMACOLOGIC AND OTC CONTRACEPTIVE METHODS

Abstinence is the only 100% effective way to prevent pregnancy and STDs. Other non-pharmacologic methods of contraception include temperature and cervical mucus tracking and the use of barrier methods. Spermicide can be used alone or with other barrier methods as another OTC option for contraception.

The temperature needs to be taken first thing each morning, prior to any other activity. A small (~1° increase) can be missed; temperature methods work best when done in conjunction with tracking changes in the cervical mucus (i.e., vaginal discharge), which has slight changes in color, texture and volume during ovulation.

TEMPERATURE AND CERVICAL MUCUS METHODS

Keeping track of body temperature and cervical mucus content are used primarily to avoid pregnancy by abstaining from intercourse on days when a woman is fertile. Tracking basal body temperature is used to predict ovulation. The typical temperature prior to ovulation is 96 – 98°F. The temperature increases to 97 – 99°F during ovulation. The changes are recorded on a calendar and used to predict ovulation (i.e., fertility) in the following months. There is an FDA-approved app, *Natural Cycles*, which can aid in tracking and predicting ovulation.

BARRIER METHODS

Barrier methods of contraception include condoms, diaphragms, caps and shields. They are non-pharmacologic options that form a physical barrier preventing passage of sperm to the oocyte.

Diaphragms, Caps and Shields

These options are soft latex or silicone barriers that cover the cervix and prevent sperm passage. They can be used with or without spermicide. The *Caya* diaphragm is a single size and does not require fitting (some diaphragms do require a prescription for fitting).

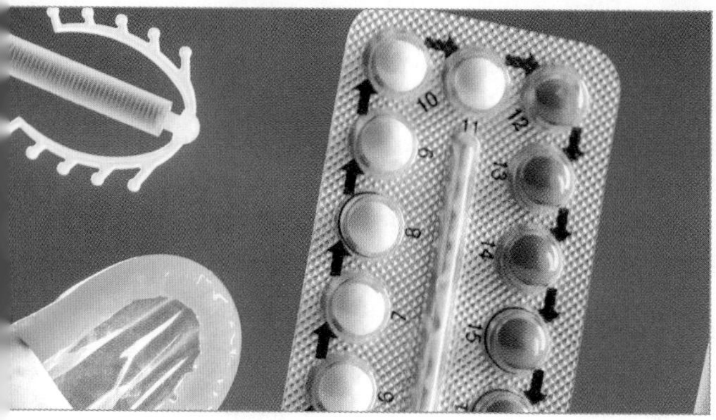

Condoms

Male condoms are a thin latex or plastic sheath worn on the penis. Female condoms are inserted into the vagina. Both are OTC. Condoms help protect against many STDs (only if latex or synthetic condoms, not "natural" sheepskin).

- Use with nonoxynol-9 spermicide is not recommended due to possible risks of tissue damage, condom breakdown and increased STD/HIV transmission.
- Lubricant makes condoms less likely to break by reducing dry friction. Never recommend oil-based lubricant for use with a latex or non-latex synthetic condom; only recommend water or silicone-based lubricants. These products are discussed in the Osteoporosis, Menopause and Testosterone Use chapter.

OTHER OTC CONTRACEPTIVE METHODS

Other OTC contraceptive methods include foams, film, creams, suppositories, sponges and jellies. These contain the spermicide nonoxynol-9. Do not use spermicide with anal sex. It is irritating and can increase the risk of STDs.

The sponge is a round piece of white, plastic foam that is inserted prior to intercourse and continuously releases spermicide. It is removed and discarded after use.

PATIENT COUNSELING FOR OTC CONTRACEPTIVE METHODS

Diaphragm

- Wash hands thoroughly. Place one tablespoon of spermicide in the diaphragm and disperse inside and around the rim.
- Pinch the ends of the cup and insert the pinched end into the vagina.
- Leave in for six hours after intercourse. Diaphragms should not be in place greater than 24 hours.
- Reapply spermicide if intercourse is repeated or diaphragm is in place for more than two hours before sex, by inserting jelly with applicator.
- Wash with mild soap and warm water after removal, air dry.
- Can be used for up to two years.

Foams, Creams, Suppositories and Jellies

- Place deep into the vagina right before intercourse where they melt (except for foam, which bubbles).

Sponge

- Place deep into the vagina right before intercourse.
- Leave in place for at least six hours after intercourse, but it can be used for up to 24 hours. Remove and discard after use.

HORMONAL CONTRACEPTIVES

Hormonal contraceptives work by inhibiting the production of FSH and LH, which prevents ovulation. They alter cervical mucus, which inhibits the sperm from penetrating the egg. If implantation of the fertilized egg in the uterus has already taken place, none of these methods are effective, and the pregnancy will proceed normally.

Available treatments include progestin-only options (pill, injectable, implant and IUD) or estrogen/progestin combinations (pill, patch and vaginal ring). The estrogen/progestin combination pills are called combination oral contraceptives (COCs). Non-oral contraceptives that contain both estrogen and progestin are referred to as combined hormonal contraceptives (CHC). The patch and the ring have unique considerations (such as how to use) but contain hormones similar to pill formulations. Contraindications are the same for the COCs and the patch or vaginal ring.

Hormonal contraceptives provide health benefits, including a decrease in menstrual pain, menstrual irregularity, endometriosis, acne, ectopic pregnancy, noncancerous breast cysts/lumps and risk of endometrial and ovarian cancer.

The FDA requires that the Patient Package Insert (PPI) be dispensed with oral contraceptives – it will be in the product packaging. The PPI has important safety information, instructions on proper use and what to do if pills are missed.

ESTROGEN AND PROGESTIN COMBINATION ORAL CONTRACEPTIVES

Most COCs contain the estrogen ethinyl estradiol (EE) and a progestin [e.g., norethindrone, levonorgestrel (LNG), drospirenone]. There are different formulations of COCs.

- Monophasic COCs have the same dose of estrogen and progestin throughout the pill pack.
- Biphasic, triphasic and quadriphasic pill packs mimic the estrogen and progesterone levels during a menstrual cycle. The type of formulation (e.g., triphasic) refers to the number of times the amounts of the hormones change (e.g., three times). The name of the pill can reflect the type (e.g., *Ortho Tri-Cyclen* is triphasic, with three different hormone "cycles").

COCs are used for other indications besides pregnancy prevention, including dysmenorrhea (menstrual cramps), premenstrual syndrome (PMS), acne (in females), anemia, (by reducing blood loss), peri-menopausal symptoms (hot flashes, night sweats), and menstrual-associated migraine prophylaxis. The use of COCs to regulate menses is first-line treatment for polycystic ovary syndrome (PCOS), a common condition (~5 – 10% of women), where infrequent, irregular or prolonged menstrual periods are common. Some women with PCOS will have hirsutism, acne, excessive weight and insulin resistance, and most women complain of fatigue.

COCs are used as first-line treatment for endometriosis (10 – 20% of women) in which endometrial tissue grows outside of the uterus. COCs reduce the symptoms of dysmenorrhea and heavy bleeding. Elagolix *(Orilissa)* is FDA-approved for moderate to severe pain associated with endometriosis.

Drospirenone is a unique progestin used in some COCs to reduce adverse effects commonly seen with oral contraceptives. It is a mild potassium-sparing diuretic which decreases bloating, PMS symptoms and weight gain; drospirenone-containing products are also associated with less acne, as they have lower androgenic activity.

PROGESTIN-ONLY PILLS

Progestin-only pills (POPs, mini-pills) contain no estrogen, and have 28-days of active pills in each pack. POPs prevent pregnancy by suppressing ovulation, thickening the cervical mucus to inhibit sperm penetration and thinning the endometrium. POPs are primarily used in women who are lactating (breastfeeding). Estrogen decreases milk production. POPs can be useful for women with a contraindication or intolerance to estrogen and can be started soon after delivery (3 – 6 weeks postpartum). It is not safe to use estrogen this soon after delivery because of an increased risk of thrombosis. POPs require good adherence; the pill must be taken within three hours of the scheduled time. POPs are sometimes used for migraine prophylaxis, and are safe in women who have migraines with aura; estrogen cannot be used with this type of migraine, due to the risk of stroke.

NON-ORAL HORMONAL CONTRACEPTIVES

Xulane Contraceptive Patch

The patch has the same side effects, contraindications and drug interactions as COCs, except that the patch causes a higher systemic estrogen exposure; do not use in anyone with clotting risk factors. Less effective in women > 198 pounds. Do not use in women > 35 years old who smoke.

Vaginal Contraceptive Rings

The vaginal rings have the same side effects, contraindications and drug interactions as oral contraception. These are small, flexible rings that are inserted into the vagina once a month. The exact position of the ring in the vagina does not matter.

Injectable Contraception

The injection *(Depo-Provera, Depo-subQ Provera)* is depot medroxyprogesterone acetate (DMPA), a progestin. It suppresses ovulation, thickens cervical mucus, and causes thinning of the endometrium. DMPA is given by IM (150 mg) or SC (104 mg) injection every 3 months.

Intrauterine Devices (IUDs)

IUDs are long-acting, reversible forms of contraception. Some IUDs contain hormones to exert their effects. IUDs are discussed in more detail later in the chapter, in the Long-Acting Reversible Contraceptives section.

CONTRACEPTION AND MENSTRUAL PERIODS

Most COC formulations involve 28 days (4 weeks) of pills, with 21 – 24 pills containing active hormone and the remaining pills containing no hormone (many use placebo pills, some contain iron or folate). During week 4 (the inactive pills), bleeding (menses) occurs for 3 – 7 days. Fewer inactive pills results in a shorter hormone-free interval and shorter bleeding time. Women who take COCs often have lighter bleeding because the endometrium remains relatively thin. For the contraceptive patch or vaginal ring, bleeding occurs during the patch-free or ring-free interval (week 4). About half of medroxyprogesterone acetate users will be amenorrheic (no menses) after 1 year of use.

Extended cycle COCs involve 84 days of active hormonal pills followed by 7 days of inactive or very low dose estrogen pills. With this schedule, bleeding occurs every 3 months, rather than every month. By taking continuous contraception, it is possible to suppress menses altogether. This involves taking hormonal pills only (no placebo pills). *Amethyst* is approved for this; other COCs and CHCs are used in this way, though it is off-label. With continuous use, it can be difficult to tell if a woman becomes pregnant. Spotting (breakthrough bleeding) occurs commonly with continuous contraception, which can lead to discontinuation. It is important to counsel patients that this typically resolves after 3 – 6 months of continuous use.

SELECT CONTRACEPTIVE TYPES

This is not a comprehensive list. For exam purposes, consider patient-specific factors that help in selecting an agent and understand the counseling points that are unique to each formulation.

PRODUCT TYPE	DESCRIPTION
General tips for contraceptive names: ■ "Lo" indicates ≤ 35 mcg E; less E causes less estrogenic side effects. Ex: *Loestrin* ■ "Fe" indicates an iron supplement included. Ex: *Loestrin Fe* ■ "24" indicates a shorter placebo time: 24 active + 4 placebo = 28 d cycle. Ex: *Minastrin 24 Fe*	
Pills	
Monophasic Formulations	Provides the same dose of P and E throughout the active pill days. Example: Junel 1/20 contains 1 mg norethindrone and 20 mcg EE
Junel Fe 1/20, Microgestin Fe 1/20, Sprintec, Loestrin, Yasmin, *Apri, Aviane, Cryselle, Gildess Fe, Junel, Levora, Nortrel, Ocella, Ortho-Cyclen, Portia, Zovia*	21/7 pill pack contains 21 active hormonal pills, 7 inactive pills
Loestrin 24 Fe, Yaz, *Beyaz, Minastrin 24 Fe, Nikki*	24/4 pill pack contains 24 active hormonal pills, 4 inactive pills
Lo Loestrin Fe	24/2/2 pill pack contains 24 active combined hormonal pills, 2 pills of just EE, and 2 inactive pills (with iron); very low dose estrogen used (EE 10 mcg)
Biphasic, Triphasic Formulations	Formulations with "phasic" in the name indicate that the hormone doses are delivered in "phases"; one or both of the hormone doses change during the active pill days
Ortho Tri-Cyclen, Tri-Sprintec, TriNessa, *Kariva, Nortrel 7/7/7, Trivora, Velivet*	3 different weeks (7/7/7) or "tri" indicates a triphasic formulation
Quadriphasic Formulations *Natazia*	Hormone dose changes over the 21-24 days to mimic menstrual cycle (four phases of estradiol valerate and progestin dienogest)
Extended Cycle Formulations	Period occurs every 3 months
Jolessa	84 days of EE + LNG followed by 7 days of placebo
Seasonique, *Camrese, Camrese Lo, Amethia*	84 days of EE + LNG followed by 7 days of low dose EE
Continuous Formulations	No inactive pills (taken continuously); no period occurs
Amethyst	28 days of EE + LNG with no placebo pills
Drospirenone Containing Formulations	Mild potassium sparing diuretic to reduce bloating and other effects
Yasmin, Yaz, *Gianvi, Loryna, Ocella, Zarah, Angeliq, Nikki, Safyral, Syeda, Vestura, Beyaz (Safyral & Beyaz contain folate)*	Contraindicated in renal or liver disease Monitor potassium, kidney function during use
Patch	
Transdermal patch	Higher AUC than pills
Xulane	Weeks 1-3: apply once weekly; week 4: off
Ring	
Vaginal ring	Lower AUC than pills
NuvaRing, *Annovera*	Insert monthly: in x 3 weeks; remove x 1 week *Annovera*: reusable vaginal ring; wash and store when it is removed, then reinsert; used for 1 year
Progestin-Only Pill (The Mini-Pill/Pop)	
Errin, Camila, Nora-BE	All contain a fixed dose of norethindrone; take active tablet daily (no placebo days) "Nor" in the name indicates it contains norethindrone
Injection	
Depo-Provera	Contains depot medroxyprogesterone (DMPA); injected every 3 months (150 mg IM or 104 mg SC) "Pro" in the name indicates it contains a progestin

ADVERSE EFFECTS OF HORMONAL CONTRACEPTIVES

Adverse Effects Due to Estrogen

Side effects of estrogen include nausea, breast tenderness/fullness, bloating, weight gain and elevated blood pressure. Formulations with lower estrogen doses are more tolerable, but insufficient estrogen can lead to breakthrough bleeding (spotting). If spotting occurs early- to mid-cycle, consider switching to a formulation that contains a higher estrogen dose. It is recommended to wait three monthly cycles before changing the dose to see if spotting resolves.

Serious adverse effects are rare, but can include thrombosis, including heart attack, stroke and DVT/PE. The risk for clots increases as the woman ages, if she smokes, if she has diabetes or hypertension, if she requires prolonged bed rest and if she is overweight. The higher the estrogen dose or exposure (e.g., with *Xulane* transdermal patch), the higher the clotting risk. When evaluating risks from use of the pill, also consider risks with an unintended pregnancy: the risk of blood clots during pregnancy and postpartum is much higher than clotting risk with any birth control pill formulation.

RISKS OF HORMONAL CONTRACEPTIVES

BOXED WARNINGS

All estrogen-containing products (pills, ring, patch)

- Do not use in women > 35 years old who smoke due to risk of serious cardiovascular events

Estrogen + progestin transdermal patch (*Xulane*)

- Increased risk of venous thromboembolism (DVT/PE) compared to COCs

Depo-Provera

- Loss of bone mineral density with long-term use

DO NOT USE ESTROGEN WITH THESE CONDITIONS

History of DVT/PE, stroke, CAD, thrombosis of heart valves or acquired hypercoagulopathies

History of breast, ovarian, or liver cancer; liver disease; uncontrolled hypertension (e.g., > 160/100 mmHg); severe headaches or migraines with aura (especially if > 35 years of age); diabetes with vascular disease; unexplained uterine bleeding; others (vary by formulation)

Adverse Effects Due to Progestin

Progestin can cause breast tenderness, headache, fatigue and changes in mood. If late-cycle breakthrough bleeding occurs, a higher progestin dose may be required.

Drospirenone has a slightly higher risk of clotting, and should not be used in women with clotting risk. It can also result in increased potassium; do not use with kidney, liver or adrenal gland disease as these can increase potassium. On a patient case, review the potassium level. It should be in the normal range (3.5 – 5 mEq/L).

The injectable depot medroxyprogesterone acetate can cause a loss in bone mineral density. This can be especially important for teens and young women who are still accumulating bone mass. Minimally, women should be taking adequate calcium and vitamin D (see recommendations in the Osteoporosis, Menopause & Testosterone Use chapter).

SEVERE & RARE ADVERSE EFFECTS OF ESTROGEN

The dose of estrogen in birth control pills used to be much higher – with a higher risk of clotting. Current formulations have lower estrogen doses and lower risk of clotting. To be safe, patients should be able to recognize symptoms of a DVT, PE and less common clots.

Remember: **ACHES**

Abdominal (stomach) pain that is severe

- ❑ Can indicate a ruptured liver tumor or cyst (mesenteric or pelvic vein thrombosis), or the pain could be due to liver problems, gallbladder problems or an ectopic pregnancy.

Chest pain

- ❑ Sharp, crushing, or heavy pain can indicate a heart attack. Shortness of breath can indicate a PE (a blood clot in the lungs).

Headaches

- ❑ Sudden and severe with vomiting or weakness/numbness on one side of the body can indicate a stroke.

Eye problems

- ❑ Blurry vision, flashing lights or partial/complete vision loss can indicate a blood clot in the eye.

Swelling or sudden leg pain

- ❑ Can indicate a DVT (a blood clot in the leg).

CONSIDERATIONS FOR DRUG SELECTION

TYPE OF PATIENT	PRODUCT SELECTION CONSIDERATIONS
Acne	Use COC with lower androgenic activity (e.g., *Ortho-Cyclen)* or no androgenic activity (i.e., *Yaz, Yasmin).*
Breastfeeding	Choose POPs or nonhormonal method. See Postpartum below.
Estrogen contraindication (including clotting risk)	Choose POPs or nonhormonal method.
Migraine	If with aura, choose POPs or nonhormonal method; do not use estrogen. If no aura, choose any method.
Fluid retention/bloating	Choose a product containing drospirenone.
Heavy menstrual bleeding (menorrhagia)	The COC *Natazia* and the levonorgestrel-releasing IUD *Mirena* are indicated for this condition. COCs with only 4 placebo pills (rather than 7) or continuous/extended regimens will minimize bleeding time.
Hypertension	If BP is uncontrolled, some estrogen formulations are contraindicated. Choose POPs or nonhormonal method.
Mood changes or disorder	Use monophasic COC – extended cycle or continuous with drospirenone is preferred.
Nausea	Take at night, with food; can consider decreasing estrogen dose or switching to a POP, vaginal ring or nonhormonal method (ideally after a 3 month trial).
Overweight	Choose any method. Counsel patient about the possibility of reduced effectiveness with the contraceptive patch. Do not use DMPA if trying to avoid further weight gain.
Postpartum	Do not use CHCs for 3 weeks, or for 6 weeks if patient has additional risk factors for VTE. Can use POPs or nonhormonal method during this time.
Premenstrual dysphoric disorder	Choose *Yaz* or antidepressant; see Depression chapter.
Spotting/"breakthrough bleeding"	Common when initiating extended cycles or continuous regimens; usually resolves within 3-6 months. When starting conventional formulations, wait 3 cycles before switching. If early or mid-cycle spotting occurs, the estrogen dose may need to be increased. If later in the cycle, the progestin dose may need to be increased.
Wishes to avoid monthly cycle/menses	Use extended (91-day) or continuous formulations. Alternative: monophasic 28-day formulation and skip placebo pills.

DRUG INTERACTIONS WITH HORMONAL CONTRACEPTIVES

Some forms of contraception can have decreased efficacy when used with other drugs; this can require use of a back-up contraception method such as condoms/spermicide. If the interaction is long-term in nature, an IUD or the birth control injection can be considered. The birth control injection does not have drug interactions since it bypasses first-pass metabolism. With all new drugs being dispensed to a patient using contraception, the package insert should be checked to avoid missing an interaction that could decrease the contraceptive efficacy. If in doubt, it is safest to use back-up.

Drug Interactions that Decrease Hormonal Contraception Efficacy

- Some antibiotics (e.g., rifampin, rifabutin and rifapentine; these are all strong inducers)
  - With rifampin, the induction can be prolonged; a back-up method of contraception is needed for six weeks after rifampin has been discontinued
- Anticonvulsants (carbamazepine, oxcarbazepine, phenytoin, primidone, topiramate, lamotrigine, barbiturates and perampanel)
- St. John's wort
- Smoking tobacco
- Ritonavir-boosted protease inhibitors (PIs), bosentan *(Tracleer)*, mycophenolate *(CellCept, Myfortic)*
- Colesevelam: separate by at least 4 hours
- *Byetta:* take contraceptive at least one hour prior to injection

Risks with Hepatitis C Treatment

- *Technivie* and *Viekira Pak* cannot be used with any formulation containing ethinyl estradiol due to the risk of liver toxicity
- With all new hepatitis C drugs being dispensed to a patient using contraception, the package insert should be checked to avoid missing an interaction that could cause toxicity

Drospirenone Drug Interactions

- Risk of increased K; caution must be used with K-sparing agents, including aldosterone antagonists, potassium supplements, salt substitutes (KCl), ACE inhibitors, angiotensin receptor blockers, heparin, canagliflozin and calcineurin inhibitors (see hyperkalemia discussion in Renal Disease chapter)

STARTING BIRTH CONTROL PILLS

Combination Oral Contraception

In general, it takes seven days of hormonal pills to achieve contraceptive efficacy.

- Start today (also called "quick start"). Best practice recommendation. Maximizes time protected from unintended pregnancy. This method requires back-up (nonhormonal) contraception for seven days.
- Sunday start. Starts the Sunday after onset of menstruation. This is commonly used if the patient prefers that menstruation occur during the week and is complete before the following weekend. It can lead to missed doses if the patient inadvertently runs out of refills over the weekend. This method requires back-up (non-hormonal) contraception for seven days.

COCs can also be started on the first day of menses. If started within five days after the start of the period, no back-up method of birth control is needed; protection is immediate. If not within five days, use back-up for seven days.

Progestin-Only Pills

- Start at any time. Use another method of birth control for the first 48 hours of progestin-pill use – protection begins after two days. All come in 28-day packs and all pills are active.

LATE OR MISSED PILLS – INSTRUCTIONS FOR TYPICAL FORMULATIONS

Missed pills are a common cause of contraceptive failure, particularly if the hormone-free interval is extended. These are the standard instructions from the CDC; when answering questions in practice, check the package insert for the individual product. For the exam, you should know the general approach to missed doses: start as soon as remembered. If more than one COC pill is missed, back-up contraception is required and if missed pills/days are in the third week of the cycle, omit the hormone-free week and start the next package of pills right away without skipping any days; back-up contraception should be used for seven days. See the following table for further information. Requirements for POPs are also included.

Missed Doses for Standard Cycle (28 days)

<table>
<tr><th></th><th></th><th>WEEK 1</th><th>WEEK 2</th><th>WEEK 3</th><th>WEEK 4</th></tr>
<tr><td rowspan="7">COCs</td><td rowspan="3">1 late or missed pill
(< 48 hours since last dose)</td><td colspan="3">Take missed pill as soon as possible and take next dose on schedule (even if that makes 2 pills in 1 day).</td><td rowspan="7"></td></tr>
<tr><td colspan="3">Back-up contraception required? No</td></tr>
<tr><td colspan="3">EC*: Not usually needed. Consider if missed doses earlier in the same cycle or in week 3 of the previous cycle.</td></tr>
<tr><td rowspan="4">2 missed pills
(≥ 48 hours since last dose)</td><td colspan="3">Take the most recent missed pill as soon as possible (discard any other missed pills). Take next dose on schedule (even if that makes 2 pills in 1 day).</td></tr>
<tr><td colspan="2"></td><td>Omit hormone-free week: start next pack of pills right after finishing current pack.**</td></tr>
<tr><td colspan="3">Back-up contraception required? Yes, x 7 days</td></tr>
<tr><td>EC*: Consider if unprotected sex in last 5 days.</td><td colspan="2">EC*: Can be considered.</td></tr>
<tr><td rowspan="3">POPs</td><td rowspan="3">If > 3 hours past scheduled time</td><td colspan="4">Take pill as soon as possible and take next dose on schedule.</td></tr>
<tr><td colspan="4">Back-up contraception required? Yes, x 48 hours</td></tr>
<tr><td colspan="4">EC*: Consider if unprotected sex in last 5 days.</td></tr>
</table>

**EC = emergency contraception*

***If unable to start a new pack right away, use back-up contraception until 7 days of the new pack have been taken*

COC PATIENT COUNSELING

- Most women can take birth control pills safely. However, some women are at higher risk of developing serious conditions that can be life-threatening. The risks increase significantly if you:
  - Have or have had clotting disorders, heart attack, stroke, angina, cancer of the breast or sex organs, jaundice or malignant or benign liver tumors.
  - Smoke; cigarette smoking increases the risk of serious effects on the heart and blood vessels. This risk increases with age and with heavy smoking and is quite marked in women over 35 years of age. Women who use oral contraceptives should not smoke.
- Alert your healthcare provider immediately if any symptoms of a blood clot develop (use ACHES; see previous Study Tip Gal).
- If you are having unusual, non-menstrual vaginal bleeding, see your prescriber before you start using the pill.
- Most side effects of the pill are mild and not serious. The most common are nausea, bleeding between menstrual periods (spotting), weight gain and breast tenderness. These side effects, especially nausea, often improve after three months of use. Taking the pill with food or at night helps to reduce the nausea.
- Discuss with your pharmacist if you start any new medicines, including OTC products or antibiotics for an infection.
- Take the pill at the same time each day; pick a time of day that you will remember.

Drospirenone Formulations

- This medication can increase the potassium level in your blood. You may need to have lab work periodically.

PATIENT COUNSELING FOR NON-ORAL FORMULATIONS

Xulane Contraceptive Patch

- This is a thin, beige, plastic patch that is placed on clean, dry skin of buttocks, stomach, upper arm or upper torso once a week for 21 out of 28 days. Do not apply to breasts.
- Start on either day 1 (no back-up needed) or Sunday (back-up seven days if not day 1).

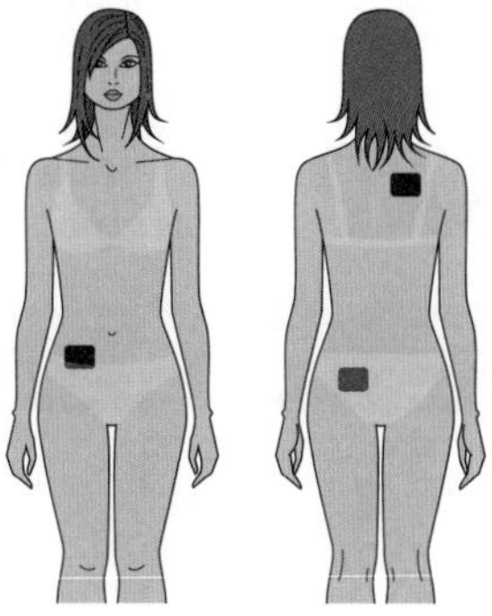

Xulane (back, abdomen, or buttock)

- If patch becomes loose or falls off > 24 hours during the three weeks of use or if > 7 days have passed during the fourth week where no patch is required, there is a risk of pregnancy. A back-up method should be used for one week after starting a new patch.

NuvaRing Vaginal Contraceptive Ring

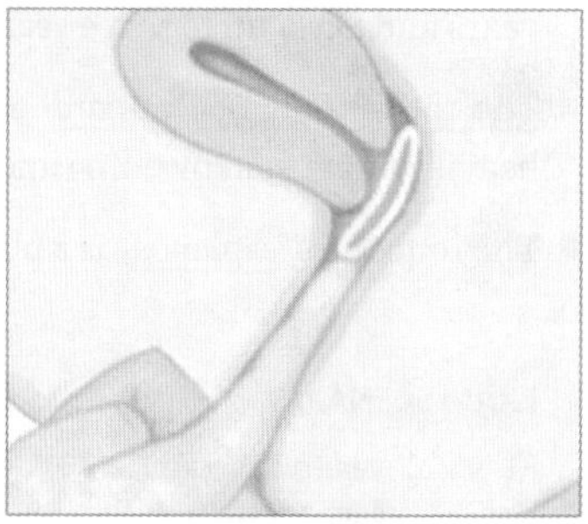

© https://www.nuvaring.com/inserting-nuvaring/

- The ring is inserted into the vagina once a month. It is kept in place for three weeks and taken out for one week before replacement with a new ring. The ring is effective for up to four weeks and, though not FDA-approved, can be kept in place to prevent a period. If the ring is kept in place for > 4 weeks: confirm no pregnancy, then insert a new ring and use back-up contraception until the new ring has been in place for seven continuous days.
- The exact position of the ring in the vagina does not matter.
- An optional applicator can be used to assist with insertion.
- Starting therapy and no hormonal contraceptive use in preceding cycle: insert the ring the first day of menstrual bleeding. If inserted on days 2 – 5 of cycle, back-up contraception should be used for the first seven days in the first cycle.
- If the ring is expelled or removed:
  - Weeks 1 and 2: if ring is out > 3 hours, rinse with cool to lukewarm water and reinsert. Use back-up contraception for seven days while the ring is in place, consider EC if intercourse within last five days.
  - Week 3: discard and insert a new ring. Use back-up contraception for seven days while the ring is in place.
- Store for up to four months at room temperature (refrigerate prior to dispensing).

Annovera Vaginal Contraceptive Ring

- This is a reusable vaginal ring. It is inserted and kept in place for three weeks, then removed for one week. While removed, wash the ring and store in provided case. Repeat this every four weeks for one year.

Injectable Contraception (Medroxyprogesterone)

- This medication can decrease the amount of mineral stored in your bones, which can increase your risk of developing bone fractures. Consume the recommended daily intake of calcium and vitamin D.
- You might experience a change in your normal menstrual cycle. Some women experience a decrease in bleeding and many women stop having periods after one year of use.

LONG-ACTING REVERSIBLE CONTRACEPTIVES

These devices are generally not dispensed from community pharmacies. They must be placed and removed by trained healthcare professionals. They are the most effective forms of reversible contraception, and are as effective as sterilization.

- Intrauterine devices (*Mirena, Skyla, Kyleena, Liletta*) are hormonal IUDs. These cause lighter menstrual bleeding and minor or no cramping. *Mirena* is FDA-approved for heavy menstrual bleeding. *Liletta, Mirena* and *Kyleena* can be used up to five years and *Skyla* up to three years. About 20% of women using *Mirena* will become amenorrheic.
- The copper-T IUD (*Paragard*) can be used for EC and/or regular birth control, and can be used up to 10 years, but causes heavier menstrual bleeding and cramping, which can be painful. Some women prefer this nonhormonal method.
- The implant (*Nexplanon*) is a plastic rod that is placed subdermally and releases the progestin etonogestrel for three years.

EXAM SCENARIO

KL is a 37-year-old female (G2 P2)* with antiphospholipid syndrome, diagnosed 2 years ago after a second DVT. She takes aspirin daily. Her last pregnancy was difficult. She requests contraception that is highly effective.

KL is 5 feet, 4 inches; 145 pounds; BP 111/77 mmHg

- Assess her medical history:
  - ❑ Estrogen is contraindicated with antiphospholipid syndrome or any clotting condition. She cannot use COCs, a vaginal ring or *Xulane*.
  - ❑ She could use POPs (the mini-pill), but the risk of unplanned pregnancy is high with missed or even late pills.
  - ❑ Another hormonal option is the *Depo-Provera* injection. Her bone health should be considered prior to use.
  - ❑ IUD placement or sterilization may be acceptable to KL.

**G2 P2 is an abbreviation for gravida and para. She has been pregnant twice and has had 2 deliveries after 24 weeks gestation.*

EMERGENCY CONTRACEPTION (EC)

TYPES OF EMERGENCY CONTRACEPTION	HOW WELL DOES IT WORK?	HOW SOON DO I HAVE TO USE IT?	HOW DO I USE IT?	WHERE CAN I GET IT?
 ParaGard IUD	FIRST 99.9% effective	Within 5 days	It's placed in the uterus by a doctor or nurse. Keeps working as super effective birth control.	From a doctor, nurse, or at a clinic. Say it's for EC so you are scheduled quickly.
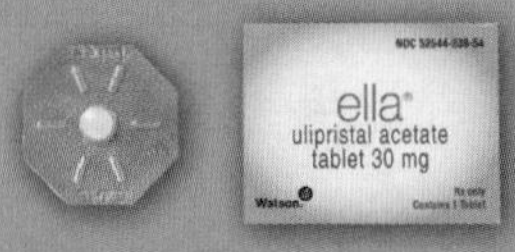 Ella	SECOND. Less effective if over 195 pounds. Try an IUD.	ASAP. Works better the sooner you take it, up to 5 days.	Take the pill as soon as you get it. Remember to use it every time you have unprotected sex.	From a doctor, nurse, or at a clinic. Get an extra pack for future emergencies.
 Plan B One-Step or a generic	THIRD. Less effective if over 165 pounds Try ella or an IUD.	ASAP. Works better the sooner you take it, up to 3 days.	Take the pill as soon as you get it. Remember to use it every time you have unprotected sex.	At a pharmacy, no prescription needed. Get an extra pack for future emergencies.

Adapted from ©Bedsider and Bixby Center at UCSF for San Francisco City Clinic www.sfcityclinic.org

Emergency contraception (EC) is a form of hormonal or nonhormonal contraception that prevents pregnancy after unprotected intercourse. The copper IUD *(Paragard)* is the most effective form of EC if inserted within five days. There are two oral EC (also known as the "morning after pill") options, levonorgestrel *(Plan B One-Step)* and ulipristal acetate *(Ella)*, that can be used within five days, with effectiveness diminishing over time. This means that the sooner EC is used, the higher the efficacy. The use of higher doses of combination oral contraceptives is no longer a common practice as it is less effective than these options, leads to more nausea/vomiting, and has more contraindications. EC has been available for 30 years and there have been no reports of serious complications or birth defects.

EC can be an important resource after unprotected sex, such as from missed pills, a condom breaking during intercourse, a diaphragm or cap that moved out of place during intercourse, or if a woman has been sexually assaulted. If sexual assault has occurred the woman may require STD treatment, including HIV post-exposure prophylaxis, HBV and HPV vaccines, and empiric antimicrobial treatment for chlamydia, gonorrhea, and trichomoniasis. Pharmacists should have referrals for other providers available to provide to patients.

Occasionally, women might use EC after sex as their regular method of birth control; this can be done when a woman has occasional (not regular) sexual activity and is willing to accept the effectiveness of the method. Depending on insurance coverage, it might also be more expensive.

LEVONORGESTREL

Plan B One-Step and generics are packaged as one 1.5 mg tab of levonorgestrel. This formulation of EC reduces the risk of pregnancy by up to 89% when started within 72 hours after unprotected intercourse. The sooner it is started, the higher the efficacy.

Plan B One-Step and generics *(Take Action, Next Choice One-Dose, Aftera, My Way, Preventeza)* are OTC with no age or other restrictions. These products can be sold in stores without a pharmacy. Per the FDA, these should be placed in the OTC aisles with the other family-planning products, such as condoms and spermicides. The generics cost $35 – $45, about $10 less than the brand *Plan B One-Step*. There is no reason to use a prescription with the formulations available OTC (unless someone wanted the 2 pill formulation), except to use insurance coverage.

If the EC is purchased OTC, there is no requirement for purchasers to sign a registry. They can purchase multiple doses and the American College of Obstetrics and Gynecologists (ACOG) recommends an additional dose for future use, if needed, since EC is more effective the sooner it is used.

- Mechanism of action: primarily works by preventing or delaying ovulation, and thickens cervical mucus.
- Preferred regimen is 1.5 mg as a single dose *(Plan B One-Step)*.
- This type of EC is indicated for up to five days (the sooner, the better) after unprotected intercourse. The package indicates to use within three days, but is used up to five days off-label according to evidence-based guidelines.
- The primary side effect is nausea, which occurs in 23% of women, and 6% have vomiting. If the woman is easily nauseated, an OTC anti-emetic (one hour prior to use, and caution if driving home due to sedation) should be recommended to avoid losing the dose. If a patient vomits within two hours of taking the medication, she should consider repeating the dose.

ULIPRISTAL ACETATE *(ELLA)*

Some patients may not wish to use ulipristal because it is a chemical cousin to mifepristone *(Mifeprex)*, also known as the "abortion pill" or RU-486. They are not the same drug and are used differently. The mifepristone product available in the U.S. is used primarily for pregnancy terminations and other non-contraceptive uses. The dose of ulipristal is much lower potency and is used to delay ovulation. It may also prevent implantation in the uterus and this is controversial for some patients.

- Given as a single 30 mg dose. Requires a prescription.
- Indicated for up to five days after unprotected intercourse. More effective than levonorgestrel if 72 – 120 hours since unprotected intercourse or if woman is overweight.
- Primary side effects are headache, nausea and abdominal pain. Some women have changes in their menstrual cycle, but all should get their period within a week. Can only use once per cycle. Use a barrier method of contraception the rest of the cycle as ovulation may occur later than normal.

PATIENT COUNSELING FOR EC

- If you vomit after taking EC you may need to take another dose. Before you do, contact a pharmacist or other healthcare provider immediately. If you get easily nauseated, the pharmacist can recommend an OTC medication that helps to lessen nausea that you can use before you take the EC pill.
- If you do not get your period in three weeks (or it is more than a week late), a pregnancy test should be taken. If you develop severe abdominal pain or irregular bleeding, you may have an ectopic pregnancy (outside of the uterus) and will need immediate medical attention.

- It is important to visit your healthcare provider for a regular birth control method and information about preventing sexually transmitted infections. If you may have contracted an infection, you should get care right away.
- You may wish to get a package of EC for future use, if needed.
- Regular hormonal contraceptives (OCs, shot, ring, patch), should be started on the same or the following day as taking the EC.
- You should only use one type of oral EC pill. Do not use two different types together.

INFERTILITY

Infertility is defined as not being able to get pregnant (conceive) after one year or longer of unprotected sex. Infertility can be due to either the male or female. This section covers drugs used in females.

Clomiphene is the first-line treatment in women with irregular or absent menstrual cycles. Clomiphene is a selective estrogen receptor modulator (SERM). Drugs that are SERMs act as estrogen agonists in some tissues and estrogen antagonists in other tissues. Clomiphene, like estrogen, causes LH and FSH to surge, which triggers ovulation. The surge in LH commonly causes hot flashes. SERMs, including clomiphene, have clotting risks.

Gonadotropins trigger ovulation by acting similar to the endogenous (naturally produced) gonadotropins FSH or LH. Gonadotropins are used after a poor response to clomiphene, or to spur egg release for procedures such as intrauterine insemination and *in vitro* fertilization.

Alternatively, human chorionic gonadotropin (hCG) or gonadotropin releasing hormone agonists (GnRHA), such as leuprolide (*Lupron*) can be used to trigger ovulation. The hCG hormone is important in pregnancy and in ovulation, where it binds to the LH receptor with a similar effect. Leuprolide and other GnRHAs are more commonly used to decrease hormone levels in breast or prostate cancer treatment.

Fertility medications, including gonadotropins and clomiphene, can cause multiple eggs to be released, which causes a risk of multiple births (see Study Tip Gal). Gonadotropins, similar to the majority of drugs that are hormones, cannot be taken orally. They are administered by SC or IM injection. This is one of the rare times a patient (or their partner) could be injecting IM, which is more painful than SC administration.

INFERTILITY DRUGS ACT LIKE ENDOGENOUS HORMONES TO TRIGGER OVULATION

↑ LH/FSH → ovulation (release of egg/s)

Clomiphene acts as estrogen to ↑ LH/FSH → cause ovulation

Gonadotropin drugs act as LH, FSH or hCG (similar to LH) → cause ovulation

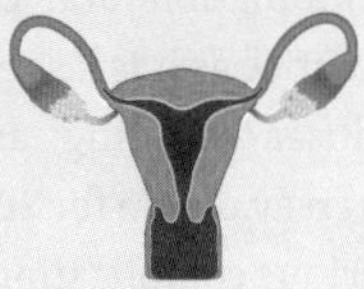

GOOD: Infertility drugs trigger ovulation (egg release)

GOOD? They can trigger the release of multiple eggs and ↑ risk of multiple births

GONADOTROPIN DRUG NAMES

Generic names include chorionic gonadotropin-recombinant, follicle stimulating hormone-recombinant, human chorionic gonadotropin-recombinant and menotropin, which contains LH and FSH extracted from the urine of menopausal females.

Brand names can include parts of the words reproduce, men(strual), follicle, gonadotropin, pregnancy and ovary, including *Menopur, Follistim, Gonal-F, Urofollitropin, Pregnyl, Novarel* and *Ovidrel.*

Select Guidelines/References

US Selected Practice Recommendations (US SPR) for Contraceptive Use, 2016 https://www.cdc.gov/reproductivehealth/contraception/mmwr/spr/combined.html (accessed 2019 Jan 11).

Emergency Contraception Information http://ec.princeton.edu/index.html (accessed 2019 Jan 11).

Association of Reproductive Health Professionals (ARHP) https://www.arhp.org/ (accessed 2019 Jan 11).

CHAPTER CONTENT

Pregnancy....707
Background....707
Lifestyle Management....707
Changes to FDA Pregnancy Categories....708
Drug Treatment....709
Common Teratogens....709
Teratogens: Danger in Pregnancy....709
Select Conditions and Preferred Management During Pregnancy....710
Lactation....712
Treating Pain....712
Known or Suspected HIV....712
Specific Medications....712

CONTENT LEGEND

= Key Drug Guy

CHAPTER 48
DRUG USE IN PREGNANCY AND LACTATION

PREGNANCY

BACKGROUND

Pregnancy typically lasts 36 – 40 weeks and is divided into three trimesters. A positive human chorionic gonadotropin (hCG+) lab result confirms pregnancy. The first trimester is when the embryo is most susceptible to birth defects caused by teratogens, though they can occur later. For a drug to be teratogenic, the drug has to cross the placenta into the fetal circulation. Teratogenic drugs should be discontinued prior to pregnancy, if possible. Pharmacokinetic changes during pregnancy can require dose and regimen changes. For example, in women being treated for hypothyroidism, an increased dose of levothyroxine will be required in order to keep thyroid hormones within normal ranges.

LIFESTYLE MANAGEMENT

Lifestyle modifications should always be considered first when treating pregnant patients. This includes encouragement to stop the use of illicit drugs, alcohol and tobacco, each of which is teratogenic. Behavioral intervention is a safe and sometimes effective strategy for prenatal smoking cessation. Refer to the Tobacco Cessation chapter.

Vitamin and Mineral Supplementation

Folate deficiency causes birth defects of the brain and spinal cord (neural tube defects). All women of childbearing age should obtain 400 mcg/day of folic acid (folate) from a combination of dietary supplements, fortified foods and their regular diet. During pregnancy, folate requirements increase to 600 mcg/day. Folate is in many healthy foods, including fortified flour and cereals, dried beans, green leafy vegetables and orange juice.

The baby's skeleton requires adequate calcium and vitamin D. If deficient in calcium, the mother's bone health will be sacrificed to provide for the baby. Pregnant women from 19 – 50 years old require 1,000 mg/day of calcium and 600 IU/day of vitamin D.

Prenatal vitamins are available by prescription and OTC. Most contain 800 – 1,000 mcg of folic acid, 400 IU of vitamin D and ~200 mg of calcium, though composition varies. Calcium is bulky and the prenatal vitamin would be large if it contained larger amounts. If the woman's dietary intake is insufficient, she may need a separate calcium and vitamin D supplement.

CHANGES TO FDA PREGNANCY CATEGORIES

The old pregnancy categories were viewed as confusing and overly simplistic. In some cases, ratings were applied incorrectly due to inadequate information on the safety risks. The new labeling is intended to provide patients and clinicians with more detailed benefit/risk data in order to make informed decisions.

New labeling requirements for pregnancy and lactation apply to prescription drugs approved since the law went into effect on June 30, 2015. The manufacturers have 3 – 5 years to add the new information for drugs approved from June 30, 2001 to the start of the new requirements in 2015. The new requirements do not apply to drugs approved before June 30, 2001, except that the Pregnancy Category will need to be removed within three years. Currently (except for drugs recently approved which reflect the 2015 requirements), the package labeling for a prescription drug can include:

- The old pregnancy category for the drug (A, B, C, D or X).
- The old pregnancy category removed and nothing else added.
- The new requirements (see table).
- The old pregnancy category and the new requirements.

Drugs with known risk from the old categories should be considered to have the same risk unless known otherwise. If a drug is Pregnancy Category X, it is contraindicated in pregnancy, which means it cannot be used in pregnancy for any reason. If a drug is Category D, it should only be used if the benefit outweighs the risk.

Previous Pregnancy Categories & Interpretation

A	Controlled studies in animals & women show no risk in the first trimester. Risk of fetal harm is remote.
B	Animal studies have not demonstrated a fetal risk, but no controlled studies in pregnant women, or animal studies show an adverse effect that was not confirmed in studies in women in first trimester.
C	Animal studies have shown harm to the fetus and there are no controlled studies in humans, or studies in humans and animals are not available; give only if potential benefit outweighs the risk.
D	Positive evidence of fetal risk is available, but the benefits may outweigh the risk with life-threatening or serious disease.
X	Studies in animals or humans show fetal abnormalities; use in pregnancy is contraindicated.

New Pregnancy Sections in Package Inserts

8.1 Pregnancy	A pregnancy risk summary is required for all medications that includes the risk of adverse developmental outcomes based on human and animal data and the drug's pharmacology. Includes any dose adjustments, maternal/fetal adverse reactions and disease risks. Includes pregnancy exposure registry information. Pregnant women should be encouraged to participate in registries, which exist for select disease states and drugs. The registries collect health information from women who take prescription drugs and vaccines when pregnant and breastfeeding. Information is also collected on the newborn baby.
8.2 Lactation	Includes whether the drug/metabolites go into human milk, the effects on the breastfed infant, and the effects on milk production. If applicable, ways to minimize exposure and monitor for adverse reactions are included.
8.3 Females & Males of Reproductive Potential	Includes any effects on fertility and requirements for pregnancy testing and contraception.

DRUG TREATMENT

If possible, use lifestyle measures to treat medical conditions in pregnant women. When this is impossible or ineffective, choose drugs carefully. Vaccination in pregnancy is covered in the Immunizations chapter.

Common Teratogens

Teratogenic drugs should be discontinued in pregnancy (preferably prior to pregnancy), but about half of pregnancies are not planned.

In the RxPrep Course Book, medications with boxed warnings and contraindications associated with teratogenicity are noted in the drug tables. The medications in the Key Drugs Guy to the right are a summary and should be known for the exam. Many of the medications included are commonly used drugs with teratogenic risk. Others are well-documented teratogens, and even though use is not common, their use in a pregnant patient is rarely, if ever, appropriate. Watch for these important teratogens when evaluating medication profiles on the exam.

Use of some medications in pregnant patients is debatable, and many medications have limited data regarding safety in pregnancy. With any medication, the drug's potential harm must be weighed against the risk of the condition not being adequately treated. For example, the use of lamotrigine in pregnancy carries a risk of congenital malformations, but seizures cause damage to both the mother and child. In some cases, a switch to a safer drug is possible, or, the woman may have had a history of poor seizure control prior to the use of lamotrigine.

Always check reputable, up-to-date resources when prescribing/dispensing to pregnant women. *Briggs' Drugs in Pregnancy and Lactation* and other resources are reviewed in the Learning Drug References chapter.

Teratogens are hazardous drugs according to USP Chapter 800, and require special handling to avoid risk to healthcare workers; see the Compounding chapters.

TERATOGENS: DANGER IN PREGNANCY

KEY DRUGS

Acne
Isotretinoin, topical retinoids (including tazarotene)

Antibiotics*
Quinolones, tetracyclines

Anticoagulants
Warfarin; see discussion of anticoagulation in pregnancy in this chapter

Dyslipidemia, Heart Failure and Hypertension
Statins, RAAS inhibitors (ACE inhibitors, ARBs, aliskiren, sacubitril/valsartan)

Hormones
Most, including estradiol, progesterone [including megestrol *(Megace)*], raloxifene, *Duavee*, testosterone, contraceptives

Migraine
Dihydroergotamine, ergotamine

Other important teratogens

Hydroxyurea	Paroxetine
Lithium	Ribavirin
Methotrexate	Thalidomide
Misoprostol	Topiramate
NSAIDs	Weight Loss Drugs
	Valproic Acid/ Divalproex

Others:
Amiodarone
Aminoglycosides
Dronedarone
Atenolol
Benzodiazepines
Carbamazepine
Dutasteride
Finasteride
Fluconazole
Voriconazole
ERAs (e.g., bosentan)
Griseofulvin
Lenalidomide
Leflunomide
Lomitapide
Methimazole
Propylthiouracil
Radioactive iodine
Phenobarbital
Phenytoin

**See Infectious Diseases I chapter for information on metronidazole, nitrofurantoin, sulfamethoxazole/trimethoprim and telavancin.*

Select Conditions and Preferred Management During Pregnancy

CONDITION	PREFERRED MANAGEMENT	NOTES
Morning Sickness, Nausea, Vomiting	Lifestyle first: eat smaller, more frequent meals, avoid spicy or odorous foods, take more frequent naps, and reduce stress, including working long hours. If lifestyle measures fail, ACOG recommends pyridoxine (vitamin B6) +/- doxylamine first line. Rx: doxylamine/pyridoxine *(Bonjesta, Diclegis).*	Ginger is rated "possibly effective" for treating morning sickness. Hyperemesis gravidarum is severe N/V, causing weight loss, dehydration and electrolyte imbalance. It will be treated under the care of an obstetrician and may require hospitalization.
GERD/Heartburn	Lifestyle first: eat smaller, more frequent meals, avoid foods that worsen GERD. If symptoms occur while sleeping, recommend elevating the head of the bed and not eating 3 hours prior to sleep. If lifestyle measures fail, recommend antacids. Calcium antacids, such as calcium carbonate *(Tums)*, are a good choice since calcium intake is often deficient.	
Flatulence	Simethicone *(Gas-X, Mylicon).*	
Constipation	Lifestyle first: ↑ fluid intake, ↑ dietary fiber intake and ↑ physical activity. If lifestyle measures fail, fiber (psyllium, calcium polycarbophil, methylcellulose), with adequate amounts of fluids, is preferred.	
Cough, Cold, Allergies	First line: first-generation antihistamines. Chlorpheniramine (drug of choice) and diphenhydramine are commonly used. The non-sedating second generation agents loratadine and cetirizine are often recommended by obstetricians during the second and third trimesters. If nasal steroids are needed for chronic allergy symptoms, budesonide *(Rhinocort)* and beclomethasone *(Beconase AQ)* are considered safest (hint: b's for babies).	Oral decongestants should not be recommended during first trimester. The cough-suppressant dextromethorphan and the mucolytic guaifenesin have limited safety data in pregnancy/lactation, but are sometimes used. Avoid liquid formulations that contain alcohol.
Pain	Non-drug options such as hot/cold packs, light massage or physical therapy can help limit or avoid the use of analgesics. ACOG continues to recommend acetaminophen first-line for mild pain during pregnancy because the perceived risk with acetaminophen may be less than the known risk with NSAIDs and opioids. There is a possible link between acetaminophen use during pregnancy and ADHD/autism in the child; the FDA is investigating the risk.	Avoid NSAIDs, including aspirin, especially in the third trimester. Opioid metabolism can affect safety risk (see Learning Drug Interactions and Pain chapters).
Asthma	Maintenance therapy (steroid): inhaled budesonide. Rescue therapy (short-acting beta agonist): inhaled albuterol.	Budesonide is also the preferred steroid for infants; the *Respules* are used in a nebulizer.
Iron Deficiency Anemia	Supplemental iron, prenatal vitamins with iron.	
Hypertension*	Labetalol, methyldopa, nifedipine.	ACE inhibitors, ARBs, aliskiren and *Entresto* are contraindicated in pregnancy.
Diabetes*	Insulin is preferred if not controlled with lifestyle. Metformin and glyburide are commonly used. The American Diabetes Association (ADA) guidelines recommend adding daily low-dose aspirin for pregnant patients with type 1 and type 2 diabetes (starting at the end of the first trimester) to lower the risk of preeclampsia.	

CONDITION	PREFERRED MANAGEMENT	NOTES
Infection*	Generally considered safe to use: penicillins (including amoxicillin and ampicillin), cephalosporins, erythromycin and azithromycin. **VAGINAL FUNGAL INFECTIONS** Topical antifungals (creams, suppositories) x 7 days. **URINARY TRACT INFECTIONS** Cephalexin 500 mg PO Q6H x 7 days. Ampicillin 500 mg PO Q6H x 7 days. Nitrofurantoin and SMX/TMP should be considered last line during the 1st trimester, and should not be used in the last 2 weeks of pregnancy. Must treat bacteriuria, even if asymptomatic with negative urinalysis. Untreated bacteriuria can lead to premature birth, pyelonephritis, and neonatal meningitis. ***TOXOPLASMOSIS*** Many people are infected with toxoplasmosis, and are asymptomatic. If a woman contracts toxoplasmosis during pregnancy, there can be grave consequences to the baby. Women can be tested prior to pregnancy with an IgG test. If unsure of the status, it is best to avoid dirty food and water (uncommon in the U.S.), unpasteurized dairy products, and cat feces (including contact with cat litter boxes), which can contain the parasite.	Do not use: quinolones (due to cartilage damage) and tetracyclines (due to teeth discoloration). **VAGINAL FUNGAL INFECTIONS** Avoid fluconazole. **URINARY TRACT INFECTION** SMX/TMP has mixed data for use in pregnancy; per ACOG, use in pregnancy (if necessary) may be acceptable. See Infectious Diseases II chapter for STI/STD management in pregnancy.
Venous Thromboembolism/ Mechanical Valves	Low molecular weight heparin (LMWH) is preferred over unfractionated heparin (UFH) for prevention and treatment of VTE in pregnant women. Pneumatic compression devices can be used or combined with LMWH in select patients. Women who require chronic warfarin therapy for mechanical heart valves or inherited thrombophilias are generally converted to LMWH during pregnancy. They may be switched back to warfarin after the 13th week of pregnancy, then back to LMWH close to delivery.	Warfarin is teratogenic. The oral factor Xa inhibitors and direct thrombin inhibitors have not been adequately studied in pregnancy and are not recommended. Monitor peak anti-Xa levels, drawn 4 hours post-dose (LMWH), or aPTT (heparin).
Hypothyroidism	Levothyroxine (will require a 30-50% dose increase during pregnancy).	Hypothyroidism must be treated during pregnancy; if left untreated, severe consequences could include miscarriage or stillbirth, preeclampsia, low birth weight, cognitive impairment and growth retardation.
Hyperthyroidism	Mild cases will not require treatment. Preferable to normalize the mother's thyroid function prior to pregnancy. Contraception should be used until the condition is controlled. If drugs are necessary (i.e., Graves' disease): propylthiouracil is preferred if trying to conceive and in the 1st trimester. After that, the decision is individualized, as both PTU and methimazole carry potential fetal risks. Historically, the patient would be switched to methimazole for the remainder of the pregnancy.	Both PTU and methimazole have a high risk for liver damage, readily cross the placenta, and can cause congenital defects. Uncontrolled maternal hyperthyroidism can cause premature delivery and low birth weight. Radioactive iodine is teratogenic and not used in pregnancy.

Managing hypertension, diabetes, HIV, bipolar disorder and certain infections during pregnancy are discussed in detail in the respective chapters.

LACTATION

The American Academy of Pediatrics (AAP) recommends that babies be exclusively breastfed for the first six months of life, as long as it is mutually desired by the mother and baby and if safety risks are not present. Babies receiving breast milk partially or exclusively should receive 400 IU of vitamin D daily until they are consuming at least one liter of vitamin D-fortified formula/day. Breastfed babies require 1 mg/kg daily of iron during months 4 - 6. See Dietary Supplements, Natural & Complementary Medicine chapter. Mothers who are breastfeeding should increase their diet by 450 – 500 kcal/day and continue prenatal vitamins and omega-3 supplements.

Excretion into breast milk is higher with drugs that are non-ionized, have a small molecular weight, a low volume of distribution and high lipid solubility. The majority of medications have low excretion into breast milk, and can be taken safely while breastfeeding. Additionally, breastfeeding can continue when the mother has a cold, influenza and with the majority of other infections. *LactMed* can be used to check for drug safety during breastfeeding (http://toxnet.nlm.nih.gov). Refer to the Learning Drug References chapter for more information.

TREATING PAIN

Codeine and tramadol should not be used by breastfeeding mothers due to risk of excessive sleepiness, breathing difficulty and/or death in the infant. Breastfed infants have died, especially in mothers taking codeine who were CYP450 2D6 ultra-rapid metabolizers. Because of the importance, this is discussed further in the Pharmacogenomics, Learning Drug Interactions and Pain chapters. Even small doses of opioids taken by the mother can cause serious side effects for the infant.

KNOWN OR SUSPECTED HIV

Breastfeeding is not recommended for women with documented HIV infection in the United States, including those women receiving antiretroviral therapy. Any woman with suspected HIV infection, should stop breastfeeding until HIV is ruled out with proper testing.

SPECIFIC MEDICATIONS

Amphetamines, amiodarone, ergotamines, lithium and statins should not be used during breastfeeding.

Metronidazole should be avoided, or the milk should be pumped and discarded for 12 – 24 hours after a single dose.

Phenobarbital is excreted in breast milk, and can result in acute withdrawal effects when breastfeeding is abruptly stopped.

Select Guidelines/References

American College of Obstetricians and Gynecologists (ACOG) Practice Guidelines, available at www.acog.org (accessed 2019 Jan 2).

CDC Recommendations for STI/STD, available at www.cdc.gov (accessed 2019 Jan 2).

CHAPTER CONTENT

Osteoporosis 713
Background 713
Risk Factors 713
Select Factors and Conditions with Osteoporosis Risk 714
Diagnosis 714
Diagnosis of Osteoporosis 714
Bone Mineral Density 714
Fracture Risk Assessment (FRAX) 714
Prevention 715
Calcium and Vitamin D Supplementation 715
Calcium and Vitamin D 715
Drug Treatment 716
Criteria for Initiating Treatment 716
Drug Summary for Osteoporosis Treatment and Prevention 716
Bisphosphonates 717
Estrogen Agonist/Antagonist Containing Products 718
Calcitonin 719
Parathyroid Hormone 1-34 719
Receptor Activator of Nuclear Factor kappa-B Ligand (RANKL) Inhibitor 720
Romosuzumab 720
Patient Counseling 721
Hormone Therapy: Health Risks and Appropriate Use 722
Menopause 723
Background 723
Estrogen-Progestin Products 723
Formulation Considerations 723
Common Hormone Therapy Products 724
"Bioidentical" Nomenclature 724
Estrogen-Progestin Patient Counseling 725
Patch Application 725
Other Products for Menopause 725
Natural Products 725
SSRIs and Ospemifene 726
Hypogonadism in Males 726
Testosterone Use 726
Testosterone Formulations 727
Testosterone Products: C-III 727
Testosterone Patient Counseling 728

CONTENT LEGEND

(💡) = Study Tip Gal

NORMAL BONE | OSTEOPOROSIS

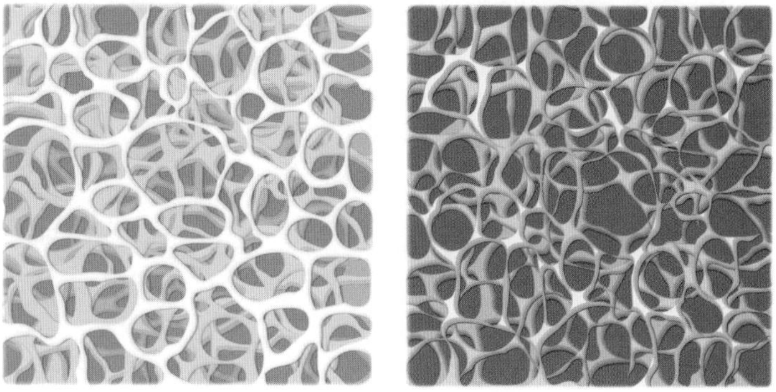

CHAPTER 49
OSTEOPOROSIS, MENOPAUSE & TESTOSTERONE USE

OSTEOPOROSIS

BACKGROUND

Osteoporosis ("porous bones") is a condition that causes bones to become weak and fragile. It is estimated that more than one-quarter of all adults in the U.S., and over half of those > 50 years of age, have osteoporosis, low bone density or low bone mass. Osteoporosis can occur in both men and women of all races; it is most common in postmenopausal women. About one in two women and one in five men will have an osteoporosis-related fracture during their lifetime. Falls are the most common cause of fractures, but with extremely porous bones, they can be caused by coughing or rolling over in bed.

The most common locations for fractures are the vertebrae (spine), the proximal femur (hip) and the distal forearm (wrist). Vertebral fractures can occur without a fall and can initially be painless (the only clue may be a gradual loss of height). Hip fractures are the most devastating type of fractures, with higher costs, disability and mortality than all other fractures combined. Hip fractures are more common after age 75 years. Wrist fractures, and other types of fractures, appear in younger people and serve as an early indicator of poor bone health.

RISK FACTORS

Osteoporosis can occur as a result of normal age-related bone loss. Bone accumulates until approximately age 30. After that, men lose bone at a rate of 0.2 – 0.5% per year and women lose bone at a similar rate, except in the 10 years after menopause when bone loss is accelerated (1 – 5% per year). Patient-specific characteristics that can contribute to osteoporosis risk include lifestyle habits, diseases and medications (see the Study Tip Gal on the following page).

SELECT FACTORS AND CONDITIONS WITH OSTEOPOROSIS RISK

Patient Characteristics
Advanced age
Ethnicity (Caucasian and Asian are at ↑ risk)
Family history
Sex (females > males)
Low body weight

Lifestyle Factors
Smoking
Excessive alcohol intake (≥ 3 drinks per day)
Low calcium intake
Low vitamin D intake
Physical inactivity

Medical Diseases/Conditions
Anorexia nervosa
Diabetes
Gastrointestinal diseases (e.g., IBD, celiac disease, gastric bypass, malabsorption syndromes)
Hyperthyroidism
Hypogonadism in men
Menopause
Rheumatoid arthritis, autoimmune diseases
Others (e.g., epilepsy, HIV/AIDS, Parkinson disease)

Medications
Anticonvulsants (e.g., carbamazepine, phenytoin, phenobarbital)
Aromatase inhibitors
Depo-medroxyprogesterone
GnRH (gonadotropin-releasing hormone) agonists
Lithium
PPIs (↑ gastric pH decreases Ca absorption)
Steroids* (≥ 5 mg daily of prednisone or prednisone equivalent for ≥ 3 months)
Thyroid hormones (in excess)
Others (e.g., heparin, loop diuretics, SSRIs, TZDs)

**Long-term use of steroids is the major drug-contributing factor to poor bone health.*

DIAGNOSIS

Bone Mineral Density

Bone is not "dead tissue"; it is living and undergoes constant remodeling. Osteoblasts are the cells involved in bone formation. Osteoclasts are the cells involved in bone resorption; they break-down tissue in the bone. Bone health is evaluated by measuring bone mineral density (BMD). The gold standard test to measure BMD and diagnose osteoporosis is a dual energy X-ray absorptiometry (DEXA, or DXA). This measures BMD of the spine and hip and calculates a T-score or a Z-score. See Study Tip Gal for information on T-scores and the thresholds for diagnosing osteoporosis and osteopenia.

All women ≥ 65 years and men ≥ 70 years should have BMD measured. BMD can be checked earlier if there is a history of a fragility fracture (e.g., a fall from standing height or lower that results in a fracture) after age 50, risk for disease- or drug-induced bone loss, a parental history of hip fracture or other clinical risk factors (e.g., smoking, alcoholism, low body weight).

If a DXA scan is unavailable, an ultrasound may be performed; ultrasounds are less expensive, portable and do not emit radiation, but they are less than optimal. Ultrasound readings provide bone density in one location, such as the heel; if low, the patient should be encouraged to get a DXA scan. Since vertebral fractures are so common in older adults, and usually lack symptoms, vertebral imaging may be done if height loss is observed or if BMD testing indicates osteopenia.

Fracture Risk Assessment Tool (FRAX)

The FRAX tool is a computer-based algorithm developed by the World Health Organization (WHO) that estimates the risk of osteoporotic fracture in the next 10 years (available at www.nof.org or www.shef.ac.uk/FRAX). It has been well-validated and the U.S. tool has adapted versions available for Caucasian, Black, Hispanic and Asian patients. Clinical risk factors included in the tool are: age, sex, weight, height, previous fracture, parental hip fracture, femoral neck BMD, smoking status, steroid use, alcohol intake, disorders strongly associated with osteoporosis (e.g., type 1 diabetes, chronic liver disease, premature menopause) and diagnosis of rheumatoid arthritis. The tool is intended for postmenopausal women and men > 50 years of age.

DIAGNOSIS OF OSTEOPOROSIS

WHAT IS A T-SCORE?
A T-score compares the patient's measured BMD to the average peak BMD of a healthy, young, white adult of the same sex.*

A DEXA (or DXA) measures BMD so a T-score can be determined.

T-scores are negative: a score at or above -1 correlates with stronger (denser) bones, which are less likely to fracture.**

WHO SHOULD HAVE BMD MEASURED?
Women age ≥ 65 years and men age ≥ 70 years.
Younger patients at high risk for fracture (see text).

INTERPRETING T-SCORE RESULTS
Normal: ≥ -1
Osteopenia (low bone mass): -1 to -2.4
Osteoporosis: ≤ -2.5

**A Z-score is calculated the same way, but compares the patient's measured BMD to the mean BMD of an age, sex and ethnicity-matched population.*

***Scores less than -1 reflect the standard deviation from the comparator group (e.g., a T-score of < -2.5 means the patient's BMD is at least 2.5 standard deviations below the average BMD for healthy, young, white adults).*

PREVENTION

Fall Prevention Measures

If the bone density is low, care must be taken to avoid falls. Factors that put a patient at increased fall risk include a history of recent falls, medications that cause sedation or orthostasis (e.g., antihypertensives, sedatives and hypnotics, narcotic analgesics, psychotropics), neurologic disorders or any condition that causes physical instability or poor coordination (e.g., Parkinson disease, dementia, prior stroke, peripheral neuropathy), impaired vision or hearing, poor health/frailty and urinary or fecal urgency. A home safety assessment should ensure that lighting is appropriate, floors are safe (throw rugs/clutter/cords have been removed), storage is at reasonable heights, bathrooms have safety bars and non-skid floors, handrails are present on all stairs and the stairs are well-lit with non-skid treads or carpet.

Preventing falls requires measures to improve muscle strength, balance and vision. Adequate corrective lenses, safe shoes and appropriate clothing (that will not cause falls) are required. If a disability is present, canes or walkers should be strongly recommended.

Lifestyle Measures

Patients with low bone density should perform regular weight-bearing exercise (e.g., walking, jogging, Tai-Chi) and muscle-strengthening exercises (e.g., weight training, yoga). They should be encouraged to stop smoking and avoid secondhand smoke, reduce alcohol intake and adopt fall prevention strategies, as described.

Calcium and Vitamin D Intake

Adequate calcium intake is required throughout life. It is critically important in children (who can build bone stores), in pregnancy (when the fetus can deplete the mother's stores) and during the years around menopause, when bone loss is rapid. Dietary intake of calcium is preferred, with supplements used if needed. Intake in excess of the recommended allowances may contribute to kidney stones, cardiovascular disease and stroke, though the evidence remains controversial.

Vitamin D is required for calcium absorption, and low levels contribute to various health conditions, including autoimmune conditions and cancer. Vitamin D deficiency in children causes rickets, and in adults it causes osteomalacia (softening of the bones). The National Osteoporosis Foundation (NOF) recommends 800 – 1,000 international units (IU) of vitamin D daily for adults age ≥ 50 years. Other organizations recommend 600 international units daily for people up to age 70 years and 800 international units daily for people ≥ 71 years. Many endocrinologists suggest a higher intake of 800 – 2,000 international units daily. The Institute of Medicine considers a safe upper limit to be 4,000 international units daily for adolescents and adults. Higher doses are needed if a vitamin D deficiency is present (see Study Tip Gal below).

Calcium and Vitamin D Supplementation

Calcium obtained through the diet is generally not enough; most women need an additional 600 – 900 mg daily (2 to 3 dairy portions) to reach recommended levels.

Calcium absorption is saturable; doses above 500 – 600 mg of elemental calcium should be divided.

Calcium carbonate has more elemental calcium per unit compared to calcium citrate, but calcium citrate has better absorption when gastric pH is increased (e.g., elderly patients, use of PPIs).

Calcium products are available in many forms (e.g., capsules, tablets, chewables, liquids, granules/powder). There is no known benefit of using more expensive formulations. Constipation is a common side effect.

Vitamin D deficiency can be treated with high doses of vitamin D2 (ergocalciferol) or vitamin D (cholecalciferol), for 8 to 12 weeks, followed by maintenance therapy (1,000 – 2,000 international units daily, or dosed to maintain target levels). See the Renal Disease chapter for information on vitamin D analogs (e.g., calcitriol).

Sunlight exposure is another source of vitamin D3. Patients should obtain any required intake from food and supplements, not sunlight, due to the risk of skin cancer.

CALCIUM AND VITAMIN D

Avoid low bone density later in life by building strong bones in children

CALCIUM

- Recommended daily intake for most adults is 1,000-1,200 mg elemental calcium
  - ❑ Do not exceed 500-600 mg of elemental calcium per dose
- Calcium carbonate (e.g., *Tums, Oscal*)
  - ❑ 40% elemental calcium
  - ❑ Absorption: acid-dependent
  - ❑ Must take with meals
- Calcium citrate (e.g., *Citracal*)
  - ❑ 21% elemental calcium
  - ❑ Absorption: not acid dependent
  - ❑ Can take with or without food

VITAMIN D

- Required for calcium absorption
- Deficiency: serum vitamin D [25(OH)D] < 30 ng/mL
- Treat deficiency with cholecalciferol (vitamin D3) or ergocalciferol (vitamin D2), dosed daily (5,000-7,000 IU) or weekly (50,000 IU)

DRUG	DOSING	SAFETY/SIDE EFFECTS/MONITORING
Calcium Supplements		
Calcium Carbonate (Os-Cal, Tums, Caltrate, Maalox, Oysco, others) 40% elemental calcium	500 mg PO TID with meals (can vary with formulation used) Total daily dose of elemental calcium should be < 2,000 mg (diet and supplements) 1 g calcium carbonate = 400 mg elemental calcium 1 g calcium citrate = 210 mg elemental calcium	**SIDE EFFECTS** Hypercalcemia, constipation, nausea **MONITORING** Ca, PO4, PTH **NOTES** Hypercalcemia is especially problematic with concomitant use of vitamin D (due to increased calcium absorption) Calcium carbonate should be taken with food Calcium citrate can be taken with or without food
Calcium Citrate (Calcitrate, Citracal, others) 21% elemental calcium		

DRUG TREATMENT

There are a number of FDA-approved options for the treatment and prevention of osteoporosis. Medications approved for prevention include bisphosphonates (except IV ibandronate) and the estrogen-based therapies, raloxifene and *Duavee*. Bisphosphonates, denosumab, parathyroid hormone analogs (e.g., teriparatide, abaloparatide) and calcitonin are indicated for treatment. These medications have primarily been studied in postmenopausal women with osteoporosis, and there is limited data in men or in those with glucocorticoid-induced osteoporosis. All prescription medications for low bone density require adequate calcium and vitamin D intake, and levels should be evaluated before initiating therapy. See Study Tip Gal below for important facts about each drug/drug class.

Criteria for Initiating Treatment

Osteoporosis	■ Postmenopausal women or men > 50 years of age with a BMD T-score ≤ -2.5 at the femoral neck, total hip or lumbar spine, OR ■ Presence of a fragility fracture, regardless of BMD
Osteopenia, if high risk	■ Low bone density (T-score between -1 and -2.5) at the femoral neck, total hip or lumbar spine, AND ■ FRAX score indicates a 10-year probability of a major osteoporosis-related fracture ≥ 20% or a 10-year hip fracture probability ≥ 3%

DRUG SUMMARY FOR OSTEOPOROSIS TREATMENT AND PREVENTION

BISPHOSPHONATES

- 1st line for the treatment or prevention of osteoporosis in most patients
- PO administration: requires staying upright for 30 minutes and drinking 6-8 oz of plain water
- Side effects: esophagitis, musculoskeletal symptoms, hypocalcemia
- Rare (but serious) side effects: osteonecrosis of the jaw (ONJ) and atypical femur fractures
- Formulations:
  - Weekly/monthly PO options
  - Quarterly/yearly IV options (if GI side effects or adherence issues with PO options)

DENOSUMAB *(PROLIA)*

- Recommended as alternative to bisphosphonates
- SC administration every 6 months
- Side effect: hypocalcemia

TERIPARATIDE *(FORTEO)*, ABALOPARATIDE *(TYMLOS)*

- Recommended for very high risk patients only (e.g., history of severe vertebral fractures)
- SC administration daily
- Side effect: hypercalcemia

RALOXIFENE *(EVISTA)*, BAZEDOXIFENE/ ESTROGENS *(DUAVEE)*

- Recommended as alternative to bisphosphonates in high risk patients of vertebral fractures
- Increase risk for VTE and stroke
- Raloxifene for patients with low-risk of VTE or high-risk of breast cancer
  - Side effect: vasomotor symptoms
- Bazedoxifene/estrogens in women with intact uterus
  - Also used as treatment for vasomotor symptoms
  - Side effects: increases the risk of breast cancer

LAST LINE OR NOT RECOMMENDED

- Estrogen (with or without progestin) for prevention only in postmenopausal women with vasomotor symptoms; use lowest possible dose for shortest duration of time
- Calcitonin for treatment only if other options are not suitable (less effective and has a risk for cancer with long term use)

Bisphosphonates

Bisphosphonates increase bone density by inhibiting osteoclast activity and bone resorption. They reduce both vertebral and hip fracture risk (except ibandronate which has only been shown to reduce vertebral fractures). Bisphosphonates are first-line for most patients for the prevention or treatment of osteoporosis. They are used to treat Paget's disease, glucocorticoid-induced osteoporosis (in men and women taking ≥ 7.5 mg daily of prednisone or prednisone equivalent) and hypercalcemia of malignancy.

DRUG	DOSING	SAFETY/SIDE EFFECTS/MONITORING
Oral Bisphosphonates		
Alendronate ***(Fosamax,*** *Binosto)* Tablet, oral solution, effervescent tablet *(Binosto)* + cholecalciferol *(Fosamax Plus D)* Tablet	**Prevention (postmenopausal women)** 5 mg PO daily or 35 mg PO weekly **Treatment (postmenopausal women and men)** 10 mg PO daily or 70 mg PO weekly *Fosamax Plus D:* 70 mg/ 2,800 IU or 70 mg/5,600 IU PO weekly **Glucocorticoid-Induced Osteoporosis** 5 mg PO daily Postmenopausal women not on estrogen: 10 mg PO daily	**CONTRAINDICATIONS** Inability to stand or sit upright for at least 30 minutes (60 minutes with once-monthly *Boniva*); abnormalities of the esophagus (e.g., esophageal stricture, achalasia); difficulty swallowing or at high risk for aspiration; hypocalcemia **WARNINGS** Osteonecrosis of the jaw [(ONJ) exposed jaw bone that is difficult to heal] – risk ↑ with invasive dental procedures, poor dental hygiene, cancer diagnosis, use of chemotherapy or corticosteroids and duration of exposure Atypical femur fractures; bone, joint or muscle pain (may be severe) Esophagitis, esophageal ulcers, erosions, stricture or perforation (rare) – follow administration instructions (see Patient Counseling section) Hypocalcemia must be corrected prior to use Renal impairment – not recommended if: CrCl < 35 mL/min: alendronate CrCl < 30 mL/min: ibandronate, risedronate **SIDE EFFECTS** Hypocalcemia, hypophosphatemia (mild, transient), abdominal pain, dyspepsia, N/V, dysphagia, heartburn, musculoskeletal pain Risedronate: headache, hypertension, skin rash, UTI, infection **NOTES** Check calcium and vitamin D levels prior to initiating treatment Due to the risk of jaw decay/necrosis, dental work should be done prior to starting treatment Aspirin or NSAIDs can worsen GI irritation – use with caution Separate oral bisphosphonates from calcium, antacids, iron and magnesium supplements by at least 2 hours Take oral bisphosphonates at least 30 minutes from food and most beverages (except water) *Binosto* (effervescent alendronate tablet) contains 650 mg Na (use with caution in Na restricted patients, such as those with heart failure, hypertension or cirrhosis) *Atelvia* is a delayed release form that requires an acidic gut for absorption; H2RAs and PPIs should be avoided completely
Risedronate *(Actonel, Atelvia)* Tablet, delayed-release tablet *(Atelvia)*	**Prevention and Treatment (postmenopausal women)** 5 mg PO daily, 35 mg PO weekly, 75 mg PO on two consecutive days/month or 150 mg PO monthly **Treatment (males)** 35 mg PO weekly **Glucocorticoid-Induced Osteoporosis** 5 mg PO daily	
Ibandronate *(Boniva)* Tablet	**Prevention and Treatment (postmenopausal women)** PO: 150 mg monthly (on the same date every month)	

DRUG	DOSING	SAFETY/SIDE EFFECTS/MONITORING
Injectable Bisphosphonates		
Ibandronate *(Boniva)* Injection	**Treatment (postmenopausal women)** 3 mg IV every 3 months Administer over 15-30 seconds	**CONTRAINDICATIONS** Hypocalcemia Zoledronic acid: CrCl < 35 mL/minute or evidence of acute renal impairment **WARNINGS** Same as oral bisphosphonates (except no GI problems) plus: Renal impairment (including injury and death due to renal failure); monitor serum creatinine before each dose; use with caution in dehydrated patients, in patients with comorbid conditions or those taking medications that can cause renal impairment Ibandronate: do not use if CrCl < 30 mL/min Zoledronic acid: use caution in patients with aspirin-sensitive asthma (can cause bronchoconstriction) **SIDE EFFECTS** Same as oral bisphosphonates (except no esophageal problems) plus: Acute phase reaction (flu-like symptoms such as fever, achiness, runny nose, headache) Zoledronic acid: edema, hypotension, fatigue, dehydration, ↓ PO4, K and Mg **NOTES** Injectable bisphosphonates are preferred if esophagitis is present, due to the risk for esophageal cancer
Zoledronic Acid *(Reclast)* ***Zometa**** – for hypercalcemia of malignancy	**Prevention (postmenopausal women)** 5 mg IV every 2 years **Treatment (postmenopausal women and men)** 5 mg IV once yearly **Glucocorticoid-Induced Osteoporosis** 5 mg IV once yearly Administer over ≥ 15 minutes	

**Brand name discontinued but name still used in practice*

Estrogen Agonist/Antagonist Containing Products

Raloxifene is an estrogen agonist/antagonist [a selective estrogen receptor modulator (SERM)], that ↓ bone resorption. Conjugated estrogens/bazedoxifene *(Duavee)* is an equine (horse) estrogen/SERM combination indicated for osteoporosis prevention in postmenopausal women with a uterus.

DRUG	DOSING	SAFETY/SIDE EFFECTS/MONITORING
Raloxifene *(Evista)*	**Prevention and Treatment (postmenopausal women)** 60 mg PO daily	**BOXED WARNINGS** ↑ risk of VTE (DVT, PE); ↑ risk of death due to stroke in women at risk for coronary events or with CAD **CONTRAINDICATIONS** VTE, pregnancy **SIDE EFFECTS** Hot flashes, peripheral edema, arthralgia, leg cramps/muscle spasms, flu symptoms, infection **NOTES** Separate raloxifene and levothyroxine by several hours Discontinue 72 hours prior to and during prolonged immobilization
Conjugated Estrogens/ Bazedoxifene *(Duavee)*	**Prevention (postmenopausal women with a uterus)** 1 tablet (0.45/20 mg) PO daily Other indications: treatment of moderate-severe vasomotor symptoms associated with menopause (same dose)	**BOXED WARNINGS** Endometrial cancer (due to unopposed estrogen use in women with a uterus); dementia (women ≥ 65 years); ↑ risk of VTE and stroke in postmenopausal women 50-79 years of age (do not use to prevent cardiovascular disease); do not use with additional estrogens **CONTRAINDICATIONS** Breast cancer (any history); undiagnosed uterine bleeding; active VTE, arterial thromboembolic disease, or known protein C, S or antithrombin deficiency; hepatic impairment; pregnancy **WARNINGS** ↑ risk of breast cancer (from use of estrogen alone) and ovarian cancer, ↑ risk of retinal vascular thrombosis, lipid effects (↑ HDL, ↑ TG, ↓ LDL) **SIDE EFFECTS** Nausea, diarrhea, dyspepsia, abdominal pain, muscle spasms **NOTES** Not recommended for women > 75 years of age Use estrogen-containing products for the shortest duration possible

Calcitonin

Calcitonin inhibits bone resorption by osteoclasts. It is less effective than other agents for the treatment of osteoporosis and, with long term use, the risk of cancer is increased. It is rarely used for this indication.

DRUG	DOSING	SAFETY/SIDE EFFECTS/MONITORING
Calcitonin (*Miacalcin*) Nasal spray, injection	**Treatment (women > 5 years postmenopause)** Nasal spray: 1 spray (200 units) in one nostril daily (alternate nostril daily) SC or IM: 100 units daily	**CONTRAINDICATION** Allergy to calcitonin-salmon **WARNINGS** Hypocalcemia (associated with tetany and seizures); ↑ risk of malignancy with long-term use; hypersensitivity reactions to salmon-derived product (e.g., bronchospasm, anaphylaxis, swelling of the tongue or throat); antibody formation Nasal spray: nasal reactions (e.g., ulceration, epistaxis, rhinitis) – nasal exams are recommended **SIDE EFFECTS** Back pain, myalgia, nausea, dizziness Injection: flushing, injection site reactions **NOTES** Keep the injection and unopened nasal spray bottles refrigerated Can be used in the management of hypercalcemia of malignancy (see the Oncology I chapter)

Parathyroid Hormone 1-34

Teriparatide and abaloparatide are analogs of human parathyroid hormone, which stimulates osteoblast activity and increases bone formation. They are used for the treatment of osteoporosis when there is a very high risk of fracture (e.g., previous history of vertebral fracture). Due to safety issues associated with long-term use, treatment duration is restricted to two years or less (see the Boxed Warning).

DRUG	DOSING	SAFETY/SIDE EFFECTS/MONITORING
Teriparatide (*Forteo*) Injection (prefilled multi-dose pen; needles not included)	**Treatment (postmenopausal women and men)** 20 mcg SC daily **Glucocorticoid-Induced Osteoporosis** 20 mcg SC daily	**BOXED WARNING** Osteosarcoma (bone cancer) in rat studies – risk dependent on dose and duration of treatment **WARNINGS** Hypercalcemia; orthostatic hypotension; do not use in patients with bone malignancy or metabolic bone diseases; use cautiously in patients with urolithiasis (urinary stones) **SIDE EFFECTS** Arthralgias, leg cramps, pain, nausea, orthostasis/dizziness *Tymlos:* ↑ uric acid, antibody development, erythema at injection site (58%) **NOTES** Keep refrigerated *Forteo* requires protection from light
Abaloparatide (*Tymlos*) Injection (pre-filled multi-dose pen; needles not included)	**Treatment (postmenopausal women)** 80 mcg SC daily	

Receptor Activator of Nuclear Factor kappa-B Ligand (RANKL) Inhibitor

Denosumab is a monoclonal antibody that binds to RANKL and blocks its interaction with RANK (a receptor on osteoclasts) to prevent osteoclast formation; this leads to ↓ bone resorption and ↑ bone mass. It is used for the treatment of osteoporosis when there is a high risk of fracture.

DRUG	DOSING	SAFETY/SIDE EFFECTS/MONITORING
Denosumab *(Prolia)* Injection ***Xgeva*** – hypercalcemia of malignancy, bone cell tumor, prevention of bone metastasis Other indications: treatment of bone loss in men receiving androgen deprivation therapy for prostate cancer and women receiving aromatase inhibitor therapy for breast cancer	**Treatment (postmenopausal women and men)** 60 mg SC every 6 months Must be administered by a healthcare professional	**CONTRAINDICATIONS** Hypocalcemia (must be corrected prior to using); pregnancy **WARNINGS** Osteonecrosis of the jaw (ONJ) – risk ↑ with invasive dental procedures, poor dental hygiene, cancer diagnosis, use of chemotherapy or corticosteroids, and duration of exposure Atypical femur fractures; bone, joint or muscle pain (may be severe) Hypocalcemia – use caution in predisposed patients (e.g., hypoparathyroidism, thyroid surgery, malabsorption syndromes, CrCl < 30 mL/min) Serious infections (e.g., skin, abdomen, urinary tract), dermatologic reactions (e.g., dermatitis, eczema, rash) **SIDE EFFECTS** Hypertension, fatigue, edema, dyspnea, headache, N/V/D, ↓ PO_4 **NOTES** If discontinued, bone loss can be rapid; consider alternative agents to maintain BMD

Romosuzumab

Romosozumab is a new FDA-approved drug for osteoporosis treatment in postmenopausal females with either a history of an osteoporotic fracture or multiple risk factors. It is recommended as an alternative to other treatments. It inhibits sclerostin, a protein that blocks bone formation.

DRUG	DOSING	SAFETY/SIDE EFFECTS/MONITORING
Romosozumab *(Evenity)* Injection	**Treatment** 210 mg SC (administered in two separate injections) monthly for up to 12 months	**CONTRAINDICATION** Hypocalcemia **WARNINGS** ↑ risk of heart attack, stroke and CVD death **SIDE EFFECTS** Arthralgia, headache and injection site reactions **NOTES** Keep the injection refrigerated and then allow to come to room temperature (at least 30 minutes) before administration Duration of therapy is limited to 12 monthly doses

PATIENT COUNSELING

All Osteoporosis Medications

- These medications do not work well if you are not taking enough calcium and vitamin D. Some products used to treat or prevent osteoporosis contain calcium or vitamin D. Discuss with your healthcare provider to see if you need to use calcium or vitamin D supplements.
- If you are using a proton pump inhibitor (e.g., *Prilosec, Prevacid)* for heartburn, discuss with your healthcare provider. These drugs may decrease the amount of calcium that is able to get into your body which can increase your fracture risk. You may need to use calcium citrate as your calcium supplement.
- Your bone and muscle strength will improve faster if you exercise. Your healthcare provider should discuss safe and healthy ways to exercise with you.

Bisphosphonates

- Take this medication first thing in the morning, before you eat or drink anything. Swallow the whole pill (do not crush or chew) with 6 – 8 oz (1 cup) of plain water. If using a weekly or monthly product, you must take it on the same day each week or month; choose a day that is easy to remember (e.g., Sunday, bridge day, book club day).
- You must take this medication while you are sitting up or standing, and then stay upright for at least 30 minutes afterwards (60 minutes with monthly *Boniva*). During this time, you cannot eat or drink anything else except more plain water. You cannot take any other medications or vitamins. You must not lie down again until after the first food of the day.
- For *Binosto*, dissolve one tablet in 4 oz (1/2 cup) of room temperature plain water. Wait five minutes to allow the tablet to dissolve, then stir for 10 seconds before drinking.
- If using an oral solution, drink at least 2 oz (1/4 cup) of plain water after taking the medication.
- *Atelvia*: this is a long-acting form of risedronate. Take the medication after breakfast with 4 oz (1/2 cup) of plain water. Sit or stand upright for at least 30 minutes after taking. Do not use acid suppressing "heartburn" therapy with this medication.
- Common side effects of this medication include GI upset (e.g., heartburn, upset stomach, pain in the stomach area), and pain in the bones, joints or muscles.
- Stop taking this medication if you develop difficult or painful swallowing, have chest pain, have very bad heartburn that does not go away or have severe pain in the bones, joints or muscles.
- Rarely, some patients have developed serious jaw-bone problems from taking this medication, which may include infection and slower healing after teeth are pulled. Tell your healthcare providers, including your dentist, right away if you have these symptoms. If you are scheduled to have dental work, you should have it done before starting the medication.
- Rarely, this medication can cause fractures in the thigh bone. Tell your healthcare provider right away if you develop thigh, hip or groin pain while on this medication.
- Do not take calcium, iron, magnesium, antacids or multivitamin supplements until later in the day.
- Missed doses:
  - Daily dosing schedule: if you miss a dose, skip that dose. Take the next dose at the regularly scheduled time.
  - Weekly dosing schedule: if you miss a dose, take it the morning after you remember (but do not take two doses on the same day).
  - Monthly dosing schedule: if you miss a dose, take it the morning after you remember, except if it is less than one week to the next dose, then skip it (do not take two doses in the same week).

Raloxifene

- Take with or without food.
- This medication can cause dangerous blood clots. If any of the following symptoms occur, it could be due to a blood clot and you should get medical treatment quickly: sudden leg pain, chest pain, shortness of breath, vision changes, an inability to speak or slurred speech or loss of movement on any side of your body.
- This medication can cause hot flashes, leg cramps, flu-like symptoms, joint pain, sweating and swelling in the feet, ankles or legs. If these occur and bother you, discuss with your healthcare provider.
- Discontinue this medication at least 72 hours prior to and during prolonged immobilization, such as after a surgery or with prolonged bed rest.

Teriparatide and Abaloparatide

- This medication helps to form new bone and increase bone strength. When tested in animals, it caused a rare form of bone cancer. It is not known if people who take the medication have the same risk. Inform your healthcare provider right away if you develop bone or joint pain.
- You may feel dizzy or lightheaded after the first few doses. This usually happens within four hours of taking the medication and goes away within a few hours. For the first few doses, inject this medication in a place where you can sit or lie down right away if these symptoms occur.

HORMONE THERAPY: HEALTH RISKS AND APPROPRIATE USE

Estrogen

- Estrogen is the most effective treatment for vasomotor symptoms.
- In women with a uterus, estrogen should be used in combination with a form of progesterone (e.g., a progestin). This is because "unopposed estrogen" increases the risk of endometrial cancer.
- Estrogens have significant safety risks (see the drug table on the following page), including boxed warnings for venous thromboembolism (VTE), stroke, dementia and breast cancer. These are of biggest concern in elderly patients.

Progestin

- A progestin (e.g., norethindrone, levonorgestrel, drospirenone) can be given as part of a combination pill (with estrogen) or as a separate tablet, most commonly medroxyprogesterone (MPA).
- Progestins can cause mood disturbances, which some women find hard to tolerate; if taken intermittently (e.g., for two weeks per month as with *Premphase*), spotting can occur which can be bothersome.
- Micronized progrestins (e.g., *Prometrium*) are considered to be safer than synthetic progestins (e.g., medroxyprogesterone).

CRITERIA FOR USE OF HORMONE THERAPY

- Healthy symptomatic women who are within 10 years of menopause, aged 60 years or younger and who have no contraindications to use.
- Extending treatment beyond age 60 years may be acceptable (e.g., patient has osteoporosis) if the lowest possible dose is used and the woman is advised of the safety risks.
- Consider quality-of-life priorities and personal risk factors (e.g., age, time since menopause, risk of blood clots, heart disease, stroke and breast cancer) before use. Patients with risk factors should use nonhormonal treatments (SSRIs, SNRIs, gabapentin or pregabalin). See the section on Other Products for Menopause.

- The medication comes in a prefilled injection pen that provides a one month supply. Each injection provides the set dose. Do not transfer the medication from the delivery device to another syringe.
- Using a new needle, inject the medication once daily in your <u>abdomen</u> (lower stomach area); *Forteo* can be injected into the thigh or abdomen. The injection sites must be rotated.
- After injecting, discard the needle in a puncture-resistant container with a tight-fitting lid (see the Medication Safety & Quality Improvement chapter). The pen should be re-capped after each use and kept in the <u>refrigerator</u>.
- You can inject at any time of the day, but pick the same time each day. If you forget, or cannot take the medication at your usual time, take it as soon as you can on that day. Do not take more than one injection in the same day.
- The pen should be <u>discarded</u> (28 days for *Forteo,* 30 days for *Tymlos)* even if some medication remains. Mark the date in the user manual when the pen is started and the date (28 or 30 days later) when the pen should be thrown away.
- <u>Do not use for more than two years</u>.

Calcitonin Nasal Spray

- Keep unused bottles in the refrigerator; once in use, the bottle may be kept at room temperature for 30 days.
- When using a new bottle, allow it to reach room temperature prior to use. Before you take the first dose, hold the bottle upright and press the two white side arms toward the bottle to release at least five sprays and until a full spray is produced (this is called "<u>priming the pump</u>"). Once the pump is primed, it does not have to be primed again if the bottle is stored in an upright position.
- To use, remove the protective cap, keep the head upright, and insert the tip of the nozzle into a nostril. Press down firmly on the pump to deliver the medication. Use the other nostril the next day.
- After 30 doses, the pump may not deliver the correct amount of medication with each spray and should be discarded.
- Call 911 if you have an allergic reaction (e.g., swelling of your face or throat, or trouble breathing).
- Some nose irritation may occur. Discuss with your healthcare provider if you get nasal crusting, dryness, redness, swelling, nose sores (ulcers) or nose bleeds.

MENOPAUSE

BACKGROUND

Menopause means that the last menstrual period was over 12 months ago. Menopause usually occurs between the ages of 40 and 58 years (the average age is 52 years). A decrease in estrogen and progesterone causes an increase in follicle stimulating hormone (FSH), resulting in vasomotor symptoms (recurrent transient episodes of flushing and sensation of heat in the upper body and face, sometimes followed by chills). Many women experience vasomotor symptoms during the menopause transition period (known as perimenopause) as estrogen production by the ovaries declines. These are often described as hot flashes and night sweats (hot flashes that occur during sleep). Sleep can be disturbed, and mood changes may be present. Due to a decline in estrogen in the vaginal mucosa, vaginal dryness, burning and painful intercourse can occur.

Some women remain largely asymptomatic during menopause, while others suffer from severe symptoms that significantly impact their quality of life. Vasomotor symptoms can last up to seven years. Women who have both of their ovaries removed, or receive chemotherapy or radiation for cancer, will experience induced menopause; the symptoms are similar but often more acute initially due to a sudden, rather than a gradual, decline in estrogen.

ESTROGEN-PROGESTIN PRODUCTS

The most effective treatment for vasomotor symptoms is systemic hormone therapy with estrogen, which causes a decrease in luteinizing hormone (LH) and more stable temperature control. Estrogen improves bone density as well, but it has a number of safety issues that must be considered when evaluating a patient for treatment; for this reason, the North American Menopause Society (NAMS) and the American Association of Clinical Endocrinologists (AACE) provide criteria for use to control vasomotor symptoms. See Study Tip Gal on the previous page for useful information on the health risks associated with hormone therapy and appropriate use.

Formulation Considerations

Transdermal, local (topical) and low-dose oral estrogen therapies have been associated with lower risks of venous thromboembolism (VTE) and stroke than standard doses of oral estrogen. Estrogen is generally well tolerated, but can cause nausea, dizziness, headaches, mood changes, vaginal bleeding, bloating and breast tenderness/fullness. Topical formulations (e.g., patch, gel, emulsion) bypass first pass metabolism, and lower doses can be used. Topical formulations may decrease the systemic estrogen exposure, causing less side effects.

Local estrogen products are preferred for patients who have vaginal symptoms only (vaginal dryness and/or painful intercourse). Any of the vaginal products included in this chapter (creams, vaginal tablets, vaginal rings) or OTC lubricants can be helpful. Common OTC lubricants and moisturizers include *Replens* and *Luvena*. A lubricant marketed specifically for dyspareunia (dry, painful intercourse) is *Astroglide*. Oil-based lubricants should not be used with condoms as they can cause the condom to tear. *Astroglide* or silicone-based lubricants are safe to recommend with condoms.

Common Hormone Therapy Products

Estradiol-containing products and conjugated estrogens are used primarily for vasomotor symptoms, vaginal atrophy and osteoporosis prevention. Oral contraceptives, used for contraception, contain ethinyl estradiol (discussed in the Contraception & Infertility chapter).

COMPONENTS	FORMULATION	SAFETY/SIDE EFFECTS/MONITORING
Topical Hormone Therapies		
17-Beta-Estradiol	Vaginal cream ***(Estrace)*** Vaginal ring ***(Estring)*** Vaginal tablet ***(Vagifem)*** Vaginal insert *(Imvexxy)*	**NOTES** Topical (vaginal) hormone therapies may have lower systemic absorption. Some absorption will occur and the safety issues discussed below should be considered
Conjugated Equine Estrogens	Vaginal cream ***(Premarin)*:** 0.625 mg/gram	
Systemic Hormone Therapies		
Estradiol	Topical gel *(Elestrin)* Transdermal patch ***(Alora, Climara, Vivelle-Dot,*** *Menostar, Minivelle)* Vaginal ring *(Femring)*	**BOXED WARNINGS** Endometrial cancer (if estrogen used without progestin in a women with a uterus); dementia (women ≥ 65 years); ↑ risk of VTE and stroke in postmenopausal women 50-79 years of age (do not use to prevent cardiovascular disease); breast cancer; use the lowest effective dose for the shortest duration possible *Evamist:* secondary exposure can cause breast budding and breast masses in prepubertal females, and gynecomastia and breast masses in prepubertal males; keep children away from spray **CONTRAINDICATIONS** Estrogen-containing products: breast cancer (any history); undiagnosed uterine bleeding; active VTE, arterial thromboembolic disease, or known protein C, S or antithrombin deficiency; hepatic impairment; pregnancy **WARNINGS** ↑ risk of breast cancer (from use of estrogen alone) and ovarian cancer, ↑ risk of retinal vascular thrombosis, lipid effects (↑ HDL, ↑ TG, ↓ LDL) **SIDE EFFECTS** Edema, hypertension, headache, weight gain, depression, nausea, abdominal pain Patch: redness/irritation of the skin Patch formulations may need to be removed prior to an MRI (see Learning Drug Formulations chapter) *CombiPatch:* store in the refrigerator prior to dispensing; once dispensed, it can be kept at room temperature for up to 6 months *Vivelle-Dot, Alora,* and *Minivelle* patches are applied twice weekly; *Climara* and *Menostar* patches are once weekly Gels and *Evamist* spray are flammable Micronized progestin (in combination with estrogen) may have a lower risk of breast cancer and cardiovascular events than synthetic progestin, medroxyprogesterone (in combination with estrogen)
17-Beta-Estradiol	Oral tablet, micronized *(Estrace)* Topical gel *(Divigel, Estrogel)* Topical spray *(Evamist)*	
Estradiol and Levonorgestrel	Transdermal patch *(ClimaraPro)* "Pro" in the name indicates a progestin	
Estradiol and Norethindrone	Transdermal patch *(CombiPatch)* Oral tablet *(Activella, Amabelz, Mimvey, Mimvey Lo)*	
Estradiol and Norgestimate	Oral tablet *(Prefest)*: cyclic treatment – estradiol x 3 days, estradiol + norgestimate x 3 days, then repeat	
Estradiol and Drospirenone	Oral tablet *(Angeliq)*	
Conjugated Equine Estrogens	Oral tablet ***(Premarin)*:** 0.3, 0.45, 0.625, 0.9, 1.25 mg Injection ***(Premarin)***	
Conjugated Equine Estrogens and Medroxyprogesterone (MPA)	Oral tablet *(Prempro)***:** 0.3/1.5, 0.45/1.5, 0.625/2.5, 0.625/0.5 mg Oral tablet *(Premphase)***:** phasic dosing – 0.625 mg on days 1-14, then 0.625/5 mg on days 15-28	
Medroxyprogesterone *Depo-Provera* – SC or IM for contraception	Oral tablets ***(Provera)*:** 2.5, 5, 10 mg	
Micronized progesterone	Oral tablet ***(Prometrium)***	
Conjugated Estrogens/Bazedoxifene	Oral tablet *(Duavee)*	

"Bioidentical" Nomenclature

Some women will prefer to use bioidentical hormones to treat symptoms, including commercially available products approved by the FDA or compounded preparations. *Bijuva* is an oral capsule and the first FDA-approved bioidentical estradiol and progesterone combination for treatment of moderate-severe hot flashes. The term "bioidentical" has different meanings; some use it to refer to hormones that have an identical structure to those found in the female body, while others use it to refer to plant-derived hormones that are compounded.

Some women and healthcare professionals believe that bioidentical hormone therapy is safer, but there are no well-designed studies to confirm risk or benefit and compounded preparations are not regulated by the FDA. Compounded products allow for patient specific formulations when the patient's needs are not met by the FDA-approved commercially available products. The AACE does not recommend bioidentical hormones to treat menopausal symptoms.

Estrogen-Progestin Patient Counseling

- Estrogen products help control menopausal symptoms but they have risks and should not be continued indefinitely. The goal is to use the lowest dose possible for the shortest period of time. When you are ready to stop treatment, discuss the best way to do so with your healthcare provider.
- Women with a uterus should not take estrogen alone as it increases the risk of cancer of the uterus.
- Report any unusual vaginal bleeding right away while you are taking estrogen. Vaginal bleeding after menopause may be a warning sign of cancer of the uterus and your healthcare provider will need to evaluate any unusual vaginal bleeding promptly.
- Using estrogens may increase your risk for heart attacks, strokes, blood clots, breast cancer and dementia. You should talk with your healthcare provider regularly about whether you still need treatment. Do not use hormone therapy to prevent heart disease, heart attacks or strokes.
- Estrogen can help keep your bones healthy. If you are using estrogen for this reason, ask your healthcare provider for help deciding if you need to take calcium and vitamin D, which are also important for healthy bones.
- Topical gels: these are applied once daily. *Divigel* should be applied to the right or left upper thigh (alternate sides daily); *Elestrin* should be applied to the upper arm and shoulder; *EstroGel* should be applied to the entire arm from wrist to shoulder. It is important that you wash your hands after applying estrogen gels.
- *Evamist* spray: each morning, spray on the inside of the forearm between the elbow and the wrist.
- If you are in the transition period of menopause (called perimenopause), you may be at risk of accidental pregnancy as your menstrual cycle has become irregular; speak with you healthcare provider about effective birth control options.

Patch Application

- Mark the schedule you plan to follow on the inner flap of your medication package, or on your calendar. If you forget to change your patch on the correct date, apply a new one as soon as you remember.

- Apply the patch to the lower abdomen, below the waistline (avoid the waistline, since clothing may cause the patch to rub off). Make sure the skin is clean, dry and free of powder, oil or lotion. Do not apply the patch to cut or irritated skin.
- Do not apply the patch to the breasts.
- If any adhesive residue remains on your skin after removing the patch, allow the area to dry for 15 minutes. Then, gently rub the area with oil or lotion to remove the adhesive from your skin.

OTHER PRODUCTS FOR MENOPAUSE

Natural Products

Natural products used for vasomotor symptoms include black cohosh, evening primrose oil, red clover, soy, flaxseed, dong quai, St. John's wort and chasteberry. The mild "plant estrogens" found in soy and red clover are called phytoestrogens; phyto means plant. These natural products may help with mild symptoms, but do not usually provide the same benefit seen with estrogens.

SSRIs and Other Drugs

Paroxetine *(Brisdelle)* is a non-hormonal FDA-approved treatment for moderate-severe vasomotor symptoms associated with menopause. The dose of paroxetine used is lower than the recommended dose for depression. Women who use *Brisdelle* should not use tamoxifen or warfarin. Paroxetine is a CYP450 2D6 inhibitor, and it will block the effectiveness of tamoxifen. SSRIs can increase the risk of bleeding in patients using warfarin. SNRIs (e.g., venlafaxine, desvenlafaxine), clonidine and gabapentin or pregabalin have shown effectiveness for treating vasomotor symptoms related to menopause, but they are not FDA-approved for this indication.

Ospemifene

Ospemifene *(Osphena)*, is an oral estrogen agonist/antagonist indicated for dyspareunia (painful intercourse) and moderate-severe vaginal dryness, which are symptoms of vulvar and vaginal atrophy due to menopause. It has risks associated with use and is not indicated for mild symptoms (topical vaginal products are safer for this purpose). Ospemifene should be used short-term for moderate-to-severe symptoms. *Intrarosa* (prasterone), a vaginally inserted steroid, is another treatment for moderate-severe dyspareunia.

SSRIs and Ospemifene

DRUG	DOSING	SAFETY/SIDE EFFECTS/MONITORING
Paroxetine (*Brisdelle*) *Paxil, Paxil CR, Pexeva* – for depression, panic disorder	7.5 mg PO QHS	**BOXED WARNING** Suicide risk (same as with other SSRIs – see the Depression chapter) **CONTRAINDICATIONS/WARNINGS** Same as with other SSRIs (see the Depression chapter) **SIDE EFFECTS** Same sexual side effects as other SSRIs (see the Depression chapter); *Brisdelle* trials showed > 10% incidence of sedation, insomnia, restlessness, tremor, dizziness/weakness, nausea, dry mouth, constipation, diaphoresis **NOTES** Lag time to effect (~4 weeks) Do not use with warfarin (↑ bleeding risk) or tamoxifen (↓ tamoxifen efficacy)
Ospemifene (*Osphena*)	60 mg PO daily Take with food	**BOXED WARNINGS/CONTRAINDICATIONS** Same as for other estrogen-containing products (see the Hormone Therapy table) **WARNING** Should not be used in women with severe hepatic impairment **SIDE EFFECTS** Hot flashes, vaginal discharge, hyperhidrosis, muscle spasms

HYPOGONADISM IN MALES

Hypogonadism in older males can be due to a normal age related decline in testosterone, or it can be secondary to a medical condition, surgical procedure or medications that lowers testosterone. Medications that can lower testosterone include opioids (especially methadone when used for opioid dependence), chemotherapy drugs used for prostate cancer (see the Oncology II chapter), cimetidine and spironolactone.

TESTOSTERONE USE

The increased use of testosterone in recent years is largely due to older males requesting treatment for "Low T" symptoms, to increase sexual interest (libido), sexual performance, muscle mass, bone density, energy, memory and concentration. The use of testosterone replacement for conditions other than the accepted medical uses is controversial, and a clear benefit of improved sexual function has not been established. The FDA has released a warning about the cardiovascular risks associated with testosterone use, and they recommend treatment only in men with low testosterone levels caused by certain medical conditions and confirmed by laboratory tests.

There have been reports of increased clotting risk in men using testosterone therapy; most men who experienced clotting may have had a higher risk at baseline and, at present, the link to testosterone use is unclear. Testosterone increases hematocrit, which can cause polycythemia and an increase in clotting risk.

Testosterone can cause noncancerous prostate growth and use is restricted in men with severe BPH. If dispensing a 5-alpha-reductase inhibitor for BPH (e.g., finasteride) that blocks the conversion of testosterone to the active form, it would not make sense to dispense another drug that provides testosterone directly. Common side effects of testosterone include increased male-pattern baldness, acne and gynecomastia.

Class wide labeling for all prescription testosterone and anabolic androgenic steroids (AAS) includes the potential for abuse and serious adverse events. When used at higher than prescribed doses, serious adverse outcomes can occur, including heart attack, heart failure, stroke, depression, hostility, aggression, liver toxicity and male infertility. Individuals abusing high doses of testosterone can have withdrawal symptoms, such as depression, fatigue, irritability, loss of appetite, decreased libido and insomnia.

Testosterone Formulations

Testosterone comes in many formulations including parenteral (IM or SC) injections, topical gels and solutions, buccal tablets and transdermal patches. The injectable forms are painful and require medical visits; patients may report that they feel symptomatic when it is getting close to the time for the next dose. The injections may increase the hematocrit more than topical formulations. *Testopel* is a small SC pellet. Testosterone undecanoate (*Jatenzo*) is a new oral formulation FDA-approved for hypogonadism only due to medical conditions, not age-related.

The gel formulations (*AndroGel* and other topical gels) are popular formulations and are relatively well-tolerated. *AndroGel* is applied to the upper body. Men who use the gel need to let it dry prior to dressing and be careful not to let others touch the application area, as this increases the risk of drug transfer. If drug transfers to a female or male child, it can cause "early virilization" and, depending on the dose received, the child could have enlarged genital organs, aggressive behavior and premature pubic hair growth. The risk of early virilization is a boxed warning and requires counseling (see the Testosterone Patient Counseling section). There are new topical formulations that reduce accidental exposure risk (e.g., *Fortesta* and *Natesto*).

Testosterone Products: C-III

TESTOSTERONE	COUNSELING
Topical Gels and Solutions	
Testosterone gel [*AndroGel* (1%, 1.62%), *AndroGel Pump* (1.62%)]	*AndroGel* 1% is applied daily to the upper arms, shoulders, and/or abdomen; the 1.62% strength should only be applied to the upper arms or shoulders (not the abdomen)
Testosterone gel 1% (*Vogelxo, Vogelxo Pump*)	Applied to upper arms and shoulders daily
Testosterone gel 1% (*Testim*)	Applied to arms and shoulders daily
Testosterone gel 2% (*Fortesta*)	Applied to front and inner thighs daily
Testosterone solution	Applied to armpits daily
Testosterone nasal gel (*Natesto*)	1 spray per nostril TID
Alternative Formulations	
Transdermal patch (*Androderm*)	2 mg, 4 mg Apply to the back, abdomen, thighs or upper arms each night
Buccal tabs (*Striant*)	30 mg to the gum region BID
Implantable pellets (*Testopel*)	SC every 3-6 months
Injections:	
Testosterone cypionate (*Depo-Testosterone*)	IM every 4 weeks (2 doses), then every 10 weeks
Testosterone undecanoate (*Aveed*)	IM every 2-4 weeks
Testosterone enanthate	IM every 2-4 weeks
Testosterone enanthate (*Xyosted*)	SC auto-injector every week
Testosterone ointment/ cream (*First-Testosterone*)	Apply as directed

SAFETY/SIDE EFFECTS/MONITORING

BOXED WARNINGS

Secondary exposure to testosterone in children can occur resulting in virilization; children should avoid contact with any unwashed or unclothed application sites in men using testosterone gel

Aveed: pulmonary oil microembolism (POME) reactions (cough, dyspnea, throat tightening, anaphylaxis) – can be life-threatening; requires observation in a healthcare setting for 30 minutes after each injection

CONTRAINDICATIONS

Breast cancer, prostate cancer, pregnancy, breast-feeding women

Aveed: allergy to castor oil or benzyl benzoate

Depo-Testosterone: serious cardiac, hepatic or renal disease

WARNINGS

↑ risk of breast cancer, prostate cancer, cardiovascular events, VTE, dyslipidemia, gynecomastia, hepatic impairment, polycythemia, priapism; may worsen BPH (↑ PSA)

SIDE EFFECTS

↑ appetite, ↑ SCr, sensitive nipples, acne, edema, hepatotoxicity, reduced sperm count, sleep apnea

Additional Issues By Formulation Type

Androderm: skin irritation

Striant: buccal irritation

Natesto: nasal irritation

Injections: pain at the site of injection

MONITORING

Testosterone levels, PSA, liver function, cholesterol, some products recommend checking hematocrit

NOTES

Gels: apply at the same time each morning; they are flammable until dry

Androderm: do not use two 2 mg patches for a 4 mg dose; after removal, treat any irritation with OTC hydrocortisone; remove the patch before an MRI

Xyosted contains sesame oil

TESTOSTERONE PATIENT COUNSELING

Testosterone Gels

- This medication should not be used by women or children. To avoid transferring the testosterone drug to women or children, it is important that you wash your hands after applying this medication and to be careful that no one touches the areas of application, especially when wet.
  - Topical testosterone is absorbed through the skin and can cause side effects or symptoms of male features in a child or woman who comes into contact with the medication. Symptoms include enlarged genitals, premature pubic hair growth, increased libido, aggressive behavior, male-pattern baldness, excessive body hair growth, increased acne, irregular menstrual periods or any signs of male characteristics.
- Testosterone can cause birth defects in unborn babies. A pregnant woman should avoid coming into contact with testosterone topical gel or with areas of a man's skin where a testosterone topical patch has been worn or the gel has been applied. If contact does occur, wash with soap and water right away.

How to apply topical gels

- Apply the medication as directed (see the application sites in the drug table) to clean, dry skin once daily in the morning. Apply only to areas that would be covered with clothing (e.g., a short sleeve t-shirt for *Androgel*). Avoid applying this medication to broken, irritated skin. Do not apply to the genitals (penis or scrotum) or breasts. Do not let others apply this medication to your body.
- Before dressing, wait a few minutes for the application site to dry completely. Keep the application site covered with clothing until you wash the areas well with soap and water.
- If you expect to have skin-to-skin contact with another person, first wash the application area well with soap and water.
- For best effects, wait at least 2–6 hours after applying the medication before showering or swimming.
- This medication is flammable until dry. Let the gel dry before smoking or going near an open flame.
- *AndroGel Pump*: before using the pump for the first time, you will need to prime the pump. To do this, push down fully on the pump three times. Do not use any *AndroGel* that came out while priming. Wash it down the sink or throw it in the trash to avoid accidental exposure to others. Your healthcare provider will tell you the number of times to press the pump for each dose.
- *AndroGel* packets: tear open the packet completely at the dotted line. Squeeze all of the *AndroGel* out of the packet into the palm of your hand. Squeeze from the bottom of the packet to the top.
- For formulations applied to the underarms: apply deodorant first.
- *Fortesta:* apply to the front and inner thighs with one finger.
- *Natesto:* prime the pump ten times first, insert the actuator into the nostril, depress slowly until the pump stops, remove from the nose while wiping the tip to transfer gel to the lateral side of the nostril, then press on the nose and lightly massage. Try not to blow your nose or sniff for one hour.

Androderm Patch

- Apply the patch each night to a clean, dry area of the skin (see the drug table for application sites). Avoid showering, washing the application site or swimming for at least three hours after application. Do not use the same site for at least seven days.
- Dispose of used patches by folding the adhesive ends together, place in a pouch or sealed container, and place in the trash away from children and pets.
- The testosterone transdermal patch may burn your skin if you wear the patch during an MRI (magnetic resonance imaging). Remove the patch before undergoing such a test.

Select Guidelines/References

Clinician's Guide to Prevention and Treatment of Osteoporosis. National Osteoporosis Foundation; 2014. https://link.springer.com/content/pdf/10.1007%2Fs00198-014-2794-2.pdf (accessed 2019 Apr 3).

American Association of Clinical Endocrinologist and American College of Endocrinology Clinical Position Statement on Menopause-2017 Update. *Endocr Pract.* 2017;23(No. 7).

Testosterone Therapy in Men With Hypogonadism: An Endocrine Soceity Clinical Practice Guideline. *J Clin Endocrinolo Metab.* 2018;103:1715-1744.

CHAPTER CONTENT

Background 729
Erectile Dysfunction 729
Drugs that Can Cause Erectile/Sexual Dysfunction 730
Non-Drug Treatment 730
Natural Products 730
Drug Treatment 730
Phosphodiesterase Type 5 (PDE-5) Inhibitors 731
PDE-5 Inhibitor Dosing Guide 731
Alprostadil (Prostaglandin E1) 733
Hypoactive Sexual Desire Disorder 733
Drug Treatment 733

CONTENT LEGEND

= Study Tip Gal = Key Drug Guy

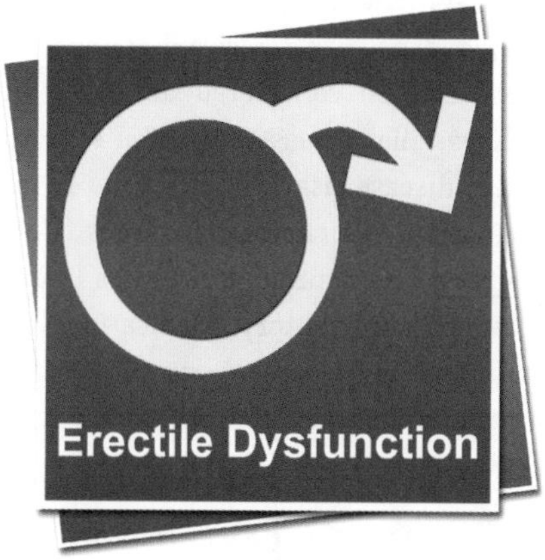

CHAPTER 50

SEXUAL DYSFUNCTION

BACKGROUND

This chapter focuses on erectile dysfunction in males and hypoactive sexual desire disorder in females. Erectile dysfunction (impotence) refers to difficulty getting or sustaining an erection that is firm enough for sex. This is a common type of sexual dysfunction in men and can generally be treated with phosphodiesterase-5 inhibitors (PDE-5 inhibitors). Males can experience other types of sexual dysfunction, including problems with ejaculation and low libido, which is sometimes due to low testosterone levels. Testosterone treatment is discussed in the Osteoporosis, Menopause & Testosterone Use chapter.

In women, sexual dysfunction can be due to either an inability to reach orgasm (anorgasmia), painful intercourse, or hypoactive (i.e., lower than normal) sexual desire disorder (HSDD). Flibanserin *(Addyi)* is the sole drug for females with sexual dysfunction, and claims to treat HSDD. In clinical trials, the benefits were modest, increasing the number of satisfying sexual events per month by 0.5 to 1, compared to placebo. It is approved for premenopausal women only, and can cause fainting.

In both males and females, sexual dysfunction can be due to the use of an SSRI or SNRI, or less commonly, another antidepressant. An alternate antidepressant can be tried that does not cause sexual side effects, such as bupropion.

ERECTILE DYSFUNCTION

The most common cause of erectile dysfunction (ED) is reduced blood flow to the penis. This can be common in patients with cardiovascular diseases, such as hypertension and atherosclerosis, and conditions that cause neuropathies, such as diabetes. Since the arteries supplying blood to the penis are smaller than those supplying blood to the heart, they can become restricted sooner than the larger vessels. ED can be considered an early warning indicator of cardiovascular disease, and men with ED who have cardiovascular disease risk factors should be referred for cardiac evaluation. Psychological issues (including depression and stress) and neurological illness (spinal cord injury, stroke) can be contributory. Medications used for other conditions, including blood pressure lowering drugs used in cardiovascular diseases, can contribute to erectile dysfunction (see Key Drugs Guy).

DRUGS THAT CAN CAUSE ERECTILE/ SEXUAL DYSFUNCTION

KEY DRUGS

Alcohol

Antidepressants
Especially SSRIs and SNRIs (including ↓ libido)

Antihypertensives
Beta blockers, clonidine, others

Antipsychotics
First-generation (e.g., chlorpromazine)
prolactin-raising second generation (e.g., risperidone, paliperidone)

BPH medications
Finasteride, dutasteride, and silodosin (mostly retrograde ejaculation)

Others

Anticancer drugs:
Leuprolide, flutamide

Anticholinergics

Atomoxetine

Digoxin

H2RAs:
Cimetidine, ranitidine

Nicotine

Opioids (chronic use, especially methadone)

NON-DRUG TREATMENT

Lifestyle changes, including weight loss, quitting tobacco and reducing alcohol intake can improve ED. Underlying diseases that can contribute to the condition should be properly managed, and any offending agents should be discontinued, if possible. Non-drug options that are beneficial in some men are vacuum erection devices, penile implants and surgery.

NATURAL PRODUCTS

Natural products used to treat ED include yohimbe, L-arginine and panax ginseng. *The Natural Medicines Database* rates L-arginine (taken in high doses) and panax ginseng as "possibly effective" for this purpose. L-arginine can cause dizziness, headache and flushing. The same side effects are caused by PDE-5 inhibitors, and the additive effects should be avoided. Yohimbe is rated as "insufficient evidence to date." Yohimbe causes gastrointestinal side effects, anxiety, and can cause more severe health concerns, including tachycardia and arrhythmias.

There are many products marketed to "treat" ED. It is important to recognize that the majority of these products contain a false list of ingredients, have not been tested and are not regulated by the FDA.

DRUG TREATMENT

PDE-5 inhibitors (sildenafil, vardenafil, tadalafil, avanafil) are first-line for the treatment of ED. These are often started at a low dose, then titrated as tolerated and to desired effect. Treatment success is defined by the patient and partner. Treatment failure could be due to a number of factors, such as lack of sexual stimulation, timing of the dose and eating a large meal with the dose. Efficacy appears to be similar among the most common PDE-5 inhibitors (sildenafil, vardenafil and tadalafil) but patients could consider switching between drugs if they do not achieve desired effect. See the PDE-5 Inhibitor table on the next page for details.

If a patient cannot tolerate or has a contraindication to PDE-5 inhibitors, alprostadil can be used instead. Alprostadil is either injected into the penis, or inserted into the penis with a urethral suppository. This treatment is invasive, painful, and short-acting.

Two of the PDE-5 inhibitors used for ED are indicated for other conditions. Tadalafil *(Cialis)* is used for benign prostatic hypertrophy (BPH) at a dose of 5 mg daily, which could treat concurrent ED. Sildenafil *(Revatio)* and tadalafil *(Adcirca)* are indicated for pulmonary arterial hypertension (PAH). Patients should not be using two PDE-5 inhibitors concurrently due to the risk of additive side effects.

The corpora cavernosa (plural) are the two spongy tubular vessels that run down the length of the penis. When the vessels are filled with blood, the penis is hard and erect.

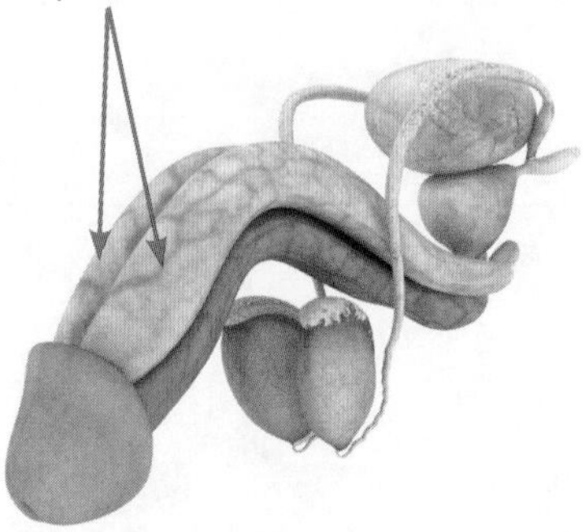

Nitric oxide (NO) → guanylate cyclase → ↑ cGMP → relaxes the smooth muscle in the arteries → blood flows into the vessels → erection.

Phosphodiesterase type 5 (PDE-5) degrades cGMP.

Phosphodiesterase Type 5 (PDE-5) Inhibitors

Following sexual stimulation, there is a local release of nitric oxide, which increases cGMP and causes smooth muscle relaxation. This permits blood to flow in, resulting in an erection (see figure on previous page). PDE-5 inhibitors block PDE-5 from degrading cGMP. PDE-5 inhibitors do not increase libido (sexual interest), which must be present for the drugs to work.

DRUG	DOSING	SAFETY/SIDE EFFECTS/MONITORING
Sildenafil (*Viagra*) *Revatio* – PAH	On-demand dosing: 25-100 mg daily PRN Start at 50 mg, take ~1 hr before sexual activity Start at 25 mg in select conditions (see Study Tip Gal)	**CONTRAINDICATIONS** Do not use with nitrates or riociguat (a guanylate cyclase stimulator). **WARNINGS** Impaired color discrimination (dose-related) – patients with retinitis pigmentosa may have higher risk. Hearing loss, with or without tinnitus/dizziness. Vision loss – rare, but can be due to nonarteritic anterior ischemic optic neuropathy (NAION). Risk factors: low cup-to-disc ratio, CAD and other vascular conditions, age > 50 yrs, Caucasian ethnicity. Avoid with retinal disorders. Hypotension, due to vasodilation. Higher risk with fluid depletion, resting BP < 90/50 mmHg, or autonomic dysfunction. Priapism, seek emergency medical care if erection lasts ≥ 4 hrs. CVD, caution with low or very high BP or recent cardiac events. If chest pain occurs, seek immediate medical help. **SIDE EFFECTS** Headache, flushing, dizziness, dyspepsia, blurred vision, difficulty with color discrimination, increased sensitivity to light, epistaxis, diarrhea, myalgia, muscle/back pain (mostly with tadalafil). **NOTES** Take with or without food. Sildenafil and vardenafil can have decreased efficacy if taken with a high-fat or large meal (common cause of treatment failure per guidelines). For ED, no more than one dose per day is recommended. *Stendra* can be taken closest to sexual activity.
Vardenafil (*Levitra*, *Staxyn* ODT)	On-demand dosing: 5-20 mg daily PRN Start at 10 mg, take ~1 hr before sexual activity Start with a lower dose of *Levitra* in select conditions (see Study Tip Gal) *Staxyn* ODT is only available as 10 mg (max dose)	
Tadalafil (*Cialis*) *Cialis* – also used for BPH *Adcirca* – PAH Lasts the longest – known as the "weekend pill"	Daily dosing: 2.5-5 mg daily Start at 2.5 mg; do not use daily dosing with severe renal or liver impairment On-demand dosing: 5-20 mg daily PRN Start at 10 mg, at least 30 min before sexual activity Start at 5 mg in select conditions (see Study Tip Gal) CrCl 30-50 mL/min: 5 mg PRN CrCl < 30 mL/min: 5 mg PRN Q72H	
Avanafil (*Stendra*)	On-demand dosing: 50-200 mg daily PRN Start at 100 mg, take 15-30 min before sexual activity Start at 50 mg in select conditions (see Study Tip Gal)	

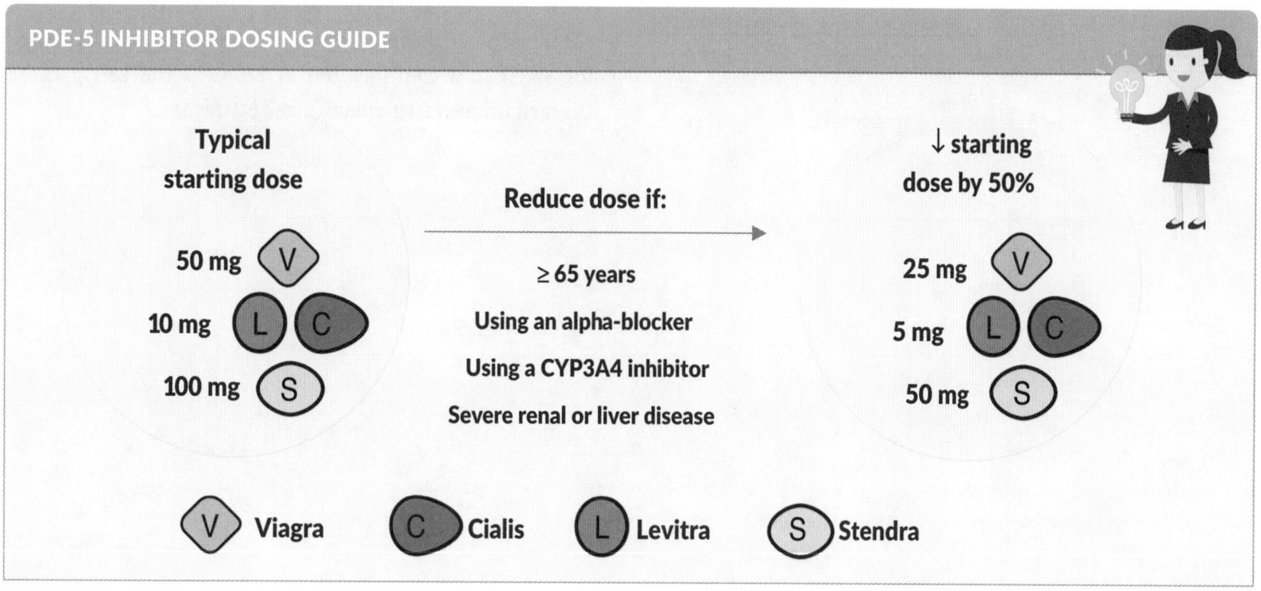

PDE-5 Inhibitor Drug Interactions

- It is an absolute contraindication to use nitrates or riociguat with PDE-5 inhibitors. These combinations can cause severe hypotension. This includes any prescription nitrates (e.g., *Nitrostat, Nitrolingual,* and *BiDil*) or illicit alkyl nitrates ("poppers" such as amyl nitrate and butyl nitrate).
  - Avoid long-acting nitrates completely. If a patient with ED has taken a PDE-5 inhibitor and develops angina, short-acting nitroglycerin should not be used until after 12 hours for avanafil, after 24 hours for sildenafil or vardenafil, and after 48 hours for tadalafil. Occasionally, if needed, nitrates are used in an acute emergency with careful monitoring.
  - Riociguat should not be administered within 24 hours of sildenafil, or within 24 hours before or 48 hours after tadalafil.
- Use caution with other agents that cause hypotension, including alpha blockers and antihypertensive drugs.
  - PDE-5 inhibitors can enhance the hypotensive effects of alpha-1 blockers. The patient should be stable on the alpha-1 blocker (without excessive dizziness/hypotension) before starting the PDE-5 inhibitor. If *Cialis* is being used to treat BPH, do not use alpha-1 blockers concurrently.
  - Alcohol can enhance hypotension with PDE-5 inhibitors.
- Moderate and strong CYP450 3A4 inhibitors (e.g., grapefruit juice, protease inhibitors, azole antifungals) increase the drug levels of PDE-5 inhibitors; lower starting doses and/or extended dosing intervals are required. Strong CYP3A4 inducers decrease drug levels; monitor effectiveness.

PDE-5 Inhibitor Patient Counseling

- Take approximately 15 minutes (avanafil), 30 minutes (tadalafil, when taken as needed), or 1 hour (sildenafil and vardenafil) before sexual activity.
- This medication can make you feel dizzy, cause headaches, flushing (red skin) and stomach indigestion. Your vision could be blurry and have color changes.
- *Cialis* can cause muscle or back pain. This usually occurs 12 to 24 hours after taking it, and can last up to two days.
- Sexual activity can put an extra strain on your heart. Stop sexual activity and get medical help right away if you have chest pain, dizziness or nausea during sexual activity.
- This medication can cause your blood pressure to drop suddenly to an unsafe level. Do not take this medication if you take drugs called "nitrates" (such as nitroglycerin) or street drugs called "poppers" (such as amyl nitrate and butyl nitrate). A sudden drop in blood pressure can cause you to feel dizzy, faint, or have a heart attack or stroke.
- This medication will not protect you or your partner from getting sexually transmitted diseases, including HIV.
- If you have an erection that lasts more than four hours or is painful, get medical help right away.
- Sudden vision loss in one or both eyes can be a sign of a serious side effect that can occur with this medication. This is rare, but if it happens, do not take any more medication and get medical help right away.
- Some people experience ringing in their ears (tinnitus) or loss of hearing in one or both ears. If you have any of these symptoms, stop taking the medication and contact your healthcare provider right away.
- After reconstitution, keep *Revatio* oral suspension (used for PAH) in a cool location or store in the refrigerator. Discard unused suspension after 60 days.

Alprostadil (Prostaglandin E1)

Alprostadil is prostaglandin E1, a vasodilator that allows blood to flow into the cavernosal arteries, which then enlarges the penis. It is either injected into the penis, or a pellet is inserted through the urethra. This treatment is invasive, painful and does not last as long as the PDE-5 inhibitors. Alprostadil is used in some men who cannot tolerate or have contraindications to PDE-5 inhibitors.

DRUG	DOSING	SAFETY/SIDE EFFECTS/MONITORING
Alprostadil (*Caverject, Caverject Impulse, Edex*) Intracavernous injection Reconstitute prior to use	Inject 1.25-2.5 mcg into the base of the penis; titrate until desired response is achieved Appropriate dose should cause erection 5-10 min after injection; lasts ~1 hr Max 1x/day, 3x/week	**CONTRAINDICATIONS** Conditions that predispose the patient to priapism (e.g., sickle cell anemia, multiple myeloma, leukemia) Intracavernous injection: anatomical deformation or fibrotic conditions of the penis, penile implants Urethral pellets: urethral stricture, balanitis, severe hypospadias and curvature, urethritis, venous thrombosis **SIDE EFFECTS** Penile pain, priapism, headache, dizziness Intracavernous injection: hematoma, bruising at injection site Urethral pellets: urethral burning or bleeding
Alprostadil (*Muse*) Urethral pellets	Insert 125-250 mcg pellet into urethra Urinate before administration Max 2x/day Refrigerate	

HYPOACTIVE SEXUAL DESIRE DISORDER

Hypoactive sexual desire disorder (HSDD) is characterized by a low sexual desire that causes marked distress or interpersonal difficulty. The low sexual desire is not due to a health condition or drug.

DRUG TREATMENT

Flibanserin exhibits agonist activity at 5-HT1A and antagonist activity at 5-HT2A receptors. The exact mechanism of how this treats HSDD is unknown. Flibanserin does not enhance sexual performance and is indicated for use in premenopausal females only.

DRUG	DOSING	SAFETY/SIDE EFFECTS/MONITORING
Flibanserin (*Addyi*)	100 mg QHS Discontinue if no benefit after 8 weeks	**BOXED WARNINGS** Contraindicated: with alcohol due to an ↑ risk of severe hypotension and syncope (REMS program required); in combination with moderate or strong CYP3A4 Inhibitors; in patients with hepatic impairment **WARNINGS** Hypotension, syncope, CNS depression **SIDE EFFECTS** Dizziness, somnolence, nausea, fatigue, insomnia, dry mouth **NOTES** Avoid in pregnancy or if breastfeeding

Flibanserin Drug Interactions

- CNS depressants: ↑ the risk of hypotension and syncope.
- Flibanserin is a major substrate of CYP3A4 and a minor substrate of CYP1A2, 2B6, 2C19, 2C8, 2C9 and 2D6. It inhibits P-gp. Concurrent moderate-strong CYP3A4 inhibitors are contraindicated.

Select Guidelines/References

Erectile Dysfunction: AUA Guideline (2018). http://www.auanet.org/guidelines/male-sexual-dysfunction-erectile-dysfunction-(2018) (accessed 2018 Dec 19).

CHAPTER CONTENT

Background ... 734
Drugs that Can Worsen BPH ... 734
Symptoms and Complications ... 735
Treatment Principles ... 735
Natural Products ... 735
Drug Treatment ... 735
Alpha Blockers ... 735
5 Alpha-Reductase Inhibitors ... 737
Phosphodiesterase-5 Inhibitors ... 738
Patient Counseling ... 739

CONTENT LEGEND

= Key Drug Guy

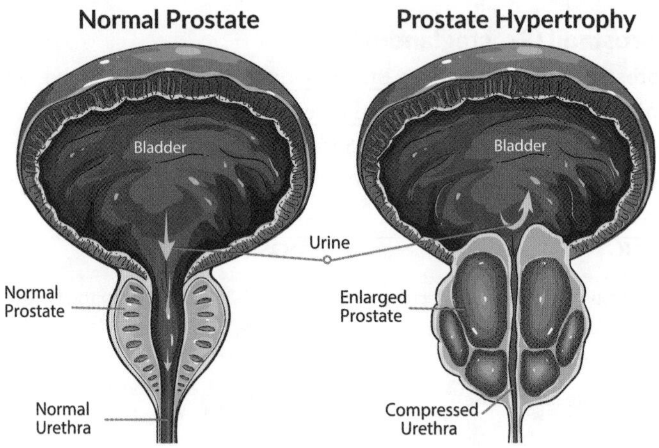

CHAPTER 51
BENIGN PROSTATIC HYPERPLASIA (BPH)

BACKGROUND

The prostate is a walnut-sized gland that surrounds the urethra of a male at the base of the bladder. As part of the male reproductive system, the main function of the prostate is to secrete fluid that becomes part of the seminal fluid carrying sperm.

The prostate is dependent on androgens (mainly testosterone) for development and maintenance of size and function. Testosterone is metabolized to dihydrotestosterone (DHT) by 5 alpha-reductase. DHT is responsible for normal and hyperplastic growth (increase in the number of cells). Benign prostatic hyperplasia (BPH) results from overgrowth of the stromal and epithelial cells of the prostate gland. The enlarged gland contributes to lower urinary tract symptoms (LUTS) via direct bladder outlet obstruction and increased smooth muscle tone and resistance.

As the prostate enlarges, the layer of tissue surrounding it stops it from expanding, causing the gland to press against or pinch the urethra. The bladder wall becomes thicker and irritated. The bladder begins to contract even when it contains small amounts of urine, causing frequent urination. Eventually, the bladder weakens and loses the ability to empty itself. The enlargement does not typically cause problems until later in life, usually around 65 years of age.

Diagnosis requires an assessment of the medical history (surgeries, trauma and current medications, including herbal and OTC drugs) and a physical exam. The physical exam

DRUGS THAT CAN WORSEN BPH

- Anticholinergics (e.g., benztropine)
- Antihistamines (e.g., diphenhydramine, chlorpheniramine)
- Caffeine
- Decongestants (e.g., pseudoephedrine)
- Diuretics
- SNRIs
- TCAs, phenothiazines and other drugs with anticholinergic properties
- Testosterone products

should include a digital rectal exam (DRE), urinalysis and serum prostate specific antigen (PSA), to rule out conditions other than BPH (primarily prostate cancer). PSA, a protein produced by prostate cells, is frequently increased in prostate cancer. It can also increase when the prostate becomes larger due to BPH, though BPH is a benign (non-cancerous) condition and does not increase prostate cancer risk.

SYMPTOMS AND COMPLICATIONS

The signs and symptoms of BPH are mainly LUTS, which includes:

- Hesitancy, intermittent urine flow, straining or weak stream of urine.
- Urinary urgency and leaking or dribbling.
- Incomplete emptying of the bladder (the bladder always feels full).
- Urinary frequency, especially nocturia (urination at night).
- Bladder outlet obstruction.

These disturbances significantly impact the quality of life for the patient. BPH rarely causes more severe symptoms, but if the blockage is severe, the urine could back up into the kidneys and result in acute renal failure. Urinary tract infections can also be present, but are uncommon. Symptoms can be similar to prostate cancer, so all patients should be referred to a prescriber for an appropriate evaluation prior to starting treatment.

TREATMENT PRINCIPLES

The severity of BPH symptoms reported by the patient guides selection of treatment. Questionnaires, such as the American Urological Association Symptom Score (AUASS) or the International Prostate Symptom Score (I-PSS), are used to quantify symptoms. The scoring systems rate how bothersome the symptoms are, with higher scores indicating more severe or bothersome symptoms. Treatment options can include watchful waiting, pharmacologic therapy or surgical intervention. Mild disease is generally treated with watchful waiting, which entails having the patient return for yearly reassessments. Moderate/severe disease is generally treated with medications, a minimally invasive procedure, or surgery such as transurethral resection of the prostate (TURP).

NATURAL PRODUCTS

The American Urological Association (AUA) guidelines do not recommend natural products for the treatment of BPH symptoms, though various natural products have been investigated. Saw palmetto has been used for BPH, but it is unlikely to be effective based on contradictory and inconsistent data. Pygeum, pumpkin seed (beta-sitosterol) and rye pollen are other natural products that have shown some improvement in BPH symptoms. Lycopene is used for prostate cancer prevention, but there is no good evidence for use in BPH. Pharmacists should not recommend natural products until the patient has seen a healthcare provider, as prostate cancer symptoms present similarly to BPH symptoms.

DRUG TREATMENT

Medications include alpha blockers (selective and non-selective), used alone or in combination with a 5 alpha-reductase inhibitor. The 5 alpha-reductase inhibitors work by decreasing prostate size, but they have a delayed onset. They should not be used in men who have BPH without prostate enlargement. Alpha blockers work quickly, but do not shrink the prostate. The two classes are often used together to get the benefits of each.

Peripherally-acting anticholinergic agents used for overactive bladder (such as tolterodine) are sometimes a reasonable option for men without an elevated post void residual (PVR) urine and when LUTS are predominately irritative. If anticholinergics are used, PVR should be < 250 – 300 mL. Anticholinergics are discussed in the Overactive Bladder chapter.

Another treatment option is the phosphodiesterase-5 (PDE-5) inhibitor tadalafil, with or without finasteride. This can be used in men with BPH alone, and can be an attractive option for men with both BPH and erectile dysfunction (ED).

ALPHA BLOCKERS

Alpha blockers are considered first-line treatment for patients with moderate to severe symptoms. They inhibit alpha-1 adrenergic receptors and relax the smooth muscle of the bladder neck, reducing bladder outlet obstruction and improving urinary flow. There are three types of alpha receptors: 1A (prostate primarily has these receptors), 1B and 1D. Terazosin and doxazosin are non-selective and have more side effects (e.g., orthostasis, dizziness, fatigue, headache) than the selective agents (tamsulosin, alfuzosin, silodosin).

Intraoperative Floppy Iris Syndrome

Alpha blockers are given to relax the smooth muscle of the bladder neck. The same receptors are present on the iris dilator muscle in the eye. With alpha-1 blockade, the iris becomes floppy, has a risk of prolapse, and the pupils do not dilate well. A majority of patients using alpha blockers will have intraoperative floppy iris syndrome (IFIS) during cataract surgery, which complicates the procedure.

If cataract surgery is required, alpha blocker treatment should be delayed until the surgery has been completed.

DRUG	DOSING	SAFETY/SIDE EFFECTS/MONITORING
Non-Selective Alpha-1 Blockers		**CONTRAINDICATIONS** Concurrent use of silodosin or alfuzosin with strong CYP3A4 inhibitors; hepatic impairment (Child-Pugh class C for silodosin, class B/C for alfuzosin); severe renal impairment (silodosin) **WARNINGS** Orthostatic hypotension/syncope, typically with the first dose, if therapy is interrupted for several days, if the dosage is increased too rapidly, or if another antihypertensive agent or PDE-5 inhibitor is started Intraoperative floppy iris syndrome has occurred in cataract surgery patients who were on or were previously treated with an alpha-1 blocker Priapism – seek medical attention if erection lasts > 4 hours Angina – discontinue if symptoms of angina begin or worsen **SIDE EFFECTS** Dizziness, fatigue, headache, fluid retention, rhinitis (tamsulosin), abnormal ejaculation (especially with tamsulosin and silodosin) **MONITORING** BP, PSA, urinary symptoms **NOTES** The non-selective agents are often given at bedtime to help minimize the initial "first dose" effect of orthostasis/dizziness. This requires careful counseling (see Patient Counseling section) as the patient likely has nocturia, and getting up at night to use the bathroom with dizziness and orthostasis can be dangerous. Alpha blockers work right away, but 4-6 weeks may be required to assess whether beneficial effects have been achieved; they do not shrink the prostate and do not change PSA levels. Take *Cardura XL* with breakfast. *Cardura XL* is an OROS formulation (see Learning Drug Formulations chapter) and can leave a ghost tablet (empty shell) in the stool. Do not use alfuzosin in patients at risk for QT prolongation. Silodosin can cause retrograde ejaculation (28%), which is reversible upon drug discontinuation. Alpha blockers can be used for bladder outlet obstruction in women (off-label).
Terazosin	Start 1 mg at bedtime; titrate slowly 10 mg at bedtime is generally effective; max dose is 20 mg at bedtime	
Doxazosin *(Cardura, Cardura XL)*	IR: start 1 mg; titrate slowly up to 4-8 mg daily, usually given at bedtime XL: start 4 mg daily with breakfast; titrate to a max of 8 mg daily	
Selective Alpha-1A Blockers		
Tamsulosin *(Flomax)* + dutasteride *(Jalyn)*	0.4 mg daily, 30 min after the same meal each day; max 0.8 mg daily	
Alfuzosin *(Uroxatral)*	10 mg daily, immediately after the same meal each day CrCl < 30 mL/min: use with caution	
Silodosin *(Rapaflo)*	8 mg daily with a meal CrCl 30-50 mL/min: 4 mg daily CrCl < 30 mL/min: do not use	

Alpha Blocker Drug Interactions

- Use caution when co-administered with PDE-5 inhibitors (*Viagra/Revatio, Cialis/Adcirca, Levitra/Staxyn, Stendra*) due to additive hypotensive effects. Patients should be stable on alpha blocker therapy before PDE-5 inhibitor therapy is initiated and the lowest dose should be used. If a patient is already taking a PDE-5 inhibitor, the alpha blocker should be started at the lowest dose, and the selective agents are preferred (over the non-selective agents). See the Sexual Dysfunction chapter.
- Use caution with other drugs that lower BP.
- Tamsulosin, alfuzosin and silodosin are major CYP450 3A4 substrates; avoid with strong CYP3A4 inhibitors.
- Silodosin cannot be used with strong P-gp inhibitors, such as cyclosporine.
- Alfuzosin can cause QT prolongation; do not use with other QT prolonging drugs. Use with caution in patients with known QT prolongation (congenital or acquired).

5 ALPHA-REDUCTASE INHIBITORS

These medications inhibit the 5 alpha-reductase enzyme, which blocks the conversion of testosterone to dihydrotestosterone (DHT). This class of medications is indicated for the treatment of symptomatic BPH in men with an enlarged prostate in combination with alpha blockers to improve symptoms, decrease the risk of acute urinary retention, and decrease the need for surgery (e.g., TURP, prostatectomy).

DRUG	DOSING	SAFETY/SIDE EFFECTS/MONITORING
Finasteride *(Proscar)* Inhibits 5 alpha-reductase enzyme, type 2 *Propecia* – for alopecia (hair loss) at lower doses (1 mg daily)	5 mg daily	**CONTRAINDICATIONS** Women of child-bearing potential, pregnancy, children **WARNINGS** May ↑ risk of high-grade prostate cancer **SIDE EFFECTS** Impotence, ↓ libido, ejaculation disturbances, breast enlargement and tenderness, rash; sexual SEs ↓ with time and return to baseline at one year of use in some men **MONITORING** PSA, urinary symptoms **NOTES** Pregnant women should not take or handle these medications as they can be absorbed through the skin and can be detrimental to fetus. Delayed onset as treatment for 6 months (or longer) may be required for maximal efficacy. 5 alpha-reductase inhibitors shrink the prostate and ↓ PSA levels. Swallow dutasteride whole. Do not chew or open as contents can cause oropharyngeal irritation. Take *Jalyn* 30 min after the same meal each day.
Dutasteride *(Avodart)* + tamsulosin *(Jalyn)* Inhibits 5 alpha-reductase enzyme, type 1 and 2	0.5 mg daily	

5 Alpha-Reductase Inhibitor Drug Interactions

- Finasteride and dutasteride are minor CYP3A4 substrates; strong CYP3A4 inhibitors can ↑ levels.
- Do not use *Proscar* in a patient using *Propecia* for hair loss.

PHOSPHODIESTERASE-5 INHIBITORS

The mechanism of action of PDE-5 inhibitors in treating BPH symptoms is not well known. They likely decrease smooth muscle and endothelial cell proliferation, decrease nerve activity, and increase smooth muscle relaxation and tissue perfusion of the prostate and bladder. Tadalafil is the only FDA-approved PDE-5 inhibitor for treatment of BPH in men with or without ED. It has been studied alone and in combination with finasteride. Tadalafil, in combination with an alpha blocker (especially a non-selective agent) can increase the risk of additive hypotension and orthostasis, especially in an elderly male.

DRUG	DOSING	SAFETY/SIDE EFFECTS/MONITORING
Tadalafil *(Cialis)* *Cialis* – also for ED ***Adcirca*** – for pulmonary arterial hypertension (PAH)	5 mg daily, at the same time each day with or without food CrCl 30-50 mL/min: 2.5 mg initially, max of 5 mg daily CrCl < 30 mL/min: do not use Use 2.5 mg if taking a strong CYP3A4 inhibitor	**CONTRAINDICATIONS** Do not use with nitrates or riociguat (a guanylate cyclase stimulator). **WARNINGS** Impaired color discrimination (dose-related) – patients with retinitis pigmentosa may have a higher risk. Hearing loss, with or without tinnitus/dizziness. Vision loss – rare, but can be due to nonarteritic anterior ischemic optic neuropathy (NAION). Risk factors: low cup-to-disc ratio, CAD and other vascular conditions, age > 50 yrs, Caucasian ethnicity. Avoid with retinal disorders. Hypotension, due to vasodilation. Higher risk with resting BP < 90/50 mmHg, fluid depletion, or autonomic dysfunction. CVD, caution with low or very high BP or recent cardiac events. If chest pain occurs, seek immediate medical help. Priapism, seek emergency medical care if erection lasts > 4 hrs. **SIDE EFFECTS** Headache, flushing, dizziness, dyspepsia, blurred vision, increased sensitivity to light, epistaxis, diarrhea, myalgia, muscle/back pain **MONITORING** BP, PSA, urinary symptoms

- For drug interactions and patient counseling for tadalafil, see the Sexual Dysfunction chapter.

PATIENT COUNSELING

ALPHA BLOCKERS

- For non-selective agents: this medication can cause a sudden drop in blood pressure. You may feel dizzy, faint, or "light-headed." When you get up from a sitting or lying position, go slowly and hold onto the bed rail or chair until you are steady on your feet. This is especially important if you take the medication at bedtime, but need to get up from bed to go to the bathroom. These side effects are more likely with the first few doses, or if you increase your dose. They can occur at any time while you are taking the drug, or if you stop and then restart treatment.
- This medication can cause side effects that could impair your thinking or reactions. You should not drive or do anything that requires you to be awake and alert until you are used to the effects of the medication. If you begin to feel dizzy, sit or lie down until you feel better.
- Drinking alcohol can make the dizziness worse, and increase night-time urination if consumed close to bedtime.
- Taking cold and allergy medications, such as decongestants and antihistamines, can make your symptoms worsen. If you need assistance, discuss what to use with your healthcare provider.
- Tell your doctor (or ophthalmologist) about the use of this medication before cataract surgery. The doctor will want to know if you have ever taken this medication.
- If you have an erection that lasts more than four hours or is painful, get medical help right away or the penis could be severely damaged.

Tamsulosin

- Do not crush, chew or break the tamsulosin tablets. Swallow them whole.
- The dose should be taken about 30 minutes after the same meal each day.

Alfuzosin

- Do not crush, chew or break the alfuzosin tablets. Swallow them whole.
- Take the dose after the same meal each day (food increases absorption).

Silodosin

- The most common side effect seen with this medication is an orgasm with reduced or no semen (dry orgasm). This side effect does not pose a safety concern and is reversible with discontinuation of the drug.
- Take the dose at the same time each day, with food.

5 ALPHA-REDUCTASE INHIBITORS

- This medication can take several months or longer to help reduce BPH symptoms. It is effective, it just takes a while to work because it shrinks the prostate slowly. If your doctor has given you another medication, called an alpha-blocker, that will work faster.
- Women who are or may become pregnant should not handle the tablets. These drugs can cause birth defects.
- Your doctor may perform blood tests or other forms of monitoring during treatment with finasteride. One of the tests that may be performed is called a PSA (prostate-specific antigen). This drug can reduce the amount of PSA in the blood.
- Tell your doctor if you experience any of these side effects: decreased sex drive, decreased volume of ejaculate, impotence or breast tenderness or enlargement.
- Taking cold and allergy medications such as decongestants and antihistamines can make your symptoms worsen. Discuss what to use with your healthcare provider if you need assistance.

Select Guidelines/References

AUA Management of Benign Prostatic Hyperplasia. Published 2010; Reviewed and Validity Confirmed 2014. http://www.auanet.org/benign-prostatic-hyperplasia-(2010-reviewed-and-validity-confirmed-2014) (accessed 2019 Jan 31).

CHAPTER CONTENT

Background 740
Pathophysiology and Etiology 741
Non-Drug Treatment 741
Drug Treatment 741
Anticholinergic Drugs 742
Anticholinergic Side Effects 742
Decreasing Risk of Dry Mouth 742
Beta-3 Agonist 743
OnabotulinumtoxinA *(Botox)* 743
Nocturia Treatment 744
Patient Counseling 744

CONTENT LEGEND

= Study Tip Gal

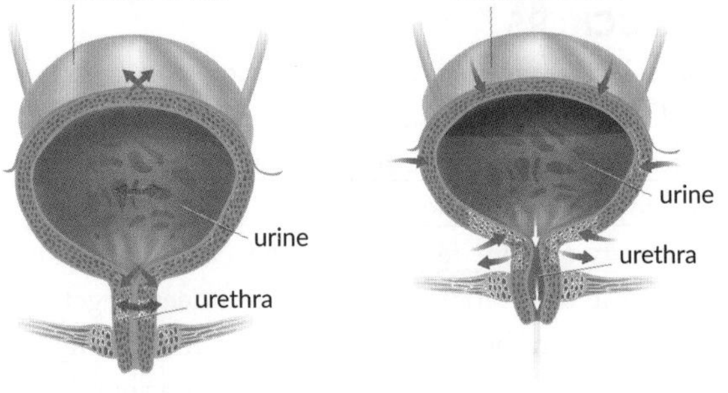

CHAPTER 52
OVERACTIVE BLADDER

BACKGROUND

Overactive bladder (OAB) is a common and debilitating urinary disorder that affects many people. It is not a normal sign of aging. OAB is a syndrome of bothersome urinary symptoms, including:

- Urinary urgency: a sudden feeling of needing to urinate. This is the primary symptom of OAB; it can occur with or without incontinence and is usually accompanied by urinary frequency and nocturia.
- Urinary frequency: voiding ≥ 8 times during waking hours.
- Nocturia: ≥ 2 awakenings in the night to urinate.
- Urinary incontinence: involuntary leakage of urine (see table for different forms).

About 1/3 of patients with OAB have incontinent episodes (OAB wet) and the other 2/3 of patients do not (OAB dry). Urge incontinence is a form of OAB wet that can be treated with the medications discussed this chapter.

FORMS OF URINARY INCONTINENCE

Urge	Patient cannot hold in urine long enough to reach the toilet. Associated with neuropathy and often present in those with diabetes, strokes, dementia, Parkinson disease or multiple sclerosis (although people without comorbidities can be affected).
Stress	Urine leaks out during any form of exertion (e.g., exercise, coughing, sneezing, laughing) as a result of pressure on the bladder.
Mixed	Combination of urge and stress incontinence.
Functional	There is no abnormality in the bladder, but the patient may be cognitively, socially or physically impaired thus hindering access to a toilet (e.g., patients in wheelchairs).
Overflow	Leakage that occurs when the quantity of urine stored in the bladder exceeds its capacity. Often occurs without the urge to urinate (BPH is the most common cause).

Many comorbidities exist in patients with OAB, including falls and fractures, skin breakdown and skin infections, UTIs, depression and sexual dysfunction. Due to embarrassment of the condition, there are many social implications of OAB, including low self-esteem, lack of sexual intimacy, social and physical isolation, sleep disturbances, limits on travel and dependence on caregivers. These can lead to a reduced quality of life. Many patients become dehydrated because they limit fluid intake. The cost of pads and adult diapers can cause a financial burden.

PATHOPHYSIOLOGY AND ETIOLOGY

The bladder is commonly referred to as a "balloon" with an outer muscular layer known as the detrusor muscle. The detrusor muscle and the bladder outlet functions are neurologically coordinated to store and expel urine. The detrusor muscle is innervated mainly by the parasympathetic nervous system (acetylcholine acting on muscarinic receptors), while the bladder neck is innervated by the sympathetic nervous system. The internal sphincter is innervated by the sympathetic nervous system and the external sphincter is innervated by the somatic nervous system. Both voluntary and involuntary contractions of the detrusor muscle are mediated by acetylcholine activation of muscarinic receptors.

In OAB, there is inappropriate stimulation of the muscarinic receptors on the detrusor muscle causing involuntary contractions and the feeling of urinary urgency. This is a contraction of the bladder even when it is not full. Of the five known muscarinic receptor subtypes, the human bladder is comprised of M2 and M3 receptors in a 3:1 ratio. The M3 receptor is responsible for both emptying contractions as well as involuntary bladder contractions. Anticholinergic drugs inhibit the effects of acetylcholine on the M2 and M3 receptors. Similar to anticholinergics, the other drug used for OAB, mirabegron, causes relaxation of the detrusor muscle (prevents contraction) but it does so by acting as a beta-3 receptor agonist.

RISK FACTORS FOR OVERACTIVE BLADDER	
Age > 40 years Diabetes Restricted mobility Obesity Neurologic conditions (e.g., Parkinson disease, stroke, dementia)	Prior vaginal delivery Hysterectomy Drugs that increase incontinence (e.g., alcohol, cholinesterase inhibitors, diuretics, sedatives) Pelvic injury

NON-DRUG TREATMENT

Behavioral therapies are considered first-line to improve OAB symptoms. These include bladder training, delayed or scheduled voiding, pelvic floor muscle exercises (Kegel exercises), urge control techniques (distraction, self-assertions), fluid management, dietary changes (avoiding bladder irritants), weight loss and other lifestyle measures

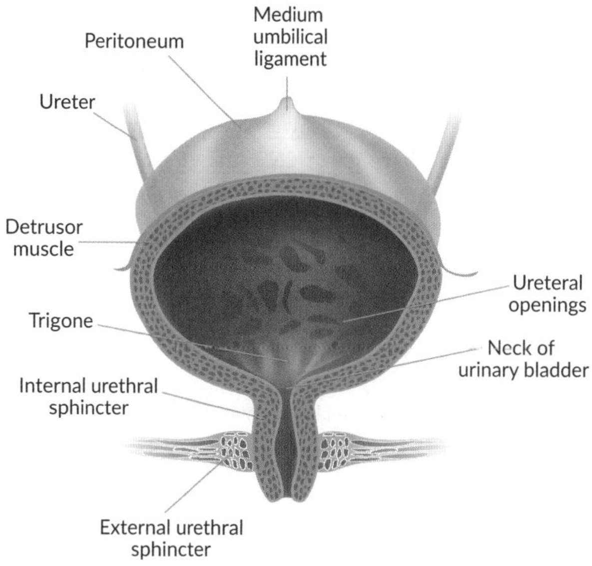

(e.g., stopping medications that can worsen OAB; or with diuretics, changing the time of administration to avoid nocturia).

Behavioral therapies can be combined with other treatment modalities, such as medications. Surgical intervention should be reserved for the rare non-neurogenic patient who has failed all other therapeutic options and whose symptoms are intolerable.

Proper technique of Kegel exercises is key. Instruct the patient to imagine that they are trying to stop urination midstream. Squeeze the muscles they would use. If they sense a "pulling" feeling, those are the correct muscles for pelvic exercise. Pull in the pelvic muscles and hold for a count of three, then relax for a count of three. Patients should work up to three sets of ten exercises per day to reduce wetting episodes.

DRUG TREATMENT

Although medications are recommended second-line, drug treatment is often used in combination with behavioral therapy to optimize symptom control and improve quality of life. The primary classes used to treat OAB symptoms are anticholinergic drugs and beta-3 receptor agonists. If a patient fails an anticholinergic agent or develops an adverse effect, it is recommended to try at least one other anticholinergic agent, a change in dose or a beta-3 receptor agonist before moving on to third-line recommendations (onabotulinumtoxinA, nerve stimulation or surgical correction). Additive anticholinergic drugs should be avoided, if possible. Indwelling catheters are used only as a last resort in select patients.

ANTICHOLINERGIC DRUGS

Anticholinergic drugs, also called antimuscarinic drugs, competitively bind to muscarinic receptors and block acetylcholine from binding. This limits contractions of the detrusor muscle. Extended-release formulations are preferred over immediate-release formulations due to a lower rate of dry mouth. Drugs that are more selective for the M3 receptor (solifenacin, darifenacin and fesoterodine) have fewer CNS side effects than the older, non-selective agents, such as oxybutynin. The Beers Criteria recommend avoiding anticholinergics in patients aged 65 years and older, due to a risk of delirium and cognitive impairment.

DRUG	DOSING	SAFETY/SIDE EFFECTS/MONITORING
Oxybutynin IR **Oxybutynin XL *(Ditropan XL)*** **Oxybutynin patch *(Oxytrol* – Rx, *Oxytrol for Women* – OTC)** Oxybutynin 10% topical gel *(Gelnique, Gelnique Pump)*	5 mg PO BID-TID 5-30 mg PO daily Apply one patch (3.9 mg/day) twice weekly (every 3-4 days; OTC patch is changed every 4 days) Apply contents of 1 sachet (or 1 pump) daily	**CONTRAINDICATIONS** Urinary retention, gastric retention, decreased gastric motility, uncontrolled narrow angle glaucoma *Oxytrol for Women* OTC: pain or burning when urinating, blood in urine, unexplained lower back or side pain, cloudy or foul-smelling urine, males, age < 18 years, urinary or gastric retention, glaucoma, accidental urine loss only due to coughing, sneezing or laughing **WARNINGS** Agitation, confusion, drowsiness, dizziness, blurred vision, hallucinations, and/or headache, which may impair physical or mental abilities; use caution if performing tasks which require mental alertness (e.g., operating machinery, driving) Angioedema of the face, lips, tongue and/or larynx **SIDE EFFECTS** Dizziness and drowsiness (greatest with oxybutynin and less with the newer, selective agents), xerostomia (dry mouth), constipation, dry eyes/blurred vision, urinary retention, application site reactions (with topical gel and patch) **NOTES** ↓ dose in renal impairment (CrCl < 30 mL/min) with fesoterodine, solifenacin, tolterodine, and trospium (do not use trospium XR) *Ditropan XL* is an OROS formulation (see the Learning Drug Formulations chapter) and can leave a ghost shell (empty shell) in the stool Oxybutynin patch and gel cause less dry mouth and constipation than oral forms *Oxytrol* patch should be placed on dry, intact skin on the abdomen, hips or buttocks; avoid reapplication to the same site within 7 days; available OTC for women ≥ 18 yrs Package labeling is not clear if metals may be present in patch; consider removing before MRI *Gelnique* should be applied to dry, intact skin on the abdomen, thighs or upper arms/shoulders; rotate application sites (do not use same site on consecutive days)
Tolterodine *(Detrol)* Tolterodine ER *(Detrol LA)*	1-2 mg PO BID 2-4 mg PO daily	
Trospium IR Trospium XR	20 mg PO BID 60 mg PO daily Take on an empty stomach	
Solifenacin *(Vesicare)*	5-10 mg PO daily	
Darifenacin *(Enablex)*	7.5-15 mg PO daily	
Fesoterodine *(Toviaz)*	4-8 mg PO daily	

Anticholinergic Drug Interactions

- Additive effects can be seen when used with other medications that have anticholinergic side effects.
- The lowest dose of tolterodine, solifenacin, darifenacin and fesoterodine should be used if the patient is taking strong CYP450 3A4 inhibitors.
- Acetylcholinesterase inhibitors used for dementia (e.g., donepezil) increase acetylcholine in the CNS. Although OAB drugs primarily stay in the periphery (outside the CNS), some patients can experience CNS side effects (e.g., memory impairment). While this is not a drug interaction, use of anticholinergic drugs in dementia can lead to decreased effect. The risk versus benefit must be considered. If there is little improvement in OAB symptoms at six weeks, the anticholinergic drug should be discontinued.

ANTICHOLINERGIC SIDE EFFECTS

Peripheral:
- Dry mouth
- Dry eyes/blurred vision
- Urinary retention
- Constipation

Central:
- Sedation
- Dizziness
- Cognitive impairment

DECREASING RISK OF DRY MOUTH

Dry mouth is a major reason that patients fail to comply with anticholinergic treatment.

Choosing a treatment that minimizes dry mouth can improve adherence.

- Try extended-release formulations (lower risk than IR formulations).
- Try oxybutynin gel or patch (lower risk than oral formulations).
- Mirabegron has a lower incidence of dry mouth and can be helpful in patients who cannot tolerate anticholinergics.

See Patient Counseling for strategies to help with dry mouth symptoms.

BETA-3 AGONIST

Mirabegron relaxes the detrusor muscle and increases bladder capacity by activating beta-3 receptors. Mirabegron has similar efficacy to anticholinergic drugs, but causes less dry mouth. It should be considered in patients who cannot tolerate anticholinergic drugs.

DRUG	DOSING	SAFETY/SIDE EFFECTS/MONITORING
Mirabegron *(Myrbetriq)*	25-50 mg PO daily CrCl 15-29 mL/min: 25 mg daily CrCl < 15 mL/min: not recommended	**WARNINGS** Angioedema of the face, lips, tongue and/or larynx, ↑ BP, urinary retention in patients with BPH and when used with anticholinergic drugs **SIDE EFFECTS** Hypertension, nasopharyngitis, UTI, headache, constipation, diarrhea, dizziness **MONITORING** BP, HR, urinary symptoms **NOTES** Efficacy seen within 8 weeks

Mirabegron Drug Interactions

- Mirabegron is a moderate CYP2D6 inhibitor. Use caution in combination with narrow therapeutic drugs metabolized by CYP2D6. Levels of metoprolol and desipramine are increased when co-administered with mirabegron. Use caution in combination with digoxin (use lowest digoxin dose and monitor levels).

ONABOTULINUMTOXINA *(BOTOX)*

Botox is a third-line treatment for patients who are refractory to first- and second-line treatment options. It affects the detrusor activity by inhibiting the release of acetylcholine.

DRUG	DOSING	SAFETY/SIDE EFFECTS/MONITORING
OnabotulinumtoxinA *(Botox)*	100 units total dose, as 0.5 mL (5 units) injections, across 20 sites (given intradetrusor) – repeat no sooner than 12 weeks from previous administration In adults treated with *Botox* for more than one indication, do not exceed a total dose of 360 units in a 3 month interval	**BOXED WARNING** All botulinum toxin products may spread from the area of injection to produce symptoms consistent with botulinum toxin effects; swallowing and breathing difficulties can be life-threatening **CONTRAINDICATIONS** Infection at the targeted injection site, urinary tract infection, urinary retention **SIDE EFFECTS** Urinary tract infection, urinary retention, dysuria **MONITORING** Post void residual volume, symptoms of OAB **NOTES** Potency units of *Botox* are not interchangeable with other preparations of botulinum toxin products Prophylactic antimicrobial therapy (excluding aminoglycosides) should be administered 1-3 days prior to, on the day of, and for 1-3 days following *Botox* administration

Botox Drug Interactions

- Aminoglycosides and drugs affecting neuromuscular transmission can increase the side effects of *Botox*.

NOCTURIA TREATMENT

The first medication FDA-approved for the treatment of nocturia in adults is desmopressin, an antidiuretic hormone analog that temporarily decreases urine production. It is administered before bed to prevent patients from having to urinate during the night.

DRUG	DOSING	SAFETY/SIDE EFFECTS/MONITORING
Desmopressin nasal spray *(Noctiva)* Desmopressin SL tab *(Nocdurna)* *DDAVP* injection – for Hemophilia A, von Willebrand's disease, diabetes insipidus *DDAVP Rhinal Tube* – for central cranial diabetes insipidus *Stimate* nasal spray – for Hemophilia A, von Willebrand's disease	**Age < 65 years and no risk for hyponatremia:** 1 spray (1.66 mcg) in one nostril 30 minutes prior to bed **Age < 65 years with risk for hyponatremia or age ≥ 65 years:** 1 spray (0.83 mcg) in one nostril 30 minutes prior to bed; can be increased to 1.66 mcg dose if no hyponatremia develops **Sublingual:** Females: 27.7 mcg 1 hour before bedtime Males: 55.3 mcg 1 hour before bedtime	**BOXED WARNING** Severe, life-threatening hyponatremia can develop **CONTRAINDICATIONS** Patients with increased risk of severe hyponatremia (e.g., excessive fluid intake, illnesses or drugs that can cause fluid or electrolyte imbalances, including chronic kidney disease, SIADH, loop diuretics, systemic or inhaled glucocorticoids) and patients with increased risk of fluid retention (e.g., uncontrolled hypertension, heart failure) **WARNINGS** Concurrent nasal conditions *(Noctiva)* **SIDE EFFECTS** Hyponatremia, headache, hypertension, rhinitis *(Noctiva)*, xerostomia *(Nocdurna)* **MONITORING** Serum Na (baseline, 1 week and 1 month)

PATIENT COUNSELING

ANTICHOLINERGICS

- This medication can cause dry mouth. The longer-lasting and topical forms tend to cause less dry mouth. If dry mouth is bothersome, discuss with your healthcare provider.
  - Avoid mouthwashes with alcohol, take small sips of water, suck on ice chips or sugar-free candy or chew sugar-free gum to help with dry mouth symptoms. Take good care of your teeth since dry mouth contributes to tooth decay.
- This medication can cause constipation. Maintain adequate intake of water and dietary fiber, including vegetables and whole-grains. A stool softener, docusate, or a laxative, senna, may be helpful. If you have any type of stomach problems, serious constipation or constipation for ≥ 3 days, you should let your healthcare provider know.
- This medication can make you feel dizzy or drowsy. Alcohol and hot temperatures can make this worse. Do not operate any dangerous machinery (such as driving a car) until you know how this medication affects your concentration and coordination.
- Doing pelvic floor muscle (Kegel) exercises in combination with this medication works better than taking the medication alone. You should get instructions on how to do this correctly, and do them for a few minutes three times daily to slowly strengthen these muscles.

Ditropan XL

- The tablet must be swallowed whole with liquid; do not crush, divide, or chew; take at approximately the same time each day.
- This medication can be taken without regard to meals.
- If you miss a dose, skip it. Take your next dose at the scheduled time. Do not take two doses within the same day.
- Part of the tablet may pass into your stool after your body has absorbed the medication. If you see the tablet in your stool, it is nothing to worry about.

Oxytrol Patch

- The patch causes less dry mouth than oral formulations.
- Open one pouch and apply one patch to clean, dry, intact skin on the abdomen, hips, or buttocks. Avoid applying the patch on your waistline, since tight clothing can rub the patch off.
- Apply to an area of skin that is under clothing and protected from sunlight.
- Do not apply the patch to areas of skin that are irritated, oily, or to where lotions or powders have been applied.

- Select a new site for each new patch (avoid reapplication to the same site within seven days). If the area around the patch becomes red, itchy or irritated, try a new site; contact your healthcare provider if the irritation continues or worsens.
- The patch may need to be removed prior to having an MRI procedure.
- Contact with water (e.g., swimming, bathing) does not change the way the drug works.

Oxybutynin Topical Gel *(Gelnique)*

- For topical use only.
- Apply to clean, dry, intact skin on the abdomen, upper arm/shoulders, or thighs. Rub into the skin until dry. Use a different site each day (do not use the same site two days in a row).
- Do not apply to recently shaved skin.
- Do not bathe, swim or shower for one hour after application.
- Wash hands after use.
- Cover treated area with clothing after gel has dried to prevent transfer of medication to others.
- Oxybutynin gel is flammable. Avoid an open flame and do not smoke until the gel has completely dried on the skin.

DESMOPRESSIN

- You need to have your sodium level tested before starting this medication and during the first month of treatment to make sure you do not experience low sodium levels, a rare but severe side effect.
- Before opening *Noctiva,* store in the refrigerator. Once open, you can keep the medication at room temperature for up to 60 days.
- *Noctiva* is a medication that is administered in the nostrils. Do not shake. The container must be primed prior to first use by pumping five sprays into the air away from the face. If you do not use the medication for more than three days, you will need to re-prime the pump by spraying it in the air two times.
- *Nocdurna* tablet is placed under the tongue until is fully disolved. Do not take the sublingual tablet with water.
- Keep *Nocdurna* in the original package until you are ready to take it in order to protect it from light and moisture.

Select Guidelines/References

Diagnosis and Treatment of Overactive Bladder (Non-Neurogenic) In Adults: AUA/SUFU Guideline. Published 2012; Amended 2014. http://www.auanet.org/guidelines/incontinence-non-neurogenic-overactive-bladder-(2012-amended-2014) (accessed 2019 Jan 31).

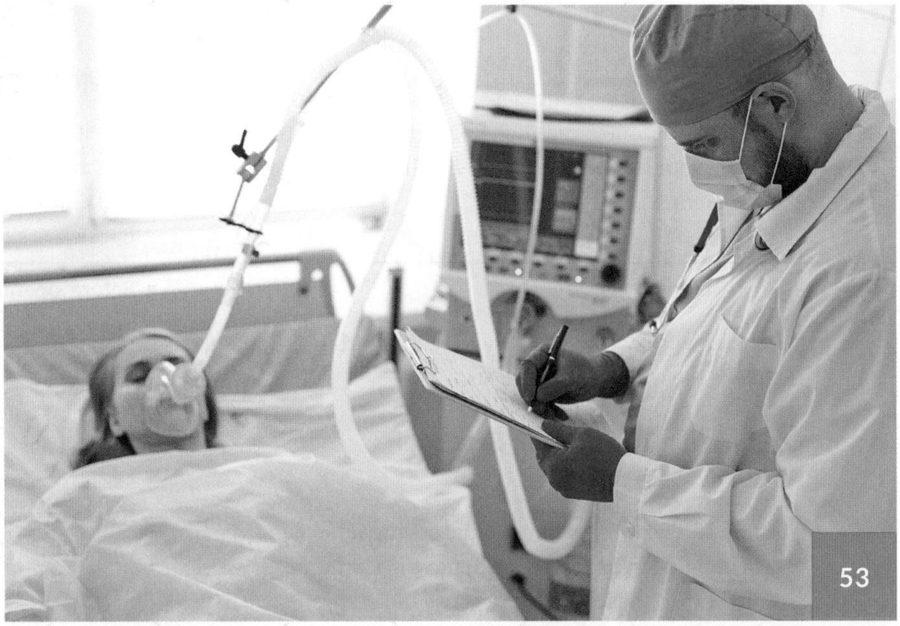

53

EXAM ROOM 1

54

55

technique
tissue
Numerous
location
occur
orthotopic
end-stage
graft
anastomoses
recipient
succeed
removed
outcome
hepatic
ranges
hyperacute
donor
well-calibrated
supporting
rejection
disease
good
quite
alcohol
must
healthy liver
live

56

57

SPECIAL POPULATIONS

CONTENTS

CHAPTER 53
ACUTE & CRITICAL CARE MEDICINE | **748**

CHAPTER 54
PEDIATRIC CONDITIONS | **763**

CHAPTER 55
CYSTIC FIBROSIS | **773**

CHAPTER 56
TRANSPLANT | **779**

CHAPTER 57
WEIGHT LOSS | **789**

CHAPTER CONTENT

Background 748
Fluids 748
Crystalloids vs Colloids 748
Electrolyte Disorders 749
Sodium 749
Potassium 751
Magnesium 751
Phosphorous 751
Other Drug Treatments in Hospitalized Patients 751
VTE Prophylaxis 751
Intravenous Immunoglobulin 752
Critical Care 752
ICU Medications that Target the Sympathetic Nervous System 753
Vasopressors 753
Dopamine Dosing 753
Vasodilators 754
Inotropes 755
Types of Shock 755
General Principles for Treating Shock 755
Hypovolemic Shock 755
Distributive Shock 755
Two Common Causes of ICU Infections 756
Acute Decompensated Heart Failure and Cardiogenic Shock 756
Treating ADHF 756
Other Common ICU Conditions 757
Pain 757
Agitation 757
Delirium 757
Stress Ulcers 760
Additional Drugs Used in the ICU and Operating Room 760
Anesthetics 760
Neuromuscular Blocking Agents 761
Hemostatic Agents 762

CONTENT LEGEND

= Study Tip Gal

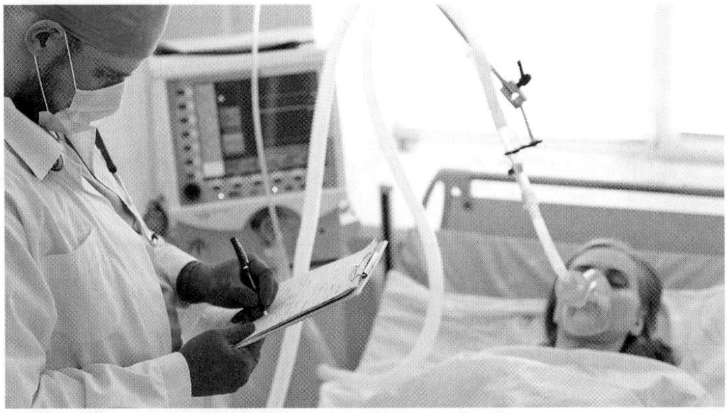

CHAPTER 53
ACUTE & CRITICAL CARE MEDICINE

BACKGROUND

When a patient is sick enough to require an advanced level of care, they are assessed for risk and admitted to either the general hospital unit (acute care) or critical care/intensive care units (ICU). If their illness has a high probability of imminent or life-threatening deterioration, treatment in the ICU is needed. The goal of critical care treatment is to stabilize the patient. If the illness is not as imminent, treatment in a general medical (acute) care unit is acceptable. The goal of acute care treatment is to diagnose and treat the illness to return the patient to their normal state of health.

Common conditions and associated medications used in hospitalized and critically ill patients are addressed in this chapter.

FLUIDS

CRYSTALLOIDS VS COLLOIDS

Hospitalized patients frequently receive IV fluids to replace losses and treat various conditions. IV fluids are categorized as crystalloids or colloids. Crystalloids contain various concentrations of sodium and/or dextrose that pass freely between semipermeable membranes. Most of the administered volume does not remain in the intravascular space (inside the blood vessels), but moves into the extravascular space or interstitial space. Crystalloids are less costly and generally have fewer adverse reactions than colloids. Some data suggest that balanced solutions (e.g., Lactated Ringers) may be preferred in certain disease states like sepsis. The chloride load provided to ICU patients can be high enough to contribute to cell injury, including renal damage. Colloids are large molecules (typically protein or starch) dispersed in solutions that primarily remain in the intravascular space and ↑ oncotic pressure. Colloids provide greater intravascular volume expansion than equal volumes of crystalloids, but are more expensive and have not shown clear clinical benefit over crystalloids.

There are many different crystalloid and colloid products available on the market, and many are available in combination formulations (e.g., D5NS). Dextrose containing products are used when water is needed intracellularly, as these products contain "free water." Lactated Ringers and normal saline are the most common agents used for volume resuscitation in shock states (see Types of Shock section). Albumin is the most commonly used colloid. It is particularly useful in patients with significant edema (e.g., cirrhosis). Albumin should not be used for nutritional supplementation when serum albumin is low. Hydroxyethyl starch use is limited secondary to its boxed warning to avoid use in critically ill patients (including sepsis) due to mortality and renal injury.

CLASS	COMMON FLUIDS
Crystalloids	**5% Dextrose (D5W)***
	0.9% NaCl (normal saline, NS)*
	Lactated Ringers (LR) – contains NaCl, KCl, $CaCl_2$, Na-lactate (lactate is converted to bicarbonate)
	Multiple electrolyte injection ***(Plasma-Lyte A**, others)*
Colloids	**Albumin 5%, 25% *(Albutein, AlbuRx*,** *Albuked, Flexbumin*, others)
	Dextran *(Dextran 40, Dextran 70)*
	Hydroxyethyl starch *(Hespan, Hextend)*

**There are various crystalloid concentrations and combinations including: D50, D5NS, D5½NS, ½NS*

ELECTROLYTE DISORDERS

Any patient (including outpatients) can experience electrolyte abnormalities, but these are common in hospitalized and critically ill patients. There are many causes (see specific deficiencies below), and some drugs deplete electrolytes and cause acute deficiency. Electrolyte abnormalities can lead to severe complications (e.g., seizures, cardiac arrhythmias, coma, death). Protocols to replace electrolytes should be followed in order to avoid toxicity. Electrolytes and their reference ranges are discussed in the Learning Lab Values & Drug Monitoring chapter.

SODIUM

Hyponatremia

Hyponatremia (Na < 135 mEq/L) can develop from many causes and is usually not symptomatic until the sodium is < 120 mEq/L, unless the serum level falls rapidly. Hyponatremia is classified according to serum osmolality and volume status:

- Hypotonic hypovolemic hyponatremia can be caused by diuretics, salt-wasting syndromes, adrenal insufficiency, blood loss or vomiting/diarrhea. The treatment is to correct the cause and administer sodium chloride IV solutions.
- Hypotonic hypervolemic hyponatremia is caused by fluid overload (e.g., cirrhosis, heart failure or renal failure). Diuresis with fluid restriction is the preferred treatment.
- Hypotonic isovolemic (euvolemic) hyponatremia is caused by the syndrome of inappropriate antidiuretic hormone (SIADH). Treatment includes fluid restriction or diuresis. Demeclocycline is frequently used off-label for SIADH.

The arginine vasopressin (AVP) receptor antagonists (conivaptan or tolvaptan) may be used to treat SIADH and hypervolemic hyponatremia. They increase excretion of free water while maintaining sodium. The role for these agents is still being determined, as they are more expensive than 3% saline and use beyond 30 days with the oral product, tolvaptan *(Samsca)*, is not recommended.

Hyponatremia should not be corrected quickly. Correcting sodium more rapidly than 12 mEq/L over 24 hours can cause osmotic demyelination syndrome (ODS) or central pontine myelinolysis, which can cause paralysis, seizures and death. Conservative correction goals are advised, as accidental overcorrection is common. Administration of desmopressin reduces water diuresis and can help avoid overcorrection.

Arginine Vasopressin Receptor Antagonists

DRUG	DOSE	SAFETY/SIDE EFFECTS/MONITORING
Conivaptan (*Vaprisol*) Injection Dual AVP antagonist [vasopressin 1A (V1A) and vasopressin 2 (V2)]	LD: 20 mg IV over 30 minutes MD: 20 mg continuous IV infusion over 24 hours. Can ↑ to 40 mg IV daily if Na does not ↑ at desired rate. Do not use > 4 days. CrCl < 30 mL/min: avoid ↓ dose in moderate and severe hepatic impairment	**CONTRAINDICATIONS** Hypovolemic hyponatremia, concurrent use with strong CYP450 3A4 inhibitors, anuria **WARNING** Overly rapid correction of hyponatremia (> 12 mEq/L/24 hours) is associated with ODS (life-threatening) **SIDE EFFECTS** Orthostatic hypotension, fever, hypokalemia, infusion site reactions (> 60%) **MONITORING** Rate of Na increase, BP, volume status, urine output
Tolvaptan (*Samsca*) Tablet Selective AVP antagonist [vasopressin 2 (V2) only]	15 mg PO daily; max 60 mg PO daily; limited to ≤ 30 days due to hepatotoxicity CrCl < 10 mL/min: avoid Avoid fluid restriction in first 24 hours of therapy	**BOXED WARNINGS** Should be initiated and re-initiated in a hospital under close monitoring of serum Na Overly rapid correction of hyponatremia (> 12 mEq/L/24 hours) is associated with ODS (life-threatening); consider slower correction with severe malnutrition, alcoholism, or advanced liver disease **CONTRAINDICATIONS** Patients who are unable to sense or respond appropriately to thirst, urgent need to raise Na, hypovolemic hyponatremia, use with strong CYP3A4 inhibitors, anuria **WARNINGS** Hepatotoxicity (avoid use > 30 days and in liver disease/cirrhosis) **SIDE EFFECTS** Thirst, nausea, dry mouth, polyuria, weakness, hyperglycemia, hypernatremia **MONITORING** Rate of Na increase, BP, volume status, urine output; signs of drug-induced hepatotoxicity

LD = loading dose, MD = maintenance dose

Hypernatremia

Hypernatremia (Na > 145 mEq/L) is associated with a water deficit and hypertonicity.

- Hypovolemic hypernatremia is caused by dehydration, vomiting, diarrhea and is treated with fluids.
- Hypervolemic hypernatremia is caused by intake of hypertonic fluids and is treated with diuresis.
- Isovolemic (euvolemic) hypernatremia is frequently caused by diabetes insipidus (DI), which can ↓ antidiuretic hormone (ADH). It is treated with desmopressin.

POTASSIUM

Hyperkalemia is often due to chronic kidney disease, and is discussed in the Renal Disease chapter. This section discusses hypokalemia.

Hypokalemia, or potassium (K) < 3.5 mEq/L, is a common occurrence in hospitalized patients. Management includes treating the underlying cause [e.g., metabolic alkalosis, overdiuresis, some medications (amphotericin, insulin)] and administering oral or IV potassium. The oral route is preferred for replacement when feasible. Oral potassium salt formulations are reviewed in the Chronic Heart Failure chapter. In general, a drop of 1 mEq/L in serum K below 3.5 mEq/L represents a total body deficit of 100 - 400 mEq. Some hospitals use potassium sliding scales that allow a healthcare provider (usually a nurse) to administer a certain dose of potassium based on the serum potassium level (see example protocol below).

EXAMPLE POTASSIUM REPLACEMENT PROTOCOL

Step 1: check phosphate level. If > 2.5 mg/dL, proceed to step 2. If ≤ 2.5 mg/dL, use separate potassium phosphate replacement protocol.

Step 2: provide replacement doses as follows.

SERUM POTASSIUM (MEQ/L)	INSTRUCTION
< 2.6	100 mEq KCl IV; contact MD
2.6-2.9	80 mEq KCl IV; contact MD
3.0-3.2	60 mEq KCl PO/IV
3.3-3.5	40 mEq KCl PO/IV

Step 3: order follow-up labs. For K < 3.2 mEq/L, recheck immediately and with AM labs. For K ≥ 3.2 mEq/L, recheck with AM labs only.

Potassium chloride premixed IVs are generally used for IV replacement. Safe recommendations for IV potassium replacement through a peripheral line include a maximum infusion rate ≤ 10 mEq/hr and maximum concentration of 10 mEq/100 mL. More rapid infusions and higher concentrations may be warranted in severe or symptomatic hypokalemia; these require a central line and cardiac monitoring. IV potassium can be fatal if administered undiluted or IV push. When hypokalemia is resistant to treatment, serum magnesium should be checked. Magnesium is necessary for potassium uptake; hypomagnesemia can worsen and/or prevent correction of hypokalemia. Magnesium should be replaced first when both hypokalemia and hypomagnesemia are present.

MAGNESIUM

Hypomagnesemia, or magnesium (Mg) < 1.3 mEq/L, is more common than hypermagnesemia. Common causes of hypomagnesemia include chronic alcohol use, diuretics, vomiting and diarrhea. Hypermagnesemia is most commonly due to renal insufficiency. When serum Mg is < 1 mEq/L with life-threatening symptoms (seizures or arrhythmias), IV replacement is recommended. Magnesium sulfate is used for IV replacement. When serum Mg is < 1 mEq/L without life-threatening symptoms, therapy can be administered IV or IM. When serum Mg is > 1 mEq/L and < 1.5 mEq/L, magnesium is replaced orally, most commonly with magnesium oxide. Magnesium replacement regimens should continue for 5 days to fully replace body stores.

PHOSPHORUS

Hyperphosphatemia is often due to chronic kidney disease, and is discussed in the Renal Disease chapter. This section discusses hypophosphatemia.

Hypophosphatemia is considered severe, and is usually symptomatic when serum phosphate (PO4) is < 1 mg/dL. Symptoms can include muscle weakness and respiratory failure. Hypophosphatemia can be associated with phosphate-binding drugs (calcium, sevelamer, antacids), chronic alcohol intake and hyperparathyroidism. When serum PO4 is < 1 mg/dL, IV phosphorus is used for replacement. Many regimens can be used, but 0.08 – 0.16 mmol/kg in 500 mL of NS over 6 hours is common. Patients must be carefully monitored and additional doses may be necessary. Patients with hypophosphatemia often have hypokalemia and hypomagnesemia that will require correction. Less severe hypophosphatemia can be treated orally and full replacement often takes one week or longer.

OTHER DRUG TREATMENTS IN HOSPITALIZED PATIENTS

Pharmacists working in the hospital setting are involved in many important initiatives to improve patient safety, optimize drug use and reduce costs. This includes medication reconciliation (see the Medication Safety & Quality Improvement chapter), antimicrobial stewardship (see the Infectious Disease I chapter), formulary review and development, developing drug use protocols and performing drug use evaluations, pharmacokinetic programs, renal dosing and IV to PO recommendations (often via protocols) and much more.

VTE PROPHYLAXIS

Hospitalized patients often have limited mobility and other risk factors for development of venous thromboembolism (VTE). Due to this increased risk, the need for VTE prophylaxis should be evaluated in all inpatients. Refer to the Anticoagulation chapter for details.

INTRAVENOUS IMMUNOGLOBULIN

Intravenous immune globulin (IVIG or IGIV) contains pooled immunoglobulin (IgG), administered intravenously. The IgG is extracted from the plasma of a thousand or more blood donors (this is the FDA's minimum; typically the IVIG is derived from between 3,000 - 10,000 donors). IVIG is given as plasma protein replacement therapy for immune deficient patients who have decreased or abolished antibody production capabilities. Initially, IVIG was used only for immunodeficiency conditions. Currently, IVIG has several FDA-approved indications and is used for a variety of off-label indications (multiple sclerosis, myasthenia gravis, Guillaine-Barré, others) with varying results. Treatment with IVIG can impair response to vaccination. Refer to the Immunizations chapter.

DRUG	DOSING	SAFETY/SIDE EFFECTS/MONITORING
Intravenous immunoglobulin *(Carimune NF, Flebogamma DIF, Gammagard, Gamunex-C, Octagam,Privigen,* *Bivigam, Gammagard S/D, Gammaked, Gammaplex, Hizentra, Hyqvia,* others)	Indication and product specific Use IBW to calculate dose Use slower infusion rate in renal and CV disease Do not freeze, shake or heat	**BOXED WARNINGS** Acute renal dysfunction can rarely occur and has been associated with fatalities; usually within 7 days (more likely with products stabilized with sucrose). Use caution in the elderly, patients with renal disease, diabetes, volume depletion, sepsis, paraproteinemia, and nephrotoxic medications Thrombosis may occur even without risk factors. For patients at risk, administer the minimum dose **CONTRAINDICATIONS** IgA deficiency (can use product with lowest amount of IgA) **WARNINGS** Use with caution in patients with CV disease (use isotonic products and low infusion rate) **SIDE EFFECTS** Headache (HA), nausea, diarrhea, injection site reaction, infusion reaction (facial flushing, chest tightness, fever, chills, hypotension – slow/stop infusion), renal failure or blood dyscrasias (both rare) **MONITORING** Renal function, urine output, volume status, Hgb **NOTES** Patients should be asked about past IVIG infusions, including product used and any reactions that occurred. Slow titration and premedication may be used Lot numbers of IVIG products administered patients must be tracked. It is a blood product

CRITICAL CARE

Patients with life-threatening injuries or illnesses require specialized care that is often initiated pre-hospital or in an emergency department and continued in the intensive care unit (ICU). Large hospitals have specialized ICUs for different types of patients (e.g., medical, surgical, cardiovascular, trauma, neurological, pediatric, neonatal). Patients in the ICU receive most of their medications intravenously (IV), with an infusion pump. This route provides rapid onset of effect and easy titration, avoids gut/absorption issues and permits administration when the patient is sedated. Although patients in the ICU are very sick, many recover and eventually go home. The Acute Physiologic Assessment and Chronic Health Evaluation II (APACHE II) is a scoring tool used to determine a patient's prognosis and estimate ICU mortality risk. The ICU mortality rate in the U.S. is ~15%.

ICU MEDICATIONS THAT TARGET THE SYMPATHETIC NERVOUS SYSTEM

VASOPRESSORS

Most vasopressors work by stimulating alpha receptors, which causes vasoconstriction (think "pressing down on the vasculature") and increases systemic vascular resistance (SVR), which increases BP. Phenylephrine is a pure alpha agonist that increases SVR without increasing HR. Epinephrine and norepinephrine are mixed alpha- and beta-agonists, causing both an increase in SVR as well as an increase in CO and HR. Dopamine is a natural precursor of norepinephrine and is recommended for use in patients with symptomatic bradycardia. Vasopressin and angiotensin II both increase SVR by unique mechanisms; they do not act on alpha receptors. Vasopressin acts directly on vasopressin receptors. Angiotensin II (*Giapreza)*, recently approved for septic and distributive shock, raises blood pressure by vasoconstriction and aldosterone release, which results in sodium and water retention. Angiotensin II is a natural hormone produced in the renin-angiotensin-aldosterone system which is discussed in detail in the Hypertension chapter. A review of the nervous system and receptor pharmacology can be found in the Learning Basic Science Concepts chapter.

DOPAMINE DOSING

Dopamine stimulates different receptors depending on the dose.

- Low (renal) dose: 1-4 mcg/kg/min
  - Dopamine-1 agonist
- Medium dose: 5-10 mcg/kg/min
  - Beta-1 agonist
- High dose: 10-20 mcg/kg/min
  - Alpha-1 agonist

DRUG	MOA	SAFETY/SIDE EFFECTS/MONITORING
Dopamine	Dose-dependent, see Study Tip Gal	**BOXED WARNING** Dopamine and norepinephrine have a boxed warning regarding extravasation; all vasopressors are vesicants when administered IV, treat extravasation with phentolamine **WARNINGS** Use extreme caution in patients taking an MAO inhibitor; prolonged hypertension may result (dopamine, epinephrine and norepinephrine) **SIDE EFFECTS** Arrhythmias, tachycardia (especially dopamine, epinephrine, vasopressin), necrosis (gangrene), bradycardia (phenylephrine), hyperglycemia (epinephrine), tachyphylaxis, peripheral and gut ischemia **MONITORING** Continuous BP monitoring (with continuous infusions), HR, MAP, ECG, urine output, infusion site for extravasation **NOTES** Solutions should not be used if they are discolored or contain a precipitate Vasopressors have no true maximum dose in the setting of shock All vasopressors are Y-site compatible with each other (except angiotensin II) Some institutions use non-weight-based infusions (mcg/min) instead of weight-based infusions (mcg/kg/min) All vasopressors should be administered via central IV line No clear evidence that low dose dopamine (renal dosing) provides benefit Epinephrine used for IV push is 0.1 mg/mL (1:10,000 ratio strength), epinephrine used for IM injection or compounding IV products is 1 mg/mL (1:1,000 ratio strength); ratio strength has been removed from labeling per the FDA
Epinephrine ***(Adrenalin)*** ***EpiPen***, others for anaphylaxis	Alpha-1, beta-1, beta-2 agonist	
Norepinephrine ***(Levophed)***	Alpha-1 agonist > beta-1 agonist	
Phenylephrine (*Neo-Synephrine, Vazculep*) *Vazculep* approved for hypotension during anesthesia	Alpha-1 agonist	
Vasopressin (*Vasostrict*) Known as arginine vasopressin (AVP) and antidiuretic hormone (ADH)	Vasopressin receptor agonist Vasoconstrictor, no inotropic or chronotropic effects	

Extravasation

Many agents used in the ICU, including vasopressors, are vesicants that cause severe tissue damage/necrosis with extravasation (leakage of drug from the blood vessel into the surrounding tissue). This is a medical emergency. To reduce the risk, every attempt should be made to infuse vasopressors through a central line. Treat vasopressor extravasation with phentolamine, an alpha-1 blocker that antagonizes the effects of the vasopressor. If extravasation occurs with norepinephrine, epinephrine or phenylephrine, stop the infusion but do not disconnect the needle/cannula and do not flush the line. Gently aspirate out (remove) the drug. Nitroglycerin ointment is sometimes used topically (off-label) as an alternative if phentolamine is unavailable.

VASODILATORS

Vasodilators administered by continuous IV infusion include nitroglycerin (NTG), nitroprusside and nesiritide. Frequent or continuous BP monitoring is required when using IV vasodilators and the dose must be decreased if hypotension or worsening of renal function is noted. NTG is often used when there is active myocardial ischemia or uncontrolled hypertension, but effectiveness may be limited after 24 - 48 hours due to tachyphylaxis (tolerance).

Nitroprusside is a mixed (equal) arterial and venous vasodilator at all doses. It has greater effect on BP than NTG, but it should not be used in active myocardial ischemia because it can cause blood to be diverted away from the diseased coronary arteries ("coronary steal"). Metabolism of nitroprusside results in formation of thiocyanate and cyanide, both of which can cause toxicity (especially in renal and hepatic insufficiency, respectively). Hydroxocobalamin can be administered to reduce risk of thiocyanate toxicity and sodium thiosulfate is used for cyanide toxicity (see the Emergency Preparedness, Toxicology & Antidotes chapter).

Nesiritide is a recombinant B-type natriuretic peptide that binds to vascular smooth muscle and increases cGMP, resulting in smooth muscle relaxation which causes vasodilation. Nesiritide produces both arterial and venous vasodilation. It has not been found to reduce mortality or hospitalizations compared to other treatments and is not commonly used.

DRUG	MOA	SAFETY/SIDE EFFECTS/MONITORING
Nitroglycerin See Ischemic Heart Disease chapter for other formulations	Low doses: venous vasodilator High doses: arterial vasodilator	**CONTRAINDICATIONS** SBP < 90 mmHg, use with PDE-5 inhibitors or riociguat **WARNINGS** Severe hypotension and ↑ intracranial pressure (ICP) **SIDE EFFECTS** HA, tachycardia, tachyphylaxis (within 24 – 48 hours of continuous administration), lightheadedness **MONITORING** BP, HR **NOTES** Requires non-PVC container (e.g., glass, polyolefin); use administration sets (tubing) intended for NTG
Nitroprusside *(Nitropress, Nipride)*	Mixed (equal) arterial and venous vasodilator	**BOXED WARNINGS** Metabolism produces cyanide (use the lowest dose for the shortest duration necessary), excessive hypotension (continuous BP monitoring required), not for direct injection (must be further diluted; D5W preferred) **WARNINGS** ↑ ICP **SIDE EFFECTS** HA, tachycardia, thiocyanate/cyanide toxicity (risk ↑ in renal and hepatic impairment) **MONITORING** BP (continuous), HR, renal/hepatic function, urine output, thiocyanate/cyanide toxicity, acid-base status, venous oxygen concentration **NOTES** Requires light protection during administration; use only clear solutions, a blue color indicates degradation to cyanide – do not use
Nesiritide *(Natrecor)*	Vasodilation via increased cGMP	**CONTRAINDICATIONS** Persistent SBP < 100 mmHg prior to treatment, cardiogenic shock (if used as the primary treatment) **SIDE EFFECTS** Hypotension, ↑ SCr **MONITORING** BP, renal function, urine output **NOTES** Limited experience with infusions lasting longer than 96 hours

INOTROPES

Inotropes increase contractility of the heart. Dobutamine is a beta-1 agonist; it increases HR and force of contraction, which increases CO. It has weak beta-2 (vasodilation) and alpha-1 agonist activity. Milrinone is a selective phosphodiesterase-3 inhibitor in cardiac and vascular tissue. It produces inotropic effects with significant vasodilation. Because both dobutamine and milrinone produce vasodilation, they should only be used when BP is adequate.

DRUG	MOA	SAFETY/SIDE EFFECTS/MONITORING
Dobutamine	Beta-1 agonist with some beta-2 and alpha-1 agonism	**SIDE EFFECTS** Dobutamine: hyper/hypotension, ventricular arrhythmias, tachycardia, angina, hypotension Milrinone: ventricular arrhythmias, hypotension **MONITORING** Continuous BP and ECG monitoring, HR, CVP, MAP, urine output, LFTs and renal function (with milrinone) **NOTES** Milrinone: dose must be reduced for renal impairment Dobutamine may turn slightly pink due to oxidation, but potency is not lost Dobutamine and milrinone often referred to as "inodilators" Because of risk of hypotension, used for inotropic effect only after adequate perfusion is achieved
Milrinone	Phosphodiesterase-3 (PDE-3) inhibitor	

TYPES OF SHOCK

Shock is a medical emergency common in ICU patients characterized by hypoperfusion usually in the setting of hypotension, defined as systolic blood pressure (SBP) < 90 mmHg or mean arterial pressure (MAP) < 70 mmHg. There are four main types of shock: (1) hypovolemic (e.g., hemorrhagic), (2) distributive (e.g., septic, anaphylactic), (3) cardiogenic (e.g., post-myocardial infarction) and (4) obstructive (e.g., massive pulmonary embolism). Diagnosis of shock is based on hemodynamic parameters. Patients may experience more than one type of shock at a time. Drugs used for shock may also be used for advanced cardiac life support (ACLS)/cardiac arrest, hypotension during surgery/anesthesia, acute decompensated heart failure (ADHF) and other critical conditions.

HYPOVOLEMIC SHOCK

Treatment of hypovolemic shock requires restoring intravascular volume and improving oxygen-carrying capacity with blood transfusion when indicated. Fluid resuscitation with crystalloids is generally recommended as first-line therapy in patients with hypovolemic shock that is not caused by hemorrhage. Blood products (packed red blood cells and fresh frozen plasma) should be administered in hypovolemic shock for patients with hemoglobin < 7 g/dL [< 10 g/dL in patients with cardiovascular (CV) disease] or patients who have a significant active bleed. If the patient does not respond to the initial crystalloid therapy ("fluid challenge"), then vasopressors may be indicated. Vasopressors will not be effective unless intravascular volume is adequate.

GENERAL PRINCIPLES FOR TREATING SHOCK

FILL THE TANK
Optimize preload with IV crystalloid bolus (as needed)

SQUEEZE THE PIPES
Peripheral vasoconstrictor (alpha-1 agonist) to ↑ systemic vascular resistance (SVR)

KICK THE PUMP
Beta-1 agonist to ↑ myocardial contractility and cardiac output (CO)

DISTRIBUTIVE SHOCK

Distributive shock is characterized by low SVR, and initially high CO followed by low or normal CO. Septic, anaphylactic and neurogenic shock are examples of distributive shock.

Sepsis and Septic Shock

Sepsis is defined as life-threatening organ dysfunction caused by a dysregulated host response to infection. See Study Tip Gal on the next page for common causes of ICU infections. Organ dysfunction can be identified by an acute change in the total Sequential Organ Failure Assessment (SOFA) score ≥ 2 points due to infection. The quickSOFA (qSOFA) is a simplified version that uses only three criteria: altered mental status, systolic blood pressure ≤ 100 mmHg and respiratory rate ≥ 22 breaths per min. SOFA and/or qSOFA have replaced the systemic inflammatory response syndrome (SIRS) criteria for screening patients likely to have sepsis. Septic shock is sepsis in the presence of persistent hypotension requiring a vasopressor to maintain MAP ≥ 65 mmHg and having a serum lactate level ≥ 2 mEq/L despite adequate fluid resuscitation.

TWO COMMON CAUSES OF ICU INFECTIONS

Mechanical ventilation: pushes air into the lungs for patients who cannot breathe on their own.

Mechanical ventilators are called respirators. Air flows into the trachea through an endotracheal tube (ET tube) placed through the mouth or nose. This is called intubation. "Weaning" refers to the process of getting the patient off the ventilator, when they are ready to breathe on their own again.

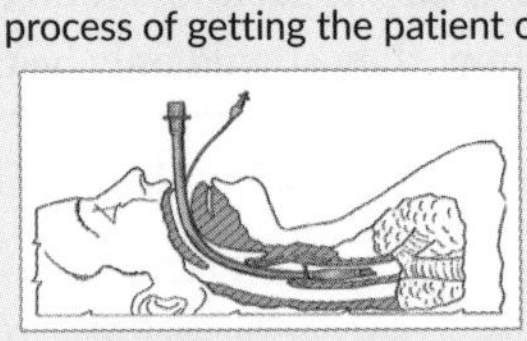

↑ time on ventilator = ↑ risk of infection, including lung infections

Pseudomonas (and a few other organisms) like the moist air in the ventilator.

Foley catheters: a common type of indwelling urinary catheter.

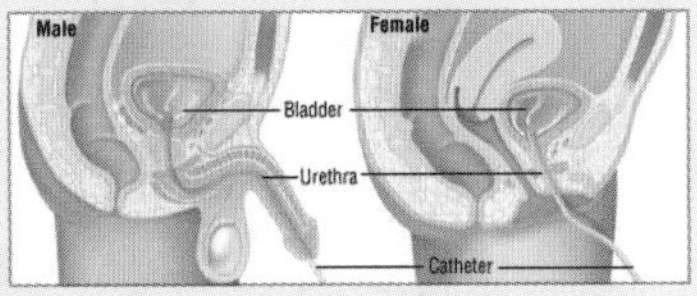

Intubated patients have an indwelling catheter that is inserted into the bladder to drain urine.

Foley catheters are the most common type.

↑ time with foley catheter = ↑ risk of bladder infection

The Surviving Sepsis Campaign is an initiative that prompts the use of selected evidence-based interventions (called "bundles") to reduce mortality from sepsis and septic shock. These bundles include early administration of broad-spectrum antibiotics and IV fluid resuscitation with IV crystalloids. When combined with additional measures, this is associated with lower overall mortality. If adequate perfusion cannot be maintained with IV crystalloids, vasopressors will be used. Norepinephrine is considered the vasopressor of choice in septic shock. Vasopressin is commonly used in addition to norepinephrine in the setting of septic shock.

ACUTE DECOMPENSATED HEART FAILURE AND CARDIOGENIC SHOCK

Patients with heart failure may experience episodes of worsening symptoms such as sudden weight gain, inability to lie flat without becoming short of breath, decreasing functionality (unable to perform their daily routine), increasing shortness of breath and fatigue. This is called acute decompensated heart failure (ADHF), and when hypotension and hypoperfusion are also present, it is called cardiogenic shock.

Clinical Presentation and Assessment

ADHF is caused by worsening HF, a cardiac event (MI, arrhythmia, valvular disease, uncontrolled hypertension) or a non-cardiac cause (e.g., non-adherence with medications or dietary restrictions, worsening renal function, infection, illicit drug use). Use of drugs that can worsen cardiac function (e.g., negative inotropes, NSAIDs/COX-2 inhibitors, drugs which cause fluid retention and direct cardiotoxic drugs) can also cause/exacerbate HF. Beta-blockers should only be stopped in an ADHF episode if hypotension or hypoperfusion is present.

Patients with ADHF present with volume overload, hypoperfusion, or both. Some patients with ADHF require invasive monitoring with a catheter that is guided through the right side of the heart into the pulmonary artery, called a Swan-Ganz or pulmonary artery (PA) catheter. The catheter provides hemodynamic measurements of congestion (pulmonary capillary wedge pressure or PCWP), hypoperfusion (cardiac output) and other measurements (SVR, CVP) useful for guiding treatment. Treatment of ADHF generally consists of diuretics, inotropes and vasodilators in various combinations depending on the patient's signs/symptoms (see Study Tip Gal).

Treating Volume Overload

The majority of patients with ADHF present with volume overload. Volume overload is treated with diuretics and possibly IV vasodilators. Loop diuretics are initially given IV since volume overload also affects the vessels of the gut and can decrease their oral absorption. If diuretic resistance develops, the dose can be increased or a thiazide-type diuretic (e.g., metolazone, chlorothiazide) can be added to the loop.

TREATING ADHF

Patients with edema (pulmonary or lower extremity), jugular venous distention (JVD) and/or ascites are **VOLUME OVERLOADED**, treatment options are:

- Loop diuretics
- Vasodilators can be added (NTG, nitroprusside, nesiritide)

Patients with ↓ renal function, altered mental status and/or cool extremities have **HYPOPERFUSION**,* treatment options are:

- Inotropes (dobutamine, milrinone)
- If the patient becomes hypotensive, consider adding a vasopressor (dopamine, norepinephrine, phenylephrine)

*Avoid vasodilators; these can ↓ BP and worsen hypoperfusion

Some patients experience both **VOLUME OVERLOAD** and **HYPOPERFUSION**, treatment options are:

- A combination of agents above

Treating Hypoperfusion

The most common cause of cardiogenic shock (or ADHF with hypoperfusion) is myocardial infarction (MI) with resulting failure of the left ventricle. Cardiogenic shock requires treatment with vasopressors and/or inotropes. The vasodilatory and inotropic properties of dobutamine and milrinone make them uniquely suited to treating ADHF in patients with both congestion and hypoperfusion when BP is adequate. If BP is inadequate, inotropes will often be used in combination with vasopressors. Inotropes are associated with worse outcomes in heart failure and should be stopped as soon as the patient is stabilized.

OTHER COMMON ICU CONDITIONS

PAIN

Opioids given IV (such as morphine, hydromorphone and fentanyl) are first-line for analgesia (to reduce pain) in the ICU, but the principles of pain management are the same for all patients (see Pain chapter for a full discussion of the opioids). The pharmacokinetic properties of the drug and the renal/hepatic function of the patient will dictate the choice of agent, because all IV opioids exhibit similar analgesic efficacy when dosed correctly. Adjuvants (e.g., acetaminophen and NSAIDs) may be appropriate depending on the type of pain. Assessment of pain (with a validated pain scale) should be performed at least every 2 – 4 hours in the ICU, and all ICU patients should be evaluated for pain at rest. Analgesia-based sedation or "analgosedation" is a sedation strategy that uses analgesia first to relieve pain and discomfort, which are primary causes of agitation. Analgosedation is associated with less time on the ventilator and shorter ICU length of stay (LOS).

AGITATION

Sedation is necessary in some ICU patients to maintain synchronized breathing with the ventilator (prevent "bucking" the ventilator), and to limit suffering in the harsh ICU environment. Agitation is managed with benzodiazepines (lorazepam, midazolam) and/or hypnotics (propofol, dexmedetomidine). Non-benzodiazepines (propofol and dexmedetomidine) are preferred for sedation and are associated with improved ICU outcomes, shorter duration of mechanical ventilation, and decrease LOS. Dexmedetomidine (*Precedex*) is the only sedative approved for use in intubated and non-intubated patients. Benzodiazepines will always have an important role in sedation of the ICU patient with seizures or alcohol/benzodiazepine withdrawal. Benzodiazepines are discussed in the Anxiety chapter.

Sedatives are used with validated sedation scales that allow for titration to light or deep sedation. Light sedation (unless contraindicated) is preferred. Some commonly used sedation scales include the Richmond Agitation Sedation Scale (RASS – see table), the Ramsay Agitation Scale (RAS) and the Riker Sedation-Agitation Scale (SAS). In some situations, the Glasgow Coma Scale is used to determine the level of consciousness (often after traumatic brain injury). Patients should be monitored every 2 – 3 hours while receiving sedation to make sure they are receiving the least amount of drug to keep them calm and pain-free. Daily interruptions of continuous infusions of sedative drugs ("sedation vacations") are used to assess the readiness to wean off/stop the sedative as soon as possible.

DELIRIUM

Delirium affects up to 80% of ventilated ICU patients and is associated with increased mortality and LOS. Delirium assessment is required. Early mobilization and control of the patient's environment (light, noise, stimuli) is recommended to decrease delirium incidence, but no medications are recommended for prevention. Providing sedation with non-benzodiazepines may decrease the incidence of delirium and/or shorten the duration in patients who already have it. There is little evidence to support the use of haloperidol for treatment of ICU delirium, although this is common in practice. Atypical antipsychotics (primarily quetiapine, which is mildly sedating and has little risk for movement disorders) can be useful (see Schizophrenia/Psychosis chapter).

RICHMOND AGITATION AND SEDATION SCALE (RASS)

SCORE	TERM	DESCRIPTION
+4	Combative	Overtly combative, violent, immediate danger to staff
+3	Very agitated	Pulls or removes tube(s) or catheter(s); aggressive
+2	Agitated	Frequent non-purposeful movement, fights ventilator
+1	Restless	Anxious, but movements not aggressive or vigorous
0	Alert and calm	
-1	Drowsy	Not fully alert, but has sustained awakening (eye opening/eye contact) to voice (≥ 10 seconds)
-2	Light sedation	Briefly awakens with eye contact to voice (< 10 seconds)
-3	Moderate sedation	Movement or eye opening to voice (but no eye contact)
-4	Deep sedation	No response to voice, but movement or eye opening to physical stimulation
-5	Unarousable	No response to voice or physical stimulation

DRUG	SAFETY/SIDE EFFECTS/MONITORING
Pain/Analgesia	
Fentanyl **Hydromorphone *(Dilaudid)*** **Morphine** Remifentanil *(Ultiva)*	See Pain chapter for additional information In critical care patients, monitor BP, HR, respiration, pain and sedation Fentanyl: less hypotension (no histamine release) than morphine, 100x more potent than morphine; rapid onset and short duration of action (half-life increases with duration of infusion), can accumulate in hepatic impairment; CYP3A4 substrate and potential for numerous drug interactions Hydromorphone: very potent, dose carefully
Agitation/sedation	
Dexmedetomidine *(Precedex)* Alpha-2 adrenergic agonist	**WARNINGS** Use with caution in patients with hepatic impairment, diabetes, heart block, bradycardia, severe ventricular dysfunction, hypovolemia or chronic hypertension **SIDE EFFECTS** Hypo/hypertension, bradycardia, dry mouth, nausea, constipation **MONITORING** BP, HR, sedation scale **NOTES** Does not require refrigeration. Duration of infusion should not exceed 24 hours per FDA labeling. Used for sedation in intubated and non-intubated patients; patients are arousable and alert when stimulated (less respiratory depression than other sedatives).
Propofol *(Diprivan)* Short-acting general anesthetic	**CONTRAINDICATIONS** Hypersensitivity to egg, egg product, soy or soy product **SIDE EFFECTS** Hypotension, apnea, hypertriglyceridemia, green urine/hair/nail beds, propofol-related infusion syndrome (PRIS – rare but can be fatal), myoclonus, pancreatitis, pain on injection (particularly peripheral vein), QT prolongation **MONITORING** BP, HR, RR, sedation scale, triglycerides (if administered longer than 2 days), signs and symptoms of pancreatitis **NOTES** Shake well before use. Do not use if there is separation of phases in the emulsion. Use strict aseptic technique due to potential for bacterial growth. Discard vial and tubing within 12 hours of use. If transferred to a syringe prior to administration, must discard syringe within 6 hours. Do not use a filter < 5 micron for administration. Does not require refrigeration. Oil-in-water emulsion (opaque, white solution); provides 1.1 kcal/mL.
Lorazepam ***(Ativan,*** *Lorazepam Intensol)* Benzodiazepine	**NOTES** Injection is formulated in propylene glycol. Total daily dose as low as 1 mg/kg/day can cause propylene glycol toxicity (acute renal failure and metabolic acidosis). In critical care patients, monitor BP, HR, RR, sedation scale, s/sx of propylene glycol toxicity (BUN, SCr, lactate, anion gap) if receiving continuous infusion. Limit use for delirium. See Anxiety chapter for additional information.

DRUG	SAFETY/SIDE EFFECTS/MONITORING
Midazolam *(Versed*)* Benzodiazepine Used specifically in acute care settings	**BOXED WARNINGS** Respiratory depression, respiratory arrest, or apnea; start at lower end of dosing range in debilitated patients and geriatric population, do not administer by rapid IV injection in neonates **CONTRAINDICATIONS** Intrathecal or epidural administration (benzyl alcohol in formulation), acute narrow angle glaucoma, use with potent CYP3A4 inhibitors **SIDE EFFECTS** Hypotension **MONITORING** BP, HR, RR, sedation scale **NOTES** Shorter acting than lorazepam if patient has normal organ function (no hepatic or renal impairment or HF). Can accumulate in obese patients (highly lipophilic) and renal impairment (active metabolite) – caution with continuous infusion.
Etomidate *(Amidate)* Nonbarbiturate hypnotic Ultra short-acting; used as an induction agent for intubation	**WARNING** Inhibits 11-B-hydroxylase which can lead to ↓ cortisol production for up to 24 hours **MONITORING** Monitor for adrenal insufficiency (hypotension, hyperkalemia), respiratory status, BP, HR, infusion site, sedation scale
Ketamine *(Ketalar)* NMDA receptor antagonist Used as an induction agent for intubation; used off-label for continuous sedation and other indications	**WARNINGS** Emergence reactions (vivid dreams, hallucinations, delirium), cerebrospinal fluid (CSF) pressure elevation, respiratory depression/apnea, may cause dependence/tolerance **MONITORING** BP, HR, respiratory status, emergence reactions, sedation scale **NOTES** Pretreatment with benzodiazepine can ↓ incidence of emergence reactions (see warnings) by 50%.
Delirium	
Haloperidol *(Haldol)*	See Schizophrenia/Psychosis chapter Commonly used, but not recommended for treatment of delirium in current guidelines
Quetiapine *(Seroquel)*	See Schizophrenia/Psychosis chapter May decrease duration of delirium

**Brand name discontinued but name still used in practice.*

STRESS ULCERS

Stress ulcers can result from the metabolic stress experienced by a patient in an ICU. Patients with critical illness have reduced blood flow to the gut as blood flow is diverted to the major organs of the body. This results in a breakdown of gastric mucosal defense mechanisms, including prostaglandin synthesis, bicarbonate production and cell turnover.

RISK FACTORS FOR THE DEVELOPMENT OF STRESS ULCERS	
Mechanical ventilation > 48H	Major burns
Coagulopathy	Acute renal failure
Sepsis	High dose systemic steroids
Traumatic brain injury	

Histamine-2 receptor antagonists (H2RAs) and proton pump inhibitors (PPIs) are the recommended agents for prevention of stress-related mucosal damage (see Gastroesophageal Reflux Disease & Peptic Ulcer Disease chapter). H2RAs can cause thrombocytopenia and mental status changes in the elderly or those with renal/hepatic impairment. Tachyphylaxis (tolerance) has also been reported. PPIs have been associated with an increased risk of GI infections (*C. difficile*), fractures and nosocomial pneumonia. Patients without risk factors should not receive stress ulcer prophylaxis (see box above).

ADDITIONAL DRUGS USED IN THE ICU AND OPERATING ROOM

ANESTHETICS

Anesthetics are used for a variety of effects including numbing of an area (local anesthesia), to block pain (regional anesthesia) or to cause a reversible loss of consciousness and sleepiness during surgery (general anesthesia). Anesthetics can be given via several routes of administration: topical, inhaled, intravenous, epidural or spinal.

COMMONLY USED ANESTHETICS
Local – lidocaine *(Xylocaine)*, benzocaine, liposomal bupivacaine *(Exparel)*
Inhaled – desflurane *(Suprane)*, sevoflurane *(Ultane)*, isoflurane *(Forane)*, nitrous oxide, others
Injectable – bupivacaine *(Marcaine, Sensorcaine)*, lidocaine *(Xylocaine)*, ropivacaine *(Naropin)*, others

Increasingly, anesthetics are being used with opioids to reduce the opioid requirement for pain control. They work by blocking the initiation and conduction of nerve impulses by decreasing the neuronal permeability to sodium ions. Most patients receiving anesthetics must be continuously monitored (vital signs and respiration). The main side effects of anesthetics include hypotension, bradycardia, nausea and vomiting and a mild drop in body temperature that can cause shivering. Overdose can cause respiratory depression. Allergic reactions are possible. Inhaled anesthetics can rarely cause malignant hyperthermia (MH). Bupivacaine, commonly used in epidurals, can be fatal if administered intravenously. Lidocaine should not be given by dual routes of administration (IV and topical).

Lidocaine/epinephrine combination products are used for some local procedures that require an anesthetic, such as inserting an IV line. The epinephrine is added for vasoconstriction, which keeps the lidocaine localized to the area where the numbing is needed. Deaths have occurred due to mix-ups with epinephrine products and lidocaine/epinephrine products. Be careful to use the proper product, concentration and route of administration.

NEUROMUSCULAR BLOCKING AGENTS

These agents cause paralysis of the skeletal muscle, including those used for respiration. Patients can require the use of a neuromuscular blocking agent (NMBA) in surgery conducted under general anesthesia, to facilitate mechanical ventilation, to manage increased intracranial pressure, to treat muscle spasms (tetany) or to prevent shivering in patients undergoing therapeutic hypothermia after cardiac arrest. The use of NMBAs is typically recommended when other methods have proven ineffective; they are not routinely used in all critically ill patients. These agents have no effect on pain or sedation. Therefore, patients should receive adequate sedation and analgesia prior to starting a NMBA. Patients must be mechanically ventilated as these agents paralyze the diaphragm. These are considered high risk medications by ISMP. All NMBAs should be labeled with a colored auxiliary label stating "WARNING, PARALYZING AGENT"; care should be taken to separate NMBAs from other solutions to avoid confusion and inadvertent administration to a patient for whom it was not intended.

There are 2 types of NMBAs: depolarizing and non-depolarizing. Succinylcholine is the only available depolarizing agent and is typically reserved for intubation. It is not used for continuous neuromuscular blockade. Succinylcholine has been rarely associated with causing MH (particularly when used with inhaled anesthetics). Resembling ACh, succinylcholine binds to and activates the ACh receptors and desensitizes them. The non-depolarizing NMBAs work by binding to the ACh receptor and blocking the actions of endogenous ACh. Patients receiving NMBAs are unable to breath, move, blink or cough. Special care must be taken to protect the skin, lubricate the eyes and suction the airway frequently to clear secretions while NMBAs are being used. Glycopyrrolate *(Robinul)* is an anticholinergic drug that can be used to reduce secretions. Numerous medications can enhance the neuromuscular blocking activity of the NMBAs, leading to toxicity (e.g., aminoglycosides, calcium channel blockers, colistimethate, cyclosporine, inhaled anesthetics, lithium, quinidine, vancomycin). Monitoring for the appropriate depth of paralysis is recommended.

DRUG	SAFETY/SIDE EFFECTS/MONITORING
Depolarizing NMBA	
Succinylcholine *(Quelicin* ***Anectine)*	Short-acting, fast onset (30-60 seconds)
Non-depolarizing NMBAs	
For all non-depolarizing NMBAs	**SIDE EFFECTS** Flushing, bradycardia, hypotension, tachyphylaxis, acute quadriplegic myopathy syndrome (AQMS) with long-term use **MONITORING** Peripheral nerve stimulator to assess depth of paralysis during continuous infusions [also called train-of-four (TOF)], vital signs (BP, HR, RR)
Atracurium	Short t½; intermediate-acting; metabolized by Hofmann elimination (independent of renal and hepatic function)
Cisatracurium *(Nimbex)*	Short t½; intermediate-acting; metabolized by Hofmann elimination (independent of renal and hepatic function)
Pancuronium	Long-acting agent, can accumulate in renal or hepatic dysfunction, ↑ HR
Rocuronium *(Zemuron)*	Intermediate-acting agent
Vecuronium	Intermediate-acting agent; can accumulate in renal or hepatic dysfunction

HEMOSTATIC AGENTS

The term hemostasis means causing bleeding to stop. A variety of hemostatic methods can be used, ranging from simple manual pressure with one finger to electrical tissue cauterization, or the systemic administration of blood products (transfusions) or hemostatic agents. The systemic hemostatic drugs work by inhibiting fibrinolysis or enhancing coagulation. Several factor products are available to treat hemorrhage in patients with hemophilia or rare factor deficiencies *(FEIBA, Coagadex, Adynovate)*. Some hemostatic drugs (e.g., *Praxbind, Andexxa)* have been approved as reversal agents for specific anticoagulants. See the Anticoagulation chapter.

There are many topical hemostatic agents and most are used surgically. These include thrombin in bandages, liquids and spray forms, fibrin sealants, acrylates and a few others (names often include "throm": *Recothrom, Thrombin-JMI, Evithrom)*. A few topical hemostatics are OTC.

DRUG	SAFETY/SIDE EFFECTS/MONITORING
Aminocaproic acid *(Amicar)* Tablet, solution, injection	**CONTRAINDICATIONS** Disseminated intravascular coagulation (without heparin); active intravascular clotting process **SIDE EFFECTS** Injection-site reactions, thrombosis **NOTES** FDA-approved for excessive bleeding associated with cardiac surgery, liver cirrhosis and urinary fibrinolysis. Do not use in patients with active clots, do not give with factor IX complex concentrates due to ↑ risk for thrombosis.
Tranexamic acid **(*Cyklokapron*,** Injection) **(*Lysteda*,** tablet)	**CONTRAINDICATIONS** IV: acquired defective color vision, active intravascular clotting, subarachnoid hemorrhage Oral: previous or current thromboembolic disease, current use of combination hormonal contraception **SIDE EFFECTS** Injection: vascular occlusion, thrombosis Oral: retinal clotting **NOTES** *Lysteda* (oral) is approved for heavy menstrual bleeding (menorrhagia). The injection is approved for bleeding with hemophilia and is often used off-label to control surgical bleeding and trauma-associated hemorrhage.
Recombinant Factor VIIa *(NovoSeven RT)* Injection	**BOXED WARNING** Risk of thrombotic events, particularly when used off-label **NOTES** FDA-approved for hemophilia and factor VII deficiency; has been used successfully off-label for patients with hemorrhage from trauma and warfarin-related bleeding events.

Select Guidelines/References

Singer M, Deutschman CS, Seymour CW, et al. The Third International Consensus Definitions for Sepsis and Septic Shock (Sepsis-3). *JAMA.* 2016; 315(8):801-10.

Rhodes A, Evans LE, Alhazzani W, et al. Surviving Sepsis Campaign: International Guidelines for Management of Severe Sepsis and Septic Shock: 2016. *Crit Care Med.* 2017; 45(3):486-552.

Devlin J, Skrobik, Y, Gelinas C et al. Clinical Practice Guidelines for the Prevention and Management of Pain, Agitation/Sedation, Delirium, Immobility, and Sleep Disruption in Adult Patients in the ICU. Crit Care Med. 2018; 46(9):1532-48.

CHAPTER CONTENT

Background 763
Safe Medication Administration 764
Newborn Baby Health 764
Apgar Scoring 764
Screening and Medications 764
Pre-term Baby Conditions 764
Patent Ductus Arteriosus 764
Persistent Pulmonary Hypertension of the Newborn 764
Respiratory Distress Syndrome 765
Over the Counter Products For Children < 12 Months Old 765
Mild Pain and Fever 765
Intestinal Gas 765
Nasal Congestion 765
Constipation 765
Common Conditions in Young Children 767
Bacterial Meningitis 767
Respiratory Syncytial Virus (RSV) 767
Croup 768
Nocturnal Enuresis 769
Drugs Not Generally Recommended in Pediatrics 770
Avoid in Pediatrics 770
Primary Toxicities from Accidental Overdose in Children 770
Vaccine-Preventable Childhood Diseases 771

PEDIATRIC TOPIC	CHAPTER
Vaccines	Immunizations
Infections (including acute otitis media)	Infectious Diseases
Cough and cold	Allergic Rhinitis, Cough & Cold
Pediculosis (lice) and diaper rash	Common Skin Conditions
Asthma	Asthma
Diabetes	Diabetes
Seizures	Seizures/Epilepsy
Iron and vitamin D recommendations	Dietary Supplements, Natural & Complementary Medicine

CONTENT LEGEND

= Study Tip Gal

CHAPTER 54
PEDIATRIC CONDITIONS

BACKGROUND

Pediatric patients have unique and important differences in drug dosing and metabolism due to physiologic differences that change as they mature. See the table below for age classifications.

AGE CLASSIFICATIONS	
Neonate	0 – 28 days
Infant	1 month – 12 months
Child	1 – 12 years
Adolescent	13 – 18 years

Infants can become seriously ill very quickly. Children must be referred to urgent care in certain situations (see box below).

Several conditions common in younger patients are covered in this chapter. Additional pediatric topics are covered elsewhere in this Course Book (see table on left).

WHEN TO SEEK URGENT CARE FOR A CHILD

- Age < 3 months old with a temperature of 100.4°F (rectal)
- Age 3 – 6 months with a temperature of 101°F (rectal)
- Age > 6 months with a temperature of 103°F (rectal)
- Any cough/cold that worsens or does not improve in several days
- Unusual, severe or persistent pain that does not go away after several hours
- Blood in the urine or stool
- Inability to sleep or drink
- Rash that looks severe or any rash with fever
- Abrasions that are dirty or deep (requiring sutures)
- Limping or unable to move an extremity
- Seizure

SAFE MEDICATION ADMINISTRATION

Household spoons should not be used for measuring medication. All liquid medications should be dispensed with an oral dosing syringe or dosing cup (oral syringes preferred; can decrease measuring errors). The parent (or caregiver) should be able to read the markings on the device when it contains medication. Instruct the parent on how to draw up the correct dose. When dispensing liquid medications that carry high risk, follow safe practice recommendations:

- Stock only one strength if a dangerous drug comes in a variety of strengths. Place the container in a high-risk bin with instructions attached to the container.
- The dose should be written in terms of total mg and in mg/kg per dose.
- The pharmacist should check that the dose is appropriate for the child's weight. Ask the parent for the child's weight if it is not available.
- The container label should include the dose (mg) and the volume (mL). Dispense with a measuring device.

With some high-risk drugs, it is preferable to administer at a medical facility, where help is available if needed.

NEWBORN BABY HEALTH

APGAR SCORING

A newborn's general condition is assessed with an Apgar score, which is taken at one minute and again at five minutes from birth. The Apgar score measures performance in five categories: heart rate, respiratory effort, color, muscle tone, and reflex irritability (the baby's response to suctioning). Each category is rated from 0 (worst score) to 2 (best score). The values are added together for a maximum score of 10. A healthy infant will initially score between 7 – 10. An infant with a lower score requires more medical care.

SCREENING AND MEDICATIONS

Just after birth, newborns are screened for congenital illnesses, such as phenylketonuria and cystic fibrosis. Standard medications given at birth include: intramuscular vitamin K to prevent bleeding, ophthalmic erythromycin or silver nitrate to prevent conjunctivitis, and the first dose of the hepatitis B vaccine. Other treatments may be given for certain patient conditions (e.g., analgesia if being circumcised, light therapy for jaundice).

PRE-TERM BABY CONDITIONS

Low Apgar scores in pre-term infants are usually due to immature lung and heart development. Support for inadequate respiration can include oxygen delivered with a face mask, continuous positive airways pressure (to push oxygen into tiny lung passages) or full ventilator support with endotracheal (mechanical) intubation. Patients on ventilators require sedatives and analgesics; see the Acute & Critical Care Medicine chapter.

Cardiovascular conditions that are common in pre-term infants include hypotension, intraventricular hemorrhage (IVH), patent ductus arteriosus (PDA) and persistent pulmonary hypertension of the newborn (PPHN).

Hypotension is treated primarily with IV fluids. Hypotension can be due to IVH, in which blood from a cranial hemorrhage is seeping into the ventricles in the brain. IVH can require blood transfusions.

PATENT DUCTUS ARTERIOSUS

The ductus arteriosus is a normal opening between the aorta and pulmonary artery in an unborn fetus. After delivery, the ductus arteriosus should close naturally. If this does not occur, it remains open (patent). This is referred to as a PDA and requires medical attention with surgery or drugs. NSAIDs (such as IV indomethacin or ibuprofen) can help the PDA to close by blocking the prostaglandins that keep the PDA open. NSAIDs must be administered within 14 days of birth to be effective. NSAIDs should not be used in the third trimester of pregnancy because they can cause the PDA to close prematurely.

PERSISTENT PULMONARY HYPERTENSION OF THE NEWBORN

When an infant is born, blood vessels in the lungs normally relax, which allows blood flow into the lungs. Failure of this process can cause PPHN. In addition to supportive care, inhaled nitric oxide (NO) to dilate the pulmonary arterioles is the standard treatment. Some of the same drugs used to treat PAH can be used for PPHN, including prostacyclin analogues and PDE-5 inhibitors; see the Pulmonary Arterial Hypertension chapter. PPHN, in infants of any age, may be linked to in utero SSRI exposure.

Pre-term infants have lungs that have not yet fully developed, which increases risk for pulmonary conditions, including respiratory distress syndrome (RDS) and respiratory syncytial virus (RSV).

RESPIRATORY DISTRESS SYNDROME

Respiratory Distress Syndrome (RDS) is caused by a deficiency of surfactant production in lungs that are not yet fully developed. Fetuses begin to produce surfactant at about week 24, and by week 35, are producing an adequate amount. Inadequate surfactant in pre-term infants causes the alveoli to collapse, which causes RDS, followed by respiratory failure and death. Most babies born ≤ 35 weeks gestation will receive surfactant very quickly after birth. Surfactant products can be recognized by either "surf" or "actant" in the name, such as poractant alfa (*Curosurf*) and calfactant (*Infasurf*).

OVER THE COUNTER PRODUCTS FOR CHILDREN < 12 MONTHS OLD

If a condition does not require urgent care, there are several over the counter (OTC) products that are deemed generally safe for use in infants. See box on first page for when to refer a pediatric patient for urgent referral.

MILD PAIN AND FEVER

Aspirin and other salicylate-containing products (bismuth subsalicylate, others) have been associated with Reye's syndrome when used in patients recovering from viral infections (especially influenza and chickenpox). These should not be recommended in anyone < 16 years old because it may not be apparent that a child is recovering from a viral illness. Acetaminophen infant drops and children's suspension are the same concentration to help reduce dosing errors in older children; previously, the infant drops were more concentrated. Acetaminophen is the most common cause of liver failure when used in doses above the safe amount. Accidental acetaminophen overdose can be due to the parent's inadvertent use of acetaminophen in multiple products. Take the time to counsel parents about this danger and the various names under which acetaminophen is packaged. Avoid ibuprofen in infants age < 6 months for pain/fever due to the risk of nephrotoxicity. To prevent dosing errors, pharmacists and parents should be aware that ibuprofen products are supplied in different dosage strengths for infants and children.

In children 6 months of age or older, acetaminophen or ibuprofen are appropriate for treating pain and fever. Often, these are given together in alternating doses (e.g., acetaminophen given first, then ibuprofen given three hours later; each drug is dosed every six hours). Ibuprofen has a longer duration of action and may provide benefit if given before sleep.

With either acetaminophen or ibuprofen infant drops, the medicine can be squirted into the child's mouth. It is acceptable to mix with a small amount of formula, but if the child does not drink the entire dose, it will be difficult to know how much of the dose was taken.

INTESTINAL GAS

Intestinal gas is a common condition with infants and causes distress post-feedings. Simethicone drops can offer mild, if any, benefit. The drug is not absorbed and is safe to use. As the child's digestive tract grows, the crying and fussiness will resolve. Parents can be comforted that symptoms will generally dissipate when the child is around 6 – 8 months old.

NASAL CONGESTION

Nasal congestion is very common in babies and is generally not serious. Children < 2 years old breathe mostly through their nose; they have not yet learned to breathe through their mouths. Smoke, including that from e-cigarettes, causes irritation; do not permit anyone to smoke near children. Using a car seat indoors to sit the child upright can help. A cool mist humidifier near the bedside can reduce congestion – especially in the winter months when the home is heated. A steamy bathroom can help relieve congestion. A parent can sit with the child outside the shower, while hot water runs. Care should be taken to avoid hot water or steam getting near the child's skin, as burns could result. Gentle suction with saline drops or spray to loosen the mucus can provide relief. Suction bulbs are sold in pharmacies.

According to FDA recommendations, OTC cough and cold medications should not be used in children age < 2 years old. Manufacturer's labels state, "do not use" in children under age 4, and the American Academy of Pediatrics has recommended against their use in patients under age 6, due to inadequate data on efficacy and the potential for medication errors and adverse effects.

CONSTIPATION

Oral polyethylene glycol 3350 (*MiraLax*) is recommended for treatment of intermittent constipation. This use is off-label and assumes the child can swallow the medication. Polyethylene glycol 3350 is dosed at 0.2 – 0.8 g/kg/day. Dietary measures (prunes or pears, either the fruit or juice) are helpful. OTC pediatric-size glycerin suppositories are commonly used for quick relief of constipation in an uncomfortable baby, although the FDA-approved indication is for children age 2 years and older. Any child with ongoing constipation issues should be seen by a pediatrician.

Select OTC Products for Infants

DRUG	DOSING	SAFETY/SIDE EFFECTS/MONITORING
Fever		
Acetaminophen (*Children's Tylenol, PediaCare Infants' Fever Reducer/Pain Reliever,* others)	10-15 mg/kg/dose every 4-6 hours (max 75 mg/kg/day) All acetaminophen oral liquid formulations (infants and children) are the same concentration: 160 mg/5 mL	For simplicity, age and weight-based dosing for infants is on the side of the dropper container Caution for incorrect dosing or overdose from use of multiple products 
Ibuprofen (*Infants' Advil Drops, Motrin Infant Drops, Advil* or *Motrin* children's suspension, others)	5-10 mg/kg/dose every 6-8 hours (max 40 mg/kg/day) Infant drop strength: 50 mg/1.25 mL Children's suspension strength: 100 mg/5 mL	Indicated for infants ≥ 6 months old Caution for nausea 
Intestinal Gas		
Simethicone (*Mylicon Infants' Gas Relief Drops, Gas Relief Infant*)	20 mg, 1-4 times/day PRN	Take after meals for mild gas pains Shake drops before using; can mix with water, formula or other liquids
Nasal dryness/congestion		
NaCl 0.9% intranasal saline solution (*Little Remedies Saline Nasal Drops, Ocean for Kids*)	2-6 drops per nostril PRN	See Allergic Rhinitis, Cough & Cold chapter; saline can be used with a suction bulb
Constipation		
Polyethylene glycol (*MiraLax*)	Age ≥ 6 months, starting dose: 0.4 gram/kg. Dose range: 0.2-0.8 gram/kg/day (max 17 grams) Dissolve in at least 4 oz water or other beverage The capful (filled to the indicated line) contains ~17 grams	Instruct parent to discuss with the pediatrician if using more than occasionally
Glycerin suppositories (*Pedia-Lax*)	1 pediatric suppository per dose Insert high into the rectum; retain for ~15 minutes	Instruct parent to discuss with the pediatrician if using more than occasionally

CLINICAL SCENARIO

The father of LC, a 9-month-old female patient, presents to a community pharmacy stating that she has a rectal temperature of 100.6°F. The father asks for a treatment recommendation for LC. He states that the child weighs 18.5 lbs.

Can this patient be treated OTC?

Yes, LC can be treated OTC based on her age (9 months) and temperature (below 101°F). No alarm symptoms are noted (e.g., if the case mentions that the patient has a rash with the fever or has not been able to sleep or drink).

What medication/s and dose/s would be appropriate?

Acetaminophen or ibuprofen (based on her age and no past medical history). Both can safely be given, and can be used together (in alternating doses).

To find the dose, first calculate LC's weight in kg: 18.5 lbs / 2.2 = 8.409 kg

Next, calculate LC's dose range for each medication:

Acetaminophen: 10-15 mg/kg/dose every 4-6 hours	Ibuprofen: 5-10mg/kg/dose every 6-8 hours
LC's dose: 84.09-126.14 mg every 4-6 hours	LC's dose: 42.05-84.09 mg every 6-8 hours

How should the father be instructed to give these medications?

Determine a dose within the range that can easily be given based on the products available:

Acetaminophen: 160 mg/5 mL	Ibuprofen children's suspension: 100 mg/5mL
LC's dose: 96 mg (3 mL) every 4-6 hours	LC's dose: 60 mg (3 mL) every 6-8 hours

The father should alternate between the two medications, keeping at least 3 hours between any doses and at least 6 hours between doses of the same medication. Ibuprofen can be given before bed to help with sleep (lasts longer).

COMMON CONDITIONS IN YOUNG CHILDREN

BACTERIAL MENINGITIS

This topic is included in the Infectious Diseases II chapter, but is emphasized here because of the unique aspects of neonatal meningitis. The fatality rate if untreated is close to 100% and the treatment recommendations are different than in other age groups. This is because the common pathogens differ and there are safety issues with use of ceftriaxone in neonates. The classic signs of meningitis are uncommon in neonates (age 0 – 28 days). Bulging fontanelles (swelling between the bones of the skull) and nuchal rigidity (inability to bend the neck) will be present in < 25% of cases; otherwise, the symptoms are non-specific. A definite diagnosis in a suspected case can be made with a lumbar puncture.

The likely pathogens causing bacterial meningitis in a neonate differ from other age groups due to the vertical transmission of organisms from the mother to the baby in the birth canal. The predominant pathogens are Group B *Streptococcus* (GBS), *Escherichia coli*, *Listeria* and *Klebsiella*. Empiric treatment of meningitis in neonates consists of ampicillin plus either cefotaxime or gentamicin.

Ceftriaxone, which is used in adults, is generally avoided in neonates. Ceftriaxone displaces bilirubin from albumin, which can cause bilirubin-induced brain damage (kernicterus). Ceftriaxone and calcium-containing solutions can precipitate, causing an embolus and death. Concurrent use in neonates is contraindicated. See the Infectious Diseases II chapter for more information on empiric treatment of bacterial meningitis.

AGE	COMMON BACTERIAL PATHOGENS	EMPIRIC TREATMENT
< 1 month	*Streptococcus agalactiae* (Group B *strep*), *Escherichia coli, Listeria monocytogenes, Klebsiella*	Ampicillin + Cefotaxime or Ampicillin + Aminoglycoside (Gentamicin)
1 – 23 months	*Streptococcus pneumoniae, Neisseria meningitidis, S. agalactiae, Haemophilus influenzae, E. coli*	Vancomycin + 3rd generation cephalosporin (Ceftriaxone or Cefotaxime)
2+ years	*N. meningitidis, S. pneumoniae*	Vancomycin + 3rd generation cephalosporin (Ceftriaxone or Cefotaxime)

RESPIRATORY SYNCYTIAL VIRUS (RSV)

Respiratory Syncytial Virus (RSV) infection occurs commonly and nearly all children have been infected by the age of two years. In older, healthy children, the symptoms mimic the common cold, but in premature babies and neonates, RSV can be deadly. RSV is a common cause of bronchiolitis (swelling and mucus build up in the bronchioles). Symptoms include low-grade fever, cough, dyspnea and cyanosis (bluish skin due to lack of oxygen). Similar to other viral infections, the treatment is primarily supportive (supplemental oxygen, IV fluids, suction of secretions). In patients with severe lower respiratory tract RSV infections with an underlying compromising condition (prematurity, cardiopulmonary disease or immunosuppression), treatment with inhaled ribavirin (*Virazole*) can be considered. This drug should not be used for routine cases.

RSV Prophylaxis

No vaccine is available for RSV and no lasting immunity develops after infection. Palivizumab (*Synagis*) is a humanized monoclonal antibody indicated for the prevention of serious lower respiratory tract disease caused by RSV in children at high risk of the disease.

RSV prophylaxis is recommended by the American Academy of Pediatrics (AAP) during RSV season (late fall, early winter, early spring). In addition to premature infants, palivizumab is used for certain infants and children < 24 months with select medical conditions that affect respiration.

Palivizumab is dosed monthly at 15 mg/kg per dose by intramuscular (IM) injection. In neonates and infants, the IM injection site is the anterolateral thigh muscle. The deltoid can be used in children once the muscle mass is adequate, which usually does not occur until at least 3 years of age. Infants should not receive more than five monthly doses during the RSV season. If the baby becomes infected with RSV, no further doses of palivizumab should be given.

WHO SHOULD RECEIVE PALIVIZUMAB (*SYNAGIS*)?

In the first year of life:

- Premature infants born at < 29 weeks gestation
- Premature infants born < 32 weeks gestation with chronic lung disease (CLD) who are < 12 months of age
- Infants < 12 months of age with certain heart conditions

CROUP

Croup, or laryngotracheobronchitis, is usually due to a viral infection which causes inflammation of the upper airway, larynx, trachea and bronchi. Bacterial infections are less common and are often associated with severe symptoms. The inflammation results in the hallmark signs of inspiratory stridor (high pitched breathing sound), barking cough and hoarseness. Croup is most common in children < 6 years old and is often worse at night. The illness is classified and treated by the severity of the symptoms.

Non-Drug Treatment

In mild cases, a child can present with only a croupy cough, which can be managed at home and should resolve within a few days. Cool mist or steam and adequate hydration may help alleviate symptoms, although evidence of benefit is lacking.

Drug Treatment for Mild, Moderate or Severe Illness

Systemic steroids (usually dexamethasone 0.6 mg/kg) are a mainstay of croup treatment for mild, moderate and severe cases. In a typical croup case presenting to an acute care setting with moderate to severe symptoms, a patient having difficulty breathing will be given a systemic steroid and then nebulized racemic epinephrine, if needed. Nebulized racemic epinephrine is a 1:1 mixture of dextro (D) isomers and levo (L) isomers (the L-isomer is the active component). If racemic epinephrine is not available, L-epinephrine is used; this is half of the drug (one of the isomers) and the dose is half of the racemic formulation.

Epinephrine is an adrenergic agonist that relaxes the bronchial smooth muscle and causes bronchodilation. When administered using a nebulizer, the onset of action is fast but the duration of action is short; it lasts up to two hours, at most. A child receiving epinephrine should be monitored for up to four hours for recurrence of symptoms. The child should not be discharged until breathing is easy with no stridor at rest and after receiving steroids to reduce the inflammation.

Some severe symptoms (e.g., stridor at rest, respiratory distress, severe retractions, mental status changes) can require respiratory support such as intubation. Antibiotics are used only if a bacterial infection is present.

System Steroids and Nebulized Epinephrine

DRUG	DOSING	SAFETY/SIDE EFFECTS/MONITORING
Dexamethasone Oral solution, injection (other forms not used in infants)	0.6 mg/kg x 1 PO/IM/IV; max 16 mg/dose	See Asthma chapter for steroid safety issues; this refers to acute use only
Nebulized: Racemic epinephrine 2.25% solution or L-epinephrine 1 mg/mL solution (10 mg racemic epinephrine = 5 mg L-epinephrine)	Racemic epinephrine dose: 0.05-0.1 mL/kg (max 0.5 mL) diluted in 2 mL NS, can repeat Q20 min PRN L-epinephrine dose: 0.5 mL/kg of 1 mg/mL solution (maximum dose: 5 mL) diluted in NS, can repeat Q20 min PRN	**WARNINGS** Caution with cardiovascular disease, cerebrovascular disease, thyroid disease, diabetes (can ↑ blood glucose) **SIDE EFFECTS** ↑ BP, ↑ HR, anxiety, arrhythmia **NOTES** Monitor for recurrent bronchospasm

NOCTURNAL ENURESIS

Nocturnal enuresis, or bed-wetting, is a normal part of a child's development and is not generally treated before age 5 years. Boys (more often than girls) can be developing nighttime bladder control until 7 years of age.

Non-Drug Treatment

Behavioral approaches are used first. Practices that can be effective include positive reinforcement, establishing a normal daytime voiding pattern and a normal bowel pattern, and establishing a normal hydration pattern. Fluid intake should be limited prior to bedtime. Bladder training exercises (such as attempting to hold the urine during the day for a set time period) are not recommended. Embarrassment should be minimized. Behavioral approaches are effective in many children and should be tried for up to three months. If behavioral methods do not result in dryness, either alarm therapy or alarm therapy with drug treatment (desmopressin) can be tried. There are numerous alarms available that attach to the underwear or pajamas and sound an alarm when wet. The child may sleep through the alarm, but generally stops voiding. When the alarm sounds a parent should wake the child and escort him or her to the bathroom.

Alarm therapy can be useful and should be considered for a minimum of three consecutive months. If unsuccessful initially, alarm therapy might work when the child is older and more motivated. Alarm therapy is effective in about two out of three children initially; many will relapse and require the intervention repeated.

Drug Treatment

Desmopressin (oral tablet) is the only preferred medication for enuresis. Desmopressin is a synthetic analogue of antidiuretic hormone (ADH); simulating ADH will ↓ nocturnal urine production. Desmopressin can be used in combination with alarm therapy.

DRUG	DOSING	SAFETY/SIDE EFFECTS/MONITORING
Desmopressin (*DDAVP*) Tablets used for enuresis Tablets, nasal spray or injection used for diabetes insipidus and hemophilia A (to control bleeding)	Start 0.2 mg PO QHS, can titrate to 0.6 mg max	**CONTRAINDICATIONS** Hyponatremia or history of hyponatremia CrCl < 50 mL/min **WARNINGS** Hyponatremia, water intoxication **SIDE EFFECTS** Headache, fatigue, possible ↓ Na due to water retention **NOTES** Limit fluid intake starting 1 hour before dose and until the next morning

DRUGS NOT GENERALLY RECOMMENDED IN PEDIATRICS

- Codeine is metabolized to morphine by the CYP450 2D6 enzyme; certain children over-express this enzyme and consequently, produce a higher than expected amount of morphine. This can result in toxicity and a possible lethal overdose. Codeine use is contraindicated in all patients age < 12 years and in those < 18 years after the most common childhood surgeries (tonsillectomy/adenoidectomy). In January 2018, the FDA changed the labeling for all prescription cough and cold medications that contain codeine or hydrocodone; they are no longer indicated in patients < 18 years old.
- Promethazine is contraindicated in children < 2 years of age due to the potential for severe and potentially fatal respiratory depression.
- Quinolones are not recommended in pediatric patients due to the possibility of adverse effects on cartilage, bone and muscle. In special cases, such as anthrax treatment, they are used on a case-by-case basis.
- Tetracyclines are not recommended in children < 8 years of age because they stain teeth and deposit into mineralizing (i.e., growing) bone and cartilage, which weakens it. One notable exception is in tick-borne Rickettsial diseases (Rocky Mountain spotted fever, ehrlichiosis and anaplasmosis). Doxycycline is the most effective treatment, and is recommended in pediatric patients, as the risk of severe illness or death outweighs the risk of tooth discoloration. See the Infectious Diseases II chapter.
- Several OTC products are not safe in young children; even OTC diphenhydramine can quickly become toxic if used in ages < 6 years.
- Topical teething products containing benzocaine increase the risk of methemoglobinemia. The FDA now recommends against their use in children < 2 years of age, and is attempting to remove these products from the market.

AVOID IN PEDIATRICS

Contraindicated

- Codeine in age < 12 years
- Tramadol in age < 12 years
- Promethazine in age < 2 years
- Ceftriaxone in neonates (1-28 days)

Not generally recommended

- Quinolones
- Tetracyclines in age < 8 years
- OTC teething medications containing benzocaine in age < 2 years
- OTC cough and cold preparations in age < 6 years (per AAP)

PRIMARY TOXICITIES FROM ACCIDENTAL OVERDOSE IN CHILDREN

Iron and acetaminophen are two common culprits of accidental overdose in children. Toddlers put anything in their mouths, especially if it looks like it could be candy. One tablet of several drug classes, including sulfonylureas, can be fatal to an infant. It is important to counsel older patients about the safe storage of medications to prevent accidental overdoses. If the child has ingested anything that could be toxic (even if the ingestion is suspected only) the poison control center should be contacted immediately for advice. Review the Emergency Preparedness, Toxicology & Antidotes chapter for further information on pediatric poisoning.

VACCINE-PREVENTABLE CHILDHOOD DISEASES

Vaccine-preventable diseases occurs more commonly than in previous years due to lower immunization rates in some areas. Recent immigrants who have not received vaccination in their home countries can also introduce diseases. Vaccine information is found in the Immunizations chapter. The symptoms of the more common vaccine-preventable diseases are included here so that the pharmacist can recognize the illness if it presents in a child. Each of the conditions below can lead to severe, permanent damage. Although chickenpox (an acute illness) generally dissipates without long-term consequences, any person who has had chickenpox is at risk for developing shingles later in life. This is a painful condition that results from reactivation of the virus in some nerves. It occurs most commonly in patients > 50 years of age and can lead to postherpetic neuralgia and chronic pain. For additional information, see Infectious Diseases III chapter.

Vaccine-Preventable Childhood Diseases

ILLNESS	CLASSIC SYMPTOMS	SYMPTOM DESCRIPTION
Measles	Koplik spots are small white spots on the inside of the cheeks (inside the mouth) that appear 2-5 days prior to the rash seen below 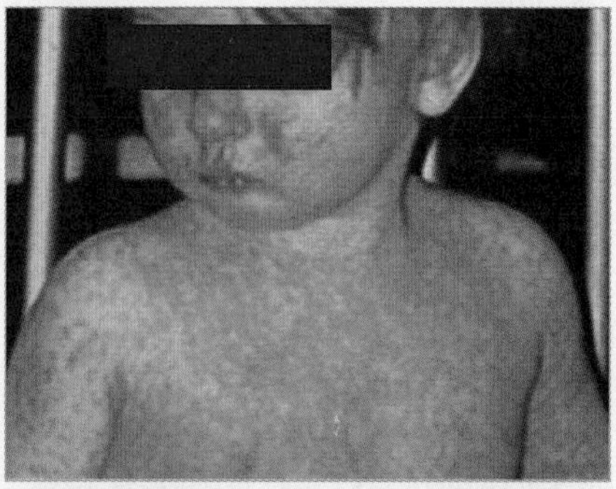	Koplik spots in mouth, maculopapular rash, fever, malaise, cough, rhinitis, conjunctivitis. Transmission is airborne and measles are highly contagious. If not immune, 90% of people who are in contact with an infected person will also become infected.
Mumps	Swollen and tender salivary glands under the ears (parotitis) 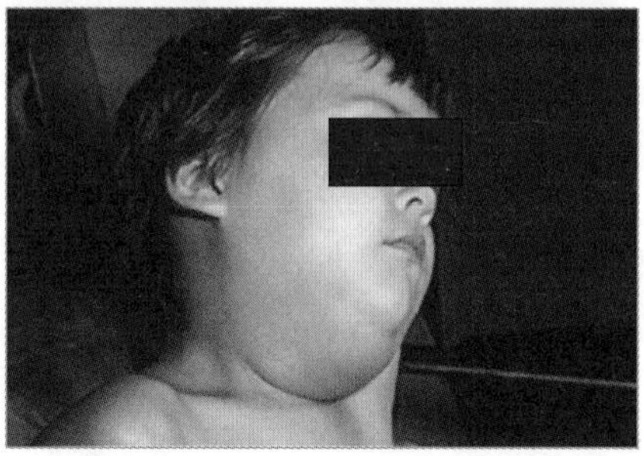	Swollen salivary glands, fever, headache, myalgia, fatigue, loss of appetite; up to 50% of patients have mild or no symptoms.
Rubella	A fine, pink rash that begins on the face and quickly spreads to the rest of the body 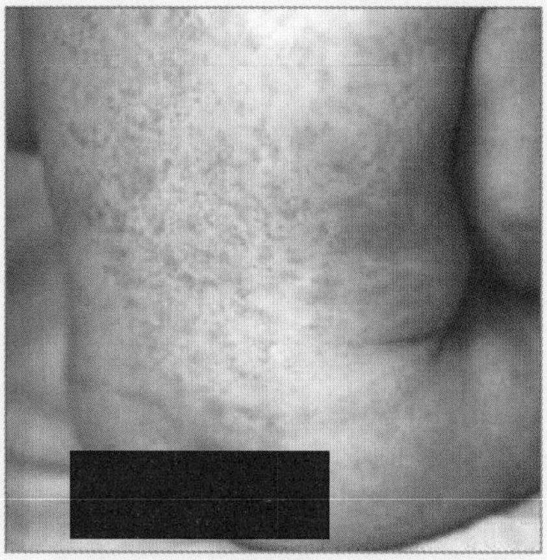	Fever, rash, swollen glands, cold-like symptoms, aching joints; up to 50% of patients have mild or no symptoms. Can cause birth defects if contracted by a pregnant woman.

ILLNESS	CLASSIC SYMPTOMS	SYMPTOM DESCRIPTION
Polio	Child with poliomyelitis 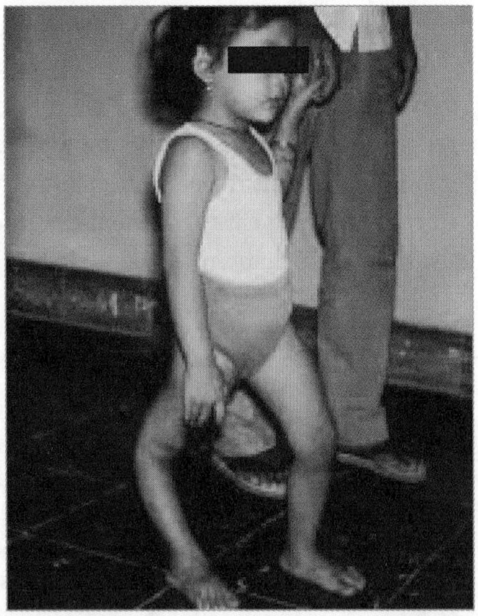	Fever, sore throat, fatigue, nausea, headache, abdominal pain; the majority have no symptoms and never know they were infected – others get severe nerve damage (paralytic polio) and later in life, post-polio syndrome, which causes progressive weakness and cognitive issues.
Pertussis (Whooping cough)	"Whoop" sounding cough; listen to a child making whooping sounds on YouTube (several parents have posted videos)	Sudden cough outbursts, fever, rhinitis, bluish skin (cyanosis), vomiting, fatigue. Can cause respiratory failure and death, especially in infants.
Rotavirus	Diarrhea, fever, vomiting	Severe, watery diarrhea that can lead to dehydration and death. Children are most likely to get rotavirus in the winter and spring (December through June).
Chickenpox (Varicella)	Chicken pox rash (spots) 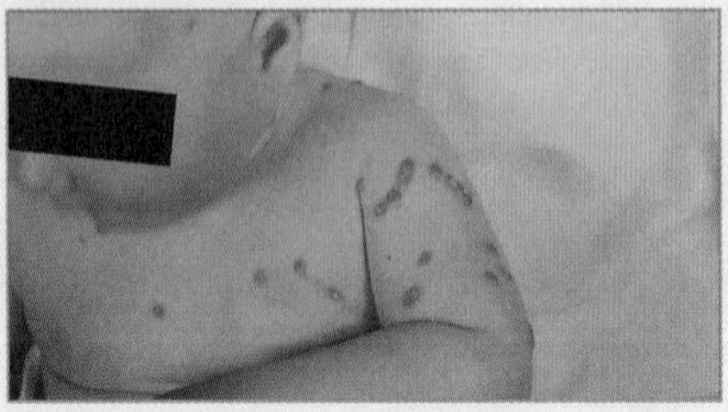 *CDC/ Susan Lindsley*	Itchy rash, fever, malaise. The rash appears as crops of sores (head, then trunk, then arms & legs), that turn into blisters, burst, then form crusts. Long-term implications include shingles (herpes zoster) with risk of ophthalmic involvement and post-herpetic neuralgia (severe pain after the infection).

Select Guidelines/References

Zoorob R, Sidani M, Murray J. Croup: an overview. *Am Fam Physician.* 2011; 83:1067-1073.

Vande Walle J, Rittig S, Bauer S, et al. Practical consensus guidelines for the management of enuresis. *Eur J Pediatr.* 2012; 171(6):971-983.

Tabbers MM, DiLorenzo C. et al. Evaluation and treatment of functional constipation in infants and children. *JPGN.* 2014; 58:258–274.

CHAPTER CONTENT

Background 773
Diagnosis 773
Signs and Symptoms 773
Drug Treatment 774
Inhaled Medications for CF 774
Lung Complications 774
Infections 774
Pancreatic Enzyme Products 776
Common Issues with Pancreatic Enzyme Products 776
CFTR Modulators 777
Other Concerns 777
Patient Counseling 778

CONTENT LEGEND

= Study Tip Gal

CHAPTER 55
CYSTIC FIBROSIS

BACKGROUND

Cystic fibrosis (CF) is caused by a mutation in the gene for the protein cystic fibrosis transmembrane conductance regulator (CFTR). The mutation causes abnormal transport of chloride, bicarbonate and sodium ions across the epithelium, leading to thick, viscous secretions. The thick mucus affects the lungs, pancreas, liver and intestines, which causes difficulty breathing, lung infections and digestive complications. The name cystic fibrosis refers to the characteristic scarring (fibrosis) and cyst formation that occurs within the pancreas. More than 75% of people with CF are diagnosed by 2 years of age, and some will eventually qualify for lung transplantation.

DIAGNOSIS

Newborn screening (NBS) is performed in the U.S. in the first 2 – 3 days after a baby is born. NBS includes testing for CF and other conditions. If the initial screening identifies a risk of CF, then a sweat chloride test (or "sweat test") is performed to confirm the diagnosis. The sweat test measures the amount of salt (chloride) in the sweat, which is high in patients with CF.

SIGNS AND SYMPTOMS

The classic symptoms of CF are salty tasting skin, poor growth and poor weight gain (despite adequate food intake), thick and sticky mucus production, frequent lung infections, coughing and shortness of breath. Patients experience obstruction of pancreatic ducts causing steatorrhea (fatty stools) and poor absorption of nutrients, including fat-soluble vitamins. Clubbing of the fingers is often present. Malnutrition and a failure to thrive can result if CF is not treated.

DRUG TREATMENT

CF is incurable. The primary goals of therapy include preventing/treating lung infections, maintaining adequate nutrition and optimizing quality of life. Most patients will receive airway clearance therapies (see table), inhaled antibiotics targeting *Pseudomonas aeruginosa* and pancreatic enzyme replacement. Advances in research have led to the development of new, targeted CFTR modulators that reduce the frequency of exacerbations and may be appropriate for some patients. Early diagnosis and a comprehensive treatment plan can improve survival and quality of life. Specialty clinics for CF can be found in many communities.

LUNG COMPLICATIONS

Multiple medications are used to help manage the thick mucus and reduce the risk of lung infections. When patients are taking several medications, administering them in the correct order is critical to maximize absorption and effect. Airway clearance therapies (e.g., bronchodilator, hypertonic saline and dornase alfa) are given before inhaled antibiotics (see Study Tip Gal for proper order).

INHALED MEDICATIONS FOR CF

ORDER	INTERVENTION	PURPOSE
1st	Inhaled bronchodilators (e.g., albuterol)	Open the airways
2nd	Hypertonic saline (e.g., *HyperSal*)	Mobilize mucus to improve airway clearance
3rd	Dornase alfa (*Pulmozyme*)	Thins mucus to promote airway clearance
4th	Chest physiotherapy	Mobilize mucus to improve airway clearance
5th	Inhaled antibiotics	Control airway infection

Most patients will require oral medications (e.g., pancreatic enzyme products, azithromycin). These can be given at any time.

INFECTIONS

Intermittent Infection

Impaired mucus clearance predisposes patients with CF to bacterial colonization and lung infections. The most common organisms early in the disease are *Staphylococcus aureus* and *Haemophilus influenzae*, followed by *Pseudomonas aeruginosa* in adolescents and adults. Acute pulmonary exacerbations are characterized by an increase in cough, sputum production with a change in sputum color (greenish), shortness of breath and a rapid decline in FEV1. Treatment often includes an extended course of antibiotics (2 – 4 weeks) and modalities to increase airway clearance.

For infections caused by *Pseudomonas aeruginosa*, two IV drugs are recommended to provide potential synergy and prevent resistance. These include aminoglycosides, beta-lactams, quinolones and others that cover *Pseudomonas aeruginosa*. See Infectious Diseases I chapter for a complete discussion of treatment options for *Pseudomonas aeruginosa*. Doses tend to be larger than normal to address altered pharmacokinetics in patients with CF, obtain therapeutic drug concentrations in lung tissue and to overcome reduced susceptibility of the bacteria chronically colonizing the airways.

Chronic Infection

Lung infections occur intermittently at first, but eventually become chronic. Chronic lung infections with *Pseudomonas aeruginosa* are associated with a more rapid decline in pulmonary function. Inhaled antibiotics are recommended for patients with chronic *Pseudomonas aeruginosa* lung infections to reduce the bacterial burden. Treatment is cycled with 28 days on therapy, followed by 28 days off. This is associated with an improvement in lung function and a reduction in the frequency of acute pulmonary exacerbations. The frequency of exacerbations is strongly associated with lung function decline and shortened survival in CF. If a patient is using a bronchodilator and/or mucolytic, these should be given prior to the antibiotic inhalation (see Study Tip Gal).

A six month trial of oral azithromycin can be considered for patients with chronic infection who are worsening on conventional treatment. Azithromycin has no direct bactericidal activity against *Pseudomonas*, but disrupts biofilm formation by the bacteria which can improve lung function and decrease exacerbations.

Treatment for Lung Complications and Infections

DRUG	DOSING	SAFETY/SIDE EFFECTS/MONITORING
Airway Clearance Therapies		
Bronchodilator (e.g., albuterol)	2-4 times daily	Refer to Asthma chapter
Hypertonic saline (*HyperSal, PulmoSal*) 4 mL unit dose vials	4 mL via a nebulizer 2-4 times daily	Hypertonic saline is a high-alert drug, especially with IV administration. For CF therapy, hypertonic saline is supplied as small ampules that are delivered via a nebulizer. *PulmoSal* is buffered to match physiologic pH of the airway surface liquid.
Dornase alfa (*Pulmozyme*) 2.5 mg single use ampule	2.5 mg daily with recommended nebulizer and compressor system Do not mix with any other drug in the nebulizer	Works by degrading extracellular DNA in the lungs to decrease mucus viscosity **CONTRAINDICATIONS** Hypersensitivity to Chinese Hamster Ovary (CHO) products **SIDE EFFECTS** Chest pain, fever, rash, rhinitis, laryngitis, voice alteration, throat irritation **NOTES** Store the ampules in the refrigerator (do not expose to room temperature ≥ 24 hours) Protect from light
Antibiotics, Inhaled – via inhalation to target *Pseudomonas aeruginosa*		
Tobramycin Inhalation Solution (*Bethkis, Kitabis Pak, TOBI*) *TOBI, Kitabis:* 300 mg/5 mL single use ampule *Bethkis:* 300 mg/4 mL single use ampule	300 mg via nebulizer Q12H x 28 days, followed by 28 days off cycle Indicated in patients ≥ 6 years who are colonized with *Pseudomonas aeruginosa* to reduce infection/hospitalization Do not mix with any other drug in the nebulizer	**SIDE EFFECTS** Ototoxicity, tinnitus, voice alteration, mouth and throat pain, dizziness, bronchospasm **NOTES** Doses should be taken at least 6 hours apart Refrigeration recommended; can be kept at room temperature up to 28 days Store in foil pouch to protect from light *TOBI:* Use with *PARI LC Plus* reusable nebulizer and *DeVilbiss Pulmo-Aide* air compressor *Bethkis:* Use with *PARI LC Plus* nebulizer and *Vios* air compressor Little systemic absorption
Tobramycin Inhalation Powder (*TOBI Podhaler*) 28 mg capsules in blister card	112 mg (4 x 28 mg caps) Q12H x 28 days, followed by 28 days off cycle Indicated in patients ≥ 6 years who are colonized with *Pseudomonas aeruginosa* to reduce infection/hospitalization	**SIDE EFFECTS** Similar to above **NOTES** Doses should be taken at least 6 hours apart Store capsules at room temperature in a dry place Use with *Podhaler* (device that comes with the capsules); do not swallow capsules Little systemic absorption
Aztreonam (*Azactam* - IV, *Cayston* - inhalation solution)	75 mg via nebulizer TID x 28 days, followed by 28 days off cycle Indicated in patients ≥ 7 years who are colonized with *Pseudomonas aeruginosa* to reduce infection/hospitalization Do not mix with any other drug in the nebulizer	**SIDE EFFECTS** Allergic reactions (may be severe), bronchospasm, fever, wheezing, cough, chest discomfort **NOTES** Doses should be taken at least 4 hours apart Refrigeration recommended (can be kept at room temperature up to 28 days) Reconstitute with 1 mL of sterile diluent (provided); give immediately Use with *Altera* nebulizer system Protect from light
Antibiotic, Oral – to ↓ inflammation and ↓ exacerbations		
Azithromycin (*Zithromax*) Off-label	< 40 kg: 250 mg 3 times/week ≥ 40 kg: 500 mg 3 times/week	**SIDE EFFECTS** In CF patients: tinnitus, nausea, risk of QT prolongation **NOTES** Do not use as monotherapy in individuals with nontuberculous mycobacteria lung infections

PANCREATIC ENZYME PRODUCTS

The thick mucus in CF obstructs pancreatic enzyme flow, resulting in a lack of these enzymes reaching the gastrointestinal tract and malabsorption. Frequent, greasy, oily, foul-smelling stools are manifestations of pancreatic insufficiency. Most CF patients need to supplement their diet with appropriate amounts of pancreatic enzyme products (PEPs). This is called pancreatic enzyme replacement therapy (PERT).

Pancrelipase is a natural product harvested from porcine pancreatic glands which contains a combination of lipase, amylase and protease. PEPs are formulated to dissolve in the more basic pH of the duodenum so they can act locally to break down fat, starches and protein. The dose is individualized for each patient and is based on the lipase component. Once PEP therapy is started, the dose is adjusted every 3 – 4 days until stools are normalized.

DRUG	DOSING	SAFETY/SIDE EFFECTS/MONITORING
Pancrelipase ***(Creon, Viokace, Zenpep****, Lip-Prot-Amyl, Pancreaze, Pertzye, Ultresa)*	**Initial** Age < 1 year: varies by product Age 1-3 years: Lipase 1,000 units/kg/meal Age ≥ 4 years: Lipase 500 units/kg/meal **Max (all ages)** Lipase ≤ 2,500 units/kg/meal or ≤ 10,000 units/kg/day; doses > 6,000 units/kg/meal are associated with colonic stricture	**WARNINGS** Fibrosing colonopathy advancing to colonic strictures (rare: higher risk with doses > 10,000 lipase units/kg/day), mucosal irritation, hyperuricemia **SIDE EFFECTS** Abdominal pain, flatulence, nausea, HA, neck pain **MONITORING** Abdominal symptoms, nutritional intake, weight, height (children), stool, fecal fat

COMMON ISSUES WITH PANCREATIC ENZYME PRODUCTS

Pancreatic enzyme replacement helps patients with CF digest food, maintain weight and improve nutrient absorption.

- PEP formulations are not interchangeable. Commonly used products are *Creon*, *Viokace* and *Zenpep*.
- *Viokace* is the only PEP that is a tablet. It is non-enteric coated and must be given with a PPI.
- All other PEPs are capsules.
  - Do not crush or chew the contents of the capsules.
  - Delayed-release capsules with enteric-coated microspheres or microtablets may be opened and sprinkled on soft, acidic foods (pH ≤ 4.5) like applesauce). Avoid foods with high pH such as dairy.
  - Do not retain the capsule contents in the mouth. Swallow immediately and follow with water to avoid mucosal irritation and stomatitis.
- Take PEPs before or with all meals and snacks. High fat meals may require higher doses.
  - Use 50% of the mealtime dose with snacks.
- Protect from moisture; dispense in original container (exceptions: *Zenpep* and some *Creon* strengths). Do not refrigerate.

CYSTIC FIBROSIS TRANSMEMBRANE CONDUCTANCE REGULATOR (CFTR) MODULATORS

Ivacaftor works by increasing the time the CFTR channels remain open, which enhances chloride transport activity. Lumacaftor and tezacaftor help correct the CFTR folding defect, which increases the amount of CFTR delivered to the cell surface. Because each drug is approved for very specific mutations, genotype testing must be performed if the patient's CF genotype is unknown.

The most common mutation in the CFTR gene is a homozygous F508del mutation (two copies of the same allele). Both combination products (*Orkambi* and *Symdeko*) are approved for the most common CF mutation.

DRUG	APPROVED MUTATION	SAFETY/NOTES
Ivacaftor (*Kalydeco*) Tablet, oral granules	At least one mutation responsive to *Kalydeco*, but not approved for the homozygous F508del mutation	**WARNINGS** ↑ LFTs, cataracts in children **NOTES** Take with high fat containing food Approved ages for use: ■ *Kalydeco:* ≥ 12 months of age ■ *Orkambi:* ≥ 2 years of age ■ *Symdeko:* ≥ 12 years of age
Lumacaftor/ivacaftor (*Orkambi*) Tablet	For homozygous F508del mutation only	
Tezacaftor/ivacaftor (*Symdeko*) Co-packaged tablets	For homozygous F508del mutation or at least one other CFTR mutation responsive to *Symdeko*	

CFTR Modulator Drug Interactions

- Ivacaftor is a substrate of CYP450 3A4 (major) and should be avoided with strong CYP3A4 inducers. Dosage adjustments may be required when CFTR modulators are used with CYP3A4 inhibitors.

OTHER CONCERNS

CF is usually diagnosed in very young children. Appropriate measures to address the patient's growth, nutrition, bone health and other CF complications are critical.

- A high-fat and calorically-dense diet is recommended to help with nutrition, normal weight and growth, increased energy needs and to prolong survival.
- Vitamin supplements are required, especially the fat-soluble vitamins A, D, E and K for normal cellular function. Calcium and vitamin D intake/absorption should be monitored to maximize bone health.
- Many patients with CF will eventually require insulin for treatment of CF-related diabetes mellitus.
- If the patient maintains good health, the chances of qualifying for a transplant are improved.

PATIENT COUNSELING

TOBRAMYCIN

TOBI Podhaler

- Do not swallow the capsules. Use the *Podhaler* device to inhale the powder in the capsules. This medication is not used with a nebulizer.
- Use a new *Podhaler* device every seven days.
- One dose consists of four capsules, inhaled one at a time. Take doses as close to 12 hours but no less than six hours apart. Inhale one capsule through the *Podhaler* device before removing the next capsule from the packaging.
- Make sure to finish the whole dose of *TOBI*. Do not leave any medication in the capsules.
- The medication comes in four weekly packs containing seven blister cards of eight capsules each (four for each morning and evening). Store capsules at room temperature in a dry place.

TOBI Inhalation for Nebulization

- Twist the ampule open and squeeze the contents into the nebulizer cup.
- Sit or stand in an upright position and breathe through your mouth (use nose clips if easier). Continue until all the medicine is gone and there is no mist being produced.
- Clean the nebulizer as instructed after each use. Every other treatment day, disinfect the nebulizer parts (except tubing) by boiling them in water for a full 10 minutes. Do not share nebulizers.

PANCREATIC ENZYME PRODUCTS

- The most common side effects are stomach pain, bloating, gas, nausea, headache and neck pain.
- The MedGuide contains important information about the medication, including a rare bowel disorder that can happen with some people.
- Take at the beginning of a meal or snack. At snacks give half of the meal-time dose. If you forget to give the medicine with the meal, wait until the next scheduled dose. Do not double the dose to make up for missed doses.
- Swallow whole. Do not let your child chew, crush or hold the medicine in the mouth or the mouth can become sore.
- If it is difficult to swallow the capsules, the contents can be sprinkled on a spoonful of soft food such as applesauce, pureed bananas or pears. Once the contents are sprinkled on the food, it needs to be used right away. Do not let your child chew it, just swallow.
- Do not mix with dairy products such as milk or yogurt.
- Have your child drink lots of non-caffeinated liquids every day.

Select Guidelines/References

ECFS Best Practice Guidelines: The 2018 Revision. *J Cyst Fibros* 2018;17:153-78.

Cystic Fibrosis Foundation: Clinical Care Guidelines. https://www.cff.org/Care/Clinical-Care-Guidelines/ (accessed 2019 Jan 16).

CHAPTER CONTENT

Background ...779
Prevention of Graft Rejection ...779
Induction Immunosuppression ...780
Maintenance Immunosuppression ...781
Drug Interactions ...785
Organ Transplant Complications ...785
Transplant Drugs: What's Used, When ...785
Cardiovascular Disease ...785
Cancer ...785
Monitoring by Patient & Health Care Team ...786
Acute Rejection ...786
Reducing Infection Risk ...786
Vaccine-Preventable Illness in Transplant Recipients ...786
Patient Counseling ...787

CHAPTER 56
TRANSPLANT

BACKGROUND

Transplantation is one of the most challenging and complex areas of modern medicine. The main goal of transplant medications is to prevent rejection. Rejection occurs when the body has an immune response to the transplanted organ, which can lead to transplant failure and can require immediate removal of the transplanted organ. Organs that have been successfully transplanted include the kidney, liver, pancreas, heart and lungs. Kidney and liver transplants are the most common.

PREVENTION OF GRAFT REJECTION

Prior to any transplant, tissue typing or crossmatching is performed to assess donor-recipient compatibility for human leukocyte antigen (HLA) and ABO blood group. A mismatch in either instance would lead to a fast, acute rejection (see box on left). This is followed by a Panel Reactive Antibody (PRA) test that is taken to gauge the degree to which the recipient is "sensitized" to foreign (or "non-self") proteins. A high score correlates with the likelihood of graft rejection and could necessitate some type of desensitization protocol prior to the transplant. Patients with a higher PRA result are likely to wait longer for a suitable donor.

An allograft is the transplant of an organ or tissue from one individual to another of the same species with a different genotype. This can also be called an allogenic transplant or homograft. A transplanted organ from a genetically identical donor (such as an identical twin) is called an isograft. An autograft (also termed autologous transplant) is a transplant in the same patient, from one site to another (e.g., autologous stem cell transplant or skin grafting).

AVOIDING AN "ABO MISMATCH" OR INCOMPATIBILITY REACTION

Type O blood does not cause an immune response when it is received by people with type A, type B, or type AB blood. This is why type O blood cells can be given to patients of any blood type. People with type O blood are called "universal donors."

Type AB blood does not react against type A, type B or type AB blood.

Type A blood reacts against type B or type AB blood.

Type B blood reacts against type A or type AB blood.

Type O blood reacts against type A, type B or type AB blood (Type O can only receive Type O).

CONTENT LEGEND

= Study Tip Gal

When the immune system recognizes the new organ as foreign and attempts to protect the rest of the body by attacking it, this is known as rejection. Rejection can be hyperacute, acute or chronic. Hyperacute rejection occurs in the operating room within hours of the transplant and is due to some type of mismatch; no treatment exists, and the transplanted organ must be removed to avoid death. Acute rejection mostly occurs within the first three months following transplant, but can occur at any time. This is discussed at the end of this chapter. Chronic rejection occurs over a long period of time and slowly leads to failure of the transplanted organ. There is no current treatment for chronic rejection.

Immunosuppressants are given just prior to transplant (induction immunosuppression), chronically after transplant (maintenance immunosuppression) and in the event of acute rejection. These medications prevent or stop the patient's own immune system from attacking the new organ.

INDUCTION IMMUNOSUPPRESSION

Induction immunosuppression is given before or at the time of transplant to prevent acute rejection during the early post-transplant period by providing a high degree of immunosuppression. It consists of a short course of effective intravenous (IV) medication, either a biological drug or monoclonal antibody (these end in -mab) sometimes combined with high-dose IV steroids.

The most commonly used induction drug is basiliximab, an interleukin-2 (IL-2) receptor antagonist. The IL-2 receptor is expressed on activated T-lymphocytes and is a critical pathway for activating T-lymphocytes to attack and reject the organ. Basiliximab does not deplete immature T-lymphocytes and therefore cannot be used for treatment of rejection (only prevention). Because the protein is humanized, infusion-related reactions are unlikely, and pre-medication is not necessary.

As an alternative to basiliximab, patients at higher risk of rejection can receive a lymphocyte-depleting medication, antithymocyte globulin. These drugs are made by injecting human T-lymphocytes into animals, allowing the animals to make antibodies against the T-lymphocytes, and then administering the animal's purified antibodies back to the human transplant recipients. Because they deplete both mature and immature T-lymphocytes, they can be used for both induction and treatment of rejection. In some cases, induction can be achieved with higher doses of the same drugs used for maintenance. Alemtuzumab, a monoclonal antibody usually used for leukemia and multiple sclerosis, can also be used off-label for induction. Induction immunosuppression is not required if the transplant is from an identical twin.

DRUG	SAFETY/SIDE EFFECTS/MONITORING
Antithymocyte globulins – Reverse rejection by binding to antigens on T-lymphocytes (killer cells) and interfering with their function.	
Antithymocyte Globulin **(*Atgam*** – Equine) **(*Thymoglobulin*** – Rabbit) Injection Dosing: normal equine doses are approximately 10-fold greater than the rabbit product (5-15 mg/kg/day vs. 1-1.5 mg/kg/day IV, respectively, for 5-14 days)	**BOXED WARNING** Administer under the supervision of a physician experienced in immunosuppressive therapy. Adequate laboratory and supportive medical resources must be readily available (e.g., epinephrine). Anaphylaxis can occur; intradermal skin testing recommended prior to 1st dose. **SIDE EFFECTS** Infusion-related reactions (fever, chills, pruritus, rash, hypotension; particularly common with the first dose), infections, leukopenia, thrombocytopenia, chest pain, hypertension, edema. **MONITORING** Lymphocyte profile (T-cell count), CBC with differential, vital signs during administration. **NOTES** Pre-medicate (diphenhydramine, acetaminophen and steroids) to lessen infusion-related reactions. Epinephrine and resuscitative equipment should be nearby.
Interleukin-2 (IL-2) receptor antagonist – Chimeric (murine/human) monoclonal antibody that inhibits the IL-2 receptor on the surface of activated T-lymphocytes preventing cell-mediated allograft rejection.	
Basiliximab (*Simulect*) Injection Dosing: 20 mg IV day 1 then repeat dose 4 days after transplant	**BOXED WARNING** Use only by physicians experienced in immunosuppressive therapy. **SIDE EFFECTS** Well tolerated; side effects listed are rated as severe and > 10%: hypertension, fever, stomach upset/nausea/vomiting/cramping, peripheral edema, dyspnea, upper respiratory irritation/infection, tremor, painful urination. **MONITORING** Signs and symptoms of hypersensitivity and infection.

MAINTENANCE IMMUNOSUPPRESSION

Maintenance immunosuppression is generally provided by the combination of:

- A calcineurin inhibitor (CNI). Tacrolimus is the first line CNI.
- An antiproliferative agent. Mycophenolate is first line in most protocols, but everolimus, sirolimus, belatacept or azathioprine can also be used.
- With or without steroids (typically prednisone). If the patient is low immunological risk, the steroids can be discontinued; otherwise, the long-term adverse effects need to be considered.

Suppressing the immune system via multiple mechanisms through different drug classes is designed to both lower toxicity risk of the individual immunosuppressants and to reduce the risk of graft rejection. Doses and goal blood levels of maintenance immunosuppression vary depending on the type of transplant, drug interactions, time from transplant, patient's risk for rejection and specific transplant center protocols. The following drug tables contain some dosing and blood level information, but remember that this varies in practice.

DRUG	DOSING	SAFETY/SIDE EFFECTS/MONITORING
Systemic steroids – Naturally occurring hormones that prevent or suppress inflammation and humoral immune responses.		
Prednisone, others	2.5-5 mg PO daily, or on alternate days	**SHORT-TERM SIDE EFFECTS** Fluid retention, stomach upset, emotional instability (euphoria, mood swings, irritability), insomnia, ↑ appetite, weight gain, acute rise in blood glucose and blood pressure with high doses. **LONG-TERM SIDE EFFECTS** Adrenal suppression/Cushing's syndrome, impaired wound healing, hypertension, diabetes, acne, osteoporosis, impaired growth in children. See Systemic Steroids & Autoimmune Conditions chapter for further information on chronic steroid use.
Antiproliferative Agents – Inhibit T-lymphocyte proliferation by altering purine synthesis.		
Mycophenolate Mofetil *(CellCept)* **Mycophenolic Acid *(Myfortic)*** Tablet, Delayed Release Tablet, Capsule, Suspension, Injection	1-1.5 g PO/IV BID *(CellCept)* or 360-720 mg PO BID *(Myfortic)*	**BOXED WARNINGS** ↑ risk of infection; ↑ development of lymphoma and skin malignancies; ↑ risk of congenital malformations and spontaneous abortions when used during pregnancy; should only be prescribed by healthcare providers experienced in immunosuppressive therapy. **SIDE EFFECTS** Diarrhea, GI upset, vomiting, leukopenia, hyper/hypotension, edema, tachycardia, pain, hyperglycemia, hypo/hyperkalemia, hypomagnesemia, hypocalcemia, hypercholesterolemia, tremor, acne, infections. **MONITORING** CBC, intolerable diarrhea, renal function, LFTs, signs of infection. **NOTES** REMS drug. *CellCept* and *Myfortic* are not interchangeable due to differences in absorption. *Myfortic* is enteric coated to decrease diarrhea (1% absolute difference with *CellCept* vs. *Myfortic*). Tablets must be protected from light; dispense in a light-resistant container, such as the manufacturer's original container. *CellCept* IV is stable in D5W only. Do not use IV if allergy to polysorbate 80. Decreases efficacy of oral contraceptives.

DRUG	DOSING	SAFETY/SIDE EFFECTS/MONITORING
Azathioprine (*Azasan, Imuran*) Tablet, Injection	1-3 mg/kg PO daily, for maintenance CrCl < 50 mL/min: adjustment required	**BOXED WARNINGS** Chronic immunosuppression can ↑ risk of malignancy (e.g., lymphomas); hematologic toxicities (leukopenia, thrombocytopenia) and mutagenic potential **WARNINGS** Patients with genetic deficiency of thiopurine methyltransferase (TPMT) are at ↑ risk for myelosuppression and may require lower dose; fetal harm, GI (severe N/V/D), hematologic (leukopenia, thrombocytopenia, anemia) and hepatotoxicity **SIDE EFFECTS** GI upset (N/V), rash, ↑ LFTs, myelosuppression **MONITORING** LFTs, CBC, renal function
Calcineurin inhibitors – Suppress cellular immunity by inhibiting T-lymphocyte activation.		
Tacrolimus (*Prograf*) Capsule, Granules for Oral Solution, Injection Extended Release Capsule – *Astagraf XL* Extended Release Tablet – *Envarsus XR* *Protopic* – topical for eczema	Initial: 0.1-0.2 mg/kg/day PO (depending on transplant type) For *Prograf*, give in 2 divided doses, every 12 hours For *Astagraf XL*, give as a single dose, every 24 hours	**BOXED WARNINGS** ↑susceptibility to infection; possible development of lymphoma; administer under the supervision of a physician experienced in organ transplantation in a facility appropriate for monitoring and managing therapy Extended-release tacrolimus associated with ↑ mortality in female liver transplant recipients (*Astagraf XL*) **SIDE EFFECTS** Hypertension, nephrotoxicity, hyperglycemia, neurotoxicity (tremor, headache, dizziness, paresthesia), hypo/hyperkalemia, hypomagnesemia, hypo/hyperphosphatemia, hyperlipidemia, QT prolongation, edema, chest pain, insomnia, generalized pain, rash/pruritus, diarrhea, abdominal pain, nausea, dyspepsia, anorexia, constipation, urinary tract infection, anemia, leukopenia, leukocytosis, thrombocytopenia, elevated liver enzymes, arthralgia **MONITORING** Trough levels, serum electrolytes (K, Phos and Mg), renal function, LFTs, BP, blood glucose, lipid profile **NOTES** *Prograf*: take consistently with or without food; food decreases absorption. Higher fat food decreases absorption the most *Astagraf XL*: take every morning on an empty stomach (1 hour before or 2 hours after a meal) *Envarsus XR*: take once daily on empty stomach, preferably in the morning Do not interchange XL to immediate release (IR) PO IR doses are 3-4 times that of IV; start oral dosing 8-12 hours after last IV dose IV is administered as a continuous infusion in a non-PVC container Numerous drug interactions: this is a CYP450 3A4 and P-gp substrate; avoid alcohol

DRUG	DOSING	SAFETY/SIDE EFFECTS/MONITORING
Cyclosporine (modified: ***Gengraf, Neoral;*** non-modified: ***Sandimmune)*** Capsule, Oral Solution, Injection ***Restasis*** drops for dry eyes	Cyclosporine (modified): initial dosing of ~8 ± 4 mg/kg/day, divided BID and then individualized to achieve target trough level Cyclosporine (non-modified): 3-10 mg/kg/day, divided BID, for maintenance, individualized to achieve target trough level IV cyclosporine (*Sandimmune*) is available; the IV dose is ⅓ of the PO dose Conversion to cyclosporine (modified) from cyclosporine (non-modified): Start with daily dose previously used and adjust to obtain pre-conversion cyclosporine trough concentration; monitor every 4-7 days and dose adjust as necessary Goal trough 100-400 ng/mL (nephrotoxicity can occur at any level)	**BOXED WARNINGS** Renal impairment (with high doses); ↑ risk of lymphoma and other malignancies, including skin cancer; ↑ risk of infection; can cause hypertension; dose adjustments must be made under the direct supervision of an experienced physician, cyclosporine (modified – *Gengraf/Neoral*) has 20-50% greater bioavailability compared to cyclosporine (non-modified – *Sandimmune*) and cannot be used interchangeably **SIDE EFFECTS** Hypertension, nephropathy, hyperkalemia, hypomagnesemia, hirsutism, gingival hyperplasia, edema, hyperglycemia, neurotoxicity (tremor, headache, paresthesia), abdominal discomfort/nausea/diarrhea, increased triglycerides, viral infections, QT prolongation **MONITORING** Trough levels, serum electrolytes (K and Mg), renal function, LFTs, BP, blood glucose, lipid profile **NOTES** Numerous drug interactions: this is a CYP3A4 and P-gp substrate IV: non-PVC sets should be used to minimize leaching of DEHP
Mammalian target of rapamycin (mTOR kinase inhibitor) – Inhibit T-lymphocyte activation and proliferation; may be synergistic with CNIs.		
Everolimus (*Zortress*) Tablet ***Afinitor*** and *Afinitor Disperz* for treatment of breast, pancreatic, neuroendocrine and renal cancers; tuberous sclerosis complex associated cancers and partial seizures	Initial: 0.75-1 mg PO BID; adjust maintenance dose if needed to reach serum trough of 3-8 ng/mL	**BOXED WARNINGS** Only experienced prescribers should prescribe everolimus, ↑ risk of infection and cancers; when used with cyclosporine, reduced doses are recommended; ↑ risk of renal thrombosis can result in graft loss; not recommended in heart transplant **WARNINGS** Angioedema, delayed wound healing, fluid accumulation, pneumonitis (discontinue drug if this develops), hyperlipidemia/hypertriglyceridemia, proteinuria, anemia, lymphocytopenia, thrombocytopenia, new-onset diabetes, male infertility **SIDE EFFECTS** Peripheral edema, hypertension, constipation, N/V/D, headache, hyperglycemia, fatigue, fever, rash/pruritus, xeroderma, acne, onychoclasis (nail disease), abdominal discomfort, stomatitis, dysgeusia, weight loss, dry mouth, risk of renal and hepatic artery thrombosis (do not use within 30 days of transplant) **MONITORING** Trough levels, renal function, LFTs, lipids, blood glucose, A1C, BP, CBC, signs of infection **NOTES.** Everolimus is a CYP3A4 substrate; use with inducers or inhibitors requires everolimus dose adjustments Must be protected from light and moisture

DRUG	DOSING	SAFETY/SIDE EFFECTS/MONITORING
Sirolimus (*Rapamune*) Tablet, Oral Solution	Usually 1-5 mg/day Serum trough concentrations are determined 3-4 days after loading doses and 7-14 days after dosage adjustments; approximate range 4-12 ng/mL, level dependent on concurrent drug use, including potent inhibitors or inducers of CYP3A4 or P-gp	**BOXED WARNINGS** ↑ risk of infection; ↑ risk of lymphoma; only experienced prescribers should prescribe sirolimus; not recommended for use in liver or lung transplantation **WARNINGS** Impaired wound healing, angioedema, fluid accumulation, decline in renal function, hyperlipidemia, latent viral infections, ↑ risk of hemolytic uremic syndrome when used with a CNI **SIDE EFFECTS** Irreversible pneumonitis/bronchitis/cough (discontinue therapy if this develops), hyperglycemia, peripheral edema, hypertension, headache, pain, insomnia, acne, constipation, abdominal pain, diarrhea, nausea, anemia, thrombocytopenia, arthralgia **MONITORING** Trough levels, LFTs, renal function, blood glucose, lipids, BP, CBC, signs of infection **NOTES** Tablets and oral solution are not bioequivalent Sirolimus is a CYP3A4 substrate; use with inducers or inhibitors requires sirolimus dose adjustments
Belatacept – Binds to CD80 and CD86 to block T-cell costimulation and production of inflammatory mediators.		
Belatacept (*Nulojix*) Injection	Initial: 10 mg/kg on days 1, 5 and then at the end of weeks 2, 4, 8, and 12 after transplantation Maintenance: 5 mg/kg at the end of week 16 after transplantation and then monthly thereafter Dose using TBW and round dose to the nearest 12.5 mg	**BOXED WARNINGS** Increased risk of post-transplant lymphoproliferative disorder (PTLD) with highest risk in recipients without immunity to Epstein-Barr Virus (EBV). Use in EBV seropositive patients only. Increased susceptibility to infection and malignancies; avoid use in liver transplant patients due to risk of graft loss and death; administer under the supervision of a prescriber experienced in immunosuppressive therapy **WARNINGS** ↑ risk of opportunistic infections, sepsis, and/or fatal infections, ↑ risk of tuberculosis (TB) - test patients for latent TB prior to initiation and treat latent TB infection prior to use **SIDE EFFECTS** Headache, anemia, leukopenia, constipation, diarrhea, nausea, peripheral edema, hypertension, hypotension, cough, photosensitivity, insomnia, urinary tract infection, pyrexia, hypo/hyperkalemia, hypophosphatemia **MONITORING** New-onset or worsening neurological, cognitive, or behavioral signs/symptoms [consider progressive multifocal leukoencephalopathy (PML), PTLD, or CNS infection]; signs/symptoms of infection, TB screening prior to therapy initiation, EBV seropositive verification prior to therapy initiation **NOTES** Use silicone-free disposable syringe (comes with drug)

DRUG INTERACTIONS

- Cyclosporine can ↓ mycophenolate and ↑ sirolimus, everolimus and some statins (which transplant patients are usually taking).
- Both cyclosporine and tacrolimus are CYP3A4 and P-glycoprotein (P-gp) substrates. Inducers of either enzyme (e.g., carbamazepine, nafcillin, rifampin) decrease the CNI concentration, and inhibitors (e.g., azole antifungals, diltiazem, erythromycin) increase the CNI concentration. Both interact with the majority of drugs.
- Tacrolimus absorption is decreased by food.
- Azathioprine is metabolized by xanthine oxidase. Avoid using azathioprine with allopurinol or febuxostat (xanthine oxidase inhibitors). Febuxostat is contraindicated. If allopurinol is used, reduce the azathioprine dose by 75%.
- Use of azathioprine with other drugs that can cause myelosuppression should be done cautiously.
- Mycophenolate can ↓ levels of hormonal contraception; mycophenolate can be ↓ by antacids and multivitamins, cyclosporine, metronidazole, PPIs, quinolones, sevelamer, bile acid resins and rifampin and derivatives. Monitor for additive myelosuppression when using mycophenolate with other marrow suppressing drugs.
- Avoid grapefruit juice and St. John's wort with either CNI.
- Caution with additive drugs that are nephrotoxic with tacrolimus and cyclosporine.
- Caution with additive drugs that raise blood glucose with tacrolimus, steroids, cyclosporine and the mTOR inhibitors (everolimus/sirolimus).
- Caution with additive drugs that worsen lipids with the mTOR inhibitors, steroids and cyclosporine.
- Caution with additive drugs that raise blood pressure with steroids, cyclosporine and tacrolimus.

TRANSPLANT DRUGS: WHAT'S USED, WHEN

Immunosuppression protocols vary by center and type of transplant.

Induction Immunosuppressants

- Basiliximab, an interleukin-2 (IL-2) receptor antagonist
- Antithymocyte globulin in patients at higher risk of rejection
- Maintenance drugs at higher doses

Maintenance Immunosuppressants

- The calcineurin inhibitors (CNIs) [tacrolimus (primarily) or cyclosporine]
- Adjuvant agents given with a CNI (to achieve adequate immunosuppression while decreasing the dose and toxicity of the individual agents)
    - Antiproliferative agents (mycophenolate or azathioprine)
    - mTOR inhibitors (everolimus or sirolimus)
    - Belatacept
- Steroids

Infection Risk Reduction

- All transplant recipients must self-monitor for symptoms of infection: fever of 100.5°F (38°C) or higher (lower if elderly), chills, sore throat, ear or sinus pain, cough, more sputum or change in color of sputum, pain with passing urine, mouth sores or a wound that does not heal
- Prophylactic drug use is likely
- Treatment of opportunistic infections is the same as in HIV; see Infectious Diseases IV chapter
- See Study Tip Gal on the next page for the discussion of vaccines

ORGAN TRANSPLANT COMPLICATIONS

CARDIOVASCULAR DISEASE

Many of the medications used to prevent transplant rejection cause metabolic syndrome. These patients are among the highest risk for cardiovascular disease (CVD), so blood pressure, blood glucose, cholesterol and weight must be tightly controlled. Specific goals based on transplant protocols are managed by specialists, including pharmacists, that have received training in transplant medicine. Blood glucose is managed according to the ADA guidelines and cholesterol to the ACC/AHA guidelines. Weight is measured at each visit, and weight loss programs are used as-needed. Refer to the individual chapters for treatment of these conditions.

CANCER

Cancer risk is higher in transplant recipients compared to the general population. Some cancer types are viral-mediated and related to immunosuppression, which causes increased cancer incidence. The cancer risk is similar to that seen with the use of immunosuppressant medications used for autoimmune conditions. For example, the Epstein-Barr virus infects most people without serious consequences. In transplant recipients, there is a marked increase in the risk of malignancies associated with the infection. Age-appropriate cancer screening needs to be performed prior to getting on the list as a transplant candidate. Screening for common cancers is routine, along with lifestyle measures known to reduce risk. Skin cancer is common with transplant, and sunscreen must be used routinely, along with sun avoidance or sun protection with clothing. In addition, CNIs cause photosensitivity. The skin should be assessed professionally at least annually.

MONITORING BY PATIENT & HEALTH CARE TEAM

Monitoring Questions

Is it a symptom of drug **toxicity**?

Is it a symptom of **organ rejection**?

Is it a symptom of an **infection**?

In addition to drug toxicity symptoms, patients need to monitor for symptoms of organ rejection. Common symptoms of acute rejection include flu-like symptoms, such as chills, body aches, nausea, cough, shortness of breath and organ-specific symptoms that depend on the transplant type. For example, heart failure symptoms or a new arrhythmia could be due to heart transplant rejection. A decrease in urine output, fluid retention, blood pressure elevation or graft tenderness could be due to kidney transplant rejection.

Immunosuppressive medications require careful monitoring (including drug trough levels for some) to minimize toxicities and the incidence of rejection.

Keep in mind which maintenance immunosuppressants have the highest incidence of certain adverse effects:

- Nephrotoxicity (tacrolimus and cyclosporine)
- Worsening or new onset diabetes (tacrolimus, steroids and cyclosporine)
- Worsening lipid parameters (mTOR inhibitors, steroids and cyclosporine)
- Hypertension (steroids, cyclosporine and tacrolimus)

ACUTE REJECTION

Acute rejection of the transplanted organ arises from either T-cell (cellular) or B-cell (humoral or antibody) mediated mechanisms. Both types can occur simultaneously. Distinguishing the type of rejection via biopsy is essential in order to determine treatment.

The initial approach is administration of high-dose steroids. For cellular rejection, the steroids and increased levels of maintenance immunosuppression are adequate to treat the rejection. For steroid-resistant rejection, administration of antithymocyte globulin is the next step. Another option for steroid-resistant acute rejection is off-label use of alemtuzumab.

Humoral rejection is more challenging to treat as the preformed antibodies against the graft must be removed and then suppressed from recurring. This process is done via a course of plasmapheresis and administration of intravenous immunoglobulin (IVIG), followed by a dose of rituximab (see the Acute & Critical Care Medicine chapter for more information on IVIG). Rituximab, a monoclonal antibody against the CD20 antigen on B-cells, will prevent further antibody development.

REDUCING INFECTION RISK

The use of potent drugs has made solid organ transplant widely available and successful. The use of strong immunosuppressants correlates with infection risk. The majority of infections are opportunistic, and these are a major cause of death in transplant recipients. Opportunistic infections caused by organisms that are ubiquitous (everywhere) in the environment, rarely cause disease in the immunocompetent host (persons with a functional immune system). Infection prophylaxis is essential; the basics are reviewed in the Study Tip Gal. Infection control must include reducing risk from transmission, such as proper hand-washing techniques (see the Medication Safety & Quality Improvement chapter), air filtration systems, keeping the mouth clean, and keeping away from dusty, crowded areas and sick people. Often the drugs used for opportunistic infection prophylaxis are used for treatment, but in larger doses and possibly given IV. Treatment can require a combination of drugs. Vaccine-preventable illness is an important consideration pre-transplant since live vaccines cannot be given post-transplant.

VACCINE-PREVENTABLE ILLNESS IN TRANSPLANT RECIPIENTS

Required vaccines are given pre-transplant if not current.

Inactivated vaccines can be given post-transplant after 3 – 6 months (once the immune system recovers from the induction immunosuppression).

Live vaccines cannot be given post-transplant.

Important vaccine-preventable illnesses in transplant:

- Influenza (inactivated, not live) annually.
- Pneumococcal vaccine in adults ≥ 19 years.
  - PCV13 first (if never received).
  - PPSV23 at least 8 weeks later.
  - Subsequent doses of PPSV23 should follow current PPSV23 recommendations for adults at high risk (5 years after the first PPSV23 dose). Some transplant centers recommend PPSV23 every 5 years.
- Varicella vaccine.
  - High risk for serious varicella infections, with a very high risk of disseminated disease if infection occurs.
  - Vaccinate pre-transplant.
  - Vaccinate close contacts. Although there is a small risk that transmission could occur (from the vaccine recipient to the transplant recipient), ACIP states that the benefits outweigh the risk of transmission.
  - If a vaccinated household contact develops a rash they are considered contagious, must avoid contact with the transplant recipient and contact their physician.
  - If the transplant patient develops a rash, they need to be seen right away.

PATIENT COUNSELING

All Immunosuppressants

- Take the medication exactly as prescribed by your healthcare provider. It is important that you take your medication at the same time every day. Stay consistent on how you take your medication.
- Never change or skip a dose of medication. Remember, if you stop taking your immunosuppressive medications, your body will reject your transplanted organ.
- Monitor your health at home and keep daily records of your temperature, weight, blood pressure, and glucose (if diabetes is present).
- Do not take any over-the-counter, herbal, or alternative medications without consulting with your healthcare provider.
- Do not get immunizations/vaccinations without the consent of your healthcare provider. Live vaccines must be avoided. Avoid contact with people who have recently received oral polio vaccine, nasal flu vaccine or zoster vaccine.
- You are more likely to develop severe infections due to your suppressed immune system. Avoid contact with people who have the flu or other contagious illness. Practice infection control techniques such as good hand washing and staying away from sick people.
- Chronic immunosuppression is associated with an increased risk of cancer, particularly lymphoma and skin cancer. Protect and cover your skin from the sun. Be sure to use sunscreen with an SPF of 30 or higher. Avoid using tanning beds or sunlamps. People who take immunosuppressive medications have a higher risk of getting skin cancer.
- If getting a blood test to measure the drug level, take your medication after you have your blood drawn (not before). It is important to measure the lowest (trough) level of drug in your blood.

Mycophenolate

- Take exactly as prescribed, every 12 hours (8 AM and 8 PM). It is important that you take your medication at the same time every day.
- If you miss a dose and it is less than four hours after the scheduled dose, take the missed dose and continue on your regular schedule. If you miss a dose and it is more than four hours after your scheduled dose, skip the missed dose, and return to your regular dosing schedule. Never take two doses at the same time. Record any missed doses.
- Take capsules, tablets and oral suspension on an empty stomach, either one hour before or two hours after a meal.
- Do not open or crush tablets or capsules. If you are not able to swallow tablets or capsules, your healthcare provider may prescribe an oral suspension. Your pharmacist can mix the medicine before giving it to you.
- Do not mix the oral suspension with any other medicine.
- This medication can cause diarrhea. Call your healthcare provider right away if you have diarrhea. Do not stop the medication without first talking with your healthcare provider. Other side effects include nausea, vomiting, abdominal pain/cramping, headache, and decreased white blood cells and platelets.
- Do not get pregnant while taking this medication. Women who take this medication during pregnancy have a higher risk of losing a pregnancy (miscarriage) during the first three months (first trimester), and a higher risk that their baby is born with birth defects. Birth control pills do not work as well with this drug.
- Do not take with antacids or multivitamins. Separate by two hours. Avoid use with bile acid resins.
- Mycophenolic acid *(Myfortic)* and mycophenolate mofetil *(CellCept)* are not interchangeable. Do not switch between products unless directed by your healthcare provider. These medicines are absorbed differently. This can affect the amount of medicine in your blood.

Tacrolimus (as *Prograf*)

- Take this medication as directed by your healthcare provider, usually every 12 hours. It is best to take on an empty stomach for best absorption. However it is taken, you must be consistent (with food or without food), and take this medication the same way every day so that your body always absorbs the same amount of drug.
- Avoid eating grapefruit or drinking grapefruit juice while being treated with tacrolimus. Grapefruit can increase the amount of tacrolimus in your bloodstream.
- Tacrolimus has many drug interactions; never start or stop any medication without first discussing the change with the transplant team first.
- Tacrolimus can cause your blood pressure to increase. You are required to check your blood pressure periodically and/or take another medication to control your blood pressure.

- Side effects of tacrolimus also include tremors/shaking, headache, diarrhea, nausea/vomiting, upset stomach, loss of appetite, tingling of the hands/feet, increased blood pressure, increased cholesterol, increased blood sugar, decreased kidney function, and an increase in potassium levels.
- Tacrolimus can cause diabetes. Tell your healthcare provider if you experience any of the following symptoms of high blood sugar: increased thirst/hunger or frequent urination.
- Tacrolimus can cause a condition that affects the heart rhythm (QT prolongation). QT prolongation can infrequently result in serious fast/irregular heartbeat and other symptoms (such as severe dizziness, fainting) that require immediate medical attention.
- High (or low) levels of potassium or magnesium in the blood can increase your risk of certain heart abnormalities called QT prolongation. This risk can increase if you use certain drugs (such as diuretics/"water pills") or if you have conditions such as severe sweating, diarrhea, or vomiting. This drug can increase or decrease your potassium and lower your magnesium levels.

Cyclosporine (as *Neoral*)

- Because different brands deliver different amounts of medication, do not switch brands of cyclosporine without your prescriber's permission and directions.
- Take cyclosporine on a consistent schedule with regard to time of day and relation to meals. Avoid eating grapefruit or drinking grapefruit juice while being treated with this medication. Grapefruit can increase the amount of the cyclosporine in your bloodstream.
- Cyclosporine has many drug interactions; never start or stop any medication without first discussing the change with the transplant team.
- *Neoral* oral solution (cyclosporine oral solution [USP Modified]) should be diluted, preferably with orange or apple juice that is at room temperature. Do not administer oral liquid from plastic or styrofoam cup. The combination of *Neoral* Oral Solution (cyclosporine oral solution, [USP Modified]) with milk can be unpalatable. *Sandimmune* can be diluted with milk, chocolate milk or orange juice. Avoid changing diluents frequently. Mix thoroughly and drink at once. Use the syringe provided to measure the dose, and rinse the container with more diluent to ensure the total dose was taken.
- Cyclosporine can also cause high blood pressure and kidney problems. The risk of both problems increases with higher doses and longer treatment with this drug.
- Side effects of cyclosporine also include increased cholesterol, headache, nausea, vomiting, diarrhea, stomach upset, increased hair growth on the face/body, tremor and acne. If any of these effects persist or worsen, notify your healthcare provider promptly.
- This medication can cause swelling and growth of the gums (gingival hyperplasia). Brush your teeth and floss daily to minimize this problem. See your dentist regularly.

Select Guidelines/References

Kidney Disease: Improving Global Outcomes (KDIGO) Transplant Work Group. KDIGO clinical practice guideline for the care of kidney transplant recipients. *Am J Transplant*. 2009; 9 (Suppl 3):S1-155.

Lucey MR, Terrault N, Ojo L et al. Long-Term Management of the Successful Adult Liver Transplant: 2012 Practice Guideline by AASLD and the American Society of Transplantation. http://www.aasld.org/sites/default/files/guideline_documents/managementadultltenhanced.pdf (accessed 2019 Feb 20).

Costanzo MR, Dipchand A, Starling R et al. The International Society of Heart and Lung Transplantation Guidelines for the care of heart transplant recipients. *J Heart Lung Transplant*. 2010; 29:914-56.

CHAPTER CONTENT

Background 789
- Medical Conditions, Drugs and Weight 789
- Select Drugs/Conditions that Can Cause Weight Gain 790

Treatment Principles 790

Drug Treatment 790
- OTC Supplements 790
- Select Drugs/Conditions that Can Cause Weight Loss 790
- Prescription Weight Loss Medications 790
  - Prescription Weight Loss Drugs: Avoid or Use Caution 791
  - Phentermine/Topiramate ER *(Qsymia)* 791
  - Naltrexone/Bupropion *(Contrave)* 791
  - Lorcaserin *(Belviq)* 791
  - Liraglutide *(Saxenda)* 792
  - Orlistat *(Xenical* and *Alli)* 792
  - Appetite Suppressants (Stimulants) 792

Patient Counseling 793

Bariatric Surgery 793
- Common Nutrient Deficiencies 793
- Medication Concerns 793

CHAPTER 57
WEIGHT LOSS

BACKGROUND

The conditions of overweight and obesity are national health threats and a major public health challenge. Data from the CDC estimates that 70.7% of U.S. adults and 33.4% of children and adolescents are overweight (BMI 25 – 29.9 kg/m^2) or obese (BMI $\geq$ 30 kg/m^2). A person who is overweight is at a higher risk for coronary heart disease, hypertension, stroke, type 2 diabetes, certain types of cancer and premature death. In addition to the health risks, being overweight reduces quality of life and causes social stigmatization and discrimination.

Weight loss must involve an "energy deficit." Calories must be decreased and/or energy expenditure increased in order to force the body to use fat as an energy source. If someone is hungry, it is difficult not to eat. Many weight loss drugs work primarily by increasing satiety (feeling full) or decreasing appetite.

MEDICAL CONDITIONS, DRUGS AND WEIGHT

Prior to starting a weight loss treatment plan, other causes of weight gain should be evaluated and managed, as appropriate. Select drugs and medical conditions can cause weight gain (see Key Drugs Guy on top of the following page). Weight will increase when a medication known to cause weight loss is discontinued, when a medication that causes weight gain is started or if a condition with weight gain is left untreated. Weight will decrease when a condition known to cause weight gain is treated.

CONTENT LEGEND

(💡) = Study Tip Gal   ( ) = Key Drug Guy

SELECT DRUGS/CONDITIONS THAT CAN CAUSE WEIGHT GAIN

KEY DRUGS

Antipsychotics (e.g., clozapine, olanzapine, risperidone, quetiapine)

Diabetes medications (insulin, meglitinides, sulfonylureas, thiazolidinediones)

Divalproex/valproic acid

Lithium

Mirtazapine

Steroids

Conditions:
Hypothyroidism

Others:

Beta-blockers

Dronabinol

Gabapentin, pregabalin

Hormones (e.g., estrogen, megestrol)

MAO inhibitors

SSRIs (paroxetine, others may be weight neutral)

TCAs (e.g., amitriptyline, nortriptyline)

Vasodilators (e.g., minoxidil)

When treating other medical conditions in overweight or obese patients, medications that cause weight gain should be avoided (if able) and preference should be given to medications that can cause weight loss (see Key Drugs Guy on the bottom right).

TREATMENT PRINCIPLES

The American Association of Clinical Endocrinologists/ American College of Endocrinology (AACE/ACE) obesity guidelines recommend various eating plans that are either reduced-calorie (daily deficit ~500 – 750 kcal) or individualized, based on personal and cultural preferences. These include Mediterranean, DASH, low-carb, low-fat, volumetric, high protein and vegetarian diets. Select patients may be candidates for very low-calorie diets.

Physical activity should increase to ≥ 150 minutes per week, performed on three to five separate days. This should include resistance exercises two or three times weekly. Behavioral interventions should be used to assist patients, depending on factors that are hindering successful weight loss. These can include self-monitoring (of food intake, exercise, weight), goal setting, stress reduction, stimulus control, use of social support structures and/or guidance by trained educators.

Weight loss medications should only be used in addition to lifestyle measures when lifestyle measures alone have failed to achieve adequate weight loss, maintain weight loss or prevent continued weight gain. In patients with weight-related complications (e.g., diabetes, dyslipidemia, hypertension, sleep apnea), weight loss medications may be started at the same time as lifestyle measures. As weight decreases, these conditions can improve. Treatment may need to be reevaluated and possibly decreased to prevent adverse effects (e.g., hypoglycemia, hypotension).

DRUG TREATMENT

OTC SUPPLEMENTS

OTC weight loss supplements commonly contain stimulants, such as bitter orange (see the Dietary Supplements, Natural & Complementary Medicine chapter), and/or excessive amounts of caffeine, which can be packaged under different names, (e.g., yerba mate, guarana and concentrated green tea powder). OTC supplements are generally ineffective and are not recommended, as they can be harmful, especially in patients with cardiovascular disease.

PRESCRIPTION WEIGHT LOSS MEDICATIONS

Prescription drugs are not appropriate for patients with small amounts of weight to lose. They are indicated when the BMI ≥ 30 kg/m^2, or the BMI ≥ 27 kg/m^2 with at least one weight-related condition, such as dyslipidemia, hypertension or diabetes. Weight loss medications are only used in addition to a dietary plan and increased physical activity. Per the AACE/ACE guidelines, the selection of a specific weight loss medication is based on the patient's comorbid conditions. Most importantly, the guidelines highlight which medications should be avoided in certain populations (see Study Tip Gal on the following page).

Older stimulant agents (e.g., phentermine, diethylpropion) are only used short-term to "jump start" a diet. The newer agents *Qsymia, Belviq, Contrave* and *Saxenda*, and the *Orlistat* formulations, can be continued long-term for weight maintenance. Weight loss drugs should be discontinued if they do not produce at least a 5% weight loss at 12 weeks.

SELECT DRUGS/CONDITIONS THAT CAN CAUSE WEIGHT LOSS

KEY DRUGS

ADHD drugs (e.g., amphetamine, methylphenidate)

GLP-1 agonists (e.g., exenatide, liraglutide)

Pramlintide

SGLT2 inhibitors (e.g., canagliflozin, empagliflozin)

Topiramate

Conditions:
Hyperthyroidism
Celiac disease
Inflammatory bowel disease

Others:

Acetylcholinesterase inhibitors (e.g., donepezil, rivastigmine, galantamine)

Antiepileptic drugs (zonisamide, ethosuximide)

Bupropion

Interferons

Thyroid drugs (e.g., levothyroxine)

Conditions:
Cystic Fibrosis
GERD or peptic ulcer disease
Lupus
Tuberculosis (active disease)

PRESCRIPTION WEIGHT LOSS DRUGS: AVOID OR USE CAUTION

PREGNANCY	HYPERTENSION	DEPRESSION	SEIZURES	TAKING OPIOIDS
Avoid all weight loss drugs	**Avoid** *Contrave* – contraindicated with uncontrolled BP (contains bupropion) **Caution** *Qsymia* – monitor HR (contains phentermine)	**Avoid in young adults and adolescents** *Contrave* – suicide risk (contains bupropion)	**Avoid** *Contrave* – lowers seizure threshold (contains bupropion) **Caution** *Qsymia* – must taper off slowly if used (contains topiramate)	**Avoid** *Contrave* – blocks opioid receptors (contains naltrexone)

Weight Loss Drugs

DRUG	DOSING	SAFETY/SIDE EFFECTS/MONITORING
Phentermine: sympathomimetic (stimulant); release of norepinephrine stimulates the satiety center which ↓ appetite **Topiramate: ↑ satiety and ↓ appetite, possibly by ↑ GABA, blocking glutamate receptors and/or inhibition of carbonic anhydrase**		
Phentermine/Topiramate ER (*Qsymia*) C-IV REMS drug due to teratogenic risk; obtain pregnancy test before treatment and monthly thereafter; use effective contraception during treatment	Start: 3.75 mg/23 mg PO QAM x 14 days; titrate up based on weight loss Max dose: 15 mg/92 mg PO QAM CrCl < 50 mL/min: max dose is 7.5 mg/46 mg/day	**CONTRAINDICATIONS** Hyperthyroidism, glaucoma, MAO inhibitor use within past 14 days, pregnancy **SIDE EFFECTS** Tachycardia, CNS effects (depression, anxiety, insomnia, suicidal thoughts, headache, paresthesias), constipation, dry mouth, ↓ HCO3, upper respiratory tract infection **NOTES** Taper off due to seizure risk
Naltrexone: ↓ food cravings	**Bupropion: ↓ appetite**	
Naltrexone/Bupropion (*Contrave*)	ER tablet: 8 mg/90 mg Week 1: 1 tab PO QAM Week 2: 1 tab PO QAM, 1 tab PO QPM Week 3: 2 tabs PO QAM, 1 tab PO QPM Week 4+: 2 tabs PO QAM and QPM Do not cut, chew, or crush; swallow whole Fatty food increases drug levels; do not take with high-fat meal	**BOXED WARNING** Not approved for treatment of major depressive disorder (MDD) or psychiatric disorders; antidepressants (bupropion) can increase the risk of suicidal thinking and behavior in children, adolescents, and young adults; not approved for use in pediatric patients **CONTRAINDICATIONS** Chronic opioid use or acute opiate withdrawal, uncontrolled hypertension, seizure disorder, use of other bupropion-containing products, bulimia/anorexia, abrupt discontinuation of alcohol, benzodiazepines, barbiturates, and antiepileptic drugs, use of MAO inhibitors within 14 days, pregnancy **WARNINGS** Use caution with psychiatric disorders, discontinue with s/sx of hepatotoxicity, can ↑ HR and BP, glaucoma **SIDE EFFECTS** N/V, constipation, headache, dizziness, dry mouth, insomnia **NOTES** Naltrexone blocks opioids and buprenorphine, which blocks analgesia; discontinue opioids or buprenorphine 7-14 days prior to use of *Contrave*
Serotonin 5-HT2C receptor agonist: ↑ satiety		
Lorcaserin (*Belviq, Belviq XR*) C-IV	IR: 10 mg PO BID XR: 20 mg PO daily	**CONTRAINDICATIONS** Pregnancy **WARNINGS** Serotonin syndrome and neuroleptic malignant syndrome-like reaction when taken with other serotonergic agents (see the Learning Drug Interactions chapter), CNS effects, ↑ risk of psychiatric disorders (including suicide risk), priapism, hypoglycemia **SIDE EFFECTS** Headache, dizziness, fatigue, nausea, dry mouth, constipation

DRUG	DOSING	SAFETY/SIDE EFFECTS/MONITORING
GLP-1 receptor agonist: ↑ satiety		
Liraglutide *(Saxenda)* Injection ***Victoza*** – for diabetes REMS program required due to risk of MTC and pancreatitis	Start: 0.6 mg SC daily x 1 week, titrate up by 0.6 mg SC daily at weekly intervals Target dose: 3 mg SC daily	**BOXED WARNING** Risk of thyroid C-cells carcinomas – seen in animal studies; risk to humans unknown **CONTRAINDICATIONS** Pregnancy; personal or family history of medullary thyroid carcinoma (MTC) or patients with Multiple Endocrine Neoplasia syndrome type 2 (MEN 2) **WARNINGS** Pancreatitis, hypoglycemia, acute gallbladder disease, gastroparesis (slows gastric emptying) **SIDE EFFECTS** Nausea (primary side effect), vomiting, diarrhea, constipation, headache, dyspepsia, fatigue, dizziness, abdominal pain and distention **NOTES** May need to ↓ insulin or sulfonylurea/meglitinide doses to ↓ risk of hypoglycemia (see the Diabetes chapter)
Lipase inhibitor: ↓ absorption of dietary fats by ~30%		
Orlistat Rx – ***Xenical*** OTC – ***Alli***	*Xenical:* 120 mg PO w/ each meal containing fat; take with meal or up to 1 hr after eating Indicated in ages > 12 years *Alli:* 60 mg PO w/each meal containing fat Must be used with a low-fat diet plan	**CONTRAINDICATIONS** Pregnancy, chronic malabsorption syndrome, cholestasis **WARNINGS** Liver damage (rare), cholelithiasis, ↑ urinary oxalate/kidney stones, hypoglycemia (in patients with diabetes) **SIDE EFFECTS** GI (flatus with discharge, fecal urgency, fatty stool) **NOTES** Take multivitamin with A, D, E, K and beta carotene at bedtime or separated by ≥ 2 hours; do not use with cyclosporine or separate by ≥ 3 hours; separate levothyroxine by ≥ 4 hours Must stick to dietary plan for both weight improvement and to help lessen GI side effects (max 30% of kcals from fat)
Appetite suppressants: sympathomimetics (stimulants), release of norepinephrine stimulates the satiety center which ↓ appetite		
Phentermine *(Adipex-P,* *Lomaira)* C-IV	15-37.5 mg PO daily, before or after breakfast, or in divided doses	**CONTRAINDICATIONS** Cardiovascular disease (e.g., uncontrolled hypertension, arrhythmias, heart failure, CAD), hyperthyroidism, glaucoma, pregnancy, breast feeding, history of drug abuse, MAO inhibitors within the past 14 days **SIDE EFFECTS** Tachycardia, agitation, ↑ BP, insomnia, dizziness, tremor, psychosis **MONITORING** HR, BP **NOTES** Used short-term, up to 12 weeks, to "jump-start" a diet Stimulants taken later in the day can cause insomnia Potential for misuse/dependence
Diethylpropion C-IV	IR: 25 mg PO TID, 1 hour before meals and mid-evening SR: 75 mg PO once at mid-morning	
Phendimetrazine C-III	IR: 35 mg PO BID-TID, 1 hr before meals ER: 105 mg PO daily, 30-60 minutes before the morning meal	
Benzphetamine C-III	25-50 mg PO daily to TID; avoid late afternoon administration	

PATIENT COUNSELING

All Weight Loss Medications

- If you do not lose an expected amount of weight within three months, this medication is not effective for you and should be stopped.
- You must be eating a modified diet and getting regular exercise while taking this medication.
- If you have diabetes and you lose weight, your blood glucose can decrease; you need to monitor your blood glucose carefully, and your diabetes medication may need to be adjusted as you lose weight.
- Do not use this drug if you are pregnant or planning to become pregnant. Attempting to lose weight during pregnancy is not safe.

Phentermine/Topiramate *(Qsymia)*

- This medication can interact with birth control pills, which can lead to unusual bleeding. At the doses prescribed, this will not increase the risk of pregnancy. Do not stop taking your birth control medication if bleeding occurs.
- Monitor your heart rate and blood pressure while taking this medication. Notify your prescriber if these become high.
- Take this medication daily in the morning. Avoid taking this medication in the evening, to prevent insomnia.

Naltrexone/Bupropion *(Contrave)*

- Do not take opioid pain relievers while taking this medication.
- Monitor your heart rate and blood pressure while taking this medication. Notify your doctor if these become abnormally high.

Lorcaserin *(Belviq and Belviq XR)*

- This medication can cause low blood glucose. Monitor your blood glucose levels carefully if you have diabetes.

Liraglutide *(Saxenda)*

- This medication may be taken at any time of the day, without regard to the time of the meal.
- Inject subcutaneously into the abdomen, thigh or arm. Make sure you rotate the site of injection.
- Do not take this medication with another medication called *Victoza*. These medications contain the same ingredient and taking them together can lead to low blood glucose.
- You may need reduced doses of other diabetes medications while you are taking this medication and as you lose weight.

Orlistat *(Xenical and Alli)*

- Take one capsule with liquid at each main meal, or up to one hour after a meal that contains fat. You should be eating a healthy diet that is low in fat in order to reduce GI side effects.
- You will need to take a daily multivitamin that contains vitamins A, D, E, and K and beta carotene. Take the multivitamin at least two hours before or after taking orlistat, or at bedtime.
- If you take levothyroxine (for low thyroid), it should be separated from orlistat by at least four hours.
- If you take cyclosporine (a transplant medication), it must be separated from orlistat by at least three hours. Discuss using orlistat with your transplant team; it is important not to change the amount of transplant medication that your body is receiving.

BARIATRIC SURGERY

Guidelines recommend weight loss or bariatric surgery for adults when BMI ≥ 40 kg/m² or when BMI ≥ 35 kg/m² with an obesity-related condition. Traditional bariatric surgery restricts food intake, which leads to weight loss. Patients must commit to a lifetime of healthy eating and regular exercise to sustain the weight loss. Some common issues associated with bariatric surgery are described below.

COMMON NUTRIENT DEFICIENCIES

- Calcium is mostly absorbed in the duodenum, which may be bypassed. Calcium citrate supplementation is preferred as it has non-acid-dependent absorption.
- Anemia can result from vitamin B12 and iron deficiency; both may require supplementation.
- Iron and calcium supplements should be taken two hours prior or four hours after antacids.
- Patients may require life-long supplementation of the fat-soluble vitamins A, D, E and K due to fat malabsorption.

MEDICATION CONCERNS

- Medications may require dose reduction, and may need to be crushed and put in liquid or used in transdermal form for up to two months post-surgery. Pharmacists need to assess which drugs can be safely crushed and provide alternatives to drugs that cannot be crushed (i.e., extended-release formulations).
- Rapid weight loss can cause gallstones. Ursodiol *(Actigall, Urso 250, Urso Forte)* dissolves gallstones and may be needed, unless the gallbladder has been removed.

Select Guidelines/References

US DHHS/DOA's 2015 - 2020 Dietary Guidelines for Americans, 8th Ed. Available at https://health.gov/dietaryguidelines/2015/guidelines (accessed 2019 Feb 14).

AACE/ACE Comprehensive clinical practice guidelines for medical care of patients with obesity. *Endoc Pract.* 2016; 22(3):1-203.

58

59

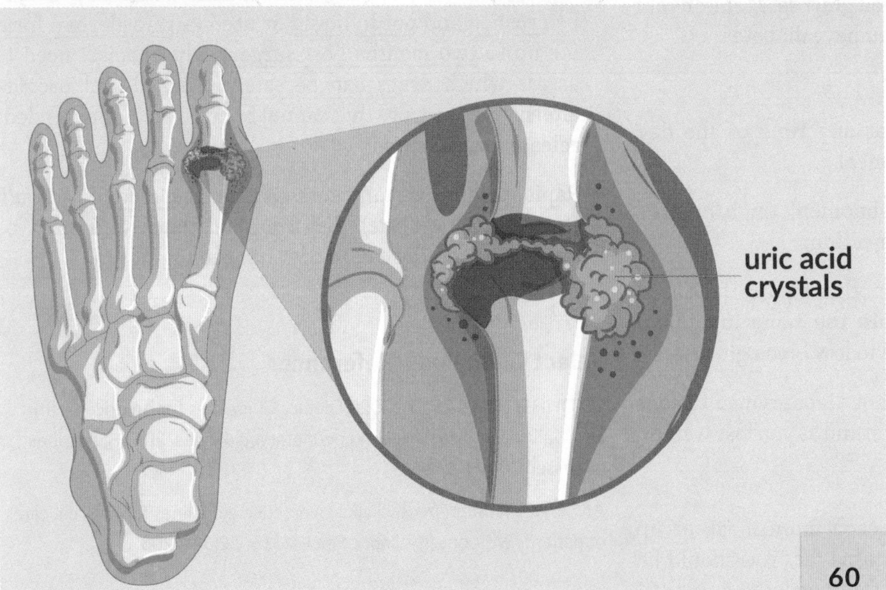

60

PAIN/RELATED CONDITIONS

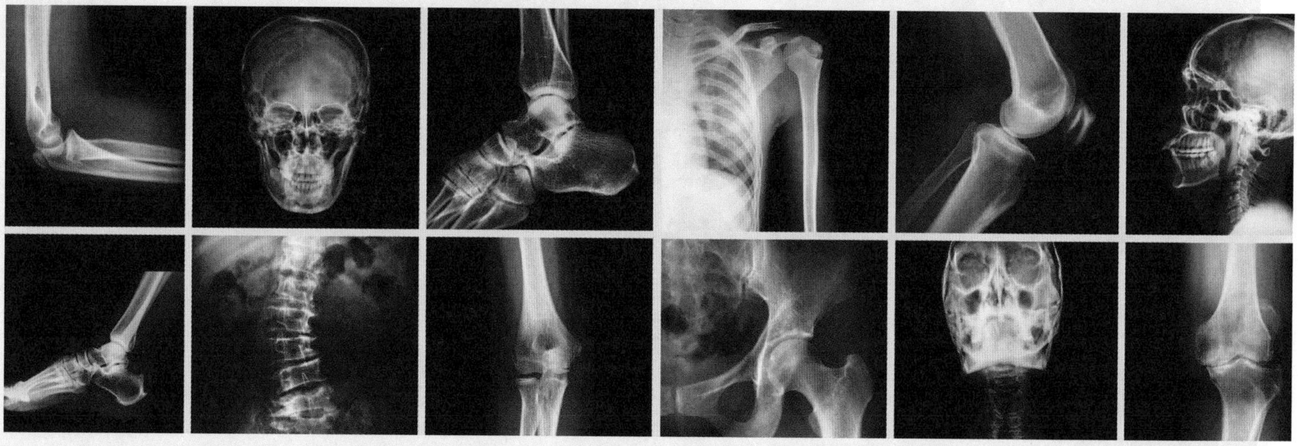

CONTENTS

CHAPTER 58
PAIN | **796**

CHAPTER 59
MIGRAINE | **818**

CHAPTER 60
GOUT | **825**

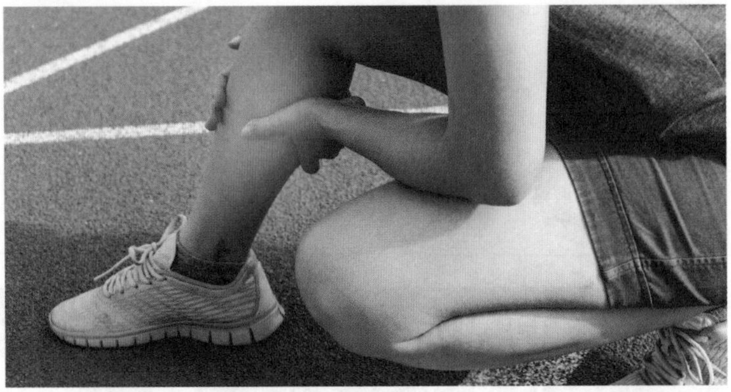

CHAPTER 58
PAIN

CHAPTER CONTENT

Background 796
Pathophysiology 796
Acute and Chronic Pain 796
Treatment Principles 797
Selecting an Analgesic Regimen 797
Non-Opioid Analgesics 797
Acetaminophen 798
Acetaminophen Overdose 798
Non-Steroidal Anti-Inflammatory Drugs 799
NSAIDs and the Ductus Arteriosus 799
Opioid Analgesics 802
Safety Concerns 802
Opioid Boxed Warnings 802
Terminology 802
Common Opioids 803
Dosing Conversions 806
Allergy 808
Opioid Allergy 808
Side Effects and Management 808
Opioid-Induced Constipation 808
Treatment of Opioid-Induced Constipation 809
Centrally Acting Analgesics 810
Opioid Abuse 811
Opioid Induced Respiratory Depression (OIRD) Risks 811
Opioid Abuse Agents 811
Opioid Overdose Management 811
Treatment of Opioid Abuse 812
Common Adjuvants for Pain Management 813
Oral Adjuvants 813
Topical Adjuvants 815
Patient Counseling 815

CONTENT LEGEND

(💡) = Study Tip Gal

BACKGROUND

Pain can be defined as the physical suffering caused by an illness or injury. Pain can lead to a significant decrease in quality of life and ability to carry out daily tasks. In 2011, the Institute of Medicine estimated that pain affects 100 million American adults.

PATHOPHYSIOLOGY

Pain is classified into two main categories (nociceptive pain and pathophysiologic pain) based on the underlying cause of the pain. Nociceptive pain occurs when sensory nerves (nociceptors) identify tissue damage. Injured tissue releases substances [such as prostaglandins (PGs), substance P, histamine] which stimulate the nociceptors to send impulses to the brain that result in feeling pain. Nociceptive pain results from injury to internal organs (visceral pain) or from an injury to the skin, muscles, bones, joints or ligaments (somatic pain, which is commonly referred to as musculoskeletal pain).

Pathophysiologic pain is different from nociceptive pain as it does not result from tissue injury or damage, but from damage or malfunction of the nervous system. This is commonly referred to as neuropathic pain. Various pain syndromes are considered pathophysiologic pain, such as fibromyalgia, diabetic neuropathy, chronic headaches, drug-induced toxicities (e.g., vinca alkaloids) and others.

ACUTE AND CHRONIC PAIN

The difference between acute and chronic pain is important because it impacts treatment decisions. Acute pain begins suddenly and usually feels sharp. It is typically nociceptive in nature, such as a fracture, burn, acute illness, surgery or childbirth. The pain can last just a few moments, or longer, and usually goes away when the cause of the pain has resolved. Acute pain can cause anxiety and physical symptoms, including sweating and tachycardia. If acute pain goes untreated, it has been shown to increase the risk for the development of chronic pain.

Chronic pain has been described as pain that persists beyond the normal healing time (or three months), but for some conditions there is no acute injury. It can persist with a visible injury (such as crushed lumbar vertebrae, causing lower back pain) or when no visible injury is present, such as with osteoarthritis (OA) or diabetic neuropathy (see Diabetes chapter). OA is a common type of chronic pain caused by a breakdown in the cartilage that pads the joint, which results in stiffness, pain and/or swelling. Chronic pain is divided into cancer pain or chronic non-cancer pain, which have separate treatment guidelines. Poorly managed chronic pain is miserable and can cause depression and physical symptoms, including muscle tension and fatigue.

TREATMENT PRINCIPLES

Pain is subjective. It is primarily measured by the patient's own description, along with observations. Patients with chronic pain should be taught to monitor and document their pain by recording the pain level, the type or quality (using words such as burning, shooting, stabbing, aching) and the time of day that the pain is better or worse. Anything that worsens or lessens the pain should be noted. This helps to evaluate pain control and give guidance on pain medication changes.

Pain scales are useful to assess pain severity. Pain is commonly rated using a numeric scale (0 = no pain, 10 = worst pain) or with the visual analog scale (see figure) for pediatric patients. The Joint Commission (TJC) standards require that pain be assessed and managed while patients are hospitalized. Hospitals must inquire about, assess, treat and re-assess pain in a timely manner using non-pharmacologic and/or pharmacologic treatments.

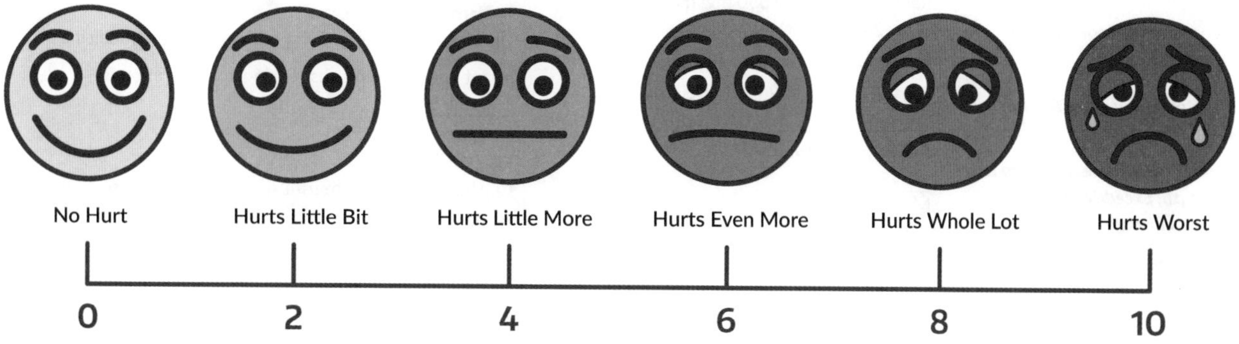

SELECTING AN ANALGESIC REGIMEN

Choosing the correct analgesic regimen is important. Pain can be treated using a stepwise approach, where the choice of drug depends on the patient's self-reported pain severity. When initially using any class of analgesic (including opioids), start low and stop at the lowest dose that adequately reduces the pain. Using medicines with multiple mechanisms of action (multimodal pain control) often produces improved pain control via additive or synergistic effects. Non-opioid analgesics [e.g., acetaminophen, non-steroidal anti-inflammatory drugs (NSAIDs)] are most commonly used for mild pain but can be added to an opioid-based regimen to reduce the total opioid dose required and provide better pain relief. Opioids are, in general, strong analgesics, most appropriate for moderate to severe pain. Adjuvants [e.g., antidepressants, antiepileptic drugs (AEDs), muscle relaxants] should be considered for all severities of pain.

NON-OPIOID ANALGESICS

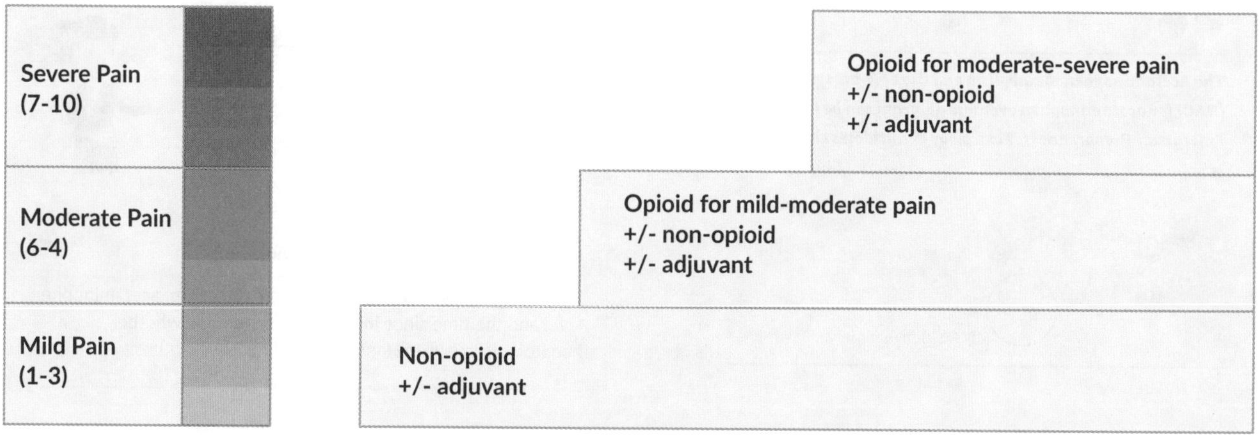

ACETAMINOPHEN

Acetaminophen reduces pain and fever (is an antipyretic) but does not provide an anti-inflammatory effect. The mechanism of action is not well defined but is thought to involve inhibition of PG synthesis in the central nervous system (CNS), resulting in reduced pain impulse generation.

DRUG	DOSING	SAFETY/SIDE EFFECTS/MONITORING
Acetaminophen (*Tylenol, FeverAll, Ofirmev,* most "Non-Aspirin" pain relievers**)** Tablet/caplet, chewable tablet, ODT, suspension, suppository, injection ***FeverAll:*** Rectal suppository ***Ofirmev:*** Injection + **hydrocodone (*Lorcet, Lortab, Norco, Vicodin*)** + **oxycodone (*Endocet, Percocet,*** *Primlev*) + **codeine (*Tylenol #2, 3, 4*)** + tramadol (*Ultracet*) + **caffeine (*Excedrin Tension Headache*)** + **aspirin/caffeine (*Excedrin Extra Strength, Excedrin Migraine,*** *Goody's Powder*) + **caffeine/pyrilamine (*Midol*)** + butalbital/caffeine (*Fioricet*) +/– codeine + diphenhydramine (*Tylenol PM*) And in multiple cough & cold products and OTC combinations	**Adults** Maximum < 4,000 mg/day from all sources Maximum of 325 mg per prescription dosing unit in combo products, per the FDA Dosing ranges and maximum doses depend on the formulation 325 mg: max 2 tabs Q4H/10 tabs per 24 hr (3,250 mg) 500 mg: max 2 tabs Q6H/6 tabs per 24 hr (3,000 mg) 650 mg ER: max: 2 tabs Q8H/6 tabs per 24 hr (3,900 mg) Rectal Suppository 650 mg: max: 1 PR Q4H/6 per 24 hr (3,900 mg) IV max: 650 mg Q4H or 1,000 mg Q6H/4-6 injections per 24 hr (4,000 mg) **Pediatrics (< 12 yrs)** 10-15 mg/kg Q4-6H Max: 5 doses/day Use weight and age based dosing table on label	**BOXED WARNING** Severe hepatotoxicity (can require liver transplant or result in death), associated with doses > 4 grams/day or use of multiple acetaminophen-containing products; risk of 10-fold dosing errors with injection **SIDE EFFECTS** Cases of severe skin rash (rare) including SJS, TEN and AGEP; stop drug, seek immediate medical help Nephrotoxicity (rare, usually with chronic overdose); generally safer than NSAIDs **SAFETY** Avoid the "APAP" abbreviation **Pediatric oral suspension** Use dosing syringe or cup provided with the medicine Infant and children's suspension concentration is 160 mg/5 mL **Injection** Concentration is 10 mg/mL (in 100 mL vials); use caution with dosing Prescribe in mg, not mL (e.g., a 75 mg dose is not 75 mL, it is 7.5 mL) All IV acetaminophen doses should be prepared in the pharmacy

Acetaminophen Drug Interactions

- Can be used with warfarin, but if used chronically (doses > 2 grams/day), acetaminophen can increase the INR. Monitor accordingly.
- Avoid or limit alcohol use due to the risk of hepatotoxicity. See Patient Counseling section.

"

The Acetaminophen Metabolism and Use of N-acetylcystyeine (NAC) for acetaminophen overdose diagram can be found in the Emergency Preparedness, Toxicology & Antidotes chapter.

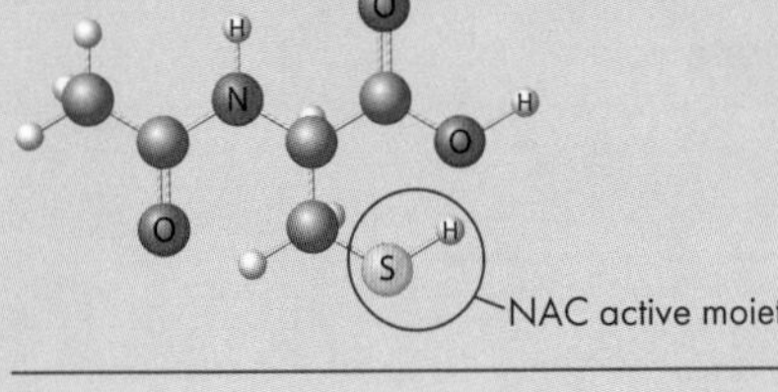

ACETAMINOPHEN OVERDOSE

The antidote for acetaminophen overdosage is N-acetylcysteine (NAC, *Mucomyst, Cetylev, Acetadote*).

- Restores intracellular glutathione.
- Available in both oral and IV formulations.

The Rumack-Matthew nomogram uses the serum acetaminophen level and the time since ingestion to determine whether hepatotoxicity is likely (and the need for NAC).

NON-STEROIDAL ANTI-INFLAMMATORY DRUGS

NSAIDs include the traditional non-selective agents (e.g., ibuprofen and aspirin) and the selective cyclooxygenase (COX) 2 inhibitors. The COX 1 and 2 enzymes catalyze the conversion of arachidonic acid to PGs and thromboxane A2 (TxA2). All NSAIDs decrease the formation of PGs which results in decreased inflammation, alleviation of pain and reduced fever. Non-selective NSAIDs block the synthesis of both COX enzymes. COX-2 selective NSAIDs block the synthesis of COX-2 only, which decreases GI risk because COX-1 protects the gastric mucosa. Blocking COX-1 decreases the formation of TxA2, which is required for both platelet activation and aggregation. Aspirin is an irreversible COX-1 inhibitor and is an effective antiplatelet agent that provides cardiovascular (CV) benefit, often referred to as cardioprotection.

Non-Aspirin Boxed Warnings

All prescription, non-aspirin NSAIDs require a MedGuide due to these risks. These warnings are not repeated in the drug tables.

- GI Risk: NSAIDs can increase the risk of serious GI adverse events including bleeding and ulceration. Patients who are elderly, have a history of GI bleed, or are taking systemic steroids, SSRIs or SNRIs are at greatest risk. Aspirin and OTC NSAIDs do not carry a boxed warning but still have this risk.
- CV Risk: NSAIDs can increase the risk of MI and stroke. Avoid use in patients with CV disease or risk factors. This warning includes all OTC non-selective NSAIDs except aspirin.
- Coronary Artery Bypass Graft (CABG) Surgery: NSAID use is contraindicated after CABG surgery. Antiplatelet therapy (commonly aspirin) is recommended after CABG surgery.

Side Effects of All NSAIDS

- NSAIDs can decrease renal clearance by reducing blood flow to the glomerulus; additional nephrotoxic agents or dehydration increases the risk. All NSAIDs should be used cautiously (or avoided) in renal failure.
- NSAIDs can increase blood pressure. Use cautiously in patients with controlled hypertension, and avoid in patients with uncontrolled hypertension.
- NSAIDs can cause premature closure of the ductus arteriosus, which can lead to heart failure in the baby. Do not use NSAIDs in the third trimester of pregnancy (≥ 30 weeks). See Study Tip Gal below.
- All NSAIDs can cause nausea. Salicylates cause worse nausea compared to other NSAIDs. Nausea can be minimized by taking with food, switching to an enteric coated or buffered product or changing to a different NSAID.

NSAIDS AND THE DUCTUS ARTERIOSUS

Before birth, the ductus arteriosus (DA) connects the pulmonary artery to the aorta, allowing oxygenated blood to flow to the baby, bypassing the immature lungs.

Do not use NSAIDs in the third trimester of pregnancy. NSAIDs can prematurely close the DA.

After birth, the DA should close on its own. In some cases, it remains patent (open) and NSAIDs can be used to help it close.

IV NSAIDs (indomethacin, ibuprofen) can be used within 14 days of birth to close a patent ductus arteriosus (PDA).

Non-Aspirin NSAIDs

DRUG	DOSING	SAFETY/SIDE EFFECTS/MONITORING
COX-1 and COX-2 Non-selective NSAIDs: all agents have GI risk, CV risk and risk in post-operative CABG setting.		
Ibuprofen ***(Advil, Caldolor, Motrin,*** *NeoProfen)* Tablet, capsule, chewable tablet, suspension, injection	**Adult** OTC: 200-400 mg Q4-6H Max: 1.2 grams/day Rx: 400-800 mg Q6-8H Max: 3.2 grams/day **Pediatric** 5-10 mg/kg/dose Q6-8H (as an antipyretic) Max: 40 mg/kg/day	**NOTES** *NeoProfen* injection is indicated for closure of PDA in premature infants. OTC: limit self-treatment to ≤ 10 days Severe skin reactions, including SJS/TEN
Indomethacin *(Indocin,* *Tivorbex)* Capsule, oral suspension, suppository, injection	IR: 25-50 mg BID-TID CR: 75 mg daily-BID *Tivorbex:* 20 mg TID or 40 mg BID-TID	**NOTES** High risk for CNS side effects (avoid in psych conditions) The IR formulation is an older NSAID approved for gout *Tivorbex* is micronized for faster dissolution IV injection is indicated for closure of PDA in premature infants

DRUG	DOSING	SAFETY/SIDE EFFECTS/MONITORING
Naproxen (OTC: ***Aleve***, Rx: *Naprelan, Naprosyn)* Tablet, capsule, suspension + sumatriptan *(Treximet)* **+ esomeprazole *(Vimovo)*** And in OTC combos with diphenhydramine and pseudoephedrine	**OTC** Pain, fever: 200 mg (220 mg naproxen Na) Q8-12H (1st dose can take 2 tabs) Max: 3 tabs in 24 hours **Rx** Inflammation, mild-mod pain: 500 mg Q12H (or 250 mg Q6-8H) Max: 1,000 mg/day (1,250 mg day 1)	**NOTES** Prescribers and patients sometimes prefer naproxen since it can be dosed BID Naproxen base 200 mg = Naproxen Na 220 mg PPI in *Vimovo* is used to protect the GI tract
Ketorolac *(Toradol, *Sprix)* Tablet, injection, nasal spray, ophthalmic *Acular*: ophthalmic	**Oral** 10-20 mg x 1, then 10 mg Q4-6H PRN Max: 40 mg/day **IV** (≥ 50 kg): 30 mg x 1 or 30 mg Q6H (↓ dose if ≥ 65 y/o) **IM** (≥ 50 kg): 60 mg x 1 or 30 mg Q6H (↓ dose if ≥ 65 y/o) **Nasal spray** *(Sprix)* < 65 y/o and ≥ 50 kg: 1 spray in each nostril Q6-8H ≥ 65 y/o or < 50 kg: 1 spray in one nostril Q6-8H	**BOXED WARNINGS** Oral ketorolac: for short-term moderate to severe acute pain only as continuation of IV or IM ketorolac (max combined duration IV/IM and PO/nasal is 5 days in adults); not for intrathecal or epidural use; avoid in patients with advanced renal disease or at risk for renal impairment due to volume depletion **WARNINGS** ↑ bleeding, acute renal failure, liver failure and anaphylactic shock **NOTES** Usually used after surgery, never before
Piroxicam *(Feldene)*	10-20 mg daily	**NOTES** High risk for GI toxicity and severe skin reactions, including SJS/TEN Used when other NSAIDs have failed; may need agent to protect gut (PPI, misoprostol)
Sulindac	150-200 mg BID	**NOTES** Sometimes used with reduced renal function, and in patients on lithium who require an NSAID
Other less-commonly used NSAIDs include: meclofenamate, mefenamic acid *(Ponstel)*, ketoprofen, fenoprofen *(Nalfon)*, flurbiprofen *(Ansaid)*, oxaprozin *(Daypro* – caution similar to piroxicam – higher risk of side effects).		
Increased COX-2 Selectivity: lower risk for GI complications (but still present), ↑ risk MI/stroke (avoid with CV risk, avoid ↑ doses and longer duration in patients at risk for CV disease), same risk for renal complications		
Celecoxib *(Celebrex)* + amlodipine *(Consensi)* - for treatment of OA pain and HTN Capsule	OA: 100 mg BID or 200 mg daily RA: 100-200 mg BID Indications: OA, RA, juvenile RA, acute pain, primary dysmenorrhea, ankylosing spondylitis	**CONTRAINDICATIONS** Sulfonamide allergy **NOTES** Highest COX-2 selectivity Avoid in pregnancy; risk greatest at ≥ 30 weeks gestation Severe skin reactions, including SJS/TEN
Diclofenac *(Voltaren,* *Cambia, EnovaRX, Flector, Pennsaid, Xrylix, Zorvolex, Zipsor)* Tablet, capsule, cream, packet, gel, kit, patch, topical solution, injection + misoprostol *(Arthrotec)*	Oral tablets: 50-75 mg BID-TID *Voltaren* (gel): 2-4 g to affected joint four times per day *Flector*: 1 patch (180 mg) to most painful area BID *Cambia*: 1 packet (50 mg) mixed in water for acute migraine *Zipsor*: 25 mg four times per day *Zorvolex*: 18 mg or 35 mg TID	**BOXED WARNING** *Arthrotec*: avoid in women of childbearing potential unless woman is capable of complying with effective contraceptive measures **NOTES** Has some COX-2 selectivity Oral diclofenac formulations are not bioequivalent even if mg strength is the same Misoprostol is used to replace the gut-protective PG to ↓ GI risk; can ↑ uterine contractions (which can terminate pregnancy) and causes cramping and diarrhea

DRUG	DOSING	SAFETY/SIDE EFFECTS/MONITORING
Meloxicam (*Mobic*, *Vivlodex*) Tablet, capsule, oral suspension	*Mobic:* 7.5-15 mg once daily *Vivlodex:* 5-10 mg once daily	**NOTES** These agents have some COX-2 selectivity *Vivlodex* capsules and other meloxicam formulations are not interchangeable
Etodolac *(Lodine)* Tablet, capsule, ER tablet	300-500 mg Q6-8H	
Nabumetone *(Relafen)* Tablet	1,000-2,000 mg daily (can be divided BID)	

Salicylate NSAIDs

DRUG	DOSING	SAFETY/SIDE EFFECTS/MONITORING
Aspirin/Acetylsalicylic Acid *(Ascriptin, Bufferin, Ecotrin,* *Durlaza)* Tablet/caplet, chewable tablet, suppository ***Ascriptin, Bufferin, Ecotrin***: EC/buffered *Durlaza* (Rx): ER capsule *Bayer "Advanced" Aspirin:* dissolves slightly faster **+ acetaminophen/caffeine *(Excedrin, Excedrin Migraine,*** *Goody's Powder)* + antacid *(Alka-Seltzer)* + caffeine *(BC Powder, Stanback)* + calcium *(Bayer Women's Low Dose)* + omeprazole *(Yosprala)* And in multiple other OTC combinations	Cardioprotection dosing: 81-162 mg once daily *Durlaza* (Rx): 162.5 mg once daily Analgesic dosing: 325-650 mg Q4-6H *Goody's Powder*: 520 mg per packet *BC*: 845-1000 mg per packet *Stanback*: 845 mg per packet	**WARNINGS** Avoid with NSAID hypersensitivity (past reaction with trouble breathing), nasal polyps, asthma. Avoid aspirin in children and teenagers with any viral infection due to potential risk of Reye's syndrome (symptoms include somnolence, N/V, lethargy, confusion). Other NSAIDs can be used in pediatrics. Severe skin rash (rare) including SJS/TEN; stop drug, seek immediate medical help. Increases the risk of bleeding. Avoid in the third trimester of pregnancy due to fetal harm. GI ulceration and bleeding can occur. **SIDE EFFECTS** Dyspepsia, heartburn, bleeding, nausea, renal impairment, ↑ blood pressure, CNS effects (fatigue, confusion, dizziness; caution in the elderly), photosensitivity, fluid retention/edema, hyperkalemia (in renal impairment or with potassium-retaining agents), blurred vision **NOTES** To ↓ nausea, use EC or buffered product or take with food PPIs may be used to protect the gut with chronic NSAID use; consider the risks from chronic PPI use (↓ bone density, ↑ infection risk) Do not use *Durlaza* or *Yosprala* when immediate effect is needed (e.g., myocardial infarction) Salicylate overdose can cause tinnitus Methyl salicylate is a popular OTC topical found in *Bengay, Icy Hot, Flexal, Thera-Gesic, Salonpas*. See Topical Agents
NON-ACETYLATED SALICYLATES		
Salsalate	Up to 3 grams/day, divided BID-TID	
Magnesium Salicylate *(Doans, Doans ES)*	580mg ES tab: 2 tablets Q6H Max: 8 tablets/day	
Choline Magnesium Trisalicylate	1 gram BID-TID or 3 grams QHS	
Diflunisal	500 mg BID-TID Max 1.5 grams daily	
Salicylate salts	No longer commonly used	

NSAID Drug Interactions

- Additive bleeding risk with other agents that can ↑ bleeding risk, such as steroids. See the Learning Drug Interactions chapter.
- Caution using aspirin with other ototoxic agents (e.g., aminoglycosides, IV loop diuretics).
- Multiple NSAIDs should not be used together, except the addition of low dose aspirin for cardioprotection when indicated. If using aspirin for cardioprotection and ibuprofen for pain, take aspirin one hour before or eight hours after ibuprofen.
- NSAIDs can ↑ the levels of lithium and methotrexate.

OPIOID ANALGESICS

Opioid drugs interact in a variety of ways with the three primary types of opioid receptors: μ (mu), κ (kappa) and δ (delta). Opioids are mu receptor agonists in the CNS, which primarily produce pain relief, but also cause euphoria and respiratory depression. These agents are primarily used to treat moderate to severe acute pain and chronic pain.

SAFETY CONCERNS

A risk evaluation and mitigation strategy (REMS) exists for all opioid medications. Primary components of the REMS include prescriber education and counseling requirements. Opioid medications have several boxed warnings (see Study Tip Gal); these are not repeated in the drug tables.

Elderly, debilitated, cachectic patients and patients with chronic pulmonary disease (conditions associated with hypoxia) or head injury/increased intracranial pressure should be monitored closely. All are at increased risk of respiratory depression. In addition, opioids have a risk of hypotension.

OPIOID BOXED WARNINGS

- Addiction, abuse and misuse can lead to overdose and death.
- Respiratory depression, which can be fatal.
- Use of any opioid with benzodiazepines or other CNS depressants, including alcohol, can increase the risk of death.
- *Kadian, Embeda, Zohydro* and *Nucynta ER*: do not consume alcohol with this medication, can cause potentially fatal overdose.
- Accidental ingestion/exposure of even one dose in children can be fatal. Never give this medication to anyone else (includes patches).
- Crushing, dissolving or chewing of the long acting products can cause the delivery of a potentially fatal dose.
- Life-threatening neonatal opioid withdrawal with prolonged use during pregnancy.

TERMINOLOGY

TERM	DEFINITION
Physiological Adaptation (Physical Dependence)	Almost all patients using chronic opioids, including abusers, become physiologically adapted to the opioid, and experience physical withdrawal symptoms when the opioid is stopped or a dose is late or missed. The symptoms include anxiety, tachycardia, shakiness and shortness of breath. The withdrawal causes much suffering. Physiological adaptation is not addiction.
Addiction	A strong desire or compulsion to take the drug despite harm. Involves drug-seeking behavior, including exaggerating the pain or physical problems, getting prescriptions from multiple prescribers and/or prescription forgery.
Pseudo-Addiction	On occasion, a patient is seen at the pharmacy who appears anxious and states they ran out of medication or are afraid of running out too early. The person seems similar to an addict, but is actually a legitimate pain patient with poorly controlled pain. The remedy is adequate analgesics, such as extended release (ER) opioids, for pain control.
Tolerance	A higher opioid dose is needed to produce the same level of analgesia that a lower dose previously provided. Tolerance develops over time with chronic opioid use. It is important to distinguish whether the higher pain severity is due to a condition (e.g., cancer that has spread), or a decrease in the drug's effectiveness due to tolerance, or both. If tolerance develops, it can be preferable to switch to another opioid, rather than increase the dose.
Opioid Hyperalgesia	Present when the opioid dose is increased to treat the pain, but the pain becomes worse rather than better. This occurs occasionally. If suspected, a different class of analgesic or a switch to another opioid should be tried.
Break-Through Pain [(BTP), end of dose pain]	Sharp spikes of severe pain that occur despite the use of an ER opioid. Must be treated with a fast acting pain agent, such as an injection, transmucosal immediate release fentanyl (TIRF) drugs (for cancer BTP only) or (less expensive, but not preferable) immediate release (IR) opioids. When multiple doses are required for BTP, a higher baseline dose can be required, or possibly a switch to a different opioid. Baseline opioids are dispensed with a BTP medication until the dose of the scheduled opioid is adequate.
Opioid-Induced Respiratory Depression (OIRD)	Usual cause of fatality in opioid overdose. Hospitalized patients receiving IV opioids must be carefully monitored for sedation and oxygen saturation.
Centrally-Acting Opioid Antagonists	There are two drugs in this group; both block opioids from binding to the mu receptor. Naloxone is used to reverse respiratory depression. Naltrexone is most commonly used in combination with an opioid to block the use of other opioids that may be taken (inappropriately) at the same time.

COMMON OPIOIDS

DRUG	DOSING	SAFETY/SIDE EFFECTS/MONITORING
Codeine C-II: codeine C-III: tablet/capsule combination products **+ acetaminophen *(Tylenol #2, 3, 4)*** C-V: oral solution combination products (e.g., cough syrups) Select combo products: + chlorpheniramine/ pseudoephedrine *(Phenylhistine DH)* + promethazine + promethazine/ phenylephrine *(Promethazine VC/Codeine)*	*Tylenol #3:* 1 tab (acetaminophen 300 mg + codeine 30 mg) Q4-6H PRN, range 15-120 mg codeine	**BOXED WARNING** Respiratory depression and death have occurred in children following tonsillectomy and/or adenoidectomy found to have evidence of being ultra-rapid metabolizers of codeine due to a CYP450 2D6 polymorphism; deaths have also occurred in nursing infants after being exposed to high concentrations of morphine because the mothers were ultra-rapid metabolizers; use with CYP3A4 inducers/inhibitors or CYP2D6 inhibitors should be carefully considered due to variable effects **CONTRAINDICATIONS** Use in children < 12 years of age; use in children < 18 years of age following tonsillectomy/adenoidectomy surgery **WARNINGS** Adolescents between 12 – 18 years who are obese or have sleep apnea or severe lung disease are at ↑ risk of breathing problems **SIDE EFFECTS** Codeine has a high degree of GI side effects including constipation **NOTES** Codeine containing cough and cold preparations are no longer indicated in patients < 18 years of age – do not use
Fentanyl *(Duragesic, Sublimaze)* C-II Injection, patch *Actiq:* oral transmucosal lozenge ("lollipop," on a stick) *Lazanda:* nasal spray *Fentora*: buccal tabs *Abstral:* tablet, SL *Subsys:* spray, SL *Onsolis:** buccal film	**Patch:** Apply 1 patch Q72H (can be Q48H) Available in 12 (delivers 12.5 mcg/hr), 25, 50, 75, and 100 mcg/hr patch strengths **Lozenge:** Always start with 200 mcg, can titrate to 4 BTP episodes/day. Only for cancer BTP.	**BOXED WARNING** Potential for medication errors when converting between dosage forms, use with strong or moderate CYP3A4 inhibitors can result in ↑ effects and potentially fatal respiratory depression, avoid exposing transdermal fentanyl to external heat **SIDE EFFECTS** Bradycardia, confusion, dizziness, diaphoresis, dehydration, dry mouth, N/V, muscle rigidity, weakness, miosis, dyspnea **NOTES** Outpatient use of fentanyl is for chronic pain management only Fentanyl is not used in opioid-naïve patients. A patient who has been using morphine 60 mg/day or equivalent for at least 7 days can be converted to a fentanyl patch. *Actiq:* cut off stick and flush unused/unneeded doses Short t½ when given IV (boluses given Q1-2H). Continuous infusion or PCA are most common Similar drugs (IV only) include alfentanil *(Alfenta)*, remifentanil *(Ultiva)*, sufentanil *(Dsuvia)* REMS program for transmucosal immediate-release fentanyl requires documentation of patient's opioid tolerance with each prescription **Fentanyl Patch** Analgesic effect can be seen 8-16 hrs after application. Do not stop other analgesic immediately (↓ dose 50% for the first 12 hrs) Do not apply > 1 patch each time Some patches need to be removed before MRI. This is specific to each formulation and manufacturer. Check the individual manufacturer package insert Dispose of patch in toilet

DRUG	DOSING	SAFETY/SIDE EFFECTS/MONITORING
Hydrocodone IR (combination products only) C-II **+ acetaminophen *(Lorcet, Lortab, Norco, Vicodin,*** *Verdrocet, Xodol)* Select combo products: + chlorpheniramine *(Tussionex Pennkinetic ER, TussiCaps)* + chlorpheniramine/ pseudoephedrine + pseudoephedrine + homatropine *(Tussigon*)* + ibuprofen *(Vicoprofen,* Ibudone)*	*Norco:* 2.5, 5, 7.5, 10 mg hydrocodone + 325 mg acetaminophen Usual starting dose: 5/325 mg Q6H	**BOXED WARNING** Refer to the acetaminophen drug table for boxed warning. Initiation of CYP3A4 inhibitors (or stopping CYP3A4 inducers) can cause fatal overdose **WARNINGS** Acetaminophen and opioids: respiratory and/or CNS depression, constipation, hypotension, skin reactions (rare), caution in liver disease (avoid or limit alcohol intake) and in CYP2D6 poor metabolizers **SIDE EFFECTS** N/V, dizziness, lightheadedness, side effects related to acetaminophen **NOTES** Hydrocodone containing cough and cold preparations are no longer indicated in patients < 18 years of age – do not use
Hydrocodone ER *(Zohydro, Hysingla ER, Vantrela ER)* C-II ER capsule: *Zohydro* ER tablet: *Hysingla ER, Vantrela ER*	*Zohydro* (capsule): start at 10 mg Q12H (opioid-naïve) Range 10-50 mg *Hysingla ER* (tablet): start at 20 mg Q24H (opioid-naïve) range 20-120 mg	**BOXED WARNINGS** Initiation of CYP3A4 inhibitors (or stopping CYP3A4 inducers) can cause fatal overdose **NOTES** Substrate of CYP3A4 (major) and CYP2D6 (minor) Preferably avoid use if breastfeeding Abuse-deterrent formulations *Hysingla:* QT prolongation has occurred at doses > 160 mg/day
Hydromorphone *(Dilaudid,* *Exalgo)* C-II Tablet, injection, solution *Exalgo:* ER tablet	Initial (opioid-naïve) Oral: 2-4 mg Q4-6H PRN IV: 0.2-1 mg Q2-3H PRN	**BOXED WARNINGS** Risk of medication error with high potency (HP) injection (use in opioid-tolerant patients only) **NOTES** Potent; start low, convert carefully. High risk for overdose Commonly used in PCAs and epidurals Can cause less nausea and pruritus *Dilaudid HP* (10 mg/mL) is a higher potency injection than *Dilaudid* (1 mg/mL) *Exalgo*: abuse-deterrent formulation (crush and extraction resistant) contraindicated in opioid-naïve patients. Two week washout required between *Exalgo* and MAO inhibitors
Methadone *(Dolophine,* *Methadose, Methadone Intensol)* C-II Tablet, soluble tablet, solution *Methadose* – 40 mg soluble tablet; for detox and maintenance treatment in opioid addicted patients only.	Initial: 2.5-10 mg Q8-12H	**BOXED WARNINGS** Life-threatening QT prolongation and serious arrhythmias (e.g., Torsades de Pointes) have occurred during treatment (most involve large, multiple daily doses), should be prescribed by professionals who know requirements for safe use, initiation of CYP450 inhibitors (or stopping inducers) can cause fatal overdose **WARNINGS** Combination with other serotonic drugs or MAO inhibitors can ↑ the risk of serotonin syndrome. Methadone also blocks reuptake of norepinephrine **NOTES** Due to variable half-life, methadone is hard to dose safely Can ↓ testosterone and contribute to sexual dysfunction Methadone is a major CYP3A4 substrate; avoid use with inhibitors or lower methadone dose

DRUG	DOSING	SAFETY/SIDE EFFECTS/MONITORING
Meperidine *(Demerol)* C-II Tablet, solution, injection	**Oral/IM:** 50-150 mg Q3-4H PRN	**WARNING** Renal impairment/elderly at risk for CNS toxicity, avoid with or within 2 weeks of MAO inhibitor **SIDE EFFECTS** Lightheadedness, dizziness, somnolence, N/V, sweating **NOTES** No longer recommended as an analgesic (especially in elderly and renally impaired). Avoid for chronic pain and even short-term in elderly. Acceptable for short-term acute or single use (e.g., sutures in ER) and used off-label for post-operative rigors (shivering) Short duration of action (pain controlled for max 3 hrs) Normeperidine (metabolite) is renally cleared and can accumulate and cause CNS toxicity, including seizures In combination with other drugs, it is serotonergic and can ↑ risk of serotonin syndrome
Morphine ER: ***MS Contin, Kadian,*** *Roxanol,* MorphaBond, Arymo ER* Injection: ***Duramorph*, *Infumorph,*** *Astramorph* C-II Tablet (IR/ER), ER capsule, injection, solution, suppository + naltrexone *(Embeda)*	**IR** (including solution): 10-30 mg Q4H PRN **ER:** 15, 30, 60, 100, 200 mg Q8-12H *MorphaBond* BID, *Kadian* daily or BID **IV** (opioid naïve): 2.5-5 mg Q3-4H PRN	**BOXED WARNINGS** Medication errors with oral solution (note strength), appropriate staff and equipment needed for intrathecal/epidural administration **SIDE EFFECTS** N/V (may need anti-emetics), dizziness, changes in mood, confusion, delirium; flushing, pruritus, diaphoresis (may need antihistamine) **NOTES** Do not use MSO4 or MS abbreviations for morphine or magnesium Do not crush or chew any ER products. *Kadian* can be opened and sprinkled on applesauce or soft food If renally impaired, start at a lower dose, or avoid morphine, due to accumulation of parent drug and/or active metabolite
Oxycodone C-II (as a single agent and in combination) Tablet/capsule (IR), ER tablet, solution IR: ***Roxicodone,*** *Oxaydo, RoxyBond* CR: ***OxyContin*** ER: *Xtampza* **+ acetaminophen *(Endocet, Percocet*,** *Primlev, Xartemis XR)* + naltrexone *(Troxyca ER)*	**IR:** 5-20 mg Q4-6H **CR:** 10-80 mg Q12H (60, 80 mg only for opioid-tolerant patients)	**BOXED WARNINGS** Initiation of CYP3A4 inhibitors (or stopping CYP3A4 inducers) can cause fatal overdose, caution with oxycodone oral solution and oral concentrate (confusion between mg and mL and different concentrations) **NOTES** *Oxaydo, OxyContin, Targiniq ER, Troxyca ER* and *Xtampza ER*: abuse-deterrent formulations *Xtampza ER* capsules can be opened and contents administered with soft food or through a gastric tube Avoid high fat meals with higher doses (except re-formulated OxyContin) If renally impaired, start at a lower dose, or avoid oxycodone, due to accumulation of parent drug and/or active metabolite
Oxymorphone *(Opana)* C-II Tablet (IR), injection	**IR** (opioid-naïve): 5-10 mg Q4-6H PRN	**NOTES** Do not use with moderate-to-severe liver impairment Use low doses in elderly, renal or mild liver impairment; there will be higher drug concentrations in these patients Take on empty stomach

**Brand name discontinued but still used in practice.*

Opioid Drug Interactions

- Caution with use together with other CNS depressants: additive somnolence, dizziness, confusion, increased risk of respiratory depression. These include alcohol, hypnotics, benzodiazepines and muscle relaxants. Avoid alcohol with all opioids, especially ER formulations.
- Increased risk of hypoxemia with underlying respiratory disease (e.g., COPD) and sleep apnea.
- Methadone: caution with agents that worsen cardiac function or increase arrhythmia risk. Caution with other serotonergic agents.
- Meperidine: caution with agents that worsen renal function, elderly patients and those with seizure history. Caution with other serotonergic agents.
- Hydrocodone, fentanyl, methadone and oxycodone are CYP3A4 substrates. Avoid use with CYP3A4 inhibitors.

DOSING CONVERSIONS

The correct dose is the lowest dose that provides effective pain relief. If the medicine is effective, but runs out too fast, do not increase the dose. This can cause respiratory depression. Rather, give the same dose more frequently. If the medication is not effective, consider increasing the dose. It is appropriate to consider switching to a different agent if:

- The dose has been increased or the interval shortened and the pain relief is not adequate
- The side effects are intolerable (patients react differently to different opioids)
- The drug is unaffordable or not included on formulary
- Changing formulations from IV to PO

For opioid conversions (not methadone) you can use ratio conversion (see table). When converting one opioid to another, round down (do not round up) and use breakthrough doses for compensation. A patient can respond better to one agent than another (likely due to less tolerance) and rounding the dose down will reduce the risk of overdose.

Steps to Convert

- Calculate total 24 hr dose requirement of the current drug.
- Use ratio-conversion to calculate the dose of the new drug. Refer to the Calculations I chapter for a review of how to set up and perform ratio-conversion calculations.
- Calculate 24 hr dose of new drug and reduce dose at least 25%. (If the problem on the exam does not specify to reduce it, just to find the equivalent dose, then do not reduce it.)
- Divide to attain appropriate interval and dose for new drug.
- Always have medication available for BTP while making changes. Guideline recommendation for BTP dosing ranges from 5 – 17% of the total daily baseline opioid dose.

DRUG	IV/IM (MG)	ORAL (MG)
Morphine	10	30
Hydromorphone	1.5	7.5
Oxycodone	–	20
Hydrocodone	–	30
Codeine	130	200
Fentanyl	0.1	–
Meperidine	75	300
Oxymorphone	1	10

Example of Opioid Conversion

A hospice patient has been receiving 12 mg/day of IV hydromorphone. The pharmacist will convert the hydromorphone to morphine ER, to be given Q12H. The hospice policy for opioid conversion is to reduce the new dose by 50%, and to use 5 – 17% of the total daily dose for BTP.

The conversion factors (the left fraction) are taken from the table from this same page. The right fraction has the patient's current total daily IV dose of hydromorphone in the denominator, and the total daily dose of morphine in the numerator:

$$\frac{\text{30 mg oral morphine}}{\text{1.5 mg IV hydromorphone}} = \frac{\text{X mg oral morphine}}{\text{12 mg IV hydromorphone}} \qquad \text{X = 240 mg of oral morphine}$$

Multiply the top left numerator (30) by the bottom right denominator (12), and then divide by the left denominator (1.5). This will give a total daily dose of morphine (PO) of 240 mg.

Reduce by 50%, as instructed in the problem:

50% of 240 mg = 120 mg, the correct dose of morphine ER would be 60 mg BID

Whenever possible, use an IR version of the long acting opioid for BTP. Typically 10 - 15% of the total daily dose is administered Q1 - 2H for BTP (~5% administered Q4H in the elderly). For example, a rescue dose of 15 mg IR morphine Q1 - 2H could be used with morphine ER 60 mg BID in the example and this would adhere to the hospice policy stated in the question. Other agents commonly used for BTP include combination agents, such as hydrocodone/acetaminophen. In an inpatient setting, injections can be given. Injections will have a faster onset and since BTP is typically severe, they can be preferable. However, if the patient does not have an existing IV line, the injection itself will cause discomfort. In real life, morphine IR may not be available. Hydrocodone/acetaminophen is often used for BTP. The hydrocodone dose is roughly the same as the morphine dose. If the patient is using acetaminophen alone for more mild pain, or the combination for moderate pain, the total daily acetaminophen intake will need to be monitored. Keep in mind that any drug that requires oral absorption will take time; if the patient has cancer pain (in which case the BTP is likely to be quite severe) a sublingual form of fentanyl can be used, which has faster onset.

Exception: Fentanyl Patches

Converting to a fentanyl patch is most commonly done using a dosing table provided in the package insert (see table and example). If converting to fentanyl using the previous chart, remember that you are finding the total daily dose in mg, and will then need to convert it to mcg (multiply by 1,000) and then divide by 24 to get the patch dose; the fentanyl patch is dosed in mcg per hour (no oral dose conversion is listed on the conversion chart because fentanyl is not absorbed orally). Some clinicians use this estimation: morphine 60 mg total daily dose = 25 mcg/hr fentanyl patch. These methods can provide different answers. For the exam, follow the specific instructions given when converting to or from fentanyl patches.

Example of Conversion to Fentanyl Patch using a Conversion Table

MJ is a 52-year-old male patient who has been using *OxyContin* 40 mg BID and *Endocet* 5-325 mg as-needed for BTP. He uses the BTP medication 2 - 3 times weekly. Using the *OxyContin* dose only, select the fentanyl patch strength that should be chosen for this patient, using the following table:

Fentanyl Conversion Table

Table 1: DOSE CONVERSION TO DURAGESIC

Current Analgesic	Daily Dosage (mg/day)			
Oral morphine	60–134	135–224	225–314	315–404
Intramuscular or Intravenous morphine	10–22	23–37	38–52	53–67
Oral oxycodone	30–67	67.5–112	112.5–157	157.5–202
Oral codeine	150–447			
Oral hydromorphone	8–17	17.1–28	28.1–39	39.1–51
Intravenous hydromorphone	1.5–3.4	3.5–5.6	5.7–7.9	8–10
Intramuscular meperidine	75–165	166–278	279–390	391–503
Oral methadone	20–44	45–74	75–104	105–134
	↓	↓	↓	↓
Recommended DURAGESIC Dose	25 mcg/hour	50 mcg/hour	75mcg/hour	100 mcg/hour

Table 1 should not be used to convert from DURAGESIC to other therapies because this conversion to DURAGESIC is conservative. Use of Table 1 for conversion to other analgesic therapies can overestimate the dose of the new agent. Overdosage of the new analgesic agent is possible

Answer: Oxycodone 80 mg daily is in the range of 67.5 - 112 mg daily which correlates to the 50 mcg/hr patch.

Methadone Conversion: Not Straight-Forward; Should Be Done By Pain Specialists

Morphine to methadone conversion ranges from 3:1 - 20:1; this is highly variable due to patient tolerance and duration of therapy. The half-life of methadone varies widely. There are separate conversion charts for pain specialists to estimate methadone dosing. This should be done only by specialists with experience in using methadone. In addition to the variable half-life, methadone is proarrhythmic and has other safety issues. Methadone is used both for the treatment of opioid addiction and for chronic pain. When used for chronic pain syndromes, it is administered 2 - 3 times per day after the proper dose is determined by titration. It should be started at very low doses of no more than 2.5 mg PO BID or TID, and escalated slowly.

OPIOIDS & CHRONIC NON-CANCER PAIN

Opioids are not first-line for chronic pain treatment and should not be used routinely. In some cases, they have benefit. When used, follow safe use recommendations:

- Establish and measure goals for pain and function. Reaching low pain rather than no pain may be reasonable.
- If using opioids, start with immediate release. *Start low and go slow.*
- Evaluate risk factors for opioid-related harm.
- Pharmacists should check their state's Prescription Drug Monitoring Program (PDMP) database. *Look for high dosages and multiple prescribers.*
- Use urine drug testing, and watch for false positives and negatives.
- Use adjunctive medications to enable a lower opioid dose.
- Avoid benzodiazepine and opioids given together, except in rare cases. *This quadruples the risk of overdose death.*
- Follow-up, taper the dose, consider discontinuation.

ALLERGY

True opioid allergies are rare. Most complaints of itching or rash are not a true allergic reaction. Symptoms of an opioid allergy (rare, but dangerous if present) include difficulty breathing, severe drop in blood pressure, serious rash, swelling of face, lips, tongue and larynx. In a true opioid allergy, use an agent in a different chemical class (see Study Tip Gal below).

Tramadol package labeling warns of increased risk of reactions to tramadol in those with previous anaphylactic reactions to opioids. Tapentadol does not have this warning in the U.S., though tramadol and tapentadol are structurally similar. If allergic to tramadol, an allergy to tapentadol is likely, and vice versa.

OPIOID ALLERGY

The common drugs in the same chemical class that cross-react with each other have **cod** or **morph** in the name. Buprenorphine has **norph** instead of **morph**.

Codeine	**Morph**ine	
Hydro**cod**one	Hydro**morph**one	Bupre**norph**ine
Oxy**cod**one	Oxy**morph**one	Heroin (diacetyl-morphine)

What to do if a morphine-type allergy is reported: in practice, make sure it is an actual allergy, and not nausea or itching. If it seems to be accurate, choose a drug in a different chemical class, such as methadone or fentanyl. Meperidine is also in a different class, but is no longer recommended as an analgesic.

SIDE EFFECTS AND MANAGEMENT

Opioid side effects usually lessen over time, except for constipation (see Study Tip Gal below). If a patient has a problem that persists or is bothersome, such as pruritus, switching to another opioid is reasonable. Hydroxyzine and diphenhydramine can be used for pruritus. Postoperative nausea and vomiting (PONV) occurs in surgical patients due primarily to the use of anesthesia and opioids. PONV is treated in the hospital with a 5HT3-receptor antagonist, such as ondansetron, or a phenothiazine, such as prochlorperazine. All oral opioids should be taken with food to lessen nausea.

Sedation and cognitive effects occur when the opioid is started or the dose is increased, and generally lessen over time. Pharmacists should advise patients not to drive or do anything potentially hazardous until they are accustomed to the medication. The use of other CNS depressants should be minimized. Alcohol should not be used with opioids.

OPIOID-INDUCED CONSTIPATION

All opioids cause constipation, referred to as opioid-induced constipation (OIC).

Opioids reduce GI tract peristalsis, making it difficult to pass a bowel movement.

Unlike CNS depression, OIC does not improve over time without treatment; it **must be anticipated and treated.**

When opioids are dosed around-the-clock, such as with an ER opioid, prophylaxis for constipation is required.

Stimulant laxatives, including senna, are the typical first-line laxative, with or without a stool softener. The stimulant laxative bisacodyl comes as a tablet (for prophylaxis) or suppository (for treatment).

If laxatives are not sufficient, specific medications for OIC that counteract the effects of the opioid receptor in the gut **(PAMORAs)** can be used.

Lubiprostone, which is used for different types of constipation, could be considered following trial of laxatives or PAMORAs.

TREATMENT OF OPIOID-INDUCED CONSTIPATION

DRUG	DOSING	SAFETY/SIDE EFFECTS/MONITORING
Peripherally-acting mu-opioid receptor antagonists (PAMORAs) - block opioid receptors in the gut to reduce constipation without affecting analgesia. PAMORAs are indicated for OIC and are only effective when constipation is secondary to use of an opioid.		
Methylnaltrexone *(Relistor)* Injection, tablet	OIC with chronic non-cancer pain: 12 mg SC daily or 450 mg PO once daily OIC with advanced illness: weight-based dose SC every other day CrCl < 30 mL/min: ↓ dose	**CONTRAINDICATION** GI obstruction **WARNINGS** Risk of GI perforation (rare reports; monitor for severe abdominal symptoms), risk of opioid withdrawal (evaluate risk vs benefit and monitor), use > 4 months has not been studied, discontinue if opioid is discontinued or if severe/persistent diarrhea **SIDE EFFECTS** Abdominal pain, flatulence, N/D **NOTES** Stay close to toilet after injecting Discontinue all laxatives prior to use Only for patients on opioids who have failed OTC laxatives Do not use routinely; can often increase laxative to obtain effect
Naloxegol *(Movantik)* Tablet	OIC with chronic non-cancer pain: 25 mg once daily in the morning on empty stomach CrCl < 60 mL/min: 12.5 mg once daily	**CONTRAINDICATIONS** GI obstruction, use with strong CYP3A4 inhibitors **WARNINGS** Risk of GI perforation (rare reports; monitor for severe abdominal symptoms), risk of opioid withdrawal (evaluate risk vs benefit and monitor) **SIDE EFFECTS** Abdominal pain, diarrhea, headache, flatulence **NOTES** Discontinue all laxatives prior to use; can reintroduce laxatives if suboptimal response after 3 days Do not use with strong CYP3A4 inhibitors. Avoid use or reduce dose to 12.5 mg daily with moderate CYP3A4 inhibitors. Do not use with grapefruit juice
Naldemedine *(Symproic)* Tablet	OIC with chronic non-cancer pain: 0.2 mg daily	**CONTRAINDICATION** GI obstruction **WARNINGS** Risk of GI perforation (rare reports; monitor for severe abdominal symptoms), risk of opioid withdrawal (evaluate risk vs benefit and monitor) **SIDE EFFECTS** Abdominal pain, diarrhea, nausea
Chloride channel activator - approved for other indications in addition to OIC.		
Lupiprostone *(Amitiza)* Capsule	OIC: 24 mcg BID	See Constipation & Diarrhea chapter

CENTRALLY ACTING ANALGESICS

Both tramadol and tapentadol are mu-opioid receptor agonists and inhibitors of norepinephrine reuptake. Tramadol also inhibits reuptake of serotonin. Both tapentadol and tramadol have the same boxed warnings as opioids (see Opioid Analgesics, Safety Concerns).

DRUG	DOSING	SAFETY/SIDE EFFECTS/MONITORING
Tramadol (*Ultram, Ultram ER,* *ConZip*) C-IV Tablet (IR/ER), ER capsule + acetaminophen (*Ultracet*)	IR: 50-100 mg Q4-6H, max 400 mg/day ER: 100 mg once daily, max 300 mg/day CrCl < 30 mL/min: IR: ↓ dose ER: do not use	**WARNINGS** Seizure risk (avoid in patients with seizure history, head trauma), risk of serotonin syndrome when used alone or with other serotonergic drugs or inhibitors of CYP2D6 or 3A4, CNS depression, respiratory depression (rare), avoid in patients who are suicidal; misuse, abuse and diversion (similar to opioids); risk of serious breathing problems in adolescents age 12-18 years with obesity, sleep apnea or lung disease; breastfeeding mothers should avoid due to ↑ risk of serious breathing problem in breastfed infants **CONTRAINDICATIONS** Use of tramadol in children < 12 years of age; use in children < 18 years of age following tonsillectomy/adenoidectomy surgery **SIDE EFFECTS** Dizziness, nausea, constipation, loss of appetite, flushing, dry mouth, dyspepsia, pruritus, insomnia (some patients find tramadol sedating but for most it is not), possible headache, ataxia Lower severity of GI side effects versus strong opioids **NOTES** Tramadol requires conversion to active metabolite by CYP2D6. Use with CYP2D6 inhibitors can have variable effects due to mixed mechanism of action of tramadol
Tapentadol (*Nucynta, Nucynta ER*) C-II Tablet (IR/ER)	IR: 50-100 mg Q4-6H ER: 50-250 mg BID CrCl < 30 mL/min: Use not recommended (not studied).	**CONTRAINDICATIONS** Use of MAO inhibitors together with or within 14 days **WARNINGS** Can increase seizure risk (avoid in patients with seizure history or seizure risk), risk of serotonin syndrome when used with other serotonergic drugs **SIDE EFFECTS** Dizziness, somnolence, nausea but lower severity of GI side effects than stronger opioids

Centrally Acting Analgesic Drug Interactions

- Caution with other agents that lower seizure threshold. Caution with other serotonergic drugs. Avoid tramadol with CYP2D6 inhibitors. Possibility of increased INR with warfarin; monitor. Tapentadol can enhance the adverse/toxic effect of MAO inhibitors; avoid use with MAO inhibitors.

OPIOID ABUSE

Prescription opioid overdose-related deaths have more than tripled from 2001 to 2014. Opioid abuse is now an epidemic in the U.S. This addiction, referred to as opioid use disorder (OUD), can be lethal. The U.S. government has created five strategies to prevent overdose death:

- Educate providers and general public about how to prevent and manage opioid overdose.
- Ensure access to treatment for patients addicted to opioids.
- Ensure ready access to naloxone (see Study Tip Gal below).
- Encourage the public to call 911.
- Encourage prescribers to use state Prescription Drug Monitoring Programs (PDMPs).

Additionally, there have been a number of FDA-approved opioids designed to help mitigate drug abuse and misuse. It is important to note that these formulations do not eliminate the ability to abuse or misuse opioids. Some opioid combination products such as *Suboxone*, *Troxyca ER* or *Embeda* are formulated with an abuse deterrent medication such as naloxone or naltrexone, while others such as *OxyContin*, *Hysingla ER* or *Arymo ER* are manufactured using specific technology designed to deter crushing, dissolving or other modifications. *Roxybond* is the first IR product to be developed with abuse deterrent technology.

OPIOID INDUCED RESPIRATORY DEPRESSION (OIRD) RISKS

An opioid prescription requires a risk/benefit assessment, and monitoring.

A prescription for naloxone should be offered to patients with elevated risk factors for OIRD.

Risk factors include:

- History of previous overdose
- Substance abuse
- Using large doses (≥ 50 morphine milligram equivalent dose)
- Using with benzodiazepines
- Comorbid illness such as respiratory and psychiatric disease

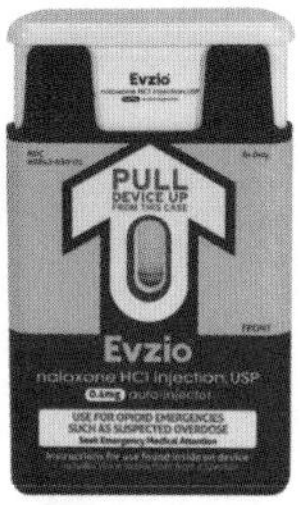

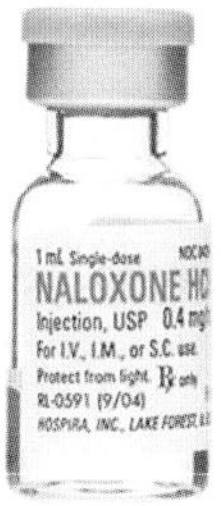

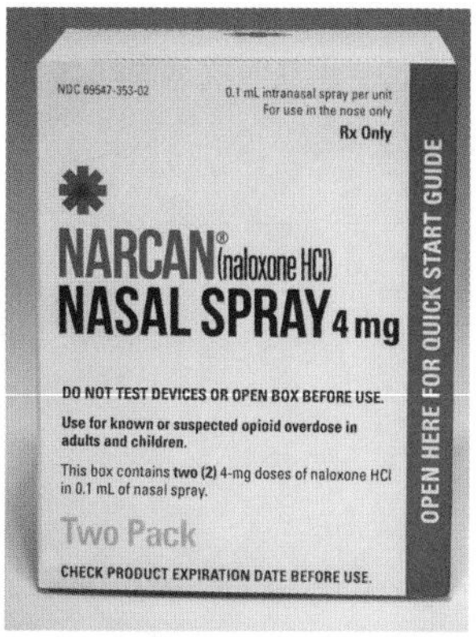

OPIOID ABUSE AGENTS

Buprenorphine is a partial mu-opioid agonist. It is an agonist at low doses and an antagonist at higher doses. It is used in lower doses to treat pain and higher doses to treat addiction. Naloxone is an opioid antagonist; it replaces the opioid on the mu receptor. Given by itself, naloxone (injection or nasal spray) is used for opioid overdose. Buprenorphine/naloxone combination products are used as alternatives to methadone for opioid dependence (buprenorphine suppresses withdrawal symptoms and naloxone helps prevents misuse).

Naltrexone is an opioid antagonist normally used to help treat alcohol and opioid dependence. It is available as a daily oral formulation and a monthly IM injection *(Vivitrol)*. Lofexidine *(Lucemyra)*, a non-opioid, alpha-2 adrenergic agonist, was approved to treat withdrawal symptoms in patients who wish to abruptly stop use of opioids altogether. While not a treatment for OUD, it is used as part of a long-term treatment plan. The non-pharmacologic treatment *reSET-O* is a digital technology FDA-cleared for OUD treatment.

Naloxone can be given if opioid overdose is suspected due to respiratory symptoms and/or symptoms of CNS depression (see Study Tip Gal below). All approved naloxone formulations can be administered for prevention of opioid overdose death. Many states have made naloxone readily available by allowing first responders and laymen to obtain naloxone in case they see someone overdosing.

OPIOID OVERDOSE MANAGEMENT

S/Sx of overdose: extreme sleepiness, slow or shallow breathing, fingernails or lips turning blue or purple, extremely small "pinpoint" pupils, slow heartbeat and/or blood pressure

If overdose is suspected, Call 911 and give naloxone

If individual is not breathing or struggling to breathe, life support measures should be performed

If there is a question about whether to give naloxone, give it, because fatality could result from not giving it

Opioid lasts longer than naloxone so monitor closely for respiratory depression and provide repeat doses, as needed

Naloxone is available in three options:

- *Evzio* (auto-injector); easy to administer with visual and voice instructions, each auto-injector provides 1 dose
- *Narcan* (nasal spray); onset of action is slower than injection, a single-use nasal spray is 4 mg administered in 1 nostril, repeat doses in alternating nostrils may be needed
- Naloxone (injection); generic formulation provided in multiple size vials, separate syringe will be needed, may need to repeat doses every 2-3 minutes until emergency medical assistance arrives

TREATMENT OF OPIOID ABUSE

DRUG	DOSING	SAFETY/SIDE EFFECTS/MONITORING
Naloxone (***Narcan***, *Evzio*, *S.O.S. Naloxone*) Injection, nasal spray *Narcan:* nasal spray *Evzio:* auto-injector	IV/IM/SC: 0.4-2 mg Q2-3 min or IV infusion at 0.4 mg/hr IM: Give in thigh through clothing, hold for 5 seconds, then call 911 Nasal spray: 1 spray (4 mg), can repeat Repeat dosing can be required (opioid can last longer than blocking agent)	**NOTES** Will cause acute withdrawal (pain, anxiety, tachypnea) in patients who are physically dependent Due to low bioavailability, can be given orally to prevent opioid-induced constipation (off-label)
Buprenorphine C-III Injection, patch, buccal film, sublingual tablet ***Belbuca:*** buccal film ***Butrans:*** patch (only for mod-severe pain in patients who need ATC opioid) *Buprenex:* injection *Probuphine* implant kit *Sublocade*: once-monthly injection **+ naloxone** (***Suboxone***: sublingual film, ***Zubsolv***: sublingual tablets, *Bunavail*: buccal film, *Cassipa*: sublingual film)	*Butrans* (opioid-naïve): 5 mcg/hr patch once weekly *Belbuca* (opioid-naïve): 75 mcg daily or Q12H *Bunavail, Suboxone, Zubsolv*: used daily for addiction and used off-label for pain **Patch Application** Apply to upper outer arm, upper chest, side of chest, upper back. Change weekly. Do not use same site for at least 3 weeks. Disposal: fold sticky sides together, flush or put in disposal unit that comes with drug **Film Application** *Belbuca* is a small film that has one white side and one yellow side. The white side should be placed on fingertip and the film is inserted between gum and cheek on the cheek. The cheek must be wet from saliva or water and patient should be instructed not to eat or drink for 30 minutes after placement of film.	**BOXED WARNINGS** *Belbuca* film, *Butrans* patch: risk of addiction, abuse and misuse; risk of serious or fatal respiratory depression; life-threatening neonatal opioid withdrawal with prolonged use during pregnancy, accidental ingestion (especially in children) can be fatal **WARNINGS** CNS depression, QT prolongation (do not exceed one 20 mcg/hr patch) **SIDE EFFECTS** Sedation, dizziness, headache, confusion, mental and physical impairment, diaphoresis, QT prolongation, respiratory depression (dose-dependent) Patch: nausea, headache, application site pruritus/rash, dizziness, constipation, somnolence, vomiting, application site erythema, dry mouth **NOTES** Do not expose patch to heat To prescribe for opioid dependence: prescribers need a Drug Addiction Treatment Act (DATA 2000) waiver. If they have it, the DEA will issue a unique identification number to the prescriber, which will start with X *Sublocade:* patients must have been taking a stable dose of transmucosal buprenorphine for 7 days prior to initiation *Cassipa* availability is currently unknown
Lofexidine (*Lucemyra*) Tablet	Initial: 0.54 mg four times daily in 5 to 6 hour intervals. Maximum duration of treatment 14 days	**WARNINGS** Risk of hypotension, bradycardia and syncope, QT prolongation, ↑ CNS depression, ↑ risk of opioid overdose after discontinuation, risk of discontinuation symptoms; must taper when discontinuing over 2 to 4 days **SIDE EFFECTS** Orthostatic hypotension, dizziness and dry mouth **NOTES** Can reduce efficacy of oral naltrexone Paroxetine and other CYP2D6 inhibitors can ↑ risk of orthostatic hypotension and bradycardia, monitor closely

Buprenorphine Drug Interactions

- Use caution with CNS depressants: additive sedation (somnolence), dizziness and confusion. These include alcohol, hypnotics, benzodiazepines and skeletal muscle relaxants.
- Use cautiously in patients taking other QT prolonging drugs or with arrhythmia risk.

COMMON ADJUVANTS FOR PAIN MANAGEMENT

Adjuvants [e.g., muscle relaxants, antiepileptic drugs (AEDs), antidepressants, topical anesthetics] are useful in pain management though they are not classified as analgesics. They can be added to opioid or non-opioid analgesics (multimodal treatment).

Adjuvants are commonly used in pain associated with neuropathy (from diabetes or spinal cord injury), postherpetic neuralgia (PHN), fibromyalgia, osteoarthritis (OA) and others. AEDs (notably pregabalin and gabapentin) are useful for neuropathic pain. Some adjuvants are being developed and labeled for specific indications. For example, a lidocaine 1.8% patch formulation, *ZTlido,* was developed and approved for PHN. In severe cases, other classes of agents, including opioids, can provide benefit. TCAs and SNRIs block norepinephrine uptake, which has shown to be beneficial in neuropathic pain. SSRIs do not have this effect.

Muscle relaxants have various, poorly-understood mechanisms of action. Some work predominantly by CNS depression leading to relaxation of skeletal muscles (e.g., carisoprodol, chlorzoxazone, metaxalone, methocarbamol), while others work by decreasing transmission of reflexes at the spinal level.

Injectable adjuvants can be used in specific cases by pain specialists. For example, clonidine injection can be added to opioids in intrathecal (epidural) pain infusion pumps for patients with cancer pain when other agents are insufficient. Only analgesics approved by the FDA for intrathecal administration should be used. Some other common injectable adjuvants include anesthetics like lidocaine injected locally to a small area for pain, for example, before a dental procedure or before placing stitches (see a list of these agents in the Acute & Critical Care Medicine chapter) or steroid injections for temporary relief in some conditions. Triamcinolone acetonide extended-release *(Zilretta)* was approved for OA knee pain and is administered by injection into the knee joint (intra-articular) to provide 12 weeks of pain relief, without opioids.

ORAL ADJUVANTS

DRUG	DOSING	SAFETY/SIDE EFFECTS/MONITORING
Antiepileptic drugs (AEDs)		
Gabapentin *(Neurontin,* *Fanatrex* compounding kit) Capsule, tablet, solution, suspension *Gralise* (tablet) – for PHN ***Horizant*** (ER tablet) – for PHN and restless legs syndrome	Initial: 300 mg TID Max 3,600 mg/day CrCl < 60 mL/min: ↓ dose and/or extend interval	**WARNINGS** Angioedema/anaphylaxis, multiorgan hypersensitivity (DRESS) reactions, suicidal thoughts or behavior (all AEDs), ↑ seizure frequency if rapidly discontinued in those with seizures, CNS effects **SIDE EFFECTS** Somnolence, ataxia, peripheral edema, weight gain, dizziness, diplopia, blurred vision, dry mouth **NOTES** Used most commonly off-label for fibromyalgia, pain (neuropathic), headache, drug abuse, alcohol withdrawal Take ER formulation with food IR, ER and gabapentin enacarbil are not interchangeable
Pregabalin *(Lyrica)* C-V Capsule, solution	Initial: 75 mg BID or 50 mg TID Max 450 mg/day CrCl < 60 mL/min: ↓ dose and/or extend interval	**WARNINGS** Angioedema, hypersensitivity reactions, risks of suicidal thoughts or behavior (all AEDs), ↑ seizure frequency if rapidly discontinued in those with seizures; can cause peripheral edema, dizziness and somnolence **SIDE EFFECTS** Somnolence, mild euphoria, peripheral edema, weight gain, ataxia, diplopia, blurred vision, dry mouth, dizziness **NOTES** Approved for use in fibromyalgia, PHN and neuropathic pain associated with diabetes and spinal cord injury

DRUG	DOSING	SAFETY/SIDE EFFECTS/MONITORING
Carbamazepine *(Tegretol, Carbatrol, Carnexiv)* Tablet (IR or ER), ER capsule, suspension, injection	Initial: 100 mg BID Max 1,200 mg/day	**NOTES** Only FDA-approved medication for the treatment of trigeminal neuralgia See Seizures/Epilepsy chapter
Antispasmodics (muscle relaxants) with analgesic effects. Use caution with other CNS depressants (e.g., alcohol, benzodiazepines and opioids) due to the additive risk of CNS depression.		
Baclofen *(Lioresal)* Tablet, injection	5-20 mg TID-QID PRN Injection given via intrathecal pump for severe spasticity	**BOXED WARNING** Abrupt withdrawal of intrathecal baclofen has resulted in severe effects (high fever, lethargy, rebound/↑ spasticity, muscle rigidity and rhabdomyolysis), leading to organ failure and death **SIDE EFFECTS** For all muscle relaxants: excessive sedation, dizziness, confusion **NOTES** Do not overdose in elderly (e.g., start low, titrate carefully), watch for additive side effects
Cyclobenzaprine *(Amrix ER, Fexmid, Flexeril)* Tablet/capsule	IR: 5-10 mg TID PRN ER: 15-30 mg once daily	**SIDE EFFECTS** Dry mouth **NOTES** Can have efficacy with fibromyalgia Serotonergic: do not combine with other serotonergic agents Can precipitate or exacerbate cardiac arrhythmias; caution in elderly or those with heart disease (similar to TCAs chemically a tricylclic almost identical to amitriptyline)
Tizanidine *(Zanaflex)* Tablet/capsule	2-4 mg Q6-8H PRN (max 36 mg/day)	**CONTRAINDICATIONS** Use with strong CYP1A2 inhibitors (e.g., fluvoxamine, ciprofloxacin) **SIDE EFFECTS** Hypotension, dry mouth, weakness, QT prolongation **NOTES** Centrally acting alpha-2 agonist
Antispasmodics (muscle relaxants) that exert their effects by sedation		
Carisoprodol *(Soma)* C-IV	250-350 mg QID PRN	**NOTES** Poor CYP2C19 metabolizers will have ↑ carisoprodol concentrations (up to 4-fold) Rapid CYP2C19 metabolizers will convert to the active metabolite meprobamate (↑ toxicity/sedation)
Metaxalone *(Skelaxin)*	800 mg TID-QID PRN	**SIDE EFFECTS** Hepatotoxic
Methocarbamol *(Robaxin,* *Robaxin-750)*	1,500-2,000 mg QID PRN	**SIDE EFFECTS** Hypotension
Rarely used muscle relaxants include dantrolene *(Dantrium* used for malignant hyperthermia), chlorzoxazone *(Lorzone)* and orphenadrine *(Norflex)*.		
SNRIs and TCAs		
Milnacipran *(Savella, Savella* Titration Pack) Tablet	Day 1: 12.5 mg daily Days 2-3: 12.5 mg BID Days 4-7: 25 mg BID Then 50 mg BID CrCl < 30 mL/min: max dose is 25 mg BID	**BOXED WARNINGS** Milnacipran is an SNRI. Antidepressants ↑ the risk of suicidal thoughts and behavior in children, adolescents, and young adults with depression and other psychiatric disorders (do not use in pediatric patients) **CONTRAINDICATIONS** Use with or within 2 weeks of MAO inhibitors, avoid with linezolid or IV methylene blue **SIDE EFFECTS** Nausea, headache, constipation, dizziness, insomnia, hot flashes **NOTES** Indicated for fibromyalgia only (not approved for depression) Do not use IV digoxin with milnacipran. Milnacipran can ↑ the toxic effect of digoxin including postural hypotension and tachycardia (particularly IV digoxin) Increased bleeding risk with anticoagulants or antiplatelets

DRUG	DOSING	SAFETY/SIDE EFFECTS/MONITORING
Amitriptyline *(Elavil)* Tablet	10-50 mg QHS, sometimes higher	**NOTES** See Depression chapter Desipramine: titrate every 3 – 7 days
Desipramine *(Norpramin)* Tablet	Initial: 25 mg daily Max 150 mg/day	
Duloxetine *(Cymbalta)* Capsule	30-60 mg/day	

TOPICAL ADJUVANTS

DRUG	DOSING/NOTES	SAFETY/SIDE EFFECTS/MONITORING
Lidocaine 5% patches *(Lidoderm)* – Rx **Lidocaine viscous gel** – Rx Lidocaine 1.8% patch *(ZTlido)* - Rx, for PHN Lidocaine 4% and lower strengths (***LidoPatch**, Lidocare*, others) – OTC	*Lidoderm:* Apply to painful area 1-3 patches/day and worn for up to 12 hrs/day Approved for PHN (shingles) pain	**SIDE EFFECTS** Minor topical burning, pruritus, rash **NOTES** Can cut into smaller pieces (before removing backing) *Lidoderm:* do not apply more than 3 patches at one time Caution with used patches; can harm children and pets; fold patch in half and discard safely Do not cover with heating pads/electric blankets
Capsaicin 0.025% and 0.075% *(Zostrix, Zostrix HP)* – OTC 8% patch *(Qutenza)* – Rx	Apply to affected area TID-QID	**SIDE EFFECTS** Topical burning, which dissipates with continued use **NOTES** *Qutenza* is given in the healthcare provider's office only – it causes topical burning and requires pre-treatment with lidocaine – applied for 1 hour and lasts for months – works in ~40% of patients to reduce pain, indicated for PHN pain ↓ TRPV1-expressing nociceptive nerve endings (↓ substance P) Onset of pain relief takes 2-4 weeks of continuous application for OTC products and 1 week for *Qutenza* (Rx)
Methyl salicylate topical OTCs ***(BenGay, Icy Hot, SalonPas*** *Precise, Thera-Gesic*, store brands) Methyl salicylate plus other ingredients **Trolamine *(Aspercreme)***	Patches, creams	**NOTES** Occasionally, topicals have caused first to third-degree burns, mostly in patients with neuropathic damage: discontinue use and seek medical attention if signs of skin injury (pain, swelling, or blistering) occur following application

PATIENT COUNSELING

ACETAMINOPHEN

- Contact your healthcare provider right away for any condition that is being self-treated if the condition worsens, lasts for more than two days, if there is a high fever (> 102.5°F), or rash, nausea, vomiting or blood in the stool (adults and children). Infants should be seen by a pediatrician.
- Many products contain acetaminophen, including prescription pain medicines and over-the-counter pain and cough and cold products. The name can be written as acetaminophen, *Tylenol*, APAP or non-aspirin pain reliever. The total daily dose of all products containing acetaminophen should not exceed 4,000 mg.
- Too much acetaminophen can cause permanent liver damage and can lead to death. This can be worsened by the use of too much alcohol. Women should not exceed one drink per day, and men should not exceed two drinks per day.

NSAIDS

- Read the MedGuide included with this medicine. This medicine can increase the chance of a heart attack or stroke that can lead to death. The risk increases in people who have heart disease. If you have heart disease, discuss using this medicine with your healthcare provider.

- This medicine can cause ulcers and bleeding in the stomach and intestines at any time during treatment. Call your healthcare provider right away if you notice red or black stools that look like tar, or if you cough or vomit blood or material that looks like coffee grounds. The risk is highest if you use higher doses, and when used long-term. To help reduce the risk, limit alcohol use while taking this medicine, and use the lowest possible dose for the shortest possible time. This medicine should not be used with steroids (such as prednisone) or anticoagulants (such as warfarin, *Pradaxa* or *Xarelto*). There are some exceptions in very high risk (clotting) patients who use both aspirin and warfarin but in general, using them together is not recommended.
- Do not use after coronary heart surgery, unless you have been instructed to do so by your healthcare provider. Do not use this medicine before any elective surgery.
- Take with food if this medicine upsets your stomach.
- Do not use this medicine if you have experienced breathing problems or allergic-type reactions after taking aspirin or other NSAIDs.
- This medicine can raise your blood pressure. If you have high blood pressure, you will need to check your blood pressure regularly; contact your prescriber with an increase in your blood pressure.
- This medicine can cause fluid and water to accumulate, particularly in your ankles. If you have heart disease, discuss use of this medicine with your healthcare provider and monitor your weight.
- This drug can make you sensitive to the sun. Limit sun exposure.
- Do not use this medicine if you are pregnant without discussing with your healthcare provider.

Diclofenac Gel

- Use the dosing card inside the package to correctly measure each dose. The dosing card is reusable so do not throw it away. Do not use more than 32 grams total of diclofenac gel each day. You should add up the amount applied to each area to make sure it is less than 32 grams:
  - The dose for your hands, wrists, or elbows is 2 grams with each application; apply four times daily and do not exceed 8 grams each day to these areas.

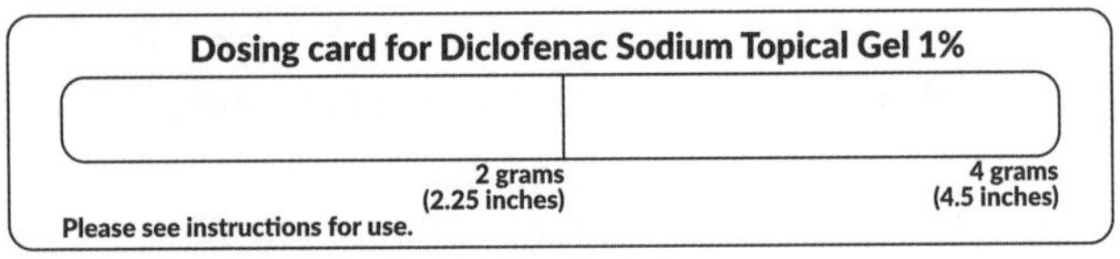

  - The dose for your feet, ankles, or knees is 4 grams with each application; apply four times daily but do not exceed more than 16 grams each day to these areas.
- Place the dosing card on a flat surface so you can read the print. Squeeze diclofenac gel onto the dosing card evenly; cover the 2 gram or 4 gram dosing area up to the dosing line.
- Using the dosing card, apply the gel to clean, dry skin that does not have any cuts or open wounds; then gently rub the gel into the skin with your hands, making sure to cover the affected area fully.
- Do not shower, bathe or wash your treated hands for at least one hour after application.

Ketorolac Nasal Spray

- Each *Sprix* bottle has enough medicine for one day. Throw away any remaining medication 24 hours after opening.
- Each bottle must be primed five times prior to first use. No additional priming is needed if additional doses are used.
- Store unopened bottles in the refrigerator. Open bottles can be kept at room temperature.

OPIOIDS

- Do not crush, chew, break or open controlled-release forms. Breaking them would cause too much drug to be released into your blood at one time.
- *Kadian* must be swallowed whole or can be opened and the entire bead contents sprinkled on a small amount of applesauce immediately prior to ingestion. The beads must not be chewed, crushed, or dissolved due to the risk of exposure to a potentially toxic dose of morphine.
- Avoid alcohol with all opioids, especially these formulations: *Kadian, Embeda, Zohydro* and *Nucynta ER*.
- To ensure that you get a correct dose, measure liquid forms with a special dose-measuring spoon or cup, not with a regular tablespoon. If you do not have a dose-measuring device, ask your pharmacist.
- This medicine will cause drowsiness and fatigue. Avoid alcohol, sleeping pills, antihistamines, sedatives and tranquilizers that can also make you drowsy, except under the supervision of your healthcare provider.
- Take with a full glass of water. Take with food or milk if it upsets your stomach. Exception: *Opana* should be taken on an empty stomach.
- Do not stop taking suddenly if you have been taking it continuously for more than 5 – 7 days. If you want to stop, your healthcare provider will help you gradually reduce the dose.

- This medicine is constipating. Increase the amount of fiber and water (at least six to eight full glasses daily) in your diet to prevent constipation (if not fluid restricted due to heart failure). Your pharmacist or healthcare provider will recommend a stronger agent for constipation if this is not adequate.
- Do not share this medication with anyone else.
- Never take more pain medicine than prescribed. If your pain is not being adequately treated, talk to your healthcare provider.

Fentanyl Patch

- Do not heat patch or skin area before or after applying. Do not cover with heating pad or any bandage. If you develop a fever while you have a patch on, call your healthcare provider.
- Apply to hairless skin on flat surface (chest, back, flank, upper arm) and change every 72 hrs. Cut hair short if necessary. Press in place for 30 seconds.
- Do not use soap, alcohol or other solvents to remove transdermal gel if it accidentally touches skin. Use large amount of water.
- Dispose of patch in toilet.
- Keep away from children and animals. Keep in child-resistant box if possible.

MUSCLE RELAXANTS

- This medicine will cause somnolence and fatigue and can impair your ability to perform mental and physical activities. Do not drive when using this medicine.
- Avoid alcohol, sleeping pills, antihistamines, sedatives, pain pills and tranquilizers that can also make you drowsy, except under the supervision of your healthcare provider.

LIDODERM PATCH

- Patches can be cut into smaller sizes with scissors before removal of the release (plastic) liner.
- Safely discard unused portions of cut patches where children and pets cannot get to them.
- Apply up to three patches at one time to cover the most painful area. Apply patches only once daily for up to 12 hr in a 24-hr period (12 hr on and 12 hr off).
- Remove patch if skin irritation occurs.
- Fold used patches so that the adhesive side sticks to itself and safely discard used patches or pieces of cut patches where children and pets cannot get to them. Even a used patch contains enough medicine to harm a child or pet.
- Do not use on broken, abraded, severely burned or skin with open lesions (can significantly increase amount absorbed).

CAPSAICIN TOPICAL

- Apply a thin film of cream to the affected area and gently rub in until fully absorbed.
- Apply 3 – 4 times daily.
- Best results typically occur after 2 – 4 weeks of continuous use. Do not use as-needed, since frequent, long-term use is required for benefit.
- Unless treating hand pain, wash hands thoroughly with soap and water immediately after use.
- If treating hands, leave on for 30 minutes, then wash hands as above.
- Do not touch genitals, nasal area, mouth or eyes with the medicine; it will burn the sensitive skin.
- The burning pain should dissipate with continual use; starting at the lower strength will help.
- Never cover with bandages or a heating pad; serious burning could result.

METHYL SALICYLATE TOPICAL

- Contact your healthcare provider if you develop a rash or excessive skin irritation while using this product or if symptoms last for more than seven days.
- Do not apply on wounds or damaged skin. Do not cover with tight bandages or apply heat.

Select Guidelines/References

CDC Guideline for Prescribing Opioids for Chronic Pain. https://www.cdc.gov/mmwr/volumes/65/rr/rr6501e1.htm (accessed 2019 April 17).

SAMHSA Opioid Overdose Prevention Toolkit. https://store.samhsa.gov/system/files/sma18-4742.pdf (accessed 2019 April 17).

Use of Opioids for the Treatment of Chronic Pain: a Statement from the American Academy of Pain Medicine. http://www.painmed.org/files/use-of-opioids-for-the-treatment-of-chronic-pain.pdf (accessed 2019 April 17).

CHAPTER CONTENT

Background 818
Causes 818
Common Migraine Triggers 819
Diagnosis 819
Non-Drug Treatment 819
Natural Products 819
Acute Drug Treatment 819
Triptans 820
Triptan Formulations 821
Ergotamine Drugs 821
Butalbital-Containing Products 821
Prophylactic Drug Treatment 822
Oral Prophylactic Agents 822
Other Prophylactic Agents 823
Medication-Overuse ("Rebound") Headaches 823
Patient Counseling 823

CONTENT LEGEND

= Study Tip Gal

CHAPTER 59
MIGRAINE

BACKGROUND

Headache treatment is a common concern in the community pharmacy. It is one of the most common complaints in neurologists' offices and the most common pain complaint seen in family practice. Most headaches are migraine and tension-type headaches.

Migraines are chronic headaches that cause significant pain for hours or days. Most migraines cause nausea, vomiting and sensitivity to light and sound. Some migraines are preceded or accompanied by sensory warning symptoms or signs (auras), such as flashes of light, blind spots or tingling in the arms or legs. Most migraines do not have an aura.

A headache accompanied by fever, stiff neck, rash, confusion, seizures, double vision, weakness, numbness, chest pain, shortness of breath or aphasia (trouble speaking) could indicate a serious cardiovascular, cerebrovascular or infectious event. Patients with these symptoms should seek immediate medical attention.

CAUSES

The cause of migraines is not well-understood. They may be caused by changes in the trigeminal nerve and imbalances in neurotransmitters, including serotonin. The decrease in neurotransmitters causes a release of neuropeptides that trigger vasodilation in cranial blood vessels.

Patients should identify and avoid "triggers" to reduce migraine incidence (see Study Tip Gal on the following page). A common type of migraine is a menstrual-associated migraine (MAM) in women. These can be treated with oral contraceptives, the estradiol patch or creams to decrease their frequency. Women who have migraine with aura are at higher risk for stroke and should not use estrogen-containing contraceptives.

COMMON MIGRAINE TRIGGERS

Hormonal Changes in Women
Fluctuations in estrogen trigger headaches in many women. Some women use monophasic oral formulations to keep estrogen levels more constant and help reduce MAM. Progestin-only pills are recommended for women with migraine with aura, due to stroke risk with estrogen-containing contraceptives.

Foods
Common offending agents include alcohol, especially beer and red wine, aged cheeses, chocolate, aspartame, overuse of caffeine, monosodium glutamate (MSG), salty foods and processed foods.

Stress
Stress is a major cause of migraines.

Sensory Stimuli
Bright lights, sun glare, loud sounds and certain scents (which may be pleasant or unpleasant odors).

Changes in Wake-Sleep Pattern
Either missing sleep or getting too much sleep (including jet lag).

Changes in the Environment
A change of weather or barometric pressure.

DIAGNOSIS

Migraine can be diagnosed when an adult has at least five attacks (not attributed to another disorder) fulfilling the following criteria:

1. Headaches last 4 – 72 hrs and recur sporadically.
2. Headaches have ≥ 2 of the following characteristics: unilateral location, pulsating, moderate-severe pain and aggravated by (or causing avoidance of) routine physical activity.
3. One of the following occurs during the headache: nausea and/or vomiting, photophobia (sensitivity to light) and phonophobia (sensitivity to sound).

NON-DRUG TREATMENT

A headache diary can assist patients in identifying triggers. Non-pharmacologic interventions involve avoiding triggers, stress management, massage, spinal manipulation or applying cold compresses/ice to the head. Acupuncture can be helpful for reducing migraines in some patients.

The medical device gammaCore provides non-invasive vagus nerve stimulation. This can help block pain signals that cause migraines and cluster headaches. The device is positioned on the neck for two 2-minute stimulations, which can be repeated x 2 if pain persists.

NATURAL PRODUCTS

Caffeine is effective in combination with acetaminophen or aspirin to treat migraine headaches; several combination products are available for this purpose. Butterbur, feverfew, magnesium, riboflavin, peppermint (applied topically) and coenzyme Q10 (each alone or in combination) have been used for prevention of migraines.

ACUTE DRUG TREATMENT

Acute (abortive) treatment is used for a headache that is already present. There are many choices for acute treatment, including OTC options: acetaminophen, *Advil Migraine* (which contains only ibuprofen), *Excedrin Migraine* (aspirin, acetaminophen and caffeine), *Aleve* (naproxen) or other drugs, including store brands of these options. OTC drugs can be tried for migraines that are mild to moderate. Prescription options for acute treatment include: serotonin receptor agonists (triptans), ergotamine- and butalbital-containing medications, opioids/opioid-combination products and diclofenac *(Cambia)* in a packet formulation that is specifically indicated for migraine treatment. Refer to the Pain chapter for a more detailed discussion of many of these medications. Opioids, butalbital-containing products, tramadol and tapentadol are not recommended due to abuse/dependence issues. If other agents have failed, these are used in select cases.

Some patients get more relief from OTC products, some from triptans and others need to use combinations of both. Always ask the patient what they have tried in the past, and if it was useful. Patients with nausea/vomiting may benefit from combined treatment with an antiemetic.

TRIPTANS

Triptans are selective agonists for the 5-HT1 receptor (1B/1D subtypes) and cause vasoconstriction of cranial blood vessels, inhibit neuropeptide release and decrease pain transmission. They are first-line for acute treatment. The safety of treating more than 3 – 5 headaches per month (product-specific) has not been established.

DRUG	DOSING	SAFETY/SIDE EFFECTS/MONITORING
Almotriptan Tablet	Initial: 6.25-12.5 mg, can repeat x 1 after 2 hrs (max 25 mg/day)	**CONTRAINDICATIONS** Cerebrovascular disease (stroke/TIA), uncontrolled hypertension, ischemic heart disease, peripheral vascular disease, history of hemiplegic or basilar migraine, use within 24 hrs of another triptan or ergotamine-type medication. See Drug Interactions for products contraindicated with MAO inhibitors and CYP450 3A4 inhibitors. **WARNINGS** Risk of ↑ blood pressure, cardiac and cerebrovascular events, arrhythmias, serotonin syndrome, medication overuse headache (MOH), seizures (sumatriptan only); caution in hepatic or renal impairment (product specific). **SIDE EFFECTS** Paresthesia (tingling/numbness), dizziness, hot/cold sensations, chest pain/tightness, dry mouth, somnolence, nausea. Triptan sensations (pressure in the chest or heaviness or pressure in the neck region) usually dissipate after administration. **NOTES** ODTs, nasal sprays and injections are useful if nausea is present. No water is required for ODTs. Nasal sprays and injections work faster. Imitrex and Zomig nasal sprays contain only 1 dose (do not prime). *Treximet*: protect from moisture; dispense in original container. *Treximet* carries all warnings associated with naproxen (see Pain chapter). **Children and Adolescents** Almotriptan tablets, zolmitriptan nasal spray and *Treximet* are approved for children and adolescents ≥ 12 years of age; rizatriptan is approved for children and adolescents 6-17 years of age. **Duration of Action** Frovatriptan has the longest half-life (26 hrs). Both frovatriptan and naratriptan are considered long-acting, but onset is slower. These can be chosen if headache recurs after dosing, lasts a long time or can be anticipated (e.g., MAM). Triptans with a shorter half-life have a faster onset: almotriptan, eletriptan, rizatriptan, sumatriptan and zolmitriptan. **Sumatriptan Injections** All are injected SC. Preferred site is lateral thigh or upper arm. Protect from light. Available as: prefilled syringe *(Imitrex)* and prefilled autoinjector *(Zembrace)*.
Eletriptan *(Relpax)* Tablet	Initial: 20-40 mg, can repeat x 1 after 2 hrs (max 80 mg/day)	
Frovatriptan *(Frova)* Tablet	Initial: 2.5 mg, can repeat x 1 after 2 hrs (max 7.5 mg/day)	
Naratriptan *(Amerge)* Tablet	Initial: 1-2.5 mg, can repeat x 1 after 4 hrs (max 5 mg/day)	
Rizatriptan *(Maxalt, Maxalt-MLT)* Tablet, ODT	Initial: 5-10 mg, can repeat x 1 after 2 hrs (max 30 mg/day)	
Sumatriptan (*Imitrex, Imitrex STATdose, Onzetra Xsail*, *Zembrace SymTouch)* Tablet, SC (autoinjector and prefilled syringe), nasal spray, nasal powder	PO: 25, 50 or 100 mg, can repeat x 1 after 2 hrs (max 200 mg/day) **Subcutaneous:** *Imitrex*: 4 or 6 mg, can repeat x 1 after 1 hr (max 12 mg/day) *Zembrace*: 3 mg, can repeat up to 4 times per day [wait a minimum of 1 hr between doses or 1 hr following use of another sumatriptan product (max 12 mg/day)] **Intranasal:** Spray *(Imitrex)*: 5, 10, or 20 mg in one nostril can repeat x 1 after 2 hrs (max 40 mg/day) Spray (Tosymra): 10 mg in one nostril can repeat x 1 after 1 hr (max 30 mg/day) Powder *(Onzetra Xsail)*: 11 mg in each nostril using nosepiece, can repeat x 1 after 2 hrs (max 44 mg/day)	
+ naproxen ***(Treximet)***	***Treximet*** Adults: *Treximet* (85-500 mg) 1 tab, can repeat x 1 after 2 hrs (max 2 tabs/24 hrs) Pediatric (12-17 yrs): *Treximet* (10-60 mg) 1 tab x 1 dose	
Zolmitriptan *(Zomig, Zomig-ZMT)* Tablet, ODT, nasal spray	PO: 1.25-5 mg, can repeat x 1 after 2 hrs Intranasal: 2.5-5 mg, can repeat x 1 after 2 hrs [max 10 mg/day (all formulations)]	

Triptan Drug Interactions

- FDA warning about combining triptans with serotonergic drugs such as SSRIs and SNRIs. Many patients take both safely, since the triptan is only taken PRN. Look for other serotonergic medications on the profile. See Patient Counseling.
- Sumatriptan, rizatriptan and zolmitriptan are contraindicated with MAO inhibitors (or within two weeks of stopping), the others are not. All of the product labels discuss the risk of serotonin syndrome.
- Use with strong CYP3A4 inhibitors: eletriptan is contraindicated; reduce the dose of almotriptan.

TRIPTAN FORMULATIONS

TABLET	ODT	NASAL SPRAY/ POWDER	INJECTION
Almotriptan Eletriptan *(Relpax)* Frovatriptan *(Frova)* Naratriptan *(Amerge)* Rizatriptan *(Maxalt)* Sumatriptan *(Imitrex)* Zolmitriptan *(Zomig)*	Rizatriptan *(Maxalt-MLT)* Zolmitriptan *(Zomig-MLT)*	**SPRAY** Sumatriptan *(Imitrex)* Zolmitriptan *(Zomig)* **POWDER** Sumatriptan *(Onzestra Xsail)*	**PREFILLED** Sumatriptan *(Imitrex)* **AUTO INJECTOR** Sumatriptan *(Imitrex STATdose, Zembrace SymTouch)*

ERGOTAMINE DRUGS

Ergotamine is a nonselective agonist of serotonin receptors, which causes cerebral vasoconstriction. In patients with contraindications to triptans or who do not find benefit with a triptan, ergotamine is generally used next.

DRUG	DOSING	SAFETY/SIDE EFFECTS/MONITORING
Dihydroergotamine *(D.H.E. 45, Migranal)* Injection, nasal spray	IM/SC/IV *(D.H.E. 45)*: 1 mg at first sign of headache, repeat hourly to a max dose of 2 mg/day (IV) and 3 mg/day (IM/SC) and max 6 mg/week Intranasal *(Migranal)*: 1 spray (0.5 mg) into each nostril, can repeat after 15 minutes, up to a total of 4 sprays (2 mg)	**BOXED WARNING** Contraindicated with potent CYP3A4 inhibitors (e.g., protease inhibitors, azoles, macrolides) due to serious and life-threatening peripheral ischemia. **CONTRAINDICATIONS** Uncontrolled hypertension, pregnancy, ischemic heart disease, angina, MI, peripheral vascular disease, hemiplegic or basilar migraine, renal/hepatic impairment, sepsis, use with pressors/ vasoconstrictive drugs. Dihydroergotamine: avoid use within 24 hours of serotonin agonists or other ergotamine-type drugs. Avoid during or within 2 weeks of discontinuing MAO inhibitors. **WARNINGS** Cardiovascular effects (avoid in any patient with baseline risk, cerebrovascular events, ergotism (intense vasoconstriction resulting in peripheral vascular ischemia and possible gangrene), cardiac valvular fibrosis, potentially serious drug interactions. **SIDE EFFECTS** Nasal spray: rhinitis, dysgeusia, nausea, dizziness. **NOTES** Nasal spray: prime by pumping 4 times. Do not inhale deeply (to let drug absorb into skin in nose). Use at first sign of attack, but can be used at any time during migraine.
Ergotamine + caffeine *(Cafergot, Migergot)* Tablet, suppository	*Cafergot* (1 mg ergotamine + 100 mg caffeine): take 2 tablets at onset of migraine, then 1 tablet every 30 min PRN to a max of 6 tablets per attack *Migergot:* 1 suppository at first sign of migraine, may repeat x 1 after 1 hr. Max: 2 suppositories per attack	

BUTALBITAL-CONTAINING PRODUCTS

Butalbital is a barbiturate. Acetaminophen/butalbital/caffeine *(Fioricet)* and aspirin/butalbital/caffeine *(Fiorinal)* are both available in combinations with codeine: *Fioricet with Codeine* and *Fiorinal with Codeine*. All of these products are federally classified as schedule III, except *Fioricet* (which is exempt). *Fioricet* remains a popular drug, but butalbital-containing products are not recommended for treating acute migraines due to abuse/dependence issues and lower efficacy. If used regularly and long-term, they must be tapered off or the patient will get worsening of headache, tremors and be at risk for delirium and seizures. Pharmacists should make sure patients do not exceed safe doses of acetaminophen and counsel on the potential for nausea and constipation with the codeine-containing formulations and additive sedation with alcohol.

PROPHYLACTIC DRUG TREATMENT

Some patients require a prophylactic (preventative) medication to decrease the frequency of migraines. These medications are taken when the patient feels well, and are not effective once a headache is present. Consider a prophylactic medication if the patient requests it, if they use acute treatments ≥ 2 days/week or ≥ 3 times per month, if the migraines decrease their quality of life or if acute treatments are ineffective or contraindicated.

Choose a prophylactic agent based on patient characteristics and the side effect profile of the medication, because efficacy data is similar for all (~50% reduction in headache days). A full trial, at a reasonable dose, should be 2 – 6 months. Many patients try more than one drug before finding one that works well for them. Oral prophylactic therapies include:

- Antihypertensives: most experience is with beta-blockers (best evidence with propranolol, timolol, metoprolol). Lisinopril, verapamil and other beta-blockers have been used.
- Antiepileptic drugs: topiramate (*Topamax* and *Trokendi XR* are approved for migraine prophylaxis in adults) and valproic acid. Topiramate causes weight loss in many patients, making it a popular choice for migraine prophylaxis.
- Antidepressants: tricyclic antidepressants (most evidence with amitriptyline) are effective. TCAs are used at lower doses for migraine prophylaxis. Venlafaxine can also be effective.
- MAM: extended-cycle oral contraceptives can be used. NSAIDs or a triptan (specifically those with longer half life: frovatriptan or naratriptan) can be started prior to menses and continued for 5 – 7 days.
- Natural products (discussed at the beginning of the chapter).

ORAL PROPHYLACTIC AGENTS

DRUG	TYPICAL DOSING RANGE	COMMENTS/SIDE EFFECTS
Beta-Blockers (see Hypertension chapter for complete discussion)		
Propranolol *(Inderal LA)*	80-240 mg, divided Q6-8H	Fatigue, ↓ HR, possible depression with propranolol (most lipophilic and non-selective)
Timolol	10 mg twice daily	Both propranolol and timolol are non-selective beta-blockers; do not use in COPD, emphysema
Metoprolol *(Lopressor, Toprol XL)*	100-200 mg daily	Metoprolol is beta-1 selective. Caution with all beta-blockers if HR is low (they ↓ HR), monitor for hypotension, dizziness
Antiepileptic Drugs (see Seizures/Epilepsy chapter for complete discussion)		
Divalproex *(Depakote)* Valproic acid *(Depakene)*	250-500 mg twice daily	**BOXED WARNINGS** Fetal harm, hepatic failure, pancreatitis **WARNINGS AND SIDE EFFECTS** Weight gain, thrombocytopenia, ↑ ammonia, alopecia, N/V, somnolence, tremor, polycystic ovarian syndrome
Topiramate *(Topamax*, *Trokendi XR)*	*Topamax*: start 25 mg QHS, titrate to 50 mg BID *Trokendi XR*: start at 25 mg once daily x 1 week; increase by 25 mg weekly to recommended dose of 100 mg daily	**WARNINGS** Fetal harm, metabolic acidosis, nephrolithiasis, ↑ ammonia, open angle glaucoma, oligohidrosis **SIDE EFFECTS** Weight loss (6-13%), somnolence, cognitive impairment, paresthesia, reduced efficacy of oral contraceptives

OTHER PROPHYLACTIC AGENTS

Calcitonin Gene-Related Peptide (CGRP) Receptor Antagonist

Calcitonin gene-related peptide (CGRP) receptor antagonist is a human monoclonal antibody that targets high levels of CGRP in the blood of patients with migraine headaches.

DRUG	TYPICAL DOSING RANGE	COMMENTS/SIDE EFFECTS
Erenumab-aooe *(Aimovig)* Injection	70 mg SC once monthly Some patients benefit from two 70 mg injections (140 mg)	**WARNINGS** Latex allergy **SIDE EFFECTS** Injection site reaction, antibody development, constipation
Fremanezumab-vfrm *(Ajovy)*	225 mg SC once monthly	**NOTES** Monoclonal antibody approved for prevention of migraine headache in adults
Galcancezumab-gnlm *(Emgality)*	240 mg SC as loading dose, then 120 mg SC once monthly	For self-administered SC injection in the abdomen, thigh or upper arm; store refrigerated in the original carton prior to use; allow the injection to sit at room temperature for at least 30 min before injecting

Botulinum Toxin

Botulinum toxin type A *(Botox)* injections are used for prophylaxis. *Botox* is for chronic migraines only (≥ 15 headache days per month).

MEDICATION-OVERUSE ("REBOUND") HEADACHES

Medication overuse headaches (MOH) result from overuse of most headache medications (e.g., NSAIDs, opioids, the butalbital-containing drugs, analgesic combination products, triptans and ergotamines, except DHE) and are characterized by headaches that occur more than 10 – 15 days per month. Pharmacists are in a position to see many patients who chronically use headache medicines, and have daily headaches. It may be best to consult with another healthcare provider if the patient seems at risk or is unlikely to successfully reduce analgesic use independently. To prevent MOH, educate patients to limit acute treatment medications to 2 – 3 times per week, at most. The most important thing is to stop the "over-used" medication. If the drug is an opioid or contains butalbital *(Fioricet, Fiorinal)*, a slow taper is needed.

PATIENT COUNSELING

All Triptans

- Side effects that you may experience include sleepiness, nausea, numbness, throat or neck pressure, dizziness, hot or cold sensations and a heaviness or pressure in the chest or neck region. These usually occur after the drug is taken and go away quickly.
- If nausea prevents you from swallowing or holding down your medication, your healthcare provider can prescribe a tablet that dissolves in your mouth, an injection or a nasal spray.
- If you have migraines that come on very quickly, a nasal spray or injection will provide faster relief.
- Serious, but rare, side effects such as heart attacks and strokes have occurred in people who have used this type of medication because of this, triptans cannot be used in patients who have had a stroke, have heart disease or have blood pressure that is not well-controlled. If any of this applies to you, inform your healthcare provider.
- This medication increases the levels of a chemical in your blood called serotonin. If it is taken with other OTC or prescription medications that also increase serotonin, toxicity can occur. Seek urgent medical care if you have symptoms of toxicity: severe nausea, dizziness and headache, diarrhea, feeling very agitated, a racing heartbeat or hallucinations.
- Take the medication with or without food, at the first sign of a migraine. It does not work as well if you wait to use it.
- If you use the orally disintegrating tablets *(Maxalt-MLT* and *Zomig-ZMT)*, peel open the blister pack and place the orally disintegrating tablet on your tongue, where it will dissolve and be swallowed with saliva. You do not need to use water. These formulations should not be used in patients with phenylketonuria, due to the sweetener.
- If your symptoms are only partly relieved, or if your headache comes back, you may take a second dose in the time period explained to you by the pharmacist.

- If you use migraine treatments more than twice a week or if they are severe, you should be using a daily medication to help prevent migraines. Discuss this with your healthcare provider.

Imitrex STATdose System

- Inject the medication just below the skin as soon as the symptoms of your migraine appear.
- The *STATdose* system includes a carrying case, a *STATdose* pen and two syringe cartridges.
- Clean the area of skin (upper outside arm or lateral thigh) with rubbing alcohol prior to administering the injection.
- Open the carrying case and pull off the tamper-proof seal from one of the syringe cartridges. Open the lid of the cartridge.
- Take the pen out of the carrying case. Load the *STATdose* pen by inserting it into the syringe cartridge and turning it clockwise. The cartridge is loaded when you are no longer able to turn the pen clockwise.
- Gently pull the loaded pen out of the carrying case. The blue button on the side triggers the injection. There is a safety feature that does not allow the injection to be triggered unless it is against your skin.
- Hold the loaded pen to the area that you have cleaned to receive the shot. Push the blue button on the top of the pen. To make sure you receive all of the medicine, you must continue to hold the pen against the skin for five seconds.
- Follow safety procedures and return the used injection needle to the cartridge. Insert the pen into the empty cartridge container. This time, turn it counterclockwise to loosen the needle. Remove the empty *STATdose* pen from the cartridge and store it in the carrying case.
- Replace the cartridge pack after both doses have been used. Discard the pack and insert a new refill.

Zembrace SymTouch

- Remove the autoinjector from the carton and check the expiration date. Inspect the medicine through the medicine window. It should be a clear, colorless to pale yellow solution.
- Clean the injection site (lateral thigh or upper arm) with an alcohol pad.
- Pull the red cap off to expose the yellow needle guard. Do not put thumb, fingers or hand over yellow needle guard.
- Press the yellow needle guard gently against the skin at a 90 degree angle.
- Press and hold the autoinjector against skin. The first "click" is the start of the injection. Continue to hold down until you hear the second "click." After the second click, hold the autoinjector against the skin for five seconds to get the full dose.
- Lift the autoinjector away from the skin. The yellow needle guard will cover the needle. Do not rub the injection site.
- Verify that you can see the red plunger in the medicine window. That means the full dose was given. Never reuse the autoinjector.
- Dispose of the autoinjector in a sharps container or heavy-duty plastic container (secure lid, leak-resistant and properly labeled as hazardous waste).

Onzetra Xsail Nasal Powder

- Open the pouch and remove the first nosepiece. Insert the nosepiece into the device until you hear it click.
- Press and release the white button to pierce the medication capsule.
- Insert the nosepiece deeply into the nose (first nostril). Rotate the device to place the mouthpiece into your mouth.
- Blow into the device with your mouth for 2 - 3 seconds to deliver medication into your nose.
- Press the clear tab to remove the first nosepiece. Check the capsule to be sure the medication is gone. Discard the first nosepiece.
- Insert the second nosepiece into the device and repeat the steps above using the second nostril.

Zomig, *Tosymra* Nasal Spray

- Blow your nose gently before use.
- Remove the protective cap.
- Hold the nasal sprayer device gently with your fingers and thumb.
- There is only one dose in the nasal sprayer. Do not prime (test) the nasal sprayer or you will lose the dose.
- Do not press the plunger until you have put the tip in your nostril or you will lose the dose. Insert into nose about a half an inch, close your mouth, press the plunger, keep head level for 10 - 20 seconds, and gently breathe in through your mouth.

Select Guidelines/References

Evidence-Based Guideline Update: Pharmacologic Treatment for Episodic Migraine Prevention in Adults. http://www.neurology.org/content/78/17/1337.full.pdf+html (accessed 2019 April 25).

CHAPTER CONTENT

Background 825
Risk Factors 825
Drugs that Increase Uric Acid 826
Drug Treatment 826
Acute Gout Attack Treatment 826
Gout Treatment Basics 827
Prophylactic Treatment 828
Tumor Lysis Syndrome 830

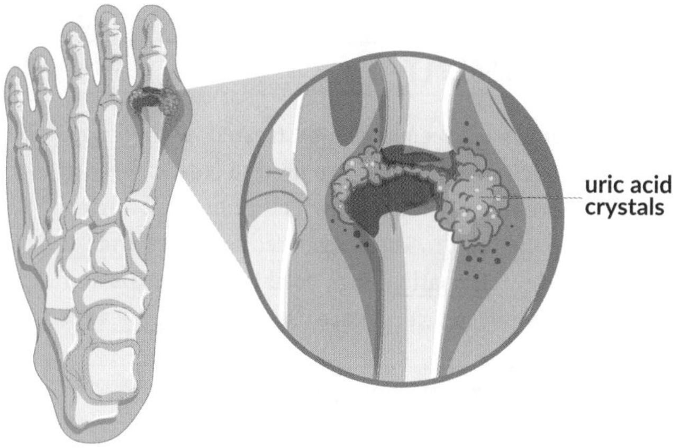

CHAPTER 60

GOUT

BACKGROUND

Gout is a type of arthritis caused by a buildup of uric acid (UA) crystals, primarily in the joints. UA is produced as an end-product of purine metabolism (see figure later in the chapter). Purines are present in many foods, and they make up one of the base pairs of DNA. Under normal conditions, UA is excreted two-thirds renally and one-third via the GI tract.

A normal serum UA level is 2 – 6.5 mg/dL in females and 3.5 – 7.2 mg/dL in males. When UA builds up in the blood, the patient can remain asymptomatic (many people with high UA, or hyperuricemia, never get gout) or the UA can crystallize in the joints, resulting in a severe, painful gout attack with burning and swelling of the affected joint. Gout attacks have a sudden onset. Gout typically occurs in one joint, most often the metatarsophalangeal joint (MTP, the big toe). If left untreated, the attacks can occur repeatedly, and damage the joints, tendons and other tissues.

In addition to a UA level, a sample of synovial (joint) fluid can be viewed under a microscope to identify if uric acid crystals are present. Various imaging studies (X-ray, US, MRI, CT) can provide an image of the affected joint.

RISK FACTORS

Risk factors for gout include male sex, obesity, excessive alcohol consumption (particularly beer), hypertension, chronic kidney disease (CKD), lead intoxication, advanced age and using medications that increase UA (see Key Drugs Guy). Changing the diet can lower risk of gout. Foods to avoid include organ meats, high-fructose corn syrup and alcohol. Foods that should be limited include fruit juices, table sugar, sweetened drinks, desserts, salt, beef, lamb, pork and seafood with high purine content (sardines, shellfish). A healthy diet, including low fat dairy products and vegetables, reduces gout risk. Weight control, smoking cessation, exercise and hydration are further ways to reduce risk.

CONTENT LEGEND

= Study Tip Gal  = Key Drug Guy 

DRUG TREATMENT

Asymptomatic hyperuricemia is not treated with drugs. Once a gout attack occurs, drugs are used to treat the acute attack and prevent future attacks, which requires lowering the UA level to < 6 mg/dL. The drugs used for acute attacks target pain and inflammation (e.g., colchicine, NSAIDs and steroids). The prophylactic drugs are used to lower UA levels.

DRUGS THAT INCREASE URIC ACID

Aspirin, lower doses
Diuretics (loops and thiazides)
Niacin
Pyrazinamide
Select pancreatic enzyme products
Calcineurin inhibitors (tacrolimus and cyclosporine)
Select chemotherapy (with tumor lysis syndrome; see end of chapter)

ACUTE GOUT ATTACK TREATMENT

Gout attacks are painful and treatment should begin as soon as possible. A single drug is recommended, which is either an NSAID, a systemic steroid or colchicine. In more severe disease, combination treatment usually includes colchicine with either an NSAID or an oral steroid. If the gout attack is localized to one or two joints, an intra-articular steroid injection (injected into the joint/s), can be helpful. If an acute attack occurs in a patient using chronic urate-lowering therapy (ULT), such as allopurinol or febuxostat, they should continue the ULT during the acute attack. Topical ice applied to the affected joints reduces pain and inflammation.

Acute Gout Attack Therapy

DRUG	DOSING	SAFETY/SIDE EFFECTS/MONITORING
Colchicine		
Colchicine (*Colcrys*, *Gloperba, Mitigare*) Tablet, liquid, capsule + probenecid	**Treatment** 1.2 mg PO (this is two 0.6 mg tablets) followed by 0.6 mg in 1 hr (do not exceed a total of 1.8 mg in 1 hr or 2.4 mg/day) Dose to be repeated no earlier than 3 days CrCl < 30 mL/min: the treatment dose is the same, but do not give again for 2 weeks **Prophylaxis** 0.6 mg once or twice daily CrCl < 30 mL/min, ↓ to 0.3 mg/day	**CONTRAINDICATIONS** Do not use in combination with a P-gp or strong CYP3A4 inhibitor with renal and/or hepatic impairment **WARNINGS** Myelosuppression, gastrointestinal symptoms (↓ dose if anorexia, N/V/D), neuromuscular toxicity (including rhabdomyolysis), avoid, if possible, with cyclosporine, diltiazem, verapamil, gemfibrozil or statins as these drugs ↑ myopathy risk **SIDE EFFECTS** Diarrhea, nausea, myelosuppression, myopathy, neuropathy (dose-dependent), ↓ vitamin B12 **NOTES** Start within 36 hours of onset of symptoms (for treatment) In elderly with CrCl < 30 mL/min: ↑ risk of myelosuppression, GI and neuromuscular adverse effects; ↓ dose and monitor, or use steroid as an alternative Wait 12 hours after a treatment dose before resuming prophylaxis dosing
NSAIDs		
Indomethacin (*Indocin*)	50 mg PO TID until attack resolved	See Pain chapter for more information
Naproxen (*Naprosyn*, others)	750 mg x 1 PO, then reduce to 250 mg Q8H until attack resolved	**NOTES** Avoid use in severe renal disease (UA is renally cleared and patients with gout often have renal insufficiency); CVD risk, bleeding (risk is lower with short duration of use)
Sulindac (*Clinoril*)	200 mg PO BID until attack resolved	
Celecoxib (*Celebrex*)	800 mg x 1 PO, then 400 mg x 1 (later in day), then 400 mg BID x 1 week	Indomethacin, naproxen and sulindac are approved for gout; other NSAIDs can be used

DRUG	DOSING	SAFETY/SIDE EFFECTS/MONITORING
Steroids: given PO, IM, IV, intra-articular or as ACTH (adrenocorticotropic hormone), which triggers endogenous glucocorticoid secretion		
Prednisone/ Prednisolone	0.5 mg/kg/day PO for 5-10 days (no taper) or 0.5 mg/kg/day for 2-5 days, then taper (reduce dose by 5 mg each day) over 7-10 days	See Systemic Steroids & Autoimmune Disease chapter for more information **NOTES** Acute side effects of steroids, including $\uparrow$ BG, $\uparrow$ BP, insomnia, $\uparrow$ appetite
Methylprednisolone (***Medrol,*** *SOLU-Medrol*)	Intra-articular: if 1-2 large joints involved Oral: Methylprednisolone dose pack	Intra-articular steroid injections stay localized and do not cause systemic side effects; repeat injections can cause joint damage
Triamcinolone	If 1-2 joints: intra-articular 10-40mg If polyarticular, IM 60 mg, may repeat once or twice Q48H	

Colchicine Drug Interactions

- Colchicine is a major substrate of CYP450 3A4 and P-gp. Fatal toxicity can occur if colchicine is combined with strong CYP3A4 inhibitors, such as clarithromycin, or a strong inhibitor of P-gp, such as cyclosporine. Check for inhibitors prior to dispensing. If using a moderate CYP3A4 inhibitor, the maximum dose for acute treatment is 1.2 mg (2 tablets).

Colchicine Patient Counseling

- At the first sign of an attack, take two tablets. You can take one more tablet in one hour. Do not use more than this amount in an hour, and do not use more than four tablets in 24 hours. Taking too much colchicine can lead to serious side effects.
- Do not take the second dose if you have upset stomach, nausea or diarrhea.
- Report any serious nausea, vomiting, diarrhea, fatigue, unusual bleeding, tingling in your fingers or toes or muscle soreness to your healthcare provider right away.
- Do not start another treatment course again for at least three days.

GOUT TREATMENT BASICS

Gout pain is severe.

Treat acute pain quickly, and use anti-inflammatory drugs: steroids (including intra-articular injections), NSAIDs (often with a high starting dose) or colchicine.

Once gout has struck (but not before), treat chronically with a prophylactic (preventive) drug: xanthine oxidase inhibitors (XOIs), allopurinol or febuxostat. Febuxostat is limited those who do not tolerate allopurinol such as in the case of hypersensitivity or when allopurinol is not effective.

An acute gout flare can occur when a XOI is started, so give initially with colchicine or an NSAID.

If XOI didn't work well enough and UA remains > 6 mg/dL:

- ✓ Add on lesinurad *(Zurampic)* or probenecid to daily XOI
- ✓ Replace the XOI with IV pegloticase *(Krystexxa)*

PROPHYLACTIC TREATMENT

Chronic ULT should be started in all patients with gout who have experienced a gout attack, have intermittent symptoms or have tophi (UA crystals that form under the skin in long-term gout). When starting chronic ULT, colchicine or NSAIDs should be used as prophylaxis to reduce the risk of attacks, which can occur when UA is lowered rapidly (possibly due to mobilization of the urate crystals).

First-line agents for ULT are the xanthine oxidase (XO) inhibitors allopurinol or febuxostat. Blocking XO stops the production of UA and produces a non-toxic end product. These drugs are titrated up (slowly for allopurinol) to lower the UA to a target level of < 6 mg/dL. Allopurinol is started at a lower dose with moderate or severe CKD. Patients who are at high risk of a severe allopurinol hypersensitivity reaction (including certain Asian groups) should be screened for the HLA-B*5801 allele prior to use.

Probenecid is a uricosuric, and is a second line agent that can be used if XO inhibitors are contraindicated or not tolerated, or can be added when the UA level is not at goal despite maximal doses of XO inhibitors. Probenecid inhibits reabsorption of UA in the proximal tubule of the nephron, which increases UA excretion. It requires adequate renal function to be effective, which many gout patients do not have. Another option when the XO inhibitor treatment is inadequate (UA remains above 6 mg/dL) is lesinurad, a uricosuric that is taken with the XO inhibitor. Pegloticase is a recombinant uricase enzyme, which converts UA to an inactive metabolite that can be easily excreted. Pegloticase is reserved for severe, refractory disease.

Uric Acid Production and Drug Treatment

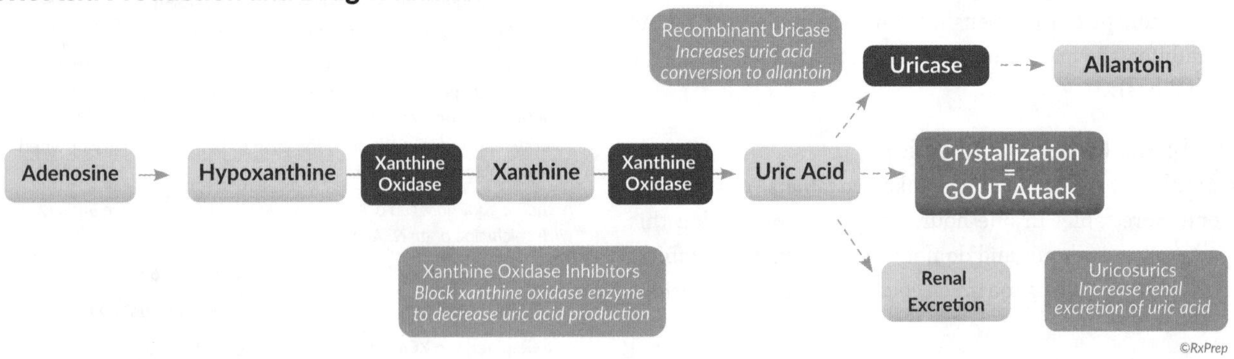

Chronic Urate Lowering Therapy

DRUG	DOSING	SAFETY/SIDE EFFECTS/MONITORING
Xanthine Oxidase Inhibitors: decrease uric acid production		
Allopurinol ***(Zyloprim, Aloprim)*** Tablet, injection + lesinurad (*Duzallo*)	Start at 100 mg daily, then slowly titrate up until UA is < 6 mg/dL (doses > 300 mg can be necessary and should be divided BID) CrCl ≤ 30 mL/min: Start at 50 mg daily, increase gradually up 300 mg/day Take after a meal (with food in stomach) to ↓ nausea	**WARNINGS** Hypersensitivity reactions, including severe rash (SJS/TEN); HLA-B*5801 testing prior to use (especially for patients of Asian descent), hepatotoxicity, bone marrow suppression **SIDE EFFECTS** Rash, acute gout attacks, nausea, diarrhea, ↑ LFTs **MONITORING** CBC, LFTs, renal function **NOTES** Higher doses used for tumor lysis syndrome (see Oncology I chapter) Due to the high rate of gout attacks when beginning ULT, use with colchicine (0.6 mg once or twice daily) or an NSAID for the first 3-6 months

DRUG	DOSING	SAFETY/SIDE EFFECTS/MONITORING
Febuxostat *(Uloric)* Tablet	Start at 40 mg daily, ↑ to 80 mg if UA not < 6 mg/dL at 2 weeks; can increase to 120 mg/day if needed CrCl < 30mL/min: max dose 40 mg daily	**BOXED WARNING** Increased risk of cardiovascular death compared to allopurinol; use should be limited to those who cannot tolerate allopurinol (e.g., hypersensitivity) or allopurinol is not effective **CONTRAINDICATIONS** Do not use with didanosine, mercaptopurine, azathioprine or pegloticase **WARNINGS** Hepatotoxicity, possible ↑ thromboembolic events (MI, stroke and cardiovascular deaths), hypersensitivity and serious skin reactions, including SJS, TEN and DRESS; gout attack **SIDE EFFECTS** Rash, nausea, ↑ LFTs, arthralgia **MONITORING** LFTs **NOTES** Due to the high rate of gout attacks when beginning ULT, use with colchicine (0.6 mg once or twice daily) or an NSAID for the first 3-6 months
Uricosurics: inhibit reabsorption of uric acid in the kidneys, which ↑ uric acid excretion		
Lesinurad *(Zurampic)* Tablet + allopurinol *(Duzallo)*	200 mg daily, in the morning, with allopurinol or febuxostat; if XOI stopped, stop lesinurad Only initiate if CrCl ≥ 45 mL/min CrCl < 30 mL/min: contraindicated	**BOXED WARNING** Acute renal failure, more common if used alone; only use with XOI **CONTRAINDICATIONS** CrCl < 30 mL/min, ESRD, dialysis, kidney transplant **SIDE EFFECTS** HA, ↑ SCr (mostly transient), renal failure, nephrolithiasis **MONITORING** SCr, CrCl **NOTES** Take in the morning with XOI, food and water; keep hydrated Use only with XOI if UA goals not reached with XOI alone
Probenecid Tablet + colchicine	Start 250 mg BID, can increase to 2 g/day CrCl < 30 mL/min: avoid	**CONTRAINDICATIONS** Do not use with aspirin therapy, blood dyscrasias, UA kidney stones (nephrolithiasis), children < 2 years, initiation in acute gout attack **WARNINGS** ↓ effectiveness with CrCl < 30 mL/min (ACR guidelines: do not use if CrCl < 50 mL/min), do not use with G6PD deficiency **SIDE EFFECTS** Hypersensitivity reactions, hemolytic anemia **NOTES** Probenecid can be used to ↑ beta-lactam levels by ↓ beta-lactam renal excretion
Recombinant Uricase: converts uric acid to allantoin, which is excreted		
Pegloticase *(Krystexxa)* Injection	8 mg IV every 2 weeks	**BOXED WARNING** Anaphylactic reactions: monitor and premedicate with antihistamines and steroids; risk is highest if UA is > 6 mg/dL, life-threatening hemolytic reactions and methemoglobinemia may occur with G6PD deficiency **CONTRAINDICATIONS** G6PD deficiency **WARNINGS** Acute gout flares can occur upon initiation; an NSAID or colchicine should be given 1 week prior to infusion and continued for at least 6 months **SIDE EFFECTS** Antibody formation, gout flare, infusion reactions, nausea, bruising, urticaria, erythema, pruritus **NOTES** Do not use in combination with allopurinol, febuxostat or probenecid (↑ risk of anaphylaxis)

Xanthine Oxidase Inhibitor Drug Interactions

- Allopurinol and febuxostat ↑ the concentration of mercaptopurine, the active metabolite of azathioprine. Do not use either drug with allopurinol or febuxostat, or ↓ dose and monitor for toxicity.
- Avoid use with didanosine; allopurinol and febuxostat can ↑ didanosine levels.
- Antacids ↓ allopurinol absorption.

Probenecid Drug Interactions

- Probenecid decreases the renal clearance of other medications when taken together, including aspirin (do not use salicylates concurrently), methotrexate, penicillins, cephalosporins and carbapenems.
- Probenecid is sometimes used with beta-lactams to ↑ the concentration of the antibiotic; this will ↑ the risk of adverse reactions. This is occasionally done with penicillin when treating neurosyphilis or other penicillin-treated infections.
- Probenecid decreases the efficacy of loop diuretics, but increases the risk of loop diuretic toxicity.

Allopurinol Patient Counseling

- Take after a meal to reduce stomach upset (higher doses can be divided). Drink plenty of fluids.
- Seek medical help if a rash develops.

TUMOR LYSIS SYNDROME

Tumor lysis syndrome (TLS) is an acute, potentially life-threatening complication of some types of chemotherapy. When cells are "lysed" open, purines are released into the blood and quickly converted to UA. This can cause acute gout and significant electrolyte abnormalities, which can lead to renal failure, cardiac arrhythmias, seizures and potential death. Prophylactic treatment includes rasburicase *(Elitek)*, a urate-oxidase enzyme, and allopurinol. See the Oncology I chapter.

Select Guidelines/References

Richette P, Doherty M, Pascual E, et al. 2016 updated EULAR evidence-based recommendations for the management of gout. *Ann Rheum Dis*. 2017;76:29-42.

ONCOLOGY

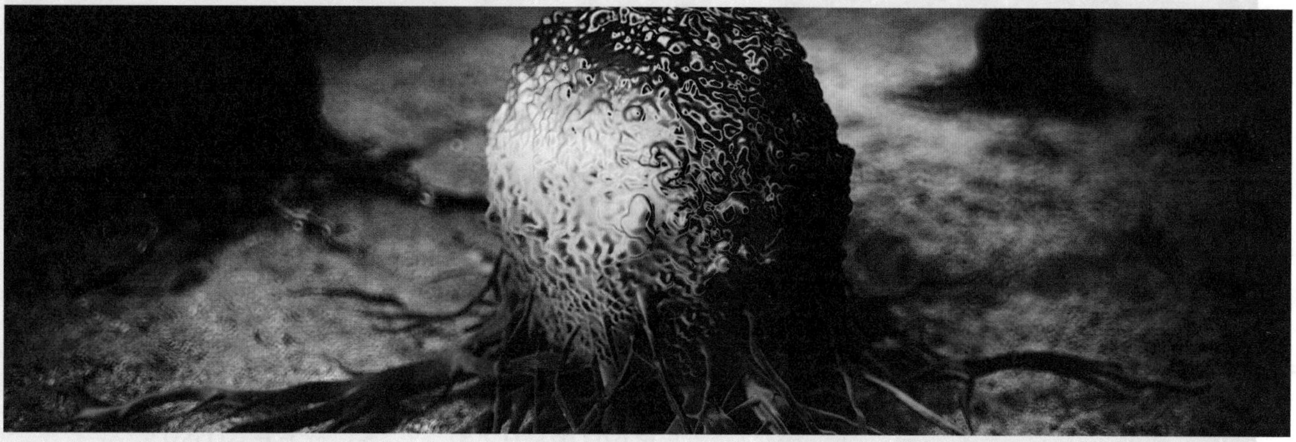

CONTENTS

CHAPTER 61
ONCOLOGY I: OVERVIEW & SIDE EFFECT MANAGEMENT | **832**

CHAPTER 62
ONCOLOGY II: COMMON CANCER TYPES & TREATMENT | **851**

CHAPTER CONTENT

Background 832
Metastatic Cancer has the Highest Fatality 833
Cancer Types and Terms 833
Select Cancer Types 833
Cancer Terms 833
Warning Signs of Cancer 834
Healthy Lifestyles Lower Cancer Risk 834
Skin Protection Lowers Skin Cancer Risk 834
Cancer Screening Guidelines for Average Risk Patients 835
Pregnancy & Breastfeeding 835
Chemotherapy Drugs are Hazardous Drugs 935
Dosing Considerations for Select Highly Toxic Drugs 835
Summary of Toxicities 836
ChemoMan and Major Toxicities of Common Chemotherapy Drugs 837
Chemotherapy Adjunctive Medications 838
Hydration, To Reduce Toxicity 838
Management of Side Effects 839
Myelosuppression Overview 839
Neutropenia 840
Anemia 841
Thrombocytopenia 842
Chemotherapy-Induced Nausea and Vomiting (CINV) 842
Other Gastrointestinal Complications 846
Irinotecan (I-Run-To-The-Can) 846
Medications for Oral Complications of Chemotherapy 847
Hand-Foot Syndrome 847
Tumor Lysis Syndrome 848
Hypercalcemia of Malignancy 849
Chemotherapy Handling, Administration and Extravasation 850
IV Administration and Extravasation 850
Timing of Vaccinations 850

We gratefully acknowledge the assistance of D. Raymond Weber, PharmD, BSPharm, BCPS, BCOP, Notre Dame of Maryland Univ. School of Pharmacy, in preparing this chapter.

CONTENT LEGEND

(💡) = Study Tip Gal

CHAPTER 61
ONCOLOGY I: OVERVIEW, TERMINOLOGY, SCREENING & SIDE EFFECT MANAGEMENT

BACKGROUND

Cancer is uncontrolled cell growth. A tumor (mass of cells) can be malignant (cancerous) or benign (non-malignant, relatively harmless). Cells that continue to grow will infiltrate normal body tissue, causing organ dysfunction, pain and death.

Cancer is caused by both external factors (such as chemicals, radiation, bacteria and viruses) and internal factors [genetic disorders (e.g., the BRCA genes, reviewed in Oncology II), hormones (e.g., estrogen is required for most breast tumors to grow) and immune disorders]. Sunlight exposure, tobacco use, excessive alcohol intake, obesity, older age, poor diet and low physical activity level increases the risk for certain cancers.

In 2018, there were 1,735,350 new cases of cancer diagnosed in the U.S; one-third of which result in fatality. Fortunately, the death rate has declined 1.8% among men and 1.4% among women (2006-2015). The declining death rate is attributed to better screening plus the use of a variety of old and new treatments. Treatment regimens are designed to be toxic to the cancer cells, but can also be highly toxic to the patient, and require careful management.

METASTATIC CANCER HAS THE HIGHEST FATALITY

Metastatic cancer is more advanced, and consequently causes most cancer fatalities. Metastases form when malignant cells break off from the primary cancer (the original site of the cancer) and travel through the lymph or blood to form new tumors in other parts of the body (see figure). A metastasis (secondary malignancy) will be the same cancer type as the primary tumor. Metastatic cancer is often not curable, and may be treated palliatively, to reduce symptoms and control further growth. If treated, the regimen will be aggressive.

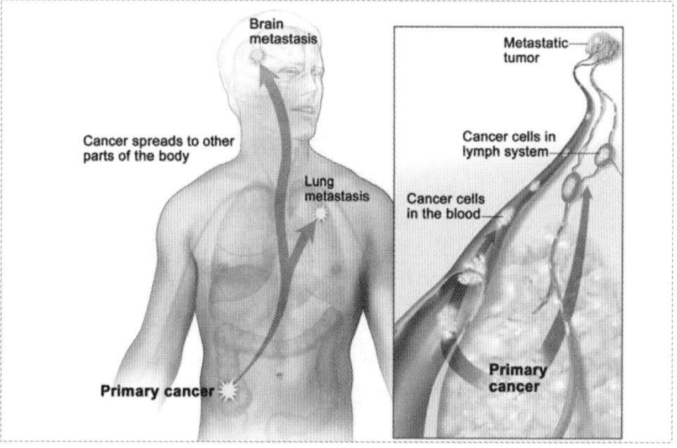

© https://www.cancer.gov/types/metastatic-cancer

CANCER TYPES AND TERMS

There are more than 100 types of cancer. Cancers are often named for the organs or tissues where the cancer forms; cancers based on the tissue type are classified as epithelial (e.g., squamous cell), connective (e.g., sarcoma), lymphoid or nerve. Diagnosis and classification is based on a sample of tissue that is excised in a biopsy. The assessment of the cancer will be aided by some type of imaging, including X-rays, CT scans, PET scans and MRIs. Blood work can identify cancers in the circulatory system (e.g., leukemia, which is cancer of leukocytes), the presence of tumor markers (i.e., chemicals produced by the tumor) and other markers (e.g., altered immunoglobulins can indicate a possibility of multiple myeloma).

SELECT CANCER TYPES

NAME	CHARACTERISTICS
Carcinoma	Cancer that starts in skin or in the tissues that line or cover internal organs.
Leukemia	Cancer of the leukocytes (WBCs); leukemia is referred to as blood cancer.
Lymphoma	Cancer of the lymphatic system.
Multiple Myeloma	A type of bone marrow cancer.
Sarcoma	Cancer in connective tissue (tissue that connects, supports, binds or separates other tissues), including fat, muscle, blood vessels and bone. Osteosarcoma is a type of bone cancer.
Skin Cancers: Basal Cell & Squamous Cell Carcinomas and Melanoma	Basal Cell and Squamous Cell Carcinoma: common, unlikely to metastasize, rather simple to remove surgically or with topical treatment. Melanoma: skin cancer that forms in the melanocytes [the skin cells that produce the pigment (melanin) that colors skin]. Least prevalent type of skin cancer (2%), but most deadly.

CANCER TERMS

TERM	DEFINITION
Adjuvant	Treatment given after the primary therapy (usually surgery) or concurrent with other therapy (usually radiation) to eradicate residual disease and ↓ recurrence.
Benign	A tumor that is not cancerous; tumors can be labeled as benign or malignant (cancerous).
Biopsy	The excision (removal, by cutting out) of a slice of tissue for microscopic examination to see if it is cancerous. A pathologist identifies if any abnormal cancer cells are present. The biopsy results are used to make a definite diagnosis.
Curative	Treatment given with the intention of curing the cancer.
Hormone (endocrine) therapy	Treatment that removes, blocks or provides hormones that slow down or kill cancer cells.
Imaging tests	Imaging is used to make images (pictures) of internal body parts, tissues, or organs (e.g., X-rays, MRIs, PET scans, CT scans).
Immunotherapy	Cancer treatment designed to boost the body's natural defenses to fight cancer, including monoclonal antibodies (drugs that end in "mab") and interferons.
Metastasis	The term for cancer that has spread to a different part of the body from the primary (starting) location.
Neoadjuvant	Treatment given before the primary therapy (which is usually surgery) to shrink the size of the tumor and make surgery more effective.

Palliative	Treatment given with the intention of reducing symptoms and/or slowing the growth of the cancer (rather than curative).
Polyp	A growth of normal tissue that sticks out from the lining of an organ, such as the colon. Polyps in the colon can become cancerous.
Radiation therapy	The use of high-energy x-rays or other particles to destroy cancer cells.
Recurrence	Cancer that has returned after a period during which it could not be detected.
Remission	The disappearance of the signs and symptoms of cancer, but not necessarily the presence of the disease (the appearance can be hidden).
Staging	A ranking system used to describe a cancer, such as how large the tumor is (the size), and if it has metastasized. The ranking can be simple, such as 0-4, or the common TNM staging where T refers to the size and extent, N is the spread to lymph nodes in which the cancer has spread, and M refers to whether the cancer has metastasized. The letters have numbers after them that provide more details.
Terminal	Cancer that cannot be cured and leads to death. Can be referred to as end-stage cancer.
Tumor markers	Different substances at higher than normal levels in the blood, urine or body tissue that identifies cancer. For example, carcinoembryonic antigen (CEA) test identifies one type of marker common in colon cancer.

WARNING SIGNS OF CANCER

The American Cancer Society (ACS) lists seven warning signs of cancer in an adult. Any of the CAUTION warning signs warrant referral to a physician.

Change in bowel or bladder habits

A sore that does not heal

Unusual bleeding or discharge

Thickening or lump in breast or elsewhere

Indigestion or difficulty swallowing

Obvious change in wart or mole

Nagging cough or hoarseness

HEALTHY LIFESTYLES LOWER CANCER RISK

Cancer can appear for no apparent reason, such as cancer in a child with no known heredity or other risk factors. Other cancers have risk that increases with some type of exposure, such as lung cancer from smoking or inhaling noxious chemicals, and skin cancer from sun exposure. Healthy lifestyles lowers the risk of different types of cancer.

- Avoid tobacco (enroll in smoking cessation program if needed).
- Maintain a healthy weight.
- Exercise regularly.
- Eat healthy with plenty of fruits and vegetables.
- Limit alcohol intake.
- Protect skin from harmful UV rays.
- Assess cancer risk, family history and individual history.
- Have regular check-ups and cancer screening tests.
- Low-dose aspirin is recommended for prevention of colorectal cancer and CVD in patients who are 50-59 years old, have ASCVD risk ≥ 10%, have ≥ 10 year life expectancy and are at low risk of bleeding.

SKIN PROTECTION LOWERS SKIN CANCER RISK

Recommendations for reducing the risk of developing skin cancer include:

- Seek shade - especially between 10 AM and 4 PM .
- Slip on a shirt - tightly woven fabrics are best.
- Slop on sunscreen - use a broad-spectrum sunscreen with an SPF of at least 15 - 30 and reapply every 2 hours.
- Slap on a hat - wear a hat with at least a 2" - 3" brim.
- Wrap on sunglasses - to protect the skin around the eyes and help prevent cataracts.

CANCER SCREENING GUIDELINES FOR AVERAGE RISK PATIENTS

CANCER	SEX	AGE	SCREENING
Breast	F	40-44 years 45-54 years ≥ 55 years	Annual mammograms are optional Begin yearly mammograms Mammograms every 2 years or continue yearly
Cervical	F	21-29 years 30-65 years	Pap smear every 3 years Pap smear + HPV (*Human papillomavirus*) test every 5 years
Colon	M/F	≥ 45 years	Stool-based tests (if positive, follow with a colonoscopy) ■ Highly sensitive fecal immunochemical test (FIT) every year ■ Highly sensitive guaiac-based fecal occult blood test (gFOBT) every year ■ Multi-targeted stool DNA test (MT-sDNA) every 3 years Visual exams of the colon and rectum: ■ Colonoscopy every 10 years ■ CT colonography (virtual colonoscopy) every 5 years ■ Flexible sigmoidoscopy (FSIG) every 5 years
Lung	M/F	55-74 years	Annual CT scan of chest if all of the following: ■ In good health ■ Have at least a 30 pack-year smoking history ■ Still smoking or quit smoking within the past 15 years
Prostate	M	≥ 50 years	If a patient opts to be tested, it involves: ■ Prostate specific antigen (PSA) test (blood test) ■ +/– a digital rectal exam (DRE)

PREGNANCY & BREASTFEEDING

Chemotherapy cannot be given during pregnancy and breastfeeding. Chemotherapy can be highly teratogenic. Male and female patients must avoid conceiving during treatment. Contraception should include barrier methods to prevent the partner from having contact with body fluids.

Pregnant women should not handle chemotherapy drugs. Males and females should be informed when a medication can cause long-term sterility.

CHEMOTHERAPY DRUGS ARE HAZARDOUS DRUGS

All chemotherapy drugs are hazardous, which means they are hazardous to the healthcare staff who can be exposed to the drug. Pharmacists, technicians, nurses and other healthcare personnel must use protective measures to limit exposure. The Compounding chapters cover safe handling of hazardous drugs.

DOSING CONSIDERATIONS FOR SELECT HIGHLY TOXIC DRUGS

DRUG	MAXIMUM DOSES	REASON
Bleomycin	Lifetime cumulative dose: 400 units	Pulmonary toxicity
Doxorubicin	Lifetime cumulative dose: 450-550 mg/m²	Cardiotoxicity
Cisplatin	Dose per cycle not to exceed 100 mg/m²	Nephrotoxicity
Vincristine	Single dose "capped" at 2 mg	Neuropathy

SUMMARY OF TOXICITIES

All pharmacists should know the major toxicities of common chemotherapeutics, and the specific drug/s most commonly associated with the toxicity. A staffing pharmacist (i.e., not an oncology pharmacist) might be dispensing a drug that requires a chemoprotectant (i.e., an antidote to reverse a toxic effect, such as dexrazoxane to prevent cardiac damage from doxorubicin) and will need to know when the chemoprotectant should be dispensed with the toxic drug. The maximum lifetime dose that can be given for select drugs is important to check before dispensing more of the same drug. The common toxicities are discussed here, and the drugs are discussed in more detail in the Oncology II chapter.

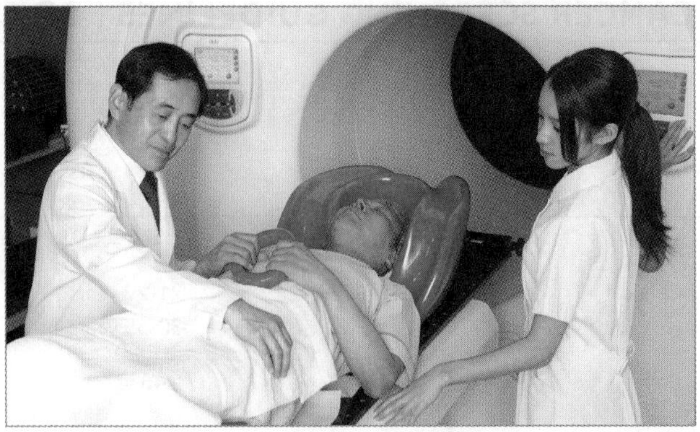

Doxorubicin has a range of maximum doses to limit cardiac toxicity. Radiation given to the sternal (i.e., chest) region will damage the heart, which lies under the sternum. In a patient who received sternal radiation, it is safer to use the lower end of the range.

Common Toxicities of Select Chemotherapeutic Agents

TOXICITY	COMMON DRUGS	MONITORING	MANAGEMENT
Myelosuppression	Almost all, except: Asparaginase, bleomycin, vincristine, most monoclonal antibodies (MAbs) and many tyrosine kinase inhibitors (TKIs)	Complete blood count (CBC) with differential, temperature, bleeding, fatigue, shortness of breath	Neutropenia: colony-stimulating factors (CSFs) Anemia: RBC transfusions, and (in palliation only) erythropoiesis-stimulating agents (ESAs) Thrombocytopenia: platelet transfusions (when very low, especially if bleeding)
Nausea & Vomiting	Cisplatin, cyclophosphamide, ifosfamide, doxorubicin, epirubicin	Patient symptoms of nausea and vomiting and low hydration	Neurokinin-1 receptor antagonist (NK1-RA), Serotonin-3 receptor antagonist (5HT3-RA), dexamethasone, metoclopramide, prochlorperazine IV/PO fluid hydration
Mucositis	Fluorouracil, methotrexate, capecitabine, irinotecan and many TKIs (afatinib, ponatinib, sorafenib, sunitinib)	S/sx of superinfection of oral ulcers with herpes simplex virus or thrush (*Candida* species)	Symptomatic treatment: mucosal coating agents, topical local anesthetics (e.g., lidocaine viscous)
Diarrhea	Irinotecan, capecitabine, fluorouracil, methotrexate and many TKIs	Frequency of bowel movements, hydration status, potassium and other electrolytes	IV/PO fluid hydration, antimotility agents (e.g., loperamide) Irinotecan: atropine for early onset diarrhea
Constipation	Vincristine, pomalidomide, thalidomide	Frequency of bowel movements	Stimulant laxatives, polyethylene glycol (PEG 3350, *Miralax*)
Xerostomia	Caused by radiation therapy to the head or neck regions	Dry mouth	Artificial saliva substitutes, pilocarpine
Cardiotoxicity	**Cardiomyopathy** Anthracyclines, HER2 inhibitors (ado-trastuzumab, trastuzumab, pertuzumab, lapatinib), fluorouracil **QT prolongation** Arsenic trioxide, many TKIs (dasatinib, nilotinib, vemurafenib, dabrafenib, trametinib, crizotinib, ceritinib, erlotinib, gefitinib, lapatinib, sorafenib, sunitinib) and leuprolide	**Cardiomyopathy** Left ventricular ejection fraction (LVEF), lifetime cumulative dose of anthracycline **QT prolongation** ECG, K, Mg, Ca	**Cardiomyopathy** Do not exceed recommended lifetime cumulative dose of 450-550 mg/m² for doxorubicin. Give dexrazoxane prophylactically in select patients receiving doxorubicin. **QT prolongation** Keep K, Mg, Ca within normal limits, consider holding therapy if QTc > 500 msec.
Pulmonary Toxicity (pulmonary fibrosis or pneumonitis)	**Pulmonary fibrosis** Bleomycin, busulfan, carmustine, lomustine **Pneumonitis** Methotrexate (primarily with chronic use), and immune therapy MAbs: atezolizumab, ipilimumab, nivolumab, pembrolizumab	Oxygen saturation, ABGs, symptoms (shortness of breath, dyspnea on exertion) Maximum lifetime dose of bleomycin 400 mg (IU)	Symptomatic management Stop therapy Corticosteroids (if an autoimmune mechanism is suspected) for immunotherapy agents

TOXICITY	COMMON DRUGS	MONITORING	MANAGEMENT
Hepatotoxicity	Antiandrogens (bicalutamide, flutamide, nilutamide), folate antimetabolites (methotrexate, pemetrexed, pralatrexate), pyrimidine analog antimetabolites (cytarabine, gemcitabine), many tyrosine kinase inhibitors, ipilimumab, pembrolizumab, nivolumab, atezolizumab	LFTs, jaundice, ascites	Symptomatic management. Consider stopping therapy. Corticosteroids if an autoimmune mechanism for PD-1 immunotherapy agents.
Nephrotoxicity	Cisplatin Methotrexate (high doses), pemetrexed, pralatrexate, carfilzomib, bevacizumab, nivolumab, pembrolizumab, ipilimumab, atezolizumab	BUN, SCr, urinalysis, urine output, creatinine clearance	Amifostine (*Ethyol*) can be given prophylactically with cisplatin to reduce the risk of nephrotoxicity. Ensure adequate hydration. Do not exceed maximum dose of 100 mg/m^2/cycle for cisplatin.
Hemorrhagic Cystitis	Ifosfamide (all doses), cyclophosphamide (higher doses, e.g., > 1 gram/m^2)	Urinalysis for blood, symptoms of dysuria	Mesna (*Mesnex*) is always given prophylactically with ifosfamide (and sometimes with cyclophosphamide) to reduce the risk of hemorrhagic cystitis. For both, always ensure adequate hydration.
Neuropathy	**Peripheral Neuropathy** Vinca alkaloids (vincristine, vinblastine, vinorelbine) Platinums (cisplatin, oxaliplatin) Taxanes (paclitaxel, docetaxel, cabazitaxel) Proteasome inhibitors (bortezomib, carfilzomib), thalidomide, ado-trastuzumab, cytarabine (high doses), brentuximab **Autonomic Neuropathy** Vinca alkaloids		Symptomatic treatment with drugs for neuropathic pain. **Vincristine** Many recommend limiting the dose of vincristine to 2 mg per week (regardless of BSA calculated dose). **Oxaliplatin** Causes an acute cold-mediated sensory neuropathy. Instruct patients to avoid cold temperatures and avoid drinking cold beverages. **Bortezomib** SC administration is associated with less peripheral neuropathy than IV administration.
Thromboembolic risk (clotting)	Aromatase inhibitors (e.g., anastrozole, letrozole), SERMs (e.g., tamoxifen, raloxifene), immunomodulators (thalidomide, lenalidomide, pomalidomide)	S/sx of DVT/PE, stroke, MI	Consider thromboprophylaxis based on the patient's risk factors.

CHEMOMAN AND MAJOR TOXICITIES OF COMMON CHEMOTHERAPY DRUGS

Chemoman is here to help with learning the major toxicities of some of the big-gun chemotherapy drugs. Use the blank version on the next page to practice drawing which part of the body is affected most by the drug.

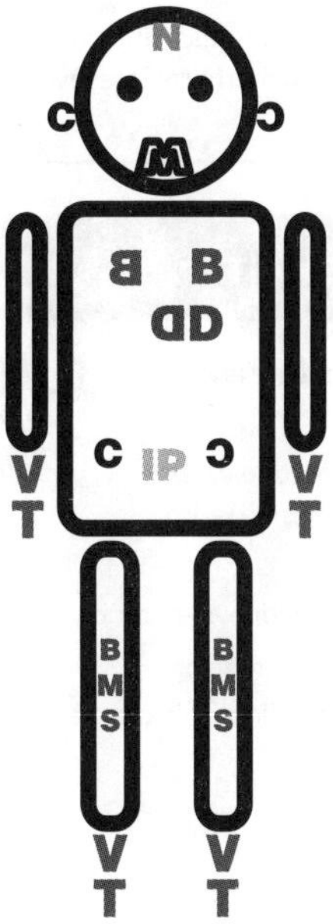

B **Bleomycin, Busulfan, Carmustine, Lomustine**
Pulmonary Fibrosis

C **Platinum-Based (Cisplatin, Carboplatin)**
Nephrotoxic/Ototoxic

D **Doxorubicin & other Anthracyclines**
Cardiotoxic

M **Methotrexate**
Mucositis

N **Nitrosoureas (Lomustine, Carmustine)**
Neurotoxicity

IP **Ifosfamide & Cyclophosphamide**
Hemorrhagic Cystitis

V **Vinca Alkaloids (Vincristine, Vinblastine & Vinorelbine)**
T **Taxanes (Paclitaxel, Docetaxel)**
Peripheral Neuropathy

BMS **Bone marrow suppression is a common toxicity of many chemotherapy agents including: alkylators, anthracyclines, platinum based compounds (cisplatin), taxanes, topoisomerase I and II inhibitors, antimetabolites and vinca alkaloids (vinblastine and vinorelbine)**

TRY YOURSELF!

B **Bleomycin, Busulfan, Carmustine, Lomustine**
Pulmonary Fibrosis

C **Platinum-Based (Cisplatin, Carboplatin)**
Nephrotoxic/Ototoxic, Nephrotoxic/ototoxic

D **Doxorubicin & other Anthracyclines**
Cardiotoxic

M **Methotrexate**
Mucositis

N **Nitrosoureas (Lomustine, Carmustine)**
Neurologic Toxicity

IP **Ifosfamide & Cyclophosphamide**
Hemorrhagic Cystitis

V
T **Vinca Alkaloids (Vincristine, Vinblastine & Vinorelbine), Taxanes (Paclitaxel, Docetaxel)**
Peripheral Neuropathy

B M S **Bone marrow suppression is a common toxicity of many major chemotherapy drugs, including: alkylators, anthracyclines, platinum-based compounds, taxanes, topoisomerase I and II inhibitors, antimetabolites and vinca alkaloids**

CHEMOTHERAPY ADJUNCTIVE MEDICATIONS

CHEMOTHERAPEUTIC DRUG	ADJUNCTIVE TREATMENT	INDICATION FOR ADJUNCTIVE TREATMENT
Cisplatin	Amifostine *(Ethyol)*	Prophylaxis to prevent nephrotoxicity
Doxorubicin	Dexrazoxane *(Zinecard)* Dexrazoxane *(Totect)*	Prophylaxis to prevent cardiomyopathy Treatment for extravasation
Fluorouracil	Leucovorin or levoleucovorin *(Fusilev)*	Given with fluorouracil to enhance efficacy (as a cofactor)
Fluorouracil or capecitabine	Uridine triacetate *(Vistogard)*	Antidote: use within 96 hours for any overdose or to treat severe, life-threatening or early onset toxicity
Ifosfamide	Mesna *(Mesnex)*	Prophylaxis to prevent hemorrhagic cystitis
Irinotecan	Atropine Loperamide	Prevent or treat acute diarrhea Treat delayed diarrhea
Methotrexate	Leucovorin or levoleucovorin *(Fusilev)* Glucarpidase *(Voraxaze)*	Given after methotrexate to ↓ myelosuppression, with mucositis (as an antidote), and with acute renal failure due to a high methotrexate level

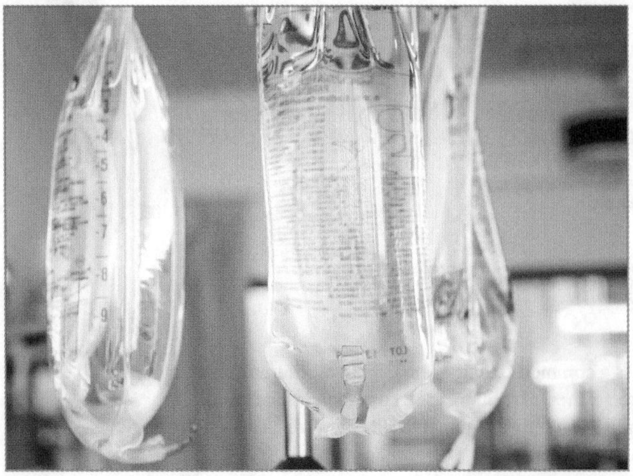

HYDRATION, TO REDUCE TOXICITY

Reduce cisplatin-induced nephrotoxicity and Ifosfamide-induced cystitis

In addition to giving the chemo-protective agent amifostine with cisplatin or mesna *(Mesnex)* with ifosfamide, remember:

When a drug damages the bladder or kidneys → get it out of the bladder and kidneys.

Hydrate the patient well with normal saline. This can also help with nausea and vomiting.

MANAGEMENT OF SIDE EFFECTS

MYELOSUPPRESSION OVERVIEW

Myelosuppression (↓ in bone marrow activity, resulting in fewer RBCs, WBCs and platelets) is a complication of most chemotherapy regimens (see figure).

- Low WBCs cause leukopenia, with increased infection risk.
- Low RBCs cause anemia, with weakness and fatigue.
- Low platelets cause thrombocytopenia, with high risk of severe/uncontrolled bleeding.

Myelosuppression Recovery

The lowest point that WBCs and platelets reach is called the nadir, which occurs (with most drugs) about 7 - 14 days after chemotherapy [the RBC nadir is much later, due to the long life span of RBCs (~120 days)].

The RBC nadir is much later, generally after several months of treatment, due to the long life span of RBCs (~120 days).

- WBCs and platelets generally recover 3 - 4 weeks post treatment. The next dose of chemotherapy is given after the WBCs and platelets have returned to a safe level.
- The next cycle of chemotherapy may need to be delayed to give more time for recovery.
- Drugs that hasten recovery can be needed. Severe cases can require a transfusion (e.g., giving packed RBCs for severe anemia).

All drugs used for myelosuppression (e.g., erythropoietin, filgrastim) are kept refrigerated and are given by subcutaneous (SC) injection. [Note that with dialysis, erythropoietin is given by intravenous (IV) injection (for anemia due to ESRD) by injecting directly into the patient's port; otherwise, it is generally given SC.]

Myelosuppression Recovery

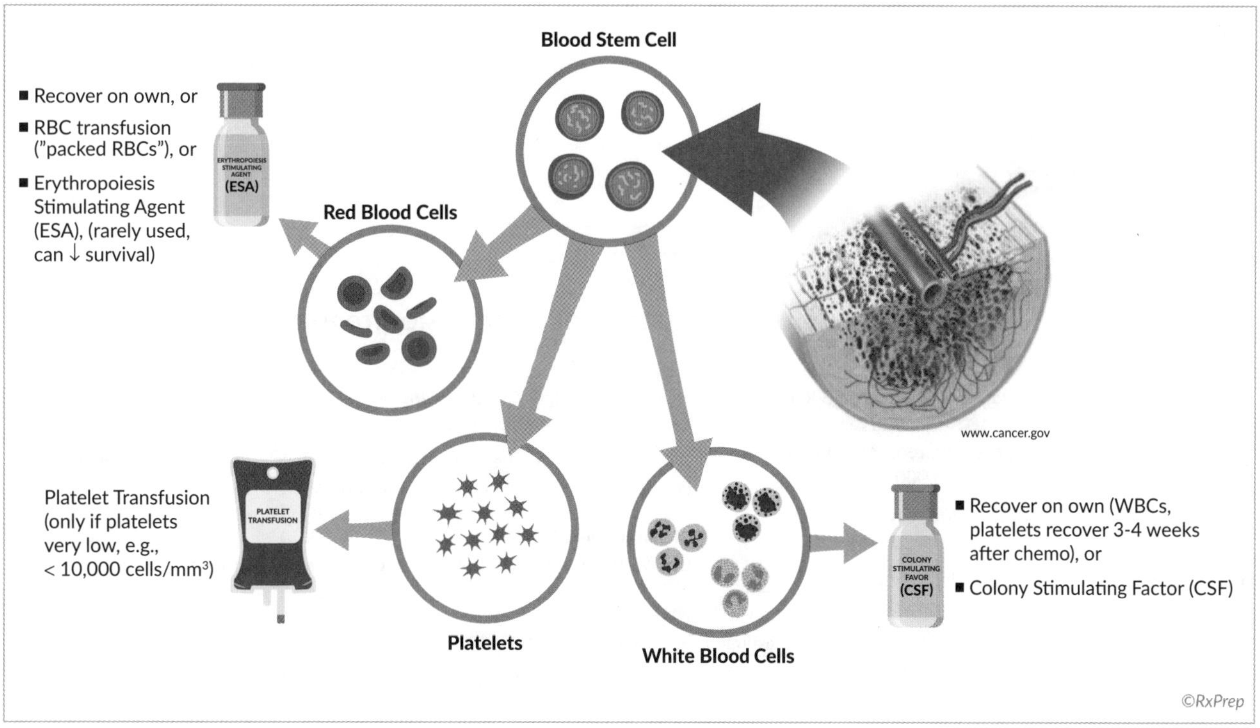

NEUTROPENIA

The more significant the neutropenia (i.e., the lower the WBC count), the higher the risk of infection.

Neutropenia Definition (American Society of Clinical Oncology)

CATEGORY	ABSOLUTE NEUTROPHIL COUNT (ANC)
Neutropenia	< 1,000 cells/mm³
Severe Neutropenia	< 500 cells/mm³
Profound Neutropenia	< 100 cells/mm³

The ANC calculation is in the Calculations IV chapter.

Growth Colony stimulating factors (G-CSFs, or simply CSFs or "myeloid growth factors") stimulate the production of WBCs in the bone marrow. Myeloid refers to the granulocyte precursor cell, which differentiates into neutrophils, eosinophils and basophils. CSFs shorten the time that a patient is at risk for infection due to neutropenia and reduces mortality from infections when given prophylactically in patients at high risk for febrile neutropenia.

All patients with > 20% chance of developing chemotherapy-induced febrile neutropenia (i.e., very high risk of infection) should receive a CSF, either G-CSF (filgrastim) or pegylated G-CSF (pegfilgrastim). GM-CSF (sargramostim), is used only for stem cell transplants.

Effect of CSFs on Neutropenia Duration

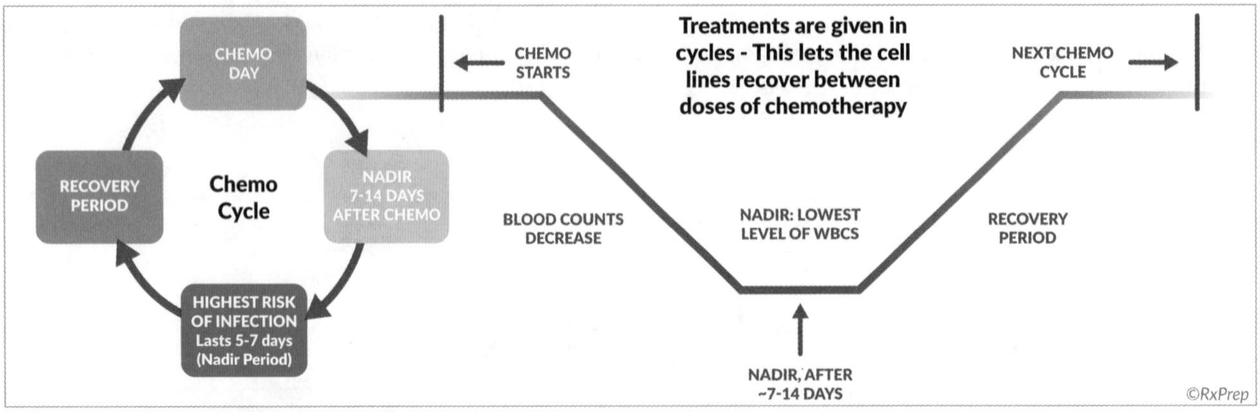

Colony Stimulating Factors (CSF)

DRUG	DOSING	SAFETY/SIDE EFFECTS/MONITORING
G-CSF **Filgrastim *(Neupogen,*** *Nivestym, Zarxio)* Tbo-filgrastim *(Granix)*	5 mcg/kg/day given IV/SC daily (round to the nearest 300 mcg or 480 mcg vial size); treat through post-nadir recovery (until ANC > 2,000-3,000 cells/mm³) 10 mcg/kg/day used for bone marrow transplant	**SIDE EFFECTS** Filgrastim/pegfilgrastim/tbo-filgrastim: bone pain, fever, glomerulonephritis, generalized rash, injection site reaction Sargramostim: fever, bone pain, arthralgias, myalgias, rash, dyspnea, peripheral edema, pericardial effusion, HTN, chest pain **MONITORING** CBC with differential, pulmonary function, weight, vital signs **NOTES** Store in refrigerator; protect vials from light Administer first dose no sooner than 24 hours after chemo; can be up to 72 hours after chemo Patients should report any signs of enlarged spleen (pain in left upper abdomen or respiratory distress syndrome) Must document when pegfilgrastim was given; should not be given within 14 days prior to the next cycle of chemo Biosimilars, depending on state law, can be interchanged for the brand
Pegylated G-CSF **Pegfilgrastim *(Neulasta)*** Pegfilgrastim-jmdb *(Fulphila)* Pegfilgrastim-cbqv *(Udenyca)*	1 prefilled syringe (6 mg) SC once per chemo cycle Pegylated filgrastim (pegfilgrastim) is longer-acting; allows for a single dose per cycle	
GM-CSF Sargramostim *(Leukine)* Limited to use in stem cell transplantation	250 mcg/m²/day given IV/SC daily; treat through post-nadir recovery	

Febrile Neutropenia

Patients receiving cytotoxic chemotherapy are at risk for infections from their own normal flora, including enteric bacteria and fungi, due to alterations in the GI mucosa caused by the chemotherapy drugs. Oncology patients commonly have a central venous access device (i.e., a central line) because many chemotherapy drugs are vesicants, and will cause severe damage if the needle falls out of the vein. The central line can cause infection from organisms on the skin or from the insertion staff/device.

If neutropenia occurs, the ability to fight infections is low, and the risk of death from sepsis increases.

Infection can be difficult to diagnose; fever may be the only sign of infection in a neutropenic patient (i.e., the increase in WBC count will not be present). Empiric antibiotics are started immediately if a fever occurs.

Neutropenia Diagnosis Requirements

FEVER	NEUTROPENIA
Oral temperature > 38.3° C (101° F) x 1 reading, or Oral temperature > 38.0° C (100.4° F) sustained for greater than 1 hour	Absolute neutrophil count (ANC) < 500 cells/mm³, or ANC that is expected to decrease to < 500 cells/mm³ during the next 48 hours

Gram-positive and Gram-negative bacteria both cause infections in febrile neutropenia, but Gram-negative bacteria have the highest risk for causing sepsis. The initial empiric antibiotics must provide adequate Gram-negative coverage, including *Pseudomonas aeruginosa*. Modification of the initial empiric antibiotic regimen can be required, based on the culture results or if the clinical situation does not improve (e.g., persistent fever).

PATIENT RISK	RISK DEFINITION	INITIAL EMPIRIC ANTIBIOTICS
Low-risk	Expected ANC < 500 cells/mm³ for ≤ 7 days No comorbidities	**Anti-pseudomonal antibiotics (oral)** Ciprofloxacin + amoxicillin-clavulanate, or Ciprofloxacin +/− clindamycin, or Levofloxacin
High-risk	Expected ANC ≤ 100 cells/mm³ for > 7 days Presence of comorbidities Evidence of renal or hepatic impairment (CrCl < 30 mL/min or LFTs > 5x ULN)	**Intravenous anti-pseudomonal beta-lactams** Cefepime or Ceftazidime or Meropenem or Imipenem-cilastatin or Piperacillin-tazobactam

ANEMIA

Hemoglobin (Hgb) levels are used to assess anemia. Normal Hgb levels are 12 - 16 g/dL for females and 13.5 - 18 g/dL for males (hematocrit is 36 - 46% females; 38 - 50% males). Anemia can recover on its own, be treated with a RBC transfusion, or rarely, with an erythropoiesis-stimulating agent (ESA) [i.e., erythropoietin, also called epoetin alfa, or the longer-acting darbepoetin alfa (*Aranesp*)]. ESAs can shorten survival and ↑ tumor progression (i.e., they can contribute to cancer recurrence). Therefore, ESAs are not recommended to be used in patients receiving chemotherapy with curative intent. This means that ESAs are only used for palliation.

To make sure that patients are aware of the risks, MedGuides are dispensed at the start of treatment. To minimize the risks of ESAs in patients with chemotherapy-induced anemia, the following requirements must be met:

- Use ESAs only in patients with non-myeloid malignancies where anemia is due to the effect of the chemotherapy
- Upon initiation of ESA therapy, there must be a minimum of two additional months of planned chemotherapy
- Initiate ESAs only when the Hgb is < 10 g/dL
- Use the lowest dose needed to avoid RBC transfusions

Serum ferritin, transferrin saturation (TSAT) and total iron-binding capacity (TIBC) will need to be assessed since ESAs will not work well to correct the anemia if iron levels are inadequate. Levels of folate and vitamin B12 may need to be evaluated, especially if there is a poor response to the ESA. For further information regarding ESAs, see the Anemia chapter.

THROMBOCYTOPENIA

Low platelets (thrombocytes) can result in spontaneous, uncontrolled bleeding. The normal range for platelets is 150,000 – 450,000/mm^3. The risk for spontaneous bleeding is increased when the platelet count is < 10,000 cells/mm^3. Platelet transfusions are generally indicated when the count falls below 10,000 cells/mm^3 (or < 20,000 cells/mm^3 if active bleed is present). Chemotherapy doses may be reduced or placed on hold until the platelet count recovers. Intramuscular injections and medications that affect platelet functioning, such as NSAIDs, should be avoided in patients who are thrombocytopenic.

CHEMOTHERAPY-INDUCED NAUSEA AND VOMITING (CINV)

Nausea and vomiting are common with chemotherapy. Patient factors which increase the risk of nausea and vomiting include: female gender, < 50 years of age, dehydration, history of motion sickness and history of nausea and vomiting with prior regimens. For chemotherapy-induced nausea and vomiting (CINV), administer antiemetics at least 30 minutes prior to chemotherapy and provide take-home antiemetic medication (such as ondansetron, prochlorperazine or metoclopramide) for breakthrough nausea and vomiting. There are 3 subtypes of CINV: acute, delayed and anticipatory.

SUBTYPE	RISK FACTORS	ONSET	MAJOR NEURO-TRANSMITTERS	DRUG THERAPY
Acute	See text above for patient risk factors	Within 24 hours after chemo	Serotonin	5HT3 receptor antagonists (5HT3-RA)
Delayed	Anthracyclines, platinum analogs, cyclophosphamide, ifosfamide, any chemo regimens with a high risk for causing acute CINV	> 24 hours after chemo	Substance P	NK1 receptor antagonists (NK1-RA), corticosteroids, palonosetron or granisetron ER SC (the only 5HT3-RAs with a labeled indication for delayed emesis)
Anticipatory	History of CINV with previous chemo regimen	Before chemo		Benzodiazepines

Nausea/Vomiting (Emesis) Treatment

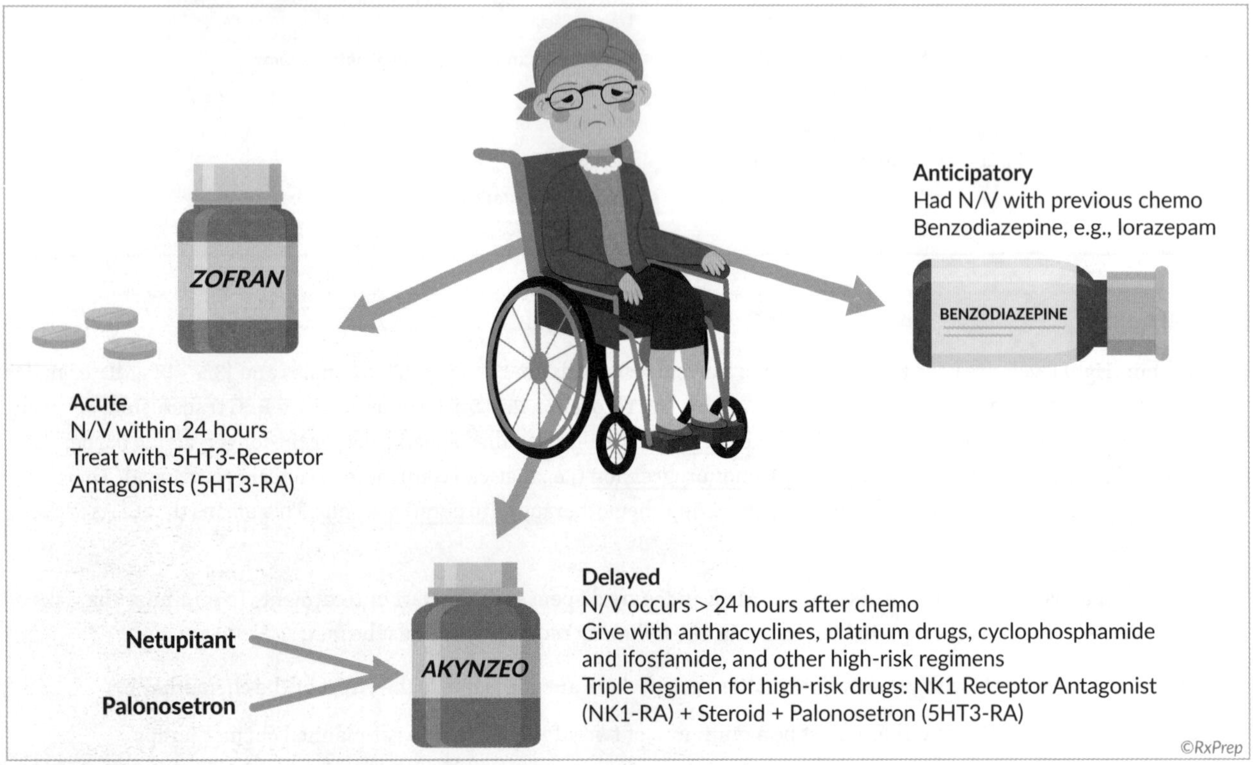

Emetic Risk Potential

Chemotherapy regimens are divided into risk groups for emetogenicity. Regimens with high emetic risk cause emesis at a frequency > 90%. Cisplatin is a high emetic risk drug. See the Common Toxicities of Select Chemotherapeutic Agents table for additional agents. Other risk categories include moderate (30 – 90%), low (10 – 30%) and minimal risk (< 10%). The majority of the MAbs and TKIs have minimal emetic risk.

Antiemetic Regimens for Acute/Delayed Nausea & Vomiting

The goal is to prevent nausea and vomiting and antiemetic regimens are started before chemotherapy. Risk of nausea and vomiting persists for three days after receiving the last dose of high emetic risk chemotherapy and for at least two days following the last dose of moderate emetic risk regimens.

5HT3-RA	NK1-RA	COMBINATION	OTHER	STEROID
Ondansetron Granisetron Dolasetron Palonosetron	Aprepitant PO Fosaprepitant IV Rolapitant	Netupitant/palonosetron *(Akynzeo)* Fosnetupitant/ palonosetron *(Akynzeo)*	Olanzapine	Dexamethasone

CHEMOTHERAPY REGIMEN	ANTIEMETIC REGIMEN
High emetic risk[a]	**3 or 4 drugs** ■ NK1-RA + 5HT3-RA + Dexamethasone ■ Olanzapine + Palonosetron + Dexamethasone ■ NK1-RA + 5HT3-RA + Olanzapine + Dexamethasone
Moderate emetic risk[a]	**2 or 3 drugs** ■ NK1-RA + 5HT3-RA + Dexamethasone ■ 5HT3-RA + Dexamethasone ■ Netupitant/palonosetron *(Akynzeo)* + Dexamethasone ■ Olanzapine + Palonosetron + Dexamethasone
Low emetic risk	**1 drug (any except NK1-RA)** ■ 5HT3-RA ■ Dexamethasone ■ Prochlorperazine ■ Metoclopramide

a. Can add lorazepam PRN, H2RA or PPI

Antiemetics for Breakthrough CINV

Despite receiving antiemetic prophylaxis for acute and/or delayed CINV, some patients may experience breakthrough nausea and vomiting. Various antiemetics may be used, including 5HT3-RAs, dopamine receptor antagonists and cannabinoids. 5HT3-RAs are usually well-tolerated by most patients, with migraine-like headaches and constipation being common side effects. They also cause minimal sedation, compared to dopamine receptor antagonists and cannabinoids. Dopamine receptor antagonists, such as prochlorperazine, promethazine and metoclopramide, are commonly prescribed, although some patients may experience unpleasant side effects. These agents commonly cause sedation and some anticholinergic side effects. Extrapyramidal symptoms (EPS) such as acute dystonic reactions can occur, especially in younger patients. Acute dystonic reactions should be treated with anticholinergics (benztropine, diphenhydramine).

Droperidol is an antiemetic in the same class as haloperidol (i.e., butyrophenones). Droperidol has restricted use (or has been removed entirely) in most hospitals due to QT-prolongation and the risk of torsades de pointes. Droperidol used to be a commonly used for postoperative nausea and vomiting (not for CINV).

Cannabinoids, such as dronabinol *(Marinol, Syndros)* and nabilone *(Cesamet)* can be used as second-line agents. These are synthetic analogs of delta-9-tetrahydrocannabinol, a naturally occurring component of *Cannabis sativa* (marijuana). Although these agents may be legally prescribed, they may cause side effects similar to *Cannabis*, such as increased appetite, sedation, dysphoria or euphoria. The DEA classifies *Cannabis* (marijuana, used in the plant form) as a schedule I drug, however it can be purchased for medical and nonmedical use in some states, and in some jurisdictions can be purchased for medical use only.

Antiemetic Agents

DRUG	DOSING	SAFETY/SIDE EFFECTS/MONITORING
Substance P/Neurokinin-1 Receptor Antagonists: inhibit the substance P/neurokinin 1 receptor, therefore augmenting the antiemetic activity of 5HT3 receptor antagonists and corticosteroids to inhibit acute and delayed phases of chemotherapy-induced emesis.		
Aprepitant *(Emend)* Capsule, suspension, injection	PO: 125 mg 1 hour before chemo on day 1, then 80 mg daily x 2 days	**CONTRAINDICATIONS** Aprepitant/fosaprepitant: do not use with pimozide or cisapride (CYP3A4 substrates) Rolapitant: do not use with thioridazine (CYP2D6 substrate) **SIDE EFFECTS** Dizziness, fatigue, constipation, weakness, hiccups **NOTES** Aprepitant/fosaprepitant/netupitant are CYP3A4 inhibitors; dose of dexamethasone should be decreased when used concurrently as an antiemetic Rolapitant is a CYP2D6 inhibitor; dose of dexamethasone should not be decreased when used concurrently as an antiemetic
Fosaprepitant *(Emend)* Injection	IV: 150 mg 30 minutes before chemo	
Netupitant + palonosetron *(Akynzeo)* Capsule Fosnetupitant + palonosetron *(Akynzeo)* Injection	PO: 300/0.5 mg 1 hour before chemo IV: 235/0.25 mg 1 hour before chemo	
Rolapitant *(Varubi)* Tablet, injection	PO: 180 mg 1-2 hours before chemo	
5HT-3 Receptor Antagonists: work by blocking serotonin, both peripherally on vagal nerve terminals and centrally in the chemoreceptor trigger zone. All may be given once prior to chemotherapy on day 1, with the exception of the granisetron transdermal patch which is started prior to day 1 of chemotherapy.		
Ondansetron *(Zofran, Zuplenz* film)	PO: 8-24 mg IV: 8-16 mg	**CONTRAINDICATIONS** Do not use 5HT3 antagonists with apomorphine *(Apokyn)* due to severe hypotension and loss of consciousness **WARNINGS** Dose-dependent ↑ in QT interval (torsades de pointes) - more common with IV Serotonin syndrome when used in combination with other serotonergic agents Constipation, progressive ileus and gastric distension *(Sustol)* **SIDE EFFECTS** Headache, constipation, fatigue, dizziness, injection site reactions *(Sustol)* **NOTES** Palonosetron PO only available in combination with netupitant *(Akynzeo)*. Of the 5HT-3 RAs, only palonosetron and *Sustol* have FDA-approval for delayed CINV
Granisetron *(Sancuso,* *Sustol)*	PO: 1-2 mg IV: 10 mcg/kg or 1 mg SC *(Sustol)*: 10 mg over 20-30 seconds Patch *(Sancuso)*: 3.1 mg/24hr patch, apply 24-48 hours before chemo; may leave in place up to 7 days	
Dolasetron *(Anzemet)*	PO: 100 mg IV: Not indicated for CINV due to ↑ risk for QT prolongation	
Palonosetron *(Aloxi)* + netupitant *(Akynzeo)* + fosnetupitant *(Akynzeo)*	IV *(Aloxi)*: 0.25 mg PO *(Akynzeo)*: 0.5/300 mg 1 hour before chemo IV *(Akynzeo)*: 0.25/235 mg 1 hour before chemo	
Corticosteroids: unknown		
Dexamethasone *(Decadron)*	All off-label dosing High risk: 12 mg PO/IV on day 1 of chemo, then 8 mg PO daily days 2-4 Moderate risk: 12 mg PO/IV on day 1 of chemo, then 8 mg PO/IV days 2-3 Low risk: 8-12 mg PO/IV on day/s of chemo	**CONTRAINDICATIONS** Systemic fungal infections, cerebral malaria **SIDE EFFECTS** Short-term side effects include ↑ appetite/weight gain, fluid retention, emotional instability (euphoria, mood swings, irritability, acute psychosis), insomnia, GI upset Higher doses ↑ BP and blood glucose (especially in patients with diabetes)

DRUG	DOSING	SAFETY/SIDE EFFECTS/MONITORING
Dopamine Receptor Antagonists: work by blocking dopamine receptors in the CNS, including the chemoreceptor trigger zone (among other mechanisms).		
Prochlorperazine (*Compazine*, *Compro)*	10 mg IV/PO Q6H PRN May give 25 mg suppository PR Q12H PRN	**BOXED WARNING** Prochlorperazine: ↑ mortality in elderly patients with dementia-related psychosis. Promethazine: do not use in children age < 2 years (risk of respiratory depression). Do not give via intra-arterial or SC administration. IV route can cause serious tissue injury if extravasation occurs. Deep IM injection is preferred (see Notes). Metoclopramide: tardive dyskinesia (TD) that can be irreversible. Discontinue metoclopramide if signs or symptoms of TD. ↑ risk of developing TD with ↑ duration of treatment and total cumulative dose. Avoid treatment with metoclopramide for > 12 weeks. ↓ dose with renal impairment. Droperidol: QT prolongation and serious arrhythmias. All patients should have a 12-lead ECG prior to receiving droperidol and continue for 2-3 hours after completing treatment. Contraindicated if baseline QT is prolonged. **WARNINGS** Symptoms of Parkinson disease may be exacerbated. Avoid use in patients with Parkinson disease. **SIDE EFFECTS** Sedation, lethargy, hypotension, neuroleptic malignant syndrome (NMS), QT prolongation, acute EPS (common in children; antidote is diphenhydramine or benztropine), can ↓ seizure threshold. Strong anticholinergic side effects (e.g., constipation) except with metoclopramide (diarrhea). **OLANZAPINE SIDE EFFECTS** Mild (sedation, orthostasis, others) when used for CINV; see Schizophrenia chapter for details. **NOTES** Droperidol is not used for CINV. It is included here due to high QT risk, and for completeness of antiemetic discussion. IM injections not feasible with ↓ PLT.
Promethazine (*Phenergan*, *Phenadoz, Promethegan)*	12.5-25 mg PO/IM/IV/PR Q4-6H PRN	
Metoclopramide (Reglan) Tablet, ODT, injection	10-40 mg PO/IV Q6H PRN For highly emetic regimens: 0.5-2 mg/kg/dose PO/IV Q6H PRN CrCl < 40 mL/min: Give 50% of the dose	
Olanzapine (*Zyprexa*) Tablet, ODT, injection Works through several mechanisms	10 mg PO on the day of chemo, and on days 2-4 5 mg PO Q4H PRN, max of 20 mg/day	
Droperidol Injection	Indicated only for post-operative N/V, not for CINV	
Cannabinoids: may work by activating cannabinoid receptors within the central nervous system and/or by inhibiting the vomiting control mechanism in the medulla oblongata.		
Dronabinol (*Marinol*, Syndros) Capsules, solution Refrigerate C-III	Labeled dosing: 5 mg/m^2 PO prior to chemo and Q2-4H after chemo for up to 6 doses/day. Most patients respond to 5 mg 3-4 times/day.	**SIDE EFFECTS** Somnolence, euphoria, ↑ appetite, orthostatic hypotension, dysphoria, lowering of the seizure threshold, use with caution in patients with histories of substance abuse or psychiatric disorders. **NOTES** Solution contains 50% alcohol.
Nabilone (*Cesamet*) No refrigeration needed C-II	1-2 mg PO BID, continue for up to 48H after last chemo dose	

Patient Counseling for Ondansetron

- Common side effects of this medication include headache, constipation, fatigue and dizziness.
- Take this medicine by mouth with a glass of water. It may be taken as needed or at scheduled times. Follow the directions on your prescription label. Do not take your medicine more often than directed.
- Do not take this medicine if you are taking apomorphine.
- If you are prescribed the oral disintegrating tablets: do not attempt to push the tablets through foil backing. With dry hands, peel back the foil of one blister and remove the tablet. Place tablet on the tongue; it will dissolve in seconds. Once dissolved, you may swallow with saliva. Administration with liquid is not necessary. Wash hands after administration.
- If you are prescribed the oral soluble film *(Zuplenz)*: with dry hands, fold the pouch along the dotted line to expose the tear notch. While still folded, tear the pouch carefully along the edge and remove the oral soluble film just prior to dosing. Place the film on the tongue, it will dissolve in a few seconds. Allow each film to dissolve completely before taking the next film if more than one is needed to reach the desired dose (i.e., 16 mg given as two 8 mg films).

OTHER GASTROINTESTINAL COMPLICATIONS

Cells of the GI tract are rapidly dividing and are therefore susceptible to being killed by chemotherapy agents that interfere with DNA replication or cell division. Damage to the epithelium of the GI tract results in diarrhea. Damage to oral mucosal epithelial cells leads to painful oral ulcerations, also called oral mucositis. Damage to the salivary glands usually caused by radiation therapy to the head or neck regions may cause dry mouth, also called xerostomia.

Chemotherapy-Induced Diarrhea

Chemotherapy-induced diarrhea (CID) can lead to life-threatening dehydration and electrolyte imbalances. Antimotility agents, such as loperamide and diphenoxylate + atropine may be prescribed to treat CID. Although the usual maximum dose of loperamide is 16 mg/day, this dose can be increased to 24 mg/day when treating CID under medical supervision. Fluorouracil, capecitabine and irinotecan commonly cause CID that occurs several days after chemotherapy. The risk of diarrhea is increased when fluorouracil (or the prodrug capecitabine) is used in combination with leucovorin or when used in patients with dihydropyrimidine dehydrogenase (DPD) deficiencies (not common). Irinotecan also causes an early onset diarrhea that occurs during the infusion of the drug and is often accompanied by symptoms of cholinergic excess such as abdominal cramping, rhinitis, lacrimation and salivation. The treatment is the anticholinergic drug atropine. Many TKIs, especially those targeting VEGF or EGF, such as sorafenib and sunitinib, commonly cause diarrhea.

IRINOTECAN (I-RUN-TO-THE-CAN)

Irinotecan causes cholinergic excess, including acute diarrhea with abdominal cramping.

Atropine can be added to the IV bag to block the patient's acute need to run to the can (i.e., toilet).

Atropine is the classic anticholinergic drug, and blocks the acute diarrhea.

Pilocarpine is the classic cholinergic drug, and causes salivation. Pilocarpine is used for xerostomia (dry mouth) caused by some cancer drugs.

Pilocarpine also causes lacrimation (tears) and is used for dry eyes.

Oral Mucositis

Chemotherapy-induced oral mucositis causes painful ulcers to form in the mouth. Symptoms begin about a week after chemotherapy (e.g., 5-FU, methotrexate). Oral mucositis is self-limiting and will dissipate. Symptoms can be severe and require treatment.

Oral mucositis causes difficulty eating, drinking, talking and cleaning the teeth. Yet, good oral hygiene (e.g., brushing with a very soft toothbrush) is important.

Viscous lidocaine 2%, magic mouthwash (i.e., various compounded preparations) and systemic analgesics will lessen pain and make it possible to talk, eat and drink. Frequent rinsing with NaCl solution (i.e., salt water) helps retain moisture. Oral mucositis increases the risk of oral *Candida* infection (thrush). Nystatin oral suspension or clotrimazole troches are used for treatment.

A patient who is not able to eat and drink could require parenteral nutrition and IV fluids.

MEDICATIONS FOR ORAL COMPLICATIONS OF CHEMOTHERAPY

DRUG	DOSING	SAFETY/SIDE EFFECTS/MONITORING
Oral Mucositis		
Mucosal Barrier Gel Spray, solution, wafer (*Episil, Gelclair, Mucotrol, MuGard, Orafate, ProThelial*)	Varies depending on product. Most are applied to the oral mucosa several times per day.	**SIDE EFFECTS** Burning, stinging sensation in the mouth
Lidocaine 2% topical solution for mouth/ throat	15 mL swish and spit/ swallowed Q3H PRN	**BOXED WARNING** Avoid use in patients < 3 years of age due to reports of seizures, cardiopulmonary arrest and death **WARNINGS** Exceeding the recommended dose can result in high plasma levels and serious adverse effects (seizures, cardiopulmonary arrest) **SIDE EFFECTS** Dizziness, drowsiness, confusion, hypotension **NOTES** Avoid ingestion of food for 60 minutes following dose due to risk of impaired swallowing and aspiration
Xerostomia		
Artificial Saliva Substitutes Spray, solution, lozenge (*Aquoral, Biotene, Caphosol, Entertainer's Secret, Moi-Stir, Mouth Kote, NeutraSal, Numoisyn, Oasis, SalivaMAX, SalivaSure*)	Varies depending on product. Most can be applied to oral mucosa PRN.	
Pilocarpine *(Salagen)*	5-10 mg PO TID Hepatic impairment: Moderate: 5 mg PO BID Severe: avoid use	**WARNINGS** Use with caution in patients with cholelithiasis, nephrolithiasis, cardiovascular disease, asthma, bronchitis, COPD **SIDE EFFECTS** Cholinergic side effects: flushing, sweating, nausea, urinary frequency **NOTES** Avoid administering with high-fat meal

HAND-FOOT SYNDROME

Hand-foot syndrome (also known as palmar-plantar erythrodysesthesia, or PPE) frequently occurs following treatment with capecitabine, fluorouracil, cytarabine, liposomal doxorubicin and the tyrosine kinase inhibitors (TKIs) sorafenib and sunitinib.

PPE occurs when small amounts of the chemotherapy drug leak out of capillaries and into the palms of the hands and soles of the feet. Heat and friction on the palms and soles increases the amount of drug in the capillaries and the amount of drug leakage. This causes tenderness and pain, inflammation and possibly peeling of the palms and soles. Methods to manage PPE are in the box below. Dose reductions or delays may be needed if symptoms do not adequately improve.

Cooling hands/feet with cold compresses provides temporary relief of pain and tenderness.

Emollients (*Aquaphor, Udder Cream, Bag Balm*) are used to retain moisture in the hands and feet. Steroids and pain medications can be helpful to lessen inflammation and pain.

HAND-FOOT SYNDROME MANAGEMENT

Limit daily activities to reduce friction and heat exposure to hands and feet.

Avoid long exposure to hot water (washing dishes, showers). Take shorter showers in lukewarm water.

Avoid use of dishwashing gloves as the rubber will hold in the heat.

Avoid increased pressure on soles of feet (no jogging, aerobics, power walking or jumping).

Avoid increased pressure on palms of hands (no use of garden tools, screwdrivers, knives for chopping or performing other tasks that require squeezing hand/s on a hard surface).

TUMOR LYSIS SYNDROME

Chemotherapy that causes tumor cell death can cause the cell wall and/or membrane to disintegrate (lyse), which releases the intracellular (inside the cell) contents into the bloodstream (see image). Tumor lysis syndrome (TLS) has occurred with most cancer types, but most commonly occurs with leukemia and non-Hodgkins lymphoma.

When the cell is lysed, the intracellular components that enter the bloodstream include potassium, phosphate, purines and pyrimidines (the base pairs that compose DNA). The phosphate that is released into the bloodstream will bind to calcium, which can cause hypocalcemia. TLS causes acute hyperkalemia (which can cause arrhythmias), hyperphosphatemia and hypocalcemia (low serum calcium, in addition to causing anorexia and nausea, can cause seizures) and hyperuricemia.

The xanthine oxidase enzyme is present in the blood and can readily convert large amounts of purines into uric acid, causing acute hyperuricemia, which crystallizes, as with gout. The uric acid crystals damage the kidneys, which can progress to acute renal failure.

Allopurinol is a xanthine oxidase inhibitor that blocks the conversion of purines into uric acid. The usual initial dose of allopurinol for gout is ~100 mg daily. For tumor lysis syndrome, higher doses (400 – 800 mg/day) are used and continued for 10 – 14 days after chemotherapy. Allopurinol is reviewed in detail in the Gout chapter.

Rasburicase is a more expensive alternative to allopurinol and can be used when allopurinol fails to control the uric acid level or is not a reasonable option (e.g., with risk of allopurinol-induced rash/severe skin reactions). Rasburicase converts uric acid to a more water-soluble metabolite (allantoin), which is easily excreted.

Both allopurinol and rasburicase are initially given with IV normal saline (NS), which increases urine output to speed up excretion of some of the excess intracellular components. IV bicarbonate solution is given to increase the urinary pH to 7.0. This causes more uric acid to solubilize, which increases excretion.

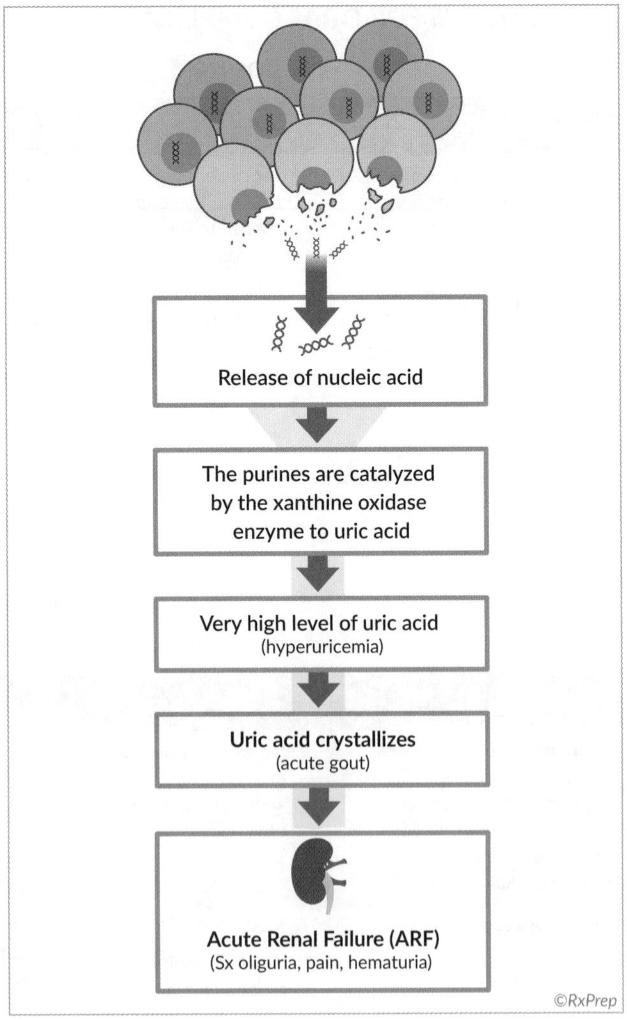

HYPERCALCEMIA OF MALIGNANCY

Certain cancers cause calcium to leach from bone, causing hypercalcemia and bones that are weak and prone to fracture. Mild hypercalcemia is typically asymptomatic and can be treated with hydration and loop diuretics.

Moderate to severe hypercalcemia (calcium > 12 mg/dL,) is symptomatic, with nausea, vomiting, fatigue, dehydration and confusion. Treatment includes IV hydration with normal saline and a medication to lower calcium levels. Calcitonin is sometimes used initially for up to 48 hours; the treatment duration is short because tachyphylaxis (tolerance) develops quickly.

An IV bisphosphate (e.g., pamidronate, zoledronic acid) is generally considered first-line. They may be given with calcitonin in severe cases. An alternative to IV bisphosphonates, is denosumab. IV bisphosphonates and denosumab are common treatment options for osteoporosis (at different doses). They have the added benefit of building bone density and reducing fractures.

Hypercalcemia of Malignancy Treatment

TREATMENT	MOA	ONSET	DURATION	DEGREE OF HYPERCALCEMIA*
Hydration with normal saline and loop diuretics	↑ renal calcium excretion	Minutes to hours	Only during length of infusion	Mild (oral or IV hydration) Moderate Severe
Calcitonin *(Miacalcin)* 4-8 units/kg IM/SC Q12H	Inhibits bone resorption, ↑ renal calcium excretion	2-6 hours	48 hours max (risk of tachyphylaxis)	Moderate Severe
IV Bisphosphonates **Zoledronic acid *(Zometa)*** 4 mg IV once, may repeat in 7 days if needed. Do not infuse over < 15 minutes due to increased risk of renal toxicity. Dose does not need to be adjusted for mild-moderate renal insufficiency when used for hypercalcemia. (Do not confuse with *Reclast*, which is dosed at 5 mg IV yearly for osteoporosis - see Osteoporosis chapter) Pamidronate *(Aredia)* 60-90 mg IV over 2-24 hrs once, may repeat in 7 days if needed.	Inhibits bone resorption by stopping osteoclast function	24-72 hours	2-4 weeks	Mild Moderate Severe
Denosumab *(Xgeva)* 120 mg SC on days 1, 8 and 15 of the first month, then monthly (Do not confuse with *Prolia*, which is dosed at 60 mg SC every 6 months for osteoporosis - see Osteoporosis chapter)	Monoclonal antibody that blocks the interaction between RANKL and RANK (a receptor on osteoclasts), preventing osteoclast formation	24-72 hours	~1 month	Moderate Severe

*Degree of hypercalcemia – Mild: corrected calcium < 12 mg/dL, Moderate: corrected calcium 12-14 mg/dL, Severe: corrected calcium > 14 mg/dL, or presence of symptoms.
Corrected Calcium (mg/dL) = Calcium (reported) + [(4 – Albumin) x 0.8]

CHEMOTHERAPY HANDLING, ADMINISTRATION AND EXTRAVASATION

IV ADMINISTRATION AND EXTRAVASATION

Chemotherapy agents are hazardous drugs that are considered carcinogenic, mutagenic or teratogenic. See the Compounding chapters for detailed information on USP 800 requirements for the compounding environment and necessary equipment.

Many chemotherapy agents are vesicants, which means they may cause tissue necrosis if the IV drug accidentally leaks from the vein into the surrounding tissue (also called extravasation). Major vesicants include anthracyclines and vinca alkaloids. Care should be taken to avoid extravasation of these drugs by administering them through central venous catheters or freshly started peripheral IV lines. If extravasation occurs, apply cold compresses (except with the vinca alkaloids and etoposide, use warm compresses) and the antidotes below depending on the drug extravasated:

- Anthracyclines: dexrazoxane (*Totect*) or dimethyl sulfoxide
- Vinca alkaloids and etoposide: hyaluronidase

Based on clinical experience, a limited number of chemotherapy agents may be administered intrathecally. This is usually accomplished by performing a lumbar puncture and injecting the drug into the cerebrospinal fluid. Drugs that can be given intrathecally include cytarabine, methotrexate, hydrocortisone and thiotepa. They must be preservative-free.

Unfortunately, accidental intrathecal administration of vincristine has been reported. Intrathecal administration of vincristine is fatal. Care must be taken to properly label vincristine to avoid accidental intrathecal administration. Do not dispense vincristine in a syringe. Vincristine is prepared in small volume IVPB solutions (50 - 100 mL) to avoid the risk of accidental intrathecal administration.

TIMING OF VACCINATIONS

Vaccination during chemotherapy should be avoided because the antibody response is suboptimal. When chemotherapy is being planned, vaccination should precede chemotherapy by ≥ 2 weeks. Patients on chemotherapy may receive the inactivated seasonal influenza vaccine in between cycles of chemotherapy. The administration of live vaccines to immunocompromised patients must be avoided. Live vaccines can generally be administered at least three months after discontinuation of chemotherapy.

Select Guidelines/References

American Cancer Society. Cancer Screening Guidelines http://www.cancer.org/healthy/findcancerearly/cancerscreeningguidelines/american-cancer-society-guidelines-for-the-early-detection-of-cancer (accessed 2019 Jan 15)

National Comprehensive Cancer Network (NCCN). www.nccn.org (accessed 2019 Jan 27)

American Society of Clinical Oncology (ASCO). www.asco.org (accessed 2019 Jan 27)

CHAPTER CONTENT

Background 851
Treatment Overview 851
Treatment Goals 852
Treatment Types 852
Lung Cancer 852
Skin Cancer 853
ABCDE – Warning Signs of Melanoma Skin Cancer ... 853
Breast Cancer 853
Identifying Breast Cancer 853
Men and Breast Cancer Risk 854
Breast Cancer Treatment 854
Monoclonal Antibodies 856
Metastatic Breast Cancer 856
Patient Counseling 857
Prostate Cancer 858
Identifying Prostate Cancer 858
Hormonal Therapies for Prostate Cancer 858
Patient Counseling 860
Chemotherapy 860
Cancer Treatments 860
Body Surface Area (BSA) Calculations 861
Traditional Cytotoxic Chemotherapy Drugs 862
Cell Cycle Independent 862
Alkylating Agents 862
Platinum-Based Compounds 863
Anthracyclines 864
To Reduce Doxorubicin Cardiotoxicity 864
Cell Cycle Specific Agents 865
Vinca Alkaloids 865
Taxanes 866
Topoisomerase I Inhibitors 866
Topoisomerase II Inhibitors 867
Pyrimidine Analog Antimetabolites 868
Folate Antimetabolites 869
Miscellaneous Agents 870
Targeted Therapies 872
Monoclonal Antibodies 872
Hints for Understanding Monoclonal Antibodies 872
Tyrosine Kinase Inhibitors 874
Common Toxicities of Tyrosine Kinase Inhibitors 876
Administration of Oral Agents 877

We gratefully acknowledge the assistance of D. Raymond Weber, PharmD, BSPharm, BCPS, BCOP, Notre Dame of Maryland Univ. School of Pharmacy, in preparing this chapter.

CONTENT LEGEND

= Study Tip Gal   = Required Formula

Breast Cancer Treatments

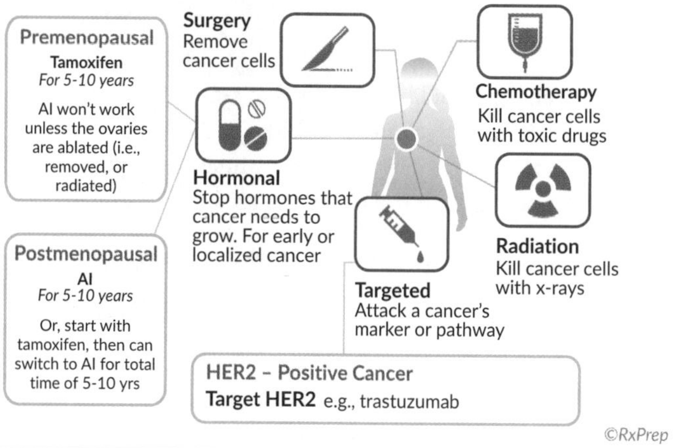

CHAPTER 62
ONCOLOGY II: COMMON CANCERS AND CANCER TREATMENT

BACKGROUND

The five most common types of cancer are basal and squamous cell skin cancer (i.e., non-melanoma), breast, lung, prostate and colorectal cancer.

The majority of this chapter reviews the use of chemotherapeutic drugs that either kill tumor cells directly (i.e., cytotoxic drugs) or prevents cell division (i.e., prevents cell growth), such as hormone-blocking drugs.

TREATMENT OVERVIEW

The term chemotherapy is used commonly to refer to cancer treatments, yet not all cancer drugs involve chemo (chemical) treatments. Cancer can be treated with surgery, radiation, chemotherapy, hormone therapy, biological therapy, targeted therapy, immunotherapy and/or vaccines. Complementary therapy (i.e., in addition to the primary treatment, such as acupuncture and medical marijuana) is commonly used among cancer patients to manage side effects and keep the body resilient.

Several key items are used in deciding the type of treatments:

- The cancer type and characteristics (e.g., a breast tumor that is estrogen-receptor positive will receive different treatment than a breast tumor that is estrogen-receptor negative).
- The stage of the cancer (the size, and how far it has metastasized, or spread).
- Patient characteristics, such as acceptable tolerability to chemotherapy.

The tolerability of chemotherapy drugs ranges from relatively mild to highly toxic; a cancer patient should be expected to have a greater benefit than harm from a regimen for the treatment to be beneficial. Cancer treatment decisions should involve the patient, their family and the healthcare team.

TREATMENT GOALS

The treatment goal could be designed to attempt to achieve remission (with curative intent) or be palliative, where cure is not the focus of care and the primary intent is to provide comfort, support and control of symptoms, such as pain.

The response to treatment can be complete or partial:

- A complete response, or complete remission, means that the treatment has destroyed all known tumors.
- A partial response, or partial remission, means that at least 50% of the tumor was eliminated, but some was not.

Some types of cancer have a higher rate of recurrence than other types which can be eradicated more readily. If a patient remains cancer-free for 5 years, it is unlikely that the cancer will recur.

TREATMENT TYPES

Surgery and radiation targets cancer that is confined locally. Other treatments can target both localized cancer and cancer cells that have spread.

Neoadjuvant therapy (e.g., radiation or chemotherapy) can be used before surgery to shrink the tumor in order to make resection more likely to reach all or most tumor cells.

Commonly, the primary treatment is surgery to remove the bulk of the tumor, if the cancer is resectable.

Adjuvant therapy (e.g., radiation and/or chemotherapy) is given after surgery in an attempt to eradicate residual disease and decrease recurrence.

Sometimes, surgery is not an option for initial treatment and radiation and/or chemotherapy is used first.

Synergistic Combination Regimens

Combination therapy is designed for synergism by using drugs with different mechanisms of action (to increase efficacy) and with different side effects (to decrease toxicity and resistance).

Chemotherapy regimens can be highly toxic. The majority of adverse effects are due to damaging effects on non-cancerous, rapidly dividing cells in the GI tract, hair follicles and bone marrow, where the production of blood cells takes place. Thus, diarrhea, alopecia and myelosuppression are common side effects. The Oncology I chapter reviews side effect management.

Patient factors including age, comorbidities and past treatments are considered when selecting a regimen. A patient's quality of life (QOL) may lead the clinician and family to choose palliative measures over a more aggressive treatment plan that could have intolerable side effects.

Due to severe side effects, the patient's physical functioning must be assessed with rating systems such as the Karnofsky and the ECOG (Eastern Cooperative Oncology Group) performance status scales.

LUNG CANCER

Lung cancer is the most common type of cancer worldwide. In the United States there are ~230,000 new cases of lung cancer annually. The three main types are nonsmall cell (~85%), small cell (~10-15%) and carcinoid (< 5%). Nonsmall cell and small cell are distinguished by the cell size; as the name implies, small cell has smaller cells.

Smoking causes ~80% of lung cancers. The other 20% is attributed to radon, asbestos fibers and exposure to various types of chemicals and pollution. A chronic cough with dyspnea can indicate lung cancer, and necessitates a visit to a physician.

Typical treatment includes surgery, followed by radiation and/or chemotherapy to destroy remaining cancer cells. The major chemotherapy drugs described in this chapter are used in various combination regimens.

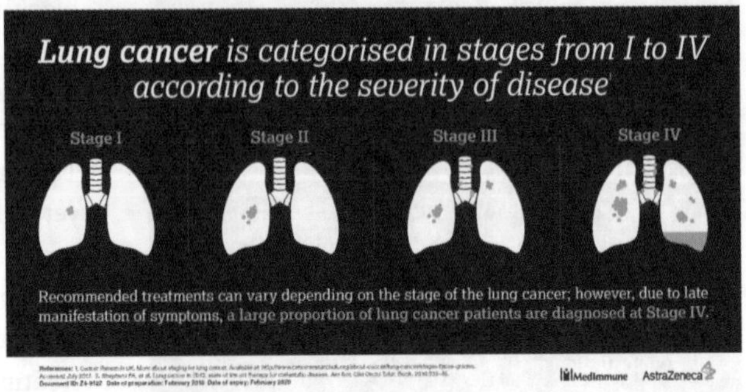

©https://www.astrazeneca.com/our-focus-areas/oncology/at-the-forefront-of-lung-cancer-treatment.html

SKIN CANCER

Skin cancer is the most common cancer in the United States. Risk factors include a history of ultraviolet (UV) light exposure (sun or tanning beds), light skin that burns easily, light hair color, immunosuppressant drugs or diseases, and a past history of skin cancer. The immune system can eliminate some early skin cancers; immunosuppressant drugs that increase the risk of skin cancer (and some lymphomas) include many transplant drugs.

There are three types of skin cancer: basal cell, squamous cell and melanoma. Basal cell and squamous cell skin cancers are common and very survivable if treated early. Melanoma is much less common but often metastasizes and accounts for ~75% of all skin cancer-related deaths. Recommendations for reducing the risk of developing skin cancer include:

- Seek shade – especially between 10 AM and 4 PM .
- Slip on a shirt – tightly woven fabrics are best.
- Slop on sunscreen – use a broad-spectrum sunscreen with an SPF of at least 15 – 30 and reapply every 2 hours.
- Slap on a hat – wear a hat with at least a 2" – 3" brim.
- Wrap on sunglasses – to protect the skin around the eyes and help prevent cataracts.

The "ABCDE" mnemonic (below) can be used to educate patients about suspicious skin spots. A suspicious skin spot, a spot that is changing over time, or a spot that looks different from other spots should be examined.

ABCDE – WARNING SIGNS OF MELANOMA SKIN CANCER

A B C D E

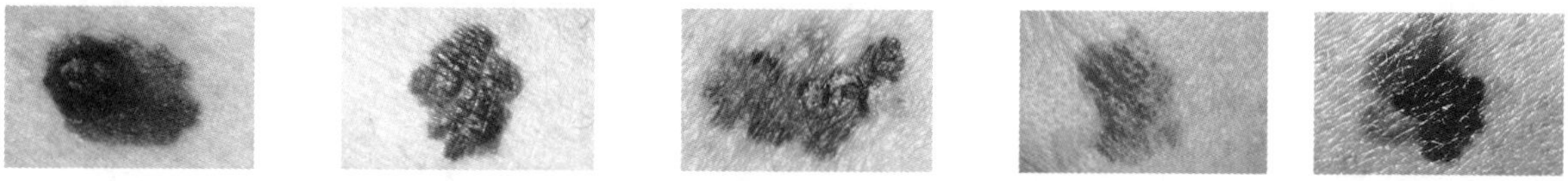

ASYMMETRY	BORDER	COLOR	DIAMETER	EVOLVING
One half of the mole does not match the other.	Edges are irregular, notched.	Color is not the same all over.	Larger than 6 mm, or the size of the tip of a pencil eraser.	Mole is changing in size, color, shape or symptoms (itching, bleeding, tenderness).

BREAST CANCER

After skin cancer, breast cancer is the most common cancer diagnosed in women in the United States. The top risk factor for developing breast cancer is being female. Estrogen is the favorite food that feeds most breast tumors, and females have more estrogen. Female breast cells are more likely to mutate because they are more active than male breast cells, which are largely inactive. Risk factors can be present at the cellular level, including genetic mutations that alter protein expression and cellular replication. Modifiable risk factors include being overweight (in postmenopausal women), low physical activity, poor nutrition and tobacco use.

Individual males have higher risk when they have a condition that increases estrogen production, including Klinefelter syndrome, described later in this section.

IDENTIFYING BREAST CANCER

Breast Self Exams

Breast Self Exams (BSE) are not used for screening, but they can help women identify a change in the look or feel of the breast or nipple, or nipple discharge, which would warrant follow-up screening.

Breast Imaging Studies

The schedule for recommended imaging varies by organization, but is roughly every year or two, beginning at age 40 or 45. Mammograms use low-dose x-rays to identify abnormal breast tissue. A few images are taken in a screening mammogram. If anything looks suspicious, a diagnostic mammogram with more images can be taken. An ultrasound is useful to differentiate between a benign fluid-filled cyst or a potentially cancerous tumor. Ultrasound is used to guide the needle during a biopsy. High-risk women can receive a magnetic resonance imaging (MRI) exam, in addition to the annual mammogram.

Biopsy follows an abnormal result. A small sample of tissue is excised (removed) with a biopsy needle and sent to pathology to identify if cancer cells are present.

Weight and Breast Cancer Risk

Postmenopausal women who are overweight have a higher breast cancer risk than lean women. Fat cells contain androgens (male sex hormones), which are converted to estrogens by the aromatase enzyme.

Regrettably, the decline in estrogen that occurs after menopause causes abdominal fat cells to store more fat, and most women gain 5 – 10 pounds in the first ten years after menopause.

BRCA1 and BRCA2 Gene Mutations are High-Risk

The BRCA1 and BRCA2 genes normally suppress tumor growth. The genes contain instructions for production of proteins that repair damaged DNA. Inherited mutations in either gene prevents cell repair, and causes a dramatic increase in breast cancer incidence. BRCA mutations were first linked to breast cancer (BR for breast, CA for cancer) but are now linked with increased risk for breast, ovarian and prostate cancers.

In a woman without either mutation, the likelihood of developing breast cancer over her lifetime is ~12%; with either mutation, the likelihood of breast cancer is ~70%. Fortunately, the risk of either mutation is low in the general population. Ethnic groups at high risk for mutations include women who are Ashkenazi Jewish (8-10%), non-Ashkenazi Jewish (2-3%) and Hispanic (4%). African-American and Asian-American women have lower risk (< 1%).

MEN AND BREAST CANCER RISK

Less than 1% of breast cancer occurs in males. The risk increases in men with a BRCA mutation, and with the presence of any condition that increases estrogen production (e.g., Klinefelter syndrome; see next section). Similar to postmenopausal women, being overweight in males increases estrogen production, which increases risk.

Klinefelter Syndrome and Breast Cancer Risk in Men

Normally, males have one X and one Y chromosome. Klinefelter syndrome is a congenital condition in which males have one Y chromosome and two or more X chromosomes. Men with Klinefelter syndrome have small testicles and are usually infertile. They produce more estrogen than is typical for males, and develop gynecomastia. Men with Klinefelter syndrome have higher breast cancer risk.

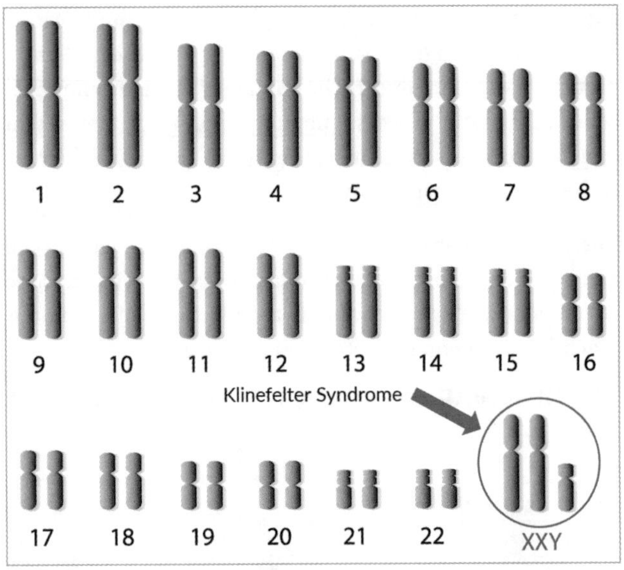

BREAST CANCER TREATMENT

The treatment of early stage breast cancer will include some combination of surgery, chemotherapy and/or radiation. Cancers that express markers on the cell surface that contribute to tumor growth will receive therapy that targets the markers, such as targeting the HER2/NEU receptor, described later. Cancers that are hormone-sensitive will be treated with hormone therapy to suppress cancer recurrence for the next 5-10 years. The choice of hormone treatment

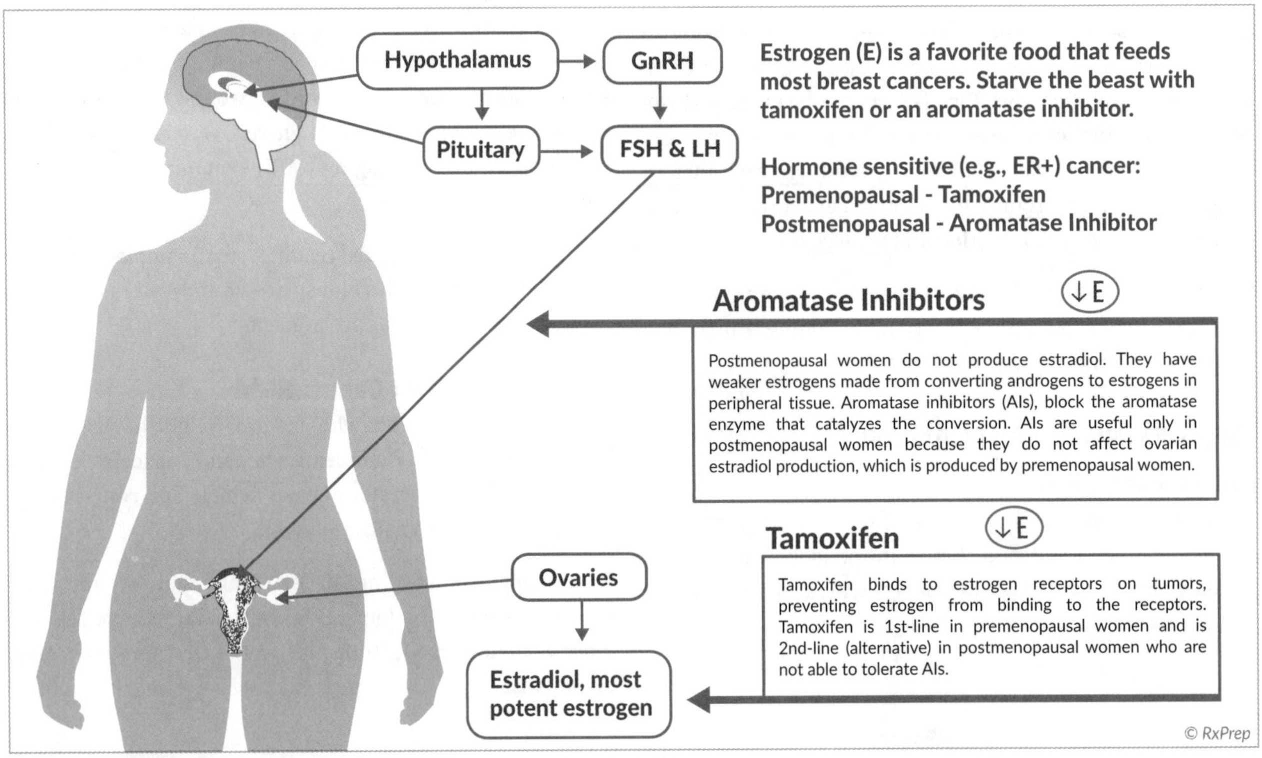

depends on the menopausal status of the patient (see diagram on the previous page).

Hormone-Sensitive Cancer Treatment

All breast tumors express some estrogen and progesterone receptors. If a tumor expresses a high percentage of either receptor type, the tumor is referred to as hormone-sensitive, and classified as estrogen receptor positive (ER+), progesterone receptor positive (PR+) or both (ER+/PR+).

Selective Estrogen Receptor Modulators (SERMs) and Aromatase Inhibitors (AIs)

The first-line treatment for premenopausal women with hormone-sensitive cancer is tamoxifen, a selective estrogen receptor modulator (SERM). Tamoxifen is an estrogen antagonist in breast cells.

Premenopausal women produce estradiol, the most potent estrogen in the ovaries; postmenopausal women do not. Postmenopausal women get most of their estrogen from the conversion of androgens into estrogen. The aromatase inhibitors reduce estrogen production by blocking the aromatase enzyme that catalyzes the conversion of androgens. AIs do not block ovarian estradiol production, which is why they are not useful treatments for premenopausal women.

Note: Raloxifene is a SERM used for breast cancer prophylaxis, not for treatment. Raloxifene increases bone density, and is indicated for osteoporosis prevention and treatment. It is used for osteoporosis in postmenopausal women who wish to use a breast cancer prophylactic drug. Raloxifene is not first-line for osteoporosis because it causes hot flashes, and has clotting risk. The other SERMs in the following table (fulvestrant and toremifene) are used in unique circumstances when tamoxifen is not a reasonable option.

In some circumstances, a premenopausal woman will be put into menopause by taking a gonadotropin-releasing hormone (GnRH) agonist (goserelin or leuprolide). GnRH agonist treatment decreases LH and FSH, which suppresses ovarian estradiol production. This makes AI treatment a reasonable option.

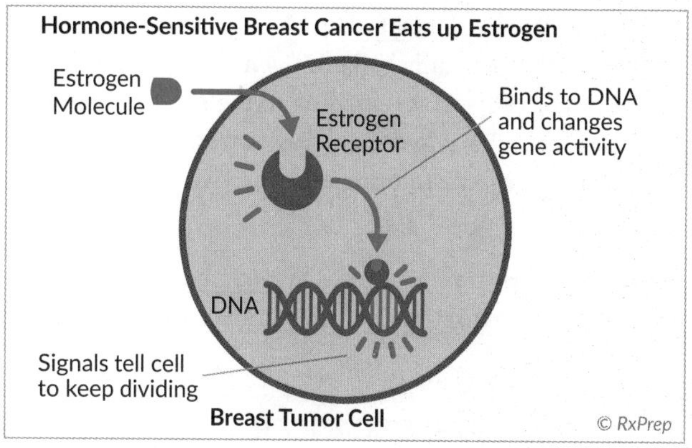

HER2 Overexpression

An oncogene is a protein that can turn a normal cell into a cancer cell; the HER2/NEU (typically referred to as HER2) oncogene promotes breast tumor growth. Approximately 20% of breast tumors over-express HER2 on the cell surface, which makes the tumor grow quickly (i.e., an aggressive malignancy; see following figure). Fortunately, there are drugs that are very effective in treating tumors that over-express HER2. The HER2 proteins on the cell surface must be coupled (dimerized) to send signals that accelerate cell division (i.e., tumor growth.) Trastuzumab *(Herceptin)* and other drugs in this class bind to the HER2 receptor, preventing dimerization. The HER2 inhibitors are used for multiple cancers that over-express HER2, and are described later in this chapter.

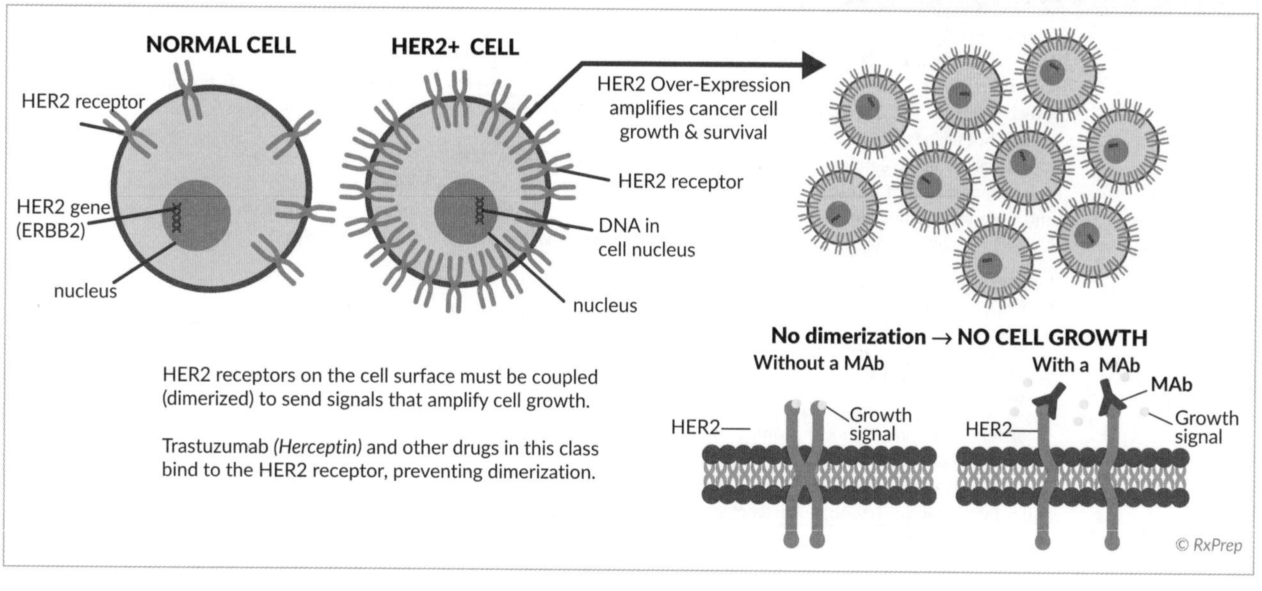

MONOCLONAL ANTIBODIES ARE ALL OVER THE RxPREP COURSE BOOK. HERE'S WHY.

Antibodies bind with high specificity to an antigen. Monoclonal means single clone; monoclonal antibody (MAb) drugs consist of many identical cloned antibodies.

MAbs are designed to attach with high specificity to an antigen. With trastuzumab, the antigen is the HER2 receptor on the tumor cell surface. Binding to the receptor prevents further signaling inside the cell. For cancer, some MAbs are used as carriers; e.g., to bring a radioactive compound into cancer cells (discussed later).

MAbs can trigger a severe reaction; some require premedication (e.g., steroid, antihistamine, acetaminophen).

METASTATIC BREAST CANCER

Breast cancer metastases are often located in the bone, lungs, liver and brain. Hormone treatment or a HER2 inhibitor will still be used, if ER/PR or HER2 is positive, respectively. Chemotherapy is given to shrink tumors and reduce further growth. Radiation is useful only for local palliation. Both chemotherapy and radiation have considerable side effects, which must be managed to reduce the impact on the patient's quality of life (QOL). Primary chemotherapy drugs used for breast cancer include capecitabine, carboplatin, cyclophosphamide, docetaxel, paclitaxel, doxorubicin and methotrexate. These are many of the big guns in chemotherapy that are described in this chapter.

Examples of MAbs in Other Chapters

The MAb rituximab (which is used for several cancers) binds to CD20 antigens on the surface of B-cells, which reduces the inflammatory response in rheumatoid arthritis. Omalizumab, in the Asthma chapter, inhibits IgE from binding to mast cells and basophils, blocking inflammation.

CDK4/6 Inhibitors and other Targeted Therapy

The CDK4/6 inhibitors in the following table are sometimes used in combination with hormone treatment in metastatic breast cancer. Another targeted treatment used with hormone-sensitive breast cancer is the mTOR inhibitor everolimus, described later in this chapter.

Number of MAb Drugs

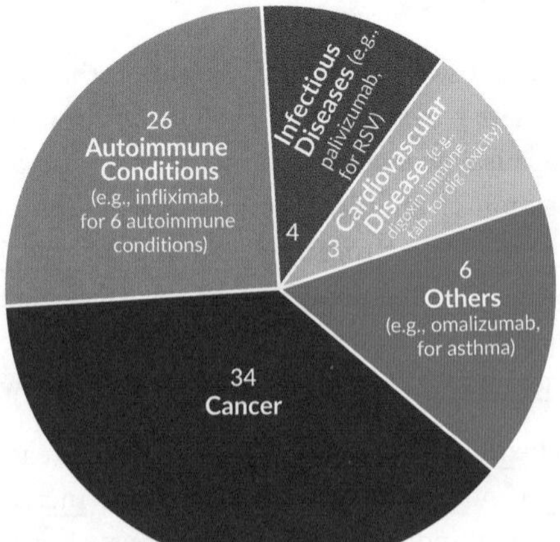

© RxPrep

Breast Cancer Hormonal Treatment and CDK4/6 Inhibitors

DRUG	UNIQUE CONCERNS	SAFETY/SIDE EFFECTS/MONITORING
Selective Estrogen Receptor Modulators (SERMs) – estrogen antagonist in breast tissue, raloxifene is also an estrogen agonist in bone		
Tamoxifen *(Soltamox)* Oral	Tamoxifen is a prodrug and is converted via CYP2D6 to the potent metabolite endoxifen. Do not use tamoxifen with CYP2D6 inhibitors, which will block the conversion. Tamoxifen causes hot flashes/night sweats, and estrogen (the usual primary treatment for hot flashes/night sweats) cannot be used. Fluoxetine and paroxetine, which are used off-label, are CYP2D6 inhibitors and cannot be used. Instead, venlafaxine is preferred for hot flashes/night sweat relief. Toremifene is an alternative option with a slow CYP2D6 metabolizer or if a drug interaction is present. Raloxifene is for breast cancer prophylaxis (not treatment); raloxifene increases bone density, and is indicated for osteoporosis prevention and treatment in postmenopausal women who require breast cancer prophylaxis.	**BOXED WARNINGS** ↑ risk of uterine or endometrial cancer (tamoxifen), ↑ risk of thromboembolic events (tamoxifen, raloxifene), QT prolongation (toremifene) **CONTRAINDICATIONS** Do not use with warfarin (tamoxifen), history of DVT/PE (tamoxifen, raloxifene), pregnancy and breastfeeding (raloxifene), QT prolongation, hypokalemia, hypomagnesemia (toremifene) **SIDE EFFECTS** Hot flashes/night sweats, vaginal bleeding/spotting, vaginal discharge/dryness/pruritus, ↓ libido, edema, weight gain, hypertension, mood changes, amenorrhea, arthralgia/myalgia, cataracts (tamoxifen) ↓ bone density; supplement with calcium/vitamin D (tamoxifen) Tamoxifen is teratogenic; contraception should be used in premenopausal women. Raloxifene is also unsafe in pregnancy, but is only used in postmenopausal women.
Fulvestrant *(Faslodex)* IM Injection		
Raloxifene *(Evista)* Oral		
Toremifene *(Fareston)* Oral		

DRUG	UNIQUE CONCERNS	SAFETY/SIDE EFFECTS/MONITORING
Aromatase Inhibitors – blocks conversion of androgens to estrogens		
Anastrozole *(Arimidex)* Oral Letrozole *(Femara)* Oral Exemestane *(Aromasin)* Oral	Higher risk of osteoporosis due to decreased bone mineral density; consider Ca and vitamin D supplementation, weight bearing exercise, DEXA screening Higher risk of CVD compared to SERMs	**CONTRAINDICATIONS** Pregnancy **SIDE EFFECTS** Hot flashes/night sweats, arthralgia/myalgia, lethargy/fatigue, N/V, rash, hepatotoxicity, hypertension, dyslipidemia
Cyclin-Dependent Kinase (CDK4/6) Inhibitors – inhibits downstream signaling and tumor growth		
Palbociclib *(Ibrance)* Abemaciclib *(Verzenio)* Ribociclib *(Kisqali)*	Avoid with CYP3A4 inhibitors or inducers (palbociclib) Avoid or reduce dose with CYP3A4 inhibitors or inducers (abemaciclib)	**SIDE EFFECTS** Neutropenia, anemia, nausea, diarrhea, fatigue, alopecia, blurred vision Risk of thromboembolic events

PATIENT COUNSELING

ALL

- Do not take any estrogen-containing medications. Estrogen is contraindicated with any history of breast cancer.
- Take adequate calcium and vitamin D (unless patient has a high calcium level from metastases). Regular walking can help your bones stay strong.

Tamoxifen

- If you forget a dose, take it when you remember, then take the next dose as usual. If it is almost time for your next dose or you remember at your next dose, do not take extra tablets to make up the missed dose.
- Do not become pregnant. If you become pregnant, stop taking this medication right away and call your healthcare provider.
- Common side effects include hot flashes and night sweats, vaginal bleeding and discharge, and a lower sex drive.
- Read the MedGuide that has been given to you. This medication can cause some serious, but rare, adverse effects, including endometrial cancer, stroke or a blood clot.
- This medication can increase the risk of getting cataracts. Your vision should be monitored.

Raloxifene

- This medication increases the chance of having blood clots; discontinue prior to a prolonged immobilization (e.g., post-surgical recovery, bed rest), and avoid long restrictions of movement during travel (e.g., an overseas plane flight).

Aromatase Inhibitors

- If you miss a dose, take it as soon as you remember. If it is almost time for your next dose, skip the missed dose.
- Common side effects include hot flashes, night sweats and joint and muscle aches.

PROSTATE CANCER

Prostate cancer is the most common cancer in men in the U.S. (lung cancer is the most common in the world). Fortunately, most prostate cancers are identified before the cancer has metastasized.

Early, non-metastatic prostate cancer can be treated with surgery, radiation, hormonal treatment or watchful waiting. Unlike breast cancer, in which treatment is almost always used, prostate cancer might not be treated, especially in an elderly man with a slow-growing tumor. In such a case, the man might die of something else before the prostate cancer could cause considerable harm.

IDENTIFYING PROSTATE CANCER

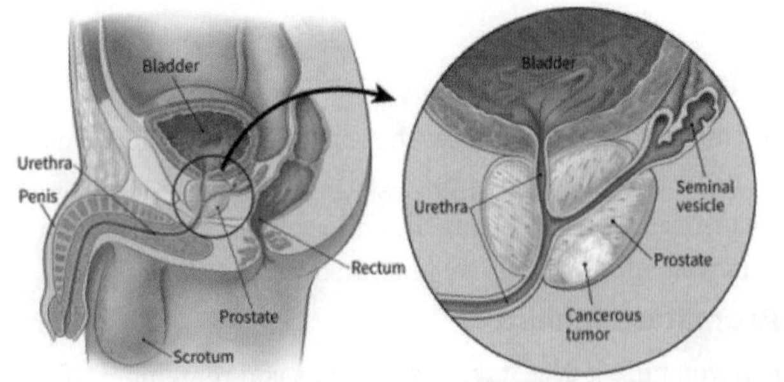

© https://www.cancer.org/cancer/prostate-cancer/early-detection/tests.html

Digital Rectal Exam

Most prostate cancers develop near the side of the prostate that can be felt with a digital rectal exam (DRE), an often uncomfortable exam for a man in which a physician inserts a gloved, lubricated finger into the rectum to palpate the prostate. If abnormal lumps or masses are felt, tissue from the prostate will be excised and sent to pathology to assess if cancerous cells are present.

Prostate Specific Antigen

Prostate-specific antigen (PSA) is produced in the prostate gland by normal and cancerous cells, and increases with most prostate cancers. PSA is measured with a blood test. A level above 4 ng/mL can indicate prostate cancer. In 15% of prostate cancers, the PSA level is within the normal range (< 4 ng/mL)

HORMONAL THERAPIES FOR PROSTATE CANCER

Similar to breast cancer, in which the primary hormone (estrogen) is blocked to prevent cancer growth, with prostate cancer, the primary hormone which is blocked is testosterone. The hormonal treatments are called androgen deprivation therapy (ADT). Androgens refers to the male sex hormones, of which testosterone is the major type. ADT is also called chemical castration.

ADT has considerable adverse effects, including impotence, weakness, hot flashes and loss of bone density. ADT is achieved with either a gonadotropin releasing hormone (GnRH) agonist (alone) or a GnRH antagonist (initially taken with an antiandrogen). Metastatic prostate cancer that has failed to respond to ADT is called "castration-resistant" and may be treated with chemotherapy.

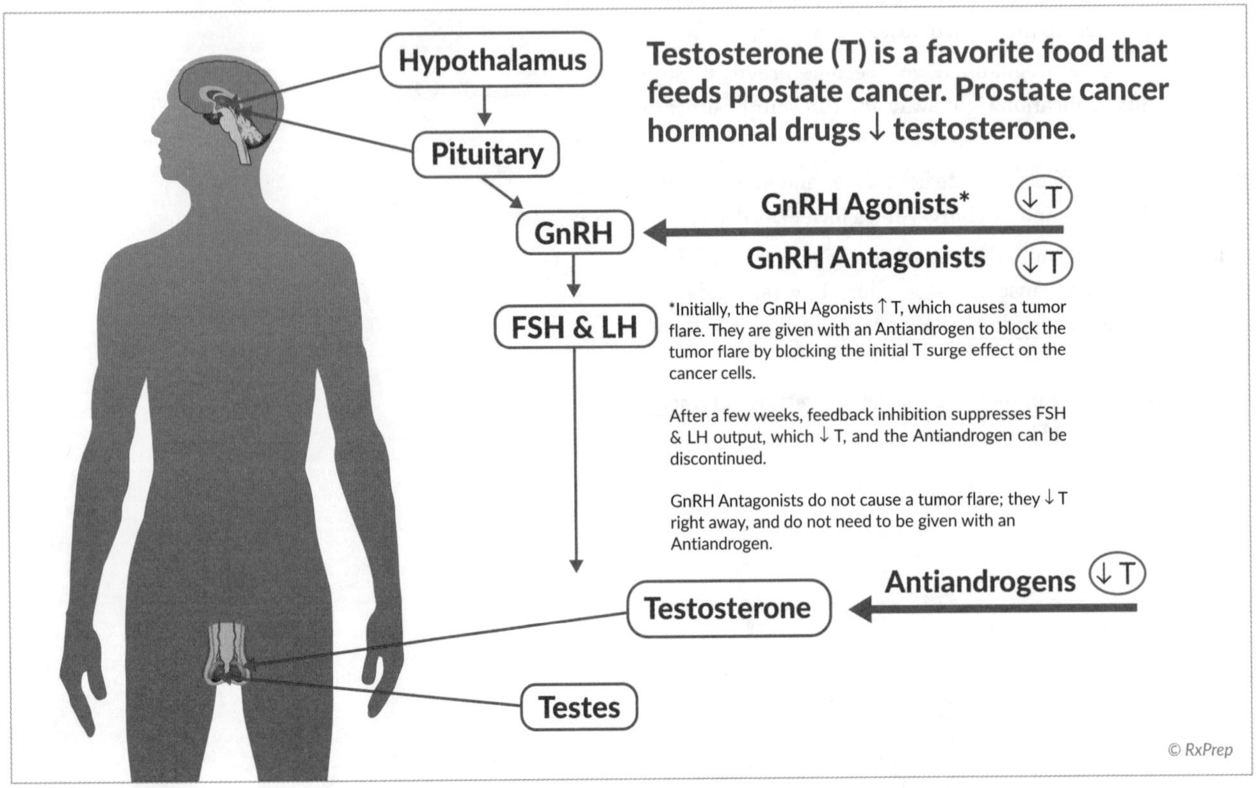

Hormonal Therapies for Prostate Cancer

DRUG	UNIQUE CONCERNS	SAFETY/SIDE EFFECTS/MONITORING
Gonadotropin-Releasing Hormone (GnRH) Agonists – also referred to as luteinizing hormone releasing hormone (LHRH) agonists, reduce testosterone through a negative feedback mechanism. They cause an initial surge in testosterone, followed by a gradual reduction. The initial surge can cause symptoms of "tumor flare," including bone pain and difficulty urinating. To prevent tumor flare, an antiandrogen is given for several weeks in conjunction with the start of a GnRH agonist.		
Leuprolide *(Lupron Depot,* *Eligard)* **Goserelin *(Zoladex)* Histrelin *(Supprelin LA, Vantas)* Triptorelin *(Trelstar)* SC or IM Injections	↓ bone density; supplement with calcium/vitamin D, use weight bearing exercise, DEXA screening may be given to identify if treatment (e.g., with a bisphosphonate) would be useful Leuprolide and goserelin can be used to treat breast cancer in women (by ovarian ablation) Tumor flare; give with concurrent antiandrogen (e.g., bicalutamide) for several weeks	**CONTRAINDICATIONS** Pregnancy Breastfeeding **SIDE EFFECTS** Hot flashes, impotence, gynecomastia, bone pain, injection site pain, osteoporosis, shrunken testicles, anxiety, peripheral edema First few weeks of treatment: bone pain, difficulty urinating QT prolongation, dyslipidemia, hyperglycemia Loss of muscle mass
Gonadotropin Releasing Hormone Antagonist – no initial surge in testosterone concentrations; an antiandrogen is not needed.		
Degarelix *(Firmagon)* SC Injection	Osteoporosis Risk: consider calcium, vitamin D supplementation, weight bearing exercise, DEXA screening No tumor flare; antiandrogen not needed	**CONTRAINDICATIONS** Pregnancy **SIDE EFFECTS** Similar to GnRH agonists, plus hypersensitivity reactions
Antiandrogens, First-Generation – competitively inhibits testosterone from binding to prostate cancer cells. They are only used in combination with a GnRH agonist.		
Bicalutamide *(Casodex)* Oral		**BOXED WARNINGS** Hepatotoxicity (flutamide), interstitial pneumonitis (nilutamide) **CONTRAINDICATIONS** Use in women, especially in pregnancy (bicalutamide); severe hepatic impairment (flutamide, nilutamide) **SIDE EFFECTS** Hot flashes, gynecomastia, edema, asthenia, hepatotoxicity, ↑ risk of CVD, N/V/D
Flutamide Oral	Causes more diarrhea than others in class	
Nilutamide *(Nilandron)* Oral	Can cause night blindness Disulfiram reactions (avoid alcohol)	
Antiandrogen, Second-Generation – unlike first generation antiandrogens, does not cause an upregulation in the expression of androgen receptors, and can be used as a single treatment.		
Enzalutamide *(Xtandi)* Oral		**CONTRAINDICATIONS** Pregnancy (partner to use effective contraception) **WARNINGS** Seizures **SIDE EFFECTS** Hypertension, peripheral edema, hot flashes, fatigue
Androgen Biosynthesis Inhibitor - interferes with a specific CYP-17 enzyme involved in the synthesis of steroid hormones in the testes and adrenal gland to decrease testosterone production. Must be taken with prednisone to cause negative feedback on the production of aldosterone and prevent symptoms of hyperaldosteronism (hypertension, fluid retention and hypokalemia).		
Abiraterone *(Zytiga)* Oral	Avoid concurrent use with strong CYP3A4 inducers; if used with a strong CYP3A4 inducer, dose adjustment required	**CONTRAINDICATIONS** Pregnancy **SIDE EFFECTS** Mineralocorticoid excess: fluid retention, ↑ BP, hypokalemia (reduce excess with concurrent prednisone) Hepatotoxicity, hyperglycemia, ↑ TGs, hypophosphatemia, hot flashes

PATIENT COUNSELING

Leuprolide for Prostate Cancer

- This medication is taken initially with another drug called an antiandrogen.
- Common side effects include hot flashes, weakness and impotence.
- During the first few weeks of treatment you may experience bone pain and difficulty urinating.

CHEMOTHERAPY

Chemotherapy regimens for all types of cancer are usually given in combinations to take advantage of synergistic relationships, and to target cells with different resistance mechanisms and at different stages of replication.

Treatment can have a curative intent, or be palliative and given to shrink the tumor size (e.g., to reduce pain caused by the tumor pressing on an organ). Chemotherapy can be given to shrink a tumor prior to surgery (to make it easier to remove) or prior to radiation (to have a smaller tumor to target).

Combination Regimens Given in Cycles

Chemotherapy regimens are usually administered in combination regimens given in 2 - 6 week cycles, followed by days or weeks without treatment. The break in treatment allows the patient time to recover from the adverse effects, including myelosuppression, which is described in the Oncology I chapter.

Example of Breast Cancer Regimen

AC is a combination of two drugs:

- **C**yclophosphamide (alkylating agent, cell-cycle independent)
- Doxorubicin (***A**driamycin*, anthracycline, multiple mechanisms, cell-cycle independent)

AC is given with cyclophosphamide and doxorubicin on day one of a 2-week cycle. The cycle is repeated 4 - 6 times every two weeks for 2 - 3 months. This regimen is highly emetogenic, requiring an aggressive antiemetic regimen, and requires filgrastim due to myelosuppression.

CANCER TREATMENTS

Traditional Chemotherapy

Traditional cancer drugs kill cancer cells (i.e., are cytotoxic) by interfering with cell division (replication). Cell cycle specific agents kill cancer cells during a specific phase/s of the cell cycle. Cell cycle non-specific agents kill cancer cells in any phase of the cell cycle (see the following figure).

Regardless of cell cycle specificity, traditional cytotoxic cancer drugs are more effective at killing cells undergoing cell division. Cancers that are characterized by more rapid cell growth, such as acute leukemias, are very susceptible

Chemotherapy and the Cell Cycle Phases

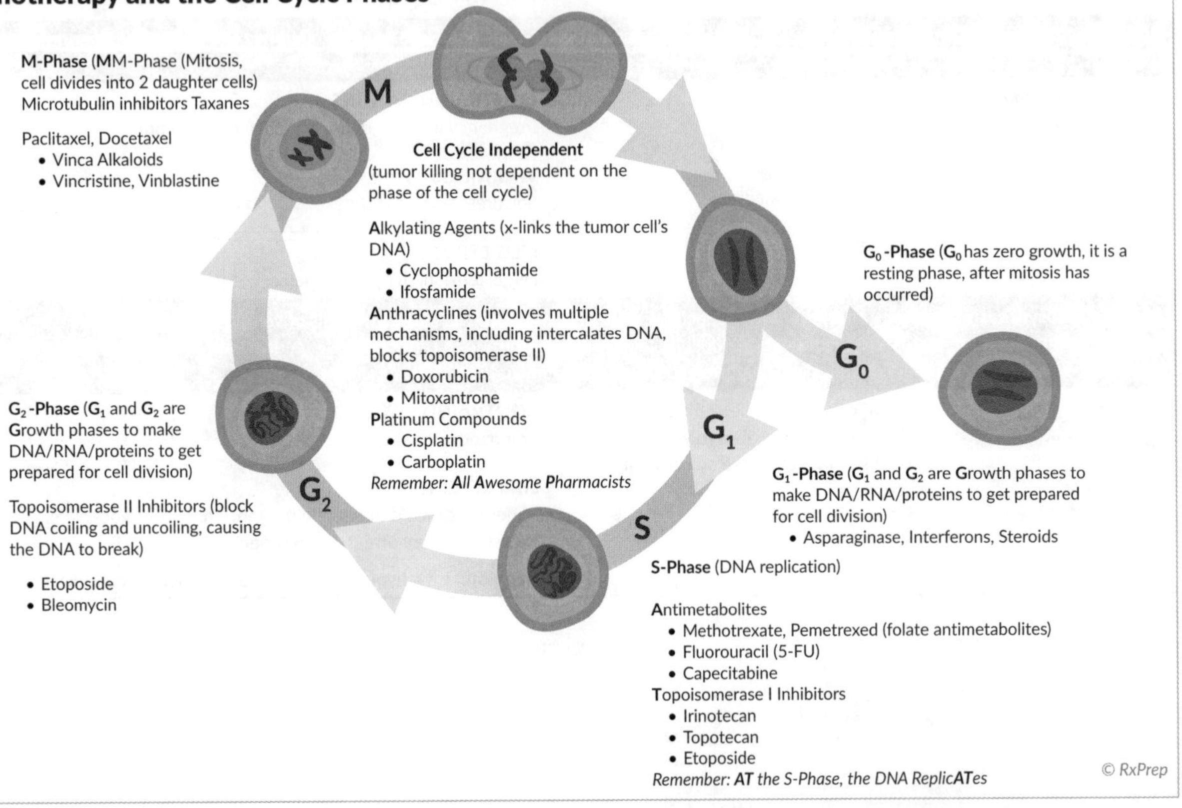

to the cytotoxic effects of traditional cytotoxic drugs. Cells in the body that are also rapidly dividing, including cells in the gastrointestinal tract and bone marrow, will be susceptible to being killed by cytotoxic drugs. This is why many cytotoxic drugs cause diarrhea, mucositis, nausea and myelosuppression (decreases in platelets, white blood cells and red blood cells, which are continuously produced in the bone marrow).

Targeted Treatment

Targeted treatment recognizes biomarkers present on cancer cells or on other cells that are essential for tumor growth. Targeted drugs include monoclonal antibodies (MAbs) and tyrosine kinase inhibitors (TKIs). See the preceding breast cancer section for a description of MAbs.

BODY SURFACE AREA (BSA) CALCULATIONS

Chemotherapy can be dosed using flat or fixed dosing, the patient's weight (mg/kg) or the body surface area (BSA). There are several BSA formulas. The ones most commonly used are Mosteller and DuBois and DuBois. Actual (or total) body weight is commonly used for calculating the dose in oncology. Use the patient's actual body weight for BSA, unless instructed otherwise.

Dubois and Dubois Equation

$$BSA\ (m^2) = 0.007184 \times [\text{Height (cm)}]^{0.725} \times [\text{Weight (kg)}]^{0.425}$$

Example

A patient has a weight of 175 pounds and height of 6'1". Calculate the patient's BSA using the DuBois and DuBois formula. Round to the nearest hundredth.

Convert weight in pounds to kilograms by dividing by 2.2: 175 lbs/2.2 = 79.5 kg

Convert height in inches to centimeters by multiplying by 2.54: 73 inches x 2.54 = 185.4 cm

$$BSA\ (m^2) = 0.007184 \times (185.4)^{0.725} \times (79.5)^{0.425}$$

$$BSA\ (m^2) = 2.03\ m^2$$

AVERAGE BODY SURFACE AREA (BSA) FOR MEN AND WOMEN

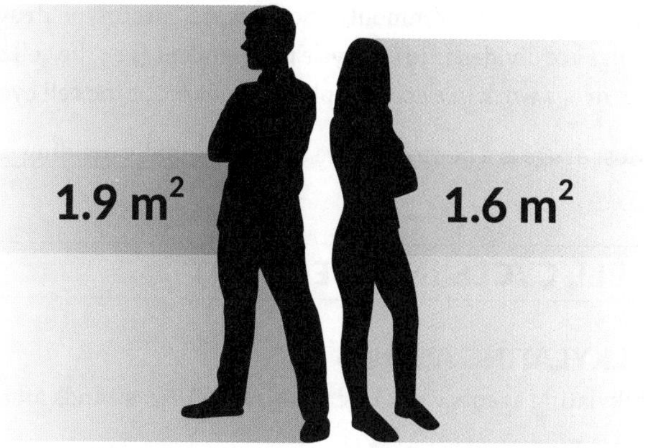

Mosteller Equation

$$BSA\ (m^2) = \sqrt{\frac{\text{Ht (cm)} \times \text{Wt (kg)}}{3{,}600}}$$

Examples

A patient has a weight of 175 pounds and height of 6'1". Calculate the patient's BSA using the Mosteller formula. Round to the nearest hundredth.

Convert weight in pounds to kilograms by dividing by 2.2: 175 lbs/2.2 = 79.5 kg

Convert height in inches to centimeters by multiplying by 2.54: 73" x 2.54 = 185.4 cm

$$BSA\ (m^2) = \sqrt{\frac{185.4\text{ cm} \times 79.5\text{ kg}}{3{,}600}} = 2.02\ m^2$$

A patient with a BSA of 2.02 m² is going to receive paclitaxel for lung cancer at a dose of 175 mg/m². Calculate the dose of paclitaxel that this patient will receive. Round to the nearest whole number.

$$175\ mg/m^2 \times 2.02\ m^2 = 354\ mg$$

A patient with a BSA of 2.02 m² is going to receive paclitaxel for lung cancer at a dose of 175 mg/m². Paclitaxel is available as a 6 mg/mL solution. If the patient's dose is 354 mg, how many milliliters will be needed for the dose?

$$354\ mg \times \frac{1\ mL}{6\ mg} = 59\ mL$$

TRADITIONAL CYTOTOXIC CHEMOTHERAPY DRUGS

Included are the commonly encountered "prototype drugs" in each class, with safety and administration information. The drugs are divided into cell cycle independent (i.e., the cell cycle does not affect the drug's killing) and cell cycle dependent (i.e., the drugs work in a specific phase or phases of the cell cycle).

Most drugs are more effective at killing rapidly dividing cancer cells since they work by interfering with the DNA replication cycle.

CELL CYCLE INDEPENDENT

ALKYLATING AGENTS

Alkylating agents work by cross-linking DNA strands and inhibiting protein synthesis and DNA synthesis.

- Can cause DNA mutations that lead to "secondary malignancies" (e.g., leukemias and lymphomas).
- Cyclophosphamide and ifosfamide produce a metabolite, acrolein, that concentrates in the bladder and can cause hemorrhagic cystitis. The chemoprotectant mesna inactivates this toxic metabolite in the bladder without interfering with the cytotoxic efficacy. Ifosfamide is always dispensed with mesna. High doses of cyclophosphamide may require mesna.

DRUG	UNIQUE CONCERNS	SAFETY/SIDE EFFECTS/MONITORING
Cyclophosphamide *(Cytoxan)* **Ifosfamide** *(Ifex)*	Hemorrhagic cystitis: ensure adequate hydration and give mesna Mesna *(Mesnex)* is a chemoprotectant that must be given prophylactically with ifosfamide and with high doses of cyclophosphamide	**BOXED WARNINGS** Myelosuppression Hemorrhagic cystitis (ifosfamide, cyclophosphamide) Pulmonary toxicity (carmustine) Neurotoxicity (ifosfamide) Hepatic necrosis (dacarbazine) **WARNINGS** Severe skin reactions, including SJS/TEN; reactivation of infections, including HBV, CMV, TB, HSV; hepatotoxicity (bendamustine) **SIDE EFFECTS** Pulmonary toxicity (busulfan, carmustine, lomustine) SIADH (cyclophosphamide) Mucositis, moderate-high emetic potential, alopecia, secondary malignancies, neurotoxicity
Carmustine *(BiCNU, Gliadel Wafer)*	Use non-PVC bag and tubing	
Dacarbazine	Protect from light (decomposed drug turns pink)	
Procarbazine *(Matulane)*	MAO inhibitor, avoid interacting drugs/foods	
Altretamine *(Hexalen)* Bendamustine *(Bendeka, Treanda)* **Busulfan** *(Myleran, Busulfex)* Lomustine *(Gleostine)* Mechlorethamine *(Mustargen, Valchlor* topical gel) Melphalan *(Alkeran, Evomela)* Temozolomide *(Temodar)*	Lomustine: fatal toxicity occurs with overdosage. Do not dispense more than one dose at a time. Both healthcare provider and pharmacist should emphasize to the patient that only one dose of lomustine is taken every 6 weeks.	
Mitomycin Free radical formation and alkylator	Vesicant, do not extravasate. Antidote is dimethyl sulfoxide (DMSO) and cool compresses Mitomycin IV solutions are a hazy blue in color and can make the urine blue-green	**BOXED WARNINGS** Bone marrow suppression, hemolytic-uremic syndrome **CONTRAINDICATIONS** Thrombocytopenia, coagulopathy, bleeding **SIDE EFFECTS** Leukopenia, thrombocytopenia, N/V, fatigue, alopecia, mucous membrane toxicity, cystitis or dysuria (from intravesical administration into bladder)

PLATINUM-BASED COMPOUNDS

Similar to alkylating agents in that they cross-link DNA and interfere with DNA synthesis and cell replication.

- Due to the platinum content, they can cause a few toxicities that are similar to symptoms of heavy metal poisoning, such as peripheral sensory neuropathy, ototoxicity and nephrotoxicity.
- Cisplatin is associated with the highest incidence of nephrotoxicity and chemotherapy-induced nausea and vomiting (CINV).
- All platinum-based compounds are renally eliminated and require dose adjustments for renal impairment.

DRUG	UNIQUE CONCERNS	SAFETY/SIDE EFFECTS/MONITORING
Cisplatin	Nephrotoxicity, ototoxicity (both cumulative) Doses are usually limited to ≤ 100 mg/m²/cycle Nephrotoxicity: monitor renal function, intake/output, Mg and K (levels may decrease) and ensure adequate IV hydration (1-2 L) before each dose Amifostine *(Ethyol)* is a chemoprotectant that can be given prophylactically to prevent nephrotoxicity Ototoxicity: perform audiograms at baseline and before each dose Highly emetogenic: see Oncology I chapter for emesis prevention	**BOXED WARNINGS** Anaphylactic-like reactions – risk increases with repeated exposure; caution when > 6 cycles of carboplatin are used Renal toxicity, ototoxicity, doses > 100 mg/m²/cycle must be confirmed with prescriber (cisplatin) Myelosuppression (carboplatin and cisplatin) **CONTRAINDICATIONS** Pre-existing renal impairment, hearing impairment (cisplatin) Myelosuppression (cisplatin and carboplatin) **SIDE EFFECTS** Peripheral neuropathy (cumulative, dose-related), myelosuppression, ↑ LFTs N/V (cisplatin, carboplatin)
Carboplatin	Myelosuppression is dose-related Doses for adults are commonly calculated by target AUC using the Calvert Formula: Total carboplatin dose (mg) = (Target AUC) x (GFR + 25) where: - AUC can range from 2-8 mg/mL x min - GFR is commonly "capped" at 125 mL/min	
Oxaliplatin	Acute sensory neuropathy: occurs 1-7 days after administration and can be exacerbated by exposure to cold, including drinking cold beverages	

ANTHRACYCLINES

Work by several mechanisms, including intercalation into DNA, inhibiting topoisomerase II, and creating oxygen-free radicals that damage cells.

- Cardiotoxicity is associated with all anthracyclines and is manifested as cardiomyopathy and heart failure. The risk for cardiotoxicity is related to the total cumulative anthracycline dose the patient has received over their lifetime. The recommended lifetime maximum cumulative anthracycline dose differs for each anthracycline, but is best defined for doxorubicin. Dexrazoxane *(Zinecard)* is a chemoprotectant indicated for prevention of doxorubicin-induced cardiotoxicity.
- Anthracyclines are strong vesicants, except for the liposomal formulations. Dexrazoxane *(Totect)* is an antidote that can be used for accidental doxorubicin extravasation. Note that dexrazoxane has two brand names, each used for a different indication.
- Protect from light during administration.

TO REDUCE DOXORUBICIN CARDIOTOXICITY:

1. Keep track of the lifetime cumulative doxorubicin dose for each patient

[Doxorubicin dose in mg/m^2/cycle] x [total number of cycles received] = Cumulative doxorubicin dose in mg/m^2

Example: [Doxorubicin 50 mg/m^2/cycle] x [6 cycles] = 300 mg/m^2

2. Lifetime maximum cumulative doxorubicin dose = 450-550 mg/m^2
3. Monitor left ventricular ejection fraction (LVEF) before and after treatment (using echocardiogram or MUGA scan)
4. Dexrazoxane *(Zinecard)*, a chemoprotectant, may be considered when the doxorubicin cumulative dose > 300 mg/m^2

DRUG	UNIQUE CONCERNS	SAFETY/SIDE EFFECTS/MONITORING
Doxorubicin *(Adriamycin)* Daunorubicin Epirubicin *(Ellence)* Idarubicin *(Idamycin PFS)* Valrubicin *(Valstar)*- only used as bladder instillation, but can have systemic toxicity N/V - give antiemetics	Potent vesicants (tissue necrosis if extravasated) Drug is red, and causes red urine discoloration Doxorubicin: do not exceed 450-550 mg/m2 (total lifetime cumulative dose) Dexrazoxane *(Totect)* for extravasation; *(Zinecard)* for cardioprotection at higher doses	**BOXED WARNINGS** Myocardial (cardiovascular) toxicity, vesicant, myelosuppression, secondary malignancy Hepatotoxicity (daunorubicin), reduce dose if impairment, (except valrubicin) Renal impairment (daunorubicin, idarubicin) **CONTRAINDICATIONS** Pre-existing myocardial insufficiency, severe hepatic impairment 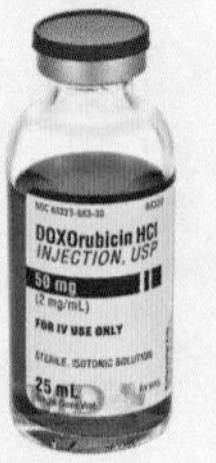
Daunorubicin and cytarabine liposomal *(Vyxeos)* Doxorubicin liposomal *(Doxil, Lipodox50)*	Liposomal formulations are not interchangeable with non-liposomal formulations	**BOXED WARNINGS** Myocardial (cardiovascular) toxicity, infusion-related reactions, myelosuppression **SIDE EFFECTS** Hand-foot syndrome
Mitoxantrone an anthracenedione, related to the anthracyclines	Irritant with vesicant-like properties Drug is blue, and causes blue urine discoloration	**BOXED WARNINGS** Myocardial (cardiovascular) toxicity, myelosuppression, secondary malignancy 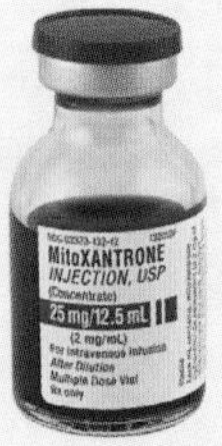

CELL CYCLE SPECIFIC AGENTS

VINCA ALKALOIDS

FOR INTRAVENOUS USE ONLY. FATAL IF GIVEN BY OTHER ROUTES.

Vinca alkaloids inhibit the function of microtubules during M phase.

- Peripheral sensory and autonomic neuropathies (constipation) are common. Neuropathies are common side effects because microtubules play an important role in transport in neurons.
  - VinCristine is associated with more CNS toxicity (neuropathy) than the other vinca alkaloids. Accidental intrathecal administration will cause a progressive paralysis and death. Label products to prevent accidental intrathecal administration (see Learning IV Medications chapter).
- VinBlastine and vinorelBine are associated with more Bone marrow suppression (myelosuppression) than vincristine.
- Vinca alkaloids are potent vesicants. Use warm compresses and hyaluronidase (off-label use) if extravasation occurs.
- Vincristine is a major substrate of CYP3A4; when given with azole antifungals there is a high risk of severe toxicities (peripheral neuropathy, seizures, paralytic ileus).

DRUG	UNIQUE CONCERNS	SAFETY/SIDE EFFECTS/MONITORING
Vincristine *(Vincasar PFS)*	Not myelosuppressive Often "capped" at 2 mg/dose, regardless of the calculated mg/m^2 dose; higher doses may be associated with ↑ risk of neuropathy	**BOXED WARNINGS** Vesicants For IV administration only (intrathecal administration is fatal) **SIDE EFFECTS** Peripheral sensory neuropathy (paresthesias), autonomic neuropathy (gastroparesis, constipation), SIADH **NOTES** To prevent inadvertent administration intrathecally, it is recommended to prepare vincristine in a small IV bag (a piggyback) rather than in a syringe
Vinblastine Vinorelbine *(Navelbine)*	Myelosuppressive	
Vincristine liposomal *(Marqibo)*	Not interchangeable with vincristine	

TAXANES

Taxanes inhibit the function of microtubules during the M phase.

- Peripheral sensory neuropathies are common side effects since the microtubules play an important role in axonal transport in neurons.
- Severe infusion-related hypersensitivity reactions (HSR) and fatal anaphylaxis can occur with all taxanes. Premedication regimens vary depending on the specific taxane.
- All taxanes are metabolized by the liver and require adjustment for hepatic impairment.
- Drug interaction: elimination of taxanes is reduced when given after cisplatin/carboplatin. Give taxanes before platinum-based compounds.

DRUG	UNIQUE CONCERNS	SAFETY/SIDE EFFECTS/MONITORING
Paclitaxel *(Taxol)*	HSR: premedicate with diphenhydramine, steroid, H2RA	**BOXED WARNINGS** Severe hypersensitivity reactions (except *Abraxane)*, myelosuppression Fluid retention (docetaxel) **SIDE EFFECTS** Peripheral sensory neuropathy, myalgias, arthralgias, hepatotoxicity, alopecia (less with cabazitaxel) **NOTES** Hypersensitivity reactions are due to the solvent systems, not the taxane. To maintain solubility, paclitaxel contains polyoxyl35/polyoxethylated castor oil (Cremophor EL); docetaxel contains Polysorbate 80. *Abraxane* is paclitaxel bound to albumin without a solvent system. Only isolated case reports of allergic reaction; no need to premedicate. Use non-PVC bag and tubing (except *Abraxane).*
Docetaxel *(Taxotere)*	HSR: premedicate with steroids for 3 days, starting 1 day prior to docetaxel Causes severe fluid retention (characterized by pleural effusion, cardiac tamponade and/or edema); premedicate with dexamethasone Some formulations contain alcohol and may cause symptoms of alcohol intoxication	
Cabazitaxel *(Jevtana)*	HSR: premedicate with diphenhydramine, steroid, H2RA	
Paclitaxel albumin-bound *(Abraxane)*	No premedication required (see Notes)	

TOPOISOMERASE I INHIBITORS

These agents block the coiling and uncoiling of the double-stranded DNA helix during S phase; causes single and double strand breaks in the DNA and prevents religation (sealing the DNA strands back together again) of single strand breaks.

DRUG	UNIQUE CONCERNS	SAFETY/SIDE EFFECTS/MONITORING
Irinotecan *(Camptosar)* *"I run to the can" (acute diarrhea)*	Acute cholinergic symptoms: flushing, sweating, abdominal cramps, diarrhea (treat with atropine) Delayed diarrhea: treat with loperamide (up to 24 mg/day) Pharmacogenomics: patients homozygous for the UGT1A1*28 allele are at ↑ risk for neutropenia and delayed diarrhea	**BOXED WARNINGS** Myelosuppression Use only when ANC > 1,500 cells/mm^3 and platelets > 100,000 cells/mm^3 (topotecan) Diarrhea (early and late) (irinotecan) **SIDE EFFECTS** N/V/D, alopecia, diarrhea, abdominal pain
Topotecan *(Hycamtin)*		

TOPOISOMERASE II INHIBITORS

Block the coiling and uncoiling of double-stranded DNA during the G2 phase; this causes single and double strand breaks in the DNA and prevents religation (sealing the DNA strands back together again) of single strand breaks.

DRUG	UNIQUE CONCERNS	SAFETY/SIDE EFFECTS/MONITORING
Etoposide IV *(Toposar)*	Infusion rate-related hypotension: infuse over at least 30-60 minutes IV preparation: prepare solution to a concentration ≤ 0.4 mg/mL to avoid precipitation (due to poor water solubility) Use non-PVC IV bag and tubing due to leaching of DEHP	**BOXED WARNING** Myelosuppression **SIDE EFFECTS** Hypersensitivity reactions, anaphylaxis, secondary malignancies
Etoposide phosphate *(Etopophos)*	Does not have solution concentration limits like etoposide (primarily used if the concentration needs to be ≥ 0.4 mg/mL) Helpful in patients with fluid restriction	
Etoposide capsules *(VePesid)*	Refrigerate capsules Etoposide IV:PO ratio is 1:2 (50% bioavailability) Doses > 200 mg need to be given in divided doses due to reduced bioavailability	
Bleomycin Blocks topoisomerase II and intercalating agent	Due to risk of anaphylactoid reactions, a test dose should be given May premedicate with acetaminophen to ↓ incidence of fever or chills ↑risk of pulmonary fibrosis when given with G-CSF (filgrastim) Not myelosuppressive Maximum lifetime dose of 400 units due to pulmonary toxicity risk	**BOXED WARNINGS** Pulmonary fibrosis, anaphylaxis **SIDE EFFECTS** Hypersensitivity reaction, pulmonary reactions (including pneumonitis, which may progress to pulmonary fibrosis), mucositis, hyperpigmentation, fever, chills, N/V (mild)

PYRIMIDINE ANALOG ANTIMETABOLITES

These agents inhibit pyrimidine synthesis during S phase; an active metabolite (F-UMP) is incorporated into RNA to replace uracil and inhibits cell growth, while another active metabolite (5-dUMP) inhibits thymidylate synthetase.

DRUG	UNIQUE CONCERNS	SAFETY/SIDE EFFECTS/MONITORING
Fluorouracil, "5-FU" *(Adrucil)* *Efudex, Carac, Tolak* and *Fluoroplex* are topical formulations used for actinic keratosis *Efudex* is also used for basal cell carcinoma	Leucovorin: given with fluorouracil to ↑ the efficacy of fluorouracil; helps fluorouracil bind more tightly to its target enzyme, thymidylate synthetase Pharmacogenomics: Dihydropyrimidine dehydrogenase (DPD) deficiency ↑ risk of severe toxicity	**BOXED WARNINGS** Significant ↑ in INR during and up to 1 month after treatment, monitor INR frequently (capecitabine) **CONTRAINDICATIONS** Severe renal impairment (CrCl < 30 mL/min) (capecitabine) **SIDE EFFECTS** Hand-foot syndrome, diarrhea, mucositis, cardiotoxicity, photosensitivity, dermatitis **NOTES** Uridine triacetate *(Vistogard)* can be given as an antidote for overdose or severe or early toxicity due to DPD deficiency
Capecitabine *(Xeloda)* 2 divided doses 12 hrs apart, given with water within 30 min after a meal	Oral prodrug of fluorouracil Pharmacogenomics: Dihydropyrimidine dehydrogenase (DPD) deficiency ↑ risk of severe toxicity	
Cytarabine conventional (called "ara-C") Cytarabine liposomal *(DepoCyt)* for intrathecal administration	Cytarabine Syndrome: fever, flu-like symptoms, myalgia, bone pain, rash	**BOXED WARNINGS** Myelosuppression, hepatotoxicity and GI toxicities (conventional) Chemical arachnoiditis (N/V, HA, fever) is common and can be fatal if untreated - give dexamethasone (liposomal formulation) **SIDE EFFECTS** Pulmonary toxicity, encephalopathy, hand-foot syndrome, neuropathy, conjunctivitis (higher doses require use of steroid eye drops)
Gemcitabine *(Gemzar)*	Infusion rate affects efficacy and toxicity; infuse per institutional protocol	**SIDE EFFECTS** Myelosuppression, flu-like symptoms, hepatotoxicity, pulmonary toxicity

EXAM SCENARIO

LK is a 34-year-old male with testicular cancer, hypertension and chronic back pain. His current medications include: hydrochlorothiazide 25 mg PO daily, naproxen 500 mg PO BID, *Lorcet* 5/325 mg PO Q4H PRN pain. He received his 4th cycle of chemotherapy with:

Paclitaxel 250 mg/m^2 IV on day 1
Ifosfamide 1000 mg/m^2 IV on days 2-5 (along with mesna)
Cisplatin 25 mg/m^2 IV on days 2-5

He returns to the clinic to receive his 5th cycle of chemotherapy and complains of numbness and tingling pain in his fingertips. His laboratory values are within normal limits with the exception of: BUN = 22 mg/dL, SCr = 2.4 mg/dL.

- **How would you characterize the type of pain LK describes?** It is consistent with sensory peripheral neuropathy.
- **What could be causing his new pain symptoms?** Paclitaxel (a taxane) is associated with sensory peripheral neuropathy, as is cisplatin (although at a lower frequency).
- **The team rules out dehydration based on the BUN/SCr ratio. What is the likely cause of his elevated SCr?** Cisplatin-induced nephrotoxicity should be suspected. No further cisplatin should be given at this time. Naproxen and hydrochlorothiazide should be held, as NSAIDs can decrease renal blood flow and diuretics could cause dehydration and potentiate further kidney damage. An alternative medication can be chosen for BP control.

FOLATE ANTIMETABOLITES

Interfere with the enzymes involved in the folic acid cycle, blocking purine and pyrimidine biosynthesis during S phase.

- Folic acid or folic acid analogs +/- vitamin B12 may be required to reduce toxicity caused by interference with the folic acid cycle (myelosuppression, mucositis, diarrhea). With high doses of methotrexate, leucovorin (or levoleucovorin) "rescue" must be given. Leucovorin is the active form of folic acid that is able to bypass the enzyme block of dihydrofolate reductase caused by methotrexate. Note that folic acid is ineffective for high dose methotrexate "rescue."
- Nephrotoxicity is associated with all the folate antimetabolites, but most frequently with high doses of methotrexate ($\geq$1 gram/m^2).

DRUG	UNIQUE CONCERNS	SAFETY/SIDE EFFECTS/MONITORING
Methotrexate *(Trexall, Otrexup, Rasuvo, Xatmep)* Doses used for cancer are much higher than doses used for RA or psoriasis. RA/psoriasis doses are given weekly, not daily. If given intrathecally, use only the preservative-free formulation of methotrexate Avoid use of MTX - this is an error prone abbreviation	"High-dose" methotrexate ($\geq$ 500 mg/m^2) requires leucovorin (folinic acid) "rescue" "Moderate-dose" methotrexate (100-499 mg/m^2) may require leucovorin rescue Levoleucovorin *(Fusilev)* is also available as the levo (L) isomer (the active biological moiety) of leucovorin and is dosed at 1/2 the dose of leucovorin; monitor methotrexate levels and renal function daily and continue leucovorin until level is $\leq$ 0.05-0.1 micromolar. Hydration and IV sodium bicarbonate must be given to alkalinize the urine and ↓ risk of nephrotoxicity caused by high doses; ensure patient does not have 3rd spacing prior to the drug (ascites, pleural effusions, severe edema) because this will delay drug clearance Glucarpidase *(Voraxaze)* will rapidly lower methotrexate levels that remain high despite adequate hydration and urinary alkalinization (with bicarb) Drug interactions: NSAIDs, salicylates, beta-lactams, proton pump inhibitors, sulfonamide antibiotics, probenecid – all ↓ clearance of methotrexate IV drug solution is yellow	**BOXED WARNINGS** Myelosuppression and aplastic anemia, renal damage, hepatotoxicity* (fibrosis and cirrhosis with long-term use), interstitial pneumonitis, dermatologic reactions (SJS/TEN), GI toxicity [nausea, diarrhea, oral stomatitis (with mucositis)], immunosuppression, tumor lysis syndrome, teratogenicity/ fetal death Renal impairment or ascites/pleural effusions: requires dose adjustments or discontinuation **SIDE EFFECTS** Nephrotoxicity (dose related), hepatotoxicity (more common with chronic use for autoimmune disease), nausea, diarrhea, stomatitis, mucositis, dizziness, sedation, hand-foot syndrome *Hepatotoxicity is more of a concern with chronic use of methotrexate for rheumatoid arthritis, especially when taken incorrectly (taken daily in error, instead of once-weekly dosing)
Pemetrexed *(Alimta)*	To ↓ risk of side effects, give folic acid, vitamin B12 and dexamethasone	**SIDE EFFECTS** Nephrotoxicity, hepatotoxicity, dermatologic toxicity (premedicate with dexamethasone)
Pralatrexate *(Folotyn)*	To ↓ risk of side effects, give folic acid and vitamin B12	**SIDE EFFECTS** Nephrotoxicity, hepatotoxicity

MISCELLANEOUS AGENTS

DRUG	UNIQUE CONCERNS	SAFETY/SIDE EFFECTS/MONITORING
Tretinoin, AKA All-trans Retinoic Acid, *ATRA* ↓ proliferation and ↑ differentiation of acute promyelocytic leukemia (APL) cells First line therapy for APL	Retinoids (vitamin A analogues) Safety issue – see Drug Use in Pregnancy & Lactation chapter Retinoic Acid-Acute Promyelocytic Leukemia (RA-APL) differentiation syndrome: fever, dyspnea, weight gain, edema, pulmonary infiltrates, pericardial or pleural effusions – treat with dexamethasone	**BOXED WARNINGS** RA-APL differentiation syndrome, leukocytosis, pregnancy **SIDE EFFECTS** Leukocytosis, RA-APL differentiation syndrome, QT prolongation, N/V/D, skin/mucous membrane dryness, hyperlipidemia, GI bleeding
Arsenic trioxide *(Trisenox)* ↑ apoptosis of APL cells and damages fusion protein PML-RAR alpha Second line therapy for acute promyelocytic leukemia (APL)	QT prolongation: monitor ECG, avoid concurrent QT prolonging agents, keep Mg, Ca, and K within normal range If acute vasomotor reactions (lightheadedness, dizziness, or hypotension) occur, prolong infusion	**BOXED WARNINGS** RA-APL differentiation syndrome, ECG abnormalities (AV block, QT prolongation), ECG and electrolyte monitoring **SIDE EFFECTS** Leukocytosis, APL differentiation syndrome, N/V/D, GI bleeding, stomatitis, electrolyte imbalance, acute vasomotor reactions (lightheadedness, dizziness, or hypotension), fatigue, edema, HA, insomnia, anxiety, infection
Asparaginase *(Erwinaze)* – derived from *Erwinia chrysanthemi* Pegaspargase *(Oncaspar)* – modified form of L-asparaginase (derived from *E. coli)* and conjugated with polyethylene glycol	Deprives leukemia cells of asparagine, which is an essential amino acid in leukemia The pegylated form (pegaspargase) allows for less frequent dosing (every 2 weeks) and less allergic reactions Monitor fibrinogen, PT, aPTT, LFTs	**CONTRAINDICATIONS** Bleeding, thrombosis or pancreatitis with prior asparaginase treatment **SIDE EFFECTS** Hypersensitivity reactions, pancreatitis, hyperglycemia, hepatotoxicity, CNS toxicity (lethargy, somnolence), encephalopathy, N/V, prolonged prothrombin time (PT/INR)
Mammalian Target of Rapamycin (mTOR) Inhibitors – Inhibit downstream regulation of vascular endothelial growth factor (VEGF) reducing cell growth, metabolism, proliferation and angiogenesis.		
Everolimus *(Afinitor, Afinitor Disperz)* Tablet, tablet for oral suspension *Zortress*-for transplant	CYP450 3A4 major substrate	**BOXED WARNINGS** See Transplant chapter for *Zortress* **CONTRAINDICATIONS** Hypersensitivity to rapamycin derivatives **SIDE EFFECTS** Mouth ulcers/stomatitis, rash, interstitial lung disease, dyslipidemia, hyperglycemia, myelosuppression, rash, pruritus, hand-foot syndrome, stomatitis, fatigue, N/V/D, peripheral edema, interstitial lung disease, renal impairment, ↑ LFTs
Temsirolimus *(Torisel)* Injection	CYP3A4 major substrate Premedicate with diphenhydramine Use non-PVC bag & tubing due to leaching of DEHP	**CONTRAINDICATIONS** Moderate to severe hepatic impairment **SIDE EFFECTS** Dyslipidemia, hyperglycemia, myelosuppression, interstitial lung disease, acute hypersensitivity reactions (polysorbate 80 solvent system), N/V/D, peripheral edema, renal impairment

DRUG	UNIQUE CONCERNS	SAFETY/SIDE EFFECTS/MONITORING
CAR T-Cell Gene Therapy – The first gene therapy approved for cancer (large B-cell lymphoma). Anti-CD19 CAR T-cell therapy involves collecting a patient's T-cells from their blood and genetically engineering them to express a specific receptor against the CD19 protein present on the lymphoma cells. These cells are then re-infused back into the patient to find and attack the lymphoma cells.		
Axicabtagene ciloleucel *(Yescarta)*	Cytokine release syndrome (CRS) and neurological toxicities. Restricted in REMS program to patients who have not responded to or who have relapsed after at least two other kinds of treatment.	**BOXED WARNINGS** Cytokine release syndrome (CRS) Neurological toxicities
Immunomodulators – Oral agents that block angiogenesis and kill abnormal cells in the bone marrow while stimulating the bone marrow to produce normal healthy cells. Usually indicated for multiple myeloma. These agents cause severe birth defects and patients must not become pregnant while using these drugs. All three have strict REMS programs.		
Lenalidomide *(Revlimid)* Pomalidomide *(Pomalyst)* Thalidomide *(Thalomid)*	Severe birth defects – only available under restricted distribution program: patient, prescriber and pharmacist must be registered with *Revlimid*, *Pomalyst* or *Thalomid* REMS program Consider prophylactic anticoagulation due to ↑ VTE risk Pharmacogenomics: myelodysplastic syndrome with a deletion 5q (del 5q) cytogenetic abnormality (lenalidomide)	**BOXED WARNINGS** Fetal risk/pregnancy, thrombosis (DVT/PE), hematologic toxicity (lenalidomide) **CONTRAINDICATIONS** Pregnancy **SIDE EFFECTS** Neutropenia, thrombocytopenia, constipation, N/V/D, fatigue, fever, cough, pruritus, rash, arthralgias, back pain, peripheral edema, DVT/PE Neuropathy, confusion, somnolence (thalidomide) Hypercalcemia (pomalidomide)
Proteasome Inhibitors – Inhibit proteasomes, which help to regulate intracellular protein homeostasis by inhibiting cell cycle progression and inducing apoptosis.		
Bortezomib *(Velcade)* SC administration has less neuropathy than IV administration	An antiviral (acyclovir, valacyclovir) can be used to prevent herpes reactivation (zoster and simplex)	**CONTRAINDICATIONS** Hypersensitivity to boron or mannitol, intrathecal administration (fatal) **SIDE EFFECTS** Peripheral neuropathy, psychiatric disturbances, insomnia, weakness, paresthesias, arthralgias/myalgias, cardiotoxicity, pulmonary toxicity, hypotension, thrombocytopenia, neutropenia, N/V/D, tumor lysis syndrome
Carfilzomib *(Kyprolis)*	Premedicate with dexamethasone and fluids ↑ alkaline phosphatase correlates with ↑ efficacy	**SIDE EFFECTS** Peripheral neuropathy (but less than bortezomib), fatigue, pulmonary toxicity, acute renal failure, tumor lysis syndrome, hepatotoxicity, anemia, thrombocytopenia, N/V/D, pyrexia, cardiotoxicity

TARGETED THERAPIES

MONOCLONAL ANTIBODIES

Monoclonal antibodies (end in "mab") work in various ways to inhibit cancer cell growth. Some bind to specific antigens or receptors on the surface of cancer cells and cause cell death. Other agents are conjugated to cytotoxic drugs or radioactive compounds. Some help to activate the immune system to recognize and destroy tumor cells. Representative monoclonal antibody targets and the associated drugs are included in the following tables (not a complete list).

- All are given as intravenous infusions.
- Most are associated with infusion-related reactions, including hypersensitivity reactions, anaphylaxis, hypotension and bronchospasm. Some infusion-related reactions may be fatal. Premedication is usually required.
- Agents that are conjugated to cytotoxic drugs are associated with additional side effects due to the cytotoxic conjugate.
- Agents that activate the immune system can be associated with potentially life-threatening autoimmune-mediated side effects.

HINTS FOR UNDERSTANDING MONOCLONAL ANTIBODIES USED IN ONCOLOGY

SUBSTEM	EXAMPLES	TARGET	MECHANISM OF ACTION	COMMON TOXICITIES
"ci" Circulatory System	Bevacizumab Ramucirumab	Vascular endothelial growth factor (VEGF) or VEGF receptor	Inhibits growth of blood vessels. Used to treat certain solid tumors, such as colon cancer and non-small cell lung cancer.	■ Inhibition of blood vessel growth → HTN → proteinuria ■ Hemorrhage or thrombosis may occur ■ Impaired wound healing (due to decreased blood flow)
"tu" Tumor	Cetuximab Panitumumab	Epidermal growth factor receptor (EGFR)	Inhibits growth factor from binding to surface of tumor cell and promoting cell growth. Used to treat certain solid tumors, such as colon cancer.	■ EGFR → epidermis → skin toxicity (acneiform rash) ■ Development of rash is correlated with response to therapy
"tu" Tumor	Trastuzumab Pertuzumab	Human epidermal growth factor receptor 2 (HER2)	Inhibits growth factor from binding to surface of tumor cell and promoting cell growth. Used to treat certain solid tumors, such as breast cancer.	■ Cardiotoxicity ■ Embryo-fetal toxicity
"tu" Tumor	Rituximab Brentuximab Daratumumab Inotuzumab	Cluster of differentiation (e.g., CD20, CD22, CD30, CD38) antigens expressed on cell surface of hematopoietic cells	Binds to antigens expressed on specific hematopoietic cells and causes cell death. Used to treat certain hematologic malignancies, such as non-Hodgkin's lymphoma, Hodgkin's lymphoma, multiple myeloma. Brentuximab vedotin *(Adcetris)* is an antibody-drug conjugate (ADC) directed to CD30, a defining marker of classical Hodgkin's lymphoma. The FDA approved this agent.	■ CD antigens are expressed on normal, as well as malignant, hematopoietic cells → suppression of specific hematopoietic cells → bone marrow suppression, increased risk for reactivation of viral infections ■ Inotuzumab ozogamicin and brentuximab vedotin are antibody-drug conjugates (ADCs); the antibody binds to the cell, which enables the cytotoxic drug to enter the tumor cell
"li" Immune System	Ipilimumab Atezolizumab Nivolumab Pembrolizumab	Immune system (PD-1, PDL-1, CTLA-4)	Interferes with the body's ability to "down-regulate" the immune system. Results in increased immune recognition of tumor antigens. Used to treat certain solid tumors, such as non-small cell lung cancer and melanoma.	■ Patient's immune system becomes overactive → potentially life-threatening immune-mediated reactions, such as colitis, hepatic toxicity, thyroid dysfunction and myocarditis, requires steroid treatment

DRUG	UNIQUE CONCERNS	SAFETY/SIDE EFFECTS/MONITORING
Vascular Endothelial Growth Factor (VEGF) Inhibitors		
Bevacizumab *(Avastin)* Bevacizumab-awwb *(Mvasi)* Ramucirumab *(Cyramza)*	Use 0.22 micron filter for ramucirumab Impairs wound healing: do not administer for 28 days before or after surgery Monitor blood pressure and proteinuria prior to each dose	**BOXED WARNINGS** Severe/fatal bleeding, GI perforation, surgical wound dehiscence (splitting open) **SIDE EFFECTS** Hypertension, proteinuria, nephrotic syndrome, heart failure, thrombosis
Human Epidermal Growth Factor Receptor 2 (HER2) Inhibitors		
Trastuzumab *(Herceptin)* Trastuzumab-dkst *(Ogivri)* Pertuzumab *(Perjeta)* Ado-Trastuzumab Emtansine *(Kadcyla)* Trastuzumab conjugated to a microtubule inhibitor	Use 0.22 micron filter for ado-trastuzumab emtansine Pharmacogenomics: test for HER2 gene expression; must have HER2 overexpression to use Monitor LVEF (using echocardiogram or MUGA scan) at baseline and during treatment	**BOXED WARNINGS** Heart failure, embryo-fetal death and birth defects (avoid pregnancy x 7 months after receiving) Severe infusion-related reactions and pulmonary toxicity (trastuzumab) Hepatotoxicity (ado-trastuzumab emtansine) Ado-trastuzumab emtansine and conventional trastuzumab are not interchangeable **SIDE EFFECTS** Infusion-related reactions, N/V/D, alopecia Ado-trastuzumab emtansine: myelosuppression, hepatotoxicity, neuropathy, pulmonary toxicity
Epidermal Growth Factor Receptor (EGFR) Inhibitors		
Cetuximab *(Erbitux)* Panitumumab *(Vectibix)*	Premedicate 1st dose with diphenhydramine Use 0.22 micron filter Pharmacogenomics: test for EGFR gene expression and KRAS mutation. EGFR positive expression correlates with better response rates in NSCLC; must be KRAS wild type to use. KRAS mutation predicts poor response to treatment in colorectal cancer *NSCLC = non-small cell lung cancer*	**BOXED WARNINGS** Severe/fatal infusion-related reactions, cardiac arrest (cetuximab) Dermatologic toxicities (panitumumab) **SIDE EFFECTS** Acneiform rash, serious skin toxicities (SJS/TEN), ocular toxicities, infusion-related reactions, N/V/D, Mg and Ca wasting **NOTES** Rash usually occurs within the 1st 2 weeks of treatment; rash from an EGFR inhibitor indicates that a patient is expected to have a better response to the drug. Advise patients to avoid sunlight, use sunscreen. Topical emollients, including topical steroids, and antibiotics, can be given prophylactically to reduce skin damage (and avoid the need for a dose reduction), and for rash treatment.
Leukocyte Cluster of Differentiation (CD) Antigens (CD20, CD30, CD19, CD3, CD38) Inhibitors		
Rituximab *(Rituxan)* Ofatumumab *(Arzerra)* Obinutuzumab *(Gazyva)*	Premedicate with diphenhydramine, acetaminophen, steroid; slowly titrate rate of first infusion to lower risk of infusion reactions Pharmacogenomics: test for B-cell antigen CD20; must be CD20 positive to use	**BOXED WARNINGS** Hepatitis B reactivation, progressive multifocal leukoencephalopathy (PML) Serious skin reactions (SJS/TEN), severe/fatal infusion-related reactions (rituximab) **SIDE EFFECTS** Rash, peripheral edema, hypertension, renal impairment, tumor lysis syndrome **NOTES** Check hepatitis B panel prior to administration Can cause severe infusion-related reactions (urticaria, hypotension, angioedema, bronchospasm, hypoxia, anaphylaxis)

DRUG	UNIQUE CONCERNS	SAFETY/SIDE EFFECTS/MONITORING
Brentuximab Vedotin *(Adcetris)* Conjugated to MMAE, a microtubule inhibitor	Pharmacogenomics: CD30 antigen must be positive for use	**BOXED WARNINGS** Progressive multifocal leukoencephalopathy **CONTRAINDICATIONS** Concurrent use with bleomycin **SIDE EFFECTS** Myelosuppression, neuropathy, pulmonary toxicity, hepatotoxicity, infusion-related reactions, SJS/TEN
Blinatumomab *(Blincyto)* Bispecific antibody targeting CD19 on B-cells and engaging CD3 on T-cells, causing lysis of B-cells	Pharmacogenomics: CD19 and CD3 antigens must be positive for use	**BOXED WARNINGS** Cytokine release syndrome, neurotoxicity **SIDE EFFECTS** Myelosuppression, hepatotoxicity, leukoencephalopathy, tumor lysis syndrome
Daratumumab *(Darzalex)* Anti-CD38 monoclonal antibody	Pharmacogenomics: CD38 antigen must be positive for use Premedicate with systemic steroid, acetaminophen and diphenhydramine	**SIDE EFFECTS** Myelosuppression, infusion-related reactions
Programmed Death Receptor-1 (PD-1) Inhibitors – When the programmed cell death (PD-1) receptor binds the PD-L1 ligand, the end result is decreased T-cell activation. PD-1 inhibitors are monoclonal antibodies that selectively inhibit PD-1 activity. This allows increased T-cell activation. Activated T-cells are capable (to some extent) of recognizing cancer cells as "non-self" or foreign, and activating the immune system against them (antitumor responses).		
Pembrolizumab *(Keytruda)*	Immune-mediated toxicities may require interruption or permanent discontinuation of treatment and treatment with steroids	**SIDE EFFECTS** Immune-mediated toxicities including: colitis, hepatotoxicity, pulmonary toxicity, nephrotoxicity (pembrolizumab), thyroid disorders, myocarditis, encephalitis, endocrinopathies, rash, weakness
Nivolumab *(Opdivo)*		
Atezolizumab *(Tecentriq)*		
Cytotoxic T-Lymphocyte Antigen-4 (CTLA-4) Inhibitor – Monoclonal antibody that binds to the cytotoxic T-lymphocyte associated antigen 4 (CTLA-4) receptors, which effectively removes the "brake" from T-cell activation. Induces antitumor responses through increased T-cell recognition of cancer cells.		
Ipilimumab *(Yervoy)*	REMS program	**BOXED WARNINGS** Fatal immune-mediated reactions (enterocolitis, hepatitis, dermatitis, endocrinopathy, neuropathy) **SIDE EFFECTS** Pneumonitis, nephrotoxicity, ocular toxicity, rash **NOTES** Immune-mediated toxicities may require interruption or permanent discontinuation of treatment and administration of steroids

TYROSINE KINASE INHIBITORS

There are a large number of different tyrosine kinase proteins that play roles in intracellular signaling pathways that control the growth and differentiation of cells. Tyrosine kinase inhibitors (TKIs) are orally administered small molecules that are active against different types of cancers. Some TKIs are "targeted" to inhibit specific abnormal tyrosine kinases that are associated with certain types of cancers. Pharmacogenomic testing must be done to identify patients likely to respond to these targeted TKIs. Other TKIs are considered to be "multitargeted." They inhibit multiple different tyrosine kinases involved in the cell signaling pathway and/or cell growth. Many TKIs have limited distribution through specialty pharmacies. The list below is not a complete list, but contains representative TKI targets and the associated drugs. For many of the TKIs, oral bioavailability may be altered if taken with food. It is very important for patients to follow the dosing instructions with regards to taking the specific TKI with or without food.

DRUG	MECHANISM/GENETICS	SAFETY/SIDE EFFECTS/MONITORING
Used in chronic myelogenous leukemia (CML) **BCR-ABL Inhibitors**		
Imatinib *(Gleevec)* Dasatinib *(Sprycel)* Nilotinib *(Tasigna)* Ponatinib *(Iclusig)* Bosutinib *(Bosulif)*	BCR-ABL gene translocation (Philadelphia Chromosome) → abnormal tyrosine kinase (occurs in ~95% of CML patients) Pharmacogenomics: must be Philadelphia chromosome (BCR-ABL) positive to use	**BOXED WARNINGS** QT prolongation (nilotinib) Vascular occlusions (strokes, MIs), heart failure, hepatotoxicity (ponatinib) **SIDE EFFECTS** Myelosuppression, N/V/D, fluid retention, edema, skin rash, ↑ LFTs, HF, QT prolongation (dasatinib, nilotinib, bosutinib); HBV reactivation (imatinib, dasatinib, nilotinib)
Used in Melanoma **BRAF Inhibitors**		
Vemurafenib *(Zelboraf)* Dabrafenib *(Tafinlar)*	BRAF mutation → abnormal tyrosine kinase that is always "on" → melanoma (occurs in ~50% of melanoma patients) Pharmacogenomics: must be BRAF V600E or V600K mutation positive to use	**WARNINGS** New malignancies such as squamous cell carcinoma and basal cell carcinoma, QT prolongation, serious skin reactions, hepatotoxicity **SIDE EFFECTS** Skin rash, photosensitivity, N/V/D, peripheral edema, fatigue, arthralgia
Mitogen-Activated Extracellular Kinase (MEK) 1 and 2 Inhibitors		
Trametinib *(Mekinist)* Cobimetinib *(Cotellic)*	Inhibits MEK, a cell signaling protein downstream from RAF Used in combination with BRAF inhibitors in patients with BRAF V600E or V600K mutations	**SIDE EFFECTS** Hypertension, HF, hepatotoxicity, skin rash, N/V/D, myelosuppression Hand-foot syndrome, QT prolongation (trametinib) Visual impairment (cobimetinib)
Used in Non-Small Cell Lung Cancer (NSCLC) **Epidermal Growth Factor Receptor (EGFR) Inhibitors**		
Afatinib *(Gilotrif)* Erlotinib *(Tarceva)* Gefitinib *(Iressa)*	EGFR mutation → abnormal tyrosine kinase that is always "on" → NSCLC (occurs in ~15% of NSCLC patients) Pharmacogenomics: must be EGFR mutation positive (exon 19 or 21) to use	**WARNINGS** Interstitial lung disease, hepatotoxicity, GI perforation, skin reactions (SJS/TEN), ocular toxicity (keratitis), fetal harm; diarrhea (afatinib/gefitinib) Renal impairment requires dose adjustment (afatinib) **SIDE EFFECTS** Acneiform rash, dry skin, pruritus, N/V/D, mucositis **NOTES** Acneiform rash from an EGFR inhibitor indicates that a patient is expected to have a better response to the drug. Advise patients to avoid sunlight, use sunscreen. Topical emollients, including topical steroids and antibiotics can be given prophylactically to reduce skin damage (and avoid the need for a dose reduction), and for rash treatment.
Anaplastic Lymphoma Kinase (ALK) Inhibitors		
Crizotinib *(Xalkori)* Ceritinib *(Zykadia)* Alectinib *(Alecensa)*	ALK gene translocation → abnormal tyrosine kinase that is always "on" → NSCLC (occurs in ~5% of NSCLC patients) Pharmacogenomics: must be ALK mutation positive to use	**WARNINGS** Hepatotoxicity, bradycardia, interstitial lung disease, QT prolongation; ocular toxicities (crizotinib), pancreatitis (ceritinib), myalgia and photosensitivity (alectinib) **SIDE EFFECTS** Skin rash, N/V/D, edema, hyperglycemia (ceritinib)

DRUG	MECHANISM/GENETICS	SAFETY/SIDE EFFECTS/MONITORING
OTHER TKIs (not a complete list)		
Lapatinib (*Tykerb*) Neratinib (*Nerlynx*)	Human Epidermal Growth Factor Receptor 2 (HER-2) inhibitors (also inhibits EGFR) Pharmacogenomics: must have HER2 overexpression to use in breast cancer	**WARNINGS** Hepatotoxicity (lapatinib, neratinib), cardiotoxicity (lapatinib), GI toxicity due to severe diarrhea (neratinib; requires antidiarrheal prophylaxis with loperamide) **SIDE EFFECTS** Diarrhea, N/V, skin rash, hand-foot syndrome
Sorafenib (*Nexavar*) Sunitinib (*Sutent*)	Multiple targets Useful in cancers where traditional therapy has little benefit, such as hepatocellular, renal and thyroid cancers	**BOXED WARNINGS** Hepatotoxicity (sunitinib) **WARNINGS** Hepatotoxicity, cardiac toxicity, hypertension, proteinuria, hemorrhagic events, SJS/TEN, impaired wound healing **SIDE EFFECTS** Skin changes, hand-foot syndrome, N/V/D, QT prolongation, thyroid dysfunction, mucositis

COMMON TOXICITIES OF TYROSINE KINASE INHIBITORS

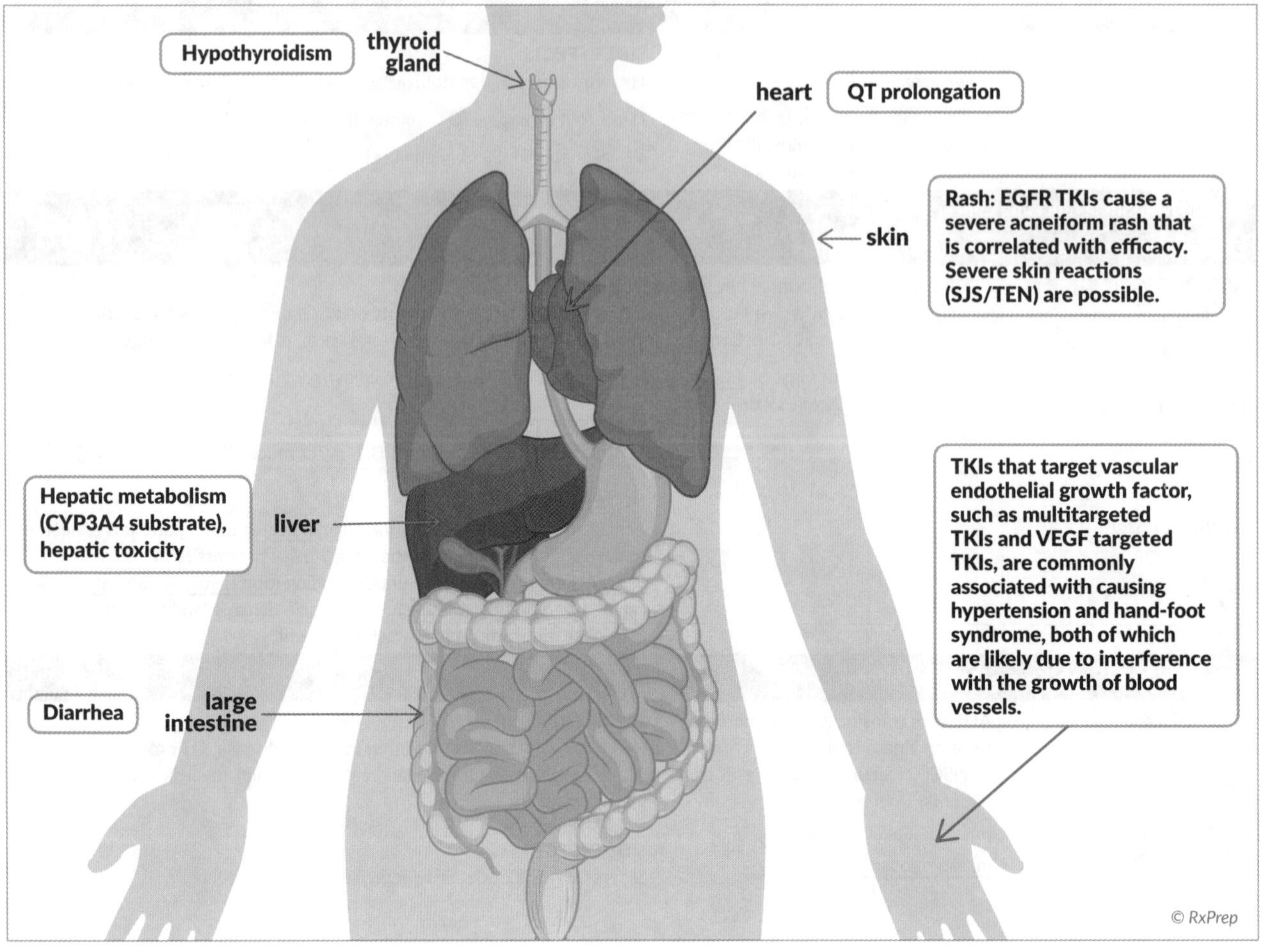

ADMINISTRATION OF ORAL AGENTS

GENERIC (BRAND)	ADMINISTRATION	SPECIAL INSTRUCTIONS
Imatinib *(Gleevec)*	Take with food or within 1 hour after a meal	Thalidomide, pomalidomide, and lenalidomide are teratogenic: female patients of reproductive potential must have 2 negative pregnancy tests prior to starting treatment and use 2 forms of birth control. REMS drugs only available through a specialty pharmacy.
Thalidomide *(Thalomid)*		
Capecitabine *(Xeloda)*		
Exemestane *(Aromasin)*		
Nilotinib *(Tasigna)*	Take on an empty stomach (1 hour before or 2 hours after food, pomalidomide is taken 2 hours before or 2 hours after food)	
Erlotinib *(Tarceva)*		
Sorafenib *(Nexavar)*		
Temozolomide *(Temodar)*		
Abiraterone *(Zytiga)*		
Pomalidomide *(Pomalyst)*		
Dasatinib *(Sprycel)*	Take without regard to food	
Sunitinib *(Sutent)*		
Tamoxifen *(Soltamox)*		
Anastrozole *(Arimidex)*		
Bicalutamide *(Casodex)*		
Lenalidomide *(Revlimid)*		
Letrozole *(Femara)*		

Select Guidelines/References

National Comprehensive Cancer Network (NCCN). www.nccn.org (accessed 2019 Feb 18)
American Society of Clinical Oncology (ASCO). www.asco.org (accessed 2019 Feb 18)

63

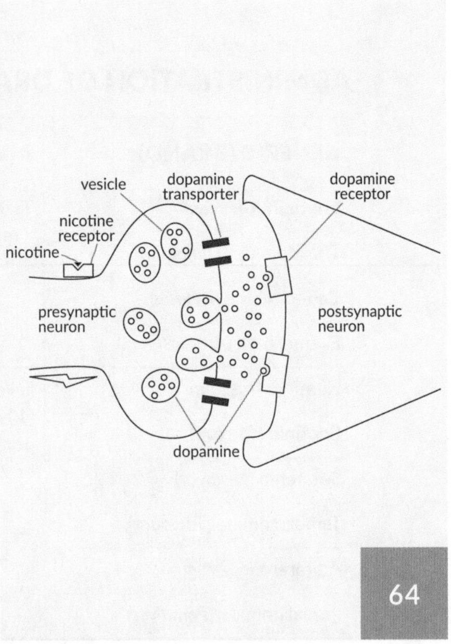

64

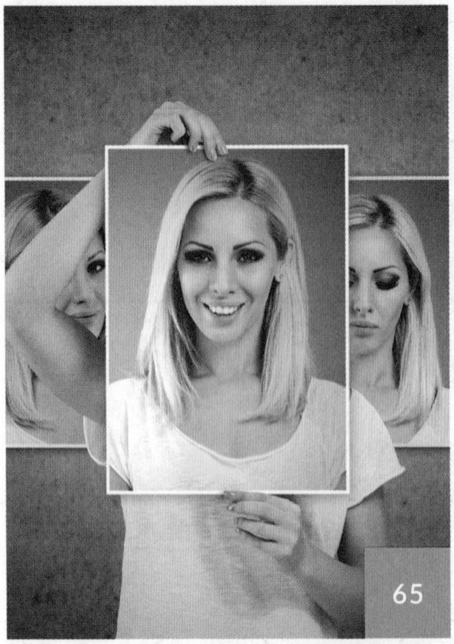

65

66

67

68

PSYCHIATRIC CONDITIONS

CONTENTS

CHAPTER 63
DEPRESSION | **880**

CHAPTER 64
SCHIZOPHRENIA/PSYCHOSIS | **892**

CHAPTER 65
BIPOLAR DISORDER | **901**

CHAPTER 66
ATTENTION DEFICIT HYPERACTIVITY DISORDER (ADHD) | **905**

CHAPTER 67
ANXIETY DISORDERS | **913**

CHAPTER 68
SLEEP DISORDERS: INSOMNIA, RESTLESS LEGS SYNDROME (RLS) & NARCOLEPSY | **918**

CHAPTER CONTENT

Background 880
Causes 880
Select Drugs that Cause or Worsen Depression 881
Diagnosis 881
Depression Diagnosis 881
Concurrent Bipolar or Anxiety Disorders 881
Natural Products 881
Drug Treatment 881
Treatment-Resistant Depression 882
Depression in Pregnancy and Postpartum Depression 882
Boxed Warnings & Medguides 882
Selective Serotonin Reuptake Inhibitors 883
SSRI and Combined Mechanism 884
Serotonin and Norepinephrine Reuptake Inhibitors 885
Antidepressants: Select Adverse Effects 885
Tricyclics 886
Dopamine and Norepinephrine Reuptake Inhibitor 886
Monoamine Oxidase Inhibitors 887
MAO Inhibitors – Keep Them Separated 887
Miscellaneous Antidepressants 888
Selecting the Best Antidepressant 888
Treatment-Resistant Depression 889
Select Adjunctive Therapy in Treatment-Resistant Depression 889
Patient Counseling 890

CONTENT LEGEND

= Study Tip Gal   = Key Drug Guy

CHAPTER 63
DEPRESSION

BACKGROUND

Major Depressive Disorder (MDD, or referred to here as "depression") is one of the most common health conditions in the world. People with depression suffer greatly with persistent feelings of hopelessness, dejection, constant worry, poor concentration, a lack of energy, an inability to sleep and, sometimes, suicidal tendencies. The statistics are sobering. In 2017, approximately 17.3 million adults in the United States experienced a major depressive episode in the past year (about 7.1% of the population). Of these, 35 percent received no treatment.

About half of those with a first episode recover and experience no further episodes. The remaining patients will experience persistent or recurrent depression and the risk of recurrence increases with each episode. After three episodes, recurrence risk is nearly 100% without ongoing treatment.

Some of the treatment problems that arise include patients who discontinue their medication without medical advice, or when medications are continued despite an inadequate response.

CAUSES

The causes of depression are poorly understood, but involve some combination of genetic, biologic and environmental factors. Neurotransmitters believed to be involved in depression include serotonin (5-HT), glutamate, acetylcholine (ACh), dopamine (DA), norepinephrine (NE) and epinephrine (EPI). 5-HT may be the most important neurotransmitter (NT) involved with feelings of well being. Certain drugs can also cause or worsen depression (see Key Drugs Guy on the following page).

DIAGNOSIS

Diagnosis and treatment of depression is difficult since it is not possible to measure brain chemical imbalances. Diagnosis relies on symptom assessment (see Study Tip Gal). The HDRS (also known as the Ham-D) is the most widely used depression assessment scale. It is designed to be used in a medical office. The patient rates their symptoms of depression on a numerical scale, and the total score indicates whether or not depression is present.

DEPRESSION DIAGNOSIS

DSM-5 criteria requires the presence of at least 5 of the following symptoms (even if they are in response to a significant loss like bereavement or financial ruin) during the same two week period (must include depressed mood or diminished interest/pleasure):

Mood - depressed
Sleep - increased/decreased
Interest/pleasure - diminished
Guilt or feelings of worthlessness
Energy - decreased
Concentration - decreased
Appetite - increased/decreased
Psychomotor agitation or retardation
Suicidal ideation
Remember: **M SIG E CAPS**

CONCURRENT BIPOLAR OR ANXIETY DISORDERS

It is necessary to rule-out bipolar disorder prior to initiating antidepressant therapy to avoid inducing mania or causing rapid-cycling (cycling rapidly between bipolar depression and mania). Screening forms for MDD now include questions designed to identify mania symptoms such as "there are times when I get into moods where I feel very speeded up or irritable."

Benzodiazepine (BZD) therapy is often used adjunctively in depression when anxiety is also present. BZDs should not be used alone; this leaves the depression untreated. BZDs can cause and/or mask depression. They can put the patient at risk for physiological dependence and withdrawal symptoms when the dose is wearing off (e.g., tachycardia, anxiety), and increase the risk of respiratory depression and death when given with certain other medications (e.g., opioids). Prescribers should also select BZDs carefully and monitor closely if patients have co-occurring substance use disorders (called Dual Diagnosis). See the Anxiety Disorders chapter for further discussion.

SELECT DRUGS THAT CAUSE OR WORSEN DEPRESSION

KEY DRUGS

ADHD medications
Atomoxetine *(Strattera)*: monitor mood

Analgesics
Indomethacin

Antiretrovirals (depression and suicidality)
Efavirenz (in *Atripla*)
Rilpivirine (in *Complera, Odefsey*)

Cardiovascular
Beta-blockers (especially propranolol)

Hormones
Hormonal contraceptives
Anabolic steroids

Other
Antidepressants: monitor for worsening mood
Benzodiazepines
Systemic steroids
Interferons
Varenicline
Ethanol

Medical conditions such as stroke, Parkinson disease, dementia, multiple sclerosis, hypothyroidism, low vitamin D levels, metabolic conditions (e.g., hypercalcemia), malignancy, OAB and infectious diseases can contribute to depression.

Others:

Methylphenidate and other stimulants

Methadone, and possibly other chronic opioid use that can lower testosterone or estrogen levels

Clonidine

Methyldopa

Procainamide

Cyclosporine

Isotretinoin

NATURAL PRODUCTS

St. John's wort, SAMe (S-adenosyl-L-methionine) or valerian may be helpful for treating depression, but there is less evidence of efficacy than with standard treatments. St. John's wort carries a weak recommendation for use in patients who are not pregnant or breastfeeding and prefer herbal treatment. Both St. John's wort and SAMe can increase the risk of serotonin syndrome and should not be used with other serotonergic agents. St. John's wort is a broad spectrum CYP450 enzyme inducer with many significant drug interactions, and it causes phototoxicity.

DRUG TREATMENT

Treatment of depression relies on a competent assessment and trial of medication/s. If a drug does not work after a suitable trial of at least 6 – 8 weeks, treatment should be reassessed (see section on Treatment-Resistant Depression). Patient history is critical in treating mental illnesses; what worked in the past, or did not work, should help guide therapy.

Mild depression should be treated with psychotherapy or medication. Moderate to severe depression should be treated with medication in addition to the option of psychotherapy. The effectiveness of the different antidepressant classes is generally comparable. The initial choice of medication should be based on the side effect profile, safety concerns and patient-specific symptoms. For most patients an SSRI or SNRI is preferred, or (with specific concurrent conditions or considerations) mirtazapine or bupropion.

Due to safety concerns (drug-drug and drug-food interactions) the use of the oral nonselective monoamine oxidase inhibitors (MAO inhibitors) such as phenelzine, tranylcypromine and isocarboxazid is restricted to patients unresponsive to other treatments. Serotonin syndrome can occur with the administration of one or more serotonergic medications (e.g., tricyclic antidepressants, fentanyl, methadone, lithium, tramadol, buspirone, amphetamines, triptans and St. John's wort). It is the most severe when an MAO inhibitor is administered with another serotonergic medication. Higher doses increase the risk. See further discussion later in the chapter and in the Learning Drug Interactions chapter.

If a drug is being discontinued, it should generally be tapered over several weeks. Withdrawal symptoms (e.g., anxiety, agitation, insomnia, dizziness, flu-like symptoms) can be quite distressing to the patient. Paroxetine, venlafaxine and some other medications carry a higher risk of withdrawal symptoms and must be tapered upon discontinuation. An exception to this rule is fluoxetine, which self-tapers because of its long half-life. Pharmacists must counsel patients on the risk of withdrawal symptoms and encourage patients to not discontinue the medication without discussing with their healthcare provider.

TREATMENT-RESISTANT DEPRESSION

Patients should receive an adequate 6 – 8 week trial at a therapeutic dose before concluding that a drug is not working. If the patient is not improving (making progress toward the treatment goal of remission) or has an incomplete response the following should be considered:

- A dose increase.
- A combination of antidepressants with different mechanisms of action.
- Augmentation with buspirone or a low dose of an atypical antipsychotic. Agents approved as augmentation therapy with antidepressants are aripiprazole *(Abilify)*, olanzapine + fluoxetine *(Symbyax)*, quetiapine extended release *(Seroquel XR)* and brexpiprazole *(Rexulti)*. Esketamine *(Spravato)* is an another option.
- Some guidelines recommend augmentation with lithium, thyroid hormone, and in some cases, electroconvulsive therapy (ECT).

DEPRESSION IN PREGNANCY AND POSTPARTUM DEPRESSION

If a woman is on antidepressants and wishes to become pregnant, it may be possible to taper the drug if the depression is mild and she has been symptom free for the previous six months. In more severe cases, medications may need to be continued or started.

Depression in pregnant women often goes unrecognized and untreated. Untreated maternal depression during pregnancy, especially in the late second or early third trimesters, is associated with increased rates of adverse outcomes (e.g., premature birth, low birth weight, fetal growth restriction, postnatal complications). The American College of Obstetricians and Gynecologists (ACOG) guidelines for mild depression in pregnancy recommend psychotherapy first, followed by drug treatment if needed. The initiation of drug treatment for depression in pregnant patients is concerning because of the risks of adverse outcomes for both the mother and the unborn baby. All drugs carry risk; the risk versus benefit must be considered individually. Historically, SSRIs have been used initially, with the exception of paroxetine, due to potential cardiac effects. The new formulation of paroxetine, *Brisdelle*, is contraindicated. Although SSRIs have historically been preferred, the FDA issued a warning regarding SSRI use during pregnancy and the potential risk of persistent pulmonary hypertension of the newborn (PPHN). Tricyclics are also commonly used, but carry their own risks and are not preferred.

Postpartum depression is common but often unrecognized and under-treated, and can have adverse outcomes for the mother, baby and family. Breastfeeding is helpful for most women for physical and emotional symptoms, and is considered beneficial for the baby. Drug safety in breastfeeding is essential. SSRIs or tricyclics are generally preferred (with the exception of doxepin, per the ACOG recommendations). Brexanolone *(Zulresso)* is the first drug with FDA-approval for postpartum depression. It is given as an IV infusion over 60 continuous hours, and can cause excessive sedation.

BOXED WARNINGS & MEDGUIDES

All antidepressants carry a boxed warning of a possible increase in suicidal thoughts or actions in some children, teenagers or young adults within the first few months of treatment or when the dose is changed. MedGuides are required for all drugs. Patients and caregivers must be advised that mood may worsen and that they should contact a healthcare provider if changes in mood, behavior, thoughts or feelings are observed. This information is not included in the drug tables that follow. Refer back to this section as needed.

Lag Effect and Suicide Prevention

Patients should be told that the medicine must be used daily, and will take time to work. It is important to inform the patient that physical symptoms such as low energy improve within a few weeks but psychological symptoms, such as low mood, may take a month or longer. Physicians and pharmacists must educate patients, family and caregivers about the risk of suicidality and screen for suicide risk. If a patient reports suicidal ideation, refer the patient to the emergency department, the suicide hotline or elsewhere for help. If someone has a plan to commit suicide, it is more likely that the threat is immediate.

SELECTIVE SEROTONIN REUPTAKE INHIBITORS

Selective Serotonin Reuptake Inhibitors (SSRIs) increase 5-HT by inhibiting its reuptake (reabsorption) in the neuronal synapse. They also weakly affect NE and DA.

DRUG	DOSING	SAFETY/SIDE EFFECTS/MONITORING
Citalopram ***(Celexa)***	20-40 mg/day Max dose: 40 mg/day Max dose in elderly (≥ 60 years): 20 mg/day	**CONTRAINDICATIONS** Concurrent use with MAO inhibitors, linezolid, IV methylene blue, or pimozide; concurrent use with thioridazine (fluoxetine, paroxetine); concurrent use with alosetron or tizanidine (fluvoxamine); concurrent use with disulfiram (sertraline solution); pregnancy (*Brisdelle*) **WARNINGS** QT prolongation: max dosing of citalopram and escitalopram due to this risk. Do not exceed citalopram 20 mg/day in elderly (≥ 60 years), liver disease, with CYP2C19 poor metabolizers or on 2C19 inhibitors. Do not exceed escitalopram 10 mg/day in elderly. SIADH, hyponatremia (elderly at higher risk), bleeding **SIDE EFFECTS** Sexual side effects: ↓ libido, ejaculation difficulties, anorgasmia, erectile dysfunction Somnolence, insomnia, nausea, dry mouth, diaphoresis (dose-related), weakness, tremor, dizziness, headache (but may help for migraines if taken continuously) Most activating: fluoxetine; take dose in AM Most sedating: paroxetine, fluvoxamine; take dose in the PM Others: take dose in the AM; if causing sedation, take in the PM Restless leg syndrome (assess whether the onset coincided with initiation of treatment) ↑ fall risk; use caution in frail patients, osteopenia/osteoporosis, use of CNS depressants **NOTES** All approved for depression and a variety of anxiety disorders, except fluvoxamine (only approved for OCD) All available in solution except fluvoxamine Sertraline is preferred in patients with cardiac risk Fluvoxamine has more drug interactions To switch to fluoxetine delayed release 90 mg/weekly from fluoxetine daily, start 7 days after last daily dose
Escitalopram ***(Lexapro*** – S-enantiomer of citalopram)	10 mg/day Max dose: 20 mg/day Max dose in elderly: 10 mg/day	
Fluoxetine ***(Prozac, Sarafem)*** + olanzapine (*Symbyax*) – for resistant depression	10-60 mg/day (max 80 mg/day); 90 mg weekly Premenstrual dysphoric disorder (PMDD): *Sarafem* 20 mg daily or 20 mg daily starting 14 days prior to menstruation through 1st full day of bleeding *Symbyax:* initial 6 mg/25 mg QHS	
Paroxetine ***(Paxil,*** *Paxil CR, Pexeva, Brisdelle)*	IR: 10-60 mg/day CR: 12.5-62.5 mg/day (max 75 mg/day for panic disorder) Each 10 mg IR = 12.5 mg CR	
Sertraline ***(Zoloft)***	50-200 mg/day Premenstrual dysphoric disorder (PMDD): 50-150 mg daily or 50-150 mg daily starting 14 days prior to menstruation through 1st full day of bleeding	
Fluvoxamine IR/ER	50-300 mg/day (daily doses > 100 mg/day should be divided BID)	

SSRI AND COMBINED MECHANISM

DRUG	DOSING	SAFETY/SIDE EFFECTS/MONITORING
SSRI and 5-HT1A Partial Agonist		**CONTRAINDICATIONS** Use within 14 days of MAO inhibitors; do not initiate in patients being treated with linezolid or methylene blue IV **WARNINGS** Seizures; avoid in patients with seizure history **SIDE EFFECTS** N/V/D, insomnia, ↓ libido (less sexual SEs compared to SSRIs and SNRIs) Vortioxetine: constipation
Vilazodone (*Viibryd, Viibryd Starter Pack*)	Start at 10 mg daily x 7 days, then 20 mg daily (dosing in patient starter kit); max 40 mg/day Take with food	
SSRI, 5-HT Receptor Antagonist and 5-HT1A Agonist		
Vortioxetine (*Trintellix*)	5-20 mg/day, with or without food	

SSRI Drug Interactions

- MAO inhibitors and serotonin syndrome or hypertensive crisis: allow a two-week washout between MAO inhibitors and SSRIs. Fluoxetine is the exception; due to its long half life (4-6 days), a five-week washout period is required if switching from fluoxetine to a MAO inhibitor.
- QT prolongation most consistently noted with citalopram and escitalopram (see max dose recommendations). Additive QT prolongation risk with other SSRIs as well; see Arrhythmias chapter for other high risk QT drugs with additive risk.
- ↑ bleeding risk when used with anticoagulants, antiplatelets, NSAIDs, ginkgo, thrombolytics.
- Fluoxetine: CYP2D6, 2C19 inhibitor. Fluvoxamine: CYP1A2, 2D6, 2C9, 2C19, 3A4 inhibitor. Paroxetine: CYP2D6 inhibitor. Note all three are 2D6 inhibitors and some other antipsychotic drugs are 2D6 substrates (e.g., aripiprazole, olanzapine). Antipsychotic drugs are sometimes used in combination; the dose of the antipsychotic may need to be lowered when given with these drugs.
- Tamoxifen requires conversion to its more active metabolite by CYP2D6. Decreased tamoxifen effectiveness occurs with fluoxetine, paroxetine and sertraline (and duloxetine and bupropion); can use venlafaxine.
- *Trintellix*: decrease dose by half when used with a strong 2D6 inhibitor (e.g., bupropion, fluoxetine, paroxetine or quinidine). Consider increasing *Trintellix* dose when a strong CYP inducer (e.g., rifampin, carbamazepine, or phenytoin) is coadministered for > 2 weeks.
- Do not use with thioridazine, pimozide or cimetidine.
- Do not initiate in patients receiving linezolid or methylene blue IV due to risk of serotonin syndrome.
- Caution with drugs that cause orthostasis or CNS depressants due to risk of falls.

SEROTONIN AND NOREPINEPHRINE REUPTAKE INHIBITORS

Serotonin and norepinephrine reuptake inhibitors (SNRIs) have a similar mechanism as SSRIs, in that they increase 5-HT through inhibiting its reuptake. SNRIs also inhibit reuptake of norephinephrine (NE). This leads to the differences in indications and side effect profiles compared to SSRIs.

DRUG	DOSING	SAFETY/SIDE EFFECTS/MONITORING
Venlafaxine *(Effexor XR)* Depression, GAD, Panic Disorder, Social Anxiety Disorder	37.5-375 mg/day (max 375 mg/day for IR and 225 mg/day for ER Different generics; check Orange Book	**CONTRAINDICATIONS** SNRIs and MAO inhibitors can potentially cause a lethal drug interaction: hypertensive crisis (see Drug Interactions section) Do not initiate in a patient receiving linezolid or intravenous methylene blue **SIDE EFFECTS** Similar to SSRIs (due to ↓ 5-HT reuptake) Side effects due to ↑ NE: ↑ HR, dilated pupils (can lead to an episode of narrow angle glaucoma), dry mouth, excessive sweating and constipation Can affect urethral resistance; caution when using SNRIs in patients prone to obstructive urinary disorders ↑ BP: risk is greatest with venlafaxine when dosed > 150 mg/day (all have risk, especially at higher doses); can ↓ dose, use antihypertensive/s or change therapy ↑ fall risk; use caution in frail patients, osteopenia/osteoporosis, use of CNS depressants **NOTES** Dose is ↓ in renal impairment; do not use levomilnacipran with CrCl < 15 mL/min or duloxetine with CrCl < 30 mL/min
Duloxetine *(Cymbalta)* Depression, Peripheral Neuropathy (pain), Fibromyalgia, GAD, Chronic Musculoskeletal Pain	40-60 mg/day (daily, or 20-30 BID); max dose 120 mg/day; doses > 60 mg/day not more effective	
Desvenlafaxine *(Pristiq,* *Khedezla)* Depression	50 mg/day (can ↑ 400 mg/day, but no benefit to > 50 mg)	
Levomilnacipran *(Fetzima)* Depression	40-120 mg/day Start at 20 mg/day x 2 days Do not open, chew or crush capsules; do not take with alcohol	

SNRI Drug Interactions

- SNRI inhibitors and MAO inhibitors can cause hypertensive crisis or serotonin syndrome if used together. A washout period is needed: 5 – 14 day (duloxetine) or seven day (venlafaxine, desvenlafaxine, levomilnacipran) washout if going from SNRI to a MAO inhibitor, 14 day washout if going from MAO inhibitor to SNRI.
- Duloxetine is a moderate CYP2D6 inhibitor.
- Additive QT prolongation risk with venlafaxine.
- Tamoxifen requires conversion to its more active metabolite by 2D6. Decreased tamoxifen effectiveness occurs with duloxetine.
- Do not initiate in patients receiving linezolid or methylene blue IV due to risk of serotonin syndrome.
- ↑ bleeding risk with concurrent use of anticoagulants, antiplatelets, NSAIDs, ginkgo, thrombolytics.
- If on antihypertensive medications, use caution and monitor (can ↑ BP), especially at higher doses.

ANTIDEPRESSANTS: SELECT ADVERSE EFFECTS

- Suicidal thoughts and behaviors: see Boxed Warnings and MedGuides section.
- Serotonin syndrome: see MAO inhibitors section and Learning Drug Interactions chapter.
- Bleeding risk ↑ with SSRIs and SNRIs when used with anticoagulants, antiplatelets, NSAIDs and other drugs/supplements that ↑ bleeding risk.
- QT prolongation (discontinue if QTc > 500 msec).
  - Citalopram doses > 40 mg not recommended (max 20 mg/day in age ≥ 60 years), escitalopram doses > 20 mg not recommended (max 10 mg/day in age ≥ 60 years).
  - Additive QT effects with SSRIs, venlafaxine, mirtazapine and tricyclic antidepressants.
- Withdrawal symptoms when discontinued abruptly (must taper), except fluoxetine due to long half-life.

TRICYCLICS

Tricyclic antidepressants primarily inhibit NE and 5-HT reuptake. They also block ACh and histamine receptors, which contributes to the side effect profile. There are two main categories of tricyclics: secondary amines and tertiary amines. Secondary amines are relatively selective for NE. Tertiary amines can be slightly more effective, but have a worse side effect profile.

DRUG	DOSING	SAFETY/SIDE EFFECTS/MONITORING
TERTIARY AMINES **Amitriptyline** *(Elavil*)* **Doxepin** – for depression, all are generic; *Silenor* is for insomnia; *Zonalon and Prudoxin* are creams for pruritus Clomipramine *(Anafranil)* Imipramine *(Tofranil)* Trimipramine *(Surmontil)* **SECONDARY AMINES** **Nortriptyline *(Pamelor)*** Amoxapine Desipramine *(Norpramin)* Maprotiline Protriptyline	**Amitriptyline** Depression: 100-300 mg/day QHS or divided doses Neuropathic pain/migraine prophylaxis: 10-50 mg QHS **Doxepin** Depression: 100-300 mg/day **Nortriptyline** Depression: 25 mg TID-QID	**CONTRAINDICATIONS** Concurrent use with MAO inhibitors, linezolid, IV methylene blue; myocardial infarction (amitriptyline); glaucoma and urinary retention (doxepin) **SIDE EFFECTS** **Cardiotoxicity** QT prolongation with overdose (monitor for suicidal ideation, as overdose can quickly cause fatal arrhythmias); obtain baseline ECG if cardiac risk factors or age > 50 years old Orthostasis, tachycardia **Anticholinergic** Dry mouth, blurred vision, urinary retention, constipation (taper off to avoid cholinergic rebound) Vivid dreams, weight gain (varies by agent and patient), sedation, sweating, myoclonus (muscle twitching – a symptom of drug toxicity) **NOTES** ↑ fall risk – especially in elderly due to combination of orthostasis and sedation Tertiary amines have increased anticholinergic properties, and are more likely to cause sedation and weight gain

**Brand discontinued but name still used in practice*

Tricyclic Drug Interactions

- MAO inhibitors and hypertensive crisis: two-week washout if going to or from an MAO inhibitor.
- Additive QT prolongation risk.
- Metabolized by CYP2D6 (up to 10% of Caucasians are poor metabolizers); check for drug interactions.

DOPAMINE AND NOREPINEPHRINE REUPTAKE INHIBITOR

DRUG	DOSING	SAFETY/SIDE EFFECTS/MONITORING
Bupropion (*Wellbutrin SR, Wellbutrin XL,* *Aplenzin, Forfivo XL*) + naltrexone *(Contrave)* – for weight management ***Zyban*** – for smoking cessation *Aplenzin* and ***Wellbutrin XL*** are approved for Seasonal Affective Disorder (SAD)	300-450 mg daily Bupropion IR is TID *Wellbutrin SR* is BID (< 200 mg/dose) *Wellbutrin XL* is daily Hydrobromide salt: *Aplenzin* Do not exceed 450 mg/day (up to 522 mg/day with *Aplenzin*) due to seizure risk	**CONTRAINDICATIONS** Seizure disorder; history of anorexia/bulimia, abrupt discontinuation of ethanol or sedatives; concurrent use with MAO inhibitors, linezolid, IV methylene blue or other forms of bupropion **WARNINGS** Neuropsychiatric adverse events possible when used for smoking cessation (can include mood changes, hallucinations, paranoia, aggression, anxiety) **SIDE EFFECTS** Dry mouth, insomnia, headache/migraine, nausea/vomiting, constipation, and tremors/seizures (dose-related), possible blood pressure changes (more hypertension than hypotension), weight loss No effects on 5-HT - sexual dysfunction is rare; can use if issues with other antidepressants Can cause CNS stimulation (anxiety, restlessness, insomnia)

Bupropion Drug Interactions

- Avoid duplication – do not use multiple formulations of bupropion in the same patient. This can be problematic due to multiple brand names and indications.
- Bupropion increases the risk of hypertensive crisis with MAO inhibitors. Allow 14 day washout when converting between bupropion and MAO inhibitors.
- Bupropion is a moderate CYP2D6 inhibitor. Tamoxifen requires conversion to its more active metabolite by CYP2D6. Decreased tamoxifen effectiveness occurs when given with bupropion.

MONOAMINE OXIDASE INHIBITORS

Monoamine oxidase inhibitors (MAOIs) inhibit the enzyme monoamine oxidase, which breaks down catecholamines, including 5-HT, NE, EPI, and DA. If these NTs ↑ dramatically, hypertensive crisis, and death can result.

DRUG	DOSING	SAFETY/SIDE EFFECTS/MONITORING
Isocarboxazid (*Marplan*)	20 mg/day in divided doses, max 60 mg/day	**CONTRAINDICATIONS** Cardiovascular disease, cerebrovascular defect, history of headache, history of hepatic disease, pheochromocytoma Concurrent use of sympathomimetics and related compounds, CNS depressants, dextromethorphan, ethanol, meperidine, bupropion or buspirone Severe renal disease (isocarboxazid, phenelzine) **WARNINGS** Not commonly used, but watch for drug-drug and drug-food interactions – if missed could be fatal Hypertensive crisis or serotonin syndrome can occur when taken with TCAs, SSRIs, SNRIs, many other drugs and tyramine-rich foods (see interactions below) **SIDE EFFECTS** Anticholinergic effects (taper upon discontinuation to avoid cholinergic rebound) Orthostasis Sedation (except tranylcypromine causes stimulation) Sexual dysfunction, weight gain, headache, insomnia
Phenelzine (*Nardil*)	15 mg TID, max 60-90 mg/day	
Tranylcypromine (*Parnate*)	30 mg/day in divided doses, max 60 mg/day	
Selegiline transdermal patch (*Emsam*) MAO-B selective inhibitor Selegiline as *Zelapar* (ODT) is for Parkinson disease	Start at 6 mg patch/day, can ↑ by increments of 3 mg to 12 mg/day	**CONTRAINDICATIONS** Use with serotonergic drugs (see Drug Interactions section), pheochromocytoma **SIDE EFFECTS** Constipation, gas, dry mouth, loss of appetite, sexual dysfunction

MAO Inhibitor Drug Interactions

- To avoid hypertensive crisis, serotonin syndrome or psychosis, MAO inhibitors cannot be used with drugs that increase concentrations of epinephrine, norepinephrine, serotonin or dopamine. Contraindicated drugs include: bupropion, buspirone, carbamazepine, cyclobenzaprine (and other skeletal muscle relaxants), dextromethorphan, oxcarbazepine, ephedrine and analogs (pseudoephedrine, phenylephrine), levodopa, linezolid, lithium, meperidine, SSRIs, SNRIs, TCAs, tramadol, methadone, mirtazapine, OTC diet pills/herbal weight loss products and St. John's wort.
- Patients taking MAO inhibitors (except selegiline patch) must avoid tyramine-rich foods, including aged cheese, pickled herring, yeast extract, air-dried meats, sauerkraut, soy sauce, fava beans and some red wines and beers (tap beer and any beer that has not been pasteurized – canned and bottled beers contain little or no tyramine). Foods can become high in tyramine when they have been aged, fermented, pickled or smoked.

MAO INHIBITORS - KEEP THEM SEPARATED

To avoid serotonin syndrome and hypertensive crisis

- 2-week washout is required between MAO inhibitors and:
  - ❑ SSRIs (see fluoxetine, below)
  - ❑ SNRIs
  - ❑ TCAs
  - ❑ Bupropion
- 5-week washout is required when changing from:
  - ❑ Fluoxetine → MAO inhibitor (due to fluoxetine's long half-life)

See Learning Drug Interactions chapter for more information on serotonin syndrome and hypertensive crisis with MAO inhibitors

MISCELLANEOUS ANTIDEPRESSANTS

DRUG	DOSING	SAFETY/SIDE EFFECTS/MONITORING
Mirtazapine *(Remeron, Remeron SolTab)* Used commonly in oncology and skilled nursing to help with sleep (dosed QHS) & to ↑ appetite (can ↑ weight gain in frail elderly)	Tetracyclic antidepressant, works by its central presynaptic alpha-2 adrenergic antagonist effects, which results in ↑ release of NE and 5-HT 15-45 mg QHS	**WARNINGS** Anticholinergic effects, QT prolongation, blood dyscrasias, CNS depression **SIDE EFFECTS** Sedation and ↑ appetite, weight gain, dry mouth, dizziness, agranulocytosis (rare)
Trazodone Rarely used as an antidepressant due to sedation. Used primarily off-label for sleep (dosed 50-100 mg QHS)	Inhibits 5-HT reuptake, blocks H1 and alpha1-adrenergic receptors IR: 150-300 mg/day in divided doses ER: 150-375 mg QHS	**CONTRAINDICATIONS** Concurrent use with MAO inhibitors, linezolid or IV methylene blue **SIDE EFFECTS** Sedation (trazodone ER may be less sedating), orthostasis (risk in elderly for falls) Sexual dysfunction and risk of priapism (painful erection longer than 4 hours, medical emergency)
Nefazodone Rarely used due to hepatotoxicity	Inhibits 5-HT and NE reuptake, blocks 5-HT2 and alpha1-adrenergic receptors 200-600 mg/day divided BID	**BOXED WARNING** Hepatotoxicity **CONTRAINDICATIONS** Hepatic disease, concurrent use with MAO inhibitors, carbamazepine, cisapride, pimozide, or triazolam **SIDE EFFECTS** Similar to trazodone, but less sedating

Drug Interactions

- Additive sedation; avoid use of any other sedating medications along with mirtazapine.
- Additive QT prolongation risk.
- Avoid use with other serotonergic drugs, due to increased risk of serotonin syndrome.
- Avoid use with MAO inhibitors due to increased risk of hypertensive crisis.

SELECTING THE BEST ANTIDEPRESSANT

Since many effective antidepressants are available, the choice of therapy should incorporate patient-specific information.

- Patient who is trying to avoid weight gain
  - ❑ Avoid mirtazapine
  - ❑ Consider: bupropion (associated with weight loss)
- Patient with cardiac issues (post MI, bradycardia, heart failure)
  - ❑ Avoid citalopram, escitalopram
  - ❑ Consider: sertraline (preferred)
- Patient at risk of seizures (seizure disorder, recent alcohol or sedative withdrawal) or history of anorexia/bulimia
  - ❑ Bupropion is contraindicated
  - ❑ Bupropion doses should not exceed 450 mg/day in any patient due to risk of seizures
- Patient with depression and pain (neuropathic or musculoskeletal)
  - ❑ Duloxetine is indicated for both
- Patient with insomnia and low body weight (i.e., weight gain desirable)
  - ❑ Mirtazapine side effects may be beneficial (sedation and weight gain)
- Patient who is trying to avoid sexual dysfunction
  - ❑ Avoid: SSRIs and SNRIs (high risk)
  - ❑ Consider: bupropion and mirtazapine (less sexual dysfunction)

TREATMENT-RESISTANT DEPRESSION

Depression that does not fully respond to two full treatment trials is considered treatment-resistant. Rule out bipolar disorder, assess medication adherence and verify that the antidepressant is at an optimal dose. This can sometimes be treated with a combination of standard antidepressants, or augment treatment with other medications. The medications in the following table are FDA-approved for treatment-resistant depression as adjunctive agents (i.e., in addition to another agent).

SELECT ADJUNCTIVE THERAPY IN TREATMENT-RESISTANT DEPRESSION

DRUG	DOSING	SAFETY/SIDE EFFECTS/MONITORING
Antipsychotics		
Aripiprazole (*Abilify, Abilify Maintena*) Tablet, ODT, solution, injection *Abilify Maintena, Aristada* (ER injections) and IR injection are used only for schizophrenia or bipolar mania	Start 2-5 mg/day (QAM), can ↑ to 15 mg/day	**BOXED WARNING** Elderly patients with dementia-related psychosis treated with antipsychotic drugs are at ↑ risk of death **CONTRAINDICATIONS** *Symbyax*: do not use with pimozide, thioridazine & caution with other drugs/conditions that cause QT prolongation **WARNINGS** Neuroleptic malignant syndrome, tardive dyskinesia (TD), falls, leukopenia, neutropenia Multiorgan hypersensitivity (drug reaction with eosinophilia and systemic symptoms, or DRESS) reactions with olanzapine (*Symbyax*) Pathological gambling and other compulsive behaviors (aripiprazole) **SIDE EFFECTS** Each of these drugs can cause metabolic issues, including dyslipidemia, weight gain, diabetes (less with aripiprazole) All can cause orthostasis/dizziness (can lead to falls) **Abilify** Anxiety, insomnia, akathisia, constipation, agitation **Olanzapine** Sedation, weight gain, ↑ lipids, ↑ glucose, EPS, QT prolongation (lower risk) **Quetiapine** Sedation, orthostasis, weight gain, ↑ lipids, ↑ glucose, EPS (lower risk) **Brexpiprazole** Weight gain, dyspepsia, diarrhea, agitation
Olanzapine/fluoxetine (*Symbyax*)	Usually started at 6 mg/25 mg capsule QHS (fluoxetine is activating, but olanzapine is more sedating), can ↑ cautiously	
Quetiapine (*Seroquel*, *Seroquel XR*)	Start 50 mg QHS, ↑ nightly to 150-300 mg QHS	
Brexpiprazole (*Rexulti*)	Start 0.5-1 mg/day, can ↑ 3 mg/day (titrate weekly)	
NMDA Receptor Antagonist		
Esketamine (*Spravato*) Nasal spray	Start 56 mg intranasally twice weekly, can ↑ to 84 mg twice weekly if tolerated Must be administered under the supervision of a health care provider; monitor for adverse effects for at least 2 hours following administration	**BOXED WARNING** Sedation and dissociative or perceptual changes, potential for abuse and misuse Due to risks, only available through a restricted distribution system under the *Spravato* REMS program

PATIENT COUNSELING

All Antidepressants

There are several counseling points that apply to all of the classes of antidepressants, listed below. See specific counseling for each class or drug in the sections that follow.

- Read the MedGuide that has been given to you. This drug can increase the risk of suicidal thinking and behavior, especially in adolescents and young adults.
- To reduce the risk of side effects, your healthcare provider may start at a low dose and gradually increase your dose.
- Take this medication exactly as prescribed. To help you remember, use it at the same time each day.
- It can take 1 – 2 weeks to feel a benefit from this drug and 6 – 8 weeks to feel the full effect on your mood. Tell your healthcare provider if your condition persists or worsens. You can try a medication in a different class. It may take more than one trial to find the right medication to help you feel better.

SSRIs

- Fluoxetine is taken in the morning; the others can be taken in the morning or at bedtime.
- This medication increases the levels of a chemical in your blood called serotonin. If it is taken with other OTC or prescription medications that also increase serotonin, toxicity can occur. Seek urgent medical care if you have symptoms of toxicity: severe nausea, dizziness and headache, diarrhea, feeling very agitated, a racing heartbeat or hallucinations.
- Some patients, but not all, have sexual difficulties when using this medicine. If this happens, talk with your healthcare provider. It may be possible to change to a medicine that does not cause these problems.
- Sertraline oral concentrate must be diluted before use. Immediately before administration, use the dropper provided to measure the required amount of concentrate; mix with four ounces (1/2 cup) of water, ginger ale, lemon/lime soda, lemonade, or orange juice only. Do not use with disulfiram.
- It is important to continue taking this medication even if you feel well. Do not stop taking this medication without consulting your healthcare provider. Some conditions can become worse when the drug is suddenly stopped. If you experience intolerable side effects, your dose may need to be slowly decreased

SNRIs

- This medication can cause nausea and stomach upset (if using venlafaxine IR, consider changing to XR).
- You may experience increased sweating; if so, discuss with your healthcare provider.
- This medication can increase your blood pressure. You should check your blood pressure regularly to make sure it stays in a safe range.
- Desvenlafaxine: when you take this medicine, you may see something in your stool that looks like a tablet. This is the empty shell from the tablet after the medicine has been absorbed by your body.
- Levomilnacipran: take the capsules whole. Do not open, chew or crush the capsules. Do not take with alcohol; this could cause the medicine to be released too quickly.
- This medication increases the levels of a chemical in your blood called serotonin. If it is taken with other OTC or prescription medications that also increase serotonin, toxicity can occur. Seek urgent medical care if you have symptoms of toxicity: severe nausea, dizziness and headache, diarrhea, feeling very agitated, a racing heartbeat or hallucinations.
- Some patients, but not all, have sexual difficulties when using this medicine. If this happens, talk with your healthcare provider. It may be possible to change to a medicine that does not cause these problems.
- Do not crush or chew extended-release formulations.

Tricyclics

- You may experience dry eyes and mouth, constipation or difficulty urinating. You can use stool softeners or a laxative for constipation and an eye lubricant for dry eyes. Dry mouth can contribute to dental decay (cavities) and difficulty chewing food. It is important to use proper dental hygiene, including brushing and flossing, while taking this medication. Sugar free lozenges can be helpful.
- This drug can cause your blood pressure to fluctuate, which can cause dizziness and lightheadedness. This can cause falls. It is important to get up slowly from the lying position or from sitting. Hold onto the bed, a bed rail or a strong table top until you feel steady.
- If you experience anxiety, or insomnia (sometimes with vivid dreams), these usually go away. If they do not, contact your healthcare provider.

Bupropion

- Avoid taking at or near bedtime, can be activating.
- This drug should not be used if you have a seizure disorder, anorexia or bulimia.
- If using for smoking cessation, inform patients to report changes in mood or behavior.

MAO Inhibitors

- Avoid interacting foods and drugs (see list in above drug interaction section). Stay away from tyramine-rich containing foods.
- Seek immediate medical care if you experience any of these symptoms: sudden severe headache, nausea, stiff neck, vomiting, a fast or slow heartbeat or a change in the way your heart beats (palpitations), tight chest pain, a lot of sweating, confusion, dilated pupils and light sensitivity.
- *Emsam* patch application: change once daily. Pick a time of day you can remember. Apply to either upper chest or back (below the neck and above the waist), upper thigh, or to the outer surface of the upper arm. Rotate sites and do not use same site two days in a row. Wash hands with soap after applying patch. Do not expose to heat. The washout period counseling (discussed previously) includes the patch.

Other Antidepressants

- Trazodone causes drowsiness and should be taken at bedtime.
- While taking trazodone, if you experience an erection lasting longer than 4 hours, seek medical immediate help.
- Mirtazapine causes drowsiness and should be taken at bedtime. This drug can increase appetite.

Select Guidelines/References

Practice Guideline for the Treatment of Patients with Major Depressive Disorder, 2010. https://psychiatryonline.org/pb/assets/raw/sitewide/practice_guidelines/guidelines/mdd.pdf (accessed 2019 Apr 13)

VA/DoD Clinical Practice Guideline for the Management of Major Depressive Disorder, 2016. https://www.healthquality.va.gov/guidelines/MH/mdd/MDDCPGClinicianSummaryFINAL1.pdf (accessed 2019 Apr 13)

Diagnostic and Statistical Manual of Mental Disorders (DSM-5).

CHAPTER CONTENT

Background 892
Pathophysiology 892
Natural Products 893
Drug Treatment 893
Medications/Illicit Drugs that Can Cause Psychotic Symptoms 893
Formulations 893
Boxed Warning/Other Warnings 894
First-Generation Antipsychotics 894
Second-Generation Antipsychotics 895
Picking the Best Antipsychotic 895
Psychosis in Parkinson Disease 898
Antipsychotic Drug Interactions 898
Patient Counseling 898
Tardive Dyskinesia 899
Neuroleptic Malignant Syndrome 900

DEFINITIONS: EXTRAPYRAMIDAL SIDE EFFECTS (EPS)

Extrapyramidal side effects (EPS) are a group of side effects related to irregular movements.

Dystonias: prolonged contraction of muscles during drug initiation, including painful muscle spasms; life-threatening if airway is compromised. Higher risk with younger males. Centrally-acting anticholinergics (diphenhydramine, benztropine) can be used for prophylaxis or treatment.

Akathisia: restlessness with anxiety and an inability to remain still; treated with anticholinergics (diphenhydramine, benztropine), benzodiazepines or propranolol

Parkinsonism: looks similar to Parkinson disease, with tremors, abnormal gait and bradykinesia; treat with anticholinergics, or propranolol if tremor is the main symptom.

Tardive dyskinesias (TD): abnormal facial movements, primarily in the tongue or mouth; higher risk with elderly females. TD can be irreversible. Must stop the drug and replace with an SGA with low EPS risk (e.g., quetiapine, clozapine).

Dyskinesias: abnormal movements; more common with dopamine replacement for Parkinson disease.

CONTENT LEGEND

= Study Tip Gal   = Key Drug Guy

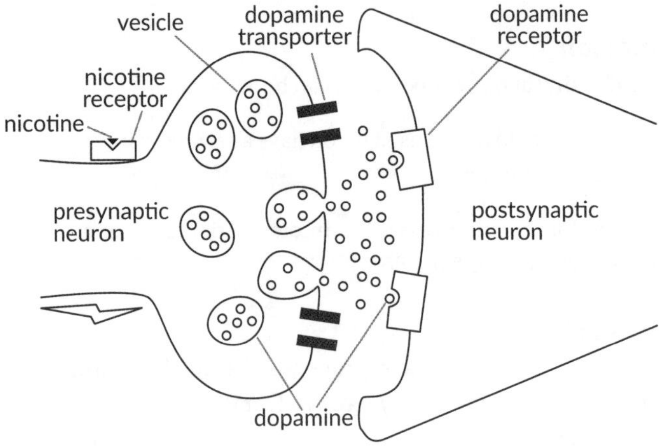

CHAPTER 64
SCHIZOPHRENIA/PSYCHOSIS

BACKGROUND

Schizophrenia is a chronic, severe and disabling thought disorder that occurs in ~1% of all societies regardless of class, color, religion or culture. The cause is multifactorial and includes altered brain structure and chemistry, primarily involving dopamine and glutamine. Genetics (inherited susceptibility) and environmental factors are important in disease development. Patients suffer from hallucinations (sensing something that is not present), delusions (false beliefs) and disorganized thinking/behavior. They can withdraw from the world around them and enter a world of psychosis, where they struggle to differentiate reality from altered perceptions. Schizophrenia ranges from relatively mild to severe. Some people can function adequately in daily life, while others need specialized, intensive care. Treatment adherence is important and often difficult to obtain, primarily due to the patient's inability to recognize their illness. Many patients with schizophrenia live a life of torment where they cannot care for themselves. This condition has one of the highest suicide rates.

The onset of symptoms usually begins in young adulthood. A diagnosis is not based on lab tests, but on the patient's behavior, which includes both negative and positive signs and symptoms (described on the following page). The Diagnostic and Statistical Manual of Mental Disorders, 5th Edition (DSM-5) is the current tool used to diagnose schizophrenia and other psychiatric disorders.

PATHOPHYSIOLOGY

Schizophrenia is a thought disorder involving abnormal neurotransmitters. Patients with schizophrenia have increased dopamine levels, and may also have changes in glutamate levels. Dopamine and glutamate modulate each other, but the role of glutamate in schizophrenia is not well understood. Genetics, environment, stressors and some drugs can also be contributing factors (see Key Drugs Guy on the following page).

DSM-5 DIAGNOSTIC CRITERIA FOR SCHIZOPHRENIA

Note: delusions, hallucinations or disorganized speech must be present

Negative signs and symptoms	Positive signs and symptoms
Loss of interest in everyday activities	Hallucinations; can be auditory (hearing voices), visual, or somatic
Lack of emotion (apathy)	Delusions: beliefs held by the patient that are without a basis in reality
Inability to plan or carry out activities	Disorganized thinking/behavior, incoherent speech, often on unrelated topics, purposeless behavior, or difficulty speaking and organizing thoughts, such as stopping in mid-sentence or jumbling together meaningless words
Poor hygiene	Difficulty paying attention
Social withdrawal	
Loss of motivation (avolition)	
Lack of speech (alogia)	

Up to 50% of patients with Parkinson disease experience hallucinations or delusions at some point during their disease course. Dopamine is critical to many central nervous system functions, including movement. Parkinson medications increase dopamine in the brain, which relieves the motor symptoms, but increased dopamine can trigger hallucinations or delusions. Treatment of psychosis in Parkinson patients can be difficult, as many antipsychotics exacerbate the motor symptoms of the disease. Pimavanserin *(Nuplazid)* is approved for psychosis in patients with Parkinson disease.

NATURAL PRODUCTS

Fish oils are being used for psychosis and other psychiatric disorders (e.g., ADHD, depression). The evidence is preliminary, but promising. Considering the debilitating nature of schizophrenia, prescription medications are usually required.

DRUG TREATMENT

Antipsychotics primarily block dopamine receptors. Newer agents also block serotonin and other receptors. Current treatments target dopamine hyperactivity, but also affect dopamine involved in focus and the ability to pay attention (leading to side effects). These drugs are effective at treating the positive symptoms of schizophrenia. The negative symptoms (e.g., lack of motivation, cognitive and functional impairment) remain for many patients and take longer to respond to antipsychotics, if at all. Researchers anticipate that a better understanding of glutamate receptors will improve functional levels. As the pathways are better understood, along with drug development, a "fine tuning" of treatment will improve results.

Side-effect profiles play an important role in selecting initial treatment for schizophrenia. Second-generation antipsychotics (SGAs) are used first-line due to a lower risk of extrapyramidal side effects (EPS). There is no need to switch patients that are stabilized on a first-generation antipsychotic and doing well. Some patients respond better to a first-generation antipsychotic (FGA).

MEDICATIONS/ILLICIT DRUGS THAT CAN CAUSE PSYCHOTIC SYMPTOMS

KEY DRUGS

Anticholinergics (centrally-acting, high doses)

Cannabis

Dextromethorphan

Dopamine or dopamine agonists (e.g., *Requip, Mirapex, Sinemet*)

Interferons

Stimulants, especially if already at risk (includes amphetamines)

Systemic steroids (typically with lack of sleep – ICU psychosis)

Illicit substances

Bath salts (synthetic cathinones, MDPV)

Cocaine, especially "crack" cocaine

Lysergic acid diethylamide (LSD, hallucinogenics)

Methamphetamine, ice, crystal

Phencyclidine (PCP)

FORMULATIONS

Long-Acting Injections: provide the benefit of increased adherence with the medication. They are used in acute care settings prior to discharge in patients without adequate resources (e.g., homelessness). Antipsychotics available as long acting injectables include *Haldol Decanoate* (every four weeks), *Risperdal Consta* (every two weeks), *Invega Sustenna* (every four weeks), *Invega Trinza* (every three months) and *Abilify Maintena* (every four weeks).

Orally Disintegrating Tablets (ODTs): used to help solve the problem of "cheeking" in an institutional setting, where the medication is hidden inside the cheek and then spit out later. The tablet dissolves rapidly in the mouth without water. Several of the SGAs are available as ODTs: clozapine, olanzapine, risperidone, aripiprazole and asenapine.

Acute IM Injections: intramuscular (IM) injections provide "stat" relief to help calm down an acutely agitated, psychotic patient for their own safety and the safety of others. They are often mixed with other drugs (called "cocktails"), such as benzodiazepines for anxiolytic and sedative effects, and anticholinergics to reduce dystonic risk (e.g., the "*Haldol* cocktail" contains haloperidol, lorazepam and diphenhydramine). Oral absorption could take up to an hour to calm the patient down. The patient will be sedated and hopefully sleep through the acute symptoms. Olanzapine and benzodiazepines should not be given together (IM) due to orthostasis risk.

BOXED WARNING/OTHER WARNINGS

Antipsychotics are not indicated for agitation control in elderly patients with dementia related psychosis. When they are used for this indication, there is an increased risk of mortality. There is a boxed warning concerning this risk, and counseling is required. Most deaths are cardiovascular (e.g., heart failure, sudden death) or infectious in nature. Several antipsychotics also carry a warning for an increased risk of stroke in patients with dementia. All antipsychotics carry a warning for falls. This information is abbreviated in the drug tables that follow; refer back to this section as needed.

FIRST-GENERATION ANTIPSYCHOTICS

First-generation antipsychotics (FGAs) work mainly by blocking dopamine (D2) receptors, and minimal serotonin (5HT2A) receptor blockade. High-potency FGAs, such as haloperidol, are associated with a high risk of EPS effects, a moderate risk of sedation and a lower risk of orthostatic hypotension, tachycardia and anticholinergic effects compared to low-potency FGAs. In contrast, low-potency FGAs are associated with a lower risk of EPS, a high degree of sedation, and a high risk of cardiovascular effects (orthostatic hypotension, tachycardia) and anticholinergic effects. Other side effects vary by the specific medication. FGAs are associated with a moderate risk of weight gain, a low risk of metabolic effects, a higher risk of EPS and a risk of sexual side effects.

First-Generation Antipsychotics (FGAs)

DRUG	DOSING	SAFETY/SIDE EFFECTS/MONITORING
Low Potency		**BOXED WARNINGS** Elderly patients with dementia-related psychosis treated with antipsychotics are at an increased risk of death compared to placebo Thioridazine: QT prolongation *Adasuve*: bronchospasm (REMS program) **SIDE EFFECTS** Sedation and EPS: lower potency drugs have ↑ sedation and ↓ EPS, and higher potency drugs have ↓ sedation with ↑ EPS Leukopenia, neutropenia, and agranulocytosis (sometimes fatal) Seizures (phenothiazines, butyrophenones), temperature dysregulation, allergic reactions; hepatic, ophthalmologic and hematologic side effects Cardiovascular effects: orthostasis, tachycardia (IV haloperidol has high risk) QT prolongation (especially with thioridazine, haloperidol, chlorpromazine) Sexual dysfunction *Adasuve*: dysgeusia (bad, bitter, or metallic taste in mouth), sedation
Chlorpromazine	300-1,000 mg/day, divided	
Thioridazine	300-800 mg/day, divided	
Mid potency		
Loxapine (*Loxitane, Adasuve*- inhalation powder for acute agitation)	30-100 mg/day, divided	
Perphenazine	8-64 mg/day, divided	
High Potency		
Haloperidol (*Haldol, Haldol Decanoate*) Oral, IV, Decanoate IM Class: butyrophenone Also used for Tourette syndrome (for tics and vocal outbursts)	Oral (tablet, solution): start 0.5-2 mg BID-TID, up to 30 mg/day IV: usually 5-10 mg Decanoate (monthly): IM only; for conversion from PO, use 10-20x the PO dose	
Fluphenazine Tablet, elixir, injectable, IM decanoate	6-12 mg/day, divided Decanoate (every 2 weeks): IM only	
Thiothixene	15-60 mg/day, divided	
Trifluoperazine	15-50 mg/day, divided	

SECOND-GENERATION ANTIPSYCHOTICS

Second-generation antipsychotics (SGAs) work by blocking dopamine (D2) and serotonin (5HT2A) receptors. Aripiprazole, brexpiprazole and cariprazine are unique: they act as D2 and 5HT1A partial agonists. Brexpiprazole also acts as a 5HT2A antagonist. SGAs have a variety of side effects (see Study Tip Gal). Metabolic side effects are a well known phenomenon with SGAs, including weight gain, lipid abnormalities and hyperglycemia, which can lead to diabetes. Although at a lower incidence than FGAs, many SGAs exhibit dose-related EPS. Hormonal issues can be problematic due to increasing prolactin levels, causing gynecomastia (painful, swollen breast tissue), galactorrhea (breastmilk production without pregnancy), sexual dysfunction and irregular or missed periods. Cardiovascular effects, including QT prolongation can be present with SGAs (ziprasidone has the highest risk). Adverse effects limit the use of a drug; for example clozapine is superior in efficacy, but has multiple boxed warnings. It is particularly known for agranulocytosis, seizures, myocarditis and high metabolic risk. Clozapine is not recommended for first-line use, but a trial should be considered for very ill patients who have had no or poor response to two trials of antipsychotic medication (at least one should be an SGA).

As with the FGAs, all SGAs have a boxed warning for an increased risk of death in elderly patients with dementia-related psychosis. An increased risk of cerebrovascular events (e.g., transient ischemic attack or stroke) is seen with SGAs, especially risperidone, paliperidone, olanzapine and aripiprazole.

Due to the potential for significant metabolic side effects when initiating antipsychotics, the American Diabetes Association (ADA) recommends screening and monitoring for overweight and obesity, dyslipidemia, hyperglycemia, hypertension and personal or family history of risk. During treatment, the patient should be monitored for changes in weight, waist circumference, plasma lipid and glucose levels and acute symptoms of diabetes.

Selecting a Second-Generation Antipsychotic

The SGAs are chosen based on several considerations, which should be identified when examining a patient case:

- Patient's past history: what drugs have helped control the symptoms (e.g., quieted the voices down), and drugs that did not help (if they were taken, and at a reasonable dose). Adherence to treatment should also be considered.
- Side effects: these can be acceptable in some patients but not in others. For example, if the patient is overweight, do not pick an agent which worsens metabolic issues. Patients with a history of tardive dyskinesia (TD), or any type of movement disorder, should avoid risperidone, paliperidone and lurasidone, which have higher risks of EPS. The Study Tip Gal below lists the drugs most likely to cause major adverse effects - avoid using them in an at-risk patient.
- When assessing treatment resistance or evaluating the best option for a partial response, it is important to evaluate whether the patient has had an adequate trial (at least 4 – 6 weeks) of an antipsychotic, including whether the dose is adequate and whether the patient has been taking the medication as prescribed.
- The prescriber's familiarity with a drug, formulary considerations and costs will also factor in to treatment selection.

PICKING THE BEST ANTIPSYCHOTIC

Each patient will respond differently to antipsychotics. A trial of different drugs may be necessary before finding the best fit.

All antipsychotics carry some risk of the following side effects. On a case, evaluate patient-specific factors to help pick the best drug and avoid drugs that could cause harm.

FGA: ↑ EPS, ↓ weight gain/metabolic side effects
SGA: ↓ EPS, but ↑ metabolic effects

EPS
Lowest risk – Quetiapine (recommended in patients with Parkinson disease who require antipsychotics)
Highest risk - FGAs, risperidone, paliperidone

Metabolic side effects
Highest risk – Clozapine, olanzapine, quetiapine
Moderate risk – Risperidone, paliperidone
Lower risk – FGAs, aripiprazole, ziprasidone, lurasidone and asenapine

QT prolongation
Highest risk – Thioridazine, haloperidol, ziprasidone

Hematological effects
Highest risk – Clozapine (agranulocytosis)

Cerebrovascular events (e.g., TIA, stroke)
Highest risk – Risperidone

↑ Prolactin
Highest risk – Risperidone, paliperidone

Seizure
Highest risk – Clozapine (dose-dependent)

Second-Generation Antipsychotics (SGAs)

DRUG	DOSING	SAFETY/SIDE EFFECTS/MONITORING
Aripiprazole (*Abilify*, *Abilify Maintena*, *Aristada* injection) Tablet, ODT, IM suspension Also approved for irritability with autism and Tourette disorder	10-30 mg PO QAM *Abilify Maintena*-IM suspension, give monthly *Aristada*-IM suspension, give every 4-8 weeks	**SIDE EFFECTS** Akathisia, anxiety, insomnia, constipation Less weight gain, some QT prolongation **NOTES** *Aristada* frequency dependent on dose
Clozapine (*Clozaril*, *FazaClo ODT, Versacloz* suspension) Only if failed to respond to treatment with 2 standard AP treatments, or had significant ADRs	300-900 mg/day, divided (start at 12.5 mg and titrate, also titrate off since abrupt discontinuation can cause seizures) Clozapine is very effective and has ↓ risk of EPS/TD, but used no sooner than 3rd line due to severe side effect potential (metabolic effects, neutropenia)	**BOXED WARNINGS, CLOZAPINE-SPECIFIC** Significant risk of potentially life-threatening neutropenia/agranulocytosis (REMS program) Bradycardia, orthostatic hypotension, syncope, and cardiac arrest; risk is highest during the initial titration period especially with rapid dose increases – titrate slowly Myocarditis and cardiomyopathy; discontinue if suspected Seizures, dose related; start at no higher than 12.5 mg once or twice daily, titrate slowly, using divided doses; use with caution in patients at seizure risk (e.g., seizure history, head trauma, alcoholism or taking medications which lower seizure threshold) **SIDE EFFECTS** Orthostasis, syncope, weight gain, ↑ lipids, ↑ glucose, somnolence, dizziness, insomnia, GI upset, sialorrhea (hypersalivation), QT prolongation, agranulocytosis, seizures, myocarditis **MONITORING** REMS: prescribers and pharmacies must be certified and patients must enroll with the Clozapine REMS To start treatment, baseline ANC must be ≥ 1,500/mm^3 Check ANC weekly x 6 months, then every 2 weeks x 6 months, then monthly Stop therapy if ANC < 1,000/mm^3 **NOTES** Smoking reduces drug levels
Lurasidone (*Latuda*)	40-160 mg/day, divided Take with food ≥ 350 kcal	**CONTRAINDICATIONS** Use with strong CYP450 3A4 inducers and inhibitors **SIDE EFFECTS** EPS, somnolence, dystonias, nausea, agitation, akathisia Nearly weight, lipid and blood glucose neutral
Olanzapine (*Zyprexa*, *Zydis ODT, Zyprexa Relprevv* injection) + fluoxetine (*Symbyax*) for treatment-resistant depression	10-20 mg QHS IM Injection (acute agitation) *Relprevv* inj suspension lasts 2-4 weeks; restricted use	**BOXED WARNING** *Zyprexa Relprevv* – sedation (including coma) and delirium (including agitation, anxiety, confusion, disorientation) have been observed following injection; must be administered in a registered healthcare facility, and patients must be monitored for 3 hours post-injection (REMS program requirements). **SIDE EFFECTS** Somnolence, weight gain, ↑ lipids, ↑ glucose, EPS, QT prolongation (lower risk), multiorgan hypersensitivity (DRESS) reactions **NOTES** Smoking reduces drug levels

DRUG	DOSING	SAFETY/SIDE EFFECTS/MONITORING
Paliperidone *(Invega, Invega Sustenna, Invega Trinza)* Active metabolite of risperidone; SEs similar	PO: 3-12 mg daily CrCl < 50 mL/min: 3 mg daily CrCl < 10 mL/min: Not recommended OROS delivery enables once daily dosing-do not break or crush *Invega Sustenna*, IM injection, give monthly *Invega Trinza*, IM injection, give every 3 months (start only after receiving *Invega Sustenna* x 4 months)	**SIDE EFFECTS** ↑ prolactin – sexual dysfunction, galactorrhea, irregular/missed periods EPS, especially at higher doses Tachycardia, headache, sedation, anxiety QT prolongation Weight gain, ↑ lipids, ↑ glucose
Quetiapine *(Seroquel,* *Seroquel XR)*	400-800 mg/day, divided BID or XR QHS	**SIDE EFFECTS** Somnolence, orthostasis, possible ocular effects Weight gain, ↑ lipids, ↑ glucose Low EPS risk – often used for psychosis in Parkinson disease QT prolongation (lower risk) **NOTES** Take XR at night, without food or with a light meal (≤ 300 kcal)
Risperidone *(Risperdal, Risperdal Consta,* *Risperdone M-TAB ODT, Perseris)* Also approved for irritability associated with autism	4-16 mg/day, divided *Risperdal Consta*: IM injection, give every 2 weeks, 25-50 mg *Perseris*: SC injection, give monthly	**SIDE EFFECTS** Somnolence EPS, especially at higher doses ↑ prolactin – sexual dysfunction, galactorrhea, irregular/missed periods Orthostasis Weight gain, ↑ lipids, ↑ glucose QT prolongation **NOTES** > 6 mg: ↑ prolactin and ↑ EPS
Ziprasidone *(Geodon)*	40-160 mg/day, divided BID Take with food Acute injection: *Geodon IM* 10 mg Q2H or 20 mg Q4H Max: 40 mg/day IM	**CONTRAINDICATIONS** QT prolongation; contraindicated with QT risk **SIDE EFFECTS** Somnolence (some have insomnia), respiratory tract infection, headache, dizziness, nausea
Asenapine *(Saphris)* Sublingual tablet	10-20 mg/day, divided BID No food/drink for 10 min after dose	**CONTRAINDICATIONS** Severe hepatic impairment **SIDE EFFECTS** Somnolence, tongue numbness; EPS (5% more than placebo), QT prolongation
Brexpiprazole *(Rexulti)*	2-4 mg daily	**SIDE EFFECTS** Weight gain, dyspepsia, diarrhea, akathisia
Cariprazine *(Vraylar)*	1.5-6 mg daily	**SIDE EFFECTS** EPS, dystonias, headache, insomnia
Iloperidone *(Fanapt)*	12-24 mg/day, divided Titrate slowly due to orthostasis/ dizziness	**SIDE EFFECTS** Dizziness, somnolence, orthostasis, tachycardia QT prolongation

PSYCHOSIS IN PARKINSON DISEASE

Pimavanserin is an inverse agonist and antagonist at serotonin 5-HT2A receptors and to a lesser extent at serotonin 5-HT2C receptors. It is approved for treatment of hallucinations and delusions associated with Parkinson disease psychosis. It does not affect dopamine receptors, and does not worsen motor symptoms of Parkinson disease.

DRUG	DOSING	SAFETY/SIDE EFFECTS/MONITORING
Pimavanserin *(Nuplazid)*	34 mg PO daily (two 17 mg tablets)	**WARNINGS** Not approved for dementia-related psychosis. See Boxed Warnings discussion. QT prolongation; avoid use with drugs that also increase the QT interval and in patients with risk factors for prolonged QT interval. **SIDE EFFECTS** Peripheral edema, confusion.

ANTIPSYCHOTIC DRUG INTERACTIONS

- All antipsychotics can prolong the QT interval. Some are considered higher risk than others. The higher risk QT prolonging SGAs are noted previously. Thioridazine, a FGA, is high-risk for QT prolongation (boxed warning). Use caution with other medications that increase risk.
- Smoking can reduce plasma levels of olanzapine and clozapine; patients who smoke can require higher doses.
- High plasma levels of risperidone and paliperidone can ↑ prolactin and cause EPS. Caution when using risperidone concomitantly with CYP2D6 inhibitors, including paroxetine and fluoxetine.
- Avoid concurrent drugs that lower the seizure threshold with clozapine.
- Some of the APs have CYP450 drug interactions which could require dosing adjustments.
- Monitoring for an increased risk of respiratory depression and hypotension when administered with benzodiazepines.
- Caution with other dopamine blocking agents such as metoclopramide *(Reglan)*, as EPS and TD risk may be increased.

PATIENT COUNSELING

All Antipsychotics

- Read the MedGuide dispensed with this medication. In addition to individual warnings, several of the drugs in this class work for depression, and these drugs include a warning for suicidality, particularly among adolescents.
- This medication can decrease hallucinations (such as voices) and can quiet the noise. It can help you to think more clearly and feel positive about yourself, feel less nervous, and take a more active part in everyday life.
- There can be a slight increased risk of serious, possibly fatal, side effects when this medication is used in older adults with dementia. This medication is not approved for the treatment of dementia-related behavior problems.
- Contact your healthcare provider right away if you experience uncontrollable movements of the mouth, tongue, cheeks, jaw, arms or legs.
- Contact your healthcare provider immediately and seek immediate medical attention if you experience fever, sweating, severe muscle stiffness (rigidity) and confusion.
- Use caution when driving, operating machinery, or performing other hazardous activities. This drug can cause dizziness, confusion and drowsiness.
- Dizziness is more likely to occur when you rise from a sitting or lying position. Rise slowly to prevent dizziness and a possible fall.
- Avoid consuming alcohol during treatment with this drug. Alcohol will increase sleepiness and dizziness and can interfere with the drug's ability to work properly.
- Tell your healthcare provider if your condition persists or worsens.

Clozapine

- This medication can cause a serious immune system problem called agranulocytosis (low white blood cells). To make sure you have enough white blood cells, you will need to have a blood test before you begin taking clozapine, and then have your blood tested regularly during your treatment.
- Clozapine can cause seizures, especially with higher doses, or if it is increased too quickly. Let your healthcare provider know if you have ever had seizures. While taking this medication, avoid activities during which a sudden loss of consciousness could be dangerous (e.g., driving, operating machinery, swimming).

- This medication can rarely cause an inflammation of the heart muscle (myocarditis). Seek immediate medical attention if you have weakness, difficult/rapid breathing, chest pain, or swelling of the ankles/legs. The risk is highest during the first month of treatment.

Olanzapine, Clozapine, Risperidone, Paliperidone and Quetiapine

- This drug has a risk of weight gain and increasing your cholesterol, blood pressure and blood glucose. These must be monitored, and treated if they occur. Talk to your healthcare provider if you experience any symptoms of high blood glucose, including excessive thirst, frequent urination, excessive hunger or fatigue.
- Your healthcare provider will order blood tests during treatment to monitor for side effects.

Different Types of Oral Formulations

- *Saphris*: place the sublingual tablet under the tongue and allow it to dissolve completely. The tablet will dissolve in saliva within seconds. Do not eat or drink for 10 minutes after taking this medication. Your tongue will feel numb afterwards.
- Aripiprazole ODT, *FazaClo, Risperdal M-Tab, Zyprexa Zydis*: Immediately upon opening the foil blister, using dry hands, remove the tablet and place in your mouth. Do not push the tablet through the foil because it can crumble. The tablet dissolves quickly so it can be easily swallowed with or without liquid.
- Most ODTs contain phenylalanine. Check with a healthcare provider before use if you have phenylketonuria (PKU).
- *Risperdal* oral solution can be administered directly from the calibrated pipette, or mixed with water, coffee, orange juice and low-fat milk; it cannot be mixed with cola or tea.
- *Latuda* should be taken with food that contains at least 350 kcal. *Geodon* is taken with food.
- Quetiapine immediate-release tablet can be taken without regard to meals. The extended-release tablet *(Seroquel XR)* should be taken without food or with a light meal (up to 300 kcal).
- Take olanzapine once daily at night because it is long-acting and sedating.
- *Invega*: part of the tablet can pass into your stool after your body has absorbed the medicine. If you see the tablet in your stool, it is nothing to worry about.

TARDIVE DYSKINESIA

Tardive dyskinesia (TD) is a complication that can occur with dopamine receptor blockade, as with antipsychotics. TD can cause irreversible symptoms that include uncontrollable movements in the tongue, face, trunk and extremities and can interfere with walking, talking and breathing. Valbenazine was the first medication approved for treatment of TD. It reversibly inhibits vesicular monoamine transporter 2 (VMAT2), a transporter that regulates monoamine uptake from the cytoplasm to the synaptic vesicle for storage and release. Deutetrabenazine, is another VMAT2 inhibitor that is approved for TD. This drug is also used to treat chorea associated with Huntington's disease.

DRUG	DOSING	SAFETY/SIDE EFFECTS/MONITORING
Valbenazine *(Ingrezza)*	Start 40 mg PO daily, increase in 1 week to 80 mg PO daily Moderate-severe hepatic impairment: adjustment required CYP2D6 poor metabolizer: consider dose reduction	**WARNINGS** Somnolence, QT prolongation (avoid in long QT syndrome)
Deutetrabenazine *(Austedo)* Also approved for chorea associated with Huntington's disease	Start 6mg PO BID, increase weekly based on response (max 48 mg/day) Concurrent strong CYP2D6 inhibitors or CYP2D6 poor metabolizer: max dose 36 mg/day	**CONTRAINDICATIONS** Hepatic impairment, administration with tetrabenazine or valbenazine, administration with an MAO inhibitor (within 14 days) **WARNINGS** Somnolence, QT prolongation (avoid in long QT syndrome)

Drug Interactions

- Avoid use with MAO inhibitors.
- Valbenazine is a substrate of CYP3A4 and 2D6. Dose reduction is required when given with strong inhibitors of CYP3A4 (e.g., itraconazole, clarithromycin) or 2D6 (e.g., paroxetine, fluoxetine).
- Valbenazine is a P-gp inhibitor and can increase digoxin concentrations. Dosage adjustment of digoxin may be required.
- Deutetrabenazine is a substrate of CYP3A4 and 2D6. Dose reduction is required when given with strong inhibitors of CYP3A4 (e.g., itraconazole, clarithromycin) or 2D6 (e.g., paroxetine, fluoxetine).

NEUROLEPTIC MALIGNANT SYNDROME

Antipsychotics used to be called neuroleptics. Neuroleptic malignant syndrome (NMS) is rare but is highly lethal. It occurs most commonly with the FGAs and is due to D2 blockade. NMS can occur, but is less common with SGAs and with other dopamine blocking agents, including metoclopramide *(Reglan)*. The majority of cases occur within two weeks of starting treatment or immediately following high doses of injectables given alongside multiple oral doses. Occasionally, patients develop NMS even after years of antipsychotic use. NMS is a medical emergency, as the intense muscle contractions can lead to acute renal injury (due to rhabdomyolysis from the destruction of muscle tissue), suffocation and death.

Signs Include

- Hyperthermia (high fever, with profuse sweating)
- Extreme muscle rigidity (called "lead pipe" rigidity), which can lead to respiratory failure
- Mental status changes
- Other signs can include tachycardia, tachypnea and blood pressure changes

Laboratory Results

- ↑ creatine phosphokinase and ↑ white blood cells

Treatment

- Taper off the antipsychotic quickly and consider another choice (quetiapine or clozapine).
- Provide supportive care: cardiorespiratory and hemodynamic support and control of electrolyte balance.
- Cool the patient down: cooling bed, antipyretics, cooled IV fluids.
- Muscle relaxation with benzodiazepines or dantrolene (*Ryanodex, Dantrium, Revonto*) is sometimes used, and some cases may require a dopamine agonist such as bromocriptine.

Select Guidelines/References

American Psychiatric Association. (2013). Diagnostic and Statistical Manual of Mental Disorders: DSM-5. Washington, D.C: American Psychiatric Association

American Psychiatric Association Guideline Watch (September 2009): Practice Guideline for the Treatment of Patients with Schizophrenia http://psychiatryonline.org/pb/assets/raw/sitewide/practice_guidelines/guidelines/schizophrenia-watch.pdf (accessed 2019 Apr 14)

CHAPTER CONTENT

Background 901
Diagnostic Criteria 901
Bipolar Mania or Illicit Drug Use? 902
Drug Treatment 902
Acute Treatment 902
Maintenance 902
Pregnancy 902
Antiepileptic Drugs 902
Second Generation Antipsychotics 903
Mood Stabilizer: Lithium 903
Lithium-Not Easy to Initiate 904

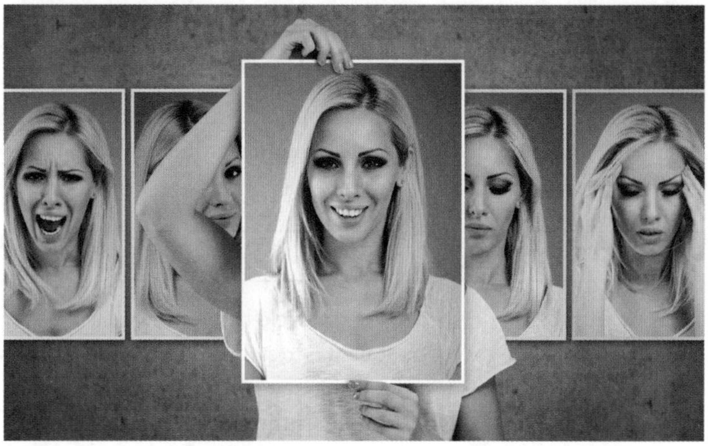

CHAPTER 65
BIPOLAR DISORDER

BACKGROUND

Bipolar disorder is a mood disorder in which moods can fluctuate from an extremely sad or hopeless state of depression to an abnormally elevated, overexcited or irritable mood called mania or hypomania. Each mood episode represents a drastic change from a person's usual mood and behavior. A mood episode that includes symptoms of both mania and depression is called a mixed state.

Bipolar disorder is classified as bipolar I or bipolar II, which differ primarily by the severity of mania the patient experiences (see Bipolar Classifications and Definitions). Another milder form not specifically addressed in this chapter is called "cyclothymic disorder" where the criteria for depression or mania are not fully met.

The prevalence of bipolar disorder is ~2.6% among U.S. adults. Bipolar disorder can lead to problems with relationships, employment and disrupt lives. It can lead to anxiety disorders, drug abuse and suicide.

BIPOLAR CLASSIFICATIONS AND DEFINITIONS

BIPOLAR I
Severe mania, and usually, bouts of intense depression.

May be psychotic/delusional and may require hospitalization.

BIPOLAR II
Hypomania, and usually, bouts of intense depression. Hypomania does not affect social/work functioning, does not cause psychosis nor require hospitalization.

People may seek help in the depressive phase (not usually in the manic phase) which can lead to a misdiagnosis of depression only.

BIPOLAR DEPRESSION
Symptoms of depressive episode are predominant including feelings of sadness or depressed mood, and/or loss of interest in activities once enjoyed.

PSYCHOSIS
Severe mental condition where there is a loss of contact with reality, involves abnormal thinking and perception (e.g., hallucinations and delusions).

DIAGNOSTIC CRITERIA

Mania
Abnormally elevated or irritable mood for at least a week (or any duration if hospitalization is needed);
≥ 3 symptoms required for diagnosis
(If mood is only irritable, ≥ 4 symptoms)

- Inflated self-esteem
- Sleeping less
- Talkative
- Jumping from one topic to the next
- Easily distracted
- Increase in goal-directed activity
- Involved with high-risk, pleasurable activities (e.g., buying sprees, sexual indiscretions, gambling)

Depression (See Depression chapter)
Common; 1 in 5 commit suicide

CONTENT LEGEND

= Study Tip Gal

BIPOLAR MANIA OR ILLICIT DRUG USE?

A toxicology screen should be taken prior to the start of treatment, and as needed, to rule-out mania due to illicit drug use.

DRUG TREATMENT

Patients with bipolar disorder usually cycle between mania and depression. The goal of treatment is to stabilize the mood without inducing a depressive or manic state. The traditional mood stabilizers, which include lithium, valproate, lamotrigine and carbamazepine, treat both mania and depression, without inducing either state. Antipsychotics, while not traditional mood stabilizers, can help to stabilize the mood when a patient with mania also has psychosis. They can be used alone or with one of the traditional mood stabilizers. Patients with bipolar disorder are more susceptible to drug-induced extrapyramidal symptoms (EPS). Use antipsychotics cautiously, especially the first generation antipsychotics (FGAs) such as haloperidol, which have a high incidence of EPS. Second generation antipsychotics (SGAs) are preferred because of a lower risk of these side effects.

Antidepressants can induce a manic episode and are not generally recommended unless the patient is on a mood stabilizer. Some SGAs have antidepressant effects. Lurasidone and olanzapine/fluoxetine *(Symbyax)* are indicated for bipolar depression and aripiprazole, brexpiprazole and quetiapine have FDA approvals for adjunctive therapy in major depressive disorder (MDD).

To select treatment, consider the following:

- The side effect profile of the drug.
- The patient's medication history and first-degree family member's medication history; if the patient or family member responded well to a drug, it may be a reasonable option.
- The drug formulations available and cost.

ACUTE TREATMENT

First-line treatment for a patient in a manic state is valproate or lithium plus an antipsychotic. For bipolar depression, first-line treatment is lithium or lamotrigine. Lurasidone and olanzapine/fluoxetine *(Symbyax)* are also approved for bipolar depression.

MAINTENANCE

After treating an acute episode, maintenance treatment can help prevent a relapse. Lamotrigine is used in bipolar depression and for maintenance treatment, but is not useful for acute mania. Lamotrigine requires a slow titration due to risk of a severe rash. Valproate and, less commonly, carbamazepine *(Equetro)* are both used for bipolar mania. Lithium, commonly used for mania, bipolar depression and maintenance, is often paired with an SGA in severe cases.

MedGuides are required with all antidepressants (primarily due to suicide risk) and with all antipsychotics (primarily due to increased risk of death in elderly patients with dementia-related psychosis).

PREGNANCY

Treating bipolar disease in pregnancy is complex. It is important to be able to identify and avoid medications that have known teratogenic effects. This includes several of the mood stabilizers that are commonly utilized.

- Valproate exposure in pregnancy is associated with increased risk of fetal anomalies, including neural tube defects, fetal valproate syndrome and long term adverse cognitive effects. It should be avoided in pregnancy, if possible, especially during the first trimester.
- Carbamazepine exposure in pregnancy is associated with fetal carbamazepine syndrome, which can cause facial abnormalities and other significant issues. It should be avoided in pregnancy, if possible, especially during the first trimester.
- Lithium exposure in pregnancy is associated with an increase in congenital cardiac malformations and other abnormalities.

In summary, lithium, valproate and carbamazepine have known fetal risk. Lamotrigine is safer, relative to the other mood stabilizers. The SGAs that are FDA-approved for bipolar disorder are also safer choices than valproate, carbamazepine or lithium. While lurasidone has the most favorable safety profile in pregnancy, it is only approved for bipolar depression.

ANTIEPILEPTIC DRUGS

See the Seizures/Epilepsy chapter for a detailed review of these medications, including drug interactions and patient counseling:

- **Lamotrigine *(Lamictal, Lamictal ODT*, *Lamictal XR*, *Lamictal Starter)***
- **Valproate/Valproic Acid Derivatives *(Depakene, Depakote*, *Depacon)***
- **Carbamazepine** *(Equetro)* – formulation approved for bipolar disorder

SECOND GENERATION ANTIPSYCHOTICS

SGAs are often used with or without lithium or valproate in patients with bipolar disorder. The medications listed are those with FDA approval for bipolar mania or bipolar depression; in practice, SGAs without FDA approval for these indications are also used. For a more complete review of the SGAs, including drug interactions and patient counseling, see the Schizophrenia/Psychosis chapter.

- **Aripiprazole *(Abilify, Abilify Maintena)***
- Asenapine *(Saphris)*
- Cariprazine *(Vraylar)*
- **Lurasidone *(Latuda)***
- Olanzapine/Fluoxetine *(Symbyax)*
- **Olanzapine *(Zyprexa*,** *Zyprexa Relprevv, Zyprexa Zydis)*
- **Quetiapine *(Seroquel*,** *Seroquel XR)*
- **Risperidone *(Risperdal, Risperdal Consta*,** *Risperidone M-Tab)*
- **Ziprasidone *(Geodon)***

MOOD STABILIZER: LITHIUM

Lithium has various proposed mechanisms including moderating the excitatory neurotransmitter glutamate levels in the brain (too much glutamate could lead to mania) and influencing the reuptake of serotonin and/or norepinephrine.

DRUG	DOSING	SAFETY/SIDE EFFECTS/MONITORING
Lithium *(Lithobid)* Tablet, capsule, solution	Start at 150-900 mg/day, divided TID, max 900-1,800 mg/day divided TID-QID Extended-release is taken BID **Therapeutic Range** 0.6-1.2 mEq/L (trough level) Acute mania may need up to 1.5 mEq/L initially	**BOXED WARNING** Serum lithium levels should be monitored to avoid toxicity **SIDE EFFECTS** GI upset (nausea, abdominal pain), cognitive effects, cogwheel rigidity, fine hand tremor, weight gain, polyuria/polydipsia, hypothyroidism (see monitoring), anorexia, hypercalcemia, cardiac abnormalities (inverted T waves), edema, worsening of psoriasis, blue-gray skin pigmentation, impotence **TOXICITY** > 1.5 mEq/L (coarse hand tremor, vomiting, persistent diarrhea, confusion, ataxia) > 2.5 mEq/L (CNS depression, arrhythmia, seizures, irreversible brain damage, coma) **MONITORING** Serum lithium levels, renal function, thyroid function (TSH, FT4), calcium, ECG (patients > 40 years old), electrolytes **NOTES** There are no CYP 450 interactions; lithium is 100% renally cleared There are many drug interactions Avoid use with other serotonergic agents

Lithium Drug Interactions

- Lithium levels ↑ with:
  - ↓ salt intake, sodium loss (e.g., with ACE inhibitors, ARBs, thiazide diuretics)
  - NSAIDs – Aspirin and sulindac are safer options
- Lithium levels ↓ with:
  - ↑ salt intake, caffeine and theophylline
- ↑ risk of serotonin syndrome if taken with lithium:
  - SSRIs, SNRIs, triptans, linezolid and other serotonergic drugs (see Learning Drug Interactions chapter)
- ↑ risk of neurotoxicity (e.g., ataxia, tremors, nausea) if taken with lithium:
  - Verapamil, diltiazem, phenytoin and carbamazepine

Lithium Counseling

- If you have worsened nausea or diarrhea, slurred speech, or feel shaky and confused, it is possible that the amount of lithium in your body has gone up. Contact your healthcare provider right away.
- You will need to have your blood checked occasionally during treatment.
- Do not crush, chew, or break any extended-release forms of lithium (*Lithobid*). The drug is specially formulated to release slowly in the body.
- Drink 8 to 12 glasses of water or other fluids (not counting any caffeinated sodas, coffee or tea) every day while taking lithium. Heavy exercise, prolonged exposure to heat or sun, excessive sweating, diarrhea, or vomiting can cause dehydration and increased side effects from lithium. Do not let yourself get dehydrated, and limit time in the sun.
- Do not change the amount of salt you consume. This will increase or decrease the amount of lithium in your body. There is a lot of salt in many fast foods, luncheon meats, frozen dinners and canned foods.
- Take the medication with food to help reduce nausea. It is often helpful to take the dose at the end of a meal, when the food is still in your stomach.
- Lithium can cause you to feel confused or "dizzy," especially when the dose is started or increased. Use caution when driving or performing other hazardous activities until you know how you feel taking this medication.
- Lithium can be harmful to an unborn baby. If you are pregnant or are planning a pregnancy, do not take lithium without first talking to your healthcare provider. Lithium can pass into breast milk. Discuss with your healthcare provider if you are breastfeeding.
- Do not stop taking this medication, even if you are feeling better.

LITHIUM-NOT EASY TO INITIATE

Common side effects
Nausea, anorexia, abdominal pain, thirst, sedation, confusion, tremor

Suggestions to help
Titrate slowly, possibly shift more of the dose to QHS

Take dose at end of a meal; food in the stomach helps

Drink adequate fluids; avoid dehydration

Dose correctly
5 mL lithium citrate solution = 8 mEq

8 mEq = 300 mg lithium carbonate tabs/caps

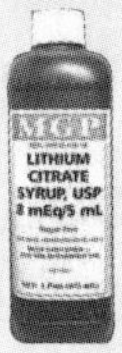

Select Guidelines/References

Diagnostic and Statistical Manual of Mental Disorders, Fifth Edition (DSM-5). Arlington VA, American Psychiatric Association, 2013.

WFSBP: Update 2012 on the long-term treatment of bipolar disorder. *The World Journal of Biological Psychiatry*. 2013;14:154–219.

APA, Treatment of Patients with Bipolar Disorder. http://psychiatryonline.org/pb/assets/raw/sitewide/practice_guidelines/guidelines/bipolar.pdf (accessed 2019 Jan 2).

VA/DOD, Management of Bipolar Disorder in Adults, 2010. http://www.healthquality.va.gov/guidelines/MH/bd/bd_305_full.pdf (accessed 2019 Jan 2).

CHAPTER CONTENT

Background 905
DSM-5 Diagnostic Criteria 906
Natural Products 906
Drug Treatment 906
Patient-Friendly Formulations for Stimulants 906
Stimulants 907
Non-Stimulants 911

CONTENT LEGEND

= Study Tip Gal

CHAPTER 66
ATTENTION DEFICIT HYPERACTIVITY DISORDER (ADHD)

BACKGROUND

ADHD is a chronic illness with primary symptoms of inattention, hyperactivity and impulsivity. People with ADHD often have difficulty focusing, are easily distracted, have trouble staying still and frequently are unable to control impulsive behavior. Primary symptoms vary; some patients are more inattentive, and others are more impulsive.

In ADHD, defects in the dopamine pathways that regulate reward anticipation and emotional self-regulation may play a role. This is why the primary focus of ADHD research is on the catecholamine system (dopamine is metabolized to epinephrine and norepinephrine). The primary treatments for ADHD are stimulant medications (e.g., methylphenidate and amphetamine drugs). Stimulants raise dopamine and norepinephrine levels.

Treatment is often challenging because similar to other psychiatric conditions, the response to an ADHD drug is highly variable among individual patients. Variability in dose and response can be due to a patient's genetics and environment, which can determine brain chemistry and affect behavior. For this reason, cognitive behavioral therapy (using psychotherapy to identify and alter thoughts and feelings, which can lead to a change in behavior), is first-line in managing ADHD. Even with strong support, some patients require medications.

ADHD is the most common neurodevelopmental disorder in children. The decision to medicate should be weighed carefully. Risks to a child with untreated ADHD can include impaired academic standing, poor social skills and risky behavior. Medications for these symptoms are helpful, but not without side effects and social stigma. Pharmacists can make sure that when medications are prescribed they are used safely, as stimulants have serious side effects and are common drugs of abuse.

About 10% of school-aged children are using ADHD medications, with boys outnumbering girls. ADHD should be considered a chronic illness; up to 80% of children will continue to exhibit symptoms into adolescence and up to 65% will continue to exhibit symptoms as an adult. As the patient ages, inattention and impulsivity can remain, and hyperactivity can decrease.

DSM-5 DIAGNOSTIC CRITERIA

INATTENTION

≥ 6 symptoms of inattention for children up to age 16, OR ≥ 5 symptoms for ages 17 and older; symptoms must have been present for at least 6 months and are inappropriate for the developmental level

Symptoms:

Fails to pay attention, has trouble holding attention, does not pay attention when someone is talking, does not follow through on instructions, fails to finish schoolwork, has difficulty organizing tasks, avoids or dislikes tasks which require mental effort, loses things, is easily distracted and is forgetful.

HYPERACTIVITY & IMPULSIVITY

≥ 6 symptoms of hyperactivity-impulsivity for children up to age 16, OR ≥ 5 symptoms for ages 17 and older; symptoms must have been present for at least 6 months and are inappropriate for the developmental level

Symptoms:

Often fidgets or squirms, leaves seat unexpectedly, runs about when not appropriate, unable to play quietly, is "on the go" as if "driven by a motor," talks excessively, blurts out answers, has trouble waiting his/her turn and interrupts or intrudes on others.

THE FOLLOWING CONDITIONS MUST BE MET:

- Several inattentive or hyperactive-impulsive symptoms were present before age 12
- Symptoms must have been present in 2 or more settings (e.g., at home, school, work, with friends or relatives, babysitters)
- Symptoms interfere with functioning, and are not caused by another disorder

NATURAL PRODUCTS

Fish oils are a natural product increasingly used for a variety of psychiatric conditions, including ADHD. Fish oils have been shown to modestly improve cognitive function and behavior in children with ADHD. Melatonin is a natural product used to help with sleep onset in individuals taking stimulants.

DRUG TREATMENT

Stimulants are first-line when using drug treatment for ADHD. Atomoxetine *(Strattera)*, a non-stimulant medication, can be tried when stimulants do not work well enough (after trials of 2 – 3 agents). *Strattera* can also be used first-line by prescribers who are concerned about the possibility of abuse by the patient or family.

Some stimulant medications come in formulations that are easier for children to swallow (see Study Tip Gal), or that are more difficult to abuse. Methylphenidate formulations (e.g., *Concerta, Ritalin*) are used first-line, mainly due to a better side effect profile. Amphetamines are also used, amphetamine/dextroamphetamine *(Adderall)* and lisdexamfetamine *(Vyvanse)*, the prodrug of dextroamphetamine. Longer-acting formulations are preferred for children, who would otherwise need a dose during the day at school, and to help maintain more steady symptom control.

PATIENT-FRIENDLY FORMULATIONS FOR STIMULANTS

Young children (and others) who cannot swallow capsules or tablets can use these long-acting formulations:

- **Suspension**: *Quillivant XR, Dyanavel XR, Adzenys ER*
- **Chewable tablet**: *QuilliChew ER, Vyvanse*
- **Capsule**, with contents sprinkled on a small amount of applesauce: *Focalin XR, Ritalin LA, Aptensio XR* and *Adderall XR*
- **Capsule**, with powder contents which can be mixed in water, orange juice or yogurt: *Vyvanse*
- **Orally-disintegrating tablet**: *Cotempla XR-ODT, Adzenys XR-ODT*
- **Patch**: *Daytrana*

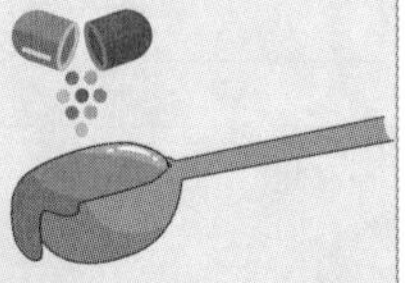

When putting capsule contents in food, use a small amount of food and do not chew the beads. Do not warm the food, and take it right away.

Guanfacine [approved in the extended-release (ER) formulation *Intuniv*] and clonidine (in the ER formulation *Kapvay*) are used alone or as adjunctive treatments. *Intuniv* or *Kapvay* can also be used to help with sleep in the evening as they are sedating. Diphenhydramine is used to help with sleep at night, but it is important to monitor for a paradoxical hyperactive reaction in some children. Another option to help with sleep is immediate-release (IR) clonidine, taken at bedtime.

Almost all ADHD medications are approved for use in adults and children ≥ 6 years of age with a few exceptions, as noted in the drug tables on the following page.

Stimulants are 1st line drugs (take in AM)
Concerta*, *Daytrana or ***Ritalin***
Vyvanse
Adderall XR and ***IR***

Non-stimulants are 2nd line (take if risk of abuse)
Strattera

Add-on medications or used alone
Intuniv
Kapvay

Zzzzz....to help sleep, at night
Clonidine IR
Diphenhydramine (OTC, 25-50 mg)
Melatonin (OTC, 2-5 mg)
Intuniv, Kapvay

STIMULANTS

CNS stimulants block the reuptake of norepinephrine and dopamine; they are highly effective for ADHD and are recommended first-line. Most stimulants are dosed every morning (IR products and some others can be given in divided doses), with doses titrated up every seven days, as-needed. Stimulants do not need to be tapered off when used as directed (i.e., not abused).

Safety Concerns

All stimulants are C-II substances and a MedGuide is required when dispensing products. This information is not repeated in the following drug tables. The Boxed Warnings, Contraindications and Warnings discussed on this page are common to most stimulant drugs. Additional safety issues unique to specific products are noted in the drug tables that follow.

Boxed Warnings

Stimulant medications have a high potential for abuse and dependence. Risk of abuse should be assessed prior to dispensing and monitored during treatment; caution should be used in patients with a history of alcohol or drug abuse. When abused long-term, tolerance and psychological dependence can occur, with varying degrees of abnormal behavior (including psychotic episodes when injected). When withdrawing treatment from someone abusing a stimulant, severe depression can occur.

Contraindications

Stimulants are contraindicated within 14 days of an MAO inhibitor. The increased levels of dopamine and norepinephrine can increase heart rate and blood pressure, leading to serious cardiovascular events in children and adults with and without preexisting cardiac disease. Patients should be assessed at baseline, and treatment should be avoided in patients with known cardiac abnormalities due to an increased risk of sudden death. Specifically, some agents are contraindicated in patients with heart failure, recent myocardial infarction, arrhythmia or moderate-severe hypertension.

Most stimulant products are also contraindicated in patients with marked anxiety, tension, agitation, glaucoma, hyperthyroidism, or history of Tourette's syndrome or other tic disorder.

Warnings

- Severe cardiovascular events (see above) and other vascular problems (e.g., priapism, Raynaud's disease) can occur with the use of stimulants.
- Stimulants can increase suicidal thoughts and behaviors, and exacerbation of mixed/mania episodes can occur in patients with pre-existing bipolar disorder; caution should be used when prescribing stimulants to any patient with a pre-existing psychiatric condition. In addition, these drugs can lower the seizure threshold and increase the risk for seizures.
- Stimulants can cause a loss of appetite. This is especially concerning in children, as it can result in a decrease in growth trajectory of the child.
- The risk of serotonin syndrome is increased when stimulants are used in combination with other serotonergic drugs (e.g., SSRIs, SNRIs, TCAs, buspirone). Refer to the Learning Drug Interactions chapter.

STIMULANTS

DRUG	DOSING	SAFETY/SIDE EFFECTS/MONITORING
Methylphenidate		
Methylphenidate IR ***Ritalin*** – tablet ***Methylin*** – oral solution, chewable tablet	Start 5 mg BID, taken 30 minutes before breakfast and lunch Max: 60 mg/day	**CONTRAINDICATIONS** *Ritalin:* pheochromocytoma, adrenal medulla tumor **WARNINGS** *Daytrana* patch: loss of skin pigmentation at application site and areas distant from the application site (can resemble vitiligo), allergic contact sensitization with local reactions (e.g., edema, papules) **SIDE EFFECTS** Nausea, insomnia, headache, irritability, blurry vision, dry mouth **MONITORING** Consider ECG prior to treatment; monitor BP and HR, cardiac symptoms, CNS effects, abuse potential and height and weight (children) **NOTES** *Metadate ER* and *Methylin ER*: duration of action is ~8 hours; can give in place of IR product once IR product is titrated and dose is equal to tablet size of ER product Methylphenidate ER tablets (all brands): swallow whole *Concerta* OROS delivery: the outer coat dissolves fast to give immediate action, and the rest is released slowly; can see a ghost tablet in stool; OROS tablets are harder to crush which decreases abuse potential *Jornay PM:* outer coating delays initial drug release 10 hours to allow for evening dosing; inner coating controls the slow release of the drug during the day *QuilliChew ER:* tablets are scored and can be broken in half *Quillivant XR:* shake bottle for at least 10 seconds prior to use *Daytrana* patch: apply 2 hours before desired effect (or as soon as the child awakens so it starts to deliver prior to school) and remove after 9 hours; alternate hips daily Some products contain phenylalanine (avoid with PKU)
Methylphenidate ER *(Aptensio XR, Ritalin LA)* Capsules that deliver a % of drug as IR and a % as ER	*Ritalin LA:* start 20 mg QAM *Aptensio XR:* start 10 mg QAM Max (both): 60 mg/day	
Methylphenidate ER ***Concerta*** – OROS tablet system *Metadate ER, Relexxii, Ritalin SR* – tablet *Adhansia XR, Jornay PM* – capsule	*Metadate ER* and *Methylin ER:* see Notes *Concerta:* start 18-36 mg QAM Max: 72 mg/day	
Methylphenidate XR *Cotempla XR-ODT* – ODT *QuilliChew ER* – Chewable tablets *Quillivant XR* – Oral suspension 25 mg/ 5 mL	*QuilliChew ER* and *Quillivant XR:* start 20 mg QAM Max: 60 mg/day *Cotempla XR-ODT:* start 17.3 mg QAM in patients 6-17 years of age Max: 51.8 mg/day	
Methylphenidate transdermal patch *(Daytrana)*	Start 10 mg/9 hr patch QAM Max: 30 mg/9hr	
Dexmethylphenidate		
Dexmethylphenidate *(Focalin, Focalin XR)* Tablet, ER capsule	IR tabs: start 2.5 mg BID, given at least 4 hours apart Max: 20 mg/day ER caps: 10 mg QAM Max: 40 mg/day	See Stimulants discussion and methylphenidate above **NOTES** Active isomer of methylphenidate; to convert from methylphenidate to dexmethylphenidate use one-half of the total daily dose of methylphenidate

DRUG	DOSING	SAFETY/SIDE EFFECTS/MONITORING
Amphetamine IR, amphetamine/dextroamphetamine IR and dextroamphetamine IR are approved in children ≥ 3 years of age. AAP guidelines do not recommend dextroamphetamine IR in children 5 years of age or younger.		
Amphetamine *Adzenys XR-ODT* – ODT *Dyanavel XR, Adzenys ER* – suspension *Evekeo* – tablet	*Adzenys XR-ODT* and *XR*: start 12.5 mg QAM (adults) or 6.3 mg QAM (children) Max: varies based on age *Dyanavel XR*: start 2.5-5 mg QAM Max: 20 mg/day	See Stimulants discussion and methylphenidate above **BOXED WARNING** Misuse can cause sudden death and serious CV events **NOTES** ER formulations cannot be substituted for other amphetamine products on a mg-per-mg basis; in most cases, the original product is discontinued and the new product initiated and titrated as per the recommended dosing schedule When converting from *Adderall XR* to *Adzenys XR-ODT* or *XR*: use 3.1 mg for each 5 mg dose of *Adderall XR* *Dyanavel XR, Adzenys ER*: shake suspension prior to use *Evekeo* is an IR tablet approved for use in children age 3 – 17 years; dosing varies by age; when dosed BID, the 2nd dose should be taken 4-6 hours after the 1st dose Avoid use of acidic foods (e.g., juice or vitamin C) as these can decrease amphetamine levels
Dextroamphetamine / Amphetamine IR *(Adderall)*	Start 5 mg QAM or BID, with 2nd dose 4-6 hours after 1st Max: 40 mg/day	
Dextroamphetamine/ Amphetamine ER *(Adderall XR*, *Mydayis)*	Start 20 mg QAM	
Dextroamphetamine *Dexedrine Spansule* – ER capsule *ProCentra* – oral solution *Zenzedi* – IR tablet	Start 5 mg QAM or BID, with 2nd dose 4-6 hours after 1st Max: 40 mg/day	
Lisdexamfetamine (prodrug of dextroamphetamine)		
Lisdexamfetamine *(Vyvanse)* Capsule, chewable tablet	Start 30 mg QAM Max: 70 mg/day	See Stimulants discussion and methylphenidate above **NOTES** Low abuse potential: prodrug composed of l-lysine (amino acid) bonded to dextroamphetamine (d-amphetamine) is hydrolyzed in the blood to active d-amphetamine; if injected or snorted, the fast effect (rush) is muted
Methamphetamine		
Methamphetamine *(Desoxyn)* tablet	Start 5 mg QAM or BID Max: 20-25 mg daily in 1-2 divided doses	See Stimulants discussion and methylphenidate above

Patient Counseling for Stimulants

- Please read the Medication Guide provided. It contains important safety information about this medication.
- This medication is a stimulant. Stimulants should not be used in patients with heart problems or serious psychiatric conditions. Notify your healthcare provider immediately if chest pain, shortness of breath, or fainting occur, or if you start seeing, hearing or believing things that are not real.
- You will need to have your blood pressure and heart rate checked regularly.
- Nausea or headache can occur when the dose is increased, or you can act "wired." This is why the dose is increased slowly at the beginning of treatment.
- This is a controlled medication and has the potential to be abused. Do not share this medication with anyone else and store it in a safe place.
- Certain food colorings and preservatives that are common in "junk" foods and candies can worsen hyperactive behavior.
- If you have trouble sleeping, the formulation can be changed or your healthcare provider can recommend OTC diphenhydramine, melatonin or prescription clonidine to take before bedtime.
- Less commonly, some patients develop repetitive movements or sounds called tics. Changing the medication dosage can make tics go away.
- For male patients: this medication can cause an erection lasting longer than four hours. If this happens, get immediate medical help to prevent long-term damage to the penis.

- For parents of children taking stimulants: your child can have a decreased appetite while taking this drug. Children seem to be less hungry during the middle of the day, but they are often hungry by dinnertime as the medication wears off. Your child should eat a healthy breakfast and pack healthy snacks for school, such as nuts, cheese and fruit. Height and weight will need to be checked regularly.
- If you have difficulty swallowing capsules and you are using a capsule formulation that can be mixed with applesauce (*Focalin XR, Ritalin LA, Adderall XR* and *Aptensio XR*), the contents can be sprinkled on a small amount of applesauce (if not warm) and used right away. Do not chew the applesauce; just swallow.
- *Concerta:* you can see a ghost tablet in your stool, but the medication has been released into the body.
- *Vyvanse* capsule: the capsule contents can be mixed in water, yogurt or orange juice, but it must be taken right away.
- *Adzenys XR-ODT* and *Cotempla XR-ODT* do not remove the tablet from the blister pack until ready to administer. Using dry hands, peel the backing off the blister pack; do not push the tablet through the foil. Remove the tablet and immediately place on the tongue and allow to dissolve. Swallow with saliva.

Daytrana Patch

- Each morning put a new patch on the hip and alternate the side each day (left hip odd days, right hip even days). Do not apply where the waist of the pants could rub it off. Apply two hours before effect is needed.
- Hold the patch on skin for 30 seconds and smooth down the edges. It should stay on during swimming or bathing. Remove the patch after nine hours so you can sleep well at night.

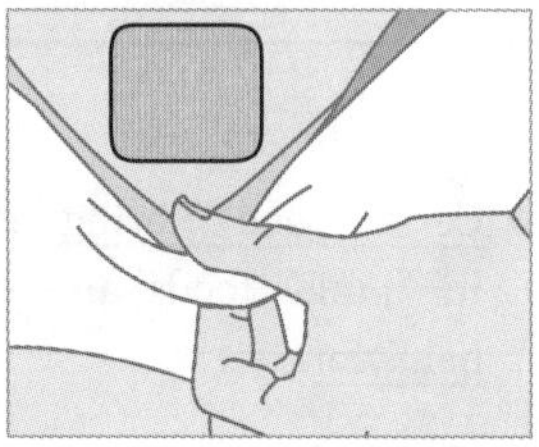

- Wash your hands immediately after applying the patch. Patches should not be reapplied with bandages, tape, or other household adhesives. Do not use hair dryers, heating pads, electric blankets, or other heat sources directly on the patch. If you have to replace a patch that has fallen off, the total wear-time for the first and second patch should not be more than a total of nine hours in one day. Do not reapply the same patch that fell off.
- When peeling off to discard, fold in half and put down the toilet or in a lidded trash can.

Quillivant XR Suspension

- The bottle must contain liquid. Return it to the pharmacist if it is still in powder form.
- Shake the bottle for at least 10 seconds. Use the dosing dispenser to measure the milliliter (mL) dose.
- Insert the tip of the dispenser into the upright bottle and push the plunger all the way down. Turn the bottle upside down and remove the correct amount; measure to the white end of the plunger.
- Use the dosing dispenser to slowly squirt the medication into the mouth. Cap tightly and rinse the dispenser with tap water or in a dishwasher. Wash after each use.
- This medication can be stored at room temperature for up to four months.

NON-STIMULANTS

These medications are second-line agents for use after trials of stimulant medications have failed, or when the prescriber is concerned about abuse potential. Non-stimulant medications for ADHD are not controlled and therefore do not have the same potential for abuse and dependence as stimulants. *Intuniv* and *Kapvay* are both old hypertension drugs which are now marketed in longer-acting formulations for ADHD (clonidine IR is also used off-label to help with sleep).

DRUG	DOSING	SAFETY/SIDE EFFECTS/MONITORING
Selective Norepinephrine Reuptake Inhibitor: approved for use in adults and children ≥ 6 years of age		
Atomoxetine ***(Strattera)*** Capsule	Start 40 mg daily Can increase after at least 3 days to 80 mg daily Max: 100 mg/day Can take in divided doses if needed (morning and late afternoon/early evening) Strong CYP450 2D6 inhibitors (e.g., paroxetine): max is 80 mg daily	**BOXED WARNING** Risk of suicidal ideation; monitor for suicidal thinking or behavior, worsening mood, or unusual behavior **CONTRAINDICATIONS** Glaucoma, pheochromocytoma, severe cardiovascular disorders, MAO inhibitor use within the past 14 days **WARNINGS** Aggressive behavior, treatment-emergent psychotic or manic symptoms, orthostasis and syncope, allergic reactions, priapism Rare, but severe hepatotoxicity (most often within 120 days of starting treatment) Serious cardiovascular events; assess at baseline and as needed during treatment and avoid use if known cardiac disease Height and weight gain can be reduced in children **SIDE EFFECTS** Headache, insomnia, somnolence, hypertension, tachycardia, dry mouth, nausea, abdominal pain, ↓ appetite, erectile dysfunction, ↓ libido, hyperhidrosis **MONITORING** HR, BP, ECG, height, weight, agitation **NOTES** Do not open the capsule – irritant
Central Alpha-2A Adrenergic Receptor Agonists: stimulate alpha adrenergic receptors in the brain; can be used alone or with stimulants		
Guanfacine ER ***(Intuniv)*** ER tablet IR tablet ***(Tenex*)*** – for hypertension	Start 1 mg daily and increase by 1 mg weekly Max: 4 mg/day (with stimulants), 7 mg/day (when used alone) Do not take with high-fat meal (↑ absorption) With strong CYP3A4 inducers: double dose With strong CYP3A4 inhibitors: ↓ dose 50%	**WARNINGS** Dose-dependent cardiovascular effects (bradycardia, hypotension, orthostasis, syncope), sedation and drowsiness Do not discontinue abruptly (can cause rebound hypertension, nervousness and anxiety (see Notes) Guanfacine: skin rash (rare, discontinue if occurs) **SIDE EFFECTS** Somnolence, dizziness, headache, fatigue, nausea, constipation, abdominal pain **NOTES** Must be tapered off to decrease the risk of rebound hypertension, nervousness and anxiety: decrease dose (0.1 mg for clonidine and at least 1 mg for guanfacine) every 3-7 days. Do not interchange ER products with IR formulations of guanfacine and clonidine or with the clonidine patch. ER tablets: do not crush, break or chew
Clonidine ER *(Kapvay)* IR tablet ***(Catapres)***, patch *(Catapres-TTS)* – for hypertension	Start 0.1 mg QHS, increase by 0.1 mg weekly Max: 0.4 mg/day Take BID, if uneven dosing with the higher dose QHS	

**Brand name discontinued but name still used in practice.*

Atomoxetine Drug Interactions

- Atomoxetine is a CYP2D6 substrate; CYP2D6 inducers or inhibitors can necessitate a change in atomoxetine dose.

Clonidine and Guanfacine Drug Interactions

- Both clonidine and guanfacine are sedating; use caution with other CNS depressants.
- Both clonidine and guanfacine lower blood pressure; use caution with other anti-hypertensives.
- Both clonidine and guanfacine come in other formulations for different indications; they should not be used together or with other formulations containing the same active drug.

Patient Counseling for Atomoxetine

- Read the Medication Guide provided. It contains important safety information about possible depression/very low mood, and possible liver damage when using this medication.
- Side effects can include headache, trouble sleeping or staying awake, dry mouth, nausea, decreased appetite, and sweating.
- Watch for symptoms of depression, unusual behavior, or thoughts of hurting yourself. Your healthcare provider will need to check you at regular visits while you are taking this medication.
- The capsule cannot be opened. If the powder from inside gets into your eyes, rinse well with water and call your healthcare provider.
- Atomoxetine can cause side effects that can impair your thinking or reactions. Be careful if you drive or do anything that requires you to be awake and alert.
- Monitor for symptoms of liver damage: weakness, abdominal pain, yellowed skin, light colored stool or darkened urine.

Select Guidelines/References

Diagnostic and Statistical Manual of Mental Disorders, Fifth Edition. Arlington, VA, American Psychiatric Association, 2013.

ADHD: Clinical Practice Guideline for the Diagnosis, Evaluation, and Treatment of Attention-Deficit/Hyperactivity Disorder in Children and Adolescents. *Pediatrics* 2011;128:1007-22.

CHAPTER 67
ANXIETY DISORDERS

CHAPTER CONTENT

Background 913
- Select Drugs that Cause Anxiety 913

Non-Drug Treatment 913

Natural Products 914

Drug Treatment 914
- Selective Serotonin Reuptake Inhibitors and Serotonin Norepinephrine Reuptake Inhibitors .. 914
- Buspirone 914
- Tricyclic Antidepressants 914
- Hydroxyzine 914
- Pregabalin 914
- Propranolol 914
- Benzodiazepines 916
- Safe Use of Benzodiazepines 916

BACKGROUND

The general population can experience occasional anxiety when faced with challenging issues at work, home or school; this is normal. The symptoms of occasional anxiety (fear, worry) and any physical symptoms (tachycardia, palpitations, shortness of breath, stomach upset, chest pain or other pain, insomnia or fatigue) resolve once the issue is gone.

When a person has an anxiety disorder, the symptoms are chronic and severe and cause great distress. The disorder can interfere with the ability to do well at school or work, and can harm relationships. The major types of anxiety disorders are generalized anxiety disorder (GAD), panic disorder (PD) and social anxiety disorder (SAD). Other disorders that have symptoms of anxiety include obsessive compulsive disorder (OCD) and posttraumatic stress disorder (PTSD). These are classified differently by the Diagnostic and Statistical Manual of Mental Disorders, Fifth Edition (DSM-5). OCD is categorized as "obsessive-compulsive and related disorders" and PTSD is categorized under "trauma and stressor-related disorders."

SELECT DRUGS THAT CAUSE ANXIETY

- Albuterol (if used too frequently or incorrectly)
- Antipsychotics (e.g., aripiprazole, haloperidol)
- Bupropion
- Caffeine, in high doses
- Decongestants (e.g., pseudoephedrine)
- Illicit drugs (e.g., cocaine, LSD, methamphetamine)
- Levothyroxine
- Steroids
- Stimulants (e.g., amphetamine, methylphenidate)
- Theophylline

NON-DRUG TREATMENT

Patients with an anxiety disorder should be assessed for comorbid conditions (e.g., hyperthyroidism) or medications that could be contributing to the problem (see Key Drugs Guy). Comorbid conditions should be treated and medications that worsen anxiety should be discontinued if possible.

Lifestyle changes can improve symptoms. Increasing physical activity, helping others, community involvement, yoga and meditation, are some of the methods that can broaden the patient's outlook and reduce stress. Cognitive Behavioral Therapy (CBT) is a type of mental health treatment in which a trained clinician helps the patient explore patterns of thinking that lead to problem-solving, relaxation techniques, worry exposure and more. In some cases, CBT provides adequate relief without the need for chronic medications.

CONTENT LEGEND

= Study Tip Gal   = Key Drug Guy

NATURAL PRODUCTS

Some patients use natural products to help treat anxiety. They may experience benefit, but some natural products have safety issues that limit use. Kava is used as a relaxant, but it can damage the liver and should not be recommended. St. John's wort, used for depression and anxiety, is a strong CYP3A4 inducer and can decrease the concentration of other medications. St. John's wort causes photosensitivity and is serotonergic. The risk of serotonin syndrome is increased when used in combination with other serotonergic medications. Valerian is used for anxiety and sleep, but some products may have been contaminated with liver toxins; if it is being used, liver function should be monitored. Passionflower appears to be safe and is rated as "possibly effective" by the *Natural Medicines Database*.

DRUG TREATMENT

There are a number of medications that can be used long-term to manage anxiety. Some antidepressant drugs have an FDA-approved indication for anxiety, and other drugs are used off-label. The selection of a drug is based on both the efficacy and the risk of adverse effects. The table below summarizes the first and second-line options that can be considered. Benzodiazepines (BZDs) should only be used short-term and are discussed in-depth later in the chapter.

Drugs Used for Anxiety

DRUG/DRUG CLASS	COMMENTS
First-Line	
Selective serotonin reuptake inhibitors (SSRIs) and serotonin norepinephrine reuptake inhibitors (SNRIs) **Escitalopram *(Lexapro)*** **Fluoxetine *(Prozac)*** **Paroxetine *(Paxil, Paxil CR,*** *Pexeva)* **Sertraline *(Zoloft)*** **Duloxetine *(Cymbalta)*** **Venlafaxine XR *(Effexor XR)***	Typically start at half the initial dose used for depression and slowly titrate to minimize anxiousness and jitteriness (common during the first couple of weeks) Do not provide immediate relief; takes at least four weeks or more at doses in the higher end of the dosing range for a noticeable effect Other drugs in the class may be used off-label for anxiety disorder Refer to the Depression chapter for more information on antidepressants
Second-Line	
Buspirone	Can be used in combination with antidepressants (e.g., when there is a poor response) Considered to be a more favorable add-on agent than benzodiazepines in elderly patients (less sedating) or if there is a risk for benzodiazepine abuse Does not provide immediate relief; takes 2-4 weeks to work when taken on a scheduled basis
Tricyclic Antidepressants **Amitriptyline** *(Elavil*)* Imipramine *(Tofranil)* Nortriptyline *(Pamelor)*	Not FDA-approved for anxiety Risk of adverse effects (e.g., anticholinergic side effects) limit use (see the Depression chapter)
Hydroxyzine *(Vistaril)*	Sedating antihistamine with anticholinergic activity FDA-approved for anxiety but does not treat the underlying condition Should not be used long-term; should be used short-term, as needed, as an alternative to benzodiazepines See the Common Skin Conditions chapter for more information
Pregabalin *(Lyrica)* C-V Gabapentin *(Neurontin)*	Not FDA-approved for anxiety but has shown benefit in patients with anxiety and neuropathic pain Has immediate anxiolytic effects similar to benzodiazepines
Special Situations	
Propranolol *(Inderal LA,* others)	Not FDA-approved for anxiety but can reduce symptoms of stage fright or performance anxiety (e.g., tremor, tachycardia) Give 10-40 mg one hour prior to an event (such as a public speech) Can cause CNS side effects (e.g., dizziness, confusion) See Hypertension chapter for more information

**Brand discontinued but name still used in practice.*

BUSPIRONE

The mechanism of action of buspirone is unknown, but its effects may be due to its affinity for 5-HT1A and 5-HT2 receptors. It does not affect GABA, an inhibitory neurotransmitter.

DRUG	DOSING	SAFETY/SIDE EFFECTS/MONITORING
Buspirone Tablet	Start 7.5 mg PO BID Can increase by 5 mg/day every 2-3 days, to a max dose of 30 mg PO BID Take with or without food, but be consistent	**WARNINGS** Do not use with MAO inhibitors or within 14 days of discontinuation; do not initiate in patients receiving linezolid or methylene blue **SIDE EFFECTS** Nausea, dizziness, drowsiness, headache, lightheadedness, excitement **NOTES** No potential for abuse, tolerance or physiological dependence When switching from a benzodiazepine to buspirone, the benzodiazepine must be tapered off slowly Avoid use in severe kidney or liver impairment

Buspirone Drug Interactions

- There is an increased risk of serotonin syndrome when used in combination with other serotonergic agents. See the Learning Drug Interactions chapter.
- Buspirone is a major substrate of CYP3A4. The dose may need to be decreased if used in combination with moderate and strong CYP3A4 inhibitors (e.g., erythromycin, diltiazem, verapamil, itraconazole). Grapefruit and grapefruit juice should be avoided.
- An increase in the buspirone dose may be required with CYP3A4 inducers, including rifampin.

Buspirone Counseling

- Common side effects can include dizziness, drowsiness, nausea and headache.
- Buspirone tablets are scored (see picture) and easily snap into pieces with finger pressure. You can take the whole tablet, one-half of a tablet or one-third of a tablet, depending on your dose.

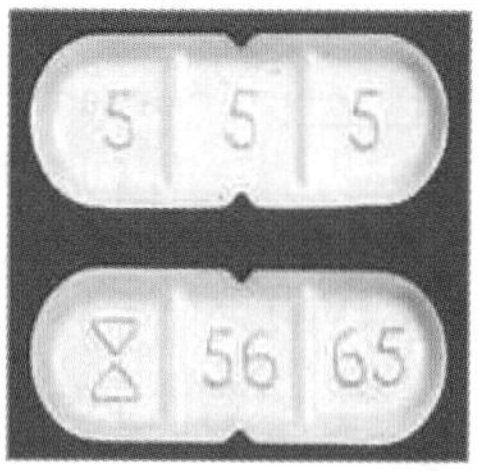

- Take this medication by mouth, with or without food. It is important to take it the same way each day so that the amount of drug absorbed will stay the same.
- This medication does not work right away, and symptoms of anxiety (e.g., restlessness) can get worse before they get better. It takes 2 – 4 weeks for this medication to help reduce your anxiety.
- Do not take buspirone with other medications that can make you sleepy, unless directed by your healthcare provider. Do not use alcohol with this medication.

BENZODIAZEPINES

- GABA: BZDs enhance GABA, an inhibitory neurotransmitter, causing CNS depression and providing anxiolytic, anticonvulsant, sedative and/or muscle relaxant properties.
- Fast relief: BZDs do not treat the underlying causes of anxiety. They work fast (and antidepressants take time to work) but they only sedate the patient.
- Short-term use: BZDs can be appropriate for short-term use, when anxiety is acute, causing extreme stress that is preventing restful sleep and disrupting life. This can be due to the recent death of a loved one, a natural disaster or another stressful situation.
- Dependence: BZDs should be used for no more than 1 – 2 weeks, and then discontinued. BZDs can be addictive, and they have physical dependence and tolerance issues. This makes it difficult to stop them when used long-term. They must be tapered off slowly.
- Elderly: in older adults, BZDs have a high risk for confusion, dizziness and falls. These risks increase with concurrent use of other CNS depressants. The L-O-T drugs (see Study Tip Gal) have a lower risk and are preferred in the elderly.

SAFE USE OF BENZODIAZEPINES

Benzodiazepines (BZDs) are highly sedating
BZDs are **NOT** preferred for anxiety. Most anxiety is due to depression (SSRIs and SNRIs are preferred).

BZDs are **NOT** preferred for sleep. First-line is non-pharmacologic treatment. Second-line is non-BZDs, like zolpidem *(Ambien)*. These drugs have some safety issues, but fewer than BZDs.

If Used, Choose a Safe Agent
The **L-O-T** drugs (**L**orazepam, **O**xazepam, **T**emazepam) are safer to use in elderly patients and those with liver impairment, since they are metabolized to inactive glucuronides.

Anxiety: UN-do anxiety with UN-**CLAD** (**C**lonazepam, **L**orazepam, **A**lprazolam, **D**iazepam).

Sleep: choose lorazepam or temazepam.

Seizures: BZDs can be given by injection for immediate control of a seizure. Diazepam is unique, it comes in a rectal gel *(Diastat AcuDial)* that can be used by a caregiver at home.

- Beers Criteria: BZDs are potentially inappropriate for use in patients age 65 and older. Occasionally, including among elderly patients, a "paradoxical" reaction occurs and the patient becomes more agitated.

DRUG	DOSING	SAFETY/SIDE EFFECTS/MONITORING
Alprazolam *(Xanax, Xanax XR,* *Alprazolam Intensol)* Tablet, ODT, oral solution	0.25-0.5 mg PO TID	**BOXED WARNING** Use with opioids can result in sedation, respiratory depression, coma and death **CONTRAINDICATIONS** Acute narrow-angle glaucoma, sleep apnea, severe respiratory insufficiency, severe liver disease (clonazepam and diazepam), myasthenia gravis (diazepam), not for use in infants < 6 months of age (diazepam oral), premature infants (lorazepam parenteral products) **WARNINGS** Physiological dependence and tolerance develop with chronic use – do not discontinue abruptly (taper slowly) CNS depression, anterograde amnesia, potential for abuse, safety risks in patients age 65 years and older (impaired cognition, delirium, falls/fractures), extravasation with IV use, paradoxical reactions, severe renal or hepatic impairment Pregnancy – crosses the placenta; can cause birth defects and neonatal withdrawal syndrome **SIDE EFFECTS** Somnolence, dizziness, ataxia, weakness, lightheadedness **NOTES** C-IV Diazepam: lipophilic, fast onset, long half-life, high abuse potential Alprazolam: fast onset, often abused due to quick action Commonly used for alcohol withdrawal syndrome: lorazepam, diazepam and chlordiazepoxide In overdose cases, the antidote is flumazenil (refer to the Emergency Preparedness, Toxicology & Antidotes chapter) Midazolam (*Versed*) used in acute care (See Acute & Critical Care Medicine chapter)
Chlordiazepoxide Capsule	5-25 mg TID-QID	
Clonazepam *(Klonopin)* Tablet, ODT	0.25-0.5 mg PO BID	
Clorazepate *(Tranxene-T)* Tablet	30 mg PO daily in divided doses	
Diazepam *(Valium,* *Diastat AcuDial, Diazepam Intensol)* Tablet, injection, oral solution, rectal gel	2-10 mg PO BID-QID	
Lorazepam *(Ativan,* *Lorazepam Intensol)* Tablet, injection, oral solution	2-3 mg PO daily in divided doses	
Oxazepam Capsule	10-30 mg PO TID-QID	

Benzodiazepine Drug Interactions

- Additive effects occur when used with CNS depressants, including pain medications, skeletal muscle relaxants, antihistamines, antipsychotics, anticonvulsants, trazodone, mirtazapine, alcohol, and others.
- Alprazolam is contraindicated with strong CYP3A4 inhibitors (e.g., ketoconazole, itraconazole). Caution should be used with moderate CYP3A4 inhibitors. Diazepam, clonazepam, chlordiazepoxide and clorazepate should be used cautiously with CYP3A4 inhibitors; lower doses may be required.
- Valproate increases the serum concentration of lorazepam.

Benzodiazepine Counseling

- Common side effects of this medication include drowsiness, dizziness, unsteadiness on your feet, lightheadedness, slow reactions and difficulty remembering what has happened. If any of these symptoms persist or worsen, contact your healthcare provider promptly.
- If you have been using the medication regularly on a daily basis (for more than 10 days), it cannot be stopped suddenly. The dose has to be decreased slowly or you will experience withdrawal symptoms (e.g., anxiety, shakiness, fast heart rate, difficulty sleeping, muscle pain), which are uncomfortable and can be dangerous.
- This medication can cause drug-seeking behavior (addictive/habit forming). Do not increase your dose, take it more frequently or use it for a longer time period than prescribed. Keep the bottle in a safe place to prevent others from taking it.
- When used for an extended time, this medication does not work as well and higher doses may be required. Talk with your healthcare provider if this medication stops working as well.
- Do not take with other medications that can make you sleepy, unless directed by your healthcare provider. Do not use alcohol with this medication.
- Avoid driving and doing other tasks or actions that require you to be alert until you see how this medication affects you.

Select Guidelines/References

American Psychiatric Association: Diagnostic and Statistical Manual of Mental Disorders, Fifth Edition. Arlington VA, American Psychiatric Association, 2013.

Locke AB, Kirst N, Shultz CG. Diagnosis and management of generalized anxiety disorder and panic disorder in adults. *Am Fam Physician* 2015;91:617-624.

Anxiety and Depression Association of America. Clinical practice review for GAD. Revised 2015. https://adaa.org/resources-professionals/practice-guidelines-gad (accessed 2019 Jan 2).

CHAPTER CONTENT

Background 918
Insomnia 918
Non-Drug Treatment 918
Natural Products 919
Drug Treatment 919
Select Drugs That Can Worsen Insomnia 919
Ez Tip for Excellent Zzzzzz (Sleep) 919
Hypnotics and Antidepressants 920
Benzodiazepines 921
Antihistamines 922
Restless Legs Syndrome 922
Drug Treatment 922
Narcolepsy 923
Drug Treatment 923

CONTENT LEGEND

= Study Tip Gal   = Key Drug Guy

CHAPTER 68
SLEEP DISORDERS: INSOMNIA, RESTLESS LEGS SYNDROME (RLS) & NARCOLEPSY

BACKGROUND

There are several types of sleep disorders. This chapter discusses the primary types for which common prescription drug treatments are available: chronic insomnia, restless legs syndrome (RLS) and narcolepsy. Another common sleep disorder is obstructive sleep apnea, which is primarily treated with non-drug measures, including continuous positive airway pressure (CPAP). A lack of restful sleep contributes to poor health and is linked to the development of a number of chronic conditions, including cardiovascular disease, mood disorders, alcoholism and depression. Patients who chronically use OTC medications for sleep should be referred to a healthcare provider.

INSOMNIA

Insomnia is the most common sleep condition and is characterized by difficulty falling asleep (sleep initiation or sleep latency), reduced sleep duration and/or poor sleep quality (e.g., awakenings after sleep onset). A diagnosis of chronic insomnia occurs when the patient has symptoms at least three times per week for at least three months, despite adequate opportunity to sleep. This often causes daytime impairment, such as being absent from work or experiencing accidents due to fatigue, somnolence, poor memory and decreased concentration.

NON-DRUG TREATMENT

Cognitive behavioral therapy for insomnia (CBT-I) is preferred and includes changes to sleep hygiene (see the flow diagram on the following page) that can reduce the need for drugs.

It is important to treat any underlying medical conditions that may be contributing (e.g., pain, shortness of breath due to heart failure, anxiety, bipolar disorder, depression, alcoholism) and discontinue medications that can worsen insomnia (see Key Drugs Guy on next page), if possible.

NATURAL PRODUCTS

Melatonin (3 – 5 mg in the evening) or valerian is used by some patients. Melatonin is also used for jet lag and can cause additive adverse effects (e.g., drowsiness, daytime somnolence) if used with other CNS depressants. It is a substrate of CYP1A2 and prolonged effects may be observed with CYP1A2 inhibitors (e.g., ciprofloxacin, fluvoxamine). Valerian is considered to have few adverse risks, but there have been isolated reports of liver toxicity; the significance of this risk is unclear. Drinking chamomile tea in the evening to feel calmer can help some patients with insomnia.

SELECT DRUGS THAT CAN WORSEN INSOMNIA

- Alcohol
- Bupropion
- Caffeine
- Decongestants (e.g., pseudoephedrine)
- Diuretics (due to nocturia)
- Fluoxetine, if taken late in the day
- Steroids
- Stimulants (e.g., methylphenidate, phentermine)
- Varenicline

DRUG TREATMENT

Sedative-hypnotics are the mainstay of insomnia treatment, but they are over-prescribed and there is a concern regarding adverse effects associated with even occasional use. It is preferable to reserve use for when non-drug treatments have failed, and to select agents with the best evidence for sleep onset and/or sleep maintenance depending on the problem identified (see the flow diagram below).

In patients using prescription agents long-term, the non-benzodiazepines are preferred over benzodiazepines due to a decreased risk of physical dependence and less daytime cognitive effects. For all medications, the lowest effective dose should be used to minimize adverse effects, and treatment should be limited to the shortest duration possible.

EXAM SCENARIO

A retired elderly male presents to his healthcare provider complaining of trouble sleeping. He has a daily routine that includes watching television and napping for much of the day.

Insomnia Guideline Recommendations

START WITH NON-DRUG TREATMENT

- Keep the bedroom dark, comfortable, and quiet
- Keep a regular sleep schedule
- Avoid daytime naps, even after a poor night of sleep, or limit to 30 mins
- Reserve the bedroom for sleep and other appropriate activities (no TV or other stimulants)
- Turn the face of the clock aside to minimize anxiety about falling asleep
- If unable to sleep, get up and do something to take your mind off sleeping
- Establish a pre-bedtime ritual to condition your body for sleep (e.g., relax with soft music, mild stretching, yoga, or pleasurable reading)
- Avoid exercising right before bedtime
- Do not eat heavy meals before bedtime
- Do not take any caffeine in the afternoon

Exam Scenario Patient Solution: **eliminate or reduce napping during the day and try taking a brisk walk earlier in the day.**

SLEEP PROBLEM PERSISTS?

PICK A DRUG TO ADDRESS THE SLEEP PROBLEM

Need help falling asleep?	Need help staying asleep?	Need help falling and staying asleep?
Eszopiclone	Doxepin	Eszopiclone
Ramelteon	Eszopiclone	Zolpidem
Zaleplon	Suvorexant	
Zolpidem	Zolpidem	

EZ Tip for Excellent Zzzzzz (sleep)

Eszopiclone
Zolpidem
in all 3 groups

Patients may self-treat insomnia with OTC first-generation antihistamines, such as diphenhydramine or doxylamine. While these can help short-term, they should not be used long-term for the treatment of insomnia. The American Academy of Sleep Medicine (AASM) guidelines state that the following treatments are not recommended for chronic use: diphenhydramine, melatonin, tiagabine, trazodone, and valerian.

Benzodiazepines (e.g. temazepam, lorazepam) can be tried for short-term treatment (such as from acute trauma), if there is no substance abuse history or current use of opioids. The Beers Criteria considers benzodiazepines, non-benzodiazepine hypnotics (e.g., zolpidem) and first-generation antihistamines as potentially inappropriate for use in patients aged 65 years and older. If benzodiazepines are used lorazepam, oxazepam and temazepam (L-O-T) are preferred in the elderly.

Hypnotics and Antidepressants

DRUG	DOSING	SAFETY/SIDE EFFECTS/MONITORING
Non-benzodiazepines: act selectively at the benzodiazepine receptors to increase GABA		
Eszopiclone *(Lunesta)* C-IV	1-3 mg PO QHS Start with 1 mg immediately before bed and increase to 2 mg or 3 mg if necessary	**WARNINGS** ↑ risk of CNS depression and next-day impairment with < 7-8 hours of sleep (especially with higher doses or coadministration of CNS depressants or alcohol), abnormal thinking and behavioral changes (can worsen depression), respiratory depression, increased risk for hazardous sleep-related activities (e.g., sleep-driving) Potential for abuse and dependence (can cause withdrawal symptoms if used longer than 2 weeks) **SIDE EFFECTS** Somnolence, dizziness, ataxia, lightheadedness, "pins and needles" feeling on the skin, can cause parasomnias (unusual actions while sleeping, which the patient may be unaware of) **NOTES** Preferred over benzodiazepines for first-line treatment due to ↓ abuse, dependence and tolerance Do not take with fatty food, a heavy meal or alcohol
Zaleplon *(Sonata)* C-IV	5-10 mg PO QHS	
Zolpidem ***Ambien, Ambien CR*** IR and ER tablets *Zolpimist* Oral spray (5 mg/spray) ***Edluar, Intermezzo*** SL tablets C-IV	*Ambien:* 5-10 mg PO QHS, max dose is 5 mg in females and elderly patients *Ambien CR:* 6.25-12.5 mg PO QHS, max dose is 6.25 mg in females and elderly patients *Zolpimist:* 1-2 sprays PO QHS *Edluar:* 5-10 mg SL QHS *Intermezzo:* 3.5 mg SL (males), 1.75 mg SL (females and those using CNS depressants)	
Orexin-receptor antagonist: blocks the orexin neuropeptide signaling system (which promotes wakefulness)		
Suvorexant *(Belsomra)* C-IV	10 mg PO QHS if at least 7 hours of sleep remaining Max dose is 20 mg daily Use 5 mg with moderate CYP3A4 inhibitors and do not exceed 10 mg daily Avoid use with strong CYP3A4 inhibitors	**CONTRAINDICATIONS** Narcolepsy **WARNINGS** Abnormal thinking and behavioral changes, worsening depression/ suicidal ideation, sleep paralysis, hallucinations, cataplexy-like symptoms (sudden loss of muscle tone), increased risk for hazardous sleep-related activities (e.g., sleep-driving) **SIDE EFFECTS** Somnolence, headache, dizziness, abnormal dreams
Melatonin receptor agonists		
Ramelteon *(Rozerem)*	8 mg PO QHS	**SIDE EFFECTS** Somnolence, dizziness **NOTES** Not a controlled substance Do not take with fatty food Contraindicated with fluvoxamine (increases serum concentration of ramelteon) Tasimelteon *(Hetlioz)* is indicated for non-24 hour sleep-wake disorder
Tasimelteon *(Hetlioz)*	20 mg PO QHS	

DRUG	DOSING	SAFETY/SIDE EFFECTS/MONITORING
Antidepressants		
Doxepin *(Silenor)*	6 mg PO QHS 3 mg if ≥ 65 years	**CONTRAINDICATIONS** Requires a 2 week washout for MAO inhibitors **SIDE EFFECTS** Somnolence, possibility of anticholinergic side effects **NOTES** Has the same risks for unusual thoughts/suicide as other antidepressants (see the Depression chapter) Generic doxepin, trazodone, and mirtazapine may be used off-label for sleep (not recommended by guidelines)

Eszopiclone, Zaleplon and Zolpidem Drug Interactions

- Use caution in combination with potent CYP3A4 inhibitors (e.g., protease inhibitors, ketoconazole, itraconazole, erythromycin and clarithromycin).
- Can cause additive effects when used with other sedating drugs, including most pain medications, muscle relaxants, antihistamines, the antidepressant mirtazapine *(Remeron)*, trazodone and alcohol.

Eszopiclone, Zaleplon and Zolpidem Patient Counseling

- Common side effects include drowsiness, lightheadedness, dizziness, "pins and needles" feeling on your skin and difficulty with coordination. You may still feel drowsy the day after taking this medication. Use caution when driving a car or operating dangerous machinery.
- This drug may (rarely) cause abnormal thoughts and behavior (e.g., more outgoing or aggressive behavior than usual, confusion, agitation, hallucinations, worsening depression, and suicidal thoughts or actions).
- You can have withdrawal symptoms when you stop taking this medication. These include unpleasant feelings, stomach and muscle cramps, vomiting, sweating and shakiness. You can also have more trouble sleeping for the first few nights after stopping the medication.
- This medication is a federally controlled substance (C-IV) because it can be abused or lead to dependence. Keep the bottle in a safe place to prevent misuse and abuse.
- *Zolpimist:* spray directly into your mouth over your tongue (once for a 5 mg dose, twice for a 10 mg dose). Prime the bottle before first time use.
- *Edluar* or *Intermezzo* SL tablets: this drug is not swallowed, it dissolves under the tongue. Do not take *Intermezzo* unless you are planning to sleep four or more hours.

Benzodiazepines

These agents enhance GABA, an inhibitory neurotransmitter, causing CNS depression. A brief summary of the agents that are FDA-indicated for insomnia is provided below; consult the Anxiety chapter for a full discussion of safety issues and patient counseling related to these drugs.

DRUG	DOSING	SAFETY/SIDE EFFECTS/MONITORING
Lorazepam ***(Ativan,*** *Lorazepam Intensol* oral solution)	0.5-2 mg PO QHS	**ALL** These are C-IV drugs; there is a risk of physical (physiological) dependence, abuse (addiction) and tolerance Lorazepam, oxazepam, and temazepam (L-O-T) are preferred for elderly patients; lorazepam and temazepam can be used for sleep; oxazepam is indicated for anxiety All benzodiazepines cross the placenta; temazepam, estazolam, and triazolam are contraindicated in pregnancy due to observed teratogenicity **NOTES** Estazolam: do not use with potent CYP3A4 inhibitors (e.g., ketoconazole, itraconazole) Triazolam: associated with higher rebound insomnia and daytime anxiety; contraindicated with azole antifungals, protease inhibitors and other CYP3A4 Inhibitors
Temazepam ***(Restoril)***	7.5-30 mg PO QHS	
Estazolam	1-2 mg PO QHS	
Quazepam *(Doral)*	7.5-15 mg PO QHS	
Flurazepam	15-30 mg PO QHS	
Triazolam *(Halcion)*	0.125-0.5 mg PO QHS	

Antihistamines

These drugs compete with (i.e., block) histamine H1 receptors.

DRUG	DOSING	SAFETY/SIDE EFFECTS/MONITORING
Diphenhydramine *(Benadryl,* store brands)	50 mg PO QHS	**SIDE EFFECTS** Sedation (tolerance to sedative effects can develop after 10 days of use), confusion (can exacerbate memory/cognition difficulty) Antihistamines may cause paradoxical excitation in young children; do not use doxylamine in children <12 years Peripheral anticholinergic side effects: dry mouth, urinary retention (makes it very difficult for males with BPH to urinate), dry/blurry vision, constipation Best to avoid use in BPH (can worsen symptoms) and glaucoma (can elevate IOP)
Doxylamine *(**Unisom**, Sleep Aid,* store brands)	25 mg PO QHS	

Diphenhydramine (and Other Sedating Antihistamines) Patient Counseling

- This medication will make you sleepy. Do not drive a car or use any dangerous machinery after taking this medication. Do not take with other drugs that can make you sleepy, unless directed by your doctor. Do not use alcohol.
- This medication can make it difficult to urinate (it will take longer for the urine to come out). You should not use this medication if you have an enlarged prostate or BPH, unless directed by your doctor.
- This medication will worsen or cause constipation.
- If you have glaucoma, discuss use with your eye doctor. It can raise the pressure in your eyes.
- Your mouth and eyes can become dry and your vision can become blurry.

RESTLESS LEGS SYNDROME

Restless legs syndrome (RLS) is an urge to move the lower legs, which is sometimes described as a "creeping" sensation. It is worse at night and is relieved with movement. RLS is thought to be due to a dysfunction of dopamine in the brain's basal ganglia circuits.

DRUG TREATMENT

The primary treatment of RLS includes dopamine agonists and the anticonvulsant gabapentin. Pramipexole *(Mirapex)* and ropinirole *(Requip)* are dopamine agonists primarily used in longer-acting formulations for Parkinson disease (PD). For RLS, the immediate-release (IR) formulation is taken 1-3 hours before bedtime. Rotigotine *(Neupro)* is a dopamine agonist that comes in a patch formulation (used for both PD and RLS). The patch is applied once daily and patients must be counseled on appropriate use (e.g., do not apply a heat source over the patch, remove the patch before an MRI procedure, rotate sites to avoid skin irritation).

Dopamine agonists cause orthostasis, somnolence and nausea that is dose-related. Even when used for RLS, the dose should be titrated up slowly. Patients should be monitored for psychiatric side effects (e.g., hallucinations, abnormal dreams) and movement disorders.

Gabapentin enacarbil *(Horizant)* is an extended-release form of gabapentin approved for postherpetic neuralgia (PHN) and RLS. The tablet is taken with food and must be swallowed whole (it cannot be crushed or chewed). For RLS, it is taken at ~5:00 PM daily. The IR formulation of gabapentin is used off-label as a less expensive alternative. Refer to the Parkinson Disease chapter for additional information on the dopamine agonists, and the Seizures/Epilepsy chapter for additional information on gabapentin.

NARCOLEPSY

Narcolepsy is excessive daytime sleepiness with cataplexy (sudden loss of muscle tone) and sleep paralysis. Narcolepsy causes sudden daytime "sleep attacks" due to poor control of normal sleep-wake cycles. The sleep attacks last a few seconds to several minutes. Patients have difficulty managing daily activities with narcolepsy; they can fall asleep while at work, school or in the middle of a conversation. In addition, sleep quality at night is poor.

DRUG TREATMENT

Narcolepsy is treated with stimulants, such as modafinil or armodafinil, or with sodium oxybate *(Xyrem)*, which is derived from the inhibitory neurotransmitter GABA. Several of the stimulants used for ADHD have an indication for narcolepsy, including dextroamphetamine, dextroamphetamine/amphetamine *(Adderall)* and various methylphenidate formulations *(Metadate ER, Methylin* and *Ritalin)*. Solriamfetol *(Sunosi)* is the newest FDA-approved drug used to improved wakefulness in adults with narcolepsy or obstructive sleep apnea. It is inhibits both dopamine and norepinephrine reuptake.

Stimulants for Wakefulness

DRUG	DOSING	SAFETY/SIDE EFFECTS/MONITORING
Modafinil *(Provigil)* C-IV	200 mg PO daily	**WARNINGS** Avoid with pre-existing cardiac conditions, caution with hepatic or renal dysfunction, psychiatric disorders and Tourette's syndrome **SIDE EFFECTS** Severe rash can be life-threatening (e.g., Stevens-Johnson syndrome), headache, insomnia, anxiety, nausea **NOTES** Other indications include obstructive sleep apnea (to help with excessive daytime sleepiness)
Armodafinil *(Nuvigil)* R-isomer of modafinil C-IV	150-250 mg PO daily	

Sodium Oxybate

This agent is derived from GABA and is indicated for narcolepsy with cataplexy. It helps with sleep at night, and is generally used with daytime stimulants.

DRUG	DOSING	SAFETY/SIDE EFFECTS/MONITORING
Sodium oxybate *(Xyrem)* Oral solution C-III (narcolepsy) C-I (illicit use) This is a "date rape" drug (the sedative GHB); a REMS program is required to ensure it is only used by patients with narcolepsy with cataplexy	Start 2.25 grams PO QHS and take again 2.5-4 hours later Titrate to effect; dosing range ~6-9 grams/night Take in ¼ cup water; lie down immediately after taking and stay in bed; sleep onset typically occurs within 5-15 minutes after taking the first dose	**BOXED WARNINGS** Strong CNS depressant; respiratory depression, coma and death can result; risk is increased when taken with other CNS depressants Restricted access through the *Xyrem* REMS Program **CONTRAINDICATIONS** Use with sedative-hypnotics or alcohol **WARNINGS** Depression, suicide, psychosis, anxiety, sleep walking **SIDE EFFECTS** Dizziness, confusion, nausea

Select Guidelines/References

Clinical practice guideline for the pharmacologic treatment of chronic insomnia in adults: an American Academy of Sleep Medicine clinical practice guideline. *J Clin Sleep Med.* 2017;13(2):307-349.

Practice guideline summary: Treatment of restless legs syndrome in adults: Report of the American Academy of Neurology. *Neurology.* 2016;87:2585-2593.

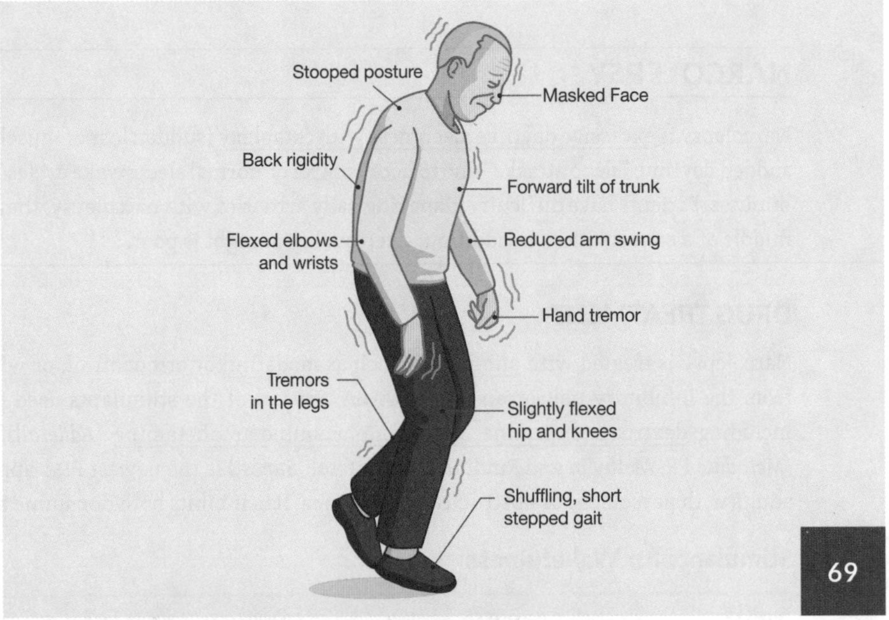
Stooped posture
Masked Face
Back rigidity
Forward tilt of trunk
Flexed elbows and wrists
Reduced arm swing
Hand tremor
Tremors in the legs
Slightly flexed hip and knees
Shuffling, short stepped gait
69

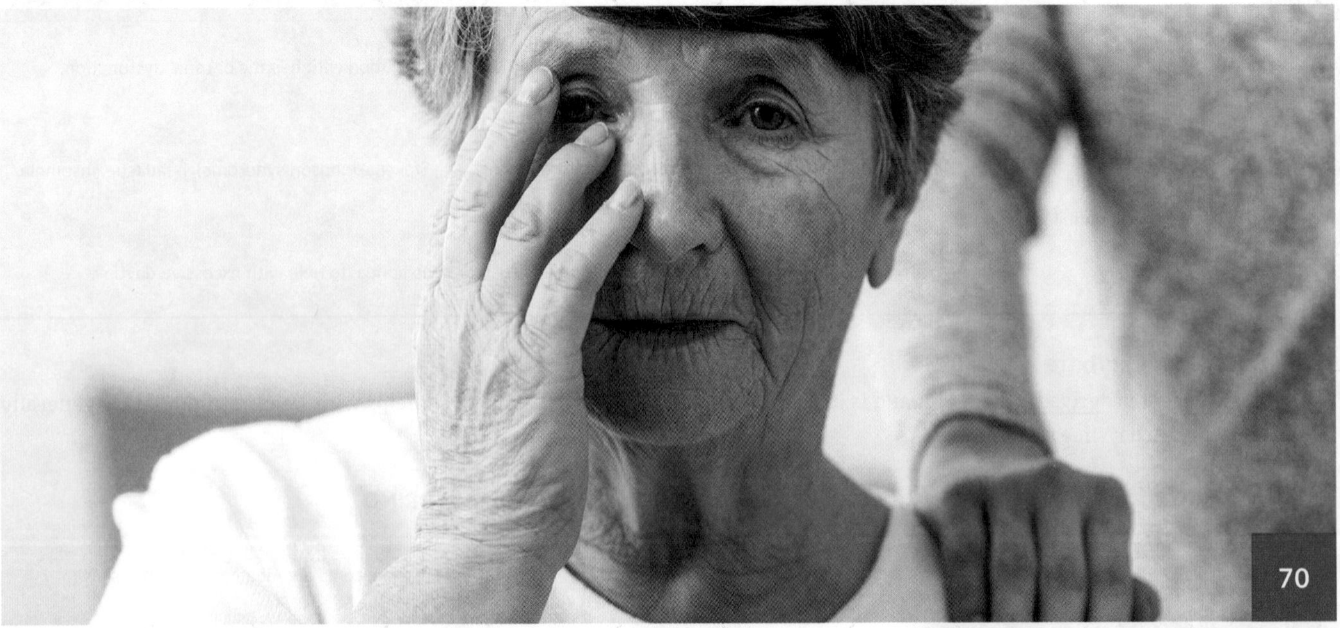
70

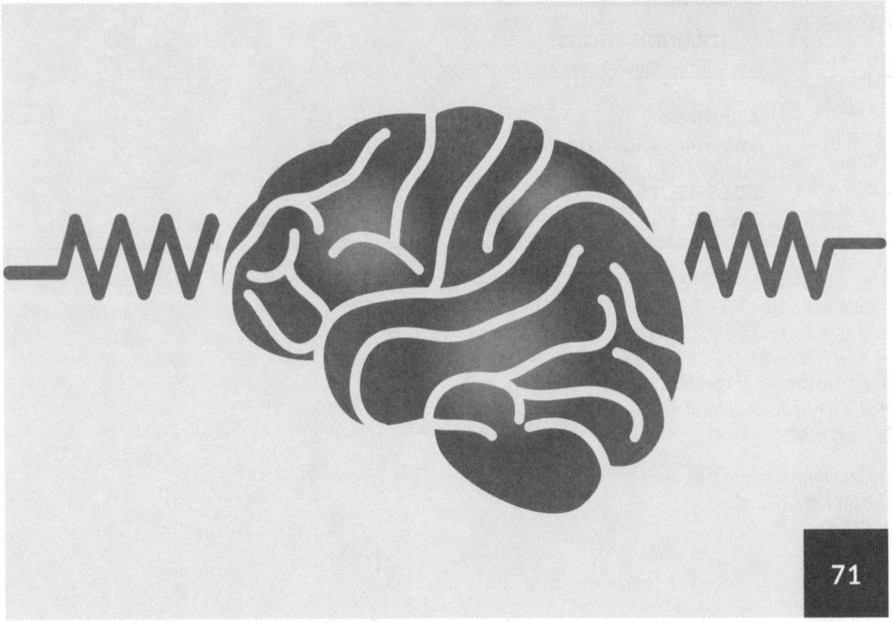
71

NEUROLOGIC CONDITIONS

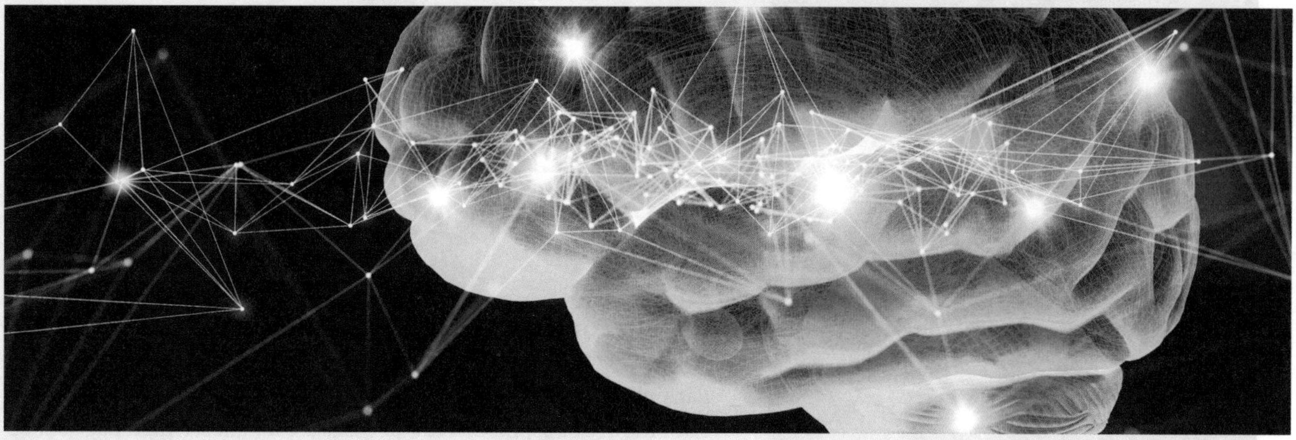

CONTENTS

CHAPTER 69
PARKINSON DISEASE | **926**

CHAPTER 70
ALZHEIMER'S DISEASE | **932**

CHAPTER 71
SEIZURES/EPILEPSY | **937**

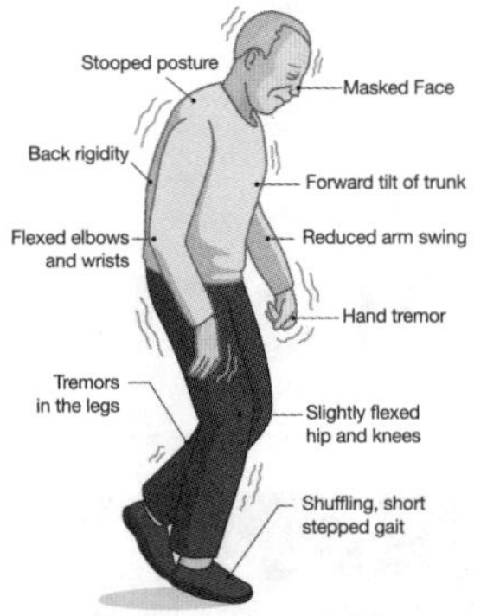

CHAPTER 69
PARKINSON DISEASE

CHAPTER CONTENT

Background 926
Dopamine Blocking Drugs that Can Worsen PD 926
Parkinson Disease: The Cause, Symptoms and Primary Drug Treatment 927
Related Psychiatric Conditions 927
Drug Treatment 927
Dopamine Replacement Drugs & Agonists 928
Carbidopa/Levodopa 928
COMT Inhibitors 928
Dopamine Agonists 928
Other Drugs for Parkinson Disease 929
Amantadine 929
Selective MAO-B Inhibitors 929
Centrally-Acting Anticholinergics 930
Alpha/Beta Agonist 930
Patient Counseling 930

CONTENT LEGEND

= Study Tip Gal   = Key Drug Guy

BACKGROUND

Parkinson disease (PD) is a neurological disorder. It usually develops after the age of 65, though 15% of cases are diagnosed under age 50. PD occurs when neurons in the substantia nigra (a part of the brain) die or become impaired. The cause of neuronal death is not well understood, but is multi-factorial. These cells produce dopamine, which allows smooth, coordinated function of body muscles and movement. When ~80% of the dopamine-producing cells are damaged, the motor symptoms of the disease appear (see the Study Tip Gal on the following page).

Motor symptoms in PD include bradykinesia (slow movement), arm/leg/trunk rigidity (stiffness), involuntary shaking and tremor and postural instability (trouble with balance and falls). Medications can cause similar symptoms, and can mimic PD or make PD worse (see Key Drugs Guy). The Abnormal Involuntary Movement Scale (AIMS) can be used to measure involuntary movements (i.e., tardive dyskinesias) from medications. Non-motor symptoms can precede motor symptoms, and may appear much earlier in the disease process. These include a loss of sense of smell (anosmia), constipation, sleep difficulties, low mood/depression and orthostasis. Biomarkers that can identify early disease, prior to visual symptoms, are a focus of research.

DOPAMINE BLOCKING DRUGS THAT CAN WORSEN PD

- Phenothiazines (e.g., prochlorperazine) used for psychosis, nausea, agitation
- Butyrophenones (e.g., haloperidol, droperidol) used for psychosis and behavior disorders or nausea
- First and second generation antipsychotics (e.g., risperidone at higher doses, paliperidone). Lowest risk with quetiapine
- Metoclopramide, a renally-cleared drug that can accumulate in elderly patients

Initially tremor appears on one-side of the body (unilateral); it will eventually spread bilaterally. Even with high doses of PD drugs and various combinations, the disease will progress, including extended periods of "off time." This is when symptoms of the disease worsen

PARKINSON DISEASE: THE CAUSE, SYMPTOMS AND PRIMARY DRUG TREATMENT

Neurons in the substantia nigra region degenerate.

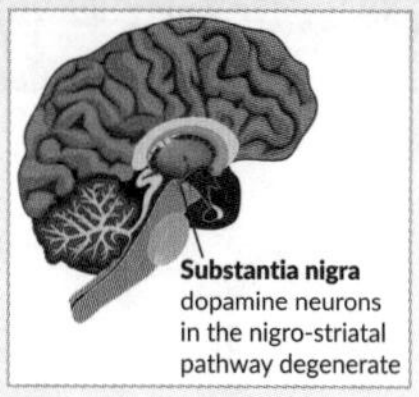

This part of the brain controls motor function, including movement and balance by releasing the neurotransmitter dopamine (DA), which fine tunes the movement instructions to other parts of the brain.

In Parkinson Disease:
Less dopamine → less instructions to the brain → movement problems, which are called the **TRAP major symptoms.**

TRAP major symptoms:	Additional Symptoms:
Tremor: when resting	Small, cramped handwriting (micrographia)
Rigidity: in legs, arms, trunk, and face (mask-like face)	Shuffling walk, stooped posture
Akinesia/Bradykinesia: lack of/slow start in movement	Muffled speech, drooling, dysphagia
Postural Instability: imbalance, falls	Depression, anxiety (psychosis in advanced disease)
	Constipation, incontinence

Primary Treatment: repleace dopamine

✓ Give a precursor to dopamine that becomes dopamine in the brain (that's levodopa, in *Sinemet).*

✓ Give a dopamine agonist that acts like dopamine.

✓ Give other drugs for specific symptoms (e.g., resting tremor).

Tremor is often the first noticeable symptom, and usually starts in one hand or foot (on just one side, unilateral) and eventually spreads to both sides (bilateral). *Resting* tremor means it appears when the hand is not moving, such as when a person's hand is resting in their lap. Initially, the tremor may be all that is treated in order to delay the need for the stronger dopaminergic drugs.

before the next dose of medication is due. An "off" episode, with muscle stiffness, slow movements and difficulty starting movement is one of the most frustrating aspects of living with the disease. Symptoms can progress to severe disability, and patients can lose the ability to walk, feed themselves and swallow food.

RELATED PSYCHIATRIC CONDITIONS

Patients with PD have a high incidence of depression. SSRIs or SNRIs are commonly used for treatment. There is some concern that they may contribute to tremor or an increased risk of serotonin syndrome in patients who are taking other serotonergic drugs. Tricyclic antidepressants, preferably the secondary amines (such as desipramine and nortriptyline), and the dopamine agonist pramipexole (reported to provide antidepressant effects), are other options.

Psychosis can occur with advanced disease, or due to side effects of drug treatment. Quetiapine is the preferred antipsychotic due to a low risk of movement disorders, but it can cause metabolic complications, including increased cholesterol and blood glucose. Clozapine has a low risk of worsening movement disorders, but has a high risk of agranulocytosis, seizures and other serious complications. Clozapine requires frequent monitoring and reporting of white blood cells. Pimavanserin *(Nuplazid)*, a 5HT2A/2C receptor inverse agonist, is FDA-approved to treat hallucinations and delusions in patients with PD. Refer to the Schizophrenia/Psychosis chapter for more information on antipsychotic drugs.

DRUG TREATMENT

Medications are used to improve movement, which also helps related issues, such as psychosis and constipation. Levodopa, a prodrug of dopamine, is the most effective agent. Carbidopa is given with levodopa (in the combination product *Sinemet)* to prevent the peripheral (i.e., outside of the CNS) metabolism of levodopa, which would destroy most of the drug before it crosses the blood-brain barrier and provides efficacy. It is important to provide the right amount of carbidopa without causing excess side effects (see the drug table on the following page). Initial treatment with carbidopa/levodopa is sometimes better tolerated in the elderly than the dopamine agonists.

Dopamine agonists are commonly used for initial treatment in younger patients, and eventually in most patients. As the disease progresses, treatment will be directed at both reducing "off" periods and limiting dyskinesias (abnormal movement). This will require multiple therapies, such as. catechol-o-methyltransferase (COMT) inhibitors and MAO-B inhibitors.

Tremor-predominant disease in younger patients can be treated with a centrally-acting anticholinergic. The considerable side effects of these drugs makes them difficult to use in elderly patients; the Beers criteria for potentially inappropriate medication use in older adults recommends to "avoid" use. Amantadine or a selective monoamine oxidase (MAO) inhibitor are other options for initial treatment of tremor. Note that for PD, selective MAO inhibitors are used; the non-selective inhibitors that are used for depression are contraindicated with dopaminergic drugs because they would block drug metabolism.

Amantadine can be useful to help with dyskinesias, in addition to tremor. Apomorphine treats severe freezing episodes that usually occur in more advanced disease, but it requires subcutaneous (SC) administration, has worrisome side effects and provides increased movement for just about an hour. Droxidopa *(Northera)* is a newer drug indicated for orthostatic hypotension, which can affect PD patients.

DOPAMINE REPLACEMENT DRUGS & AGONISTS

DRUG	DOSING	SAFETY/SIDE EFFECTS/MONITORING
Carbidopa/levodopa: levodopa is a precursor of dopamine. Carbidopa inhibits dopa decarboxylase enzyme, preventing peripheral metabolism of levodopa.		
Carbidopa/Levodopa ***Sinemet, Sinemet CR*** Tablets *Rytary* ER capsule *Duopa* Enteral suspension given via J-tube Levodopa and carbidopa available separately *Inbrija* Levodopa capsule for oral inhaler, used as needed for symptoms during off periods 70-100 mg/day of carbidopa required to inhibit dopa decarboxylase	IR (starting dose): 25/100 mg PO TID CR (starting dose): 50/200 mg PO BID CR tab can be cut in half – do not crush or chew *Rytary*: start at 23.75/95 mg PO TID if levodopa-naive; take whole or sprinkle on a small amount of applesauce *Inbrija*: 84 mg (2 capsules) inhaled up to 5 times daily as needed, max dose: 420 mg/day Titrate cautiously	**CONTRAINDICATIONS** Non-selective MAO inhibitors within 14 days, narrow angle glaucoma **SIDE EFFECTS** Nausea, dizziness, orthostasis, dyskinesias, xerostomia (dry mouth), dystonias (occasional, painful), confusion, hallucinations or psychosis Can cause brown, black or dark discoloring of urine, saliva or sweat and can discolor clothing; positive Coombs test: discontinue drug (hemolysis risk); unusual sexual urges, priapism; ↑ uric acid *Rytary:* suicidal ideation and attempts *Duopa:* GI complications **NOTES** Long term use can lead to fluctuations in response and dyskinesias Separate from oral iron and high protein foods
COMT inhibitors: increase the duration of action of levodopa; inhibit the enzyme catechol-O-methyltransferase (COMT) to prevent peripheral conversion of levodopa.		
Entacapone *(Comtan)* + levodopa/carbidopa *(Stalevo)* COMT inhibitors should only be used with levodopa	200 mg PO with each dose of carbidopa/levodopa (max = 1,600 mg/day) *Stalevo:* carbidopa/levodopa in a ratio of 1:4 with 200 mg of entacapone in each tablet (example: 12.5/50/200 mg)	**SIDE EFFECTS** Similar to levodopa, due to extending its duration **NOTES** ↓ in levodopa dose of 10-30% is usually necessary when adding on a COMT inhibitor Dyskinesias can occur earlier with COMT inhibitors Tolcapone *(Tasmar)* is another agent in the class; it is not used much due to hepatotoxicity
Dopamine agonists: act similar to dopamine at the dopamine receptor.		
Pramipexole *(Mirapex, Mirapex ER)* IR formulation also approved for restless legs syndrome (RLS)	IR: start with 0.125 mg PO TID, titrate weekly to max of 1.5 mg TID ER: start with 0.375 mg PO daily, titrate weekly to max of 4.5 mg daily ↓ dose if CrCl < 50 mL/min (90% renally excreted)	**SIDE EFFECTS** Somnolence (including sudden daytime sleep attacks), orthostasis, hallucinations, dyskinesias, dizziness, nausea, vomiting, dry mouth, peripheral edema, constipation, impulse control disorders Rotigotine patch: application site (skin) reactions, hyperhidrosis **NOTES** A slow titration (no more than weekly) is required due to orthostasis, dizziness, sleepiness Ropinirole: CYP450 1A2 substrate; caution with CYP1A2 inhibitors due to increased drug levels Bromocriptine is another agent in the class; no longer recommended **Patch** Apply once daily, at the same time each day; do not use the same site for at least 14 days; do not apply a heat source over the patch; remove the patch before an MRI; avoid if sensitivity/allergy to sulfites
Ropinirole *(Requip, Requip XL)* IR formulation also approved for RLS	IR: start with 0.25 mg PO TID, titrate weekly to max of 8 mg TID XL: start with 2 mg PO daily, titrate weekly to max of 24 mg daily	
Rotigotine *(Neupro)* Patch Also approved for RLS	Patch: start with 2 mg/24 hrs (early PD) Max dose: 8 mg/24 hours	

DRUG	DOSING	SAFETY/SIDE EFFECTS/MONITORING
Dopamine agonist injection for advanced disease: a "rescue" movement agent for "off" periods.		
Apomorphine *(Apokyn)* Injection Taken in addition to other PD medications	Start with 0.2 mL (2 mg) SC PRN (up to 5x/day); titrate by 1 mg every few days Max single dose: 0.6 mL (6 mg) Caution: dose written in mL, not mg Lasts 45-90 minutes Must be started with a test dose in a medical office	**CONTRAINDICATION** Do not use with 5HT3 antagonists (ondansetron, others) due to severe hypotension and loss of consciousness **SIDE EFFECTS** Severe N/V, hypotension, yawning, dyskinesias, somnolence, dizziness, QT prolongation **NOTES** Monitor supine and standing blood pressure For emesis prevention: give trimethobenzamide *(Tigan)* 300 mg PO TID, or a similar antiemetic, started 3 days prior to the initial dose

Carbidopa/Levodopa *(Sinemet)* Drug Interactions

- Contraindicated with non-selective MAO inhibitors (a two week separation is required).
- Iron and protein-rich foods can ↓ absorption.
- Do not use with dopamine blockers, which will worsen Parkinson symptoms (e.g., phenothiazines, metoclopramide).

OTHER DRUGS FOR PARKINSON DISEASE

DRUG	DOSING	SAFETY/SIDE EFFECTS/MONITORING
Amantadine: blocks dopamine reuptake into presynaptic neurons and increases dopamine release from presynaptic fibers. Primarily used to treat dyskinesias associated with peak-dose of carbidopa/levodopa.		
Amantadine Tablet, capsule, syrup Amantadine extended-release *(Gocovri, Osmolex ER)*	IR: 100 mg PO BID *Osmolex ER:* 137 mg PO daily, increase after 1 week to 274 mg daily *Gocovri:* 129 mg daily, increase weekly to max dose of 322 mg daily ↓ dose in renal impairment	**CONTRAINDICATIONS** ER products: eGFR < 15 mL/min/1.73 m^2 **WARNINGS** Somnolence (including falling asleep without warning during activities of daily living), compulsive behaviors, psychosis (hallucinations, delusions, paranoia) **SIDE EFFECTS** Dizziness, orthostatic hypotension, syncope, insomnia, abnormal dreams, dry mouth, constipation Cutaneous reaction called livedo reticularis (reddish skin mottling – can require drug discontinuation) **NOTES** *Gocovri* is indicated for the treatment of dyskinesia in patients receiving levodopa-based therapy
Selective MAO-B inhibitors: block the breakdown of dopamine which increases dopaminergic activity. Primarily used as adjunctive treatment to carbidopa/levodopa; rasagiline has an indication for monotherapy.		
Selegiline *(Zelapar)* Capsule, tablet (generics) *Zelapar* – ODT *Emsam* – patch; only indicated for depression	Capsule, tablet: 5 mg PO BID, with breakfast and lunch ODT: 1.25-2.5 mg daily (not recommended if CrCl < 30 mL/min) Selegiline can be activating; do not take dose at bedtime; If dosed twice daily, take the 2nd dose at mid-day	**CONTRAINDICATIONS** Use in combination with other MAO inhibitors (including linezolid), opioids, SNRIs, TCAs, others (see Drug Interactions) *Xadago*: severe hepatic impairment **WARNINGS** Serotonin syndrome, hypertension, CNS depression, dyskinesias, impulse control disorders, caution in patients with psychotic disorders (may exacerbate) or ophthalmic disorders *(Xadago)* Rasagiline, when taken as monotherapy, can cause headache, joint pain and indigestion **MONITORING** BP, signs of serotonin syndrome, visual changes *(Xadago)* **NOTES** May need to reduce levodopa dose when beginning treatment with a selective MAO-B inhibitor
Rasagiline *(Azilect)*	0.5-1 mg PO daily	
Safinamide *(Xadago)* Adjunctive treatment to carbidopa/levodopa in patients experiencing "off" episodes	Start with 50 mg once daily; after 2 weeks may increase to 100 mg once daily When stopping treatment: decrease the dose to 50 mg for one week before discontinuing	

DRUG	DOSING	SAFETY/SIDE EFFECTS/MONITORING
Centrally-acting anticholinergics: have anticholinergic and antihistamine effects. Primarily used for tremor.		
Benztropine *(Cogentin)*	0.5-2 mg TID (start QHS)	**SIDE EFFECTS** High incidence of peripheral and central anticholinergic effects: dry mouth, constipation, urinary retention, blurred vision, somnolence, confusion, tachycardia **NOTES** Avoid use in elderly patients
Trihexyphenidyl	1-5 mg TID (start 1 mg QHS)	
Alpha/beta agonist: used for neurogenic orthostatic hypotension.		
Droxidopa *(Northera)*	Start at 100 mg PO TID, can titrate every 24-48 hour to a max of 1800 mg/day Take capsule whole (do not open) with or without food; take the last dose at least 3 hours prior to bedtime (to avoid supine hypertension during sleep)	**BOXED WARNING** Supine hypertension: monitor supine BP prior to and during treatment; elevate the head of the bed and measure BP in this position; if supine hypertension cannot be managed by elevation of the head of the bed, reduce dose or discontinue **SIDE EFFECTS** Syncope, falls, headache

MAO-B Inhibitor Drug Interactions

- These drugs should not be used with foods high in tyramine content (aged or matured cheese, air-dried or cured meats, including sausages and salamis, fava or broad bean pods, tap/draft beers, Marmite concentrate, sauerkraut, soy sauce, and other soybean condiments). Avoid these foods during and for two weeks after discontinuation of the medication.
- Products containing dopamine, tyrosine, phenylalanine, tryptophan or caffeine should be avoided.
- Avoid in combination with other drugs that increase the risk of serotonin syndrome. See the Learning Drug Interactions chapter for a detailed discussion on drugs/drug classes that can have additive effects when used together.
- Rasagiline is a CYP1A2 substrate and should not be dosed above 0.5 mg daily with ciprofloxacin or other CYP1A2 inhibitors.

PATIENT COUNSELING

All Parkinson Disease Patients

- People with Parkinson Disease may be at a higher risk of getting a type of skin cancer called melanoma. It is important that you are monitored for this condition.
- Call your healthcare provider right away if you have uncontrollable movements of the mouth, tongue, cheeks, jaw, arms or legs, or if you have a fever and your body feels very hot.
- The medications used for Parkinson Disease cannot be taken with a group of drugs used for depression called MAO inhibitors. Make sure your healthcare provider knows about all the medications you use, and any changes to your medications.
- If you develop any urges, including unusual urges for sex, gambling or uncontrollable buying sprees, let your healthcare provider know.
- Your mood can change; tell your healthcare provider if your mood becomes sad, or if you have thoughts of harming yourself.
- Do not stop taking this medication suddenly. Stopping suddenly could make your condition worse.
- Avoid drinking alcohol because it will make dizziness and sleepiness worse, and could cause falls and injuries.
- If you miss a dose of any of your regular medications, take the dose as soon as you remember, except if it is close to the time for the next dose, then skip the one you forgot, and just take the regular dose.

Carbidopa/Levodopa

- Do not crush or chew any controlled-release forms of carbidopa/levodopa *(Sinemet CR)*. They are specially formulated to release slowly into your system. If necessary, the tablets can be split in half where they are scored, then swallowed without crushing or chewing.
- Use caution when driving, operating machinery or performing other hazardous activities. Carbidopa/levodopa can cause dizziness or drowsiness and can make you feel suddenly sleepy.
- This drug may cause the urine, saliva and sweat to become darker (e.g., dark brown) and can stain clothing.
- Iron can decrease the amount of medication that gets into your body; if you take iron pills they should be taken at a different time.

- Foods high in protein can reduce the amount of drug that gets into your body (protein intake is important and should not be reduced).
- *Rytary*: a high-fat or high-calorie meal can cause the drug to work slower.
- For males, if you have a painful or prolonged erection (lasting more than four hours), which is rare, stop using this drug and seek immediate medical attention.

Ropinirole and Pramipexole

- This medication can be taken with or without food. Food will help if the medication causes nausea.
- Nausea and drowsiness are the most common side effects. This medication may cause you to fall asleep while you are doing daily activities, such as driving, talking with other people or eating. If you experience increased drowsiness or dizziness, or episodes of falling asleep while performing daily activities, do not drive or participate in potentially dangerous activities.
- This drug can cause dizziness, which may be more likely to occur when you rise from a sitting or lying position. Rise slowly and use caution to prevent a fall.
- Alcohol, sleeping pills, pain medications, antihistamines, antidepressants and other drugs that cause drowsiness can make the side effects you experience with this medication worse, which could be dangerous.
- Tell your healthcare provider if you experience paranoid thoughts, have excessive worry or begin hearing voices. There is medication that may help, or the dose of your Parkinson medication may need to be changed.
- The dose of this medication will be increased slowly over time due to the risk for dizziness and sleepiness.

Rotigotine *(Neupro)* Patch

- Side effects from the patch can include ankle swelling, headache, fatigue, nausea, changes in blood pressure, difficulty getting a good night's sleep and unusual thoughts. If any of these occur and are troublesome, discuss with your healthcare provider.
- This medication can cause you to become very sleepy. Do not drive a car or operate dangerous machinery until you are sure this can be done safely.
- You may find that you sweat more than usual. It is important to drink enough fluids and avoid direct sunlight.
- The patch contains aluminum, which can burn your skin if you have certain medical procedures. The patch must be removed prior to magnetic resonance imaging (MRI) or a "cardioversion" procedure. Do not expose the patch to heat, such as heating pads.
- To apply the patch:
  - Choose the time of day that works best for you so it is easiest to remember.
  - Wear the patch for 24 hours. Remove before applying the next patch.
  - Do not apply to hairy skin, or skin that has cuts. Do not use moisturizer before applying the patch or it will not stick well.
  - After peeling off one side of the backing, apply to dry skin on the stomach, thigh, hip, side of the body, shoulder or upper arm. Press in place for 30 seconds.
  - Do not cut the patch. If the patch falls off, you can reapply with bandage tape.
  - The patch can irritate the skin. Contact your healthcare provider if you get a rash, swelling or itching that persists. Rotate the place where you place the patch. Wait at least 14 days before applying in the same location.
  - When the patch is removed, fold it in half (sticky sides together) and throw away the folded patch so that children and pets cannot reach it.

Select Guidelines/References

Parkinson disease. *Nature Reviews: Disease Primers.* 2017 Mar 23;3:1-21.

CHAPTER CONTENT

Background ... 932
Dementia Types ... 932
Screening and Diagnosis ... 933
Screening Tools ... 933
Anticholinergics & Memory Impairment ... 933
Key Drugs that Can Worsen Dementia ... 933
Natural Products ... 933
Non-Drug Treatment ... 933
Drug Treatment ... 933
Alzheimer's Disease Drugs ... 934
Acetylcholinesterase Inhibitors ... 934
Memantine ... 935
Patient Counseling ... 935

CONTENT LEGEND

= Key Drug Guy

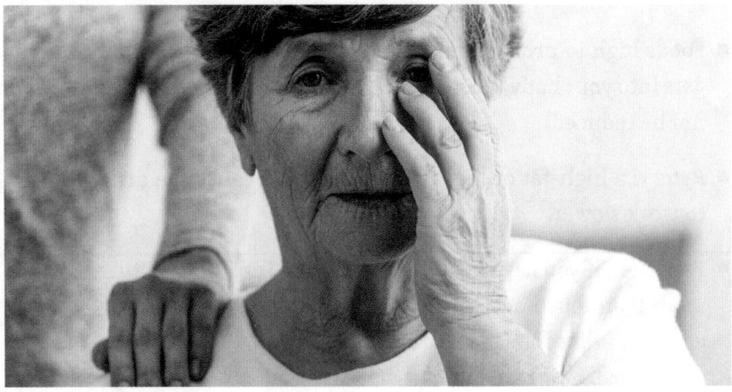

CHAPTER 70
ALZHEIMER'S DISEASE

BACKGROUND

Mild age-associated cognitive decline is normal and can cause bothersome symptoms, such as losing the car keys more often. Mild cognitive impairment (MCI) is a condition of measurable decreases in memory and mental function, but it is not severe enough to significantly interfere with daily functioning.

With dementia, the decline is more severe. Intellectual and social abilities progressively worsen, and functioning becomes impaired. The most noticeable symptom initially is memory loss. As dementia worsens, problems develop with judgment, attention, planning and personal grooming. Agitation, aggression and depression can be present, and are difficult challenges for patients and caregivers.

ALZHEIMER'S DISEASE SYMPTOMS

- Memory loss, getting lost
- Difficulty communicating, repeating words and information
- Inability to learn or remember new information
- Difficulty with planning and organizing
- Poor coordination and motor function
- Personality changes
- Inappropriate behavior
- Paranoia, agitation, hallucinations

DEMENTIA TYPES

There are different types of dementia, including Alzheimer's disease, vascular dementia and Lewy body dementia. The clinical findings in a patient can help the clinician characterize the dementia type. Alzheimer's is the most common type of dementia and has well-defined treatment, though the benefits are modest. The pathophysiology of Alzheimer's dementia involves neuritic plaques and tangles in brain tissue, which interrupt neuron signaling, and/or alteration of neurotransmitters (e.g., decreased acetylcholine).

SCREENING AND DIAGNOSIS

A definitive diagnosis of the cause and type of dementia cannot be made unless an autopsy is conducted post-mortem (after death). Researchers are developing markers and tests that can identify dementia at an early stage. With dementia that worsens over time, such as Alzheimer's disease, an early diagnosis provides a person time to plan for the future while he or she can still participate in decision making.

Initial screening should attempt to rule out causes of memory impairment which could be reversible, such as vitamin B12 deficiency, depression and infection. In some patients, the use of analgesics, benzodiazepines or other centrally-acting medications can cause or exacerbate memory loss (see Key Drugs Guy). Anticholinergics are particularly concerning and are discussed on the following page.

SCREENING TOOLS

Assessments used to identify or screen for dementia include the Folstein Mini-Mental State Exam (MMSE, a score < 24 indicates a memory disorder), the Montreal Cognitive Assessment (MoCA) and DSM-5 criteria. These screening tools ask the patient a series of questions to assess cognitive impairment (e.g., to spell a word backwards or count backwards from 100 by sevens) and/or assess functional abilities with activities of daily living (e.g., bathing, dressing, using a telephone, housekeeping).

ANTICHOLINERGICS & MEMORY IMPAIRMENT

Anticholinergics are used to treat incontinence (e.g., oxybutynin), allergies or insomnia (e.g., diphenhydramine), dystonic reactions (e.g., benztropine, diphenhydramine) and a few other conditions. A drug with strong centrally-acting anticholinergic effects can cause acute cognitive impairment and, occasionally, psychosis and hallucinations. The effect depends on the patient's baseline cognitive function, sensitivity to the drug, drug clearance, the number of drugs with additive effects and the dosing schedule. In elderly patients, centrally-acting anticholinergics should be avoided due to these risks. Anticholinergics used for overactive bladder (OAB) affect cognition modestly, but the concern is not completely alleviated. If a drug is used to treat incontinence, the reduction in symptoms should be evaluated at six weeks. If there is a lack of improvement, the drug should be discontinued.

NATURAL PRODUCTS

Vitamin E (2,000 IU daily) has been reported to benefit some patients with Alzheimer's dementia, but the findings are inconsistent. Recent trial results suggest a modest benefit in patients with mild-to-moderate disease. Ginkgo biloba is commonly used for memory, but the benefit is not well-defined. Ginkgo increases bleeding risk and should be discontinued in patients at high risk (e.g., taking warfarin or aspirin) and prior to elective surgical procedures. Other natural products that may be helpful include acetyl-L-carnitine and A-phosphatidylserine, both of which act as acetylcholine precursors. Older adults with low vitamin D levels may have an increased risk of cognitive decline, including memory loss. If vitamin D levels are low, supplementation should be provided.

KEY DRUGS THAT CAN WORSEN DEMENTIA

Antihistamines and antiemetics

Antipsychotics

Barbiturates

Benzodiazepines

Central anticholinergics (e.g., benztropine)

Peripheral anticholinergics (including incontinence and IBS drugs)

Skeletal muscle relaxants

Other CNS depressants (e.g., opioids, sedative hypnotics)

NON-DRUG TREATMENT

The vascular health of the blood vessels in the brain is vital for cognitive function. To promote vascular health:

- Keep blood glucose, blood pressure and cholesterol well-controlled.
- Engage in "thinking" activities and regular physical activity (in all age groups, physical activity enhances the growth and survival of brain cells).
- Eat a healthy diet, with fruits, vegetables, nuts, fish and with a low intake of red meat and alcohol.

DRUG TREATMENT

Acetylcholinesterase inhibitors (e.g., donepezil) are the mainstay of treatment. They are used alone, or with memantine in more advanced stages of the disease. Clinical improvement with these medications is usually modest, but at a minimum, the patient can have a slower clinical progression than with no treatment. For family members and caregivers, this may mean that the patient can feed themselves for a little while longer or use the bathroom independently for several more months. Some patients will not have noticeable improvement and can experience side effects (nausea, diarrhea, dizziness).

Patients receiving acetylcholinesterase inhibitors should be monitored for both improvement and side effects; if there is no improvement, or if side effects are intolerable, the drug can be discontinued. Discontinuation is advisable if the dementia has advanced to the point where the drug lacks clinical benefit, though this may not be acceptable to the family and in some patients there will be a noticeable deterioration when the medication is stopped.

The timing of medication administration can help reduce adverse effects. If nausea is present, administration in the evening can help. Donepezil is taken at bedtime for this reason. If insomnia is a concern, the patient can take the dose in the morning.

Memantine *(Namenda)* is approved for use alone or with donepezil for moderate-to-severe disease. *Namzaric* is a combination of donepezil and memantine. Patients stabilized on donepezil 10 mg can be switched to *Namzaric*.

Antidepressants (e.g., sertraline, citalopram, escitalopram) can be used to treat related depression and anxiety. Antipsychotics are used off-label for delusions and agitation, but there is an increased risk of death in elderly patients (see Boxed Warning in the Schizophrenia/Psychosis chapter).

NON-DRUG INTERVENTIONS TO KEEP THE BRAIN HEALTHY

- Discontinue drugs that can worsen dementia if possible (see Key Drugs Guy)
- Exercise
- Eat a healthy diet
- Control blood glucose, blood pressure and cholesterol
- Engage in activities that stimulate the brain

DRUG TREATMENT

Mild-Moderate Alzheimer's Disease?
Start an acetylcholinesterase inhibitor (donepezil, rivastigmine, galantamine)

Moderate-Severe Alzheimer's Disease?
Start an acetylcholinesterase inhibitor* (donepezil, rivastigmine, galantamine) and/or memantine

**Combination treatment with memantine is more likely to delay progression of disease than monotherapy*

Disease Worsens?
Use combination treatment: acetylcholinesterase inhibitor + memantine

At each patient visit, assess if the patient has any drug side effects, has started any new medications that can worsen dementia and if the medication is helping.

Do not titrate medications too quickly.

Adjust the timing and administration of medications if it will help with side effects (see text and drug table).

©RxPrep

ALZHEIMER'S DISEASE DRUGS

DRUG	DOSING	SAFETY/SIDE EFFECTS/MONITORING
Acetylcholinesterase inhibitors: inhibit centrally-active acetylcholinesterase, the enzyme responsible for hydrolysis (breakdown) of acetylcholine; this causes an ↑ in acetylcholine		
Donepezil *(Aricept)* ODT, tablet + memantine *(Namzaric)*	Start: 5 mg QHS, can increase to 10 mg QHS after 4-6 weeks Moderate-to-severe disease: can increase to 23 mg QHS after ≥ 3 months of 10 mg QHS	**WARNINGS** Bradycardia, heart block, fainting (due to vagotonic effects), QT prolongation – use with caution in patients with cardiac conduction abnormalities **SIDE EFFECTS** Insomnia, nausea, vomiting, diarrhea, tremors, weight loss **NOTES** Patients weighing < 50 kg can experience more side effects Donepezil is dosed QHS to help ↓ nausea *Exelon* patch and donepezil ODT have less GI side effects *Exelon* patch: apply the first patch the day after the last oral dose; apply daily at the same time each day; rotate sites – do not use the same site for 14 days *Exelon* capsules and galantamine IR should be taken with breakfast and dinner; galantamine ER should be taken with breakfast Galantamine solution can be mixed with liquid; drink immediately If stable on donepezil 10 mg, can switch to *Namzaric* (start at the lowest dose of memantine 7 mg/donepezil 10 mg QHS and titrate no more frequently than weekly)
Rivastigmine *(Exelon)* Capsule, patch	Capsule: start 1.5 mg BID Can increase every 2 weeks to a max dose of 6 mg BID Patch: start with 4.6 mg/24 hrs Can increase every 4 weeks (to 9.5, then 13.3 mg/24 hrs, which is the max dose) Hepatic impairment: max patch dose is 4.6 mg/24 hrs	
Galantamine *(Razadyne, Razadyne ER)* Tablet, capsule, solution	IR tablet or solution: start 4 mg BID ER capsule: start 8 mg daily Can increase every 4 weeks (usual dose range is 16-24 mg daily) Severe hepatic/renal impairment: do not use	

DRUG	DOSING	SAFETY/SIDE EFFECTS/MONITORING
Memantine: blocks NMDA (N-methyl-D-aspartate) receptors, which inhibits glutamate (an excitatory neurotransmitter) from binding and ↓ abnormal neuron activation		
Memantine (*Namenda*, *Namenda XR, Namenda Titration Pack)* Tablet, ER capsule, oral solution + donepezil (*Namzaric*)	IR: start with 5 mg daily Titrate weekly (no sooner) by 5 mg to a max dose of 10 mg BID (doses beyond 5 mg are given twice daily) ER: start with 7 mg daily Titrate weekly (no sooner) by 7 mg to a max dose of 28 mg daily Can switch IR 10 mg BID to ER 28 mg daily; begin ER the day after the last IR dose CrCl < 30 mL/min: do not exceed 5 mg BID or 14 mg XR daily	**SIDE EFFECTS** Dizziness, HA, diarrhea or constipation, hyper/hypotension **NOTES** Take without regard to meals ER capsule and *Namzaric*: do not crush or chew; capsules can be opened and contents sprinkled on applesauce (swallow immediately) Oral solution: use provided dosing device and squirt slowly into the corner of the mouth (do not mix with any other liquids)

Acetylcholinesterase Inhibitor Drug Interactions

- Use caution with other drugs that can lower heart rate (e.g., beta-blockers, diltiazem, verapamil, digoxin) and with drugs that cause dizziness (e.g., antipsychotics, alpha blockers, skeletal muscle relaxants, hypnotics, opioids).
- Drugs that have anticholinergic effects can reduce efficacy. Discontinue incontinence drugs if there is no benefit.
- These drugs can increase gastric acid secretion; use cautiously with NSAIDs, due to the risk of GI bleeding.

PATIENT COUNSELING

ACETYLCHOLINESTERASE INHIBITORS

- These medications can cause nausea. Taking the medication with food can help (or at bedtime with donepezil). If nausea remains a problem, talk to your doctor about changing to a longer acting formulation or the *Exelon* patch, which have a lower risk for nausea.
- The dose of this medication may increase, but it is started low due to the risk of dizziness, falls and nausea. Use caution when moving from a sitting to a standing position. It is best to avoid alcohol when using this medication.
- Tell your healthcare provider which prescription and over-the-counter medications you are taking; other drugs can worsen memory problems.
- If you have nausea, weakness and dark, tarry-looking stools, let your healthcare provider know. Be careful to watch for this if you have had stomach bleeding or ulcers in the past.
- If you experience sleep problems (insomnia), you can take the medication in the morning. If you have trouble swallowing the medication, there is a formulation that dissolves in your mouth that can be used instead.

Exelon Patch Instructions

- Apply a new patch at the same time each day to the upper or lower back, upper arm or chest; rotate applications site. Do not use the same site within 14 days.
- Remove the protective liner from one side of the patch. Place the sticky side of the patch on the application site, then remove the second side of the protective liner. Press the patch down firmly until the edges stick well.
    - Do not apply to an area of the skin that is hairy, oily, irritated, broken, scarred or calloused.
    - Do not place the patch under tight clothing or apply it to an area where cream, lotion or powder has recently been applied. Do not let the patch get hot from the sun or any other heat; this can cause too much medication to get into your body.
- Let your healthcare provider know if the skin gets a rash or becomes irritated from the patch.
- After 24 hours, remove the used patch. Do not touch the sticky side. Fold the patch in half with the sticky sides together and dispose of it safely.

MEMANTINE

- Take this medication by mouth, with or without food. When you first start taking this medication, you will take it once daily. Once your dose increases, you will take it twice daily unless you are prescribed a long-acting formulation (dosed once daily).
- For the oral liquid: read the instruction sheet that comes with the bottle. Follow the directions exactly. Use the oral syringe that comes with the product to measure out your dose. Swallow the medication directly from the syringe. Do not mix it with water or other liquids.
- For the capsule: if you have trouble swallowing, open the capsule and sprinkle the medication on applesauce. Eat the applesauce right away but do not chew it. Do not crush or chew the capsule.
- You can experience dizziness; use caution when moving from a sitting to a standing position. It is best to avoid alcohol and other drugs that make you feel dizzy when using this medication.
- If you become constipated from this medication, ask your healthcare provider to recommend an over-the-counter medication that helps relieve the constipation.

Select Guidelines/References

Rabins PV, Rovner BW, Rummans T, et al. APA Guideline Watch (October 2014): Practice Guideline for the Treatment of Patients with Alzheimer's Disease and Other Dementias. https://psychiatryonline.org/pb/assets/raw/sitewide/practice_guidelines/guidelines/alzheimerwatch.pdf (accessed 2019 Feb 25).

CHAPTER CONTENT

Background 937
Drugs that Can Lower the Seizure Threshold 938
Classification of Seizure Types 938
Acute Seizure Management 938
Diastat Acudial Dispensing 939
Chronic Seizure Management 939
Non-Drug and Alternative Treatments 939
Antiepileptic Drugs 939
AED Mechanisms of Action 940
AED Cousins 940
Take Your Vitamins on AEDs! 940
Common Broad-Spectrum Antiepileptic Drugs 941
Lamictal Starter Kits: Colors Help Safety 941
Common Narrow-Spectrum Antiepileptic Drugs 943
Phenytoin/Fosphenytoin Administration 946
Other Antiepileptic Drugs 947
Concerns with AEDs 949
Adjusting Phenytoin Doses 949
Phenytoin Correction for Albumin < 3.5 949
AEDs Have a Lot of Drug Interactions 949
AEDs are CNS Depressants 949
Patient Counseling 950

FIRST AID FOR SEIZURES

First aid for seizures involves responding in ways that can keep the person safe until the seizure stops by itself:

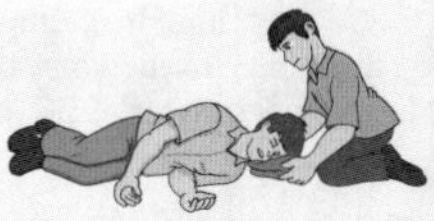

- Prevent injury by clearing the area around the person of anything hard or sharp.
- Ease the person to the floor and put something soft and flat, like a folded jacket, under the head. Turn the person gently onto one side. This will help keep the airway clear.
- Remove eyeglasses and loosen ties or anything around the neck that may make breathing difficult.
- Time the seizure. If the seizure continues for longer than five minutes without signs of slowing down, or if the person has trouble breathing, appears to be injured, in pain or has an unusual recovery, call 911.
- Do not hold people down or try to stop their movements.
- Contrary to popular belief, it is not true that people having a seizure can swallow their tongue. Do not put anything in the person's mouth.
- Do not attempt artificial respiration except in the unlikely event that a person does not start breathing after the seizure has stopped.

CONTENT LEGEND

= Study Tip Gal   = Key Drug Guy   = Required Formula

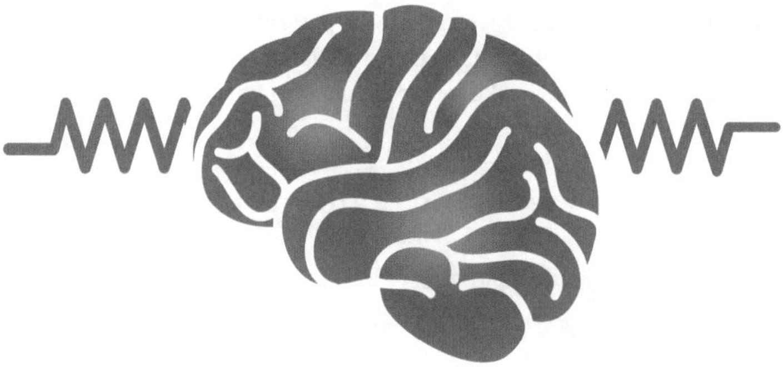

CHAPTER 71

SEIZURES/ EPILEPSY

BACKGROUND

A seizure occurs when excitatory neurons produce a sudden surge of electrical activity in the brain. Seizures can be caused by temporary conditions such as fever (common in children), infection, alcohol withdrawal, hypoglycemia or electrolyte abnormalities; in these cases, treating the underlying cause stops the seizure. Some drugs can lower the threshold for seizures and this makes a person more susceptible to a seizure. These drugs should be avoided in a person with history of seizures. See Key Drugs Guy on the next page.

Epilepsy is a chronic seizure disorder. This is a broad-spectrum condition; there are different types of seizures, and different types of medications are used to treat them. Seizure medications are called antiepileptic drugs (AEDs). Seizure types vary from uncontrolled jerking movements (tonic-clonic seizures) to a subtle momentary loss of awareness (absence seizures). Seizures can damage and destroy neurons, which causes brain damage and can be life-threatening.

The incidence of epilepsy is highest in the young and the elderly. One-third of new cases in the U.S. each year (50,000 of 150,000) are in children and adolescents. Seizures caused by a high fever in infants and young children do not usually lead to epilepsy. The elderly are at risk for seizures due to conditions that are more prevalent in the elderly, including dementia, brain tumors and, most commonly, damage from a stroke.

Motor vehicle accidents, gunshot wounds and other causes of severe head trauma damage the brain and can trigger seizures; emergency room treatment for severe head injuries often includes seizure prophylaxis or treatment. There is no identifiable cause or event that leads to seizures in half of all cases; these are attributable to some combination of genes and environment. About 500 genes have been linked to specific seizure types.

Individuals with epilepsy are evaluated for age of onset, seizure type, seizure frequency, description of witnessed seizure, identifiable causes or triggers and a thorough neurologic (brain and brain function) exam. An electroencephalogram (EEG), the most common test used to diagnose epilepsy, records electrical activity in the brain. An EEG can show abnormal patterns even when the patient is not having a seizure. Brain imaging with a CT or MRI can identify some conditions that can provoke seizures, including brain tumors or damage from a stroke.

DRUGS THAT CAN LOWER THE SEIZURE THRESHOLD

KEY DRUGS

Bupropion
Clozapine
Theophylline
Varenicline
Carbapenems (esp. imipenem)*
Lithium*
Meperidine*
Penicillin*
Quinolones*
Tramadol*
*High doses and renal impairment ↑ risk

Others:
Acyclovir
Cephalosporins
Lindane
Mefloquine
Metoclopramide
Valacyclovir

CLASSIFICATION OF SEIZURE TYPES

Seizure types are classified into three main types based on where the seizure starts in the brain: focal seizures, generalized seizures and unknown onset seizures.

Focal seizures start on one side of the brain, but can spread to the other side. Generalized seizures start on both sides of the brain. Seizures are classified as unknown onset seizures if the location of the beginning of the seizure is not known (e.g., the seizures are unwitnessed or occur during the night).

Focal seizures are further classified based on the patient's awareness during the seizure. If a focal seizure results in no loss of consciousness, it is called a focal aware seizure, previously known as a simple partial seizure. If the patient experiences loss of consciousness, it is called a focal seizure with impaired awareness, previously known as a complex partial seizure. Patients with generalized seizures experience loss of consciousness or are unaware during the seizure event.

All seizure types can be described based on the patient's symptoms. Motor symptoms include sustained rhythmical jerking movements (clonic), limp or weak muscles (atonic), muscle twitching (myoclonus) and rigid or tense muscles (tonic). Non-motor symptoms include changes in sensation, emotions, thinking or cognition. Generalized seizures with non-motor symptoms are called absence seizures, which typically present as staring spells.

ACUTE SEIZURE MANAGEMENT

Most seizures last less than two minutes, and do not require medical intervention. Seizures that continue longer cause more brain damage and can be fatal. Status epilepticus (SE) is a seizure lasting beyond five minutes because the normal mechanisms that terminate seizures are not working. At 30 minutes, long-term damage can occur. This is a medical emergency, and emergency treatment should begin with any seizure that lasts longer than five minutes.

SE is divided into phases (see figure below). Initial treatment is a benzodiazepine injection. Intravenous (IV) access can be difficult during a seizure; if it is not possible to connect an IV line, midazolam can be given intramuscularly (IM).

If the patient is not receiving urgent medical care (i.e., not in a medical facility), diazepam rectal gel *(Diastat AcuDial)*, or intranasal or buccal midazolam are non-injection options. The *Diastat AcuDial* is given to patients (or caregivers, such as parents) who are at risk of long-lasting seizures; dispensing and counseling requirements are essential (see Study Tip Gal).

STATUS EPILEPTICUS TREATMENT

0-5 minutes
Stabilization phase

Time the seizure
Start EEG, oxygen may be needed
Check AED levels, electrolytes, if BG low- treat with D25-D50

↓

5-20 minutes
Initial treatment phase

If seizure continues:
Give IV lorazepam *(Ativan)*
Alternatives if IV unavailable: IM midazolam *(Versed)* or rectal diazepam *(Diastat)*

↓

20-40 minutes
Second treatment phase

If seizure continues:
Give regular AED: IV fosphenytoin, valproic acid, levetiracetam (phenobarbital if others are unavailable)
If seizure lasts longer, there is no clear treatment

DIASTAT ACUDIAL DISPENSING

Each package contains two rectal syringes prefilled with diazepam rectal gel.

- Syringes come in 2.5, 10 and 20 mg.
- Syringes MUST be dialed to the right dose and locked BEFORE DISPENSING (see below).
- Once locked, the green band should say "READY," and the syringe cannot be unlocked.
- When counseling, check both syringes with the patient before they leave the pharmacy, to ensure the syringe is dialed and locked.
- See Patient Counseling section for administration. instructions.

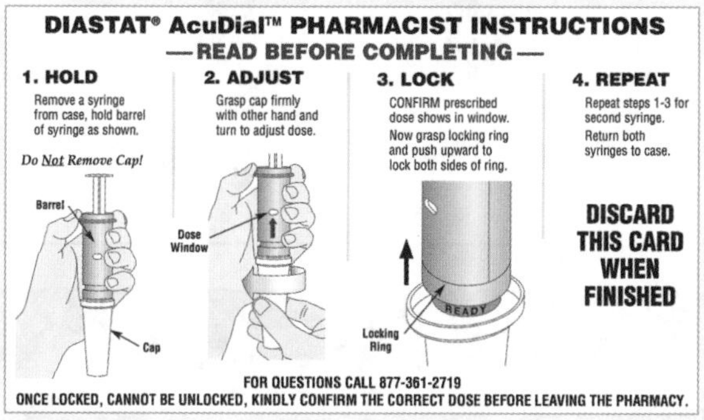

DIASTAT® AcuDial™ PHARMACIST INSTRUCTIONS
—READ BEFORE COMPLETING—

1. HOLD
Remove a syringe from case, hold barrel of syringe as shown.
Do Not Remove Cap!

2. ADJUST
Grasp cap firmly with other hand and turn to adjust dose.

3. LOCK
CONFIRM prescribed dose shows in window.
Now grasp locking ring and push upward to lock both sides of ring.

4. REPEAT
Repeat steps 1-3 for second syringe.
Return both syringes to case.

DISCARD THIS CARD WHEN FINISHED

FOR QUESTIONS CALL 877-361-2719
ONCE LOCKED, CANNOT BE UNLOCKED, KINDLY CONFIRM THE CORRECT DOSE BEFORE LEAVING THE PHARMACY.

CHRONIC SEIZURE MANAGEMENT

AEDs are first-line treatment for epilepsy. The initial one or two drugs will provide adequate control in approximately 70% of cases. Seizures that are resistant to AEDs need to be addressed another way; uncontrolled seizures cause brain damage and can be fatal. AEDs should not be stopped abruptly as this can lead to seizures.

NON-DRUG AND ALTERNATIVE TREATMENTS

Non-drug and alternative options for chronic seizure treatment include medical marijuana (cannabis), a ketogenic diet, vagal nerve stimulation or surgical intervention. The Embrace smartwatch is a FDA-approved medical device that monitors seizures in adults and children 6 years of age and older.

Medical Marijuana (Cannabis)

Pharmacy exams focus on drugs with well-defined medical use; medical marijuana (cannabis) is not currently a tested topic, except when components have been made into prescription drugs. Cannabidiol, or CBD (*Epidiolex*), was approved by the FDA as the first marijuana-derived medication to treat two rare forms of epilepsy. There are patients with resistant seizures who have received some degree of seizure control with medical cannabis. Pharmacists should consider the impact of additive CNS side effects, primarily from the tetrahydrocannabinol (THC) component (e.g., somnolence, euphoria, possible anxiety and paranoia), and the potential for drug interactions from the THC and CBD components.

Ketogenic Diet

A ketogenic diet can be used in patients with refractory seizures (not responding to medications). The diet contains high fats, normal protein and low carbohydrates (usually a 4:1 ratio of fats to combined protein and carbohydrates). This forces the body to break down fatty acids into ketone bodies as an energy source. Ketone bodies pass into the brain and replace glucose. This elevated ketone state is called ketosis, and can lead to a reduction in seizure frequency.

ANTIEPILEPTIC DRUGS

A few AEDs are used for isolated conditions, such as ethosuximide for absence seizures. Broad-spectrum AEDs treat different seizure types. Lamotrigine, levetiracetam, topiramate and valproic acid treat focal and generalized seizures. Several narrow-spectrum AEDs are used commonly, including carbamazepine, lacosamide, oxcarbazepine, phenobarbital, phenytoin and fosphenytoin. Pregabalin and gabapentin are not listed with common AEDs. Pregabalin and gabapentin are used commonly, but not for epilepsy; they are used to treat neuropathic pain. The other AEDs are used less commonly, but there are some important issues, such as vision loss with vigabatrin.

AED MECHANISMS OF ACTION

Benzodiazepines	↑ GABA
Valproic acid	↑ GABA
Phenobarbital	Enhance/potentiate GABA effect
Levetiracetam	Ca channel blocker and ↑ GABA
Ethosuximide	T-Type Ca channel blocker
Pregabalin/ Gabapentin	Ca channel blocker
Oxcarbazepine	Na and Ca channel blocker
Carbamazepine	Na channel blocker
Lamotrigine	Na channel blocker
Phenytoin / Fosphenytoin	Na channel blocker
Topiramate	Na channel blocker

A seizure occurs when excitatory (activating) neurons produce a sudden surge of electrical activity in the brain. The sudden electrical surge is caused by a receptor malfunction or an imbalance of neurotransmitters (NTs).

A deficiency of the inhibitory NT, gamma-aminobutyric acid (GABA), or an excess of the excitatory NT, glutamate, can result in a seizure, as shown here:

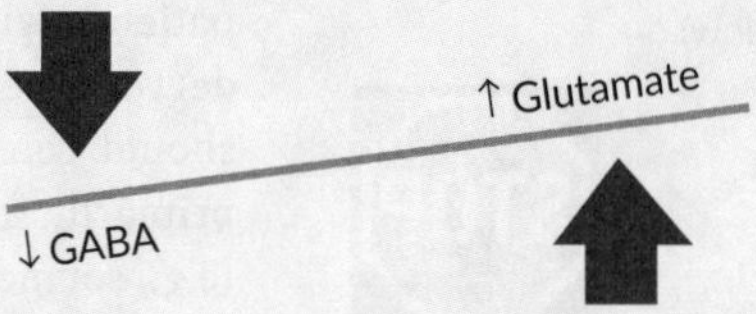

AEDs ↓ abnormal electrical activity by either:

- ↑ GABA
- ↓ Glutamate
- Blocking (or altering) Ca channels, which slows down or stops transmission of the electrical signal
- Blocking Na channels, which decreases the neurons firing rate

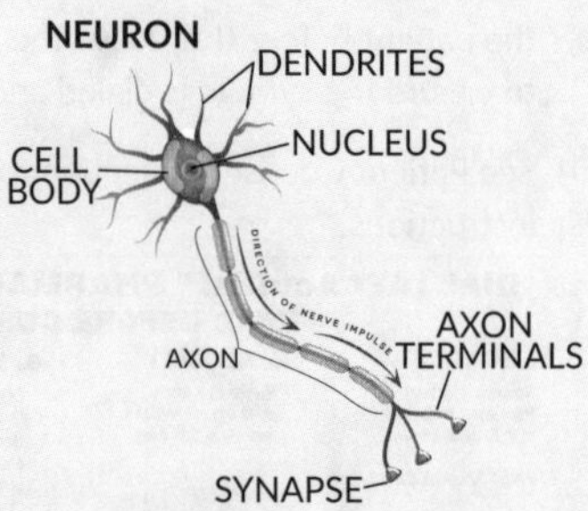

AED COUSINS

Some AEDs have family members, with similar side effects and safety considerations.

- Carbamazepine, Oxcarbazepine and Eslicarbazepine
  - Hyponatremia, rash, enzyme inducers
- Gabapentin and Pregabalin
  - Weight gain, peripheral edema, mild euphoria
  - Used primarily for neuropathic pain
- Phenobarbital and Primidone (prodrug of phenobarbital)
  - Sedation, dependence/tolerance/overdose risk, enzyme inducers
- Topiramate and Zonisamide
  - Weight loss, metabolic acidosis
  - Nephrolithiasis and oligohidrosis/hyperthermia (in children)

TAKE YOUR VITAMINS ON AEDs!

Supplement with:

- ALL AEDs: calcium and vitamin D
- Women of childbearing age: folate
- Valproic acid: possibly carnitine (see drug table)
- Lamotrigine: if alopecia, supplement with selenium and zinc

COMMON BROAD-SPECTRUM ANTIEPILEPTIC DRUGS

Lamotrigine

DRUG	DOSING	SAFETY/SIDE EFFECTS/MONITORING
Lamotrigine (*Lamictal, Lamictal ODT, Lamictal Starter Kit, Lamictal XR,* *Subvenite, Subvenite Starter Kit-Blue, Green, Orange*) Tablet, Chewable, ODT	**Initial:** Weeks 1 and 2: 25 mg daily Weeks 3 and 4: 50 mg daily Week 5 and on: can ↑ by 50 mg daily every 1-2 weeks **Maintenance Dose:** 300-400 mg daily, divide BID, unless using XR (daily)	**BOXED WARNING** Serious skin reactions, including SJS/TEN (rate of rash is greater in pediatrics than adults); ↑ risk with higher than recommended starting doses, dose escalation, or when used with valproic acid **WARNINGS** Risk of aseptic meningitis, blood dyscrasias, multiorgan hypersensitivty (DRESS) reactions, serious rare immune system reaction (hemophagocytic lymphohistiocyosis [HLH]) that can be fatal **SIDE EFFECTS** N/V, somnolence, rash, tremor, ataxia, impaired coordination, dizziness, diplopia, blurred vision, alopecia (supplement selenium and zinc) **MONITORING** Rash **NOTES** Discontinue if there is any sign of hypersensitivity reaction or unspecified rash. Use starter kit packaging when starting to ensure correct dosing (see Study Tip Gal).

Lamotrigine Drug Interactions

- Valproic acid ↑ lamotrigine concentrations more than two-fold. Use lower dose starter kit (blue box).
- Carbamazepine, phenytoin, phenobarbital, primidone, lopinavir/ritonavir, atazanavir/ritonavir and rifampin ↓ lamotrigine levels by 40%. Use the higher dose starter kit (green box).
- Oral estrogen-containing contraceptives ↓ lamotrigine; higher maintenance doses of lamotrigine may be needed.

LAMICTAL STARTER KITS: COLORS HELP SAFETY

Orange:
- Standard starting dose
- Use if no interacting medications

Blue:
- Lower starting dose
- Use if taking valproic acid

Green:
- Higher starting dose
- Use if taking an enzyme inducer (e.g., carbamazepine, phenytoin, phenobarbital, primidone), and not taking valproic acid

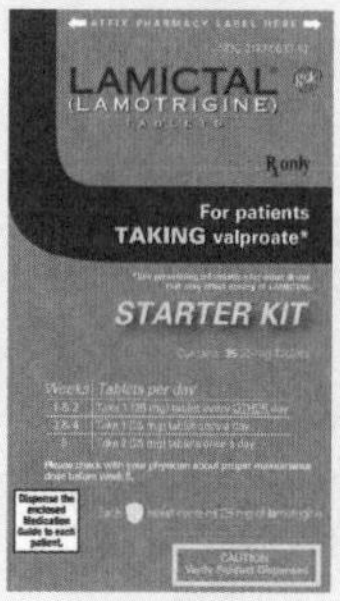

Levetiracetam

DRUG	DOSING	SAFETY/SIDE EFFECTS/MONITORING
Levetiracetam (*Keppra, Keppra XR,* *Roweepra, Roweepra XR, Spritam*) Tablet, Oral Solution, Injection	**Initial:** 500 mg BID or 1,000 mg daily (XR) **Maximum:** 3,000 mg/day **CrCl ≤ 80 mL/min:** ↓ dose IV:PO ratio 1:1	**WARNINGS** Psychiatric reactions, including psychotic symptoms, somnolence, fatigue, suicidal behavior, anaphylaxis, angioedema, coordination difficulties, severe skin reactions (SJS/TEN), hematologic abnormalities (mainly anemias), ↑ BP, loss of seizure control during pregnancy **SIDE EFFECTS** Irritability, dizziness, weakness, asthenia, vomiting (children and adolescents) **NOTES** No significant drug interactions

Topiramate

DRUG	DOSING	SAFETY/SIDE EFFECTS/MONITORING
Topiramate (*Topamax*, *Topamax Sprinkle)* Topiramate Extended-Release (*Qudexy XR, Trokendi XR)* Capsule, Extended-Release Capsule, Tablet Also used for migraine prophylaxis	**Initial:** Week 1: 25 mg BID (IR) or 50 mg daily (XR) Weeks 2-4: ↑ by 25 mg BID (IR) or 50 mg daily (XR) each week Week 5 and on: ↑ by 100 mg weekly until max dose or therapeutic effect **Maximum:** 400 mg/day **CrCl < 70 mL/min:** ↓ dose by 50% *Topamax Sprinkle*: swallow whole or open and sprinkle on a small amount of soft food (do not chew; swallow immediately)	**CONTRAINDICATIONS** *Trokendi XR* only: alcohol use 6 hours before or after dose, *Qudexy XR* only: patients with metabolic acidosis who are taking metformin **WARNINGS** Hyperchloremic nonanion gap metabolic acidosis, oligohidrosis (reduced perspiration)/hyperthermia (mostly in children), nephrolithiasis (kidney stones), acute myopia and secondary angle-closure glaucoma, hyperammonemia (alone and with valproic acid), visual problems (reversible), fetal harm **SIDE EFFECTS** Somnolence, dizziness, psychomotor slowing, difficulty with memory/concentration/attention, weight loss, anorexia, paresthesia **MONITORING** Electrolytes (especially bicarbonate), renal function, hydration status, eye exam (intraocular pressure)

Topiramate Drug Interactions

- Topiramate is a weak inhibitor of CYP2C19 and inducer of CYP3A4.
- Phenytoin, carbamazepine, valproic acid and lamotrigine can ↓ topiramate levels.
- Topiramate can ↓ oral contraceptive effectiveness, (especially doses ≥ 200 mg/day). Non-hormonal contraception is recommended.
- Topiramate can ↓ the INR in patients on warfarin; monitor closely.

Valproic Acid

DRUG	DOSING	SAFETY/SIDE EFFECTS/MONITORING
Valproic acid (*Depakene, Depacon*) *Depakene* – Capsule, Syrup *Depacon* – IV **Divalproex (*Depakote, Depakote ER, Depakote Sprinkle*)** *Depakote* – Delayed-Release (DR) Tablet *Depakote ER* – Extended-Release (ER) Tablet *Depakote Sprinkle* – capsules can be opened and sprinkled on food Also used for bipolar and migraine prophylaxis	**Initial:** 10-15 mg/kg/day **Maximum:** 60 mg/kg/day **Therapeutic Range:** 50-100 mcg/mL (total level) If the albumin is low (< 3.5 g/dL), the true valproic acid level will be higher than it appears – adjust with the same formula used for phenytoin. DR and ER tablets are not bioequivalent, ↑ total daily dose 8-20% when converting from DR to ER tablets	**BOXED WARNINGS** Hepatic failure: usually during first 6 months of therapy, children < 2 years and patients with mitochondrial disorders (mutations in mitochondrial DNA polymerase gamma gene [POLG]) are at ↑ risk; fetal harm (neural tube defects and ↓ IQ scores); pancreatitis **CONTRAINDICATIONS** Hepatic disease, urea cycle disorders, prophylaxis of migraine in pregnancy, known POLG-related disorder or suspected if < 2 years of age **WARNINGS** Hyperammonemia (treat with carnitine in symptomatic adults only), hypothermia, dose-related thrombocytopenia (↑ bleeding risk), multiorgan hypersensitivty (DRESS) reactions **SIDE EFFECTS** Alopecia (supplement selenium and zinc), weight gain, N/V, headache, anorexia, abdominal pain, dizziness, somnolence, tremor, edema, polycystic ovary syndrome, diplopia, blurred vision **MONITORING** LFTs (baseline and frequently in the first 6 months), CBC with differential, platelets

Valproic Acid Drug Interactions

- Valproic acid is an inhibitor of CYP2C9 (weak) and a substrate of CYP2C19 and 2E1 (minor).
- Valproic acid can ↑ levels of lamotrigine, phenobarbital, phenytoin, warfarin and zidovudine.
- Salicylates displace valproic acid from albumin (↑ levels).
- Carbapenem antibiotics can ↓ the levels of valproic acid.
- Estrogen-containing hormonal contraceptives can ↓ valproic acid levels.
- Use caution with valproic acid and lamotrigine due to risk of serious rash; use lower starting dose of lamotrigine and titrate slowly.
- Use with topiramate can lead to hyperammonemia with or without encephalopathy.

COMMON NARROW-SPECTRUM ANTIEPILEPTIC DRUGS

Carbamazepine

DRUG	DOSING	SAFETY/SIDE EFFECTS/MONITORING
Carbamazepine *(Tegretol, Tegretol XR,* *Carbatrol, Epitol)* Capsule, Tablet, Chewable, Oral Suspension *Equetro* – for bipolar disorder Also used for trigeminal neuralgia	**Initial:** 200 mg BID (or divided QID for suspension) **Maximum:** 1,600 mg/day (some patients can require more) **Therapeutic Range:** 4-12 mcg/mL	**BOXED WARNINGS** Serious skin reactions, including SJS/TEN: patients of Asian descent should be tested for HLA-B*1502 allele prior to initiation; if positive for this allele, carbamazepine cannot be used (unless benefit clearly outweighs risk); aplastic anemia and agranulocytosis; discontinue if significant myelosuppression occurs **CONTRAINDICATIONS** Myelosuppression, hypersensitivity to TCAs, use of MAO inhibitors within past 14 days, use with nefazodone or boceprevir, use with delavirdine or other non-nucleoside reverse transcriptase inhibitors (NNRTIs) that are substrate of CYP3A4 **WARNINGS** Risk of developing a hypersensitivity reaction can be ↑ in patients with the variant HLA-A*3101 allele, multiorgan hypersensitivty (DRESS) reactions, hyponatremia (SIADH), hypothyroidism, mild anticholinergic effects, cardiac conduction abnormalities, liver damage, fetal harm **SIDE EFFECTS** Dizziness, drowsiness, ataxia, N/V, dry mouth, pruritus, photosensitivity, blurred vision, rash, ↑ LFTs, alopecia **MONITORING** CBC with differential and platelets prior to and during therapy, LFTs, rash, eye exam, thyroid function tests, electrolytes (especially Na), renal function Monitor levels within 3-5 days of initiation and after 4 weeks due to autoinduction. **NOTES** Enzyme inducer, autoinducer – ↓ level of other drugs and itself

Carbamazepine Drug Interactions

- Carbamazepine is an autoinducer and will ↓ its own levels.
- Carbamazepine is a strong inducer of many enzymes (CYP1A2, 2C19, 2C8/9, 3A4) and P-glycoprotein (P-gp). It will ↓ the levels of many drugs, including other seizure medications, aripiprazole, levothyroxine, warfarin and hormonal contraceptives. Use of an alternative, non-hormonal contraceptive is recommended.
- Carbamazepine is a major CYP3A4 substrate; inhibitors will ↑ carbamazepine levels and inducers will ↓ carbamazepine levels. Do not use with nefazodone or NNRTIs.
- Carbamazepine suspension should not be taken together with other liquid medications (especially chlorpromazine) or diluents, as precipitates can form.

Lacosamide

DRUG	DOSING	SAFETY/SIDE EFFECTS/MONITORING
Lacosamide *(Vimpat)* C-V Tablet, Oral Solution, Injection	**Initial:** 50-100 mg BID **Maximum:** 400 mg/day **CrCl ≤ 30 mL/min:** maximum dose is 300 mg/day IV:PO ratio 1:1	**WARNINGS** Prolongs PR interval and ↑ risk of arrhythmias; obtain an ECG prior to use and after titrated to steady state in patients with or at risk of cardiac conduction problems. Multiorgan hypersensitivty (DRESS) reactions, syncope, dizziness, ataxia **SIDE EFFECTS** N/V, headache, diplopia, blurred vision, ataxia, tremor, euphoria **MONITORING** ECG (baseline and at steady state) in at-risk patients

Lacosamide Drug Interactions

- Lacosamide is a substrate of CYP2C19 (minor), 2C9 (minor), 3A4 (minor) and an inhibitor of CYP2C19 (weak). Caution with inhibitors of CYP2C19, 2C9 and 3A4 as they can ↑ lacosamide levels.
- Use caution with medications that prolong the PR interval (e.g., beta-blockers, calcium channel blockers, digoxin) due to the risk of AV block and bradycardia.

Oxcarbazepine

DRUG	DOSING	SAFETY/SIDE EFFECTS/MONITORING
Oxcarbazepine *(Trileptal,* *Oxtellar XR)* Tablet, Oral Suspension *(Trileptal)* Extended-Release Tablet *(Oxtellar XR)*	**Initial:** 300 mg BID *(Trileptal)*; 600 mg daily *(Oxtellar XR)* **Maximum:** 2,400 mg/day **CrCl < 30 mL/min:** start 300 mg daily Carbamazepine to oxcarbazepine dose conversion: 1.2-1.5x carbamazepine dose	**CONTRAINDICATIONS** Hypersensitivity to eslicarbazepine **WARNINGS** ↑ risk for serious skin reactions(SJS/TEN), consider screening patients of Asian descent for HLA-B*1502 prior to initiating therapy, multiorgan hypersensitivity (DRESS) reactions, hypersensitivity reactions to carbamazepine have 25-30% cross-sensitivity to oxcarbazepine Hyponatremia, hypothyroidism, potential worsening of seizures **SIDE EFFECTS** Somnolence, dizziness, N/V, abdominal pain, diplopia, visual disturbances, ataxia, tremor **MONITORING** Serum Na levels especially during first 3 months of therapy, thyroid function, CBC **NOTES** *Trileptal* oral suspension: must be used within 7 weeks once original container is opened. XR tablet: take on empty stomach 1 hour before or 2 hours after meals.

Oxcarbazepine Drug Interactions

- Oxcarbazepine is a weak CYP3A4 inducer and CYP2C19 inhibitor, but is not an autoinducer. Strong CYP3A4 inducers can ↓ oxcarbazepine levels. Oxcarbazepine and its active metabolite, MHD, can ↑ levels of fosphenytoin, phenytoin and phenobarbital.
- Oxcarbazepine doses ≥ 1200 mg/day can significantly ↑ phenytoin levels. Phenytoin levels should be monitored carefully as dose reductions may be needed.
- Oxcarbazepine can ↓ hormonal contraceptive levels significantly. Use of a non-hormonal contraceptive is recommended.

Phenobarbital

DRUG	DOSING	SAFETY/SIDE EFFECTS/MONITORING
Phenobarbital C-IV Tablet, Oral Solution, Elixir, Injection	**Initial:** 50-100 mg BID or TID **Therapeutic Range:** 20-40 mcg/mL (adults) 15-40 mcg/mL (children)	**CONTRAINDICATIONS** Severe hepatic impairment, dyspnea or airway obstruction, previous addiction to sedative-hypnotics, intraarterial administration **WARNINGS** Habit forming, paradoxical reactions including hyperactive or aggressive behavior, (in acute pain and pediatric patients), hypotension when given IV, serious skin reactions (SJS/TEN), respiratory depression, fetal harm **SIDE EFFECTS** Somnolence, cognitive impairment, dizziness, ataxia, physiological dependence, tolerance, hangover effect, depression, folate deficiency **MONITORING** LFTs, CBC with differential

Phenobarbital Drug Interactions

- Phenobarbital (and primidone which is the prodrug) is a strong inducer of most enzymes, including CYP1A2, 2C8/9, 3A4 and P-gp. These two drugs can ↓ the levels of many drugs metabolized by these enzymes.
- Phenobarbital and primidone can ↓ hormonal contraceptive levels significantly. Use of an alternative, non-hormonal contraceptive is recommended.

Phenytoin/Fosphenytoin

DRUG	DOSING	SAFETY/SIDE EFFECTS/MONITORING
Phenytoin ***(Dilantin, Dilantin Infatabs**, Phenytek)* Capsule, Chewable, Oral Suspension, Injection (IV only)	**Loading dose:** 15-20 mg/kg **Maintenance dose:** up to 300-600 mg/day Fosphenytoin is dosed in phenytoin equivalents (PE): 1 mg PE = 1 mg phenytoin (fosphenytoin 1.5 mg = 1 mg PE) IV:PO ratio 1:1 **Therapeutic Range:** 10-20 mcg/mL (total level) 1-2.5 mcg/mL (free level)	**BOXED WARNINGS** Phenytoin IV administration rate should not exceed 50 mg/minute and fosphenytoin IV should not exceed 150 mg PE/minute or 2 mg PE/kg/min (use the slower rate); if given faster, hypotension and cardiac arrhythmias can occur. **CONTRAINDICATIONS** Previous hepatotoxicity due to phenytoin **WARNINGS** Extravasation (leading to Purple Glove Syndrome, characterized by edema, pain and bluish discoloration of the skin which can sometimes lead to tissue necrosis), avoid phenytoin in patients with a positive HLA-B*1502 and in patients who have had a severe rash with carbamazepine, multiorgan hypersensitivty (DRESS) reactions, fetal harm, bradycardia, ↑ risk of serious skin reactions (SJS/TEN), fraction of unbound (free) drug is higher with renal or hepatic failure or ↓ albumin, blood dyscrasias, caution in cardiac disease, hepatic and renal impairment, hypothyroidism **SIDE EFFECTS** **Dose-related (toxicity):** Nystagmus, ataxia, diplopia/blurred vision, slurred speech, dizziness, somnolence, lethargy, confusion **Chronic:** Gingival hyperplasia, hair growth, hepatoxicity, skin thickening (children), morbilliform rash (measles-like), rash, peripheral neuropathy, ↑ BG, metallic taste, connective tissue changes, enlargement of facial features (lips) **MONITORING** LFTs, CBC with differential IV: continuous cardiac (ECG, BP, HR) and respiratory monitoring
Fosphenytoin *(Cerebyx)* Injection (IV/IM) Prodrug of phenytoin		

See adjusting phenytoin doses for low albumin on p. 949

Phenytoin/Fosphenytoin Drug Interactions

- Phenytoin and fosphenytoin are strong inducers of several enzymes, including CYP2B6, 2C19, 2C8/9, 3A4, P-gp and UGT1A1; they are substrates of CYP2C19 (major), 2C9 (major) and 3A4 (minor). Phenytoin and fosphenytoin can ↓ the concentration of many drugs including other AEDs, contraceptives and warfarin.
- Use of an alternative, non-hormonal contraceptive is recommended with chronic phenytoin.
- Both have high protein binding, and can displace other highly-protein bound drugs or be displaced by other highly-protein bound drugs, causing an ↑ in levels, that can lead to toxicity.

PHENYTOIN/FOSPHENYTOIN ADMINISTRATION

IV Fosphenytoin
- Do not exceed 150 mg PE/minute
- Monitor BP, respiratory function and ECG
- Lower risk of purple-glove syndrome than phenytoin

IV Phenytoin
- Do not exceed 50 mg/minute (slower infusion)
- Monitoring same as above
- Requires a filter
- Dilute in NS, stable for 4 hours, do not refrigerate

NG-tube Phenytoin
- Enteral feedings (e.g., tube feeds) ↓ phenytoin absorption
- Hold feedings 1-2 hours before and after administration

OTHER ANTIEPILEPTIC DRUGS

DRUG	SAFETY/SIDE EFFECTS/MONITORING
Benzodiazepines, including: Clobazam *(Onfi, Sympazan)* C-IV Tablet, Oral Suspension, Oral Film	**BOXED WARNINGS** Concurrent use with opioids can result in profound sedation, respiratory depression and death **WARNINGS** Serious skin reactions (SJS/TEN), paradoxical reactions including hyperactive or aggressive behavior, anterograde amnesia **NOTES** Cause physiological dependence, tolerance, drooling, pyrexia
Brivaracetam *(Briviact)* Tablet, Oral Solution, Injection C-V	**WARNINGS** Behavioral reactions including psychotic symptoms, irritability, depression, aggressive behavior and anxiety; bronchospasm and angioedema **MONITORING** Somnolence and fatigue, caution driving or operating machinery **NOTES** No added therapeutic benefit when used in combination with levetiracetam
Cannabidiol *(Epidiolex)* Oral Solution C-V	**WARNINGS** Somnolence and sedation; hepatotoxicity, risk is ↑ when used with valproic acid **MONITORING** Baseline LFTs **NOTES** For treatment of seizures associated with Lennox-Gastaut and Dravet Syndrome (rare epilepsies) in patients ≥ 2 years
Eslicarbazepine *(Aptiom)* Tablet Oxcarbazepine - active metabolite	**NOTES** Same warnings and side effects as oxcarbazepine including ↓ Na (monitor) plus warning for drug-induced liver injury, (monitor LFTs) Inducer of CYP3A4 (moderate)
Ethosuximide *(Zarontin)* Capsule, Oral Solution Used for absence seizures	**WARNINGS** Serious skin rash (SJS/TEN), blood dyscrasias, multiorgan hypersensitivty (DRESS) reactions **SIDE EFFECTS** N/V, abdominal pain, weight loss, hiccups, dizziness, somnolence **MONITORING** LFTs, CBC with differential, urinalysis, platelets, signs of rash, trough serum concentration
Felbamate *(Felbatol)* Tablet, Oral Suspension	**BOXED WARNINGS** Hepatic failure, aplastic anemia **MONITORING** LFTs, CBC, serum levels of other AEDs **NOTES** Informed consent needs to be signed by patient and prescriber prior to dispensing.
Gabapentin *(Neurontin)* Capsule, Tablet, Oral Solution, Oral Suspension *(Fanatrex* compounding kit) *Gralise* – postherpetic neuralgia (PHN) *Horizant* (gabapentin enacarbil) – PHN and restless legs syndrome	**WARNINGS** Angioedema, peripheral edema **SIDE EFFECTS** Dizziness, somnolence, peripheral edema, weight gain, ataxia, diplopia, blurred vision, dry mouth, mild euphoria **MONITORING** Edema/weight gain **NOTES** Often used for neuropathic pain treatment See Pain chapter for more details

DRUG	SAFETY/SIDE EFFECTS/MONITORING
Perampanel *(Fycompa)* C-III Tablet, Oral Suspension	**BOXED WARNING** Neuropsychiatric events (dose-related) including irritability, aggression, anger, paranoia, and others mostly in the first 6 weeks **NOTES** Substrate of CYP3A4 (major)
Pregabalin *(Lyrica)* C-V	**NOTES** Warnings, side effects and monitoring are the same as gabapentin Also used for diabetic or spinal cord injury neuropathic pain, PHN, fibromyalgia See Pain chapter for more details
Primidone *(Mysoline)*	**NOTES** Prodrug of phenobarbital and phenylethylmalonamide (PEMA) - both are active metabolites See phenobarbital drug table for more details
Rufinamide *(Banzel)* Tablet, Oral Suspension	**CONTRAINDICATIONS** Patients with familial short QT syndrome due to QT shortening (dose-related) **NOTES** Take with food
Stiripentol *(Diacomit)* Capsule, Oral Suspension	**WARNINGS** Loss of appetite/weight loss, delirium/hallucinations (rare) **MONITORING** CBC and hepatic function, weight, mood **NOTES** To be taken with clobazam
Tiagabine *(Gabitril)* Tablet	**WARNINGS** Worsening of seizures/new onset seizures when used off-label for other indications, serious skin reactions (SJS/TEN) **NOTES** Take with food
Vigabatrin *(Sabril, Vigadrone)* Tablet, Packet for Solution	**BOXED WARNING** Causes permanent vision loss (≥ 30% of patients) **MONITORING** Eye exam at baseline, every 3 months during therapy and 3-6 months after discontinuation **NOTES** Only available through a restricted program called the Vigabatrin REMS Program
Zonisamide *(Zonegran)* Capsule	**CONTRAINDICATIONS** Hypersensitivity to sulfonamides **WARNINGS** Same as topiramate except: no hyperammonemia warning and there is risk of serious skin reactions (SJS/TEN); multiorgan hypersensitivty (DRESS) reactions **SIDE EFFECTS** Side effects similar to topiramate, including oligohidrosis/hyperthermia (primarily in children) and risk of nephrolithiasis

CONCERNS WITH AEDs

AEDs should be selected based on individual patient factors, including seizure type, age, childbearing potential and school and career requirements. The right AED for one patient may not be appropriate for another patient with the same seizure type. Below are factors to consider when selecting an AED for a particular patient.

Monitoring

All AEDs require monitoring of seizure frequency (to ensure efficacy) and mental status (to minimize adverse effects). Some AEDs (e.g., phenytoin, valproic acid, carbamazepine and phenobarbital) have therapeutic drug level ranges that are monitored to control seizures and keep the toxic effects to a minimum. Drug levels are commonly obtained when treatment is started, with dose adjustments, with suspected toxicity, and to check adherence. The metabolism of phenytoin can become saturated; when there are no enzymes left to metabolize the drug, a small increase in the dose can lead to a large increase in the drug concentration. See Study Tip on Adjusting Phenytoin Doses. It is important to monitor levels and make dose changes carefully.

ADJUSTING PHENYTOIN DOSES

Phenytoin has Michaelis-Menten kinetics, also called saturable kinetics.

If the enzymes have become saturated, small ↑ in dose can cause a large ↑ in drug level.

If albumin is low (< 3.5 g/dL), and CrCl ≥ 10 mL/min, adjust the total level with the formula:

$$\text{Phenytoin correction} = \frac{\text{Total phenytoin measured}}{(0.2 \times \text{albumin}) + 0.1} \dagger$$

Free levels do not require correction.

See the Pharmacokinetics chapter for more details.

† Use serum phenytoin in mcg/mL and albumin in g/dL

EXAM SCENARIO

A patient has a total phenytoin level of 13 mcg/mL and recent labs as follows: SCr 1.1 mg/dL, albumin 3.1 g/dL. What is the corrected phenytoin level (round to the nearest TENTH)?

Phenytoin Correction = 13 / (0.2 x 3.1) + 0.1

= 18.1 mcg/mL

Drug Interactions

Many AEDs are enzyme inducers and lower the concentration of other medications, including other AEDs (see Study Tip Gal). Valproic acid is an enzyme inhibitor, which is usually not a big issue, except with lamotrigine. The two are often used together. Increased lamotrigine levels increase the risk of severe rash.

AEDs HAVE A LOT OF DRUG INTERACTIONS

Enzyme Inducers

- Carbamazepine
- Oxcarbazepine
- Phenytoin
- Fosphenytoin
- Phenobarbital
- Primidone
- Oral contraceptives

Enzyme Inhibitor

- Valproic acid (↑ lamotrigine)

CNS Depression

All AEDs have to cross the blood-brain barrier to prevent seizures. Regardless of the specific mechanism of action, all AEDs depress electrical activity in the brain. All AEDs cause CNS depression (e.g., dizziness, confusion, sedation and ataxia/coordination difficulties) and increase risk for impairment, falls and injuries. The degree of CNS depression is an important consideration when selecting treatment for adults, who need to perform well at work, and for children, who need to perform well in school.

AEDs ARE CNS DEPRESSANTS

AEDs **DEPRESS** electrical activity in the brain; they are CNS-**DEPRESS**ants, and cause dizziness, confusion, sedation and ataxia/coordination difficulties.

These ↑ the risk for impairment, falls and injuries.

Some AEDs cause more CNS depression than others; this is an important consideration for school-age children, and for frail elderly at risk for falls.

Bone Loss

AEDs can cause bone loss and increase fracture risk. All patients on AEDs should be supplemented with calcium and vitamin D. Bone loss can occur as soon as two years after the start of an AED. Modifiable factors that affect bone density should be addressed (see Osteoporosis, Menopause & Testosterone Use chapter).

Suicide Risk and Rash

All AEDs have a warning for suicide risk and require monitoring of mood by the patient and caregivers. This information is not repeated in the drug tables. Many AEDs can cause serious skin rash, including risk for Stevens-Johnson syndrome (SJS) and toxic epidermal necrolysis (TEN). Higher blood levels increase the risk.

Use in Pregnancy

Several of the older AEDs (e.g., clonazepam, phenobarbital, primidone, phenytoin, fosphenytoin, carbamazepine and valproic acid) have known teratogenic risk. Valproic acid has the highest risk, including neural tube defects and impaired cognitive function in the child (decreased IQ).The risk profiles of newer AEDs are not well defined, and most have some degree of risk.

Congenital malformations occur more commonly in children exposed to AEDs *in utero*. Most are minor, but some are not, including cardiac defects (e.g., atrial septal defect, Tetralogy of Fallot, patent ductus arteriosus and pulmonary stenosis), urogenital defects and neural tube defects. Neural tube defects occur most commonly in children born to mothers taking carbamazepine or valproic acid. Women of childbearing age on AEDs should receive daily folate supplementation.

Because of the teratogenic effects, women of childbearing age on AEDs should prevent pregnancy through contraception. Many AEDs reduce efficacy of oral contraceptives. Alternative non-hormonal contraception options, such as an intrauterine device (IUD), are preferred.

AEDs contribute to bone loss, as discussed previously. In pregnancy, the mother provides calcium for the baby to grow bone. This leads to an additive need for extra calcium. The mother must receive adequate supplementation of calcium and vitamin D while pregnant and taking an AED.

Blood levels of AEDs can change throughout pregnancy and postpartum. Monitoring drug levels throughout this time frame is very important. The levels of all AEDs decline during pregnancy, with some being more affected than others. Low AED levels can lead to seizures. Seizures during pregnancy can be harmful to the baby. Dose increases can be needed. In the postpartum period, AED levels increase, and decreased doses are commonly needed. Monitoring levels in the postpartum period is necessary to minimize side effects.

Use in Children

In addition to cognitive impairment and coordination difficulty, there are drug-specific risks in children taking AEDs. Topiramate and zonisamide can cause reduced or lack of sweating (i.e., hypohidrosis) in young children. This means that exposure to the sun should be limited, which affects playtime and sports. Lamotrigine-induced rash, with risk of fatality, occurs more commonly in children.

Administering medications to children can be difficult as many are unable to swallow tablets and capsules. AEDs that are often used in children come in formulations that are easy to swallow, including lamotrigine (ODT, chewable tablets) and levetiracetam (ODT, oral solution).

Half of the children with epilepsy outgrow the condition. A child who remains seizure-free for one to two years can often be tapered off AEDs safely without repercussions.

PATIENT COUNSELING

All Antiepileptic Drugs

- This drug can cause suicidal thoughts or actions in a very small number of people (about 1 in 500). Call your healthcare provider right away if you experience thoughts about suicide or dying, new or worsening depression or anxiety, panic attacks, irritability or other unusual behavior.
- Do not stop taking this medication without consulting your healthcare provider. Seizures can become worse when the drug is suddenly stopped. When stopping therapy, the dose needs to be gradually decreased.
- Seizure medications can impair judgment, thinking and coordination. You can experience dizziness and drowsiness, especially when starting therapy. Do not drive, operate heavy machinery or do other dangerous activities until you know how this medication affects you.
- This medication can cause additional drowsiness and dizziness when taken with other drugs such as alcohol, barbiturates, benzodiazepines, hypnotics, opioids and skeletal muscle relaxants. Avoid use of other sedating drugs, if possible.
- Avoid drugs that can lower the seizure threshold. Avoid St. John's wort with all seizure medications.
- Use caution with different generic substitutions; try to stick to the same manufacturer. Small dosage variations can result in loss of seizure control.
- These medications can lower the amount of calcium and vitamin D in your body; it is recommended to supplement with calcium and vitamin D while taking this medication.

Carbamazepine

- The most common side effects include sleepiness, dizziness, nausea, vomiting and problems with coordination. Take with food to decrease stomach upset.
- Carbamazepine can cause rare but very serious (possibly fatal) skin reactions. If you are of Asian descent, you should have a blood test prior to using this medicine to determine if you are at greater risk of developing a serious skin reaction. Serious skin reactions usually develop within the first few months of treatment. Seek immediate medical attention if you feel weak and feverish, develop a skin rash, hives, sores in your mouth or blistering or peeling of the skin.
- Carbamazepine can cause rare but serious blood problems. You will need to have your blood checked to make sure this is not occurring. Contact your healthcare provider right away if you develop fever, sore throat, other infections, easy bruising or bleeding, red or purple spots on your body or severe weakness and tiredness.

- This medicine can cause birth defects if taken during pregnancy. Do not take carbamazepine without first talking to your healthcare provider if you are pregnant or planning a pregnancy.

Diazepam Rectal Gel

- Before leaving the pharmacy, be sure to check that each syringe has the correct dose visible in the display window and the green "READY" band is visible.
- Your healthcare provider will tell you exactly when to use this medication to control seizures. If you are uncomfortable or unsure of how to use the medication (see figure at end of chapter), discuss with your healthcare provider.
- After giving this medication, stay with the person for four hours and watch for changes in breathing or color, or unusual symptoms or recovery. Call 911 if the seizure continues 15 minutes after giving the medication.
- For the 10 or 20 mg syringe, dispose of any remaining medication in the sink or toilet as shown below before discarding. This step is not needed for the 2.5 mg syringe.
- This medication can be habit forming and should be kept in a safe place to prevent others from taking it, and away from children.

Lamotrigine

- The most common side effects of this medication are sleepiness, dizziness, rash, nausea, vomiting, insomnia, lack of coordination and blurred or double vision.
- This medication can cause a serious skin rash. These serious skin reactions are more likely to happen in the first 2 to 8 weeks of treatment (but it can happen in people who have taken the medication for any period of time). Call your healthcare provider right away if you develop a fever, skin rash, hives, swollen lymph glands, sores in the mouth or around your eyes or unusual bleeding or bruising.
- This medication can rarely cause aseptic meningitis, which is a serious inflammation of the protective membrane of the brain. Call your healthcare provider right away if you develop a stiff neck, headache, fever, abnormal sensitivity to light, muscle pains, chills and/or confusion.
- Swallow tablets whole.
- The ODT formulation should be placed on the tongue and moved around the mouth to rapidly disintegrate.
- Chewable tablets can be swallowed whole, chewed, or mixed in water or diluted fruit juice. If mixed, take the whole amount right away.

Levetiracetam

- Take levetiracetam with or without food.
- Swallow the tablets whole. Do not chew, break or crush tablets. Ask your healthcare provider for levetiracetam oral solution or dissolvable tablet if you cannot swallow tablets.
- If taking levetiracetam oral solution, be sure to use a medicine dropper or medicine cup to help you measure the correct amount of levetiracetam oral solution. Do not use a household teaspoon or tablespoon.
- This medication can cause serious skin reactions, although this is rare. Seek immediate medical attention if you feel weak and feverish, develop a skin rash, hives, sores in your mouth or blistering or peeling of the skin.

Oxcarbazepine

- This medication can cause low sodium concentrations in the blood. Symptoms of low blood sodium include nausea, tiredness or lack of energy, headache, more frequent or more severe seizures and confusion.
- Take oxcarbazepine with or without food. Take oxcarbazepine extended-release (*Oxtellar XR*) on an empty stomach at least one hour before or two hours after food. Swallow whole.
- Before taking oxcarbazepine oral suspension, shake the bottle for at least ten seconds and use the oral dosing syringe to withdraw the amount of medicine needed. The dose can be taken directly from the oral syringe or can be mixed in a small glass of water immediately prior to swallowing. Rinse syringe with warm water after use and allow to dry thoroughly. Discard any unused portion after seven weeks of first opening the bottle.
- This medication can cause serious skin reactions, although this is rare. Seek immediate medical attention if you feel weak and feverish, develop a skin rash, hives, sores in your mouth or blistering or peeling of the skin.

Phenobarbital

- This medication can cause abuse and dependence and can slow your thinking and reflexes. Do not drive, operate heavy machinery, or do other dangerous activities until you know how this medication affects you.
- This medicine can cause birth defects if taken during pregnancy. Do not take phenobarbital without first talking to your healthcare provider if you are pregnant or planning a pregnancy.

Phenytoin

- The most common side effects of this medication include sleepiness, dizziness, unsteady walking, confusion and slurred speech.
- This medication can cause a serious skin rash. Call your healthcare provider right away if you develop a skin rash, hives, fever, swollen lymph glands, sores in the mouth or unusual bleeding or bruising.
- This medicine can cause the gums in your mouth to grow, and be more likely to decay. Brush and floss regularly; do not miss dental cleanings or appointments.

- This medicine can cause birth defects if taken during pregnancy. Do not take phenytoin without first talking to your healthcare provider if you are pregnant or planning a pregnancy.
- If using the suspension, shake the bottle well before each dose.
- Use this medication regularly in order to get the most benefit from it. It is important to take all doses on time to keep the amount of medicine in your body at a constant level.

Topiramate

- The most common side effects of this medication include sleepiness, dizziness, tingling of the arms and legs, weight loss and loss of appetite. This medication can cause confusion, problems with concentration, attention, memory or speech.
- This medication can cause eye problems. Please contact your healthcare provider right away if you experience a sudden decrease in vision with or without eye pain and redness. Rarely, this medicine can increase the pressure in the eye. This can lead to permanent loss of vision if not treated.
- Topiramate can cause decreased sweating and increased body temperature. Children in particular should be watched for signs of decreased sweating and fever especially in hot weather. Keep your child out of direct sunlight and heat and have the child drink plenty of water when going outside when it is hot.
- Topiramate can increase the level of acid in your blood. Contact your healthcare provider right away if you feel tired, have a loss of appetite, feel changes in heartbeat, or have trouble thinking clearly.
- Topiramate sprinkle capsules can be swallowed whole or can be opened and sprinkled on a teaspoon of soft food. Drink fluids right after eating the food and medicine mixture to make sure it is all swallowed. Do not chew the food and medicine mixture. Do not store any medicine and food mixture for later use.
- Drink plenty of fluids during the day. This helps prevent kidney stones while taking this medication.
- This medicine can cause birth defects if taken during pregnancy. Do not take without first talking to your healthcare provider if you are pregnant or are planning a pregnancy. An increased risk of oral clefts (cleft lip and/or palate) has been observed, particularly following first trimester exposure.

Valproic Acid

- Common side effects with this medication include nausea, vomiting, sleepiness, weakness, increased appetite, weight gain, double or blurry vision and hair loss.
- This medication can rarely damage the liver. This is more likely to occur in the first six months of therapy. Call your healthcare provider right away if you develop severe fatigue, vomiting, loss of appetite, pain on the right side of your stomach, dark urine, light stools or yellowing of your skin or whites of your eyes.
- In rare cases, valproic acid has caused severe, sometimes fatal, cases of pancreatitis (inflammation of the pancreas). Call your healthcare provider right away if you have severe stomach pain that you can also feel in your back or have nausea or vomiting that does not go away. These symptoms can be early signs of pancreatitis.
- Do not crush, chew or break the capsules. Swallow them whole.
- Measure the liquid form of valproic acid with a special dose-measuring spoon or cup, not a regular teaspoon or tablespoon. If you do not have a dose-measuring device, ask your pharmacist for one.
- This medicine can cause birth defects if taken during pregnancy. Do not take without first talking to your healthcare provider if you are pregnant or are planning a pregnancy. Malformations of the face, head, brain and spinal cord have been reported (neural tube defects such as spina bifida). In addition, children born to mothers taking valproic acid products while pregnant can have impaired mental development.
- Take with food to help avoid stomach upset.
- You will need to have blood tests during treatment. It is important for your healthcare provider to know how much medication is in the blood and how well your liver is working.

Select Guidelines/References

Evidence-Based Guideline: Treatment of Convulsive Status Epilepticus in Children and Adults: Report of the Guideline Committee of the American Epilepsy Society. *Epilepsy Curr.* 2016;16(1):48-61.

Operational Classification of Seizure Types by the International League Against Epilepsy. 2017 Update. https://www.ilae.org/files/dmfile/Operational-Classification--Fisher_et_al-2017-Epilepsia.pdf (accessed 2019 Feb 1).

HOW TO ADMINISTER AND DISPOSAL

Diastat® (diazepam rectal gel) **Diastat® AcuDial™** (diazepam rectal gel)

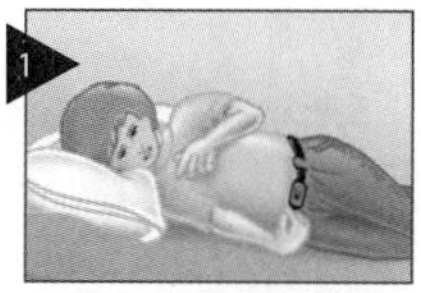
1 — Put person on their side where they can't fall.

2 — Get medicine.

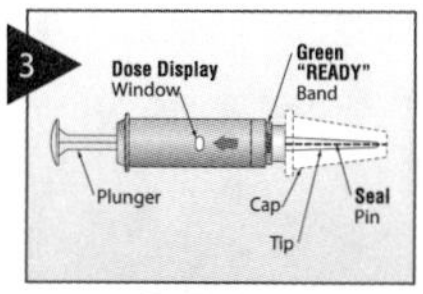

3 — Get syringe.
Note: Seal Pin is attached to the cap.

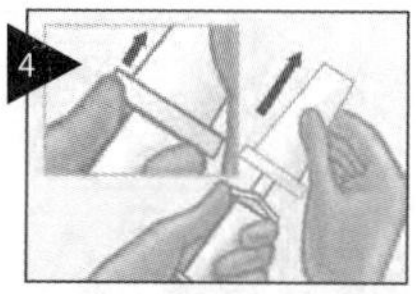
4 — Push up with thumb and pull to remove cap from syringe. **Be sure Seal Pin is removed with the cap.**

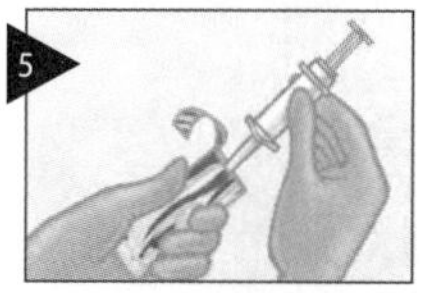
5 — Lubricate rectal tip with lubricating jelly.

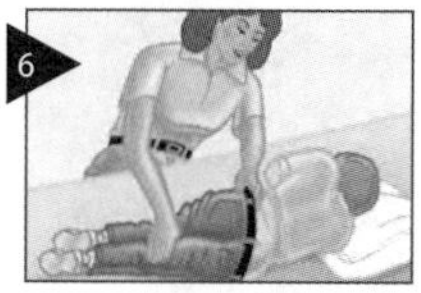
6 — Turn person on side facing you.

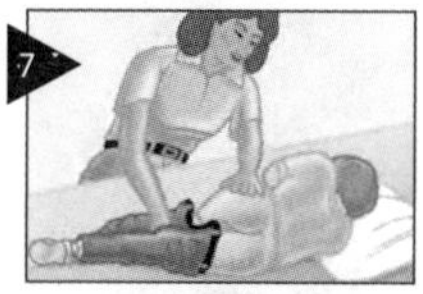
7 — Bend upper leg forward to expose rectum.

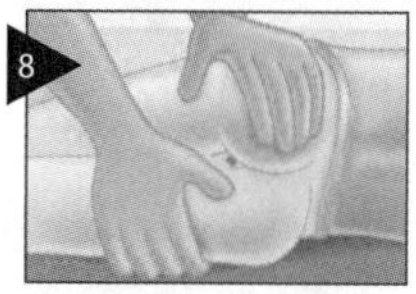
8 — Separate buttocks to expose rectum.

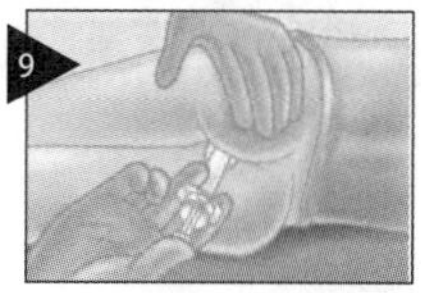
9 — Gently insert syringe tip into rectum.
Note: Rim should be snug against rectal opening.

SLOWLY COUNT OUT LOUD TO THREE...1...2...3

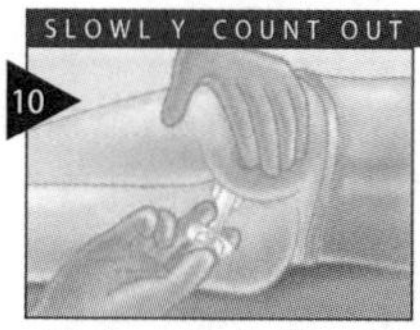
10 — Slowly count to 3 while gently pushing plunger in until it stops.

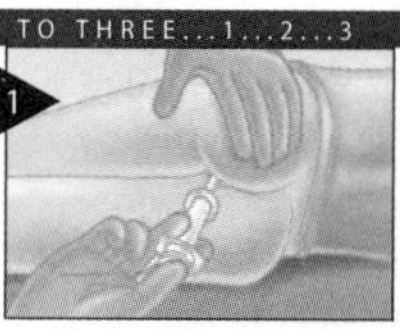
11 — Slowly count to 3 before removing syringe from rectum.

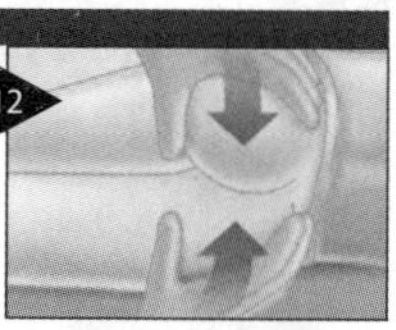
12 — Slowly count to 3 while holding buttocks together to prevent leakage.

ONCE DIASTAT® IS GIVEN

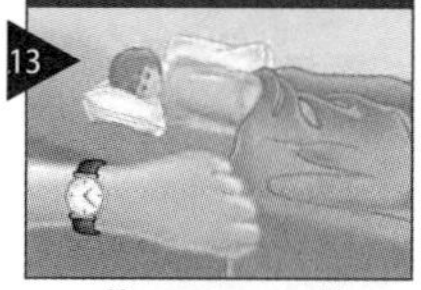
13 — Keep person on side facing you, note time given and continue to observe.

DISPOSAL INSTRUCTIONS FOR DIASTAT ACUDIAL

14a

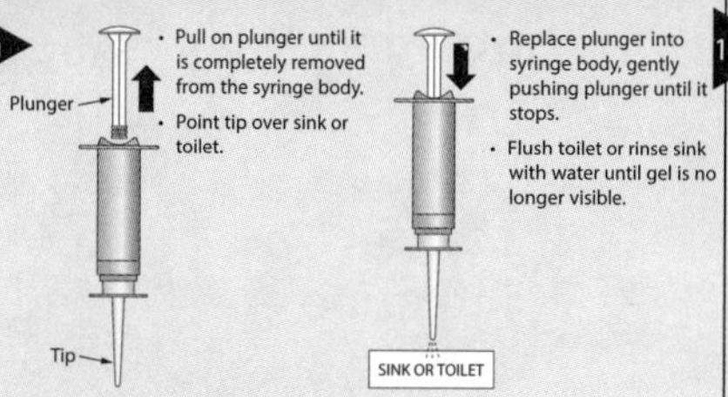

- Pull on plunger until it is completely removed from the syringe body.
- Point tip over sink or toilet.
- Replace plunger into syringe body, gently pushing plunger until it stops.
- Flush toilet or rinse sink with water until gel is no longer visible.

This step is for Diastat® AcuDial™ users only
At the completion of step 14a:
- Discard all used materials in the garbage can.
- Do not reuse.
- Discard in a safe place away from children.

DISPOSAL FOR DIASTAT 2.5 MG

14b

At the completion of step 13:
- Discard all used materials in the garbage can.
- Do not reuse.
- Discard in a safe place away from children.

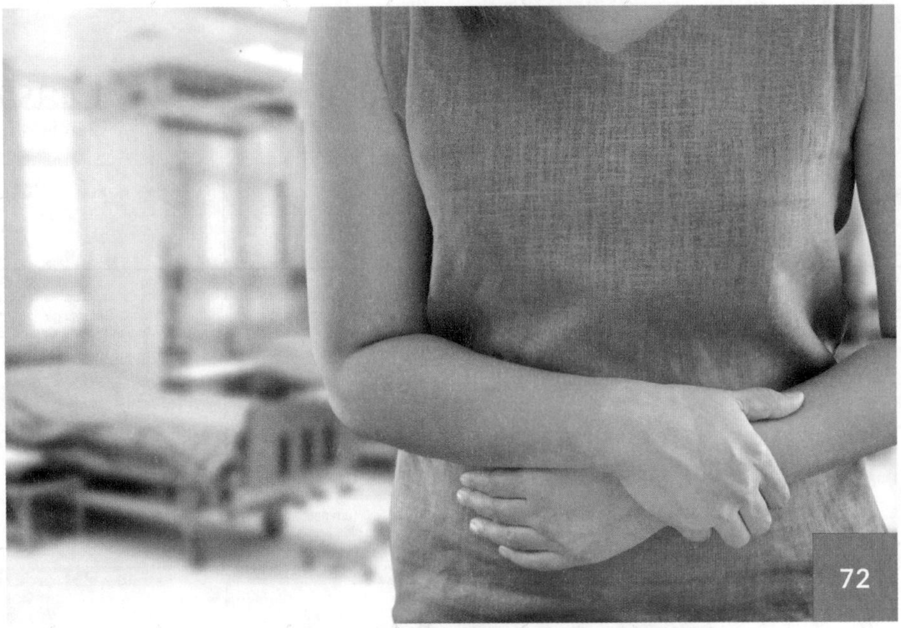

72

73

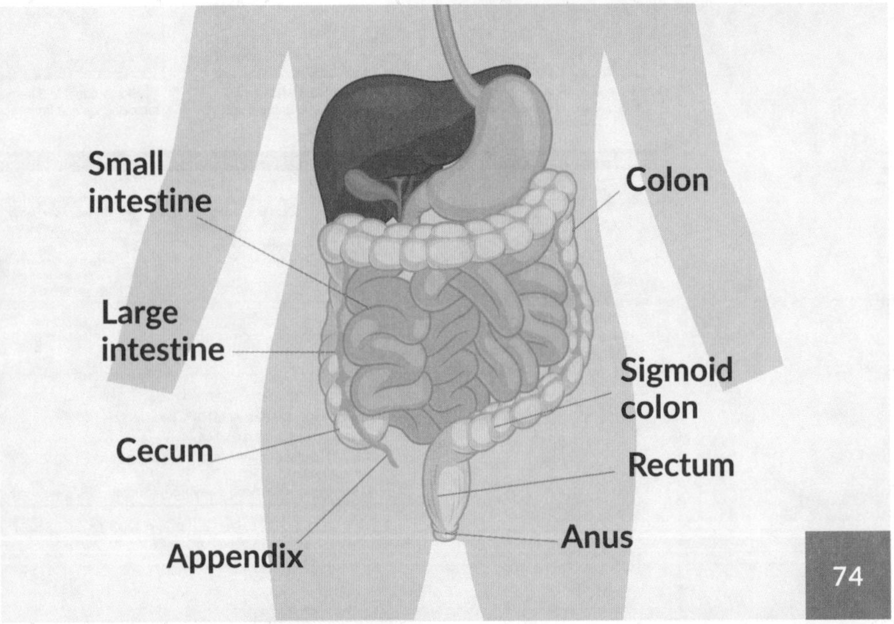
Small intestine
Colon
Large intestine
Sigmoid colon
Cecum
Rectum
Anus
Appendix

74

75

GASTROINTESTINAL CONDITIONS

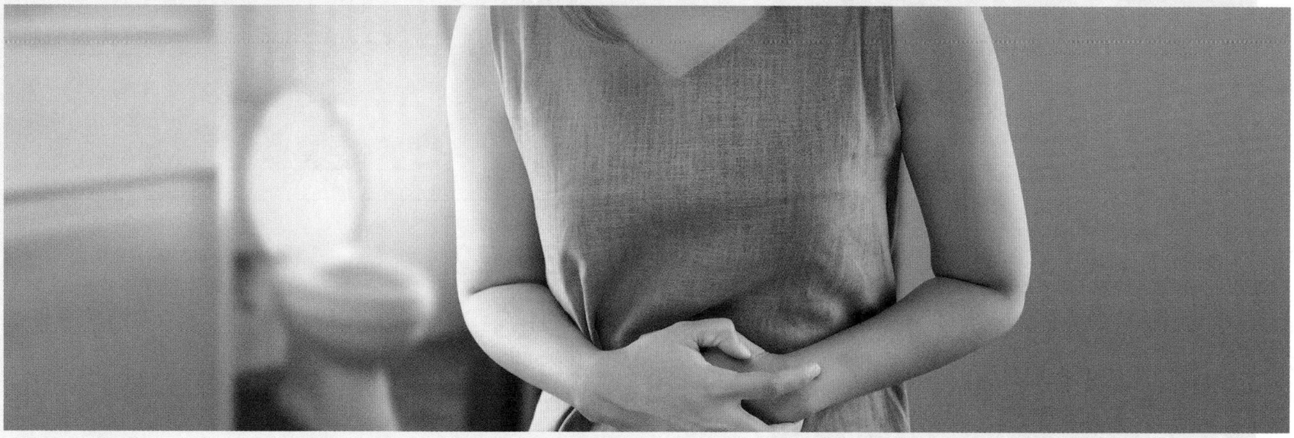

CONTENTS

CHAPTER 72
GASTROESOPHAGEAL REFLUX DISEASE & PEPTIC ULCER DISEASE | **956**

CHAPTER 73
CONSTIPATION & DIARRHEA | **966**

CHAPTER 74
INFLAMMATORY BOWEL DISEASE | **975**

CHAPTER 75
MOTION SICKNESS | **983**

CHAPTER CONTENT

Gastroesophageal Reflux Disease 956
Background 956
Screening and Diagnosis 956
Key Drugs that Can Worsen GERD Symptoms 957
Treatment Principles 957
Drug Treatment 957
Antacids 957
Histamine-2 Receptor Antagonists 958
Proton Pump Inhibitors 958
H2RA and PPI Formulations to Know 959
Risks Associated with Acid-Suppression Therapy 959
Metoclopramide and Other Medications 960
Drug Interactions 960
Key Drugs with Decreased Absorption 960
Peptic Ulcer Disease 961
Background 961
H. Pylori Detection and Management 961
Non-Steroidal Anti-inflammatory Drug-Induced Ulcers 963
Background 963
Prevention and Treatment 963
Cytoprotective Drugs 963
Patient Counseling 964

CONTENT LEGEND

= Study Tip Gal = Key Drug Guy

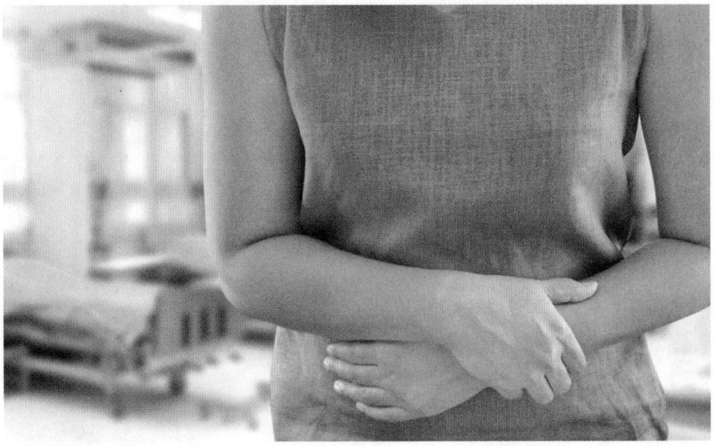

CHAPTER 72
GASTROESOPHAGEAL REFLUX DISEASE & PEPTIC ULCER DISEASE

GASTROESOPHAGEAL REFLUX DISEASE

BACKGROUND

Parietal cells in the epithelial lining of the stomach, when stimulated by histamine, acetylcholine and the hormone gastrin, secrete hydrochloric acid (HCl) through the H^+/K^+-adenosine triphosphatase (ATPase) pump, also known as the proton pump. Gastrin also aids in digestion by stimulating stomach muscle contractions. Acidic gastric contents are normally prevented from backflow into the esophagus by a protective ring of muscle fibers called the lower esophageal sphincter (LES). Patients with gastroesophageal reflux disease (GERD) have reduced LES pressure (muscle tone), and gastric contents can backflow into the esophagus.

SCREENING AND DIAGNOSIS

Typical GERD symptoms include heartburn (daytime or nocturnal), hypersalivation and regurgitation of acidic contents into the mouth or throat. Less common symptoms include epigastric pain, nausea, cough, sore throat, hoarseness or chest pain, which can be difficult to distinguish from cardiac pain.

Diagnosis is based on patient-reported symptoms (duration, daytime and/or nocturnal occurrence), frequency (≥ 2 times per week) and risk factors (e.g., family history, diet and eating habits, sleep position); invasive testing is not required when typical symptoms are present.

GERD can decrease quality of life and lead to esophageal erosion, strictures, bleeding and Barrett's esophagus (abnormal cell growth in the esophageal lining which can lead to esophageal cancer). If a patient has alarm symptoms (see next page) or there is concern for a more serious condition, endoscopy can be performed to further investigate the problem. Patients who are refractory to GERD treatment may benefit from 24-hour esophageal pH monitoring.

KEY DRUGS THAT CAN WORSEN GERD SYMPTOMS

Aspirin/NSAIDs	Iron supplements
Bisphosphonates	Nicotine replacement therapy
Dabigatran	Steroids
Estrogen products	Tetracyclines
Fish oil products	

TREATMENT PRINCIPLES

The vast majority of patients self-treat GERD symptoms with OTC products and do not seek medical attention unless this fails. It is common for a pharmacist to be the first healthcare encounter for a patient with GERD symptoms. Patients should be referred for further evaluation if they do not respond to lifestyle modifications and/or two weeks of self-treatment with OTC products, or if alarm symptoms are present [odynophagia (painful swallowing), dysphagia, frequent nausea and vomiting, hematemesis, black bloody stools, unintentional weight loss].

Treatment should include lifestyle modifications and drugs. Infrequent heartburn (< 2 times per week) can be treated with OTC antacids or histamine-2 receptor antagonists (H2RAs), used as needed (PRN). An eight week course of a proton pump inhibitor (PPI) is the initial drug treatment of choice for GERD, and is used to heal any erosive esophagitis. There are no major differences in efficacy between the available PPIs. After eight weeks, treatment should be interrupted; if symptoms return, maintenance therapy is needed.

GERD Treatment Algorithm

Lifestyle Modifications

- Weight loss (if overweight or recently gained weight)*
- Elevate the head of the bed with foam wedges or blocks
- Avoid eating high fat meals within 2-3 hours of bedtime
- Avoid foods/beverages that trigger reflux (patient-specific): caffeine, chocolate, acidic/spicy foods, carbonated beverages

↓

Initial Drug Treatment

PPI once daily for 8 weeks

- Can increase to twice daily if partial response or if nocturnal symptoms are present

↓ *Stop treatment at 8 weeks; if symptoms return, start maintenance therapy*

Maintenance Treatment

- 1st line: PPI at the lowest effective dose**
- Alternative: H2RA, if there is no erosive esophagitis and it relieves symptoms
- Not recommended: metoclopramide or sucralfate

**Weight loss has the best evidence for improvement of symptoms*

***Can include intermittent or on-demand dosing (see PPI section of text)*

DRUG TREATMENT

Antacids

Antacids work by neutralizing gastric acid (producing salt and water), which increases gastric pH. Since antacids do not require systemic absorption, they provide relief within minutes, but the duration of relief is short (30 – 60 minutes). Antacids can be purchased OTC and are suitable for mild, infrequent symptoms. Patients using antacids containing aspirin (e.g., *Alka-Seltzer)* should be made aware of the serious bleeding risk if used too frequently; see Patient Counseling.

DRUG	DOSING	SAFETY/SIDE EFFECTS/MONITORING
Calcium carbonate *(Tums,* others) **+ magnesium *(Mylanta Supreme,*** others) **+ simethicone (anti-gas) *(Maalox Advanced Maximum Strength,*** others)	Many formulations including suspensions, chewable tablets, capsules Dosing varies by product; many require administration 4-6 times per day	**WARNINGS** Aluminum and magnesium: can accumulate with severe renal dysfunction (not recommended if CrCl < 30 mL/min); risk of bleeding with aspirin-containing products (see Patient Counseling) **SIDE EFFECTS** Unpleasant taste Calcium: constipation, bloating, belching Aluminum: constipation, hypophosphatemia Magnesium: loose stools (use with aluminum may counter-balance) **NOTES** Calcium-containing antacids may be preferred in pregnancy (see Drug Use in Pregnancy and Lactation chapter) *Alka-Seltzer* contains > 500 mg Na per tablet which can worsen edema in patients with heart failure or cirrhosis
Magnesium hydroxide *[Milk of Magnesia (MOM),* others] + aluminum *(Gaviscon, Mag-Al,* others) **+ aluminum + simethicone** (***Mylanta Classic***, others)		
Sodium bicarbonate + aspirin + citric acid (*Alka-Seltzer*, others)		

Histamine-2 Receptor Antagonists

H2RAs reversibly inhibit H2 receptors on gastric parietal cells, which decreases gastric acid secretion. H2RAs are used PRN for infrequent or mild heartburn but have a slower onset than antacids. They can be used as maintenance therapy for GERD in patients without esophageal erosions. They are also used for patients who complete eight weeks of PPI treatment and are able to remain symptom-free on an H2RA since this could decrease side effects associated with long-term use of PPIs (see Risks Associated with Acid Suppression Therapy section). If used for ulcer healing or hypersecretory conditions (e.g., Zollinger-Ellison syndrome), higher doses are needed.

DRUG	DOSING	SAFETY/SIDE EFFECTS/MONITORING
Famotidine ***(Pepcid, Pepcid AC,*** others) Rx and OTC: tablet, chewable tablet, suspension Rx: injection + calcium carbonate and magnesium hydroxide *(Pepcid Complete)* OTC: chewable tablet + ibuprofen *(Duexis)* Rx: tablet	**OTC** 10-20 mg 1-2 times daily PRN **Rx** 20 mg BID	**WARNINGS** Confusion, usually reversible [risk factors: elderly, severely ill, renal impairment (see Notes)]; vitamin B12 deficiency with prolonged use (≥ 2 years) Famotidine: ECG changes (QT prolongation) with renal dysfunction Ranitidine: ↑ ALT **SIDE EFFECTS** Headache, agitation/vomiting in children < 1 year Cimetidine (high doses): gynecomastia, impotence **NOTES** Onset of relief: within 60 minutes Duration: 4-10 hours May be used in pregnancy when clinically indicated Decrease dose when CrCl < 50 mL/min (famotidine, ranitidine, nizatidine) or CrCl < 30 mL/min (cimetidine) Cimetidine can ↑ SCr, without causing renal impairment Avoid cimetidine due to drug interactions and side effects To relieve symptoms, take PRN; to prevent symptoms, take PRN 30-60 minutes before food or beverages that cause heartburn Tachyphylaxis (tolerance to acid suppressing effects) can occur if used on a scheduled basis
Ranitidine ***(Zantac, Ranitidine Acid Reducer,*** others) Rx and OTC: tablet, capsule, syrup Rx: injection	**OTC** 75-150 mg 1-2 times daily PRN **Rx** 150 mg BID	
Nizatidine Rx: capsule, oral solution	**Rx** 150 mg BID	
Cimetidine Rx and OTC: tablet, oral solution	**OTC** 200 mg 1-2 times daily PRN **Rx** 400 mg Q6H	

Proton Pump Inhibitors

PPIs irreversibly bind to the gastric H^+/K^+-ATPase pump in parietal cells. This shuts down the proton pump and blocks gastric acid secretion. PPIs are the most effective medications for GERD; an eight week course of treatment is recommended for relief of symptoms and to heal erosions that may be present. All PPIs have similar efficacy, though an individual patient may respond better to one drug over another. If used for maintenance therapy long-term, the lowest effective dose should be used and the need for treatment should be assessed regularly. Intermittent use (PPI taken for a short period of time after relapse of GERD symptoms) and on-demand use (PPI taken only when symptoms occur) are additional options.

Recommended Administration of Oral PPIs

DRUG	MEAL	TIMING
Esomeprazole *(Nexium)*	Before breakfast	At least 60 minutes before
Lansoprazole *(Prevacid, Prevacid SoluTab)*		Time not specified
Omeprazole *(Prilosec)*		Time not specified
Omeprazole + sodium bicarbonate *(Zegerid)*		60 minutes before (can control nocturnal symptoms if given at bedtime)
Dexlansoprazole *(Dexilant)*	Without regard to meals	Without regard to meals
Pantoprazole *(Protonix)*		Tablet: without regard to meals Oral suspension: 30 minutes before a meal
Rabeprazole *(Aciphex, AcipHex Sprinkle)*		Tablet: without regard to meals Capsule sprinkles: 30 minutes before meal

Proton Pump Inhibitor Products

DRUG	DOSING	SAFETY/SIDE EFFECTS/MONITORING
Dexlansoprazole *(Dexilant)* Rx: capsule	**Rx** 30-60 mg daily	**WARNINGS** *C. difficile*-associated diarrhea (CDAD), hypomagnesemia, vitamin B12 deficiency with prolonged use (≥ 2 years), acute interstitial nephritis (hypersensitivity reaction), cutaneous and systemic lupus erythematosus, increased incidence of osteoporosis-related bone fractures in high-dose or long-term (≥ 1 year) therapy **SIDE EFFECTS** Headache, nausea, diarrhea (all mild and infrequent) IV *Protonix*: thrombophlebitis, severe skin reactions (SJS/TEN) **NOTES** Onset: 1-3 hours; duration > 24 hrs for most PPIs PPIs may diminish the therapeutic effect of clopidogrel, avoid use of omeprazole and esomeprazole while on clopidogrel; rabeprazole or pantoprazole have less risk May be used in pregnancy when clinically indicated Pantoprazole and esomeprazole are the only PPIs available IV Do not crush, cut, or chew tablets or capsules Dexlansoprazole, esomeprazole, lansoprazole, omeprazole and rabeprazole capsules can be opened (not crushed), mixed in applesauce and swallowed immediately (without chewing) *Zegerid* 20 mg and 40 mg have the same Na bicarbonate content (1100 mg); do not substitute two 20 mg capsules/packets for one 40 mg capsule/packet because the patient will receive twice the amount of Na; caution in patients on Na restricted diet (e.g., heart failure, cirrhosis) *First-Omeprazole, Omeprazole+Syrspend SF Alka* and *First-Lansoprazole* are suspension compounding kits that contain pre-measured powdered drug, suspension liquid (with flavoring) and mixing tools *Esomep-ESZ* is a kit that contains capsules with Pill Swallowing Spray
Esomeprazole *(Nexium, Nexium IV, Nexium 24HR-OTC,* *Esomep-EZS*, others) Rx and OTC: capsule, tablet Rx: injection, packet for oral suspension + naproxen 375 or 500 mg *(Vimovo)* Rx: tablet	**OTC** 20 mg daily **Rx** 20-40 mg daily	
Lansoprazole *(Prevacid, Prevacid SoluTab, Prevacid 24HR-OTC,* *First-Lansoprazole*, others) Rx and OTC: capsule, ODT Rx: suspension	**OTC** 15 mg daily **Rx** 15-30 mg daily	
Omeprazole *(Prilosec, Prilosec OTC,* *First-Omeprazole, Omeprazole+Syrspend SF Alka)* Rx and OTC: capsule, tablet Rx: packet for oral suspension OTC: ODT + sodium bicarbonate *(Zegerid, Zegerid OTC)* Rx and OTC: capsule, packet for oral suspension + aspirin 81 or 325 mg *(Yosprala)* Rx: tablet	**OTC** 20 mg daily **Rx** 20-40 mg daily	
Pantoprazole *(Protonix)* Rx: tablet, injection, packet for oral suspension	**Rx** 40 mg daily	
Rabeprazole *(Aciphex, AcipHex Sprinkle)* Rx: tablet, capsule sprinkle	**Rx** 20 mg daily	

H2RA AND PPI FORMULATIONS TO KNOW

- H2RAs and PPIs are very common medications. Sometimes suspensions, solutions or ODT formulations are needed (e.g., infants, children, adults unable to swallow tablets/capsules). Non-oral formulations are used when patients are NPO.

	OTC	ODT	ORAL SOLUTION/SUSPENSION	INJECTION
H2RA	Cimetidine Famotidine Ranitidine		Cimetidine Famotidine Nizatidine Ranitidine	Famotidine Ranitidine
PPI	Esomeprazole Lansoprazole Omeprazole	Lansoprazole Omeprazole	Lansoprazole **Packets for suspension:** Esomeprazole Omeprazole Pantoprazole	Esomeprazole Pantoprazole

Risks Associated with Acid-Suppression Therapy

Long-term use of PPIs causes chronic changes in gastric pH. This can promote growth of microorganisms and increase the risk of GI infections, including *C. difficile* and possibly pneumonia (due to reflux of gastric contents beyond the oral cavity). PPIs also increase the risk of osteoporosis and fractures. The Beers Criteria recommend that PPIs not be used beyond eight weeks in elderly patients unless there is a clear indication (e.g., high risk due to chronic NSAID use, demonstrated need for maintenance therapy).

Metoclopramide and Other Medications

Other medications historically used for GERD treatment include the cytoprotective drugs, misoprostol and sucralfate, and the prokinetic drug, metoclopramide. There is currently no role for these medications in the management of GERD and they are not recommended by guidelines. Misoprostol and sucralfate can be used for peptic ulcer disease, which is discussed later in the chapter. Metoclopramide and erythromycin are most commonly used when patients have coexisting gastroparesis.

Metoclopramide is a dopamine antagonist. At higher doses, it blocks serotonin receptors in the chemoreceptor zone of the CNS (see the Oncology I chapter). It also enhances the response to acetylcholine in the upper GI tract, causing enhanced motility and accelerated gastric emptying (peristaltic speed) and ↑ LES tone.

DRUG	DOSING	SAFETY/SIDE EFFECTS/MONITORING
Metoclopramide ***(Reglan)*** Tablet, ODT, oral solution, injection	10-15 mg QID 30 min before meals and at bedtime Has a short duration of action (food must be present in the gut) Not recommended for use > 12 weeks	**BOXED WARNING** Can cause tardive dyskinesia (a serious movement disorder, often irreversible); there is increased risk with high doses, long-term treatment (> 12 weeks) and in elderly patients **CONTRAINDICATIONS** GI obstruction, perforation or hemorrhage, history of seizures, pheochromocytoma, combination with other drugs likely to increase extrapyramidal symptoms (EPS) **WARNINGS** EPS (including acute dystonia), parkinsonian-like symptoms, rare neuroleptic malignant syndrome (NMS), depression **SIDE EFFECTS** Drowsiness, restlessness, fatigue, cardiovascular (hypertension, pro-arrhythmic), diarrhea **NOTES** CNS side effects are dose-related and more common in the elderly – ↓ dose in patients with CrCl < 40 mL/min (use 50% of normal dose) Avoid use in patients with Parkinson disease

DRUG INTERACTIONS

There are many types of interactions between acid-suppressing drugs and other medications. This section highlights the most important interactions for antacids, H2RAs and PPIs, but it is not all-inclusive. As appropriate, refer to other chapters (e.g., HIV, Hepatitis & Liver Disease, Infectious Diseases).

Antacids, H2RAs and PPIs

- Some drugs require an acidic gut for absorption, including enteric-coated or delayed-release products that can dissolve and release drug prematurely if the gastric pH is increased. The Key Drugs Guy to the right shows some important drugs that can have decreased absorption when given concurrently with antacids, H2RAs and PPIs.
  - Due to the short duration of action of antacids, this type of interaction can often be alleviated by separating administration of the interacting drugs (see Antacids section below).
  - The following should be avoided completely when taking H2RAs or PPIs: delavirdine, dasatinib, pazopanib and the delayed-release formulation of risedronate *(Atelvia)*. Erlotinib, rilpivirine and velpatasvir/sofosbuvir *(Epclusa)* are additional medications that should be avoided in combination with PPIs.

KEY DRUGS WITH DECREASED ABSORPTION

Drugs that require an acidic gut (absorption ↓ by antacids, H2RAs and PPIs)

- Antiretrovirals: rilpivirine (NNRTI*), atazanavir (PI*)
- Antivirals: ledipasvir, velpatasvir/sofosbuvir
- Azole antifungals: itraconazole, ketoconazole, posaconazole oral suspension**
- Cephalosporins (oral): cefpodoxime, cefuroxime
- Iron products
- Mesalamine
- Risedronate delayed-release
- Tyrosine kinase inhibitors: dasatanib, erlotinib, pazopanib

Oral drugs/drug classes that antacids bind

- Antiretrovirals (INSTIs): bictegravir, dolutegravir, elvitegravir, raltegravir
- Bisphosphonates
- Isoniazid
- Mycophenolate
- Quinolones
- Sotalol
- Steroids (especially budesonide)
- Tetracyclines (less of a concern with doxycycline and minocycline)
- Thyroid products

**NNRTI = non-nucleoside reverse transcriptase inhibitor, PI = protease inhibitor*

***Absorption decreased by H2RAs and PPIs only*

Antacids

- Antacids can decrease the absorption of some drugs by binding or adsorbing to them. It is necessary to separate administration of antacids from select drugs (see Key Drugs Guy on previous page). The timing of separation varies; for most products, avoiding antacids 2 – 4 hours before or 2 – 6 hours after is recommended.

H2RAs

- Use caution with CNS depressants (especially in the elderly) due to the risk of additive delirium, dementia and cognitive impairment. Use lower doses in patients with renal impairment.
- Avoid using famotidine with highest risk QT-prolonging drugs (see the Arrhythmias chapter).
- Cimetidine is a moderate inhibitor of CYP450 2C19 and a weak inhibitor of other enzymes (e.g., CYP3A4 and CYP1A2). Avoid use with dofetilide and use caution with other drugs, including amiodarone, calcium channel blockers, clopidogrel, phenytoin, SSRIs, theophylline and warfarin.

PPIs

- All PPIs inhibit CYP2C19; most are weak inhibitors but omeprazole and esomeprazole are moderate inhibitors. PPIs can ↑ the levels of citalopram, phenytoin, tacrolimus, voriconazole and warfarin. Do not use PPIs with nelfinavir.
- Omeprazole and esomeprazole can ↓ the effectiveness of clopidogrel (a prodrug) through CYP2C19 inhibition. Avoid using these drugs together.
- PPIs can inhibit renal elimination of methotrexate, leading to ↑ serum levels and risk of methotrexate toxicities.

Metoclopramide

- Avoid in patients receiving medications for Parkinson disease (antagonistic effect). Avoid in combination with antipsychotic drugs, droperidol, promethazine, tetrabenazine and trimetazidine due to an increased risk of adverse effects. When used in combination with SSRIs, SNRIs or TCAs, monitor for possible EPS, NMS and serotonin syndrome.

PEPTIC ULCER DISEASE

BACKGROUND

Peptic ulcer disease (PUD) occurs when there is mucosal erosion within the gastrointestinal tract. Unlike gastritis, the ulcers in PUD extend deeper into the mucosa. Most ulcers occur in the duodenum, but a small percentage also occur in the stomach. Ulcers can be observed with an upper gastrointestinal endoscopy. The three most common causes of PUD are *Helicobacter pylori (H. pylori)*-positive ulcers, nonsteroidal anti-inflammatory drug (NSAID)-induced ulcers and stress ulcers, which occur in critically ill and mechanically-ventilated patients (see the Acute & Critical Care Medicine chapter). *H. pylori*, a spiral-shaped, pH-sensitive, gram-negative bacterium that lives in the acidic environment of the stomach, is responsible for the majority of peptic ulcers (70 – 95%). Less common causes of PUD are hypersecretory states (e.g., increased gastric acid in Zollinger-Ellison syndrome), viral infections (e.g., cytomegalovirus), radiation therapy and infiltrative diseases (e.g., Crohn's Disease).

Under normal conditions, a physiologic balance exists between gastric acid secretion and the gut's mucosal defense and repair mechanisms, which include mucus and bicarbonate secretion, mucosal blood flow, prostaglandin synthesis, cellular regeneration and epithelial cell renewal. These mechanisms protect the GI mucosa from damage caused by NSAIDs (including aspirin), *H. pylori*, acid, pepsin and other GI irritants.

Symptoms

The primary symptom of PUD is dyspepsia, a gastric pain which can feel like a gnawing or burning sensation in the middle or upper stomach. If the ulcer is duodenal (usually caused by *H. pylori*), pain is typically worse 2 – 3 hours after eating (when the stomach is empty); eating food or taking antacids lessens the pain. With gastric ulcers (primarily from NSAIDs), eating generally worsens the pain. Other symptoms include heartburn, belching, bloating, cramping, nausea and anorexia.

H. PYLORI DETECTION AND MANAGEMENT

Diagnostic Tests

H. pylori infection, if left untreated, can lead to gastric cancer. The infection should be treated if testing is positive. Common, non-invasive, diagnostic tests for *H. pylori* include the urea breath test (UBT), which identifies gas (CO_2) produced by the bacteria, and the fecal antigen test, which detects *H. pylori* in the stool. PPIs, bismuth and antibiotics should be discontinued two weeks prior to these tests to avoid false negative results.

Drug Treatment

There are several combination regimens available to treat *H. pylori* (see the table on the following page). Due to failure rates with triple therapy (often caused by clarithromycin resistance), the American College of Gastroenterology (ACG) guidelines now recommend quadruple therapy first-line. The use of triple therapy first-line is only recommended if clarithromycin resistance rates are low (< 15%) and the patient has no previous history of taking a macrolide antibiotic (for any reason).

First-Line *H. Pylori* Treatment Regimens

DRUG REGIMEN	NOTES
Bismuth Quadruple Therapy: take for 10-14 days Use first-line, especially if local resistance rates to clarithromycin are high (≥ 15%), the patient has had a previous macrolide exposure or a penicillin allergy, or triple therapy failed (if used first)	
Bismuth subsalicylate 300 mg QID + **Metronidazole 250-500 mg QID +** **Tetracycline 500 mg QID +** **PPI BID (or esomeprazole 40 mg daily)** Or use a 3-in-1 combination product + PPI: *Pylera* (bismuth subcitrate potassium 420 mg + metronidazole 375 mg + tetracycline 375 mg) QID + PPI BID	Tinidazole may be substituted for metronidazole If the patient cannot tolerate a PPI, substitute a H2RA (e.g., ranitidine 150 mg BID, famotidine 40 mg daily, nizatidine 150 mg BID) Swallow all capsules in the *Pylera* regimen (3 capsules per dose) **Alcohol Use** Do not use metronidazole **Pregnancy/Children** Do not use tetracycline during pregnancy or in children < 8 years of age **Salicylate Allergy** Do not use bismuth subsalicylate
Concomitant Therapy: take for 10-14 days Alternate first-line treatment consisting of a four-drug regimen; preferred over clarithromycin triple therapy if a macrolide is used	
Amoxicillin 1,000 mg BID + **Clarithromycin 500 mg BID +** **Metronidazole 250-500 mg QID +** **PPI BID (or esomeprazole 40 mg daily)**	Tinidazole may be substituted for metronidazole
Clarithromycin Triple Therapy: take for 14 days Use only if local resistance rates to clarithromycin are low (< 15%) and the patient has had no previous exposure to a macrolide	
Amoxicillin 1,000 mg BID + **Clarithromycin 500 mg BID +** **PPI BID (or esomeprazole 40 mg daily)** Or use a 3-in-1 combination product with PPI: *Prevpac* (amoxicillin + clarithromycin + lansoprazole) *Omeclamox-Pak* (amoxicillin + clarithromycin + omeprazole)	Penicillin allergy: replace amoxicillin with metronidazole 500 mg TID or use quadruple therapy (see above) *Prevpac* contains all medications on one blister card; take the entire contents of one card (divided BID) every day for 14 days *Omeclamox-Pak* is a combination package, swallow capsules and tablets whole

Other *H. pylori* Treatments

Sequential therapy (PPI plus amoxicillin for 5 – 7 days, followed by a PPI, clarithromycin and metronidazole for the remaining 5 – 7 days), hybrid therapy (PPI plus amoxicillin for seven days, followed by a PPI, amoxicillin, clarithromycin and metronidazole for seven days) and quinolone-based regimens are other options presented in the guidelines, though the level of evidence for these treatment recommendations is weaker.

Do not make drug substitutions in *H. pylori* eradication regimens. H2RAs should not be substituted for a PPI, unless the patient cannot tolerate a PPI. Other antibiotics within a class should not be substituted (for example, do not use ampicillin instead of amoxicillin). If the PPI is continued beyond 14 days, this is to help ulcer healing; it should not be continued indefinitely.

NON-STEROIDAL ANTI-INFLAMMATORY DRUG-INDUCED ULCERS

Background

NSAIDs, including aspirin, can cause gastric mucosal damage by two mechanisms: direct irritation of the gastric epithelium and systemic inhibition of prostaglandin synthesis (by inhibiting COX-1). The chronic use of NSAIDs increases the risk for gastric (GI) ulcers. Patients are at high-risk if they have any of the risk factors shown in the box to the right.

RISK FACTORS FOR NSAID-INDUCED ULCERS
Age > 60 years
History of PUD (including *H. pylori*-induced)
High-dose NSAIDs
Using > 1 NSAID (e.g., NSAID plus aspirin)
Concomitant use of anticoagulants, steroids or SSRIs

Prevention and Treatment

The choice of NSAID can be important when assessing the risk for GI ulcers and bleeding. All NSAIDs elevate blood pressure and decrease renal blood flow; they should be used with caution in any person with cardiovascular or renal disease. NSAIDs with selective inhibition of COX-2 (e.g., celecoxib) have decreased GI risk but increased cardiovascular (CV) risk compared to non-selective NSAIDs. NSAIDs that approach the selectivity of celecoxib are meloxicam, nabumetone, diclofenac and etodolac.

Patients with high GI risk (or a history of ulcers) who take non-selective NSAIDs can use concurrent PPI treatment to prevent or decrease the risk of ulcers and bleeding, but the long-term risks of acid-suppression therapy need to be considered. The cytoprotective drug, misoprostol, is an alternative option to a PPI, but diarrhea, cramping and its four times per day dosing contribute to poor patient compliance. Combination products specifically marketed to reduce the risk of NSAID-induced ulcers include naproxen/esomeprazole (*Vimovo*), ibuprofen/famotidine (*Duexis*) and diclofenac/misoprostol (*Arthrotec*); these are indicated to relieve symptoms of osteoarthritis and rheumatoid arthritis in patients at risk of GI ulcers. *Yosprala*, a combination of aspirin and omeprazole, is approved for secondary prevention of cardiovascular and cerebrovascular events in patients at risk for aspirin associated ulcers.

If possible, both non-selective NSAIDs and COX-2 selective drugs should be avoided in patients with both high GI and high CV risk. Naproxen may be the preferred NSAID in patients with low-moderate GI risk and high CV risk. A COX-2 selective drug, with or without a PPI, can be used in patients who do not have CV risk factors.

If an ulcer develops, it should be treated with a PPI for eight weeks, and NSAIDs should be discontinued. If PPIs cannot be used, high dose H2RAs or sucralfate are other options.

Cytoprotective Drugs

Misoprostol is a prostaglandin E1 analog that replaces the gastro-protective prostaglandins removed by NSAIDs. Sucralfate is a sucrose-sulfate-aluminum complex and can interact with albumin and fibrinogen to form a physical barrier over an open ulcer. This protects the ulcer from further insult by HCl acid, pepsin and bile, and allows it to heal.

DRUG	DOSING	SAFETY/SIDE EFFECTS/MONITORING
Misoprostol *(Cytotec)* + diclofenac 50 mg *(Arthrotec)*	200 mcg PO QID with food; if not tolerated, may ↓ to 100 mcg QID; take with meals and at bedtime	**BOXED WARNING** Warn patients this is an abortifacient and not to give this drug to others; do not use to ↓ NSAID-induced ulcers in women of childbearing potential unless capable of complying with effective contraceptive measures **SIDE EFFECTS** Diarrhea, abdominal pain **NOTES** Use of psyllium *(Metamucil)* can help decrease diarrhea
Sucralfate *(Carafate)* Tablet, suspension	1 gram PO QID before meals (empty stomach) and at bedtime	**WARNING** Caution in renal impairment; sucralfate is in an aluminum complex and can accumulate **SIDE EFFECTS** Constipation **NOTES** Drink adequate fluids and use laxatives PRN for constipation Difficult to use due to binding interactions (separate antacids by 30 minutes and other drugs 2 hrs before and 4 hrs after)

PATIENT COUNSELING

ANTACIDS, H2RAS AND PPIS

- Lifestyle counseling: refer to the treatment algorithm earlier in the chapter.
- If you are self-treating your heartburn with medication for more than 14 days, or more than two times per week, you should discuss your symptoms with a healthcare provider.
- Seek urgent or emergent care if you have trouble or pain when swallowing food, bloody stools, or vomit with blood or material that looks like coffee grounds.
- This medication can prevent other drugs from getting into the body. Check with a healthcare provider to see if you need to separate this medication from other drugs you are taking.

Antacids

- This medication provides immediate relief, but lasts only about 30 – 60 minutes. If you need a medication that lasts longer, ask your healthcare provider.
- Do not use aluminum or magnesium products if you have kidney disease, or antacids with sodium if you require a sodium restricted diet (e.g., heart failure, high blood pressure, kidney disease).
- Magnesium-containing products can cause loose stools. Aluminum-containing products can cause constipation.
- Antacids with aspirin (e.g., *Alka-Seltzer*) have caused serious bleeding events and should be avoided. Your risk of bleeding is higher if you are > 60 years of age, have a history of stomach ulcers or bleeding problems, take blood-thinning medication, steroids, OTC pain relievers (e.g., *Motrin, Aleve*) or drink more than three alcoholic beverages per day.

H2RAs

- This medication provides heartburn relief in about 30 – 45 minutes and lasts 4 – 10 hours. If your symptoms remain bothersome, discuss with your healthcare provider.
- If elderly: this medication can cause you to be confused, dizzy or have memory problems. This can be more likely if you also have kidney disease. If you notice these symptoms, you should discuss them with your healthcare provider.

PPIs

- It is important to take this medication correctly to stop heartburn and other reflux symptoms. Some products work best when taken 30 – 60 minutes before a meal, often breakfast; others can be taken without regard to meals. Refer to the Recommended Administration of Oral PPIs table and counsel according to the specific product.
- This medication does not work immediately; you need to take it every day, as instructed, to get relief.
- Your risk of getting severe diarrhea, caused by an infection in your intestines, is increased with this medication. Call your healthcare provider if you have watery stool, stomach pain and a fever that does not go away.
- Using this medication for longer than a year can increase your risk of bone fractures. Make sure your calcium and vitamin D intake is optimal. If you are taking calcium products for your bone health, calcium citrate works best.
- You should not stop this medication abruptly as you may experience acid rebound. Discuss how to stop treatment with your healthcare provider.
- This medication can cause low levels of magnesium in your body. Tell your healthcare provider right away if you have dizziness, jitteriness, abnormal heartbeat, seizures, jerking movements or shaking, or weak, cramping or aching muscles.
- *Prevacid SoluTab* contains the sweetener aspartame. Do not use if you have phenylketonuria (PKU).
- Do not crush or chew any tablets or capsules. *Prevacid SoluTab* and omeprazole orally disintegrating tablets should be placed on the tongue and allowed to dissolve; any small particles can be swallowed without water.

METOCLOPRAMIDE

- Do not drive, operate machinery or perform other dangerous tasks until you know how this drug affects you.
- Avoid drinking alcohol while taking this drug. Alcohol may increase drowsiness and dizziness.
- Contact your healthcare provider right away if you experience any unusual body movements, such as shakiness, stiffness, or uncontrollable movements of the mouth, tongue, cheeks, jaw, arms or legs.

H. PYLORI COUNSELING

- For all *H. pylori* regimens: these medications are used together for stomach ulcers caused by an infection. It is very important that you take the medication as prescribed and complete the course of treatment.

- It is common to have some <u>diarrhea</u> while taking these medications. If it becomes severe or watery, contact your healthcare provider. Other side effects to watch for are headache, a bad taste in the mouth or any sign of allergy, like a skin rash.

- A darkening of your tongue and stool may occur. It goes away when you stop taking this medication.

- *Prevpac:* each card has your dose (four pills) for the morning and the evening. Take your dose before breakfast and before dinner.

- *Pylera:* to treat your stomach ulcers correctly, you need two prescriptions, *Pylera* and a prescription for an acid reducing medication. Take the acid reducing medication, as directed, for the same number of days as *Pylera*, but you should not continue taking it after that unless your healthcare provider has said to continue. Take *Pylera* (three capsules) four times each day with a full glass of water (after breakfast, lunch, dinner and at bedtime). Swallow the capsules whole.

- If your treatment includes metronidazole (includes *Pylera*), you should avoid alcohol products during treatment and for at least three days after stopping, as you may have headaches, flushing, cramps and an upset stomach.

Select Guidelines/References

Katz PO, Gerson LB, Vela MF. Guidelines for the diagnosis and management of gastroesophageal reflux disease. *Am J Gastroenterol.* 2013;108:308-28.

American College of Gastroenterology (ACG) clinical guideline: treatment of *Helicobacter pylori* infection. *Am J Gastroenterol.* 2017;112:212-238.

CHAPTER CONTENT

Constipation ... 966
- Background ... 966
- Non-Drug Treatment ... 966
- Drugs that are Constipating ... 967
- Drug Treatment ... 967
- Laxative Agents Used for Bowel Prep ... 967
- Which OTC to Recommend for Constipation ... 967
- Treatment for Constipation Associated with Irritable Bowel Syndrome ... 968
- Bulk-Forming Agents ... 968
- Osmotics ... 968
- Stimulants ... 969
- Emollients (Stool Softeners) ... 969
- Lubricants ... 969
- Osmotics for Whole Bowel Irrigation ... 970
- Lubiprostone ... 970
- Guanylate Cyclase C Agonists ... 971
- Peripherally-Acting Mu-Opioid Receptor Antagonist ... 971
- Serotonin 5HT-4 Receptor Agonist ... 971

Diarrhea ... 972
- Background ... 972
- Select Drugs that Can Cause Diarrhea ... 972
- Non-Drug Treatment ... 972
- Drug Treatment ... 972
- Treatment for Diarrhea Associated with Irritable Bowel Syndrome ... 973
- Peripherally-Acting Mu-Opioid Receptor Agonist ... 974
- Patient Counseling ... 974

CONTENT LEGEND

= Study Tip Gal = Key Drug Guy

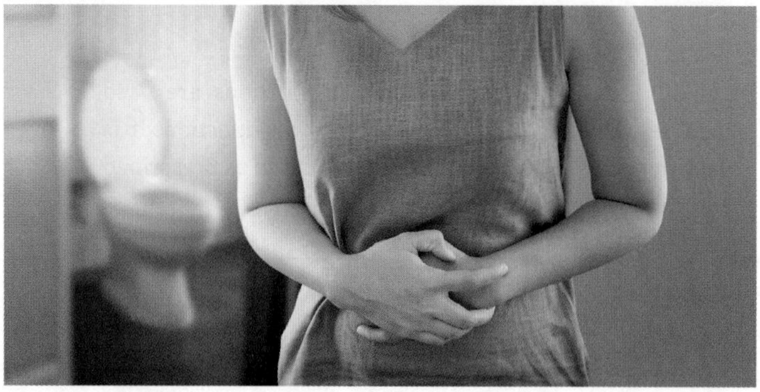

CHAPTER 73
CONSTIPATION & DIARRHEA

CONSTIPATION

BACKGROUND

Constipation is generally defined as infrequent stool passage (less than three bowel movements per week) or difficulty in passing stools (e.g., straining, lumpy/hard stools, pushing for more than 10 minutes, requiring digital evacuation of stool or sensation of incomplete evacuation). Constipation can be caused by diet, lifestyle, drugs (see Key Drugs Guy), GI disorders, pregnancy and other medical conditions (see box below). If the cause of constipation is unknown, it is idiopathic. When constipation persists for several weeks or longer, it is chronic. When idiopathic constipation occurs frequently and is associated with chronic or recurrent abdominal discomfort that is relieved by defecation, it is termed irritable bowel syndrome with constipation (IBS-C).

MEDICAL CONDITIONS THAT CAN CAUSE CONSTIPATION	
Irritable bowel syndrome (constipation-predominant)	Cerebrovascular events
Anal disorders (anal fissures, fistulae, rectal prolapse)	Parkinson disease
Multiple sclerosis	Spinal cord tumors
	Diabetes
	Hypothyroidism

NON-DRUG TREATMENT

Non-drug treatments are preferred for constipation. These include increasing fluid intake (64 oz daily recommended), limiting caffeine and alcohol intake (to avoid dehydration) and increasing physical activity. Replacing refined foods with whole grain products, bran, fruits, vegetables, beans and other foods high in fiber is useful. It is important to avoid delays in going to the bathroom when the urge to defecate is present (time to use the bathroom may need to be scheduled for young children). If possible, drugs that are constipating should be discontinued.

DRUG TREATMENT

If symptoms do not improve with lifestyle measures, and/or if a constipating drug cannot be stopped, drug therapy for constipation can be used. The American Gastroenterological Association (AGA) guidelines recommend gradually increasing fiber intake (dietary and as supplements) with the possibility of adding on an osmotic agent [e.g., milk of magnesia, polyethylene glycol (PEG)] or a stool softener (e.g., docusate). These are available OTC (PEG is available OTC as *MiraLax* and by prescription in a larger container).

If the patient needs to defecate quickly, a suppository (bisacodyl or glycerin) will provide fast relief. Preferably, these should be administered 30 minutes after a meal when GI peristalsis has increased, but they can be used at any time of day.

Fiber products (such as psyllium) are the first-line treatment in most cases, and the treatment of choice in pregnancy. In addition to providing benefit for constipation, psyllium modestly improves cholesterol and blood glucose levels. Psyllium requires adequate fluids. This can be difficult for some (e.g., an elderly female with incontinence would not likely be willing to increase fluid intake). A reasonable alternative is to use a stool softener, such as docusate. This is commonly needed for patients using iron supplements, as iron makes the stool hard and compact and it is difficult for fiber to mix in to soften the stool.

Patients using chronic opioids will often require a stimulant laxative, because the opioids reduce the ability to push out the stool. Certain opioids are more constipating than others (e.g., morphine causes more constipation than fentanyl) but all are constipating, and some patients have more constipation than others. Oral stimulants (senna, bisacodyl) can be taken at bedtime. Senna is the usual first-line oral stimulant agent. These agents take ~10 hours to work. The patient should have a bowel movement the following morning.

The stool softener docusate is given with the stimulant laxative if the stool is hard. If the stool is not hard but the patient cannot push it out ("moosh with no push"), a stimulant alone is the usual treatment. There are newer options for opioid-induced constipation (OIC) for patients who do not find relief with a stimulant plus a stool softener.

OTC treatment is appropriate for short-term (< 7 days). If no improvement, patients should see a healthcare provider.

DRUGS THAT ARE CONSTIPATING

KEY DRUGS

Aluminum antacids

Anticholinergic drugs, or drugs with similar properties (e.g., TCAs, antihistamines, phenothiazines, antispasmodics, urge incontinence agents)

Non-DHP calcium channel blockers (especially verapamil)

Clonidine

Colesevelam

Iron

Opioids

Sucralfate (contains an aluminum complex)

Others:

5-HT3 receptor antagonists (e.g., ondansetron)

Aripiprazole

Milnacipran

Phentermine/topiramate

Ranolazine

Tramadol, tapentadol

Varenicline

WHICH OTC TO RECOMMEND FOR CONSTIPATION

ADULTS
Most adults – fiber (*Metamucil*)

On opioids – senna, or a bisacodyl suppository if the patient needs fast relief

On iron or stool is very hard – docusate

For adults that need to go soon but need something gentle – glycerin suppository

CHILDREN
For a child that needs to go quickly – glycerin suppository

If no improvement in < 7 days, refer patient to a healthcare provider.

LAXATIVE AGENTS USED FOR BOWEL PREP

Laxatives can also be used for bowel prep before a colonoscopy. A successful colonoscopy requires a complete and thorough bowel prep. Several of the agents (the PEGs, and occasionally sodium phosphate) are used for both bowel prep and as laxatives. Sodium phosphates *(Fleet Enema, Osmoprep)* can cause fluid and electrolyte abnormalities, and are particularly risky in patients with renal or cardiac disease. Because of this, they are contraindicated for OTC laxative use (oral solution) in heart failure, renal impairment or with electrolyte abnormalities. Some PEG formulations are only used for bowel prep, such as *Golytely*.

General counseling for bowel prep agents must include when to take the agent, what the patient can consume during the bowel cleansing process (e.g., after they have started using the bowel prep agent) and what must be avoided. Although usually safe and well-tolerated, in certain patients, fluid and electrolyte loss could be critical. Use extra caution in patients with cardiovascular disease, renal insufficiency, and if taking loop diuretics (due to additional fluid loss) and NSAIDs. Refer to the Notes section in the Osmotics for Whole Bowel Irrigation table for instructions on what is acceptable to consume with these agents.

TREATMENT FOR CONSTIPATION ASSOCIATED WITH IRRITABLE BOWEL SYNDROME

Many of the same modalities mentioned above are used to treat IBS-C, including bulking agents and osmotic laxatives; other drugs might be needed to treat pain/abdominal discomfort (e.g., dicyclomine). Lubiprostone, linaclotide and plecanatide are approved for both IBS-C and chronic idiopathic constipation (CIC). Due to cost considerations, polyethylene glycol is often used first and will provide relief in many cases.

BULK-FORMING AGENTS

Bulk-producing laxatives create a gel-like matrix in the stool, soaking up fluid in loose stool and adding bulk to the stool.

DRUG	DOSING	SAFETY/SIDE EFFECTS/MONITORING
Psyllium *(Metamucil)* Capsule, powder Sugar-free options available	2.5-30 g/day in divided doses	**CONTRAINDICATIONS** Fecal impaction, GI obstruction (psyllium) **SIDE EFFECTS** Gas, bloating, bowel obstruction (if strictures present), choking (if powder forms are not taken with enough liquid) **NOTES** Onset of action 12 to 72 hours Take 2 hours before/after other drugs (caution with other drugs that stick to fiber) Adequate fluids are required. This may be inappropriate for patients who require fluid restriction (e.g., heart failure), have difficulty swallowing (e.g., Parkinson disease), or who are at risk for fecal impaction (e.g., intestinal ulcerations, stenosis)
Calcium polycarbophil *(FiberCon)* Caplet	1,250 mg 1-4 times/day	
Methylcellulose *(Citrucel)* Caplet, powder	Caplet: 1-6 g/day Powder: 2-6 g/day	
Wheat Dextrin *(Benefiber)* Tablet, chewable tablet, powder	4 grams (2 teaspoons) in 4-8 oz of liquid or soft food TID	

OSMOTICS

Osmotic laxatives contain large ions or molecules that are poorly absorbed. These draw fluid into the bowel lumen through osmosis, which distends the colon and increases peristalsis.

DRUG	DOSING	SAFETY/SIDE EFFECTS/MONITORING
Magnesium hydroxide *(Milk of Magnesia)*, magnesium citrate, magnesium sulfate	MgOH: 2.4-4.8 g QHS or in divided doses	**CONTRAINDICATIONS** Anuria (sorbitol), low galactose diet (lactulose), GI obstruction *(MiraLax)* **SIDE EFFECTS** Electrolyte imbalance, gas, dehydration Suppositories: rectal irritation **NOTES** Onset of action 30 minutes to 96 hours (oral), 15-30 minutes (rectal) Milk of magnesia: contains magnesium, caution with renal impairment and do not use with severe renal impairment Glycerin suppository used commonly in children who need to defecate quickly Lactulose used commonly for hepatic encephalopathy
Polyethylene glycol 3350 *(MiraLax,* *GaviLax, GlycoLax,* others)	17 g in 4-8 oz of water daily	
Glycerin *(Fleet, Pedia-Lax, Sani-Supp)* Suppository: adult & pediatric sizes	Insert 1 suppository into the rectum (PR)	
Sorbitol Solution, enema	PO: 30-150 mL (70% solution) PR: 120 mL (25-30% solution)	
Lactulose *(Constulose, Enulose, Generlac, Kristalose)*	10-20 g daily	

STIMULANTS

These drugs directly stimulate colonic neurons causing peristaltic activity.

DRUG	DOSING	SAFETY/SIDE EFFECTS/MONITORING
Senna *(Ex-Lax, Senokot,* others) + docusate *(Senna Plus, Senna S,* others)	17.2-50 mg PO daily-BID	**WARNINGS** Avoid use with stomach pain, N/V, or a sudden change in bowel movements that lasts > 2 weeks **SIDE EFFECTS** Abdominal cramping, electrolyte imbalance, rectal irritation (suppository) **NOTES** Onset of action 6-12 hours (oral), 15-60 minutes (rectal) Ideally, give 30 minutes after a meal (for ↑ peristalsis) Chronic opioid use often requires a stimulant laxative
Bisacodyl *(Dulcolax,* others) EC tablet, enema, suppository	PO: 5-15 mg daily Do not crush or chew enteric coated tablets; do not take within 1 hr of milk, dairy products or antacids Suppository: 10 mg PR daily; if too soft to insert, can cool in fridge or cold water first	

EMOLLIENTS (STOOL SOFTENERS)

Emollients, also called stool softeners, soften fecal mass and make defecation easier. Emollients reduce the surface tension of the oil-water interface of the stool, allowing more water and fat to mix with the stool.

DRUG	DOSING	SAFETY/SIDE EFFECTS/MONITORING
Docusate sodium *(Colace)*, docusate calcium, docusate potassium Many formulations (e.g., capsule, enema, oral syrup) + senna *(Senna Plus, Senna S,* others)	Docusate sodium: PO: 50-360 mg daily or in divided doses Enema: 283 g/5 mL PR daily-TID	**CONTRAINDICATIONS** Abdominal pain, N/V, use with mineral oil (see below), OTC use > 1 week **NOTES** Onset of action 12 to 72 hours (oral), 2-15 mins (rectal) Preferred when straining should be avoided (e.g., postpartum, post-MI, anal fissures, hemorrhoids) Use when stool is hard and/or dry

LUBRICANTS

Lubricants coat the bowel and the stool mass with a waterproof film. This keeps moisture in the stool and makes defecation easier.

DRUG	DOSING	SAFETY/SIDE EFFECTS/MONITORING
Mineral oil Oral, enema	Dose varies with product	**CONTRAINDICATIONS** Age < 6 years, pregnancy, bedridden patients, elderly, use > 1 week, difficulty swallowing **NOTES** Onset of action 6-8 hours (oral), 2-15 mins (rectal). Oral formulation generally not recommended due to safety concerns; potential risk of aspiration (lipid pneumonitis) Take a multivitamin at a different time due to malabsorption of fat-soluble vitamins Do not take docusate and mineral oil together (it increases absorption of mineral oil)

OSMOTICS FOR WHOLE BOWEL IRRIGATION

DRUG	DOSING	SAFETY/SIDE EFFECTS/MONITORING
Polyethylene glycol solution *(Colyte, GaviLyte-C, GaviLyte-G, Gavilyte-N, GoLytely, MoviPrep, NuLytely, Plenvu, TriLyte)* *NuLytely, TriLyte* are sulfate-free; may taste better	Drink 240 mL every 10 minutes until 4 liters are consumed *MoviPrep:* drink 240 mL every 15 minutes until 2 liters are consumed *Plenvu:* drink 480 mL over 30 minutes, then 480 mL clear liquid over 30 minutes; then repeat Preferable to split the dose, such as half the night before, and half the morning of the procedure	**BOXED WARNING** Nephropathy *(OsmoPrep)* **CONTRAINDICATIONS** Ileus, gastrointestinal obstruction, gastric retention, bowel perforation, toxic colitis, toxic megacolon Acute phosphate nephropathy, gastric bypass or stapling surgery *(OsmoPrep)* Severe renal impairment *(Prepopik)* **SIDE EFFECTS** N/V, abdominal discomfort, bloating, arrhythmias, fluid/electrolyte abnormalities, seizures; gout flare *(Suprep)* **NOTES** Onset of action within 1-6 hours The following food items are acceptable to consume the day prior to colonoscopy: "clear liquid diet," which can include water, clear broth (beef or chicken), juices without pulp (apple, white cranberry, white grape, lemonade), soda, coffee or tea (without milk or cream), clear gelatin (without fruit pieces), popsicles (without fruit pieces or cream) The following food items cannot be consumed prior to colonoscopy: anything with red or blue/purple food coloring (including gelatin and popsicles), milk, cream, tomato, orange or grapefruit juice, alcoholic beverages, cream soups, and solid or semi-solid foods
Sodium picosulfate, magnesium oxide, and citric acid *(Prepopik, Clenpiq)* Combination of a stimulant and osmotic laxative (enables lower fluid intake)	*Prepopik:* 150 mL x 2 doses *Clenpiq:* 160 mL x 2 doses	
Sodium phosphates *(Fleet Enema, OsmoPrep)*	*Fleet Enema:* contents of one 4.5 oz enema as a single dose *OsmoPrep:* 32 tablets and 2 quarts of clear liquid	
Sodium sulfate, potassium sulfate and magnesium sulfate *(Suprep Bowel Kit)*	Night before the procedure: drink 480 mL, then 960 mL clear liquid; Morning of: repeat	

LUBIPROSTONE

Lubiprostone works by activating chloride channels in the gut, leading to increased fluid in the gut and peristalsis. It is approved for CIC, OIC with chronic non-cancer pain and IBS-C in adult women.

DRUG	DOSING	SAFETY/SIDE EFFECTS/MONITORING
Lubiprostone *(Amitiza)*	CIC & OIC: 24 mcg BID IBS-C: 8 mcg BID ↓ dose with mod-severe liver impairment	**CONTRAINDICATIONS** Mechanical bowel obstruction **SIDE EFFECTS** Nausea, diarrhea, headache, hypokalemia **NOTES** Take with food and water to decrease nausea; swallow whole, do not break, chew or crush Consider alternative treatment in patients taking methadone (↓ lubiprostone effects)

GUANYLATE CYCLASE C AGONISTS

Linaclotide and plecanatide are agonists of guanylate cyclase C, which increases chloride and bicarbonate secretion into the intestinal lumen, increasing the speed of GI transit and reducing abdominal pain. They are both used for CIC and for IBS-C.

DRUG	DOSING	SAFETY/SIDE EFFECTS/MONITORING
Linaclotide *(Linzess)* CIC in adults IBS-C in adults Capsule	CIC: 145 mcg PO daily IBS-C: 290 mcg PO daily Take at least 30 minutes before breakfast on an empty stomach	**BOXED WARNING** Do not use in pediatric patients; high risk of dehydration that can cause death **CONTRAINDICATIONS** Age < 6 years, mechanical GI obstruction **SIDE EFFECTS** Diarrhea, abdominal distension, flatulence, headache **NOTES** Swallow whole; do not break, chew or crush *Linzess* capsules *Trulance* tablets can be crushed and *Linzess* capsules can be opened; put in 1 teaspoonful of applesauce or 30 mL of room temperature water; the mixture must be swallowed immediately *Linzess:* must be protected from moisture; original container has a desiccant
Plecanatide *(Trulance)* CIC in adults IBS-C in adults Tablet	3 mg PO daily Administer with or without food	

PERIPHERALLY-ACTING MU-OPIOID RECEPTOR ANTAGONIST

Peripherally-acting mu-opioid receptor antagonists (PAMORAs) act on mu-opioid receptors found in the GI tract, decreasing constipation. Alvimopan is only for hospitalized patients and is given prior to surgery to reduce the risk of ileus that can occur post-op. Methylnaltrexone *(Relistor)*, naloxegol *(Movantik)* and naldemedine *(Symproic)* are only used in patients taking opioids who have OIC. These agents are discussed in the Pain chapter.

DRUG	DOSING	SAFETY/SIDE EFFECTS/MONITORING
Alvimopan *(Entereg)* Post-surgical patients to ↓ risk of post-operative ileus REMS drug	12 mg PO, 30 min-5 hrs prior to surgery, and 12 mg BID for up to 7 days total (maximum 15 doses) Used inpatient only	**BOXED WARNING** Potential risk of MI with long-term use **CONTRAINDICATIONS** Patients who have taken therapeutic doses of opioids for > 7 consecutive days prior to use **SIDE EFFECTS** ↓ K, dyspepsia, anemia, urinary retention, back pain

SEROTONIN 5HT-4 RECEPTOR AGONIST

Prucalopride is a selective, high affinity 5HT-4 receptor agonist. This causes a muscle contraction, increased gastrointestinal motility through a release of acetylcholine. Prucalopride is indicated for CIC and is also used for OIC with chronic non-cancer pain off-label.

DRUG	DOSING	SAFETY/SIDE EFFECTS/MONITORING
Prucalopride *(Motegrity)*	CIC: 2 mg PO daily CrCl < 30 mL/min: 1 mg PO daily Avoid use in ESRD with HD	**CONTRAINDICATIONS** Intestinal perforation or obstruction due to structural or functional disorder of the gut wall, obstructive ileus, severe inflammatory conditions of the GI tract (Crohn's disease, ulcerative colitis, toxic megacolon) **WARNINGS** Suicidal ideation, severe diarrhea usually in first week of treatment, if persistent diarrhea, discontinue therapy **SIDE EFFECTS** Headache, nausea, diarrhea, abdominal pain **MONITORING** Worsening of depression or emergence of suicidal thoughts

DIARRHEA

BACKGROUND

Diarrhea occurs when there is an increase in the number of bowel movements, or stools are more watery and loose than normal. When the intestines push stools through the bowel before the water in the stool can be reabsorbed, diarrhea occurs. Abdominal cramps, nausea, vomiting or fever can be present. When idiopathic diarrhea is recurrent and associated with chronic or reoccurring abdominal discomfort that is relieved by defecation, it is termed irritable bowel syndrome with diarrhea (IBS-D).

Most cases of diarrhea are viral, have a quick onset and usually resolve within a few days without treatment. Diarrhea can be idiopathic, caused by diseases, drugs (see Key Drugs Guy), food poisoning or by consuming contaminated food/water (e.g., travelers' diarrhea, see Travelers chapter). *E. coli* is the most common bacterial cause. The treatment of diarrhea caused by a bacterial infection is discussed in the Infectious Diseases II chapter.

SELECT DRUGS THAT CAN CAUSE DIARRHEA

- Antacids containing magnesium
- Antibiotics, especially broad-spectrum antibiotics, clindamycin, and erythromycin (which has prokinetic activity); diarrhea may be infectious (e.g., *C. difficile)*
- Antineoplastics
- Colchicine
- Laxatives
- Metoclopramide
- Misoprostol
- Quinidine

Patients who experience diarrhea after consuming milk or milk products could be lactose intolerant. Rule out lactose intolerance as the cause of the diarrhea by stopping the use of dairy products. Lactose intolerance can be confirmed through testing.

NON-DRUG TREATMENT

Management of diarrhea includes fluid and electrolyte replacement, especially in moderate-severe cases and in the elderly, children, or adults with chronic medical conditions. For fluid and electrolyte loss, replace fluids with oral rehydration solutions (ORS), which are available at stores and pharmacies *(Pedialyte, Infalyte)* in developed countries. *Gatorade* or similar products can be used as alternatives.

DRUG TREATMENT

Most patients with non-infectious diarrhea who require symptomatic relief can use short-term bismuth subsalicylate *(Pepto-Bismol)* or loperamide if needed. Bismuth subsalicylate exhibits both antisecretory and antimicrobial effects when used as an antidiarrheal. Loperamide and diphenoxylate are antimotility agents that slow intestinal motility, prolonging water absorption.

TREATMENT FOR DIARRHEA ASSOCIATED WITH IRRITABLE BOWEL SYNDROME

In most cases, loperamide offers acceptable relief. Rifaximin *(Xifaxan)* is an antibiotic with approval for IBS-D. It is costly, and relapse often occurs within several months of treatment. Alosetron *(Lotronex)* is useful for women only, but has restricted use due to the risk of ischemic colitis. The pain/abdominal discomfort of IBS-D can be managed with additional agents, including antispasmodics (e.g., dicyclomine) and antidepressants in select patients.

DRUG	DOSING	SAFETY/SIDE EFFECTS/MONITORING
Antidiarrheals		
Bismuth subsalicylate *(Pepto-Bismol,* others) Chewable tablet, suspension	525 mg every 30-60 mins PRN or 1,050 mg every 60 mins PRN Max: 4,200 mg/day for up to 2 days	**CONTRAINDICATIONS** Salicylate allergy, use with other salicylates, ulcer, coagulopathy, black/bloody stool **SIDE EFFECTS** Black tongue/stool, salicylate toxicity if used excessively (early s/sx include tinnitus, N/V, increased respiratory rate, diaphoresis) **NOTES** Caution in patients on aspirin therapy, anticoagulants, or those with renal insufficiency Children and teenagers who are recovering from the flu, chickenpox, or other viral infections should not use this drug due to the risk of Reye's syndrome
Loperamide *(Imodium A-D,* *Loperamide A-D, Anti-Diarrheal, Diamode,* others)	4 mg PO after the first loose stool, then 2 mg after each subsequent loose stool Max: 16 mg/day OTC max: 8 mg/day 1 tab = 2 mg	**BOXED WARNING** Torsades de pointes, cardiac arrest and sudden death with doses higher than recommended. Do not exceed the recommended dose. **CONTRAINDICATIONS** Abdominal pain without diarrhea, children < 2 years, acute dysentery (bloody diarrhea and high fever), acute ulcerative colitis, pseudomembranous colitis *(C. difficile)*, bacterial enterocolitis caused by invasive organisms (toxigenic *E. coli, Salmonella, Shigella*) **SIDE EFFECTS** Abdominal cramping, constipation, nausea, QT prolongation **NOTES** Self-treatment should not be > 48 hours Loperamide is sometimes abused, as it causes a mild opioid-like "high" in large quantities. To encourage safe use, the FDA is working with manufacturers to use blister packs or other single-dose packaging, and to limit the number of doses in a package
Diphenoxylate/ atropine *(Lomotil)* Diphenoxylate 2.5 mg with atropine 0.025 mg C-V Diphenoxylate inhibits excessive GI motility and propulsion; atropine is anticholinergic and is used to discourage abuse (subtherapeutic amount)	Diphenoxylate 5 mg (2 tablets) up to four times daily Max: 20 mg/day Improvement of acute diarrhea is usually seen within 48 hours; if not seen within 10 days, discontinue	**CONTRAINDICATIONS** Diarrhea caused by enterotoxin-producing bacteria or pseudomembranous colitis *(C. difficile)*, obstructive jaundice, pediatric patients < 6 years of age cannot use tablets **SIDE EFFECTS** Sedation, constipation, urinary retention, tachycardia, blurred vision, dry mouth, depression, hallucinations Atropinism (hyperthermia, tachycardia, flushing, urinary retention, dryness of the skin and mucous membranes), especially in pediatric patients with Down syndrome **NOTES** Tablets not recommended for use in children < 13 years; liquid formulation for use in children > 2 years
Antispasmodic		
Dicyclomine *(Bentyl)* Tablet, capsule, solution	20 mg QID Max: 80 mg/day for < 2 weeks (can increase to 40 mg QID after 1 week, if symptoms respond) Take 30-60 minutes before meals	**CONTRAINDICATIONS** GI obstruction, severe ulcerative colitis, reflux esophagitis, acute hemorrhage with cardiovascular instability, obstructive uropathy, breast feeding, narrow-angle glaucoma, myasthenia gravis, breastfeeding women, infants < 6 months of age **WARNINGS** Anticholinergic (caution in patients ≥ 65 years, per Beer's Criteria), caution in mild-moderate ulcerative colitis (can cause toxic megacolon or paralytic ileus) **SIDE EFFECTS** Dizziness, dry mouth, nausea, blurred vision

PERIPHERALLY-ACTING MU-OPIOID RECEPTOR AGONIST

Eluxadoline is a mu-opioid receptor agonist (in contrast to the PAMORAs, which are mu-receptor antagonists). While the PAMORAs compete and displace the binding of opioids to receptors in the periphery to reduce constipation, eluxadoline binds to the opioid receptors as an agonist to treat diarrhea. It is indicated for IBS-D where the diarrhea is difficult to treat with usual measures.

DRUG	DOSING	SAFETY/SIDE EFFECTS/MONITORING
Eluxadoline (*Viberzi*) C-IV	100 mg PO BID in patients with a gallbladder May decrease to 75 mg BID if unable to tolerate 100 mg dose Take with food	**CONTRAINDICATIONS** Patients without a gallbladder, biliary duct obstruction, sphincter of Oddi dysfunction/disease, pancreatic disease, alcoholism, patients who drink > 3 alcoholic drinks/day, severe hepatic impairment (Child-Pugh class C), history of severe constipation, known GI obstruction **WARNINGS** Pancreatitis (with or without sphincter of Oddi spasm), sphincter of Oddi spasm (which can cause pancreatitis), CNS depression **SIDE EFFECTS** Constipation, nausea, abdominal pain, rash, dizziness, upper respiratory infections, nasopharyngitis **MONITORING** S/sx of pancreatitis or sphincter of Oddi spasm (e.g., abdominal pain that radiates to the back or shoulder, nausea and vomiting), LFTs

PATIENT COUNSELING

All Diarrhea Cases

- Contact your healthcare provider if you have a high fever (> 101°F), severe abdominal pain or blood in your stool that does not get better in two days. For female patients: contact your healthcare provider if you are pregnant.
- Drink fluids with electrolytes while you have diarrhea to prevent dehydration. *Pedialyte* and *Infalyte* are good options. *Gatorade* or similar products can also be used as an alternative.
- Additional counseling for parents of children with diarrhea:
  - If your child is less than 6 months old you should have the infant seen by a healthcare provider.
  - If your child has diarrhea and fever/cold symptoms are present, aspirin should not be given. Aspirin can cause a rare but serious condition called Reye's Syndrome in children. For the treatment of fever or mild pain, refer to the Pediatrics Conditions chapter.

Bismuth Subsalicylate Patient Counseling

- Do not use if you have an allergy to salicylates (including aspirin and NSAIDs, like ibuprofen).
- Tell your healthcare provider prior to starting this medication if you are also taking a salicylate like aspirin.
- Do not give to children and teenagers who have flu signs, chickenpox, or other viral infections due to the chance of Reye's syndrome.
- Some products have phenylalanine. If you have PKU, do not use.
- This medication can make your tongue and stool dark; this is normal. Contact your healthcare provider right away if you notice tarry or bloody stools or if you are throwing up blood or a substance that looks like coffee grounds.
- If you notice a ringing in the ears or a loss of hearing while taking this medicine, stop taking it and contact your healthcare provider.
- Do not take for longer than two days without the approval of your healthcare provider.

Select Guidelines/References

American Gastroenterological Association (AGA) Medical Position Statement on Constipation. *Gastroenterology*. 2013;144:211–217.

CHAPTER CONTENT

Background 975
Ulcerative Colitis 975
Crohn's Disease 976
CD and UC Comparison 976
Diagnosis 976
Lifestyle Measures, Supportive Care and Natural Products 976
Drug Treatment 976
Maintenance of Remission: Comparison of Common CD and UC Treatments 977
Steroids 978
Aminosalicylates 979
Thiopurines 980
Methotrexate and Cyclosporine 980
Anti-TNF Agents, Interleukin Receptor Antagonists and Janus Kinase Inhibitors 980
Integrin Receptor Antagonists 981
Patient Counseling 981

CONTENT LEGEND

= Study Tip Gal

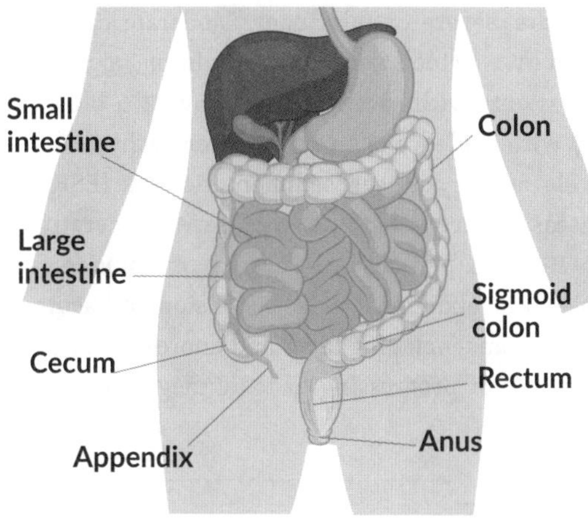

CHAPTER 74
INFLAMMATORY BOWEL DISEASE

BACKGROUND

Inflammatory bowel disease (IBD) is a group of inflammatory conditions of the colon and small intestine. The major types of IBD are ulcerative colitis and Crohn's disease. The classic symptom is bloody diarrhea. Other symptoms include rectal urgency, tenesmus (a feeling of having to pass stools, even if the colon is empty), abdominal pain, fatigue and in some cases, weight loss, night sweats, nausea, vomiting and constipation (e.g., ulcerative colitis limited to the rectum). IBD is a chronic, intermittent disease; symptoms can be mild to severe during flares (or exacerbations) and minimal or absent during periods of remission. Flares can occur at any time, and can be triggered by infections, use of NSAIDs or certain foods. Food triggers are patient specific but can include fatty foods and gas-producing foods (e.g., lentils, beans, legumes, cabbage, broccoli, onions). Food triggers can be avoided or food can be prepared in a way that improves tolerability.

IBD can be mistaken for irritable bowel syndrome (IBS), as they have similar symptoms (e.g., abdominal pain, bloating, gas, and either constipation or diarrhea). Unlike IBD, IBS does not cause inflammation and is not as serious of a condition. Drugs used to treat IBS primarily treat constipation or diarrhea; refer to the Constipation & Diarrhea chapter for drug specifics.

ULCERATIVE COLITIS

Ulcerative colitis (UC) is characterized by mucosal inflammation confined to the rectum and colon with superficial ulcerations. When UC is limited to the descending colon and rectum, it is called distal disease and can be treated with topical (rectal) treatment. Inflammation limited to the rectum is called proctitis. The larger the affected area (e.g., extensive UC), the worse the symptoms. When the disease flares, patients can have numerous stools per day, often with pain, which can significantly decrease quality of life. UC is classified as mild, moderate, severe or fulminant. Moderate disease is characterized by > 4 stools per day with minimal signs of toxicity, and patients with severe disease have ≥ 6 bloody stools per day with evidence of toxicity [fever, tachycardia, anemia, or an elevated erythrocyte sedimentation rate (ESR)]. Fulminant disease refers to patients with severe ulcerative colitis with > 10 stools per day, and severe symptoms (e.g., continuous bleeding, abdominal pain, distension and acute, severe toxic symptoms including fever and anorexia). These patients are at risk of progressing to toxic megacolon and bowel perforation.

CROHN'S DISEASE

Crohn's disease (CD) is characterized by deep, transmural (through the bowel wall) inflammation that can affect any part of the GI tract. The ileum and colon are most commonly affected. Damage to the bowel wall can cause strictures (narrowing of the bowel) and fistulas (abnormal connections or openings in the bowel). Symptoms of CD include chronic diarrhea (often nocturnal), abdominal pain, and weight loss. Perianal symptoms [e.g., bleeding, fissures (tears)] can be present before bowel symptoms.

CD AND UC COMPARISON

CLINICAL FEATURES	CD	UC
Diarrhea	Bloody or non-bloody	Bloody
Fistulas/ Strictures	Common	Uncommon
Location	Entire GI tract (especially the ileum & colon)	Colon (especially the rectum)
Depth	Transmural	Superficial
Pattern	Non-continuous, "cobblestone" appearance	Continuous
Smoking	Risk factor	Protective

DIAGNOSIS

IBD can be difficult to diagnose because the symptoms mimic other common conditions (e.g., constipation, diarrhea, infections, anorexia/bulimia and peptic ulcer disease). These conditions must be ruled out before a diagnosis is made. Laboratory blood tests (for inflammatory markers, such as CRP) and stool testing (e.g., fecal calprotectin test) can be helpful, but usually a colonoscopy with tissue biopsy is needed to make the diagnosis. A colonoscopy allows the healthcare provider to visualize the entire colon. A sigmoidoscopy might be used for UC, which is similar to a colonoscopy but only evaluates the end part of the intestine, closest to the rectum. Endoscopy (scope through the mouth) might also be used if upper GI symptoms are present. Imaging tests (e.g., CT, MRI) can be helpful for diagnosis as well.

LIFESTYLE MEASURES, SUPPORTIVE CARE AND NATURAL PRODUCTS

As previously mentioned, patients with IBD should adapt their diet to avoid foods that are more likely to trigger flares. In general, eating smaller, more frequent meals that are low in fat and dairy products can be helpful. It is usually best to drink plenty of water. Alcohol and caffeinated beverages that can stimulate the GI tract should be avoided, as well as carbonated beverages that can be gas-producing. The patient should watch for avoidable problems; both sorbitol and lactose are classified as excipients (or binders) and are present in various medications to help hold tablets together. Sorbitol is also used as a sweetener in some diet foods; it has laxative properties and can cause considerable GI distress in some patients. Lactose will worsen GI symptoms if the patient is lactose-intolerant.

Some patients may use antidiarrheals or antispasmodic drugs [e.g., dicyclomine (*Bentyl*)] to help manage symptoms of diarrhea; these should be used cautiously, and under the supervision of a healthcare provider, as they need to be avoided in select patients with IBD (e.g., severe disease, acute exacerbations, post-bowel resection). See the Constipation & Diarrhea chapter for more information on these products. Vitamin supplements (e.g., B12, vitamin D, calcium, iron) can help prevent deficiencies related to malabsorption. Nicotine has been shown to worsen CD but can be protective in UC. Nicotine patches have been used as an adjunct therapy for UC, but adverse effects (e.g., nausea, dizziness) limit the benefits.

The probiotics *Lactobacillus* or *Bifidobacterium infantis* can reduce abdominal pain, bloating, urgency, constipation or diarrhea in some patients. Fish oils with EPA and DHA (omega-3 fatty acids) can help fight inflammation, although the evidence for benefit is minimal. Some natural products that might be useful include peppermint (in oils or teas), chamomile tea and Indian frankincense.

DRUG TREATMENT

Treatments for IBD are used for induction of remission (they treat exacerbations or active disease) and/or maintenance of remission. Short courses of oral or IV steroids are commonly used to treat acute exacerbations in both UC and CD. Systemic steroids are not recommended for maintenance of remission and will usually be tapered over 8 – 12 weeks once remission is achieved.

In UC, aminosalicylates (active component is 5-aminosalicylic acid, or 5-ASA) are used for maintenance therapy in most patients with distal UC or mild extensive disease. For patients with moderate-severe UC that extends beyond the colon and rectum, other immunosuppressive medications [e.g., thiopurines, anti-tumor necrosis factor (TNF) drugs, tofacitinib and cyclosporine] can be used (see Study Tip Gal below).

For mild CD that is limited to the ileum and proximal colon, budesonide is preferred. In moderate-severe cases, immunosuppressive medications [e.g., thiopurines, anti-TNF agents, methotrexate, interleukin (IL) receptor antagonists] can be used. Steroids might be needed for severe cases of CD. Integrin receptor antagonists (e.g., vedolizumab) are used in patients with IBD that is refractory to other therapies or that is steroid-dependent.

Some of the more common drugs used to treat UC and CD are shown in the tables below. Additional agents [e.g., IV steroids, anti-TNF agents (infliximab, adalimumab, certolizumab), methotrexate, interleukin receptor antagonists (ustekinumab)] are discussed fully in the Systemic Steroids & Autoimmune Conditions chapter.

INDUCTION OF REMISSION

OPTIONS FOR CD*
- Steroids (± thiopurine or methotrexate)
- Anti-TNF ± thiopurine
- Interleukin receptor antagonist

OPTIONS FOR UC*
- 5-ASA (oral and/or rectal) ± [steroids (oral or rectal) or thiopurine]
- Anti-TNF ± thiopurine
- IV cyclosporine
- Tofacitinib *(Xeljanz)*

**Selection of agents and route of administration are based on the clinical status of the patient (e.g., severity of illness, location of disease), past treatments (successful and failed therapies), inpatient versus outpatient status and more.*

MAINTENANCE OF REMISSION: COMPARISON OF COMMON CD AND UC TREATMENTS

CROHN'S DISEASE

Mild disease of the ileum and/or right colon
- Oral budesonide for ≤ 3 months; after this course, discontinue treatment or change to thiopurine or methotrexate

Moderate-severe disease*
- Anti-TNF agents**
  - Adalimumab *(Humira)*
  - Infliximab *(Remicade)*
  - Certolizumab *(Cimzia)*
- Thiopurine (azathioprine, mercaptopurine)
- Methotrexate
- IL receptor antagonist
  - Ustekinumab *(Stelara)*

Refractory to above treatments and/or steroid dependent
- Integrin receptor antagonists
  - Vedolizumab
  - Natalizumab

ULCERATIVE COLITIS

Mild disease
- Mesalamine (5-ASA) rectal and/or oral preferred

Moderate-severe disease*
- Anti-TNF agents**
  - Adalimumab *(Humira)*
  - Infliximab *(Remicade)*
  - Golimumab *(Simponi)*
- Thiopurine (azathioprine, mercaptopurine)
- Cyclosporine
- Janus kinase inhibitor
  - Tofacitinib *(Xeljanz)*

Refractory to above treatments and/or steroid dependent
- Integrin receptor antagonists
  - Vedolizumab

**Agents can be used as monotherapy or in combination*

***The biosimilars adalimumab-atto (Amjevita), adalimumab-adbm (Cyltezo), adalimumab-adaz (Hyrimoz), infliximab-dyyb (Inflectra), infliximab-abda (Renflexis) and infliximab-qbtx (Ixifi) are also FDA-approved for IBD*

STEROIDS

DRUG	DOSING	SAFETY/SIDE EFFECTS/MONITORING
Oral Steroids		
Prednisone Tablet *(Deltasone)* Oral solution *(Prednisone Intensol)* Delayed-release tablet *(Rayos)*	5-60 mg daily	**CONTRAINDICATIONS** Systemic fungal infections, live vaccines **SIDE EFFECTS** Short-term: ↑ appetite/weight gain, fluid retention, emotional instability (euphoria, mood swings, irritability), insomnia, GI upset, higher doses can cause an ↑ in BP and blood glucose Long-term: adrenal suppression/Cushing's syndrome, immunosuppression/impaired wound healing, ↑ BP, ↑ blood glucose, cataracts, osteoporosis, others; refer to the Systemic Steroids & Autoimmune Conditions chapter **NOTES** **All Steroids** For management of acute flares; avoid long-term use if possible Can use alternate day therapy (ADT) to ↓ adrenal suppression and other adverse effects If used longer than 2 weeks, must taper to avoid withdrawal symptoms If long-term use is required, assess bone density (optimize calcium and vitamin D intake and consider bisphosphonates if needed) **Budesonide** Undergoes extensive first-pass metabolism; ↓ systemic exposure than other oral steroids Swallow whole – do not crush, chew or break
Budesonide *(Entocort EC, Uceris)* *Entocort EC*: 3 mg extended release capsule (for CD only) *Uceris*: 9 mg extended release tablet (for UC only)	**Induction (CD and UC):** 9 mg PO once daily in the morning for up to 8 weeks **Maintenance (CD only):** 6 mg PO once daily for 3 months, then taper	
Rectal Steroids		
Hydrocortisone *(Cortenema, Cortifoam)*	**Induction and/or Maintenance** *Cortenema:* 1 enema (100 mg) QHS for 21 days or until remission, then taper *Cortifoam:* 1 applicatorful (90 mg) 1-2 times daily for 2-3 weeks, then every other day thereafter; taper after long-term therapy	**CONTRAINDICATIONS** *Cortifoam*: obstruction, abscess, perforation, peritonitis, fresh intestinal anastomoses, extensive fistulas and sinus tracts *Cortenema*: ileocolostomy in immediate/early post-op period **NOTES** Rectal steroids are indicated for UC only Not proven effective for maintenance of remission; maintenance use is limited to mild-moderate distal UC as an alternative to rectal and/or oral aminosalicylates Budesonide rectal foam: propellant is flammable; avoid fire and smoking during and after use
Budesonide rectal foam *(Uceris)*	**Induction** 1 metered dose BID x 2 weeks, then 1 metered dose daily x 4 weeks (1 metered dose = 2 mg budesonide)	

Budesonide Drug Interactions

- Budesonide is a major substrate of CYP450 3A4. Avoid strong and moderate inhibitors of CYP3A4, including grapefruit juice and grapefruit products.
- Use of steroids with other immunosuppressants can increase the risk of serious adverse events.
- Antacids can cause enteric coated oral budesonide to dissolve prematurely due to ↑ gastric pH. Separate administration of antacids by two hours.

AMINOSALICYLATES

Aminosalicylates are indicated for treatment of UC; the mechanism of action is unknown, but they appear to have a topical anti-inflammatory effect in the gastrointestinal tract. Mesalamine (5-ASA) is the primary aminosalicylate used in the U.S.; it is well tolerated and available in both oral and rectal formulations. The other aminosalicylates (sulfasalazine, balsalazide, olsalazine) are available in oral form only and must be converted to mesalamine to have an effect. Sulfasalazine is used less commonly due to the many side effects associated with the sulfapyridine component.

DRUG	DOSING	SAFETY/SIDE EFFECTS/MONITORING
Mesalamine ER ER capsules *(Apriso, Delzicol, Pentasa)* ER tablets *(Asacol HD, Lialda)* Enema *(Rowasa)* Suppository *(Canasa)*	**Induction (oral therapy for 6-8 weeks and/or rectal therapy for 3-6 weeks)** *Asacol HD:* 1.6 g PO TID *Delzicol:* 800 mg PO TID *Lialda:* 2.4-4.8 g PO daily *Pentasa:* 1 g PO QID Suppository: 1 g rectally QHS, retain for at least 1-3 hours Enema: 4 g rectally QHS, retain in the rectum overnight for approximately 8 hours **Maintenance** *Apriso:* 1.5 g PO daily *Delzicol:* 1.6 g PO in 2-4 divided doses *Lialda:* 2.4 g PO daily *Pentasa:* 1 g PO QID Enema: 2 g rectally QHS, or 4 g QHS every 2-3 days	**CONTRAINDICATIONS** Hypersensitivity to salicylates or aminosalicylates **WARNINGS** Acute intolerance syndrome (cramping, acute abdominal pain, bloody diarrhea); caution in patients with renal or hepatic impairment; delayed gastric retention (e.g., due to pyloric stenosis) can delay release of oral products in the colon; hypersensitivity reactions (including myocarditis, pericarditis, nephritis, hematologic abnormalities and other internal organ damage) – more likely with sulfasalazine than mesalamine; ↑ risk of blood dyscrasias in patients > 65 years of age *Apriso* contains phenylalanine; do not use in patients with phenylketonuria (PKU) *Rowasa* enema contains potassium metabisulfite, may cause an allergic-type reaction **SIDE EFFECTS** Abdominal pain, nausea, headache, flatulence, eructation (belching), nasopharyngitis **MONITORING** Renal function, CBC, hepatic function, s/sx of IBD **NOTES** Mesalamine is better tolerated than other aminosalicylates Rectal mesalamine is more effective than oral mesalamine and rectal steroids for distal disease/proctitis in UC; can use oral and topical formulations together Swallow capsules/tablets whole; do not crush, chew, or break due to delayed-release coating *Apriso:* do not use with antacids (dissolution is pH-dependent)
Sulfasalazine Tablets *(Azulfidine)* ER tablets *(Azulfidine EN-tabs)*	**Induction** 3-4 g PO divided TID or QID, titrate to 4-6 g PO daily divided QID **Maintenance** 2 g PO daily divided TID or QID	Refer to the Systemic Steroids & Autoimmune Conditions chapter **CONTRAINDICATIONS** Salicylate allergy, sulfa allergy, intestinal or urinary obstruction, porphyria **NOTES** Doses should be taken at ≤ 8 hour intervals Can reduce dose if GI intolerance occurs
Balsalazide Tablet *(Giazo)* Capsule *(Colazal)*	**Induction** *Colazal:* 2.25 g (three 750 mg capsules) PO TID for 8-12 weeks *Giazo* (approved in males only): 3.3 g (three 1.1 g tablets) PO BID for up to 8 weeks	**CONTRAINDICATION** Salicylate allergy **WARNINGS** Gastric retention (e.g., due to pyloric stenosis) can delay release of drug in the colon; acute intolerance syndrome; caution in patients with renal or hepatic impairment **SIDE EFFECTS** Headache, abdominal pain, N/V/D **MONITORING** Renal function, LFTs, s/sx of IBD **NOTES** *Colazal* capsule can be opened and sprinkled on applesauce; beads are not coated, so mixture can be chewed if needed; when used this way, it can cause staining of the teeth/tongue
Olsalazine *(Dipentum)* Capsule	**Maintenance** 500 mg PO BID Take with food	**CONTRAINDICATION** Salicylate allergy **SIDE EFFECTS** Diarrhea, abdominal pain **MONITORING** CBC, LFTs, renal function, symptoms of IBD

THIOPURINES

The thiopurines, azathioprine and mercaptopurine, are immunosuppressive drugs, sometimes referred to as "immunomodulators." They do not have an FDA indication for IBD but are recommended as an option in guidelines for induction and maintenance of remission, often in combination with other drugs.

DRUG	DOSING	SAFETY/SIDE EFFECTS/MONITORING
Azathioprine *(Azasan, Imuran)* Tablet, injection	1.5-3 mg/kg/day IV or PO CrCl < 50 mL/min: adjustment required PO: taking after meals or in divided doses may ↓ GI side effects	**BOXED WARNINGS** Chronic immunosuppression ↑ risk of malignancy in patients with IBD (especially lymphomas); mutagenic potential; risk for hematologic toxicities **WARNINGS** Hematologic toxicities (e.g., leukopenia, thrombocytopenia, anemia); patients with a genetic deficiency of thiopurine methyltransferase (TPMT) are at ↑ risk for myelosuppression GI hypersensitivity reactions (severe N/V/D, rash, fever, ↑ LFTs), serious infections, hepatotoxicity **SIDE EFFECTS** N/V/D, rash, ↑ LFTs **MONITORING** LFTs, CBC (weekly for 1st month), renal function, s/sx of malignancy **NOTES** Consider TPMT genetic testing before starting (see Pharmacogenomics chapter) Azathioprine is metabolized to mercaptopurine; do not use the thiopurines in combination Aminosalicylates inhibit TPMT; caution with use in combination Allopurinol inhibits a pathway for inactivation of azathioprine; azathioprine dose reduction required if used in combination
Mercaptopurine *(Purixan)* Tablet, oral suspension	1-1.5 mg/kg/day CrCl ≤ 50 mL/min: adjustment required	Same as azathioprine above (except no boxed warning) plus: **NOTES** Take on an empty stomach Avoid old terms "6-mercaptopurine" and "6-MP"; they ↑ the risk of overdose due to administration of doses 6-fold higher than normal

METHOTREXATE AND CYCLOSPORINE

Methotrexate is an immunosuppressive drug with anti-inflammatory properties. It does not have an FDA indication for IBD, but it is recommended by the guidelines for induction and maintenance of remission in moderate-severe CD in patients who cannot tolerate azathioprine. It is dosed once weekly by IM or SC injection. See the Systemic Steroids & Autoimmune Conditions chapter for information on methotrexate. Cyclosporine is an immunosuppressive drug recommended for severe UC. It can be given orally or via IV continuous infusion. See the Transplant chapter for more information on cyclosporine.

ANTI-TNF AGENTS, INTERLEUKIN RECEPTOR ANTAGONISTS AND JANUS KINASE INHIBITORS

The anti-TNF agents, (e.g., infliximab) are monoclonal antibodies that bind to human TNF-alpha, preventing induction of proinflammatory cytokines (e.g., interleukins). They are used in patients with moderate-severe UC or CD, often in combination with a thiopurine. See the Study Tip Gal earlier in the chapter for information on which specific anti-TNF agents are FDA-approved for UC and CD.

Ustekinumab *(Stelara)* is a monoclonal antibody that binds to and interferes with IL-12 and IL-23. It is FDA-approved for moderate-severe CD and can be used in patients who have not yet failed or are intolerant to anti-TNF treatment. Tofacitinib *(Xeljanz)* is an oral tablet that inhibits janus kinase (JAK) enzymes, which are involved in stimulating immune cell function. It is FDA-approved to treat moderate-severe UC. These medications are discussed further in the Systemic Steroids & Autoimmune Conditions chapter.

INTEGRIN RECEPTOR ANTAGONISTS

Natalizumab and vedolizumab are monoclonal antibodies that bind to subunits of integrin molecules, blocking the ability of integrin to interact with adhesion molecules and preventing inflammatory cells from migrating into gastrointestinal tissue. They are indicated for induction and maintenance of remission in patients with IBD who have responded inadequately, or who cannot tolerate, conventional therapies or in patients who are steroid-dependent.

DRUG	DOSING	SAFETY/SIDE EFFECTS/MONITORING
Natalizumab *(Tysabri)* Injection Approved for Crohn's disease and multiple sclerosis	300 mg IV over 1 hour every 4 weeks Discontinue if no response by 12 weeks	**BOXED WARNING** Progressive multifocal leukoencephalopathy (PML); PML is an opportunistic viral infection of the brain that leads to death or severe disability; monitor for mental status changes; risk factors include: anti-JCV antibodies, ↑ treatment duration and prior immunosuppressant use Only available through the REMS TOUCH Prescribing Program **WARNINGS** Herpes encephalitis and meningitis, hepatotoxicity, hypersensitivity (antibody formation), immunosuppression/infections **SIDE EFFECTS** Infusion reactions, headache, fatigue, arthralgia, nausea, rash, depression, gastroenteritis, abdominal/back pain **NOTES** Cannot be used with other immunosuppressants Stable in NS only; do not shake If taking steroids when initiating *Tysabri*, begin tapering when the onset of benefit is observed; stop *Tysabri* if patient cannot taper steroids within 6 months of initiation
Vedolizumab *(Entyvio)* Injection Approved for Crohn's disease and ulcerative colitis	300 mg IV over 30 min at 0, 2, and 6 weeks, then every 8 weeks Discontinue if no benefit by week 14	**WARNINGS** Infusion reactions, hypersensitivity reactions, infections, liver injury, PML All immunizations must be up to date before starting; should not receive live vaccines during treatment unless benefit outweighs risk **SIDE EFFECTS** Headache, nasopharyngitis, arthralgia, antibody development **MONITORING** LFTs, s/sx of infection, hypersensitivity, neurological symptoms (to monitor for PML), routine TB screening **NOTES** Refrigerate and store in original packaging to protect from light Swirl during reconstitution, do not shake; after reconstitution, use immediately or refrigerate up to 4 hours (do not freeze) Cannot be used with other immunosuppressants

PATIENT COUNSELING

MESALAMINE

- *Asacol HD* and *Delzicol:* you might see a ghost tablet (empty shell) in the feces; the drug has been absorbed into your body and the tablet is empty.
- *Rowasa* enema: for best results, empty the bowel immediately before use.
    - *Rowasa* is an off-white suspension. Enema contents can darken over time when removed from the foil pouch. If the enema has dark brown contents, throw it away.
    - Remove the bottle from the pouch and shake well. Remove the protective sheath from the applicator tip. Hold the bottle at the neck to prevent any of the medication from being discharged.
    - Best results are obtained by lying on the left side with the left leg extended and the right leg flexed forward for balance. Gently insert the lubricated applicator tip into the rectum to prevent damage to the rectal wall, pointed slightly toward the navel.

- Grasp the bottle firmly, and then tilt slightly so that the nozzle is aimed towards the back; squeeze slowly to instill the medication. Steady hand pressure will discharge most of the medicine. After administering, withdraw and discard the bottle.
- Remain in position for at least 30 minutes, or preferably all night for maximum benefit.
- *Rowasa* can cause staining of surfaces, including clothing and other fabrics, flooring, painted surfaces, marble, granite, vinyl and enamel. Take care in choosing a suitable location for administration of this product.

- *Canasa* suppository: for best results, empty your bowel immediately before use.
    - This medication should be used at bedtime. Detach one suppository from the strip. Remove the foil wrapper carefully while holding the suppository upright. Do not handle the suppository too much; it can melt from the heat from your hands and body.
    - Insert the suppository, with the pointed end first, completely into your rectum, using gentle pressure. You can put a little bit of lubricating gel on the suppository if you have trouble.
    - For best results, keep the suppository in your rectum for at least 1 – 3 hours.
    - *Canasa* can cause staining of surfaces, including clothing and other fabrics, flooring, painted surfaces, marble, granite, vinyl and enamel. Keep *Canasa* away from these surfaces to prevent staining.

HYDROCORTISONE RECTAL FOAM *(CORTIFOAM)*

- Preparation: shake the foam container well for 5 – 10 seconds before each use. Hold the container upright on a level surface and place the tip of the applicator onto the nose of the container cap. Pull the plunger past the fill line on the applicator barrel. To fill the applicator barrel, press down firmly on the cap flanges, hold for 1 – 2 seconds and release. Wait 5 – 10 seconds for the foam to expand and fill the applicator barrel. Repeat until the foam reaches the fill line, then remove the applicator from the container.

- Use: hold the applicator firmly by the barrel (thumb and middle finger on the barrel "wings") and place the index finger on the plunger. Insert the tip gently into the anus and push the plunger to expel the foam. Withdraw the applicator. The foam container should never be inserted into the anus - only the applicator.

- After use, take apart and clean all parts with warm water for next use. Store at room temperature. Each aerosol container should deliver 14 doses.

BUDESONIDE RECTAL FOAM *(UCERIS)*

- This medication is for rectal use only. The *Uceris* rectal foam kit has two aerosol canisters and 28 lubricated applicators. Each canister contains 14 doses of foam.

- Empty your rectum completely before use. Attach a disposable applicator to the nozzle. Warm the canister in your hands and shake well for 10 – 15 seconds before using. Choose a position to administer – standing, lying or sitting on the toilet. The easiest way to use *Uceris* is to keep one foot on the floor and place the other foot onto a firm surface such as a stool or chair.

- Turn the canister upside down and place your forefinger on top of the pump dome. Insert the applicator into the rectum as far as it is comfortable. Push down with your forefinger on the pump dome one time and hold it for about two seconds. Release finger pressure on the pump dome and hold the applicator in place for 10 – 15 seconds. Remove the applicator from the anus, detach it from the canister and dispose of it in the plastic bag provided.

- Administer the evening dose before bedtime and try not to have a bowel movement until morning.

Select Guidelines/References

World Gastroenterology Organization Global Guidelines: Inflammatory Bowel Disease. Updated 2015. http://www.worldgastroenterology.org/guidelines/global-guidelines/inflammatory-bowel-disease-ibd (accessed 2019 Mar 1).

American College of Gastroenterology (ACG) Clinical Guideline: Management of Cronh's Disease in Adults. Am J Gastroenterol 2018;113:481–517.

American Gastroenterological Association (AGA) Clinical Practice Guidelines on the Management of Mild-to-Moderate Ulcerative Colitis. Gastroenterology 2019;156:748-764.

CHAPTER 75
MOTION SICKNESS

CHAPTER CONTENT

Background 983
Non-Drug Treatment 983
Drug Treatment 983
- Motion Sickness Drugs 984
- *Transderm Scop* Counseling 985
- Scopolamine *(Transderm Scop)* Patch 985

DEFINITIONS

Nausea
The uncomfortable, queasy feeling that one may vomit.

Treatment
The chemoreceptor trigger zone (CTZ) in the CNS contains receptors for dopamine (DA), serotonin (5HT) and acetylcholine (Ach). Each receptor can set off a chemical pathway leading to nausea and vomiting. Blocking the receptors reduces nausea.

- Blocking 5HT with 5HT-3 receptor antagonists (e.g., ondansetron)
- Blocking DA with phenothiazines (e.g., prochlorperazine)
- Blocking 5HT and DA with metoclopramide (a prokinetic that moves food through the gut)

Nausea due to chemotherapy is treated with 5HT-3 receptor antagonists and various other medications; see Oncology I chapter.

Vertigo

Dizziness, with the sensation that the environment is moving or spinning. Vertigo is typically due to an inner-ear condition that affects balance.

Treatment
- Vestibular (inner-ear) suppressants, including antihistamines (e.g., meclizine, dimenhydrinate) and benzodiazepines

5HT-3 receptor antagonists are not useful for vertigo because they do not affect the inner ear

Motion Sickness
Dizziness, with a sensation of being off-balance and woozy due to repetitive motions, such as a boat moving over waves or an airplane flying in turbulent weather.

Treatment
- Anticholinergics (e.g., scopolamine) and antihistamines (e.g., meclizine)

CONTENT LEGEND

(💡) = Study Tip Gal

BACKGROUND

Motion sickness (kinetosis) is a common condition that is also called travel/car sickness, seasickness or airsickness. Symptoms are nausea, dizziness and fatigue. People can get motion sickness on a moving boat, airplane, car, or amusement park ride. Symptoms can be triggered in some patients by movies or video games.

NON-DRUG TREATMENT

Some patients find benefit with a wrist band that presses on an acupuncture point located on the inside of the wrist, about the length of 2 fingernails up the arm from the center of the wrist crease. One popular brand is *Sea-Band*.

Ginger, in teas or supplements, is used commonly for nausea. Some patients with motion sickness find it helpful. Peppermint may also be helpful. The best way to stop motion sickness, if possible, is to stop the motion.

DRUG TREATMENT

Antihistamines and anticholinergics are recommended for motion sickness. Scopolamine *(Transderm Scop)*, an anticholinergic, is most commonly prescribed. It is not more effective than generically-available OTC drugs but is applied topically (behind the ear) and is taken less frequently (lasts three days).

Antihistamines used for motion sickness include cyclizine (*Marezine*), diphenhydramine (*Benadryl*), dimenhydrinate (Dramamine) and meclizine (*Bonine, Dramamine All Day Less Drowsy*). Dimenhydrinate, meclizine and cyclizine are long-acting piperazine antihistamines and are a little less sedating than other antihistamines, but they are still sedating. All of the antihistamines have anticholinergic effects similar to scopolamine. Oral medications must be taken 30 - 60 minutes prior to the needed effect.

Medications for motion sickness cause drowsiness and impair judgment. Pilots, ship crew members, or anyone operating heavy equipment or driving a car should not take them. Sometimes combinations of products (such as scopolamine to reduce nausea, taken with a stimulant, such as dextroamphetamine, to counteract the drowsiness from the scopolamine) are used but these combinations have significant risk and should not be routinely recommended.

Traditional antiemetics are discussed in the Oncology I chapter. Promethazine is prescription only and should not be used in children due to risk of respiratory depression. All promethazine products carry a boxed warning to avoid use in children less than 2 years old and strongly cautioning use in children age 2 and older (see Pediatric Conditions and Allergic Rhinitis, Cough & Cold chapters). Metoclopramide and the 5HT-3 receptor antagonists (e.g., ondansetron) are generally not effective for motion sickness.

MOTION SICKNESS DRUGS

DRUG	DOSING	SAFETY/SIDE EFFECTS/MONITORING
Scopolamine 3-day patch *(Transderm Scop)*	**Motion Sickness** Apply 1 patch behind the ear at least 4 hrs before the effect is needed. May use a new patch every 3 days PRN. **Preoperative (e.g., cesarean section)** Apply 1 patch the night before surgery or 1 hr prior to surgery. Remove patch 24 hrs after surgery.	**CONTRAINDICATIONS** Hypersensitivity to belladonna alkaloids, angle closure glaucoma **SIDE EFFECTS** Dry mouth, CNS effects [drowsiness, dizziness, confusion (can be significant in elderly, frail), hallucinations (rare)], stinging of the eyes and pupil dilation (if eyes are touched after handling), risk of ↑ IOP, tachycardia (rare) **NOTES** Refer to patient counseling below Primarily for motion sickness, occasionally used inpatient Do not use in children
Dimenhydrinate *(Dramamine)* Tablet, injection	**Motion Sickness** Oral: 50-100 mg Q4-6 hrs **Nausea and vomiting** IM,IV: 50-100 mg Q4 hrs	**WARNINGS** CNS depression (may impair physical or mental abilities, caution in elderly), worsening of BPH symptoms, and can ↑ IOP (glaucoma) **SIDE EFFECTS** Dizziness, drowsiness, dry mouth, blurry vision, tachycardia **NOTES** There are various OTC formulations of *Dramamine* with different ingredients. *Dramamine Original Formula* contains only dimenhydrinate. *Dramamine All Day Less Drowsy* contains only meclizine
Meclizine *(Dramamine All Day Less Drowsy*, *Bonine, Motion-Time, Travel Sickness)*	25-50 mg PO 1 hour before travel, can repeat Q24 hrs PRN	**WARNINGS** CNS depression (may impair physical or mental abilities, caution in elderly), worsening of BPH symptoms, and can ↑ IOP (glaucoma) **SIDE EFFECTS** Sedation, dry mouth, dry/blurry vision, tachycardia **NOTES** Meclizine is commonly used for vertigo; it was previously branded as *Antivert*

TRANSDERM SCOP COUNSELING

- Peel off the clear backing from the patch and apply it to a clean, dry, hairless area of the skin behind the ear. Press firmly for at least 30 seconds to make sure the patch sticks well, especially around the edges. The patch will slowly release the medication into your body over three days. Apply at least four hours before activity that will cause motion sickness.
- Be sure to wash your hands thoroughly with soap and water before and immediately after handling the patch, so that any drug that might get on your hands will not come into contact with your eyes. Wash the area behind the ear where the patch was removed.
- For motion sickness lasting longer than three days, remove the current patch and apply a new one. Only one patch should be worn at any time.
- This drug causes significant drowsiness. Avoid alcohol and other drugs that make you tired.
- The most common side effect is dryness of the mouth. Other common side effects are drowsiness, blurry vision and widening of the pupils (especially if the drug is on your hands and you touch your eyes). Rarely, some people get disoriented, and others can get confusion, hallucinations or heart palpitations. If any of these occur, remove the patch and contact your healthcare provider.
- Remove the patch before an MRI or it will burn your skin.

SCOPOLAMINE (*TRANSDERM SCOP*) PATCH

For N/V due to motion sickness or anesthesia/surgery

- Apply at least 4 hours before needed or the night before surgery
- Press firmly to skin behind ear for 30 seconds
- Try to avoid placing the patch over hair or when the patch is removed- the hair may be removed too
- Lasts 3 days; if continued treatment needed, remove the first patch and place a new patch behind the other ear

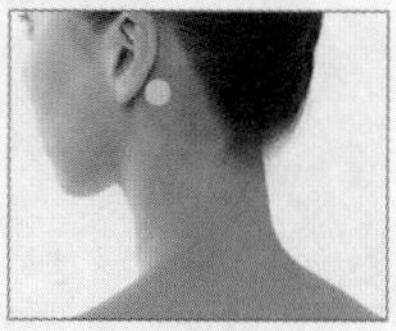

- Wash hands after applying
- Painful/mydriasis if gets in eyes
- Remove prior to an MRI

Do not drive: high level of sedation, dizziness, confusion—(worse in the elderly; anticholinergics are not well-tolerated in elderly; avoid use when possible).

76

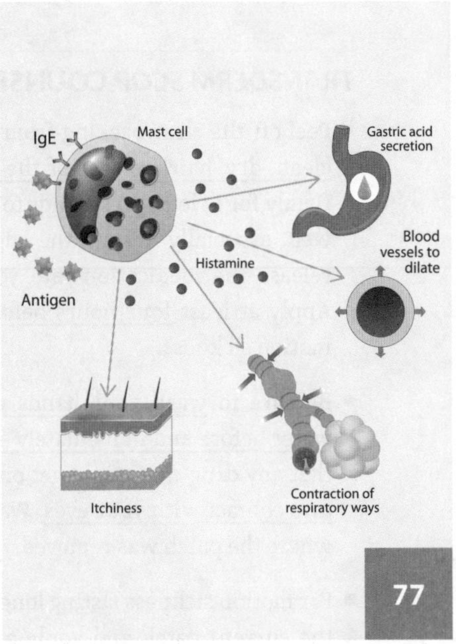

77

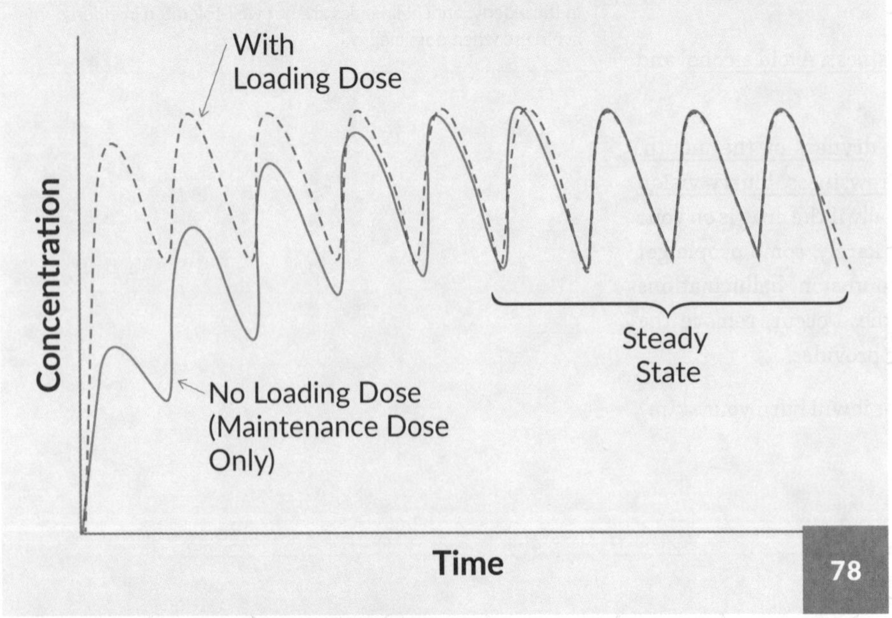

78

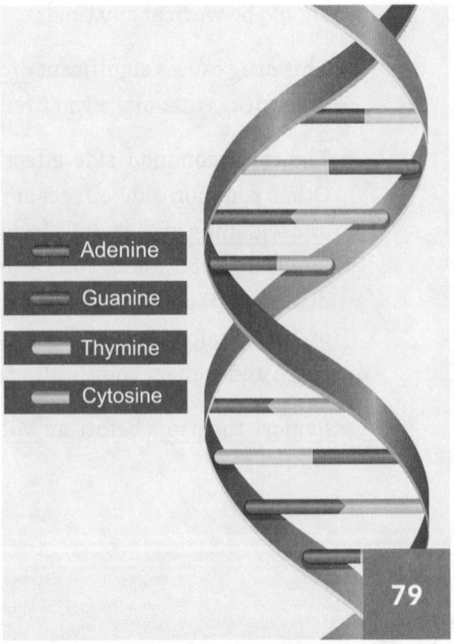

79

80

81

PHARMACY FOUNDATIONS PART 2

CONTENTS

CHAPTER 76
MEDICATION SAFETY & QUALITY IMPROVEMENT | **988**

CHAPTER 77
DRUG ALLERGIES & ADVERSE DRUG REACTIONS | **1000**

CHAPTER 78
PHARMACOKINETICS | **1009**

CHAPTER 79
PHARMACOGENOMICS | **1020**

CHAPTER 80
DIETARY SUPPLEMENTS,
NATURAL & COMPLEMENTARY MEDICINE | **1024**

CHAPTER 81
EMERGENCY PREPAREDNESS,
TOXICOLOGY & ANTIDOTES | **1033**

CHAPTER CONTENT

Background 988
Medication Errors 988
System-Based Causes 988
Response 989
Reporting 989
Organizations that Specialize in Error Prevention 989
Evaluation and Quality Improvement 990
The Joint Commission (TJC) 990
National Patient Safety Goals 990
Select National Patient Safety Goals 990
Common Methods to Reduce Medication Errors 991
Avoid "Do Not Use" Abbreviations 991
Tall Man Lettering 991
Do Not Use Abbreviations 991
High-Alert Drugs 991
Medication Therapy Management 992
Medication Reconciliation 992
Indications and Proper Instructions on Prescriptions 993
Use of The Metric System 993
Do Not Identify Medications Based on Packaging Alone 993
Avoid Multiple-Dose Vials 993
Safe Practices For Emergency Medications/Crash Carts 994
Dedicate Pharmacists To High Risk Areas 994
Monitor for Drug-Food Interactions 994
Education 994
Five Rights of Medication Administration 994
Use of Technology and Automated Systems 995
Computerized Prescriber Order Entry and Clinical Decision Support 995
Barcoding 995
Automated Dispensing Cabinets 995
Patient Controlled Analgesia Devices 996
Infection Control in Hospitals 996
Common Types of Hospital-Acquired (Nosocomial) Infections 996
Universal Precautions to Prevent Transmission 997
Catheter-Related Bloodstream Infections 997
Hand Hygiene 997
Safe Injection Practices 998
Sharps Disposal 998

CONTENT LEGEND

= Study Tip Gal

CHAPTER 76
MEDICATION SAFETY & QUALITY IMPROVEMENT

BACKGROUND

A study from the Institute of Medicine (IOM), *To Err is Human* (1999), increased awareness of the prevalence of medical errors. This study found that up to 98,000 Americans die each year in U.S. hospitals due to preventable medical errors, 7,000 from medication errors alone. These numbers understated the problem because they did not include preventable deaths due to medical treatments outside of hospitals. Since the release of the IOM study, there has been a greater focus on the quality of healthcare provided in the U.S. The Joint Commission (TJC) and the Institute for Safe Medication Practices (ISMP) are two organizations actively involved in improving medication safety.

MEDICATION ERRORS

The formal definition of a medication error developed by the National Coordinating Council for Medication Error Reporting and Prevention (NCC MERP) is "any preventable event that may cause or lead to inappropriate medication use or patient harm while the medication is in the control of the healthcare professional, patient, or consumer." This can include errors made in prescribing, order communication, product labeling and packaging, compounding, dispensing, administration, education and monitoring.

Do not confuse medication errors with adverse drug reactions (ADRs). ADRs are generally not avoidable, although they may be more likely to occur if the drug is given to a patient at high-risk for certain complications. Refer to the Drug Allergies & Adverse Reactions chapter for a discussion of ADRs.

A sentinel event is an unexpected occurrence involving death or serious physical or psychological injury, or risk thereof. When a sentinel event occurs, it is important to find out what went wrong and implement measures to prevent it from happening again.

SYSTEM-BASED CAUSES

Experts in medication safety agree that the most common cause of medication errors is a problem with the design of the medical system itself, not usually an individual making an error. Instead of blaming the "new pharmacist" or the "lazy technician" (or the prescriber), healthcare professionals should find ways to improve the system. Errors will always occur, but the goal is to design systems to prevent medication errors from reaching the patient. Some "at risk" behaviors that can compromise patient safety are included below.

AT-RISK BEHAVIORS THAT CAN COMPROMISE PATIENT SAFETY

Drug and Patient-Related
- Failure to check/reconcile home medications and doses
- Dispensing medications without complete knowledge of the medication
- Not questioning unusual doses
- Not checking/verifying allergies

Communication
- Not addressing questions/concerns
- Rushed communication

Technology
- Overriding computer alerts without proper consideration
- Not using available technology

Work Environment
- Trying to do multiple things vs.focusing on a single complex task
- Inadequate supervision and orientation/training

RESPONSE

Institutions should have a plan in place for responding to medication errors. The plan should address the following:

- Internal notification: who should be notified within the institution and within what time frame?
- External reporting: who should be notified outside of the institution?
- Disclosure: what information should be shared with the patient/family? Who will be present when this occurs?
- Investigation: what is the process for immediate and long-term internal investigation of an error?
- Improvement: what process will ensure that immediate and long-term preventative actions are taken?

EXAMPLE OF AN ADR (NOT A MEDICATION ERROR)

A 55-year-old female has a history of herpes zoster. She has no other known medical conditions. The patient reports considerable "shingles pain" that "runs from my back through my left breast." She received a prescription for pregabalin. The patient returned to the clinic with complaints of ankle swelling, which required drug discontinuation.

This problem would not be attributable to a medication error made by the prescriber of pregabalin or by the pharmacist who dispensed it. Rather, this is a side effect that can occur with the use of this drug.

ERRORS OF OMISSION AND COMMISSION

Error of Omission

Something was left out that is needed for safety

Example: failing to warn a patient about an important side effect with a new medication

Error of Commission

Something was done incorrectly

Example: prescribing bupropion to a patient with a history of seizures

REPORTING

Medication errors, preventable adverse drug reactions, hazardous conditions and "close calls" or "near misses" should be reported. Medication errors are reported to the appropriate bodies so that changes can be made to the system to prevent similar errors in the future. Without reporting, these events may go unrecognized and will likely happen again because others will not learn from the incident.

In a pharmacy, the staff member who discovers the error should immediately report it using the established reporting structure to the appropriate office (e.g., corporate office, the owner of an independent pharmacy, designated hospital office). Many state boards of pharmacy require quality assurance programs to promote pharmacy processes to prevent medication errors. Error investigations need to take place quickly (often as soon as within 48 hours of the incident) so that the sequence of events remains clear to those involved. Many states mandate the ethical requirement that errors be reported to the patient and the prescriber as soon as possible.

Many medication error reporting systems within hospitals are electronic; however, some hospitals still maintain a paper reporting system. The hospital's Pharmacy and Therapeutics (P&T) committee and Medication Safety Committee (or similar entity) should be informed of the error.

ORGANIZATIONS THAT SPECIALIZE IN ERROR PREVENTION

Organizations that specialize in error prevention can analyze the system-based causes of errors and make recommendations. The ISMP National Medication Errors Reporting Program (MERP) is a confidential national voluntary reporting program that provides expert analysis of the system causes of medication errors and provides recommendations for prevention.

Medication errors and close calls can be reported on the ISMP website (www.ismp.org). Professionals and consumers should be encouraged to report medication errors using this site even if the error was reported internally. When there are many reports of a particular error, the manufacturer may be required to take measures to increase safety (e.g., REMS program, name change, packaging change).

Every pharmacist should make it a practice to read medication error reports and use the information to improve their own practice setting.

EVALUATION AND QUALITY IMPROVEMENT

A root cause analysis (RCA) is a retrospective investigation of an event that has already occurred which includes reviewing the sequence of events that led to the error. The information obtained in the analysis is used to design changes that will hopefully prevent future errors.

The RCA can be of great value in capturing both the big picture perspective and the details of the error. Targeting corrective measures at the identified root cause is the best way to prevent similar problems from occurring in the future. A single intervention is not likely to prevent all future errors. Thus, RCA is often considered to be a repetitive process, and is frequently viewed as an important continuous quality improvement (CQI) tool.

An analysis can also be done prospectively to identify pathways that could lead to errors and to identify ways to reduce the error risk. Failure mode and effects analysis (FMEA) is a proactive method used to reduce the frequency and consequences of errors. FMEA is used to analyze the design of the system in order to evaluate the potential for failures, and to determine what potential effects could occur when the medication delivery system changes in any substantial way or if a potentially dangerous new drug will be added to the formulary.

THE JOINT COMMISSION (TJC)

The Joint Commission on Accreditation of Healthcare organizations (TJC) is an independent, not-for-profit organization that accredits and certifies more than 17,000 healthcare organizations and programs in the U.S., including hospitals, healthcare networks, long-term care facilities, home care organizations, office-based surgery centers and independent laboratories. TJC focuses on the highest quality and safety of care and sets standards that institutions must meet to be accredited. An accredited organization must undergo an on-site survey at least every three years and surveys can be unannounced.

NATIONAL PATIENT SAFETY GOALS

National patient safety goals (NPSGs) are set annually by TJC for different types of healthcare settings (e.g., ambulatory care, behavioral health, hospital). Each goal includes defined measures called "Elements of Performance" that must be met. These will be included in the institution's protocol. The Study Tip Gal and text describe some of the most important 2019 hospital NPSGs related to medication safety.

NPSG 03.05.01: Reduce the likelihood of harm associated with anticoagulant therapy.

There are many important elements to this goal including the requirements to use standardized dosing protocols and programmable pumps for heparin and to provide education to patients and families. Protocols should include starting dose ranges, alternate dosing strategies to address drug-drug interactions, communication with the dietary department to address drug-food interactions, requirements for a baseline INR, frequency of INR monitoring and monitoring for bleeding and HIT.

NPSG 03.06.01: Maintain and communicate accurate patient medication information.

This includes medication reconciliation, providing written information to the patient and conducting discharge counseling. The medication name, dose, frequency, route and indication (at the minimum) should be confirmed. Refer to the section on Medication Reconciliation later in this chapter.

NPSG 07.03.01; 07.04.01; 07.05.01; 07.06.01: Implement evidence-based practices to reduce healthcare associated infections.

These include recommendations to prevent healthcare-associated infections with multidrug-resistant organisms

SELECT NATIONAL PATIENT SAFETY GOALS

NPSG 01.01.01: Use at least **two patient identifiers** when providing care, treatment and services.

- Appropriate identifiers: name, medical record number, date of birth
- Inappropriate non-patient specific identifiers: zip code, physician name, room number

NPSG 02.03.01: Report critical results of tests and diagnostic procedures on a timely basis.

- Includes lab and blood culture results; protocols must include acceptable length of time for reporting.

NPSG 03.04.01: Label all medications, medication containers and other solutions on and off the sterile field in perioperative and other procedural settings.

- Numerous errors have been associated with removing medications from their original containers and placing them into unlabeled containers.

NPSG 03.05.01: Reduce the likelihood of harm associated with **anticoagulant** therapy (see text).

NPSG 03.06.01: Maintain and communicate accurate patient medication information (see text).

NPSG 07.01.01: Comply with the Centers for Disease Control (CDC) hand hygiene guidelines.

(e.g., MRSA, *C. difficile*, VRE, multidrug-resistant gram-negative bacteria). The elements of performance address care of central lines, bloodstream infections, post-surgical infections and catheter-associated urinary tract infections.

COMMON METHODS TO REDUCE MEDICATION ERRORS

AVOID "DO NOT USE" ABBREVIATIONS

Abbreviations are unsafe and contribute to many medical errors. TJC standards include recommendations against the use of unsafe abbreviations. The minimum list of "Do Not Use" abbreviations per TJC is shown in the table. ISMP also publishes a list of error-prone abbreviations, symbols, and dosage designations which includes those on TJC's list and many others. All institutions accredited by TJC are required to have a list of abbreviations that may not be used in the facility. This list must include all of the abbreviations from the TJC "Do Not Use" list, and any additional abbreviations selected by the institution (e.g., those that have resulted in significant errors at the site in the past). The unapproved abbreviation list should be readily accessible in the institution (e.g., wall charts, pocket cards). It is best to try to avoid abbreviations entirely. Electronic prescribing can virtually eliminate errors associated with poor handwriting. Despite this, handwritten prescriptions and progress notes are still used in many settings. See Study Tip Gal.

DO NOT USE	POTENTIAL PROBLEM	USE INSTEAD
U, u (unit)	Mistaken for "0" (zero), the number "4" (four) or "cc"	Write "unit"
IU (International Unit)	Mistaken for IV (intravenous) or the number 10 (ten)	Write "International Unit"
Q.D., QD, q.d., qd (daily) Q.O.D., QOD, q.o.d., qod (every other day)	Mistaken for each other Period after the Q mistaken for "I" and the "O" mistaken for "I"	Write "daily" Write "every other day"
Trailing zero (X.0 mg) Lack of leading zero (.X mg)	Decimal point is missed resulting in a 10-fold dosing error	Write X mg Write 0.X mg
MS	Can mean morphine sulfate or magnesium sulfate	Write "morphine sulfate"
MSO_4 and $MgSO_4$	Confused with one another	Write "magnesium sulfate"

TALL MAN LETTERING

Look-alike, sound-alike medications are a common cause of medication errors. Poor handwriting and similar product labeling aggravate the problem. Drugs that are easily mixed up should be labeled with tall man letters (the letters that are different are tall man). Here are two examples:

- *CeleXA, CeleBREX*
- *predniSONE, prednisoLONE*

Using tall man letters, which mix upper and lower case letters, draws attention to the dissimilarities in the drug names. The letters that are upper cases are the ones that are different between the two look-alike, sound-alike drugs. Safety-conscious organizations (e.g., ISMP, FDA, TJC) have promoted the use of tall man letters as one means of reducing confusion between similar drug names. The FDA's and ISMP's approved tall man lettering information is available at: http://www.ismp.org/tools/tallmanletters.pdf.

Drug dictionaries within computer systems and automated dispensing cabinets (ADC) often have alerts that prompt the provider to confirm that the correct medication is being ordered or withdrawn. For example a warning may appear on the screen of the ADC which will state: "This is *DILAUDID*. Did you want hydroMORPHONE?" to avoid confusion with morphine.

DO NOT USE ABBREVIATIONS

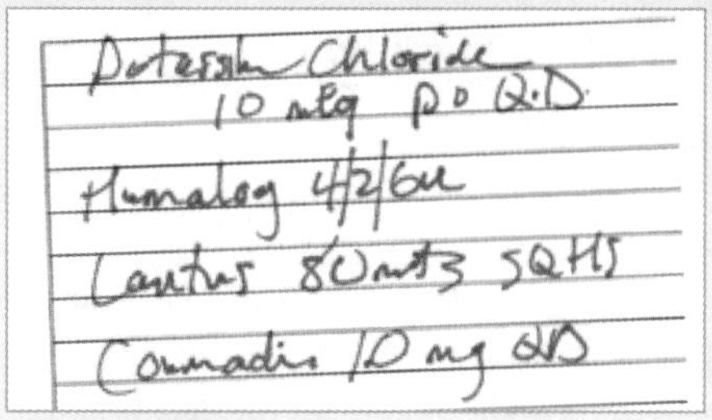

How often should the potassium be given?

Is that 8 or 80 units of *Lantus*?

Coumadin 1 or 10 mg? Once daily or four times per day?

HIGH-ALERT DRUGS

Drugs with a heightened risk of causing significant patient harm if used in error, should be designated as high-alert. See the box on the following page for some examples from multiple patient-care settings. The ISMP "high-alert" list is available at: http://www.ismp.org/Tools/highAlertMedicationLists.asp. ISMP's list represents the most common agents that are high risk, but an institution's list may include additional drugs based on experience in that setting.

High-alert medications can be used safely by developing protocols or order sets for use, using premixed products whenever possible, limiting concentrations available in

HIGH ALERT MEDICATIONS

Acute Care, Community/Ambulatory and/or Long-Term Care Settings

- Anesthetics, IV or inhaled (e.g., propofol)
- Antiarrhythmics, IV (e.g., amiodarone)
- Anticoagulants/Antithrombotics (e.g., heparin, warfarin)
- Chemotherapeutics (e.g., methotrexate)
- Epidural/intrathecal drugs
- Hypertonic saline (greater than 0.9%)
- Immunosuppressants (e.g., cyclosporine)
- Inotropics (e.g., digoxin)
- Insulins (e.g., insulin aspart, insulin U-500)
- Magnesium sulfate injection
- Opioids
- Oral hypoglycemics (e.g., sulfonylureas)
- Parenteral nutrition
- Potassium chloride and phosphates for injection
- Sterile water for injection

the institution and stocking high-alert products only in the pharmacy. See an example of safe use precautions for insulin and potassium chloride on the next page. Protocols for high-risk drugs increase appropriate prescribing and reduce the chance of errors from inappropriate prescribing.

Examples of Safe-Use Precautions

DRUG	PRECAUTIONS
Insulin	If U-500 is stocked, specify conditions under which it is to be used, which product will be stocked (vials and U-500 syringes vs. pens), and how doses will be supplied Standardize all insulin infusions to one concentration Develop protocols for insulin infusions, transition from infusion to SC and sliding scale orders; use standard orders for management of hypoglycemia Do not use "U" for units; always label with "units" or "units = mL", but never just "mL" Do not place insulin in automated dispensing cabinets; all insulin orders should be reviewed by a pharmacist prior to dispensing
Potassium Chloride	Remove all KCl vials from floor stock; all KCl infusions prepared in the pharmacy Use premixed containers Use protocols for KCl delivery which include indications for IV administration, maximum rate of infusion, maximum allowable concentration, guidelines for when cardiac monitoring is required, stipulation that all KCl infusions must be given via a pump, prohibition of multiple simultaneous KCl solutions (e.g., no IV KCl while KCl is being infused in another IV) Allow for automatic substitution of oral KCl for IV KCl, when appropriate Label all fluids containing potassium with a "Potassium Added" sticker

Any drug that is high-risk for significant harm if dispensed incorrectly can be placed in a medication bin that provides a visual alert to the person pulling the medication. The bin can be labeled with warnings and include materials (placed inside the bin) that should be dispensed with the drug (such as oral syringes or MedGuides). In the hospital setting, certain drugs are classified as "high-alert" and these can be placed in bins labeled with dispensing requirements.

MEDICATION THERAPY MANAGEMENT

Errors may be discovered during a comprehensive medication review (CMR), through the process of medication therapy management (MTM). A personal medication record (PMR) is prepared, and a medication-related action plan (MAP) is developed, preferably by a pharmacist-led team. The next steps involve interventions, referrals, documentation and plans for follow-up. Patients targeted for MTM include those with multiple chronic conditions who are taking multiple drugs and are likely to incur annual costs for covered drugs that exceed a predetermined level. Computer databases are used to identify patients with certain high-risk conditions (such as heart failure or uncontrolled diabetes) who are generally using many medications (some systems tag patients taking many chronic medications daily) and assign a pharmacist (preferably) to review profiles for proper use.

The pharmacist can form a partnership with the patient and prescriber to remedy any issues or lapses. Often, these reviews identify missed therapy such as lack of an ACE inhibitor or ARB in patients with diabetes and albuminuria, missing beta-blocker therapy post-MI, missing bisphosphonate therapy with high-dose chronic steroids, and others, since these are easily searchable in databases. A popular MTM initiative is to improve nonadherence in heart failure patients due to the high-rate of ED visits due to decompensated heart failure. MTM is also used to identify cost-savings, by promoting switches to generics or more affordable brands, or by suggesting patient assistance programs or low income subsidies for eligible members.

MEDICATION RECONCILIATION

Medication reconciliation involves comparing a patient's medication orders to all of the medications that the patient has been taking (home medications including OTC and dietary supplements). This reconciliation is done to avoid medication errors such as omissions, duplications, dosing errors or drug interactions.

Medication reconciliation ("med rec") was previously done on paper forms, but it is now usually performed within the electronic health record (EHR). Prescribers can view side-by-side lists of home medications and ordered medications and address any discrepancies. This process is most effective when complete and accurate information is entered into the patient's medical record. For this reason, pharmacy departments are often actively involved in documenting home medication use and performing medication reconciliation. In many hospitals, admission orders for a patient cannot be entered into the electronic system until medication reconciliation is completed by a physician, pharmacist or nurse.

Medication reconciliation should be done at every transition of care in which new medications are ordered or existing orders are rewritten. Transitions of care include changes in setting, service, practitioner or level of care. Common examples are hospital admission, transfer into or out of an ICU and at hospital discharge. This process comprises five steps:

1. Develop a list of current medications
2. Develop a list of medications to be prescribed
3. Compare the medications on the two lists
4. Note discrepancies and make clinical decisions based on the comparison
5. Communicate the new list to appropriate caregivers and to the patient

Discharge medication reconciliation is an opportunity for the prescriber to address any of the patient's home medications that were "on hold" during the hospitalization and which medications used during the hospitalization should be continued when the patient goes home. Discrepancies are addressed and the patient is educated. Though most often discussed in the hospital context, medication reconciliation can be equally important in ambulatory care, as many patients receive prescriptions from more than one outpatient provider and may go to several pharmacies.

EXAMPLE OF THE BENEFIT OF MEDICATION RECONCILIATION

Ann is an 82-year-old female. Her only medication for the previous ten years has been atenolol 25 mg daily. Ann recently developed influenza. She began to have trouble breathing and was taken to the hospital. It was discovered that Ann had pneumonia and heart failure. She was prescribed lisinopril, carvedilol and furosemide. Ann was discharged to transitional care and received the new medications plus her home medication (atenolol). The consultant pharmacist conducted a medication review to reconcile the medications and, after discussion with the physician, the pharmacist wrote an order to discontinue the atenolol.

INDICATIONS AND PROPER INSTRUCTIONS ON PRESCRIPTIONS

An indication for use that is written on the prescription (such as lisinopril 10 mg once daily for hypertension) helps pharmacists ensure appropriate prescribing and drug selection.

Using the term "as directed" is not acceptable on prescriptions because the patient often has no idea what this means and the pharmacist cannot verify a proper dosing regimen. Occasionally, this term is used on the bottle along with a separate dosing calendar, such as with warfarin. It would be preferable to write "use per instructions on the dosing calendar" since the patient may not understand how to take the medication and may not be aware that a separate dosing calendar exists.

USE OF THE METRIC SYSTEM

Measurements should be recorded in the metric system only. Prescribers should use the metric system to express all weights, volumes and units. Computer systems generally have a drop-down menu for selecting the correct units (e.g., lb vs. kg) and easily converting between units. It is critical to record the correct units, since many calculations (CrCl or eGFR) and dosing checks are performed automatically by the EHR system based on the height and/or weight recorded for the patient. With the increasing prevalence of overweight and obesity in the U.S., it is not uncommon to care for patients weighing 100 kg (or more); but serious errors can occur if this weight was intended to be 100 lb.

DO NOT IDENTIFY MEDICATIONS BASED ON PACKAGING ALONE

Look-alike packaging can contribute to errors. If unavoidable, separate look-alike drugs in the pharmacy and patient care units, or repackage. Never rely on the package to identify the right drug product. Pharmacies frequently have to purchase products from different manufacturers (and these may look vastly different).

EXAMPLE OF AN ERROR DUE TO MISIDENTIFICATION OF A CONCENTRATION BASED ON THE PACKAGING

The intravenous catheters of three neonates in a NICU unit were flushed with the adult therapeutic dose of heparin (10,000 units/mL) rather than the heparin flush dose of 10 units/mL. This accident did not result in fatalities although two of the babies required the reversal agent protamine. Three babies died from a similar incident the previous year at a different hospital. The overdose was administered because the nurse thought she was using a lower concentration of heparin.

Due to the high-risk associated with heparin overdose, high concentration heparin vials should not be present in patient care areas. Instead, therapeutic doses should be sent by the pharmacy department.

AVOID MULTIPLE-DOSE VIALS

Multiple-dose vials pose risk for cross-contamination (infection) and over-dosing. If used, they should be (ideally) designated for a single patient and labeled appropriately. Discard the remainder when the patient is done with the medication, or is discharged.

SAFE PRACTICES FOR EMERGENCY MEDICATIONS/CRASH CARTS

Staff must be properly trained to handle emergencies and use crash cart medications. The medications should be unit dose and age-specific, including pediatric-specific doses. A weight-based dosing chart can be placed in the trays used in the pediatric units. If a unit dose medication is not available, it is best to have prefilled syringes and drips in the cart (to the extent possible) because it is easy to make a mistake under the stress of a code. The emergency medications should be stored in sealed or locked containers in a locked room and replaced as soon as possible after use (through a cart exchange so that the area is not left without required medications). Monitor the drug expiration dates. Trained pharmacists should be present at codes when possible.

CODE BLUE

A code blue refers to a patient requiring emergency medical care, typically for cardiac or respiratory arrest. The overhead announcement and/or paging system will provide the patient's location. The code team (often including a pharmacist) will rush to the room and begin immediate resuscitative efforts.

DEDICATE PHARMACISTS TO HIGH RISK AREAS

The intensive care unit (ICU), pediatric units and emergency departments are units with a high incidence of preventable medication errors. Pharmacists working in these units can assist in identifying and preventing medication errors by developing process improvements designed to reduce errors.

MONITOR FOR DRUG-FOOD INTERACTIONS

Check for drug-food interactions routinely and involve the nutrition department (also called "dietary") when the profile includes drugs with a high rate of food interactions (e.g., warfarin), or medications that interact with enteral feedings (i.e., tube feedings). For example phenytoin administration via feeding tube requires that enteral feeding be held for 1 – 2 hours before and after the dose.

EDUCATION

Staff education programs such as "in-services" should be provided whenever new high-alert drugs are being used in the facility, to introduce new procedural changes aimed at preventing medication errors and to introduce any new guidelines. The information provided in these "in-services" should be unbiased and should not be provided in a skewed manner by drug company representatives. Many hospitals now limit access of pharmaceutical companies and representatives due to the inherent bias.

Patients can play a vital role in preventing medication errors when they have been encouraged to ask questions and seek satisfactory answers about their medications before drugs are dispensed at a pharmacy. If a patient questions any part of the medication dispensing process, whether it is about the drug's appearance, dose or something else, the pharmacist must be receptive and responsive (not defensive). All patient inquiries should be thoroughly investigated before the medication is dispensed. The written information about the medications should be at a reading level that is appropriate for the patient.

It may be necessary to provide pictures or other means of instruction to patients who do not speak English or are unable to read English. Attempts must be made to communicate to the patient in their language, using on-site staff or dial-in translation services.

FIVE RIGHTS OF MEDICATION ADMINISTRATION

One recommendation is to use the "five rights" when administering medications to help prevent medications errors. The "five rights" are a quick double check that should be performed by a healthcare professional every time when giving a medication (see figure). The "five rights" are an example of a best practice in medication safety, but cannot prevent errors alone and must be combined with other system-based error prevention methods. Barcoding (discussed later in this chapter) is an example of a technological tool that has been implemented in medication administration to assist in ensuring the "five rights."

USE OF TECHNOLOGY AND AUTOMATED SYSTEMS

COMPUTERIZED PRESCRIBER ORDER ENTRY AND CLINICAL DECISION SUPPORT

Computerized physician/provider order entry (CPOE) is a computerized process that allows direct entry of medical orders by prescribers. Directly entering orders into a computer has the benefit of reducing errors by minimizing the ambiguity resulting from handwritten orders. A much greater benefit is seen with the combination of CPOE and clinical decision support (CDS) tools. Clinical guidelines and patient labs can be built into the CPOE system and alerts can notify a prescriber if the drug is inappropriate, or if labs indicate that the drug could be unsafe (such as a high potassium level and a new order for a potassium-sparing agent). CPOE can include standard order sets and protocols. An example of an on-screen alert from a CDS system is shown below. This alert appears when a prescriber attempts to order citalopram with a dose greater than 40 mg/day. In addition to medication orders, CPOE is used for laboratory orders and procedures. In most hospitals, pharmacists are actively involved in creating, updating and monitoring the CDS tools. One aspect of CQI is monitoring, reporting trends and addressing alert overrides.

CITALOPRAM DOSE RANGE

FDA notified healthcare professionals and patients that the antidepressant Celexa (citalopram) should no longer be used at doses greater than 40 mg per day because it can cause abnormal changes in the electrical activity of the heart. In addition, studies did not show a benefit in the treatment of depression at doses higher than 40 mg per day. Read the MedWatch safety alert by clicking "References" linked to the FDA Drug Safety Communication.
Thank you

Alert Action

○ Cancel citalopram
○ Override

References | OK

BARCODING

Barcoding may be the most important medication error reduction tool available right now. The barcode follows the drug through the medication use process to make sure it is being properly stocked (such as in the right space in the pharmacy or in the right pocket in the dispensing cabinet), through compounding (if required) and to the patient. The barcode is used at the bedside to identify that the correct drug (by scanning the barcode on the drug's packaging) is going to the right patient (by scanning the barcode on the patient's wristband) and confirms that the dose is being given at the right time. The nurse may have a badge barcode to track who administered the dose. Barcodes are now on many pumps and can prevent errors involving medications being given IV that are not meant to be administered in this manner. When a medication is scanned and administered using barcode technology, the administration can automatically populate on the medication administration record (MAR), thus avoiding the time associated with manual charting of medication administration.

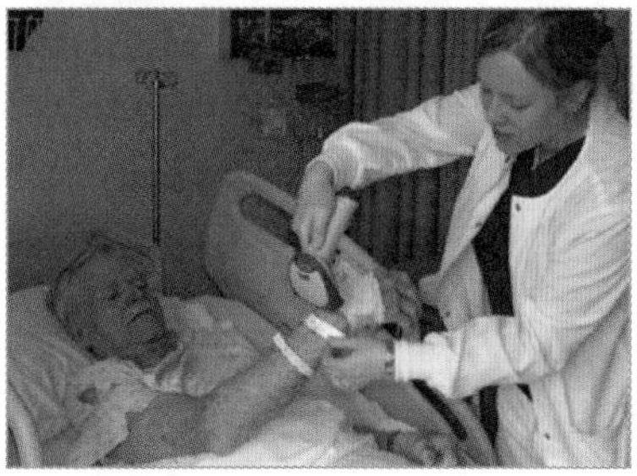

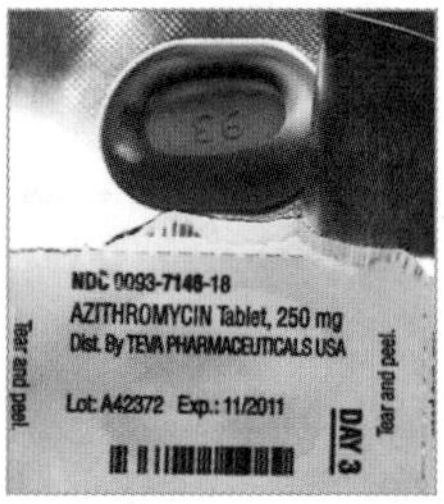

AUTOMATED DISPENSING CABINETS

Most pharmacy interns will have seen automated dispensing cabinets (ADCs) while on clinical rotations. Common names are *Pyxis, Omnicell, ScriptPro* and *AccuDose*. Over half of the hospitals in the U.S. now use ADCs. In many hospitals, they have replaced patient cassettes that had to be filled at least once daily and exchanged.

Practical Benefits of ADCs

The drug inventory and medication can be automated when drugs are placed into the cabinet and removed. Controlled drug security can be improved (versus the previous method of keeping the controlled drugs locked in a metal cabinet or in a drawer in the nurses' station). The drugs are easily available at the unit and do not require individual delivery from the pharmacy. ADCs provide alerts, usage reports and work well with barcoding.

Methods to Improve ADC Safety

- TJC requires that the pharmacist review the order before the medication can be removed from the ADC for a patient, except in special circumstances (an override). The override function should be limited to true emergencies and all overrides should be investigated.
- The most common error associated with ADC use is giving the wrong drug or dose to a patient. The patient's MAR should be accessible to practitioners while they are removing medications from the ADC. Barcode scanning improves ADC safety. The drug can be scanned to make sure it is going into the right place in the cabinet and can ensure that the right drug is being pulled. Prior to administration, the patient's wristband can be scanned to make sure the drug is going to the right patient.

- Look-alike, sound-alike medications should be stored in different locations within the ADC. Using computerized alerts, ideally pop-up alerts that require a confirmation when medications with high potential for mix-up in a given setting are selected, can help reduce error risk.
- Certain medications should not be put into the ADCs, including insulin, warfarin and high-dose narcotics (such as hydromorphone 10 mg/mL and morphine 20 mg/mL).
- Nurses should not be permitted to put medications back into the medication compartment because it might be placed in the wrong area; it is best to have a separate drawer for all "returned" medications.
- If the machine is in a busy, noisy environment, or in one with poor lighting, errors increase.

PATIENT CONTROLLED ANALGESIA DEVICES

Opioids are effective agents used for moderate to severe post-surgical pain and are the mainstay of treatment. These may be administered with patient controlled analgesia (PCA) devices. PCAs allow the patient to treat pain quickly (there is no need to call the nurse and wait for the dose to arrive) and allow the administration of small doses, which helps reduce side effects (particularly over-sedation). PCA drug delivery can mimic the pain pattern more closely and provide good pain control. Increasingly, the PCA is administered with anesthetics for a synergistic benefit in pain relief.

PCA Safety Considerations

- The devices can be complex and require set-up and programming. This is a significant cause of preventable medication errors. PCAs should be used only by well-coordinated healthcare teams.
- Patients may not be appropriate candidates for PCA treatment. They should be cooperative and should have a cognitive assessment prior to using the PCA to ensure that they can follow instructions.

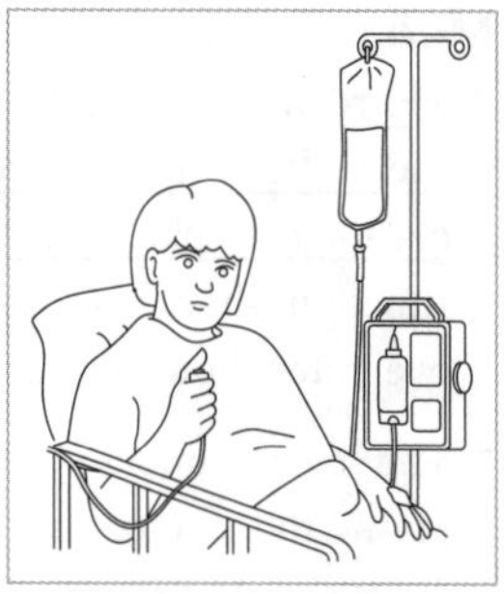

- Friends and family members should not administer PCA doses. This is a TJC requirement.
- PCAs do not frequently cause respiratory depression, but the risk is present. Advanced age, obesity and concurrent use of CNS depressants (in addition to higher opioid doses) increases risk.

PCA Safety Steps

- Limit the opioids available in floor stock. Use standard order sets (set drug dosages, especially for opioid-naïve patients) so that drugs are not over-dosed.
- Educate staff about HYDROmorphone and morphine mix-ups.
- Implement PCA protocols that include independent double-checking of the drug, pump setting, and dosage. The concentration on the MAR should match the PCA label.
- Use barcoding technology. Some infusion pumps incorporate barcoding technology. Scanning the barcode on the PCA would help ensure the correct concentration is entered during PCA programming. It will also ensure that the right patient is getting the medication.
- Assess the patient's pain, sedation and respiratory rate on a scheduled basis.

INFECTION CONTROL IN HOSPITALS

Nearly two million infections occur in hospitals annually – about one infection for every twenty patients. Hospital infections cause avoidable illness and death and add enormous financial costs. Many of these infections are preventable if proper techniques are followed. Many states now require hospitals to report infection rates and Medicare can refuse reimbursement for hospital-acquired infections that are largely avoidable.

It is important to properly clean surfaces, including bed rails, eating trays and other room surfaces. Healthcare professionals should be careful not to be sources of infection from contaminated clothing (including white coats and ties). Organisms that spread via surface contact include VRE, *C. difficile*, noroviruses and other intestinal tract pathogens.

COMMON TYPES OF HOSPITAL-ACQUIRED (NOSOCOMIAL) INFECTIONS

- Urinary tract infections from indwelling catheters (very common). Remove the catheter as soon as possible – preventing catheter associated infections is one of TJC's NPSGs.
- Blood stream infections from IV lines (central lines have the highest risk) and catheters
- Surgical site infections (see the Infectious Diseases II chapter)
- Decubitus ulcers
- Hepatitis
- *Clostridium difficile*, other GI infections
- Pneumonia (mostly due to ventilator use), bronchitis

UNIVERSAL PRECAUTIONS TO PREVENT TRANSMISSION

Universal precautions is an approach to infection control that treats human blood and bodily fluids as if they are known to be infectious for HIV, HBV and other bloodborne pathogens. Contact with bodily fluids should be avoided through the use of good hand hygiene and, in select cases, the use of gowns, masks or patient isolation.

There are three categories of transmission-based precautions defined by the CDC:

Contact Precautions

- Intended to prevent transmission of infectious agents which are spread by direct and indirect contact with the patient and the patient's environment.
- Single patient rooms are preferred. If not available, keep ≥ 3 feet spatial separation between beds to prevent inadvertent sharing of items between patients.
- Healthcare personnel caring for these patients wear a gown and gloves for all interactions that may involve contact with the patient or contaminated areas in the patient's room.
- Contact precautions are recommended for patients colonized or infected with MRSA and VRE and patients with *C. difficile* infection.

Droplet Precautions

- Intended to prevent transmission of pathogens spread through close respiratory contact with respiratory secretions.
- Single patient rooms are preferred. If not available, keeping ≥ 3 feet spatial separation and drawing a curtain between beds is especially important for diseases transmitted via droplets.
- Healthcare personnel wear a mask (a respirator is not necessary) for close contact with the patient. The mask is donned upon entry to the patient's room.
- Droplet precautions are recommended for patients with active *B. pertussis*, influenza virus, respiratory syncytial virus (RSV), adenovirus, rhinovirus, *N. meningitidis*, and group A streptococcus (for the first 24 hours of antimicrobial therapy).

Airborne Precautions

- Intended to prevent transmission of infectious agents that remain infectious over long distances when suspended in the air.
- Patient should be placed in an airborne infection isolation room (AIIR). An AIIR is a single-patient room that is equipped with special air and ventilation handling systems. The air is exhausted directly to the outside or re-circulated through HEPA filtration before being returned.
- Healthcare personnel wear a mask or respirator (N95 level or higher), depending on the disease, which is donned prior to room entry.
- Airborne precautions are recommended for patients with active pulmonary tuberculosis, measles or varicella virus (chickenpox).

CATHETER-RELATED BLOODSTREAM INFECTIONS

- The most important and most cost-effective strategy to minimize catheter-related bloodstream infections (CRBSI) is through aseptic technique during catheter insertion, including proper handwashing and utilization of standard protocols/catheter insertion checklist.
- It is also important to minimize use of intravascular catheters, if possible, through intravenous to oral route protocols and setting appropriate time limits for catheter use. For example, peripheral catheters should be removed/replaced every 2 – 3 days to minimize risk for infection.
- Other strategies shown to reduce the risk of CRBSI, include the use of skin antiseptics (2% chlorhexidine), antibiotic impregnated central venous catheters, and antibiotic/ethanol lock therapy, but must be weighed against the potential risk for increased rates of resistance.

HAND HYGIENE

Numerous studies show that proper hand hygiene by those working in healthcare settings reduces the spread of nosocomial infection. Alcohol-based hand rubs (gel, rinse or foam) are considered more effective in the healthcare setting than plain soap or antimicrobial soap and water, but soap and water are preferable in some situations. Fingernails should be clipped short and no jewelry should be worn under gloves (this can harbor bacteria and tear the gloves).

Antimicrobial hand soaps that contain chlorhexidine (*Hibiclens*, others) may be preferable to reduce infections in healthcare facilities. Triclosan may also be better but this compound gets into the water supply and has environmental concerns.

When to Perform Hand Hygiene

CDC/Amanda Mills

- Before entering and after leaving patient rooms and between patient contacts if there is more than one patient per room.
- Before donning and after removing gloves (use new gloves with each patient).
- Before handling invasive devices, including injections.
- After coughing or sneezing.
- Before handling food and oral medications.

Use Soap and Water (not Alcohol-Based Rubs) in These Situations

- Before eating.
- After using the restroom.
- Anytime there is visible soil (anything noticeable on the hands).
- After caring for a patient with diarrhea or known *C. difficile* or spore-forming organisms; alcohol-based hand rubs have poor activity against spores. Handwashing physically removes spores.
- Before caring for patients with food allergies.

Soap and Water Technique

- Wet both sides of hands, apply soap, rub together for at least 15 (slow) seconds.
- Rinse thoroughly.
- Dry with paper towel and use the towel to turn off the water.

Alcohol-Based Hand Rubs Technique

- Use enough gel (2 – 5 mL or about the size of a quarter).
- Rub hands together until the rub dries (15 – 25 seconds).
- Hands should be completely dry before putting on gloves.

Hand-Hygiene for Sterile Compounding

- Refer to the Compounding chapters.

SAFE INJECTION PRACTICES

Outbreaks involving the transmission of blood borne pathogens (e.g., HIV, hepatitis B or C) or other microbial pathogens to patients (and occasionally to healthcare workers) continue to occur due to unsafe injection technique. The majority of safety breaches involve the reuse of syringes in multiple patients, contamination of IV bags with used syringes, failure to follow basic injection safety when administering IV medications and inappropriate care or maintenance of glucometer equipment that is used on multiple patients.

SAFE INJECTION PRACTICES FOR HEALTHCARE FACILITIES

- Never administer an oral solution/suspension intravenously; fatal errors have occurred. Use oral syringes (which are difficult or impossible to attach to a needle for IV injection) and label oral syringes "for oral use only."
- Never reinsert used needles into a multiple-dose vial or solution container. Single-dose vials are preferred over multiple-dose vials, especially when medications will be administered to multiple patients.
- Needles used for withdrawing blood or any other bodily fluid, or used for administering medications or other fluids should preferably have "engineered sharps protection" which reduces the risk of an exposure incident by a mechanism such as drawing the needle into the syringe barrel after use.
- Never touch the tip or plunger of a syringe.
- Disposable needles that are contaminated (e.g., with drugs, chemicals or blood products) should never be removed from their original syringes, unless no other option is available. Throw the entire needle/syringe assembly (needle attached to the syringe) into the red plastic sharps container.
- Immediately discard used disposable needles or sharps into a sharps container without recapping.
- Sharps containers should be easily accessible and not allowed to overfill; they should be routinely replaced.

If a needle-stick (percutaneous exposure) occurs with a used needle, contact the proper department at a healthcare facility immediately. If post exposure prophylaxis (PEP) is required (for HIV and/or hepatitis), acting quickly is important. In the outpatient setting, instruct the patient to wash the area right away with soap and water, and contact their healthcare provider. See Human Immunodeficiency Virus chapter for details on PEP medication regimens.

SHARPS DISPOSAL

Patients who use injectable medications should have a disposal container and be instructed to put needles and other sharps in the container immediately after use. Sharps should be disposed of in an FDA-cleared sharps container, which is puncture resistant, labeled or color-coded appropriately, closeable and leak-proof. They come marked with a line that indicates when the container should be considered full (about ¾ full). Never compress or "push down" on the contents of any sharps container.

If an FDA-cleared container is not available, some community guidelines recommend using a heavy-duty plastic household container as an alternative (e.g., a plastic laundry detergent container). The container must be leak and puncture-resistant with a tight-fitting lid.

The entire needle/syringe assembly is discarded. Do not instruct patients to remove the needle or attempt to cut it. The only time that recapping a needle is permitted is when the sharps container is not immediately available; in that case, use the one-hand method to recap until the sharps container can be reached: (1) Place the cap on a table or counter next to something firm to push the cap against; (2) Hold the syringe with the needle attached and slip the needle into the cap without using the other hand. Push the capped needle on the firm surface to "seat" the cap onto the needle using only the one hand. Sharps disposal guidelines and programs vary. The local trash removal services or health department should have the available service/s, and the pharmacy can provide this information to patients. Services include drop boxes or supervised collection sites (such as in a hospital, pharmacy, police or fire station), household hazardous waste collection sites, mail-back programs and residential special waste services pick-up.

Select Guidelines/References

Institute for Safe Medication Practices. www.ismp.org (accessed 2019 Mar 6).

The Joint Commission. www.jointcommission.org (accessed 2019 Mar 6).

MMWR Guideline for Hand Hygiene in Health-Care Settings October 25, 2002, 51(RR16);1-44.

CHAPTER CONTENT

Background ... 1000
Adverse Drug Reactions ... 1001
Type A Reactions ... 1001
Type B Reactions ... 1001
FDA Tools to Reduce Adverse Drug Reactions ... 1001
Boxed Warnings ... 1001
Contraindications, Warnings and Precautions ... 1001
Adverse Reactions ... 1001
Risk Evaluation and Mitigation Strategies ... 1002
Medication Guides ... 1002
Assessing Causality of an Adverse Drug Reaction ... 1002
Characterizing an Adverse Drug Reaction ... 1002
ADR Reporting ... 1003
Intolerances, Sensitivities and Idiosyncratic Reactions ... 1003
Stomach Upset/Nausea ... 1003
Intolerance or Allergy? ... 1003
Mild Rash ... 1004
Photosensitivity ... 1004
Drugs Most Commonly Associated with Photosensitivity ... 1004
Thrombotic Thrombocytopenic Purpura ... 1004
Drugs Commonly Associated with TTP ... 1004
Severe Skin Reactions ... 1004
Drugs Commonly Associated with Severe Skin Reactions ... 1005
Drug Allergies ... 1005
Anaphylaxis ... 1005
Epinephrine Auto-Injector Administration ... 1006
Drugs Commonly Associated with Allergic Reactions ... 1006
Beta-Lactams ... 1006
A Penicillin Allergy, Or Not? ... 1007
Sulfa Drugs ... 1007
Opioids ... 1007
Heparin ... 1007
Biologics ... 1007
NSAIDs ... 1007
Contrast Media ... 1007
Peanuts and Soy ... 1007
Eggs ... 1007
Skin Testing and Desensitization ... 1008
Penicillin Skin Testing ... 1008
Induction of Drug Tolerance (Desensitization) ... 1008

DEFINITIONS

Mild or Severe Reactions to Histamine Release

Urticaria (hives)
A rash with red/pinkish raised patches. The patches have varied shapes and sizes.

Pruritis (itching)
Any rash or reaction that causes itching can be referred to as with pruritus.

Erythema
Redness on skin from superficial (near the surface) capillaries, often due to inflammation, often with pruritis. When pressed down, the red skin that is due to erythema will blanch (whiten) temporarily because the blood flow is blocked. Erythematous refers to an area on the skin, such as a patch, with erythema.

Angioedema
Swelling caused by edema in the deeper dermal, cutaneous and sub-mucosal tissue.

Morbilliform
Macular or maculopapular (or both), with 1-10 mm lesions. In between the lesions is healthy skin.

CONTENT LEGEND

= Study Tip Gal   = Key Drug Guy

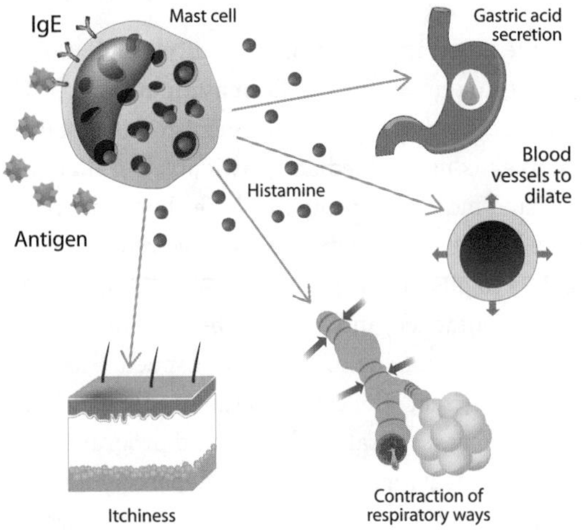

CHAPTER 77
DRUG ALLERGIES & ADVERSE DRUG REACTIONS

BACKGROUND

Adverse drug reaction (ADR) is a term that encompasses all unintended pharmacologic effects of a drug when it is administered correctly and used at recommended doses. ADRs should not be confused with medication errors, which can include overdose and administration mistakes, and are discussed in the Medication Safety & Quality Improvement chapter. ADRs result in substantial morbidity and mortality, and reports are increasing; over one million reports with serious outcomes were logged with the FDA in 2018 (including 197,060 deaths).

Although side effects or adverse effects can occur in anyone, some patients are more susceptible than others. For example, some degree of renal damage can occur with use of an aminoglycoside for longer than seven days. However, in patients with underlying renal impairment, nephrotoxicity is more likely to occur and may happen after a shorter duration.

ADVERSE DRUG REACTIONS VS. ERRORS

Adverse Drug Reaction (ADR)
Effects from a drug when it is administered correctly. ADRs are typically dose-related; the ADR severity increases with higher doses/reduced clearance.

Medication Error
Someone did something wrong, such as giving a medication dose to the wrong person.

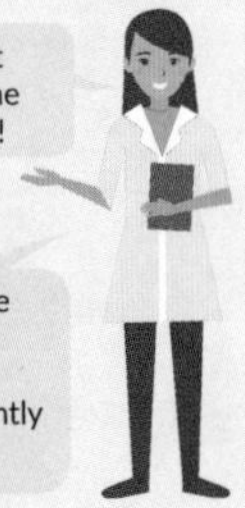

ADVERSE DRUG REACTIONS

ADRs are categorized into two types: predictable (Type A) and unpredictable (Type B) reactions.

TYPES OF ADRS

Type A reactions (most ADRs)
Dose-dependent and predictable based on the drug's pharmacology

Type B reactions
Idiosyncratic – **not predictable** from drug's pharmacology

- Can be influenced by patient-specific factors
- Examples: rash with lamotrigine, rash with abacavir, Stevens-Johnson Syndrome

Mr. Bean, you are starting doxazosin for prostate enlargement. It will make your blood pressure drop when you stand up. This will make you dizzy. We will Increase the dose slowly. Start by taking the medication at bedtime.

Mr. Mortensen, you are going to take *Plavix* to keep the arteries to your heart open so blood can get through. *Plavix* can cause a severe rash called TTP. This rash is not common, but if it happens, call your doctor right away.

TYPE A REACTIONS

Type A reactions are dose-dependent, related to the known pharmacologic actions of the drug, can occur in any patient and range from mild to severe. Type A reactions are the most common and account for an estimated 80% of ADRs. An example of a Type A reaction is orthostatic hypotension with doxazosin. If a patient starts doxazosin at 1 mg QHS, they will have much less orthostatic hypotension and dizziness than if the medication is started at a 4 mg dose. Because of this risk, the dose should be slowly titrated upward.

TYPE B REACTIONS

Type B reactions are generally not dose-dependent, are unrelated to the pharmacologic actions of the drug and can be influenced by patient-specific factors. Type B reactions include:

- Drug allergies
- Pseudoallergic reactions (e.g., redman syndrome with rapid vancomycin infusion, itching after opioid administration)
- Drug intolerances (e.g., nausea with codeine)
- Idiosyncratic reactions (e.g., Stevens-Johnson syndrome)

Drug allergy refers to an immune-mediated response to a medication or excipient (inactive ingredient). True drug allergies, or hypersensitivity reactions, are classified into four types:

This is the classic-type of IgE-mediated allergic reaction. Mostly due to histamine release from basophils.

- Type I reactions: immediate (within 15-30 minutes of drug exposure).
  - Reactions include urticaria, bronchospasm, angioedema and anaphylaxis
  - Severity ranges from minor inconvenience to death
- Type II reactions: minutes to hours after drug exposure.
  - Examples: hemolytic anemia and thrombocytopenia
- Type III reactions: immune-complex reactions; occur 3-10 hours after drug exposure.
  - Example: drug-induced lupus erythematosus
- Type IV reactions: delayed hypersensitivity reactions; can occur anywhere from 48 hours to several weeks after drug exposure.
  - Example: PPD skin test for tuberculosis (peaks at 48 – 72 hours)

FDA TOOLS TO REDUCE ADVERSE DRUG REACTIONS

BOXED WARNINGS

A boxed warning indicates a risk of death or permanent disability from a drug (e.g., increased risk of venous thromboembolism and death from stroke with raloxifene).

The risk of fatality can be due to prescribing or dispensing errors. For example, conventional amphotericin b deoxycholate has a boxed warning not to exceed 1.5 mg/kg. Fatalities have been caused by using the lipid amphotericin dosing (typically 3 – 6 mg/kg) for conventional amphotericin.

CONTRAINDICATIONS, WARNINGS AND PRECAUTIONS

Mrs. Jones, you cannot get *Evista* because you had a DVT in the past.

Contraindications indicate that the drug cannot be used in that patient. The risk will outweigh any possible benefit (e.g., a history of venous thromboembolism is a contraindication to the use of raloxifene). If there are no known contraindications for a drug, the section will state "None."

Mrs. Smith, you could get a DVT from *Evista* because you sleep on the couch all day.

Warnings and precautions include serious reactions that can result in death, hospitalization, medical intervention, disability or teratogenicity (e.g., raloxifene has a warning for venous thromboembolism). Warnings and precautions may or may not change a prescribing decision.

ADVERSE REACTIONS

Mrs. Ngo, you are starting *Evista*. You might get hot flashes and achy joints.

Adverse reactions refer to undesirable, uncomfortable or dangerous effects from a drug (e.g., arthralgia from raloxifene). The risk-benefit assessment is patient-specific (e.g., arthralgia from raloxifene will be more of a concern in an unfit patient with chronically sore joints, versus a fit patient with no sore joints).

RISK EVALUATION AND MITIGATION STRATEGIES

Risk Evaluation and Mitigation Strategies (REMS) are risk management plans required by the FDA for some drugs. They are developed by the manufacturer and approved by the FDA to ensure the benefits of a drug outweigh the risks. REMS programs can include a Medication Guide or Patient Package Insert, communication plan, Elements to Assure Safe Use (ETASU) or an Implementation System.

REMS can include a variety of approaches. For example, the REMS for a drug could require physicians or pharmacies to have special certification to prescribe or dispense the drug, patients enroll in a registry so that ADRs can be tracked or that lab testing is completed before dispensing. Examples include the clozapine REMS, the iPLEDGE program for isotretinoin and the REMS to reduce the misuse of long-acting opioids. The list of REMS drugs continues to grow. When studying from this book, note the many drugs that have REMS requirements.

MEDICATION GUIDES

Medication Guides (or MedGuides) present important adverse events that can occur with over 300 medications. MedGuides are FDA-approved patient handouts that are written in non-technical language and are considered part of the drug's labeling. If a medication has a MedGuide, it should be dispensed with the original prescription and with each refill. Some medications dispensed while inpatient require MedGuides and these should be available to the patient or family upon request. It is not necessary to dispense them to inpatients routinely because the patient is being monitored. MedGuides are required for many individual agents and some entire classes of medications (including anticonvulsants, antidepressants, long-acting opioids, NSAIDs, ADHD stimulants and atomoxetine).

ASSESSING CAUSALITY OF AN ADVERSE DRUG REACTION

When an ADR occurs, the Naranjo Scale (a validated causality assessment scale) can help determine the likelihood that a drug caused an adverse reaction. Based on the questionnaire, a probability score is calculated. A score ≥ 9 = definite ADR; 5 – 8 = probable ADR; 1 – 4 = possible ADR; 0 = doubtful ADR.

QUESTION	YES	NO	DO NOT KNOW
Are there previous conclusive reports on this reaction?	+1	0	0
Did the adverse event appear after the suspected drug was given?	+2	–1	0
Did the adverse reaction improve when the drug was discontinued or a specific antagonist was given?	+1	0	0
Did the adverse reaction appear when the drug was readministered?	+2	–1	0
Are there alternative causes that could (on their own) have caused the reaction?	–1	+2	0
Did the reaction reappear when a placebo was given?	–1	+1	0
Was the drug detected in any body fluid in toxic concentrations?	+1	0	0
Was the reaction more severe when the dose was increased or less severe when the dose was decreased?	+1	0	0
Did the patient have a similar reaction to the same or similar drugs in any previous exposure?	+1	0	0
Was the adverse event confirmed by any objective evidence?	+1	0	0

CHARACTERIZING AN ADVERSE DRUG REACTION

When patients report an adverse drug reaction, pharmacists must ask the right questions in order to determine whether an adverse reaction is an intolerance or drug allergy:

- What reaction occurred (e.g., a mild rash, a severe rash with blisters, trouble breathing)?
- When did it occur? About how old were you?
- Can you use similar drugs in the same class? For example, if a penicillin allergy is reported, ask if the patient has ever used *Keflex*.
- Do you have any food allergies or a latex allergy?

Some food allergies (e.g., soy, peanut) have implications for certain drugs or formulations. Latex allergies should be collected because some drugs require tubing, have latex vial stoppers or require gloves for administration. All allergies should be noted in the patients record.

ADR REPORTING

Side effects, adverse events and allergies should be reported to the FDA's MedWatch program, which is called the FDA Adverse Event Reporting System (FAERS), that provides a central collection point for problems caused by drugs. Vaccines are an exception and are reported under a different program called VAERS. See Immunizations chapter for more information.

The FDA can require Phase IV (post-marketing safety surveillance programs) for approved drugs and biologics, and collects and analyzes the reports to better understand the drug safety profile in a real world setting. When drugs are studied in trials, high-risk patients are typically excluded. Yet in real life settings, some high-risk patients will receive the medication. Post-marketing reports also help identify side effects that occur less frequently. If a drug causes a reaction in 1 out of every 3,000 people, the problem may not be apparent in a smaller clinical trial. For this reason, community-based adverse event reporting is critical.

EXAMPLE: ADR INCIDENCE IN REAL LIFE VS. CLINICAL TRIAL

When spironolactone was studied in heart failure patients during the RALES trial, patients with renal insufficiency or elevated potassium levels were excluded due to the known risk of additional hyperkalemia from the use of spironolactone. The drug was found to have benefit in advanced heart failure patients and doctors in the community began to use it in their heart failure patients. In this real life setting, patients with renal insufficiency or elevated potassium were occasionally prescribed spironolactone, and arrhythmias and sudden death due to hyperkalemia were reported.

Reporting is voluntary but has important implications for safe medication use. Healthcare professionals and patients can report adverse events to the drug manufacturer, who is required by law to send the report to the FDA. The MedWatch form used for reporting can be found online. Reports can also be made by calling the FDA directly. MedWatch is also used for reporting problems with biologics, medical devices, some dietary supplements and cosmetics.

If the FDA receives enough reports that a drug is linked to a particular problem, the manufacturer can be required to update the labeling (e.g., package insert). In especially risky cases, a drug safety alert is issued to prescribers, usually before the labeling is changed.

EXAMPLE: ADR REPORTS LEAD TO FDA REQUIREMENT FOR SAFETY LABELING CHANGES

Oseltamivir *(Tamiflu)* was initially released without any warning of unusual behavior in children. The FDA received enough reports that they issued a warning to prescribers in 2006. After many more reports, in 2008, the FDA required the manufacturer to update the prescribing information to include a precaution about hallucinations, confusion and other strange behavior in children.

Example of a Posting on the FDA Website of Phase IV Monitoring

DRUG	USAGE	ADVERSE EVENT REPORTS	NOTES
Dulaglutide *(Trulicity)*	Diabetes mellitus, type 2	Serious hypersensitivity reactions	FDA is evaluating the need for regulatory action.

INTOLERANCES, SENSITIVITIES AND IDIOSYNCRATIC REACTIONS

STOMACH UPSET/NAUSEA

Stomach upset or nausea is often incorrectly reported as an allergy. It should be listed on the patient profile because the drug bothered the patient and, if possible, should be avoided in the future, but this is not an allergy and should not prevent drugs in the same class from being used. This is more accurately categorized as an intolerance. Electronic medical records allow for documentation of intolerances separate from allergies. An example of an intolerance is the patient who has stomach upset with codeine (but not hydrocodone or other drugs in the morphine class) or from erythromycin (but not azithromycin or other macrolides).

INTOLERANCE OR ALLERGY?

Gather enough information to determine the type of reaction.

Example:
A patient reports getting a stomach ache from *Chantix*.

Possibilities:
I did not eat anything until dinner because Chantix made me nauseous. (Intolerance)

I got nauseous, I felt dizzy and I had trouble breathing. (Allergy)

Intolerances are less serious complaints, such as nausea or constipation. As the drug bothers the patient, it should be avoided, if possible.

Allergies are an immune system response, and range from mild (e.g., pruritus) to severe (e.g., Stevens Johnson syndrrome). Allergies can affect multiple areas:

- Facial swelling, bronchoconstriction with a severe drop in BP
- Weakness, fever and severe rash

EXAMPLE: INTOLERANCE REPORTED INCORRECTLY AS A DRUG ALLERGY

CG received acetaminophen 300 mg/codeine 30 mg *(Tylenol #3)* for pain relief after a dental extraction. She got very nauseated from the medicine. When she was admitted to the hospital several years later for a left hip replacement, she reported to the intake coordinator that she was "allergic" to codeine. The intake coordinator did not attempt to clarify the reaction. The hospital's pain management protocol calls for hydromorphone in a patient-controlled analgesic device for postoperative pain control. The physician used a less desirable option for pain control due to the reported allergy.

MILD RASH

Opioids cause a non-allergic release of histamine from mast cells in the skin, causing itching and hives in some patients. This is particularly problematic in the inpatient setting after surgery, when opioid-naïve patients receive the medication or when non-naïve patients receive higher-than-normal doses. Pruritus due to this or other causes, if not severe, can be reduced or avoided if the patient is pre-medicated with an antihistamine, such as diphenhydramine.

PHOTOSENSITIVITY

Photosensitivity can occur when sunlight reacts with a drug in the skin and causes tissue damage that looks like a severe sunburn on sun-exposed areas; this occurs within hours of sun exposure. A type IV (delayed hypersensitivity) reaction can also occur with sun exposure and some medications. It appears as a red, itchy rash that can spread to areas that were not exposed to sun and occurs within days of sun exposure.

When dispensing medications that can cause photosensitivity, it is important to advise the patient and/or their caregivers to limit sun exposure and to use sunscreens that block both UVA and UVB radiation (these are labeled broad spectrum). See Key Drugs Guy below.

DRUGS MOST COMMONLY ASSOCIATED WITH PHOTOSENSITIVITY

KEY DRUGS

- Amiodarone
- Diuretics (thiazide and loop)
- Methotrexate
- Oral and topical retinoids
- Quinolones
- St. John's wort
- Sulfa antibiotics
- Tacrolimus
- Tetracyclines
- Voriconazole

Others:

- Antihistamines (1st generation)
- Carbamazepine
- Chloroquine
- Coal Tar
- Fluorouracil
- Griseofulvin
- NSAIDs
- Quinidine
- Tigecycline

THROMBOTIC THROMBOCYTOPENIC PURPURA

Thrombotic Thrombocytopenic Purpura (TTP) is a blood disorder in which clots form throughout the body. The clotting process consumes platelets and leads to bleeding under the skin and the formation of purpura (bruises) and petechiae (dots) on the skin. TTP can be fatal and should be treated immediately with plasma exchange. Common drugs that can cause TTP are listed in the Key Drugs Guy on the right.

SPOTS AND RASHES

Papules
Raised spots

Macules
Flat spots

Purpura
Red/purple skin spots (lesions) due to bleeding underneath the skin. Purpura includes small and large spots:

Petechiae	Smaller lesions	< 3 mm
Ecchymoses	Larger lesions	> 5 mm

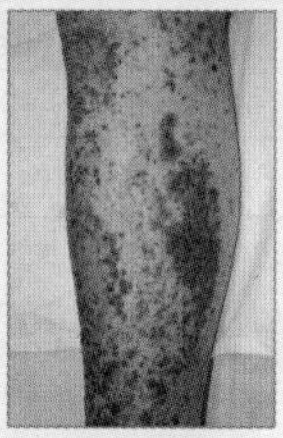

Purpura, with petechiae and ecchymoses (TTP rash)

Hematoma
A collection of blood under the skin due to trauma (injury) to a blood vessel, resulting in blood leaking into the surrounding tissue. Drugs that can cause hematoma include heparin, low molecular weight heparin (LMWH), some other anticoagulants and phytonadione (vitamin K) if given mistakenly as an IM injection.

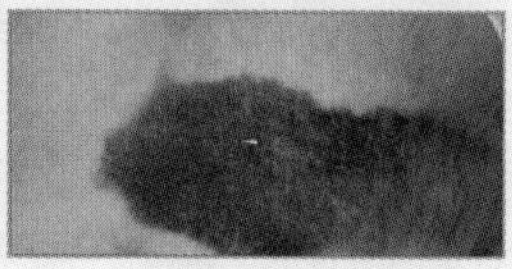

Hematoma

DRUGS COMMONLY ASSOCIATED WITH TTP

KEY DRUGS

- Clopidogrel
- Sulfamethoxazole

Others:

- Acyclovir
- Famciclovir
- Quinine
- Valacyclovir

SEVERE SKIN REACTIONS

There are several severe skin reactions that can be caused by drugs, including Stevens-Johnson syndrome (SJS), toxic epidermal necrolysis (TEN), and drug reaction with eosinophilia and systemic symptoms (DRESS). All of these can be life-threatening and require prompt treatment. Although the OTC analgesics acetaminophen and ibuprofen are generally considered to be safe, cases of severe reaction have been reported, which highlights the unpredictable nature of these reactions. Drugs most commonly associated with these severe skin reactions are listed in the Key Drugs Guy on the following page.

Stevens-Johnson Syndrome and Toxic Epidermal Necrolysis

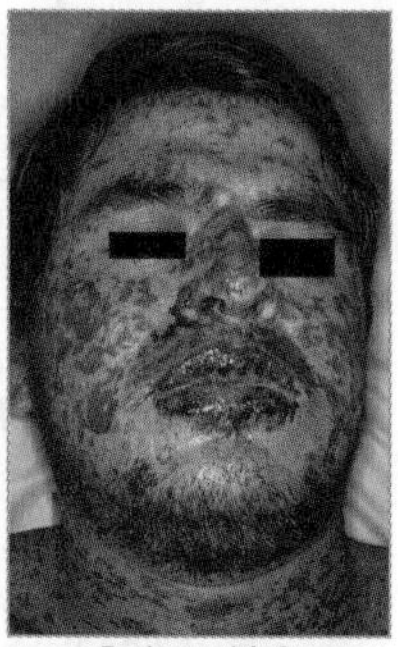

Patient with Stevens-Johnson Syndrome

Stevens-Johnson Syndrome and Toxic Epidermal Necrolysis SJS and TEN involve epidermal detachment and skin loss that is equivalent to third degree burns. SJS and TEN generally occur 1 – 3 weeks after drug administration, and almost always more than 72 hours after drug administration. These reactions can result in severe mucosal erosions, a high body temperature, major fluid loss and organ damage (eyes, liver, kidney, lungs). SJS and TEN are commonly classified by the percent of skin detachment. The key to treating both is to stop the offending agent as soon as possible. In addition, patients will receive fluid and electrolyte replacement, wound care and pain medications. Systemic steroids are contraindicated in TEN, but may be used in SJS, though benefit is controversial. Due to the severity of the mucosal involvement, antibiotics are often necessary to prevent or treat an infection.

Drug Reaction with Eosinophilia and Systemic Symptoms

DRESS can include a variety of skin eruptions accompanied by systemic symptoms such as fever, hepatic dysfunction, renal dysfunction and lymphadenopathy, but rarely involves mucosal surfaces. Treatment consists of stopping the offending agent, although symptoms may continue to worsen for a period of time after the agent has been discontinued.

DRUG ALLERGIES

Some drugs are more commonly associated with drug allergies than others. Penicillins and sulfonamides are two classes that cause the most drug allergies. For a true drug allergy to occur, the person must have taken the drug previously. Initial exposure will cause a Type I hypersensitivity reaction, resulting in IgE production, which primes the body to release excessive histamine at the next drug exposure. This section describes drug allergy reactions and treatment, but keep in mind that similar treatment can be used for non-drug allergies. A pharmacist who is dispensing an epinephrine auto-injector for other types of allergies will provide the same instructions.

Some medications (e.g., phytonadione, contrast media) are associated with a pseudoallergic reaction, sometimes called an anaphylactoid reaction. It is not IgE-mediated, but the clinical appearance and treatment are similar to that of anaphylaxis.

A reaction without breathing difficulty can sometimes be treated by simply stopping the offending drug. Antihistamines can be used to counteract the histamine release that causes itching, swelling and rash. Systemic steroids, and sometimes NSAIDs, can be used to decrease swelling. Severe swelling may necessitate a steroid injection. Epinephrine is used to reverse bronchoconstriction if the patient is wheezing or has other signs of trouble breathing.

ANAPHYLAXIS

Anaphylaxis is a severe, life-threatening allergic reaction that occurs within seconds to minutes of drug exposure. Anaphylaxis can occur after an initial exposure and subsequent immune response, but some drugs can cause anaphylaxis with the first exposure. A patient experiencing anaphylaxis may have generalized urticaria (hives), swelling of the mouth and throat, difficulty breathing or wheezing sounds, abdominal cramping and hypotension (which can cause dizziness, lightheadedness or loss of consciousness). Symptoms can develop quickly, within seconds or minutes; treatment must be administered immediately.

Anyone with serious allergies to food, drugs or serious medical conditions (including hypoglycemia that may require glucagon) should wear a medical identification bracelet. This will alert emergency responders and many can be linked to the patient's health profile that is accessible through a 24-hour information center.

DRUGS COMMONLY ASSOCIATED WITH SEVERE SKIN REACTIONS

SJS/TEN	Clopidogrel	Terbinafine
Amiodarone	Darunavir	Tiagabine
Bupropion	Deferasirox	Varenicline
Caspofungin	Etravirine	Voriconazole
Celecoxib	Fosphenytoin	Zonisamide
Clindamycin	Hydroxychloroquine	
	Ibuprofen	**DRESS**
	Isavuconazonium	Doxycycline
	Isoniazid	Fosphenytoin
	Macrolides	Gabapentin
	Metronidazole	Lacosamide
	Minocycline	Minocycline
	Oseltamivir	Olanzapine
	Oxcarbazepine	Oxcarbazepine
	Peramivir	Sulfasalazine
	Phenobarbital	Terbinafine
	Piroxicam	Valproate
	Quinine	Vancomycin
	Quinolones	

KEY DRUGS

- Abacavir
- Allopurinol
- Carbamazepine
- Ethosuximide
- Lamotrigine
- Modafinil
- Nevirapine
- Penicillins
- Phenytoin
- Sulfamethoxazole

Anaphylaxis Treatment

An anaphylactic reaction requires immediate emergency medical care. The patient or family should be instructed to call 911 if anaphylaxis occurs. Treatment includes epinephrine injection ± diphenhydramine ± steroids ± IV fluids. To avoid blocking the airway, nothing should be placed under the head or in the mouth. Swollen airways can be quickly fatal; patients who have had such a reaction should carry a single-use epinephrine auto-injector (*EpiPen, EpiPen Jr, Auvi-Q, Adrenaclick, Symjepi* or generic equivalent) as they may be at future risk. These are generally available as epinephrine 1 mg/mL (previously labeled as 1:1000) in dosages of 0.3 mg (adult dose) or 0.15 mg (pediatric dose) of epinephrine. The 0.15 mg dose is for patients 15 – 30 kg (*EpiPen Jr* dose).

EPINEPHRINE AUTO-INJECTOR ADMINISTRATION

For *EpiPen*:

- Remove from the carrying case and pull off the blue safety release.
- Keep thumb, fingers and hand away from the orange (needle) end of the device.
- Inject into the middle of the outer thigh only at a 90 degree angle.

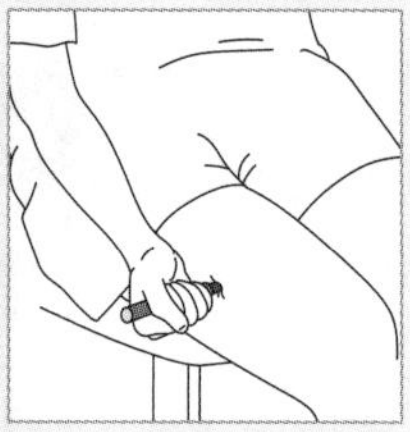

- Hold the needle firmly in place while counting to 3.
- Remove the needle and massage the area for 10 seconds.
- After injection, the orange tip will extend to cover the needle. If the needle is visible, it should not be reused.

For all epinephrine auto-injectors:

- It is normal to see liquid remaining in the device after injection.
- Call for emergency help because additional care may be needed.
- A second dose (in the opposite leg) may be given if needed prior to arrival of medical help.
- Refrigeration is not required.
- All products can be injected through clothing.
- Check the device periodically to make sure the medication is clear and not expired.

Symjepi is only available in 0.3 mg (indicated for patients 30 kg and up), and *Auvi-Q* is also available in 0.1 mg (for patients weighing 7.5 – 14 kg). The patient's emergency kit should also include emergency contact information and diphenhydramine tablets (25 mg x 2), which should be taken only if there is no tongue/lip swelling.

Patient Counseling for Epinephrine Auto-Injectors

- Tell your family, caregivers and others where you keep your epinephrine auto-injector and how to use it, as you may not be able to speak in an allergic emergency.
- It is important to keep the thumb, fingers and hand away from the needle end of the device, as injection can cause vasoconstriction and necrosis.
- When injecting an uncooperative child, hold leg firmly to avoid bending or breaking the needle.
- Skin infections can occur after injection. Report any prolonged redness, swelling, warmth or tenderness at the injection site.

For *Adrenaclick:*

- Remove the two gray end caps while keeping the thumb, fingers and hand away from the red tip.
- Inject in the middle of the outer thigh, hold needle firmly in place on the thigh for 10 seconds, then massage area for 10 seconds.
- After injection, examine the red tip. If the needle is visible, the dose has been received. If the needle is not visible, repeat the injection step. When complete, place the cap over the needle.

For *Symjepi:*

- Pull off cap, holding the syringe with the fingers (avoiding the needle).
- Inject in the middle of the outer thigh, hold needle firmly in place on the thigh for two seconds, then massage area for 10 seconds.
- After injection, slide the safety guard out over the needle.

For *Auvi-Q:*

- Pull off the outer case, then follow the voice instructions to administer. Hold needle firmly in place on the thigh for five seconds.

DRUGS COMMONLY ASSOCIATED WITH ALLERGIC REACTIONS

While any drug can lead to an allergic reaction, some are known to do so more than others. These are discussed below. Often the drug that caused a reaction can be replaced with another drug. Patch testing by an allergist is the most reliable way to determine if a person is truly allergic to a drug, but it does not provide any information regarding certain types of rashes (e.g., SJS or TEN).

BETA-LACTAMS

Penicillin is a beta-lactam antibiotic and there are many related compounds in this family, including nafcillin, ampicillin, piperacillin and others. Anyone who is allergic to one of the penicillins should be presumed to be allergic to all penicillins and should avoid the entire group, unless they have been specifically evaluated for this problem.

Cephalosporins are structurally related to penicillin. People with a history of penicillin allergy have a small risk of also having an allergic reaction to a cephalosporin or carbapenem. Risk of cross-reactivity is low, but it is prudent on the NAPLEX exam to avoid any beta-lactam with a stated allergy to another, unless there is no acceptable alternative agent. A notable exception is in acute otitis media (AOM); the American Academy of Pediatrics recommends use of 2nd or 3rd generation cephalosporins in patients with a non-severe penicillin allergy, due to toxicities and decreased efficacy of alternative AOM therapies in children.

Aztreonam (a monobactam) is considered safe in patients with penicillin allergies.

A PENICILLIN ALLERGY, OR NOT?

About 10% of people report they have a penicillin "allergy," but the CDC reports the true incidence of an IgG-mediated (Type I hypersensitivity) reaction to penicillin is ~1%. When a "penicillin allergy" is reported, broad-spectrum antibiotics are often used, which increases resistance and cost.

It can be best to test: a negative skin test result should be followed by an oral drug. Give an oral drug "challenge" dose before the full treatment dose. For a positive test or a past severe skin reaction (SJS/TEN, DRESS, etc), don't give the drug.

Remember: if penicillin allergy AND syphilis in pregnancy or HIV:

- Must test, and if positive, desensitize.
- Penicillin is the only acceptable treatment.

Good news report!

- Many cephalosporins can be safely tolerated despite a penicillin allergy in acute otitis media infection (e.g., allergy to penicillin/amoxicillin, give cefdinir, cefpodoxime, ceftriaxone or cefuroxime).

SULFA DRUGS

Reactions are most commonly reported with sulfamethoxazole (in *Bactrim)*, and the patient should avoid using sulfasalazine, sulfadiazine and sulfisoxazole. The package labels for "non-arylamine" sulfonamides [thiazide diuretics, loop diuretics (except ethacrynic acid), sulfonylureas, acetazolamide, zonisamide and celecoxib], as well as cidofovir, darunavir *(Prezista)*, fosamprenavir and tipranavir contain warnings or contraindications for use in patients with sulfa allergy, although they usually do not cross react with a sulfamethoxazole allergy. The risk of cross-reactivity with sulfamethoxazole, thiazides and loop diuretics is very low, and in clinical practice the reaction is usually not considered significant when these drugs are needed. Even so, the patient should be aware to watch for a possible reaction. Some other sulfa-type groups also have low risk of cross-reactivity. On the NAPLEX exam you should recognize the possible interaction. Sulfite or sulfate allergies do not cross react with sulfonamides. The rotigotine patch, orphenadrine injection, the *Rowasa* mesalamine enema, some dobutamine formulations and some eye drops contain sulfites.

OPIOIDS

Opioid intolerance due to histamine release is common; however, true opioid allergy is uncommon. See Pain chapter for information on opioid allergy and treatment options.

HEPARIN

See Anticoagulation chapter for information on heparin-induced thrombocytopenia (HIT).

BIOLOGICS

Biologics (e.g., rituximab) can cause hypersensitivity reactions, among other ADRs. Desensitization is possible for some agents in patients who need a biologic but have had a prior poor reaction. See the following page for more information regarding desensitization processes.

NSAIDS

Reactions to NSAIDs, including aspirin, can either be a drug sensitivity or a true allergic reaction. A drug sensitivity can cause rhinitis, mild asthmatic-type reactions, or skin reactions. If a true allergy is present, the patient will experience urticaria, angioedema and occasionally anaphylaxis. COX-2 selective NSAIDs may be used in practice, but on the NAPLEX exam it is prudent to avoid all NSAIDs.

CONTRAST MEDIA

Contrast media (used in CT scans) can cause anaphylactoid reactions and delayed skin reactions. Systemic steroids and antihistamines are sometimes used to prevent reactions if contrast media is needed in a patient who has had a prior reaction.

PEANUTS AND SOY

It is important for the pharmacist to be aware if a patient has a peanut allergy. Peanuts and soy are in the same family and can have cross-reactivity. Soy is used in some medications. Parents of children with peanut allergies should be CPR-trained and have ready access to an epinephrine auto-injector. Most likely, a reaction will be due to consuming peanuts or soy unknowingly in food products. Drugs to avoid with peanut or soy allergy: clevidipine *(Cleviprex)*, propofol *(Diprivan)*, progesterone in *Prometrium* capsules.

EGGS

If a patient has a true allergy to eggs, they cannot use clevidipine *(Cleviprex)*, propofol *(Diprivan)* or Yellow Fever vaccine (chicken eggs are used in vaccine production). For influenza vaccine, ACIP states that even patients who have had more severe symptoms when consuming eggs (such as wheezing, requiring epinephrine, hypotension or cardiovascular changes) can receive any indicated inactivated vaccine. Administration should be supervised by a healthcare provider who is able to recognize and treat severe allergic reactions. *Flublok*, which is made using recombinant techniques and contains no egg protein, is one option in patients with severe reactions to consuming eggs, but is not preferentially recommended by ACIP. If a severe reaction to an influenza vaccine occurs, regardless of which ingredient is suspected, that patient should not receive further doses of any influenza vaccine formulation.

SKIN TESTING AND DESENSITIZATION

PENICILLIN SKIN TESTING

A penicillin allergy is the most common drug allergy in the U.S., reported in about 10% of the general population. A true penicillin allergy has been found to be present in only about 10% of those that are reported. Some patients report a penicillin "allergy" when their reaction was more properly categorized as an intolerance (e.g., nausea or diarrhea). In other cases, patients may have had a true allergic reaction to penicillin in the past, but over time, the antibodies can wane and the patient may be able to safely receive penicillins. Due to concerns of cross-reactivity with cephalosporins and carbapenems, a penicillin allergy can severely limit the selection of antibiotics available to treat infectious diseases. Patients who report a penicillin allergy have been shown to more often receive broad-spectrum antibiotics that cause more collateral damage, such as quinolones, and antibiotics with greater toxicity potential, such as vancomycin. The goal of penicillin skin testing is to identify patients who are at the greatest risk of a Type I hypersensitivity reaction if exposed to a systemic penicillin.

The penicillin skin test uses the components of penicillin that most often cause an immune (allergic) response. *Pre-Pen* (benzylpenicilloyl polylysine injection) contains the major determinants of penicillin allergy and is used with very dilute solutions of penicillin G. A step-wise skin test is done: a skin prick test followed by intradermal testing. A localized reaction around the *Pre-Pen* or penicillin G test site indicates a high risk of a reaction to systemic penicillin and the patient should not receive it. A patient with a negative skin test, (no reaction to the test solutions) can be considered to be at the same risk as a patient in the general population who does not report a penicillin allergy. Skin testing only predicts an IgE-mediated reaction. Regardless of skin test results, a patient should never be re-challenged with an agent that caused SJS or TEN.

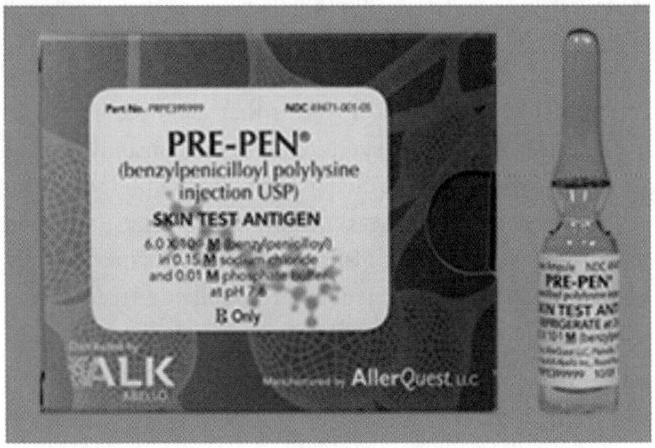

INDUCTION OF DRUG TOLERANCE (DESENSITIZATION)

In many cases when a drug allergy is present, an alternative medication can be chosen. When no acceptable alternative is available, induction of drug tolerance (often referred to as desensitization) may be recommended. For example, if a pregnant patient has syphilis and a penicillin allergy, the CDC recommends desensitization and penicillin treatment, rather than using second-line agents (see Infectious Diseases II chapter).

Desensitization is a step-wise process that begins by administering a very small dose of the medication and then incrementally increasing the dose at regular time intervals up to the target dose. This modifies the patient's response to the medication and temporarily allows safe treatment. The desensitization procedure must take place in a medical setting where emergency care can be provided if a serious reaction occurs. Treatment with the agent must start immediately following the desensitization procedure and must not be interrupted. If doses are missed, the drug-free period allows the immune system to re-sensitize to the drug and serious hypersensitivity reactions (including anaphylaxis) could occur with subsequent doses.

Induction of drug tolerance is a more accurate term than desensitization, because the process does not "cure" the patient of an allergy, and the reaction should not be removed from the patient's medical record. If the drug is required on a separate occasion, the process must be repeated. Desensitization protocols exist for a number of antimicrobial agents, some biologics and a few other medications (such as aspirin). Desensitization should never be attempted if an agent has previously caused SJS or TEN.

Select Guidelines/References

Food and Drug Administration MedWatch program http://www.fda.gov/Safety/MedWatch/ (accessed 2019 Apr 5)

Drug Allergy: An Updated Practice Parameter. *Ann Allergy Asthma Immunol.* 2010 Oct;105:259-273.

CHAPTER CONTENT

Background ... **1009**
Absorption ... **1009**
Drug Absorption ... 1010
Local vs Systemic Effects ... 1010
Dosage Form Dissolution and Drug Solubility ... 1010
Bioavailability ... 1010
Bioavailability Formula ... 1011
Distribution ... **1011**
Calcium and Phenytoin Correction Formulas ... 1012
Volume of Distribution ... 1012
Volume of Distribution (Vd) Formula ... 1012
Metabolism ... **1013**
Excretion ... **1013**
Clearance and Area Under the Curve ... 1013
Zero vs First Order Pharmacokinetics ... 1015
Michaelis-Menten Kinetics ... 1015
Dose Adjustments for Michaelis-Menten Kinetics ... 1015
Elimination Rate Constant ... 1016
Predicting Drug Concentrations ... 1016
Half-Life ($t_{1/2}$) and Steady State ... 1017
Loading Dose ... **1019**
Loading Dose (LD) Formula ... 1019
Therapeutic Drug Monitoring ... **1019**

CONTENT LEGEND

= Study Tip Gal = Required Formula

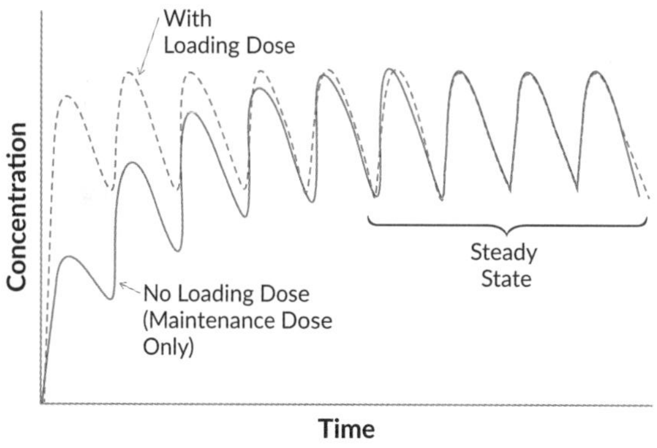

CHAPTER 78
PHARMACOKINETICS

BACKGROUND

Pharmacokinetics is what the human body does to a drug and pharmacodynamics is what the drug does to the human body. Pharmacokinetics involves the study of drug absorption, distribution, metabolism and excretion (often abbreviated ADME) over time. Mathematical relationships are used to describe these processes. Clinicians use pharmacokinetics to assess drug levels and optimize drug therapy. Pharmacodynamics refers to the relationship between the drug concentration at the site of action, and both therapeutic and adverse effects.

ABSORPTION

When a drug is given intravascularly (e.g., intravenously or intra-arterially), absorption is not required because the drug directly enters the bloodstream (systemic circulation). If a drug is administered extravascularly, drug absorption occurs as the drug moves from the site of administration to the bloodstream (see Study Tip Gal on the next page). Some examples of extravascular administration include oral, sublingual, buccal, intramuscular, subcutaneous, transdermal, inhaled, topical, ocular, intraocular, intrathecal and rectal.

When a drug is given orally, it passes from the stomach to the intestine. Most oral drug absorption occurs in the small intestine because of the large surface area and permeable membrane. After gut absorption, the drug enters the portal vein and travels to the liver. Some drugs are extensively metabolized in the liver before reaching the systemic circulation; this is called first pass metabolism (discussed later). Some drugs are transported through the bile back to the gut where they can be reabsorbed. This is called enterohepatic recycling (see the Learning Drug Interactions chapter).

Absorption of oral drugs occurs via two primary processes: passive diffusion across the gut wall or active transport. Passive diffusion is movement of drugs from an area of high concentration (e.g., the gut lumen) to an area of lower concentration (e.g., the blood). Energy is not required for passive diffusion. Active transport occurs when drugs are moved across the gut wall via transporter proteins that are normally used to absorb nutrients from food.

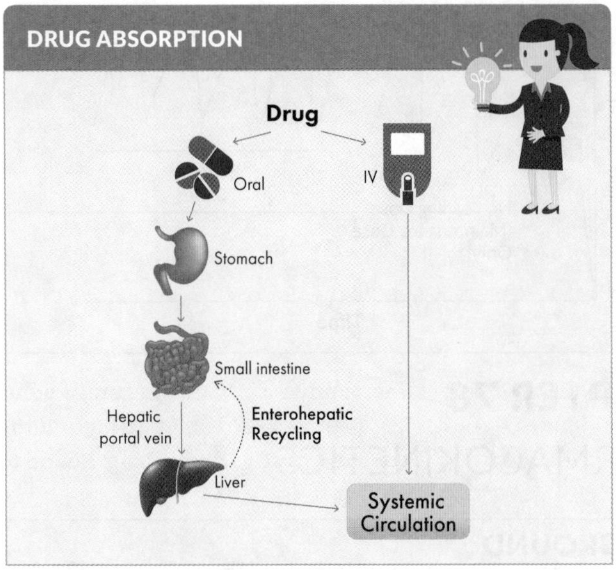

LOCAL VS SYSTEMIC EFFECTS

Drugs administered extravascularly can be divided into two categories: drugs intended for local effects and drugs intended for systemic effects. Drugs intended for local effects are often applied topically where the drug effect is needed. Examples of this include eye drops for glaucoma (e.g., latanoprost), dermal preparations for psoriasis (e.g., coal tar preparations) and nasal sprays for allergies (e.g., fluticasone nasal spray). Topical administration of a drug can produce therapeutic effects while minimizing systemic toxicity due to lower systemic exposure, but some topical formulations are designed to deliver a systemic dose (e.g., *Duragesic* patch). The extent of topical absorption is affected by many factors, including presence of open wounds on the skin (increased absorption) and the amount of drug applied.

Drugs intended for systemic effects are generally administered to facilitate absorption to the circulatory system. Examples of drugs intended for systemic effects are oral tablets for seasonal allergies (e.g., loratadine), suppositories for fever (e.g., acetaminophen) and sublingual tablets for angina (e.g., nitroglycerin SL). Some percentage of a drug intended for systemic effect moves from the site of administration into the systemic circulation.

DOSAGE FORM DISSOLUTION AND DRUG SOLUBILITY

When an oral dosage form is ingested, it begins to dissolve in the gastrointestinal (GI) tract and the active ingredient is released from the dosage form (typically a compressed tablet or a capsule). This is called dissolution. The rate of dissolution depends on the inactive ingredients used to make the dosage form. Drugs that dissolve rapidly in the mouth [e.g., sublingual (SL) and orally dissolving tablet (ODT) formulations] will have faster absorption. Many drugs are made using polymers that help slow down the release of the drug in a controlled way. This can provide less variability in drug concentrations and reduce the dosing frequency. In general, the rate of absorption by dosage form will follow this order (fastest to slowest): IV, SL, ODT, immediate release tablet, extended release tablet.

Most immediate release formulations dissolve and get absorbed rapidly, but some can be destroyed in the gut (primarily by hydrolysis, or lysis with water) making them less available for absorption. Drug formulations have been developed with protective coatings to limit drug degradation in the stomach (acidic) but permit dissolution in the intestine (basic). Examples of drugs with these protective coatings include enteric coated formulations such as *Dulcolax* and *Entocort EC*.

If a drug has poor absorption, one of the methods used to increase the dissolution rate is to reduce particle diameter, which increases surface area. Drugs with very small particle diameters are referred to as micronized, which means the diameter was measured in micrometers, but sometimes refers to even smaller particle sizes measured in nanometers. Progesterone and fenofibrate are examples of drugs with poor oral absorption that have been developed in micronized formulations. The rate of dissolution is described by the Noyes-Whitney equation.

Following dissolution, the drug that is released from the dosage form can be dissolved in GI fluids. The rate and extent to which the drug dissolves depends on the drug's solubility. Poorly soluble drugs are generally lipophilic, or lipid-loving. Freely soluble drugs are generally hydrophilic, or water-loving. As a drug moves through the GI tract, only dissolved drug is absorbed into the bloodstream. Poorly soluble drugs generally have poor systemic absorption, and highly soluble drugs often have good systemic absorption.

BIOAVAILABILITY

The extent to which a drug is absorbed into the systemic circulation is called bioavailability. Bioavailability is the percentage of drug absorbed from extravascular (e.g., oral) relative to intravascular administration (e.g., IV). It is affected by absorption, dissolution, route of administration and other factors. Bioavailability is reported as a percentage from 0 to 100%. A drug with good absorption has high bioavailability (> 70%), while a drug with poor absorption has low bioavailability (< 10%). Levofloxacin and linezolid have high bioavailability. With these two drugs, nearly 100% of the oral dose is absorbed, and the oral and IV doses are the same. In many hospitals, these drugs are automatically converted from IV to oral in the same dose by protocol, called a therapeutic interchange or IV to PO protocol.

Bisphosphonates, like ibandronate, have low oral bioavailability, so the oral dose (150 mg PO monthly) must be much higher than the IV dose (3 mg IV every 3 months) to produce the therapeutic effect.

Bioavailability can be calculated using the area under the plasma concentration time curve, or AUC. The AUC represents the total exposure of drug following administration.

Absolute bioavailability, represented by F, is calculated using the following equation:

$$F(\%) = 100 \times \frac{AUC_{extravascular}}{AUC_{intravenous}} \times \frac{Dose_{intravenous}}{Dose_{extravascular}}$$

1. A pharmacokinetic study of an investigational drug was conducted in healthy volunteers. Following an IV bolus dose of 15 mg, the AUC was determined to be 4.2 mg x hr/L. Subjects were later given an oral dose of 50 mg and the AUC was determined to be 8 mg x hr/L. Calculate the absolute bioavailability of the investigational drug. Round to the nearest whole number.

$$F(\%) = 100 \times \frac{\frac{8\ mg \times hr}{L}}{\frac{4.2\ mg \times hr}{L}} \times \frac{15\ mg}{50\ mg} = 57\%$$

Different dosage forms of the same drug (e.g., tablet vs solution) may have different bioavailabilities. The formula below can be used to calculate an equivalent dose of a drug when the dosage form is changed:

$$\text{Dose of New Dosage Form} = \frac{\text{Amount Absorbed from Current Dosage Form}}{\text{F of New Dosage Form}}$$

DISTRIBUTION

Distribution is the process by which drug molecules move from systemic circulation to the various tissues and organs of the body. Distribution occurs for intravascular and extravascular routes of administration. It depends on the physical and chemical properties of the drug molecule and interactions with membranes and tissues throughout the body. Drugs distribute throughout the body based on the drug's lipophilicity, molecular weight, solubility, ionization status and the extent of protein binding. Factors that favor passage across membranes and greater drug distribution to the tissues include high lipophilicity, low molecular weight, unionized status and low protein binding. Human plasma contains many proteins, and albumin is the primary protein responsible for drug binding. Only the unbound (free) form of a drug can interact with receptors, exert therapeutic or toxic effects and be cleared from the body. If a drug is highly protein-bound (> 90%) and serum albumin is low (< 3.5 g/dL), then a higher percentage of the drug will be in the unbound form.

Though the unbound form of the drug is responsible for the therapeutic effect, many drug assays cannot differentiate between bound and unbound (active) drug. When assessing levels of highly protein bound compounds (e.g., phenytoin, calcium), a patient with low serum albumin has more of the unbound (active) compound in the serum, and can experience therapeutic or even adverse effects at what appears to be a normal or subtherapeutic drug level. This issue can be overcome by obtaining a "free" phenytoin level or ionized calcium level. Free phenytoin and ionized calcium only measure the unbound portion, so no adjustment is required for hypoalbuminemia. Otherwise, adjustment of the total level is required. The correction formulas allow us to determine what the concentration would be if albumin was normal. With hypoalbuminemia, the corrected level of a highly protein bound drug will be higher than the total level reported by the lab. This is discussed further in the Calculations III and Seizures/Epilepsy chapters.

CALCIUM AND PHENYTOIN CORRECTION FORMULAS

$Ca_{corrected}$ (mg/dL) = $calcium_{reported\ (serum)}$ + [(4.0 – albumin) x (0.8)] †

Phenytoin corrected* (mcg/mL) $= \frac{\text{Total phenytoin measured}}{(0.2 \times \text{albumin}) + 0.1}$ ‡

† Use serum calcium in mg/dL and albumin in g/dL (standard units in the U.S.) in the corrected calcium formula.

‡ Use serum phenytoin in mcg/mL and albumin in g/dL (standard units in the U.S.) in the corrected phenytoin formula.

**Same formula is used for valproic acid correction.*

2. A pharmacist receives a call from a provider asking for assistance with two patients in the clinic. Both patients have a seizure disorder and are taking phenytoin. Patient A is seizure free, but is experiencing symptoms of toxicity. Patient B has a higher phenytoin level and is doing fine. Both patients have normal renal function. Which of the following statements is/are true of this scenario? (Select ALL that apply.)

LAB	REFERENCE RANGE	PATIENT A	PATIENT B
Phenytoin level (total)	10-20 mcg/mL	14.3	17.8
Albumin	3.5-5 g/dL	2.1	4.2

A. Patient B's corrected phenytoin level will be lower than the total level reported.
B. Patient A's corrected phenytoin level will be lower than the total level reported.
C. Patient A's corrected phenytoin level will be higher than the total level reported.
D. Patient A has a greater percentage of bound phenytoin.
E. Patient A has a greater percentage of unbound phenytoin.

The correct answers are (C and E). The corrected phenytoin level for Patient A (using the formula provided) is 27.5 mcg/mL. Increased unbound phenytoin is contributing to the patient's side effects.

VOLUME OF DISTRIBUTION

The volume of distribution (V or Vd) is how large an area in the patient's body the drug has distributed into, and is based on the properties of the drug (discussed previously). The volume of distribution relates the amount of drug in the body to the concentration of the drug measured in plasma (or serum). When a dose of drug is administered (e.g., 1,000 mg), a concentration (e.g., 12 mcg/mL) from a sample of biological fluid can be measured and reported. To convert between amounts and concentrations, a volume is needed. The equation for volume of distribution is:

SUBSCRIPTS IN FORMULAS

Vd can be written as V_d and ke can be written as k_e. Subscripts are not used in this chapter for simplicity.

$$Vd = \frac{\text{Amount of drug in body}}{\text{Concentration of drug in plasma}}$$

The Vd is determined from the amount of drug in the body after the dose is given.

3. A 500 mg dose of gentamicin is administered to a patient, and a blood sample is drawn. The concentration of gentamicin is measured as 25 mcg/mL (which is the same as 25 mg/L). What is the volume of distribution of gentamicin in this patient?

$$Vd = \frac{500\text{ mg}}{25\text{ mg/L}} = 20\text{ L}$$

Vd is a theoretical value, which is why it is sometimes called the "apparent" volume of distribution. Vd is not an exact physical volume that is measured, but is a helpful parameter used to make inferences regarding how widely a drug distributes throughout the body.

METABOLISM

Metabolism is the process by which a drug is converted from its original chemical structure into other forms to facilitate elimination from the body. The original chemical form is called the parent drug and the additional forms are called metabolites. Metabolism can occur throughout the body. The gut and liver are primary sites for drug metabolism due to high levels of metabolic enzymes in these tissues.

Blood from the gut travels to the liver before it reaches the rest of the body. First-pass metabolism is the hepatic metabolism of a drug before it reaches the systemic circulation, which can dramatically reduce the bioavailability of an oral formulation. First-pass metabolism of lidocaine is so extensive that the drug cannot be given orally – it must be given IV. Some drugs with extensive first-pass metabolism can be given orally, but in much higher doses than IV doses (e.g., propranolol). Many non-oral, extravascular methods of administration (e.g., transdermal, buccal, sublingual) bypass first-pass metabolism entirely. About 50% of a drug given rectally bypasses the liver.

Enzyme metabolism involves Phase I reactions (oxidation, reduction and hydrolysis), followed by Phase II (conjugation) reactions. Phase I reactions, which can terminate the activity of the drug or convert a prodrug into its active form, provide a reactive functional group on the compound that permits the drug to be attacked by Phase II enzymes. For example, breaking carbon bonds or adding a hydroxyl group to a drug makes the drug more hydrophilic - this means more of the drug stays in the blood, the blood then passes through the kidneys, and the drug is renally excreted. Glucuronidation and other Phase II reactions create compounds that are more readily excreted in the urine and bile. Cytochrome P450 (CYP450) enzymes, located mainly in the liver and intestines, metabolize the majority of drugs. Metabolism is described in detail in the Learning Drug Interactions chapter.

EXCRETION

Excretion is the process of irreversible removal of drugs from the body. Excretion can occur through the kidneys (urine), liver (bile), gut (feces), lungs (exhaled air) and skin (sweat). The primary route of excretion for most drugs is the kidneys (renal excretion). Renal excretion can be increased by adjusting acidity of the urine. For a weak base, increase excretion by acidifying the urine. For a weak acid, increase excretion by alkalinizing the urine.

P-glycoprotein (P-gp) efflux pumps play a role in absorption and excretion of many drugs (see Learning Drug Interactions chapter). Renal excretion is discussed in the Renal Disease and Calculations chapters.

CLEARANCE AND AREA UNDER THE CURVE

Clearance (Cl) describes the rate of drug removal in a certain volume of plasma over a certain amount of time. Since the liver and kidneys clear most of the drug (and these organs do not usually speed up or slow down), most drug elimination occurs at a steady rate (called the rate of elimination). This is true of drugs that follow first order kinetics (discussed later in the chapter). The term clearance is used to describe the efficiency of drug removal from the body. Clearance is described by the following equation:

$$Cl = \frac{\text{Rate of Elimination (Re)}}{\text{Concentration}}$$

4. A dose of gentamicin is given to a patient, and urine is collected from the patient for 4 hours after drug administration. It is determined that 300 mg of gentamicin was eliminated during that time period, and the measured plasma concentration at the midpoint of the collection was 12.5 mg/L. Calculate the patient's gentamicin clearance.

$$Cl = \frac{300 \text{ mg of gentamicin } / \text{ 4 hours}}{12.5 \text{ mg/L}} = 6 \text{ L/hr}$$

or

$$Cl = \frac{300 \text{ mg of gentamicin}}{4 \text{ hours}} \times \frac{L}{12.5 \text{ mg}} = 6 \text{ L/hr}$$

The rate of elimination (Re) has units of mass per time (e.g., mg/hr), and drug concentration has units of amount per volume (e.g., mg/L); units of mass (mg) cancel out and clearance has units of volume per time (e.g., L/hr). Because the rate of elimination is difficult to assess clinically, another method is used to calculate the clearance of a drug from the body:

$$F \times Dose = Cl \times AUC$$

The area under the curve (AUC) is the most reliable measurement of a drug's bioavailability because it directly represents the amount of the drug that has reached the systemic circulation. The clearance for extravascular administration is calculated with this formula:

$$Cl = \frac{F \times Dose}{AUC}$$

Following IV administration, bioavailability (F) = 1, which can be inserted into the previous equation to determine clearance for a drug given intravenously:

$$Cl = \frac{Dose}{AUC}$$

---

5. A patient is currently receiving 400 mg of gentamicin IV once daily and, based on measured serum concentrations, the AUC is determined to be 80 $^{mg \times hr}/_{L}$. Calculate the patient's gentamicin clearance.

$$Cl = \frac{400 \text{ mg}}{\frac{80 \text{ mg} \times \text{hr}}{L}} = 5 \text{ L/hr}$$

ZERO VS FIRST ORDER PHARMACOKINETICS

Most drugs follow first order elimination or "first order kinetics," where a constant percent of drug is removed per unit of time. For example, a 325 mg dose of acetaminophen is eliminated at the same rate as a 650 mg dose. With zero order elimination, a constant amount of drug (mg) is removed per unit of time, no matter how much drug is in the body. The following table provides an example of zero order and first order elimination of a 2 gram dose of a drug.

	ZERO ORDER			FIRST ORDER		
Hour	**Amount of Drug (mg)**	**Percent Removed in Previous Hour**	**Amount (mg) Removed in Previous Hour**	**Amount of Drug (mg)**	**Percent Removed in Previous Hour**	**Amount (mg) Removed in Previous Hour**
0	2,000			2,000		
1	1,700	15	300	1,600	20	400
2	1,400	17.65	300	1,280	20	320
3	1,100	21.43	300	1,024	20	256

MICHAELIS-MENTEN KINETICS

Phenytoin, theophylline and voriconazole exhibit Michaelis-Menten kinetics (also called saturable, mixed order or non-linear kinetics). The maximum rate of metabolism is defined as the Vmax (see figure on the right). The concentration at which the rate of metabolism is half maximal is defined as the Michaelis-Menten constant (Km). At very low concentrations (much less than the Km), the rate of metabolism mimics a first order process. At most concentrations approaching and exceeding the Km, the rate of metabolism becomes mixed. At even higher concentrations relative to the Km, the rate of metabolism approaches zero order (e.g., Vmax). Throughout this process, an increase in dose leads to a disproportionate increase in drug concentration at steady state. The rate of phenytoin metabolism approaches the maximum at accepted therapeutic concentrations. Because of this, phenytoin dose adjustments should be made in small increments (30 – 50 mg) when the serum concentration is > 7 mcg/mL.

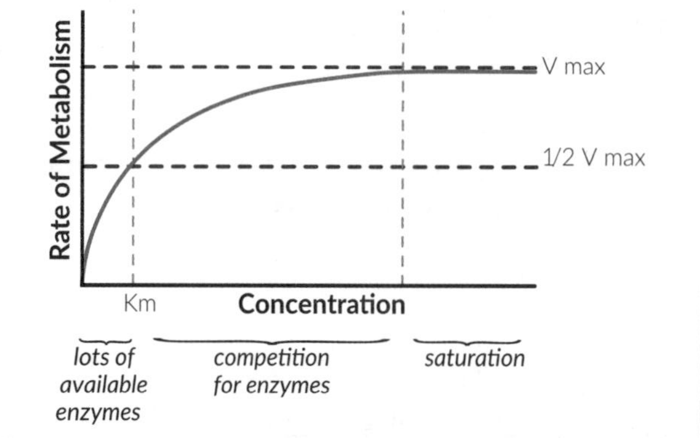

DOSE ADJUSTMENTS FOR MICHAELIS-MENTEN KINETICS

Most drugs follow first order (linear) kinetics.

- At steady state, doubling the dose approximately doubles the serum concentration.

Some drugs (phenytoin, theophylline and voriconazole) follow Michaelis-Menten (also called non-linear, saturable or mixed order) kinetics.

- Doubling the dose of these drugs can more than double the serum concentration.
  - Using a proportion to calculate a new dose is not appropriate.
- Dosing adjustments must be made cautiously to avoid toxicity.

6. A patient has been using phenytoin 100 mg three times daily. The phenytoin level was drawn and found to be 8.8 mcg/mL (reference range 10 – 20 mcg/mL). The prescriber doubled the dose to 200 mg three times daily. The patient started to slur her words, felt fatigued and returned to the clinic. The level was repeated and found to be 23.7 mcg/mL. Which of the following statements is accurate regarding the most likely reason for the change in phenytoin level?

A. Phenytoin half-life is reduced at higher doses.
B. Phenytoin volume of distribution increases at higher doses.
C. The patient's serum albumin level likely increased.
D. Phenytoin bioavailability can decrease at higher doses.
E. Phenytoin metabolism can become saturated at higher doses.

The correct answer is (E). The most likely explanation for the increase in phenytoin level is that when the dose was doubled, the metabolism became partially or completely saturated, and the steady-state level increased dramatically.

ELIMINATION RATE CONSTANT

The elimination rate constant (ke) is the fraction of the drug that is eliminated (cleared) per unit of time. It is calculated from the Vd and the clearance:

$$ke = \frac{Cl}{Vd}$$

7. A drug has the following pharmacokinetic parameters: Vd = 50 liters and Cl = 5,000 mL/hour. Calculate the elimination rate constant of the drug.

$$ke = \frac{5\ L/hr}{50\ L} = 0.1\ hr^{-1}$$

Be certain that the values are converted to units that properly cancel out in the equation. The ke is 0.1 hr^{-1} (meaning that 10% of the drug remaining is cleared per hour).

Predicting Drug Concentrations

The ke can be used to predict the concentration of a drug at any time (t) after the dose using the below calculations. The second formula is derived from the first.

$$C_2 = C_1 \times e^{-kt}$$

$$ke = \frac{\ln(C_1/C_2)}{t}$$

Where C1 = the first or higher drug concentration (sometimes the peak concentration), C2 = the second (or lower) drug concentration (at time = t). E = the base of the natural log.

8. A patient received a dose of gentamicin. Just after the infusion, it is known that the drug level was 10 mg/L, and the patient's ke = 0.22 hr^{-1}. Calculate the predicted concentration after 8 hours.

$$C_2 = 10\ mg/L \times e^{-0.22 \times 8}$$

$$C_2 = 10\ mg/L \times 0.172 = 1.72\ mg/L$$

9. A patient being treated with vancomycin had a supratherapeutic trough of 28 mcg/mL. If his ke = 0.15 hr⁻¹, predict how long it will take for the trough to decrease to his goal therapeutic trough (15 mcg/mL). Round to the nearest hour.

$$0.15\ hr^{-1} = \frac{\ln(28 / 15)}{t} = 4.16\ hr,\ or\ 4\ hours$$

HALF-LIFE AND STEADY STATE

The time required for the drug concentration (and drug amount) to decrease by 50% is called the elimination half-life ($t_{½}$). For example, it takes 5 hours for theophylline concentrations to fall from 16 to 8 mg/L. The half-life of theophylline is 5 hours. It takes 5 more hours for the drug concentration to fall from 8 mg/L to 4 mg/L. Half-life is independent of the drug concentration for drugs exhibiting first-order kinetics.

Half-life is more clinically meaningful than ke. The half-life of a drug can be calculated from the ke:

$$t_{½} = \frac{0.693}{ke}$$

The half-life of a drug can be used to calculate the time required for drug washout (complete elimination) or the time required to achieve steady-state (refer to the table below). When a fixed dose is administered at regular intervals, the drug accumulates until it reaches steady state where the rate of drug intake equals the rate of drug elimination. The time required to reach steady state depends on the elimination half-life of the drug. It takes ~5 half-lives to reach steady state, assuming the drug follows first-order kinetics (described previously) in a one-compartment distribution model (the drug is rapidly and evenly distributed throughout the body) and no loading dose has been given. Similarly, 5 half-lives are required to eliminate more than 95% of the drug if no additional doses are given. The most clinically useful information is obtained from drug levels collected at steady state.

# OF HALF-LIVES	ELIMINATION (NO ADDITIONAL DOSES GIVEN) % OF DRUG REMAINING IN THE BODY	ACCUMULATION (MULTIPLE DOSES GIVEN) % OF STEADY-STATE ACHIEVED
1	50	50
2	25	75
3	12.5	87.5
4	6.25	93.8
5	3.13	96.9

10. Tetracycline has a clearance of 7.014 L/hr and a volume of distribution of 105 L. Calculate the half-life of tetracycline (round to the nearest tenth) and the time required for elimination of greater than 95% of the drug from the body.

$$ke = \frac{Cl}{Vd} = \frac{7.014\ L/hr}{105\ L} = 0.0668\ hr^{-1}$$

$$t_{1/2} = \frac{0.693}{ke} = \frac{0.693}{0.0668\ hr^{-1}} = 10.4\ hours$$

The time required is 10.4 hours x 5 half-lives = 52 hours

11. The serum concentration of Drug A over time is plotted in the figure below. What is the half-life of Drug A?

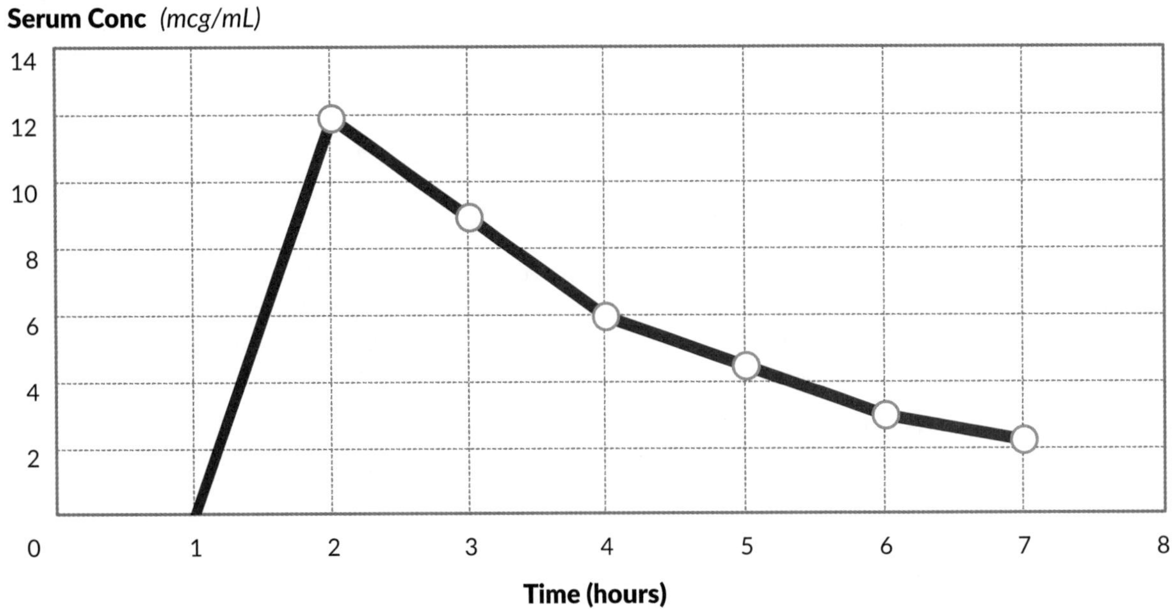

The drug concentrations can be presented in a figure (as shown) or in a list. Identify two times (in hours) where the drug concentration has decreased by half to find the half-life:

- At 2 hours the concentration is 12 mcg/mL and at 4 hours the concentration is 6 mcg/mL.
- It takes 2 hours for the concentration to decrease by 50%, so the half-life is 2 hours.

12. A patient was receiving Drug B for 1 week. The drug was held on June 1st due to an elevated serum concentration. Based on the serum concentrations obtained on June 1st after the drug was held (shown below), what is the half-life of Drug B?

TIME	CONCENTRATION OF DRUG B
1400	12 mcg/mL
1500	8.5 mcg/mL
1600	6 mcg/mL
1700	4.3 mcg/mL
1900	2.1 mcg/mL

The drug concentration fell by 50% (from 12 mcg/mL to 6 mcg/mL) in 2 hours, so the half-life of Drug B is 2 hours. This is a different way of presenting the same information from the previous problem.

13. A patient receives 200 mg of a drug with a half-life of 5 hours. How much of the drug remains after 10 hours?

- 10 hours = 2 half-lives
- 50 mg of the drug remains after 10 hours

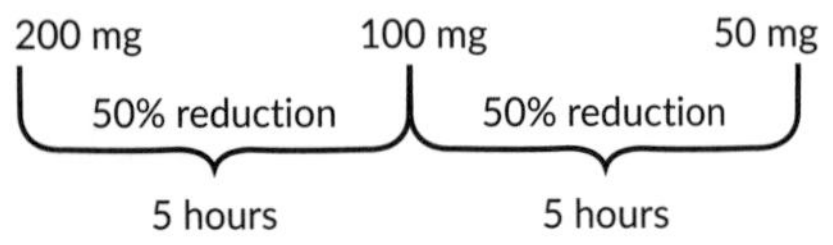

LOADING DOSE

Administration of a loading dose can be necessary to rapidly achieve therapeutic concentrations of a drug. When the half-life of a drug is long relative to the frequency of administration, several doses must be administered before steady state is achieved.

14. A patient will be started on daily oral digoxin for management of atrial fibrillation. The following pharmacokinetic parameters for oral digoxin are known: F = 0.6, Vd = 500 L and Cl = 120 L/day. When would steady state be reached? Round to the nearest day.

$$ke = \frac{Cl}{Vd} = \frac{120 \text{ L/day}}{500 \text{ L}} = 0.24 \text{ days}^{-1}$$

$$t_{1/2} = \frac{0.693}{ke} = \frac{0.693}{0.24 \text{ days}^{-1}} = {}^{\sim}2.89 \text{ days}$$

$$\text{Steady State} = 5 \text{ half-lives} \times 2.89 \text{ days} = {}^{\sim}14 \text{ days}$$

It is beneficial to administer a loading dose to achieve the targeted levels more quickly in this case. The loading dose can be determined with the following equation:

$$\text{Loading Dose} = \frac{\text{Desired Concentration} \times \text{Vd}}{\text{F}}$$

15. Using the pharmacokinetic parameters provided in the previous question, what oral loading dose of digoxin is appropriate to rapidly achieve a peak concentration of 1.5 mcg/L?

$$\text{Loading Dose} = \frac{\text{Desired Concentration} \times \text{Vd}}{\text{F}} = \frac{1.5 \text{ mcg/L} \times 500 \text{ L}}{0.6} = 1{,}250 \text{ mcg or } 1.25 \text{ mg}$$

THERAPEUTIC DRUG MONITORING

Some medications are monitored with drug levels to reach dosing goals and avoid toxicity (see Learning Lab Values & Drug Monitoring chapter). If drug levels are too high, toxicity can occur. If drug levels are too low, the patient's condition might not adequately be treated. To prevent either toxicity or inadequate treatment, an adjustment of the dosing regimen is needed.

The peak level is the highest concentration in the blood the drug will reach. The trough level is the lowest concentration the drug will reach in the blood, and is drawn just before the next dose (or some short time before the dose is due). When adjusting a dosing regimen, changing the dose generally affects the peak, and changing the interval/frequency generally affects the trough. For aminoglycosides, it is usually preferred to extend the dosing interval (i.e., give the dose less often) instead of decreasing the dose, because it maximizes the killing ability of the antibiotic.

Therapeutic drug monitoring optimizes drug therapy by enhancing efficacy (e.g., overcoming resistance) and reducing toxicity associated with overdosing or drug accumulation.

CHAPTER CONTENT

Background 1020
Dominant and Recessive Traits 1020
Definitions 1021
Pharmacogenomic Testing and Pharmacist Action 1022
Does a Positive or Negative Test Require Action? 1023
Select Drugs with Pharmacogenomic Implications 1023

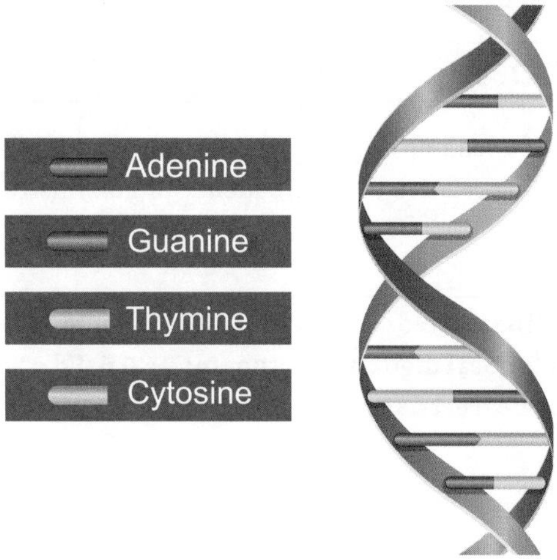

CHAPTER 79
PHARMACOGENOMICS

BACKGROUND

Pharmacogenomics is the science which examines inherited variations in genes that determine a patient's response to a drug. It is estimated that genetic factors contribute 20 – 40% of the differences in drug metabolism and response between patients. The goal of pharmacogenomics is to identify these factors and design treatments with improved efficacy and reduced adverse reactions. Pharmacogenomics is called "personalized medicine" because drugs can be avoided entirely or used preferentially, based on a person's genotype. The genotype is an individual's unique genetic instructions (the coding in the DNA), which determines response and tolerability of drugs.

Historically, Hit-or-Miss

Psychiatric prescribing has historically been hit-or-miss; it was not possible to predict patient response or tolerability of psychiatric medications. Today, analyzing the availability or lack of genes that influence efficacy (response) and the likelihood of adverse events can guide prescribing.

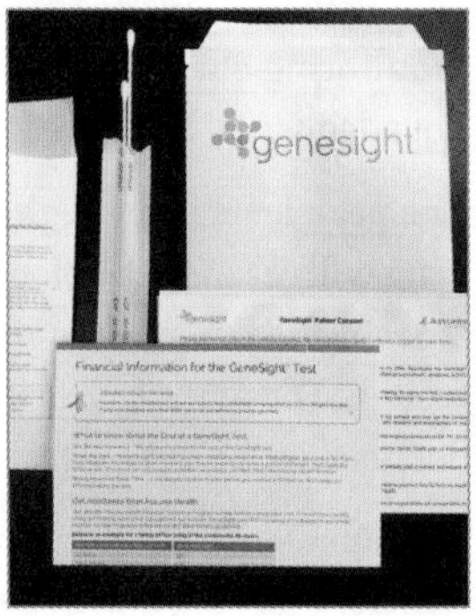

Pharmacogenomics is Becoming Mainstream

Pharmacogenomic testing is now simpler, which is making services more mainstream. Many tests are conducted on DNA extracted from a sample of saliva. Health insurance plans cover the cost of some pharmacogenetic tests if prescribed by a medical provider.

DOMINANT AND RECESSIVE TRAITS

Dominant and recessive genotypes describe the inheritance patterns of certain traits. They can be used to determine how likely it is for a certain phenotype to pass from parent to offspring.

CONTENT LEGEND

= Study Tip Gal   = Key Drug Guy

Each parent contributes one copy (allele) of each gene to the offspring. The differences in the alleles cause variations in protein production (expression), which contribute to the phenotype, such as brown or blonde hair. The phenotype will also be influenced by the offspring's environment.

A dominant allele produces a dominant phenotype in individuals who have one copy of the allele, which can come from just one parent. For a recessive allele to produce a recessive phenotype, the individual must have two copies, one from each parent (see figure on right).

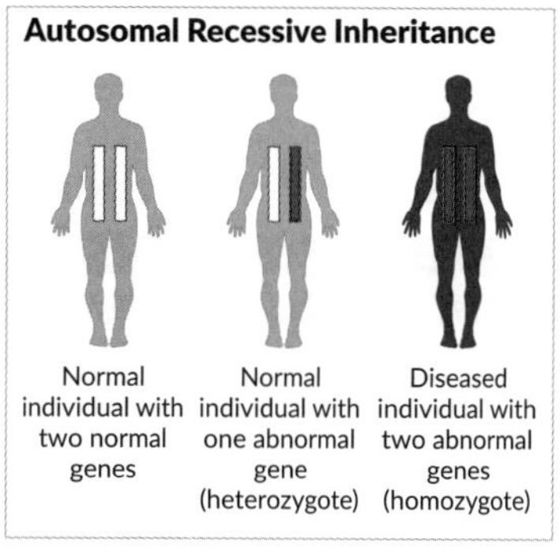

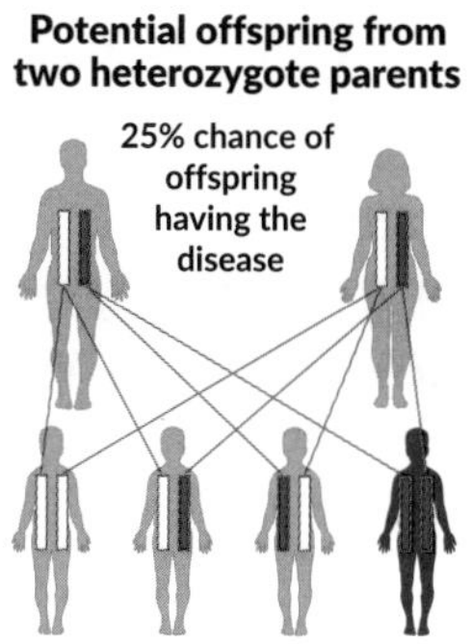

DEFINITIONS

TERM	DEFINITION
Deoxyribonucleic acid (DNA)	The genetic information that is inherited from both parents that is present in two long chains of nucleotides, joined together by hydrogen bonds and twisted into a double helix. The strands of DNA are very long. DNA is the main component of chromosomes.
Nucleotide	Subunit of the nucleic acids DNA and RNA. Each nucleotide contains a nitrogen base, a five-carbon sugar (deoxyribose in DNA, and ribose in RNA), and a phosphate group. In DNA, the bases consist of two purines (adenine and guanine) and two pyrimidines (thymine and cytosine). In RNA, uracil is present instead of thymine.
Chromosome	Tightly packed structure within the cell nucleus, consisting of DNA and proteins. Chromosomes contain genes. Human cells contain 23 pairs of chromosomes.
Gene	Specific sequence of nucleotides that code (provide instructions) for a single protein. A gene is similar to a recipe, or a set of instructions, on how to make a protein. Since proteins make up the entire life form, genes are referred to as the "blueprint" of life.
Allele	The specific form of a gene. Alleles are either wild-type or variants. Wild-type is usually the most commonly occurring allele. Two identical alleles make up a homozygous genotype (e.g., CYP450 2C19 *1/*1), and two different alleles make up a heterozygous genotype (e.g., CYP2C19 *1/*3).
Genotype	The set of unique genes that determine a specific trait in an individual.
Phenotype	An observable trait (outward expression) of the genotype, such as hair color, or an inherited trait that is not outwardly visible, such as sickle cell disease.
Haplotype	A group of genes or DNA variations inherited from a single parent that exist on the same chromosome and are likely to be inherited together.
Single nucleotide polymorphism (SNP)	A change in a single nucleotide in a genetic sequence (e.g., C replaced by G). SNPs are the most common genetic polymorphism in DNA. An SNP can be harmless, or it can result in a disease. SNPs are responsible for the majority of individual variability in response to a drug. Example: in cystic fibrosis, an SNP results in defective coding for a protein involved in sweat and mucus production.
Structural variation (SV)	SVs are polymorphisms, like SNPs, except that they are longer. They involve a large portion of DNA. SVs, like SNPs, can be harmless or associated with a certain risk or disease.
Polymorphism	An inherited variation in the DNA sequence (such as a SNP or SV).
Poor metabolizer	A person with significantly reduced or no enzyme activity. This would lead to reduced or no metabolism (breakdown) of a drug through that particular enzyme. This might mean a patient should avoid drugs metabolized by that enzyme or needs to use a modified dose to prevent adverse effects.
Ultra-rapid metabolizer	A person with high enzyme activity. This leads to fast metabolism of a drug through that particular enzyme. This means a patient would quickly metabolize a prodrug to its active form and/or eliminate a drug faster than expected.

PHARMACOGENOMIC TESTING AND PHARMACIST ACTION

DRUG	TEST	SIGNIFICANCE/POPULATION	RESULT/ACTION
Human leukocyte antigen (HLA) testing: the major histocompatibility complex, class I, B (HLA-B) is an important gene in the immune system.			
Abacavir *(Ziagen)* + Abacavir-containing combination drugs	HLA-B*5701	Serious and fatal hypersensitivity reactions have occurred. Patients who are HLA-B*5701 positive are at ↑ risk for a hypersensitivity reaction. Test all patients prior to starting.	If positive, do not use.
Allopurinol *(Zyloprim, Aloprim)*	HLA-B*5801	Increased risk of Stevens-Johnson syndrome (SJS) in patients testing positive for HLA-B*5801. Discontinue at first sign of allergic reaction, including skin rash. **Population** Consider testing high-risk individuals (Korean patients with renal impairment or with Han Chinese or Thai ancestry).	If positive, do not use.
Carbamazepine *(Tegretol*, others) **Oxcarbazepine *(Trileptal)*** **Phenytoin *(Dilantin***, others) Fosphenytoin *(Cerebyx)*	HLA-B*1502	Serious skin reactions, including SJS and toxic epidermal necrolysis (TEN), have occurred. The HLA-B*1502 allele (more common in Asian populations) are at ↑ risk of serious skin reactions. Test all Asian patients before starting carbamazepine; testing is suggested for oxcarbazepine, optional for phenytoin and fosphenytoin.	If positive, do not use (unless benefit clearly outweighs risk).
CYP450 polymorphisms: polymorphisms of various CYP450 enzymes may be responsible for much of the variability in response to certain medications. These polymorphisms could affect any population, but the tests are not yet routinely performed in clinical practice.			
Clopidogrel *(Plavix)*	CYP2C19	Clopidogrel is a prodrug. It must be converted to the active metabolite by CYP2C19. The CYP2C19*1 allele is fully functional, whereas the *2 and *3 alleles indicate reduced metabolism (less active metabolite formed). CYP2C19*2 or *3 alleles are poor metabolizers and have ↑ cardiovascular events.	If the patient has the CYP2C19*2 or *3 alleles, consider alternative treatment.
Codeine	CYP2D6	Codeine (a prodrug) is metabolized to morphine via CYP2D6. Ultra-rapid metabolizers, due to extensive conversion to morphine metabolite, will be at ↑ risk of opioid overdose. Over-production of morphine can cause ↑ CNS effects, including respiratory depression. Infant deaths occurred when nursing mothers who were ultra-rapid metabolizers took codeine for pain. Excessive morphine was passed to the infant through breast milk.	If CYP2D6 ultra-rapid metabolizer, do not use (toxicity risk). If CYP2D6 poor metabolizer, do not use (lack of efficacy).
Warfarin *(Coumadin, Jantoven)*	CYP2C9*2 and *3, VKORC1	Increased bleeding risk due to decreased function of alleles and haplotypes (CYP2C9*2 and 2C9*3) and VKORC1 G > A variant.	If these allele variations are present, start with a lower dose.

DRUG	TEST	SIGNIFICANCE/POPULATION	RESULT/ACTION
Other Pharmacogenomic Tests			
Trastuzumab *(Herceptin)* Ado-trastuzumab emtansine *(Kadcyla)* Pertuzumab *(Perjeta)* Trastuzumab-dkst *(Ogivri)* Trastuzumab-dttb *(Ontruzant)* Trastuzumab-qyyp *(Trazimera)* Lapatinib *(Tykerb)*	HER2 gene expression	These drugs are HER2 inhibitors; they require overexpression of HER2 for efficacy. HER2 negative status and those with weakly positive (1+) tumors do not respond well.	If tumor is HER2 negative, drugs are not effective.
Cetuximab *(Erbitux)* Panitumumab *(Vectibix)*	KRAS mutation	Only patients who are KRAS mutation-negative (are wild-type) should receive these medications. They are not effective in patients with colorectal cancer who are positive for the KRAS mutation (~40% of patients).	If positive for a KRAS mutation, do not use.
Azathioprine *(Azasan, Imuran)*	Thiopurine methyltransferase (TPMT)	Low/absent TPMT activity ↑ risk of severe, life threatening myelosuppression (↓ WBCs, ↓ RBCs, ↓ platelets); patients with intermediate TPMT activity are also at ↑ risk for myelosuppression with lower severity.	If TPMT activity is low/absent, start at a very low dose or use an alternative treatment.
Capecitabine *(Xeloda)* **Fluorouracil** *(Adrucil)*	DPD deficiency	Dihydropyrimidine dehydrogenase (DPD) deficiency ↑ risk of severe toxicity (diarrhea, neutropenia, neurotoxicity).	If DPD deficient, do not use.

Refer to Key Drugs Guy below for drugs with required or strongly recommended pharmacogenomic testing per the package labeling.

DOES A POSITIVE OR NEGATIVE TEST REQUIRE ACTION?

Avoid the drug when the pharmacogenomic test is POSITIVE

- Positive HLA-B testing indicates ↑ risk of hypersensitivity: avoid the drug.
- Positive KRAS mutation (often called "KRAS mutant") predicts poor response: avoid the drug.

Avoid the drug when pharmacogenomic test is NEGATIVE

- Negative HER2 expression indicates poor response: avoid HER2 inhibitors.

SELECT DRUGS WITH PHARMACOGENOMIC IMPLICATIONS

KEY DRUGS

Testing required/strongly recommended:

Abacavir and any combination products containing abacavir

Azathioprine

Carbamazepine

Cetuximab and panitumumab

Trastuzumab, ado-trastuzumab, lapatinib and pertuzumab

May consider testing, though not yet routine:

Allopurinol

Capecitabine and fluorouracil

Clopidogrel

Codeine

Phenytoin and fosphenytoin

Warfarin

Select Guidelines/References

Clinical Pharmacogenetics Implementation Consortium (CPIC) Guidelines. https://cpicpgx.org/guidelines/ (accessed 5 Mar 2019).

CHAPTER CONTENT

Background 1024
Natural Medicine 1024
Differences Between Dietary Supplements and Drugs 1025
Dietary Supplement Labeling 1025
Interactions with Prescription Drugs 1025
Supplements that Increase Bleeding Risk 1025
Supplements with Risk of Liver Toxicity 1026
Supplements with Risk of Cardiac Toxicity 1026
Medical Foods 1026
Commonly Used Supplements 1027
Safety Issues with Common Supplements 1028
Vitamin Supplementation 1030
Calcium & Vitamin D 1030
Folic Acid (Folate) 1030
Vitamin E 1030
Iron 1030
Drugs That Cause Nutrient Depletion 1031
Conditions with Recommended Supplements 1031
Homeopathic Products 1032

CONTENT LEGEND

= Study Tip Gal

CHAPTER 80
DIETARY SUPPLEMENTS, NATURAL & COMPLEMENTARY MEDICINE

BACKGROUND

Complementary medicine refers to health practices (e.g., dietary supplements and acupuncture) that are used with conventional medicine (e.g., physician visits and prescription medications). In the last decade, yoga and meditation had the largest increases in use.

The term alternative medicine is used when conventional medicine is not used.

Complementary medicine is used more commonly in the United States, with dietary supplements used by 75% of adults.

NATURAL MEDICINE

'Natural medicine' is a general umbrella term that includes herbals (plant products), vitamins, minerals and many substances that are not plant-derived but exist in nature, such as glucosamine from shellfish. The FDA uses the term "dietary supplements," which will be used here.

Dietary supplements are regulated by the Dietary Supplement Health and Education Act (DSHEA) of 1994. DSHEA requires the manufacturer to ensure that their products are safe before they are marketed. In contrast, drugs must be proven safe and effective before they can be sold. Once the supplement is marketed, the FDA has the responsibility for showing that a supplement is "unsafe," before it can take action to restrict use or remove it from the marketplace. The company selling or distributing the supplement must forward adverse event reports to the FDA. Adverse events from supplements can be reported to the FDA's Safety Reporting Portal, which sorts safety issues to the correct FDA site.

Manufacturers cannot make claims that the product treats or cures a condition.

DIFFERENCES BETWEEN DIETARY SUPPLEMENTS AND DRUGS

Supplement safety is the manufacturer's responsibility, which should be proven prior to release. After release, the FDA can remove a supplement if it is found to be unsafe.

- In contrast, drugs must have proven safety and effectiveness (to the FDA) prior to release.

Supplements cannot claim to treat, cure or mitigate (lessen) a condition (e.g., melatonin helps you fall asleep faster).

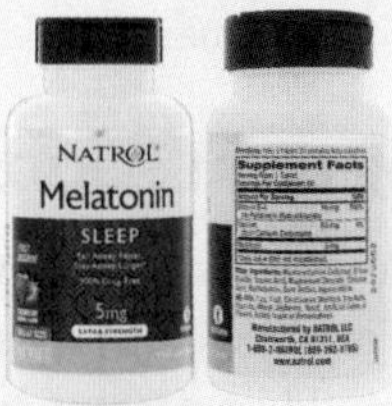

- In contrast, drug claims are based on FDA approval (e.g., zolpidem treats insomnia).

SUPPLEMENTS

- The Supplement Facts label is similar to the label required on food products. It includes the ingredients, quantities, serving size, servings/container, calories, calories from fat, total fat and saturated fat, cholesterol, sodium, carbohydrate, dietary fiber, sugars, protein, vitamin A, vitamin C, calcium and iron, when present in measurable amounts.

OTC DRUGS

- The OTC Drug Facts label includes ingredients, purpose, uses, warnings, instructions, excipients and how to avoid an allergic reaction. OTC drugs can include a package insert similar to prescription drugs; this depends on the product's approval process.

PRESCRIPTION DRUGS

- Much more detailed information, which is in the package insert; see the Learning Drug References chapter.

Health claims are limited to the nutrient content, the relationship to health and the impact on normal body structure or function, such as "calcium builds strong bones," and "fiber maintains bowel regularity." Products that make claims on the structure or function of the body (e.g., antioxidants maintain cell integrity) must state in a "disclaimer" that the FDA has not evaluated the claim.

Risks with natural products are usually dose-dependent; higher doses have higher risk. Supplements can pose safety risks in certain patients. Four areas of particular concern are supplements that interact with prescription drugs, increase bleeding risk or cause cardiotoxicity or hepatotoxicity.

DIETARY SUPPLEMENT LABELING

The claims on supplement labels are limited (see above) because the supplements have not had rigorous trials to determine safety and efficacy. The Supplement Facts label includes the recommended daily intake (RDI) and the amounts present in the product.

Label Updates

The RDIs have been changed for some common vitamins and minerals. Additionally, some of the products will have new measurement units. The labeling is not yet required, but some labeling has been updated already.

- One that will cause confusion is folic acid, which will have units listed on labels in DFE instead of in micrograms.
  - Folic acid 600 mcg DFE = 400 mcg of folic acid daily, the RDA for women in child-bearing years and pregnancy.

INTERACTIONS WITH PRESCRIPTION DRUGS

St. John's Wort

St. John's wort (SJW) has several important drug interactions to be aware of.

- SJW induces CYP450 3A4, 2C19, 2C9, 1A2 and p-glycoprotein (P-gp), which lowers levels of other drugs (with possible treatment failures).
  - Do not use with many drugs, including oral contraceptives, transplant drugs and warfarin.
- SJW is serotonergic and is often implicated in serotonin syndrome.
  - Do not use with MAO inhibitors, including linezolid.
  - Concurrent use with other serotonergic drugs can be dangerous, especially at higher doses, including SSRIs and SNRIs.
- SJW causes photosensitivity and requires counseling on sun protection and avoidance.
  - Photosensitivity risk increases when taken with other photosensitizing drugs, including diuretics, retinoids, quinolones, sulfamethoxazole, tetracyclines and transplant drugs (e.g., tacrolimus); see Drug Allergies & Adverse Drug Reactions chapter.
- SJW may lower the seizure threshold. Caution is required when taking multiple drugs that lower the seizure threshold (e.g., bupropion, quinolones, tramadol, penicillin and carbapenems) or in anyone with a history of seizures; see Seizures/Epilepsy chapter.

SUPPLEMENTS THAT INCREASE BLEEDING RISK

Several natural medicines have the potential to increase bleeding risk.

- The "5 Gs": garlic, ginger, ginkgo, ginseng and glucosamine
- Fish oils (at higher doses)
- Vitamin E
- Dong quai
- Willow bark (a salicylate); do not use with anticoagulants. Other supplements should not be given concurrently with warfarin; see Anticoagulation chapter.

SUPPLEMENTS WITH RISK OF LIVER TOXICITY

Natural products can be hepatotoxic.

- Black cohosh (used for menopausal symptoms)
- Chaparral, comfrey
- Kava (used for stress/anxiety)
- Green tea "extracts" may be a health concern; see below.

SUPPLEMENTS WITH RISK OF CARDIAC TOXICITY

Cardiotoxic supplements will have higher risk in patients with cardiac conditions, but can cause toxicity in anyone.

- Ephedra was removed from the market due to reports of cardiac toxicity. Bitter orange (Citrus aurantium or synephrine) replaced ephedra in many products.
  - Ephedra and bitter orange/synephrine are stimulants with dose-dependent cardiac toxicity. Increases blood pressure and heart rate. There are reports of myocardial infarction, stroke and arrhythmias.
- DMAA (dimethylamylamine) is an amphetamine derivative that is used in body-building/performance-enhancement products, including powdered supplement mixtures.
  - DMAA has cardiac toxicity, including increasing blood pressure and heart rate.
- Licorice contains glycyrrhizin; artificially flavored licorice products do not contain this compound.
  - Glycyrrhizin, taken in excess can lower potassium and increase blood pressure.
- Yohimbe is used to increase libido and for erectile dysfunction.
  - Yohimbe raises blood pressure, increases heart rate and has seizure risk.

Caffeine and Health Risks

Caffeine taken in usual doses is not harmful; in excessive doses, caffeine can raise blood pressure and increase heart rate.

- Caffeine is present in supplements for weight loss, energy and body-building. Many have high caffeine content.
- Caffeine is present in black tea, green tea, cocoa (including chocolate), yerba mate, guarana and kombucha (fermented tea).
- Green tea "extract" (with various unknown contents) has been linked to liver damage in body-building products.

Caffeine and Health Benefits

Caffeine is not all bad; it is the most popular drug in the world, with several benefits.

- Caffeine increases alertness, helps with weight management and can be useful in treating headaches.
- Green tea, in reasonable amounts, helps lower LDL and triglycerides. The table that follows includes other supplements with beneficial cardiovascular effects.

MEDICAL FOODS

Medical foods are not medications, nor are they supplements. They are compounds used to meet a nutritional need, which should be used under medical supervision, yet they do not require a prescription. Medical foods are not covered by most insurance plans.

FDA Requirements for Medical Foods

The FDA requires medical foods to be:

- Taken enterally (i.e., by mouth, or with an enteral feeding tube).
- Taken under the supervision of a healthcare professional.
- Intended to treat a condition with a known nutritional requirement.

Medical Food Use is Increasing

Commonly used medical foods includes l-methylfolate, an active form of folate *(Deplin)* used for depression, L-methylfolate, B6 and B12 *(Metanx)* used for neuropathic pain and phosphatidylserine conjugated to different forms of enriched omega-3 fatty acids (*Vayacog* and *Vayarin*), used for mild cognitive impairment and ADHD, respectively.

Safety Concerns

A medical food used for osteoarthritis, flavocoxid *(Limbrel)* has been linked to hepatotoxicity and pneumonitis. The FDA has requested that the manufacturer recall all lots.

Generally Recognized As Safe

Some of the supplements in the following table (e.g., chamomile, cinnamon, synephrine) are used in food products. The FDA labels food additives as Generally Recognized As Safe (GRAS) when the additive is considered safe when used as intended. When used in doses that are higher than the intended dose, the safety profile will change, and could include toxicity. All ingredients in a medical food must be GRAS.

COMMONLY USED SUPPLEMENTS

CONDITION	TREATMENT
Anxiety	Valerian
	Passionflower
	Kava
	Chamomile
	St. John's wort
	5-Hydroxytryptophan (5-HTP)
ADHD	Omega-3 fatty acids, "fish oils", polyunaturated fatty acids (PUFAs), contains docosahexaenoic acid (DHA) and eicosapentaenoic acid (EPA)
Cold Sores (Aphthous Ulcers/Canker Sores)	L-lysine
Colds and Flu	Echinacea
	Zinc
	Vitamin C (ascorbic acid)
	Probiotics (e.g., *Bifidobacterium animals, Lactobacillus acidophilus)*
Dementia/ Memory	Ginkgo
	Vitamin E (alpha-tocopherol)
	Vitamin D
	Acetyl-L-carnitine
	Vinpocetine, used for memory, neuroprotection, weight loss
Depression	St. John's wort
	SAMe (S-adenosylmethionine), used for depression, osteoarthritis
	Valerian
	5-HTP
Diabetes	Alpha lipoic acid, used for diabetic neuropathy, memory, neuroprotection
	Bitter melon
	Cinnamon
	Chromium
	Ginseng

CONDITION	TREATMENT
Dyslipidemia	Red yeast rice (contains a natural form of lovastatin)
	Garlic controversial benefit; small ↓ CH and LDL
	Omega-3 fatty acids, "fish oils"
	Plant sterol (beta-sitosterol)
	Fibers (Barley, psyllium, and oat bran)
	Artichoke extract
Dyspepsia	Calcium
	Magnesium
	Peppermint
	Chamomile
Energy/Weight Loss	Bitter orange (synephrine component)
	Caffeine
	Guarana, green tea powder (contain caffeine)
Erectile Dysfunction	Ginseng
	L-arginine
	Yohimbe
Heart Failure, Heart Health (general)	Coenzyme Q10 (ubiquinone), used as adjunctive treatment with HF medications
	Hawthorn
	Omega-3 fatty acids, "fish oils"
Hypertension	Omega-3 fatty acids, "fish oils"
	L-arginine
	Coenzyme Q10
	Garlic controversial benefit; small ↓ in systolic BP
	Fiber (psyllium, oats, and wheat bran)
	Potassium
Gastrointestinal Health	Fibers (for diarrhea, constipation; examples: psyllium (in *Metamucil*), barley, and oat bran)
	Chamomile
	Peppermint
	Probiotics *(Lactobacillus, Saccharomyces boulardii, Bifidobacterium infantis* strains)
	Horehound (GI health, constipation)
	Wheatgrass (GI health, detoxification)
Inflammation	Omega-3 fatty acids, "fish oils"
	Flax seeds/oil, converted to DHA and EPA
	Turmeric

CONDITION	TREATMENT
Insomnia/Sleep	Melatonin used for sleep (taken QHS) and to help prevent/treat jetlag (0.5 to 2 mg taken pre-flight and higher doses, such as 5 mg, post-flight)
	Lemon balm
	Passionflower
	Valerian
	Chamomile
	Coenzyme Q10 (If due to heart failure)
	5-HTP and L-tryptophan
Liver Disease	Milk thistle
Menopause	Black cohosh
	Dong quai
	Evening primrose oil; provides essential fatty acids (gamma-lineloic acid, or GLA)
	Soy, red clover, Panax ginseng contain mild phyto- (plant) estrogens
Migraine, Prophylaxis	Feverfew
	Butterbur
	Magnesium
	Riboflavin (vitamin B2)
	Coenzyme Q10
	Guarana (for caffeine) or other caffeine sources
Motion Sickness	Ginger
	Peppermint

CONDITION	TREATMENT
Osteoarthritis	Glucosamine (best evidence with sulfate salts)
	Chondroitin
	SAMe (S-adenosylmethionine), used for depression, osteoarthritis
	Turmeric (↓ inflammation/pain)
Osteoporosis	Calcium
	Vitamin D
	Soy
	Ipriflavone
Prostate Health	Saw palmetto (used often, may be ineffective)
	Lycopene
	Pygeum
	Pumpkin seed (contains beta-sitosterol)
Skin Conditions	Aloe vera (for lichen planus, psoriasis, HSV, burns)
	Tea tree oil (for acne, dandruff, fungal infections)
	Topical vitamin D (for psoriasis, seborrheic keratosis, diaper rash-vitamin A & D ointment)
	Biotin (hair loss, ↑ nail and hair thickness)
UTI	Cranberry
	Yogurt
	Probiotics (*Bifidobacteria*, *Lactobacillus* strains)
Weight Loss	Garcinia cambogia

SAFETY ISSUES WITH COMMON SUPPLEMENTS

TREATMENT	NOTES, SAFETY ISSUES
5-HTP	Serotonergic, ↑ risk with other serotonergic drugs
Artichoke extract	Allergic reactions (uncommon), cross-sensitivity with other members of Asteraceae family (e.g., asters, chamomile, chrysanthemum, echinacea, ragweed)
Bitter melon	↓ blood glucose (BG); caution with hypoglycemic drugs
Bitter orange (synephrine component)	Stimulant; dose-related ↑ BP, ↑ HR, arrhythmia risk
Black cohosh	May be hepatotoxic Do not use with medications for heart failure: ACE inhibitors, ARBs, beta-blockers, amiodarone
Caffeine	Dose-related (with high doses) dizziness, agitation, irritability, ↑ BP, ↑ HR
Chamomile	Allergic reactions (uncommon), cross-sensitivity with other members of Asteraceae family (e.g., ragweed, asters, chrysanthemums, artichoke)
Chondroitin	Bleeding risk at higher doses, ↑ INR with warfarin

TREATMENT	NOTES, SAFETY ISSUES
Dong quai	Increased bleeding risk (e.g., with concurrent use of anticoagulants, antiplatelets, salicylates)
Echinacea	Controversial safety with autoimmune disorders; use cautiously with other members of Asteraceae family (e.g., ragweed, asters, chamomile, chrysanthemums, artichoke)
Evening primrose oil; provides essential fatty acids (gamma-lineloic acid, or GLA)	Provides essential fatty acids (gamma-lineloic acid, or GLA); anti-inflammatory
Feverfew	Mouth ulceration (inflammation of the oral cavity/tongue), increased bleeding risk (e.g., with concurrent use of anticoagulants, antiplatelets, salicylates)
Fibers (barley, psyllium and oat bran)	GI effects, if not used to fiber intake
Garcinia cambogia	May be serotonergic
Garlic	↑ bleeding risk
Ginger	↑ bleeding risk
Ginkgo	↑ bleeding risk; discontinue in advance of surgery
Ginseng	↑ bleeding risk
Guarana, green tea powder (contains caffeine)	See caffeine, above
Hawthorn	Positive inotrope; avoid concurrent use with digoxin (additive effect), ↓ BP; caution for additive effect with BP-lowering drugs
Kava	Avoid due to hepatotoxicity
L-arginine	L-arginine converts into nitric oxide, ↓ BP and ↑ dizziness, caution for additive effect with BP-lowering drugs; avoid concurrent use with nitrates
Melatonin	When used chronically for sleep, endogenous melatonin can be decreased, resulting in dependency for sleep
Omega-3 fatty acids, "fish oils"	↑ bleeding risk with high doses, can ↑ LDL
Passionflower	QT prolongation; avoid with QT risk/other QT-prolonging drugs
Potassium	Potassium levels should be measured in a lab, and dosed accordingly (not with OTC supplements)
Probiotics	Separate use from oral antibiotics, safety concern with use of live bacteria in immune-compromised states
Red yeast rice (contains a natural form of lovastatin)	CYP450 inhibitors (e.g., amiodarone) will ↑ red yeast level; red yeast rice ↓ coenzyme Q10, which may ↑ myopathy risk
SAMe (S-adenosylmethionine), used for depression, osteoarthritis	Serotonergic, ↑ risk with other serotonergic drugs ↑ bleeding risk, do not use in bipolar due to ↑ risk manic behavior
Soy, red clover, Panax ginseng mild phyto-(plant) estrogens	Soy might increase breast cancer risk in postmenopausal women, who are not producing estradiol
St. John's wort	Many drug interactions (inducers, ↓ other drug levels except ↑ levels of prodrugs), serotonergic, photosensitivity
Valerian	Sedation, CNS depressant; risk with concurrent CNS depressants
Vinpocetine	Vinpocetine is derived from a plant product and is semi-synthetic; the FDA is reviewing status as a supplement
Vitamin C (ascorbic acid)	False-negative stool occult blood 48 to 72 hours after ascorbic acid ingestion
Vitamin E (alpha-tocopherol)	Do not exceed 400 IU daily; bleeding risk, CVD risk
Yohimbe	↑ BP, ↑ HR, seizure risk
Zinc	Nasal products can cause loss of smell

VITAMIN SUPPLEMENTATION

VITAMINS	NAMES
Vitamin A	Retinol
Vitamin B1	Thiamine
Vitamin B2	Riboflavin
Vitamin B3	Niacin
Vitamin B6	Pyridoxine
Vitamin B9	Folic Acid
Vitamin B12	Cobalamin
Vitamin C	Ascorbic Acid

People who consume a balanced diet typically do not require vitamin supplementation. Many people have poor diets that are low in nutritional value, and may require a vitamin supplement to prevent nutrient deficiencies. Calcium and vitamin D intake remains insufficient for the majority of adults and children. Folate intake among women of child-bearing age can be insufficient. A lack of thiamine (vitamin B1) is common in alcoholism, and can be due to malabsorption, including from Crohn's Disease, and can occur after obesity surgery, with advanced HIV and from a few other conditions. Thiamine deficiency can cause Wernicke's encephalopathy. Symptoms of Wernicke's include mental confusion, ataxia, tremor and vision changes. As the symptoms of Wernicke's fade, Korsakoff syndrome tends to develop (also called Korsakoff psychosis), which is permanent neurologic (mental) damage. Pharmacists are part of the solution to problems associated with vitamin deficiencies. Anticonvulsants can contribute to calcium deficiency; supplementation with calcium and vitamin D is required for most patients. There are other individual drugs that deplete nutrients, require a supplement to work properly or require a supplement to reduce toxicity (see table on the following page).

CALCIUM & VITAMIN D

For all prescription medications for low bone density (osteopenia or osteoporosis) adequate calcium and vitamin D supplementation should be recommended, if dietary intake is inadequate. Low levels of vitamin D impairs calcium absorption. Patients who do not receive enough vitamin D from the sun or diet can benefit from supplementation with both calcium and vitamin D. Calcium and vitamin D supplementation is an essential topic for pharmacists since they often recommend OTC products. Product type and selection is discussed in the Osteoporosis, Menopause & Testosterone Use chapter.

The American Academy of Pediatrics (AAP) makes the following recommendations for infants and children:

- Exclusively breastfed infants or babies drinking less than 1 liter of baby formula need 400 IU of vitamin D daily. *Poly-Vi-Sol* products (discussed later) or generics are acceptable.
- Older children who do not drink at least 4 cups of vitamin D fortified milk also need vitamin D supplementation.

FOLIC ACID (FOLATE)

Folate deficiency causes birth defects of the brain and spinal cord (neural tube defects). All women of childbearing age should obtain 400 mcg/day of folic acid. During pregnancy, folate requirements increase to 600 mcg/day. Folate should be taken at least one month before pregnancy and continued for the first 2 – 3 months of pregnancy. Once pregnant, the woman will likely take a prescription prenatal vitamin which is continued throughout the pregnancy since it also contains calcium (not enough, about 200 mg) and some iron. Folate is in many healthy foods, including fortified cereals (some of which are not healthy), dried beans, leafy green vegetables and orange juice. Multivitamins usually contain an amount in the recommended range. Prescription prenatal vitamins usually contain 1,000 mcg, or 1 mg, of folate. The newer birth control pills *Beyaz* and *Safyral* contain folate, however it is less expensive to use a different birth control pill with a supplement. *Beyaz* and *Safyral* contain the potassium-sparing progestin drospirenone, with ethinyl estradiol and levomefolate.

VITAMIN E

It is unusual to have a vitamin E deficiency, since it is present in many foods. Vitamin E in foods is considered healthy, but excess intake in supplements is considered a health risk (particularly CVD risk); patients should not exceed 400 IU daily.

IRON

AAP Iron Recommendations

AGE	TREATMENT
0 – 4 months	Supplemental iron is not required.
4 – 6 months	Formulas contain adequate iron; supplementation is not required. Breastfed babies need 1 mg/kg/day from 4-6 months old and until consuming iron-rich foods. At about 6 months most breastfed babies get about half their calories from other foods, which may be adequate.
6 – 12 months	Need 11 mg/day of iron. Food sources are preferred; supplement as-needed.
1 – 3 years	Need 7 mg/day of iron. Food sources are preferred; supplement as-needed.

Pre-Term Infants

- Preterm (< 37 weeks) breastfed infants should receive 2 mg/kg/day of elemental iron supplementation from age 1 – 12 months. Most preterm formula-fed infants receive enough iron from formula, but some still require supplementation.

Adolescent Girls

- Adolescent girls are at risk of anemia once menstruation begins. During this time, females should consume a diet high in iron-rich foods such as beans, eggs, fortified-cereals and meats. Some will need an oral iron supplement.

Iron-Only Supplements (generics available)

Check the label on iron drops because the amount of iron provided by the dropper ranges from 10 – 15 mg.

- *Fer-In-Sol* Iron Supplement Drops
- *Feosol* tablets and caplets

Vitamin Supplements with Iron

- *Poly-Vi-Sol* Vitamin Drops With Iron: use if both vitamin D and iron are needed
- Others: *Flintstones* Children's Chewable Multivitamin plus Iron, *Pokemon* Children's Multiple Vitamin with Iron and store brands

DRUGS THAT CAUSE NUTRIENT DEPLETION

DRUG	DEPLETED NUTRIENT	CHAPTER
Acetazolamide	Calcium, potassium	Travelers, Glaucoma
Antiepileptic drugs (including carbamazepine, lamotrigine, oxcarbazepine, phenobarbital/primidone, phenytoin, topiramate, valproic acid/divalproex, zonisamide)	Calcium*	Seizures/Epilepsy, Bipolar Disorder, others
Amphotericin B	Magnesium, potassium	Infectious Diseases III
Isoniazid	Vitamin B6	Infectious Diseases II (for neuropathy prevention)
Loop diuretics	Potassium	Hypertension, Heart Failure
Metformin	Vitamin B12	Diabetes
Methotrexate	Folate	Autoimmune, Oncology II
Orlistat	Beta-carotene, fat-soluble vitamins	Weight Loss
Proton Pump Inhibitors	Magnesium, vitamin B12 (> 2 years of treatment)	GERD
Sulfamethoxazole	Folate	Infectious Diseases I

**A supplement is needed for most patients using these drugs. Calcium should be given with vitamin D, if needed.*

CONDITIONS WITH RECOMMENDED SUPPLEMENTS

CONDITION	RECOMMENDED SUPPLEMENT	CHAPTER
Alcoholism	Vitamin B1, folate	Hepatitis & Liver Disease
Microcytic Anemia	Ferrous sulfate	Anemia
Macrocytic Anemia	Vitamin B12 and/or folate	Anemia
Pregnancy	Folate, calcium, vitamin D, pyridoxine (for nausea)	Pregnancy
Osteopenia/Osteoporosis	Calcium, vitamin D	Osteoporosis, Pregnancy
Osteomalacia (Rickets)	Calcium, vitamin D	
Chronic Kidney Disease	Vitamin D	Renal Disease, Bipolar Disorder (for lithium side effect)
Scurvy	Vitamin C	
Crohn's Disease (and possibly ulcerative colitis)	Patient specific-depends on levels; can require iron, zinc, folate, calcium, vitamin D, B vitamins	Inflammatory Bowel Disease
Bariatric Surgery	Various; patient-specific, refer to chapter	Weight Loss

HOMEOPATHIC PRODUCTS

Homeopathy is based on "the law of similars" or the concept that "like is cured by like." This is the belief that giving very small amounts of a substance, which in its undiluted form causes similar symptoms of the illness, will protect the patient or cure them of the illness. The quantity of homeopathic substances in a product are reported in X or C dilution scales. X represents a 1:10 dilution and C represents a 1:100 dilution of solute:solvent. The number in front of the X or C is the number of subsequent dilutions. The more dilute a substance is, the more "potent" it is considered.

Most evidence does not support the validity of homeopathy; however, many are advocates. The remedies may provide a placebo benefit or may be labeled as homeopathic but actually contain measurable concentrations of drugs, nutrients or dietary supplements. In 2010, *Hyland's Teething Tablets* were recalled due to cases of belladonna toxicity. The amount of belladonna could be measured and was unsafe. It is tempting to use the term "homeopathic" on a label. It sounds nice, and if a manufacturer labels a product "homeopathic", they are permitted to make health claims, while dietary supplements are not allowed by law to claim benefit for particular conditions. There have been other recent examples of products labeled as homeopathic which actually were not. Always check the quantity of ingredients.

Select Guidelines/References

National Center for Complementary and Integrative Health (NCCIH). Use of complementary health approaches in the U.S. National Health Interview Survey. https://nccih.nih.gov/research/statistics/NHIS/2012/natural-products (accessed 2019 Apr 15).

Baker RD, Greer FR. Diagnosis and prevention of iron deficiency and iron-deficiency anemia in infants and young children (0-3 years of age). Pediatrics. 2010;126(5):1040-50.

CHAPTER CONTENT

Emergency Preparedness 1033
Toxicology 1034
Prevention of Accidental Overdose 1034
Initial Overdose Management 1034
Hospital Overdose Management 1035
Common Symptomatic Treatment 1035
Decontamination with Activated Charcoal 1035
Antidotes for Common Poisonings 1035
Acetaminophen 1036
N-Acetylcysteine Treatment 1036
Opioids 1036
Initial Management of Suspected Opioid Overdose 1036
Additional Antidotes 1037
Antidotes for Common Bites and Stings 1039

CONTENT LEGEND

(💡) = Study Tip Gal

CHAPTER 81

EMERGENCY PREPAREDNESS, TOXICOLOGY & ANTIDOTES

EMERGENCY PREPAREDNESS

Pharmacy staff can be involved in the response to a disaster, which can include natural disasters (e.g., floods), industrial accidents, terrorist attacks that involve the release of biological and chemical agents, and disasters from radioactive, nuclear or explosive devices.

Pharmacists should be primarily involved in the planning and execution of pharmaceutical distribution and medication management during a disaster. Legal issues regarding dispensing a drug during an emergency (such as with the Emergency Prescription Assistance Program), are discussed in RxPrep's MPJE Course.

It is most important for the pharmacy staff involved in preparing for an emergency to be well-informed about likely threats in their locality and to coordinate the drug components included in the emergency response plans with the federal, regional/state and local agencies responsible for the plan development and maintenance. The pharmacists involved with these efforts should ensure that any drug stockpiling efforts are in agreement with these plans. Pharmacists should discourage inappropriate stockpiling by individual institutions that are not involved with the emergency response plans. Pharmacists should be familiar with emergency protocols for their institution or workplace, including those for evacuation, disaster preparedness, mass dispensing (if required) and poisoning emergencies.

Communications concerning emergency planning and response requires an electronic network that should include the hospital pharmacy department directors and local pharmacies that can serve the needs of the community. The network should be used to transmit urgent information related to emergency preparedness and to circulate important new information related to pharmacist involvement on disaster response teams, such as a new biological threat, or a heightened state of emergency. Pharmacists involved from a hospital setting should be familiar with the recommendations of the American Society of Health-System Pharmacists (ASHP). The CDC pages on Emergency Preparedness and Response include recommendations for exposure to biological agents, information on current disease outbreaks and treatment for chemical and radiation exposure. One of the antidotes for exposure to radioactive iodine (KI, potassium iodide) is reviewed in the Thyroid Disorders chapter because it is used for other purposes.

TOXICOLOGY

Toxicology is the study of poisonous chemicals, which includes drugs at unsafe doses. Children are the most common victims of accidental poisoning in the U.S. The top categories of exposures in children are to cosmetics/personal care products, analgesics and cleaning substances. Accidental poisoning is common among the elderly, primarily due to mental or physical impairment, the use of multiple drugs and reduced elimination of the drug from the body. Poisoning can be due to illicit (illegal) drug use or FDA-approved drugs (e.g., opioids), taken alone or in combination with other drugs including fixed dose combinations (e.g., hydrocodone and acetaminophen). Poisoning can be intentional, such as with attempted suicide, or as an act of revenge or in situations such as drug-facilitated sexual assault.

PREVENTION OF ACCIDENTAL OVERDOSE

To reduce accidental poisoning in children, child-resistant (C-R) containers are helpful, but are not foolproof. These are required for prescription drugs unless waived by the patient (or the provider for a single exception), or with specific substances that are excluded from this requirement, such as nitroglycerin sublingual tablets. Non-prescription (OTC) drugs that require C-R containers include anything containing iron, acetaminophen, salicylates, NSAIDs, diphenhydramine, "imidazoline" vasoconstrictors such as naphazoline and oxymetazoline and drugs that have been switched from Rx to OTC status. Non-drug compounds that are dangerous if swallowed require C-R packaging, such as turpentine. A list of drugs that must have C-R packaging is provided in the RxPrep MPJE Course, since this is a federal legal requirement. Common C-R packaging includes screw caps that require more than a simple turn to open (such as pressing down with the palm when turning to open), unit-dose packaging and the card adherence and safety packaging (*Optilock*) that requires the user to press on one side while pulling the medication card out of the other side. *Optilock* packaging can help with adherence since each dose is labeled with the day it should be taken (see image above).

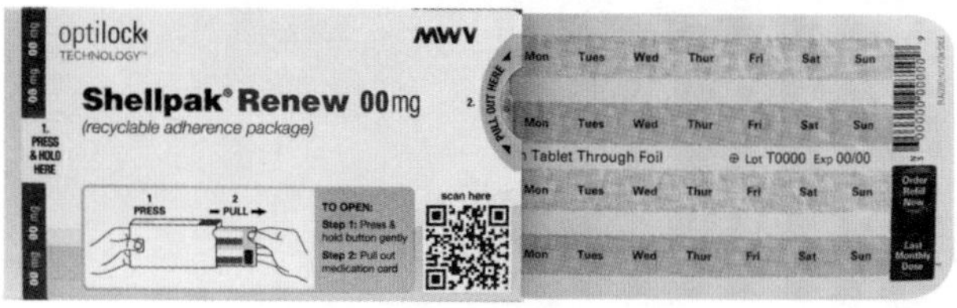

INITIAL OVERDOSE MANAGEMENT

If poisoning is suspected, anyone can contact Poison Control by phone (1-800-222-1222) to receive guidance and recommendations. Basic first aid for poisonings should be initiated immediately after the exposure.

- For topical exposure, remove contaminated clothing and run water over the skin for 10 minutes, then wash with soap and rinse to remove the poison from the skin.
- For ocular exposure, remove contact lenses and rinse eye/s with a gentle stream of water for at least 15 minutes.
- For oral ingestion, remove any remaining substance/s from the mouth. If there are symptoms of burning or irritation, drink a small amount of water or milk immediately.
- For inhaled exposure, move to fresh air immediately. Stay away from toxic fumes and/or gases.
- For ingestion of button batteries (commonly found in electronics), give two teaspoons of honey every 10 minutes while seeking immediate medical care. Ingestion can be fatal within hours, and honey or sucralfate can slow damage to the esophagus and airway.

Ipecac syrup, used previously to induce emesis for certain exposures, is no longer recommended or commercially available but remains in many home medicine cabinets. Instruct others not to give ipecac syrup, or use any other mechanism to induce vomiting.

If the patient is unconscious, having difficulty breathing, appears agitated or is having a seizure, call 911. If the patient is not breathing and/or has no pulse, initiate basic life support until emergency help arrives. The ABCs (Airway, Breathing and Circulation) must be addressed. First, check to see if the patient has a pulse; immediately start chest compressions (CPR) if no pulse is present. Breathing support, including assisted ventilation, may be required. This maintenance of the ABCs is commonly referred to as supportive care, and is the mainstay of treatment until medications are cleared from the body. Patients must be transported to the nearest hospital to receive specialized care for overdoses of this severity.

HOSPITAL OVERDOSE MANAGEMENT

Correct identification of the ingested substance/s is helpful to correctly treat and support the patient. Pharmacists can assist in identifying ingested substances by interviewing family members or calling the patient's pharmacy. For some substances, specific antidotes or dialysis may be used. Antidotes for common overdoses are discussed later in the chapter. In many cases of overdose, more than one drug is involved and more than one antidote may be required.

If the specific cause of the overdose remains unknown, patients are treated with supportive care and symptomatic treatment to minimize symptoms of the overdose (see Study Tip Gal below). Some overdoses have specific symptoms that can help healthcare providers identify the exposure or ingestion (e.g., anticholinergic overdose, see table).

Several of the most dangerous compounds do not cause immediate symptoms when toxic. The clinician should consider the formulation, quantity and timing of ingestion of these substances. For example, in an acetaminophen overdose the patient can remain asymptomatic or have non-specific symptoms (such as nausea, abdominal pain, fatigue) until end organ toxicity (liver failure) becomes apparent.

COMMON SYMPTOMATIC TREATMENT

Many different medications can cause similar symptoms following overdose. Typically, these symptoms are managed similarly regardless of ingested drug.

Symptom: management

Agitation: sedatives, such as benzodiazepines

Bradycardia: atropine, inotropes

Seizure: benzodiazepines

Hypertension: IV vasodilator

Hypoglycemia: dextrose

Hypotension: IV fluids, vasopressors

QRS widening: sodium bicarbonate

Sedation: protection of airway with intubation

DECONTAMINATION WITH ACTIVATED CHARCOAL

Activated charcoal is used in the emergency treatment of specific types of orally ingested drugs and is an early step in some overdose protocols. Activated charcoal needs to be given quickly and is most effective when used within one hour of ingestion. The idea is to stop the absorption of as much of the drug as possible while it is still in the gut. The charcoal adsorbs the drug, which prevents GI absorption and systemic toxicity. The dose of activated charcoal is 1 g/ kg. Typically, only one dose of activated charcoal is administered. Multiple-doses should only be considered if a patient has ingested a life-threatening amount of carbamazepine, dapsone, phenobarbital, quinine or theophylline.

Prior to using activated charcoal, the airway should be protected (with intubation, if needed) to prevent aspiration. Aspiration is the inhalation of foreign material, usually vomit, and can cause lung irritation leading to respiratory failure or respiratory infections. Some ingested compounds can increase the risk of aspiration [such as with hydrocarbons (petroleum products including gasoline and paint thinner)] and care must be taken to protect the airway with these ingestions. Activated charcoal is contraindicated when the airway is unprotected (the patient is unconscious, cannot clear their throat and/or hold their head upright), or with intestinal obstruction, a gastrointestinal tract that is not intact or with decreased peristalsis. Potential complications include transient constipation, bowel obstruction and regurgitation. If administered via an incorrectly placed nasogastric tube, there is an increased risk of aspiration, with consequent pulmonary complications (including death).

ANTIDOTES FOR COMMON POISONINGS

Antidotes are substances that stop the harmful effects of the poison (or overdosed drug). Many are used off-label in the management of poisonings. According to 2017 American Association of Poison Control Centers (AAPCC) data, the most commonly ingested substances are analgesics, household cleaning substances, cosmetic products, sedative hypnotics, antipsychotics, antidepressants, antihistamines and cardiovascular medications. Analgesics includes both prescription (e.g., opioids) and non-prescription (e.g., acetaminophen) pain medications. Because of the frequency of these overdoses, they will be covered individually. The remaining antidotes are found in the table.

ACETAMINOPHEN

Acetaminophen is the most common cause of drug-induced liver injury (DILI); excessive ingestion can lead to hepatotoxicity. Hepatotoxicity is a dose-dependent adverse effect caused by the increased metabolism of acetaminophen by CYP450 2E1 to *N*-acetyl-*p*-benzoquinone imine (NAPQI). NAPQI can covalently bind to liver cell proteins and cause liver injury, and ultimately, liver failure (see figure). Acetaminophen overdose presents in four phases:

- Phase 1 (1 – 24 hours): commonly asymptomatic or non-specific symptoms, such as nausea and vomiting.
- Phase 2 (24 – 48 hours): hepatotoxicity evident on labs (e.g., elevated INR, AST/ALT); any symptoms from phase 1 usually subside.
- Phase 3 (48 – 96 hours): fulminant hepatic failure (e.g., jaundice, coagulopathy, renal failure and/or death).
- Phase 4 (> 96 hours): the patient recovers or receives a liver transplant.

In order to prevent hepatotoxicity, acetaminophen toxicity must be identified early and the antidote, N-acetylcysteine (NAC), given quickly. NAC works by increasing glutathione, which increases glutathione-S-transferase (GSH). GSH converts NAPQI to mercapturic acid, which can safely be excreted from the body. If NAPQI has already bonded to hepatocytes, the damage is irreversible.

When the acetaminophen level is available and the exposure has occurred within the past 24 hours, it is used as the basis for treatment. To determine the risk of hepatotoxicity following acetaminophen ingestion, acetaminophen blood levels are drawn and plotted on the Rumack–Matthew nomogram in comparison to the time from ingestion. If there is possible or probable hepatotoxicity, NAC should be started. NAC is available in both oral and IV formulations (see Study Tip Gal).

N-ACETYLCYSTEINE TREATMENT

N-acetylcysteine (*Cetylev* effervescent tablets for oral solution or *Acetadote IV*).

Restores hepatic glutathione (acts as a glutathione substrate).

Oral: 140 mg/kg x 1, followed by 70 mg/kg every 4 hours x 17 additional doses. Repeat the dose if emesis occurs within 1 hour of administration.

Intravenous: 150 mg/kg IV over 60 minutes, followed by 50 mg/kg IV over 4 hours, followed by 100 mg/kg IV over 16 hours.

Acetaminophen Metabolism and Use of N-acetylcysteine (NAC)

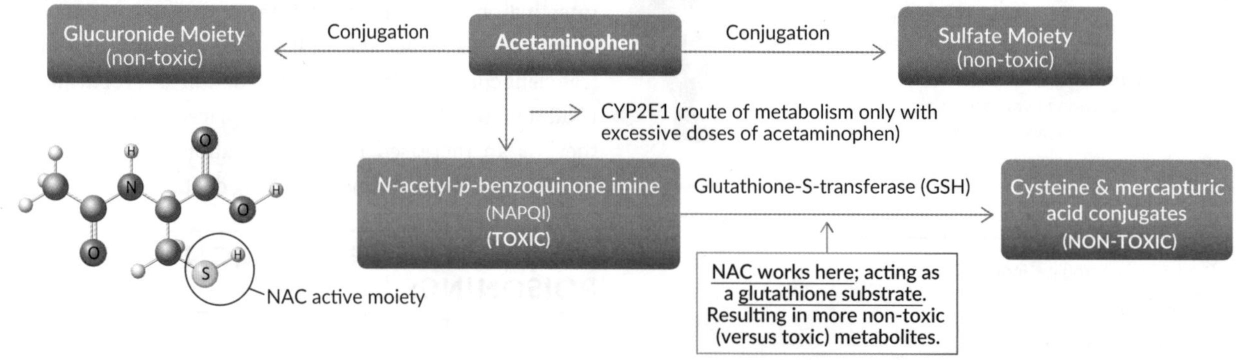

OPIOIDS

Opioid abuse, overdose and related deaths have become an epidemic in the U.S. Acute opioid overdose can lead to life-threatening respiratory depression and sedation. The depressant effects of opioids can easily be reversed if the appropriate antidote, naloxone, is administered quickly. There are minimal to no adverse effects associated when giving naloxone to a patient who did not ingest any opioids (see Study Tip Gal). In many states, pharmacists can dispense naloxone without a prescription to patients at risk for opioid-induced respiratory depression. Various naloxone products are currently available and are covered in the Pain chapter.

INITIAL MANAGEMENT OF SUSPECTED OPIOID OVERDOSE

Contact 911 if patient is unconscious, having difficulty breathing, agitated, or is having a seizure.

Ensure patient's airway, breathing and circulation is maintained.

Attempt to identify substance/s of overdose:

Opioid overdose can present as slowed breathing, pinpoint pupils, altered mental status and/or unconsciousness.

Administer naloxone if any potential for opioid overdose. Naloxone is not harmful if opioids are not present.

When in doubt, give naloxone. It could save a life.

ADDITIONAL ANTIDOTES

DRUG OVERDOSE	SYMPTOMS/TREATMENT
Anticholinergics: atropine, diphenhydramine, dimenhydrinate, scopolamine, *Atropa belladonna* (deadly nightshade), jimson weed	Symptoms: "red as a beet": flushing, "dry as bone": dry skin and mucous membranes, "blind as a bat": mydriasis with double or blurry vision, "mad as a hatter": altered mental status, "hot as a hare": fever Primarily supportive care, rarely physostigmine is given; physostigmine inhibits the enzyme that breaks down acetylcholine (ACh), acetylcholinesterase, which ↑ ACh and ↓ anticholinergic toxicity
Anticoagulants: warfarin, direct thrombin inhibitors, factor Xa inhibitors, heparin, low molecular weight heparins	Agent specific: see Anticoagulation chapter for more details **Phytonadione (vitamin K)**: warfarin **Prothrombin complex concentrate *(Kcentra)***: warfarin, factor Xa inhibitors **Protamine**: heparin, low molecular weight heparin **Idarucizumab *(Praxbind)***: dabigatran **Andexanet Alfa *(Andexxa)***: apixaban, rivaroxaban
Benzodiazepines	**Flumazenil** *(Romazicon)*: can cause seizures when used in patients on benzodiazepines chronically; sometimes used off-label for non-benzodiazepine hypnotic overdose (e.g., zolpidem), but not routinely recommended
Beta-blockers	Glucagon (if unresponsive to symptomatic treatment) High dose insulin with glucose may be used in patients refractory to glucagon Lipid emulsion to enhance elimination of some lipophilic drugs
Calcium channel blockers	Same as beta-blockers plus: Calcium (chloride or gluconate): administer calcium IV only, avoid fast infusion, monitor ECG, do not infuse calcium in same line as phosphate-containing solutions
Cyanide: smoke inhalation, nitroprusside in high doses/long durations/renal impairment	Hydroxocobalamin *(Cyanokit)* Sodium thiosulfate + sodium nitrite *(Nithiodote)*
Digoxin, oleander, foxglove	**Digoxin Immune Fab *(DigiFab)*** Each *DigiFab* 40 mg vial binds ~0.5 mg digoxin; when the amount ingested or digoxin level is unknown, the max adult dose is 20 vials Interferes with digoxin levels drawn after it has been given
Ethanol (alcoholic drinks)	If suspected to be a chronic alcohol user, administer thiamine (vitamin B1) to prevent Wernicke's encephalopathy (neurological damage)
5-fluorouracil (5-FU), capecitabine	Uridine triacetate *(Vistogard, Xuriden)*
Heavy metals: arsenic, copper, gold, lead, mercury, thallium	Dimercaprol: arsenic, gold, mercury [or lead in conjunction with calcium disodium edetate (CaNa2 EDTA)] Penicillamine: copper Succimer *(Chemet)*, dimercaptosuccinic acid *(DMSA)*: lead Ferric hexacyanoferrate, ["Prussian blue" *(Radiogardase)*]: thallium
Hydrocarbons: petroleum products, gasoline, kerosene, mineral oil, paint thinners	Do not induce vomiting; keep patient NPO due to aspiration risk
Insulin or other hypoglycemics	Dextrose injection or infusion (drip) Glucagon (when IV or oral dextrose cannot be administered) Sulfonylurea-induced hypoglycemia: octreotide *(Sandostatin)*
Isoniazid	Pyridoxine (vitamin B6), benzodiazepines and/or barbiturates For acute neurotoxicity (seizure, coma), administer IV pyridoxine Oral pyridoxine 10 – 50 mg is used daily with isoniazid to prevent neuropathies
Iron Aluminum	Deferoxamine *(Desferal)*, deferiprone *(Ferriprox)* and deferasirox *(Exjade, Jadenu)* – for iron overload from blood transfusions
Local anesthetics (bupivacaine, mepivacaine, ropivacaine) and other lipophilic drugs	IV lipid emulsion 20% Symptomatic treatment for seizures (benzodiazepines)

DRUG OVERDOSE	SYMPTOMS/TREATMENT
Organophosphates (OPs), including industrial insecticides (malathion, others) and nerve (warfare) gases (sarin, others)	Atropine and pralidoxime or in combination *(DuoDote, ATNAA)* OPs block acetylcholinesterase, which increases ACh levels; atropine is an anticholinergic and blocks the effects of ACh to reduce the cholinergic SLUDD symptoms: salivation, lacrimation, urination, diarrhea/defecation Pralidoxime treats muscle weakness and relieves paralysis of respiratory muscles by reactivating cholinesterase that was inactivated by exposure to the OPs
Methotrexate	Leucovorin (folinic acid), levoleucovorin *(Fusilev)*, glucarpidase *(Voraxaze)*: for rescue after high-dose in cancer treatment, after an accidental overdose, or to ↓ toxicity and counteract the effects of impaired elimination
Methemoglobinemia resulting from medications like topical benzocaine (in *OraGel* or teething products), dapsone, nitrates or sulfonamides.	Methylene blue *(ProvayBlue)* Methylene blue is contraindicated in patients with G6PD deficiency; avoid administration with SSRIs and SNRIs
Mushrooms (amatoxin-containing)	Silibinin *(Legalon SIL)* is the flavonoid in milk thistle, sometimes used for hepatoprotection Symptomatic treatment for severe muscarinic symptoms (bradycardia) with atropine
Naphthalene, from mothballs	Methylene blue *(ProvayBlue)*
Neostigmine, pyridostigmine	Pralidoxime *(Protopam)*: counteracts the muscle weakness and/or respiratory depression secondary to overdose of anticholinesterase medications used to treat myasthenia gravis
Nicotine, including e-cigarettes	Supportive care Atropine is a muscarinic receptor antagonist and should be given to treat symptomatic bradycardia Benzodiazepines should be given to treat seizures
Paralytics (e.g., rocuronium bromide, vecuronium bromide, pancuronium bromide)	For reversal of the effects of neuromuscular blockade in adults undergoing surgery: Neostigmine methylsulfate *(Bloxiverz)*: rocuronium, vecuronium and pancuronium Atropine or glycopyrrolate can be given to prevent bradycardia from neostigmine Sugammadex *(Bridion)*: rocuronium and vecuronium
Salicylates	General concept: for a weak base, increase excretion by acidifying the urine, and for a weak acid, increase excretion by alkalinizing the urine Salicylates are acidic. Sodium bicarbonate is an alkalinizing agent and is given to alkalinize the urine; this will decrease the drug reabsorption and increase the excretion of the salicylates and other weak acids
Stimulant overdose: amphetamines, including ADHD and weight loss drugs, cocaine, ephedrine, caffeine, theophylline, MDMA (ecstasy)	Supportive care for agitation or seizures (benzodiazepines)
Toxic alcohols: ethylene glycol (antifreeze), diethylene glycol, methanol	Fomepizole *(Antizol)* is preferred Ethanol (2nd line)
Tricyclic antidepressants (TCAs)	Overdose can quickly cause fatal arrhythmias Sodium bicarbonate: to decrease a widened QRS complex Supportive care for agitation or seizures (benzodiazepines), if present Vasopressors may be needed for hypotension
Valproic acid or topiramate-induced hyperammonemia	Levocarnitine *(Carnitor)*

ANTIDOTES FOR COMMON BITES AND STINGS

TOXIN	ANTIDOTE	COMMENTS
Animal bites	Rabies vaccine *(RabAvert, Imovax Rabies)* with Human rabies immune globulin *(HyperRAB S/D, Imogam Rabies HT)*	High-risk animal bites or exposure (no previous rabies vaccination): give vaccine and human rabies immune globulin (HRIG). Vaccine given 1 mL IM in the deltoid (adults) or thigh (children, infants) on days 0, 3, 7, 14 and immune globulin is given 20 units/kg on day 0, infiltrated around wound site and a location separate from vaccine site. HRIG is not useful after day 7 of vaccine or in previously immunized individuals. Clean wound with soap and water. Tetanus shot is required if it has been at least 10 years since the last booster shot. See the Immunizations chapter for more details.
Black Widow spider bites	Antivenin for *Latrodectus mactans*	Predominantly found in southern and western states. Children and frail elderly are at highest risk for severe injury. The primary treatment is supportive care (opioids for pain management and benzodiazepines for muscle spasms).
Scorpion stings	Antivenin immune FAB *Centruroides (Anascorp)*	Scorpions with venom potent enough to cause clinically severe symptoms are found mainly in the southwest.
Snake bites: eastern coral snake, Texas coral snake, copperhead snake, rattlesnake	**Crotalidae polyvalent immune FAB *(CroFab)*** for copperhead and rattlesnake bites Crotalidae Immune F(ab')2 *(Anavip)* for rattlesnake bites	Do not use ice; do not cut/suck out venom; transport patient to healthcare facility.

CLINICAL SCENARIO

A patient is found down, unarousable, with slow and shallow breathing at home by a family member. It is unknown how long the patient has been in this state. Unlabeled bottles of liquid and pills are found at the scene.

Initial Overdose Management

First, it is important to maintain the ABCs. Given the slow and shallow breathing, the patient may need to be intubated. The family should call 911.

Hospital Management

Continue to maintain the ABCs (intubate the patient if needed). Check the patient's vitals (blood pressure, heart rate) and blood glucose. Hypoglycemia is easy to detect and correct.

Pharmacists role: help identify possible substances that could have been ingested. Obtain a medication history from family/pharmacy. Assist team with supportive care based on symptoms and antidote selection based on physical exam findings and laboratory results.

Possible Actions

Always treat the most life-threatening overdose first (the substance causing impaired ABCs).

- Significant somnolence and depressed breathing could be an opioid overdose. Naloxone should be administered.
- Hypoglycemia: give dextrose (IV or PO) or glucagon if unable to give dextrose. If the patient was on a sulfonylurea, can give octreotide.
- Benzodiazepines: check a urine drug screen for benzodiazepines. Consider flumazenil (caution: can cause seizures if the patient takes it chronically).
- Toxic alcohols: check an anion gap. If significantly elevated, check levels of ethanol, methanol, propylene glycol and treat with fomepizole.
- Antidepressants (especially if this was a known/suspected suicide attempt): TCAs – check ECG and give sodium bicarbonate if QRS is widened.
- Acetaminophen (opioids are commonly prescribed in combination with acetaminophen): obtain an acetaminophen level. Use the Rumack-Matthew nomogram to determine if NAC should be given.

Select Guidelines/References

National Library of Medicine TOXNET. http://toxnet.nlm.nih.gov (accessed 2019 Apr 13).
Lexi-Comp Toxicology Online. http://online.lexi.com/lco/action/home/tox (accessed 2019 Apr 13).
CDC, Emergency Preparedness. http://emergency.cdc.gov (accessed 2019 Apr 13).

PATIENT CASES

CONTENTS

CHAPTER 82

CASES, EXAM-STYLE PRACTICE | **1042**

CHAPTER CONTENT

Case #1 1042
Case #1 Questions 1044
Case #2 1045
Case #2 Questions 1046
Case #3 1047
Case #3 Questions 1048
Answers to Case Questions 1049

CHAPTER 82
CASES, EXAM-STYLE PRACTICE

CASE #1

History of Present Illness: DD is a 67-year-old white male who works as a manager in a shipping and receiving department. He presents for follow-up of fatigue, right and left-sided finger stiffness/soreness, and right-sided hip stiffness/pain. He recently had a rheumatoid factor ordered that was reported as 86 U/mL. Other complaints include decreased sexual desire, productive cough, dyspnea on exertion and poor sleep quality.

Past Medical History: hypertension, depression, anxiety, COPD

Family History: father deceased (stroke), mother still living with dementia

Social History: drinks alcohol socially on weekends, former smoker (quit approximately 4 years ago)

Allergies: *Vasotec* (cough)

Vitals: height: 5' 11", weight: 168 lbs, BP 148/88 mmHg, HR 88 BPM, RR 18 BPM

Physical Exam: rhonchi bilaterally, some SOB. Pain as described in the history of present illness. Active bowel sounds, last bowel movement earlier today. Some lower extremity edema.

MEDICATIONS:	NEW PRESCRIPTIONS:	
Amlodipine 10 mg PO daily	Methotrexate 7.5 mg PO weekly	
Atenolol 25 mg PO daily	Topical Pain Gel (Compound)	
Celexa 40 mg PO daily	Ketamine HCl	20 g
Zolpidem 10 mg PO QHS	Lidocaine HCl	8 g
Spiriva Respimat 2 inhalations daily	Ketoprofen	20 g
Welchol 3.75 grams PO daily	Polyethylene glycol	15 g
Omeprazole 20 mg PO daily	*Span 80*	7.5 g
	Sorbic acid	400 mg
	Poloxamer 30% gel	qs ad 175 g

Assessment and Plan: rheumatoid arthritis. See medication orders above. Follow up in 6 – 8 weeks for clinical assessment and laboratory monitoring. Add a long-acting beta-2 agonist for COPD. Patient prefers once daily medications (consult pharmacy for recommendation).

Labs (6 weeks later):

Na (135-146 mEq/L)	133	WBC (4-11 x 10^3 cells/mm^3)	3.1
K (3.5-5.3 mEq/L)	4.3	Hgb (13-17 g/dL)	11.8
Cl (98-110 mEq/L)	102	Hct (38-50%)	35
HCO3 (21-33 mmHg)	26	Platelets (150-450 x 10^3 cells/mm^3)	198
BUN (7-25 mg/dL)	14	PMNs (45-73%)	21
Creatinine (0.6-1.2 mg/dL)	0.9	Bands (3-5%)	25
Glucose (65-99 mg/dL)	122	Lymphocytes (20-40%)	40
Ca (8.5-10.5 mg/dL)	8.8	Monocytes (2-8%)	10
A1C (%)	6.2	Eosinophils (0-5%)	3
AST (10-40 U/L)	23	Basophils (0-1%)	1
ALT (10-40 U/L)	34	Total cholesterol (< 200 mg/dL)	168
BNP (< 100 pg/mL)	92	HDL (> 50 mg/dL)	38
Albumin (3.5-5 g/dL)	3.6	LDL (< 100 mg/dL)	120
RF (< 60 U/mL)	44	TG (< 150 mg/dL)	188
CCP Ab Ig (< 20 units)	43	10-year ASCVD risk (%)	22

Test your knowledge on this case with the questions on the following page.

CASE #1 QUESTIONS

1. Which of DD's medications can decrease A1C?

   A. Amlodipine
   B. *Welchol*
   C. Methotrexate
   D. *Spiriva Respimat*
   E. *Celexa*

2. Which medication is indicated for DD?

   A. Glipizide
   B. Rosuvastatin
   C. Lisinopril
   D. Calcium carbonate
   E. Iron dextran

3. Place the instructions for use of DD's current COPD maintenance inhaler in the correct order.

   A. Open the cap
   B. Press the dose release button and breathe in slowly
   C. Turn the clear base until it clicks
   D. Hold your breath as long as possible
   E. Breathe out fully away from the inhaler

4. Which inhaler should the pharmacist recommend for DD?

   A. *Proventil HFA*
   B. *Flovent HFA*
   C. *Combivent Respimat*
   D. *Arcapta Neohaler*
   E. *Trelegy Ellipta*

5. What is the percentage strength (w/w) of lidocaine in the compounded topical pain gel? (Round to the nearest TENTH.)

6. What is the purpose of *Span 80* in the compounded topical pain gel?

   A. Emollient
   B. Surfactant
   C. Preservative
   D. Sweetener
   E. Acidifier

7. What is the most likely role of sorbic acid in the compounded topical pain gel?

   A. Levigating agent
   B. Diluent
   C. Preservative
   D. Thickening agent
   E. Lubricant

8. What would be an appropriate beyond use date for the compounded topical pain gel?

   A. 7 days
   B. 14 days
   C. 30 days
   D. 3 months
   E. 6 months

9. Which medication is most likely causing DD's complaint of decreased sexual desire?

   A. Amlodipine
   B. *Celexa*
   C. *Welchol*
   D. Zolpidem
   E. Methotrexate

10. Calculate DD's absolute neutrophil count. (Round to the nearest WHOLE number.)

CASE #2

History of Present Illness: HG is a 69-year-old black female who was admitted to the hospital on January 5th with fever, chills, shortness of breath and right lower extremity swelling. Her initial work up revealed the following:

EF: 25%; CXR: bilateral fluid overload but no consolidations or infiltrates; Lower Extremity Ultrasound: positive right popliteal DVT; Urine Culture: > 100,000 CFUs/mL gram negative rods

Past Medical History: hypertension, dyslipidemia, type 2 diabetes, heart failure, peripheral neuropathy

Allergies: *Bactrim* (hives)

Home Medications: metformin 1,000 mg PO BID, *Altace* 5 mg PO BID, furosemide 20 mg PO daily, *Coreg* 6.25 mg PO BID, *Cymbalta* 30 mg PO daily, St. John's wort, cassia cinnamon 3 grams PO daily

ADMISSION ORDERS AND NOTES (JANUARY 5TH)

Continue all home medications except metformin and furosemide	*Lasix* 40 mg IV Q12H
Lantus 20 units SC daily	Enoxaparin – pharmacy to dose per protocol
Humalog 6 units SC TID-AC	Warfarin – pharmacy to dose per protocol
Humalog SC PRN per correction dose protocol	*Unasyn* 1.5 g IV Q6H
(Blood glucose goal = 140 mg/dL)	Nitroglycerin 100 mg/250 mL x 12 hours, titrate per protocol

Vitals (January 7th): height: 5' 1", weight: 126 lbs, BP 144/92 mmHg, HR 87 BPM, RR 18 BPM, T 98.7°F

Labs (January 7th):

Glu (65-99 mg/dL)	154
A1C (%)	7.5
Na (135-146 mEq/L)	133
K (3.5-5.3 mEq/L)	3.1
Cl (98-110 mEq/L)	102
HCO3 (21-33 mmHg)	22
BUN (7-25 mg/dL)	12
Creatinine (0.6-1.2 mg/dL)	1.4
INR	1.8

WBC (4-11 x 10^3 cells/mm^3)	8.2
RBC (3.8-5.1 x 10^6/mcL)	4.6
Hgb (12-16 g/dL)	12.1
Hct (36-46%)	38
Plt (150,000-400,000 cells/mm^3)	150
Anti-Xa (units/mL)	Pending
Total cholesterol (< 200 mg/dL)	166
HDL (> 50 mg/dL)	38
TG (< 150 mg/dL)	188

Urine Culture: *Klebsiella pneumoniae*

ANTIBIOTIC	MIC DILUTION	MIC INTERPRETATION
Amoxicillin/Clavulanate	< 8/4	S
Cefazolin	< 2	S
Ciprofloxacin	< 1	S
Gentamicin	< 2	S
Nitrofurantoin	< 32	S
Piperacillin/Tazobactam	< 16	S
Trimethoprim/Sulfamethoxazole	< 2/38	S

INR Report

DATE	INR
January 5	1.2
January 6	1.6
January 7	1.8
January 8	2.1

Test your knowledge on this case with the questions on the following page.

CASE #2 QUESTIONS

1. Which medication has the same mechanism of action as the beta-blocker HG takes at home?

   A. Esmolol
   B. Nadolol
   C. Nebivolol
   D. Labetalol
   E. Atenolol

2. The medical team wants to switch HG's IV *Lasix* to an equivalent oral dose. What dose should be recommended?

   A. 20 mg twice daily
   B. 40 mg once daily
   C. 40 mg twice daily
   D. 80 mg once daily
   E. 80 mg twice daily

3. Once stable, which intervention should be made to HG's home medication list?

   A. Change furosemide to chlorthalidone
   B. Add *Entresto*
   C. Increase the dose of *Coreg*
   D. Add lisinopril
   E. Add *Norvasc*

4. If the enoxaparin doses are administered at 0600 and 1800, what time should the anti-Xa level have been drawn?

   A. 0530
   B. 0630
   C. 1000
   D. 1400
   E. 1800

5. How many milliliters of *Lantus* will be administered with each dose?

6. Which of the following statements is true regarding *Lantus*?

   A. It can be mixed with regular insulin
   B. It can be given at bedtime
   C. It peaks at approximately 18 hours
   D. It is stable at room temperature for 42 days
   E. It is available as 500 units/mL

7. The hospital uses *Lantus* vials and *Humalog KwikPen* 200 units/mL. How many milliliters are contained in each *Humalog KwikPen* device?

   A. 0.03 mL
   B. 0.09 mL
   C. 1.5 mL
   D. 3 mL
   E. 10 mL

8. Based on HG's current insulin regimen, what is her correction factor? (Round to the nearest WHOLE number.)

9. Which of HG's medications can increase the risk of bleeding when used with warfarin?

   A. *Cymbalta*
   B. Metformin
   C. St. John's wort
   D. *Coreg*
   E. *Altace*

10. HG is most likely using cinnamon to treat:

    A. Dyslipidemia
    B. Depression
    C. Heart failure
    D. Diabetes
    E. Anxiety

CASE #3

PATIENT PROFILE

Patient Name	EG								
Address	1365 Stephens Avenue								
Age:	48	**Sex:**	M	**Race:**	African American	**Height:**	5'10"	**Weight:**	143 pounds
Allergies	Morphine – itching, Sulfa-rash								

DIAGNOSES	HOME MEDICATIONS
Epilepsy	Phenytoin 300 mg PO nightly
Barrett's esophagus	

MEDICATIONS

Date	Prescriber	Drug/Strength/Sig
10/9	Marks	Phenytoin 100 mg IV Q8 hours
10/9	Smith	D5NS IV infusion @ 50 mL/hr
10/9	Smith	Propofol IV infusion, starting at 5 mcg/kg/min. Titrate by 5 mcg/kg/min every 10 minutes to achieve a RASS of -2. Max dose 40 mcg/kg/min.
10/9	Smith	Morphine 2.5 mg IV Q3 hours prn severe pain
10/15	Smith	NS bolus 1000 mL IV x 1
10/15	Smith	Meropenem 1 gram IV Q8 hours
10/15	Smith	Tobramycin IV per pharmacy protocol (Hartford Nomogram)
10/15	Smith	Dexmedetomidine IV infusion, starting at 0.2 mcg/kg/hour. Titrate by 0.1 mcg/kg/hour every 30 minutes to achieve a RASS of -1. Max dose 0.7 mcg/kg/hour.
10/15	Taylor	Parenteral nutrition IV per pharmacy protocol
10/25	Doner	Enteral nutrition (Jevity 1.5) at 10 mL/hour
10/25	Doner	Phenytoin 100 mg via PEG tube

LAB/DIAGNOSTIC TESTS

Test	Normal Value	Results			
		Date: 10/9	**Date:** 10/15	**Date:** 10/19	**Date:** 10/25
Glu	65–99 mg/dL	102	118	101	110
Na	135-146 mEq/L	137	140	143	138
K	3.5-5.3 mEq/L	4.4	4.6	6.1	4.2
Cl	98-110 mEq/L	106	107	108	102
CO2	21-33 mEq/L	26	26	24	24
BUN	7-25 mg/dL	14	17	45	15
Creatinine	0.6-1.2 mg/dL	1.2	1.3	3.1	1.1
Alb	3.5-5 g/dL	2.9		3.2	
TG	< 150 mg/dL		507		
AST	10-40 units/L	23	40		
ALT	10-40 units/L	27	52		
WBC	4-11 x 10^3/mm^3	6.2	14.6	8.9	
PLT	150-450 x 10^3/mm^3	250	267	258	
Hgb	13-17 g/dL	11.3	10.8	10.6	
Hct	40-52%	43	37	38	
MCV	80-100 fL	65			
MRSA nasal swab		Positive			
Phenytoin, total (mcg/mL)				9	

PROGRESS NOTES

Date	Notes
10/9 at 1700	Vitals: BP 144/88 mmHg, HR 86 BPM, T 37°C; Patient admitted to the ICU s/p esophageal surgery. Plan: patient will remain intubated, sedated and NPO x 14 days. Will convert home medications to IV and start IV fluids.
10/15 at 1300	Vitals: BP 90/46 mmHg, HR 92 BPM, T 39°C; Patient remains intubated and sedated on propofol. Patient noted to have increased sputum production with increased purulence and increasing oxygen requirements. Plan: obtain chest X-ray and send blood and sputum cultures to evaluate for infection, and start broad spectrum antibiotics. DC propofol and start dexmedetomidine. DC IV fluids and start parenteral nutrition.
10/19 at 1100	Vitals: BP 130/76 mmHg, HR 56 BPM, T 36.5°C; Patient is less responsive and noted to have some seizure like activity. Urine output has decreased overnight. Peaked T-waves are noted on EKG. Plan: obtain EEG, BMP and phenytoin level.
10/25 at 1400	Vitals: BP 131/72 mmHg, HR 80 BPM, T 37°C; Patient remains stable; percutaneous G-tube (PEG) placed; extubated. Plan: DC parenteral nutrition and start enteral nutrition. DC IV phenytoin and administer medications via PEG

Test your knowledge on this case with the questions on the following page.

CASE #3 QUESTIONS

1. Based on his admission labs on 10/9, EG likely has a diagnosis of:

   A. Dyslipidemia
   B. Gout
   C. Iron deficiency anemia
   D. Osteoporosis
   E. Diabetes

2. The hospital stocks 500 mg/50 mL bottles of propofol. At what rate (mL/hour) should the nurse start the infusion on 10/9?

3. The medical team asks about a recommendation for VTE prophylaxis. Which of the following would be appropriate for EG? (Select **ALL** that apply.)

   A. Enoxaparin 40 mg subcutaneously daily
   B. Heparin 5,000 units subcutaneously Q8 hours
   C. *Lovenox* 1 mg/kg subcutaneously Q12 hours
   D. Rivaroxaban 15 mg PO BID
   E. Unfractionated heparin 80 units/kg IV once, followed by an infusion starting at 18 units/kg/hr and adjusted per dosing protocol

4. By 10/15, EG's propofol has been titrated up to 40 mcg/kg/min to achieve adequate sedation. Propofol is changed to dexmedetomidine. What adverse effect of propofol is the team concerned about?

   A. Anemia
   B. Emergence reaction
   C. Hyponatremia
   D. Pancreatitis
   E. Propylene glycol toxicity

5. On 10/15, EG's chest X-ray shows a focal opacity in the right upper lobe. The gram stain of the respiratory culture shows numerous white blood cells with many gram-positive cocci in clusters. Meropenem and tobramycin are ordered. What additional antibiotic should be recommended?

   A. Daptomycin
   B. Ciprofloxacin
   C. Linezolid
   D. Nafcillin
   E. *Unasyn*

Questions 6-7 relate to the Hartford nomogram for tobramycin dosing discussed in the Infectious Diseases I chapter.

6. The hospital policy for tobramycin dosing is to use the Hartford nomogram for extended interval dosing and round doses to the nearest 20 mg. What dose of tobramycin should EG receive based on the order from 10/15?

7. The tobramycin level was drawn 9 hours after the start of the infusion and the result was 4.8 mcg/mL. Based on the nomogram, what dosing interval should be ordered for EG?

   A. Q12H
   B. Q24H
   C. Q36H
   D. Q48H
   E. Q72H

8. On 10/15, the medical team orders parenteral nutrition per pharmacy. The pharmacist calculates EG's protein requirement to be 80 grams daily. Using a 15% amino acid solution, how many milliliters will be required to provide the daily protein requirement? (Round the final answer to the nearest WHOLE number.)

9. On 10/19, EG experiences seizure like activity. Which of his medications can lower the seizure threshold?

   A. *Diprivan*
   B. Meropenem
   C. Morphine
   D. *Dilantin*
   E. Tobramycin

10. What is EG's corrected phenytoin level on 10/19? (Round the final answer to the nearest TENTH.)

11. Which of the following can be used for the electrolyte abnormality on 10/19? (Select **ALL** that apply.)

    A. IV calcium gluconate
    B. IV conivaptan
    C. IV albumin
    D. IV insulin
    E. IV pamidronate

CASE #1 ANSWERS

1-**b**, refer to the Diabetes chapter

2-**b**, refer to the Dyslipidemia chapter

3-**c,a,e,b,d**, refer to the Chronic Obstructive Pulmonary Disease chapter

4-**d**, refer to the Chronic Obstructive Pulmonary Disease and Asthma chapters

5-**4.6%**, refer to the Calculations II chapter

6-**b**, refer to the Compounding chapters

7-**c**, refer to the Compounding chapters

8-**c**, refer to the Compounding chapters

9-**b**, refer to the Depression and Sexual Dysfunction chapters

10-**1426**, refer to the Calculations IV chapter

CASE #2 ANSWERS

1-**d**, refer to the Hypertension chapter

2-**e**, refer to the Chronic Heart Failure chapter

3-**c**, refer to the Chronic Heart Failure chapter

4-**c**, refer to the Anticoagulation chapter

5-**0.2 mL**, refer to the Diabetes chapter

6-**b**, refer to the Diabetes chapter

7-**d**, refer to the Diabetes chapter

8-**47**, refer to the Diabetes chapter

9-**a**, refer to the Learning Drug Interactions and Anticoagulation chapters

10-**d**, refer to the Dietary Supplements, Natural & Complementary Medicine chapter

CASE #3 ANSWERS

1-**c**, refer to the Anemia chapter

2-**1.95 mL/hour**, refer to the Calculations IV chapter

3-**a,b**, refer to the Anticoagulation chapter

4-**d**, refer to the Acute & Critical Care Medicine chapter

5-**c**, refer to the Infectious Diseases II chapter

6-**460 mg**, refer to the Infectious Diseases I chapter

7-**b**, refer to the Infectious Diseases I chapter

8-**533 mL**, refer to the Calculations III chapter

9-**b**, refer to the Seizures/Epilepsy chapter

10-**12.2 mcg/mL**, refer to the Seizures/Epilepsy chapter

11-**a,d**, refer to the Renal Disease chapter

INDEX

Quick Guides

Common Medical Abbreviations: 39
Diagnostic Tests: 27
How to Use the RxPrep Course Book: 14
Medical Terms: 30
Required Formulas: 25
Top Inpatient Drugs: 19
Top OTC Drugs: 23
Top Outpatient Drugs: 15

Study Tip Gals

"Color" Drug References: 89
A Penicillin Allergy, or Not?: 1007
ACE Inhibitors and ARBs for Albuminuria: 293
Acetaminophen Overdose: 798
Acne Treatment Summary: 574
Adjusting Phenytoin Doses: 949
Administration (Food) Requirements: 434
Adult Treatment Goals (ADA): 641
AED Cousins: 940
AEDs are CNS Depressants: 949
AEDs Have a Lot of Drug Interactions: 949
AFib: Rate vs. Rhythm Control: 509
Aminoglycosides: Good News, Bad News: 355
Anticholinergic Side Effects: 742
Anticoagulants are for Blood Clots: 526
Antidepressants: Select Adverse Effects: 885
AOM Treatment in Kids: When to Consider Observation: 379
ART Adverse Effects by Class and Agent: 435
Assessing and Treating Iron Deficiency Anemia: 544
Avoid in Pediatrics: 770
Blood Pressure Monitoring: 460
C. difficile Guideline Recommendations: 394
Calcium and Vitamin D: 715
Calories Provided from Macronutrients: 151
CAP Patient Assessment (Stepwise Approach): 382
Central Tendency Calculations: 202
ChemoMan and Major Toxicities of Common Chemotherapy Drugs: 837
Chemotherapy Adjunctive Medications: 838
Classifying Drugs with Vaughan Williams. 508
Coagulation Cascade: 527
Common Conversions: 117
Common Issues with Pancreatic Enzyme Products: 776
Common IV Fluids: 129
Common Migraine Triggers: 819
Common Resistant Pathogens: 346
Common Symptomatic Treatment: 1035
Comparison of Hepatitis Viruses: 303
Complications of Diabetes: 639
Concentrated Insulin Products: 656
Conversion between Anticoagulants: 532
COPD vs Asthma: 618
Cough and Cold Combo Products: What's in a Name?: 565
CrCl vs. GFR: 292
CYP Inducers: 59
CYP Inhibitors: 60
DAA Mechanisms and Regimens: 303
Decreasing Risk of Dry Mouth: 742
Depression Diagnosis: 881
Determining Add-On Treatment Based on Patient Risk: 448
Determining Statin Treatment Intensity Based on Patient Risk: 445
Determining the BUD For CSPs: 284
Diagnosis of Osteoporosis: 714
Diagnostic Criteria: 638
Diastat Acudial Dispensing: 939
Differences Between Dietary Supplements and Drugs: 1025
Diphenhydramine In Pharmacy; It's Everywhere: 559
Dispense in Original Container: 436
Dissociation Particles vs. Valence: 146
Do Not Use Abbreviations: 991
Does a Positive or Negative Test Require Action?: 1023
Dopamine Blocking Drugs that Can Worsen PD: 926
Dopamine Dosing: 753
Dose Adjustments for Michaelis-Menten Kinetics: 1015
Dosing Considerations for Select Highly Toxic Drugs: 835
Drug Absorption: 1010
Drug Summary for Osteoporosis Treatment and Prevention: 716
Drug Treatment of ACS: 482
Drug-Induced Raynaud's: 686
Drugs for Travelers' Diarrhea: 335
Drugs of Choice/Active Drugs for Specific Pathogens: 369
Epinephrine Auto-Injector Administration: 1006
Ez Tip for Excellent Zzzzzz (Sleep): 919
Factors to Consider When Selecting Drug Treatment: 662
Final Volume of Compounded IV Solutions: 171
Follow the Rules of Math: 127
General Principles for Treating Shock: 755
Glaucoma Treatment Goal: Decrease IOP: 567
Gonorrhea & Chlamydia: They Often Go Together: 396
Gout Treatment Basics: 827
H2RA and PPI Formulations to Know: 959
Height in Inches: 168
Hints for Understanding Monoclonal Antibodies: 872
Hormone Therapy: Health Risks and Appropriate Use: 722
How to Chew Nicotine Gum: 632
How to Round on the Exam: 117
Hydration, To Reduce Toxicity: 838
Hyperglycemic Crises Treatment: 661
Hypertension Guideline Recommendations: 461
Identifying Medication Therapy Problems: 110
Immunosuppression from Steroids: 674
Infertility Drugs Act Like Endogenous Hormones to Trigger Ovulation: 706
Influenza Vaccine Tips: 325
Inhaled Medications for CF: 774
Initial Management of Suspected Opioid Overdose: 1036
Initiating Basal-Bolus Insulin: 656
INSTI-Based Regimen (INSTI + 2 NRTIs): 418
Insulin Conversions: 657
Interferons: 307
Interpreting ABGs: 177
Interpreting Confidence Intervals: 205
Intolerance or Allergy?: 1003
Invalid Contraindications to Vaccination: 320
Irinotecan (I-Run-To-The-Can): 846
ISO Air Quality in the PEC: 233
Key Features of Carbapenems: 353
Key Features of Cephalosporins: 352
Key Features of INSTIs: 430
Key Features of Macrolides: 359
Key Features of Nitrofurantoin: 368
Key Features of NNRTIs: 423
Key Features of NRTIs: 420
Key Features of Penicillins: 350
Key Features of PIs: 425
Key Features of Quinolones: 358
Key Features of Sulfamethoxazole/ Trimethoprim 361
Key Features of Tetracyclines 360

Key Issues with Azole Antifungals: 400
Lab Tests for Liver Disease: 309
Lamictal Starter Kits: Colors Help Safety: 941
Levothyroxine Tablet Colors: 667
Lithium-Not Easy to Initiate: 904
Lyme Disease or Ringworm?: 397
Maintenance of Remission: Comparison of Common CD and UC Treatments: 977
Managing Myalgias: 446
MAO Inhibitors – Keep Them Separated: 887
Math is Ready for NAPLEX When: 197
MDIs and DPIs: 607
Multidose Pens (No Needle Included): 659
N-Acetylcysteine Treatment: 1036
Nicotine Patch Administration: 632
NSAIDs and the Ductus Arteriosus: 799
Opioid Allergy: 808
Opioid Boxed Warnings: 802
Opioid Induced Respiratory Depression (OIRD) Risks: 811
Opioid Overdose Management: 811
Opioid-Induced Constipation: 808
Parkinson Disease: The Cause, Symptoms and Primary Drug Treatment: 927
Patch Frequency: 97
Patient-Friendly Formulations for Stimulants: 906
PDE-5 Inhibitor Dosing Guide: 731
Pediatric Cough and Cold Treatment - Caution Needed: 564
Penicillin Pregnancy Puzzler: 396
Pharmacodynamics: Pharmaco + Dynamics: 55
Pharmacokinetics: Pharmaco + Kinetics: 57
Pharmacopeias: 226
Phenytoin/Fosphenytoin Administration: 946
PI and PK Booster Drug Interactions: 429
Picking the Best Antipsychotic: 895
Pneumococcal Vaccine Indications, Sequence and Intervals: 328
Prescription Weight Loss Drugs: Avoid or Use Caution: 791
Ratio Relationships: 125
Ready to Submit Your Answer?: 127
Receptor Pharmacology: 49
Reducing Particle Size & Cake Baking: 271
RIPE Therapy for TB: 386
Risk with Concurrent Use of Benzodiazepines and Opioids: 56
Rounding Rules for NNT and NNH: 210
S/Sx of Hyperthyroidism: 668
S/Sx of Hypothyroidism: 665
S/Sx of Thyroid Storm: 669
Safe Use of Benzodiazepines: 916
Scopolamine (*Transderm Scop*) Patch: 985
Select Contraceptive Types: 699
Select Drugs and Conditions that Alter Vital Signs: 109
Select Drugs with Pharmacogenomic Implications: 1023
Select Factors and Conditions with Osteoporosis Risk: 714
Select National Patient Safety Goals: 990
Selecting the Best Antidepressant: 888
Setting Up Proportions: 118
Severe & Rare Adverse Effects of Estrogen: 700
Signs and Symptoms of Stroke: 518
Signs and Symptoms of Systolic Heart Failure: 490
Spirometry: Tests Lung Function (How Well the Lungs Work): 600
Statin Equivalent Doses: 446
Steps for Treating Severe Hyperkalemia: 299
Steroids: Least Potent to Most Potent: 673
Suppositories: 277
Symptoms of Common STIs: 395
Take Your Vitamins on AEDs!: 940
The Heart's Natural Pacemaker and Arrhythmias: 505
The HLB Number: 257
Timing of Perioperative Antibiotics: 377
To Reduce Doxorubicin Cardiotoxicity: 864
Transplant Drugs: What's Used, When: 785
Treating Acute Inflammation with Steroids: 674
Treating ADHF: 756
Treatment Algorithm: 642
Treatment Approach for Stable Ischemic Heart Disease: 475
Treatment Considerations for Tobacco Cessation: 631
Treatment of Chronic Systolic Heart Failure: 492
Triptan Formulations: 821
Two Common Causes of ICU Infections: 756
Vaccine Timing & Spacing: 319
Vaccine-Preventable Illness in Transplant Recipients: 786
Warfarin Tablet Colors: 535
Which OTC to Recommend for Constipation: 967
With a Spacer, More Drug Gets Into The Lungs: 611

Key Drug Guys

Common Drugs Known to Cause Vision Changes or Damage: 571
Common Drugs with Diluent Solution Requirements: 101
Common Drugs with Filter Requirements: 103
Do Not Refrigerate: 103
Drug Conversions: 125
Drugs Commonly Associated w/ Severe Skin Reactions: 1005
Drugs Commonly Associated w/ TTP: 1004
Drugs for Secondary Prevention After ACS: 488
Drugs Most Commonly Associated w/Photosensitivity: 1004
Drugs that are Constipating: 967
Drugs that Can Cause Erectile/ Sexual Dysfunction: 730
Drugs that Can Increase Blood Pressure: 460
Drugs that Can Increase IOP: 567
Drugs that Can Lower the Seizure Threshold: 938
Drugs that Can Raise Blood Glucose: 641
Drugs that Can Worsen BPH: 734
Drugs that Increase Uric Acid: 826
Drugs with Leaching/Adsorption/ Absorption Issues with PVC Containers: 101
Hazardous Drugs on the NIOSH List: 228
Key Drugs that Can Worsen Dementia: 933
Key Drugs that Can Worsen GERD Symptoms: 957
Key Drugs with Decreased Absorption: 960
Key IV Hypertension Medications: 472
Key Vaccines in Sickle Cell Disease: 551
Medications/Illicit Drugs that Can Cause Psychotic Symptoms: 89
No Renal Dose Adjustment Required: 370
Protect From Light During Administration: 104
Select Drugs and Conditions that can Cause Hypothyroidism: 665
Select Drugs that are Contraindicated in CKD: 294
Select Drugs that Can Cause Diarrhea: 972
Select Drugs That Can Cause Drug-Induced Lupus Erythematosus (DILE): 682
Select Drugs that Can Cause Hemolytic Anemia: 549
Select Drugs that Can Cause Pulmonary Fibrosis: 598
Select Drugs that Can Increase or Prolong the QT Interval: 508
Select Drugs that Can Lower Blood Glucose: 660
Select Drugs That Can Worsen Insomnia: 919
Select Drugs that Cause Anxiety: 913
Select Drugs that Cause Kidney Disease: 292
Select Drugs that Cause or Worsen Depression: 881
Select Drugs that Cause or Worsen Heart Failure: 491
Select Drugs that Raise Potassium Levels: 298
Select Drugs that Require ¯ Dose or ≠ Interval in CKD: 294
Select Drugs with Boxed Warning for Liver Damage: 310
Select Drugs/Conditions that Can Cause Weight Gain: 790
Select Drugs/Conditions that Can Cause Weight Loss: 790
Select Drugs/Conditions that Can Raise LDL and/or Triglycerides: 443
Single Tablet Regimens: 419
Teratogens: Danger in Pregnancy: 709
Therapeutic Drug Levels: 80
Travel Vaccines: 336

Numbers

3% Saline: 749
5 Alpha-Reductase Inhibitors: 735, 737, 739
5-alpha Reductase Type 2 Inhibitor: 577
5-fluorouracil (5-FU: 1037
5-FU: 846, 868
5HT-3 Receptor Antagonists: 66, 508, 808, 836, 842, 843, 844, 967, 984
5-Hydroxytryptophan: 1027, 1028
50% Insulin Lispro Protamine Suspension, 50% Insulin Lispro Solution: 655
70% Insulin Aspart Protamine Suspension, 30% Insulin Aspart Solution: 655
70% NPH, 30% Regular: 655
75% Insulin Lispro Protamine Suspension, 25% Insulin Lispro Solution: 655

A

Abacavir: 228, 418, 419, 420, 435, 436, 1001, 1005, 1022
Abacavir/lamivudine: 419
Abaloparatide: 95, 716, 719, 721
Abatacept: 101, 103, 681
Abciximab: 103, 483, 486
Abelcet: 371, 399
Abemaciclib: 857
Abilify: 882, 889, 896, 903
Abilify Maintena: 95, 889, 893, 896, 903
Abiraterone: 859, 877
Abraxane: 866
Abreva: 407, 576
Absorica: 575
Abstral: 93, 803
Acanya: 575
Acarbose: 648
Accolate: 607
Accupril: 466, 494
Accuretic: 462
Acebutolol: 469
ACE Inhibitors: 67, 73, 293, 298, 361, 461, 462, 466, 468, 473, 482, 483, 488, 492, 493, 494, 496, 497, 499, 504, 640, 647 701, 710, 904
Acetadote: 798
Acetaminophen: 56, 68, 94, 103, 309, 310, 379, 488, 552, 564, 565, 572, 710, 757, 765, 766, 770, 797, 798, 801, 803, 804, 805, 810, 815, 819, 821, 856, 867, 873, 874, 1004, 1010, 1036
Acetaminophen/butalbital/caffeine: 821
Acetaminophen/codeine: 1003
Acetazolamide: 339, 568, 1007, 1031
Acetic Acid: 179
Acetylcholinesterase Inhibitors: 109, 686, 742, 933, 934, 935, 1037
Acetyl-L-Carnitine: 933, 1027
Aciphex: 958, 959
AcipHex Sprinkle: 958, 959
Acitretin: 228, 691
Aclidinium: 606, 621
Aclidinium/formoterol: 606
Aclovate: 589
Actemra: 681
Acticlate: 359
Actigall: 793
Actiq: 93, 803
Activase: 487, 519
Activated Charcoal: 677, 1035
Activella: 724
Actonel: 667, 717
Actoplus Met: 643
Actoplus Met XR: 643
Actos: 112, 646
Acular: 570, 800
Acuvail: 570
Acyclovir: 61, 70, 102, 103, 168, 294, 370, 407, 408, 409, 411, 576, 871, 938, 1004
Aczone: 575
Adalat CC: 464, 472
Adalimumab: 95, 679, 680, 977
Adamantanes: 405, 406
Adapalene: 575
Adasuve Inhalation Powder: 894
Adcetris: 874
Adcirca: 479, 731, 736, 738
Adderall: 906, 907, 909, 923
Adderall XR: 93, 906, 907, 909, 910
Addyi: 733
Adefovir: 308
Adempas: 479, 592, 593
Adenocard: 515
Adenosine: 510, 515, 593
Adhansia XR: 908
Adipex-P: 792
Adlyxin: 649, 650, 651, 659
Admelog: 653, 655, 659
A&D Ointment: 581
Ado-trastuzumab: 836, 837, 873, 1023
Adrenaclick: 1005, 1006
Adrenalin: 20, 753
Adrenergic Alpha-2 Agonists: 568
Adriamycin: 860, 864
Adrucil: 868, 1023
Advair: 111
Advair Diskus: 605, 606, 610, 614, 622
Advair HFA: 605, 606
Advil: 766, 799
Advil Migraine: 819
Adynovate: 762
Adzenys ER: 906, 909
Adzenys XR-ODT: 906, 909, 910
Aemcolo: 335
AeroChamber: 611
Aerospan: 606
Afatinib: 836, 875
Afinitor: 783, 870
Afinitor Disperz: 783, 870
Afrezza: 653, 655, 659
Afrin: 94, 561
Aftera: 705
Aggrastat: 486
Aggrenox: 521
Aimovig: 823
Airborne: 562
AirDuo RespiClick: 605, 606, 615
Ajovy: 823
Akynzeo: 843
Alavert OTC: 560
Alaway: 569
Albendazole: 582
Albenza: 582
Albiglutide: 649
Albuked: 749
Albumin: 101, 103, 104, 749
AlbuRx: 749
Albutein: 749
Albuterol: 46, 49, 299, 599, 604, 610, 611, 621, 710, 774, 775
Alcaftadine: 569
Alclometasone Dipropionate: 589
Alcohol: 73, 79, 367, 460, 730, 741, 805, 814, 931, 950
Aldactazide: 462
Aldactone: 313, 468, 497
Aldara: 396
Aldosterone Receptor Antagonists (ARAs): 73, 361, 291, 298, 468, 488, 492, 494, 497, 647, 701
Alecensa: 875
Alectinib: 875
Alemtuzumab: 685
Alendronate: 545, 717
Aleve: 800, 964
Alfalfa: 535
Alfuzosin: 69, 305, 428, 429, 508, 735, 736, 739
Alimta: 869
Alirocumab: 450, 456
Aliskiren: 67, 73, 298, 361, 461, 466, 467, 473, 504, 710
Aliskiren/Hydrochlorothiazide: 462
Alka-Seltzer: 801, 957, 964
Alkeran: 862
Alkylating Agents: 837, 838, 860, 862
All-trans Retinoic Acid: 870
All Day Allergy: 560
Allegra 24HR: 560
Allegra Allergy: 560
Allegra Allergy Childrens: 560
Allegra D: 560
Aller-Chlor: 559
Alli: 667, 792, 793
Allopurinol: 294, 422, 608, 828, 829, 830, 848, 1005, 1022
Almotriptan: 820, 821
Alocril: 569
Aloe Vera: 1028
Alogliptin: 648, 662
Alogliptin/pioglitazone: 643
Alomide: 569
Aloprim: 828, 1022
Alora: 97, 98, 724
Alosetron: 69, 70, 883, 973
Aloxi: 844
Alpha-1 Agonist: 753
Alpha-1 Blockers: 49
Alpha-2 Adrenergic Agonist: 758, 911
Alpha-2 Agonist + Diuretic: 462
Alpha-adrenergic Agonists: 560
Alpha/Beta Agonist: 930
Alpha Blockers: 66 472, 571, 735, 739, 935
Alphagan P: 568
Alpha-Glucosidase Inhibitor: 648
Alpha Lipoic Acid: 638, 1027
Alpha-Tocopherol: 1029
Alprazolam: 916, 917
Alprazolam Intensol: 916
Alprostadil: 733
Alrex: 570
Altabax: 389
Altace: 466, 494
Alteplase: 102, 104, 487, 518, 519
Altoprev: 90, 447, 456
Altreno: 575
Altretamine: 862
Aluminum: 66, 431, 667, 957, 964, 1037
Aluminum Acetate Solution: 585
Aluminum Antacids: 967
Aluminum Hydroxide: 295
Aluminum + Simethicone: 957
Alvesco: 605, 606, 607, 613
Alvimopan: 971
Amantadine: 405, 406, 927, 929
Amaryl: 645
Amatoxin: 1038
Ambien: 111, 916, 920
Ambien CR: 920
AmBisome: 371, 399
Ambrisentan: 228, 596
Amerge: 820, 821
Amethia: 699
Amethyst: 698, 699
Amidate: 759
Amifostine: 69, 837, 838, 863
Amikacin: 355, 356, 383, 385, 414
Amiloride: 67, 468
Amiloride/Hydrochlorothiazide: 462
Aminoglycosides: 68, 69, 73, 168, 292, 294, 355, 361, 369, 377, 382, 386, 388, 392, 399, 688, 761, 767, 774, 1019
Aminopenicillins: 348, 349
Aminophylline: 125, 167, 168, 183, 608
Aminosalicylates: 979, 980
Aminosyn: 151, 153, 154, 156
Amiodarone: 52, 60, 62, 63, 64, 66, 69, 70, 78, 101, 103, 304, 310, 428, 429, 448, 465, 470, 499, 500, 508, 511, 512, 516, 532, 535, 571, 596, 598, 665, 667, 712, 961, 992, 1004, 1005, 1029
Amitiza: 809, 970
Amitriptyline: 52, 508, 790, 815, 886, 914
Amjevita: 679
Amlodipine: 69, 447, 448, 464, 593, 800
Amnesteem: 575
Amoxapine: 886
Amoxicillin: 52, 349, 350, 354, 370, 372, 379, 380, 382, 387, 392, 393, 395, 397, 535, 711, 962
Amoxicillin + Clarithromycin + Lansoprazole: 962
Amoxicillin + Clarithromycin + Omeprazole: 962
Amoxicillin/Clavulanate: 349, 350, 354, 370, 379, 380, 381, 382, 390, 392, 841
Amphetamine: 52, 905, 909, 1026
Amphetamine/dextroamphetamine: 906, 909
Amphetamines: 64, 460, 592, 686, 712, 882, 893, 906, 1038
Amphotericin B: 69, 73, 101, 102, 103, 292, 294, 361, 371, 399, 404, 414, 751, 1031

Amphotericin B Deoxycholate: 399, 1001
Amphotericin B + Flucytosine (5-FC): 404
Amphotericin B Lipid Complex: 399
Ampicillin: 101, 349, 369, 370, 371, 378, 382, 387, 711, 767
Ampicillin/Sulbactam: 101, 349, 354, 369, 371, 377, 390, 391
Amprenavir: 70, 426
Ampyra: 685
Amrix ER: 814
Amylin Analog: 652
Anabolic Steroids: 443, 881
Anafranil: 886
Anakinra: 681
Analgesics: 69, 70, 552, 881, 933
Anaplastic Lymphoma Kinase (ALK) Inhibitors: 875
Anascorp: 1039
Anastrozole: 857, 877
Anavip: 1039
Ancef: 351
Ancobon: 399
Andexanet Alfa: 531, 536, 1037
Andexxa: 531, 536, 762, 1037
Androderm: 97, 98
AndroGel: 94
Androgen Biosynthesis Inhibitor: 859
Androgens: 228
Anectine: 761
Anesthetics: 109, 760, 813, 992
Angeliq: 699, 724
Angiomax: 533
Angiotensin II: 458
Angiotensin II Receptor Blocker (ARB): 504
Angiotensin Receptor and Neprilysin Inhibitor (ARNI): 492
Anidulafungin: 402
Annovera: 699, 703
Anoro Ellipta: 606, 621, 622, 627
Ansaid: 800
Antabuse: 310
Antacids: 57, 66, 73, 305, 358, 360, 372, 373, 431, 438, 545, 751, 801, 830, 957, 717, 960, 961, 721
Antara: 452, 457
Anthracenedione: 864
Anthracyclines: 100, 104, 105, 836, 837, 838, 842, 850, 860, 864
Anthralin: 690
Antiandrogen: 858, 859
Anti-arrhythmics: 688
Antiarrhythmics: 66, 109, 294, 428, 508, 992
Anticholinergics: 109, 567, 686, 734, 735, 744, 741, 742, 843, 893, 930, 933, 1037, 1038
Anticoagulants: 62, 67, 69, 228, 454, 482, 483, 526, 527, 528, 529, 530, 532, 534, 535, 538, 539, 543, 816, 884, 885, 1025, 1029, 1037
Anticoagulants/antiplatelets: 428
Anticoagulants/Antithrombotics: 992
Anticonvulsants: 428, 431, 701, 1002, 1030
Antidepressants: 65, 66, 67, 70, 409, 460, 797, 813, 881, 882, 931, 934, 1002
Anti-Diarrheal: 973
Antidiuretic Hormone (ADH): 291, 769
Antiemetics: 66, 844, 933
Antiepileptic Drugs (AEDs): 68, 409, 797, 813, 937, 939, 946, 949, 1031
Antifreeze: 1038
Antihistamines: 68, 109, 557, 559, 560, 563, 564, 565, 567, 710, 734, 856, 922, 931, 933, 967, 983, 984, 1004, 1007
Antimetabolites: 837, 838
Antimotility Agents: 846
Antimuscarinics: 69
Antineoplastics: 228, 972
Antiplatelet Agents: 67, 69, 454, 476, 479, 482, 485, 529, 532, 534, 535, 543, 884, 885, 1029
Antiproliferative Agents: 781
Antipsychotics: 65, 69, 70, 109, 358, 359, 688, 790, 884, 893, 894, 898, 900, 926, 933, 934, 935
Antiretrovirals: 228, 881
Antispasmodics: 814
Antistaphylococcal Penicillins: 348, 349
Antithymocyte globulin: 780
Anti-TNF Agents: 682, 977
Anti-tuberculosis Medications: 294
Antitussive: 381
Antivenin Immune FAB Centruroides: 1039
Antizol: 1038
Anu-Med: 582
Anusol: 582
Anxiolytics: 65
A-phosphatidylserine: 933
Apidra: 653, 655, 659
Apixaban: 62, 67, 69, 294, 359, 386, 428, 527, 530, 531, 532, 536, 538, 539, 1037
Aplenzin: 631, 886
Apokyn: 929
Apomorphine: 228, 508, 927, 929
Appetite Suppressants: 460
Apraclonidine: 568
Apremilast: 691
Aprepitant: 69, 70, 535, 843, 844
Apri: 699
Apriso: 979
Aptensio XR: 906, 908, 910
Aptiom: 947
Aptivus: 427
Aquanil: 586
Aquaphor: 578, 847
Aquoral: 847
Aranesp: 298, 547, 548, 841
Arava: 677
ARBs: 67, 73, 110, 293, 298, 361, 461, 462, 466, 467, 473, 483, 492, 493, 495, 496, 497, 499, 504, 640, 647, 701, 710, 904
Arcapta Neohaler: 606, 622, 628
Aredia: 849
Arformoterol: 606, 622
Argatroban: 67, 75, 528, 530, 533
Arginine Vasopressin (AVP) Receptor Antagonists: 749
Arginine Vasopressin Receptor Antagonists: 750
Aricept: 934
Arimidex: 857, 877
Aripiprazole: 69, 70, 95, 882, 884, 889, 893, 895, 896, 902, 903, 943, 967
Aripiprazole ODT: 899
Aristada: 889, 896
Arixtra: 96, 527, 530, 532
Armodafinil: 923
Armour Thyroid: 665, 666
ARNI: 466
Arnuity Ellipta: 605, 606, 627
Aromasin: 857, 877
Aromatase Inhibitors: 714, 720, 857
Arsenic: 508, 1037
Arsenic Trioxide: 836, 870
Arthrotec: 800, 963
Artichoke Extract: 1027, 1028, 1029
Arymo ER: 805, 811
Arzerra: 873
Asacol HD: 979, 981
Ascorbic Acid: 545, 562, 1027, 1029, 1030
Ascriptin: 476, 521, 801
Asenapine: 893, 897, 903
Asmanex HFA: 605, 606
Asmanex Twisthaler: 605, 606, 610
Asparaginase: 836, 870
Aspercreme: 815
Aspirin: 52, 56, 57, 67, 78, 453, 457, 475, 476, 477, 479, 482, 483, 484, 487, 488, 519, 520, 521, 529, 539, 565, 639, 678, 704, 710, 765, 798, 799, 819, 821, 829, 830, 904, 933, 957, 959, 961, 963, 964, 718, 973, 717
Aspirin/Acetylsalicylic Acid: 801
Astagraf XL: 782
Astelin: 560
Astepro: 560
Asthmanefrin: 604
Astramorph: 805
Astroglide: 723
Atacand: 467, 494
Atazanavir: 62, 69, 70, 305, 420, 426, 428, 429, 434, 435, 438, 448, 508, 534, 648
Atazanavir + Ritonavir: 419
Atazanavir/ritonavir: 428, 941
Atelvia: 717, 721
Atenolol: 469
Atenolol/Chlorthalidone: 462
Atezolizumab: 836, 837, 872, 874
Atgam: 780
Ativan: 758, 916, 921
ATNAA: 1038
Atomoxetine: 70, 508, 730, 881, 906, 911, 912, 1002
Atorvastatin: 63, 69, 428, 445, 447, 448, 456
Atovaquone: 337, 413, 414
Atovaquone: 414
ATRA: 870
Atracurium: 761
Atralin: 575
Atripla: 294, 419, 434, 881
Atropa Belladonna: 1037
Atropine: 49, 69, 836, 838, 846, 866, 1035, 1037, 1038
Atrovent HFA: 621, 623
Atypical Antipsychotic: 882
Atypical Antipsychotics: 443, 757
Aubagio: 683, 685
Augmentin: 349, 350, 370, 372
Augmentin ES-600: 349, 379
Auryxia: 296
Austedo: 899
Auvi-Q: 1005, 1006
Avage: 575
Avalide: 462
Avanafil: 66, 69, 294, 424, 478, 479, 498, 730, 731, 732
Avandia: 646
Avapro: 110, 467
Avastin: 101, 873
Aveeno: 585
Avelox: 103, 357, 370
Aviane: 699
Avibactam: 346
Avita: 575
Avodart: 737
Avonex: 683, 684
Avycaz: 351
Axicabtagene Ciloleucel: 871
Azacitidine: 101
Azactam: 354, 775
Azasan: 782, 980, 1023
AzaSite: 569
AzaSite Eye Drops: 358
Azathioprine: 79, 228, 682, 781, 782, 785, 977, 980, 1023
Azelaic Acid: 574, 575
Azelastine: 558, 560, 569
Azelex: 574, 575
Azilect: 929
Azilsartan: 467
Azilsartan/Chlorthalidone: 462
Azithromycin: 60, 335, 358, 359, 369, 370, 373, 379, 380, 381, 382, 387, 393, 395, 396, 413, 414, 532, 569, 619, 711, 774, 775, 1003
Azo: 393
Azole Antifungals: 60, 63, 66, 358, 359, 400, 402, 404, 508, 535, 641, 785
Azopt: 568
Azor: 462
Aztreonam: 53, 294, 354, 369, 377, 383, 388, 391, 775, 1006
Azulfidine: 676, 979

Azulfidine EN-tabs: 979

B

B-12 Compliance: 546
Babylax: 94
Bacille Calmette-Guerin (BCG) Vaccine: 384
Bacitracin: 585
Bacitracin/neomycin/polymyxin B/ Hydrocortisone: 585
Baclofen: 69, 814
Bactrim: 101, 103, 360, 373, 1007
Bactrim DS: 360
Bactroban: 94, 389, 585
Bactroban Nasal: 368, 374
Bag Balm: 847
Baloxavir Marboxil: 380, 405, 406
Balsalazide: 979
Banzel: 948
Baraclude: 308
Barbiturates: 68, 401, 402, 701, 821, 933, 950, 1037
Baricitinib: 677
Barley: 1027, 1029
Basaglar: 654, 655, 657, 659
Basiliximab: 780
Bath Salts: 893
Baxdela: 357
Bayer: 476, 521
Bayer "Advanced" Aspirin: 801
Bayer Women's Low Dose: 801
Baza: 579
Bazedoxifene: 718, 724
BC Powder: 801
BCR-ABL Inhibitors: 875
Bebulin: 537
Beclomethasone: 558, 605, 606, 710
Beconase AQ: 558, 710
Bedaquiline: 385
Belatacept: 781, 784
Belbuca: 812
Belimumab: 101, 682
Belladonna: 69, 1032
Belsomra: 920
Belviq: 660, 790, 791, 793
Belviq XR: 791, 793
Benadryl: 559, 563, 922, 984
Benazepril: 466
Benazepril/Amlodipine: 462
Benazepril/Hydrochlorothiazide: 462
Bendamustine: 862
Bendeka: 862
Benefiber: 968
BenGay: 815
Benicar: 110, 467
Benicar HCT: 462
Benlysta: 101, 682
Benoxyl: 575
Benralizumab: 602, 609
Bentyl: 973
Benzac: 575
BenzaClin: 575
Benzalkonium Chloride: 568, 571, 689
Benzamycin: 575
Benzocaine: 50, 760, 770, 1038
Benzodiazepine Injection: 938
Benzodiazepines: 56, 68, 69, 109, 757, 758, 805, 808, 814, 881, 893, 900, 914, 916, 917, 920, 921, 933, 940, 947, 950, 1035, 1037, 1038
Benzonatate: 563
Benzoyl Peroxide: 574, 575
Benzphetamine: 792
Benztropine: 69, 567, 734, 843, 845, 930, 933
Benzyl Alcohol: 583
Benzylpenicilloyl Polylysine: 1008
Besifloxacin: 569
Besivance: 569
Beta-1 Agonist: 753, 755
Beta-1 and Beta-2 Blockers (Non-Selective): 470
Beta-1 Blockers: 49
Beta-1 Selective Blockers: 469
Beta-1 Selective Blocker with Nitric Oxide-Dependent Vasodilation: 469
Beta-2 Agonist: 46, 73, 622
Beta-3 Agonist: 743
Beta-3 Receptor Agonists: 741
Beta-adrenergic Receptor Antagonists: 496
Beta Agonists: 109, 641
Beta Blockers: 56, 63, 109, 443, 465, 469, 470, 473, 477, 482, 483, 488, 492, 496, 499, 503, 508, 509, 510, 511, 512, 567, 572, 641, 660, 686, 688, 790, 881, 935, 943, 1037
Beta-Blockers:568, 822
Betagan: 568
Beta-lactam Antibiotics: 294, 348, 354, 369, 372, 382, 678, 774, 830, 869, 1006
Beta-lactamase Inhibitor: 346, 350, 369
Betamethasone: 579, 673
Betamethasone Dipropionate: 588
Betamethasone Valerate: 588
Betapace: 515
Betapace AF: 294, 515
Betaseron: 683, 684
Betaxolol: 60, 469, 568
Bethanechol: 49
Bethkis: 775
Betimol: 568
Betoptic-S: 469, 568
Betrixaban: 67, 527, 530, 531, 532, 538
Bevacizumab: 101, 460, 872, 873
Bevacizumab-awwb: 873
Bevespi: 90
Bevespi Aerosphere: 606, 621, 622
Bevyxxa: 527, 530, 531
Beyaz: 699, 1030
Biaxin: 358, 370, 373
Biaxin XL: 358
Bicalutamide: 859, 877
Bicillin C-R: 349, 395
Bicillin L-A: 349, 350, 395, 396
BiCNU: 862
Bictegravir: 61, 418, 419, 430, 431, 435
BiDil: 492, 498, 682
Biktarvy: 294, 418, 419, 430, 431
Bile Acid Binding Resins: 451, 648
Bile Acid Resins: 66
Bile Acid Sequestrants: 443, 449, 451, 453, 457
Bimatoprost: 567, 571, 577
Binosto: 717, 721
Bioclusive: 98
Bio-Statin: 403
Biotene: 847
Biotin: 1028
Bisacodyl: 808, 967, 969
Bismuth Subcitrate Potassium: 962
Bismuth Subsalicylate: 334, 360, 373, 765, 962, 972, 973
Bisoprolol: 469, 483, 496
Bisoprolol/Hydrochlorothiazide: 462
Bisphosphates: 57, 66, 73, 294, 296, 545, 716, 717, 721, 849
Bitter Melon: 1027, 1028
Bitter Orange: 1026, 1027, 1028
Bivalirudin: 67, 483, 530, 533
Bivigam: 752
Black Cohosh: 725, 1026, 1028
Black Tea: 1026
Bleomycin: 598, 686, 835, 836, 837, 838, 867
Bleph-10: 569
Blinatumomab: 874
Blincyto: 874
Bloxiverz: 1038
Bonine: 984
Boniva: 717, 718, 721
Bonjesta: 710
Boro-Packs: 585
Bortezomib: 508, 871
Bosentan: 69, 228, 305, 310, 535, 596, 645, 701
Bosulif: 875
Bosutinib: 508, 875
Botox: 686, 743, 823
Botulinum Toxin: 228, 686, 823
BRAF Inhibitors: 875
Brentuximab: 872
Brentuximab Vedotin: 874
Breo Ellipta: 605, 606, 622, 627
Brevibloc: 469
Brexanolone: 882
Brexpiprazole: 69, 70, 882, 889, 895, 897, 902
Bridion: 1038
Brilinta: 485
Brimonidine: 567, 568, 570
Brinzolamide: 568
Brisdelle: 882, 725
Brivaracetam: 947
Briviact: 947
Broad-spectrum AEDs: 939
Brodalumab: 691
Bromelain: 535
Bromfed DM: 564
Bromfenac: 570
Bromocriptine: 79, 648, 900
Brompheniramine: 69, 564, 565
Brompheniramine/ pseudoephedrine/ dextromethorphan: 564
Bronchodilators: 381, 618, 619
Brovana: 606, 622
Budesonide: 558, 605, 606, 609, 622, 672, 710, 977, 978, 982
Budesonide/formoterol: 606
Bufferin: 476, 521, 801
Bulk-producing Laxatives: 968
Bumetanide: 493
Bumex: 493
Bunavail: 812
Bupivacaine: 50, 760, 1037
Buprenex: 812
Buprenorphine: 69, 97, 98, 508, 808, 811, 812
Bupropion: 64, 70, 109, 353, 631, 633, 791, 884, 886, 887, 888, 891, 938, 1005, 1025
Bupropion IR: 631
Bupropion SR: 631
Burow's: 585
Buspirone: 64, 67, 68, 69, 882, 887, 907, 914, 915
Busulfan: 836, 837, 838, 862
Busulfex: 862
Butalbital: 798, 819, 821, 823
Butenafine: 579
Butoconazole: 581
Butrans: 97, 98, 812
Butterbur: 819, 1028
Butt Paste: 581
Butyrophenones: 843, 894, 926
Bydureon: 649, 650, 651, 659
Bydureon BCise: 649, 650
Byetta: 649, 650, 659, 701
Bystolic: 469
Byvalson: 462

C

Cabazitaxel: 866
Cabergoline: 228
Caduet: 447
Cafergot: 821
Caffeine: 65, 460, 734, 790, 798, 801, 819, 821, 930, 1026, 1027, 1028, 1029, 1038
Caladryl: 585
Calamine Lotion + Pramoxine: 585
Calan: 465, 512
Calan SR: 465, 512
Calcifediol: 70, 297
Calcimimetic: 297
Calcineurin Inhibitors: 64, 65, 67, 69, 578, 690, 701, 781, 782
Calcipotriene: 690
Calcitonin: 73, 716, 719, 720, 722, 719
Calcitonin Gene-Related Peptide (CGRP) Receptor Antagonist: 823
Calcitrate: 715
Calcitrene: 690
Calcitriol: 70, 297, 715

Calcium: 57, 66, 82, 102, 103, 125, 291, 431, 667, 793, 801, 857, 940, 950, 714, 716, 715, 717, 721
Calcium Acetate: 183, 295
Calcium Antacids: 710
Calcium Carbonate: 183, 295, 710, 715
Calcium Carbonate and Magnesium Hydroxide: 958
Calcium Channel Blockers (CCBs): 464, 472, 477, 593, 640, 686, 688, 761, 943, 961, 1037
Calcium Chloride: 159
Calcium Citrate: 183, 715, 721
Calcium gluconate: 159, 299
Calcium Hydroxylapatite: 433
Calcium Polycarbophil: 710, 968
Caldolor: 799
Calfactant: 765
Caltrate: 715
Cambia: 93, 800, 819
Camila: 699
Camphor: 564, 565
Campral: 310
Camptosar: 866
Camrese: 699
Camrese Lo: 699
Canagliflozin: 67, 73, 294, 298, 361, 647, 662, 662
Canasa: 979, 982
Cancidas: 101, 402
Candesartan: 467, 494
Candesartan/Hydrochlorothiazide: 462
Cangrelor: 485
Cannabidiol: 939, 947
Cannabinoids: 843, 845
Cannabis: 893, 939
Capecitabine: 70, 535, 836, 838, 846, 847, 868, 877, 1023, 1037
Capex: 589
Caphosol: 847
Capoten: 494
Capsaicin: 640, 815, 817
Captopril: 466, 494
Captopril/Hydrochlorothiazide: 462
Carac: 868
Carafate: 372, 963
Carbachol: 568
Carbamazepine: 59, 62, 65, 69, 70, 72, 73, 74, 78, 80, 228, 305, 401, 402, 424, 427, 428, 429, 532, 535, 608, 640, 648, 665, 701, 785, 814, 884, 887, 902, 904, 939, 940, 941, 942, 943, 949, 950, 951, 1004, 1005, 1022, 714
Carbamide Peroxide: 572
Carbapenems: 346, 348, 353, 369, 388, 391, 392, 942, 830, 938, 1025
Carbatrol: 814, 943
Carbidopa: 927, 928
Carbidopa/Levodopa: 928, 929, 930
Carbinoxamine: 559
Carbonic Anhydrase Inhibitors: 568
Carbonyl Iron: 544
Carboplatin: 837, 838, 863, 866
Carbowax: 264
Cardene IV: 464
Cardizem: 465, 512
Cardizem CD: 465, 512
Cardizem LA: 465, 512
Cardura: 736
Cardura XL: 94, 736
Carfilzomib: 101, 871
Carimune NF: 752
Cariprazine: 895, 897, 903
Carisoprodol: 69, 814
Carmustine: 836, 837, 838, 862
Carnexiv: 814
Carnitine: 940
Carnitor: 1038
CaroSpir: 313, 468, 497
Carteolol: 568
Cartia XT: 465, 512
Carvedilol: 49, 62, 70, 93, 469, 470, 483, 492, 496
Casodex: 859, 877
Caspofungin: 101, 102, 371, 402, 1005
Cassipa: 812
Catapres: 471, 911
Catapres-TTS: 97, 98, 473, 911
Catapres-TTS Patch: 471
Catecholamines: 496
Catchol-O-methyltransferase (COMT) inhibitors: 927, 928
Caverject: 733
Cayston: 354, 775
CBD: 939
CCBs: 364, 461
CCR5 Antagonist: 431
Cefaclor: 351, 370, 392
Cefadroxil: 351, 370, 387
Cefazolin: 351, 352, 354, 377, 387, 388
Cefdinir: 351, 352, 370, 372, 379, 382, 392, 545, 1007
Cefditoren: 351
Cefepime: 102, 350, 351, 352, 354, 369, 382, 383, 388, 391, 841
Cefixime: 93, 351, 395
Cefotan: 351
Cefotaxime: 350, 351, 352, 354, 378, 767
Cefotetan: 350, 351, 352, 354, 369, 377
Cefoxitin: 350, 351, 352, 354, 369, 377, 388
Cefpodoxime: 351, 370, 379, 382, 392, 1007
Cefprozil: 351, 370
Ceftaroline: 350, 352, 354, 369, 390
Ceftaroline Fosamil: 351
Ceftazidime: 350, 351, 352, 354, 369, 383, 388, 391, 841
Ceftazidime/Avibactam: 350, 351, 352, 354, 369
Ceftibuten: 351, 370, 371
Ceftin: 351
Ceftolozane/Tazobactam: 350, 351, 352, 354, 369
Ceftriaxone: 52, 53, 59, 102, 313, 350, 351, 352, 354, 377, 378, 379, 382, 386, 387, 388, 392, 395, 396, 767, 1007
Cefuroxime: 351, 352, 354, 370, 372, 377, 379, 382, 388, 397, 1007
Celebrex: 50, 800, 826, 991
Celecoxib: 50, 54, 70, 800, 826, 963, 1005, 1007
Celestone: 673
Celexa: 883, 991
CellCept: 101, 701, 781, 787
Centrally-Acting Alpha-2 Adrenergic Agonists: 471
Central Nervous System Depressants: 68
Cephalexin: 351, 352, 354, 370, 372, 387, 389, 392, 711
Cephalosporins: 74, 75, 346, 348, 350, 351, 352, 369, 377, 379, 380, 392, 393, 395, 535, 549, 711, 767, 830, 938, 1006, 1007
Cequa: 689
Cerebyx: 946, 1022
Ceritinib: 508, 836, 875
Certain Dri: 578
Certolizumab: 977
Certolizumab Pegol: 95, 679
Cesamet: 843, 845
Cetacort: 589
Cetirizine: 69, 560, 569, 710
Cetraxal: 357
Cetrorelix: 228
Cetuximab: 872, 873, 1023
Cetylev: 798, 1036
Cevimeline: 689
Chamomile: 1026, 1027, 1028, 1029
Chantix: 631, 1003
Chaparral: 1026
Chemet: 1037
Chemotherapeutics: 835, 837, 838, 841, 992
Children's Flonase: 558
Children's Tylenol: 766
Chloramphenicol: 228, 365, 546
Chlordiazepoxide: 916, 917
Chlorhexidine: 389
Chloroquine: 508, 571, 1004
Chlorothiazide: 463, 756
Chlorpheniramine: 69, 559, 564, 565, 710, 734, 804
Chlorpheniramine/codeine: 564
Chlorpheniramine/hydrocodone: 564
Chlorpheniramine/ Pseudoephedrine: 803, 804
Chlorpromazine: 53, 104, 508, 730, 894, 943
Chlorpropamide: 644
Chlorthalidone: 463
Chlor-Trimeton: 559
Cholecalciferol: 297, 715, 717
Cholestyramine: 82, 93, 451, 667, 677
Choline Magnesium Trisalicylate: 801
Cholinesterase Inhibitors: 741
Chondroitin: 1028, 1029
Chorionic gonadotropin-recombinant: 706
Chromium: 638, 1027
Chrysanthemum: 1028, 1029
Cialis: 479, 731, 732, 736, 738
Ciclesonide: 558, 605, 606
Ciclopirox: 580
Cidofovir: 228, 410, 414, 1007
Cilastatin: 353
Cilostazol: 69
Ciloxan: 357, 569
Cimduo: 420
Cimetidine: 60, 69, 70, 402, 608, 730, 884, 958, 961
Cimzia: 679, 977
Cinacalcet: 73, 297
Cinnamon: 638, 1026, 1027
Cinqair: 609
Cipro: 357, 370, 373
Ciprodex: 357, 572
Cipro ER: 392
Ciprofloxacin: 66, 69, 161, 313, 357, 358, 369, 370, 372, 373, 381, 383, 387, 388, 392, 393, 569, 608, 841
Ciprofloxacin and Dexamethasone: 572
Ciprofloxacin and Hydrocortisone: 572
Cipro HC: 357, 572
Cipro XR: 357
Cisapride: 305, 428, 429, 844
Cisatracurium: 761
Cisplatin: 68, 69, 73, 292, 361, 399, 686, 835, 836, 837, 838, 842, 863, 866, 868
Citalopram: 66, 69, 508, 883, 884, 885, 934, 961
Citracal: 183
Citric Acid: 970
Citrucel: 968
Citrus Aurantium: 1026
Cladribine: 685
Claravis: 575
Clarinex: 560
Clarithromycin: 60, 62, 63, 69, 358, 359, 369, 370, 373, 380, 382, 387, 413, 414, 448, 499, 512, 532, 608, 648, 900, 921, 961, 962
Claritin D: 560
Claritin OTC: 560
Claritin RediTabs OTC: 560
Clavulanate: 346
Clearasil: 575
Clear Eyes: 689
Clear Eyes Redness Relief: 570
Clemastine: 559
Clenpiq: 970
Cleocin: 366, 370, 373
Cleocin-T: 366
Clevidipine: 156, 443, 464, 465, 1007
Cleviprex: 464, 1007
Climara: 97, 724

ClimaraPro: 97, 724
Clindacin ETZ: 366
Clindacin-P: 366
Clindacin Pac: 366
Clindagel: 366
Clindamycin: 366, 369, 370, 373, 377, 380, 387, 389, 396, 414, 575, 841, 972, 1005
Clindamycin + Primaquine: 414
Clindesse: 366
Clinisol: 153
Clinoril: 826
Clobazam: 228, 947
Clobetasol Propionate: 588
Clobex: 588
Clomid: 90
Clomiphene: 577, 706
Clomipramine: 508, 886
Clonazepam: 228, 916, 917
Clonidine: 48, 63, 68, 97, 98, 109, 465, 470, 471, 473, 511, 512, 730, 813, 881, 907, 911, 912, 725
Clopidogrel: 60, 67, 70, 424, 476, 477, 479, 483, 484, 485, 487, 488, 521, 529, 639, 645, 961, 1004, 1005, 1022
Clorazepate: 916, 917
Clotrimazole: 93, 397, 403, 404, 579, 581, 846
Clozapine: 69, 72, 74, 111, 184, 508, 552, 641, 790, 893, 895, 896, 898, 899, 900, 938, 1002
Clozaril: 896
CNS Depressants: 933
Coagadex: 762
Coal Tar: 576, 690, 1004
Cobalamin: 1030
Cobicistat: 60, 62, 63, 69, 70, 110, 402, 419, 420, 425, 428, 429, 431, 434, 439, 448, 532, 534
Cobimetinib: 875
Cocaine: 460, 592, 686, 893, 1038
Cocoa: 1026
Codeine: 61, 65, 68, 70, 294, 563, 564, 565, 770, 798, 803, 806, 808, 821, 1001, 1003, 1022
Coditussin DAC: 564
Coenzyme Q10: 446, 461, 535, 1027, 1028
Cogentin: 930
Colace: 969
Colazal: 979
Colchicine: 62, 69, 228, 294, 305, 359, 428, 429, 447, 452, 546, 826, 827, 828, 829, 972
Colcrys: 826
Colesevelam: 451, 648, 701, 967
Colestid: 451
Colestipol: 451
Colistimethate: 70, 73, 365, 369, 383, 399, 761
Colistimethate Sodium: 365
Colistin: 70, 365
Collagenase: 585
Colloidal Oatmeal: 585
Coly-Mycin M: 365
Coly-Mycin S: 572
Colyte: 970
Combigan: 568
Combination Oral Contraceptives (COCs): 697, 702
CombiPatch: 724
Combivent Respimat: 621, 624
Combivir: 420
Comfrey: 1026
Compazine: 845
Complera: 294, 419, 434, 881
Compro: 845
Comtan: 928
COMT Inhibitors: 928
Concentrated Regular Insulin: 654, 655
Concerta: 89, 94, 686, 906, 907, 908, 910
Conivaptan: 62, 73, 447, 532, 749, 750
Conjugated Equine Estrogens: 724
Conjugated Estrogens/ Bazedoxifene: 718, 724
Consensi: 800
Constulose: 312, 968
Contrast Media: 1005, 1007
Contrave: 790, 791, 793, 886
ConZip: 810
Copaxone: 95, 683, 684
Copper: 1037
Copper IUD: 705
Cordran: 588, 589
Coreg: 470, 473, 496
Coreg CR: 93, 470, 473, 496, 504
CoreMino: 359, 575
Corgard: 311, 470
Corlanor: 492, 500
Cormax: 588
Cortaid: 589
Cortef: 673
Cortenema: 978
Corticosteroids: 836, 837, 844
Corticotropin: 683
Cortifoam: 978, 982
Cortisol: 70
Cortisone: 70, 673
Cortisporin: 585
Corvert: 515
Cosentyx: 691
Cosopt: 568
Cotellic: 875
Cotempla XR-ODT: 906, 908, 910
Cough Suppressants: 563, 565
Cough Syrups: 641
Coumadin: 534, 1022
Cozaar: 467, 494
Cranberry: 1028
Creon: 93, 776
Cresemba: 66, 103, 401
Crestor: 447
Crisaborole: 578
Crixivan: 426
Crizotinib: 508, 836, 875
Crofab: 1039
Crofelemer: 433
Cromolyn: 569
Crotalidae Immune F(ab')2: 1039
Crotalidae Polyvalent Immune FAB: 1039
Cruex: 579
Cryselle: 699
Cubicin: 101, 363, 371
Cubicin RF: 363, 371
Curosurf: 765
Cutivate: 588, 589
Cyanide: 79, 178, 1037
Cyanocobalamin: 546
Cyanokit: 1037
Cyclin-Dependent Kinase (CDK4/6) Inhibitors: 857
Cyclizine: 984
Cyclobenzaprine: 69, 814, 887
Cyclooxygenase (COX) 2 Inhibitors: 493, 756, 799
Cyclophosphamide: 682, 836, 837, 842, 860, 862
Cycloset: 648
Cyclosporine: 60, 62, 63, 64, 65, 67, 69, 73, 78, 228, 292, 294, 298, 305, 361, 364, 399, 443, 447, 448, 449, 451, 460, 470, 496, 499, 596, 641, 682, 689, 736, 761, 783, 785, 788, 793, 826, 881, 977, 980, 992
Cyclosporine Emulsion: 570
Cyltezo: 679
Cymbalta: 111, 815, 885, 914
Cymzia: 95
CYP1A2 Inhibitors: 930
Cyproheptadine: 69
Cyramza: 873
Cytarabine: 847, 868
Cytomel: 665, 666
Cytotec: 963
Cytotoxic T-Lymphocyte Antigen-4 (CTLA-4) Inhibitor: 874
Cytovene Injection: 410
Cytoxan: 862
Cytra-2: 300

D

DAAs: 304, 305
Dabigatran: 62, 67, 294, 359, 386, 470, 496, 528, 532, 533, 534, 536, 538, 539, 541, 957, 1037
Dabrafenib: 836, 875
Dacarbazine: 104, 862
Daclatasvir: 62, 304
Daklinza: 304
Dalbavancin: 362, 369, 371, 390
Dalfampridine: 685
Daliresp: 111, 622
Dalteparin: 67, 529, 536
Dalvance: 362
Danazol: 448
Dandrex: 576
Dantrium: 900
Dantrolene: 900
Dapagliflozin: 294, 647, 662
Dapsone: 69, 75, 413, 414, 549, 574, 1038
Dapsone gel: 575
Dapsone: 414
Daptomycin: 75, 76, 101, 363, 369, 371, 387, 390, 391
Daratumumab: 872, 874
Darbepoetin Alfa: 228, 298, 547, 841
Darifenacin: 69, 70, 742
Darunavir: 57, 69, 305, 419, 420, 425, 429, 434, 435, 438, 439, 448, 1005, 1007
Darunavir + Ritonavir: 419
Darunavir/ritonavir: 428
Darzalex: 874
Dasabuvir: 62, 70, 305
Dasatinib: 508, 592, 836, 875, 877
Daunorubicin: 864
Daunorubicin and Cytarabine Liposomal: 864
Dayhist Allergy 12 HR Relief: 559
Daypro: 800
DayQuil Cough: 563
Daytrana: 97, 98, 906, 907, 908, 910
DDAVP: 769
DDAVP Injection: 744
DDAVP Rhinal Tube: 744
Deadly Nightshade: 1037
Debrox: 572
Decadron: 673, 844
Decongestants: 109, 460, 557, 560, 564, 565, 734
DEET: 336
Deferasirox: 553, 1005, 1037
Deferiprone: 228, 552, 553, 1037
Deferoxamine: 103, 544, 553, 1037
Degarelix: 859
Degludec: 654
Delafloxacin: 357
Delstrigo: 419
Delsym: 563
Delta-9-tetrahydrocannabinol: 843
Deltasone: 673, 978
Delzicol: 979, 981
Demadex: 493
Demerol: 805
Denavir: 407, 576
Dengvaxia: 337
Denosumab: 716, 720, 720
Depacon: 902, 942
Depakene: 822, 902, 942
Depakote: 822, 902, 942
Depakote – Delayed-Release: 942
Depakote ER: 111, 942
Depakote Sprinkle: 93, 942
Deplin: 1026
DepoCyt: 868
Depo-Medrol: 673
Depot medroxyprogesterone acetate: 698, 699, 700, 714
Depo-Provera: 698, 699, 700, 704, 724
Derma-Smoothe/FS Oil: 589
DermAtop: 589
Descovy: 294, 418, 420, 422
Desenex Jock Itch: 579
Desferal: 103, 544, 1037
Desflurane: 760

Desiccated Thyroid: 666
Desiccated USP (T3 and T4): 666
Desipramine: 815, 886, 927
Desirudin: 533
Desitin: 581
Desloratadine: 560
Desmopressin: 73, 744, 745, 750, 769
Desmopressin SL: 744
Desonate: 589
Desonide: 589
DesOwen: 589
Desoximetasone: 588
Desoxyn: 909
Desvenlafaxine: 885, 725
Detemir: 654
Detrol: 742
Detrol LA: 94, 742
Deutetrabenazine: 899, 900
Dexamethasone: 62, 357, 378, 570, 673, 768, 836, 844
Dexedrine Spansule: 909
Dexilant: 93, 958, 959
Dexlansoprazole: 93, 958, 959
Dexmedetomidine: 63, 103, 465, 470, 511, 512, 757, 758
Dexmethylphenidate: 93, 908
DexPak: 673
Dexrazoxane: 228, 836, 838, 850, 864
Dextran: 749
Dextroamphetamine: 64, 70, 906, 909, 923, 984
Dextroamphetamine/amphetamine: 923
Dextroamphetamine/amphetamine ER: 93
Dextromethorphan: 64, 67, 70, 563, 565, 710, 887, 893
Dextromethorphan/promethazine: 564
D.H.E. 45: 821
DHS Tar: 690
Diacetyl-morphine: 808
Diacomit: 948
Diamode: 973
Diamox: 339
Diastat AcuDial: 916, 938, 939
Diazepam: 70, 916, 917
Diazepam Intensol: 916
Diazepam Rectal Gel: 938, 951
Diazoxide: 592, 641
Diclegis: 710
Diclofenac: 69, 70, 94, 97, 98, 570, 800, 819, 963
Diclofenac Gel: 816
Diclofenac/misoprostol: 963
Diclofenac Potassium: 93
Dicloxacillin: 349, 350, 389
Dicyclomine: 69, 968, 973
Didanosine: 76, 372, 422, 434, 435
Diethylene glycol: 1038
Diethylpropion: 592, 792
Differin: 575
Dificid: 367, 394
Diflorasone Diacetate: 588
Diflucan: 370, 400, 581
Diflunisal: 801
DigiFab: 512, 1037
Digitek: 499, 512
Digox: 499, 512
Digoxin: 62, 63, 80, 100, 109, 294, 465, 470, 485, 492, 496, 499, 500, 504, 509, 510, 511, 512, 516, 571, 593, 730, 935, 943, 992, 1019, 1029, 1037
Digoxin Immune Fab: 1037
Dihydroergotamine: 67, 228, 821
Dihydropyridine Calcium Channel Blockers: 109
Dihydropyridine CCBs: 464
Dihydropyridines (DHP): 464
Dilantin: 101, 161, 946, 1022
Dilantin Infatabs: 946
Dilatrate SR: 498
Dilaudid: 758, 804
Diltiazem: 60, 62, 63, 69, 448, 464, 465, 470, 483, 496, 508, 511, 512, 532, 593, 785, 826, 904, 915, 935
Dilt-XR: 512
Diltzac: 512
Dimenhydrinate: 984, 1037
Dimercaprol: 1037
Dimercaptosuccinic Acid: 1037
Dimethylamylamine: 1026
Dimethyl Fumarate: 683, 685
Dinoprostone: 228
Diovan: 467, 494
Diovan HCT: 462
Dipentum: 979
Dipeptidyl Peptidase 4 (DPP-4) Inhibitor: 76, 642, 645, 648, 660, 662
Diphenhydramine: 69, 508, 559, 563, 564, 565, 584, 710, 734, 770, 798, 800, 843, 845, 873, 893, 907, 920, 922, 933, 984, 1004, 1005, 1006, 1037
Diphenoxylate: 846, 972
Diphenoxylate/atropine: 973
Diprivan: 465, 758, 1007
Diprolene: 588
Diprolene Cream AF, 0.05%: 588
Dipyridamole: 67, 520
Dipyridamole/aspirin: 521
Direct-acting Antivirals (DAA): 428
Direct Acting Antivirals (DAAs): 303
Direct Renin Inhibitor: 467
Direct Renin Inhibitor + DIURETIC: 462
Direct Thrombin Inhibitors: 75, 528, 533, 539, 540, 711, 1037
Direct Vasodilators: 471
Disopyramide: 294, 508, 513
Disulfiram: 310, 367, 608, 883
Ditropan XL: 742, 744
Diuretics: 73, 78, 298, 443, 462, 472, 497, 734, 741, 1004, 1025
Diuril: 463
Divalproex: 228, 790, 822, 942
Divigel: 724, 725
DMARDs: 74, 675
DMSA: 1037
Doans: 801
Doans ES: 801
Dobutamine: 49, 64, 104, 755, 756, 757, 1007
Docetaxel: 837, 838, 866
Docosanol: 407, 576
Docusate: 457, 544, 545, 967, 969
Docusate Calcium: 969
Docusate Potassium: 969
Docusate Sodium: 969
Dofetilide: 66, 294, 364, 431, 508, 515, 961
Dolasetron: 843, 844
Dolophine: 804
Dolutegravir: 62, 76, 418, 419, 430, 434, 435, 438, 545
Domeboro Soothing Soak: 585
Donepezil: 66, 508, 686, 933, 934, 935
Dong Quai: 535, 725, 1025, 1028, 1029
Dopamine: 49, 70, 100, 104, 631, 753, 756, 893, 930
Dopamine Agonists: 648, 893, 900, 927, 929
Dopamine Receptor Antagonists: 843, 845
Doral: 921
Doravirine: 419, 423, 435
Doripenem: 353, 354
Dornase Alfa: 774, 775
Doryx: 337, 359
Dorzolamide: 568
DoubleDex: 673
Dovato: 419
Dovonex: 690
Doxazosin: 49, 66, 472, 571, 735, 736, 1001
Doxepin: 70, 508, 882, 886, 921
Doxercalciferol: 297
Doxil: 864
Doxorubicin: 100, 105, 835, 836, 837, 838, 847, 860, 864
Doxorubicin Liposomal: 864
Doxycycline: 66, 337, 359, 360, 369, 370, 371, 373, 380, 381, 382, 389, 395, 396, 397, 545, 575, 770, 1005
Doxylamine: 69, 710, 920, 922
Doxylamine/pyridoxine: 710
Dramamine: 984
Dritho-Crème: 690
Dronabinol: 68, 433, 790, 843
Dronedarone: 60, 62, 63, 66, 69, 70, 228, 305, 428, 429, 448, 499, 508, 512, 514, 532, 534, 598
Droperidol: 66, 508, 843, 845, 926, 961
Drospirenone: 67, 697, 698, 700, 701, 703, 722, 724
Drospirenone-containing COCs: 73, 298, 361
Droxia: 552
Droxidopa: 927, 930
Duac: 575
Duaklir Pressair: 606, 621, 622
Duavee: 716, 718, 724
Duetact: 643
Duexis: 958, 963
Dulaglutide: 649, 1003
Dulcolax: 969, 1010
Dulera: 605, 606, 613
Duloxetine: 69, 70, 294, 640, 815, 884, 885, 888, 914
DuoDote: 1038
Duopa: 928
Dupilumab: 578, 602, 609
Dupixent: 578, 609
Duraclon: 471
Duragesic: 97, 98, 803, 1010
Duramorph: 805
Durlaza: 476, 521, 801
Dutasteride: 69, 111, 228, 730, 737
Dutoprol: 462
Duzallo: 828, 829
Dyanavel XR: 906, 909
Dyazide: 462, 468
Dymista: 558, 560
Dyrenium: 468

E

Echinacea: 562, 1027, 1028, 1029
Echinocandins: 73, 402, 404
Ecotrin: 476, 521, 801
Edarbi: 467
Edarbyclor: 462
Edecrin: 493
Edex: 733
Edluar: 93, 920
Edoxaban: 62, 67, 294, 386, 428, 527, 530, 531, 532, 539
Edurant: 423
E.E.S.: 358
Efavirenz: 69, 70, 305, 401, 402, 419, 423, 424, 434, 435, 437, 648, 881
Effer-K: 501
Effexor XR: 885, 914
Effient: 484
Efinaconazole: 580
Efudex: 868
Egrifta: 433
Elagolix: 698
Elavil: 815, 886, 914
Elbasvir/grazoprevir: 304, 428
Elestat: 569
Elestrin: 724, 725
Eletriptan: 820, 821
Elidel: 578, 690
Eligard: 859
Elimite: 583
Eliquis: 82, 527, 529, 530, 531
Elitek: 830
Elixophyllin: 608
Ella: 705
Ellence: 864
Elocon: 588
Elocon Ointment, 0.1%: 588
Eltrombopag: 548
Eluxadoline: 974

Elvitegravir: 419, 430, 431, 435, 439
Elvitegravir/cobicistat/emtricitabine/tenofovir Disoproxil Fumarate: 439
Embeda: 805, 811, 816
Emend: 844
Emergen-C Immune+: 562
Emgality: 823
Empagliflozin: 294, 647, 662
Emsam: 97, 887, 891, 929
Emtricitabine: 76, 418, 419, 420, 421, 422, 434, 435, 436, 439
Emtricitabine/tenofovir: 433
Emtricitabine/tenofovir Alafenamide: 439
Emtricitabine/tenofovir Disoproxil Fumarate/rilpivirine: 439
Emtriva: 421
Enablex: 742
Enalapril: 70, 466, 494
Enalaprilat: 70, 466
Enalapril/Hydrochlorothiazide: 462
Enbrel: 95, 104, 679, 680
Enbrel SureClick: 679
Endari: 553
Endocet: 798, 805
Endonuclease Inhibitors: 405, 406
Endothelin Receptor Antagonists (ERAs): 593, 596
Enfuvirtide: 432
Engerix-B: 336
EnovaRX: 800
Enoxaparin: 67, 95, 96, 103, 167, 294, 529, 536, 540
Enstilar: 690
Ensure: 151, 160
Entacapone: 928
Entecavir: 228, 308
Entereg: 971
Entertainer's Secret: 847
Entocort EC: 672, 978, 1010
Entresto: 467, 492, 495, 504, 710
Entyvio: 981
Enulose: 312, 968
Envarsus XR: 782
Enzalutamide: 859
Enzyme Inhibitor: 949
Epaned Powder: 466, 494
Epanova: 454, 457
Epclusa: 304, 305, 960
Ephedra: 1026
Ephedrine: 562, 887, 1038
Epidermal Growth Factor Receptor (EGFR) Inhibitors: 873, 875
Epidiolex: 939, 947
Epiduo: 575
Epiduo Forte: 575
Epinastine: 569
Epinephrine: 46, 56, 64, 74, 104, 132, 491, 562, 760, 761, 768, 887, 1005
Epinephrine Auto-injector: 1005, 1006
Epinephrine Auto-injectors: 1006
EpiPen: 95, 753, 1005, 1006
EpiPen Jr: 1005
Epirubicin: 836, 864
Episil: 847
Epitol: 943
Epivir: 421
Epivir HBV: 308
Epivir-HBV: 421, 436
Eplerenone: 67, 69, 291, 428, 468, 497
Epoetin Alfa: 298, 547, 841
Epogen: 107, 298, 547
Epoprostenol: 593, 595
Eprosartan: 467
Eptifibatide: 483, 486
Epzicom: 420
Equetro: 902, 943
Eravacycline: 359
Eraxis: 402
Erbitux: 873, 1023
Erelzi: 679
Erenumab-aooe: 823
Ergocalciferol: 297, 715
Ergot Alkaloids: 400, 401, 402
Ergotamine: 305, 819, 820, 821
Ergotamines: 712
Ergot Derivatives: 428, 429
Erlotinib: 836, 875, 877, 960
Errin: 699
Ertapenem: 52, 53, 101, 353, 354, 369, 371, 377, 388, 391
Ertugliflozin: 647
Erwinaze: 870
Ery: 358
Erygel: 358
EryPed: 358
Ery-Tab: 358
Erythrocin: 358
Erythromycin: 60, 63, 69, 358, 359, 382, 395, 448, 499, 512, 532, 569, 575, 608, 711, 785, 915, 921, 972, 1003
Erythromycin Ethylsuccinate: 358
Erythropoiesis Stimulating Agents (ESAs): 74, 298, 460, 538, 545, 547, 548
Esbriet: 598
Escitalopram: 66, 69, 508, 883, 884, 888, 914, 934
Esketamine: 882, 889
Eslicarbazepine: 59, 228, 665, 940, 947
Esmolol: 469
Esomep-EZS: 959
Esomeprazole: 60, 70, 93, 476, 477, 484, 485, 800, 958, 959, 961, 962
Estazolam: 921
Estrace: 724
Estradiol: 97, 228, 724
Estradiol/Drospirenone: 724
Estradiol/Levonorgestrel: 97, 724
Estradiol/Norethindrone: 724
Estradiol/Norgestimate: 724
Estring: 724
EstroGel: 724, 725
Estrogen Agonist/antagonist: 718, 725
Estrogen-containing Hormonal Contraceptives: 942
Estrogens: 98, 228, 443, 535, 538, 539, 667, 716, 718, 724, 722, 725
Eszopiclone: 920, 921
Etanercept: 95, 104, 679, 680, 690
Etelcalcetide: 297
Ethacrynic Acid: 493, 1007
Ethambutol: 294, 384, 385, 386, 414, 571
Ethanol: 178, 881, 1037, 1038
Ethinyl Estradiol: 69, 428, 448, 451, 697, 701, 1030
Ethinyl Estradiol-containing Products: 305
Ethinyl Estradiol/norelgestromin: 97
Ethosuximide: 940, 947, 1005
Ethylene glycol: 79, 178, 1038
Ethyol: 837, 838, 863
Etodolac: 801, 963
Etomidate: 759
Etopophos: 867
Etoposide: 850, 867
Etravirine: 70, 305, 424, 434, 435, 535, 1005
Eucerin: 578
Eucrisa: 578
Evamist: 724, 725
Evekeo: 909
Evening Primrose Oil: 535, 1028, 1029
Everolimus: 64, 65, 298, 781, 783, 785, 856, 870
Evista: 82, 718
Evithrom: 762
Evoclin: 366
Evolocumab: 450, 456
Evomela: 862
Evotaz: 429, 434
Evoxac: 689
Evzio: 811, 812
Exalgo: 804
Excedrin: 801
Excedrin Extra Strength: 798
Excedrin Migraine: 798, 801, 819
Excedrin Tension Headache: 798
Exelon: 97, 934, 935
Exemestane: 857, 877
Exenatide: 228, 649, 650, 662
Exenatide Extended Release: 649
Exforge: 462
Exforge HCT: 462
Exjade: 553, 1037
Ex-Lax: 969
Exparel: 760
Expectorants: 563, 565
Extavia: 683, 684
Extended-Spectrum Penicillins: 348, 349
Extina: 400, 579
Ezetimibe: 62, 445, 446, 447, 448, 449, 452, 456, 639
Ezogabine: 508

F

FA-8: 546
Fabior: 575
Factor VIIa Recombinant: 537
Factor Xa Inhibitors: 530, 532, 536, 539, 540, 711, 1037
Famciclovir: 70, 407, 408, 409, 1004
Famotidine: 294, 305, 438, 958
Famvir: 407, 408, 409
Fanapt: 897
Fanatrex: 813
Fareston: 856
Farxiga: 647
Fasenra: 609
Faslodex: 856
FazaClo: 899
FazaClo ODT: 896
Febuxostat: 828, 829, 830
FEIBA: 762
Felbamate: 69, 310, 947
Felbatol: 947
Feldene: 800
Felodipine ER: 464
Femara: 857, 877
Femhrt: 305
Femring: 724
Fenofibrate: 53, 111, 449, 452
Fenofibric Acid: 452
Fenoglide: 452, 457
Fenoprofen: 800
Fentanyl: 64, 65, 67, 69, 93, 97, 98, 757, 758, 803, 805, 806, 807, 882, 967
Fentanyl Patch: 807, 817
Fentora: 93, 803
Feosol: 1031
Feraheme: 545
Ferate: 544
Fer-In-Sol: 544, 1031
FeroSul: 544
Ferralet 90: 544
FerraPlus 90: 544
Ferretts: 544
Ferrex 150: 544
Ferric Carboxymaltose: 545
Ferric Citrate: 296
Ferric Hexacyanoferrate: 1037
Ferric Pyrophosphate Citrate: 545
Ferrimin 150: 544
Ferriprox: 553, 1037
Ferrlecit: 101, 545
Ferrous Fumarate: 544
Ferrous Gluconate: 544
Ferrous Sulfate: 544, 1031
Ferumoxytol: 545
Fesoterodine: 742
Fetzima: 885
FeverAll: 94, 798
Feverfew: 819, 1028, 1029
Fexmid: 814
Fexofenadine: 69, 560
Fiasp: 653, 655, 659
Fiber: 461, 710
FiberCon: 968
Fibers: 1027, 1029
Fibrates: 76, 443, 446, 449, 452, 457
Fibricor: 452, 457
Fibrinolytics: 482, 487, 488, 529
Fidaxomicin: 367, 369, 394

Filgrastim: 90, 839, 840
Finacea: 574, 575
Finasteride: 228, 242, 577, 730, 735, 737, 739
Fingolimod: 66, 228, 508, 683, 685
Fioricet: 798, 821, 823
Fioricet with Codeine: 821
Fiorinal with Codeine: 821
Firmagon: 859
First-generation Antipsychotics (FGAs): 894, 902
First-Lansoprazole: 959
First-Omeprazole: 959
Firvanq: 361, 370
Fish Oils: 67, 444, 454, 457, 461, 535, 906, 1025, 1027, 1029
Flagyl: 312, 366, 370, 373
Flagyl ER: 312
Flarex: 570
Flavocoxid: 1026
Flaxseed: 725, 1027
Flebogamma DIF: 752
Flecainide: 70, 429, 508, 514
Flector: 97, 98, 800
Fleet: 968
Fleet Enema: 967, 970
Flexbumin: 749
Flexeril: 814
Flibanserin: 62, 424, 428, 733
Flintstones Children's Chewable Multivitamin Plus Iron: 1031
Flolan: 595
Flomax: 736
Flonase: 565
Flonase Allergy Relief: 94, 558
Flonase Sensimist: 558
Florone Ointment, 0.05%: 588
Flovent: 558
Flovent Diskus: 605, 606
Flovent HFA: 605, 606, 613
Flublok: 1007
Fluconazole: 60, 69, 70, 228, 294, 370, 371, 400, 401, 402, 403, 404, 414, 508, 535, 581, 596, 711
Flucytosine: 399, 414
Fludrocortisone: 671
Flumadine: 406
Flumazenil: 916, 1037
Flunisolide: 558, 606
Fluocinolone: 357
Fluocinolone Acetonide: 588
Fluocinonide: 588
Fluorometholone: 570
Fluoroplex: 868
Fluorouracil: 70, 836, 838, 846, 847, 868, 1004, 1023
Fluoxetine: 64, 70, 882, 883, 884, 887, 889, 890, 896, 900, 914
Fluphenazine: 894
Flurandrenolide: 588
Flurazepam: 921
Flurbiprofen: 570, 800
Flutamide: 310, 730, 859
Fluticasone: 94, 558, 560, 605, 606, 621, 622, 1010
Fluticasone Propionate: 588, 589
Fluticasone/salmeterol: 606
Fluticasone/vilanterol: 606
Fluvastatin: 70, 445, 446, 447, 456, 535
Fluvoxamine: 64, 69, 70, 535, 608, 883, 884
FML Forte: 570
FML Liquifilm: 570
Focalin: 908
Focalin XR: 93, 906, 908, 910
Folate: 310, 451, 457, 546, 667, 676, 695, 698, 699, 1026
Folate Antimetabolites: 869
Folic Acid: 546, 695, 1025, 1030, 1031
Follicle Stimulating Hormone-recombinant: 706
Follistim: 706
Folotyn: 869
Fomepizole: 1038
Fondaparinux: 67, 75, 96, 294, 527, 530, 532, 538
Forane: 760
Forfivo XL: 631, 886
Formoterol: 605, 606, 621, 622
Fortamet: 14, 643
Fortaz: 351
Forteo: 95, 716, 719, 722
Fosamax: 667, 717
Fosamax Plus D: 717
Fosamprenavir: 69, 70, 426, 434, 435, 448, 1007
Fosaprepitant: 70, 843, 844
Foscarnet: 73, 100, 410, 414, 508
Foscavir: 410
Fosfomycin: 368, 369, 392, 393
Fosinopril: 466, 494
Fosinopril/Hydrochlorothiazide: 462
Fosnetupitant: 844
Fosnetupitant/palonosetron: 843, 844
Fosphenytoin: 70, 228, 546, 608, 939, 944, 946, 949, 1005, 1022
Fosrenol: 296, 358, 360
Foxglove: 1037
Fragmin: 529
FreAmine: 151, 153, 155
Fremanezumab-vfrm: 823
Frova: 820, 821
Frovatriptan: 820, 821
Fulphila: 840
Fulvestrant: 856
Fungi-Nail: 579
Furadantin: 368
Furosemide: 103, 125, 299, 313, 492, 493
Fusilev: 838, 869, 1038
Fusion Inhibitors: 432
Fuzeon: 432
Fycompa: 948

G

Gabapentin: 90, 294, 640, 790, 813, 914, 939, 940, 722, 725
Gabapentin Enacarbil: 922, 947
Gabitril: 948
Galantamine: 508, 934
Galcancezumab-gnlm: 823
Gammagard: 752
Gammagard S/D: 752
Gammaked: 752
Gammaplex: 752
Gamunex-C: 752
Ganciclovir: 70, 228, 294, 353, 410, 414
Garcinia Cambogia: 1028, 1029
Gardasil: 396
Garlic: 67, 444, 461, 535, 638, 1025, 1027, 1029
Gas Relief Infant: 766
Gas-X: 710
Gatifloxacin: 357
GaviLax: 968
GaviLyte-C: 970
GaviLyte-G: 970
Gavilyte-N: 970
Gaviscon: 957
Gazyva: 873
G-CSF: 840
Gefitinib: 836, 875
Gelclair: 847
Gelnique: 742, 745
Gelnique Pump: 742
Gemcitabine: 868
Gemfibrozil: 63, 70, 305, 446, 447, 448, 449, 452, 595, 608, 644, 645, 646, 826
Gemifloxacin: 357, 380, 382, 392, 395
Gemzar: 868
Generlac: 312, 968
Gengraf: 783
Gentak: 569
Gentamicin: 54, 59, 80, 102, 355, 356, 378, 383, 386, 387, 392, 395, 569, 767, 1012, 1014, 1016
Genvoya: 294, 305, 419, 422, 429, 434, 439, 532, 534
Geodon: 897, 903
Gianvi: 699
Giapreza: 753
Giazo: 979
Gildess Fe: 699
Gilenya: 683, 685
Gilotrif: 875
Ginger: 67, 535, 710, 1025, 1028, 1029
Ginkgo Biloba: 67, 933, 535, 884, 885, 1025, 1027, 1029
Ginseng: 67, 535, 638, 1025, 1027, 1028, 1029
Glatiramer Acetate: 95, 683, 684
Glatopa: 683, 684
Glecaprevir/pibrentasvir: 304
Gleevec: 875, 877
Gleostine: 862
Gliadel Wafer: 862
Glimepiride: 70, 451, 645
Glimepiride/pioglitazone: 643
Glipizide: 70, 451, 645
Glipizide XL: 645
Gloperba: 826
GlucaGen: 660
Glucagon: 660, 1037
Glucagon-like Peptide 1 (GLP-1) Agonists: 76, 642, 645, 649, 650, 660, 662, 792
Glucarpidase: 838, 869, 1038
Glucerna: 151, 160, 161
Glucophage: 14, 643
Glucophage XR: 112, 643
Glucosamine: 67, 535, 1025, 1028
Glucotrol: 645
Glucotrol XL: 645
Glucovance: 643
Glulisine: 653
Glumetza: 14, 643
Glyburide: 70, 294, 451, 596, 637, 645, 662, 710
Glycerin: 94, 967, 968
Glycerin Suppositories: 766
GlycoLax: 968
Glycoprotein IIb/IIIa Receptor Antagonists: 75, 482, 483, 486
Glycopyrrolate: 298, 606, 621, 622, 761, 1038
Glycopyrrolate/formoterol: 606
Glycopyrrolate/indacaterol: 606
Glycopyrronium: 578
Glynase: 645
Glyset: 648
Glyxambi: 643
GM-CSF: 840
GnRH Antagonists: 706, 714, 858, 859
Gocovri: 929
Goldenseal: 535
Golimumab: 95, 103, 679, 680, 977
GoLytely: 264, 970
Gonadotropins: 706
Gonal-F: 706
Goody's Powder: 798, 801
Goserelin: 859
Gralise: 813, 947
Granisetron: 92, 843, 844
Granix: 840
Grastek: 562
Green Tea: 535, 546
Green Tea: 1026, 1027, 1029
Griseofulvin: 403, 1004
G Tussin AC: 564
Guaifenesin: 563, 565, 710
Guaifenesin/codeine: 564
Guaifenesin/codeine/pseudoephedrine: 564
Guanfacine: 109, 907, 911, 912
Guanfacine IR: 471
Guanylate Cyclase C Agonists: 971
Guarana: 790, 1026, 1027, 1028, 1029
Guselkumab: 691
Gynazole-1: 581
Gyne-Lotrimin: 581

H

Halcinonide: 588
Halcion: 921
Haldol: 95, 759, 893, 894
Haldol Decanoate: 893, 894

Halobetasol Propionate: 588
Halog: 588
Haloperidol: 66, 69, 70, 79, 508, 759, 843, 893, 894, 902, 926
Haloperidol Decanoate: 95
Harvoni: 304, 305
Havrix: 336
Hawthorn: 1027, 1029
HC 1% Lotion: 586
HCV Protease Inhibitors: 303
Head & Shoulders: 576
Hectorol: 297
Hemangeol: 470
Hemocyte: 544
Hemostatic Agents: 762
Heparin: 67, 73, 75, 102, 298, 577, 701, 711, 990, 992, 993, 1004, 714
HepFlush: 528
Hepsera: 308
HER2 Inhibitors: 836
Herbals: 460
Herceptin: 101, 873, 1023
Heroin: 808
Hespan: 749
Hetlioz: 920
Hexalen: 862
Hextend: 749
Histamine-2 Receptor Antagonists (H2RAs): 160, 294, 305, 431, 544, 545, 546, 717, 760, 957, 958, 961
Histrelin: 859
HIV Protease Inhibitors: 305
Hizentra: 752
HMG-CoA Reductase Inhibitors: 444
Homatropine: 804
Horehound: 1027
Horizant: 813, 922, 947
Hormonal Contraceptives: 881
HP Acthar: 683
Humalog: 653, 655, 656, 659
Humalog Mix 50/50: 655, 659
Humalog Mix 75/25: 655
Human Chorionic gonadotropin-recombinant: 706
Human Epidermal Growth Factor Receptor 2 (HER2) Inhibitors: 873, 876
Humira: 95, 679, 680, 977
Humulin Mix 70/30: 655, 659
Humulin N: 654, 655, 659
Humulin R: 654, 659
Humulin R U-500: 654, 655, 656, 658, 659
Hyaluronidase: 850
Hycamtin: 866
Hydralazine: 109, 471, 498, 682
Hydralazine and Nitrates: 492
Hydrea: 552
Hydrocarbons: 1037
Hydrochlorothiazide: 111, 140, 60, 462, 463, 468, 469, 515, 868
Hydrocodone: 64, 65, 69, 70, 563, 564, 770, 798, 805, 806, 808, 1003
Hydrocodone ER: 804
Hydrocodone IR: 804
Hydrocortisone: 357, 575, 581, 586, 671, 673, 850, 978, 982
Hydrocortisone Butyrate: 589
Hydrocortisone Probutate: 589
Hydromorphone: 102, 757, 758, 804, 806, 808, 1003
Hydroxocobalamin: 754, 1037
Hydroxychloroquine: 571, 577, 676, 682, 1005
Hydroxyethyl Starch: 749
Hydroxyurea: 552
Hydroxyzine: 69, 586, 914
Hyland's Teething Tablets: 1032
HyperRAB S/D: 1039
HyperSal: 774, 775
Hypertonic Saline: 774, 775, 992
Hypnotics: 65, 68, 805, 933, 935, 950
Hyqvia: 752
Hyrimoz: 679
Hysingla ER: 804, 811
Hytone: 589
Hyzaar: 111, 462

I

Ibalizumab-uiyk: 432
Ibandronate: 545, 716, 717, 718, 718
Ibrance: 857
Ibudone: 804
Ibuprofen: 54, 379, 453, 457, 479, 503, 564, 565, 572, 765, 766, 799, 804, 958, 974, 1004, 1005
Ibuprofen/famotidine: 963
Ibutilide: 66, 508, 515
Icatibant: 228
Iclusig: 875
Icosapent Ethyl: 454
Icy Hot: 815
Idamycin PFS: 864
IDArubicin: 536, 864
Idarucizumab: 101, 533, 536, 1037
Ifex: 862
Ifosfamide: 836, 837, 842, 862, 868
IL-4 Antagonist: 578
Ilevro: 570
Iloperidone: 897
Iloprost: 595, 686
IL Receptor Antagonist: 977
Ilumya: 691
Imatinib: 875, 877
Imdur: 498
Imipenem: 938
Imipenem/cilastatin: 353, 354, 382, 383, 390, 391, 841
Imipramine: 886, 914
Imiquimod: 396
Imitrex: 94, 95, 96, 820, 821, 824
Imitrex STATdose: 820, 821, 824
Immune globulins: 104
Immunosuppressants: 62, 69, 74, 405, 443, 460, 787, 871, 980, 853, 992
Imodium: 394
Imodium A-D: 334, 973
Imogam Rabies HT: 1039
Imovax Rabies: 1039
Imuran: 782, 980, 1023
Imvexxy: 724
Inbrija: 928
Incruse Ellipta: 606, 621, 627
Indacaterol: 606, 621, 622
Indapamide: 463
Inderal: 311
Inderal LA: 470, 822, 914
Inderal XL: 470
Indinavir: 69, 426, 434, 435, 532
Indocin: 799, 826
Indomethacin: 764, 799, 826, 881
Infants' Advil Drops: 766
Infasurf: 765
INFeD: 545
Inflectra: 679
Infliximab: 47, 101, 103, 679, 690, 977, 980
Influenza Vaccine: 379, 1007
Infumorph: 805
Ingrezza: 899
Inhaled Anesthetics: 761
Inhaled Corticosteroids (ICS): 76, 602, 604, 605
Inhaled Epinephrine: 602
Injectafer: 545
InnoPran XL: 470
Inotropes: 992, 1035
Inotuzumab: 872
Inspra: 468, 497
INSTIs: 431, 435, 438
Insulin: 65, 73, 95, 104, 101, 125, 160, 298, 299, 358, 470, 637, 642, 645, 653, 656, 657, 660, 661, 662, 710, 751, 790, 992, 1037
Insulin Aspart: 653, 655, 992
Insulin Degludec: 655, 656
Insulin Detemir: 655
Insulin Glargine: 654, 655, 656
Insulin Glulisine: 655
Insulin Lispro: 653, 655
Insulin NPH/Insulin Regular: 112, 654, 655, 657, 661
Insulin U-500: 992
Inteferon Alfas: 641
Integrase Strand Transfer Inhibitors (INSTIs): 430
Integrilin: 486
Integrin Receptor Antagonists: 977, 981
Intelence: 424
Intensol: 673, 804
Interferon: 303
Interferon-alfa-2b: 307
Interferon Beta: 683
Interferon Beta-1a: 684
Interferon Beta-1b: 228, 684
Interferons: 78, 665, 881, 893
Interleukin-2 (IL-2) Receptor Antagonist: 780
Intermezzo: 93, 920
Intralipid: 151, 155, 156
Intranasal Cromolyn: 561
Intranasal Ipratropium Bromide: 561
Intranasal Steroids: 557, 558, 560
Intrarosa: 725
Intravenous Immune globulin: 688, 752
Intron A: 307
Intuniv: 907, 911
Invanz: 101, 353
Invega: 897, 899
Invega Sustenna: 95, 893, 897
Invega Trinza: 893, 897
Invirase: 427
Invokamet: 643
Invokamet XR: 643
Invokana: 112, 647
Iodides: 669
Iodinated Contrast Media: 644
Ionil-T: 690
Iopidine: 568
Ipecac: 1034
Ipilimumab: 836, 837, 872, 874
IPOL: 336
Ipratropium: 621
Ipratropium Bromide: 621
Ipriflavone: 1028
Iprivask: 533
Irbesartan: 467
Irbesartan/Hydrochlorothiazide: 462
Iressa: 875
Irinotecan: 836, 838, 846, 866
Iron: 66, 105, 125, 451, 457, 544, 545, 547, 667, 698, 699, 770, 957, 960, 967, 717, 1030, 721
Iron Chews: 544
Iron Dextran: 545
Iron Sucrose: 101, 545
Isavuconazole: 70
Isavuconazonium: 60, 66, 70, 103, 371, 400, 401, 402, 404, 508, 1005
Isentress: 418, 430, 434
Isentress HD: 430
Isocarboxazid: 49, 64, 67, 882, 887
Isoflurane: 760
Isoniazid: 61, 69, 70, 178, 310, 371, 384, 385, 386, 682, 1005, 1031, 1037
Isoproterenol: 48, 49, 104, 132
Isopto Carbachol: 568
Isopto Carpine: 568
Isordil Titradose: 498
Isosorbide Dinitrate: 498
Isosorbide Dinitrate + Hydralazine: 498
Isosorbide Dinitrate IR/ER: 498
Isosorbide Mononitrate: 498
Isotretinoin: 90, 228, 571, 574, 575, 881, 1002
Isradipine: 464
Istalol: 568
Itraconazole: 60, 62, 69, 400, 401, 402, 403, 404, 414, 424, 448, 499, 512, 532, 580, 648, 900, 915, 917, 921
Itraconazole Solution: 371
Ivabradine: 69, 228, 428, 492, 499, 500, 504
Ivacaftor: 777

IvaRest: 585
Ivermectin: 90, 583
IV Lipid Emulsions: 443
Ixekizumab: 691
Ixiaro: 336
Ixifi: 679

J

Jadenu: 553, 1037
Jalyn: 737
Jantoven: 534, 1022
Janumet: 643
Janumet XR: 643
Janus Kinase Inhibitor: 977
Januvia: 648
Jardiance: 647
Jentadueto: 643
Jentadueto XR: 643
Jevity: 151, 160
Jevtana: 866
Jimson Weed: 1037
Jolessa: 699
Jornay PM: 908
Jublia: 580
Juluca: 419, 434
Junel: 699
Junel Fe 1/20: 699
Juxtapid: 455

K

Kadcyla: 873, 1023
Kadian: 93, 805, 816
Kaletra: 427, 434
Kalydeco: 777
Kanamycin: 385
Kaon-Cl: 501
Kapspargo Sprinkle: 469, 496
Kapvay: 471, 907, 911
Karbinal ER, RyVent: 559
Kariva: 699
Kava: 914, 1026, 1027, 1029
Kayexalate: 300, 667
Kazano: 643
Kcentra: 536, 537, 1037
Keflex: 111, 351, 352, 370, 372, 389, 1002
Kenalog: 588, 673
Kengreal: 485
Keppra: 81, 90, 103, 941
Keppra XR: 941
Keri: 578
Kerosene: 1037
Kerydin: 580
Ketalar: 759
Ketamine: 759
Ketoconazole: 60, 69, 70, 305, 310, 389, 400, 402, 404, 424, 448, 532, 534, 535, 576, 579, 648, 917, 921
Ketoprofen: 800
Ketorolac: 570, 800
Ketorolac Nasal Spray: 816
Ketotifen: 569
Kevzara: 681
Keytruda: 874
Khedezla: 885
Kineret: 681
Kionex: 300
Kisqali: 857
Kitabis Pak: 775
Klonopin: 916
Klor-Con: 501
Klor-Con 10: 501
Klor-Con/EF: 501
Klor-Con M10: 501
Klor-Con M15: 501
Klor-Con M20: 501
Kogenate: 107
Kombiglyze XR: 643
Kombucha: 1026
Kristalose: 312, 968
Krystexxa: 829
K-Tab: 501
Kyleena: 704
Kynamro: 455
Kyprolis: 101, 871

L

Labetalol: 470, 710
Lacosamide: 939, 943, 1005
Lactated Ringers: 749
Lactose: 92
Lactulose: 76, 312, 968
Lamictal: 902, 941
Lamictal CD: 93
Lamictal ODT: 92, 902, 941
Lamictal Starter: 902
Lamictal Starter Kit: 941
Lamictal XR: 902, 941
Lamisil: 403, 405, 580
Lamisil AT: 579, 580
Lamivudine: 308, 418, 419, 420, 421, 422, 435, 436
Lamotrigine: 64, 65, 93, 701, 709, 902, 939, 940, 941, 942, 949, 950, 951, 1001, 1005, 1031
Lanolin: 578
Lanoxin: 499, 512
Lansoprazole: 958, 959
Lanthanum: 358, 360, 667
Lanthanum Carbonate: 296, 358, 360
Lantus: 654, 655, 656, 657, 659
Lapatinib: 508, 836, 876, 1023
L-arginine: 461, 1027, 1029
Lasix: 493
Lastacaft: 569
Latanoprost: 567, 1010
Latanoprostene Bunod: 567
Latisse: 567, 571, 577
Latuda: 896, 899, 903
Laxatives: 431, 457, 686, 836, 972
Lazanda: 803
Ledipasvir: 62, 305
Leflunomide: 70, 228, 310, 552, 677, 685
Legalon SIL: 1038
Lemon Balm: 1028
Lemtrada: 685
Lenalidomide: 871, 877
L-epinephrine 1 Mg/mL Solution: 768
Lescol: 447
Lescol XL: 447
Lesinurad: 828, 829
Letairis: 596
Letermovir: 410
Letrozole: 857, 877
Leucovorin: 413, 414, 838, 846, 868, 1038
Leukine: 840
Leukocyte Cluster of Differentiation (CD) Antigens (CD20, CD30, CD19, CD3, CD38) Inhibitors: 873
Leukotriene Receptor Antagonists (LTRAs): 602, 607
Leuprolide: 95, 706, 730, 836, 859, 860
Levalbuterol: 604
Levaquin: 357, 370, 373
Levemir: 654, 655, 659
Levetiracetam: 103, 939, 940, 941, 950, 951
Levitra: 426, 479, 731, 736
Levobunolol: 568
Levocarnitine: 1038
Levocetirizine: 560
Levodopa: 70, 75, 545, 549, 887, 927, 928
Levofloxacin: 66, 357, 369, 370, 371, 372, 373, 378, 380, 382, 383, 385, 388, 392, 393, 395, 413, 414, 841
Levoleucovorin: 838, 869, 1038
Levomefolate: 1030
Levomilnacipran: 885, 890
Levonorgestrel: 69, 577, 697, 705, 722, 724
Levonorgestrel-releasing IUD: 701
Levophed: 753
Levora: 699
Levothyroxine: 54, 66, 125, 161, 168, 296, 451, 545, 608, 665, 666, 711, 793, 718
Levoxyl: 666
Lexapro: 426, 883, 914
Lexiva: 426
L-glutamine Oral Powder: 553
Lialda: 979
LiceMD: 583
Licorice: 460, 535, 1026
Lidex-E Cream, 0.05%: 588
Lidex Ointment, 0.05%: 588
Lidocaine: 50, 97, 508, 513, 760, 813, 847
Lidocaine 1.8% Patch: 815, 846
Lidocaine Viscous: 815, 836
Lidocare: 815
Lidoderm: 97, 98, 409, 815, 817
LidoPatch: 815
Lifitegrast: 570, 689
Liletta: 704
Limbrel: 1026
Linaclotide: 968, 971
Linagliptin: 648
Linagliptin/empagliflozin: 643
Lindane: 938
Linezolid: 49, 64, 67, 75, 363, 364, 369, 370, 371, 382, 383, 387, 390, 391, 571, 660, 883, 884, 885, 886, 887, 888, 904, 915, 1025
Linzess: 971
Lioresal: 814
Liothyronine: 666
Liotrix: 666
Lipase Inhibitor: 792
Lipid Amphotericin: 1001
Lipid Emulsion: 151
Lipids: 103
Lipitor: 447
Lipodox50: 864
Lipofen: 452, 457
Lipoglycopeptides: 362
Liposomal: 414
Liposomal Amphotericin B: 399, 404
Liposomal Bupivacaine: 760
Lip-Prot-Amyl: 776
Liquifilm: 570, 264
Liraglutide: 649, 792, 662
Liraglutide/insulin Degludec: 643
Lisdexamfetamine: 61, 64, 70, 93, 906, 909
Lisinopril: 466, 492, 494
Lisinopril/Hydrochlorothiazide: 462
Lithium: 58, 62, 64, 67, 78, 80, 116, 294, 504, 577, 665, 712, 761, 762, 790, 882, 887, 902, 903, 904, 714
Lithobid: 903, 904
Little Noses Decongestant Drops: 561
Little Remedies Saline Nasal Drops: 766
Livalo: 447
Lixisenatide: 649
Lixisenatide/insulin glargine: 643
L-lysine: 1027
L-methylfolate: 1026
Local Anesthetics: 688
Locoid: 589
Lodine: 801
Lodoxamide: 569
Loestrin: 699
Loestrin 24 Fe: 699
Loestrin Fe: 699
Lofexidine: 812
Lokelma: 300
Lo Loestrin Fe: 305, 699
Lomaira: 792
Lomitapide: 228, 310, 448, 455
Lomotil: 394, 973
Lomustine: 836, 837, 838, 862
Long-acting Beta-2 Agonists (LABAs): 602, 604, 619, 622
Long-acting Muscarinic Antagonists (LAMAs): 602, 619
Lonhala Magnair: 606, 621
Loop Diuretic: 63, 68, 69, 73, 125, 292, 361, 399, 462, 492, 503, 641, 493, 678, 714, 756, 830, 849, 967, 1031
Loperamide: 334, 393, 686, 836, 838, 846, 866, 972, 973
Loperamide A-D: 973
Lopid: 452, 457

Lopinavir: 305, 426, 427, 428, 448
Lopinavir + Ritonavir: 427
Lopinavir/ritonavir: 433, 435, 532, 941
Lopressor: 469, 473, 496, 822
Lopressor HCT: 462
Loprox: 580
Loratadine: 69, 560, 710, 1010
Lorazepam: 101, 103, 757, 758, 893, 916, 917, 920, 921
Lorazepam Intensol: 758, 916, 921
Lorcaserin: 67, 592, 660, 791, 793
Lorcet: 798, 804
Lortab: 798, 804
Loryna: 699
Losartan: 467, 494
Losartan/Hydrochlorothiazide: 462
Lotemax: 570
Lotensin: 466
Lotensin HCT: 462
Loteprednol: 570
Lotrel: 462
Lotrimin AF: 579
Lotrimin Ultra: 579
Lotrisone: 579
Lotronex: 973
Lovastatin: 63, 64, 69, 305, 359, 428, 429, 445, 446, 447, 448, 456, 485, 511, 512, 1027, 1029
Lovaza: 454, 457
Lovenox: 95, 96, 103, 529
Low Molecular Weight Heparin (LMWH): 75, 80, 294, 483, 527, 528, 529, 530, 535, 536, 538, 539, 540, 711, 1004
Loxapine: 894
Loxitane: 894
L-tryptophan: 67, 1028
Lubiprostone: 968, 970
Lucemyra: 811, 812
Lucentis: 640
Lugol's Solution: 669
Luliconazole: 579
Lumacaftor/ivacaftor: 777
Lumify: 568, 570
Lumigan: 567
Lunesta: 920
Lupiprostone: 809
Lupron: 706
Lupron Depot: 95, 859
Lurasidone: 305, 428, 429, 896, 902, 903
Luteinizing Hormone Releasing Hormone (LHRH) Agonists: 859
Luvena: 723
Luxiq Foam, 0.12%: 588
Luzu: 579
Lycopene: 735, 1028
Lyrica: 813, 914, 948
Lysergic Acid Diethylamide (LSD: 893
Lysine: 573, 576

M

Maalox Advanced Maximum Strength: 957
Macitentan: 228, 596
Macrobid: 368, 374, 392
Macrodantin: 368, 374
Macrolides: 57, 60, 66, 335, 358, 359, 373, 382, 508, 532, 535, 1003, 1005
Mag-Al: 957
Magnesium: 57, 66, 431, 667, 819, 957, 958, 964, 717, 721
Magnesium Citrate: 968
Magnesium Hydroxide: 957, 968
Magnesium Oxide: 751, 970
Magnesium Salicylate: 801
Magnesium Sulfate: 751, 992, 968, 970
Ma Huang: 460
Malarone: 337
Malathion: 583, 1038
Mammalian Target of Rapamycin (mTOR) Inhibitors: 64, 65, 783, 785, 856, 870
Mannitol: 69, 79, 100, 103, 522
MAO-B Inhibitors: 927, 929, 930
MAO Inhibitors: 49, 50, 64, 67, 364, 386, 460, 559, 561, 563, 790, 810, 882, 883, 884, 885, 886, 887, 888, 891, 900, 907, 911, 915, 1025
Maprotiline: 886
Maraviroc: 310, 431
Marcaine: 760
Marezine: 984
Marijuana: 843, 939
Marinol: 433, 843, 845
Marplan: 49, 887
Marqibo: 865
Matulane: 862
Mavenclad: 685
Mavyret: 304, 305
Maxalt: 820, 821, 823
Maxalt-MLT: 820, 821, 823
Maxidex: 570
Maxipime: 351
Maxitrol: 569
Maxzide: 462, 468
Maxzide-25: 462, 468
Mayzent: 685
MDMA (ecstasy): 1038
MDPV: 893
Mebendazole: 582
Mechlorethamine: 862
Meclizine: 69, 686, 984
Meclofenamate: 800
Medrol: 673, 674, 827
Medrol Therapy Pack: 673
Medroxyprogesterone: 228, 695, 698, 703, 722, 724
Mefenamic Acid: 800
Mefloquine: 938
Megace ES: 433
Megestrol: 433, 790
Meglitinides: 642, 644, 655, 660, 662, 790
Mekinist: 875
Melatonin: 81, 906, 907, 919, 920, 1025, 1028, 1029
Meloxicam: 69, 70, 111, 801, 963
Melphalan: 862
Memantine: 93, 933, 934, 935, 936
Menactra: 336
Menopur: 706
Menostar: 97, 724
Menotropin: 706
Men's Rogaine: 471
Menthol: 564, 565
Menveo: 336
Meperidine: 67, 70, 294, 805, 806, 887, 938
Mephyton: 537
Mepivacaine: 1037
Mepolizumab: 602, 609
Mercaptopurine: 79, 977, 980
Meropenem: 353, 354, 382, 383, 390, 391, 392, 841
Meropenem/Vaborbactam: 353
Merrem: 353
Mesalamine: 94, 977, 979, 1007
Mesalamine ER: 979
Mesna: 837, 838, 862
Mesnex: 837, 838, 862
Mestinon: 688
Metadate ER: 908, 923
Metamucil: 967, 968, 1027
Metanx: 1026
Metaxalone: 67, 814
Metformin: 14, 75, 79, 294, 451, 546, 637, 642, 643, 644, 662, 710, 7
Metformin/alogliptin: 643
Metformin/canagliflozin: 643
Metformin/dapagliflozin: 643
Metformin/empagliflozin: 643
Metformin/ertugliflozin: 643
Metformin/glipizide: 643
Metformin/glyburide: 643
Metformin/linagliptin: 643
Metformin/pioglitazone: 643
Metformin/repaglinide: 643
Metformin/saxagliptin: 643
Metformin/sitagliptin: 643
Methadone: 64, 65, 66, 67, 69, 70, 358, 359, 422, 424, 428, 508, 730, 804, 805, 807, 881, 882, 887, 970
Methadose: 804
Methamphetamines: 70, 562, 592, 686, 893, 909
Methanol: 79, 178, 1038
Methazolamide: 568
Methimazole: 228, 668, 682, 711
Methocarbamol: 814
Methotrexate: 69, 75, 96, 105, 225, 242, 310, 598, 608, 675, 676, 677, 678, 679, 680, 830, 836, 837, 838, 846, 850, 869, 961, 977, 980, 992, 1004, 1031, 1038
Methoxy-polyethylene glycol: 264
Methylcellulose: 710, 968
Methyldopa: 75, 78, 79, 471, 545, 549, 682, 710, 881
Methyldopa/Hydrochlorothiazide: 462
Methylene Blue: 49, 64, 67, 75, 549, 883, 884, 885, 886, 888, 915, 1038
Methylin: 908, 923
Methylnaltrexone: 809, 971
Methylphenidate: 64, 93, 94, 97, 686, 881, 905, 906, 908, 909, 923
Methylprednisolone: 414, 673, 827
Methyl Salicylate Topical: 815, 817
Metipranolol: 568
Metoclopramide: 67, 294, 648, 836, 842, 843, 845, 898, 926, 929, 938, 960, 961, 964, 972, 984
Metolazone: 463, 493, 756
Metoprolol: 49, 56, 70, 125, 470, 822
Metoprolol Succinate: 469, 483
Metoprolol Succinate ER: 496
Metoprolol Succinate Extended Release: 469
Metoprolol Succinate/ Hydrochlorothiazide: 462
Metoprolol Tartrate: 469, 496
Metoprolol Tartrate/ Hydrochlorothiazide: 462
Metoprolol XL: 511
Metreleptin: 446
Metro: 312, 366
MetroCream: 366
Metrogel: 366
MetroGel-Vaginal: 366
MetroLotion: 366
Metronidazole: 70, 103, 312, 366, 367, 369, 370, 371, 373, 377, 388, 393, 396, 535, 712, 785, 962, 1005
Mevacor: 447
Mexiletine: 508, 513
Miacalcin: 720, 719
Micafungin: 371, 402, 403
Micardis: 467
Micardis HCT: 462
Miconazole: 579, 581
Miconazole + Zinc Oxide + Petrolatum: 581
Micort-HC: 589
Microgestin Fe 1/20: 699
Micro-K: 93, 501
Micronized glyburide: 645
Microzide: 463
Midazolam: 305, 424, 428, 429, 757, 759, 916, 938
Midol: 798
Mifeprex: 705
Mifepristone: 228, 705
Migergot: 821
Miglitol: 648
Migranal: 821
Milk of Magnesia: 957, 967, 968
Milk Thistle: 309, 1028, 1038
Millipred: 673
Milnacipran: 814, 967
Milrinone: 755, 756, 757
Miltefosine: 228
Mimvey: 724
Minastrin 24 Fe: 699

Mineralocorticoid Receptor Antagonists (MRAs): 497
Mineral Oil: 537, 969, 1037
Minitran: 97
Minivelle: 724
Minocin: 359, 373, 575
Minocycline: 66, 359, 360, 364, 369, 371, 373, 389, 545, 575, 682, 1005
Minolira: 575
Minoxidil: 471, 790
Minoxidil Topical: 577
Miostat: 568
Miotics: 568
Mipomersen: 310, 455
Mipomersin: 228
Mirabegron: 70, 508, 743
MiraLax: 264, 765, 766, 967, 968
Mirapex: 893, 922, 928
Mirapex ER: 928
Mirena: 701, 704
Mirtazapine: 64, 67, 68, 69, 70, 508, 790, 887, 888, 891, 921
Misoprostol: 228, 800, 963, 972
Mitigare: 826
Mitogen-Activated Extracellular Kinase (MEK) 1 and 2 Inhibitors: 875
Mitomycin: 100, 862
Mitoxantrone: 105, 683, 864
Mobic: 801
Modafinil: 69, 70, 305, 686, 923, 1005
Moderiba: 306
Moexipril: 466
Moexipril/Hydrochlorothiazide: 462
Moi-Stir: 847
Mometasone: 558, 605, 606
Mometasone/formoterol: 606
Mometasone Furoate: 588
Monistat 3: 581
Monobactam: 354
Monoclonal antibodies (MAbs) 432, 720, 836, 856, 861, 872
Monoket: 498
Montelukast: 93, 561, 607, 608, 609
Monurol: 368
Mood Stabilizers: 902
Morgidox: 359
MorphaBond: 805
Morphine: 55, 56, 61, 70, 93, 104, 294, 482, 483, 757, 758, 805, 806, 808, 967
Motegrity: 971
Motion-Time: 984
Motrin: 766, 799, 964
Motrin Infant Drops: 766
Mouth Kote: 847
Movantik: 809, 971
MoviPrep: 970
Moxatag: 349, 350
Moxeza: 357, 569
Moxifloxacin: 66, 103, 294, 357, 369, 370, 371, 372, 378, 380, 382, 385, 388, 391, 392, 414, 569
MPA: 722, 724
MS Contin: 805
Mucinex: 563, 565
Mucinex Allergy: 560
Mucinex D: 560
Mucomyst: 798
Mucosal Barrier Gel Spray: 847
Mucotrol: 847
MuGard: 847
Multaq: 514
Multivitamins: 66, 457, 969
Mu-opioid Receptor Agonists: 809, 810, 811
Mupirocin: 94, 368, 374, 389, 585
Mupirocin Nasal: 368
Muscle Relaxants: 688, 817
Muse: 733
Mushrooms: 1038
Mustargen: 862
Mvasi: 873
Myalept: 446
Myambutol: 386
Mycamine: 402
Mycelex: 93, 403
Mycophenolate: 73, 101, 228, 296, 701, 781, 785, 787
Mycophenolate Mofetil: 682, 781, 787
Mycophenolic Acid: 781
Mydayis: 909
Myfortic: 701, 781, 787
Mylanta Classic: 957
Mylanta Supreme: 957
Myleran: 862
Mylicon: 710
Mylicon Infants' Gas Relief Drops: 766
Myorisan: 575
Myrbetriq: 743
Mysoline: 948
Mytesi: 433
My Way: 705

N

Nabilone: 68, 843, 845
Nabumetone: 801, 963
N-acetylcysteine (NAC): 798, 1036
Na-channel Blockers: 510
NaCl 0.9% Intranasal Saline Solution: 766
Nadolol: 311, 470
Nadolol/Bendroflumethiazide: 462
Nafarelin: 228
Nafcillin: 100, 305, 349, 350, 354, 387, 785, 1006
Naldemedine: 809, 971
Nalfon: 800
Naloxegol: 809, 971
Naloxone: 56, 68, 811, 812, 1036
Naltrexone: 95, 310, 791, 805, 811
Naltrexone/Bupropion: 793
Namenda: 934, 935
Namenda Titration Pack: 935
Namenda XR: 93, 935
Namzaric: 934, 935
Naphazoline: 570
Naphthalene: 1038
Naprelan: 800
Naprosyn: 800, 826
Naproxen: 488, 800, 819, 820, 826, 959
Naproxen/esomeprazole: 963
Naratriptan: 820, 821
Narcan: 811, 812
Nardil: 49, 887
Naropin: 760
Nasacort 24 HR: 565
Nasacort Allergy 24HR OTC: 558
Nasal Allergy 24HR OTC: 558
Nasalcrom: 561
Nasal Wetting Agents: 557
Nascobal: 546
Nasonex: 558
Natalizumab: 101, 552, 685, 977, 981
Natazia: 699, 701
Nateglinide: 69, 644
Natrecor: 754
Natroba: 583
Natural Penicillins: 349
Nature-Throid: 666
Navelbine: 865
Nebivolol: 469
Nebivolol/Valsartan: 462
Nebulizer Solution 0.02%: 621
Nedocromil: 569
Nefazodone: 63, 69, 310, 448, 648, 888, 943
Nelfinavir: 69, 425, 427, 428, 433, 434, 435, 961
Neomycin: 312, 585
Neomycin/Bacitracin/Polymyxin B: 569
Neomycin/Colistin/Hydrocortisone/Thonzonium: 572
Neomycin/Polymyxin B/Dexamethasone: 569
Neo-Polycin: 569
NeoProfen: 799
Neoral: 783, 788
Neosporin Original: 585
Neostigmine: 1038
Neostigmine Methylsulfate: 1038
Neo-Synephrine: 561, 753
Nepafenac: 570
Neprilysin Inhibitor: 495
Nepro: 160
Neptazane: 568
Neratinib: 876
Nerlynx: 876
Nesina: 648
Nesiritide: 754, 756
Netaglinide: 70
Netarsudil: 568
Netupitant: 844
Netupitant/Palonosetron: 843, 844
Neuac: 575
Neulasta: 840
Neupogen: 840
Neupro: 97, 98, 922, 928, 931
Neuraminidase Inhibitors: 405, 406
Neurohormones: 458
Neurokinin-1 Receptor Antagonist (NK1-RA): 836, 842, 843
Neuromuscular Blocking Agents: 109, 761
Neurontin: 813, 914, 947
Neut: 300
NeutraSal: 847
Nevanac: 570
Nevirapine: 69, 228, 310, 424, 435, 1005
Nexafed: 561
Nexavar: 876, 877
Nexium: 93, 958, 959
Nexium 24HR-OTC: 959
Nexium IV: 959
Nexplanon: 704
Next Choice One-Dose: 705
Nexterone: 511
Niacin: 78, 444, 446, 447, 453, 457, 641, 1030
Niacor: 453
Niaspan: 453, 457
Nicardipine IR: 464
Nicardipine SR: 464
NicoDerm CQ: 97, 630
Nicorette: 630
Nicorette Mini: 630
Nicotine: 97, 630, 632, 633, 730, 957, 1038
Nicotine Polacrilex: 630
Nicotine Replacement Therapy: 65
Nicotinic Acid: 453
Nicotrol Inhaler: 630
Nicotrol NS: 630
Nifedipine: 64, 69, 464, 483, 593, 686, 710
Nifedipine ER: 464
Nifedipine IR: 464
Nikki: 699
Nilandron: 859
Nilotinib: 508, 836, 875, 877
Nilutamide: 859
Nimbex: 761
Nimodipine: 523
Nintedanib: 598
Nipride: 754
Nisoldipine ER: 464
Nitazoxanide: 393
Nithiodote: 1037
Nitrates: 66, 109, 477, 478, 482, 483, 488, 498, 738, 1029, 1038
Nitric Oxide: 593, 764
Nitro-Dur: 97
Nitrofurantoin: 75, 294, 368, 369, 374, 392, 393, 549, 598, 711
Nitroglycerin: 66, 97, 101, 102, 478, 481, 483, 488, 686, 754
Nitroglycerin Patches: 480
Nitroglycerin Sublingual: 93, 479, 1010
NitroMist: 478, 480
Nitropress: 754
Nitroprusside: 104, 754, 756, 1037
Nitrosoureas: 837, 838
Nitrostat: 93
Nitrous Oxide: 760
Nivestym: 840

Nivolumab: 836, 837, 872, 874
Nix: 583
Nizatidine: 958
Nizoral: 400, 404, 576
Nizoral A-D: 400, 576
NMDA Receptor Antagonist: 759
NNRTIs: 424, 435, 437, 943
Nocdurna: 744, 745
Noctiva: 744, 745
Nonabsorbable Disaccharides: 312
Nonbarbiturate Hypnotic: 759
Non-Dihydropyridine (non-DHP) Calcium Channel Blockers: 60, 63, 109, 464, 465, 483, 499, 500, 509, 510, 511, 512, 967
Non-dihydropyridines (non-DHP): 464
Non-nucleoside Reverse Transcriptase Inhibitors (NNRTIs): 423
Nonoxynol-9: 697
Non-selective ARA: 497
Non-Selective Beta-Blocker and Alpha-1 Blockers: 470, 496
Non-selective Beta-blockers: 49, 311, 473
Non-Steroidal Anti-Inflammatory Drugs (NSAIDs): 62, 67, 68, 69, 73, 292, 294, 298, 309, 313, 358, 361, 399, 460, 463, 483, 485, 488, 493, 495, 497, 503, 504, 529, 532, 534, 535, 543, 552, 647, 671, 675, 682, 678, 710, 756, 757, 764, 797, 799, 815, 816, 822, 823, 826, 828, 842, 869, 884, 885, 904, 935, 957, 963, 967, 974, 1002, 717, 1004, 1005
Non-Stimulants: 906, 907, 911
Non-vitamin K Oral Anticoagulants: 539
Nora-BE: 699
Norco: 798, 804
Norepinephrine: 64, 100, 104, 458, 491, 753, 756, 810, 887
Norethindrone: 428, 448, 451, 697, 722, 724
Norgestimate: 724
Norinyl: 305
Noritate: 366
Normal Saline: 129, 661, 749
Norpace: 513
Norpace CR: 513
Norpramin: 815, 886
Northera: 927, 930
Nortrel: 699
Nortrel 7/7/7: 699
Nortriptyline: 790, 886, 914, 927
Norvasc: 464
Norvir: 429
Novantrone: 683
Novarel: 706
Novasource: 160
Novolin 70/30: 655
Novolin N: 654, 655
Novolin N ReliOn: 654
Novolin R: 654, 659
Novolin R ReliOn: 654
Novolog: 653, 655, 657, 659
Novolog 70/30: 659
Novolog Mix 70/30: 655
NovoSeven RT: 537
Noxafil: 370, 401, 404
NP Thyroid: 665, 666
NRTIs: 79, 294, 310, 418, 419, 422, 435, 436
NS5B Polymerase Inhibitors: 303
Nucala: 609
Nucleoside/nucleotide Reverse Transcriptase Inhibitors (NRTIs): 420
Nucleoside/Tide Reverse Transcriptase Inhibitors (NRTIs): 307
Nucynta: 810
Nucynta ER: 810, 816
Nulojix: 784
NuLytely: 970
Numoisyn: 847
Nuplazid: 893, 898
Nutracort: 589
NuvaRing: 90, 305, 699, 703
Nuvessa: 366
Nuvigil: 923
Nuzyra: 359
Nyamyc: 403
Nymalize: 523
Nystatin: 370, 403, 404, 846
Nystatin Suspension: 403
Nystop: 403

O

Oasis: 847
Oat Bran: 1027, 1029
Obinutuzumab: 873
Ocean: 565
Ocean for Kids: 766
Ocella: 699
Ocrelizumab: 685
Ocrevus: 685
Octagam: 752
Octreotide: 311, 641, 660
Ocudose: 568
Ocuflox: 357, 569
Ocupress: 568
Odactra: 562
Odefsey: 294, 419, 422, 434, 439, 881
Ofatumumab: 873
Ofev: 598
Ofirmev: 103, 798
Ofloxacin: 357, 387, 393, 395, 569
Ogivri: 873, 1023
Olanzapine: 69, 91, 95, 508, 641, 790, 843, 845, 884, 889, 893, 895, 896, 899, 903, 1005
Olanzapine/Fluoxetine: 882, 889, 902, 903
Oleander: 1037
Olmesartan: 451, 467
Olmesartan/Amlodipine: 462
Olmesartan/Amlodipine/Hydrochlorothiazide: 462
Olmesartan/Hydrochlorothiazide: 462
Olodaterol: 606, 621, 622
Olopatadine: 560, 569
Olsalazine: 979
Olumiant: 677
Olux Foam: 588
Omadacycline: 359
Omalizumab: 602, 609, 856
Ombitasvir: 62, 305
Omeclamox-Pak: 962
Omega-3 Acid Ethyl Esters: 454
Omega-3-carboxylic Acids: 454
Omega-3 Fatty Acids: 1026, 1027, 1029
Omeprazole: 60, 70, 426, 438, 476, 477, 484, 485, 521, 801, 958, 959, 961
Omeprazole + Sodium Bicarbonate: 958
Omeprazole+Syrspend SF Alka: 959
Omnaris: 558
Omnicef: 351, 370, 372
Omnipred: 570
OnabotulinumtoxinA: 741, 743
Oncaspar: 870
Oncology Agents: 460
Ondansetron: 66, 69, 92, 508, 843, 844, 846, 967, 984
Ondansetron ODT: 92
Onfi: 947
Onglyza: 648
Onsolis: 803
Ontruzant: 1023
Onzetra Xsail: 820, 824
Opana: 805, 816
Opdivo: 874
Opioids: 55, 56, 61, 64, 65, 67, 68, 109, 125, 409, 485, 552, 640, 710, 760, 761, 797, 802, 803, 808, 809, 811, 812, 814, 819, 823, 881, 933, 950, 967, 969, 971, 992, 996, 1001, 1002, 1004, 1007, 1036
Opsumit: 596
OptiChamber: 611
OptiHaler: 611
OptiPranolol: 568
Oracea: 359, 373
Oracit: 300
Orafate: 847
OraGel: 1038
Oralair: 562
Oral Contraceptives: 67, 451, 460, 608, 650, 652, 1025
Oralube: 689
Orapred ODT: 673
Orbactiv: 362
Orencia: 101, 103, 681
Orenitram: 595
Organophosphates: 1038
Orilissa: 698
Oritavancin: 70, 75, 362, 369, 371, 390
Orkambi: 777
Orlistat: 537, 667, 790, 792, 793, 1031
Orphenadrine: 1007
Ortho-Cyclen: 699, 701
Ortho Tri-Cyclen: 697, 699
Ortho Tri-Cyclen Lo: 305
Oscal: 183
Oseltamivir: 294, 380, 405, 406, 411, 1003, 1005
Oseni: 643
Osmitrol: 103, 522
Osmolex ER: 929
Osmolite: 151, 160, 162
Osmoprep: 967, 970
Osmotic Laxatives: 968
Ospemifene: 725
Osphena: 725
Otezla: 690, 691
Otiprio: 357
Otovel: 357
Otrexup: 96, 676, 678, 869
Ovide: 583
Ovidrel: 706
Oxacillin: 349, 350, 354
Oxaliplatin: 101, 863
Oxaprozin: 800
Oxaydo: 805
Oxazepam: 916
Oxazolidinones: 363
Oxcarbazepine: 59, 65, 69, 73, 228, 305, 308, 424, 665, 701, 887, 939, 940, 944, 947, 949, 951, 1005, 1022, 1031
Oxtellar SXR: 944, 951
Oxtellar XR: 944
Oxybutynin: 49, 69, 90, 97, 567, 742, 933
Oxybutynin IR: 742
Oxybutynin Topical Gel: 742, 745
Oxybutynin XL: 742
Oxycodone: 56, 64, 65, 69, 70, 798, 805, 806, 808
OxyContin: 805, 811
Oxymetazoline: 94, 560, 561
Oxymetazoline Hydrochloride 1% Cream: 574
Oxymorphone: 805, 806, 808
Oxytrol: 97, 742
Oxytrol For Women - OTC: 742
Oxytrol Patch: 744
Ozempic: 649, 651, 659
Ozenoxacin: 389
Ozurdex: 570

P

P2Y12 Inhibitors: 74, 482, 483, 484, 485, 488, 529
Pacerone: 511
Paclitaxel: 837, 838, 866, 868
Paclitaxel albumin-bound: 866
Paint Thinners: 1037
Palbociclib: 857
Paliperidone: 79, 95, 508, 730, 895, 897, 899, 926
Palivizumab: 767
Palonosetron: 843, 844
Pamelor: 886, 914
Pamidronate: 228, 849
Pamix: 582

Pancreatic Enzyme Products: 774, 776, 778
Pancreaze: 776
Pancrelipase: 93, 776
Pancuronium: 761, 1038
Pancuronium Bromide: 1038
Pandel: 589
Panitumumab: 872, 873, 1023
Pantoprazole: 958, 959
Paragard: 704, 705
Paralytics: 1038
Parathyroid Hormone Analogs: 716
Paricalcitol: 297
Paritaprevir: 62, 69, 305

Paritaprevir/nritonavir/ombitasvir + Dasabuvir: 304
Paritaprevir/ritonavir/nombitasvir: 304
Parnate: 49, 887
Paroxetine: 64, 68, 69, 70, 228, 790, 882, 883, 884, 900, 725, 725
Parsabiv: 297
Pasireotide: 228
Passionflower: 914, 1027, 1028, 1029
Pataday: 569
Patanase: 560
Patanol: 569
Patiromer: 299, 300, 667
Paxil: 883, 914
Paxil CR: 883, 914
Pazeo: 569
PCSK9 Inhibitors: 446, 445, 448, 450, 456, 639
PediaCare Infants' Fever Reducer/ Pain Reliever: 766
Pedia-Lax: 766, 968
PEG 3350: 836
Pegaspargase: 870
Pegasys: 307
Pegfilgrastim: 840
PEG-filgrastim: 264
Pegfilgrastim-cbqv: 840
Pegfilgrastim-jmdb: 840
Peginterferon Beta-1a: 684
PegIntron: 307
Pegloticase: 75, 549, 828, 829
Pegylated G-CSF: 840
Pegylated Interferon-alfa-2a: 307
Pegylated Interferon-alfa-2b: 307
Pegylated Interferon Beta: 683
Pembrolizumab: 836, 837, 872, 874
Pemetrexed: 869
Penciclovir: 70, 407, 408, 576
Pen G: 369
Penicillamine: 1037
Penicillin: 57, 58, 354, 380, 387, 396, 938, 1006, 1007, 1008, 1025
Penicillin G: 1008
Penicillin G Aqueous: 349
Penicillin G Aqueous Crystalline: 395
Penicillin G Benzathine: 349, 350, 395, 396
Penicillin G Benzathine and Penicillin G Procaine: 349
Penicillin G Procaine: 395
Penicillins: 75, 346, 348, 535, 549, 711, 830, 1005
Penicillin VK: 350, 370, 371, 372, 389
Penicillin V Potassium: 349
Penlac: 580
Pennsaid: 800
Pentamidine: 67, 73, 101, 103, 104, 298, 371, 413, 414, 508, 660
Pentasa: 979
Pentetate Calcium Trisodium: 228
Pentoxifylline: 608
Pentrax Gold: 690
Pen VK: 349
Pepcid: 958
Pepcid AC: 958
Pepcid Complete: 958
Peppermint: 819, 1027, 1028
Pepto-Bismol: 334, 394, 972, 973
Peramivir: 380, 405, 406, 1005
Perampanel: 701, 948
Percocet: 798, 805
Perforomist: 606, 622
Perindopril: 466, 494
Perindopril/Amlodipine: 462
Peripherally-acting mu-opioid Receptor Antagonists (PAMORAs): 971, 974
Perjeta: 873, 1023
Permethrin: 336, 583
Perphenazine: 894
Perseris: 897
Pertuzumab: 836, 872, 873, 1023
Pertzye: 776
Petrolatum: 581
Petrolatum + Zinc Oxide: 581
Pexeva: 883, 914
Pfizerpen-G: 349
P-gp Inhibitor: 900
Phenadoz: 845
Phenazopyridine: 392, 393
Phencyclidine (PCP): 893
Phendimetrazine: 592, 792
Phenelzine: 49, 64, 67, 882, 887
Phenergan: 845
Phenobarbital: 59, 62, 65, 69, 70, 75, 305, 308, 424, 427, 428, 429, 535, 546, 608, 647, 712, 939, 940, 941, 942, 944, 945, 949, 951, 1005, 714

Phenothiazines: 66, 508, 734, 926, 929, 967
Phenoxybenzamine: 228
Phentermine: 460, 592, 791, 792, 967
Phentermine/Topiramate: 793
Phentolamine: 49, 753
Phenylalanine: 92, 372, 899, 930
Phenylephrine: 49, 64, 460, 560, 561, 565, 582, 753, 756, 887
Phenylhistine DH: 803
Phenylketonuria: 92
Phenylpropanolamine: 562
Phenytek: 946
Phenytoin: 59, 62, 65, 69, 70, 75, 76, 80, 101, 103, 127, 161, 228, 305, 308, 424, 427, 428, 429, 451, 532, 535, 546, 608, 647, 648, 665, 701, 884, 904, 939, 941, 942, 944, 946, 949, 951, 961, 1005, 1011, 1012, 1015, 1016, 1022, 714
PhosLo: 183, 295
Phoslyra: 295
Phosphate: 102
Phosphate Binders: 66, 73, 296
Phosphodiesterase-3 Inhibitor: 755
Phosphodiesterase-4 (PDE-4) Inhibitors: 578, 619, 622
Phosphodiesterase-5 Inhibitors (PDE-5): 47, 66, 69, 428, 483, 498, 570, 571, 593, 686, 731, 736, 738, 764
Phosphodiesterase-5 (PDE-5) Inhibitor: 735
Phosphodiesterase Inhibitors: 109
Physicians EZ Use B-12: 546
Physostigmine: 1037
Phytonadione: 536, 537, 1004, 1005, 1037
Pifeltro: 423
Pilocarpine: 49, 568, 689, 836, 846, 847
Pilopine HS: 568
Pimavanserin: 893, 898
Pimecrolimus: 552, 578
Pimozide: 69, 305, 400, 401, 402, 428, 429, 844, 883, 884
Pindolol: 470
Pin-X: 582
Pioglitazone: 69, 70, 646, 662
Piperacillin/Tazobactam: 102, 103, 382, 383, 390, 391, 392, 349, 350, 369, 388, 841
Piperazine Antihistamines: 984
Piperonyl Butoxide: 583
Pirfenidone: 598
Piroxicam: 800, 1005
Pitavastatin: 63, 445, 446, 447, 512
Plan B One-Step: 705
Plant Sterol: 1027
Plaquenil: 676
Plasma-Lyte A: 749
Plavix: 70, 90, 475, 476, 484, 521, 1022
Plax: 689
Plazomicin: 355, 392
Plecanatide: 968, 971
Plegridy: 683, 684
Plenvu: 970
Pneumovax 23 (PPSV23): 379, 601, 639
Pokemon Children's Multiple Vitamin with Iron: 1031
Policosanol: 535
Polyethylene glycol (PEG): 264, 766, 765, 836, 967, 968
Poly-L-Lactic Acid: 433
Polymyxins: 73, 292, 294, 361, 365, 369, 383, 585
Polysaccharide Iron Complex: 544
Polysporin: 585
Polytrim: 569
Poly-Vi-Sol: 1030, 1031
Pomalidomide: 836, 837, 871, 877
Pomalyst: 871, 877
Ponatinib: 836, 875
Ponstel: 800
Poractant Alfa: 765
Portia: 699
Posaconazole: 60, 62, 69, 370, 371, 400, 401, 402, 404, 413, 414, 424, 448, 641
Potassium: 73, 93, 298, 461, 1027, 1029
Potassium Acetate: 158
Potassium Bicarbonate and Potassium Citrate: 501
Potassium Chloride: 125, 158, 501, 751, 992
Potassium Iodide: 669
Potassium Iodine: 669
Potassium-sparing Diuretics: 158, 294, 361, 468, 698
Potassium Sulfate: 970
Proton Pump Inhibitors (PPIs): 73, 75, 305, 424, 428, 431, 714, 715, 717, 962

Pradaxa: 528, 533, 816
Pralatrexate: 869
Pralidoxime: 1038
Praluent: 450
Pramipexole: 922, 927, 928, 931
Pramlintide: 642, 652, 660, 662
PrandiMet: 643
Prandin: 644
Prasterone: 725
Prasugrel: 67, 69, 483, 484, 485, 488
Pravachol: 447
Pravastatin: 63, 445, 446, 447, 512
Praxbind: 101, 533, 536, 762, 1037
Prazosin: 472
Precedex: 63, 103, 465, 470, 511, 512, 757, 758
Precise: 815
Precose: 648
Pred Forte: 570
PredForte: 567
Pred Mild: 570
Prednicarbate: 589

Prednisolone: 70, 567, 570, 673, 827
PrednisoLONE: 991
Prednisone: 70, 412, 414, 671, 673, 674, 675, 781, 816, 714, 717
Prednisone Intensol: 673, 978
Prefest: 724
Pregabalin: 294, 640, 790, 813, 914, 939, 722, 725
Pregabalin/Gabapentin: 940
Pregnyl: 706
Premarin: 724
Premphase: 722, 724
Prempro: 724
Preparation H: 582
Pre-Pen: 1008
Prepopik: 970
Prestalia: 462

Prevacid: 958, 959, 721
Prevacid 24HR-OTC: 959
Prevacid SoluTab: 958, 959, 964
Prevalite: 451
Preventeza: 705
Prevnar (PCV13): 379, 601, 639
Prevpac: 962, 965
Prevymis: 410
Prexxartan: 467
Prezcobix: 420, 425, 429, 434
Prezista: 425, 1007
Prilosec: 958, 721
Prilosec OTC: 959
Primaquine: 75, 337, 549
Primatene Mist: 604
Primaxin I.V.: 353
Primidone: 65, 69, 70, 75, 535, 546, 608, 701, 940, 941, 945, 948, 949, 1031
Primlev: 798, 805
Prinivil: 466, 494
Pristiq: 885
Privigen: 752
ProAir Digihaler: 604
ProAir HFA: 111, 604, 613
ProAir RespiClick: 604, 610, 615
Probenecid: 57, 349, 358, 678, 826, 828, 829, 830, 869
Probiotics: 1027, 1028, 1029
Probuphine: 812
Procainamide: 72, 74, 78, 80, 294, 508, 511, 513, 577, 682, 881
Procaine: 50
Procarbazine: 862
Procardia: 464
Procardia XL: 94, 464, 472
Pro-C-Dure: 673
ProCentra: 909
Prochlorperazine: 66, 836, 842, 843, 845, 926
Procrit: 107, 298, 547
Pro-Ex Antifungal: 579
Profilnine: 537
Progesterones: 69, 228, 722, 724
Progestin-only Pills: 698, 702
Progestins: 228, 443, 716, 722, 724
Proglycem: 592
Prograf: 782, 787
Programmed Death Receptor-1 (PD-1) Inhibitors: 874
Proguanil: 337
Prolia: 716, 720
Promacta: 548
Promethazine: 100, 564, 770, 803, 843, 845, 961, 984
Promethazine/codeine: 564
Promethazine/Phenylephrine: 803
Promethazine/phenylephrine/codeine: 564
Promethazine VC/Codeine: 564, 803
Promethegan: 845
Prometrium: 722, 724
Propafenone: 70, 429, 499, 508, 512, 514, 608
Propecia: 577, 737
Prophylactic Penicillin: 551
Prophylaxis: 838
Propofol: 156, 443, 465, 508, 757, 758, 992, 1007
Propranolol: 49, 68, 69, 70, 311, 470, 608, 686, 822, 881, 914
Propranolol/Hydrochlorothiazide: 462
Propylene glycol: 79, 178
Propylthiouracil (PTU): 228, 310, 667, 668, 682, 711
Proscar: 577, 737
Prostacyclin: 595
Prostacyclin Analogues: 593, 764
Prostaglandin Analogs: 567
Protamine: 528, 529, 536, 1037
Protease-Activated Receptor-1 Antagonist: 487
Protease Inhibitors (PIs): 60, 63, 386, 425, 428, 429, 435, 443, 448, 508, 641, 648
Proteasome Inhibitors: 871
ProThelial: 847
Prothrombin Complex Concentrate: 536, 537, 538, 1037
Protonix: 958, 959
Proton Pump Inhibitors (PPIs): 394, 488, 543, 544, 545, 546, 682, 721, 760, 869, 1031
Protopam: 1038
Protopic: 578, 690, 782
Protriptyline: 886
ProvayBlue: 1038
Proventil HFA: 604
Provera: 724
Provigil: 923
Prozac: 883, 914
Prucalopride: 971
Prudoxin: 886
Prussian Blue: 1037
Pseudoephedrine: 64, 460, 560, 561, 562, 565, 686, 734, 800, 804, 887
Psorcon Cream, 0.05%: 588
Psorcon Ointment, 0.05%: 588
Psoriasin: 690
Psyllium: 710, 967, 968, 1027, 1029
Pulmicort Flexhaler: 605, 606, 610, 614
Pulmicort Respules: 605, 616
PulmoSal: 775
Pulmozyme: 774, 775
Pumpkin Seed: 735
Pumpkin Seed: 1028
Purixan: 980
Pygeum: 735, 1028
Pylera: 962, 965
Pyrantel Pamoate: 582
Pyrazinamide: 78, 294, 384, 385, 386
Pyrethrin: 583
Pyridium: 392, 393
Pyridostigmine: 688, 1038
Pyridoxine: 310, 385, 710, 1030, 1031, 1037
Pyrilamine: 798
Pyrimethamine: 413, 414
Pyrimidine Analog Antimetabolites: 868
Pyrithione Zinc: 576

Q

Qbrelis: 466, 494
Qbrexza: 578
Qnasl: 558
Qnasl Childrens: 558
Qsymia: 790, 791, 793
Qtern: 643
Quazepam: 921
Qudexy XR: 942
Quelicin: 761
Questran: 93, 451
Questran Light: 93
Quetiapine: 69, 508, 641, 757, 759, 790, 889, 897, 899, 900, 902, 903, 926, 927
Quetiapine Extended Release: 882
QuilliChew ER: 906, 908
Quillivant XR: 906, 908, 910
Quinapril: 466, 494
Quinapril/Hydrochlorothiazide: 462
Quinidine: 62, 69, 70, 75, 78, 400, 401, 402, 429, 499, 508, 511, 512, 513, 549, 682, 761, 884, 972, 1004
Quinine: 508, 549, 660, 1004, 1005
Quinolones: 57, 66, 161, 294, 296, 335, 353, 357, 358, 359, 369, 372, 377, 378, 380, 382, 385, 387, 392, 393, 508, 535, 545, 641, 660, 688, 711, 770, 774, 785, 938, 1004, 1005, 1008, 1025
Quinupristin/Dalfopristin: 76, 101, 104, 364, 369, 371
Qutenza: 815
QVAR: 605
QVAR RediHaler: 605, 606, 607, 610, 613

R

RabAvert: 1039
Rabeprazole: 958, 959
Rabies Vaccine: 1039
Racemic Epinephrine 2.25% Solution: 768
Racepinephrine: 604
Radiesse: 433
Radiesse Plus: 433
Radioactive Iodine: 711
Radiocontrast Dye: 73, 399
Radiogardase: 1037
Radiographic contrast Dye: 292
Radiographic Contrast Dye: 361
Ragweed: 1028, 1029
Ragwitek: 562
Raloxifene: 82, 83, 228, 716, 718, 721, 716, 718
Raltegravir: 62, 76, 418, 419, 430, 431, 434, 435, 439
Raltitrexed: 546
Ramelteon: 70, 920
Ramipril: 466, 494
Ramucirumab: 872, 873
Ranexa: 477
Ranibizumab: 640
Ranitidine: 294, 730, 958
Ranitidine Acid Reducer: 958
RANKL Inhibitor: 720
Ranolazine: 62, 69, 305, 429, 448, 470, 475, 477, 478, 480, 496, 508, 967
Rapaflo: 736
Rapamune: 784
Rapivab: 406
Rasagiline: 49, 64, 67, 69, 228, 929, 930
Rasburicase: 75, 104, 549, 830, 848
Rasuvo: 676, 678, 869
Rayaldee: 297
Rayos: 673, 978
Razadyne: 934
Razadyne ER: 934
ReadySharp Betamethasone: 673
Rebetol: 306
Rebif: 683, 684
Reclast: 718
Recombinant Tissue Plasminogen Activator: 487
Recombivax HB: 336
Recothrom: 762
Red Clover: 725
Red Clover: 1028, 1029
Red Yeast Rice: 444
Red Yeast Rice: 1027, 1029
Reese's Pinworm Medicine: 582
Refissa: 575
Refresh: 570, 689
Reglan: 845, 898, 960
Relafen: 801
Relenza Diskhaler: 406
Relexxii: 908
Relistor: 809, 971
Relpax: 820, 821
Remeron: 888
Remeron SolTab: 92, 888
Remicade: 101, 103, 679, 977
Remifentanil: 758
Remodulin: 595
Renagel: 296
Renflexis: 679
Renin-angiotensin-aldosterone System (RAAS): 67, 313, 458, 466, 467
Renova: 111, 575
Renvela: 296, 358
ReoPro: 103, 486
Repaglinide: 69, 70, 452, 644, 645
Repatha: 450
Replens: 723
Requip: 90, 893, 922, 928
Requip XL: 928
Reslizumab: 602, 609
Respules: 710
Restasis: 570, 689, 783
Restoril: 921
Retacrit: 298, 547
Retapamulin: 389
Retavase: 487
Reteplase: 487
Retin-A: 575
Retin-A Micro: 575

Retinoids: 443, 574, 690, 870, 1004, 1025
Retinol: 1030
Retrovir: 422
Revatio: 479, 731, 732, 736
Revefenacin: 606, 621
ReVia: 310
Revlimid: 871, 877
Revonto: 900
Rexulti: 882, 889, 897
Reyataz: 426
Rhinocort: 710
Rhinocort Allergy OTC: 558
Rhofade: 574
Rho Kinase Inhibitors: 568
Rhopressa: 568
Ribasphere RibaPak: 306

Ribavirin: 228, 303, 306, 307, 767
Ribociclib: 857
Riboflavin: 819, 1028, 1030
RID: 583
Rifabutin: 59, 65, 69, 305, 385, 386, 401, 402, 414, 701
Rifadin: 385
Rifamate: 385
Rifampin: 57, 59, 62, 63, 65, 69, 70, 75, 105, 305, 308, 367, 369, 371, 384, 385, 386, 387, 401, 402, 424, 428, 429, 431, 532, 534, 535, 549, 595, 608, 646, 647, 648, 701, 785, 884, 915, 941
Rifamycin: 335
Rifapentine: 59, 69, 70, 384, 701
Rifater: 385
Rifaximin: 312, 335, 367, 393, 973
Rilpivirine: 419, 423, 424, 434, 435, 437, 508, 881, 960
Rimantadine: 405, 406
Riociguat: 228, 478, 479, 498, 592, 593, 732, 738
Riomet: 14, 643
Risedronate: 545, 717, 721, 717
Risperdal: 897, 899, 903
Risperdal Consta: 95, 893, 897, 903
Risperdal M-Tab: 899
Risperdone M-TAB ODT: 897
Risperidone: 70, 79, 95, 508, 730, 790, 893, 895, 897, 899, 903, 926
Risperidone M-Tab: 903
Ritalin: 906, 907, 908, 923
Ritalin LA: 93, 906, 908, 910
Ritalin SR: 908
Ritonavir: 57, 60, 62, 63, 69, 70, 303, 305, 401, 402, 419, 425, 426, 427, 428, 429, 431, 434, 435, 448, 532, 596, 608, 648, 701
Rituxan: 680, 873
Rituximab: 680, 685, 872, 873, 1007
Rivaroxaban: 62, 67, 69, 294, 359, 386, 428, 527, 530, 531, 532, 536, 538, 539, 541, 1037
Rivastigmine: 97, 934
Rizatriptan: 820, 821
Robafen: 563
Robafen AC: 564, 565
Robafen DM: 565
Robaxin: 814
Robaxin-750: 814
Robinul: 761
Robitussin Cough + Chest Congestion DM: 565
Robitussin D: 560
Robitussin DM: 563
Robitussin Mucus + Chest Congestion: 563
Rocaltrol: 297
Rocephin: 351
Rocuronium: 761, 1038
Rocuronium Bromide: 1038
Roflumilast: 619, 622
Rogaine: 577
Rolapitant: 843, 844
Romazicon: 1037
Ropinirole: 69, 922, 928, 931
Ropivacaine: 760, 1037
Rosadan: 366
Rosiglitazone: 70, 646, 655
Rosuvastatin: 60, 63, 428, 445, 446, 447, 448, 512
Rotigotine: 97, 98, 922, 928, 931, 1007
Rowasa: 94, 979, 981, 982, 1007
Roweepra: 941
Roweepra XR: 941
Roxanol: 805
Roxicodone: 805
Roxybond: 805, 811
Rozerem: 920
RU-486: 705
Rufinamide: 948
Ryanodex: 900
Rye Pollen: 735
Rytary: 928, 931
Rythmol SR: 514

S

Sabril: 948
Sacubitril: 495
Sacubitril/Valsartan: 67, 467, 492, 495, 504
Safinamide: 929
Safyral: 699, 1030
Salagen: 689, 847
Salicylates: 57, 67, 73, 68, 178, 488, 535, 765, 801, 869, 942, 1025, 1029, 1038
Salicylate Salts: 801
Salicylic Acid: 574, 690
Saline: 101, 557, 565
SalivaMAX: 847
Salivart: 689
SalivaSure: 847
Salmeterol: 428, 604, 606, 609, 622
Salonpas: 97, 98, 815
Salsalate: 801
SAMe: 881, 1027, 1028, 1029
Samsca: 749, 750
Sancuso: 92, 844
Sandimmune: 783
Sandostatin: 311
Sani-Supp: 968
Santyl: 584, 585
Saphris: 897, 899, 903
Saquinavir: 69, 305, 427, 434, 435, 448, 508
Sarafem: 883
Sarecycline: 359, 575
Sargramostim: 840
Sarilumab: 681
Sarin: 1038
Savaysa: 527, 530, 531
Savella: 814
Savella Titration Pack: 814
Saw Palmetto: 735, 1028
Saxagliptin: 62, 69, 648, 662
Saxagliptin/dapagliflozin: 643
Saxenda: 649, 790, 792, 793
Scopolamine: 97, 98, 567, 686, 983, 984, 985, 1037
Seasonique: 699
Secnidazole: 366, 396
Second-generation (atypical) antipsychotics: 641, 893, 895, 896, 902
Secret Clinical Strength: 578
Secukinumab: 691
Sedating Antihistamines: 68, 69
Seebri Neohaler: 606, 621, 628
Segluromet: 643
Selective ARA: 497
Selective Estrogen Receptor Modulators (SERMs): 82, 718, 228, 535, 538, 539, 706
Selective Monoamine Oxidase-B Inhibitors: 67
Selective Norepinephrine Reuptake Inhibitor: 911
Selective Serotonin Reuptake Inhibitors (SSRIs): 64, 66, 67, 68, 73, 485, 529, 532, 534, 535, 508, 592, 790, 882, 884, 887, 714, 722, 725, 883, 907, 914, 890, 1025
Selegiline: 49, 64, 67, 97, 887, 929
Selenium: 940, 941
Selenium Sulfide: 576
Selexipag: 595
Selsun: 576
Selzentry: 431
Semaglutide: 649, 662
Senna: 457, 808, 967, 969
Senna Plus: 969
Senna S: 969
Senokot: 969
Sensipar: 297
Sensorcaine: 760
Serevent Diskus: 604, 606, 622
Seroquel: 759, 889, 897, 903
Seroquel XR: 882, 889, 897, 903
Serotonin-3 Receptor Antagonist (5HT3-RA): 836
Serotonin 5-HT2C Receptor Agonist: 791
Serotonin 5HT-4 Receptor Agonist: 971
Serotonin Norepinephrine Reuptake Inhibitors (SNRIs): 64, 67, 68, 485, 529, 532, 534, 535, 907, 885, 914, 1025
Serotonin Receptor Agonists: 819
Sertraline: 66, 69, 70, 508, 883, 884, 888, 890, 914, 934
Sevelamer: 296, 358, 667, 751, 785
Sevelamer Carbonate: 296
Sevelamer Hydrochloride: 296
Sevoflurane: 508, 760
Seysara: 359, 575
Shingrix: 90
Shohl's Solution: 300
Shopko Athletes Foot: 579
Short-acting Beta Agonists (SABAs): 602, 604, 609, 619
Short-acting Bronchodilator: 599
Short-acting Muscarinic Antagonist (SAMA): 602, 619
Siklos: 552
Sildenafil: 47, 66, 69, 305, 429, 478, 479, 498, 571, 598, 730, 731, 732
Silenor: 886, 921
Silibinin: 1038
Siliq: 691
Silodosin: 730, 735, 736, 739
Simbrinza: 568
Simethicone: 710, 766, 957
Simethicone Drops: 765
Simponi: 95, 679, 680, 977
Simponi Aria: 679
Simponimod: 685
Simulect: 780
Simvastatin: 60, 63, 64, 69, 110, 305, 359, 428, 429, 444, 445, 446, 447, 448, 449, 452, 456, 485, 511, 512
Sinemet: 893, 927, 928, 929
Sinemet CR: 94, 928
Singulair: 93, 561, 607, 615
Sinuva: 558
Sirolimus: 62, 64, 65, 69, 228, 401, 402, 781, 784, 785
Sirturo: 385
Sitagliptin: 69, 648
Sitagliptin/ertugliflozin: 643
Sitavig: 407, 576
Sivextro: 363
Skelaxin: 814
Skeletal Muscle Relaxants: 68, 69, 686, 887, 933, 935, 950
Sklice: 583
Skyla: 704
Sleep Aid: 922
Slo-Niacin: 453
Slow Fe: 544
Slow Iron: 544
Smoflipid: 151, 156
SNRIs: 460, 508, 686, 722, 725, 734, 882, 814, 887, 890
Sodium: 291
Sodium Acetate: 157, 179
Sodium Bicarbonate: 57, 102, 299, 300, 661, 958, 959, 1035, 1038
Sodium Bicarbonate + Aspirin + Citric Acid: 957

Sodium Chloride: 749
Sodium Citrate/Citric Acid Solution: 300
Sodium Ferric Gluconate: 101, 545
Sodium glucose Co-transporter 2 (SGLT2) Inhibitors: 294, 443, 638, 642, 645, 647, 660, 662
Sodium Oxybate: 923
Sodium Phosphates: 157, 967, 970
Sodium Picosulfate: 970
Sodium Polystyrene Sulfate: 667
Sodium Polystyrene Sulfonate: 299, 300
Sodium Sulfate: 970
Sodium Thiosulfate: 754
Sodium Thiosulfate + Sodium Nitrite: 1037
Sodium Zirconium Cyclosilicate: 299, 300
Sofosbuvir: 62, 304, 511
Sofosbuvir/ledipasvir: 304, 422
Sofosbuvir/velpatasvir: 304
Sofosbuvir/velpatasvir/voxilaprevir: 304
Solifenacin: 508, 742
Soliqua: 643, 659
Solodyn: 359, 373, 575
Solosec: 366
Solriamfetol: 923
Soltamox: 856, 877
Solu-Cortef: 673
Solu-Medrol: 673
SOLU-Medrol: 827
Soma: 814
Sonata: 920
Sorafenib: 508, 836, 846, 847, 876, 877
Sorbitol: 92, 968
Soriatane: 691
Sorilux: 690
Sorine: 515
S.O.S: 812
Sotalol: 66, 294, 508, 510, 515
Sotylize: 515
Sovaldi: 304
Spectracef: 351
Spinosad: 583
Spiriva: 111
Spiriva HandiHaler: 606, 621, 625
Spiriva Respimat: 606, 608, 621
Spironolactone: 67, 228, 291, 313, 468, 497, 574, 577, 1003
Spironolactone/Hydrochlorothiazide: 462
Sporanox: 90, 400, 404, 580
Sporanox PulsePak: 400
Spravato: 882, 889
Sprintec: 699
Spritam: 941
Sprix: 800, 816
Sprycel: 592, 875, 877
SPS: 300
SSKI: 669
SSRI, 5-HT Receptor Antagonist and 5-HT1A Agonist: 884
SSRI and 5-HT1A Partial Agonist: 884
Stalevo: 928
Stanback: 801
Starlix: 644
Statins: 60, 63, 69, 76, 125, 294, 444, 445, 446, 447, 449, 482, 488, 450, 452, 453, 456, 511, 639, 641, 712, 826
Stavudine: 76, 422, 432, 435
Staxyn: 479, 736
Staxyn ODT: 731
Steglatro: 647
Steglujan: 643
Stelara: 691, 977, 980
Stendra: 479, 731, 736
Steroids: 73, 74, 79, 125, 381, 443, 460, 543, 641, 667, 671, 683, 690, 710, 714, 768, 781, 790, 816, 826, 827, 856, 859, 866, 868, 872, 873, 881, 893, 957, 960, 1005
Stimate Nasal Spray: 744
Stimulant Laxative: 969
Stimulants: 64, 109, 881, 893, 905, 906, 907, 908, 909, 910, 911, 1026
Stiolto Respimat: 606, 621, 622, 624
Stiripentol: 948
St. John's Wort: 59, 62, 63, 64, 67, 69, 70, 305, 308, 401, 402, 424, 428, 429, 431, 532, 535, 608, 648, 701, 725, 785, 881, 882, 887, 914, 1004, 1025, 1027, 1029
Stool Softeners: 457, 969
Strattera: 881, 906, 907, 911
Streptomycin: 355, 385, 414
Stribild: 110, 294, 305, 419, 422, 429, 430, 434, 439, 532, 534
Striverdi Respimat: 606, 622, 624
Stromectol: 583
Suave: 576
Sublimaze: 803
Sublocade: 812
Suboxone: 811, 812
Subsys: 93, 803
Subvenite: 941
Subvenite Starter Kit-Blue, Green, Orange: 941
Succimer: 1037
Succinylcholine: 761
Sucralfate: 66, 360, 372, 431, 667, 963, 967
Sucroferric Oxyhydroxide: 296
Sudafed: 561
Sudafed PE: 561, 565
Sugammadex: 1038
Sular: 464
Sulbactam: 346
Sulfacetamide: 569
Sulfadiazine: 414, 1007
Sulfamethoxazole/Trimethoprim: 63, 67, 70, 72, 73, 75, 103, 294, 298, 313, 360, 361, 369, 370, 371, 373, 378, 387, 389, 392, 393, 413, 575, 711, 1004, 1005, 1007, 1025, 1031
Sulfasalazine: 75, 546, 598, 676, 979, 1005, 1007
Sulfatrim: 370
Sulfisoxazole: 1007
Sulfonamides: 75, 361, 678, 869, 948, 1005, 1038
Sulfonylureas: 358, 364, 452, 470, 642, 644, 645, 655, 660, 662, 790, 992, 1007
Sulindac: 800, 826, 904
Sumatriptan: 94, 95, 96, 800, 820, 821
Sumavel DosePro: 96
Sunitinib: 508, 836, 846, 847, 876, 877
Sunosi: 923
Supprelin LA: 859
Suprane: 760
Suprax: 93, 351, 395
Suprep Bowel Kit: 970
Surmontil: 886
Sustiva: 423
Sustol: 844
Sutent: 876, 877
Suvorexant: 428, 920
Syeda: 699
Sylatron: 307
Symbicort: 605, 606, 613, 622
Symbyax: 882, 883, 889, 896, 902, 903
Symdeko: 777
Symfi: 294, 419, 434
Symfi Lo: 294, 419, 434
Symjepi: 1005, 1006
Symlin: 652, 659
Sympathomimetics: 686, 792
Sympazan: 947
Symproic: 809, 971
Symtuza: 294, 419, 422, 429, 434
Synacort: 589
Synagis: 767
Synalar: 588, 589
Syndros: 433, 843, 845
Synephrine: 1026, 1027, 1028
Synercid: 101, 104, 364
Synjardy: 643
Synjardy XR: 643
Synthetic Cathinones: 893
Synthroid: 111, 666
Systane: 570, 689
Systemic Dexamethasone: 424

T

T3: 666
Taclonex: 690
Tacrolimus: 62, 64, 65, 67, 69, 73, 78, 101, 228, 292, 294, 296, 298, 305, 361, 399, 443, 508, 552, 578, 641, 678, 781, 782, 785, 787, 788, 961, 1004, 1025
Tadalafil: 66, 69, 294, 478, 479, 498, 730, 731, 732, 735, 738
Tafinlar: 875
Tafluprost: 567, 571
Take Action: 705
Taltz: 691
Tamiflu: 406, 411, 1003
Tamoxifen: 69, 70, 443, 856, 857, 877, 884, 725
Tamsulosin: 111, 735, 736, 739
Tanzeum: 649
Tapazole: 668
Tapentadol: 67, 640, 810, 819, 967
Tarceva: 875, 877
Tarka: 462
Tarsum: 690
Tasigna: 875, 877
Tasimelteon: 920
Tavaborole: 580
Taxanes: 101, 103, 837, 838, 866
Taxol: 866
Taxotere: 866
Tazarotene: 575, 690
Tazicef: 351
Tazobactam: 346
Tazorac: 575
Taztia XT: 512
Tbo-filgrastim: 840
Tea Tree Oil: 1028
Tecentriq: 874
Tecfidera: 683, 685
Technivie: 304, 305, 701
Tedizolid: 363, 364, 369, 371, 390
Teflaro: 351
Tegaderm: 98
Tegretol: 814, 943, 1022
Tegretol XR: 943
Tekturna: 467
Tekturna HCT: 462
Telavancin: 75, 228, 362, 369, 390, 508
Telavancin/Oritavancin: 362
Telmisartan: 467
Telmisartan/Amlodipine: 462
Telmisartan/Hydrochlorothiazide: 462
Temazepam: 228, 916, 920, 921
Temodar: 862, 877
Temovate: 588
Temozolomide: 862, 877
Temsirolimus: 870
Tenecteplase: 487
Tenex: 471, 911
Tenofovir: 76, 294, 422, 435, 436, 439
Tenofovir Alafenamide: 294, 418, 419, 420, 421, 437
Tenofovir Alafenamide (TAF): 308
Tenofovir Disoproxil fumarate: 294
Tenofovir Disoproxil Fumarate (TDF): 308, 418, 419, 420, 421, 434, 437, 439
Tenofovir Disoproxil Fumarate/emtricitabine: 419
Tenofovir Powder: 434
Tenoretic: 462
Tenormin: 469
Terazol 7: 581
Terazosin: 472, 735, 736
Terbinafine: 403, 404, 405, 579, 580, 682, 1005
Terbutaline: 48, 49
Terconazole: 581

Teriflunomide: 70, 228, 310, 677, 683, 685
Teriparatide: 95, 716, 719, 721
Tersi: 576
Tesamorelin: 433
Tessalon Perles: 563
Testosterone Products: 47, 79, 94, 97, 98, 228, 734
Tetrabenazine: 961
Tetracyclines: 360, 395, 575, 57, 66, 161, 296, 359, 364, 373, 535, 545, 711, 770, 962, 957, 960, 1004, 1025, 1017
Tetrahydrocannabinol (THC): 939
Tetrahydrozoline: 561, 570
Tezacaftor/ivacaftor: 777
T/Gel: 576
Thalidomide: 836, 837, 871, 877
Thalomid: 871, 877
Theo-24: 608
Theochron: 608
Theophylline: 47, 62, 65, 69, 80, 109, 125, 167, 168, 183, 359, 602, 608, 619, 904, 938, 961, 1015, 1038
Thera-Gesic: 815
Thiamine: 310, 1030, 1037
Thiazide: 640, 641
Thiazide Diuretic: 468
Thiazide Diuretics: 73, 294, 461, 462, 493, 756, 1007
Thiazides: 462
Thiazolidinediones: 642, 645, 646, 660, 662, 714, 790
Thionamides: 668
Thiopurines: 977, 980
Thioridazine: 66, 70, 508, 883, 884, 894, 898
Thiotepa: 103, 104, 850
Thiothixene: 894
Thrombin-JMI: 762
Thrombolytics: 526, 529, 532, 534, 884, 885
Thrombopoietin Nonpeptide Agonist: 548
Thymoglobulin: 780
Thyroid: 666
Thyrolar: 666
ThyroSafe: 669
Tiagabine: 920, 948, 1005
Tiazac: 465, 512
Ticagrelor: 62, 67, 69, 428, 448, 483, 484, 485, 488
Ticalast: 558, 560
Ticaspray: 558
Tigecycline: 104, 105, 364, 369, 391, 535, 1004
Tikosyn: 515
Tildrakizumab-asmn: 691
Timolol: 470, 567, 568, 572, 822
Timolol GFS: 568, 572
Timoptic: 470, 568, 572
Tinactin: 579
Tindamax: 366
Tinidazole: 366, 367, 393, 396, 962
Tiotropium: 606, 608, 621, 622
Tiotropium/olodaterol: 606
Tipranavir: 62, 69, 76, 305, 310, 427, 434, 435, 448, 1007
Tirofiban: 483, 486
Tirosint: 666
Tirosint-SOL: 666
Tivicay: 418, 430, 439
Tivorbex: 799
Tizanidine: 373, 508, 814, 883
TNKase: 487
Tobacco: 608
TOBI: 775, 778
TOBI Podhaler: 775, 778
TobraDex: 569
TobraDex ST: 569
Tobramycin: 80, 355, 356, 383, 397, 569
Tobramycin/Dexamethasone: 569
Tobramycin Inhalation Powder: 775
Tobramycin Inhalation Solution: 775
Tobrex: 569
Tocilizumab: 681
Tofacitinib: 552, 677, 977, 980
Tofranil: 886, 914
Tolak: 868
Tolazamide: 644
Tolbutamide: 644
Tolcapone: 310
Tolnaftate: 579
Tolsura: 400
Tolterodine: 69, 94, 567, 735, 742
Tolterodine ER: 742
Tolvaptan: 69, 749, 750
Topamax: 567, 822, 942
Topamax Sprinkle: 942
Topicort Cream/Ointment, 0.25%: 588
Topicort Gel, 0.05%: 588
Topicort LP Cream, 0.05%: 588
Topiramate: 70, 73, 76, 109, 228, 294, 567, 644, 701, 791, 822, 939, 940, 942, 948, 950, 952, 967, 1031, 1038
Topiramate ER: 791, 942
Topoisomerase I and II Inhibitors: 837, 838
Topoisomerase II Inhibitors: 867
Topoisomerase I Inhibitors: 866
Toposar: 867
Topotecan: 866
Toprol XL: 94, 469, 473, 496, 503, 822
Toradol: 800
Toremifene: 856
Torisel: 870
Torsemide: 493
Tosymra: 820, 824
Totect: 838, 850, 864
Toujeo: 654, 655, 656, 657, 659
Toviaz: 742
Tracleer: 596, 701
Tradjenta: 648
Tramadol: 64, 65, 67, 69, 70, 353, 488, 640, 798, 808, 810, 819, 882, 887, 938, 967, 1025
Tramadol ER: 294
Trametinib: 836, 875
Trandolapril: 466, 494
Trandolapril/Verapamil: 462
Transderm Scop: 97, 98, 983, 984, 985
Tranxene-T: 916
Tranylcypromine: 49, 64, 67, 882, 887

Trastuzumab: 101, 836, 837, 872, 873, 1023
Trastuzumab-dkst: 873, 1023
Trastuzumab-dttb: 1023
Trastuzumab-qyyp: 1023
Travasol: 153
Travatan Z: 567
Travoprost: 567
Trazimera: 1023
Trazodone: 64, 67, 68, 69, 70, 428, 508, 888, 891, 920, 921
Treanda: 862
Trelegy Ellipta: 606, 621, 622
Trelstar: 859
Tremfya: 691
Treprostinil: 595
Tresiba: 654, 655, 656, 659
Tretinoin: 575, 870
Tretin-X: 575
Trexall: 676, 869
Treximet: 800, 820
Triamcinolone: 558, 673, 827
Triamcinolone Acetonide: 588
Triamcinolone Acetonide ER: 813
Triamterene: 67, 468
Triamterene/Hydrochlorothiazide: 462
Triazolam: 228, 305, 428, 429, 921
Tribenzor: 462
Tricor: 452, 457
Tricyclic Antidepressants (TCAs): 64, 66, 67, 69, 70, 109, 428, 460, 567, 508, 640, 734, 790, 814, 882, 885, 886, 882, 887, 890, 907, 914, 927, 967, 1038
Tridesilon: 589
Triethanolamine: 572
Triferic: 545
Trifluoperazine: 894
Triglide: 452, 457
Trihexyphenidyl: 69, 567, 930
Trileptal: 944, 1022
Trilipix: 452, 457
TriLyte: 970
Trimetazidine: 961
Trimethoprim: 370, 373, 575
Trimethoprim/Polymyxin B: 569
Trimethoprim/Sulfamethoxazole: 535
Trimethoprim (TMP): 360, 414
Trimipramine: 886
TriNessa: 699
Trintellix: 884
Triostat: 665, 666
Triple Paste: 581
Triptans: 67, 819, 820, 821, 823, 882, 904
Triptorelin: 859
Trisenox: 870
Tri-Sprintec: 699
Triumeq: 418, 419, 421, 439
Trivora: 699
Trizivir: 420
Trogarzo: 432
Trokendi XR: 822, 942
Trolamine: 815
TrophAmine: 153
Trospium IR: 742
Trospium XR: 742
Troxyca ER: 805, 811
Trulance: 971
Trulicity: 649, 651, 659, 1003
Trusopt: 568
Truvada: 418, 420, 433, 434, 439
Tryptophan: 930
Tudorza Pressair: 606, 621, 626
Tumor Necrosis Factor (TNF) Alpha Inhibitors: 679
Tums: 183, 295, 710, 715
Turmeric: 1027, 1028
TussiCaps: 564, 804
Tussigon: 804
Tussionex: 564
Tussionex Pennkinetic ER: 804
Tuzistra XR: 564
Twinrix: 336
Twynsta: 462
Tybost: 429, 532, 534
Tygacil: 364
Tykerb: 876, 1023
Tylenol: 798, 815
Tylenol #2, 3, 4: 803
Tylenol #3: 1003
Tylenol PM: 798
Tymlos: 95, 716, 719, 722
Typhim Vi: 335, 336
Tyramine: 364
Tyrosine: 930
Tyrosine Kinase Inhibitors (TKIs): 78, 460, 665, 836, 847, 861, 874
Tysabri: 101, 685, 981
Tyvaso: 595

U

Uceris: 978, 982
Udder Cream: 847
Udenyca: 840
Ulesfia: 583
Ulipristal Acetate: 228, 705
Uloric: 829
Ultane: 760
Ultiva: 758
Ultracet: 798, 810
Ultram: 810
Ultram ER: 810
Ultravate: 588
Ultresa: 776
Umeclidinium: 606, 621, 622
Umeclidinium/fluticasone: 622
Umeclidinium/vilanterol: 606
Unasyn: 101, 349
Undecylenic Acid: 579

Unfractionated Heparin (UFH: 75, 483, 527, 528, 529, 530, 535, 536, 538, 540, 711
Unisom: 922

Unithroid: 666
Uptravi: 595
Uricosurics: 829
Uridine Triacetate: 838, 868, 1037
Uristat: 393
Urofollitropin: 228, 706
Uroxatral: 736
Urso 250: 793
Ursodiol: 793
Urso Forte: 793
Ustekinumab: 691, 977, 980
Utibron Neohaler: 606, 621, 622, 628

V

Vabomere: 353
Vagifem: 724
Valacyclovir: 61, 70, 294, 407, 408, 409, 411, 871, 938, 1004
Valbenazine: 899, 900
Valchlor: 862
Valcyte: 370, 410
Valerian: 881, 914, 919, 920, 1027, 1028, 1029
Valganciclovir: 70, 228, 294, 370, 410, 414
Valium: 916
Valproate: 127, 577, 902, 903, 917, 1005
Valproic Acid: 64, 70, 75, 76, 80, 93, 310, 549, 790, 822, 902, 939, 940, 941, 942, 949, 952, 1031, 1038
Valrubicin: 864
Valsartan: 467, 494, 495
Valsartan/Amlodipine: 462
Valsartan/Amlodipine/Hydrochlorothiazide: 462
Valsartan/Hydrochlorothiazide: 462
Valstar: 864
Valtrex: 407, 408, 409, 411
Vancocin: 361
Vancomycin: 59, 68, 69, 73, 74, 80, 99, 103, 167, 292, 294, 346, 361, 369, 370, 377, 378, 382, 383, 386, 387, 390, 391, 394, 399, 761, 767, 1001, 1005, 1008, 1017
Vandazole: 366
Vanos Cream, 0.1%: 588
Vanoxide-HC: 575
Vantas: 859
Vantrela ER: 804
Vaprisol: 750
VAQTA: 336
Vardenafil: 66, 69, 478, 479, 498, 730, 731, 732
Varenicline: 631, 633, 881, 938, 967, 1005
Varubi: 844
Vascepa: 454, 457
Vascular Endothelial Growth Factor (VEGF) Inhibitors: 873
Vaseretic: 462
Vasodilators: 109, 790
Vasopressin: 291, 311, 491, 753
Vasopressors: 100, 103, 753
Vasostrict: 311, 753
Vasotec: 466, 494
Vasotec IV: 466
Vaxchora: 335, 336
Vayacog: 1026
Vayarin: 1026
Vazculep: 753
Vectibix: 873, 1023
Vecuronium: 761, 1038
Vecuronium Bromide: 1038
Vedolizumab: 977, 981
Velcade: 871
Veletri: 595
Velivet: 699
Velpatasvir: 305
Velpatasvir/sofosbuvir: 960
Velphoro: 296
Veltassa: 300, 667
Vemlidy: 308
Vemurafenib: 836, 875
Venlafaxine: 69, 70, 640, 882, 884, 890, 725
Venlafaxine XR: 914
Venofer: 101, 545
Ventavis: 595
Ventolin HFA: 604, 610, 613
VePesid: 867
Verapamil: 60, 62, 63, 69, 448, 465, 470, 483, 496, 499, 508, 511, 512, 532, 593, 608, 826, 904, 915, 935, 967
Verdeso: 589
Verdrocet: 804
Verelan: 465, 512
Verelan PM: 465, 512
Veripred: 673
Versacloz: 896
Versed: 759, 916
Verzenio: 857
Vesicare: 742
Vesicular Monoamine Transporter 2 (VMAT2): 899
Vestura: 699
Vfend: 370, 401, 404
Vfend IV: 401
Viagra: 479, 731, 736
Vibativ: 362
Viberzi: 974
Vibramycin: 359, 370, 373
Vibramycins: 337
Vicks Sinex: 561
Vick's VapoRub: 565
Vicodin: 798, 804
Vicoprofen: 804
Victoza: 112, 649, 651, 659, 792
Vidaza: 101
Videx: 372, 422
Videx EC: 422
Viekira: 305
Viekira Pak: 63, 304, 305, 424, 701
Viekira XR: 304, 424
Vigabatrin: 228, 571, 939, 948
Vigadrone: 948
Vigamox: 357, 569
Viibryd: 884
Viibryd Starter Pack: 884
Vilanterol: 605, 621, 622
Vilanterol/fluticasone: 621
Vilazodone: 884
Vimovo: 800, 959, 963
Vimpat: 943
Vinblastine: 100, 837, 838, 865
Vinca Alkaloids: 100, 850, 837, 838, 865
Vincasar PFS: 865
Vincristine: 99, 100, 835, 836, 837, 838, 850, 865
Vincristine Liposomal: 865
Vinorelbine: 837, 838, 865
Vinpocetine: 1027, 1029
Viokace: 776
Viracept: 427
Viramune: 424
Viramune XR: 424
Virazole: 306, 767
Viread: 308, 421
Virtussin A/C: 564
Virtussin DAC: 564
Visine: 570
Vistaril: 586, 914
Vistogard: 838, 868, 1037
Vitamin A: 310, 1028, 1030
Vitamin B1: 310, 1030, 1031, 1037
Vitamin B2: 1028, 1030
Vitamin B3: 453, 1030
Vitamin B6: 310, 710, 1026, 1030, 1037
Vitamin B9: 546, 1030
Vitamin B12: 546, 1026, 1030, 1031
Vitamin C: 545, 562, 1027, 1029, 1030, 1031
Vitamin D: 73, 79, 82, 310, 446, 638, 857, 933, 940, 949, 950, 714, 715, 716, 721
Vitamin D2: 715
Vitamin D3: 715
Vitamin D Analogs: 297
Vitamin E: 67, 535, 933, 1025, 1027, 1029, 1030
Vitamin K: 530, 534, 536, 537, 538, 1004
Vitamin K Antagonists: 527, 530
Vitamin K Receptor Antagonists: 447
Vivelle: 724, 725
Vivelle-Dot: 97, 724
Vivitrol: 95, 811
Vivlodex: 801
Vivotif: 335, 336
Voltaren: 94, 800
Vorapaxar: 428, 487
Voraxaze: 838, 869, 1038
Voriconazole: 60, 69, 70, 228, 294, 370, 371, 400, 401, 402, 404, 424, 428, 448, 535, 571, 961, 1004, 1005, 1015
Vortioxetine: 884
Vosevi: 304, 305
Vraylar: 897, 903
Vusion: 581
Vytorin: 447, 449
Vyvanse: 61, 93, 686, 906, 907, 909, 910
Vyxeos: 864
Vyzulta: 567

W

Warfarin: 56, 57, 59, 62, 63, 65, 67, 69, 70, 75, 76, 80, 82, 107, 160, 161, 228, 358, 359, 360, 361, 362, 364, 367, 386, 402, 447, 451, 452, 453, 454, 485, 488, 509, 511, 527, 530, 532, 534, 535, 537, 538, 539, 540, 541, 577, 593, 608, 711, 816, 856, 933, 942, 943, 946, 961, 992, 993, 994, 996, 1022, 1025, 725
Welchol: 451, 648
Wellbutrin SR: 631, 886
Wellbutrin XL: 631, 886
Westhroid: 666
Wheat Bran: 1027
Wheat Dextrin: 968
Wheatgrass: 1027
Willow Bark: 535
Willow Bark: 67, 1025
Wintergreen Oil: 535
Wixela Inhub: 605, 606, 622
Women's Rogaine: 471
WP Thyroid: 666

X

Xadago: 929
Xalatan: 567
Xalkori: 875
Xanax XR: 916
Xanthine Oxidase (XO) Inhibitors: 785, 828, 830, 848
Xarelto: 527, 529, 530, 531, 816
Xarelto Starter Pack: 531
Xartemis XR: 805
Xatmep: 676, 869
Xeljanz: 677, 977, 980
Xeljanz XR: 677
Xeloda: 868, 877, 1023
Xelpros: 567
Xenical: 667, 792, 793
Xepi: 389
Xerava: 359
Xgeva: 720
Xhance: 558
Xifaxan: 312, 367, 973
Xigduo XR: 643
Xiidra: 570, 689
Ximino: 359, 575
Xodol: 804
Xofluza: 405, 406
Xolair: 609
Xolegel: 400
Xopenex: 604
Xrylix: 800
Xtampza: 805
Xtandi: 859
Xulane: 97, 305, 698, 699, 700, 703, 704
Xultophy: 643, 659
Xuriden: 1037

Xylocaine: 513, 760
Xyrem: 923
Xyzal Allergy 24HR OTC: 560

Y

Yasmin: 699, 701
Yaz: 699, 701
Yellow Fever Vaccine: 1007
Yerba Mate: 790, 1026
Yervoy: 874
Yescarta: 871
YF-VAX: 336
Yogurt: 1028
Yohimbe: 1026, 1027, 1029
Yohimbine: 460
Yosprala: 476, 521, 801, 959, 963
Yupelri: 606, 621

Z

Zafirlukast: 70, 535, 607, 608
Zaleplon: 920, 921
Zanaflex: 373, 814
Zanamivir: 380, 405, 406
Zanfel: 585
Zantac: 958
Zarah: 699
Zarontin: 947
Zarxio: 840
Zegerid: 958, 959
Zegerid OTC: 959
Zelapar: 887, 929
Zelboraf: 875
Zembrace SymTouch: 820, 821, 824
Zemdri: 355, 392
Zemplar: 297
Zemuron: 761
Zenpep: 776
Zenzedi: 909
Zepatier: 304, 305, 424, 428
Zephrex-D: 561
Zerbaxa: 351
Zerit: 422
Zerviate: 569
Zestoretic: 462
Zestril: 466, 494
Zetia: 449
Zetonna: 558
Ziac: 462
Ziagen: 420, 1022
Ziana: 575
Zicam Extreme Congestion Relief: 561
Zidovudine: 228, 420, 422, 435, 942
Zileuton: 69, 607, 608
Zilretta: 813
Zinc: 66, 310, 562, 577, 940, 941, 1027, 1029, 1031
Zinecard: 838, 864
Zioptan: 567, 571
Ziprasidone: 66, 228, 508, 895, 897, 903
Zipsor: 800
Zirgan Ophthalmic gel: 410
Zithranol: 690
Zithromax: 358, 373, 775
Zithromax Tri-Pak: 358
Zocor: 110, 447, 456
Zofran: 844
Zohydro: 804, 816
Zoladex: 859
Zoledronic Acid: 228, 718
Zolmitriptan: 820, 821
Zoloft: 883, 914
Zolpidem: 69, 70, 916, 920, 921, 1025
Zolpidem SL: 93
Zolpimist: 920
Zometa: 718
Zomig: 820, 821, 823, 824
Zomig-ZMT: 820, 823
Zonalon: 886
Zonegran: 948
Zonisamide: 73, 228, 940, 948, 950, 1005, 1007, 1031
Zontivity: 487
Zortress: 783, 870
Zorvolex: 800
Zostrix: 815
Zostrix HP: 815
Zosyn: 349, 350
Zovia: 699
Zovirax: 370, 407, 408, 409, 411, 576
Z-Pak: 358
ZTlido: 813, 815
Zubsolv: 812
Zulresso: 882
Zuplenz: 846
Zuplenz Film: 844
Zurampic: 829
Zyban: 631, 886
Zyclara: 396
Zydis ODT: 896
Zyflo CR: 607
Zykadia: 875
Zyloprim: 828, 1022
Zymaxid: 357
Zypitamag: 447
Zyprexa: 845, 896, 903
Zyprexa Relprevv: 95, 896, 903
Zyprexa Zydis: 92, 899, 903
Zyrtec D: 560
Zytiga: 859, 877
Zyvox: 363, 370

Image Credits

Some images have been modified from their original state. All images are being used for illustrative purposes only. Any person depicted in the content is a model.

www.istockphoto.com;
www.123rf.com;
www.vectortoons.com;
Michael Varouhas

REQUIRED FORMULAS

Calculations *(page numbers refer to RxPrep 2020 Course Book)*

Liquid (Volume) Conversions p. 117

tsp (t) = 5 mL, tbsp (T) = 15 mL
1 fl oz = 30 mL (approx.); 29.57 mL (actual)
1 cup = 8 oz, 240 mL (approx.); 236.56 mL (actual)
1 pint = 16 oz, 480 mL (approx.); 473 mL (actual)
1 quart = 2 pints, 960 mL (approx.); 946 mL (actual)
1 gallon = 4 quarts, 3,840 mL (approx.); 3,785 mL (actual)

Solid (Weight) Conversions p. 117

1 kg = 2.2 pounds (lbs)
1 oz = 28.4 grams (g)
1 lb = 454 g
1 grain = 65 mg (approx.); 64.8 mg (actual)
mEq to mmol is 1:1 for monovalent ions, 1:0.5 for divalent ions

Height Conversions p. 117

1 inch (in) = 2.54 centimeters (cm)
1 meter (m) = 100 cm

Percentage Strength p. 128

$$\% \text{ w/v} = \frac{X \text{ g}}{100 \text{ mL}} \qquad \% \text{ w/w} = \frac{X \text{ g}}{100 \text{ g}} \qquad \% \text{ v/v} = \frac{X \text{ mL}}{100 \text{ mL}}$$

Ratio Strength p. 132

Percentage strength = 100 / Ratio strength
Ratio strength = 100 / Percentage strength

Parts Per Million (PPM) p. 134

PPM → Percentage strength — Move the decimal left 4 places
Percentage strength → PPM — Move the decimal right 4 places

Specific Gravity (SG) p. 135

$$SG = \frac{\text{weight of substance (g)}}{\text{weight of equal volume of water (g)}} \quad \text{or} \quad SG = \frac{\text{g}}{\text{mL}}$$

Dilution & Concentration (Changing Strength or Volume) p. 136

Q1 x C1 = Q2 x C2 — Q1 = old quantity, Q2 = new quantity, C1 = old concentration, C2 = new concentration

Alligation p. 137

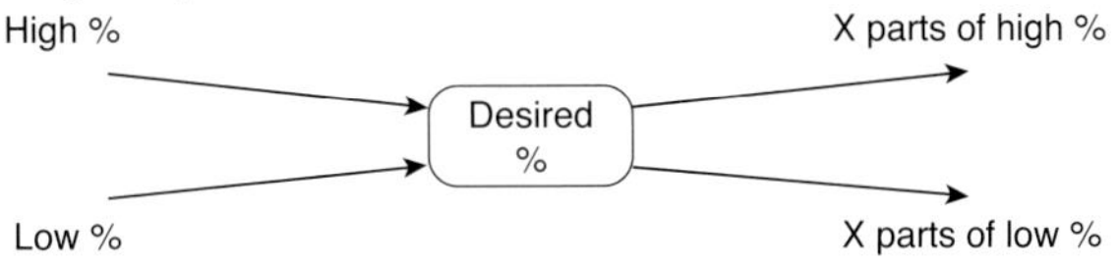

Use proportions to calculate amount of high % and/or low % required

Osmolarity p. 139

$$\text{mOsmol/L} = \frac{\text{Wt of substance (g/L)}}{\text{MW (g/mole)}} \times (\text{\# of particles}) \times 1{,}000$$

Isotonicity (E Value) p. 142

$$E = \frac{(58.5)(i)}{(\text{MW of drug})(1.8)}$$

Moles or Millimoles p. 144

$$\text{mols} = \frac{\text{g}}{\text{MW}} \quad \text{or} \quad \text{mmols} = \frac{\text{mg}}{\text{MW}}$$

Milliequivalents p. 146

$$\text{mEq} = \frac{\text{mg x valence}}{\text{MW}} \quad \text{or} \quad \text{mEq} = \text{mmols x valence}$$

Corrected Calcium for Albumin < 3.5 (not needed with ionized Ca) p. 159

$Ca_{corrected}$ (mg/dL) = $calcium_{reported(serum)}$ + [(4.0 – albumin) x (0.8)]

Parenteral Nutrition Calories p. 151

Dextrose Monohydrate = 3.4 kcal/gram — ILE 10% = 1.1 kcal/mL
Amino Acid Solutions = 4 kcal/gram — ILE 20% = 2 kcal/mL
ILE 30% = 3 kcal/mL

Enteral Nutrition Calories p. 151

Carbs, Protein = 4 kcal/gram — Fat 9 kcal/gram

Determining Fluid Needs p. 149

When weight > 20 kg: 1,500 mL + (20 mL)(weight in kg – 20)
**can estimate using 30-40 mL/kg/day*

Total Energy Expenditure p. 150

TEE = BEE x activity factor x stress factor

Grams of Nitrogen From Protein p. 152

$$\text{Nitrogen (g)} = \frac{\text{protein intake (g)}}{6.25}$$

Cockcroft-Gault Equation p. 175

$$\text{CrCl (mL/min)} = \frac{140 - (\text{age of patient})}{72 \times \text{SCr}} \times \text{weight (kg) (x 0.85 if female)}$$

Body Mass Index (BMI) p. 166

$$\text{BMI (kg/m}^2) = \frac{\text{weight (kg)}}{[\text{height (m)}]^2} \quad \text{or} \quad \frac{\text{weight (lb)}}{[\text{height (inches)}]^2} \times 703$$

Ideal Body Weight (IBW) p. 167

IBW (males) = 50 kg + (2.3 kg) (number of inches over 5 feet)
IBW (females) = 45.5 kg + (2.3 kg) (number of inches over 5 feet)

Adjusted Body Weight ($AdjBW_{0.4}$) p. 167

$AdjBW_{0.4}$ = IBW + 0.4(TBW – IBW)

Selecting Patient Weights p. 168

All drugs (if underweight)	Total Body Weight (TBW)
Most drugs (if normal weight or obese)	TBW
<u>Exceptions</u>	
Acyclovir, Aminophylline, Levothyroxine, Theophylline (normal weight, obese)	IBW
Aminoglycosides (obese)	$AdjBW_{0.4}$

Flow Rates Drop Factor (drops/min) p. 169

$$\frac{\text{\# drops}}{\text{mL}} \times \frac{\text{mL}}{\text{hr}} \times \frac{\text{hr}}{60 \text{ min}} = \frac{\text{\# drops}}{\text{min}}$$

Dehydration p. 174

BUN:SCr > 20:1

Arterial Blood Gas (ABG) p. 177

ABG: pH/pCO_2/pO_2/HCO_3/O_2 Sat

1. pH < 7.35 → acidosis and pH > 7.45 → alkalosis
2. Respiratory: pCO_2 < 35 → alkalosis and pCO_2 > 45 → acidosis
   Metabolic: HCO_3 > 26 → alkalosis and HCO_3 < 22 → acidosis
3. Which abnormal value (pCO_2 or HCO_3) matches the pH from Step #1?
   Ex: ↓ pH + ↑ pCO_2 → <u>respiratory</u> acidosis
   Ex: ↓ pH + ↓ HCO_3 → <u>metabolic</u> acidosis

Anion Gap p. 178

Anion gap (AG) = Na – Cl – HCO_3

pH Calculations p. 179

Weak acid: $$pH = pK_a + \log\left[\frac{\text{salt}}{\text{acid}}\right]$$

Weak base: $$pH = pK_a + \log\left[\frac{\text{base}}{\text{salt}}\right]$$

Percent Ionization p. 182

Weak acid: $$\% \text{ ionization} = \frac{100}{1+10^{(pKa-pH)}}$$

Weak base: $$\% \text{ ionization} = \frac{100}{1+10^{(pH-pKa)}}$$

Absolute Neutrophil Count (ANC) p. 184

ANC (cells/mm³) = WBC x [(% segs + % bands)/100]

Answering Case-Based Exam Questions

Temperature Conversions (Fahrenheit ↔ Celsius) p. 108

°C = (°F – 32)/1.8 — °F = (°C x 1.8) + 32

Biostatistics **Mean, Median and Mode p. 202**

Mean - average value

Median - value in the middle of an ordered list

Mode - value that occurs most frequently

Risk, Relative Risk (RR) p. 207, Relative Risk Reduction (RRR) & Absolute Risk Reduction (ARR) p. 208

$$\text{Risk} = \frac{\text{Number of subjects with unfavorable event in group}}{\text{Total number of subjects in group}}$$

$$\text{RR} = \frac{\text{Risk in treatment group}}{\text{Risk in control group}}$$

$$\text{RRR} = \frac{(\text{\% risk in control group} - \text{\% risk in treatment group})}{\text{\% risk in the control group}}$$

ARR = (% risk in control group) – (% risk in treatment group)

Number Needed to Treat or Harm (NNT, NNH) pp. 209-210

$$\text{NNT or NNH} = \frac{1}{\text{ARR}^*}$$

*expressed as decimal

Odds Ratio (OR) p. 210

Exposure	Outcome Present	Outcome Absent
Present-Cases	A	B
Absent-Controls	C	D

$$\text{OR} = \frac{AD}{BC}$$

Hazard Ratio (HR) p. 211

$$\text{HR} = \frac{\text{Hazard rate in the treatment group}}{\text{Hazard rate in the control group}}$$

Sensitivity and Specificity p. 214

Test Result	HAVE Condition	No Condition
Positive	A	B
Negative	C	D
Total	A + C	B + D

Sensitivity = [A/(A + C) x 100]

Specificity = [D/(B + D) x 100]

Common Skin Conditions

Time to Burn (TTB) p. 514

TTB (with sunscreen in min) = SPF X TTB (without sunscreen)

Diabetes

Initiating Basal-Bolus Insulin in Type 1 Diabetes p. 656

1. Calc TDD 0.6 units/kg/day using TBW
2. Divide into 1/2 basal & 1/2 rapid-acting. If using NPH/R, use 2/3 & 1/3.
3. Split rapid-acting among meals

Insulin-to-Carbohydrate Ratio: Rule of 500 for Rapid-Acting Insulin p. 656

$$\frac{500}{\text{total daily dose of insulin (TDD)}} = \text{grams of carbohydrate covered by 1 unit of rapid-acting insulin}$$

Insulin-to-Carbohydrate Ratio: Rule of 450 for Regular Insulin p. 656

$$\frac{450}{\text{total daily dose of insulin (TDD)}} = \text{grams of carbohydrate covered by 1 unit of regular insulin}$$

Correction Factor: 1,800 Rule for Rapid-Acting Insulin p. 657

$$\frac{1{,}800}{\text{total daily dose of insulin (TDD)}} = \text{correction factor for 1 unit of rapid-acting insulin}$$

Correction Factor: 1,500 Rule for Regular Insulin p. 657

$$\frac{1{,}500}{\text{total daily dose of insulin (TDD)}} = \text{correction factor for 1 unit of regular insulin}$$

Correction Dose p. 657

$$\frac{\text{(blood glucose now) - (target blood glucose)}}{\text{correction factor}} = \text{correction dose}$$

Dyslipidemia **Friedewald Equation p. 443**

$$\text{LDL} = \text{TC} - \text{HDL} - \frac{\text{TG}^*}{5}$$

*do not use if TG > 400

Non-Sterile Compounding

Minimum Weighable Quantity (MWQ) p. 252

$$\text{MWQ} = \frac{\text{Sensitivity Requirement}}{0.05}$$

Oncology II

BSA Calculations, using Mosteller p. 861

(review how to use Dubois-Dubois)

$$\text{BSA (m}^2\text{)} = \sqrt{\frac{\text{Ht (cm) x Wt (kg)}}{3{,}600}}$$

Pharmacokinetics

Bioavailability (F) p. 1011

$$F (\%) = 100 \times \frac{AUC_{extravascular}}{AUC_{intravenous}} \times \frac{Dose_{intravenous}}{Dose_{extravascular}}$$

Volume of Distribution (Vd) p. 1012

$$\text{Vd} = \frac{\text{Amount of drug in body}}{\text{Concentration of drug in plasma}}$$

Clearance p. 1013

$$\text{Cl} = \frac{\text{F x Dose}}{\text{AUC}} \quad \text{or} \quad \text{Cl} = \text{ke x Vd}$$

Elimination Rate Constant (ke) p. 1016

$$\text{ke} = \frac{\text{Cl}}{\text{Vd}}$$

Predicting Drug Concentrations p. 1016

$$C_2 = C_1 \times e^{-kt}$$

$$\text{ke} = \frac{\ln (C_1/C_2)}{t}$$

Half-Life ($t_{1/2}$) p. 1017

$$t_{½} = \frac{0.693}{\text{ke}}$$

Loading Dose (LD) p. 1019

$$\text{LD} = \frac{\text{Desired Concentration x Vd}}{\text{F}}$$

Seizures/Epilepsy **Phenytoin Correction for Albumin < 3.5 (not needed with free phenytoin) p. 949**

$$\text{Phenytoin}_{\text{corrected}} \text{ (mcg/mL)} = \frac{\text{Total phenytoin measured}}{(0.2 \times \text{albumin}) + 0.1}$$

(can also be used for valproic acid)

DOSE CONVERSIONS *(ORAL, UNLESS NOTED)*

KCl Solution (Oral) to Tablets p. 147 (see problem #61)

KCl 10% = 20 mEq/15 mL, KCl 20% = 40 mEq/15 mL

Calcium Salts p. 148

Calcium Carbonate = 40% elemental calcium

Calcium Citrate = 21% elemental calcium

Aminophylline ↔ Theophylline p. 148

Aminophylline to **T**heophylline: **M**ultiply by 0.8 (remember: **ATM**)

Theophylline to Aminophylline: Divide by 0.8

Loop Diuretics p. 493

Ethacrynic acid	50 mg	Bumetanide	1 mg
Furosemide	40 mg	Furosemide IV:PO = 1:2	
Torsemide	20 mg	Other Loops IV:PO = 1:1	

Metoprolol Conversions p. 496 (IV:PO = 1:2.5)

Iron, Elemental Conversions p. 544

Ferrous Sulfate = 20% elemental iron (e.g., 325 mg x 0.2 = 65 mg)

Insulin Conversions p. 657

Usually, 1:1 conversion

Exceptions:

NPH dosed BID → glargine dosed daily, use 80% of NPH dose

Toujeo → *Lantus* or *Basaglar*, use 80% of *Toujeo* dose

Steroids p. 673

Cortisone	25 mg	**M**ethylprednisolone	4 mg
Hydrocortisone	20 mg	**T**riamcinolone	4 mg
Prednisone	5 mg	**D**examethasone	0.75 mg
Prednisolone	5 mg	**B**etamethasone	0.6 mg

(remember: **C**ute **H**ot **P**harmacists and **P**hysicians **M**arry **T**ogether & **D**eliver **B**abies)

Opioids (methodology) p. 806

Statins p. 446

Pitavastatin	2 mg	**L**ovastatin	40 mg
Rosuvastatin	5 mg	**P**ravastatin	40 mg
Atorvastatin	10 mg	**F**luvastatin	80 mg
Simvastatin	20 mg		

(remember: **P**harmacists **R**ock **A**t **S**aving **L**ives and **P**reventing **F**atty-deposits.)